jeffrey bernard

talking HORSES

illustrated by
michael heath

fourth estate
london

First published in Great Britain in 1987 by
Fourth Estate Ltd
113 Westbourne Grove
London W2 4UP

British Library Cataloguing in Publication Data

Bernard, Jeffrey
    Talking horses.
    1.   Horse-racing — Anecdotes, facetiae,
    satire, etc.
    I.   Title
    798.4'00207   SF335.5
    ISBN 0-947795-02-2

Illustrated by Michael Heath
Typeset in Palatino by York House Typographic Ltd, London W7
Printed and bound by The Bath Press Ltd, Bath, Avon.

The author and publishers would like to thank the *Spectator*
and *The Sporting Life* for permission to use material that
originally appeared in their columns.

contents

foreword   7

part i: a year at the races   11
          (with occasional run outs)

part ii: the races   123

foreword

WHEN I WAS ABOUT SIXTEEN AND DOING TIME AT A DISGUSTING naval college called Pangbourne, a boy called Vickers was given twelve strokes of the cane – the maximum – for running a book. I was deeply impressed. That put gambling in the same wicked league as drinking and sex, and if it was that bad then I wanted some of it. So I started to read the racing pages in the Saturday papers and pretty soon I too was laying a few bets.

It didn't take long to get me hooked. Once you've risked about ten times more than you can afford and savoured the flow of adrenalin it's hard to get excited about anything else. Even my passion for my mother faded into the background. She looked like a cross between Maria Callas and Ava Gardner and I fancied her so much it nearly drove me bonkers. This new obsession with horseracing didn't exactly further the career she had planned for me as an Officer and Gentleman, though. I fell at the first by getting chucked out of the Outward Bound course designed for future high-fliers in the Blue Funnel line, and went straight to Soho to become a layabout.

I got jobs navvying and dishwashing and, believe it or not, boxing. I had been quite handy at school so I used to go down to Jack Solomon's gym and spar with 'The Aldgate Tiger', British and European Featherweight Champion Al Phillips. Rather than cash in hand my reward was a visit to the café next door. One day, Phillips gave me concussion, then Solomon took me to the café for a cup of coffee, a cheese roll and a cigarette. I was once greedy enough to climb into the ring with one of the greatest of all featherweights, Sandy Saddler, for eight quid a round, the equivalent of two weeks' wages. I didn't know what I was doing for the next three days.

Anyway, hanging around Soho wondering what to do with myself I kept being assailed by this brilliant idea of having a bet on a horse. The first time this brainwave came to me I borrowed five shillings, picked two of Manny Mercer's mounts – since I was always overhearing pub talk about what a genius the man was – and did them both in a double. You never forget the names of your first two winners: Burnt Grass and Cherry Heering. The bookmaker paid me in an alley, which made it all the more wicked, and I was almost rich. Thirty-seven years later, the struggle goes on.

Another day some years later I was sitting in the pub doing bugger all – I was supposed to be working as a stage hand – when a bookmaker friend of mine walked in and told me *The Sporting Life* were advertising for a columnist. For want of anything better to do I applied, and to my astonishment I was hired. My brief was to privide half a page twice a week, on Wednesdays and Saturdays. This was the early seventies, but I thought my wage of fifty quid was a bit of an insult, even for a stage hand. I started work the day Nijinsky came second in Le Prix de l'Arc de Triomphe.

I didn't waste words pretending I knew much about horses or waxing lyrical about such and such a trainer as if I'd known him since the cradle. I wrote about what horseracing meant to me and just about everyone else: losing money. I described all the traps and pitfalls of punting and how I fell into them with tedious regularity, and I took the piss out of the racing Establishment. The readers lapped it up. Odd things used to happen to me on 'The Life'. One night I woke up in a field outside Pontefract and I still have no idea how I got there. Another time I remember opening my eyes to find myself in bed with Barry Brogan – a great jockey, it is true, but not my idea of a desirable bed companion. And I once spent the night with a girl in the ditch of the celebrated Pond Fence at Sandown. I don't know how we met or what was so enticing about the Pond Fence – perhaps I was pointing out to her that obstacle's peculiar hazards. Anyway, we got on famously.

Exactly a year after I started this job I was sacked. There was a National Hunt dinner at a hotel in Kensington, to which I was invited as guest of honour to present an award to the woman point-to-point rider of the year. I had to give a speech – something I'd never done before – and I was nervous as hell. I went to *The Sporting Life* at the crack of dawn to start work on it. Smithfield Market was open, and I thought that if I had a couple of drinks to get me going I'd probably write rather a good one. I drank steadily from six in the morning to seven in the evening, at which time I arrived at the hotel and immediately passed out. Two waiters had to carry me upstairs and put me to bed. The next day I flew to Paris for the Arc de Triomphe. I'd been so pissed I couldn't remember anything at all. Henry Cecil walked up to me in the paddock at Longchamp and said, 'Hello, Jeffrey, what a pity you've been sacked.' It was the first I'd heard of it, but anyway, that was that. Except that I put my whole week's wages on Mill Reef and won what for me was quite a tidy sum.

This wasn't quite the end of my career as a racing journalist. Richard Ingrams dreamed up the idea of having a racing column in *Private Eye* and asked me to do it under the pseudonym 'Colonel Mad'. They were great people to work for because they let me say anthing I wanted and I had a good time taking the Mickey out of all the intolerably pompous people I'd met since I first got obsessed with horses. Of course racing people loved it. They are mostly lunatics and nutcases who live in a world of their own, can only talk about what some wretched three-year-old did yesterday or might do tomorrow, have never been to the theatre or read a book, and can't tell a Chippendale chair from a kitchen stool. What was strange was that even readers who knew nothing about racing became intrigued by the barmy people I was writing about.

Needless to say I lost this job, too. Lord Gnome began to disapprove of me. It didn't improve matters when I was interviewed once and the reporter had the rare gall to actually print what I said. He asked me why I'd fallen into disfavour with his Lordship and I told him: 'I fuck, I drink and I back horses. Not only does he do none of these things, but he can't.' Nigel Dempster took over the column and they called him 'Colonel Bonkers'. But there was a snag: Dempster isn't funny.

This brief account of my career is to give you some insight into why this is such an exceptional book. And I mean *exceptional*. Most books about racing are terrible hack jobs by jumped up sub-editors who can't write. The rest are dreary rags-to-riches 'autobiographies' about some hard-done-by apprentice who starts life in a rat-infested loft in Newmarket but by sheer talent and force of character becomes a champion jockey, and gets his just reward on his retirement when the Queen summons him to Buckingham Palace and presents him with a silver cigarette box. A famous jockey once asked me to ghost his life story. It would have been a very boring job without much money in it, but I said I'd do it if he owned up. He stared at me as if I'd gone mad. 'What do you mean, own up?' I told him there'd be no point in trotting out another achingly dull racing book unless he spilt the beans about the horses he'd pulled, the owners he'd conned – explained, in fact, exactly what a devious bastard he was. By this time he knew I was in urgent need of psychiatric attention. 'I'd get my badge taken away . . . I'd be warned off . . . I could never show my face in Lambourn again . . . ' he spluttered. I told him in that case I wasn't interested.

Of course there are exceptions – for instance, *Men and Horses I Have Known* by George Lambton, Jack Leach's *Sods I Have Cut on the Turf* and best of all, *The History of the Derby Stakes* by Roger Mortimer, one of the funniest raconteurs in the business. And not every racing journalist is a hack. Richard Baerlein is not only a serious punter but a good writer, too; and Charles Benson and Clive Graham, both of whom were 'The Scout' on the *Daily Express*, were always worth reading.

Come to think of it, men like these have forgotten more about racing than I will ever know. Who hasn't?

part i:

a
year at the
RACES
(with occasional run outs)

1

I ONCE WENT TO AN EVENING MEETING AT WINDSOR, GOT absolutely pissed, lost every penny in my pocket, and had no idea how to get back to London after the last. I was almost the final person to leave the racecourse and, standing desolately in the car-park, I suddenly saw a beautiful white Rolls Royce slowly approaching. I stood in its way and signalled to it to stop. It stopped. The owner, as suave as a film-star, asked what he could do for me. I said, 'I'm pissed and potless. Will you please take me to the Dorchester immediately and buy me a drink.' I'd never seen him before and I've never seen him since, but he was absolutely charming. He recognised someone who'd done their bollocks and was feeling thirsty. He drove me straight to the American Bar and stood me a huge one. We never introduced ourselves. He just filled me up and then gave me the taxi fare to get back to Soho.

That is typical of what happens at the races. You wouldn't find it at a football game or a cricket match. The racing world is stuffed with lunatics, criminals, idiots, charmers, bastards and exceptionally nice people. When you're on form and don't mind losing a few notes, a day at the races is one of the most magical days you can imagine, and the lure of the ever-changing racing circus soon becomes irresistible. What follows is a loosely chronological description of my shambling progress through a racing year, with plenty of red herrings and tangents. It runs from about August 1976 to September 1977 because I happen to have that year documented. But it

could be any year, last year, next year. Except that you get a
different bunch of horses to bankrupt yourself on.

On the first Saturday in August I decided Newmarket was
good enough for me. The crowds at Goodwood, and at Royal
Ascot come to that, always put me off attending these classier
meetings. The Sloane Square mob get in the way of the racing
and there are just too many people who go to be seen and who
aren't really at the races at all. So I picked Newmarket, and got
there early enough to go up to the gallops with Bill Marshall.

I watched him go up the new gallop on Long Hill sitting
tight on an old enemy of mine, Peranka. On the Tuesday
before, that horse had run pretty well enough in the Stewards'
Cup to finish fifth, but not well enough to prevent a hefty hole
being made in my pocket. Marshall was then training from the
Eve Lodge Stable, the yard Lester Piggott had built about three
years previously and from which he now trains with some
success. Even then, if you happened to be wondering whether
Lester was a millionaire yet or not, you just had to look at the
set-up and estimate how much it must have cost to build a
brand-new yard with eighty boxes in it and with automatic
feeding devices.

As soon as I arrived on the course an hour before the first
race I knew I'd done the right thing in not going to the Nassau
Stakes at Goodwood. All the old faces were here. The first one
I bumped into was the late Tommy Turner, who used to stand
up on the rails for William Hill in the old days. Tommy was
typical of the older generation of racing professionals. Under
his soft brown hat there was a face as ripe as a windfall. I once
saw him make a book at Worcester while at the same time,
between races, he managed to consume an entire bottle of
Courvoisier in the Members' Bar. I hasten to add it was an
accurate book which showed the old firm a profit. Remi-
niscing about Worcester I remarked how odd it was that it was

the only track in England that actually had a pub on the course itself. He said that sadly they'd pulled it down, but then he went on to tell me about the other convenience in Worcester. He said that there was a pub *inside* the cemetery grounds, which made it a very short journey if you weren't feeling up to scratch.

The first race was won by Etienne Gerard, a giant of a two-year-old, and it started a lot of arguments in the bar after. I'd always thought that Brigadier Gerard was a fluky horse and I was already convinced that it would be madness to pay vast sums for his progeny at that early stage of his career as a stallion. His sire, Queen's Hussar, was a goodish horse who threw a few goodish horses, but the Brigadier was the only really top class one. Well, I know he was more than top class. But he was a long way then from being proved as a great sire, and I'm sad to say that subsequently Brigadier Gerard's dismal career at stud has proved me to have been right on that rare occasion.

Bill Marshall bought yet another bottle of champagne when he heard that he had won the first race of the day at Thirsk with Minstrel Song, ridden by his son Richard. Then I went with him to watch him saddle up The Guvnor for the fourth race. It's always interesting to go with a trainer into the paddock and meet the jockey and listen to the riding instructions. Alan Bond had the mount, and there was a fair amount of optimism in the air that in receipt of two stone from Berkeley Square The Guvnor might bring it off. 'Keep him up with the others all the time, because he loves to be in the thick of things, and then see if you can make a run for it three furlongs out.'

At that moment, Rhodomontade's jockey walked by to mount his horse and Marshall said, 'Oh shit. He heard us.' This was followed by a lot of laughing and I felt as though I was in the middle of a schoolboy conspiracy. Sadly for all the connections, The Guvnor came third and Berkeley Square lived up to his name by demonstrating a fair amount of class.

Incidentally, the fortunes of Alan Bond in the ten years since that day at Newmarket illustrate as well as anything the ups and downs of racing. Bond had been champion apprentice in both 1974 and '75, in both years beating his nearest rival Richard Fox. When he was then invited by Henry Cecil to become the new stable jockey, the world seemed to lie at his feet. But his association with Cecil was short and disastrous and from then on it was all downhill. He rode fewer and fewer winners until at the beginning of 1987 it was announced he was leaving these shores to try and make a living somewhere else. And it wasn't because he lacked talent. Bad luck breeds bad luck and too much of that leads to you going out of fashion. There's nothing as unloved in racing as an unfashionable jockey, and when you're deeply unfashionable you may as well hang up your boots. Richard Fox, on the other hand, is currently a popular and successful lightweight.

I didn't have a bet in the next race but then at the very last moment, as they were going into the stalls for the sixth, I got hit over the head by a hunch and, running like Last Tycoon himself towards the bookies, I got a fiver on Bicoque. As they raced past us inside the final furlong it seemed like a mess of a blanket finish. Then they announced that Bicoque had won by a head. There was more agony to come in the form of a stewards' enquiry which went on for fifteen minutes and then they gave the all clear. Bicoque the winner at 33-1. But you know what really kills me about betting on the horses? You're never happy. I'm not, anyway. I sat there under the trees sipping the last dregs of the Bollinger, cursing myself for not having put a tenner on. It was pathetic, really, and got me to thinking that a psychiatrist I know probably hit the nail on the head when he described punting as 'collecting injustices'.

A couple of weeks later and I was bound for Newbury to back Oats in the Geoffrey Freer. A day at the races can be nearly made or broken by the race train. I had recently taken to this form of transport for two reasons. Firstly, I had sensibly decided to give up driving before I killed somebody. This, by the way, led to the necessity, when living in the wilds of Berkshire, of sending myself a postcard every day so that the postman had to drive out the three miles from the village to deliver it and I would get a ride back with him to the pub. Secondly, I had recently been driven to the races by the first English model to appear as a centrefold for *Playboy*. She was driving a brand new Aston Martin, and when I nervously complained about the speed we were going she said, 'Oh, I'm not in top yet . . .' She suddenly put it up to another gear that I hadn't imagined even existed and there we were doing a hundred and sixty down the M4.

When I first started going to the more distant courses by train some twenty years ago I looked forward to those journeys almost as much as I looked forward to the racing itself. Traditionally, the restaurant car to Salisbury, for example, would be taken over by bookmakers, their workmen – the tictac men, clerks, runners etc – the spivs and the touts. Out would come the cards for kaluki or gin rummy, and out would come the most fantastic yarns of villainy and chicanery that would keep me spellbound and laughing for most of the journey. On the return journeys, the generosity of the bookmakers would be, on occasions, stupendous.

At one time, the race trains to and from York during the August meeting were, I think, the only trains on British Rail to carry champagne. They didn't carry it for long. After Peterborough, the passengers carried it. Brighton races were almost worth going to for the journey alone and I once came back from Chepstow on a train that was something like a nightclub travelling at eighty mph. But it was not all fun. Some services were and are shameful. If you ever miss the first of the two trains that are the specials to Newbury, you might just as well forget it. I did just that on this occasion and found myself going down on a nasty, buffetless, corridorless pay-train of the sort British Rail lay on to give you an inkling of what it must have been like to have been a Jew in Germany a few years ago. Anyway, once at Newbury the nasty taste of the journey didn't in fact last very long. I kicked off with 10-1 winner Destino and there's no better way of starting a day. The winner of the first race always gives you the necessary confidence as well as the enemy's money to play around with. So when Oats got beaten a head and I lost only a tenth of my winnings it wasn't a knockout blow. I spoke to trainer Peter Walwyn after the race and he seemed pleased enough with the animal's performance. He said he'd go much better in the St Leger and with a month more to work on the horse, he was happy enough. Maybe, I began thinking, the money was only lent. Maybe. The winner Swell Fellow started at 16-1 and I felt rather bad about that one. Ten minutes before the off I had been talking to an ex-colleague, Alan Jamieson, who used to be on the *Sun*, when he turned to me and said, 'Shall I put my cash on Swell Fellow or buy a bottle of Bollinger?' 'Buy the Bollinger,' I told him, 'Swell Fellow's got no bloody chance.' Yes, well, people shouldn't listen to people, should they?

It was at that point that Roger Mortimer appeared at the bar and gave me a short but fascinating lecture on matters of stallions covering mares. His theory, an interesting one and one that might connect with humans possibly, is that a stallion needs to be something of a shit to be good at stud. He told me that the great racehorse The Tetrarch was very sweet-natured and found sex a most fearful bore. He only got a hundred and twenty foals, eighty of which won. When he covered a mare, apparently they had to keep dead quiet because if he heard someone sawing a piece of wood or drop a bucket, it put him right off. St Simon, on the other hand who was a bit of a bastard and who would eat a groom for breakfast, got five hundred and fifty foals. It reminds me of that great stallion Hyperion, who had an odd idiosyncracy for a horse. As a general rule, animals don't take in all that much that isn't immediate, but Hyperion, they say, in his old age, was fascinated by aeroplanes and if one flew overhead while he was covering a mare, he'd stop and follow it around with his head and eyes until it was out of sight.

But back to the races. The day continued well enough and in the fifth race Princess of Verona obliged at 3-1, but I was disappointed with the ladies on show that day. Now it's a fairly well-known fact that racing doesn't attract many grey people. Racing folk tend to be either the salt and mustard of the earth or they're utterly ghastly. But there used to be some wonderful-looking women at the racetrack. Where are they now? Discussing the serious shortage with a trainer at Newbury that day I was fascinated by the way – and it's simply a habit not an insult – he referred to them as though they were horses. I had observed this before though, come to think of it. I once asked Fred Winter what he thought of a certain trainer's mistress and he said, 'Oh, she's very moderate.' The trainer I spoke to that Saturday decribed one woman there as being 'of little account'. My day ended with buying a drink for one whom Mr Winter and his colleagues would describe as 'Promising, useful, scope'

bernard's guide to gambling types

The next time you go to the races resist the temptation to dive straight into the business of losing money for a few minutes and watch the various sorts of punters as they go about their business. There are eight types that I know of:

1.   **The really big punter** is the one I most like to watch. He gambles vast sums and win or lose he looks incredibly bored with the whole proceedings. The braver bookies twitch nervously as he approaches, their brains rehearsing odds and fizzing with calculations in case he has a bet with them. He'll risk five grand in just the same voice as he'll order a cup of tea.

2.   **Rich idiot**, I call him. A successful businessman who likes to gamble, but whose main motivation is to impress

Bernard's Gambling Types – No. 1

*The Really Big Punter . . . gambles vast sums, and win or lose he
looks incredibly bored with the whole proceedings.*

whichever young girl he happens to be with. The girls
with type two, incidentally, are either models, someone
else's daughter, actresses, 'in showbusiness' or on holiday
from Kenya. That's to say, amateur brasses. He'll always
tell anyone who can be bothered to listen that he's very
well up on the day.

3.   **The non-punter**. He wanders round the paddock
sucking thoughtfully on a cigar someone gave him
pretending that he's trying to make up his mind which
horse to bet on. In fact he's not going to bet on any of
them. He imagines he might be mistaken for a wealthy
and knowledgeable punter, or even an owner. On Monday
morning he'll tell the receptionist at the second-hand car
showroom where he works that he had a 'fair afternoon –
not much, just a few hundred up'. She won't believe him,
but won't bother to tell him so, either. He owes two
weeks rent.

4.   **The compulsive punter** is usually to be found in the
Members' Bar, sweating, shouting, losing badly or
winning as though it's his divine right. Very unsociable,
impatient and intolerant of others, the indulges in boring
post-mortems after the last race when everyone else is
going home and his girlfriend has just left with type two.

5.   **Women gamblers**. Your average one is probably
between forty and fifty although she has the constantly-
twitching but well-manicured hands of a woman of sixty.
She chain smokes, uses too much perfume, wears too
much jewellery and covers herself to an absurd extent
with each-way bets. Don't try to talk to her. She'll think
you're trying to pick her up. If you are, you'll have to earn
every penny of it, and she knows all about gigolos. Her
husband left her a million and she smiled all the way to
the funeral, and now she's the sort of woman who has
lunch alone at the Ritz. She's also a shrewd nut and
probably wins in the long run.

6.   **Young gamblers**. Japanese students, Persian
remittance men, boys between public school and work,
and boys between rich aunts and a carpet in Wandsworth

comprise this tiresome lot. There is admittedly the odd deb's delight or a redundant Rajah who finds the 2.30 at Kempton the nearest he can get to pig-sticking, but they're mostly amateur students. They haven't a quarter the amount of money they give the impression of having and they've seen someone win in the movies so they think they can. They're suckers for tips and think they can make a fortune backing favourites. They tend to pass out in the Gents, lose their girlfriends to types one, two, three and four and are usually going to see their probation officers when they say they're going to Fortnum's.

7.   **I don't like to talk about this lot. I'm one of them**. They're simply out of their depths. They know they can't win, but they'll risk it 'just this once'. They bet beyond their means, go mad when they win and cry all the way home on the train when they lose. Their cup doth not runneth over and there's a nasty tendency towards bitterness which takes the form of swearing loudly in the Gents when it's empty. They also retreat there to have a private roll call of their rapidly dwindling wad from time to time. They gamble while under the influence of alcohol and/or the astrological columns and they're even mad enough to gamble to 'get out of trouble'. That's why they're always in it. Like most dogs they have their day. About once in a lifetime.

8.   **Losers**. Losing is written right across the faces of some people, and it's hard to define. There's a slightly watery look about the eye and a tendency towards ash on the waistcoat or chipped nail varnish depending on the sex. There's a nervous twitch of the lips that promises to be a brave smile or the harbinger of tears – you can never tell which. There's the touching gesture of bravado in the form of a nonchalantly produced wallet that contains one last tenner. There's a seemingly wise and knowing nod of the head which is realy the burden of remorse. There's *Raceform* on the table at home with the last three weeks' installments missing. There's the old and faded trilby and the hired binoculars and the cigarettes plucked from packets of ten. At 6pm when they return to their dreadful little flat in Tooting even the cat knows they've lost. On

Bernard's Gambling Types No. 4

*The Compulsive Punter is to be found in the Members' Bar, sweating,
shouting, losing badly . . .*

Monday at the office the clerk spots them looking at the
day's runners at Southwell and Bangor. There's a
Luncheon Voucher for lunch and then an afternoon of
wishful thinking to be got through.

After that, it's gin and tonic time. Things don't seem to
be so bad after all. Now's the time to flash the teeth in a
brave smile and afford the big spender all the sympathetic
laughter you can muster. You too can be a big spender. It's
nearly payday anyway and you're due for a run of luck.
Saturday could be the day. Just one brave bet at 20-1 could
swing it. Just one selling-plater that stays the course. And
may God have mercy on our souls.

2

A WEEK AFTER NEWBURY I HAD TO REVISE MY OPINIONS ON THE
shortage of attractive women at the races when I went to
Kempton Park. The feature race was the Playboy Nursery
Handicap Stakes and, thanks to the sponsors, who are no
longer in the bookmaking business, the course was liberally
littered with bunnies. I examined one of these animals at
moderately close quarters and came away full of admiration at
the way they'd been turned out. Their costumes could have
been designed by Brunel. The bra works on the cantilever
system and is not so much a repository but more a launching
pad. How apt then that their race should have been won by
Showpiece, a bay colt by Daring Display out of Magic Thrust,
and thanks be to the good goddess Venus that I had a fiver on
it at 5-1. After the race there was a presentation in the unsaddling enclosure and then the photographers asked the late Sir
Gordon Richards to pose for the odd snap with a bunny called
Penny. This was an amazing sight. Sir Gordon, the best friend
the punters ever had, was then in his seventies and had

definitely stopped growing. His head came exactly level with
Penny's cantilever constuction and try as the old maestro did
to look her straight in the eye his twinkling orbs kept dropping
to her Brunel-encased breasts.

Exhausted by this display of hypnotism, I sat down on a
bench with a couple of jockeys outside the weighing room. It
was much the same story there. I couldn't see a horse for the
quantity of behinds. In front of me there was a wall of black-
stockinged legs and white tails which played strange tricks
with what little there was left of my concentration. Nevertheless, somehow I managed to follow Showpiece with Sousa
who won the Geoffrey Hamlyn Handicap Stakes at 7-1. That
was really thanks to his nicely unsecretive trainer, Michael
Stoute, who dropped me a heavy hint earlier in the day that
his horse would win. Now, ten years on, Stoute has twice been
champion trainer, establishing a record for prize money won
in one season in 1986, and is widely acknowledged as one of
the great masters of his art.

By this time, I was on the crest of a tiny wave flecked with
Louis Roederer spume and I was in half a mind to make a
complete pig of myself by going on to the White City dog
track, now sadly pulled down, after the last race at Kempton.
But my old friend Chris Smith put me off. He's a tic-tac man
and something of a character and when I asked him if he'd
mark my card at the dogs later on he begged me to go straight
home. 'Don't go to the dogs, don't go, son. You've got no
bleedin' chance and I'm here to tell you that I owe every
bookmaker on the bloody track.' I quote Mr Smith just to show
you that bookmakers and their workmen get into just as much
trouble as we mugs. Well, almost.

Not so long ago, there was a bookmaker with a chain of
betting shops and a compulsion to play *chemin de fer* for very
heavy stakes who was encouraged to go on playing up to the
hilt so that the casino owners could step in and buy his betting
shops for a rock-bottom price. Not many people are safe from
gambling once they've tasted the delicious flavour of a big win

The Playboy Handicap

. . . the photographers asked the late Sir Gordon Richards to pose for the odd snap with a bunny called Penny. This was an amazing sight.

and bookmakers are no exception. Had I won a fraction more at Kempton Park I might have been tempted to go on to White City to lay a couple of short-priced favourites, but remembering the doleful look in Chris Smith's eyes I went straight home.

I was soon wishing I'd stayed at home on the Tuesday too instead of going to York for the first day of the big August meeting. Earlier in the season, on advance information from Chantilly, I had backed Empery ante-post to win the Derby at 20-1, so naturally I was looking forward to seeing my old friend again. The news that he wasn't after all going to run in the Benson and Hedges Gold Cup (now the Matchmaker International) wasn't the best start to the day that I could have wished for and then when Crow got beaten by Wollow I viewed the finish with mixed feelings. I had had a fair bet on Crow at 10-1, but on the other hand I was glad to see an English-trained horse win the race. I had mixed feelings about York in general terms too, as well as about the big race. It is without doubt one of the finest meetings in the calendar and the course is a cracker but it was so uncomfortable watching racing among so many people – about thirty thousand then and probably even more now – that I resolved to stick to the television at home in the future. It really isn't a sort of inverted snobbery that makes me prefer going to one of the 'gaffs' on a Wednesday or Thursday. The York people run the course very well and the atmosphere is always good, but all those people in the heat can make it a shattering day. Disaster was averted only by an invitation halfway through the afternoon from Bill Marshall to join him in the trainers' luncheon room.

On the next Saturday I attended the last evening meeting of the year at Windsor. They're odd things, evening meetings. The first race was at 5.30pm and the last one around 8pm. I'm not entirely sure I like them, although Windsor has its points. The executive at least seem to like racing, which is half the battle, but it feels slightly odd to start one's hooliganism at teatime. Royal Match won yet again and even though he was one of the best handicappers in training at the time he was such an incredible tribute to his trainer, the late Ryan Jarvis, that the horse just went on winning and winning. Ryan's son Willie has recently made a very bright start to his own training career. A former assistant to Henry Cecil, he now has a strike rate almost to rival his old guvnor and has already broken his duck at Royal Ascot with his smart colt Colmore Row.

That evening at Windsor, I had taken as my companion for the betting, one Fred Dipper, a pub acquaintance from Lancashire who bet in fifties and hundreds, in those days, and who didn't know the difference between those employed by United Dairies and those sired by Sea Bird II. Over the years I've bumped into a lot of characters like this one and they've all of them never failed to irritate me. Basically, they're men who gamble fairly heavily and with a modicum of success on a form of animated roulette that they don't understand. I'm beginning to twig the secret of their success. It's simply an utter contempt for money, regarding it simply as pieces of paper, and that in turn makes for supreme confidence. At Windsor that night, I tore a page from his book and found it rather nerve-racking. By the fifth race, I was so much down I was nearly drowning in self-pity and fiscal damage. Then I thought I'd put my betting boots on and wager like Fred. I had my last, but really my last, twenty-five pounds in the world on a one-paced horse called Sweet Reclaim and it just got up to win at 11-4 by half a length. I didn't want to go through that again. I decided to stick in the future to being pretentiously knowledgeable, and the heart and pocket would last much longer. Fred meanwhile has no doubt gone on backing winners out of sheer blind ignorance and nerve.

If you ever take anyone racing for the first time and, presumably, intend for them to like the business, then I must advise you not to try them out with Kempton Park. This is an extremely dodgy and usually rather boring racetrack. Of course, it has its compensations. There are bars, bookmakers, races that are won by winners and the grass is green, but my experience of it the Monday after the Windsor evening meeting, a Bank Holiday, made me more reluctant than ever to visit the place again.

The whole afternoon was so ghastly that not even the backing of Briar Patch, who won at 12-1, could entirely compensate for the hour of boredom and fuss that it took to reach the place and park the car, and the entrance money that it took to get into the Ring. Nerves were steadied and cooled by the sight of Briar Patch's trainer, the late Ryan Price. I'd been told he'd given a remarkable interview on television at York a few days previously in which he'd claimed to be a 'bloody genius'. Captain Price was without doubt one of, if not the most remarkable people in the business. I suppose what really used to upset the few people who were upset by him was the bald fact that he really was a genius or pretty close to whatever that may be.

He trained the first winner of the afternoon as well, which steamed in at 15-1. There was no stopping him in those days. And he seemed to be pretty sure that his Marquis de Sade would win the St Leger in a couple of weeks.

Half way through the afternoon I fell in with a big punting owner from Wales, Paddy Gallagher, who was unlucky enough to have his horse scratched from the big handicap of the day. Paddy had fancied it and I hate to think how much he would have put on it. Five years previously I had bumped into him at Sandown Park and he asked me to accompany him to the rails where he was going to collect from the bookmakers for a win he'd had the previous week with a hurdler at Cheltenham called Bumble Boy. I swear it took his man on the rails twenty minutes to count the stuff out. When I reminded him of the episode he rightly said, 'Don't forget the bad days.'

infantile megalomania

In my opinion the only point in betting is to earn money
when you're skint. I bet because I'm greedy and want to
get something for nothing. And a word of advice, ignore
tips. The nearer to the horse's mouth, the worse they are.

It has been suggested that in a few hundred years' time
gamblers will be forced by law to have psychiatric
treatment. It's a very simple sickness, completely infantile
for a start. It's also a chronic complaint that invariably lasts
for life. The gambler, after all, is the one person who is
completely unmoved by experience. In the beginning, it's
a disease that's comparable to the megalomania that
possesses all babies: when they want milk, they cry and
they get it.

Where do I get all this from? The answer is Edmund
Bergler, an American pshychoanalyst who wrote a book
on the psychology of gambling. He says that the placing of
a bet is an unconscious provocation of a situation wherein
the gambler will be defeated. His hate-filled and seemingly
self-defensive attacks on self-constructed enemies are
made for the purpose of enjoying an unconscious
masochistic pleasure. He could have fooled me. But I do
realise that some gamblers want to lose. Time and time
again I've noticed, and I don't need an analyst to point it
out, that nearly all gambling reminiscences and post-
mortems concern losses and not winnings. Invariably,
when recollecting the past, gamblers will say: 'I'll never
forget that day. I got beaten for a thousand quid by a neck
and a short head.'

For some strange reason, punters have short memories
when it comes to winnings. There are of course the odd
exceptions that prove this rule. One of them is a man I
know who is so clinically unique he should be stuffed and
mounted in the Natural History Museum. In fact this is a
very real possibility.

He devoted years to the formbook with little tangible
success, but as luck would have it he did a ten-bob
accumulator one day and won two thousand pounds.
(This was many years ago.) He immediately gave up his
job and flew his wife and mistress to the south of Spain,

where they spent a happy month fighting over him and
occasionally pouring bottles of cheap wine over his head.
And of course that's where it all went. To his head,
I mean.

He returned to England armed with an inordinate
amount of conceit, arrogance, bitterness and fifteen
shillings. He'd done it once, he said, and there was no
good reason why he shouldn't do it again. Every day. The
last I heard of him he was working as a messenger on a tit
magazine. His classic case of paranoia and delusions of
grandeur shuffled in with a persecution complex is typical
of the sort of man who likes to think of himself as being a
'classical' gambler, according to Bergler.

This is simply the gambler who deceives himself that his
gambling is an intellectual exercise, rather like a game of
chess. Outwardly he gives the impression that he's
desperately keen to win, but underneath he enjoys his
daily stint of self-commiseration and he is, in fact, never
happy until he has received his 'daily dose of injustice'.
The classical gambler has a greater capacity for suffering
than he has an ability to enjoy success.

I particularly like Bergler's summing up of the *real*
gambler. He is marked by the following characteristics or
clinical symptoms:-

1   Gambling is a typical, chronic and repetitive experience
in his life.
2   Gambling absorbs all his other interests like a sponge.
3   He is pathologically optimistic about winning and
never learns his lesson when he loses.
4   He cannot stop when he is winning.
5   No matter how great his initial caution, the true
gambler eventually risks more than he can afford.
6   He seeks and enjoys an enigmatic thrill which cannot
be logically explained since it is compounded of as much
pain as pleasure.

I once had a friend, a compulsive gambler and habitual
loser, who eventually cancelled his subscription to 'The
Life' as it offered too much temptation. He further stated
that he owed a lot of money and was being sued for the
rates. 'There's one good thing about being skint though,'

he told me. 'It keeps the mind lively and generally puts one on one's toes.'

Well, of course it does. I know it's an expensive way of keeping fit but, by God, it works. There's nothing like a bailiff on the doorstep or a brief in King's Bench to keep one up to the mark. I can recommend trouble for anyone who's complacent about life. Just think of the amount of winners that the Marchioness of Tavistock would suddenly have if she were overdrawn at Hambros, or the number of successes Charles St George would chalk up if the exhaust pipe on his Bentley fell off. It doesn't bear thinking about. If the roof fell in at Sunningdale, John Banks might even lay a loser.

It's not the sort of philosophy they teach at Trinity or Magdalen I know, but perhaps they should. If Lester's cigar had gone out and he wasn't offered a light, I'd hate to think what might have happened to Sir Gordon's record. No. It's obviously the thing to do. Go skint.

I remember having a perfectly miserable day at Fontwell Park one week, backing winner after winner until I met Jack Cohen. He bought me a drink, a cup of tea, a cigar and lent me the fare home. He then told me that I was a lousy good-for-nothing. Life suddenly had some sort of meaning again and it was a tremendous relief to back the last two losers. Oh yes. I shall always be grateful to him for that.

Once you are skint, all sorts of ways of trying to earn a bob or two come to mind. In the old days, people used to write begging letters, Bohemians in particular. I know one chap who used to average five a day, it didn't matter who to, just anyone from out of the telephone directory. Quite respectable people used to do it to vague acquaintances: 'I'm trying to write a book. Could you let me have five hundred quid? . . . ' But there are no longer the patrons like there used to be. There was one multi-millionaire a good few years ago who used to have a string of writers, some very famous, on his payroll, each receiving a fiver or a tenner a week. It used to make him feel good.

On the other hand Harry Diamond, the photographer, always walks along with his head held down at an odd angle. You think he's depressed or something when you first meet him. But he's not. He's watching the gutter,

Clinical Symptom of REAL Gambler No. 5

No matter how great his initial caution, the true gambler eventually risks more than he can afford.

hoping he might come across a fifty-pence piece. He once
took a photograph of Frank Norman and me in Old
Compton Street. I thought it was just some joky snapshot.
The next day Harry came round and asked for ten pounds
for the print. I gave him a fiver reluctantly, in fact very
reluctantly. It now serves as a memento of the days when
I thought that drinking whisky was some sort of a career.

Personally, I used to like to shoot craps. It's a
marvellous game because you're participating yourself. It's
not as if you're just being dealt the cards. The best game I
ever had was in The Pair of Shoes in Hertford Street, quite
a posh club years ago, which was run by Eric Steiner, a
very nice man and a good punter, one of the few ever to
beat Nick the Greek at cards. That was at poker in Las
Vegas in the fifties. The game lasted three days and they
just broke off occasionally to have a shower, a change of
clothes and some eggs and bacon.

At the time of my big win in The Shoes I was on the
bum, dishwashing. Eric knew this and for a few weeks
before Christmas he'd been well aware of what was going
on. The club served free drinks if you were punting. I
used to go in and have a pound on red and a pound on
black every night and so ate and drank for nothing, unless
zero came up. One night I had had more than just the
one. Playing craps, I had a fiver on seven and then passed
out. Somone tapped me on the shoulder and woke me up
to tell me seven had come up five consecutive times.
That's got to be somewhere near a world record. I had an
enormous pile of chips in front of me and luckily I had
enough sense to cash them in and walk out. It was
Christmas Eve and I was assured of enjoying myself after
all. The only snag was that I left half my winnings in the
bloody taxi.

There was another gambling club in Berkeley Square I
used to frequent. Before his deportation, George Raft came
up to me one night and told me Continuation would win
the Royal Hunt Cup. I knew he knew bugger all about
racing, but as he was a bit of a gangster I thought I'd put a
fiver on it. It pissed in at 25-1 and the next week he left the
country — in a hurry.

It's hard to understand why rich people still like to bet,
but they do. Robert Sangster is a shrewd punter with a lot

of nerve. I was having a drink with him at Newbury one
September when Fred Binns walked past. Robert said,
'Oh, by the way Fred, while you're there, can I have £5000
to win Detroit in the Arc?' I asked him why he was
putting five thousand pounds on his own filly to win a
race that boasted prize money of a hundred and fifty
thousand and would enhance her paddock value by a
million or more. 'Just for interest's sake,' he replied. And I
don't know whether it's true, but the Queen is reputed to
have small bets on her horses. Just a tenner at a time.
While Charles St George, a millionaire, does a yankee
every Saturday.

3

WITH THE ST LEGER APPROACHING THAT DISMAL BANK HOLIDAY
at Kempton soon faded from my memory. Despite trainers'
tips for other horses I became more and more convinced that
Crow, the French-trained and Yves Saint-Martin-ridden
contender, would win. The St Leger, the last classic, comes in
for a lot of knocking these days but it is still an important and
significant event in the racing calendar. Several winners of the
race in this century have become very important stallions and
they include Bayardo – grandsire of Hyperion, Swynford,
Hurry On, Solario and Fairway. More recently, the St Leger
has been won by many good, and some great, horses and it
seems strange that the race attracts so little enthusiasm, especially as it is often a very exciting contest to watch. The other
French challenger that year was to be ridden by that very good
French-based jockey, Bill Pyers.

I met Bill Pyers in Chantilly once and he was doing a stint
behind the bar of the hotel I use there, The Hotel du Château.
Pyers was acting barman because he said that Chantilly bored

him, but on the whole I can recommend the place. The Hotel du Château is at the end of the town and it lies behind what the French call the stables and what looks a bit like Buckingham Palace. At the end of the racecourse there's the Château du Chantilly which looks like something out of a fairy story and there's a mist and dew on the course every morning, even during the hottest of summers. By the railway station, at the other end of the town, there's the café where all the jockeys, trainers and pressmen from Paris gather, drink and natter. Behind the scenes it's a very posh place. On one visit there I looked round the stables then run by Jean Michel de Choubersky and owned by Rothschild and I looked at the house at the end of the yard and remarked how lucky he was to have such a place to live in. He said it wasn't his house but the head lad's. Later, I had lunch at his château and when I left he gave me some advice about the return trip to London. 'When you go through Paris,' he said, 'why don't you drop into the Tour D'Argent? You can get a very nice snack there.' Well, thank you Jean. Anyway, it's nothing like any racing place in England, and if you're ever passing that way it's well worth a look.

So is Lambourn, and the Lurcher Show there, organised and run by Peter Tabor, an ex-assistant trainer of Fred Winter's, and held on the Sunday after my bad experiences at Kempton, was an event I shall remember for the rest of my life. They say that you should keep your horses in the worst company and yourself in the best. Well, as far as racing company goes I was certainly in the best on this occasion. There was a marvellous lunch *chez* Peter Walwyn and I took a look around the yard that houses the older horses before that. I don't know whether you've ever tried talking to horses but they don't take a lot of notice. That yard was full of friends with the exception of Après Demain, an old enemy who had cost me dear and one which I had backed for the last time on the day beore. I asked him about the twenty quid I had lost and got very little response.

After the dog show in a nearby field in which spectators overcome by fresh air and the beer tent kept falling asleep, there were a few drinks to be had by the side of Mr Walwyn's swimming pool. Walwyn himself appeared wearing trunks and, taking a running dive into the pool, he shouted, 'Thank you, English Prince.' It seems he shouts the same message every time he takes to the water. English Prince's Irish Derby victory paid for the pool. Après Demain, I thought bitterly, hadn't paid for the tonic water that was consumed around the edge of it, the bastard. Anyway, sitting there with Joe Mercer and Jimmy Lindley and Edward Underdown was a very pleasant way of passing the evening, especially as Lindley and Mercer both backed up my opinion that Crow would win the St Leger. Even Fulke Walwyn spoke to me, and he hadn't done that for five years, since I'd remarked that his famous chaser The Dikler looked like a cart horse and he had got very upset.

This event had taken place in Lambourn one morning when I happened upon a rustic scene full of old-world charm and reminiscent of a Constable water-colour. Two men stood holding two horses by the verge in the lane opposite the Malt Shovel. The horses were eating grass contentedly and I noticed that one of them, on closer inspection, was one of the most magnificent cart horses I'd ever seen. They munched away, the birds sang in the trees, and I exchanged 'good mornings' with the stable men. Then I said: 'That's a nice looking horse you've got there,' pointing to the monster one, and added, 'I should think he could plough a field by himself in ten minutes.' At this, the horse looked round at me, made a nasty noise and then tried to kick me into the Malt Shovel before gargling time. I was extremely frightened, broke out into an immediate sweat and cowered in the doorway of the pub. I'm frightened of horses, it should be known, but this one was terrifying. The man soothed him, turned to me and said, 'This is The Dikler.' Well, Fulke Walwyn is just about the greatest trainer of jumpers there's ever been and I need hardly remind myself or you that about two years after that incident

The Dikler went on to win chasing's Blue Riband, the Cheltenham Gold Cup. But I still think he was a horrible-looking
animal.

The Malt Shovel is a very pleasant little pub opposite Fulke
Walwyn's yard. What's nicer about it than a London pub is
standing in the window and watching his and Fred Winter's
strings walking back after working on the Downs. What you
mustn't do if you go there is to take notice of everthing you
hear. You can be given fifty tips in the time it takes to drink a
pint of beer with the stable lads. You can then move on to the
Red Lion and get another fifty tips to beat the fifty you just got.
But still, it's a pleasant way to pass a morning.

I'm happy to say that Crow subsequently won the St Leger,
but the race had complications. I had lunch with a man shortly
afterwards who is well known in racing circles, has sponsored
an important race or two and has friends in well-manured
places. Another French horse in the St Leger, Campero, had
run like a pig, but his connections had vehemently denied that
the horse had been doped. My informant told me otherwise.

Before the race, two of the French challengers, Campero
and Secret Man, had run against each other and finished
within one and a half lengths of each other on two occasions.
That year the St Leger was run on 11 September and, ten days
before that, Campero stood at 8-1 in most of the ante-post lists
and Secret Man at 9-1. On the day of the race, Campero
opened at 7-1 and started at 9-1. Secret Man, on the other
hand, opened at 8-1 and started at 15-2. In the event Crow won
easily enough from Secret Man, but Campero was beaten by
approximately thirty lengths. *Raceform* said, 'Campero looked
well, prominent till the eighth furlong, beaten in straight.'
There are no more reliable publications in racing than *Raceform*, both the formbook and the red *Notebook*.

My informant went on to tell me that he was in the presence
of Campero's connections and, although he admits that
they're lousy losers on the other side of the Channel, he says
that they were shocked, flabbergasted, amazed, choked and

puzzled. The horse had been aimed at the St Leger for ages. They expected it to run really well. At least, Maurice Zilber, the horse's trainer, did.

Now it so happens, and this is where there might be a little crunch, that days after, when Zilber was talking to the owner, the latter owned up to having had thirty thousand pounds to win on Campero. This is quite surprising and not a very small bet for a businessman to have on the first horse he'd ever owned. When you consider that the same owner, to the best of Zilber's knowledge, had never been on a racecourse before, then you realise that it was an enormous bet even by old-fashioned standards.

When I was told this, I immediately asked my informant, 'How could he get such a bet on?' since bookmakers, generally speaking, lost their nerve in the 'thirties'. Well, he said, he'd checked on that and all the big boys had admitted that it had been a particularly strong market for the St Leger. Lots of people had shovelled it on that year.

Now it was odd that all the doped horses that season – as far as one could tell, that is – had been doped to win and not to lose. How then did anyone get at Campero to stop it? It must have been got at over here in England. Remembering that Jockey Club security had had well-publicised lapses, it was fairly safe to assume that someone got at the beast at Doncaster itself. When? When the horse was at exercise. How? Easily. By putting something in the manger. How? Easy again. It was a fact then, even if it might be a little more difficult now, that any man carrying a bucket in one hand and preferably wearing a cloth cap could get into anywhere where they kept valuable racehorses in this country.

If you don't believe that, I can tell you that I had recently spent an undisturbed half-hour in a yard that housed what then must have been five million pounds worth of horseflesh. One man looked at me and said, 'Mornin' guvnor,' and another just grinned at me and went on his way. I know, for a fact, that you can't do that on courses like Longchamp. I also know, for a fact, that ten years ago you could wander fairly freely around stable courses in this country. So anyway, *who* had Campero stopped?

Obviously that's what was intriguing, and still is, because once you've cleared the owner and trainer the field is wide open. I'll tell you another thing about bookmakers and, hoping you've worked out that thirty thousand pounds at 8-1 is a liability of two hundred and forty thousand pounds, a very good friend of mine had recently reported the not unusual sight of one of the biggest bookmakers in the country having lunch with one of the best jockeys in the country in one of the best restaurants in the country. I wouldn't be at all surprised if he still doesn't retain a couple to pull the odd favourite, but that's another matter . . . And remember, if you back losers and whether they've been doped or not, then there are sound-proof booths for moaners. Meanwhile, I was forming the opinion that if there was a guard dog with teeth in Newmarket and a watchman who was not permanently sloshed at Chantilly, then Welsh Flame might win the forthcoming Cambridgeshire, and Ivanjica the Prix de L'Arc de Triomphe.

pulling the fast one

It's not only trainers and jockeys who resort to sharp practices, gamblers cheat too. I suppose the most common scam used to be betting after time. In America, some time ago, they went to an enormous amount of trouble to get the man who relayed the racecourse commentaries to the bookmakers' offices to delay his commentaries for just one minute. They cleaned up packets before they were tumbled. There are endless dodges used by betting shop employees to mistime bets and you might wonder why they bother since they always get caught. It's the really petty stuff that intrigues me, though. A friend who is an

ex-runner for a bookie told me a fairly sordid story when I
last met him. He said he was standing in a pub one day
where he used to take bets when a woman said to him
that he'd dropped something and pointed to a bit of paper
on the floor. Without much thinking he thanked her,
picked it up and put it in his pocket. Of course, it was a
slip for a race that had just been run. He found out later
that her husband got the results on the phone, she'd then
write out a winning bet and drop it on the floor by the
nearest bookmaker.

The same man also told me about the strange graffiti on
the wall of the Gents in a south London pub. He was idly
gazing at it one day during an inter-race slash when he
noticed that nearly all the words written had more than
four letters. They were in fact the names Gentle Art,
King's Petition and Prince Pan, which is exactly how they
finished in the 1963 running of the Woodcote Stakes.
Someone had been very fly in getting the results on the
dot, tearing down to the Gents to write them up on the
wall where someone else would come in and see them
and write out a quick bet after time. Oddly enough it
never occurs to this friend of mine to admit that he was
a bit of a mug. I'm less surprised than he is that he is no
longer in the bookmaking business. Incidentally, he's a
very strange bird indeed. He now manages an old
people's home, but he's always got wads of readies on
him when he comes up to the West End. I suspect that
quite a few wills are written in his favour by people who
discover too late that he's standing on the oxygen tube.
But that's another matter.

The coup I liked the best that never came off was the
Francasal affair. If you don't remember it, they put in a
ringer at Bath one day, cut the telephone wires to London
so that the money couldn't get back and spoil the price
and then they plunged on the horse which was returned,
I think, at 100-8. The only other method I know of backing
winners is to study form and take no notice of anyone.
I've been doing that for years and the larder is still empty.

4

BEFORE TRYING OUT MY HUNCHES FOR THE CAMBRIDGESHIRE and the Arc de Triomphe, it was time to cross to Ireland for the Irish St Leger. There are things and people that can only happen over there and the place was still the friendly madhouse it has always been. At Waterford, where I first stopped for a couple of nights, I visited a golf club and saw a painted notice at the entrance of the place that would make an English golfer turn pale with horror. The notice said, 'Members are forbidden to train geyhounds on the links.'

It was wonderfully typical of the country. Inquiring about the notice I learned that the procedure was one of getting the dog you really wanted to work out to run with two others. What they do is to get someone to stand on the green and wave a handkerchief at the men holding three dogs on the tee. The men on the tee let one go and then another and when the first one's gone fifty yards they let the important dog go another fifty yards later. Apparently the third dog tries like a lunatic to catch up the other two and the gallop, as it were, brings him on a ton. When I asked the man who took me up to the place whether the other members got annoyed at this sort of activity he told me that, no they didn't, they just leant on their clubs and made rapid bets as to whether the third dog would catch the other two.

What was so Irish was that the man who introduced me to the place was a local and highly respected doctor who had been temporarily barred from my hotel for three months for breaking a chandelier in the restaurant. You could look for years, and sadly without success, in England to find a doctor like that. The good doctor also happened to own a load of property and a bar that I reckon was one hundred yards long. He told me that he thought it would be a nice idea to have his own place to drink in, had bought it for thirty-five thousand pounds, spent the same amount on it and was now going in for breeding cattle. Someone else said they thought he'd be a millionaire within five years, and then they introduced me to the local big deal dentist.

By the time I met him there'd been three races at Newbury, he was a hundred and fifty quid down and he couldn't stand up. He mumbled something about wanting a 'getting out' bet, so I told him what I thought might win the next. It lost. He lost another fifty quid and staggered off into the early afternoon. Just after that bit of disaster someone else came into the bar and told me that the waiter in the hotel had been easvesdropping on our conversation over breakfast and, thinking that three English racing journalists might know what they were talking about, had followed our tips. He went down by no less than three hundred pounds.

I couldn't believe it at first. I mean, can you imagine an English waiter with enough nerve to bang on three hundred pounds hearsay? Anyway, the two days in Waterford ended in disaster. We drove up to the Curragh on Saturday morning with empty pockets and sore heads. Both were soon revived. At the Curragh I was treated like visiting royalty in the way that the Irish always treat nonentities. I was taken to the oak-lined, champagne-filled, private rooms occupied by the men that ran the course. Compared to England it was an unbelievable scene. They wouldn't even let the Stewards of the course in the place it was so posh and yet there I was drinking what they called shampoo with the director of the course, Joe McGrath, and his brother the director of the Irish Hospital Sweeps, Paddy McGrath, who was reputed to have one hundred and fifty million in his current account. He turned to me half way through the afternoon and said, 'I can't understand why they call us the McGrafia.' Then he told me he couldn't sell or buy shares without the knowledge of it sending firms broke or ridiculously up-market.

For the two hours before the St Leger itself we all scanned the form to try to find something that would beat the odds-on favourite Meneval. I opted for Navarre. Meneval won easily, smoothly and by eight lengths. Piggott won three races altogether during the afternoon and I wasn't on a single one of them. Lesson. Don't be greedy. Short-priced winners are better than any kind of loser and it's as well to remember that not only do you win a little, but you actually get your wretched stake back. That night in Dublin the doctor came to the rescue with a financial injection. I said that I was a bit sick of racing and just wanted to go out and have a drink in those haunts where I'd drunk with the likes of Behan years before.

'A drink,' he said. 'Well, you'll be needing twenty pounds.'

'No,' I said, 'a drink means about five pounds.' (This was all of ten years ago, remember.)

'You might run into trouble,' he said and pressed the twenty quid into my hand.

'And when will you be wanting it back?' I asked, slipping into Irish.

'Next year at Royal Ascot,' he said.

Of all people who take themselves too seriously, the English racing classes ought to plead guilty and I mean more guilty than even those in the entertainment business. Offer some criticism to a jockey, poke some fun at a trainer and the heavens open up. I was once told I was responsbile for one trainer's heart attack. I had simply remarked, somewhat facetiously, that he covered the distance of ground between his yard and his local pub at a speed reminiscent of The Tetrarch. (He should have been so well bred!) The man exploded and apparently made some remark to the effect that trainers of racehorses were due respect because they trained racehorses. Well, well. What a funny lot some of them are. The trouble is that most of the genuinely funny ones are across the sea in Ireland.

Take Mick O'Toole. I once stayed the weekend with him at the Curragh. They're two days I shall never forget, though I can't remember them. He showed me round his yard on the morning I arrived. I used to pretend to be knowledgeable about horses on appearance, but I'm not. That's something you have to be brought up to. But on this occasion I was showing off, pretending I knew. Mick pulled a horse out of a box and said, 'There's a nice little fella here we've got.' 'He looks very good,' I replied. 'He looks as though he should stay three miles.'

Mick's retort was to the point. 'Jesus, Jeffrey, you're a fool. He couldn't stay bloody two miles in a fucking horsebox.'

Then we went to the pub. His wife prevailed on us to be back for lunch: 'There's a lovely joint in the oven . . .' The pub was owned by Pat Eddery's father, Jimmy, and we arrived at opening time. Mick cautioned me: 'The old woman, she really means it. I daren't mess up the lunch. We can only have the one.' We were still there seven hours later.

The next day – it must have been about ten minutes away – he took me to the dogs in Dublin at Selhurst Park. Now since O'Toole was at one time in his early days a dog trainer I was more than eager that he should mark my card. He was quick to reassure me: 'You've got nothing to worry about, Jeffrey, just follow me.' My resources were limited. I was there on feeble expenses from some magazine. There were eight dog races that night and I backed everything Mick told me to. Together, we backed eight consecutive losers.

He was tremendously amused by our going skint, but I found it very hard to raise a smile since I have a genuine loathing for running out of money when I'm abroad. Actually, I'm not that fond of running out of money at Harringay, Ascot or in my betting shop, but giving handouts to bookies in Ireland or the Paris-Mutuel in France is ghastly. Anyway, O'Toole whistled all the way back to the Shelbourne hotel with me whining beside him: 'I just don't know what to do, Mick. You've screwed me up completely. I haven't got a pot to piss in.' I've never seen a man raise a float so quickly as he did. Within three minutes his pockets were running over and he 'saw me alright'. I tried to pay him back a day or so later but he refused: 'Keep it, Jeffrey. You don't owe me anything. You're a guest in my country.' He has a lot of friends does Mr O'Toole, he puts his money where his mouth is when he has a bet and I've never known the man complain when his horses do get stuffed.

I'd very much like to take a few of the humourless and pompus English trainers over to the Curragh and around his yard to show them that you don't have to imitate Colonel Blimp to train horses. Con Collins who trains over there is another case, and he has extraordinary ideas of what hospitality consists of. When I called in at his establishment I was shown into a sitting room and then a maid came in carrrying a tray on which were poised a glass, a bottle of Scotch whisky, a bottle of Irish, a bottle of gin, a bottle of brandy and a bottle of vodka. 'Mr Collins will be with you in five minutes and he says you're to ring the bell if you need any more to drink', she said.

I was still musing about the different types you meet in racing when I attended the Newmarket sales soon after the Irish St Leger. I only saw one record broken and that had nothing to do with horses. The record in question was a drink one. I saw one trainer from the West Country move into the bar at 10am, buy himself a large whisky and sit rooted to the spot for five hours without budging except to replenish his glass. This beat, by two hours, a record I'd seen set by an Irish trainer six years previously at Ballsbridge. Now I'm not sitting in judgement on the man, particularly since it took me five hours of my own time to observe, console and accompany him. The method is surprisingly successful, though on the face of it you'd think it would be tremendously difficult to buy, let alone bid for, a horse if you don't see one and aren't in the ring.

For all his five-hour sessions in the bar, my boozy friend is the heart and soul of racing. He once won one of the biggest handicaps in the calendar, only had fifty quid on the horse and celebrated the victory for four weeks. He treats his staff well, tells his owners they're fools if they are and by so doing loses their custom, and he's ridden over the sticks himself and

broken more bones than banks. He never moans when he has
a bad run and he doesn't gloat when he beats his colleagues
and rivals. He doesn't suffer rich fools gladly and so he's
unfashionable. When he does train a winner, the butcher,
baker and garage-keeper appear at his backdoor within four
hours. He lends impecunious stable boys money, gives
handouts to anyone in the business who needs them if he can
and he cries all the way to the bank. He's in his fifties now and
it's unlikely he'll ever strike it rich, but he can show the young
trainers a thing or two. Thank God for him, and for making the
sales, the courses and the bars worth visiting.

the good, the bad and the ugly

Trainers, by and large, move in mysterious ways.
Originally they were known as 'training grooms'. The title
was appropriate. They fed and cantered the horses and
took their orders from owners who knew as much about
the business as they did. It was the Hon George Lambton
who first made racehorse training a posh occupation
round about the turn of the century. It was he, by the
way, who made my favourite snob remark of all time. As
an undergraduate at Cambridge he rode regularly to
Newmarket to ride work, and one day on the Heath a
gentleman work-watcher asked him what college he went
to. 'I don't know,' replied Lambton, 'Trinity I suppose.'
   Since then the training of horses has gathered about it
an utterly disproportionate glamour – equalled only by the
ridiculous reverence heaped on fashion photographers
who are known to sleep with their models. I fancy you
detect a note of sour grapes in my tone; if there is one,
then it is because I'm fairly convinced that with the help of
a good Irish head lad I too could train the likes of a
Nijinsky, a Sea Bird II or a Shergar. In fact, I'm pretty sure
that a horse of the stamp of Nijinsky could be galloped up

the side of a slag heap every morning and still win the
Derby.

Perhaps it's not quite as simple as that, and yes, of
course, there are trainers who are tremendously skilful.
Richard Hannon is one. He has won the Two Thousand
Guineas twice, both times with comparatively cheap
horses – Mon Fils and Don't Forget Me. Cheap horses are
a feature of his Marlborough yard. He often takes on the
bigger, classier yards and beats them. Such has been his
success that he is now capable of training more winners
then any but the ten or so biggest stables in the country.

Quite apart from his brilliance as a trainer he is also an
unusually inventive gambler. About ten years ago his wife
had triplets, two boys and a girl. One night after his wife
and children had gone to bed, Richard was downstairs
enjoying a drink with a merry band of lunatic, punting-
mad Irishmen when he had a brilliant idea. He crept
upstairs, got hold of the triplets, brought them down to
the sitting room and arranged them on the sofa. 'Now,' he
announced, 'we're going to play Find the Lady.' So there
were the triplets gurgling happily on the sofa while all
around them Richard's Irish friends were bunging on ten-
pound notes, twenties, fifties, until finally a fortune had
piled up on each of the babies. Then Richard would
remove their nappies with a flourish and pay the punters
who had found the lady. Then the game would start
again: 'All out of the room,' Richard would bellow, 'while I
shuffle them.' This marvellous source of income naturally
came to an end when the babies grew old enough for their
sexes to become too obvious, but before then fortunes
were gambled on this real-life version of the three-card
trick.

Richard got very merry when Mon Fils won the Guineas
at fifty to one. 'Fuck you all,' he told the press. 'I'll never
have to work again.' Of course he was back at the yard on
Monday morning as usual.

I used to go to the sales with Dave Hanley, Eddie
Reavey, Richard Hannon and my friend from Lambourn
Doug Marks. On one occasion one of their number, I
won't say who, never actually clapped eyes on a horse. He
was in the bar all day every day for three days. But he
consulted the catalogue from time to time and, on the

strength of the breeding alone, sent someone out to bid for him. He ended up with a couple of decent animals and, as I've already said, it is a system I can recommend, especially to those trainers whose yards are stuffed with hand-picked million-dollar purchases that look good but won't do a tap.

Hanging round the sales is where you meet racing characters more than on the track, and you really do meet some idiots. How they get to be entrusted with millions of pounds worth of horseflesh is one of racing's enduring mysteries. Typical of this sort is the young, arrogant trainer who treats the stable lads the way he treated fags at school. There's even a PR man in the business who's so shabby that when he was an assistant trainer he actually did beat his stable staff. Anyway, this young idiot trainer appears at the sales in the morning in jodhpurs, roll-neck jersey and Barbour and immediately drops house points for boasting about his hangover. He then spends most of the morning trying to ingratiate himself with anyone with a title and more than a hundred thousand in his account. A disgusting sight.

In the afternoon he appears on the stands in a curly-brimmed soft hat and sounds off at full volume in an accent borrowed from St James's Street until about nine in the evening, at which time the wheels fall off his act and he roars off with his chums to some unspeakable olde worlde pub masquerading as a restaurant. Here they revert to prefect days at school, chuck bread rolls at people and scream at their lady friends, all of whom are called Arabella or Emma.

I know one trainer of this type who managed to book Lester Piggott to ride one of his horses. He had a hefty punt on it, but they were beaten a neck. This twit said to Lester afterwards: 'That's it, Lester. You'll never ride for me again.' Dry as you like Lester replied: 'Oh well, I'd better hang up my boots then, hadn't I?'

A band of trade union officials once bought a horse and sent it to this same idiot. One day they organised a coach trip to the yard to see the animal. There were two coach loads of proud, expectant owners, armed with sandwiches and Thermos flasks, all set for a visit to the stables to see their noble beast followed by an excellent day at the races, all for two quid a head. When they arrived at the training establishment, nothing stirred. Not a cock was crowing, not a stable lad in sight. Baffled, perplexed, they piled out of the coaches and wandered up to the house. They looked through a downstairs window. All they could see was their chosen trainer, in his dinner jacket, lying on a sofa and snoring, two empty champagne bottles on the table beside him. His career as a trainer was short-lived.

I don't want to give the impression that every trainer is a sozzled prat who looks as if someone's just waved a British Rail Race Day 'Special' pork pie under his nose. Take Bill Marshall, for instance, one of the most likeable characters of the Turf. He flew his own Spitfire from South Africa to England in 1940 and said to the RAF: 'Here's a plane and here's a pilot. Help yourself.' He shot down plenty of German planes and was awarded the DFC. Eventually he was shot down himself and was incarcerated in a prisoner-of-war camp. Needless to say he escaped, walked from Bavaria to the north coast of France, nicked a boat and made it back to England. He couldn't speak a word of German and so anyone who asked awkward questions on the way was making a big mistake. Bill used to train at Edenbridge, from where he sent out Raffingora to break the course record at Epsom over five furlongs (hand timing) and thus become the fastest horse in the world. He's only a tiny skinny fellow, but not one to provoke. After he moved to Newmarket he had a row with a colossus of a lorry driver who was trying to dump some supplies Bill hadn't ordered. When things got really heated, Bill simply laid him out with a punch that wouldn't have disgraced Sugar Ray Robinson.

He was one of the very few trainers who actually rode work rather than watching from the back of a hack. Some days he used to ride out three lots, not bad for a man in his fifites. Some of the old brigade of Newmarket trainers thought he was a bit of a nut, but Bill used to say it kept him fit and cleared the liver of any left-over champagne. When he retired he went to Barbados to sit in the sun and drink rum. But he soon got bored of that and now, aged about seventy, he is champion trainer over there. When not working he can be found sitting on a boat with a fishing rod in one hand and a rum punch in the other muttering to himself, 'This is the life.'

I can never understand how some of the biggest trainers who have up to two hundred horses in their yards keep track of them all, but you can't argue with success – look at Henry Cecil, he trains enough horses to fill the card at Newmarket for an entire season. And yet the man has a compulsive habit of collecting white shoes and is tee-total – which, I am reluctant to say, gives the lie to the idea that water is the refuge of half-wits. Barry Hills commands a similarly huge operation at Robert Sangster's complex at Manton. Hills made his money on a horse called Frankincense, which he backed down from 66-1 to 100-8 to win the Lincoln, enabling him to rise overnight from travelling head lad to trainer. That's the sort of story that makes people like me broke.

I suppose you have to love horses to be any good with them, and I don't. The girl who did the late Ryan Price's national winner Kilmore was so deeply attached to the animal that she wanted to take it on holiday with her. 'Where the hell are you going to go?' the Captain asked. 'Well, Guvnor, I'm going to a hotel in Bournemouth and I though he could stay on the lawn outside.' He was a great character, Ryan Price. He once employed a stable girl who was rather well-endowed. When he saw her having difficulty mounting a horse he would shout: 'Just throw your tits over and the rest will follow.'

But it doesn't do to get too obsessed with racing at the expense of everything else, though I don't see why you should take that sort of advice from me. One day I was being driven back from the races by an old pisspot of a trainer along with his wife Maisy and one of the gutsiest jockeys ever, whom I'd better call K, a real tough nut. He used to kick dead-beat horses into enormous fences in an absurdly fearless manner, but that day he'd ridden one of this trainer's horses without success. Anyway, this trainer and I were in the front of the car, with Maisy and K in the back. Maisy had her head concealed under an old tartan blanket and it was quite clear to me what was going on. The poor old trainer was rambling away about horses as usual: 'You know, K, I think perhaps we ought to try that horse over a different trip next time . . . Give him two and a half miles in the soft and he could be anything,

especially if we let him make his own running . . . ' It was
lucky he was talking to K not Maisy. Her mouth was full,
and it wasn't a lollipop she was sucking.

5

THE FLAT SEASON EVENTUALLY CAME TO AN END, PRODUCING ITS
usual bag of mixed results. In the Cambridgeshire, Welsh
Flame ran as though he was carrying two tons through a bog. I
had a nice win at the Arc de Triomphe, but then dropped the
lot on the Dewhurst. I'll save the details of my disastrous
Champion Stakes day, experienced from the not so safe
distance of Soho, for later. It was now time to turn the
attention to the jumps. I was soon wishing that it wasn't.

The poshest racecourse in England, Ascot, has an extraordinary grandstand. As far as I'm concerned it's a multi-million-
pound concrete shambles. On Black and White day, at the end
of November, I met at least six people who'd got lost in it. The
escalators make it seem like something between an air terminal and a modern hospital. Come to that, I suppose it's a bit
like a large store with no goods. Anyway, that's not my main
beef. Neither is the fact that there are more bars in the
grandstand than there are pubs in Brighton.

What I can't stand about the place is that it's so bloody hard
to win money there. The horse cracked up by so many as being
the star of Fred Winter's stable was not only returned at an
unbackably short price, it then got well and truly outstayed by
a rival. By the time Napoleon Brandy had been beaten in the
second race I was making full use of the bar facilities in that
dreadful stand. It was then that one of Toby Balding's owners
came to my rescue. His name was Harry Beccle and he saved
the day for me. Harry is an Eastender who'd already done

pretty well for himself, well enough anyway to send his son to a posh prep school. When he went to watch him run in the hundred yards, surrounded by po-faced parents, he suddenly heard to his horror his own voice screaming out, 'Come on my son!' A dead give-away if ever there was one. He even managed to make me laugh when the wrong horse won the big race. By this time I was thinking of taking a part-time job, but I still didn't realise that I was about to lose more than I'd ever lost in one day's racing.

Meanwhile, Harry went on laughing at his own jokes and when someone picked him up on it he said with incredible logic, 'I laugh at my own jokes because it's the first time I've heard them.' By now I was falling for that silly old thing of picking prices and not horses, and by backing to get out of trouble I was getting deeper into it. I managed to forget my troubles for a few minutes when a lot of us watched the Night Nurse v Bird's Nest race on television. I looked at Bob Turnell's face as much as I looked at the television set: watching a trainer's face when he's got something in a big race is one of my favourite occupations. I stood next to Bernard van Cutsem a few years ago when his two-hundred-and-ten-thousand-pound charge Crowned Prince got stuffed at Newmarket. It was unnecessary to look at the race. I could read it in his face. As the face got longer, I knew that Crowned Prince was finding nothing.

On this occasion when Bird's Nest came to the second flight from home, Mr Turnell's entourage started bobbing up and down. By the time he cleared the last they were jumping up and down, almost hitting the ceiling. Bob Turnell was one of the greatest National Hunt trainers in post-war years. I am one of the greatest losers.

I'd arrived at Ascot determined to back one particular horse. Harry put me off it, and it was all his fault. Another runner couldn't be beaten, he said, and I went along with him especially since it was a better price. What folly, what insanity. I was now breaking into the weekend money, having done the housekeeping money after losing the gas and light money. With one race to go Harry was still laughing – I think his pockets might have been deeper than mine – and I was near tears. Fred Winter's representative was a certainty for the last race. Everyone knew it. So it was the second horse of the day to start at an unbackable price. Of course, what I should have done was to shovel everything on, float a quick loan and bang that on too. But off I went looking for outsiders again. It's a funny thing that it never occurs to one, when one's having a nervous breakdown that is, that outsiders are outsiders because they're not very good. So I backed almost everything in the wretched race that was more than 6-1.

I couldn't even bring myself to watch it. I stood on a balcony and took the occasional peep round the corner while hoping that the racecourse commentator had got his colours confused. But, damn it, the last peep I took revealed the unmistakable colours of the favourite zooming across the finishing line like Ribot. By now it was getting dark. The champagne was running out and a sausage roll left over from some other meeting was playing havoc with my guts. The girl I was with was looking at me with more disbelief than pity. I made the usual futile remarks about Monday being another day and Harry quite rightly pointed out that so was Tuesday.

Switching to large ports to fend off the evening air and general *angst*, we stayed in the bar until the course was almost deserted. I sat there uttering the usual clichés about racing teaching one to lose. Suddenly, for the life of me, I couldn't see what was so good about learning to lose.

It was a different woman who accompanied me to Sandown Park the next week, and she'd never been racing before. It's always fascinating in a ghastly sort of way to take someone to the races for the first time because they inevitably ask such daft questions. At one point this particular lady asked me why did the horses have tissue paper stuck to the inside of their hind quarters. I couldn't think what the hell she was talking about, gingerly approached the rear end of a horse in the

Black and White Day, Ascot

BEFORE   AFTER

Another runner couldn't be beaten, he said, and I went along with him especially since it was a better price. What folly, what insanity.

unsaddling enclosure and realised she was referring to the white foam that horses sweat.

She did make the interesting observation that racing people look conspiratorial, tend to talk out of the side of their mouths and invariably look as though they're up to no good. I've got so used to them that I don't notice, but she was right. A jockey we were with that day talked to us as though he was operating a ventriloquist's dummy and it was while sitting with him that I had the month's most embarassing moment. An owner new to racing joined us at our table in the bar. Thinking himself a bit of a lad, he suddenly leant forward and said to this jockey, 'I suppose you've pulled a few in your time?' This is roughly like asking a police officer, 'Taken any good bribes this week?' The amount of people in racing who don't engage brain before operating mouth sometimes seems to grow daily.

For the first three races my companion attempted to pick the winners by what she called cosmic means. When that failed, she turned to astrology. I pointed out to her that the sun signs method might be slightly unbalanced since horses are born in the first half of the year leaving everything from Leo to Sagittarius pretty blank. When I told her, just to make converstion mind you, that Park Top and I shared a birthday on 27 May she became even more convinced that it was all in the stars. I'm glad to say that she then went completely skint.

Two questions that newcomers to racing are continually asking is 'What's going to win?' and 'What won?' You might think that when something wins by ten lengths or so that it would be unnecessary to ask, but they always do. The other thing they always tell you is what a wonderful life you lead if you write about racing. There's an assumption that you never back losers and that the champagne in the Members' Bar is free.

'Why don't you ask that trainer what's going to win?' is another phrase that keeps popping up. I never ask trainers for tips and I've always been convinced that it's bad form. Why the hell should any trainer tell the world when he thinks he might have a touch? I'd keep very quiet about it if I trained and thought I had something that might win the next at 10-1. In fact, trainers in this country are tremendously co-operative with the press. In France they show journalists round the back to the tradesmens' entrance.

After the last race we dillied and we dallied in the bar with a few of the spivs and the touts and the lady then told me what wonderful warm human beings they were. She obviously thought it was just like *Guys and Dolls*. I pointed out to her on the way home that they were desperate men who'd been up to more tricks and dodges than she'd dreamt of, but she wasn't having any of it. I then realised that she'd unknowingly become hooked on racing and in only one afternoon. I suppose that's what gets all of us punters at it in the beginning. On the Turf there are men for all occasions. There are cultured men, kind men, good men, hooligans and absolute bastards. I've never believed the old adage that on the Turf as under it all men are equal, but you certainly get all sorts. She took a particular shine to Jack Doyle, the bloodstock agent, and kept telling me how sexy he was. I pointed out to her that he was Irish and therefore couldn't be sexy but she would have it. Then she got it all wrong when she reminded me that it was he who originally bought Bruni for seven thousand six hundred pounds. She thought it was good business since that was such a lot of money. I told her it was good business because it was so little money and she began trying to work that one out. I supposed that in a few weeks she'd know it all. Show someone a horserace, wait until they back their first winner and they think they invented the game.

the false messiah

To see a newcomer to racing getting hooked, then
stumbling, then crashing, is like watching a man falling off
the top of a building in slow motion. Take Antonio.
Antonio was the Portuguese barman who served in the
Soho pub I used to frequent. He gave the impression of
being carefree, but really he was manic. His addiction to
matters concerning the Turf began one day when he put
fifty pence on a horse of Scobie Breasley's called Hittite
Glory. The animal trotted up at 100-1 and Antonio got the
idea that he could repeat the performance every day for
the rest of his life. The fact that he didn't know one end of
a horse from the other made things awkward for him and
watching him study the midday *Evening Standard* (as it
then was) was sadly like watching a junkie who can't
remember how a hypodermic's put together.

Anyway, someone told him I knew the odd trainer and
horses, and he started asking me to mark his card for him
every day. As far as Antonio went, looking back on it, it
was already too late to shout a warning. I simply tried to
cushion the inevitable sickening thud by giving him a few
winners on the way down, but I think the results may
have speeded up his descent. I started off by giving him
a couple of good things each day and then astounded
myself by giving him four out of four which he did in a
yankee. The very next day I gave him a nourishing 32-1
double, followed by another winner the day after which
cruised in at 9-1.

I then began to fear for his sanity although I had always
thought he was suspect in the head. In two lousy weeks
only, he suddenly knew it all, and one night I nearly killed
him when he, like a baby trying to walk by himself for the
first time, actually had the nerve to venture an opinion.
'That horse Wollow, he's no good,' he said. So crass was
the remark that I can very nearly savour it now, but at the
time I was tremendously tempted to jump over the
counter and hit him over the head with a bottle of his own
revolting Mateus Rosé. I know a teacher at St Martin's
School of Art who felt much the same when one of his

students told him that Rembrandt couldn't paint, and there was Antonio, only one and a half flat seasons, a yankee and a couple of doubles old, telling me that Wollow was no good. They really make me want to weep, do newcomers to racing.

I debated whether or not I should intentionally give Antonio a couple of pigs to back in the hope that it would put him off and shut him up for good, but even that harsh measure isn't as easy as it sounds. In the fifties and in the same pub I used to have a pound bet with a friend every day in which we'd try to go through the card naming a horse in every race that would *not* get placed. Time after time I thought, and we both thought, we'd done it and then some hack would get its nose in the frame at 20-1.

But if only Antonio's lunacy had stopped there. It didn't. He acquired an irritating habit of telling me that the Portuguese discovered the world. Surely, I asked him the first time he said it, you mean a part of it? No. Apparently not. Before Mr Ferdinand Magellan's trip there was nothing. Worse was to come. Antonio then began falling under the spell of one 'Irish' Des, a man who claimed that Lester Piggott couldn't ride racehorses. God preserve us from people like that. Perhaps it's a bit like what Stevenson said about marriage. Betting on a horse is a step so grave and decisive that it attracts light-headed, variable men by its very awfulness. It could even be simpler. Maybe I just happened to use a pub frequented by two lunatics.

Impersonating God, giving tips in other words, is a tricky business. Many tips are simply flushed away. I sometimes think, when the game is really bad that is, that the easiest way out would be to get up in the morning, just shove fifty quid in the loo and then pull the chain. What fascinates me is the way that people react to losing tips.

Inured as I am to personal disaster, I have come to regard losing bets over the past few years as losses of bits of paper. I don't mean to sound flash by that. I just mean that I don't expect miracles but don't mind them when they come to pass. On the other hand, when I do get what I think is a genuine bit of information, then I feel bound and obliged to pass it on.

The False Messiah

. . . and then astounded myself by giving him four out of four which he did in a yankee.

I once lumbered a friend of mine, a painter of some repute, with two complete stinkers. He is a fearless gambler and I guessed he must have lost a thousand pounds on the two. I met him on the next Monday morning over coffee and he uttered not a single word of reproach. Lovely and as it should be. I ran across him once in a betting shop. I was moaning because I was down a little 'How's it going?' he asked. 'Awful. I've just lost twenty-five quid and I'm really fed up. How about you?' 'Not so good either,' he replied. 'I've just lost two thousand seven hundred, including the tax.' It was only two-thirty. There had only been two races. (Another painter of my acquaintance used to owe a mad Irish bookmaker so much money that he had to keep painting his portrait for nothing. If you see a show of his, look out for pictures of 'The Pink Man'.)

But others accept losing tips with less equanimity than my painter friend. What I'm getting at is the fact that there are those who mistakenly accept the hunch as gospel. They're not Christians, just punters and I wish to God that they'd get it right. A tip is an opinion. It might be a strong opinion – one stated with some conviction – but it's still just an opinion and if all of them were bang on target then there wouldn't be such things as horse races. Worse than tipping losers to bad losers is tipping winners to idiots and then not backing them yourself.

I was having a shave in a barber's shop in Old Compton Street one Monday morning and the man operating the cut-throat asked me what I fancied. For a moment I couldn't answer him since I'd noticed the most extraordinary thing. Instead of using tissue paper to wipe the razor on after every clean sweep of the chin, he was using betting slips nicked from the local betting shop. Having digested that, I went on to say that a certain horse of Fred Winter's might oblige at a long price. Gastronomic and alcoholic events that followed prevented me from having a wager that afternoon. In the evening, when I read that the horse had won at 12-1, I choked.

At one time in my life, I found myself being followed and I didn't like it. Amost every time I stuck a bet with my unlicensed bookmaker in the local pub the wager was duplicated by a woman called Eva. She had a sort of faith in me that was more dumb than blind. It had started in the spring. I had called round to her flat – it was more of a 'salon' than a flat actually – to discuss the previous day's appalling behaviour and to borrow some money from her. She asked me if there was, by any chance, a particular nag that I fancied that day. I told her that I'd been waiting for a certain hurdler which was running that afternoon and she gave me a tenner to put on for her. That evening, I presented her with a hundred pounds and it was that evening that she got the idea that winning a hundred on a horse was as easy as falling out of a taxi.

In fact, I suspect that she got the idea that winning a hundred was something that could be done on every race, never mind once a day. Well, we had our ups and downs, did Eva and I, and that was the beginning of the best run of luck I'd had for a very long time. We took to having snacks in the Connaught and I went on making inspired guesses and, d'you know, we just couldn't go wrong.

Then came the inevitable period when I couldn't pick anything that even made the frame, never mind won. Well, nearly. But the plucky little woman still followed me. It put me in something of a quandary. In the first place the said Eva, hereinafter referred to as the PLW (for plucky little woman), had the extraordinary idea that money is pieces of paper. In view of that you might think it odd of me to have a conscience about tipping her losers, but it doesn't work like that.

It's something that you just can't help feeling bad about. The nitty gritty of the business is the fact that I can't bear putting money on for someone else even when it's their wretched choice. If you're betting on credit and sticking on for other people you can do your money by the time they send out the cheques or the bills and you've still got to find the readies for your friends. Is that quite clear? I thought it was a terrible sentence. Another thing that's unbearable about getting involved with others is the person who has a go at you when they lose. It's unforgivable in fact. The PLW didn't do that; she was as good as gold, or in her case platinum. What she did do when she lost was bathe me in one of those looks that labradors give you after you've kicked them and which mean, 'I hope you didn't hurt your foot.'

No, what then began troubling my conscience was the fact that my luck turned again and I had two very nourishing touches on horses trained by J. Webber. On both occasions I snuck off round the corner to put the money on, having told the PLW that I wasn't betting that day. I was almost in her boots because I was tipped both animals and the man that gave them to me was furious that I didn't put more on. Megalomania had reared its ugly head. Winning tipsters want to play God a little.

Can you imagine it? That man was actually angry that his tips hadn't made me rich. I can understand it in a way because I can remember feeling slightly irritated with the PLW when I'd given her a winner and she'd said I'm wonderful but hadn't gone on and on saying it. Then, of course, there's superstition and the more you try and despise that the more superstitious you get. On the quiet, I began thinking that the PLW might have been a jinx on me. I knew logically that what she happened to be doing at closing time couldn't possibly affect the performance of a horse in tomorrow's three o'clock at Ripon, but I *felt* it. Mind you, there wasn't much I could do about it. She was hell-bent on throwing pieces of paper at the bookmaking fraternity and if one is doomed to make that kamikaze trip to Carey Street then one might as well have company.

That reminds me. Just about the most honest thing that could ever have been uttered in a bankruptcy court was the classic remark made by the actor Valentine Dyall, radio's 'The Man in Black'. The Recorder asked him, 'To what do you attribute your downfall?' Mr Dyall replied, 'Two-and-a-half-mile handicap hurdles.' What I'd like to know is what about the bloody summer sprint handicaps? Come to that, what about the Bollinger in the Members' Bar, and the novice chases, and the hunter-chasers? It's one hell of a struggle, isn't it?

6

EARLY IN DECEMBER I WENT DOWN TO LAMBOURN TO SEE MY trainer. God, how I've longed to be able to say that. The rich owners of this world may be well used to the phrase, but I get a kick out of being able to use it at last. Let me explain. In a moment of lunacy, I had invested in a part-share in a two-year-old and now here I was being driven by Doug Marks, his usual eccentric self, up to the gallops to watch my filly have a lesson in how to gallop. It was only her third outing and she was accompanied by three three-year-olds. I was quite pleased with myself for naming her Deciduous, since she was by Shiny Tenth out of Elm Leaf, but it seemed I'd given her a name which for some strange reason her trainer had great difficulty in pronouncing.

That morning we decided to settle for his calling her 'your horse'. It suited me and exaggerated that feeling of ownership. It was the first time I'd had a good look at her. She was all chestnut with hardly one white hair, on the small side as would be anyone who wouldn't be two until 1 January. She had a nice intelligent head and seemed quite alert and lively. I watched her do two gallops of approximately three furlongs each and although she was very green she stayed with the three-year-olds, tucked in behind them, with something that looked amazingly like enthusiasm. Perhaps horses actually like galloping, I thought, but it looked like fearfully hard work to me.

Back in the yard I went into Boom Docker's box and had a good look at him. Doug reminded me how well he had run in the Grand National the previous March until being brought down at Becher's the second time around. I watched a video recording of the race and Doug made one of his usual 'funnies'.

'Yes,' he said, 'when I saw him still standing and going well as they passed the stands, I thought to myself, I must start feeding that horse.' Incredible as it may seem, there are a few owners thick enough to take that sort of remark seriously. They'd better stay away from Mr Marks. I remember one Newmarket sales when two Americans approached Doug and asked him if they could have a look at a horse he was going to sell. They were interested in buying him and wanted a good look at him before he went into the sale ring. I walked with them to the box and Doug got the lad to bring him out and walk him around. To the astonishment of the Americans and all standers-by, Doug then got hold of the lad and walked him around.

'A nice little mover,' he said. 'I picked him up for thirty bob the other day in Huddersfield. Got him from a remand school. I know he's a bit plain, but he should make up into quite a nice sort.'

Doug used to send me these ridiculous letters about Deciduous: 'Geoff Baxter rode her out at work this morning. She galloped so well she's bound to win a race.' I couldn't afford to own her. She was syndicated and I just had a leg, but she raced in my name and colours and I never met the other owners.

On Boxing Day I went to Kempton Park. In spite of two great races, the experience was awful and I made my annual resolution never to return. Traditionally, one takes one's hangover to Kempton to give it an airing, but when fifty thousand or so like-minded people are at it, then a day at the races becomes a gigantic and uncomfortable scrum.   British Rail, as only they can do it, had started the day off in lunatic style. They'd put on what they laughingly called a 'special' to Kempton and they said it would leave from platform sixteen. A few hundred binoculared fanatics gathered at the end of that platform and waited patiently for twenty minutes and then it was announced that the 'special' would leave from platform five after all. We charged the length of Waterloo and stood champing at that platform for ten minutes until another announcement told us to go back to platform sixteen. The return charge was fairly spectacular. I maimed at least two children and one woman with my briefcase and saw one red setter crumple from a blow on the head from a pair of race glasses. But eventually we got on our 'special' and discovered what was so special about it. It kept stopping. Once on the racecourse I realised that the entire outing was a ghastly mistake. Only at Wembley have I seen so many dreadful people loafing with intent. You could hardly see a horse for the crowd and getting a drink in any of the bars was fifteen minutes hard graft.

That horseracing is largely a matter of opinion was nicely proved in and after the first race. I had a fancy for Bob Turnell's King Neptune and banged a fiver on its nose. The horse made serveral mistakes, but managed to get second, beaten by a couple of lengths. As soon as they passed the post my man on the rails said, 'I thought like you, Jeff, and put forty quid on the bleedin' animal. It wasn't trying a yard, was it? A diabolical liberty, that's what it was.' He continued his slander and I walked back to the grandstand past two men who were discussing the same horse and jockey. 'That Andy Turnell,' one of them was saying. 'he's bloody brilliant. No other jockey could have got within twenty lengths of the winner.' I had to subscribe to the latter view and a lack of moral fibre it was that prevented me from telling my bookmaker that he was talking rubbish. The trouble is, when a bookmaker gives you the best available price or a point over the odds, then you need to keep him sweet. What made him think that the Turnell combination wasn't interested in winning the race was beyond me.

Just before the big race, the King George VI, I realised it was hopeless to try and see the horses in the paddock so I watched and listened on a television set in the trainers' and owners' bar. Would to God I wasn't so easily led. I'd fancied Royal Marshall II all the way from London and then I allowed Dick Pitman's commentary to ruin things. He went on about what a nasty, mean, scraggy individual that horse was and put me right off. My fault, not his. What was so galling though was to

hear, after Royal Marshall had won at 16-1, the trainer Tim
Forster said the horse was always at his best when he looked
like that. I took a really close look at him outside the weighing
room when he was being unsaddled and I must say the beast
looked as though it had just done two years' solitary in
Parkhurst.

Before that race, by the way, Dramatist had won an epic
hurdle from Night Nurse and Bird's Nest. It was pleasing to
hear from Richard Baerlein, as he handed me a glass of
revolting racecourse medium sherry, that he'd napped the
winner in the *Guardian*. I was to remember Mr Baerlein a week
later. Meanwhile I ended the day at Kempton on a classic note.
I like to lose my money scientifically but the holiday spirit put
me in the mood for hunches and when I met a bookmaker in
the bar just before the last who asked me if I'd lay him Brief
Chance I told him yes. The horse hacked up at 9-2 and it must
have been the sherry that made me lay him. A couple of points
over 9-2 and there would have been an embarrassing scene
with me welshing or walking back to London.

Before I staggered off the course, I mentioned to Mr Baerlein
that Roger Mortimer had been waxing eloquently to me a
couple of weeks before about Fred Rimell's horse Hiram
Maxim. Richard said he wasn't sure whether the horse had
turned into a pig or whether he'd temporarily lost his form.
But the horse stayed fixed in my mind for the next few days.
And what a next few days. They ended up with my seeing the
New Year in in a ward of the Royal Free Hospital where they
told me I might have to be put down.

Anyway, between comas and cold hard-boiled eggs,
someone shoved a *Guardian* under my nose and I saw that not
only was Hiram Maxim running, but that Richard Baerlein had
napped it. His napping it stirred some semblance of
confidence in me and I screamed for the telephone trolley to
be wheeled to my bedside. Phone calls to Soho were made and
Hiram Maxim was backed along with The Dealer and The Bo-
Weevil. Hiram Maxim won at 9-1, The Dealer at 2-1 and The

Bo-Weevil at 8-11. The night nurse told me I was looking in tremendously good nick when she came on duty later. I began wondering whether it wouldn't be a good idea to give punting patients in hospitals false results if they lose and then tell them the truth later when they've recovered. Of course, actual winners are the best tonic and it's terribly difficult to take doctors seriously when you're lying there knowing that you're going to collect when you get out. What do you think was whispered into Lazarus's ear?

The Schweppes Gold Trophy at Newbury has now had its name changed but to most people will still be known as 'The Schweppes'. It is run at a time of year when the weather often causes it cancellation. When the snow stays away it is my favourite race of the season, being a sucker for tricky handicaps. That year I fancied Josh Gifford's good horse Tiepolino. He had been gelded in the previous spring and had taken a bit of time to get over it, according to his trainer. He actually sounded slightly puzzled when he told me, but it's an operation that I'm pretty sure would take me more than a year to get over.

The race itself was a terrific contest. I thought my own personal drought was coming to an end for a moment when Tiepolino made a move in the straight, but it wasn't to be. Apart from the excellence of the racing at Newbury that day the company I kept was almost perfect. I met an old Russian gentleman in the bar who'd fled his country in 1917 and who confessed to me that he now made an extremely precarious living out of insurance companies by throwing himself in front of the occasional taxi. His subsequent injuries had made him pretty doddery, but he somehow managed to hobble from course to course when in funds after an accident.

After The Schweppes I took a long hard look at the customers in the grandstand. Much as I love racing I can't help finding regular racegoers, for the most part, quite ridiculous. As usual there were hundreds and hundreds of Lucindas and Ruperts and the thing that always strikes me about them is

The Schweppes

As usual there were hundreds and hundreds of Lucindas and Ruperts . . .

that they are completely out of touch with reality. That's to say they have barely any experience of life beyond the boundaries of Annabel's and Badminton. One wonders what the hell they'd do if they suddenly had to earn a living with their two hands. Apart from that lot there were the lunatic set that I preferred to pass the time of day with like 'Dennis the Chest', 'Jimmy the Spiv' and Lulu Mendoza. God preserve and keep such characters, because the bloody horses won't. One of them told me quite a good story about that cynical ex-jockey Dave Dick. I'd remarked about Dick Pitman's commentaries that I thought he spoiled them by the tremendous effort he made to talk posh. I was then told that when Pitman was riding, Dave Dick said to Fred Winter one day, 'Now that you've taught him to speak like you, why don't you teach him to fucking ride like you?' Cruel on poor Dick Pitman but pithy.

Shortly after The Schweppes I went over to see Deciduous again and the ground was so hard because of the frost that she was simply trotting round the lanes of Lambourn. I'm no expert at judging horses on looks, and when they've got their winter coats it becomes absolutely impossible for me. She looked perky enough and gave me the warm glow of ownership, but she looked horribly like a chesnut-coloured doormat. Doug Marks though thought she was a bit of a cracker and I began rosily looking forward to a touch with her in April or May.

behind closed doors

Lambourn, most famous of all racing villages, I can only describe as an extraordinary sort of alfresco nuthouse. The kernel of the village is the market square, where stable boys booze along with racing pros and fringe types like myself who drop by for the occasional gargle. Drive or

stagger for five miles in any direction from here and you
come to the outer shell, inhabited by the rich landowners,
trainers and suchlike, who behave in much the same
lunatic way but on a smarter level.

There's an air of Irish languor about Lambourn. Time is
measured by the licensing laws, when in effect – opening
hours enjoy a sort of *Dr Who*-style time-lag. Mornings are
there for the beauty of the gallops, afternoons for physical
resuscitation, and evenings for social and sexual
intercourse. Another odd thing about Lambourn is its
veneer. You can be sure that strangers, English and
foreign alike, who drive through the place think they're
passing through what's known as a 'sleepy' English
village. After all, there are roses clambering over a few
porches and very little noise to disturb the booze-loud
glade. But you know what they say about what goes on
behind closed doors. Newmarket is tame as a zoo by
comparison. In Lambourn they let the animals wander
about; in Newmarket they dress them up and take them
for walks.

Doug Marks is one of the best-loved inmates of the
nuthouse that is Lambourn. A silly oak sign outside his
house used to bear the name Lethornes, until his wife Pam
got fed up with racing and left him temporarily, and Doug
changed the name to Bleak House. He is a crafty punter.
He doesn't bet often, but wins whenever he does. He once
trained a horse called Singing Bede which broke a course
record at Goodwood, steaming in at longish odds. Of
course Doug had his money down. He was a good jockey
in his day, winning the Thousand Guineas and the Oaks
as an apprentice on a filly that would only go for him,
Godiva. Then he developed a problem with his spine and
had to spend two or three years in hospital. Doug likes to
make out he's a bit daft on occasion. Frankie Vaughan is
one of his owners and he once danced around the
cashpoint outside Marks and Sparks in Newbury singing
'Give Me the Moonlight'.

Then there is Freddie Maxwell, who was probaly unique
among trainers in that racing was only the second
obsession in his life. The first was croquet. I can remember
seeing him screaming blue murder and tearing his hair out
because Joe Mercer and Jimmy Lindley told him that they

had planted dandelion seeds all over his lawn. They were only teasing, of course. He looked rather like a little Irish gnome, and could talk the hind leg off a donkey. But his achievements were fine by any standards: he helped teach Lester Piggott his trade; trained one of the fastest fillies of all time in Cawston's Pride; and won the Ascot Gold Cup with Precipice Wood. He is still to be found in Lambourn, not in the market square or with his horses, but on the croquet lawn or in the middle of his artichoke and asparagus beds.

As I've mentioned before, the highlight of the Lambourn year is Lurcher Show day, which used to be held on Peter Walwyn's land but has now been relegated to Newbury racecourse. Peter Walwyn was champion trainer twice in the mid-seventies and won the Derby with Grundy. At this time he had two retained jockeys, Pat Eddery and Frank Morby, and the team was invincible wherever they ran their horses, from Bath to Pontefract. Peter is a lovely man, and Bonk, his wife, is one of the nicest people I have met in fifty years. Although I hate parties, I made an exception for the one they used to give on Lurcher Show day. There was always a huge marquee stuffed full of smoked salmon, roast beef, champagne and people. One year I took Tom Baker, the actor, down there with me. I introduced him to Fred Winter. Eddery filled up his glass. Lester Piggott tripped over his feet. Tom said to Peter Walwyn: 'Thank you very, very much for all this. It's the most amazing party I've every been to.' Peter was not at all taken aback: 'Oh yes, well, thank you Tom . . . You know, it's awfully nice to have a few friends pop in for a drink on a Saturday, isn't it?'

The lurchers themselves never held much fascination for me but the people who bring them from miles around to show them and race them are an extraordinary bunch. They are a sort of hotch-potch of Sloane Ranger, gipsy, racing type and farmer. The lurchers – half greyhound and half anything you like – aren't all that prepossessing. I once asked Jimmy Lindley if they were intelligent. He gazed at them racing up the temporary track and said, 'You've got to be pretty daft to chase something that's dead.'

Needless to say it's an excellent day for gambling talk of

all kinds. The engaging Roger Mortimer, a raconteur of some skill, told me an odd story about Richard Baerlein's father. It seems that many years ago the gentleman decided to calculate the chances of life after death. For this purpose he required his family to give him a pile of sandwiches and a Thermos flask of coffee and he then retired to his room for the weekend. On Monday morning he emerged from his study and announced that the chances were 'little better than five to two against'. The matter was closed and never referred to again . . .

7

THE THING THAT DELIGHTS ME MOST ABOUT RACECOURSE CON-MEN is their method of approach. One man at Kempton Park in early March who tried to chat me up had a good new one for openers. 'I'm on the brink of something great,' he said to me. 'Count me out,' I said. I liked that; the use of the words 'brink' and 'great'. It made such a nice change from that stale approach that you should always beware of which is, 'I'll tell you what I'll do with you.' That's a dead give-away, since the word 'do' lets you know straightaway that you're going to be used in some way to their advantage.

Nevertheless, it's sad that the straighter racing gets the fewer characters you see about. I wish I'd seen the dreaded chalk-and-water men at the dogs in the old days. These were a nasty bunch of strong-arm men who wandered in and out of bookmakers' pitches carrying a bucket of water and an old cloth. They offered to wipe the bookmakers' boards after each race for a half-crown. If the offer wasn't accepted the bookmaker would get duffed up.

Apart from the fellow who told me he was on the brink of something great, the crowd at Kempton were an amiable

bunch of alfresco boozers. I went to the meeting with a Soho
publican called Charlie Stevenson who used to be a tic-tac
man up North before he decided to make a profession out of
his hobby. In between no less than eight bottles of Bollinger he
managed to win seven hundred and fifty pounds, which is a
good illustation of keeping your head when all about you are
losing their all.

An appalling bit of vanity stopped me from backing the 20-1
winner Don't Hesitate. And I mean sheer vanity. I fancied the
horse to beat Pendil in receipt of 31lb, and I approached my
man on the rails with the intention of sticking a tenner on it.
Now it frequently happens, when I'm transacting my tiny
business on the rails, that the bookmakers go in for a bit of
banter at my expense. They shout out things like, 'Hey
Charlie, guess what Jeff's backed? He must be mad.' On this
particular day, thanks to Mr Stevenson's Bollinger, I was
taking myself a touch too seriously and I didn't want a load of
mickey-taking on the lines of 'The madman's at it again, Bill.
He's gone and backed Don't Hesitate.' So, idiot that I am, I
switched to Brown Admiral and lost my tenner instead of
winning two hundred pounds.

Oh, well. It was still one of the best days' racing I'd had for
an age. There was one hell of a tip for the last winner,
Mourndyke. As so often happens in this game someone must
have done too much talking. I'd heard from an inside source
three days previously that it was going to be off and we
thought we'd get something in the region of 5-1, with luck
maybe 11-2, on the day. To my irritation, when I got to
Kempton, the world and his wife seemed to know about
Mourndyke. According to *The Sporting Life* betting report in
the Monday's edition, 'After isolated offers of 4-1 were quickly
taken, Mourndyke was heavily laid from 3-1 to 9-4 (including
two bets of £2000 – £800 and £2250 – £1000).' As for the race,
Mourndyke drew clear approaching the last flight and won
comfortably.

It seems that as time goes by it gets harder and harder to

keep good things dark. You can't imagine a leak from an organisation like the 'Druid Lodge Confederacy' or the 'Netheravon Syndicate' as it was sometimes called in the old days. This was a group of extremely clever and very heavy betting owners that was generally thought to have been founded by Mr A. P. Cunliffe who won the Derby in 1913 with Aboyeur. The brain behind the organisation was probably Captain Wilfred Purefroy, one of the hardest nuts ever seen on the Turf; the other members were Mr J. H. Peard, Captain Frank Forester and Mr E. A. Wigan. Cunliffe died in 1942. He was the poorest of the confederacy and he left one hundred and fifty thousand. When Hackler's Pride won the Cambridgeshire in 1903 and again in 1904, they won something in the region of a quarter of a million.

It's an old adage that no man will commit suicide when he's holding an ante-post voucher. This made it almost certain that I would live at least until Grand National day. In a mad moment in Compton I had struck a twenty-two pound bet: a one pound each-way yankee on the next four big betting races. I had Dramatist at 9-1 for the Champion Hurdle, Border Incident at 16-1 for the Gold Cup, Rhodomantade at 16-1 for the Lincoln and Gay Vulgan at 16-1 for the Grand National. The bookmaker in Compton, Steve Fisher, doubled the bet and came in with me since it wasn't worth his while holding it. So he made it a two pound each-way yankee and put it on with one of the big firms. Without bothering to think about it or work it out I asked him why wasn't it worth his while? He whipped out a pencil and paper, made some rapid calculations and said, 'Well, your share will come to fifty-two thousand if they all oblige.' Needless to say they didn't. None of them.

That year's festival meeting at Cheltenham will be remembered for the death of Lanzarote in the Gold Cup more than for anything else. I had met the horse the year before on my annual spring visit to Fred Winter's yard. We went into Lanzarote's box armed with a packet of Polo mints and –

normally fairly terrified of racehorses – the first thing that struck me about him was what a marvellous nature he had. Amost black in colour, he had looked magnificent and I foolishly thought that Fred's eulogy was more than tinged with sentiment. As a result I tended to underrate the horse until his fatal accident and I don't think I was alone in that. Apart from his Champion Hurdle victories I shall always remember what cracking races he used to run at Kempton Park.

I personally had the worst Cheltenham I've ever experienced. I watched the first two days of it on the most wretched black-and-white television set in Muriel Belcher's Colony Room Club in Dean Street, financially bled to death and spent the rest of the time removing intoxicated publishers and the like from my line of vision. Almost everything I backed to win came second and almost everything I backed each-way came fourth or fifth.

On Thursday I decided to brave the crowds and put my press badge into use. I was driven down to the course by a friend and noted in the car that Meladon and Davy Lad might win. I then did my usual nonsense of changing my mind at the last minute. The only winner I had all day was Rusty Tears in the last, which won at a pretty miserable 7-4. Meanwhile, there was some attactive lunacy in the form of a few hundred drunken Irishmen celebrating St Patrick's Day plus Meladon, Davy Lad and Rusty Tears, and there was some incredible hospitality.

Behind the stands there must have been nothing less than a hundred tents hired for the private parties. My guide to them was Charles Benson, then 'The Scout' on the *Daily Express*, and his knowledge of parties is encyclopaedic. The Piper-Hiedsieck people, who then sponsored the Gold Cup, were giving the stuff away in bucketfuls and at that point I was utterly unaware of the fact that one of my companions was dangerously close to saturation point. It wasn't until we all came to rest in Jake Morley's tent that I could actually see

The Cheltenham Festival Meeting

. . . a remarkable thing happened that I've never seen afflict a drunk before. **Rigor mortis** *actually set in although the patient was far from dead.*

disaster. My friend and companion suddenly keeled over a crate of tonics, came to rest in a horizontal position with his head almost bursting through the canvas of the tent, and then a remarkable thing happened that I've never seen afflict a drunk before. *Rigor mortis* actually set in although the patient was far from dead. It's tremendously difficult to remove someone who's completely rigid, so we had to leave him to make his own natural and somewhat lengthy recovery. Now what I like about racing people is that it's typical of them that they took hardly any notice of the event at all. I mean, imagine that scene at something like the Chelsea Flower Show. There'd be considerable tut-tutting. At Cheltenham they just said, 'What's the matter with him?' 'He's passed out.' 'Really? Have another gin.'

There were further Cheltenham troubles after it was all over. I woke up on the Friday utterly potless and had to suffer the indignity of walking up to Great Portland Street to ask Victor Chandler's henchman Bill Brett for the measly thirteen pounds and twenty pence that they owed me on Rusty Tears. That really was rock bottom.

from bookie to shrink

If you're interested in observing incipient lunacy at close quarters, you should go to a betting shop in Berkshire where most of the customers can only just reach the counter. Most stable lads are compulsive punters and if you worked in this particular shop just about all you'd see of them would be their grubby little hands reaching up with tenners clutched in them. When they're in the chips they really shovel it on. Of course, their downfall in the long run is that they always fall in love with the two they do, and even if they're second-rate selling-platers they still back them and back them. Some boys or girls are lucky

enough to look after champions. I remember meeting the
lad who did Bolkonski when I went up to Newmarket
during the stable lads' strike. All the other lads in the pub
were teasing him mercilessly because although this lad
was on strike, he still heaved himself out of bed at the
crack of dawn and walked to the Heath to watch
Bolkonski work. He told me that the sight of that horse
galloping made the hair on the back of his neck stand up.
It certainly must have stood up when Bolkonski won the
Guineas at 33-1.

   But you don't have to work in a racing stable to get
involved with horses and some of my own likes and
dislikes are quite illogical. For some reason or another I
could never get worked up about Grundy, magnificent as
he was. Perhaps it was because I always had quite the
wrong hunch that *this* time he would get beaten and then
I'd be annoyed with myself for having opposed him. In
retrospect, I always think of the gallant Bustino when
I think of that epic race for the King George VI and Queen
Elizabeth Stakes, even though Grundy won. You can get
to almost hate a horse for no good reason. Canisbay, the
1965 Eclipse winner, fell into that category. Not only did
he beat one of my favourite horses, Roan Rocket, but he
was a chesnut and I've got a daft prejudice about
chesnuts. Some know-all was giving me a lecture just
before the race about chesnuts and instead of cocking him
a deaf 'un I stood there mesmerised by this talk about all
chesnuts being 'ungenerous'. Well, some of them are, but
plenty aren't and there are a few descendents of Hyperion
who've got and had got plenty of guts. I fancied Canisbay,
then went off him, then he won at 20-1.

   But the love and hate isn't all through the pocket.
I never had a bet on Arkle and I only backed Brigadier
Gerard once at the beginning of his racing career. That
anyone could have ever wanted to see two horses like
those beaten for the sake of a few shillings is beyond me.
But if you really want to see pigs at close quarters you
should spend an afternoon in the betting shop in Frith
Street. I use the place sometimes because it's adjacent to
a few of my haunts, but it's racing's Chamber of Horrors.
The punters therein are mostly Italian and Cypriot and

horseracing to them is a sort of animated roulette. In the
winter they scream for favourites to fall till I'd really like
to put a few of them up on a steeplechaser and send them
round Aintree for three miles. Not far away from that
shop there's the one in Gerrard Street that's used by the
Chinese, and they bet like men possessed. Possessed by
something that makes them very quiet, mind you, but
possessed nevertheless. In yet another betting shop I
know there's a man who's still in love with Harry Wragg.
He must be getting on a bit to have seen Harry win the
1928 Derby on Felstead, but after nearly every race he will
insist on telling anyone present how Felstead and Wragg
would have murdered the entire field.

I back my losers and occasional winners with Victor
Chandler in Great Portland Street. His father, old Victor
Chandler, owned Brighton and Walthamstow dog
stadiums and came into a lot of money after the war. I
first got to know him on the racetrack and one day shortly
after I met him I heard him say to his clerk, Val, as I
approached, 'Good news, boys, here comes the lunch
money.'

I once owed Victor about twenty quid, a fortune to me
then and nothing to him. I'd been avoiding him for weeks.
One day he came into the Members' Bar at Newbury, so
I pretended I'd droppped something on the floor and hid
under the table. After I'd been there about five minutes, a
hand appeared bearing an enormous whisky. Victor's face
followed and met mine: 'Hello, Jeffrey. I should think you
need this pretty badly.'

Percy Thompson, who worked for him, was the biggest
punter in England, bar none. He'd chalk up the prices on
the board, write down the bets, then he'd phone another
bookmaker and have ten grand on. He had one hundred
thousand pounds on Tudor Minstrel to win the Derby,
and he was merely a clerk.

To this day there is a picture of Sterope, the dual
Cambridgeshire winner, in young Victor's office. It's there
because his dad had fifty grand on it at 40-1 in 1948. That's
another story that makes people like me broke.

The last time I was in hospital a couple of years ago
Victor came to visit me, and as he left he said, 'You'll be
needing a couple of bob for buying things like toothpaste

and the newspaper in the morning,' He then shoved a hundred quid under my pillow, which goes to show there are such things as generous bookmakers.

And while on the subject of gambling and hospitals, I was once sent to a very odd establishment in Surrey which is like a punters' research clinic. I lay in bed trembling for a day or two and, when I came to, a nurse told me I'd been raving and saying things like 'I'll take evens.' 'Did I ask for my wife?' I enquired. 'No. But you did ask for The Life.'

In the next bed there was an Irishman who told me that he'd been psychologically unable to work for ten years. 'At one point', he informed me, 'the mention of the word "work" made me feel physically sick.' The psychiatrist in the place was Irish too. On the third day of my confinement, he came along and sat down beside my bed with a great wad of papers, an instrument for measuring blood pressure, a thermometer and a mid-day newspaper. I thought he was going to ask me the story of my life, but not a bit of it. He went straight to he point: 'Do you think Tiernascragh can beat Phaestus?' I had a look at the weights and told him no. 'You really are in a bad way,' he told me, and left to go back Tiernascragh and thus prove I was mad.

When he came back he told me he'd won on the horse but that he'd had a saver on Phaestus just in case I'd happened to know what I was talking about. 'We had a journalist in here once who was so good at tipping we kept him in for five months.'

8

WE NOW CAME TO THE BEGINNING OF THE NEW FLAT SEASON AND I hoped I could start to do a bit better. One lives in hope. I knew it was wise to leave the Lincoln alone, but it was there and so I had to have a bet. The nearer it got to the day the more

The Punters' Research Clinic

'We had a journalist in here once who was so good at tipping we kept him in for five months.'

I liked the look of Harry Wragg's horse, Fluellen. This one had been reported to have done one hell of a gallop on the Saturday before at Newmarket. He was to be ridden by Pat Eddery and seemed to have an excellent chance. After having great difficulty getting a run, he was eventually beaten a neck into second at 9-1.

Almost the next thing I was aware of was my Grand National party. I had asked a lot of people from the local boozer to come to my flat to watch the race on television. Fifteen of them turned up. The fifteen included three pornographers, one bookmaker, two divorcees, a printer, a journalist, and a ne'er-do-well with his long-suffering wife. I was postive that Red Rum couldn't possibly win for a record-breaking third time and I laid him from here to kingdom come. He won. Luckily, I also took an enormous amount of money on whether Charlotte Brew would finish the course at all. Since I knew the horse that she was riding was inexperienced and hopeless, I felt safe in laying 8-1 against her completing the course. How she got to the twenty-seventh fence still remains something of a mystery to me. But don't be alarmed, I didn't end up winning or anything foolish like that. I took ninety pounds in cash from my guests, went to my local in the evening and lost the lot playing spoof. There is a message there. When you're ahead, don't push it.

I have to report that my local at the time very nearly became out of bounds to me. In a moment of lightheaded foolishness I found myself laying horses in there the next Saturday too. I then worked out it would cost me sixty-six pounds the next time I went in there for a drink, and I couldn't think of many drinks that were worth sixty-six pounds.

I began eyeing the Guineas and soon came to the conclusion that the Two Thousand would surely be won by Tachypous. If not, another suicide attempt. In the One Thousand Guineas I thought I'd probably take a chance with the Newmarket long shot Haco. But aside from the Guineas there was a fearfully important race coming up at Wolverhampton on Monday, 2

May. It was the race I was awaiting with bated, pastis-smelling breath as it was to mark the first racecourse appearance of my filly Deciduous. Geoff Baxter had been continuing to ride her in work and Doug Marks was still writing me boring business letters about the price of oats and hay, but there had been a large number of postscripts to the effect that Deciduous had been galloping really well. Trainers have a tendency to exaggerate the merits of their charges, using phrases like 'He's jumping out of his skin,' and 'He can catch pigeons on the gallops.' My own favourite exaggeration is the one they use after the horse has won a race. Even if it's only got up by a neck the trainer will say, 'He won doing hand-springs.'

I travelled up to Wolverhampton from Euston with an extremely hard nut, physically that is, of a bookmaker who warned me to expect nothing of Deciduous – as if I didn't already know – and during the journey, discussing people who've gone down the drain via the Turf, he came out with what, for me, was the saying of the week. 'Yes,' he said, 'this racing game tames bleedin' tigers.' Quite so. While Haco had been unplaced in the One Thousand, Tachypous had gone down by a length in the Two Thousand Guineas at 12-1, having drifted from sevens.

It was the first time I'd been to Wolverhampton for six years and I'd forgotten just how underrated a track it is. Forget the town, the track is very worthwhile going to if ever you have the bad luck to be in that part of the world. There's a good restaurant in the Members' where you can sit and eat and drink *and* see every yard of how you're losing your money.

As soon as I got to the track I walked over the course to see Deciduous being saddled up. She was walking around the tiny paddock with the others, awaiting their various trainers, and she looked really sweet. There's something very touching about looking at two-year-olds who've never been out. You know they don't really know what its's all about, and when you're personally involved you realise what a hell of a thing it is: you wonder how on earth they must feel when they see that seemingly endless stretch of gallop in front of them from the stalls. They're just big babies. Deciduous looked in very good nick and the only fault you could find was that she needed a bit more time and a bit more muscle on her arse, which is where it counts and where the propulsion comes from.

I'd been pretty sure from the day before that she wasn't going to win, since Doug Marks had written to me from Lambourn warning me that on the evidence of home gallops she didn't like soft going. Her dainty feet got stuck in too far. But if she had won and I hadn't had a penny on her I would have been furious. In the end I made a sort of compromise, not too little and certainly not too much, and had a fiver each way. In the parade ring she certainly wasn't put to shame by any of the other runners. By the time the jockeys walked in to mount the adrenalin was fairly bubbling and here was one of my fantasies at last about to become reality. In fact it was a tremendous let-down. I thought Taffy Thomas would walk up to me, tug his forelock and address me as 'Sir', instead of which he walked over and said, 'Hallo, Jeff. How's it all going then?'

I'd forgotten while I fantasised that I used to get legless some time previously in Taff's local, the White Lion in Newmarket. Anyway, Doug told Thomas, 'Win if you can' and I went into the Ring to place my bet while they cantered down to the start. It came as something of a shock to me when I saw that Deciduous had opened at as little as 4-1 and was third favourite. Did someone know something that the connections didn't? In fact, what the hell was going on? I didn't have to wait long to find out. She started drifting and ended up being returned at 10-1.

From the off I knew she was going to get stuffed since she came out of the stalls very slowly, but it was some consolation to see my colours making some sort of headway as they came to the half-way stage. At the death she finished eighth of the fifteen runners with Thomas sitting pretty quietly on her having not knocked her about. Eighth of fifteen in the 2.15 at Wolverhampton, the Lichfield Maiden Fillies' Stakes, run over five furlongs. Those were the bare facts. But dear oh Lord, what a lot more there is to it when you're personally involved.

Just how much one's life can be affected by racing, and more particularly by the love of a good horse, is illustrated by the career of my friend Conan Nicholas. I first met him over thirty-five years ago in a desolate Soho pub. He told me that he'd first got interested in racing when he was reading *The Times* in the bath and noticed there was a horse called Dante entered for the Derby. Being a bit of a literary bloke, he was delighted that someone should have named a horse after a poet.

Anyway, the idea of Dante obsessed him and he forced his wife to pawn all her belongings so that he could back him at every price down to 100-30 at the off. That did it. He never looked back. Mind you, he very nearly never looked at all. He got a very bad eye infection some time later and refused to see a doctor. His wife told me that he insisted on going to the man who tried to save Dante's eyesight.

For the next few years he had his ups and downs, with possibly more downs than ups, and they affected his health quite badly. He used to nearly have a fit when he backed a loser and the excitement of the opening of the betting shops almost finished him altogether. His next setback was his marriage. He'd decided one day to go to Ascot to see the great Ribot. As he was leaving his flat his wife said, 'Haven't you forgotten something?' 'No,' he said. 'You have,' she replied. 'It's your daughter's birthday party today. What's more important to you, Conan, your daughter or Ribot?' 'Quite frankly, my dear.' he said, 'Ribot.' And he closed the door behind him.

Then he got this bee in his bowler about Fred Winter. We had our biggest win ever on Sky Pink at Cheltenham and from that moment on Conan used to refer to Fred as 'God'. He started to talk like a lunatic all the time. The crunch came with the bad weather. There was no racing for a few weeks at one

Cat Hurdling

It soon became clear that one cat, Kier Hardie, was head and shoulders above the rest.

point and Conan introduced us to what he called 'cat hurdling'.

These events took place along the corridors of his large Battersea flat. The hurdles were made of wooden rods with cloths draped over them. There were four hurdles in all and the cats were induced to jump them (a) by not having been fed for a bit and (b) by placing a saucer of tinned salmon by the front door, which was the finishing post. It soon became clear that one cat, Keir Hardie, was head and shoulders above the rest. Or, if you prefer it, a good eight ounces in front of the other runners.

Conan then had a brilliant idea. He decided to handicap the cats. One Saturday he held an invitation handicap hurdle and tied, with a bit of sticking plaster, an eight-ounce kitchen scale weight on to that animal's back. A film editor from Wimbledon brought along a very fierce tabby and besides the two hometrained runners, Keir Hardie and Nye Bevan, there was also a tabby from Chelsea called Scobie. Like all other mug punters, we thought the film director's animal hadn't come all the way from Wimbledon for the fresh air, and so he was made a redhot favourite at 6-4.

There was tremendous tension in the paddock (the kitchen). After all, we were racing for a prize of twenty cigarettes and a bottle of Chablis. Then they were off. Keir Hardie, from the gate, quite obviously resented the handicapper's judgement and ran sideways like a horse fighting for its head. The tabby went completely mad and Scobie won quite easily, although he flattened the last flight. Much to everyone's embarrassment, we subsequently discovered that the Wimbledon menace had been bunged a pep pill and the film man was warned off.

Somehow the whole business never quite caught on, but Conan never gave up. Even after the weather cleared up he was still at it. I called round one morning and his wife said to me, 'If you're looking for Conan, he's out on the gallops.' I crossed the road to Battersea Park and there he was, walking

about with a cat on a lead. It was Keir Hardie. I said, 'Hallo.'
And Conan simply said, 'Just wait till he gets the sun on his
back.'

ups 'n' downs

The National is one of my best races – after something like
thirty-five of the wretched events I fancy myself
something of an expert at it. As the great day approaches
and every housewife in the country is blindfolding herself
with a duster and poising a finger over the pinsticker's
guide, I find myself thinking that it must be the easiest bet
of all the big handicaps. Merryman II and Nicolaus Silver,
for instance, stood out like sweet cherries. I even backed
Russian Hero, Ayala and Maori Venture, none of which
had much of a shout on paper. But the thing about the
National is that you can always eliminate most of the
horses on one of two grounds: inability to jump and
inability to stay – both vital in the longest major
steeplechase with those old-fashioned Aintree fences
along the way.

The dodgy one to judge is staying power. Russian Hero
– famous simply because it was tipped by what was then
the *Daily Worker* – had never previously won over more
than two and a half miles; Specify was another National
winner that wasn't supposed to have the stamina. The
complicating factor is that a good jockey can persuade a
decent middle-distance horse to stay by getting it to *hack*
round for the first circuit. It was Fred Winter who first
drew my attention to this when he dismounted from one
of his National winners and told the press in the most
disarming way that the first circuit had been sweet as
hunting.

Fred Winter once helped me back a winner at Aintree,
but I never felt very good about this one. He was showing
me his yard at Lambourn and took me round the stable
lads' hostel. Being the middle of the day it was deserted,

exept for a solitary lad lying on his bunk with his head
swathed in bandages. I asked what had happened.
Apparently this was the lad who did Anglo and the brute
had almost brained him with a kick to the skull which
needed thirty-five stitches. I mumbled something feeble
about how sorry I was. Fred looked at it rather differently.
'Actually,' he said as we left the hostel, 'I feel rather
optimistic. It shows Anglo's really on his toes.' I thought
this somewhat callous, but it didn't stop me backing Anglo
come the National six weeks later.

At the time it was a rather horrific and embarrassing
experience. I was very short of readies, unemployed and
living with a paranoid girl of great wealth who quite
rightly thought that everyone was after her money. We
had a party on Grand National day and as I watched
Anglo skip over the last few fences and draw farther and
farther away as though he was having a little canter on the
Lambourn Downs, I could have won an Oscar for my
acting. I knew that if the lady in question tumbled the
fact that I'd just backed a 50-1 winner, then I wouldn't see
much of it since it would be levied as a love tax. But I
managed to hold my head in my hands and moan and
moan and utter phrases like 'stuffed again'. Inwardly
I was jumping over the then unsullied moon.

I have suffered far worse at the Derby. I don't mean
especially from the financial point of view, though I've
bled as much on Epsom Downs as any man; no, it's just
that it's not worth going to the Derby unless things are
absolutely right for you on the day. By this I mean getting
there in good time, getting there in a car (and not on that
travelling luntic asylum known as the Derby Day 'Special'
train) but avoiding the ghastly traffic jams, and cadging an
invitation to someone's box to escape being trampled on
by a hundred thousand twice-a-year punters who don't
know a betting slip from a Chinese laundry ticket. Also,
I refuse to wear a morning suit as I already look daft
enough in my usual clothes to raise laughs from the
bookmakers.

Nijinsky's Derby was one of the worst. A great horse,
but the price wasn't good enough for me, so I hunted
around for a long shot and of course came away with
a fractured pocket. At least it was a lovely day, and

The Derby

In a trance I slowly put cold pieces of cod in my mouth and watched the Rolls Royces glide majestically by.

sunshine always alleviates impecunity. Mill Reef will
always stick in my mind because I was absolutely
convinced it wouldn't win, and had to run the last mile
and a half uphill to the course because of the damned
traffic, arriving just in time to see the bugger sail first past
the post. I did have the sense to recoup my money by
backing him for the Arc de Triomphe that October, the day
I lost my job. After the race my Irish trainer friend Mick
O'Toole, who had also won, bought the entire stock of
Dom Perignon in the paddock bar.

In spite of my interest in – sorry, I mean obsession with
racing it wasn't until Charlottown's Derby that I actually
clapped eyes on the brutes in the flesh. I did my usual
thing. I went down to Epsom with a hundred pounds, a
gigantic sum in those days, as they say (and come to that I
couldn't half do with another ton now), intending to
shove the lot on Charlottown, so impressed had I been
with its running in the Lingfield Derby Trial Stakes. I don't
need to tell you that I changed my mind five minutes
before the off and did my lot. After the last race I
remember standing by a fish and chip stall crying. No one
noticed since it was pouring with rain. In a trance I slowly
put cold pieces of cod in my mouth and watched the Rolls
Royce glide majestically by.

I don't believe I've told you yet which are the greatest
racehorses of my time, and it's not an opinion I intend to
keep to myself. They are Sea Bird II, Ribot and Dancing
Brave; then Nijinsky and Mill Reef.

9

THE BIG YORK SPRING MEETING CAME AND WENT. TELEVISION
punters who for some reason or other couldn't get to the
course, heard a most interesting comment during an inter-race
interview when the old master, Harry Wragg, ex-pilot of three
Derby winners, was asked about the prospects of his Mecca-

Dante winner Lucky Sovereign staying the Derby distance. He said, 'Any horse will stay if it's settled properly.' Bold words, dogmatic and a tremendous generalisation.

The next Saturday at Newbury I quoted this quote to that genuine expert John Hislop and, slightly to my surprise, he disagreed. 'So how come Hard Ridden won the Derby,' I asked him, 'since he was by Hard Sauce, a seven-furlong horse?' 'Ah,' said Mr Hislop, 'Hard Sauce may have been a seven-furlong horse, but *theoretically* he should have stayed.' We were beginning, or at least he was beginning, to get into the complicated realms of throwbacks. When I mentioned that another Derby winner, the great Sir Ivor, was also thought not to be able to last the Derby distance Hislop again went into a fairly complicated spiel explaining that there again Sir Ivor was so stoutly bred on the dam's side two generations back that the question of his stamina never arose very seriously. It should be remembered that Hislop bred Brigadier Gerard and wrote a fascinating book about it which, along with Andrew Devonshire's *Park Top* and John Oaksey's *Mill Reef*, is amongst the best ever books about an individual horse.

The races at Newbury treated me well on the Friday and the Saturday. I backed three winners on each day, paid for the weekend's expenses and still had a few bob left over. Relkino ran a magnificent race in the Lockinge Stakes and I grabbed the early 5-1 offered about it by Ladbroke's. Not a bad price for a horse that had finished second to Empery in the previous year's Derby. Richard Hannon was kind enough to advise me to have a bet on one of his on which I nicked another 5-1 and Robert McAlpine forced some champagne down my throat, which seemed rather odd ten minutes after one of his foremen on the motorway navvying gang had bought me a bottle of plonk.

On the Sunday I had a cursory glance round Major Dick Hern's yard and had a really good look at those two stars Relkino and Boldboy. Relkino was a magnificent-looking horse, Boldboy too – but a fairly tempermental and dangerous one. There was another Classic prospect lurking in the yard as well and that was the Queen's Oaks hope, Dunfermline. The way she had won at Newmarket last time had convinced me she had one hell of a chance.

Turning to the Derby, I had been expecting some information from France, but all I'd had so far was an eyewitness report from Charles Benson of the gallop that the favourite Blushing Groom had done on the course at Chantilly some ten days previously. 'Not so much impressive,' he said, 'but breathtaking'. But I was still not rowing in with that one. There was a huge doubt on breeding as to whether he would get the trip. I might have changed my mind if Lester Piggott had been engaged to ride him. So what the hell to back?

I would look no further than Durtal for the Oaks with a possible saver on Dunfermline, but the Derby picture was, as usual, getting no clearer as the day drew nearer. Recently I had begun to take notice of The Minstrel and now that Lester was definitely riding you couldn't not take this one into account. And then came the news that Robert Sangster, his owner, had turned down an offer of one million pounds for the horse – well that spoke for itself. One million was a pretty hefty sum of money for a horse *before* it had won the Derby and it meant, in fact, that the animal was worth more then, having not even yet won a race that season, than Grundy was *after* he had won the Derby. This was the beginning of the period which is only now coming to an end when bloodstock prices began leaping out of all proportion to ever more dizzy-making levels. On Blushing Groom, who had at least already shown his paces that year, the Aga Khan had just completed a deal with some Americans that put his value at four million six hundred thousand dollars.

This makes for conjecture as to just how much various men could be syndicated for at stud. I suppose Leonardo da Vinci would have stood for a few bob if he could have gone through with it, but in present day terms some American film star would be the guvnor. But I wander. Though I'd never been so undecided about a big race since I'd taken up giving money to bookmakers, I finally settled for Caporello, The Minstrel and a French horse, Montcontour, in that order.

Meanwhile, day-to-day life on the Turf had been getting me down. At Kempton Park one Friday evening I stood in a rain-lashed freezing gale and did my pieces. It's odd that losing money on a sunbaked afternoon in the middle of the week at a track like Salisbury when you're in good company and holding on to a fortified and ice-cold Pimms can be akin to a positive pleasure. Losing in physical discomfort though is doubly painful.

And following my horse Deciduous was becoming something of a strain. Scratched from a race at Wolverhampton in the last week of May – and me trekking all the way there not realising she'd been withdrawn – and then a few days later at last running really well and getting just touched off. Before the event, at Lingfield, Doug Marks and I could only see one better-looker in the parade ring. Then when she went down to the start, ears pricked and pulling a little, I really thought, for the first time, that she'd get in the frame.

I followed Mr Marks to the rails thinking he might have a pony on her and I was more than a little surprised when he put on a hundred pounds and then, two mintues later, pressed it further. I had a tenner at 6-1 and then climbed on to the stand. I watched the race in a bit of a daze and then when Philip Waldron appeared in my fairly revolting colours – the race card said pink, but they were more like raspberries going off – and he looked as though he'd hit the front at the furlong pole, just for a second I thought we'd won. At the line she was beaten a neck and half a length. A very encouraging run and a fraction unlucky. The next day, in *The Sporting Life*, George Ennor who did their 'close-up' wrote: 'Deciduous, always well there, every chance one furlong out, not much room, ran on.' It was the 'not much room' which was the only bit of bad luck. In fact, in the unsaddling enclosure after, Waldron said that if he'd been second he would have objected. Oh well, that's racing.

It was a pretty expensive day, as it happened. My cynical companion of the afternoon had already persuaded me to buy champagne as soon as we arrived at the course saying, 'If you wait till after your horse has run you might not have anything to celebrate,' and subsequent results did little to improve things.

A far better day's sport in many ways was at Sandown Park a few days earlier. I went with two publicans and my seven-year-old daughter. I was extremely touched halfway through the afternoon when, observing them on their sixth bottle of Bollinger, she remarked, 'Actually, I'm not supposed to have anything to do with people like you.' Not a bad judge already, I thought.

going off course

When not at the races, betting can take on some unusual patterns. I used to bet a lot with a friend who liked to play the amateur bookmaker. Convinced as he was that all punters are as thick as planks, he eventually came unstuck with an architect, a publican and myself. When there was an evening meeting it was quite a pleasant way to wager. We sat outside premises that shall remain nameless and our amateur used to go to the phone for a show. Then we would strike our bets, then he'd telephone for the results and, if we'd won, he'd pay out in readies on the spot. We were fearfully unpopular with his wife who would have liked to have him home for supper at 7.30 pm, but he was not allowed to leave us until after the last race. I had a confrontation with her on this matter and when I explained to her that no man can be led astray who doesn't *want* to be led astray, she poured an Amer Picon citron over my head. It is a slow-drying and sticky substance, and I lived for a few minutes in the hope that

Sandown Park

I went with two publicans and my seven-year-old daughter.

it might turn my hair brown.

Once, when all four of the Saturday's meetings were called off, I found myself in a pub with a bookmaker and nothing whatsoever to bet on. I tried the old one of betting him that the next person to walk through the door would be a man, but he wasn't having any. Oddly enough the next person was a woman, and he would have won. She was accompanied, I recall, by a nice old- fashioned chap who held the door open for her. As a last resort – if you can call Hackney a resort – I had two losing dog bets and then ambled in a desultory and sulky way along Piccadilly. Almost opposite the Ritz, by the way, there used to be and probably still is a rather extraordinary betting shop owned by the William Hill Organisation. It's situated in what must have been once a rather magnificent house.

Décor apart, it's very handy for a punt if you're having tea in the Ritz. The last time I partook of the cucumber sandwich bit there with a lady friend I kept sneaking over the road telling her I was going to the Gents, and coming back with a longer and longer face each time. She evidently thought I had prostate trouble, as opposed to the old fiscal complaint, and I think she was definitely put off me. I suppose the thing is to own up about the betting, but there are girls who would and could never understand that the four-thirty at Sedgefield was more important than them. Wild horses *can* drag you away.

I once leapt out of bed on a Saturday morning shouting a vow to give up backing horses for good and ever. By midday, like an alcoholic twitching for the first hair of the dog, I was looking around for something to bet on. It really is a bloody disease. As bad luck would have it I bumped into my amateur bookmaker friend in Dean Street. We had an idle chat and then, contemplating the weather and gazing at the heavens, I heard my voice say 'What odds will you lay me that it rains before one o'clock?' I was laid two pounds at 2-1 and my request for 20-1 against sleet during the weekend was refused.

Feeling a twinge of guilt at having had a bet at all, but consoling myself that at least I hadn't backed a wretched horse yet, I then had two pounds at 1-2 that the sex of the first customer in the York Minster at opening time would be male. This seemed to me to be something of a racing certainty since I was sure as a man could be that I'd be the first person in the pub. But my luck was really stinking. I was beaten a head by the cleaning lady.

It was after that, while lingering over a refreshing aperitif, that my eye accidentally caught sight of the racing page in *The Times*. Saturday, of course, is the punter's pitfall day. It's sheer folly to try and go through four or five meetings on a Saturday and I felt really pleased about my new resolution to eschew the Turf. Then, glancing at the runners in the Joe Coral Northumberland Plate, it occurred to me that Grey Baron stood one hell of a chance of winning even with his top weight of 10st 1lb. I could of course make him my one final and definitely last bet of all time apart from the obligatory double on Connors and Evert to win their Wimbledon finals. Well, Grey Baron came in third, which made my eyes water a bit, and then I lost a fiver playing my last ever game of spoof.

By now, guilt and remorse, not to mention considerable *angst*, had set in and when at 4 pm, I found myself in an afternoon club staring longingly at a fruit machine, I was damn nigh weeping. Well, a couple of five pence pieces wasn't going to do much harm, was it? The second one I put in produced the jackpot and that totted up to seven pounds fifty. God, fate, luck and love had obviously returned to my side and, as it happened, I realised I was just in time to get on a good thing in the four-twenty at Newcastle. I plunged in heavily. The name of that particular beast still rings in my ears, and how Gold Loom came to be beaten a short head and half a length is something I still haven't quite recovered from.

Let me give you an account of a more typical Saturday's betting away from the course, Champion Stakes day a few years ago to be precise. Take it as a warning. I got out of bed feeling the usual strange mixture of optimism and fear and worked really hard on the afternoon's cards all morning, concentrating to such effect on the Newmarket events that I'd forgotten two recorded deliveries and a final demand by the time I met my bookmaker in Soho. That was at 11.30 am. It was what happened between then and the first race that caused ruination and that was two bottles of a rather astringent white wine. By the time they came under orders for the first, the wit was utterly out. It was five minutes before the Champion Stakes though that I suddenly got a very strong hunch that Rose Bowl was going to get beaten. But by what? Certainly not by the eventual 22-1 winner, Vitiges. I thought Malacate might have a squeak so I put a hurried fiver each way on him. I then read a glowing account of a recent gallop by Konafa and put five pounds on her. Just one more glass of wine before the off and it occurred to me that what with the Bruce Hobbs string being in such good form and his horse Jolly Good having displayed a certain relish for soft going last time out at Lingfield, he must represent really good value at 25-1, so I had a rushed and wildly optimistic each way on that one too as they were going into the stalls.

Half an hour later I had a sudden thought about the Cesarewitch. Grinling Gibbons is about to get stuffed, I said. Furthermore, I mumbled inwardly to myself, it won't be by John Cherry since nothing is going to win this test of stamina humping 9st 13lb on its back even if it is largely in the form of Lester Piggot. I then had a wonderful experience and a rare one. It was a vision. Tug of War was hacking into the final furlong, drawing away from the field and doing hand-springs. So I backed him. A minute later, and just to be on the safe side, I had a saver on Belfalas. It was John Cherry's year.

As you can imagine, funds were now running out. There was only one thing for it – get out of trouble by backing a few jumpers at Kempton Park. Two hours later, sitting under a portrait of a disapproving-looking Mustafa Kemal in a Turkish restaurant, the proprietor approached me with a large, free glass of Raki. It was on the house, he said, because he hated to see anyone look as sad as I did.

THE MINSTREL AND DUNFERMLINE DULY WON THE DERBY AND the Oaks respectively. Meanwhile the continuing saga of the wretched Deciduous was beginnning to get on my nerves, get me down and get me into debt. She ran for the third time on 20 June at a Monday evening meeting at Wolverhampton and came in a well beaten fourth. For once I couldn't go to the course and see her, but the next time she sees me, I thought, I hope she has the decency to lower her eyes and blush a little. She actually opened up as the 7-2 favourite before drifting out to 5-1 and that surely must have been a bookmaker's 'come-on'. At the beginning of the day Terry Wogan, then on the breakfast 'show' on Radio 2, had put the block on her by tipping her and, at the same time, had blown my cover on *Private Eye* as Colonel Mad. Then, later in the day, I phoned up Victor Chandler who kindly let me have a credit account for the day and I put twenty quid on her.

It's a fact that I didn't give a hoot about losing twenty pounds, or a very tiny hoot, but what was beginning to drive me mad was this crazy emotional involvemment with Deciduous just because my name appeared in print after hers on the race card and in *The Sporting Life*. When the result of the race came over the blower in the betting shop I was biting my nails and realising how my mother must have felt when I got expelled from school. Before the race, I went in to the 'French' pub for 'just the one' and to pick up a friend to accompany me to the shop and there was a sudden flood of money for Deciduous from various Spanish waiters and people at the bar. You see, that's another thing about having a geegee. Everyone you know is on your side and then when the horse trails in fourth there's a certain amount of lip-curling and boring banter. Even if the horse wins, it's the owner that always carries the penalty.

After the race I retired to another pub to lick my wounds
since I couldn't face explanations to a mob of irate Spaniards
and, sitting there, having a moan like I'm having now , some
twit had the nerve to say, 'Well, just think how Robert
Sangster must have felt when Durtal was injured at the start of
the Oaks and had to be withdrawn with the race at her mercy.'
In answer to that I can only say that whatever Robert Sangster
feels it's cushioned by having a few million quid in his current
account. Furthermore, when Mr Sangster feels like selling a
horse he's at liberty to do so and since his horses are his own
or in partnerships with friends he can sell a horse without
having nine angry coal-miners coming after him with picks.
God alone knew how you got out of a syndicate financially
intact if no one wanted to buy your share. Anyway, I now
began waiting explanations and excuses from Doug Marks
who would, no doubt, have something funny and uplifting to
say about the race.

Personally, I began thinking we'd better send her to Chantilly where they get up to so many dodges on the quiet that
sometimes I think they could get a donkey to win the Derby.
Actually, this is something I'd love to have the time and
money to investigate properly. I'm not one of those people
who go about saying that racing is all bent, in fact I think it's
far straighter than most people do. But I have a shrewd
suspicion that French racing is distinctly murky. Which
reminds me, by the way, of my favourite French racing joke
which is actually true. An Australian jockey who will have to
remain nameless got a retainer to ride for a big stable at
Chantilly, duly arrived and they found that he couldn't speak
a word of French. They got an interpreter to him who said,
'Now the first thing you'll have to learn is a phrase the guvnor
might use when he gives you the leg up at Longchamp
tomorrow. It's "*Pas aujourd'hui*" and it means not today.'

What a pity that as far as Deciduous was concerned I was
beginning to think that it wasn't yesterday, today or
tomorrow. And there I will leave the sad subject except to tell

Soho

After the race I retired to another pub to lick my wounds.

you that no, she never did win a race. I later had another
syndicated horse. This one was named Colonel Mad after my
Private Eye column, was by Tower Walk and was trained by
James Bethell. I was soon at the receiving end of the usual
amount of rubbish. One of those involved with the syndicate
used to ring me up and say, 'He galloped very well yesterday.
Could possibly win the Two Thousand Guineas.' Such information was not entirely accurate. Colonel Mad was once
placed at 25-1 and the height of his achievements was to win a
very small event over hurdles at somewhere like Devon and
Exeter. Needless to say, I forgot to be there that day and thus
avail myself of the quite generous odds about him. He was
eventually sold to someone in Switzerland. What anyone in
Switzerland saw in an unsuccessful gelding called Colonel
Mad is one of those little puzzles that I have never managed to
solve.

the luck of the draw

Allow me to refer you to another learned book on
gambling *The Psychology of Gambling* edited by Jon Halliday
and Peter Fuller. The book is a very serious and
disconcerting one and although I've always prided myself
on having the ability to 'own up', I realised on reading it
that my owning up has always been sheer surface stuff.

For example, I never knew until I read this learned tome
that I gambled because I really feel lousy about it and not
only want to lose on the nags to punish myself for this
blinding practice but, to rub it in further, also want to kill
my father. Speaking as an anal retentive who thought that
Her Majesty's Dunfermline would be outclassed in the
1977 St. Leger by the likes of Alleged and the French
contingent, I always put my punting down to the simple
business of asking questions. My main, first and foremost
question has always been: 'Is fate, God, luck and love on

my side?' The second question has usually been: 'Can I win enough money on such and such a horse to enable me to avoid actual work?'

But I come not to knock Freud, Halliday or Fuller for they are honourable men although I wouldn't mind offering a shade of odds that none of them ever did or ever has had a bet. Heavens above, can you imagine the trouble Freud would have had betting? If, as I believe to be the case, Freud turned up one hour early to catch a train, then can you imagine the trouble he would have had trying to get a bet on the three-thirty while the two-thirty was still being run? Obviously he would have been an obsessive and compulsive ante-post plunger. And, like most obsessive and anally-orientated punters, he would have shown a marked tendency to knock the bookmaker.

What really gets my nanny tote is the clumsy way, or at least inexperienced way, that clever men, intellectuals and academic men get their teeth stuck into vicarious problems. Should you ever have the bad luck or spare time to be asked and then go to a party given by the sort of people who live in Docklands and who write for the *Sunday Times* and then hear the subject of compulsive gambling crop up, you'll find it a racing certainty that some bright spark – usually a feature writer who earns about fifty thousand a year and whose one assignment in the year is to take a trip to the Dordogne to find out how some poof celebrity cooks aubergines – is bound to mention Dostoevsky. There'll then be a lot of wise shakings of the heads and at least two people with After Eight stains on their waistcoats will knowingly murmur : 'Christ yes. Did you read *The Gambler*? Absolutely fantastic.' No one ever seems to have tumbled that what's so bloody despicable about Dostoevsky is that he was a really lousy punter. Not just usually bad, but really awful. You wouldn't have passed the time of day with him in a betting shop.

I don't mean that to be a social worker you need to have been a one-time psychopath brought up in a slum, but I do think that you need to have done a little more than an exam-sitting. (Show me a GP who knows anything about alcoholics who isn't one.) What I'm laboriously and clumsily trying to get at is that you've got to be there to

know what it's like to be there. Messrs Halliday and Fuller
have written a splendid introduction – nearly half the
book in fact, the rest of it consisting of some eight essays –
but it's all theory.

I know a historian can write about Waterloo without
having fought at it, but I just don't see how two blokes
can explain gambling who haven't sweated, panted and
drooled over a race card. At the beginning of this
admirably unsatisfying and fascinating book that leaves
most of the questions unanswered or glibly explained *à la*
Freud, there are three quotes. To my amazement one of
them begins: 'Sitting here contemplating a load of bills
from various bookmakers, I can suddenly remember what
made me fall in love with horseracing. There was a boy at
school . . . ' The quote is credited to Jeffrey Bernard, 'A
Year at the Races', *New Statesman* 1 June 1973. And I think
that's where we came in.

God forgive me for ever having been so glib about my
Oedipal background but as I've got this far I may as well
continue. As a disastrous day's punting at Newmarket
never fails to rub in, results depend a little on breeding but
a lot more on the luck of the draw. The proof of the
pudding is in human beings. Take my own infamous
career on the Turf. I was sired by a scenic designer who
was himself by a theatrical impressario out of an actresss.
My dam was a singer who was by an itinerant pork
butcher out of a gypsy.

Another strange example is the case of a Yorkshire-bred
friend of mine. He comes from really sound stock being as
he is by a dispensing chemist out of a Salvation Army
contralto. Full of promise, he came to London at the
outbreak of the war, attempted to take the publishing
world by storm and now, forty years later, he earns a
living writing pornography in the snug of a public house
behind what used to be Bourne and Hollingsworth. Taking
matters like these into consideration is what the Jockey
Club ought to be doing. Where they say the draw has little
effect they should double-check and reorganise draining
in cases of slightest camber or move the running rails so as
to prevent fields splitting into two groups. My Yorkshire
friend and I have been running with the group on the
stands side for the past forty years and from where I'm

The Psychology of Gambling

*Speaking as an anal retentive who thought Her Majesty's
Dunfermline would be outclassed in the 1977 St Leger . . .*

standing, you lot on the far side have got a ten length advantage. And we're entering the final furlong.

11

ECLIPSE DAY AT SANDOWN PARK WAS FASCINATING. LESTER Piggot proved once again and for the umpteenth time that he's about as romantic as a woman with a display of the coolest, coldest and most cerebral raceriding that it can have been my pleasure and displeasure to watch. When I say displeasure I am of course talking through my pocket. As usual, I started off by fancying the winner, Artaius, before the off and then went off it after having listened and taken too much notice of people whose opinions didn't matter a damn.

Sound advice came from my old friend Bill Marshall. We were discussing the prospects of the French challenger Arctic Tern who had a terrible reputation for travelling badly. He said, 'Don't go and look at the horses in the paddock. The sight of them doesn't necessarily give you a clue.' I said that surely one could get some idea of whether an animal was fit and happy and he replied, 'No. I've had horses sweat up and look like pigs and they've cantered in and I've had them look like they've been French polished and they've run like cows.' By and large I agree with him, although it's certainly a fact that when horses are well and in good nick, as with human beings it shows in obvious ways. They positively shine, look well-muscled and keen and happy.

Later I managed to get Vincent O'Brien, trainer of the winner, to one side and ask him something that had always intrigued me about racing: horses losing weight and gaining it. O'Brien had always weighed his horses on a weigh-bridge, something that has now become almost common practice among trainers, and he told me that in sheer sweat a horse can lose as much as ten kilos during a race, something like 22 lb. If they eat up well after and recover the poundage, then he had a pretty fair idea that they'd recovered well and had suffered no ill effects from the race. Loose livers with bathroom weighing machines, please take note.

Towards the end of the month, it seemed that I wasn't the only person who thought that Crow would win the King George VI and Queen Elizabeth Diamond Stakes. Bets struck in the Ring just before the off included £5000 – £1000, £9000 – £2000, £18000 – £4000, £12000 – £3000, £4500 – £1000 three times, £3750 – £1000, and £3500 – £1000. The Minstrel won. He must have been one of the bravest horses of all time and yet people went on knocking him on looks, constantly criticising his four white stockings, white blaze and flashy chestnut colouring. You might just as well have said that no one who looked like Olivier in his younger days could have possibly been any great shakes at acting.

The highlight of Glorious Goodwood was the sight of Artaius and Lester following up in the Sussex Stakes, and it took some of the pain out of the previous three weeks when, in the last day, I backed Tumbledownwind at 5-2 and Homeboy who won very easily at 16-1, though of course I didn't have enough on. That weekend was, for me, one of those that you don't get to savour unless you associate with the sort of people your old headmaster would have described as being 'bad hats'. Mine anyway. The paradox about them is that they seemingly drift toward ruination in the most idle way. In actual fact, drifting is an art that requries enormous energy and effort. Come to think of it, it needs a little judgement. It's no good drifting toward Carey Street in bad company. One must laugh along the way. This can be done at Goodwood. I suppose it can be done at some of the dump tracks too, but it's preferable to go down the steepest hill. And there's one thing I'll say about Goodwood, and I'm a dreadful inverted snob about racecourses, and that's that the view standing by the rails on the finishing post is second to none. Shrewd judges, I suppose, back horses that win by such streaks that they don't have to stand on the line. I was driven to Goodwood by a couple of publicans from Soho who are just about the strongest analgesics I've come across. They forced seafood down my throat, a little drink, and then pushed me out into the sunshine to mix with the likes of Edward Underdown – Steward at Newbury and gentleman actor – and Jimmy Lindley who must be about the most articulate jockey it's ever been my pleasure to meet.

The Benson and Hedges Gold Cup and St Leger both produced upsets, with Relkino and Dunfermline beating the two hot-pots of O'Briens, Artaius and Alleged. For me, a couple of the lesser meetings stand out in the memory, like Sandown Park on the day the Variety Club sponsored a race and they had that farce of a marquee they always put up by the paddock and call the 'Celebrity Tent'. Always keen to have a look at a name if only for future dropping, I fiddled myself an invitation into the tent and looked around for a celebrity to stare at. The only people you might have ever heard of in the place were Liz Fraser and John Junkin. The three of us stared at each other for a while, picked out three losers and had a drink while hundreds of people were actualy daft enough to stand around the tent staring at us inside. What on earth is it that makes people want to ogle those they've seen on television? God alone knows. Just as odd to my mind is the fact that thespians really live it whatever they say.

By the end of the day I could just about see the light at the end of the tunnel. I'd been trying to pick winners from a hospital bed for two weeks and that's very tricky. It's particularly difficult studying the form of a race when some wretched student, nervous and with trembling hand, is trying to extract the few drops of blood the bookmakers have been kind enough to leave you. The light at the end of this particular tunnel came in the form of one of Richard Hannon's charges who duly obliged in the last at 5-1.

the guvnor

I once went to Newmarket to interview Lester Piggot for
The *Sunday Times*. He rode two hot-pots for a big trainer
on the gallops that morning and when he got off the
second one he said it was a Derby prospect. On the way
back to his house we came across a loose horse that had
obviously thrown its stable lad on the way home and was
now standing stupidly in the middle of the road. It was
the Derby prospect. I pointed it out to Lester and
suggested we stopped and got hold of it – after all, it could
easily be smashed up by a car. Lester smiled rather
wickedly: 'No, Jeffrey. You never catch hold of a loose
horse. You can spend all bloody day hanging on to it.'
I thought this a charmingly cynical approach.

At the end of the morning I explained that I had to get
back to Newbury for the races. 'You're an idiot,' he told
me succinctly. 'Don't you realise I'm riding there this
afternoon? You can have a lift in my aeroplane.' So we
flew to Newbury in his four-seater with Geoff Wragg and
another trainer. I got out at the races, and said thank you
very much and thought nothing more of it. A week later
I got a bill for thirty-five quid. A little later, a reminder
followed. Incensed by this display of parsimony I told one
of the stalls handlers about it. This same man found
himself loading Lester into the stalls one day soon after.
'Lester' he said, 'that thirty-five quid bill you sent to Jeff –
he's very annoyed about it . . . ' Apparently when the
stalls opened Lester was laughing so much that he almost
fell off.

Lester is astute and funny, but his humour is dry and
abrasive and when teamed up with a brain that fires on all
cylinders it is easily misunderstood. Most of the stories
about his meanness are really about Lester winding people
up, teasing them – like the day he gave Willie Carson a lift
back from York one sweltering August day. Lester told his
chauffeur to pull up at a garage selling ice cream. 'Get
three,' he told the man, who returned shortly and handed
over three cones to Lester. Carson put his hand out for
one, but Lester simply turned to him and said: 'They're

mine, get your own.' This sort of incident, purely an experiment to see how discomfited Carson could look, has been exaggerated to make Lester seem pathologically mean, which he isn't. He's just tight.

I can remember sitting outside a café in Chantilly feeling bored and depressed and anxious about my fast-dwindling expenses – the afternoons are horribly dead even in that lovely place – and who should walk by but Lester. I never thought that worried, taut, serious face would be a cheering sight off a horse but I nearly burst into a couple of verses of 'We'll Meet Again' *à la* Vera Lynn. But Lester didn't stop to say hello. That might have cost him a glass of red wine.

It's not true either that he never smiles, though it doesn't look as if there'd be room between the crags. I remember a day at Ascot when he landed the King George VI and Queen Elizabeth Diamond Stakes with a brilliant ride on that gutsy horse The Minstrel. He then went on to win the Brown Jack Stakes on the Queen's horse Valuation. In the enclosure afterwards he was talking to the Queen and beaming like the cat that's got the cream. I gather that the Queen had said to him: 'You made it look so easy.' And with an admirable lack of false modesty he had replied: 'Ma'am, it *was* easy.'

Another occasion sticks in the mind. Soon after Vincent O'Brien sacked him, Lester popped up and beat one of O'Brien's best horses by a short head in a thrilling finish. O'Brien was standing miserably in the unsaddling enclosure. Lester walked past him on his way to the scales and gave him a huge grin. 'Will you be needing me again?' were his only words.

As in all departments, Lester Piggot talks a great deal of sense about gambling. I once told him the story of an Italian waiter in Frith Street who put his life's savings on a horse that Lester was riding and which started at 6-5. You don't back horses like that with your life's savings, not unless you're mad, but this man did, and Lester got stuffed that day – beaten by a very small margin – a neck or half a length. The waiter was reduced to hysteria and suddenly began screaming in the betting shop: 'Alla my life I givva my wife good food . . . My children havva the shoes on their feet . . . They eata well, they're clothed, I

The Bad Loser

If you lose your wages, well that's your fault.

paya the rent . . . And now this fucking bastard Piggott,
he kill me, he ruin my life . . . ' In a little while he was
transferred to the Middlesex Hospital in a straight-jacket.
When Lester heard this story, he simply remarked that
people like that are idiots. And he was right. After all, no
one twists your arm to have a bet. If you lose your wages,
well that's your fault.

I don't envy the racing correspondents who, now that
he's a trainer (and naturally a successful one), have to try
and get statements from Lester after one of his horses has
won. He is certainly no orator and tends to reply in short,
sharp, grumpy monosyllables. But for my money he's the
Guvnor of all time. There's a long-standing debate about
who was the greatest, Lester or Gordon Richards. No
contest. After all, Gordon could ride almost anything, but
Lester had many fewer mounts because of his weight
problems. His genius is unique – he's a Jack Dempsey, a
Joe Davis, a Donald Bradman.

12

LATE SEPTEMBER FOUND ME AGAIN AT NEWBURY, THIS TIME FOR
a specific purpose. I could hardly remember – it had been that
long – when I had first started fancying Peter Walwyn's
Formidable for the Mill Reef Stakes. All I do know is that I just
couldn't see it getting beat and was armed with the necessary
amount to back up my judgement to the hilt. As the runners
were cantering down to the start, I spotted Phil Bull
approaching a rails bookmaker. Now Phil Bull, the Halifax
sage, is the ex-schoolmaster who founded *Timeform* and who
knows more about racing than just about anyone in the world.
So I followed him and did a spot of eavesdropping. 'I'll have
two thousand pounds to win Tumbledownwind,' I heard the
great man say. I immediately abandoned my own strong fancy

Formidable and plunged in heavily on the other. Tumble-downwind led until the distance after his usual fast start, but then Formidable was shaken up by Eddery and quickly asserted his superiority. It was Bull that had once described racing as 'the great triviality,' but that was little consolation to me now.

The two days racing at Newbury had been something of a glut of horse manure what with staying in the place for two nights, eating, drinking and socialising there, at night as well as during the day, losing money, then getting some back and then, eventually going down with most flags flying. My own particular flag on this occasion was the white flag of surrender.

Last year, however, my luck changed. I had a yankee up and won over £2,000, a big win for a very small punter. It was the sort of win that hooks a boy on racing, but it occurred to me that since it had taken thirty-five years to arrive at that win punting was indeed a mug's game. I decided to take up making a book among my friends and acquaintances in a very small, fun way. The law didn't see it quite like that and my luck changed again. I got nicked, having been under surveillance by H.M. Customs for three months (always on Saturdays – double time?), no less. It took nine policemen and three customs men in one wagon, and one squad car to arrest me. Little me. I sometimes wonder at just how much public expense. They recovered the vital sum of £31.12p in evaded betting tax and fined me £200 with £50 costs. As the Press at the time more or less said, the law is indeed an ass. Here, never published before, are some of the more ridiculous excerpts from the charge record, *verbatim*.

From the statement of David Bailey, Officer of Customs and Excise:

'On 13th June, 1986 at approximately 14.00 hours I entered the Coach & Horses Public House, Greek Street, London W1. A television set was switched on showing racing from Sandown and York. A man, who I now know to be Jeffrey Bernard said "Does anyone want anything on this?", just as the 3.00 race

The Arrest

It took nine policemen and three Customs men to arrest me.
Little me.

from Sandown was starting . . . [20th June 1986] After the 2.45 race at Newmarket, Jeffrey Bernard handed coins to a woman. A man addressed as Alan on a previous visit to the premises asked Mr Bernard "Did anyone have it?" Mr Bernard pointed to the woman to whom he had just handed the coins. During the build-up to the 3.05 race, the Irish Sweeps Derby, Jeffrey Bernard said to a man, "Dino (or Tino), do you want a bet?"

'I asked a man at the bar for the running number of a horse called Bonhomie. He consulted his newspaper and replied. At this point Mr Bernard said to me, "Do you want a bet?" I handed him two £1 coins and asked for Bonhomie. Two other customers handed Mr Bernard coins and both asked for Bonhomie. Mr Bernard said to a female companion, "I'm fucked if Bonhomie wins." Bonhomie lost and I left the premises at approximately 15.18 hours.'

From the Statement of Paul David Denham, Officer of Customs and Excise:

'On 5th July 1986 at approximately 1320 hours I entered the Coach and Horses. Mr Bernard was sat at the bar. He had the racing page of the *Times* newpaper folded up in front of him on the bar. At 13.45 hours Mr Bailey entered the premises. We sat at the bar next to Mr Bernard and in front of the television . . . Mr Bailey bet £2 on High Plains. I bet £2 on Morgan's Choice . . . My selection Morgan's Choice won the race. Mr Bernard said to me, "I'm glad you won, if High Plains had won I would have been in trouble." He asked me the starting price of my selection. I told him 9-2. Mr Bernard said "So I owe you £11." He gave me £11 and said to customers around him 'That's why they bet with me, because they don't have to pay any tax" . . .

'On 30th August 1986 at approximately 1325 hours I entered the Coach and Horses. There I met Mr Bailey. Mr Bernard was sat at the bar. The television was showing racing from Sandown . . .

'On 20th September 1986 at approximately 1330 hours I entered the Coach and Horses with Mr Bailey. Mr Bernard was sat at the bar. The television was switched on showing racing. Shortly before the first race at 1340 hours Mr Bernard took a folded up racing page from the *Times* newspaper and placed it in front of him on the bar . . . I bet £2 on Irish Passage . . . My selection won at a starting price of 5-1. Mr Bernard pointed to me and said "You had a winner." He handed me a £10 note from his trouser pocket and two £1 coins that were on the bar. The return of the 12 represents no tax deduction . . . Before the start of the 3.00 race at Newbury, Mr Bernard asked me what I thought would win the race. I told him "Print" . . . I then bet £2 on Print . . . My selection, Print, won the race. As soon as the race finished, and before Mr Bernard had paid me, Police and Customs Officers entered the public house at approximately 1505 hours.

From the Record of Interview between myself and A. Cummings at Vine Street Police Station

Cummings Do you pay tax on the bets you take to the government?

Bernard No, well how could I? I'm not a licensed bookmaker.

Cummings Do you think its against the law not to pay tax?

Bernard I do now, as I told Inspector Gardner I always have treated it as a joke between friends. I always take bets from friends not from strangers. Also the governor of the Coach & Horses knows nothing about this, he caught me once and said I'd be barred for life. He knows nothing about today at all.

Cummings Why do the regulars bet with you rather than go to the Mecca around the corner?

Bernard They regard it as fun and are too lazy to walk to the betting shop to desert their drink. It's a joke between us. I think they're fools and they think I'm one.

Cummings Do they bet with you because you don't charge tax?

Bernard No it's just a game. Nobody's that mean, at least my friends aren't.

Cummings I accept it's a bit of fun but don't you think they do it for the tax advantage as well?

Bernard No they don't, it's really as though we're ribbing each other we're taking the piss out of each other in a way.

Cummings How well do you have to know someone before you take bets of them?

Bernard Friends and acquaintances, not strangers. Most of the people are good mates.

Interview temporarily ceased. Doctor to see Mr Bernard (16.57). P.C. Emment and Bernard leave the room.

Bernard and P.C. Emment re-entered the room at 17.04. Interview recommenced . . .

Cummings How well do you have to know someone before you bet with them?

Bernard Friends or acquaintances, never from a stranger.

Cummings Would you be surprised to know you've accepted bets from Customs Officers.

Bernard If I have I must have been pissed at the time, which is quite likely. Have I? Did they win? I hope they got it on expenses if they lost.

Bernard I have never knowingly taken a bet from a stranger put it that way. And if I have I have assumed that they were in the company that I was with in the same way that if you're with a group of people you don't buy them all a drink and exclude one person.

Cummings On one occasion an officer overheard you say "that's why they bet with me, they don't have to pay any tax". Do you still say that that wasn't one of their reasons for betting with you?

Bernard I've only got your word that he said that and you've only got his word.

Cummings Today you mentioned that you were concerned that there were police officers in the pub. Why?

Bernard Because it had been pointed out to me earlier that what I was doing was illegal, by one of the people backing horses with me.

Cummings When was it pointed out to you that it was illegal to accept bets?

Bernard I don't remember exactly a few weeks, well when Norman Balan [*sic*] said that he'd bar me, in the summer about three months ago.

Cummings Did you think at that time that it would be against Customs laws as well?

Bernard That was pointed out to me then.

Cummings What customs law were you told you'd be breaking?

Bernard VAT.

Cummings Is that the tax on the betting in other words?

Bernard Yes betting tax not VAT, betting tax.

Cummings Are you saying that you've known since the middle of the summer that you've been breaking Customs laws on betting tax accepting bets?

Bernard Yes.

Cummings When roughly were you told this?

Bernard June.

Cummings And which Customs law would you be breaking?

Bernard Betting tax, evading Betting tax.

Cummings So is it fair to say that since some time in June that in accepting bets you've known you're evading Betting tax?

Bernard Yes, I've cost the Government about three pounds a week in tax. I'm guilty, I'm not daft. I'm not lying to you or the police.

Cummings Can I just run through the bets you've laid to-day?

Bernard Yes, fifty nine, I think Inspector Gardner said.

Cummings Have you marked all details of bets you've accepted?

Bernard Yes, but not what I've paid out.

Bernard examines the sheet from the Times showing racing.

Cummings The 1.40 at Ayr. Did you take six bets totalling seven pounds?

Bernard Yes.

Bernard 2.10 six pounds, four pounds on the 2.40, twenty pounds on the 2.00 Newbury, twelve pounds 2.30 Newbury,

twenty pounds 3.00 Newbury and that's when I got arrested.
Cummings Do you keep a record anywhere of bets you've
accepted previous days?
Bernard No, I win or lose and go home.
Cummings No more questions.
Interview terminated at 17.29 hours.

**About a month after this coup, the arresting officer, Inspector
Gardner, was promoted to Chief Detective Inspector.**

part ii:
the
RACES

What follows is a list of all the Group races on the Flat in Britain, all Group 1 Flat races in France and Ireland, and a few elsewhere. It is intended as an entirely fallible guide to the more interesting races, the more enjoyable meetings and the more obvious pitfalls, and you follow any advice it contains at your peril.

Each season the racing calendar changes as races improve or decay. What is presented here is a typical modern season, so both the dates and the prize money are approximate. Only results up to the time of going to press (30 July 1987) have been taken into account.

The following notation has been used:

GRP — Group
m   — miles
f   — furlongs
f&y — furlongs/yards
3y   — three-year-olds
4y+ — four-year-olds and older
F   — fillies
C   — colts
G   — geldings

the flat

DONCASTER   March 26-28

The opening of the British Flat racing season at Doncaster is a dismal affair. The best advice is to stay at home. The weather is usually wet and windy, the ground more suited to jumping and the racing of little account. The 'highlight' of the meeting is

THE (WILLIAM HILL) LINCOLN HANDICAP (£30,000, 1m 4y+). This historic first leg of the 'Spring Double' (the second leg being the Grand National) was first run as the Lincolnshire Handicap at Lincoln in 1853 and was transferred, on the closure of that course, to Doncaster in 1965, since when more ink has been wasted each year on the effects of the draw than on any other aspect of the race. The facts are that since work on the straight was carried out a few years ago it has proved almost impossible for high-drawn horses to win. The field is invariably huge and picking the winner is a tricky business. And remember that luck in running can play a major part in the race. The best advice is to concentrate on the better fancied horses, drawn low, starting at up to 14-1, keep your bet small and make it an each-way one.

NEWBURY   April 10-11

The quality of the racing, if not the weather, is guaranteed at the Newbury Spring Meeting. Newbury is one of the fairest, best-managed and most enjoyable tracks in the country – but beware: finding winners here is notoiously difficult and the record of favourites is one of the worst of the season. The three best races of the meeting are:

THE (GAINSBOROUGH STUD) FRED DARLING STAKES (GRP 3 – £20,000 7f60y, 3yF). This first of the trials for the Thousand Guineas is named after the great former champion trainer and is occasionally won by a good filly. Favourite backers fare reasonably well.

THE (CLERICAL MEDICAL) GREENHAM STAKES (GRP 3 – £25,000, 7f, 3yC+G) is the first of the trials for the Two Thousand Guineas, originally staged over a mile in 1906. The race has been won by some good and great horses in recent years, like Risk Me, Kris, Wollow, Boldboy and Mill Reef, but treat the Greenham with the utmost caution. Since the war, only Wollow has gone on to win the Guineas and some very good horses, like Grundy, have been defeated in it before going on to greater things.

THE (LANES END) JOHN PORTER (E.B.F.) STAKES (GRP 3, £27,500, 1½m, 4y+), named after another great trainer of the past, is the first good race for older horses of the season but is full of pitfalls. Tread warily and remember that the 1983 winner Teenoso was defeated on his 1984 reappearance in this, a Group 3 contest.

NEWMARKET   April 14-16
The Craven Meeting is traditionally the one when even the smartest of trainers, the Henry Cecils and Dick Herns, may deign to have their first runners of the year.

THE (JUDDMONTE FARMS) NELL GWYNNE STAKES (GRP 3 – £17,500, 7f, 3yF) is the second of the trials for the Thousand Guineas and a much more reliable one than the Fred Darling, having been won in recent years by future winners of the first Classic, such as Flying Water, One in a Million, Fairy Footsteps, Pebbles and Oh So Sharp. A good filly installed as

favourite often represents a sound investment, though you may have to take a short price. Bear in mind that the astounding Henry Cecil has won six of the last nine runnings. THE (LADBROKE) EUROPEAN FREE HANDICAP (£22,500, 7f, 3y), the first of the two long-standing Two Thousand Guinea trials at the meeting, can lay claim to being the classiest handicap of the season as many of the runners at this stage have Classic pretensions. In the 1987 renewal, for example, the top-weight winner, Noble Minstrel, was officially rated only 15lb behind top-rated Reference Point in the 1986 list of two-year-olds, while the runner-up, Midyan, went on to be third in the Guineas before taking the Jersey Stakes at Royal Ascot. As a guide to Classic form, however, the Free handicap is less than reliable and only Privy Councillor and Mrs Mcardy have gone on to success in the Guineas since 1962, while picking the winner is a tricky affair.
THE EARL OF SEFTON E.B.F. STAKES (GRP 3 – £22,500, 1m1f, 4y+) is the second race of any account for older horses since the start of the season.
THE (CHARLES HEIDSIECK CHAMPAGNE) CRAVEN STAKES (GRP 3 – £15,000, 1m, 3yC+G). The Craven is the least valuable but most important of the Group races at this meeting, and its result invariably has some bearing on the Two Thousand Guineas. The last two years have been typical. In 1986 Dancing Brave won the Craven and went on to spread-eagle his field in the Guineas. In 1987 Don't Forget Me was only second in the Craven to Ajdal but then won the Guineas with Ajdal only fourth. So the conclusion must be: ignore the Craven form at your peril, but for goodness sake don't take it on trust.

EPSOM   April 21-22
The prestige of the first Epsom meeting of the season has been sinking for many years. It was once a proud three-day affair, boasting some important and famous races. Now reduced to two days, its two 'Classic trials', the Princess Elizabeth Stakes

and the Blue Riband Trial, are without Group status and have little bearing on Classic form. The famous old races, the City and Suburban Stakes and the Great Metropolitan Handicap, have fared contrastingly. While the former can offer £16,000 to the winner, the latter, first run in 1846 over 2¼ miles and one of the spectacles of the season, has disappeared completely from the calendar, being replaced by a sad apology of its former self, the Great Metropolitan 40th Anniversary of the Photo Finish Handicap, run over a predictable 1½ miles and worth a mere £2,000 or so more than its predecessor was ten years ago.

SANDOWN   April 24-25

THE TRUSTHOUSE FORTE MILE (GRP 2 – £30,000, 1m, 4y+), a new race of only three years' standing, is now the first British Group 2 event of the season. Won by the great Pebbles, the 11-8 favourite, in 1985, the subsequent two renewals have been slightly sub-standard affairs.

THE GUARDIAN CLASSIC TRIAL (GRP 3 – £25,000, 1¼m, 3yC+G) is the first of the season's Derby trials and can lay claim to being the best simply because four Derby winners – Troy, Henbit, Shergar and Sharastani – all first won this event impressively on their seasonal reappearances. Favourites have a reasonable record, though there is the occasional surprise result. Best tip: follow Dick Hern.

THE GORDON RICHARDS E.B.F. STAKES (GRP 3 – £25,000, 1¼m, 4y+) was formerly known as the Westbury Stakes until renamed after the death of the great jockey in 1987. It has a good record for favourites but is seldom won by a really good horse. This race and the Guardian Trial are run on Saturday, and both are overshadowed by the great jump race the Whitbread Gold Cup. All in all, it is one of the most entertaining race days of the year.

ASCOT   April 29

A good day's racing on the Wednesday before the start of the big Guineas meeting at Newmarket and well worth a visit. The (Insulpak) Victoria Cup is a competitive and valuable handicap over seven furlongs, the E.B.F. Garter Stakes the first two-year-old race of the year of any note, and the White Rose Stakes a now devalued Classic trial over 1¼ miles.

THE (INSULPAK) SAGARO (E.B.F.) STAKES (GRP 3 – £27,500, 2m, 4y+) is named after the great recently deceased stayer and run over two miles. Don't ignore it, as it's handy as a guide to the Ascot Gold Cup.

NEWMARKET   April 30-May 2

The first Classics of the season always seem to arrive before anyone is really ready for them, and the weather is usually more wintry than springlike. The Pretty Polly Stakes, the Classic trial for fillies over 1¼ miles, has only 'listed' status but is often won by a really good horse, like Dunfermline and Indian Skimmer.

THE (GENERAL ACCIDENT) 1000 GUINEAS STAKES (GRP 1 – £85,000, 1m, 3yF) is not a bad race for punters and is usually won by a well-fancied and proven filly. The best advice is to select such a runner from a big stable that knows what it's doing and back it each-way. That way you should get a run for your money.

THE (GENERAL ACCIDENT) JOCKEY CLUB STAKES (GRP 2 – £25,000, 1½m, 4y+), very often an exciting race to watch but a graveyard for favourites and best left alone, as a surprise result is the norm. It is usually won by a good second-rater, the only outstanding victor of recent years being the great Ardross.

THE (GENERAL ACCIDENT) 2000 GUINEAS (GRP 1 – £100,000, 1m, 3yC+F) is a similar race to the fillies' Guineas and is usually won by a proven, fancied horse from a fashionable yard, though there are some shock results to contend with, often coming in a sequence. The last of these was in the mid-to-late seventies when, with the exception of Wollow's year, the Classic was won by horses starting at 50-1, 9-2, 33-1,

20-1, 28-1, 20-1 and 14-1. There was a similar bad spell in the early-to-mid sixties and it could be that another unsettling period is due.

THE PALACE HOUSE STAKES (GRP 3 – £20,000, 5f, 3y+) is significant for two reasons. It is the first Group sprint contest of the season and the first Group race where three-year-olds are pitted against older horses and thus the first opportunity to compare the two generations. As a betting medium it is best left alone.

CHESTER   May 5-7

A charming and historic meeting which has recently fallen on hard times with some of its races devalued and the vastly important TV coverage removed. Nevertheless, for anyone with a few days off, a visit to Roodeye can't be too warmly recommended.   Chester is the smallest flat course in Britain and favours the sharp-actioned horse at the expense of the out-and-out galloper. A low draw and a fast break are essential in races up to a mile. Despite its popularity, Chester is the sort of course that will suffer if the lobby who want to streamline racing get their way. Their argument, a purely economic one, is that racing would become a more profitable concern if the number of courses was drastically reduced. Why have the Dee Stakes at Chester, they would ask, when a similar race at Kempton or Doncaster would be just as good or better? Such a view is of course hopelessly short-sighted. The reason that British racing is pre-eminent in Europe, and possibly now the world, is because the owners – the Arabs included – love the facts that, unlike in the USA, the European season has a beginning, a middle and an end, and that, more so than in France, the contrasting tracks from the vast expanses of Newmarket to trappy little Chester add significantly to the fascination of the game.

THE (DALHAM) CHESTER VASE (GRP 3 – £25,000, 1½m65y, 3yC+F) received an enormous boost as a Derby trial when in successive years in the early eighties Henbit and Shergar won

the race, both favourites. They were exceptions to the rule, however, and though other good horses have won the event, it is better watched than gambled on; fields tend to be very small, thus making each-way bets impossible. Dick Hern has won the Vase three times in recent years and his overall record at Chester is magnificent. The (Ladbroke) Chester Cup first staged in 1824, is a marvellous handicap run over an extended 2¼ miles and won in the past by such good horses as John Cherry and Sea Pigeon (twice), but the last Oaks heroine thrown up by the Cheshire Oaks was Lupe back in 1970. The second Group race at the meeting is
THE ORMODE E.B.F. STAKES (GRP 3 – £27,500, 1m5f85y, 4y+) in which short-priced favourites have a particularly good record, while the ancient Dee Stakes, a Derby trial, has a record of upsets but is often won by a good horse such as Sir Harry Lewis, the 1987 Irish Derby hero.

LINGFIELD   May 9
THE (HIGHLAND SPRING) DERBY TRIAL (GRP 3 – £47,500, 1½m, 3y). This exceptionally rich trial used to be mainly of interest because of the similarity of Lingfield's mile and a half to that of Epsom. In the last five years its prestige has been boosted considerably by the wins of Teenoso and Slip Anchor. Juliette Marney (1975) was the last Oaks winner to win Lingfield's (Marley Roof Tiles) Oaks Trial.

LONGCHAMP   May 3 and 10
Either
LE PRIX GANAY (GRP 1 – £55,000, 1m2½f, 4y+C+F)
or
LE PRIX (DUBAI) POULE D'ESSAI DES POULAINS (GRP 1 – £107,500, 1m, 3yC) is the first French Group 1 race of the season, the latter being their equivalent to our Two Thousand Guineas. Considering that British trainers won £960,946 in France in the 1986 season, their record in this race is pathetic, with only Guy Harwood's Recitation having been successful

in the last quarter-century.

YORK   May 12-14

The York May Meeting offers a superb three days' racing on one of the best courses in the world, and Lester Piggott's favourite.

THE (TATTERSALLS) MUSIDORA STAKES (GRP 3 – £37,000, 1m2½f, 3yF) is the big Oaks trial, and of the five most recent winners one went on to Classic glory. A word of warning: despite some small fields, or perhaps because of them, favourites are highly unreliable.

THE MECCA-DANTE STAKES (GRP 2 – £80,000, 1m2½f, 3yC+F) is the equivalent Derby trial and, fabulously valuable, the only Classic trial to have attained Group 2 status in Britain. Won in recent years by Shirley Heights, Shahrastani and Reference Point, it is one of the best guides to what will happen at Epsom. As in the Musidora, don't trust the favourite and, if in doubt, back Henry Cecil's representative. He has won five of the last nine runnings.

THE YORKSHIRE CUP (GRP2 – £27,500, 1¾m, 4y+) is a lovely race which can be won by an out-and-out stayer or by a speedier type. The great Ardross only just failed to win the Arc de Triomphe (1½m) and won the Ascot Gold Cup (2½m) twice, each time taking in the Yorkshire Cup on the way. The form often holds up quite well, and Dick Hern and Henry Cecil are the men to follow.

THE DUKE OF YORK STAKES (GRP 2 – £27,500, 6f, 3y+) is the first Group race over six furlongs in the season. Tread carefully: favourites oblige only once in a blue moon.

NEWBURY   May 15

Slip away if you can to Newbury for this excellent day's racing – all the better for being on a Friday and thus free of the Sloane Square mob which infests the course on Saturdays. The highlight of the afternoon is

THE (JUDDMONTE) LOCKINGE STAKES (GRP 2 – £30,000,

1m, 3y+) in which the Classic generation is eligible to meet its elders over the straight mile, although it is quite often not represented. The best advice is to go each way on an animal likely to be an improving sort and from a big stable.

THE CURRAGH   May 16

THE AIRLIE/COOLMORE IRISH 2000 GUINEAS RACE (GRP 1 – IR£100,000, 1m, 3y) is the first Irish Classic and Group 1 race of the season. As a betting medium it is a tricky contest, and is often the scene of an upset. Of six English Two Thousand Guineas winners to attempt the double since 1969, Right Tack and Don't Forget Me succeeded while High Top, Nebbiolo, To-Agori-Mou and Lomond all failed. This does not mean that the Irish Guineas is a better race than the English, however, and of English Guineas failures who went on to win the Irish version, Wassl (1983) and Grundy (1975) are English-trained examples.

LONGCHAMP   May 17

Two Group 1 races,
LE PRIX LUPIN (GRP 1 – £55,000, 1m2½f, 3yC+F)
and
LE PRIX (DUBAI) POULE D'ESSAI DES POULICHES (GRP 1 – 1m, 3yF) head a high-class Sunday card in France. The first race is effectively a rich trial for the French Derby and Oaks. The second is the French Thousand Guineas. Unless you're an expert on French form, stay well clear. Astoundingly, no British-trained horse has won the Poule d'Essai in the last quarter-century.

GOODWOOD   May 20-21

Goodwood is perhaps the most beautiful racecourse in Britain, even the world, and should be visited by anyone interested in the sport. It has many turns and slopes, and the agile horse is at an advantage over the resolute galloper. The five-furlong course is one of the fastest in the country, speed from the gate and a good draw (high) being needed to cope with its continual descent. This 'May Meeting' is now rather devalued, though the two Listed Classic trials – the (Sheraton Park Tower) Lupe Stakes and the (N.M. Schroders) Predominate Stakes – have both produced Classic winners in the past.

THE CURRAGH   May 23
THE (GOFFS) IRISH 1000 GUINEAS RACE (GRP1 – £92,500, 1m, 3yF) has recently become a benefit for English trainers, who have won the last four runnings, and ten since 1967. Best advice at the moment is to stick with an English runner at an each-way sort of price and ignore favourites – they have a disastrous record.

LONGCHAMP   May 24
Another fascinating Sunday card in France features
LE PRIX SAINT-ALARY (GRP – £52,500, 1¼m, 3yF)
and
LE PRIX DU CADRAN (GRP 1 – £35,000, 2½m, 4y+)

SANDOWN   May 25-26
Sandown is one of the most comfortable and up-to-date courses in Britain and offers consistently good quality racing both on the flat and over the jumps. Long-striding gallopers are at home here, but make sure your selection has the necessary stamina to win whichever race you're betting on, as Sandown's uphill straight is a true test. This particular meeting, tucked away at the beginning of the week, is recommended.
THE (MAPPIN AND WEBB) HENRY II STAKES (GRP 3 – £20,000, 2m, 4y+) has produced four Ascot Gold Cup winners since 1967. It has long been the regret of many racing *aficionados* that these long-distance events have been devalued as speed has become more and more fashionable at the expense of stamina; for the connoisseur, however, there is no more exciting a spectacle than a race such as this. British trainers are

beginning to prove that they can go over to the USA and beat the Americans without recourse to drugs or 'medication'. If this trend continues, British racing will be unarguably the best in the world. That is when the Jockey Club should and must act to protect and enhance the races in the Pattern of two miles and more by greatly increasing their value, if necessary at the expense of the sprint races. (That sounds too glib to work, but isn't it worth a try?)

THE (SEARS) TEMPLE STAKES (GRP 2 – £27,500, 5f, 3y+) is just such a sprint. It has been won by decent horses in its time, the most recent being Never So Bold in 1985, but is this sixty second dash really so much more important than the Henry II Stakes?

THE BRIGADIER GERARD STAKES (GRP 3 – £17,500, 1¼m, 4y+), once farmed by Noel Murless in the late sixties in its previous incarnation, has been won by such cracking good horses as Commanche Run and Kalaglow in recent years and is a fitting tribute to the great Brigadier over his best distance. The second day of the meeting, on which this race is run, has good claim to being the best evening meeting of the year and also features the (Precocious) National Two-Year-Old Stakes over five furlongs and a couple of competitive handicaps.

LONGCHAMP   May 30

Those punters fed up with Sunday licensing laws and with access to a private plane could do worse than pop over to France for

LE PRIX D'ISPAHAN (GRP1 – £55,000, 1m1f55y, 4y+C+F) and

LE PRIX JEAN PRAT (ECURIE FUSTOK) (GRP 1 – £70,000, 1m1f55y, 3yC+F).

EPSOM   June 3-6

Epsom could be described as the oddest racecourse in the country. It has many disagreeable features. It is a terrible place to get to on a busy raceday. The amenities fall far short of providing satisfactorily for a large crowd. The paddock is so far away from the stands and weighing-room that the jockeys have to go down by minibus. On Derby Day it is at its worst and best. If you want to sample the atmosphere, then a day out on the downs can be fun for those with great stamina and wallets fitted with anti-theft devices. If you want to see the race itself and don't have access to a private box then for goodness sake stay at home and watch it on television.

The racetrack is an extraordinary switchback unparalleled anywhere in the world, a blueprint of what not to do for any twentieth-century racecourse designer. On the other hand, the Derby course itself is still considered by many to be the supreme test of the racehorse, and it is this rather than any sense of history that has kept the Derby at the top of the tree in a very competitive world. Winning it is still the most important and famous victory in the career of any European owner, trainer or jockey, and a horse with a combination of speed, stamina, agility and good temperament is ideally required.

For the spectator, the sense of occasion, the vagaries of the course and the exposed but highly debatable form of the horses make the Derby one of the most exciting races of the calendar. It is a pity that with the obvious exceptions of those listed below, the quality of the supporting races over the four days is simply not good enough; the authorities would do well to dispense with some of the lesser fare and make the Derby meeting into a three-day or even a two-day event.

THE DIOMED STAKES (GRP3 – £20,000, 1m110y, 3y+) has a habit of getting the bookmakers off to a good start.

THE (EVER READY) DERBY STAKES (GRP 1 – £285,000, 1½m, 3yC+F) is on the whole a good betting race. In the last quarter- century only four horses have won it at odds of more than 10-1 while in recent years the simple method of betting on the favourite and second favourite would have produced a handsome profit. In the face of all the fact and figures hurled about each year, stick to the same principles that go for so many top-class races: pick a fancied horse from a good stable,

ridden by a good jockey and capable of either holding its
already good form or, better still, of improving on it. Having
made your choice, let no man put you off.

THE (HANSON TRUST) CORONATION CUP (GRP1 –
£55,000, 1½m, 4y+) is run over the Derby course and distance
but is a very different race, mainly because of the very small
fields it attracts – only twice in the last twenty-five years have
there been even ten runners. Favourites have a good record,
but there have been two shock results in the last six years, both
at 20-1. First run in 1898, the Coronation Cup's roll of honour
features many of the great names of the century.

THE (GOLD SEAL) OAKS STAKES (GRP 1 – £150,000, 1½m,
3yF) was first run in 1779 and thus predates the colts' equivalent, the Derby, by one year. Favourites have an uncertain
record, despite the smaller fields, and there have been some
hard luck stories in recent years. The best betting advice is the
same as that given for the Derby. While the prestige of this
great contest has remained undiminished over the years, it
has recently been in danger of being ignored by the public,
staged as it was in 1987 at 4.05 on a busy Saturday afternoon. It
is exactly the sort of race that could form the centre-piece of a
marvellous Sunday's racing, as in France. But the Powers That
Be consider that a desultory stroll with the dog, the tingling
excitement of 'Songs of Praise', and an early bed are better
antidotes to the gloom of the Sabbath, and who are we to
argue?

CHANTILLY   June 6

It's strange that the French think it's all right to stage their
Derby and Oaks on Sundays, along with many other great
races. Well they're Catholics, aren't they? Godless.

LE PRIX DU JOCKEY CLUB (LANCIA) (GRP1 – £212,500,
1½m, 3yC+F) is their equivalent of the Derby and, apart from
two Irish-trained and Robert Sangster-owned victors in the
early eighties, they've managed to keep it to themselves. After
all, English trainers have better and more interesting things to

be doing on a Sunday afternon, like . . . er . . .

CHANTILLY   June 14

LE PRIX DE DIANE (HERMES) (GRP 1 – £150,000, 1m2½f, 3yF) is the French equivalent of our Oaks though 1½ furlongs shorter in distance, and the British record in the race is less shameful than in the other French Classics, with Highclere, Mrs Penny, Madam Gay and Indian Skimmer all successful since 1974.

ROYAL ASCOT   June 16-19

Royal Ascot is quite simply the best four days' racing in the world on one of the best racecourses in the world. The snag is the people. Such is the throng that the racegoer now has the choice of seeing the horses either in the paddock or in the race; to achieve both is almost impossible. You will find you spend a lot of time in the dreaded concrete tunnel, complete with traffic light system, that links Tattersals to the Paddock. Gold Cup day on the Thursday is the most crowded, and King's Stand day on the Friday is the least. If your intention is merely to see the hats or to take the air, then you'll no doubt have a lovely, if expensive, day out, though you'd be well advised to avoid the Royal enclosure where the number of dubious people loitering with intent seems to grow every year.

The course itself is a stiff, testing one with a short run-in of less than three furlongs, but tough, resolute gallopers seem to thrive here. There are races at all distances from five furlongs to 2¾ miles and, despite the dictates of the modern breeders, the Gold Cup remains the highlight of the week. Whatever you do, don't forget your umbrella. Storms and cloudbursts are as much a part of the tradition as the top hats and strawberries.

THE QUEEN ANNE STAKES (GRP 2 – £45,000, 1m, 3y+) has steadily been growing in importance and was upgraded to Group 2 status in 1985. It is the only mile race at the meeting

open to older horses, but three-year-olds who have won
Group 1 contests, like the Guineas, are excluded. Since 1985
the Queen Anne has been won by three top-class milers –
Rousillon, Pennine Walk and Then Again – and the bad record
of favourites is beginning to improve. Henry Cecil has been
top trainer at Royal Ascot for six of the last nine years (setting a
new post-war record of seven winners in 1987), and he won
this race for four years running from 1981 to 1984.

THE PRINCE OF WALES'S STAKES (GRP2 – £47,500, 1¼m,
3y+) since its introduction in 1968 has been won by some very
good and great horses, such as Royal Palace, Connaught,
Brigadier Gerard, Ela-Mana-Mou and Mtoto, but it has to be
said that the field is not always up to scratch. Avoid the few
representatives of the Classic generation like the plague – they
have yet to score a victory – and never trust the favourite
either. The best advice is to go each-way on a horse with recent
winning form from one of the big yards.

THE ST JAMES'S PALACE STAKES (GRP 2 – £42,500, 1m, 3y)
is nearly always won by a really good horse and, except for
Horage and Half a Year, all the last ten winners had run
prominently in either the English or Irish Two Thousand
Guineas, while the last- named was the only one not to have
run as a two-year-old. Finding that really good horse,
however, is not so easy, as it is usually the winning of this race
that proves their worth, and while Two Thousand Guineas
victors such as Right Tack, Brigadier Gerard, Bolkonski and
To-Agori-Mou have gone on to win the St James, others, most
recently Don't Forget Me, have tasted defeat. This superb race
is better watched than gambled on, especially as the likes of
Radetzsky (16-1, 1976) and Horage (18-1, 1983) can pull off the
occasional shock result. The previous year's Coventry Stakes
winner has won three of the last six renewals.

THE COVENTRY STAKES (GRP3 – £32,500, 6f, 2y) is the
richest of the five two-year-old races at the meeting and is also
the first Group two-year-old contest of the season. It is worth
briefly considering the changing pattern of two-year-old

racing. In the old days it was usual to produce two-year-olds with Classic ambitions at the royal meeting, but this is a rare occurrence now; such animals are seen out later in the season and will fulfill their promise in such races as the Dewhurst at Newmarket or the Futurity at Doncaster. Indeed, the fashion in the most recent past has been for trainers to expose their two-year-old Classic hopes less than ever. In 1986 Reference Point won the Futurity, topped the Free Handicap and went on to win the 1987 Derby, but the fact that this progress was exceptional rather than normal illustrates the current state of the art. The Coventry Stakes is usually won by a sharp sort who has already clocked up a success. Beyond that, it's hard to say. The record of favourites is unstable, and longish-priced winners are regular. Don't be put off a representative from one of the smaller yards if you fancy it, and then don't lose sight of the winner because he could come in useful to you a year later. Three of the last six winners – Horage, Chief Singer and Sure Blade – went on to win the next season's St James's Palace Stakes.

THE KING EDWARD VII STAKES (GRP2 – £52,500, 1½m, 3yC+G), known as the 'Ascot Derby' for obvious reasons, is usually either won by a horse beaten at Epsom, like Lanfranco and Love the Groom in the last two years, or by one which is on the way to even better things, like Ile de Bourbon and Shareef Dancer, who went on to take the King George and Queen Elizabeth Stakes and the Irish Derby respectively. Shock results are about as rare as a winning favourite or second favourite and this advice won't surprise you: select a fancied each-way chance from a big stable, particularly that of Dick Hern or Henry Cecil both of whom have good records in the race. This first day at Ascot is arguably the best of the four days and is completed by the Ascot Stakes, a handicap (one of six at the meeting) run over the Gold Cup trip of 2½ miles. The second day opens with

THE JERSEY STAKES (GRP 3 – £22.500, 7f, 3y) is for three-year-olds that haven't won a Group 1 or 2 event, and is a sort of halfway house sort of race for horses stepping down from a mile or stepping up from six furlongs. It is won by both improving handicappers and by Classic disappointments.

THE QUEEN MARY STAKES (GRP3 – £30,000, 5f, 2yF) is occasionally won by a good filly like Amaranda or Forest Flower, but more often by an early sort who subsequently fails to set the world alight. Risk your money at your peril. Favourites have a bad record and since 1977 starting prices of the winners have ranged from 50-1 to 6-4 on. Good recent form is almost essential, but most of the runners have that or they wouldn't be in the race.

THE ROYAL HUNT CUP (HANDICAP) (£30,000, 1m, 3y+) is one of the great betting races of the meeting. Many people get very excited about this charge down the straight mile while others wonder why it retains its prominence at the centre of such a marvellous card. Picking the winner from the inevitably huge field requires divine guidance. Those that must have a bet should restrict themselves to a low-drawn horse, not carrying too much or too little weight and starting at 14-1 or less. If you get it right, then pack it all in. Such outrageous good fortune simply can't last.

THE CORONATION STAKES (GRP 2 – £45,750, 1m, 3yF), on the other hand, is one of the safer betting races of the meeting; as often as not won by the favourite, a real upset is extremely rare. The race has an extremely close connection with the Irish Thousand Guineas and is very often won by a filly that has run in and frequently won that Classic. The 1987 winner Milligram was typical. Second in the Irish Guineas, she started a red-hot favourite for the Coronation and, carrying sackfuls of money and confidence, absolutely skated home by seven lengths. Her price of 5-4 on (touched Evens) was nothing to get excited about, but a short-priced winner is a great deal better than the most extravagantly-priced loser. The second day at Royal Ascot is completed by the Queen's Vase (two miles) and the Bessborough Handicap (1½ miles). The big day, Gold Cup day, kicks off with

THE CORK AND ORRERY STAKES (GRP 3 – £25,000, 6f, 3y+). On a roll of honour which resembles something from the Cheltenham Festival, the names of Irish trainers figure nine times in the last eighteen runings of the Cork and Orrery, a sprint which is inevitably overshadowed by the Group 1 King's Stand a day later and is often won by a second-rater. From a betting point of view this race is best left alone and not even the market or the form book are of much help.

THE NORFOLK STAKES (GRP 3 – £22,500, 5f, 2y) is open to colts, geldings and fillies, and it is an anomaly that it should be worth considerably less than the Queen Mary Stakes, which is restricted to fillies. The winner has to be an extremely fast horse, usually with a proven record and fancied; of course this description will always apply to several of the contenders, and backing the favourite would prove a fast road to ruin. Strangely, backing the second favourite over the past ten years or so would have proved very profitable.

THE GOLD CUP (GRP 1 – £52,500, 2½m, 4y+), one of the crowning glories of the racing year and long may it remain so. Everyone knows about the modern problems of long-distance races and staying horses and they are not easily surmountable. Certainly the Gold Cup these days often attracts small fields and occasionally they are sub-standard. But next time you're being bored by the sort of person who makes a hobby of slagging off the famous old race and its Group 1 status, just remind them of the marvellous triple victories of Sagaro in the mid-seventies, of the breath-taking performances of the great dual winners Le Moss and Ardross, and of the roar the crowd on any of a staggering eleven occasions when that great tactician Lester Piggott came to take this race. Remind them also that the Gold Cup form is as reliable as any and that a couple of quid on the favourite is more likely than not to make you money.

THE RIBBLESDALE STAKES (GRP 2 – £45,000, 1½m, 3yF) is the fillies' equivalent of the King Edward VII Stakes, but while Derby runners are common in the colts' race, Oaks runners are rare in the Ribblesdale. Whatever you do, don't go near the favourite. It's almost a certainty it'll get stuffed. As so often, an each-way bet on a contender with form from a good stable is recommended. The Chesham Stakes for two-year-olds and the King George V Handicap complete the third day. By the Friday, the crowds have often thinned a little and the strawberries and the ladies behind the Tote windows have a slightly tired look. The racing, starting with the Windsor Castle Stakes for two-year-olds is still of the highest quality and the sun quite often shines.

THE HARDWICKE STAKES (GRP 2 – £37,500, 1½m, 4y+) is often the target for a horse that is just under top class and is looking for a nice Group contest. If you must have a bet, ignore the favourite, back the second favourite when there are less than eight runners, and have an each-way stab – usual rules apply – when there are eight or more.

THE WOKINGHAM STAKES (HANDICAP) (£22,500, 6f, 3y+) is a frenzied cavalry charge of a contest as a huge field dashes towards the post in about seventy-five seconds. The best thing to do, you might think, would be to stay at home and snip up your tenners with the kitchen scissors. Extraordinarily, the truth is that this appalling-looking handicap is well worth an investment. There are certain rules. Make sure your selection is well-drawn (usually low) and not carrying more than about 8st 8lb. But the best rule of all is simply to back the favourite. Three have won in the last five years (admittedly after rather a long dearth) and the profit to five bets of a pound would have been £21.50. Of course, it can't continue like this.

THE KING'S STAND STAKES (GRP 1 – £60,000, 5f, 3y+) is the richest race of the meeting and the first hurdle in the European five-furlong sprinting triple crown, completed by the William Hill Sprint Championship at York and Le Prix de L'Abbaye at Longchamp, though many winners of the King's Stand step up to the extra furlong of the July Cup at Newmarket on their next run. Always a thrilling race to watch, the King's Stand has been won by many champions in the past, though the fate of favourites is uncertain. The Royal meeting is completed by the Britannia Handicap and the Queen Alexandra Stakes, the longest Flat race of the season. As a footnote to this four-day feast of racing, it has to be conceded that those who say that Royal Ascot should allow sponsorship of races are probably right, but oh, how nice it is not to have these historic race-names cluttered up with the ugly brand names of every product under the sun. And it is about time that the Jockey Club insisted on the retention of the old names in new sponsored titles. Or does everybody think that the 'William Hill Sprint Championship' has more dignity than the 'Nunthorpe Stakes'?

THE CURRAGH   June 27
THE (BUDWEISER) IRISH DERBY (GRP 1 – £330,000, 1½m, 3y), talking of sponsorship, has been elevated in recent years from being a comparatively unimportant affair to being the second most valuable race in Europe after the Arc de Triomphe. In every other way it still has to be content with playing second fiddle to Epsom, and it is almost invariably won by the winner of the Epsom Derby or by a horse that was beaten in the great English Classic.

NEWMARKET   June 27
THE (VAN GEEST) CRITERION STAKES (GRP 3 – £17,500, 7f, 3y) is the centre of a less than scintillating card at Headquarters.

LONGCHAMP   June 29
LE GRAND PRIX DE PARIS (GRP 1 – £107,500, 1¼m, 3yC+F) has been won by English-trained horses for four of the last seven runnings. In line with modern trends, it has now been shortened from its old distance of 1 mile 7½ furlongs.

HAYDOCK   July 4
Haydock is an oval, galloping track with a 4½-furlong run-in.

THE (HARP-LAGER) LANCASHIRE OAKS (GRP 3 – £30,000, 1½m, 3yF) is a nice race for fillies and is sometimes won by a good one, while the historic Newton Cup (Handicap) and the Cock of the North Stakes for two-year-olds make up an entertaining day's racing for a knowledgeable and appreciative crowd.

SANDOWN   July 4
THE (CORAL) ECLIPSE STAKES (GRP 1 – £117,500, 1¼m, 3y+), a very great contest and always an exciting race, also provides the first top-class clash between the current Classic generation and their elders, and the score in recent years is just about even. The race commemorates the great horse and was first run in 1886 since when it has been won by many of the most famous names in racing. Rather naturally, a proven record with at least one Group victory is needed to win the Eclipse and there is no better warm-up than the Prince of Wales Stakes at Royal Ascot: Royal Palace, Connaught, Brigadier Gerard, Trepan, Gunner B, Ela-Mana-Mou and Mtoto all completed this double. There is also a strong link with the Derby. In recent years Derby winners and runners-up have both won and lost the race. Shock results are extremely rare – July is the best month of the season for reliability of form – and the winner is nearly always a much-fancied contender, but beware of odds-on favourites and fillies. Both have a bad record. Eclipse day at Sandown is more often than not bathed in warm summer sunshine, the crowd is a manageable size – Wimbledon and Henley are rival events – and this chance to see some of the best horses in Europe should not be missed, though the supporting card is rather less than mouth-watering.

SAINT-CLOUD   July 5
LE GRAND PRIX DE SAINT-CLOUD (GRP 1 – £127,500, 1½m, 3y+C+F), following hot on the heels of the Eclipse, is another clash between the two generations, over an extra quarter-mile.

English trainers have a proud recent record in the contest, having won four of the last six runnings.

NEWMARKET   July 7-9

The Newmarket July Meeting, held on the special July course, is a very enjoyable event, all straw hats and strawberries and usually blessed with good weather. The racing is of the highest standard.

THE (HILLSDOWN) CHERRY HINTON STAKES (GRP 3 – £27,500, 6f, 2yF) is sometimes won by a very good filly like Forest Flower, Mrs Penny or Mysterious, and the bookmakers have a ridiculous habit of quoting the winner for the next year's Thousand Guineas, though Mysterious (1973) was the last filly to complete the double. There have been some long-priced upsets, but if you fancy the favourite, here is a race to steam in and have a bet.

THE PRINCESS OF WALES'S STAKES (GRP 2 – £32,500, 1½m, 3y+), another race in which to support a genuine, worthy favourite; money can be made by doing so. It is worth remembering that the score between three-year-olds and older horses is about even, that recent winning form is desirable but not essential, and that Major Dick Hern has won six of the last fourteen runnings.

THE CHILD STAKES (GRP 2 – £30,000, 1m, 3y+F) is yet another good race for favourites and it is unnecessary to look further than a worthy one. Three-year-olds have a better record than their elders simply because they are represented in far greater numbers.

THE (ANGLIA TELEVISION) JULY STAKES (GRP 3 – £25,000, 6f, 2yC+G) has been won by all sorts of two-year-olds and good winning form is almost the only common bond. Don't trust the favourite.

THE (NORCROS) JULY CUP (GRP 1 – £50,000, 6f, 3y+) is the second of the four great English and French sprint races and the only one of six rather than five furlongs. Since 1976 four horses have gone on from winning the King's Stand to taking the July Cup in the same year, while Habibti completed the double in different years. Five horses have gone on from winning the July Cup to victory in the William Hill Championship. Three outstanding sprinters, Lochnager, Solinus and Never So Bold clocked up the treble in the same year, while Habibti did it in different years (again). The July Cup is always a thrilling contest to watch, and favourites have a decent record.

THE CURRAGH   July 11
THE (GILLTOWN STUD) IRISH OAKS (GRP 1 – £100,000, 1½m, 3yF) must cause the Irish authorities some distress as, since 1968, eleven runnings have been won by English-trained fillies and four by French. In the same period five fillies have completed the Epsom/Irish Oaks double: Altesse Royale, Juliette Marny, Fair Salinia, Blue Wind and Unite. A feature of the betting is that nearly every winner has been prominent in the market, with many at short prices, while a real upset is almost unheard of.

MAISONS-LAFITTE   July 19
LE PRIX ROBERT PAPIN (GRP 1 – £37,500, 5½f, 2yC+F) is the first European Group 1 race for two-year-olds and is currently dominated by fillies, some of them extremely good like the 1982 heroine Ma Biche. English trainers used to win this event back in the sixties and early seventies but now seem to have forgotten about it.

ASCOT   July 25
THE PRINCESS MARGARET STAKES (GRP 3 – £15,000, 6f, 2yF)
is followed by
THE KING GEORGE VI AND QUEEN ELIZABETH (DIAMOND) STAKES (GRP 1 – £185,000, 1½m, 3y+). The King George and Queen Elizabeth can claim to be the most important event in the European horse-racing calendar,

barring the Epsom Derby. Its only rival is Le Prix de L'Arc de Triomphe. The French race is far more valuable and has a glamour all of its own, but it is run at the end of the season when the going is often on the soft side and among the contenders there are always a number of tired horses that have gone over the top. The King George, on the other hand, is run at the height of the season on ground which is usually perfect and there can be no excuses for the beaten horses. Also it is invariably won by a very good or great horse. The list of winners of the last twenty running speaks eloquently for itself: Busted, Royal Palace, Park Top, Nijinsky, Mill Reef, Brigadier Gerard, Dahlia (twice), Grundy, Pawneese, The Minstrel, Ile de Bourbon, Troy, Ela-Man-Mou, Shergar, Kalaglow, Time Charter, Teenoso, Petoski and Dancing Brave. If that list is not impressive enough, let's put it another way. The last twenty winners also won one Irish Two Thousand Guineas, four English Two Thousand Guineas, eight English Derbys, five Irish Derbys, two English Oaks, one Irish Oaks, One French Oaks, five Coronation Cups, seven Eclipses, three Benson and Hedges Gold Cups, one St Leger, two Arcs, three Champion Stakes and one Washington International. The case rests.

NEWCASTLE   July 27
THE BEESWING STAKES (GRP 3 – £20,000, 7f, 3y+) is the only
Group race at this testing, gallopers' circuit where stamina is at a premium. Favourites have a good record in the Beeswing.

GOODWOOD   July 28 – August 1
The 'Glorious Goodwood' meeting is well worth a visit. The fashionable trainers stroll around in lightweight suits and straw hats, attempting to appear languid and unruffled, the ladies wear large, rather silly hats and Lester Piggott looks inscrutable in a pair of blue shades. The racing is superb, starting with

THE MOLECOMBE STAKES (GRP 3 – £20,000, 5f, 2y) and the THE (WILLIAM HILL) STEWARDS' CUP (HANDICAP) (£42,500, 6f, 3y+). Lord March has now introduced the SCHWEPPES GOLDEN MILE HANDICAP (£52,000, 1m, 3y+) and hopes that the new race and the Stewards' Cup will provide a tremendous betting double for the punters. The latter, first run in 1840, always draws a huge field and is won by 50-1 shots and 5-1 shots. The good news is that favourites have a remarkably good record for such a competitive handicap. Stick to them – in the last thirteen years they've produced a profit of £23.50 to a pound stake. The first day ends with

THE GORDON STAKES (GRP 3 – £25,000, 1½m, 3y).

THE (P & OCL) RICHMOND STAKES (GRP 2 – £37,500, 6f, 2y) opens the second day. It is seldom won by a really top-class animal and shock results are regrettably common. The highlight of the meeting, and since sponsorship one of the most important and valuable races in the European calendar, is

THE (SWETTENHAM STUD) SUSSEX STAKES (GRP 1 – £155,000, 1m, 3y+). Three-year-olds have a marvellous record in the Sussex, as they do in the King George and Queen Elizabeth, and have won sixteen of the last twenty runnings; favourites too have a habit of living up to their reputation. Here is a race to savour, and if you fancy the favourite and it's a three-year-old, then strap on your betting boots. The list of past winners is a suitably impressive one and eight winners of the Thousand Guineas and Two Thousand Guineas have gone on to success here since the war. On the third day

THE LANSON CHAMPAGNE VINTAGE STAKES (GRP 3 – £15,000, 7f, 2y) is often won by a good two-year-old, like the subsequent Two Thousand Guineas winner Don't Forget Me in 1986, and is the first Group two-year-old race over seven furlongs, while

THE GOODWOOD CUP (GRP 3 – £22,500, 2m5f, 3y+) is a superb long-distance race first run in 1812, the second step for the Cup horses after the Ascot Gold Cup and the longest of the four. Since the war, eleven Ascot winners have gone on to win at Goodwood and ten Goodwood winners have gone on to win the Doncaster Cup. Favourites have a good record, but this is an event to watch rather than bet on.

THE KING GEORGE STAKES (GRP 3 – £22,500, 5f, 3y+) rounds off the third day. The centre-piece of the fourth day is the Extel Stakes (Handicap) for three-year-olds over 1¼ miles. Incredibly, Luca Cumani has won the last three runnings.

THE (VODAFONE) NASSAU STAKES (GRP 2 – £37,500, 1¼m, 3yF). Favourites have an unshaky record in this nice event, which is occasionally won by a very good filly, but there is seldom a major upset.

PHOENIX PARK   August 9

Ireland too sensibly makes use of Sunday afternoons to stage horseracing.

THE (HEINZ "57") PHOENIX STAKES (GRP 1 – £165,000, 6f, 2y) is currently the most valuable two-year-old race in Europe, though the new and controversial Goffs' Million race planned by Jonathon Irwin for 1988 will take its place at the top. In 1986 the Phoenix Stakes produced a memorable contest with the clash of Minstrella and Forest Flower, the former just prevailing by a short head.

NEWBURY   August 14-15

This is a nice Friday/Saturday meeting featuring
THE (TRUSTHOUSE FORTE) HUNGERFORD STAKES (GRP 3 – £25,000, 7f60y, 3y+)
and
THE (WALMAC INTERNATIONAL) GEOFFREY FREER STAKES (GRP 2 – £40,000, 1m5f60y, 3y+) which is often won by a good horse and is a good race for favourites.

DEAUVILLE   August 16

French racing has meanwhile moved to the summer resort of Deauville where casinos combine with the Pari-Mutuel to

relieve the punters of their money. There are two Group 1
contests during the excellent series of races, the first of which
is
LE PRIX (DU HARAS DE FRESNAY-LE-BUFFARD) JACQUES
LE MAROIS) (GRP 1 – £75,000, 1m, 3y+C+F) which is sponsored by Stavros Niarchos via his well-known stud.

YORK   August 18-20
The York August meeting is one of the most popular and
important of the season, featuring no less than three Group 1
events. The weather is usually good, the horses fast and the
crowd huge.
THE MATCHMAKER INTERNATIONAL (GRP 1 – £145,000,
1m2½f, 3y+) is the first of the three great 1¼ mile contests
that stretch into the autumn via the Phoenix Park and
Newmarket Champion Stakes. The Matchmaker, formerly the
Benson and Hedges Gold Cup, was first run in 1972 and soon
acquired a reputation for being a graveyard for famous horses;
in recent years the race has settled down into a more reliable
contest, and favourites now have quite a reasonable record,
though upsets like Cormorant Wood's 1984 victory at 15-1 do
still occur.
THE YORKSHIRE OAKS (GRP 1 – £50,000, 1½m, 3yF) has
been won by eight Epsom Oaks winners since the war but,
good race though it is, is often taken by a high-class filly
looking for a fat consolation prize. Only one horse has won at
longer odds than 9-1 since the war so don't waste time looking
for lively outsiders. A fancied each-way chance from one of
the big stables is the best bet, and favourites have a dismal
record.
THE (TOTE) EBOR HANDICAP (50,000, 1¾m, 3y+), run on
the second day, is a fabulously rich long-distance handicap
first run in 1843. The shortest-priced winner in the last ten
years was the 6-1 returned against the second-favourite Primary in 1986. The favourite that year, the well-backed White
Mill, came sixteenth. This race is best left alone. There are

many other far more enjoyable ways to spend your money.
THE (SCOTTISH EQUITABLE) GIMCRACK STAKES (GRP 2 –
£37,500, 6f, 2y) is an ancient race for two-year-olds first staged
in 1846. These days it is usually won by the sort of animal who
is most likely to make his name over short distances and the
last really great horse to win it was Mill Reef back in 1970.
Favourites have a bad record.
THE (WILLIAM HILL) SPRINT CHAMPIONSHIP (GRP 1 –
£60,000, 5f, 3y+) is the third and last of the great English sprint
contests and has close links with the other two, as suggested
earlier. It is always highly competitive and exciting to watch
but the dangers of betting on such a race can be pointed up by
the extraordinary starting prices for the three-times winner
Sharpo: 3-1, 14-1 and 13-1. The last Group race of the meeting
is
THE LOWTHER STAKES (GRP 2 – £20,000, 6f, 2yF).

SANDOWN   August 21
THE (GLEN INTERNATIONAL) SOLARIO STAKES (GRP 3 –
£25,000, 7f, 2y). Two-year-old racing moves towards centre
stage at this time in the season, and Group juvenile races start
coming thick and fast. This is a nice contest often won by a
decent animal, and favourites have a good record.

DEAUVILLE   August 23
LE PRIX MORNY (GRP 1 – £40,000, 6f, 2yC+F) is the first
Group 1 race for two-year-olds and the only one in France out
of the five such races over six furlongs. This is an important
event and has been won by some top-class performers in the
past, like Blushing Groom and Super Concorde, and it is
therefore extraordinary that British trainers have such an
appalling record in it. In 1986 they weren't even represented.

GOODWOOD   August 21-22
THE WATERFORD CANDELABRA STAKES (GRP 3 – £25,000,

7f, 2yF) is the centrepiece of the Friday card. Punters should be warned – the favourite is nearly always turned over. On the Saturday, THE WATERFORD CRYSTAL MILE (GRP 2 – £45,000, 1m, 3y+), a very good race and often exciting to watch. Sandwiched in between the Group 1 mile contests, the Sussex Stakes and the Queen Elizabeth Stakes, it has strong links with both. In the last twenty years, six Sussex winners have gone on to take the Waterford Crystal either in the same season or the next, and five winners of the Waterford have gone on to win the Queen Elizabeth six times (Brigadier Gerard scoring twice). The Waterford Crystal Mile is usually won by a really good horse, and sometimes by a great one.

ARLINGTON PARK   August 30
THE BUDWEISER-ARLINGTON MILLION (GRADE 1 – £450,000, 1¼m, 3y+) was won in 1985 by a five-year-old gelding, Teleprompter, trained in Richmond in Yorkshire by Bill Watts, owned by Lord Derby and starting at 142-10. This at a stroke reaffirmed that English and European horses could fly into the States and lift some of the top prizes. There have been some disappointments since but the comparisons between European and American racehorses and training methods should prove to be one of the most fascinating aspects of the next few years.

KEMPTON   September 4
The executive of United Racecourses must get sick and tired of the disparaging remarks made so often about Kempton Park. They've done their best over the years to make the best of it but it's impossible to change the atmosphere of a place, and the truth is that Kempton will never be voted 'Racecourse of the Year'. The six furlong straight that is laid down diagonally across the course can make for confusing viewing, and it must be remembered that the position of the stalls makes a huge difference, particularly when the ground is soft. When placed

on the far side, high numbers are favoured, when on the near side, low drawn horses have the advantage. The only Group race run at Kempton is THE (BONUSPRINT) SEPTEMBER STAKES (GRP 3 – £20,000, 1m3f30y, 3y+).

HAYDOCK   September 5
THE VERNONS SPRINT CUP (GRP 2 – £47,500, 6f, 3y+) is often won by a very good horse, including five July Cup winners in the last twenty years.

LONGCHAMP   September 6
LE PRIX DU MOULIN DE LONGCHAMP (ECURIE FUSTOK) (GRP 1 – £115,000, 1m, 3y+C+F) has received a recent boost in prize money and, restricted to three-year-olds, is the last European Group 1 mile event for that generation. A win like that of Sonic Lady in 1986 can have great bearing on the mile championship.

PHOENIX PARK   September 6
THE PHOENIX CHAMPION STAKES (GRP 1 – £275,000, 1¼m, 3y+) is a new race, only three seasons old. With its fabulously rich purse and its position – sandwiched in between the Matchmaker International and the Champion Stakes at Newmarket – it has quickly made its mark and is now established as one of the most important races in Europe.

DONCASTER   September 9-12
The long run-in of nearly five furlongs make the final stages of long distance races held here particularly exciting. It is overall a very fair track on which stamina is no disadvantage.
THE PARK HILL STAKES (GRP 2 – £35,000, 1¾m127y, 3yF) is to all intents and purposes the fillies' St Leger, though very much less valuable, and was first run in 1839. Many decent animals have won it, but finding the winner is not easy and

recent prices have ranged from odds-on favourites to 25-1 shots. Highlights of the second day include
THE KIVETON PARK STAKES (GRP 3 – £25,000, 7f, 3y+)
and
THE DONCASTER CUP (GRP 3 – £25,000, 2¼m, 3y+) in which favourites have a sparkling record though their prices are sometimes prohibitively short. It has been won ten times since the war by the winner of the Goodwood Cup.
THE MAY HILL (E.B.F.) STAKES (GRP 3 – £15,000, 1m, 2yF) is the first Group race for two-year-olds (fillies) over a mile.
THE LAURENT PERRIER CHAMPAGNE STAKES (GRP 2 – £40,000, 7f, 2y), run on the Friday and an important two-year-old contest. It has been won in recent years by Grundy, Wollow and Don't Forget Me, all of whom went on to Classic glory, and by many other fine horses.
THE (HOLSTEN PILS) ST LEGER STAKES (GRP 1 – £125,000, 1¾m167y, 3yC+F) is the last and oldest of the great Classic races, first run in 1776. For many years the arguments have raged. The St Leger's detractors say that recent trends have reduced its status, point to the decline in its quality, and suggest that it should be reduced in length and opened up to older horses. Thank goodness the Powers That Be have paid no attention. The French and Irish mucked about with their equivalent races and succeeded only in burying them in obscurity. The facts of the matter are that the St Leger is never less than a fascinating contest, and is often one of the most thrilling spectacles of the season. What is more, it has received several boosts in the last two or three years and is showing signs of a long overdue revival. Ever more generous sponsorship has substantially raised the prize-money. In an unforgettable 1984 contest, and in very controversial circumstances, Lester Piggott won it for the eighth time thereby surpassing the all-time Classic record set up by Frank Buckle, who won his first Classic in 1792. Then in 1985 the great race was won by the Triple Crown heroine Oh So Sharp. It is immediately preceded by

THE BRIAN SWIFT CHILDERS STAKES (GRP 2 – £20,000, 5f, 2y) in which favourites have a good record.

GOODWOOD   September 11
THE SCOTTISH EQUITABLE SELECT STAKES (GRP 3 – £17,500, 1¼m, 3y+) is a handy Group 3 contest that was thrust into prominence in 1986 when won by Dancing Brave en route for his victory in the Arc.

LONGCHAMP   September 13
LE (TRUSTHOUSE FORTE) PRIX VERMEILLE (GRP 1 – £80,000, 1½m, 3yF) is a key race for the Arc de Triomphe. San San, Allez France, Ivanjica, Three Troikas and All Along are fillies who won the Vermeille in recent years before going on to take the Arc in the same or the next season.

THE CURRAGH   September 13
Two valuable and important two-year-old races are staged at this Sunday afternoon meeting. They are
THE MOYGLARE STUD STAKES (GRP 1 – £70,000, 6f, 2yF) and
THE (GUINNESS PEAT) NATIONAL STAKES (GRP 1 – £70,000, 7f, 2yC+F)

AYR   September 16-19
Ayr is a good, fair, well-drained track and this meeting is always popular with professionals and public alike, though sadly the TV coverage of the excellent and historic four days has been greatly reduced. The best races are the Doonside Cup, the Harry Rosebery Challenge Trophy, the (Ladbroke) Ayr Gold Cup and the Firth of Clyde Stakes.

NEWBURY   September 19
A popular Saturday card that also features the competitive (Coral) Autumn Cup is crowned by
THE (ROKEBY FARMS) MILL REEF STAKES (GRP 2 – £30,000,

6f, 2y) which is sometimes won by a really top-class animal like Mon Fils, Formidable and Forest Flower.

BELMONT PARK   September 19
THE TURF CLASSIC (GRADE 1 – £300,000, 1½m, 3y+) is a highly valuable American contest that is suitable for European animals. In 1985 the French won it with Noble Fighter. In 1986 the Jeremy Tree-trained Damister was second.

LONGCHAMP   September 19
LE PRIX DE LA SALAMANDRE (GRP 1 – £45,000, 7f, 2yC+F) is a race that can have considerable bearing on the next season's Classics. This excellent Sunday card also includes Le Prix du Prince d'Orange (Grp 3) and Le Prix de Lutece (Grp 3).

ASCOT   September 24-26
This three-day meeting kicks off with
THE CUMBERLAND LODGE STAKES (GRP 3 – £20,000, 1½m, 3y+) and rises to a superb climax on the Saturday.
THE HOOVER FILLIES' MILE (GRP 2 – £30,000, 1m, 2yF) has been moved up from earlier in the week and is a good race for favourites.
THE QUEEN ELIZABETH II STAKES (GRP 1 – £140,000, 1m, 3y+) has in 1987 been elevated to Group 1 status and carries vastly increased prize-money, as part of the new look to this meeting henceforward to be known as The Festival of British Horseracing, thus righting the imbalance in the past between Group 1 races for three-year-olds and up in France and those in England. It now takes its place as the last of such races in the European Pattern and will therefore play a huge part in deciding the mile championship. Even as a Group 2 contest it was won by some formidable names, including Shadeed, Teleprompter, To-Agori-Mou, Known Fact, Kris, Rose Bowl and Brigadier Gerard.
THE ROYAL LODGE STAKES (GRP 2 – £35,000, 1m, 2y) has

been won by future Derby winners like Royal Palace and
Shirley Heights, and the day is completed by a favourites'
race,
THE (TRUSTHOUSE FORTE) DIADEM STAKES (GRP 3 –
£25,000, 6f, 3y+)

NEWMARKET   September 30 – October 3
Two-year-old racing comes to the fore at this, the 'Cambridgeshire Meeting'. Newmarket is the headquarters of racing and
uniquely has not just one but two racecourses, the Rowley Mile
and the July Course. Both courses share the first mile but then
turn right towards two different sets of stands. Neither are to
everyone's taste and the viewing leaves a lot to be desired, but
both should be visited. The wide open spaces of the Heath and
the gallops and the broad long, testing straights can be found
nowhere else.
THE (TATTERSALLS) CHEVELEY PARK STAKES (GRP 1 –
£37,500, 6f, 2yF) and
THE (TATTERSALLS) MIDDLE PARK STAKES (GRP 1 –
£37,500, 6f, 2y) are matching contests of great importance. Both
have produced their share of Classic winners, but neither can be
regarded as a reliable guide. As betting mediums they are also
rather shaky and both can produce the odd upset.
THE JOCKEY CLUB CUP (GRP 3 – £22,500, 2m24y, 3y+) is the
last in the fine series of long distance contests that grace the
English Flat season and has been won by many great horses,
including the three-times victor High Line (1969-1971). Favourites have a wonderful record and despite very small fields are
often returned at reasonable prices. If you fancy the market
leader, then here is a race where you can fairly safely put your
money where your mouth is.
THE (WILLIAM HILL) CAMBRIDGESHIRE HANDICAP
(£40,000, 1m½f, 3y+) is one of the great betting races of the
season and is the first half of the 'Autumn Double' (completed
by the Cesarewitch). The best advice is to stay clear of the whole
caper. It is a bookmakers' benefit and William Hill and the Tote

put their names to the two races in the sure and happy knowledge that the money they lose in sponsorship is only a small proportion of the money they get back from the punters. Favourites have a ghastly record and if you're still not scared off, then here are the winners' starting-prices in the last eight years: 10-1, 16-1, 33-1, 35-1, 20-1, 50-1, 22-1 and 33-1. Enough said. The Saturday card is completed by THE SUN CHARIOT STAKES (GRP 2 – £27,500, 1¼m, 3y+F).

LONGCHAMP   October 4

There is nowhere else to be but in France on this first Sunday in October for what is the best day's racing in the European horse racing calendar.

LE PRIX MARCEL BOUSSAC (GRP 1 – £45,000, 1m, 2yF) is a race of great importance and Classic significance. Suffice it to say that the last two runnings were won by Midway Lady and Miesque who between them went on to win two English Thousand Guineas and an English Oaks among other victories.

LE PRIX DE L'ABBAYE (GRP 1 – £40,000, 5f, 2y+) is the last great sprint of the European season and the roll of honour lists many of the champion sprinters over the years. The astounding fact is that the French themselves have failed to win their own race since 1978, since when victory has gone to six English and two Irish trained runners.

LE (TRUSTHOUSE FORTE) PRIX DE L'ARC DE TRIOMPHE (GRP 1 – £400,000, 1½m, 3y+) is arguably Europe's greatest race. Its only shortcomings are that the ground is sometimes uncomfortably soft and that some contenders may be over the top by this stage of the season. Never rule out a lightly raced colt or filly that you know to be rapidly improving or who has been laid out for the race. Fillies and mares have a remarkably good record, especially in recent years. Favourites have a shaky history. Down the years, the Arc has been won by many of the very greatest names in the sport and it is always an enthralling and thrilling contest, and the hitherto rather poor English record has been improved in recent years by the victories of Rainbow Quest and Dancing Brave.

ASCOT   October 10
Before turning its attention to the jumping game, Ascot stages one last Saturday's Flat racing, including
THE PRINCESS ROYAL STAKES (GRP 3 – £20,000, 1½m, 3y+F) and
THE CORNWALLIS STAKES (GRP 3 – £17,500, 5f, 2y), which is a good race for favourite backers.

THE CURRAGH   October 11
THE (JEFFERSON SMURFIT) MEMORIAL IRISH ST LEGER (GRP 1 – £62,500, 1¾m, 3y+) has not been enhanced by opening it to older horses as the authorities had hoped. Now it just seems like any other race, especially as its prize-money is nothing to get excited about.

LONGCHAMP   October 11
LE GRAND CRITERIUM (GRP 1 – £65,000, 1m, 2yC+F) has been won by some top-class Classic contenders like Blushing Groom, Super Concorde, Irish River and Green Forest. English horses have a poor record.

NEWMARKET   October 15-17
The 'Cesarewitch Meeting' features
THE (RICARD) CHALLENGE STAKES (GRP 3 – £25,000, 7f, 3y+) on the first day and then, on the Friday, stages the highlight of the British two-year-old season:
THE (WILLIAM HILL) DEWHURST STAKES (GRP 1 – £45,000, 7f, 2yC+F). Until recently, this race was the best guide of all to the next season's Classic races. Nijinsky and Mill Reef won it in '69 and '70, then Grundy, Wollow and The Minstrel in '74, '75 and '76. The changing pattern of training methods has now made it less likely that the Derby hero will first win the Dewhurst, but it is still often won by a very smart horse, like El Grand Senor or Ajdal, and along with the William Hill Futurity it

is replayed on video more often than most contests by those searching for Classic clues during the dark winter months. In spite of the occasional shock result, the form stands up pretty well on the whole, and favourites have fared decently. The other important race on the Friday card is
THE (CHEVINGTON STUD) ROCKFEL STAKES (GRP 3 – £17,500, 7f, 2yF).

THE (DUBAI) CHAMPION STAKES (GRP 1 – £100,0000, 1¼m, 3y+) is a tricky contest for the punter, partly because, as in the Arc, there is always the danger that your fancy has gone over the top by this stage of the season. Favourites have an absolutely appalling record. If in doubt back a filly – they have a fine history in the race, as do French-trained horses. Do not be put off having a punt on an outsider, as they quite often pop up, and remember that three-year-olds have a much better chance than the older generations. The best advice is to keep your powder dry. Invest instead on the second favourite in
THE (TOTE) CESAREWITCH HANDICAP (£35,000, 2m1f, 3y+), the second leg of the 'Autumn Double'. Over the last decade this method would have produced a healthy profit.

WOODBINE, TORONTO   October 18
THE ROTHMANS INTERNATIONAL CHAMPIONSHIP (GRADE 1 – £225,000, 1m5f, 3y+) is another North American race suitable for European horses. The Michael Stoute trained Shadari only narrowly failed to win it in 1986.

NEWBURY   October 22 and 24
This meeting, with a day's jumping in between, features
THE (MATCHMAKER) HORRIS HILL STAKES (GRP 3 – £50,000, 7f60y, 2y), which is extremely well-endowed for its status, and
THE ST SIMON STAKES (GRP 3 – £20,000, 1½m, 3y+).

DONCASTER   October 24
THE WILLIAM HILL FUTURITY STAKES (GRP 1 – £50,000, 1m,

2yC+F) received a huge bost in prestige in 1986 when it was won by Reference Point, who went on to top the Free Handicap and win the 1987 Derby. Until then the race had acquired a reputation of uncertain results that had little bearing on the next season's Classics. Henry Cecil has won three of the last five runnings.

LONGCHAMP   October 25
The last two European Group 1 races are
LE PRIX DE LA FORET (GRP 1 – £40,000, 7f, 2yC+F)
and
LE PRIX ROYAL-OAK (GRP 1 – £40,000, 1m7½f, 3y+) which used to be the equivalent to the St Leger but which is now thrown open to older horses.

SANTA ANITA   October 31
THE BREEDERS' CUP SPRINT (GRADE 1 – £325,000, 6f, 3y+)
THE BREEDERS' CUP MILE (GRADE 1 – £325,000, 1m, 3y+)
THE BREEDERS' CUP TURF (GRADE 1 –£650,000, 1½m, 3y+).
These incredibly valuable American races caused a great stir in Britain in 1986 when they were contested by some of our best horses and shown on TV. In fact results were disappointing, especially the eclipse of Dancing Brave after a long hard season, but the French-trained Last Tycoon scored a superb victory in the Mile, and it is just a question of time before English-trained horses avenge the defeats.

LAUREL PARK   November 14
THE WASHINGTON INTERNATIONAL (GRADE 1 – £200,000, 1¼m, 3y+). Won by Karabas in 1969, since when only a handful of English horses have even reached the frame in this great race. France, on the other hand, has a terrific record having won it eleven times since 1962.

TOKYO   November 22
THE JAPAN CUP (GRADE 1 – £400,000, 1½m, 3y+). A truly

international contest which has been won in the last six years by
two American horses, one Irish, two Japanese and one English.

the jumps

Jumping is very much the poor relation of the Flat. Prize-money
bears no comparison and nor does the breeding side. But for
many people the winter game is much more appealing. They
will tell you that it is still first and foremost a sport and not the
highly commercialised industry that is the Flat today. They will
point to the bravery of the National Hunt horses and jockeys, to
the greater thrill and spectacle. They will talk disparagingly of
many of those involved in the Flat and suggest that jumping
attracts an altogether 'nicer', more genuine crowd – people that
love horses more than money.

The truth is that such *aficionados* are in the minority, but they
do have a point. Nothing is more enjoyable than a good afternoon at the races in the depths of winter, and it doesn't have to
be at Cheltenham or Ascot. Tremendous sport can be found at
any one of the 'gaff' tracks that are sprinkled liberally all over the
country. The long, exhausting season lasts from the end of July
to the end of the next May. The bookmaker wins and the punter
loses at much the same rate as on the Flat. What follows is a list of
some of the major meetings and races in Britain.

Wednesday October 28: This is the first meeting of the season of
any great importance and presents a nice card for anyone who
can get the time off. The main race is THE CROCKFORDS
TROPHY H'CAP CHASE (£12,500, 2m). Ascot is a superb course
for jumping but it is a testing one, especially when the ground is
soft.

Saturday November 14: Cheltenham is the Mecca of the jumping world. Set in a natural ampitheatre, the old and new courses, both very similar, provide some of the most thrilling racing of the year. The fences are stiff, and the extremely testing uphill finish has been the scene of more heartbreaks and snatched triumphs than any other course in the country. THE MACKESON GOLD CUP H'CAP CHASE (£17,500, 2½m) is the first great race of the jumping year. First staged in 1960, Fred Rimell won it four times in a row from 1968 to 1971 (twice with Gay Trip) while Fred Winter has landed three of the last five renewals.

On the same day Newcastle features THE FOODBROKERS AND PRIMULA 'FIGHTING FIFTH' HURDLE (GDE 2 – £10,000, 2m120y). Newcastle is more prominent as a jumping track than it is on the Flat, and its gradually rising half-mile home straight makes it a true test of stamina.

Friday and Saturday November 20-21: Ascots' A.T. CROSS ASCOT HURDLE (GDE 2 – £17,500, 2½m) has two strange things about it, firstly a good record for favourites and secondly a habit of being won by the same top-class horse in consecutive years. The Champion Hurdler Lanzarote won it in 1974 and '75, Dramatist in '76 and '77, Connaught Ranger in '79 and '80 and another Champion, Gaye Brief, in '84 and '85. The supporting race on the Friday is THE HURST PARK NOVICES CHASE (GDE 2 – £10,000, 2m) which was won in 1985 by Desert Orchid. On the Saturday, THE H. and T. WALKER GODDESS H'CAP CHASE (20,000, 2½m) was won in 1981 by the great Wayward Lad.

Friday and Saturday November 27-29: Newbury is as good and successful a jumping track as it is a Flat one. The feature of the Friday card is THE B.M.W. SERIES FINAL H'CAP CHASE (£12,500, 3M) which is open to five-year-olds and above who have been placed in one of the B.M.W. series of races but who haven't won a chase before the current year.

The Saturday is one of the best attended and most popular jumping days of the season. The main snag is the large number of Ruperts and Carolines in trilbys and horsey scarves that treat the place like one huge wine-bar. The best tip is to arm yourself with a hip-flask and position yourself out on the course itself by the water-jump or one of the other fences in the home straight. Unlike some other courses that should know better, Newbury encourages its customers to get close to the real excitement and thrill of the race where the mud flies, the whips crack and the jockeys curse. THE GERRY FIELDEN HURDLE (GDE 2 – £7,500, 2m100y) has been won by many good horses, including the Champion Hurdlers Comedy of Errors and Lanzarote in 1972 and '73, but it is inevitably overshadowed by the big race, THE HENNESSY COGNAC GOLD CUP H'CAP CHASE (£17,500, 3¼m82y), one of the most exciting races of the season. Stand on the course opposite the packed stands. If the favourite lands safely over the last in front of the field, then the roar of the crowd is one of the most thrilling sounds in the whole calendar. And the favourite quite often does just that. Races like the Hennesy transcend their handicap status and are far nobler affairs than many such similarly endowed events on the Flat. This particular race, for example, has been won by such stars as Mandarin (twice), Mill House, Arkle (twice), Bregawn, Brown Chamberlin and Burrough Hill Lad.

Saturday December 5: Sandown is one of the most exciting jumping arenas in the country. There are seven fences along the back straight and the last three are so close together that an inexperienced or unwary combination of horse and jockey can easily be caught out. The course is a real test of stamina and is concluded by an uphill run-in of 300 yards. The big race today is THE MECCA BOOKMAKERS H'CAP HURDLE (£12,500, 2m).

Saturday December 12: Cheltenham stages THE (GLEN

INTERNATIONAL) BULA HURDLE (GDE 2 – £10,000, 2m), which lists Salmon Spray, Pendil, Bula, Comedy of Errors (twice), Sea Pigeon, Bird's Nest (three times) and Ekbalco on its roll of honour, and THE GLEN INTERNATIONAL GOLD CUP H'CAP CHASE (£12,500, 2½m). This race has also been won by very good horses like Pendil and Combs Ditch but is one to treat with caution. Upsets are common, so go for an each-way bet and don't ignore a lively outsider.

Saturday December 19: Pre-Christmas cheer and misery can be found at Ascot. THE H.S.S. HIRE SHOPS HURDLE (£5,000, 2m, 4 and 5y) has been won by many up-and-coming stars like Lanzarote, Grand Canyon and See You Then, while many an established champion has taken THE LONG WALK HURDLE (GDE 2 – £7,500, 3¼m). THE S.G.B. H'CAP CHASE (£15,000, 3m) has been won by Arkle, Midnight Court and Grand Canyon. If in doubt, back the favourite.

Boxing Day December 26: This meeting at Kempton is attended by more hangovers than any other. THE KING GEORGE VI (RANK) CHASE (GDE 1 – £37,500, 3m) is the most important steeplechase after the Cheltenham Gold Cup. It has been won by many of the most famous names in the game and recently the heroic Wayward Lad won it three times in four years. The amazing Dickinson family captured the prize six times in the seven years between 1978 and '85 with three different horses and four different jockeys. This is a race to watch and savour rather than to bet on, and it almost makes Christmas worthwhile.

Saturday December 28: Chepstow is a charming track with constantly changing gradients and five fences in the home straight. THE (CORAL) WELSH NATIONAL H'CAP CHASE (£22,500, 3¾m) has been won in recent years by the Grand National winners Rag Trade and Corbière and by the Gold Cup hero Burrough Hill Lad. Jenny Pitman has carried off three of the last five renewals with a different horse each time, and, extraordinarily, the last seven victors have all been seven-year-olds.

Wetherby is a popular Yorkshire track with easy bends and a long home straight. This is one of the biggest days there and the centre-piece of the card is THE CASTLEFORD H'CAP CHASE (GDE 2 – £12,500, 2m50y). Meanwhile Kempton carries on the good Christmas work with THE (TOP RANK) CHRISTMAS HURDLE (GDE 1 – £20,000, 2m) which has been won by Lanzarote and Dawn Run.

Saturday January 9: This meeting at Sandown has suffered its fair share of abandonments but offers an outstanding day's racing when the weather allows. The two big contests are THE ANTHONY MILDMAY – PETER CAZALET MEMORIAL H'CAP CHASE (£12,500, 3m5f118y) and THE (ROUX RESTAUR-ANTS) TOLWORTH HURDLE (GDE 2 – £6,000, 2m).

Saturday January 23: Haydock Park has resisted the temptation to soften up the jumping and is renowned for its stiff drop fences. THE CHAMPION HURDLE TRIAL (GDE 2 – £7,500, 2m) and THE PETER MARSH CHASE H'CAP (£12,500, 3m) are top-class races, the latter being won by the subsequent Gold Cup winner The Thinker in 1987.

Kempton stages THE (BIC RAZOR) LANZAROTE H'CAP HURDLE (£10,000, 2m).

Saturday February 6: THE (F.U.'S JEANS) GAINSBOROUGH H'CAP CHASE (GDE 2 – £17,500, 3m118y) takes pride of place on this Sandown card. Recent winners include Bula, Diamond Edge (twice), Bregawn, Observe, Burrough Hill Lad (three times, including a walkover) and Desert Orchid. THE (BONANZA JEANS) OTELEY HURDLE (£7,500, 2m) also has an impressive roll of honour: Lanzarote (twice), Sea Pigeon (twice), Desert Orchid and See You Then.

Saturday February 13: The English weather is less unpredictable than many people imagine, as an investigation of the racing calendar proves. Royal Ascot week is always stormy, Eclipse day heralds a heatwave, the Cheltenhham Gold Cup is usually run in a blizzard. Schweppes Gold Trophy day at Newbury stands plumb in the middle of what is often the nastiest period of the winter. Since 1969 the meeting has been abandoned no less than eight times. Schweppes perhaps understandably came to the recent conclusion that there were better ways to promote their fizzy drinks, and the Tote have gallantly, if rashly, stepped in. What is now THE TOTE GOLD TROPHY H'CAP HURDLE (£22,500, 2m100y) is one of the most fiercely contested and fascinating handicaps of the winter months. It is also one of the most dangerous for the punter. If you can pick the winner then there is no reason why you shouldn't go on to disprove the Theory of Relativity between drinks in the Members' Bar. The last few winners have started at 10-1, 16-1, 13-1, 20-1, 25-1, 14-1 and 16-1. There was a time when it was good enough simply to back Ryan Price's candidate and make your fortune, but those great days are sadly past. The supporting race is THE GAME SPIRIT H'CAP CHASE (GDE 2 – £10,000, 2m160y). Beware – as a betting race it is almost as dangerous.

Saturday February 20: The best place to be today is at Newcastle for THE TOTE EIDER H'CAP CHASE (£7,500, 4m1f), a lovely long-distance event that will inevitably include a few candidates warming up for the Grand National. If you can't be there, then try Chepstow for THE AYNSLEY CHINA CUP CHASE (£10,000, 2½m), supported by THE (FOODBROKERS) PERSIAN WAR NOVICES HURDLE (GDE 2 – £7,500, 2½m).

Thursday February 25: There are a couple of good races at lowly Wincanton which are often used by horses bound for Cheltenham glory. They are THE KINGWELL PATTERN

HURDLE (GDE 2 – £10,000, 2m)and THE JIM FORD CHAL-LENGE CUP CHASE (£7,500, 3m1f), which has an exceptional record for favourites though you can expect some cramped odds.

Saturday February 27: THE TOTE PLACEPOT HURDLE (£10,000, 2m, 4y) is a good race for the young generation of four-year-old hurdlers at Kempton, while THE RENDLESHAM HURDLE (GDE 2 – £7,500, 3m) is an event for their elders and betters.

Saturday March 5: As the countdown to the Cheltenham Festival begins in earnest, Haydock is the place to be this Saturday where THE JOHN CRAIG VICTOR LUDORUM HURDLE (GDE 2 – £7,500, 2m, 4y), THE TIMEFORM CHASE (£12,500, 2½m) and THE GREENALL WHITLEY BREWERIES H'CAP CHASE (£15,000, 3m) form the core of a superb day's racing. For those stranded in the south, Newbury's meeting offers a good alternative.

Saturday March 12: Sandown's (WILLIAM HILL) IMPERIAL CUP H'CAP HURDLE (£12,500, 2m) offers punters an opportunity to give needy bookmakers an early Easter present. There is still a shell-shocked punter wandering around the home counties who once found the 14-1 winner of this event, Prayukta, in 1980. This unreliable though Fred Winter-trained animal was beautifully nursed and cajoled around the inside rail by John Francome. Avoid this punter like the plague. Knowing that he will never have such luck again, it is his only topic of conversation.

Tuesday, Wednesday and Thursday March 15-17: The Chel-tenham Festival is the climax of the jumping calendar. This marvellous feast of racing is attended by any lover of the sport who can beg, borrow or steal the time off, including several thousand Irishmen all with huge wads of notes and many wearing dog-collars. The fate of favourites at the Festival is dismal and huge amounts of luck are needed for the hard-pressed punter to stay afloat in the often bog-like conditions.

On the Tuesday the very first race offers a good opportunity to get off to a losing start as THE WATERFORD CRYSTAL SUPREME NOVICES' HURDLE (GDE 1 – £25,000, 2m) is frequently won by an Irish mud-lark, but not the one that the invading hordes have backed down to favouritism. The Irish also love to win THE ARKLE CHALLENGE TROPHY CHASE (GDE 1 – £22,500, 2m), another graveyard for favourites, and have won six of the last eleven runnings. Starting prices for recent winners are normally in double figures. THE (WATER-FORD CRYSTAL) CHAMPION HURDLE CHALLENGE TROPHY (GDE 1 – £45,000, 2m) is the crowning achievement of a hurdler's career, and in 1987 the great See You Then joined the elite band of triple winners. This thrilling race has the rare distinction of being quite kind to favourite backers. THE WATERFORD CRYSTAL STAYERS HURDLE (GDE 1 – £22,500, 3m1f), THE KIM MUIR MEMORIAL CHALLENGE CUP H'CAP CHASE (£12,500, 3m) and THE CHELTENHAM GRAND ANNUAL CHALLENGE CUP H'CAP CHASE (£15,000, 2m) round off the first day.

The Wednesday opens with THE SUN ALLIANCE NOVICES HURDLE (GDE 1 – £27,500, 2½m) and continues with the big race of the day, THE QUEEN MOTHER CHAMPION CHASE (GDE 1 – £27,500, 2m) which is often one of the most exciting races of the meeting, though not always living up to its grand title. The Dickinsons have won this race four times in the last six years (three times with Badsworth Boy) and when they're not winning it, then the Irish nearly always are. The best advice to punters who have any money left is to back the second favourite. THE CORAL GOLDEN HURDLE FINAL H'CAP (£15,000, 3m1f) is often won by one of the better fancied horses who isn't carrying more than about 10st 8lb. The question is which one? THE SUN ALLIANCE CHASE (GDE 1 – £30,000, 3m) is almost never won by a first or second favourite and a crystal ball, preferably made by Waterford, is recommended for the last two races of the day.

Only punters who spend the rest of the year imagining they're Napoleon go anywhere near Thursday's opening race, THE (DAILY EXPRESS) TRIUMPH HURDLE (GDE 1 – £27,500, 2m, 4y), the four-year-old championship. It is also a very tough contest for the horses and there are trainers who dislike it so much that they won't have a runner in it. THE (CHRISTIES) FOXHUNTER CHASE CHALLENGE CUP (£10,000, 3¼m) is an exciting contest for amateur riders and then comes the big one itself, THE (TOTE) CHELTENHAM GOLD CUP CHASE (GDE 1 – £60,000, 3¼m), the Blue Riband of the winter sport. Despite the depressing fact that it is very unusual for an outright favourite to win, form on the whole stands up fairly well in the Gold Cup, and real shock results are a rarity. In 1986 the ill-fated mare Dawn Run, helped by the newly-increased allowance to the fairer sex, became the first horse ever to complete the Champion Hurdle/Gold Cup double. No horse has yet regained his crown after losing it and a dual victory has not been achieved since L'Escargot's in 1971. The best advice about the remaining three races of the Festival, THE (RITZ CLUB) NATIONAL HUNT H'CAP CHASE (£20,000, 3m1f), THE COUNTY H'CAP HURDLE (£12,500, 2m) and THE CATHCART CHALLENGE CUP CHASE (£12,500, 2½m), is to ignore the first and third, but to invest on favourite and second favourite in the 'County', a method which has showed a handsome profit in recent years.

Thursday, Friday and Saturday April 7-9: Only a few years ago the Grand National Meeting at Liverpool was quite a sad affair. Sparsely attended, jumping races were mixed with a few desultory events on the Flat and even the future of the great race itself was in jeopardy. Now, thanks to Jockey Club intervention, good sponsorship and positive management from the Aintree authorities, the same three days have been transformed into a thriving, crowd-pulling festival. The first

day features THE WHITBREAD GOLD LABEL CHASE
(£12,500, 3m1f) and THE WHITBREAD TROPHY H'CAP
CHASE (£10,000, 2¾m), which illustrate the difference
between Aintree's two courses – the Mildmay, with its normal
track, softish fences and tight bends, and the Grand National
course with its famous gigantic obstacles and the long run-in
that has seen so many triumphs and tragedies.

The second day highlights are THE GLENLIVET HURDLE
(£15,000, 2m, 4y) and THE (R.E.A. BOTT) FOX HUNTERS
CHASE (£7,500, 2¾m). This last-named is the race that every
amateur dreams of winning and, run over the National fences,
provides many thrills and spills.

Grand National day itself begins with THE (CAPTAIN
MORGAN) AINTREE H'CAP CHASE (GDE 2 – £15,000, 2m).
This is followed by THE (SANDEMAN) AINTREE HURDLE
(GDE 2 – £15,000, 2m5½f), which has been won by Champion
Hurdlers like Monksfield and Gaye Brief but has also seen
upsets like the defeat of See You Then. THE (SEAGRAM)
GRAND NATIONAL H'CAP CHASE (£65,000, 4½m) is a law
unto itself and must be considered as such. It is the richest event
in the jumping calendar and yet it is only a 'listed' handicap. It
causes more excitement than the Gold Cup or the Derby but is
invariably won by a mere handicapper. Though it is run over the
exceptional distance of 4½ miles, it is usually won by a horse
who is happier at shorter trips and has the speed to stay out of
the trouble-spots. The ability to jump well is an obvious necessity. Finding the winner is no easy task, but the National is not
quite the lottery that some people claim. Apart from four upsets
at 25-1, 40-1, 50-1 and 28-1, all the winners since 1972 have been
much-fancied horses starting at 14-1 or less, and investing on the
second favourite over the last decade would have produced a
substantial profit. Detractors of the National, and they are
common enough, are continually sniping at the race, and when
there are tragedies, like the deaths of Alverton and Dark Ivy,
certain public bodies and organisations are always quick to
orchestrate opposition to the staging of the contest.

The Jockey Club have sensibly declined to tamper any more with the fences. To do so would be to lose the unique quality of the contest.

Saturday April 16: Ayr has none of the idiosyncracies of Aintree, being a flat and oval track. THE (WILLIAM HILL) SCOTTISH NATIONAL H'CAP CHASE (£25,000, 4m120y) is a valuable and hotly-contested race. The last Grand National winner to do the double was the great Red Rum in 1974 after winning the second of his three Liverpool victories. The supporting race is THE (LONDON AND NORTHERN GROUP) FUTURE CHAMPION NOVICES CHASE (GDE 2 – £10,000, 2m).

Saturday April 23: THE WHITBREAD GOLD CUP H'CAP CHASE (£35,000, 3m5f18y) is the centrepiece of a fantastic mixed day's racing at Sandown that also features the Guardian Classic Trial on the Flat and is the oldest sponsored steeplechase in the calendar, as well as being one of the most popular. But picking the winner of this last great chase of the season is no easy matter.

Monday May 2: On this Bank Holiday Monday, with the Flat season well into its stride and only two days after the Two Thousand Guineas, Haydock rather incongruously stages the last big race of the dying jumping season THE SWINTON INSURANCE BROKERS TROPHY H'CAP HURDLE (£20,000, 2m).

It is essential to keep an eye on the Irish jumping scene during the winter. The chances are that come March they'll be over at Cheltenham in force attempting to lift some of the top prizes. And many of the top English horses are bred in the Emerald Isle. It is still possible to hear a smart English trainer, when asked where he found one of his stars, utter the time-honoured words: 'Well, I was over in Ireland some time back to take the air, and I saw this nice-looking animal standing in the corner of a field . . . '

Here is a short list of some of the top Irish events (prize money in Irish pounds):

Saturday December 5: Fairyhouse. THE HOLSTEN PILS CHASE (£7,500, 2¼m) and THE HOLSTEN H'CAP HURDLE (£17,500, 2m).

Tuesday and Wednesday September 22-23: Listowel. THE DAWN LIGHT BUTTER H'CAP HURDLE (£12,500, 2m, 4y) and THE GUINNESS KERRY H'CAP CHASE (£15,000, 3m).

Saturday December 12: Punchestown. THE DURKAN BROTHERS INTERNATIONAL PUNCHESTOWN CHASE (£10,000, 2½m)

Saturday to Tuesday September 26-29: Leopardstown. THE DENNYS GOLD MEDAL NOVICES' CHASE (£15,000, 2m), THE FINDUS BEEFBURGER HURDLE (£10,000, 2½m), THE FINDUS H'CAP CHASE (£22,500, 3m), THE BLACK AND WHITE WHISKY CHAMPION CHASE (£35,000, 2½m) and THE SEAN P. GRAHAM MEMORIAL HURDLE (£35,000, 2m).

Saturday January 2: Naas. THE SLANEY HURDLE (£7,500, 2m3f).

Saturday January 9: Leopardstown. THE LEE & CO. SHOP LOCAL CHASE (£10,000, 2½m) and THE LADBROKE H'CAP HURDLE (£35,000, 2m).

Saturday February 7: Leopardstown. THE (WESSEL) ARKLE PERPETUAL CHALLENGE CUP CHASE (£10,000, 2¼m), THE (WESSEL CABLE) CHAMPION HURDLE (£22,500, 2m) and THE HAROLD CLARKE LEOPARDSTOWN CHASE (£15,000, 3m).

Saturday February 13: Leopardstown. THE VINCENT O'BRIEN IRISH GOLD CUP (£50,000, 3m).

Wednesday February 24: Thurles. THE PURCELL EXPORTS HURDLE (£10,000, 2m).

Saturday February 27: Punchestown. THE DINERS CLUB CHASE (£12,500, 2½m).

Sunday and Monday April 17-18: Fairyhouse. THE JAMESON IRISH GRAND NATIONAL H'CAP CHASE (£65,000, 3½m) and THE POWER GOLD CUP CHASE (£15,000, 2½m).

HISTORY
OF
WORLD
TRADE
IN
MAPS

Published by Collins
An imprint of HarperCollins Publishers
Westerhill Road
Bishopbriggs
Glasgow G64 2QT

www.harpercollins.co.uk

First Edition 2020

© HarperCollins Publishers 2020

Text © Philip Parker 2020

Maps © see Acknowledgements on page 222

A catalogue record for this book is available from the British Library

ISBN 978-0-00-840929-6

10 9 8 7 6 5 4 3 2 1

Printed in Slovenia by GPS Group

MIX
Paper from
responsible sources
FSC™ C007454

This book is produced from independently certified FSC™ paper to ensure responsible forest management.

For more information visit: www.harpercollins.co.uk/green

If you would like to comment on any aspect of this book, please contact us at the above address or online.
e-mail: collins.reference@harpercollins.co.uk

 facebook.com/collinsref

@collins_ref

HISTORY
OF
WORLD
TRADE
IN
MAPS

Philip Parker

Contents

7   INTRODUCTION

ANCIENT TRADE

10   ÇATALHÖYÜK AND
NEOLITHIC TRADE

12   TRADE IN ANCIENT EGYPT

14   GREEK AND PHOENICIAN TRADE

18   TRADE IN THE ANCIENT NEAR EAST

20   PETRA AND THE
FRANKINCENSE ROUTE

22   ROMAN TRADE

26   THE PERIPLUS AND ROME'S
EASTERN TRADE

28   TRADE IN LATE ANTIQUITY

32   THE AMBER ROAD

MEDIEVAL TRADE

36   CHARLEMAGNE AND
CAROLINGIAN TRADE

40   TRADE IN THE ISLAMIC WORLD

44   EUROPE AND THE WORLD IN 1300

46   THE TRANS-SAHARAN GOLD TRADE

48   THE SILK ROAD

52   MARCO POLO AND THE SILK ROAD

56   THE RISE OF THE
MARITIME REPUBLICS

60   THE VENETIAN TRADING EMPIRE

62   BRUGES AND THE CLOTH TRADE

66   PLAGUES AND PANDEMICS

70   THE HANSEATIC LEAGUE

72   THE VOYAGES OF ZHENG HE

TRADE IN THE AGE OF DISCOVERY

74   THE JOINING OF THE WORLD

78   THE PORTUGUESE TRADING
EMPIRE IN AFRICA

80   CIRCUMNAVIGATING THE GLOBE

84   OTTOMAN TRADE IN
THE 16TH CENTURY

86   AZTEC TRADE

88   THE SILVER TRADE

90   PIRATES AND PRIVATEERS

92   NEWFOUNDLAND AND
THE COD TRADE

96   THE DUTCH AND MANHATTAN

100   THE HUDSON'S BAY COMPANY
AND THE FUR TRADE

102   TRADE AND THE BIRTH OF
THE UNITED STATES

106   SOUTH AMERICA AND THE SPANISH

110   THE PORTUGUESE AND
THE SPICE TRADE

116   THE DUTCH EAST INDIA COMPANY

118   THE PORTUGUESE AND
       THE JAPAN TRADE

122   PORTUGAL'S CHINA TRADE

126   SWEDEN, RUSSIA AND
       NORTH EUROPEAN TRADE IN
       THE 16TH CENTURY

TRADE, REVOLUTION AND EMPIRE (c. 1700–1900)

130   THE BRITISH IN INDIA

134   THE SLAVE TRADE

138   THE SUGAR TRADE

140   THE COTTON TRADE

144   THE COFFEE TRADE

146   THE CHINA TEA TRADE AND
       THE CLIPPERS

150   THE AGE OF STEAM

154   WORLD CITIES

156   IMPERIALISM AND TRADE

160   THE ERIE CANAL

164   THE SUEZ CANAL

166   THE PANAMA CANAL

168   THE US TRANSCONTINENTAL
       RAILROAD

172   THE TRANS-SIBERIAN RAILWAY

176   THE CAPE TO CAIRO RAILWAY

178   THE WOOL TRADE

182   REFRIGERATION AND
       THE MEAT TRADE

186   THE COAL TRADE

TRADE IN THE INDUSTRIAL AGE (1900 - PRESENT)

190   THE SECOND INDUSTRIAL
       REVOLUTION

192   A SMALLER WORLD

196   TARIFFS AND TRADE

200   THE OIL TRADE

204   ELECTRONICS AND THE INTERNET

208   BANKING AND FINANCE

212   TOURISM AND TRADE

216   TRADE BLOCS

218   THREATS TO WORLD TRADE

222   ACKNOWLEDGEMENTS

"... The progress of freedom depends more upon the maintenance of peace, the spread of commerce, and the diffusion of education, than upon the labours of Cabinets and Foreign-offices."

Richard Cobden, 1850

Introduction

Trade, the fulfilling of a want or need by the exchange of goods with another group that has a surplus of it, is one of the most ancient human activities. As early as 11,000BC unknown traders took obsidian, a volcanic glass that produces sharp blades, 80 miles across the Aegean Sea from the island of Melos to Franchthi Cave on the Greek mainland. They did so because there was a profit to be made, and their actions created a network of ties between communities that bound them together in a mutually advantageous association. Adam Smith, the Scottish philosopher and founder of modern economics, understood well that mankind is a trading animal: in his seminal work *The Wealth of Nations* (1776), he declared that man has a "propensity to truck, barter and exchange". As the pace of economic change has grown ever more furious since Smith's time, that propensity has only intensified, until today mobile phones from China, coffee from Brazil, wine from Australia or cheese from France create a global shopping basket for consumers of which their ancestors could never have dreamed.

Trade is one of the hidden catalysts of world history. It helped bring in the agricultural surpluses that the earliest cities, such as Uruk and Ur in 5th-millennium BC Mesopotamia, needed to grow and thrive, and drove exploration and conquest, from the expeditions sent by the Egyptian pharaoh Hatshepsut to the fabled Land of Punt (possibly in modern Somalia) around 1470BC. Without the impetus of trade, Han Chinese traders would not have brought knowledge of silk and paper westwards along the Silk Road, Arab merchants would not have penetrated the Sahara in the 10th century, in search of gold, but bringing Islam with them, and Christopher Columbus would not have crossed the Atlantic in 1492 in the hope of

The 1375 Catalan Atlas shows Mansa Musa, a West African ruler, whose Malian kingdom dominated the trans-Saharan gold trade.

finding a shortcut to the source of valuable spices, but as an unintended consequence leading the second European expedition to reach the Americas – 500 years after the long-forgotten voyages of the Vikings there – and ushering in the first epoch of globalisation.

This book tells the story of world trade, from the hesitant barter of the Neolithic to the instantaneous transmission of cryptocurrencies in the information age. It does so through the medium of maps. Almost as ancient a way of visualising the world as trade itself, maps began as imprints on Mesopotamian clay tablets and today sit in computer tablets that can contain the whole world in fine detail. What these very different forms of cartography have in common is that they tell us much about how cultures have seen the world, their preoccupations, their limitations and even their propaganda.

Maps tell stories, and the history of trade is brimming with such narratives. Those selected for this volume are largely contemporary to the eras whose history they illustrate – with some exceptions for epochs when maps were rare, non-existent or partial. The extraordinary story of the monsoon trade across the ancient Indian Ocean in the early years of the Roman Empire is told by a reconstruction of a 1st-century AD merchant's manual, the epic saga of the Silk Road – which carried goods between China and the Middle East and Europe for a millennium and a half – unfolds in a 12th-century Chinese map, the trading networks that spanned the Americas before Columbus are illustrated with a contemporary Aztec map of their great capital Tenochtitlán, and the ways in which the world has seemed to grow smaller are explained far more concisely through maps of early 20th-century submarine telegraph cables and the building of the Suez Canal in the 1860s than ten thousand words could achieve. Closer to our own time, the explosive growth of the internet and the huge changes it has wrought on our society are almost impossible to grasp – yet a map of its information trunks and nodes brings home that this too is a form of trade.

Most of the maps in the central portion of this book tell the story from a European perspective. By creating maps of the regions which they encountered, European explorers both marked the way for those who followed afterwards, and symbolically took possession of the land, despite in almost every case the presence of long-established peoples who had no say in being mapped into becoming subjects of a European monarch. Although trade was an important motive for this mapping, it was not the only one; while Europeans hoped to profit from the

lands they conquered and colonised, the extraction of wealth that could be achieved in the short term by naked violence and the simple expansion of the lands under their control pleased monarchs who cared neither how they were acquired or what means were necessary to exploit them. Maps are an expression of power, an ordering of the world in the way in which the cartographer, or his patron, desired. Step-by-step as Europe gained more knowledge of the continents outside its borders, and its tentative probes into them grew into empires of force, those maps increased in detail and sophistication. Then, just as Europe has lost its pre-eminence in the information sphere, first, to the United States and, more recently, to Japan, China and other Asian powers, its monopoly on the

An 1869 map of the Suez Canal shortly after its opening. It allowed more rapid trade flows between Europe and Asia.

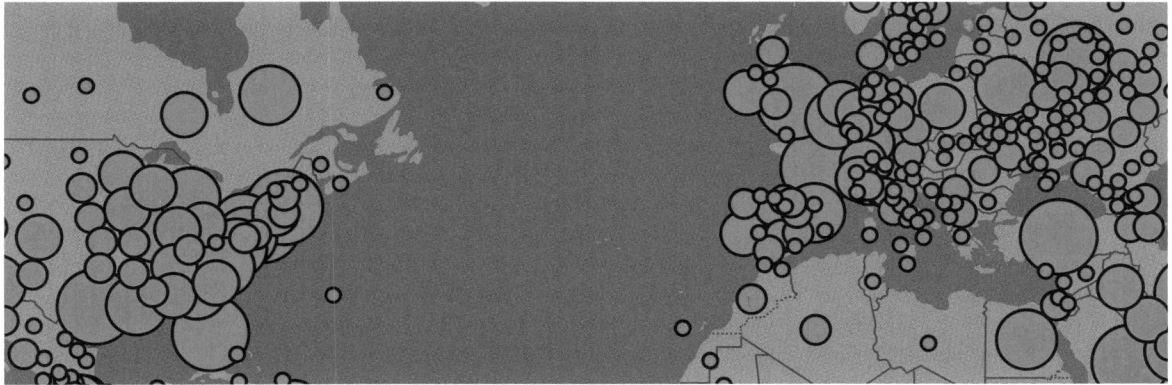

A map of the hotspots in the 2020 COVID-19 pandemic, produced using data from Johns Hopkins University.

world of mapping and, tellingly, its dominance of world trade have slipped. If information is power, and maps are a visual expression of it, the line of cartography that links Rome's itinerary maps to the European Renaissance mapmakers and the red-hued maps of the British Empire may have run its course, and that power, just as the trade that underpins and magnifies it, may become more diffused.

As the world has changed, so too has trade, and in many cases it has been the instrument of those changes. It is not just the commodities – from that ancient obsidian to the modern tantalum, a key component in mobile phones – that have shifted as tastes and technology have developed, but the arenas in which it is conducted have also changed. Columbus's expeditions and the equally vital, but often disregarded voyage of Vasco da Gama around Africa to the west coast of India in 1497 in search of pepper and other spices made new connections which ultimately reshaped the geopolitics of the world. Europe's encounter with the Americas – which the newcomers referred to as the "New World", ignoring the presence of long-established civilizations there – quickly led to the establishment of Spanish and Portuguese empires and, in short order, the subjugation of India, the colonisation of North America and Australia, and the distribution of almost every spare scrap of territory elsewhere to European imperialist powers.

Over the long span of history the names of the trading hegemons have altered. The Roman Empire, the Spanish Habsburgs, the Venetian Republic, and the British East India Company rose and fell as the tides of war and patterns of commerce ebbed and flowed. China, a trading superpower from the 2nd century BC to the 14th century AD, subsided into comparative impotence, until it re-emerged to become – so far – the 21st century's most successful trading nation. Many of the challenges and threats they and individual merchants faced have remained the same. The struggle to dominate resources is ever-present, with the one-sixth of global oil production that goes through the narrow and contested Strait of Hormuz as potentially destabilising as the stranglehold on silver production that the Spanish achieved from their mine in Potosí (in Bolivia) in the 16th century. War and disease have ravaged trade as much as they have populations, with the Black Death in 1348, the Spanish flu in 1918-19 and the 2020 COVID-19 pandemic leading to temporary cessations in the flow of trade.

Yet trade, the urge to acquire and the need to bargain, has always overcome these obstacles and if it ceased, our civilisation would fall. Far more than a bare chronicle of events or a list of kings and presidents, these five-dozen maps present the very lifeblood of history.

Çatalhöyük and Neolithic Trade

Dimly discernible on the mural from the Neolithic town of Çatalhöyük near Konya, in southern Anatolia, are a pattern of black rectangles and, in the background of the left-hand section, the shape of a peak etched in red. This scene, dating from around 6200BC, is very possibly the world's oldest map, showing a settlement plan of the cube-like Çatalhöyük dwellings and the Hasan Daği volcano, some 90 miles away, in full eruption. Its 6,000 or so inhabitants earned a living from farming and their settlement was full of cult sites dedicated to the auroch cattle that ensured their prosperity.

As well as a danger, Hasan Daği provided Çatalhöyük with a blessing, for it is one of the very rare sites where obsidian – a razor-sharp black volcanic glass – can be mined. Founded around 7000BC, the town was at the centre of one of the world's first known trade networks, its obsidian blades turning up hundreds of miles away in Iran and Cyprus and forming part of a regular trade with the early walled town of Jericho.

Even at this very early date, trade arose where there was a need, or at least a demand, for raw materials and finished items which were in short supply locally. The obsidian trade predated even Çatalhöyük, as small quantities of it have been found at Franchthi Cave in southwestern Greece dating to around 11,000BC. These originated on the island of Melos and must have been transported 80 miles by sea. Obsidian seems to have been something of a Neolithic status symbol, and by the 6th millennium BC, it appears in the western Mediterranean after the discovery of a source on Sardinia.

Obsidian was not the only commodity traded across long distances in Neolithic times. Shells circulated hundreds of miles from the shores where they were collected, with cowries from the Red Sea reaching 'Ain Ghazal in Jordan. A particularly active network took spondylus shells – found only in the Mediterranean and whose colourful spiny form made them prized for jewellery – on routes through the Balkans as far as Slovakia, where they are found in levels dating to c. 5000BC, and even to Épône, 40 miles west of Paris.

The journeys to carry these Stone Age luxuries must have been arduous, sometimes taking months. Occasionally we have evidence of trackways which were carved out on the most trafficked routes or in particularly difficult sections, such as the Sweet Track, built through the marshy Somerset Levels around 3800BC and the Hærevejen (the "Ox Road"), laid out along the neck of Denmark's Jutland peninsula at about the same time.

Of the ancient traders, however, we know almost nothing. The only tantalising glimpse is the corpse of Ötzi, found frozen on a glacier high on the Italian–Austrian border in 1991. The Iceman, as he is nicknamed, died around 3200BC, bleeding to death from an arrow wound in his back. Among his possessions was a copper axe blade, which contained impurities of arsenic and lead that betray the origin of the metal in southern Tuscany. How it came to be traded, or even if it was acquired there by Ötzi himself, we cannot know, but it and Çatalhöyük's obsidian are clear evidence that, from the earliest, mankind was a trading animal.

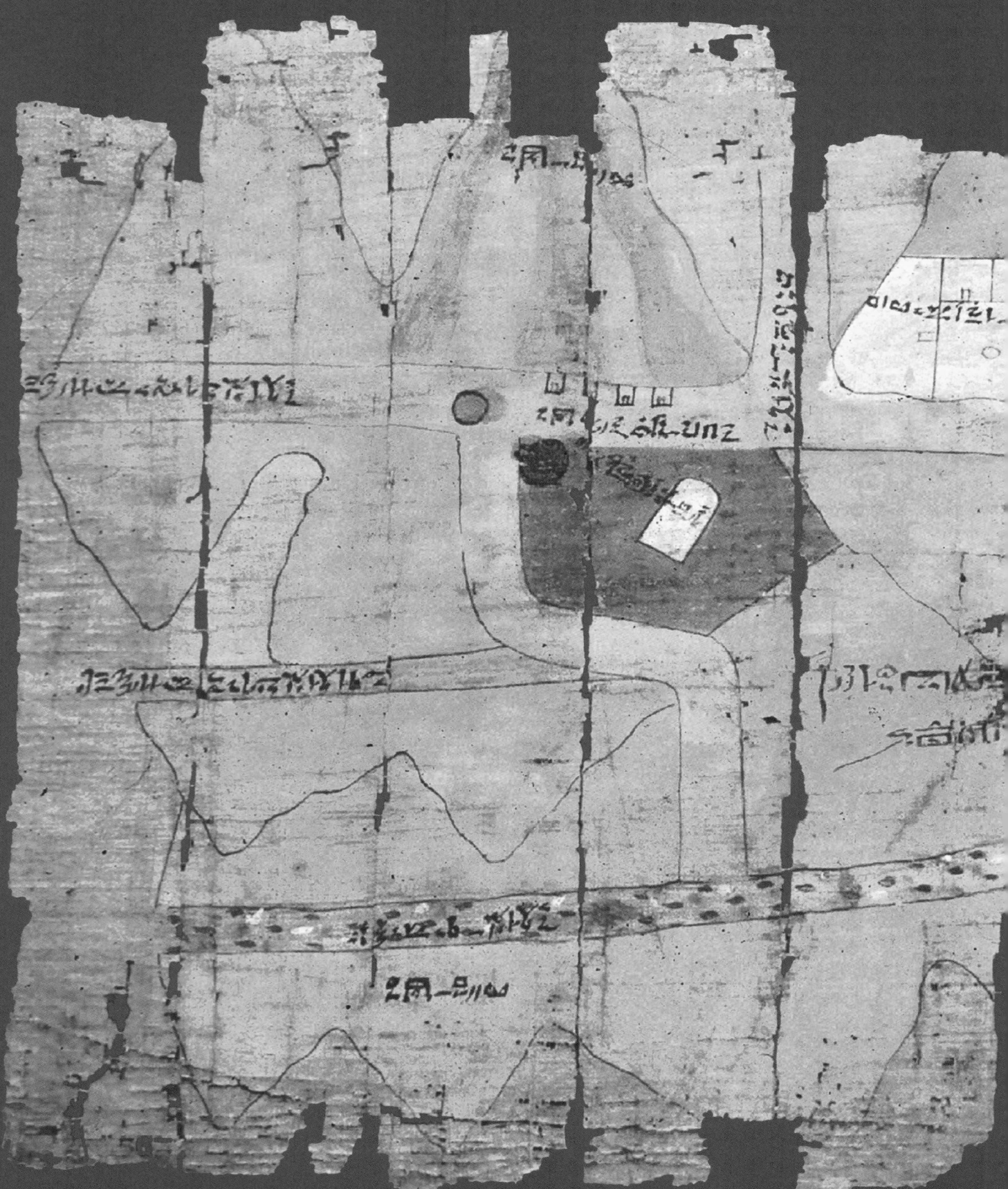

Trade in Ancient Egypt

Unearthed by agents acting for the French consul in Egypt in the 1820s, the 2.8-metre-long Turin Papyrus (of which a section is shown), probably drawn up during the reign of Pharaoh Ramesses IV (c. 1151-1145BC), gives a precious insight into Egypt's trading and economic history.

Although the annual flooding of the Nile enriched ancient Egypt's soil and provided it with ample sources of food, its rulers had to look elsewhere for minerals, metals and luxury goods. The mines and trade routes from which these flowed back into Egypt involved hazardous traverses of the desert. The papyrus shows one such route, Wadi Hammamat, depicted as a bold line in the lower portion, with hills shown by conical forms. Labels indicate features such as "mountains of gold", which formed the probable destination of the expedition for which the map was drawn up (as well as building stone, such as the greenish greywacke, which was prized for carving royal statuary).

Wadi Hammamat also acted as a main conduit for trade northwards, through Sinai, into Palestine and the city-states of Mesopotamia. Even before the unification of Egypt around 3100BC, there is evidence of cedar being imported from Lebanon – Egypt had a chronic shortage of wood – and lapis lazuli from Badakshān in Afghanistan, its sole known source in ancient times. To protect their trade, the Egyptians established trading colonies in Palestine, and under the New Kingdom from around 1550BC, incorporated it into their empire.

To the south, the Egyptians sent expeditions down the Nile, which then proceeded overland to trade with a variety of kingdoms based in modern Sudan. In the Middle and New Kingdoms, fortified bases were established as far as Buhen, around 800 miles south of the capital at Memphis. Although one expedition led by Harkhuf, the governor of Elephantine under Pepi II (c. 2278-2184BC), is said to have brought back a dancing dwarf which pleased the pharaoh far more than any of the other goods, the main items that came from the southern lands, first Yam, and then Irem, were wood, ivory, gold, and aromatic resins such as myrrh. Accompanying these commodities were a multitude of slaves.

The principal destination for this southern trade under the New Kingdom (c. 1570-1069BC) was the Land of Punt, whose precise location is unknown, but probably lay in modern Yemen or Somalia. The best-known expedition was despatched by Hatshepsut, one of Egypt's very few female pharaohs, around 1470BC. Its progress is depicted in friezes on the walls of her imposing funerary temple at Deir el-Bahri near the Valley of the Kings. These show 80-foot-long galleys, laden with grain and textiles, which in Punt receive a return cargo of large trees (probably myrrh, which the Egyptians wanted to try to grow themselves). The accompanying inscription lists myrrh, ebony, ivory, gold, cinnamon, apes, monkeys, dogs and panther skins as amongst the goods brought back to the queen.

These were high-value items, and as Egypt's power waned, and it was subjected to occupation by Assyrians and Persians, its ability to project its power and trade in luxuries diminished. Trade routes shifted to the Arabian Peninsula and bypassed Egypt, and by the 6th century BC, the mines of Wadi Hammamat and the trade routes to Punt were silent.

Greek and Phoenician Trade

The Mediterranean is outlined in multicoloured hues in this map portraying the situation around 550BC, taken from a historical atlas published in 1923. It shows the world's first empires built on trade: those of the Phoenicians and Greeks, whose colonists occupied the coastlines to such an extent that the Greek philosopher Plato was moved to remark that "like frogs around a pond, we have settled upon the shores of this sea".

The Phoenicians came first, coalescing as a people around 1200BC. Their prosperity was based on the cities of the Lebanese seaboard, most notably Tyre and Sidon, whose hinterland was amply provided with cedar, a hard and aromatic wood, the demand for which from Egypt and Mesopotamia was insatiable. As befits a merchant people, they took their name from one of their commodities, *phoinix*, a fabulously expensive purple dye extracted from crushed shells of the murex snail.

By 1000BC Phoenician traders were venturing westwards into the Mediterranean in search of raw materials such as copper from Cyprus, silver from Spain and tin from Cornwall. Their coast-hugging vessels needed waystations, which over time turned into colonies. Among the first were Gades (the future Cadiz), founded before 1000BC, and Carthage (founded in 814BC). Many have survived into the present, such as Malaka (Malaga) in Spain, Tingis (Tangier) in Morocco, and Icosium (Algiers) in Algeria. Farther afield they traded ivory from Punt (Somalia or Yemen), amber from the Baltic, sheep from Arabia, and emeralds from Yemen.

"Tyre, the crowning city, whose merchants are princes", as the Book of Isaiah put it, soon had competition from the Greek city-states, which began establishing colonies around 800BC. Some, such

as al-Mina in Syria or Naucratis on the Nile Delta, were purely trading posts, but overpopulation in Greece led to the dispatch of substantial numbers of colonists who established miniature versions of their mother city-states, such as Syracuse in Sicily (founded by Corinth in 733BC) and Cyrene in North Africa, established in 631BC by settlers from Thera.

The Greek colonies in southern Italy became so tightly clustered that the area was known as Magna Graecia ("Great Greece") and the Greeks encroached on areas the Phoenicians had regarded as their domain, setting up colonies at Emporion on Spain's east coast around 575BC and Massalia (Marseilles) in southern France, c. 600BC. As well as importing grain and other raw materials such as copper from their new colonies, the Greeks in the homeland exported luxury goods such as fine pottery, wine and textiles to the colonists. With a strategic eye, they established settlements astride key trade routes, such as Byzantium, founded by colonists from Megara in 668BC, which controlled access to the Black Sea. This was vital, because much of Greece's grain had to travel this way, leading Athens to establish a large naval force to patrol the Aegean and contributing to its defeat in the Peloponnesian War (431-404BC) after the Spartans captured Byzantium in 411BC.

By then the heyday of the Greek and Phoenician trading worlds was over. The Greek city-states retained a notional independence until their absorption by Rome in 146BC, the same year that Carthage, the last flagbearer of the Phoenician world, was taken and razed to the ground by Roman troops at the end of the Third Punic War.

Tanais

Olbia

Lake Maeotis
(Sea of Azov)
Phanagoria

Tauric
Cherso-
nese
Panticapaeum
Theodosia

Cauc

Pityu

Di

Heraclea
Chersonesus

PONTUS EUXINUS
(BLACK SEA)

Istrus
Tomi

Callatis

Sinope
Amisus
Cera

Odessus

Mesambria

PAPHLYGONIA
Cotyora

Apollonia

pidaurus

Selymbria
Byzantium
Calchedon
Chalcedon

THRACE

Heraclea

Halys R.

CAPPADOCIA

Lissus

Perinthus

MACEDONIA
Amphipolis
Abdera

BITHYNIA

Epidamnus
(Dyrrhachium)

Ainos

Propontis

Cius

ASIA MINOR

Cyzicus

Apollonia

Chalcidice

Thasos

Parium
Lampsacus

MYSIA

PHRYGIA

Methone

Sestus

Abydus

Olynthus
Potidaea
Dodona

Sane

Hellespont

Ilium

LYDIA

Thessaly

Lesbos

Sardis

orcyra

Histiaea

Euboea

Phocaea

Smyrna

Ambracia

AEG

Chios

Ionia
Ephesus

Anactorium
Leucas

Aeto
lia

Thebes

Erythrae

Ithaca

Chalcis

Samos

Miletus

CARIA

Cephallenia

Corinth

Athens

Halicarnassus

CILICIA

Elis

Megara

Delos

Naxos

PAMPHYLIA

Tarsus

Argos

Cyclades

LYCIA

Sparta

Melos

Thera

Cnidus

Rhodes

Phaselis

Selinus

Soli

Salamis

Cythera

Cythera

Citium

Bybl

Gydonia

Cnossus

Itanus

CYPRUS

PHOENICIA

Sido

CRETE

Tyre

Ha
Ara

IONIAN SEA

N

EAN

SEA

Cyrene

Hesperis

Barca

CYRENAICA

Naucratis

EGYPT

Libyan

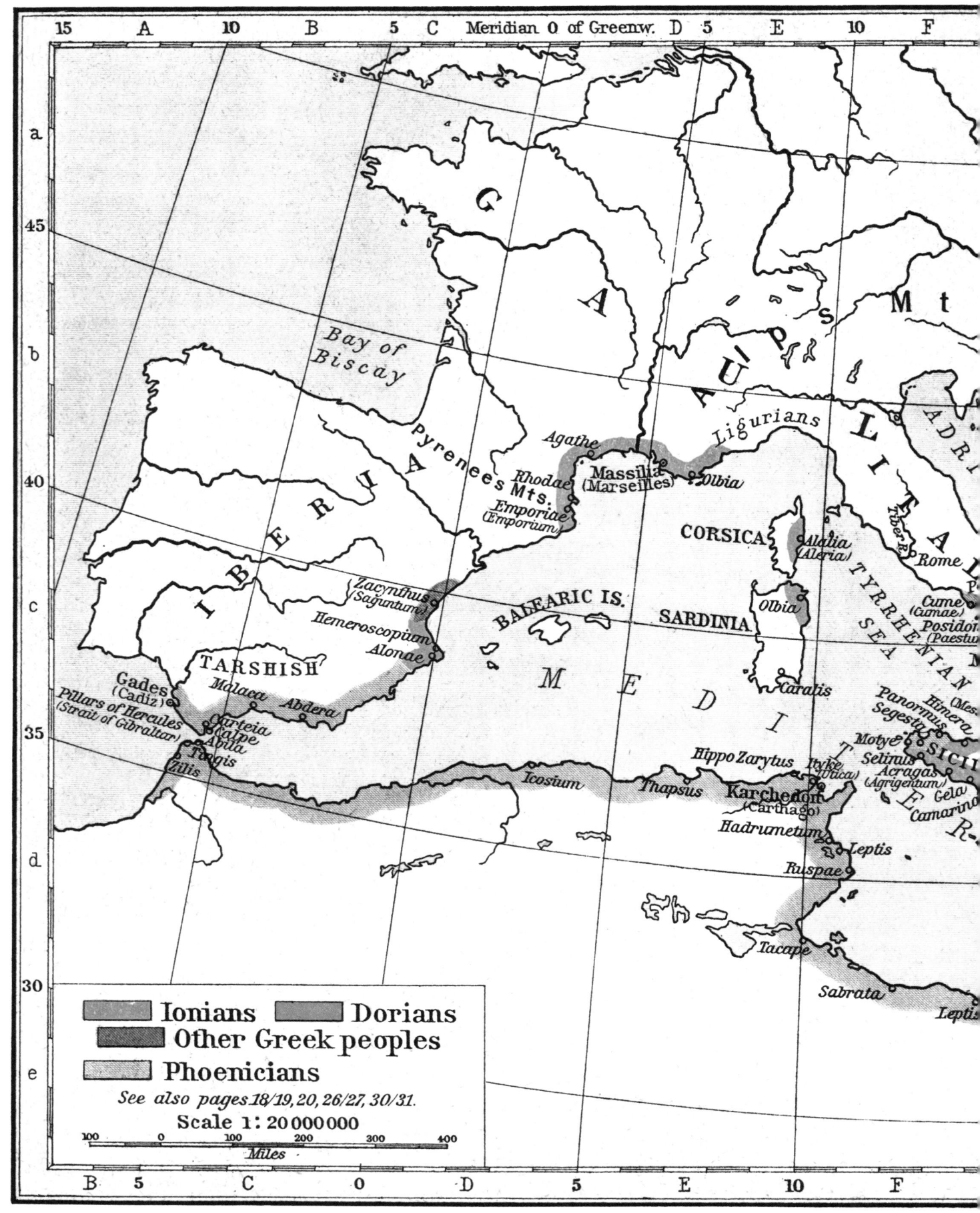

15   A   10   B   5   C   Meridian 0 of Greenw.   D   5   E   10   F

a

45

b

40

c

35

30

e

*Bay of
Biscay*

Pyrenees Mts.

I B E R I A

TARSHISH

Gades
(Cadiz)

Pillars of Hercules
(Strait of Gibraltar)

Malaca

Abdera

Carteia
Calpe
Abila
Tingis
Zilis

G

A

U

L

Agathe

Rhodae
Massilia
(Marseilles)
Emporiae
(Emporium)

Zacynthus
(Saguntum)

Hemeroscopium

Alonae

A L P s

Ligurians

Olbia

CORSICA

BALEARIC IS.

SARDINIA

Olbia

Alalia
(Aleria)

Caralis

M   E   D   I

Icosium

Thapsus

M   t

I T A L

ADRI

Tiber

Rome

Cume
(Cumae)
Posidon
(Paestu

T Y R R H E N I A N

SEA

Himera
(Mes

Panormus
Segesta   SICIL
Motye
Selinus   Acragas
(Agrigentum)   Gela
Camarino

R.

Hippo Zarytus   Ityke
(Utica)
Karchedon
(Carthago)

Hadrumetum

Leptis

Ruspae

Tacape

Sabrata

Leptis

Ionians   Dorians
Other Greek peoples
Phoenicians

See also pages 18/19, 20, 26/27, 30/31.

Scale 1 : 20 000 000

100   0   100   200   300   400
Miles

B   5   C   0   D   5   E   10   F

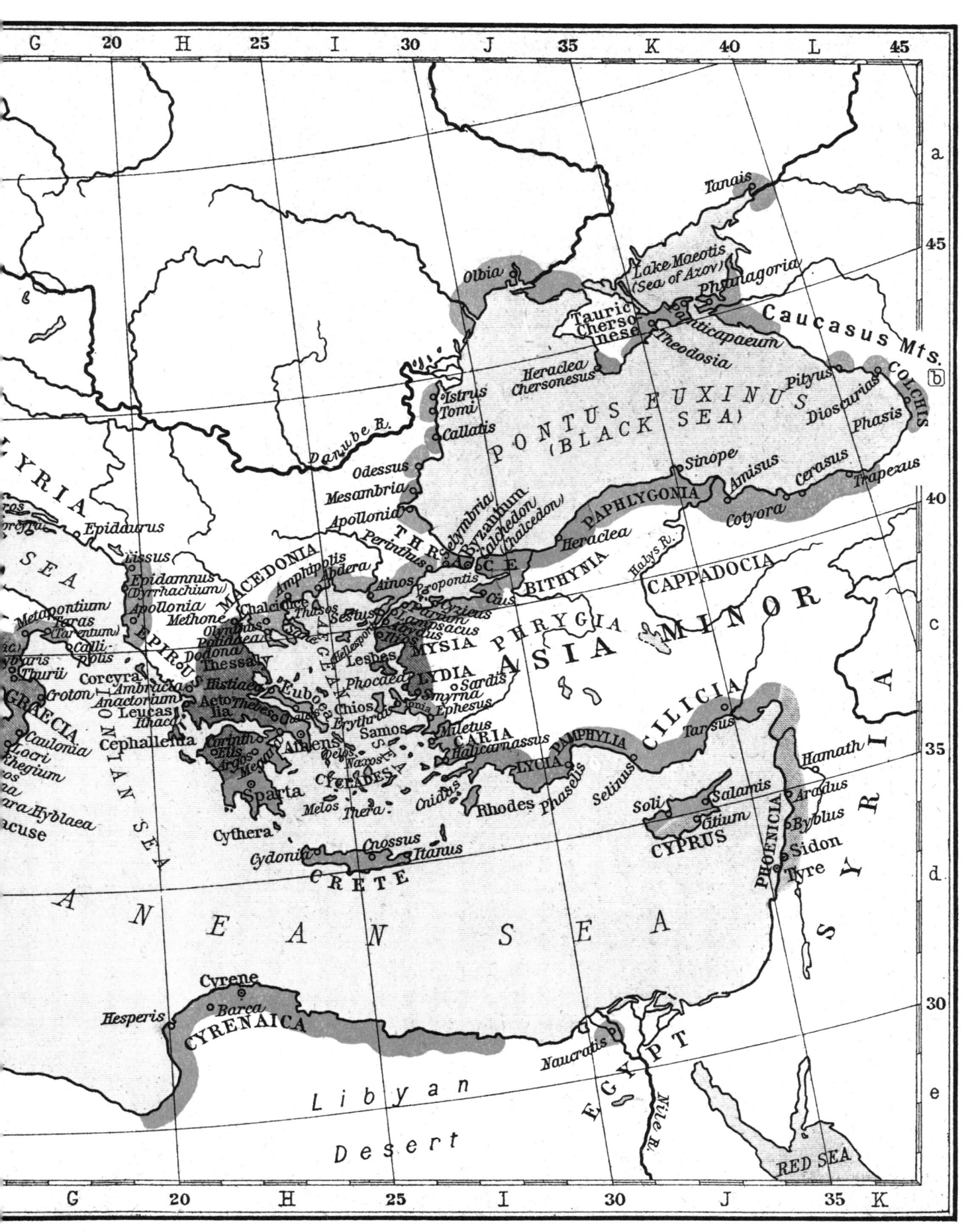

G   20   H   25   I   30   J   35   K   40   L   45

a

Tanais

45

Olbia

Lake Maeotis
(Sea of Azov)   *Phanagoria*

Tauric   *Panticapaeum*
Cherso-   *Theodosia*
nese   *Pityus*   Caucasus Mts.

b

Heraclea   *Pityus*   COLCHIS
Chersonesus   *Dioscurias*

Istrus   PONTUS EUXINUS   *Phasis*
Tomi   (BLACK SEA)
Callatis   *Cerasus*   *Trapezus*

Danube R.   *Sinope*   *Amisus*
Odessus   *Cotyora*

40

Mesambria   PAPHLYGONIA
Apollonia   *Selymbria* *Heraclea*
Y R I A   *Epidaurus*   THRACE   *Byzantium*   *Halys R.*
Perinthus   *Chalcedon*   BITHYNIA   CAPPADOCIA
S E A   *Lissus*   MACEDONIA   *Abdera*   *Cius*
Epidamnus   *Amphipolis*   *Ainos*   *Propontis*   ASIA MINOR

c

(Dyrrhachium)   *Chalcidice*   *Cyzicus*
Metopontium   *Apollonia*   *Thasos*   *Lampsacus*   PHRYGIA
Taras   *Methone*   *Olynthus*   *Sestus*   MYSIA   LYDIA
(Tarentum)   EPIRUS   *Potidaea*   *Hellespont*
Calli-   *Dodona*   *Thessaly*   Lesbos   *Sardis*
polis   *Sybaris*   *Phocaea*   *Smyrna*
Thurii   Corcyra   *Histiaea*   Chios   *Ephesus*
GRAECIA   *Ambracia*   *Thebes*   *Erythrae*   Ionia   CILICIA
Anactorium   Aetol-   *Euboea*   Samos   *Tarsus*
Caulonia   ia   Ithaca   CARIA   *Miletus*

35

Locri   Leucas   *Corinth*   Delos   *Halicarnassus*   PAMPHYLIA
Rhegium   Cephallenia   *Elis*   Naxos   LYCIA   *Hamath*
Hyblaea   *Argos*   Athens   CYCLADES   *Phaselis*   *Soli*   Salamis   *Aradus*
cuse   IONIAN SEA   Megara   Rhodes   *Selinus*   *Citium*   *Byblus*
Sparta   *Melos*   Cnidus   CYPRUS   *Sidon*
Cythera   *Thera*   PHOENICIA   *Tyre*
Cnossus   S Y R I A
Cydonia   *Itanus*

d

CRETE

A N E A N S E A

Cyrene

30

Hesperis   *Barca*
CYRENAICA
Naucratis
EGYPT

e

L i b y a n
Nile R.
D e s e r t
RED SEA

G   20   H   25   I   30   J   35   K

Trade in the Ancient Near East

The clay tablet contains the earliest map of the world, or at least the view of its Babylonian creator around 600BC. The Earth is shown as a flat disk girdled by an encircling ocean beyond which lie fabulous lands lit by perpetual sunlight or shrouded in eternal darkness. At the very centre, naturally, sat Babylon, then the world's largest city (with around 200,000 inhabitants) and the heart of an extensive trade network that stretched into the Mediterranean and east to Iran and beyond.

Those trading contacts were already over 3,000 years old, for the first cities, which appeared in Mesopotamia just before 4000BC, could not sustain themselves on locally available commodities. The cities of the south lacked timber and stone for building, and those in the less fertile north needed the barley and oil more abundant in the south. Uruk – which by 3300BC was Mesopotamia's megalopolis, occupying a site of over 250 acres – was at the core of the first large-scale long-distance trade, with regular contacts into Anatolia, eastern Iran and south Asia. As copper-working became more established in the later 4th millennium BC, its merchants travelled throughout Anatolia in search of ore, and trading outposts were set up at Tell Qannas on the Euphrates in Syria – which had over 7,000 inhabitants – and in Anatolia and the Iranian plateau.

In time, Uruk's hegemony collapsed and by 2700BC its place had been taken by Ur, whose royal tombs, filled with artefacts of gold, lapis lazuli, carnelian and silver, speak of a burgeoning trade in luxuries. By the 25th century BC Ur's abundant archives, written in cuneiform script, contained records of its ships sailing south to Dilmun (modern Bahrain), from where they brought back timber. Within a century,

Sargon of Akkad, the world's first empire builder, was boasting that Dilmun had submitted to him and that his ships travelled as far as Magan (Oman) and Meluhha (probably the Indus Valley civilisation of Pakistan and northwest India).

This first global trading system brought back precious stones, pearl, ivory and ebony from Meluhha, diorite and copper to Ur and was dominated by a specialised class of merchants called the *alik Tilmun* ("those who go to Dilmun") who established consortia backed by silver from city-state rulers and other merchants. Their investment contracts, which demanded a specified return, survive in large numbers. We even know the name of one of the early trading magnates, Ea-Nasir, whose warehouses stored consignments of copper as large as 18 tons and whose ships transported silver and metal rings to Dilmun in payment. To regulate this trade, early law codes such as that of Hammurabi of Babylon, c. 1750BC, laid down the maximum interest that could be levied by merchants and made the giving of receipts mandatory.

By 1500BC the trade to India had declined as the Indus Valley culture collapsed, though the Mediterranean end of the system still thrived, as shown by a ship from around 1350BC found wrecked at Ulu Burun off Bodrum in Turkey which was carrying half a ton of tin. Around 200 years later, the entire economy of the western Mediterranean disintegrated as its settled cultures were overwhelmed by raiders. The world that the Babylonian tablet portrays is very much a phoenix risen from those ashes.

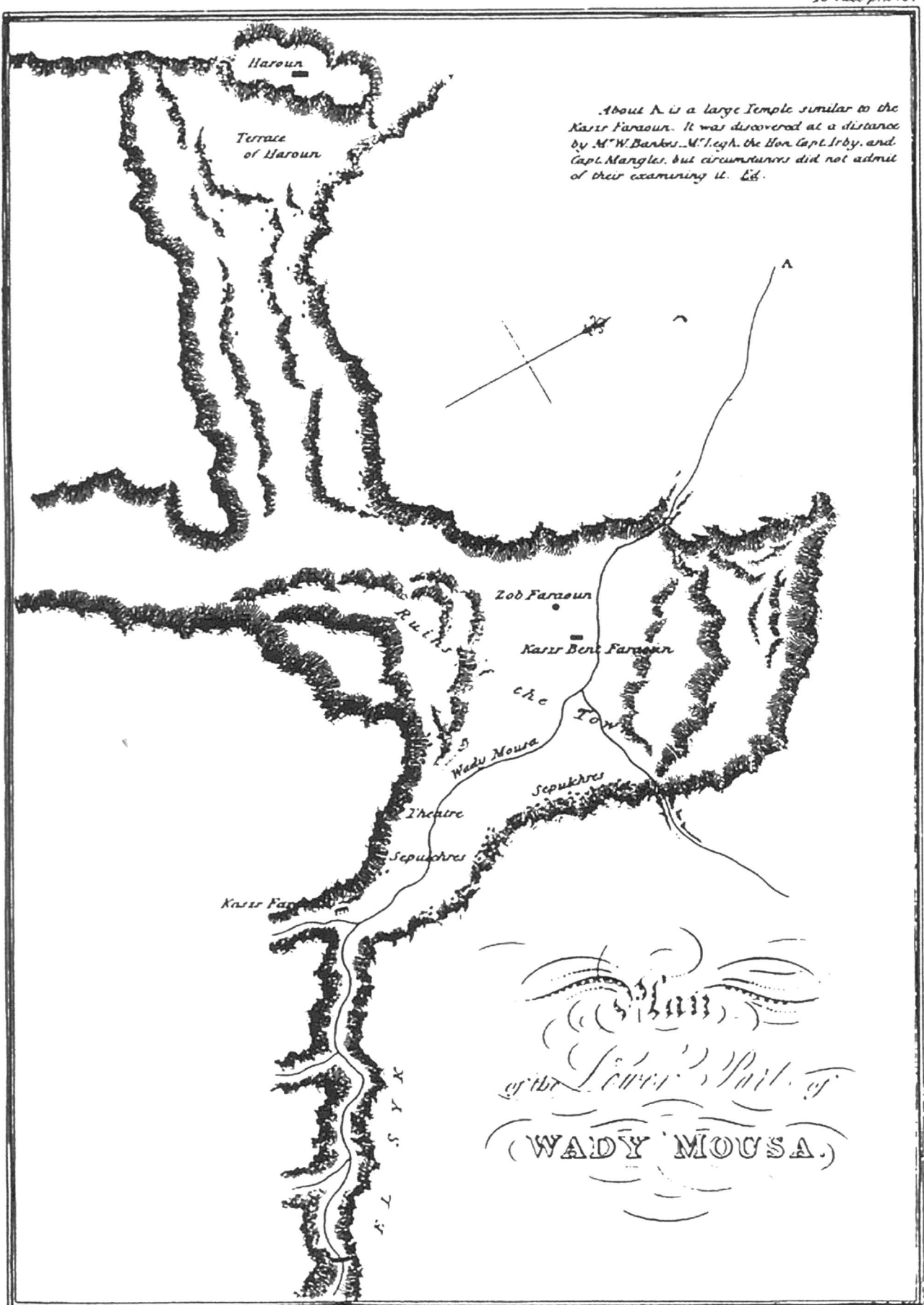

To face p. 248.

About A. is a large Temple similar to the
Kasr Faraoun. It was discovered at a distance
by Mr W. Banks, Mr Legh, the Hon. Capt. Irby, and
Capt. Mangles, but circumstances did not admit
of their examining it. Ed.

Haroun

Terrace
of Haroun

Zob Faraoun

Kasr Bent Faraoun

Ruins of

the Town

Wady Mousa

Sepulchres

Theatre

Sepulchres

Kasr Far

EL SYK

Plan

of the Lower Part of

WADY MOUSA.

J. L. Burckhardt del.

Published as the Act directs by John Murray Albemarle Street London May 1st 1822.

Petra and the Frankincense Route

The map shows Wady Mousa (now Wadi Musa) in modern Jordan, the cleft-like Siq, a narrow gorge providing a hidden entrance to the rose-red city of Petra with its spectacular collection of rock-cut tombs. It comes from the account of Johann Ludwig Burckhardt, who rediscovered the ancient town in 1812, when, disguised as Sheikh Ibrahim ibn Abdallah, he prevailed on his guide to let him venture into the area – renowned as the site of the tomb of Moses's brother Aaron – to pray.

Burckhardt had come across one of the ancient world's premier merchant towns, the entrepôt for a trade which yielded it fabulous wealth. For Petra controlled the northern end of the incense route from southwest Arabia. Frankincense (*Boswellia sacra*) and myrrh (*Commiphora myrrha*) are both derived from the sticky sap of desert trees native to modern Yemen. As early as the 1st century AD the Roman naturalist Pliny the Elder described how local tribes cut incisions into the barks of the trees and collected the oozing sap on palm mats. This they left to dry for several weeks before collecting it and transporting it on camels to the north.

The overland route traversed a series of caravan cities which sprang up to control the trade, most notably Ma'rib, the capital of the Sabaean kingdom. There the priests extracted a 10 per cent toll, one of many along the way which inflated the price so that when it finally reached Rome, a pound of frankincense cost the equivalent of two weeks' wages for a skilled labourer. Though the Yemeni tribes retained their independence, outside powers sought to control the caravan cities. In the late 8th century BC, the Assyrian king Tiglath-Pileser III attacked Gaza at the route's northern end, and when Petra became urbanised in the late 4th century BC, its Nabataean rulers suffered persistent assaults from neighbouring Greek kingdoms, though all failed.

In 24BC, the Romans decided to strike at the source of the trade, sending an expedition under Aelius Gallus, the prefect of Egypt. Unwisely, Gallus accepted the services of Syllaeus, the chief minister of the Nabataean kingdom, as a guide. With every interest in thwarting Roman control of the incense route, he took the Roman on a twisting desert odyssey, and when they finally reached Ma'rib six months later, the legions were so exhausted and debilitated by disease and thirst that after six days' perfunctory siege they turned tail and left.

Rome got its revenge in AD106, when the Emperor Trajan annexed Petra virtually unopposed, which allowed ever greater quantities of frankincense and myrrh to flow into the empire for use in religious rituals, as medicinal cures and simply as incense to counter the malodorous vapours of urban life. Much of the trade by then was in any case bypassing the traditional land route by going up the Red Sea to ports such as Myos Hormos and Berenice in southeastern Egypt before being transhipped to the Delta. The collapse of the western Empire in the 5th century brought a steep decline in the incense trade, and although it continued to prosper in the Islamic world and found a later market in the modern perfume trade, by the 21st century production of frankincense in Yemen was down to a few thousand tons and the price had sunk to around £2 a kilo. Once an exotic luxury, it had joined pepper and cloves as an everyday commodity.

Roman Trade

The elongated sheet of parchment shows a flattened view of Asia Minor and Egypt, with Constantinopolis (Constantinople) clearly visible on the left with its enthroned figure of the city's patron goddess Tyche and a column set up in honour of its founder, the Emperor Constantine. The map forms part of the *Tabula Peutingeriana*, or Peutinger Table, a 13th-century copy – probably of a 4th-century original – that shows major routes throughout the Roman Empire and its periphery.

The map's curious form, showing distances between towns, rather than attempting any accurate representation of the landscape, is typical of what we know of Roman mapping. What was most important was the itineraries, and the representation of the roads, which formed the arteries of Roman land transportation. Along this system, which began with the construction of the Via Appia in 312BC connecting Rome with southern Italy, went official travellers, couriers – who took advantage of the horse-changing stations every nine miles or so – and merchants, whose covered wagons etched deep ruts into the surface of a system which ultimately extended to over 240,000 miles.

Rome began as an unpromising settlement on a collection of central Italian hills in 753BC, but by the 1st century AD it had a population of over a million and its emperors governed a vast domain stretching from the Tyne to the Tigris. The army of some 300,000 men ensured a *Pax Romana* ("Roman Peace") which fuelled prosperity. Its sheer size and growing number of cities created a vast integrated market for goods which the regions within the empire could not themselves produce. *Terra sigillata*, high-quality red pottery stamped by its makers, travelled from factories around Arettium (Arezzo) and southern Gaul to reach virtually every province of the empire; iron and salt, both imperial monopolies, travelled inwards to Rome.

Bulkier goods were transported by sea – as the shipping costs were as little as 1/28th of the land price – departing or arriving at the vast port of Ostia, near Rome, with its huge *horrea* or warehouses and guilds of *negotiatores*, or merchants. Grain came in massive convoys from Alexandria to supply the grain dole of 70 pounds per month, which was being handed out to some 200,000 free males over the age of 11 by the 2nd century. Rome's demand for olive oil and wine too was insatiable: the city consumed 150 million litres of wine a year, transported in pottery amphorae so numerous that their shattered shards still form the base of Monte Testaccio, a 120-foot high mound near the River Tiber.

The merchants' manifests were not confined to these essential goods. Along the roads and in the merchant vessels, which could surpass 300 tons in size, travelled a vast panoply of goods and people: pork, a particular favourite of Roman legionaries; garum, a pungent sauce made from fish (including the intestines) fermented for weeks in vast vats in North Africa, which was bafflingly popular among Roman gourmands; glass, animals' hides, papyrus and – a more sinister aspect of ancient trade – a constant stream of captives from newly conquered provinces to feed the slave markets of the centre.

RATE SAVRICA.

MEOTE.

fossa facta p seruos scutarij por

ΣΑΥΣ ΕΕΙΒΙ

Cabacos. Myς ... Hermoca. Chimerium.
Sololime. ac ... Teagina. Humphi. O

Sorices.

ΣΙΗ Σ P

ΒΟ

ΦΟ

Philias. xx. Thimea. xu. Sycas. Chrysopolis. rouisort. xx

YTIHI. Calcedonia. B Γ
xvin. xxxvn.

A Constan tino polis. HS ANTIOCHIA

Melentiana. HS AGARAS

Regio. xu. SIHS

Proπ

aelca x ΣΗΣΙΛΕΒΟΓ L HS prdcitnessis. Pylae

ROHESOS Leuct.

Macrontecos. Vicar. ... Velo. Lmie

odisia. xxiu. Lemnos Egria.

Callipoli. Se Lamasco. Parnum. Priapos. xx
xu. Se xxu.
A
Egria. Lesbos Micale Bioruhe xxiu. audo. ouu.

Certih Icaria. Perpies Thao. Vardano.

Chalara Harpaton S ... S
Subrita. Cortin. Thomusa.
xxxu. xxiu. Cnoso. xvi. Vresonesso. xvi.
Lithum. xvi.
Ledena. xu. xvi. Inata. arcade. xxx. Blenna. xx. Hie
Eisia. R xxxu.
C ETIC a
ac a

IX.

1.

2.

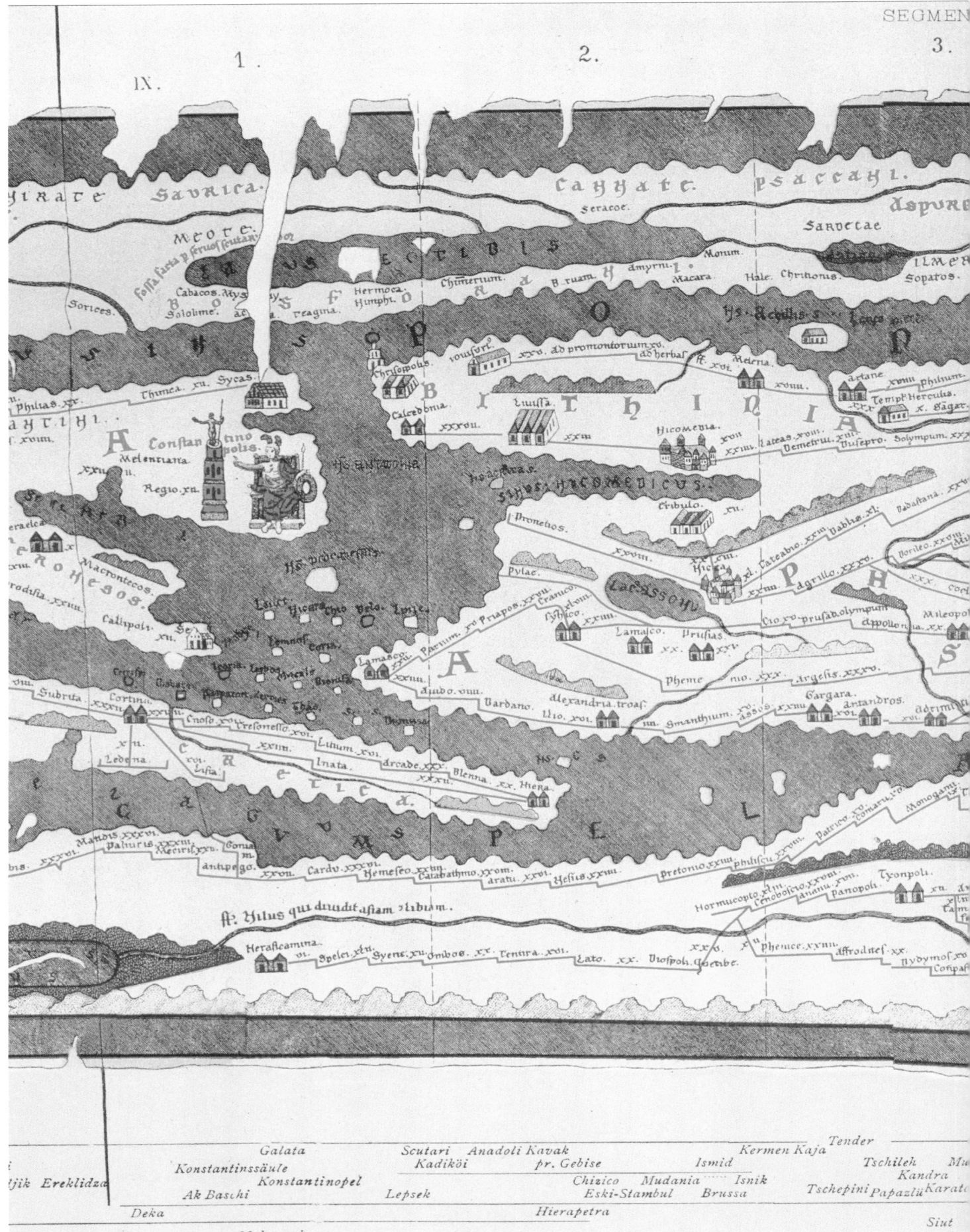

	Galata	Scutari	Anadoli Kavak		Kermen Kaja	Tender	
	Konstantinssäule	Kadiköi	pr. Gebise		Ismid		
i	Konstantinopel			Chizico Mudania	Isnik	Tschileh	Mi
tjik Ereklidza				Eski-Stambul Brussa		Tschepini Kandra	
	Ak Baschi	Lepsek				Papazlü Karat	
	Deka		Hierapetra				
	Maharraka					Siut	

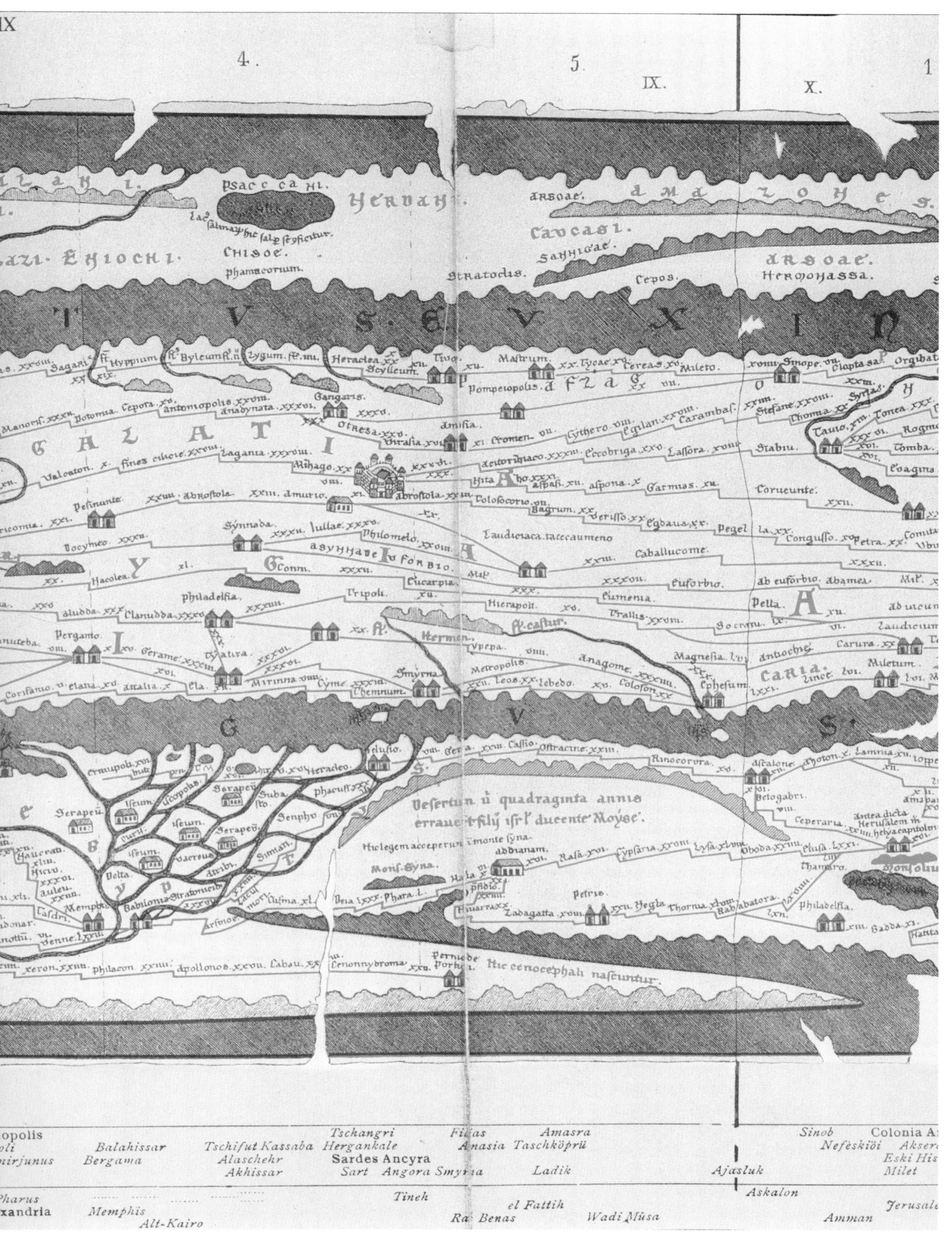

ERYTHRAEI SIVE RVBRI MARIS PERIPLVS, olim ab Arriano descriptus, nunc verò ab Abrah. Ortelio ex eodem delineatus.

VLYSSIS ERRORES, ex Conatib. Geographicis Ab. Ortelij.

The Periplus and Rome's Eastern Trade

The Roman Empire's vast size and the huge wealth of its upper classes – the senators and equestrians who monopolised its public offices – meant that it constituted the ancient world's largest market for luxury goods. This 1603 colour engraving of the 1597 map by the Flemish cartographer Abraham Ortelius illustrates an unexpected account of this trade, the *Periplus of the Erythrean Sea*, a mid-1st-century AD manual for merchants trading in the Indian Ocean.

Many of those merchants were Roman, but they had not established the trade. Its origins lay in Ptolemaic Egypt, and the foundation of the port of Berenice by Ptolemy II in 275BC, when he sent an expedition in search of war elephants. The new harbour became an entrepot for trade deeper into Nubia, for aromatic gums from Somalia and frankincense and myrrh from the ports of Arabia.

India, though, lay beyond the scope of these Hellenistic voyages and it was not until the discovery of the monsoon winds some time in the 2nd or 1st century BC that western merchants were able to travel there by sea. This advance is variably ascribed to Eudoxus of Cyzicus, who received information about the winds from an Indian mariner shipwrecked off Berenice in 118 BC, or Hippalus, to whom the Periplus attributes the first voyage to India.

Rome gained access to this trade after its absorption of Egypt as a province in 30BC (following the defeat and suicide of Cleopatra) and soon its merchants were making the long trip to India, setting out in July for a three-week voyage via the Gulf of Aden and then returning in November on the westerly monsoon winds. Some headed north to the ports of Barbaricon and Barygaza (in modern Gujarat), where they traded wines, metal and coral for spices and cotton fabric. Larger numbers turned south to Nelcynda and Muziris in Kerala, where they bartered gold and silver for pearls, gemstones and pepper. Their enforced three-month sojourns waiting for favourable return conditions left their mark, and hoards of thousands of Roman coins have been unearthed there, while the Peutinger Table, at its very margin, shows a Temple of Augustus in Muziris, where Roman merchants could show dutiful deference to the imperial cult.

The trade was clearly lucrative, and a papyrus from Muziris values the cargo from a single merchant ship at nearly 9 million sesterces, enough to purchase 3,000 large gemstones or a couple of good-sized farms. As the Roman state took as much as 35 per cent of the value of goods in tariffs, trade represented a significant contribution to its coffers. Amongst the more valuable south Indian cargoes was pepper, which was in such demand that around 16,000 tons of it were exported to the empire each year. It was so prized that the sole surviving Roman cookbook, that of Apicius from the 1st century AD, includes it as an ingredient in 349 out of its 468 recipes. The Germanic barbarians who overwhelmed the Roman Empire in the 4th and 5th centuries developed a taste for it too, and when the Gothic warlord Alaric menaced Rome in 408, part of the price he demanded for departing was 3,000 pounds of pepper. More than gold, silver or its diminished legions, pepper had, even if for a short time, saved Rome.

Trade in Late Antiquity

The Madaba map, a mid-6th-century representation of the Byzantine Near East, is a mosaic masterpiece. It shows a dense network of towns in Egypt, Palestine and Syria, although, as a fundamentally Christian piece of art, its undisputed centrepiece is the over-large representation of Jerusalem, with the Church of the Holy Sepulchre at its centre.

The apparent prosperity of the region in late antiquity – the centuries either side of the collapse of the Roman Empire in the West in 476 – may come as a surprise. The overrunning of the western provinces by Germanic barbarians in the 4th and 5th centuries had caused the collapse of a complex trading system which spanned a vast distance from Hadrian's Wall in northern Britain to the Rhine, the Danube and the borders of Persia. The vast grain shipments from Alexandria which had fed the empire, the export of high-quality *terra sigillata* pottery, and the arms factories needed to equip the half-million soldiers of the late Roman army all dried up. In Britain, long-distance trading declined catastrophically and although high-quality goods such as Coptic bowls still arrived from Egypt (and were interred in the grave of a 7th-century king of East Anglia at Sutton Hoo), these were an exception.

In the East, where the Eastern Roman (known to historians as Byzantine) Empire weathered the crisis, things were very different. In Egypt, 6th-century papyri reveal a world where complex financial and commercial activity survived, and imperial tax collectors were unceasing in their predations. The large numbers of copper coins that survive on archaeological sites indicate that small-scale commercial transactions in local markets continued, and there was even an expansion of commercial settlement in the limestone zone of northern Syria, where towns as such Serjilla were established in the 5th century and thrived on the olive oil trade.

Byzantine goods circulated within the empire (which succeeded in holding onto eastern North Africa, Turkey, the Near East and the Balkans), but an export trade of sorts also remained. North African red-slip tableware and olive oil, which had dominated the market in the western Mediterranean, still appear on coastal sites in the 6th century. That links persisted even as far as India is suggested by the gift of an elephant from a "king of the Indians" to the Emperor Heraclius (reigned 610-41). New trading routes were even pioneered, from Clysma (Suez) to the Aksumite kingdom of northern Ethiopia and Yemen, while imperial patronage of building projects ensured the survival of the marble quarries of Proconnesus on the island of Marmara.

Yet the late antique flourishing illustrated by the beautiful mosaic town plans of the Madaba map was not to last. Plague hit the Byzantine Empire in 541-42, and a protracted struggle with the Persian Sasanian Empire to the east both sapped manpower and morale. It had more direct effects on trade, as from the 6th century the Romans forbade the sale of copper and iron to the Persians, while the Persians imposed punitive tariffs, inflating the price of silk travelling westward. The conquest of the Byzantine Near East by Islamic armies in the 630s dealt a deathblow to the old system. Trade survived, but its form, the trading centres and the political masters who directed that trade were transformed in the centuries that followed (see pages 40–3).

The Amber Road

The map, from the Amber Combine in Kaliningrad, is a modern portrayal of a region which was for a long time the sole source of one of trade's most mysterious commodities. The amber of which it is composed was mined along northern Europe's Baltic coastline, a region from where, for the past 5,000 years, the lustrous shiny gemstone has been exported southwards down a network of trade routes to the Mediterranean and beyond.

A fossilised form of resin which had oozed from ancient pine trees around 40 million years ago, amber fascinated the ancients. Around 600BC, the Greek scholar Thales of Miletus noted that when rubbed, it attracted straw, the first recorded observation of static electricity. Other ancient authors were attracted to more fantastical theories. The Roman naturalist Pliny thought amber was the solidified tears of the Heliades, the daughters of the sun god, as they lamented the death of their brother Phaethon, who had taken their father's chariot and driven it too close to the Earth, almost scorching it to ashes. The 1st-century AD physician Dioscorides believed it might be the solidified urine of lynxes, with the fierier-coloured samples coming from the male.

Whatever its origins, amber was highly prized for use in jewellery. From the Baltic, where it could be easily harvested from beaches, it was traded down the Vistula and Dniester rivers and then to the Danube, from where it was filtered east down into the Balkans or west to the Adriatic. Amber beads were found both in Mycenaean graves in Greece dating from around 1500BC and on the funerary breast ornament of the Egyptian pharaoh Tutankhamun, who died in 1323BC.

By the time of the Roman Empire, amber was the height of fashion. So keen were the Romans to discover its source that under Nero (reigned 54-68), the master of the imperial gladiatorial school sent a mission to investigate. Though the details of where its leader went are shadowy, he came back weighed down with hundreds of pounds of amber. From then, the Roman amber route thrived, and large quantities of Roman coins are found in the southern Baltic, peaking between 138 and 180.

But then, as pressure from barbarian tribes on the Roman frontier grew after the 3rd century, the Amber Road was cut and trade almost ceased. It was not revived until the Teutonic Knights conquered Prussia between 1226 and 1283 and secured a monopoly on the amber trade (saving only a few exemptions, including the fishermen of Gdansk). A tradition of amber working grew up in Russia, whose most notable piece was the Amber Room, a jewel- and amber-encrusted extravaganza made in 1701 from almost 100,000 pieces, which Frederick I of Prussia installed in the Berlin Palace. Peter the Great so admired it on a visit that he was given it as a gift, and had it transported to St Petersburg, where it ended up in the Catherine Palace. There it remained until 1941, when invading German troops dismantled it and shipped it back to the castle at Königsberg (now Kaliningrad). At some point in 1945, the room disappeared, whether in the bombing of the town by Allied aircraft or looted by Soviet troops when they took the town in April is unknown.

The fate of the Amber Room, one of the most spectacular interiors in history, remains as mysterious as the origins of amber itself did to the ancient world.

БАЛТИЙСКОЕ МОРЕ

ЗАЛИВ
КУРСКИЙ

СВЕТЛОГОРСК

ЯНТАРНЫЙ

ПОЛ

КАЛИНИНГРАД

БАЛТИЙСК

ЗАЛИВ КАЛИНИНГРАДСКИЙ

БАГРАТИОНОВСК

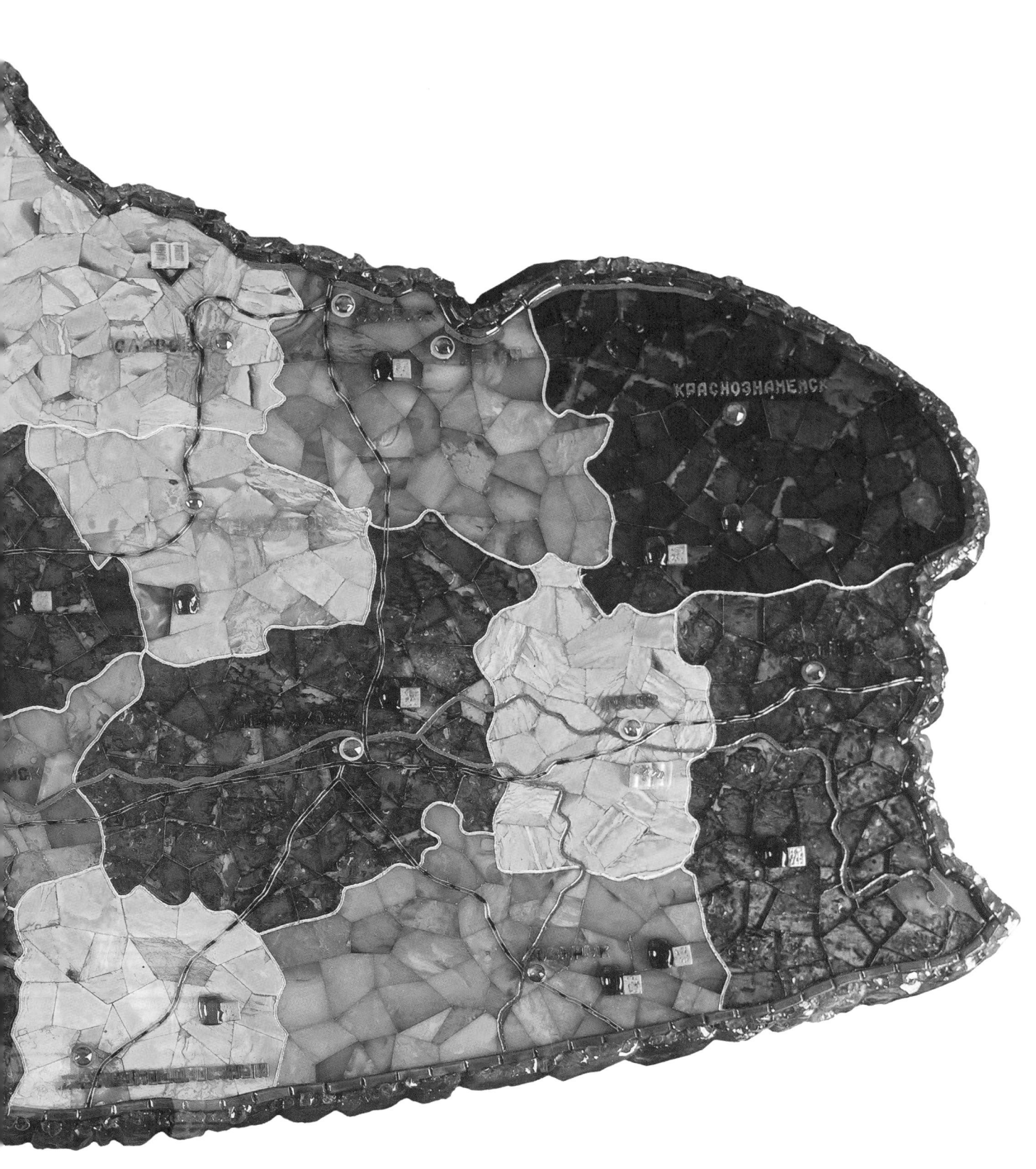

Charlemagne and Carolingian Trade

The Flemish cartographer Petrus Bertius's 1623 map of the Carolingian Empire of Charlemagne shows the 8th-century Frankish emperor's conquests stretching from his French heartland out into Saxony, the north of Spain and as far as northern Hungary. It was the nearest Europe had come to unity since the fall of the Roman Empire. Bertius knew a thing or two about the pitfalls of disunity: raised in the Netherlands during its 80-year revolt against the Spanish, he had fallen foul of his ardently Protestant peers at Leiden University for his pro-Catholic views and had defected to the France of Louis XIII, to whom he dedicated this map.

Charlemagne built on the work of his father Pepin the Short (reigned 751-768), who had deposed the last of the moribund Merovingian dynasty, installed himself as king and reinvigorated the realm. Charlemagne's 46-year reign saw a series of campaigns of conquest, which culminated in his coronation as emperor in 800. Although the levers available to him to encourage economic growth and trade were as nothing compared to those of the old Roman emperors, a decree in 802 enforced uniform measures throughout Francia and a new currency, the *livre carolinienne*, based on a pound of silver, set a standard for the rest of Europe.

Northwest European trade was already reviving, based around *emporia*, or trading centres, along the coastline, such as Quentovic near Étaples in France, Dorestad in the Netherlands and Hamwic (Southampton) in England. As well as acting as the conduits for local goods such as the Ipswich ware pottery found in large numbers in eastern England, they helped the movement of grain, wine, furs and luxury goods which sparked the economy of Europe to life.

The revival was comparatively short-lived. In 793 the first attack by Scandinavian raiders hit Lindisfarne in northeastern England. For 150 years the coastlines of northwestern Europe were terrorised by Viking warriors who radically disrupted political and economic life. Charlemagne's empire disintegrated in the 830s, ravaged by these raids and civil wars between his grandchildren. The emporia contracted and, as ever in times of political turmoil, trade shrank.

Yet the Vikings themselves were also traders – if opportunistic ones – and from the 760s they set up small posts in the east such as Staraya Ladoga, near modern St Petersburg, and then pushed inland down the Volga towards Novgorod and Kiev. They alternately attacked and traded with Constantinople and established links with Arab traders, which led to huge quantities of Arabic silver coins (or dirhams) appearing in hoards back in Scandinavia. One Viking trader, Ohthere, even appeared at the court of Alfred the Great (despite his countrymen's attempts to conquer England) and told the assembled court of his trading in the far north of Norway, where he levied tribute on the local Finnish tribes, taking animal skins and whale bones to barter farther south.

Charlemagne too established long-distance trade and diplomatic links, and in 802 he received an Asian elephant named Abul Abbas from the Abbasid caliph Harun al-Rashid. It was the first such beast seen in northern Europe since antiquity, and the emperor was so proud of it that in 810 he sent it on an expedition against the Danes, intending to terrify them into submission. Unfortunately, the beast expired just after the crossing of the Rhine.

Elephants, like empires, were ephemeral things.

IMPERII
CAROLI MAGNI
et vicinarum regionum
DESCRIPTIO,
Dedicata et inscripta
LVDoVICo,
REGI, VICToRI,
ET DEFENSORI eCCLeSIæ
CHRIStI.
ab Auctore Petro Bertio
zyusdem Cosmographo.

ABODRITI
WENEDI
AISTI
WILZI, SCLAVI
WELATABI
LILONES SMELDINGI
SCLA VI
SORABI
SCLAVI
BOIEMANI SCLAVI
Mara hen ses sclaui
ICARIA
STIRIA
PANNONIA
SVPERIOR
WINIDI
PANNONIA
INFERIOR
CROATIA
ISTRIA
LIBVRNIA
Dalmatia

MARE ADRIATICVM.

MARE HETRVSCVM

CALABRI

MARE IONIVM

NEI PARS

DACIA MEDITER
RANEA
DACIA
RI
PENSIS
DACIA ALPESTRIS

Moesia
Superior
Moesia inferior
BVLGARIA
THRA CIA

PONTI
EVXINI
PARS

MACEDO
NIA

THESSALIA

ACHAIA

POLOPON
NESVS
MESSE

Propontis

ASIÆ
PARS

MARE ÆGÆVM
MARE MYR
TOVM MARE ICARIVM

CYCLADES
INSVLÆ

MARE CRETICVM

CRETA

MARE CARPA
THIVM

MARE LIBYCVM

NOMINA MENSIVM FRANCICA
Carolus Magnus mensibus iuxta patriam linguam vocabula imposuit, quam ante id
tempus partim Latinis partim Barbaris nominibus appellarentur. Eginhardus in eius vita

Ianuarius,	Wintermonth.	Iulius.	Hewimonth.
Februarius,	Hornung.	Augustus.	Arenmonth.
Martius.	Lintzmonth.	September.	Herbstmonth.
Aprilis.	Ostermonth.	October.	Wynmonth.
		November.	Windmonth.

وهذه صورة العراق

وامام دجلها ان المصرة البصرة مدينة عظيمة لم تكن في ايام العجم وانما احطها المسلمون ايام
عمر بن الخطاب ومصرها عتبة بن غزوان عنه خطط وقد اكلها وسط اليوم طريفها البادية مقدشا

Trade in the Islamic World

Abu Ishaq al Istakhri's late 10th-century map of Iraq, shown on the left, comes from his *Book of Roads and Kingdoms*, a compilation of knowledge about the Islamic Empire and the wider world, which included 21 provincial maps, a world map and texts describing them. Beautifully drawn, yet stylised, it shows the River Tigris boldly striking through the map's centre, with the round city of Baghdad, the capital of the Abbasid empire, at its centre. Roads linking main centres are displayed, but there is little of the surrounding geographical features. It is a map whose focus is links and caravans, as befits a trading culture.

Right from its origins, Islam and trade were inextricably linked: the Prophet Muhammad was a merchant in his early adulthood, trading as far as Syria, and his home town Mecca sat athwart a northern Arabian trade and pilgrimage route that brought it great prosperity. When Islamic armies emerged from the Arabian Peninsula in the 630s, conquering first Syria and Palestine, and then Egypt and Persia, they seized the western end of the traditional trading networks that had led from China to the Mediterranean. By the 720s, when they completed the conquest of Khorasan – the region east and north of Persia, which included venerable trading cities such as Samarkand – the role of Muslim merchants in this eastern trade was unrivalled. Present in China as early as the 7th century, they established mercantile colonies in Canton (now Guangzhou) and Zaitun (now Quanzhou), bringing back silk, ceramics and paper. The last was much in demand at the caliphal court at Baghdad, where the Bayt al-Hikma – the "House of Wisdom" established by al-Mansur (reigned 754-775) – acted as a centre for translating classical manuscripts into Arabic. The Chinese Tang and, later, Song emperors were more than happy to encourage this trade, as the state levied a tax of 30 per cent of the value of inbound goods.

On the return journey, via newly established trading settlements at Nishapur, Isfahan and Hamadan, went silk, horses and grain.

Baghdad, itself another of al-Mansur's foundations in 762, was geographically well placed at the heart of this huge trading network, but as the Abbasid empire fragmented in the 9th century, its grip on trade weakened. Groups such as the Samanids (819-999) gained control of the eastern empire and diverted trade from China and India northwards through Russia, from where tens of thousands of Arabic dirhams made their way to treasure hoards in Scandinavia.

As so often in the history of trade, periods of political unity brought upturns in mercantile fortunes. When the Seljuks reunited much of the western part of the former Islamic Empire under their rule from the late 10th century, trade once again revived, even with the Christian Byzantine Empire to the north (although after the stunning Seljuk defeat of Emperor Romanos IV at Manzikert in 1071, which led to the near collapse of the empire, it dried up again).

The collapse of the Seljuk Empire after the death of Malik Shah in 1092 brought further turmoil to the Levant, and the arrival of the army of the First Crusade in Syria in 1097 – which captured a slice of the coast of Syria and Palestine and established a series of Christian-ruled states there – threatened to stifle the Muslim rulers' westward trade.

Yet it did not do so, for as well as the military confrontation of the Crusades, there were long-standing links between Christians and Muslims in the Mediterranean. The 1154 world map of the Arab geographer al-Sharif al-Idrisi, shown overleaf, demonstrates this occasional surprising closeness.

Born in Morocco to the ruling Idrisid house, he travelled for almost a decade in Europe, including to France and England, before arriving in Sicily in 1138. There, he took service at the court of Roger II, whose enlightened policies included a keen appreciation of the value of Islamic scholarship. In order to "know accurately the details of his land and master them with precise knowledge" Roger commissioned al-Idrisi to compile a world map. This was completed in 1154 and was, in its original form, inscribed on an enormous silver disc.

Al-Idrisi's world broadly reflects Arab knowledge of the time, though its outlines of Spain and Italy – realms closely tied to Roger's – are more refined (and those of the British Isles and Scandinavia sketchy in the extreme). The Mediterranean lands still had a sense of unity. Grain travelled from Alexandria, as it had done for over a millennium, but now diverted to Baghdad rather than Rome or Constantinople. Into the Islamic states established in Iberia after the Muslim invasion of 711 flowed precious stones, silk and gold from the south and east, with slaves, timber and grain arriving from the Christian kingdoms to the north.

By the 11th century, as economic activity in Europe in general revived, the rise of maritime republics in Italy such as Genoa and Venice (see pages 56–9) further restored the integration of the Mediterranean

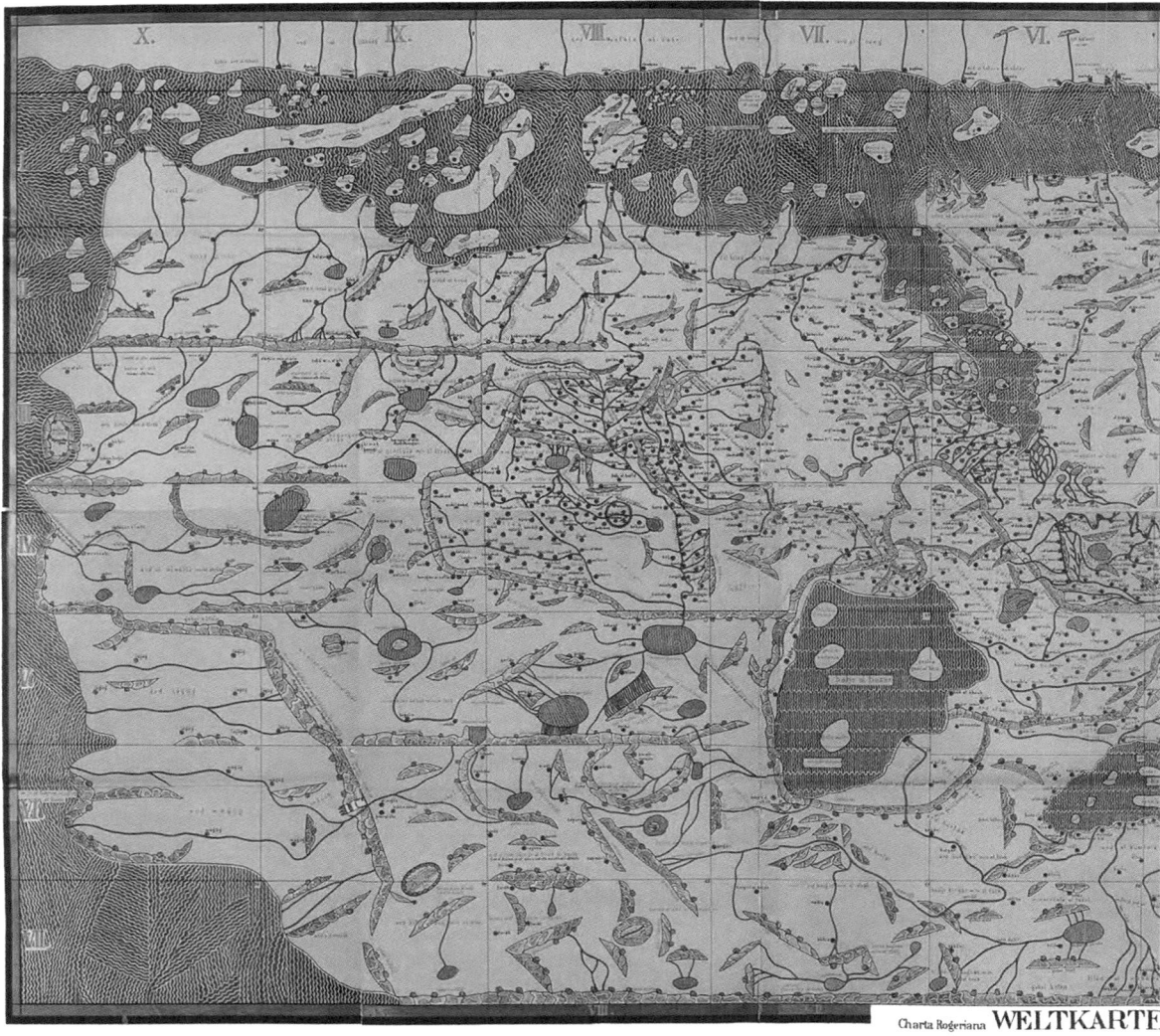

world, as the Italian galleys travelled east in search of sugar and spices, trading equally with the Christian Crusader states and their supposed Muslim enemies.

The Muslim world itself, despite an increasing level of political fragmentation – as the last remnants of the Abbasid caliphate were brutally snuffed out by Mongol invaders in 1258 – retained a sense of cultural unity which helped trading networks survive. In 1325 the Moroccan traveller Ibn Battuta could still set out on a lengthy odyssey from his home town of Tangier that took him across the Islamic world, to Egypt and Mecca, and then to India. There he spent several years in the service of the erratic sultan of Delhi Muhammad ibn Tuhgluq, whose acquisitive nature

extended to scholars as well as provinces, and who forced his guest to act as a *qadi*, a religious judge. On escaping the sultan's clutches, Ibn Battuta made his way via the Maldives and the Malay Peninsula to visit Zaitun in China, where he complained that the local fashion for paper money meant nobody would take his silver dirham coins. Finally, in 1349 he returned home to Morocco, living proof that seven centuries after their first establishment, the trading networks of the Islamic world were still vibrant and active.

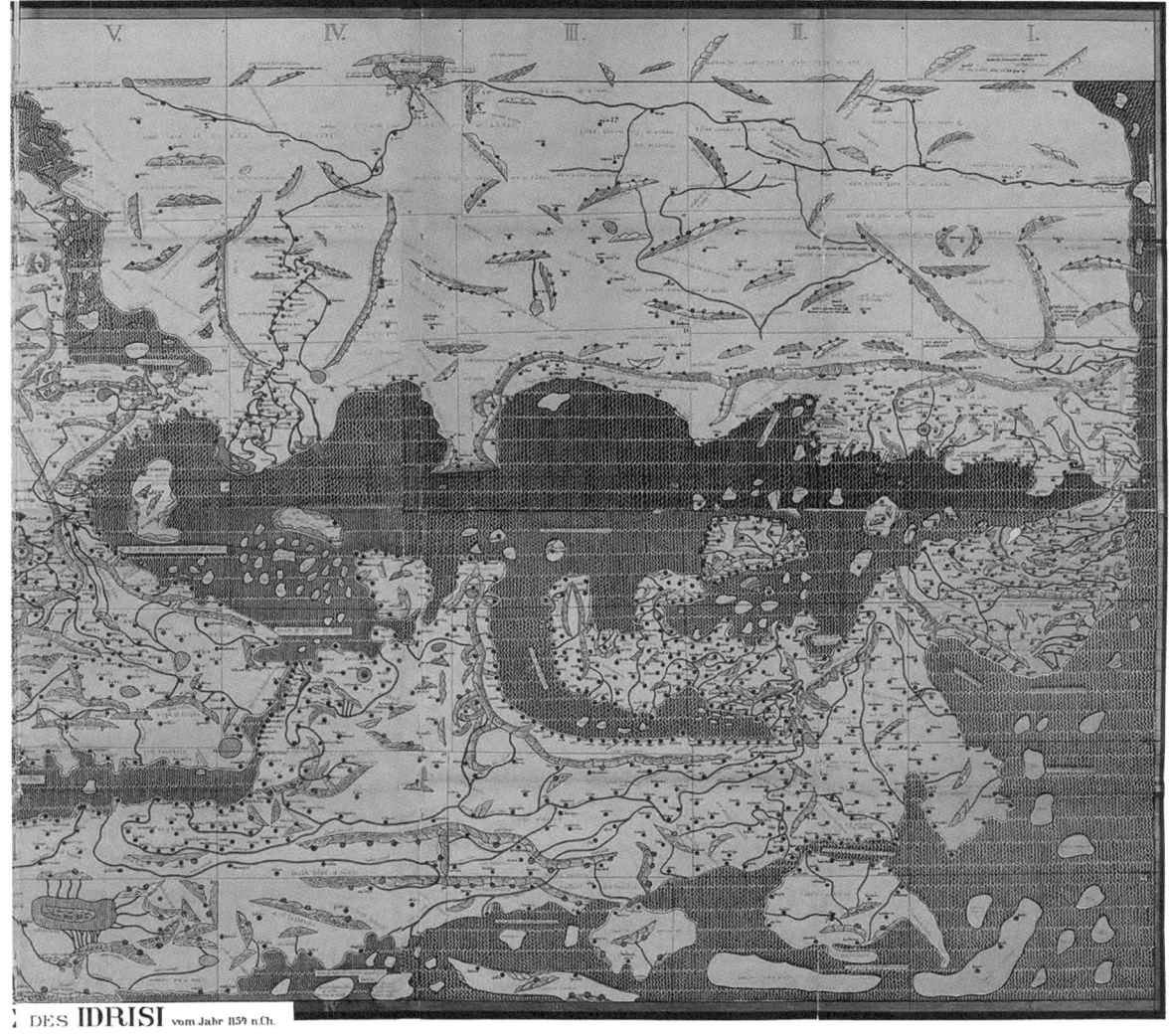

DES IDRISI vom Jahr 1159 n.Ch.

Europe and the World in 1300

The Hereford *Mappa Mundi* is a hauntingly beautiful medieval view of the world. Compiled around the year 1300, it is more a theological statement than a geographical one and bears the name of "Richard of Haldingham or Lafford". The author's knowledge, or at least his attention to detail, was sketchy, as the gilded labels for Europe and Africa have been switched. He was more comfortable with the Christian narrative, as biblical events, such as the expulsion of Adam and Eve from the Garden of Eden, predominate, while unicorns and mandrakes populate the corners of the globe where the compiler's direct sources were lacking.

It is an irony that the *Mappa Mundi* was created just as knowledge of the world outside Europe was growing and European traders were again accessing wider trading networks. The continent's economy was expanding, fuelled by advances such as the three-field system (in which crops were rotated, which increased the land's productive yield) which helped the population grow from around 40 million in 1000 to around double that three centuries later. Commercial fairs, most notably those in Champagne – whose cycle of six fairs, centred around Bar-sur-Aube, Lagny, Provins and Troyes in eastern France drew traders from as far afield as Germany and northern Italy – also helped reinvigorate long-distance trade.

Among those who took advantage of the more favourable conditions were Catalan merchants, operating from bases in Majorca and Valencia which King Jaime of Aragon had seized from Muslim emirs in 1229 and 1238. They established merchant colonies along the coast of north Africa, at Ceuta, Bougie (now Bejaïa) and Tunis, where they bought gold dust, wool, dried fruits and slaves in exchange for grain, cloth and silver. The Catalans pushed even farther, aided by their development of portolan charts – mariners'

maps based on practical observation rather than biblical analysis – and reached the Canary Islands, which they attempted, unsuccessfully, to colonise in the 1340s.

In the east, the keenness of European powers to circumvent the grip of the Muslim states on the western end of the Silk Road led them to send ambassadors to the court of the Mongol khans, whom they believed they might convert to Christianity. The Franciscan friar John of Plano Carpini set out with letters from Pope Innocent IV in 1245, but was rewarded only with a peremptory demand from the new khan Güyük that the Pope come and swear allegiance to him. William of Rubruck, another Franciscan, sent out by Louis IX of France, reached the Mongol court at Karakorum in 1254. He was received politely, but inconclusively by Möngke Khan, although he did provide a detailed account of Mongol customs, such as the felt yurts in which they lived, and encountered Nestorian Christians and several European traders, including a French silversmith.

There were travellers who went the other way too. The Uighur Nestorian monk Rabban Bar Sauma departed China in the 1270s on a pilgrimage to the Holy Land, but political instability in the region prevented him from reaching his destination and he settled in Persia, from where, in 1287 the ruling Ilkhan Argun despatched him as an ambassador to the Pope and European kings. Among those whom he met were Philip IV of France, Pope Nicholas IV and, on a side trip to Bordeaux, Edward I of England. Ironically, just as the compiler of the *Mappa Mundi* was struggling to comprehend the outer margins of the world, that world had already come to England.

The Trans-Saharan Gold Trade

In one sense Abraham Cresques's 1375 map, known as the "Catalan Atlas", is a straightforward portolan chart. Its characteristic lines criss-cross in the sea to create a pattern of diamonds and a guide for 14th-century sailors to the maritime routes and coastlines of the lands to which they ventured. Yet the Catalan Atlas's true interest lies in the interior, lavishly decorated with illustrations, most notable of which is the enthroned king in the far south, his gold crown and sceptre a symbol of the wealth of a man who is reflecting on the huge nugget of gold held in his hand.

This monarch, Mansa Musa of Mali, was the heir to a long-standing tradition of gold-trading across the vast sandy expanse of the Sahara Desert even farther south and beyond the scope of the Catalan Atlas. Made possible through the importation of camels into North Africa from Arabia and their adoption as pack animals, the gold trade helped the rise of a series of West African empires, beginning with the Ghana kingdom, which until the 11th century dominated the routes that terminated at Sijilmasa in Morocco and Ifriqiya in Tunisia.

The Arabs brought both settlers to the northern fringes of Africa and the new religion of Islam, but the Ghana rulers, though becoming Muslims, resisted political penetration by the newcomers and managed to keep secret the sources of their wealth, in gold mines at Bure and Bambouk in the Senegal Valley. The caravans which traversed the desert brought salt from the mines at Idjil in the western desert, as well as slaves, captured or bought in the savannah lands south of the Sahara. Some 28 million of them ended up in the slave markets of North Africa and the Middle East by the late 17th century, although, as up to 80 per cent died on the gruelling journey – a toll far higher even than that of the slave ships of the Middle Passage across the Atlantic (see pp 134–5) – the economic and social cost to societies on which the slave traders preyed was devastating.

Even so, gold remained the principal commodity demanded by markets and rulers around the Mediterranean. Yet by the 12th century, Ghana's power had waned as the network of trade routes extended further southwards, enriching local rulers there, while the strengthening of political power in Morocco under the Almoravids and Marinids threatened Ghana's northern flank. It lost control of the gold trade and was supplanted by the Mali Empire founded by Sundiata Keita in about 1235. His descendant Mansa Musa, who came to the throne about 1312, was a man who embraced religion and wealth with equal vigour. In 1324, he resolved to fulfil his duty as a devout Muslim and perform the haj, or pilgrimage to Mecca. He did not stint on his preparations and his caravan was 60,000-strong, including 12,000 young slaves clad in garments of fine silk. As outriders, 500 of these went ahead bearing staffs of pure gold to warn of his coming. When the caravan reached Cairo, its spending was so lavish that the value of gold instantly sank and prices in the markets soared. The seemingly limitless resources of the Malian king became so stretched that he was forced to borrow from moneylenders. On his final return to Mali, having collected sundry religious scholars and architects to beautify his capital at Niani, he paid off hias Cairo creditors in one go, causing the price of gold to crash again. It was an early example of the dangers of market manipulation.

Built on gold, Mansa Musa's empire was soon tarnished. When the Moroccan traveller Ibn Battuta visited his successor Mansa Suleiman in 1352, he was fobbed off with gifts of bread rather than the customary gold. The empire began to dissolve in the 15th century, displaced by the empire of Songhai. Even this faced a new competitor in the gold trade in the form of the Portuguese, whose 14th-and 15th-century explorations along the coast of West Africa were in part motivated by a desire to bypass the trans-Saharan routes. Before long, new sources of gold and silver from South America reduced the importance of the trans-Saharan trade (though not the links between West Africa and Europe, which, as Europeans seized direct control of parts of the coast, became, if anything, more direct). Lords of the desert the Songhai may have been, but they were no longer the kings of the gold trade.

The Silk Road

The 12th-century stone map of China, displayed overleaf, shows an empire united and self-contained. Yet the inclusion of lands beyond its borders is a hint that, for all its strength and wealth, China depended on trade, and the most vital artery for this was also its most vulnerable: the collection of routes arcing from its western border, which became known as the Silk Road.

By the time this map was constructed in 1136, that network was already under threat. The Song dynasty, which had begun rather unpromisingly in 960, when its first ruler Taizu was declared emperor by his troops as he lay helpless after a monumental drinking bout, became one of China's most splendid. Under it the country became an economic powerhouse as more productive strains of rice from southeast Asia provided an agricultural bounty, and the construction of the Grand Canal linked its capital Bianjing (now Kaifeng) on the Yellow River with the southern waterways centred on the Yangtze.

Yet Song China had a nomad problem, as had previous dynasties, the Han and the Tang. The Silk Road – whose name was in fact coined by the 19th-century German scholar Ferdinand von Richthofen – carried far more than silk, but its most precious commodity was both an attractive target for nomadic raiders such as the Xiongnu (cousins to the Huns who devastated the late Roman Empire) and a useful diplomatic incentive for them to desist.

The merchant caravans which snaked out of the gates of the Song capital, and its rather more splendid Tang predecessor Chang'an (which in the 8th century had a million inhabitants, which made it the world's largest city), were generally secure until they crossed China's frontiers. Those borders had been pushed far to the west by the Han emperor Wudi (141-87BC), whose efforts to form an alliance with the Yuezhi nomads against the Xiongnu, their mutual foe, had resulted in the occupation of a string of oasis towns such as Dunhuang, Turfan, Khotan and Kashgar.

This spearhead of Chinese-controlled territory in central Asia opened up tantalising prospects. It put Han merchants within striking distance of the Iranian plateau and marked the first real opening of the full length of the Silk Road. That 4,000-mile (6,500-kilometre) distance from Chang'an to the Mediterranean was rarely traversed in its entirety by a single merchant, but a series of camel trains, middlemen and barters transferred goods between two empires – the Roman and Chinese – which were scarcely aware of each other's existence. That silk did reach the Roman Empire is clear: Pliny the Elder lamented in his *Natural History* (AD77) that fashionable ladies in Rome were so fond of it that its import was costing the huge sum of 100 million sesterces a year and threatened to beggar the empire.

The first stages of the long journey – which would take up to a year for any intrepid enough to brave it – would be familiar enough to many merchants. Pressing on towards the Tarim Basin, the caravans reached Dunhuang, the main staging post in China's central Asian empire, and from there the routes diverged. A northerly one exited the city through the Jade Gate and edged to the north of the forbidding Taklimakan Desert, whose nicknames – "the sea of death" and "the place you enter but do not leave" – give an indication of why the straighter route across its red sand dune expanse was rarely attempted. The northern way passed through the Turfan oasis, and at Kashgar rejoined its southern counterpart (which began at Dunhuang's Sun Gate), which instead visited Khotan and Yarkand. From there the road became more precipitous, involving navigating the foothills of the Tien Shan range and the perilous crossing of the Pamirs, before reaching more level ground in Iran.

Along this vast distance, a huge variety of goods were traded. Eastwards came ivory, silver (in payment for the silk) and novel plants such as saffron and the narcissus (which became a favourite subject for Chinese court painters). New foodstuffs travelled east also, including grapes and spinach, which was in great demand for Daoist adepts, whose search for an elixir of life made them prone to ingesting poisons to which they believed it an antidote. Most of all, however, the Chinese wanted horses, and in particular a breed they called the "heavenly horse", which was believed to sweat blood and be related to dragons, which made it both fierce and swift. They also craved jade, whose translucent quality gave it an association with immortality. The only known source was near Khotan, and it was used to ensheath the royal dead of the Han dynasty in funerary suits. As late as the 15th century, a huge 1.8-metre-long slab of it (the largest known single piece of jade) formed the lid to the sarcophagus of the last great Mongol conqueror, Timur.

Ideas and new techniques were less tangible – but just as important – travellers along the Silk Road. Paper, produced in China from around AD105, went westwards in the baggage of Arab merchants and gradually supplanted papyrus and parchment, making the production of books more economical. In the opposite direction went Buddhism, which reached China from its Indian homeland around the first century AD and soon established itself as an alternative to the native Confucianism. It set down such deep roots that Chinese Buddhist pilgrims such as Xuanzang trekked the far southern reaches of the Silk Road, back down into India in search of Buddhist religious tracts. When he returned in 645, after an 18-year odyssey, he came with a trove of over 600 texts, which led Emperor Taizong, who had expressly refused permission for him to travel, to shower him with honours (all of which the pious monk refused).

Yet, by the 11th century, the Song control over its frontiers was slipping. New confederations such as the Xi Xia and the Tangut took great slices out of the Song's western provinces, and in the north Jurchen nomads pressed hard against the Great Wall. With their security no longer guaranteed, merchants began to favour maritime routes where they could, and trade along the Silk Road dried up. In 1126, the Jurchen invaded, captured Bianjing and drove the Song southwards, where they set up an imperial capital in exile at Hangzhou. Although the Jurchen became partially Sinicised, rebranding themselves as the Jin dynasty and trying to encourage trade, a disunited China shorn of its precious oasis trading towns was not such an attractive prospect for traders. The emergence of a new nomadic power, the Mongols, and the destructive whirlwind that their warlord Genghis Khan unleashed on China in 1215 – whose effects killed an estimated 35 million of its population of 115 million – then threatened to destroy the Silk Road entirely. That it did not and that the Silk Road in fact enjoyed a new golden age are testament to the power of trade (see pages 48–55).

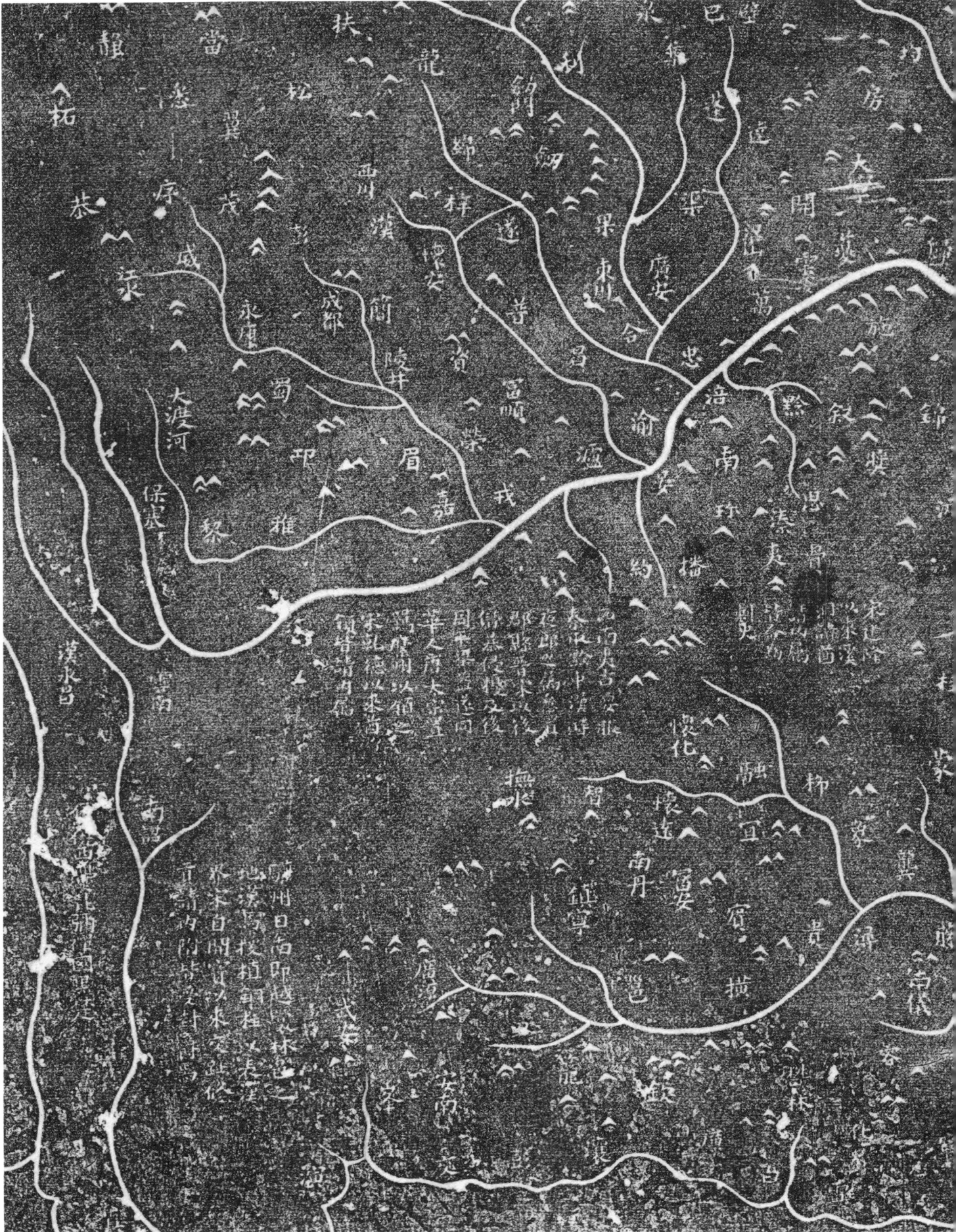

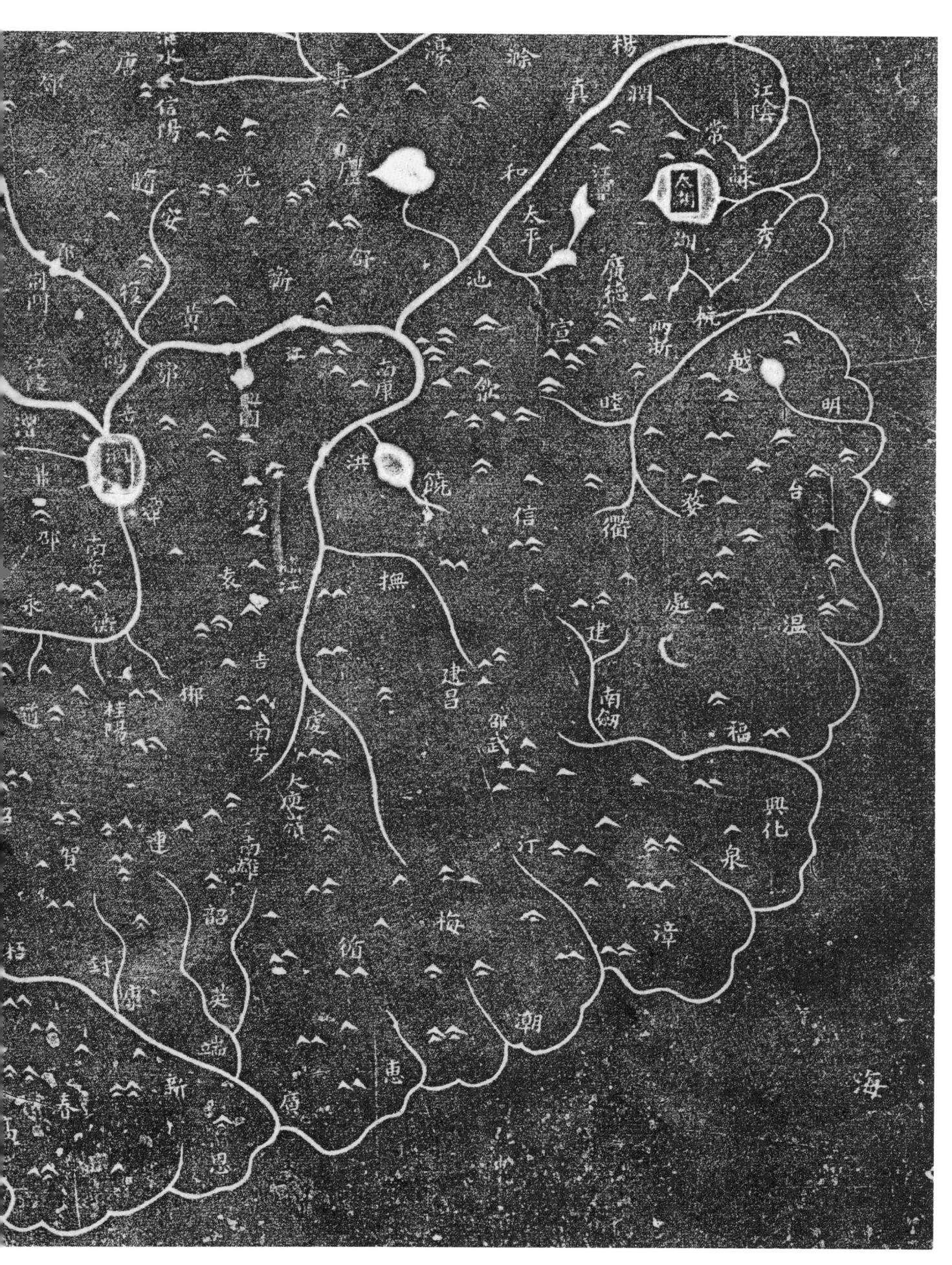

Marco Polo and the Silk Road

Fra Mauro's world map of 1459, oriented with south at the top, is a cartographic masterpiece. Commissioned by Afonso V of Portugal, its high degree of accuracy and scope – it is among the first western maps to portray Japan (labelled as Cipangu) – must have pleased its patron. Although its creator was a Camaldolese monk, his base in Venice allowed him access to the finest sources from his home city's substantial trading empire.

Among those were the travel accounts of the young Venetian merchant Marco Polo, who had spent 20 years travelling in the Mongol Empire between 1275 and 1295. The Mongols had fallen like a thunderbolt on northern China, overcoming its northern Jin overlords by 1215. It was a startling achievement by a people who had only united under Genghis Khan nine years before. These horse-borne nomads seemed unlikely to bring anything more than economic doom to a region whose native Chinese Song dynasty had been confined to southern China by the Jin – themselves originally a nomad group – in 1126. Their onslaught was so destructive that China lost a third of its population of 115 million.

It looked certain to spell the end for the Silk Road. Yet, on the contrary, the sheer expanse of the Mongol Empire – which expanded into Persia in the 1250s and as far as Baghdad, which they brutally sacked in 1258 – left its entire length in the hands of a single political master. This stability allowed trade once again to flare into life under the aegis of a *Pax Mongolica* (Mongol Peace). The Mongol institution of the *ortaq*, a partnership under which merchants received financial backing from a member of the Mongol ruling establishment, ensured traders could

operate under the protection of the state, and the *yam*, an imperial postal system, guaranteed that information (and profit) flowed freely.

Into this world Marco Polo arrived at the court of Kublai Khan in 1275, brought there by his father and uncle, who were acting as semi-official envoys between the Mongols and the Pope. Instead of returning home, he secured a position as a roving ambassador, reporting to Kublai on conditions in the provinces, an urgent necessity once the Mongols overcame the last Song resistance and conquered southern China in 1276. When finally he returned home to Venice in 1295, few believed his fantastic tales of lands where cows were sacred, or where a black substance that burnt oozed from vents in the ground. It was only Polo's capture in a naval battle against the Genoese in 1298 and the literary skills of his cellmate Rustichello da Pisa, to whom Marco dictated his memoirs, that ensured his reports survived.

That they did was very much to the profit of Fra Mauro, who plundered them for information for his map. By then, the Silk Road had already closed once more. The Mongol Empire fractured after the death of Kublai Khan in 1294, the squabbling khanates into which it dissolved unable to provide the security within which the long-distance trade prospered. Then, the rise of the Ottoman Empire from the 14th century created a block to European merchants travelling eastward. Although he portrayed the whole world – as it was then known – much of it now consisted of lands through which travellers, and trade, could no longer safely pass.

The Rise of the Maritime Republics

Cristoforo de Grassi's lavish 1597 painting of his home city's port, shown overleaf, harks back to an earlier age. Begun by another painter in 1481, it shows the victorious Genoese fleet entering harbour after a victory against the Ottoman Turks. Proudly dominating the scene is the Lanterna, Genoa's lighthouse, which had welcomed back generations of their predecessors, both mariners and merchants, to the safety of the mother republic.

Genoa's first lighthouse was built in the 12th century, when the city's pre-eminence was far from assured. It formed part of a wave of Italian maritime republics that emerged as European commerce revived in the central Middle Ages. With its central location, Italy was well placed to plug into growing networks in both northern Europe and the Mediterranean. At first, though, much Genoese activity was little more than piracy – in 1087 a joint Pisan-Genoese fleet raided Muslim-controlled Mahdia in Tunisia, bringing back a store of loot – but the commercial activities of Pisa, Genoa and Venice, the principal republics, grew in sophistication.

With its position on the Ligurian coast, Genoa traded north into France and Rhineland Germany and south into the western Mediterranean, where a struggle with Pisa – enriched by its role as a gateway for the textile industry of Tuscany – ended in a defeat for the Pisans at Meloria in 1284. Venice, meanwhile, looked east, assisted by its heritage as a former Byzantine city, which gave it valuable commercial privileges in what was left of the empire.

The cities were aided by their republican constitutions – although heavily dominated by merchant families – which freed them from the crippling exactions that monarchies tended to impose on commercially successful towns. They were also agile, taking advantage of the Crusades to establish bases in the new Latin kingdoms set up after the First Crusade (1096-99). The privileges which the Genoese and Venetians acquired in exchange for transporting and supplying the Crusaders were valuable enough, but the access they gained to the spice trade from the East was even more lucrative. Pepper and ginger were in particular demand in Europe and in return the Italians brought silver, olive oil, and – despite religious qualms against it – slaves.

The Genoese secured even greater privileges when they supported the Byzantines to recover Constantinople in 1261, after its half-century of occupation by western Crusaders. From new commercial colonies at Pera, on Chios in the Aegean, and at Caffa on the Black Sea, Genoa's merchants ranged far and wide, exporting alum and cotton from Turkey, sugar from Cyprus and salt from Ibiza, and establishing contacts as far afield as Flanders and London. The profits were staggering – a single voyage could yield a profit of 100 per cent. Yet the bounty did not last. The rivalry with Venice sapped both cities' strength, and an attritional war that ended with the defeat of Genoa at Chioggia in 1381 was so ruinously expensive that the Genoese accepted the imposition of French sovereignty in 1396.

By the time of Grassi's painting, Genoa's heyday was long over and that of Venice too. The Ottoman Empire, which began as a tiny emirate in western Anatolia in the late 13th century, and which had progressively expanded at the expense of the Byzantine Empire, spilling over into the Aegean and the Balkans from the 14th century, provided a potent competitor. As the empire grew more sophisticated, its merchants took control of key trade routes, particularly into the Black Sea, excluding the maritime republics from the critically important grain trade and extracting privileges from those western traders, such as the Venetians, whom the Ottoman sultan suffered to trade in his domains. By the time Venetian-held Cyprus fell to the Ottomans in 1571, the age of the maritime republics was largely a distant memory.

URBIS GENUÆ PICTURÆ
INIURIA FERE CONSUMPTÆ
EXEMPLUM ILLIUS VETUSTATIS
CAUSA P̄ PRĒS COMMUNIS
MANDARUNT ANNO MDXLVII

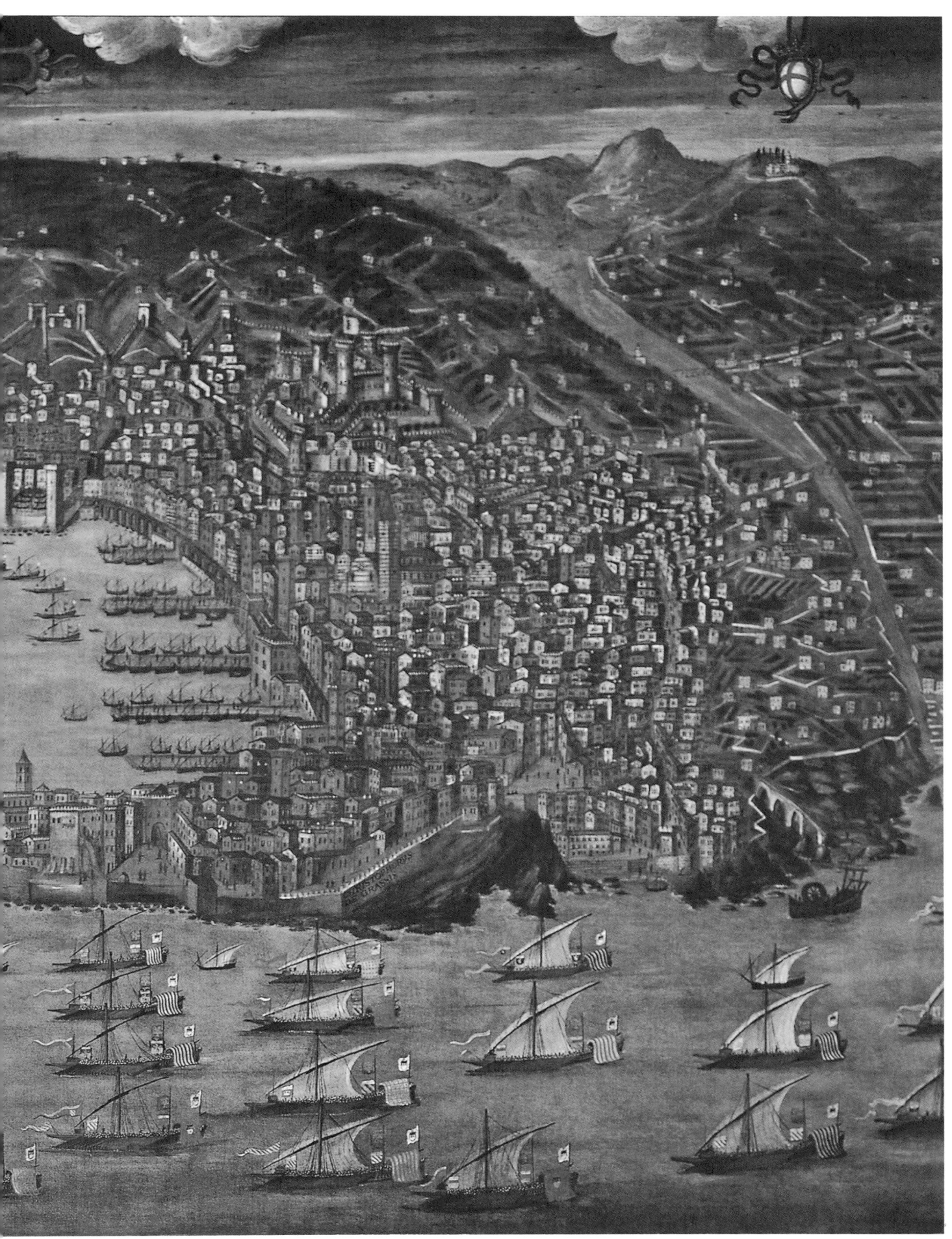

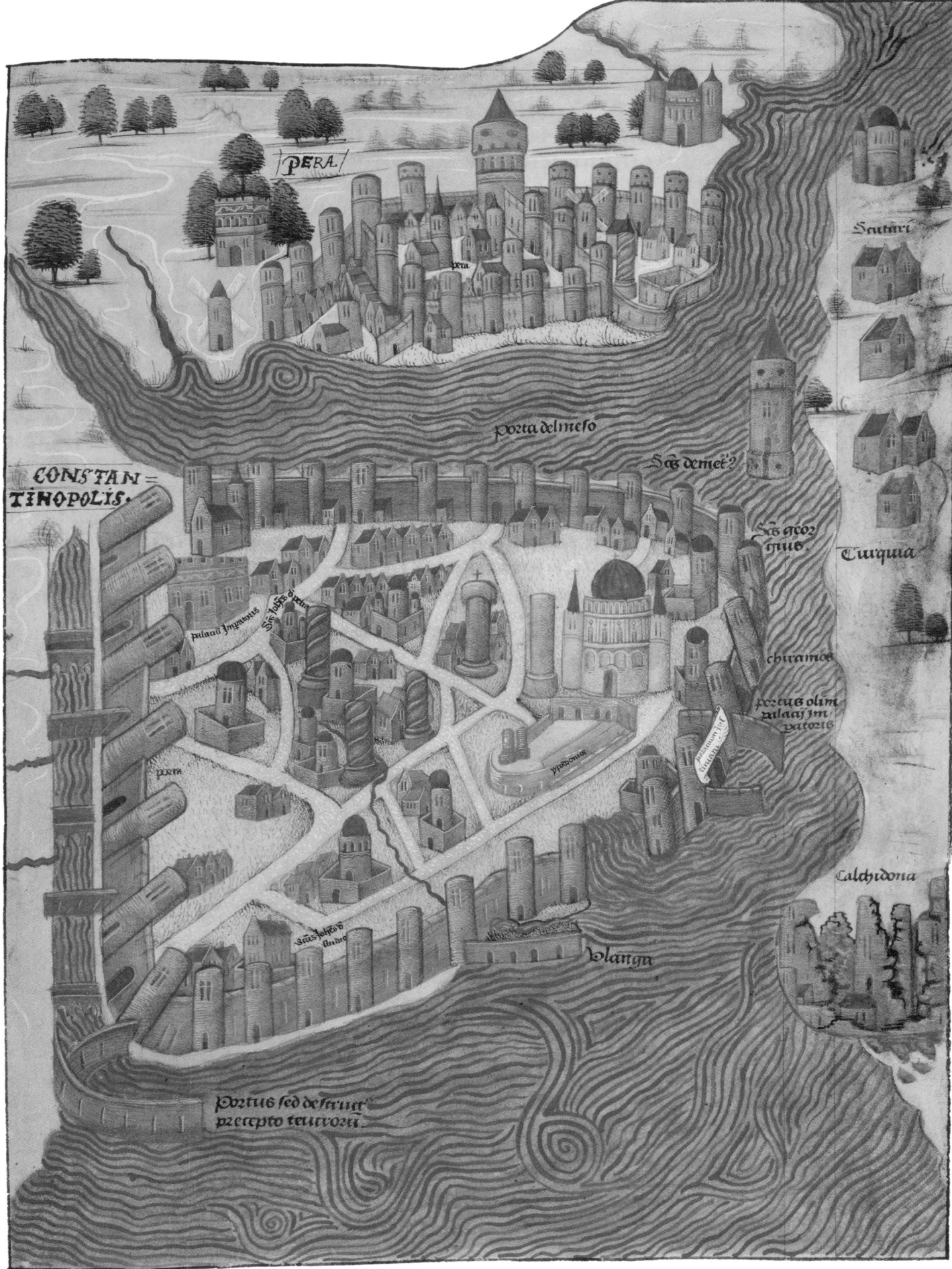

PERA.

pera

Porta del mefo

CONSTAN=
TINOPLIS.

Sᶻᵒ demeᵗ᷑

Sᶻᵒ geoᵗ
gnius

Scutari

Turquia

palaciū Imparius

Sᶜᵗⁱˢ lucꝰ ᵈ pᵉᵗᵉ

chiramos

portus olim
palacij im
patoris

porta

Dᵃlacium Impᵉ
ᵗᵗacioᵗᵘ

Ypodomos

Sᶜᵗⁱˢ Johᵉˢ ᵈ
Studio

Vlanga

Calchidonia

Portus fed deftruᵗᵗ
ꝑ ereptᵒ teutᵗonu

The Venetian Trading Empire

The map of Constantinople, drawn by the Florentine Franciscan friar Cristoforo Buondelmonti after a visit in the 1420s, shows a city on the brink of catastrophe. The imperial monuments and the grand church of Hagia Sophia shown on the right of the map would fall in 1453 to the new power in the region, the Ottoman Turks.

The Ottoman advance threatened another power, that of Venice, which had come far from its humble beginnings as an offshore haven for refugees escaping the barbarian invasions of the 5th century. Originally a Byzantine city, Venice had a love-hate relationship with its parent. Its wealth was founded on trade in slaves and silver with the Byzantine-controlled coastline of the eastern Adriatic, and multiplied further after it received the right to trade freely in the empire as a reward for its aid in a campaign against the Normans in 1081.

The Crusades brought further opportunities, as the Venetians helped ferry the Christian armies to the Levant and in 1124 were granted trading privileges in the new Crusader states there (as well as one-third of the city of Tyre). Grain, olive oil, sugar and wine flowed in to feed a city that expanded to over 110,000 inhabitants in 1340, as well as increasing quantities of spices, most notably pepper, of which the fast Venetian galleys were transporting 3.5 million pounds by the 15th century. With a strong merchant aristocracy and the development of the *commenda*, a mercantile contract that allowed investors to take a defined proportion of both risk and profits, the city's future seemed assured.

The Venetians were masters of strategy and arch-manipulators who were quite happy to maintain close diplomatic relations with the schismatic (in western eyes) Byzantines and the non-Christian Turks. Trade and Venice's prosperity outweighed all

other considerations – sometimes to the frustration of other European powers – but occasionally Venetian manoeuvring trumped good tactical sense. A long rivalry with Genoa endangered their eastern commerce: their temporary replacement by the Genoese as Byzantium's favoured trading partner caused Venice's rulers first to transport the fleet of the Fourth Crusade in 1204, and then to divert it to Constantinople, which it sacked and occupied.

As a reward the Venetians became the "lords of a quarter and half of a quarter" of the Byzantine Empire which the westerners divided between them. They did not exult for long, for in 1261 the Byzantines retook Constantinople and granted all trading privileges to the Genoese. Chastened, the Venetians turned more and more to trading with the rising Muslim powers, first the Mamluks of Egypt and then the Ottomans, which led in 1322 to Venice's merchants being excommunicated by the Pope. Manipulative as ever, the Venetians simply transferred trade to Lajazzo, a Christian enclave in Cilicia (in modern-day Turkey), and religious scruples were satisfied.

The Venetians were exchanging ambassadors with the Ottomans as early as 1397, and so when Mehmet II took Constantinople in 1453, they had prepared the ground well. Their fleets still visited Alexandria and the Black Sea, and wealth poured into the doge's coffers. It was instead the voyage of Vasco da Gama to India in 1497 that caused their downfall: the Venetian pepper trade collapsed in the decades that followed. Venice turned gradually inwards and became embroiled in wars in the Italian peninsula that sapped its strength. Although the Venetians held onto Cyprus until 1571 and Crete as late as 1669, by the time Napoleon put an end to the republic's independence in 1797, its days of trading glory were long gone.

Bruges and the Cloth Trade

Flemish cartographer Frans Hogenberg's map of Bruges appeared in his *Civitates Orbis Terrarum*, a compilation of city plans produced between 1572 and 1617. He had done the main city of his home province proud: its dense network of streets almost fills its city walls, surrounded by a fertile countryside.

At its centre, clearly visible atop the market hall is the belfry, the city's clock tower, constructed in the 1240s. The wealth that funded it came from cloth. Flanders was amongst the most densely populated and industrialised regions in northern Europe: Bruges alone had 46,000 inhabitants in 1340, around half the number of London. As land was reclaimed from the sea, the region's fertility allowed a cluster of medium-sized towns to appear, and a cycle of fairs based in Bruges, Ypres, Lille and Torhout that drew in merchants from the Rhineland, France and England.

What attracted them was textiles. Flanders had long been a producer of woollen cloth and the need for raw material to feed its looms sent Flemish merchants to Britain, where they were found as far north as Berwick in 1248, creating a symbiosis between Flanders and England that tied them together economically and diplomatically.

There were signs early on that Bruges's cloth empire relied on uncertain foundations. As silting cut it off from the sea, outports had to be established, first at Damme in 1180 and then at Sluys in 1280. The increasing importance of the English trade was a weakness too, and in 1270 a full-blown trade war broke out when the Countess of Flanders accused Henry III of not respecting the privileges of Flemish merchants. This led the English king to ban the export of wool to Flanders.

Foreign merchants, who established themselves in Bruges in large numbers – with over 200 merchants from the Hanseatic League settled there by the mid-15th century – were a sign both of success and of vulnerability: their loyalties were fickle and they could just as easily move elsewhere. The setting up by Edward I of England in 1294 of a staple, a single port through which the cloth trade had to go, further loosened the control of the Bruges merchant aristocracy. It was situated there for only a dozen years in the 14th century and from 1363 was fixed for almost two centuries in English-controlled Calais. The Hundred Years' War between France and England was a further blow, as punitive taxes were levied on wool exports to fund the English armies, rising from 6.5 shillings per sack in 1275 to more than six times that level in 1341.

England had developed its own finished cloth trade and so exported less and less wool to Bruges (down to 14,000 sacks annually, from 35,000 half a century before) and exported ever more of its own cloth. The establishment in 1421 of an English mercantile colony in Bruges's upstart rival Antwerp was a sign that the Flemish city's reign as king of cloth was almost over. A ruinous revolt against its Austrian Habsburg overlords ended in defeat in 1485, and by 1511 only a dozen Hanseatic merchants were left in the city. When Henry Wadsworth Longfellow wrote his poem about the Belfry of Bruges in 1845, imagining the "Lombard and Venetian merchants with deep-laden argosies", they were but ghosts.

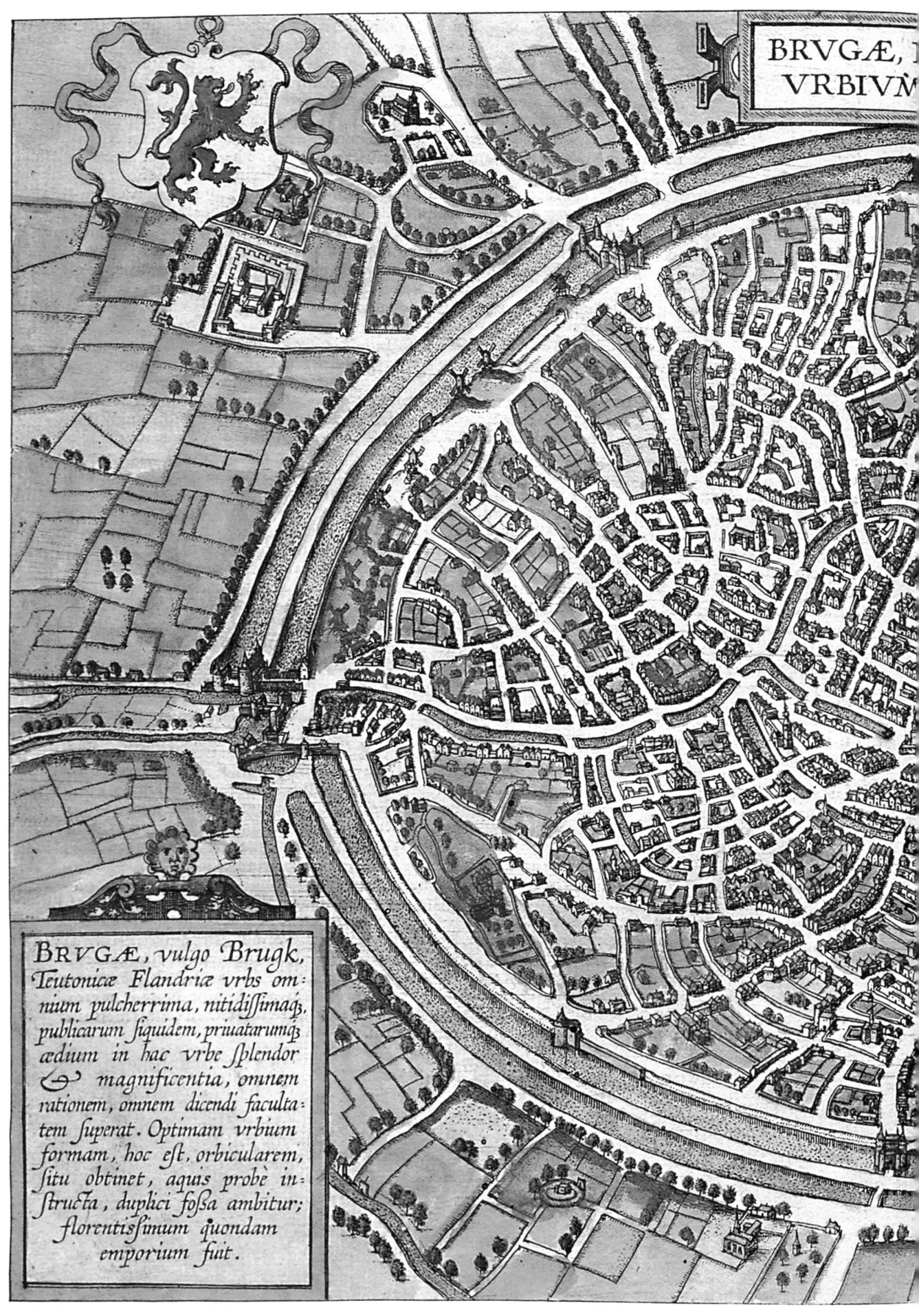

BRVGÆ,
VRBIVM

BRVGÆ, *vulgo* Brugk,
Teutonicæ Flandriæ vrbs om-
nium pulcherrima, nitidiſſimaǭ,
publicarum ſiquidem, priuatarumǭ
ædium in hac vrbe ſplendor
& magnificentia, omnem
rationem, omnem dicendi faculta-
tem ſuperat. Optimam vrbium
formam, hoc eſt, orbicularem,
ſitu obtinet, aquis probè in-
ſtructa, duplici foſſa ambitur;
florentiſſimum quondam
emporium fuit.

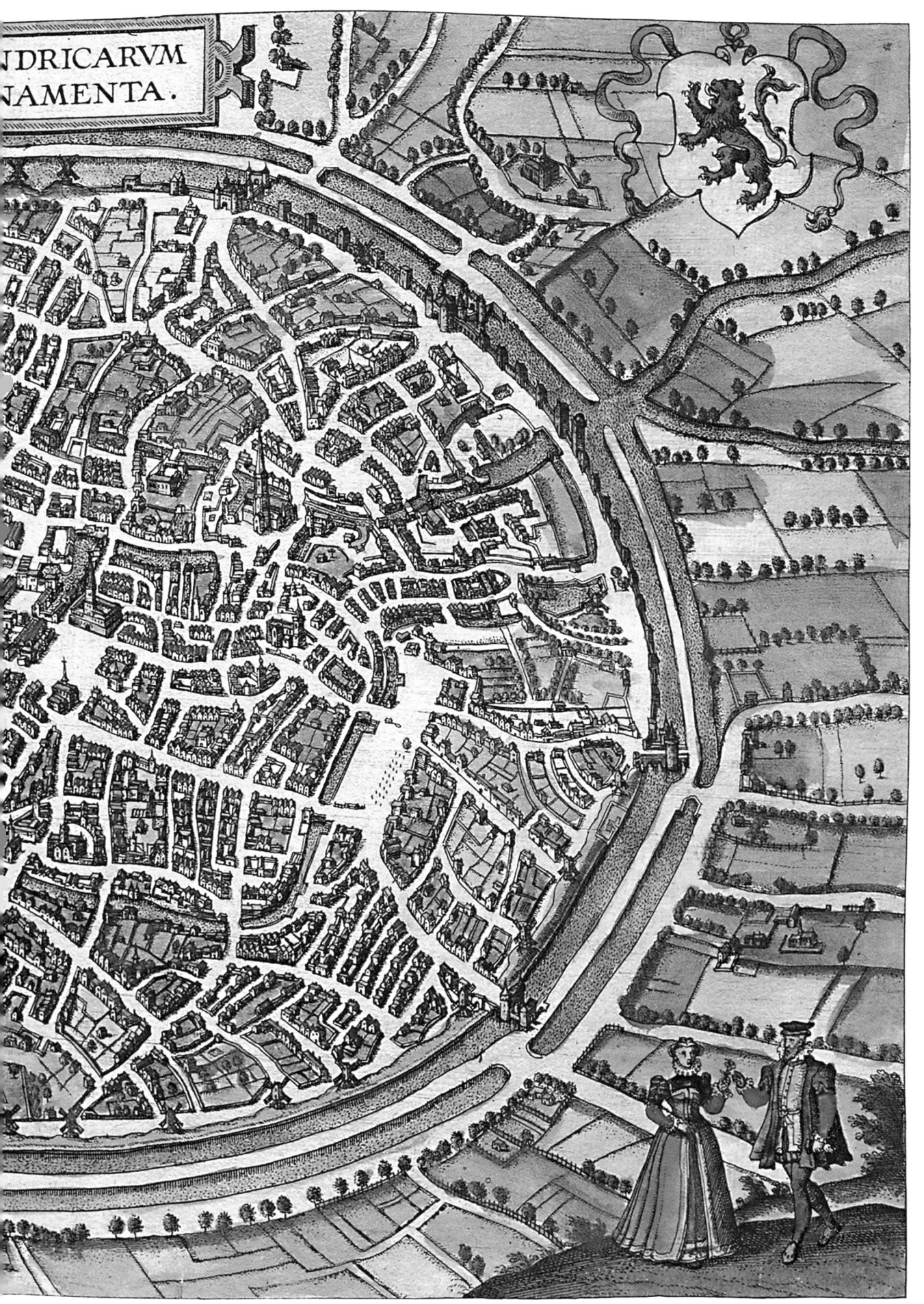

NDRICARVM
NAMENTA.

Plagues and Pandemics

The Catalan Atlas shown overleaf, produced around 1375 by the father and son cartographers Abraham and Jehuda Cresques in the Spanish town of Palma de Mallorca, portrays an image of Europe and North Africa criss-crossed by a dense network of maritime trading routes. Yet scarcely 30 years beforehand those same trade routes had carried the greatest disaster to befall medieval Europe: the Black Death.

Merchants were the medieval world's most inveterate travellers, their caravans and baggage animals acting as ready conduits for the transmission of disease. The plague bacillus *Yersinia pestis* is normally endemic to the Central Asian steppes, where various types of rodent act as reservoirs. When black rats too became infected, the disease spread rapidly through their fleas, which were as happy to bite humans as rodents once their host had died.

In AD541 the plague made its first certain appearance in history, when it struck the Byzantine Empire during the reign of Justinian. The historian Procopius described its advent in Egypt, and the buboes, or swellings of the lymph glands, which accompanied victims' death agonies. At its peak, ten thousand died per day in the imperial capital Constantinople, and trade collapsed in a weakened empire, which, unable to pay or even raise soldiers, succumbed with surprising ease to the Arab Muslim invasions of the 630s.

Plague is a disease of trade, and the decline in trading networks this dislocation caused blocked the main avenues for its spread. The reopening of the Silk Road during the *Pax Mongolica* (Mongol Peace) from the 13th century, though, removed an important epidemiological barrier. Ironically it was the Mongols themselves who acted as the agents of disaster. Plague had reappeared on China's borders around 1331, and by 1346 had reached the Crimea, where it struck the Mongol army besieging the Genoese-controlled port of Caffa (now Feodosiya). As his troops succumbed, the Mongol khan Janibeg performed an early act of bioterrorism by ordering infected corpses to be lobbed into the city. Soon the Genoese too were dying, and, terrified, they fled.

In October 1347, 12 of their galleys docked at the Sicilian port of Messina. Within days, the dead choked the town's streets, and the Black Death scythed northwards through Italy, reaching the Alps by the autumn. Late in the year it struck France, via the port of Marseilles, and then England the following summer. The death rate was appalling, and between a third and half of the population of Europe died. In Europe alone, it claimed the lives of 25 million people. The toll was even worse in the Middle East and, in particular, Egypt.

The world – and with it trade – was rewritten. After months of paralysis, society began to rebuild itself, but in a different form. Labour shortages led to a new balancing between the previously powerless peasantry, who were able to demand higher wages (in Navarre in Spain they doubled between 1350 and 1401-05) and better land tenure. As a consequence, the feudal system began to wither away, and land-intensive activities such as sheep and cattle farming replaced labour-hungry crop-rearing in many areas.

Waves of plague epidemics continued to strike Europe, the Middle East and China in the 14th century (and did not die off completely until the 19th century), generally carrying away the young, who had no resistance, and retarding both population and economic growth. The death toll from the Black Death would not be equalled until the "Spanish" flu pandemic of 1918-19. Possibly originating among US servicemen in Kansas, after the United States joined the First World War in April 1917, the infection spread across Europe and from there to the rest of the world. It received its nickname because Spain, as a non-combatant in the war, was not subject to wartime censorship and so its newspapers reported the disease's spread there freely. Up to 50 million people died worldwide (roughly three times the death toll of the war itself), and many businesses and individuals suffered terrible economic hardship. Although the effects on trade are difficult to disentangle from the devastation caused in Europe by the war and the subsequent rebound, it was a while before output recovered. It was a warning that in an increasingly connected world, the progress of the Black Death from the Crimea to England would seem like a leisurely stroll.

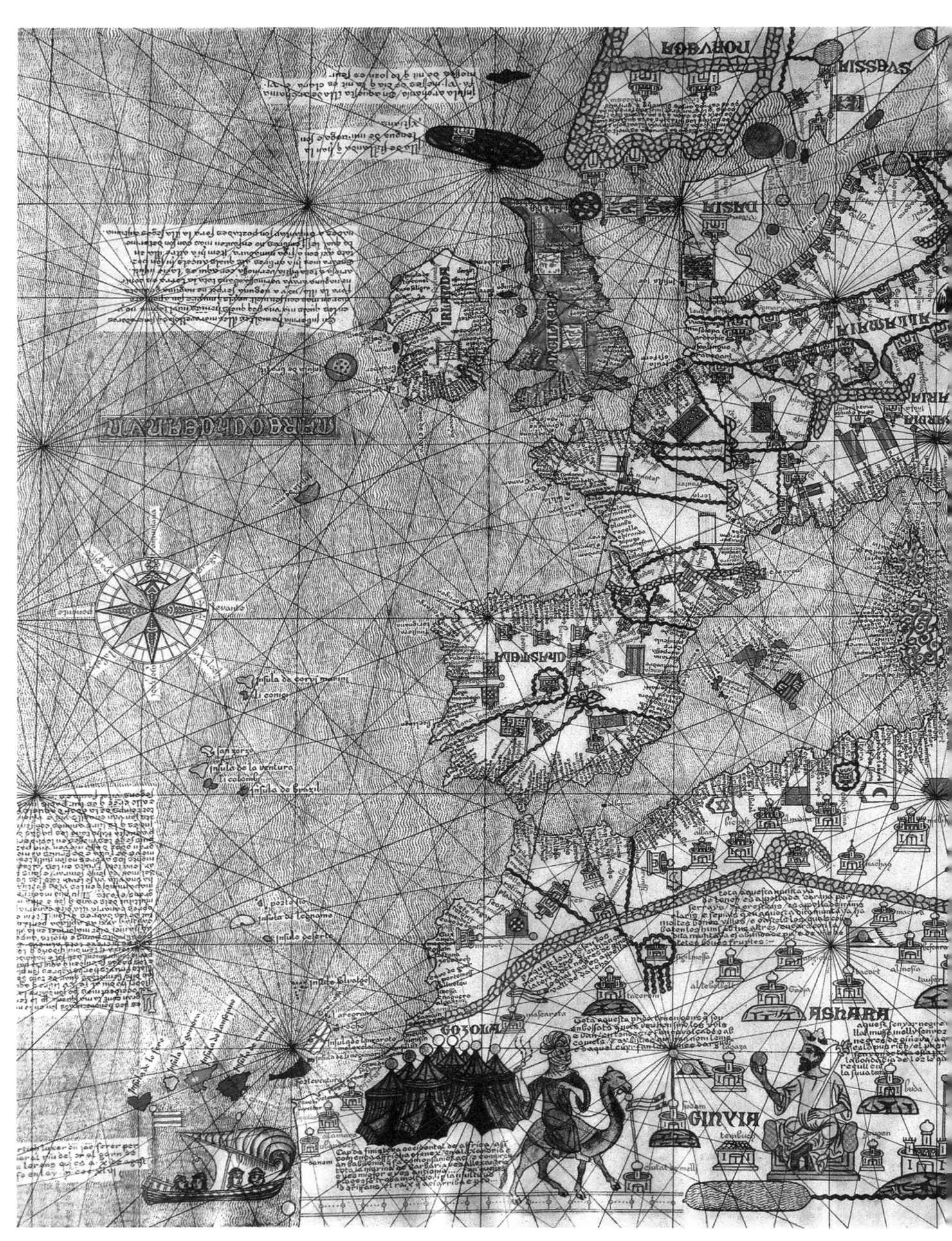

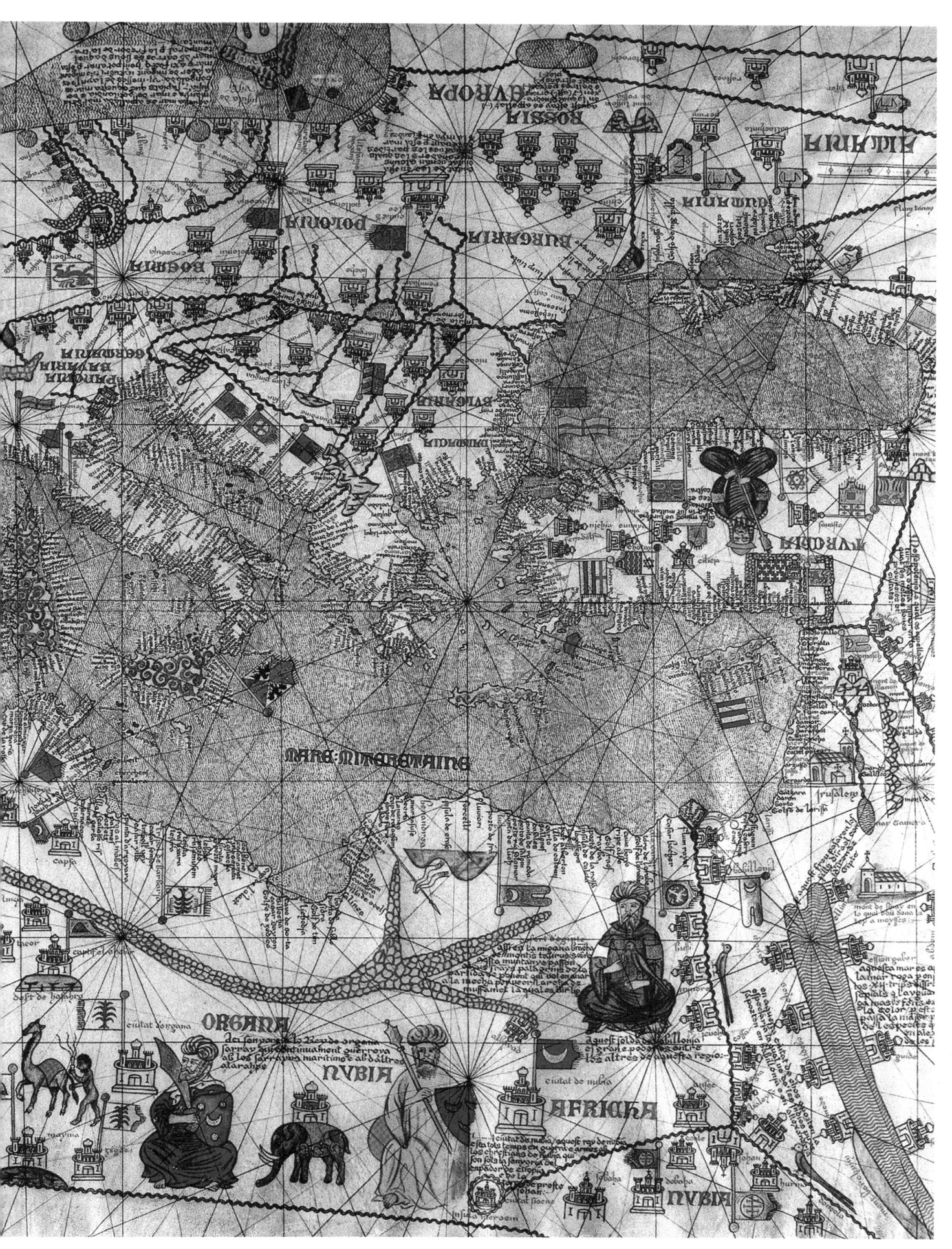

The Hanseatic League

The map by the Antwerp cartographer Abraham Ortelius, taken from his 1570 *Theatrum Orbis Terrarum* ("Theatre of the World") – the first proper world atlas, with maps of a uniform format bound together in a single volume covering the entire world as known to Europeans, as opposed to a disparate collection of sheets compiled from diverse sources – shows another theatre, that of trade and the field of operations of the Hanseatic League, one of history's greatest trading organisations.

The German word *Hanse* originally referred to any association of merchants, but it gradually came to be applied to larger organisations and then a single one which by the 14th century dominated trade in north Germany and the Baltic. It had its roots in the rebuilding of Lübeck, just east of the Jutland peninsula, by Duke Henry the Lion of Saxony from 1158. The town became a magnet for traders, who by 1160 had also established a community at Visby on the island of Gotland, which gave them a strategic lock on trade travelling east and west through the Baltic Sea. Although German merchants had long co-operated when they traded in foreign lands, now more formal links were established. In 1210 Lübeck and Hamburg agreed a common law between them, strengthened by a pact in 1241 to act against pirates. Gradually more towns joined this Hanse, which spun off new satellite settlements along the Baltic coast, at Reval (modern Tallinn), Danzig (Gdansk) and Dorpat (Tartu).

Farther west, where Cologne merchants had obtained a charter of privileges from Henry II of England in 1157 and secured a favoured position in Bruges, the Baltic Hanse gradually forced its way in. In 1282 the Cologne Hanse was absorbed by it. The Hanseatic League, as it had now become, grew to around 170 members, although it never possessed formal institutions such as officials or a central treasury, and was governed only by a Diet which met intermittently from 1356, and to which many towns did not send representatives.

The Hanse merchants monopolised Baltic trade, taking furs from Novgorod, amber and grain from the southern Baltic, timber from Poland, and above all herring and other fish, which were dried as "stockfish" and carried through the Sound – the narrow strait between Denmark and Sweden – to markets in England, France and the Netherlands. In return the Hanse imported necessities such as cloth, brokered through overseas headquarters – or Kontore – at London, Bergen, Bruges and Novgorod, which dominated the commercial life of their host nations.

From the 14th century, the Hanse underwent a slow decline. Constant friction with Denmark led to outright war in 1367-70. Although the Hanseatic League were the victors and secured free passage through the Sound, they had lost Visby to Denmark, while the Union of Poland and Lithuania in 1386 and that of Denmark, Sweden and Norway in 1397 created powerful new rivals. The strengthening of princely power in Germany stripped more cities from the Hanse's grasp, and the penetration by the Dutch in the 16th century of the Baltic herring industry, the heart of Hanseatic wealth, undermined it further. By 1669, when the Hanseatic Diet met for the last time, only nine towns turned up. Surviving only as a theoretical compact between Lübeck, Hamburg and Bremen, the Hanseatic League lingered on until a few years before German Unification in 1871. By then, the Hanse was remembered only as a byword for trading excellence, a theatre on which the curtain had long gone down.

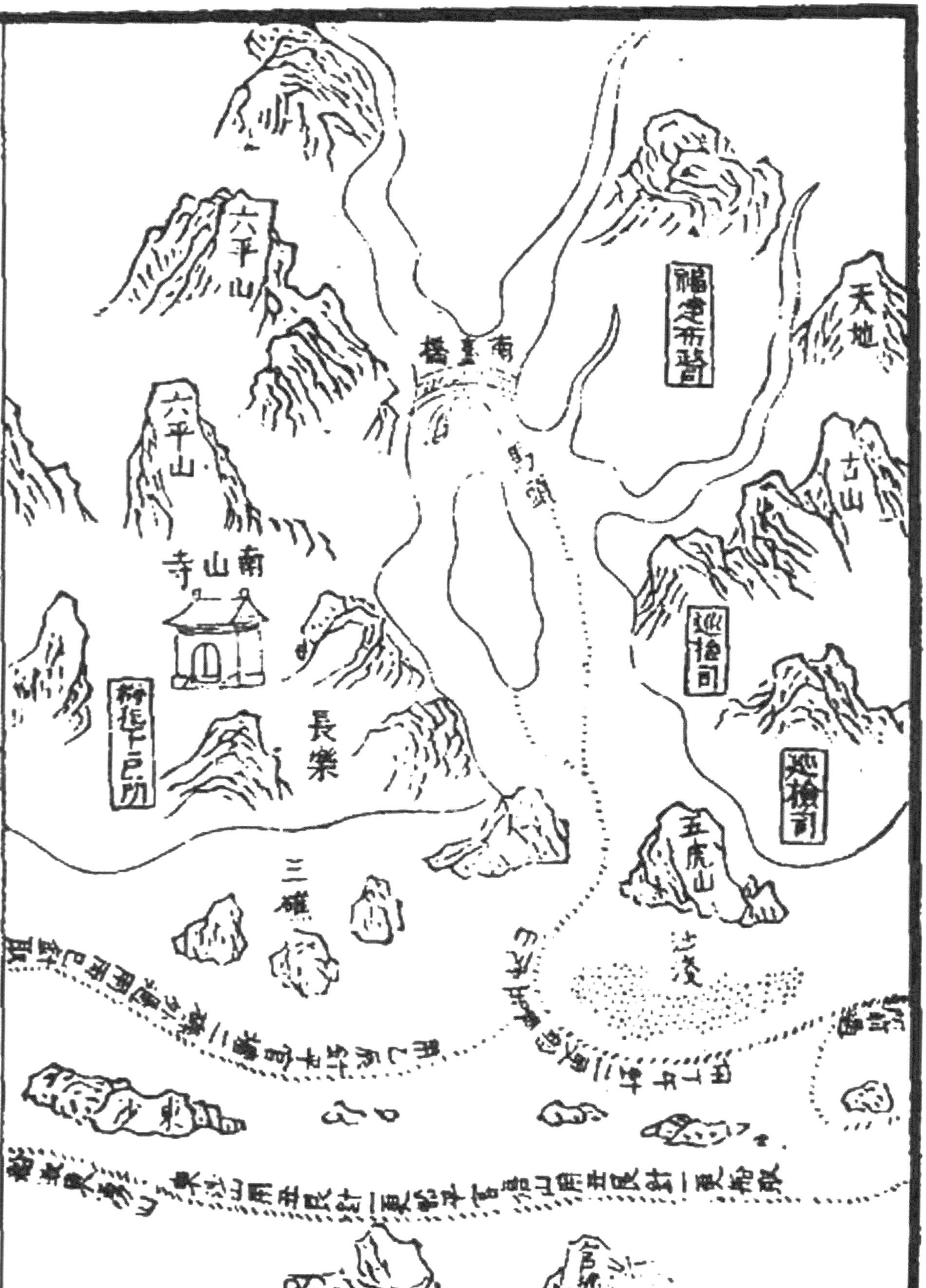

The Voyages of Zheng He

The map shows the initial stages of one of the medieval world's most spectacular journeys of exploration, which linked China to the East African coast in a brief, tantalising set of voyages, whose discoveries were never followed up. Accompanying Ma Huan's 1416 *Overall Survey of the Ocean*, an account of those voyages, it shows the coastline of Fujian Province with, in its centre, the port of Changle, from which several of them departed.

With the overthrow of the Mongol Yuan dynasty by the Ming in 1368, China had turned inwards and long-distance voyages were discouraged. The policy was changed again by the Yongle emperor, who ascended to the throne in 1402. He entrusted the task to his protégé Zheng He, employed in his service ever since he was captured at the age of about 10 during an uprising and castrated to make him a eunuch. Appointed in 1405 as admiral of the Imperial fleet, Zheng ordered the building of a vast flotilla of 300 vessels, including 62 enormous *baochuan*, or "treasure ships", which were as long as 300 feet, and had up to 12 masts.

In late summer 1405 he set out for Java, pausing to clear pirates out of the Strait of Malacca and present a gift of silver and a cloak to the sultan of Malacca as a sign that China's emperor would protect him from his Siamese enemies. This was no ordinary mercantile expedition, but a way of projecting Chinese power, and establishing a network of tributary states extending into the Indian Ocean. On the second voyage, 1408-09, he visited Ceylon, where the local ruler Alagakkonara attacked the fleet, but was seized and carried back to China, where he had to submit to the emperor. On a fourth voyage (1413-15) he ventured as far as Hormuz, and brought back envoys from more than 30 nations, many of whom were returned home on the next voyage (1417-19).

The sixth voyage, from 1421-22, made even more spectacular progress, with some vessels sailing down the East African coast as far as Sofala in Mozambique. They brought back exotic gifts: ostriches from Barawa, zebras from Mogadishu, and from the sultan of Aden several giraffes, whose resemblance to the *qilin* – a creature from Chinese myth said to presage an age of prosperity – caused great excitement. Yongle died in 1424, and having lost his patron, Zheng He struggled to gain support for new ventures. Finally, the Xuande emperor sanctioned one last voyage, which in 1431 took the much-travelled route via Sumatra and reached as far west as Hormuz. As a devout Muslim, Zheng He took the opportunity to perform the haj, the pilgrimage to Mecca, but he died just before the fleet returned to China in 1433.

No new Chinese flotilla set out into the Indian Ocean, and later Ming emperors gradually tightened restrictions. In 1525 the destruction of large ocean-going vessels was ordered. Zheng He's achievements were largely forgotten, though a temple was established in his honour in Malacca. In the end his voyages had been more floating diplomatic missions than any attempt at establishing lasting trading connections. They were virtually edited out of historical memory: in China, where subsequent emperors preferred to forget them; and in Europe, where the idea that the "discovery" of new lands was an enterprise undertaken solely by Europeans had become embedded. Yet it is a tantalising thought that had his fifth voyage pressed just a little farther, it would have been a Chinese fleet that rounded the tip of southern Africa first, over 80 years before Vasco da Gama did so in 1497.

The Joining of the World

The 1507 map by Freiburg cartographer Martin Waldseemüller portrays the moment that the world became whole. It shows the name of the new – to Europeans, at least – continent discovered by the Genoese mariner Christopher Columbus in 1492, which, ironically was not named after Columbus at all, but one of his rivals, the more able self-publicist Amerigo Vespucci.

Columbus had not expected to fill in a blank in the map, but to sail straight through it. His westward voyage across the Atlantic was motivated by the great trading mirage of the Middle Ages, a way to access the riches of the Spice Islands of the East without having to traverse lands controlled by Muslim powers. Columbus used judicious cherry-picking of ancient sources to convince himself that the distance between Portugal and Japan was a mere 2,500 miles (as opposed to the more than 10,000 miles it truly is). This comparatively puny expanse, Columbus reasoned, could be easily crossed by the ocean-going caravels of the time.

In 1484 Columbus secured an audience with Portugal's King João II and argued his case. The royal advisers turned him down, doubting his assertions about the narrowness of the western ocean. Spurned, Columbus turned to Spain in 1486, but his case became bogged down in a committee of specialists set up by Ferdinand of Aragon and Isabella of Castile. So, it was only on August 3, 1492 that Columbus's little fleet of caravels, the *Pinta, Niña* and *Santa María*, sailed from the Spanish port of Palos, took a westward swerve at the Canaries and began the long voyage into the unknown. It took 36 long days, but finally, with the crew on the point of mutiny, land was sighted, most probably San Salvador in the Bahamas.

On that first voyage, Columbus surveyed the Bahamas, Cuba and Haiti, vainly searching for the cities of Japan and China he confidently expected to encounter. Cuba he thought might be Cathay (China) and Haiti just possibly the biblical land of Sheba. Nonetheless, when he returned home on March 15, 1493, his cargo of captured Arawak people, parrots and pineapples caused a sensation, and the small quantity of gold he had found ensured the dispatch of more expeditions.

More importantly, his pioneering voyage marked the start of the "Columbian Exchange" of foodstuffs and ideas between the Old World and the New. Tomatoes, maize and potatoes crossed the Atlantic to become staples in Europe, and cassava displaced traditional crops in Africa. Chillies, cocoa, peanuts and tobacco all made the journey, together with cotton, which revolutionised the textile trade. In the other direction went onions, grapes, apples, pigs, horses, cattle and the domestic cat. There were more disturbing exchanges too. To provide a labour force on their plantations, the Spanish and Portuguese began importing slaves, mostly from West Africa, and between 1525 and 1866 around 12.5 million Africans were forced to cross the Atlantic into enslavement.

Disease was the deadliest fellow traveller. Native Americans had no resistance to infections such as measles, influenza and smallpox, whose ravages undermined the ability of the Inca and Aztec Empires to resist the Spanish and killed up to 90 per cent of the pre-contact population of the Americas. In the Columbian Exchange the indigenous Americans got by far the worse end of the bargain.

HIR⁹

TERRA VLTERI INCOGNITA

PARIAS

OCCEANVS OCCIDENTALIS

CIRCVS 80

CIRCVLVS ARCTICVS

ISABELLA INSVLA

SPAGNOLLA INSVLA

OCCIDENTALES OCCEANVS

CANCRI

ATHLANTICVM

Iste infule per Columbum ge
ner fem aluftrantem ex iuſ
to re, ſi Caſtelle inuente ſunt.

TOTA ISTA PROVINCIA INVENTA EST PER MANDATVM REGIS CASTELLE

TERRA VLTRA

EQVINOCTI

SINVS SPE

GETVLIA

LIBIA INTER
IOR

CAPRICO

INCOGNITA

CAPVT Sandtauas
Sandimdatis

AMERICA

REGNVM MVSAMELI DEONOIA
EQVINOCTIA
ICHTIOPHAGI ETHIOPES
AGANGINE ET HIOPES
REGNVM ORGVENE
XILICES ETHIOPES
REGNVM NVBIE
AFFRICA
ETHIO
AGIZIMBA REGIO E

280

290

300

310

320

SINVS MAGNVS AF

APRICORN

CHOR⁹

ZEPHIR⁹

CLAVDII PTHOLOMEI ALLEX
ANDRINI COSMOGRAPHI

OCCEANVS OCCIDENTALIS

MARE GLACIALE SIVE CONGELA

AFRICVS

AMERICA

AFFRICA

LYBONOTH⁹

NOTVS

UNIVERSALIS   COSMOGRAPHIA   SECVNDVM PTHOLOMAEI TRA   DITIONEM

AMERICI VESPVCII

AQVILO   CECIAS

SVBSOLANVS

ASIA

CHATAY

INDIA MERI
DIONALIS

OCEANVS ORIENTALIS INDICVS

SERICA
REGIO

SCITHIA EXTRA IMAV

INDIA EXTRA
GANGEM

REGNVM
AVREVM

VVLTVRNVS
EVRVS

SINVS GANGETICVS

TAPROBANA
INSVLA

IAVA
MAIOR

EQVINOCTIALIS

INDIA

REGNVM
VALIS

OCEANVS INDICVS MERIDIONALIS

ZEYLAN

IAVA MINOR

TROPICO CAPRICORNI

EVRONOTVS

O MADAGASCAR

110   120   130   140   150   160   170   180   190   200   210   220   230   240   250   260

ET   AMERICI   VESPVCII   ALIORV QVE   LVSTRATIONES.

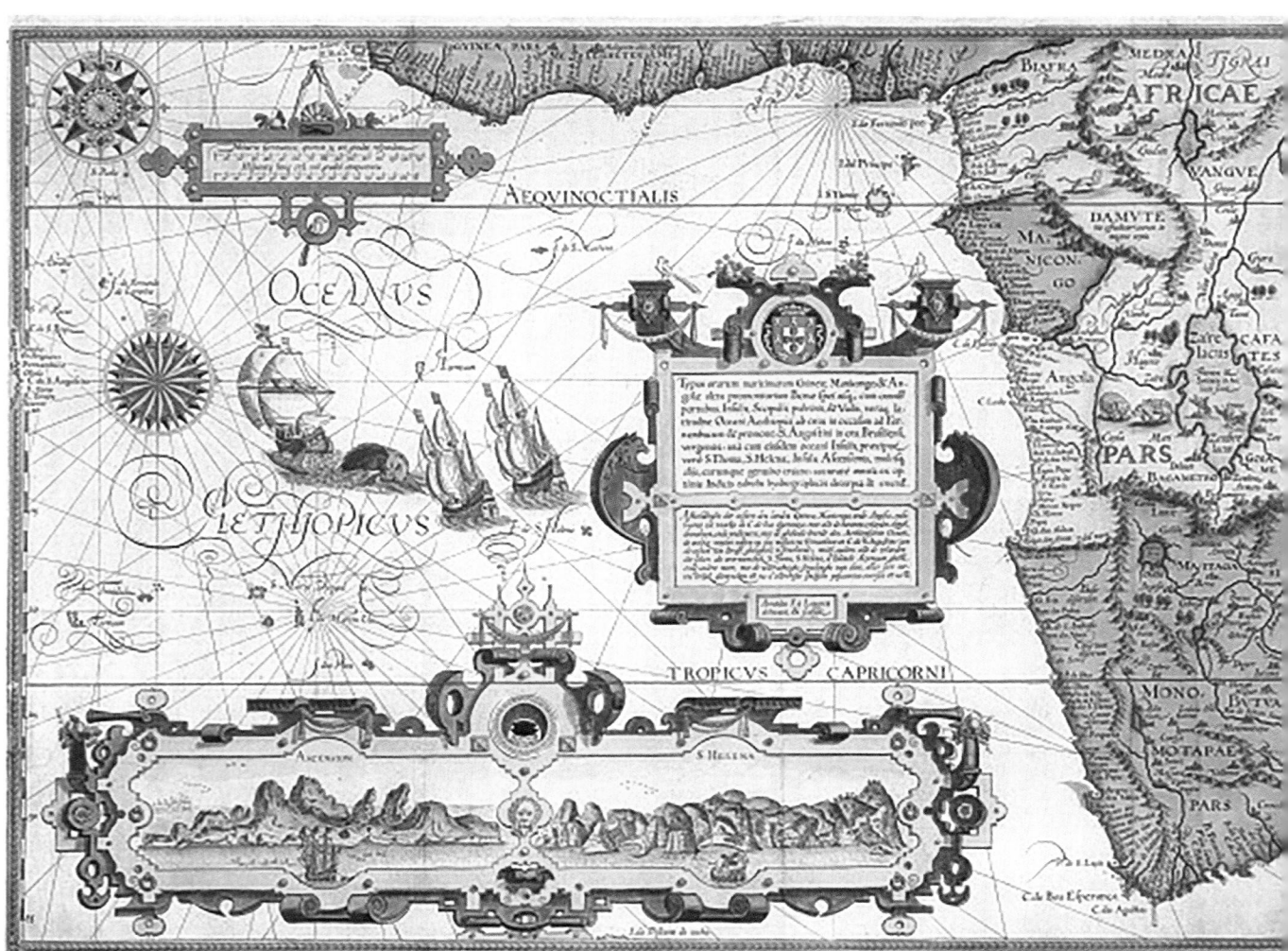

The Portuguese Trading Empire in Africa

Arnoldus Florentius van Langren's 1594 world map shows the arena of Portugal's first imperial venture, a thrust down the west coast of Africa, which created a trading empire (of which van Langren's Dutch compatriots would all too soon seize a share).

The Portuguese engagement with Africa began in 1415, when its forces seized Ceuta, intended to act as a bridgehead into the trans-Saharan gold trade. The results ultimately proved disappointing as the Moroccans retained control of the route. Nonetheless, the Ceuta expedition had consequences. One of the princes who took part in it, the Infante Dom Henrique (also known as Prince Henry the Navigator), returned home determined to find a back door into African commerce. From his residence at Sagres he sent out a series of expeditions, latterly in caravels, whose manoeuvrability and ability to sail windwards made them ideal for exploration. A succession of expeditions inched their way down the coast, rounding Cape Bojador in 1434 and reaching Arguin on the west coast of Mauritania in 1443, Senegal in 1446, the Cape Verde Islands in 1456 and as far as the mouth of the Congo in 1482.

On Cape Verde and the islands of the Gulf of Guinea (and on the Azores, settled from 1439) the Portuguese were able to produce wheat, sugar and timber for consumption back home, as well as establishing ties with traders on the African mainland. They sold cloth, salt and beads in exchange for kola nuts, animal skins, carved wooden artefacts, but above all slaves. The growth of the sugar industry in the São Tomé region in the late 15th century accelerated the flow. As with most trading ventures by the Spanish and Portuguese, little happened without the direction – or at least the tacit approval – of the Crown, and the São Tomé industry began with the allocation in 1485 of half the island to João de Paiva, with the direction that he plant sugar cane there. More merchants followed his lead, a trend which further increased after the establishment of relations with the Kingdom of Kongo in 1491, until by the 1550s

there were 60 sugar mills operating, producing over 2,000 tons of sugar annually.

To protect this growing commercial empire, the Portuguese established a series of forts, first at Arguin in 1445 and then at Elmina in modern Ghana in 1481-82, which acted as staging posts where slaves were bought in exchange for bark cloth and currency shells. They extended their exploration farther east after Vasco da Gama's pioneering voyage to India in 1497, allying themselves with the Sultan of Melinde (in Kenya) and setting up trading bases at Kilwa and Sofala. Although the hoped-for bonanza in gold failed to materialise, from the 1530s Portuguese merchants sailed up the Zambezi into central Africa, trading in gold and ivory and securing a hold on the gold-producing regions of northern Zimbabwe that lasted until the 1690s.

By then the Portuguese trading empire in Africa was on the retreat. Sugar production moved to Brazil from the 1530s, and warfare with the Kingdom of Kongo threatened the supply of slaves, as did the vigorous resistance of Queen Nzinga, who between 1620 and 1657 fought against the Portuguese occupation of her coastal kingdom of Ndongo in northern Angola and then established a new power base at Matamba, blocking Portuguese slave traders from access farther inland and forcing them to deal with African middlemen. Nzinga also exploited European rivalries, making diplomatic approaches to the Dutch, who encroached steadily on Portuguese territory, capturing Elmina in 1637 and launching several attempts to seize the Portuguese settlement at Luanda in Angola (founded in 1576). The French and English entered the slave trade by establishing a presence in west Africa, and Portugal's forced unification with Spain in 1580 (after King Sebastian died in a quixotic attempt to shore up the Portuguese position in Morocco in the face of Ottoman Turkish advances) further sapped its will to exploit Africa. Van Langren's map was of a region where the future would not be Portuguese.

Circumnavigating the Globe

The map, with its golden-haired cherubs representing the winds, comes from a 1544 world atlas by the Genoese cartographer Battista Agnese. Its outline of North America, blurring off into a void, highlights that the manner in which the jigsaw of the continents fitted together was still imperfectly known. The route marked on it, that of the pioneering circumnavigation instigated by the Portuguese captain Ferdinand Magellan, marked the moment when this geographical fog began to lift.

The primary motivation for Magellan's voyage, however, was trade rather than cartographic curiosity. The voyage by Columbus in 1492 had sparked a row with Portugal, which believed it had an equal right to the lands Columbus had claimed for Spain. This was patched up by the Treaty of Tordesillas, signed in June 1494, which awarded all lands west of a line 370 leagues (1,185 miles) west of the Cape Verde islands to Spain and those to the east of it to Portugal.

There was, however, a loophole. If the line were continued to the other side of the world, it just might put the Spice Islands and their trove of nutmeg and cloves inside the Spanish rather than the Portuguese sphere of influence. Magellan had spent seven years in the Indies – taking part in the capture of Malacca in 1511 – and knew them well. His proposal to lead a voyage there had been rebuffed by Manuel I of Portugal and so, in partnership with the cartographer Ruy Faleiro, in 1517 he took his idea to Charles I of Spain instead, who rapidly approved it.

In August 1519 Magellan set out from Seville with a fleet of five ships and around 270 crew. The initial stages of the voyage were turbulent. There was a certain irony in the fact that Magellan's real aim was what medieval Europeans had always regarded as a "New World" (East Asia), which had actually been Columbus's intended destination and not the Americas, to which the explorer and arch-self publicist Amerigo Vespucci attached the term "New World" more durably in the decade before Magellan's voyage. Needless to say, neither of these regions was in the least bit "new" in the eyes of its inhabitants, who had lived there for millennia.

Magellan struggled to find the strait at the tip of South America which Faleiro had assured him would be there, and two ships deserted. Finally, on November 28, the remaining three completed a stormy passage of the strait (later named after Magellan) and entered the vast Pacific Ocean. By ill chance Magellan's fleet was crossing at virtually its widest point and by the time they reached Guam 99 days later the crew was starving and scurvy-ridden. A survey of the Philippines ended in disaster on April 27, 1521, when Magellan was killed on Mactan during a confrontation with Lapulapu, a local ruler who had rejected Magellan forcing on him both conversion to Christianity and subjection to the rajah of the neighbouring island of Cebu. With the expedition down to barely 100 men, the remnant was forced to burn the *Concepción*, and in December the *Trinidad* had to be left behind in the Moluccas. So it was that in command of the final ship, the *Victoria¸* Magellan's successor Juan Sebastián de Elcano set out on the long voyage home. He lost more men to starvation and 13 were captured by the Portuguese on going ashore at Cape Verde for supplies, but when the 18 survivors reached Spain on September 6, 1522, the cargo of 26 tons of cloves they were carrying made them rich. Elcano was showered with honours, including a new coat of arms featuring 12 cloves, three nutmegs and two crossed sticks of cinnamon.

Sadly for Spain, the expedition proved inconclusive regarding on which side of the line the Spice Islands lay, and a further treaty in 1529 awarded them definitively to Portugal. The extent of Magellan and Elcano's feat, though, is indicated by the fact that it was not successfully repeated until the Englishman Sir Francis Drake did so over half a century later, in 1577-80 on board the *Golden Hind*.

terra de bacalaos
insule felis
C · DE · S · AGOSTIN ·
BRAZIL ·
RIO · DE · LA ·
PLATA
LIBIA · ITERIOR ·
AVRITANI
EVROPA ·

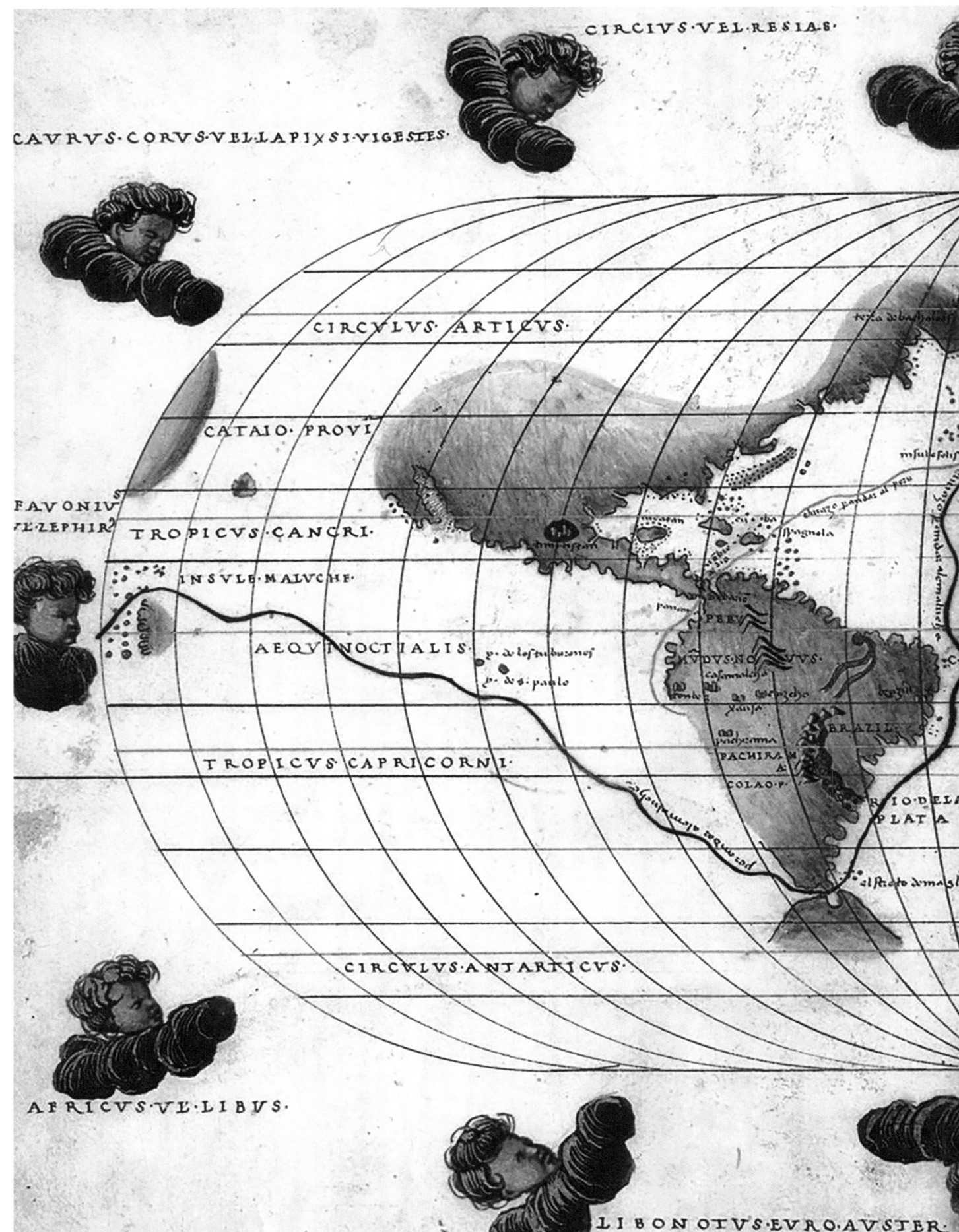

CIRCIVS·VEL·RESIAS·

CAVRVS·CORVS·VEL·LAPIX·SI·VIGESIES·

CIRCVLVS·ARTICVS·

terra·de·bacthalos̄

CATAIO·PROVI

insula·folis

FAVONIV
VEL·ZEPHIR

TROPICVS·CANCRI·

INSVLE·MALVCHE·

spagnola

PERV

AEQVINOCTIALIS·

p̄·de·los·tubuenos
p̄·de·s·paulo

MVDVS·NOVVS·

TROPICVS·CAPRICORNI·

BRAZIL·

R·IO·DELA
PLATA

PACHIRA
COLAO·P

el·streto·de·magl

CIRCVLVS·ANTARTICVS·

AFRICVS·VL·LIBVS·

LIBONOTVS·EVRO·AVSTER·

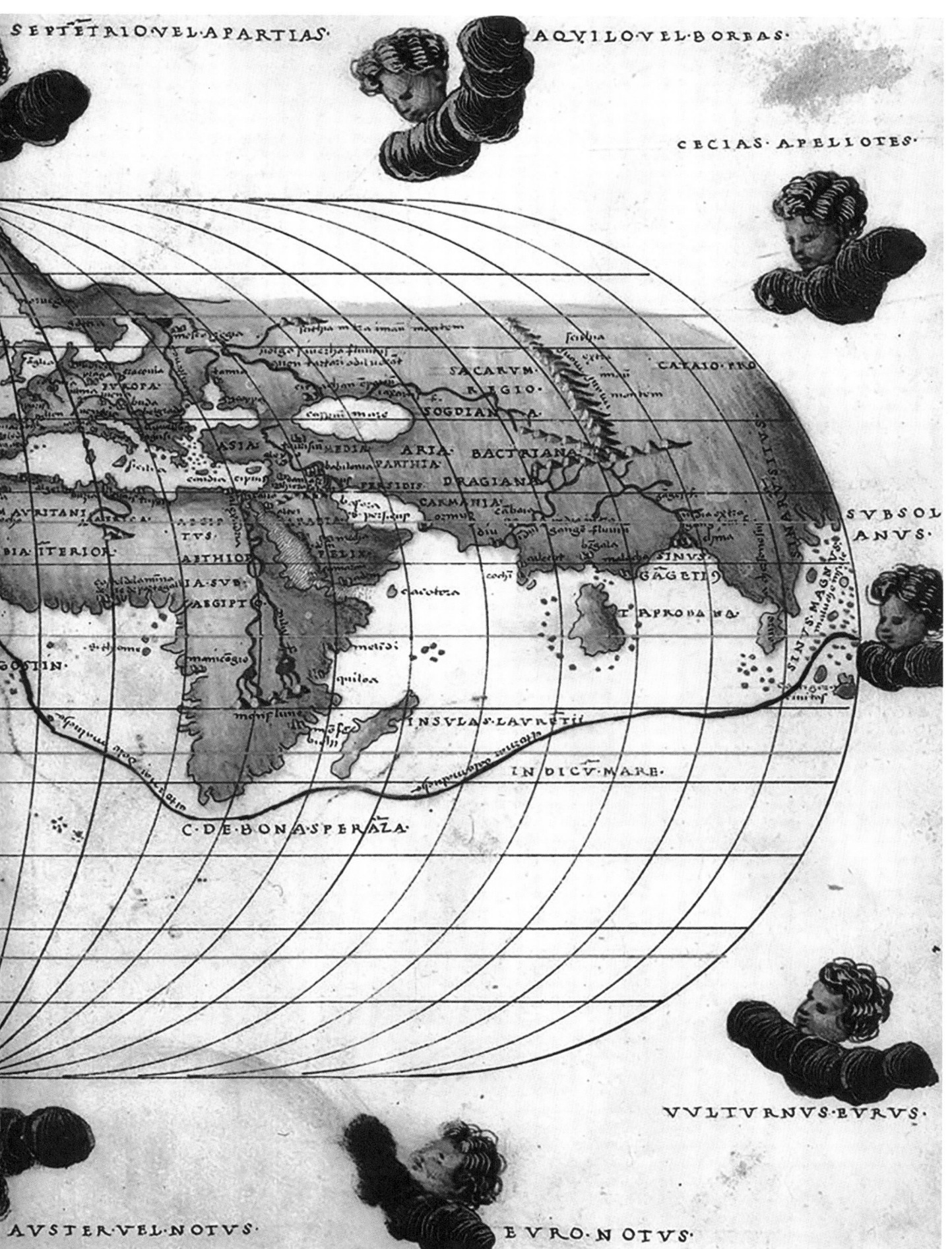

SEPTETRIO VEL APARTIAS.   AQVILO VEL BORBAS.

CECIAS. APELIOTES.

SACARVM.
REGIO.
SOGDIANA.

CATAIO. PRO

IVROPA

ASIA

MEDIA   ARIA. BACTRIANA.
PARTHIA
PERSIDIS. DRAGIANA.

MAVRITANI

BIA. ITERIOR.

TVS.

CARMANIA.

AETHIOP

FELIX.

IA. SVB.

AEGIPTO.

GAGETIS

SINVS

SVBSOL
ANVS.

TAPROBANA.

SINVS. MAGNVS

GOSTIN.

INSVLAS. LAVRETII.

C. DE BONA SPERAZA.

IN DICV. MARE.

VVLTVRNVS. EVRVS.

AVSTER. VEL NOTVS.   EVRO. NOTVS.

Ottoman Trade
in the 16th Century

Drawn on gazelle skin parchment in 1513 by the Ottoman admiral and cartographer Piri Reis, the map shows the breadth of Muslim – and in particular Ottoman Turkish – knowledge of the world. Only a third of it survives, displaying an accurate outline of the coasts of Europe and part of the Mediterranean, and a reasonable attempt at those of North and South America. Sadly, the part that shows much of the Ottoman trading world is lost.

By the time Piri Reis drew up his map, the Ottoman Empire controlled much of the Balkans, Anatolia, western Iraq, Palestine and Syria, and would within four years capture Egypt too. This vast expanse of land blocked its enemies from gaining access to the trade networks that fed into trade from India and China. The conquest of Kaffa on the Crimean peninsula in 1475 made the Black Sea a virtual Ottoman lake and gave the sultans access to the vast grain resources of the area and control over the north–south routes between Russia and the Mediterranean which the Genoese had previously dominated. In the early 16th century the growth of the Turkish fleet drove Venetian galleys out of the eastern Mediterranean, cutting the Italians out of the spice trade they had monopolised for centuries (and providing an extra impetus to cultivate the sea routes via Africa and the Americas).

It was in one such battle, at Zonchio in 1499, that the young Ahmed Muhiddin Piri cut his teeth in the service of his uncle Kemal Reis, a corsair turned imperial admiral. The Venetians were bested and slunk back into the safe harbour of the republic. Piri took part in other key engagements that enabled the Ottomans to reach the zenith of their power, participating in the Siege of Rhodes in 1522 that saw the expulsion of the Knights of St John. In 1547 he

rose to the ranks of Reis (admiral) and commander of the Ottoman fleet in Egypt. His downfall came from the need of the Ottoman sultan to secure the eastern trade routes. In 1552 he was dispatched to dislodge the Portuguese who had occupied the strategic island of Hormuz which blocked the maritime route through the Persian Gulf. His failure led to his execution in 1554. His advanced age, at almost 90, did not sway an unforgiving court.

Ottoman trade still thrived, with the export of primary produce such as grapes, figs, wheat and olive oil to Europe in exchange for manufactured goods and the import of luxuries such as silk and lacquers from the east, which had to be paid for in silver. The gradual contraction of the empire after its failure to take Vienna in 1683 together with the loss of other key trade nodes – in 1630 the Yemenis seized Bab al Mandab, which controlled access to the Red Sea – began its slow economic strangulation.

With expansion no longer yielding profits from plunder or providing rewards for the nobility, taxes rose, and once fertile land became unprofitable. The thirst of the empire for European manufactures after the Industrial Revolution and the penchant of 19th-century sultans for engaging in expensive but ineffective reforms to remodel their army and bureaucracy on western lines piled up massive debts. By the time the Piri Reis map was rediscovered in 1929 by a German theologian sifting through uncatalogued parchments at the Topkapi Palace in Istanbul, the Ottoman Empire was no more, having been replaced six years earlier by the modern Turkish Republic.

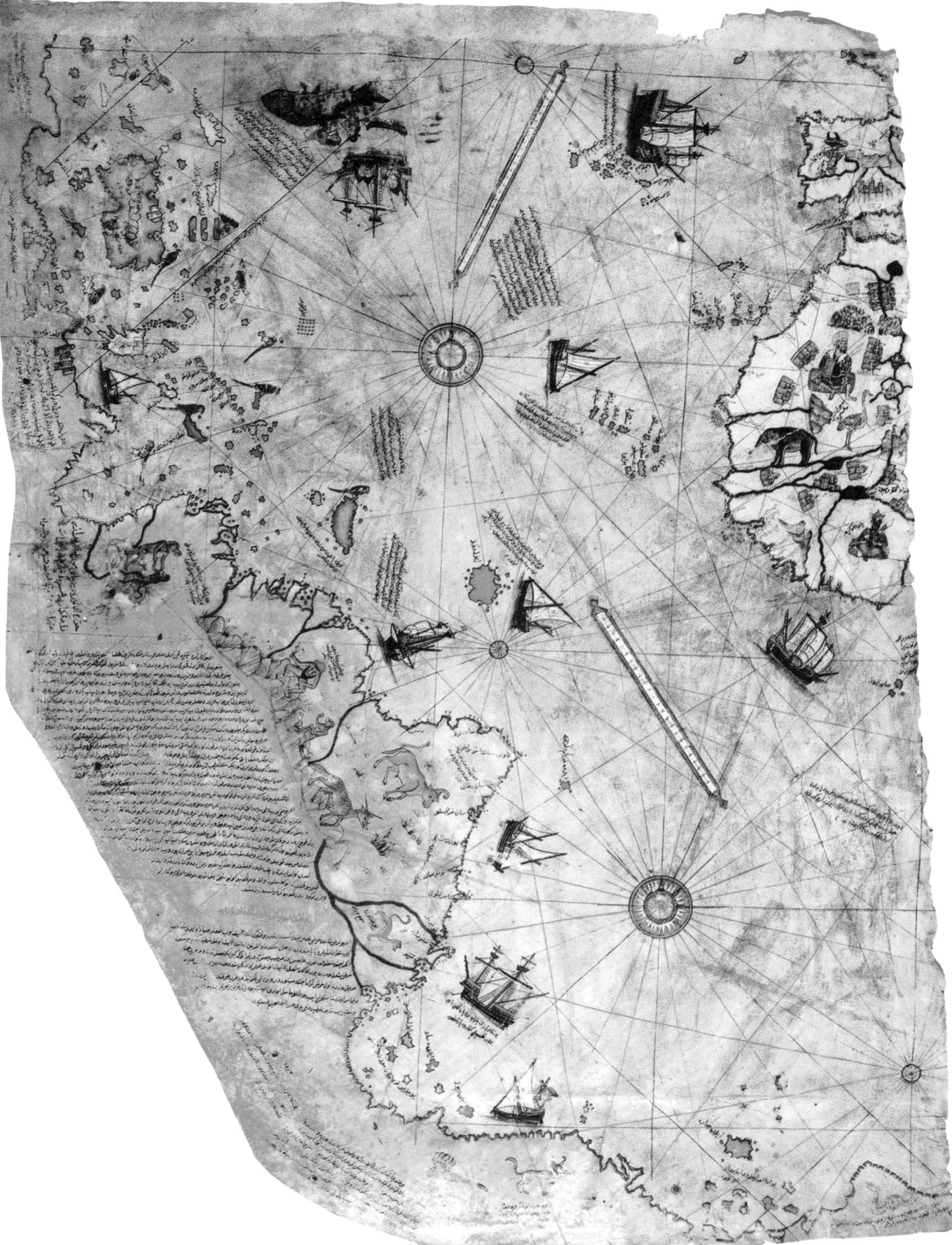

Aztec Trade

The map shows a proudly Aztec view of their history. Taken from the Codex Mendoza – a history of the Aztec people composed in 1541, some twenty years after the Spanish conquest – it is illustrated in traditional style, with the map making no attempt at topographical accuracy. Instead it tells a story, with the Aztec imperial capital of Tenochtitlán at its centre, identified by an eagle clutching a cactus (a reference to the city's foundation myth in which the Aztecs were bidden by a god to establish a settlement when they saw such a sight). The city's temples are shown – complete with skull racks for sacrificial victims – and the four waterways represent the causeways that linked the island-city to the mainland.

The Aztec Empire, which stretched from the north of present-day Mexico to Guatemala in the south, was a trading state. Although it was knit together by fear of the Aztec army and by the taking of hostages for sacrifice, local markets existed in every town in which local goods such as tomatoes and maize were bartered or exchanged for cacao beans, which formed a basic form of currency. Over longer distances, more exotic goods flowed to Tenochtitlán in the form of tribute demanded by the *tlatoani*, the Aztec emperor. Rubber came from Veracruz, chocolate from Chiapas, jaguar pelts from the Yucatán, cacao and obsidian from Honduras, gold from Costa Rica, and feathers for head-dresses from the tropical regions of Central America.

In Tenochtitlán itself, the markets were enormous. The principal one, near the sacred and royal precinct in the heart of the city, took place daily. When the Spanish first entered the Aztec capital in 1519, the conquistador Hernán Cortés remarked that "There is one square, twice as large as that of Salamanca, all surrounded by arcades, where daily more than sixty thousand souls buy and sell, and where are found all the kinds of merchandise produced in these countries."

The merchants who carried goods around the empire – on their backs, as the Aztecs had no large beasts of burden or wheeled vehicles – were a specialised class known as the *pochteca*. With relatively high social status, but below that of warriors, they enjoyed the protection of the state, and the Aztecs frequently went to war with neighbours such as the Huastecs who had murdered merchants. They had their own god, Yacatecuhtli, an earth deity distinguished by his merchant's staff, and before they set out on journeys, they engaged in elaborate rituals, such as affixing paper images of their patron god to their staffs, sacrificing quails and washing their hair (which was forbidden once a trading journey was under way). As well as being simple merchants, the *pochteca* acted as spies, particularly a subclass known as the *oztomeca* ("disguised merchants") who risked travelling through lands from which the Aztecs were normally excluded.

The whole edifice of Aztec trade and the *pochteca* came crashing down when Cortés captured Tenochtitlán on August 13, 1521, after a three-month-long siege. Moctezuma II, the *tlatoani* at the time the Spanish landed two years before, was already dead and, deprived of political leadership, the empire simply imploded. With it disappeared the tribute-based system which had driven long-distance trade. By the time the Codex Mendoza was composed, the *pochteca* were no more.

Acaitli

ọcelopa

Teensiceuh

Xocoyol

tenuch

Huexotl

Xomimilo

Xiuhtacal

Hqua

tenochtitlan

colhuacan. pueblo.

tenayucan. pueblos

The Silver Trade

Commodore George Anson's map commemorates the moment in June 1743 when he interrupted one of the early modern world's most lucrative trading routes. The yellow line straight across the Pacific marks the westward journey of the Manila galleons, the Spanish silver bullion ships which for 250 years from 1565 carried the precious cargo from Acapulco in Mexico to the Philippines, while the red line shows its return route. It was Anson's singular fortune to be one of just four captains to capture one of those treasure ships.

Spain's conquest of the Aztec Empire in Mexico (in 1521) and the Inca Empire of Peru (1533) brought it huge new territories, but the difficulty of exploiting them meant its new empire was initially a financial black hole. The discovery of a massive silver vein at Potosí in Bolivia in 1545 changed the equation. The development of a mercury mine at Huancavelica in 1565, which had been exploited at first on a small scale, meant the silver ore could be extracted cheaply and

in huge quantities. Miners, merchants and fortune-seekers flooded in, and by 1600 Potosí had ballooned into a metropolis of 160,000 inhabitants, which made it as large as London. Like any mining boom town, it was a desperate, dangerous place, with more taverns per head than any other city in the Spanish empire, where vast fortunes could be made, but, equally, where death came easily: in 1616 a massive dam burst nearly swept the settlement away, and a series of plagues in the early 18th century killed a third of its population. As well as by European fortune-seekers, the mines were initially largely worked – and managed – by indigenous Andean peoples, some 10,000 of them by the 1570s, who monopolised the refining process. In compensation for the backbreaking, hazardous work, many took their official or unofficial pay in silver. African slaves, transported from Congo or Angola, worked largely as silversmiths or in the Potosí mint, with relatively few sent to the silver mines themselves. By the late 16th century, around 290 tons of silver were being extracted a year, much of it heading straight

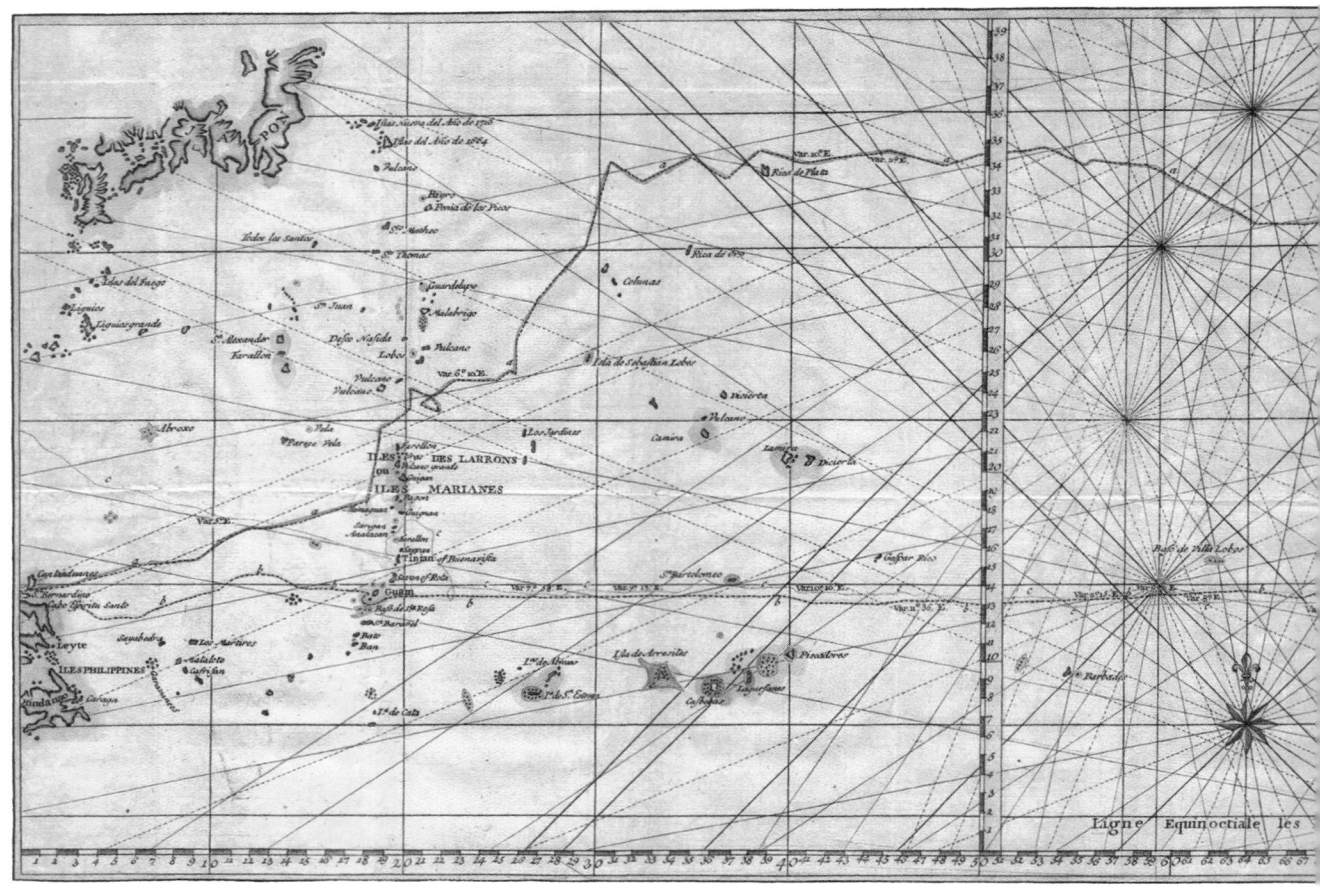

back across the Atlantic to Spain, where the Crown took 20 per cent of its value, fuelling an inflation that ruined the kingdom's economy.

Around 40 tons of silver a year went westwards, a route made possible by the Spanish occupation of the Philippines in 1565 and the discovery that year of a return route making use of westerly winds to reach Mexico. From then, each February a silver-laden galleon and a swarm of protective warships crossed the Pacific to Manila, where its silver cargo was used to buy porcelain, silks and other luxuries from Chinese traders. China's lack of silver mines and the high value the Chinese placed on silver (a ratio of 1:5 versus gold, as opposed to 1:12 in Europe) ensured a ready demand. The return cargo made its way back to Acapulco, shown overleaf, yielding a return of 100 to 300 per cent for investors, and making Mexico City one of the most fashionable cities in the world.

Such a valuable load was an irresistible target for raiders, but only twice in two centuries had the Manila galleon been captured (in 1587 and 1709). Then, during the War of the Austrian succession, Anson was tasked to proceed with a squadron of ships to disrupt Spanish interests. By the time he reached Macao in China in November 1742, his flagship the *Centurion* was the only survivor. Undaunted and having heard *Nuestra Señora de Covadonga*, the Manila galleon, was due, he made for Manila Bay, where, after a brief engagement he captured the ship and 35 tons of silver.

The event was a sensation and ensured Anson's promotion to admiral and the success of his account, *Voyage Round the World*, in which the map appears. For the Spanish Manila galleons, it was not quite the end, but the silver trade tailed off, as the Potosí mine was exhausted and other countries muscled into the China trade. By the time the last galleon sailed in 1815, Spain's near monopoly on silver had long been broken.

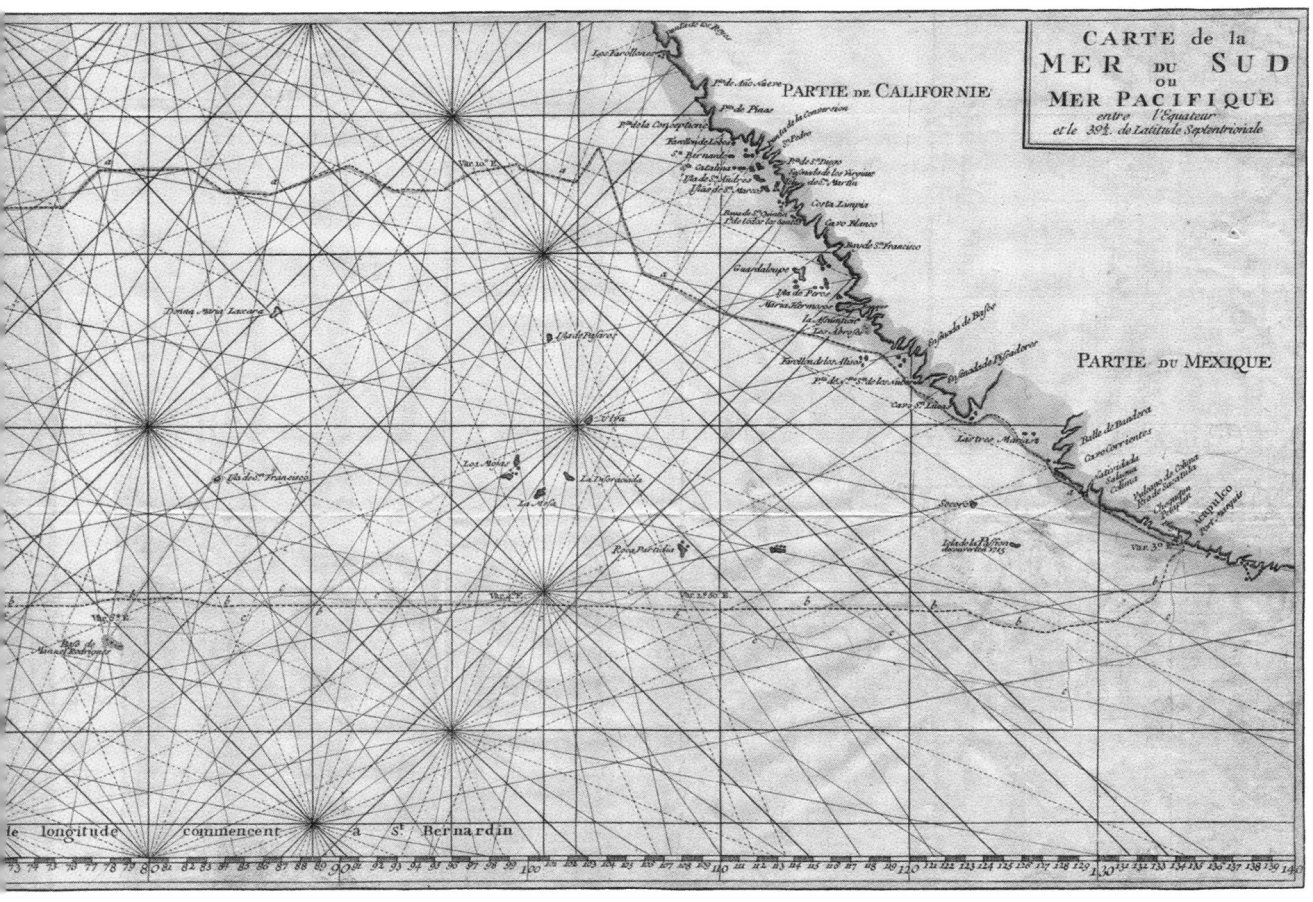

Pirates and Privateers

The 1589 map by the Italian artist Baptista Boazio shows various stages in the assault three years before by the English sea captain Francis Drake on the Spanish-held town of Cartagena de Indias (in modern Colombia). At the bottom the English fleet approaches, while English marines surge across a narrow strip of land at its centre. Published by Boazio in 1589, to accompany Walter Bigges's *A Summarie and True Discourse of Sir Francis Drake's West Indian Voyage*, it also illustrates a centuries-old truth, that trade and piracy were sometimes indistinguishable.

Piracy had been the scourge of maritime trading routes since ancient times, and a young Julius Caesar made his name in 75BC by clearing out a nest of Cilician pirates who had previously held him to ransom. It flourished wherever central authority was weak or sought to stifle trade with monopolistic regulations. In 1503, Spain established the *Casa de Contratación* (the House of Trade) which forbade anyone but Spanish ships from trading in the Americas, on pain of death, while even Spanish captains had to carry official certificates.

This system worked while the Spanish control in the Americas was unchallenged, but over time semi-independent colonies of adventurers and escaped slaves established themselves on islands such as Tortuga in the Caribbean. Then, as tensions rose from the mid-16th century between Spain and France, England and the Netherlands, state-sponsored expeditions were dispatched to break the Spanish grip on the region. Captains such as John Hawkins acted under letters of marque, an all too convenient English tradition by which private individuals were licensed to undertake military action on behalf of the state.

These privateers wrought havoc on Spanish possessions in the Caribbean. Drake began his maritime career on one of Hawkins's voyages in 1567 and, seeing the massive profits to be had by plundering Spanish silver, he returned again in 1571 and 1573. Queen Elizabeth I too was grateful

for the damage he inflicted on the Spanish and the silver which helped fund her campaigns against them, and in 1585 granted him permission to go to the Caribbean again with a fleet of 29 ships and over 1,600 soldiers. With this force, he stormed Santo Domingo on Hispaniola and then headed for the much more enticing target of Cartagena. The Cartagenans had been forewarned and had mustered militia, while the geography of the town made it hard for Drake to use his normal tactic of a seaborne feint masking a landward assault. Even so, he managed on February 9, 1586 to outflank Cartagena's earth wall at low tide and enter the town. He then proceeded to extort a ransom, burning houses when Cartagena's leading citizens refused to pay up. To avoid the town being reduced to ashes, they finally handed over a satisfactory haul of 107,000 pesos. In all of this, of course, the indigenous people had no say. Economically and socially marginalised by the Spanish conquest, they saw their numbers reduced by epidemic diseases brought over from Europe to which they had no resistance, and by the harshness of the *encomienda* system of labour requisition imposed by the Spanish. A smallpox epidemic which began in Cartagena in 1588, just two years after Drake's attack, affected them especially severely. To them, the handing over of a haul of silver in a dispute between two rival bands of European conquerors was a footnote to the story of their demographic collapse.

Over time, the French and British presence in the Caribbean moved from occasional raiding to outright conquest. They established plantations, notably on Jamaica, acquired by Britain from the Spanish in 1655, and constructed a colonial society in which London-based merchants, financiers and nobles extracted the lion's share of the profits, followed by European planters and overseers, with the Africans enslaved and transported to work receiving little but suffering and toil. Squeezed out too were the settlements of adventurers, escaped slaves and pirates which had dotted the Caribbean. In France and Britain's vision of empire, these sparks of independence had no place. In particular, they turned against the pirates, men upon whom in previous generations they had showered money and knighthoods. In 1670, the Royal Navy had just two ships in the Caribbean, but by 1718 it had 124 vessels patrolling and hunting down pirates. Many of those they hunted might well have pointed out that the legal difference between their depredations and those of the privateers was a simple piece of paper, easily bought. They might also have noted that while many of the seamen aboard Royal Navy ships had been impressed into service involuntarily, those aboard the pirate vessels generally served of their own free will and could expect a share of the prizes they captured that far exceeded the less democratic notions of the British fleet. The Caribbean pirates enjoyed a last flourishing, with towering figures such as Blackbeard (Edward Teach) and William "Captain" Kidd terrorising the region, but when Bartholomew Roberts – the most successful of all, who had taken over 400 vessels captive – was cut to pieces by a Royal Navy broadside off the coast of Gabon in 1722, their golden age was over.

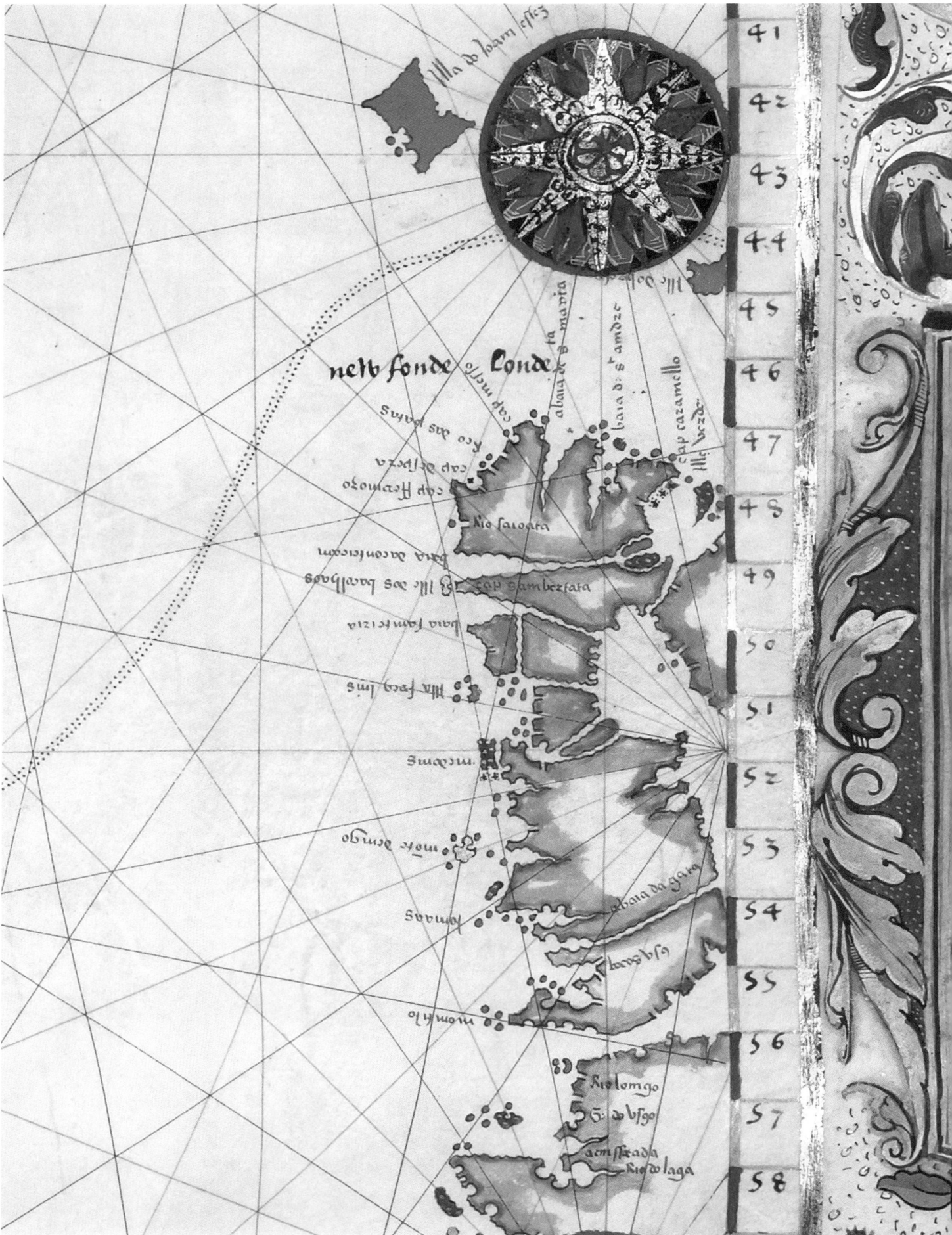

netb fonde Conde

Illa do Ioam esses

Rio das bavas
cap de Spera
cap Hermoso
Rio faroata
baia a conseicom
Illa das bacalbaos
baia fam kriza
Illa fera ins
incomu.
mote amigo
bavas
momfilo

cap de marta
abara de maria
baia de s ambze
cap cazamello
Illa verde
cap gambezfata
abara da gata
kens bfa
Riolomgo
G de bfgo
a em strada
Rio de laga

41
42
43
44
45
46
47
48
49
50
51
52
53
54
55
56
57
58

Newfoundland and the Cod Trade

A ship returns from Newfoundland in Jean Rotz's map – which has south at the top – from his 1542 *Boke of Idrographie*. A Franco-Scottish cartographer who had moved to England in the hope of royal patronage, Rotz diplomatically dedicated his atlas to Henry VIII.

The inclusion of Newfoundland might have been a sore point, for it represented disappointed hopes for England's infant empire in the New World. When the Italian mariner Giovanni Caboto (or John Cabot) lobbied Henry VII for funds to mount an expedition to the New World, the king – eager for Spain not to take all the glory – readily accepted, and in spring 1497 Cabot set out from Bristol across the Atlantic. What he encountered in Newfoundland was not piles of gold, but cod, so much that "the sea there is full of fish that can be taken not only with nets but with fishing baskets". When he got back, the king was unimpressed, granting him a paltry pension of £20 a year and the sop of the title "Grand Admiral". But the cod eventually proved to be a bonanza so valuable that in the 18th century William Pitt the Elder referred to it as "British gold".

Before long French, Spanish, Portuguese and English fishermen were setting out each year in spring, remaining throughout the summer to collect their haul. The English took theirs onto land, where it was dried on racks and salted ready for transporting back in the autumn, while the others preferred to salt it on board and dry it back home. So when small settlements began to be established on Newfoundland in the early 17th century, it was the English who inhabited them. By the mid-16th century the Newfoundland cod fisheries were providing around 60 per cent of the fish consumed in England, bringing prosperity to ports such as Bristol, Plymouth and Dartmouth, from where 70 or 80 vessels were setting out each year by the 1620s. Yet foreign ports, such as La Rochelle in France and Bilbao in Spain, also depended on the trade. This led to periodic clashes, until a raid led by Bernard Drake on the Portuguese fishing fleet in 1585, and the aftermath of the defeat of the Spanish Armada three years later, led Spain and Portugal to pull their fishermen back from Newfoundland.

The French and British were left to jockey for supremacy, with the British gaining very much the upper hand, particularly after the Napoleonic Wars. A trade grew up linking Britain's North American colonies to the Caribbean, where cod provided a cheap source of food on slave plantations and was exchanged for molasses, sugar, indigo and cotton to be sold in Britain for a handsome profit.

Through the vicissitudes of war, a temporary failure of the fishing shoals in the decade after 1715, and the decline of the English West Country ports, the fishing trade survived. The cod catch peaked at 810,000 tons in 1968, which led to fears that the depleted shoals might collapse completely. In 1977 Canada (of which Newfoundland had become a part in 1949) declared a 200-mile maritime zone to keep international fleets out, and in 1992 a ten-year moratorium on all cod fishing was imposed. Five centuries after Cabot initiated it, the "gold" of the Newfoundland cod trade was almost exhausted.

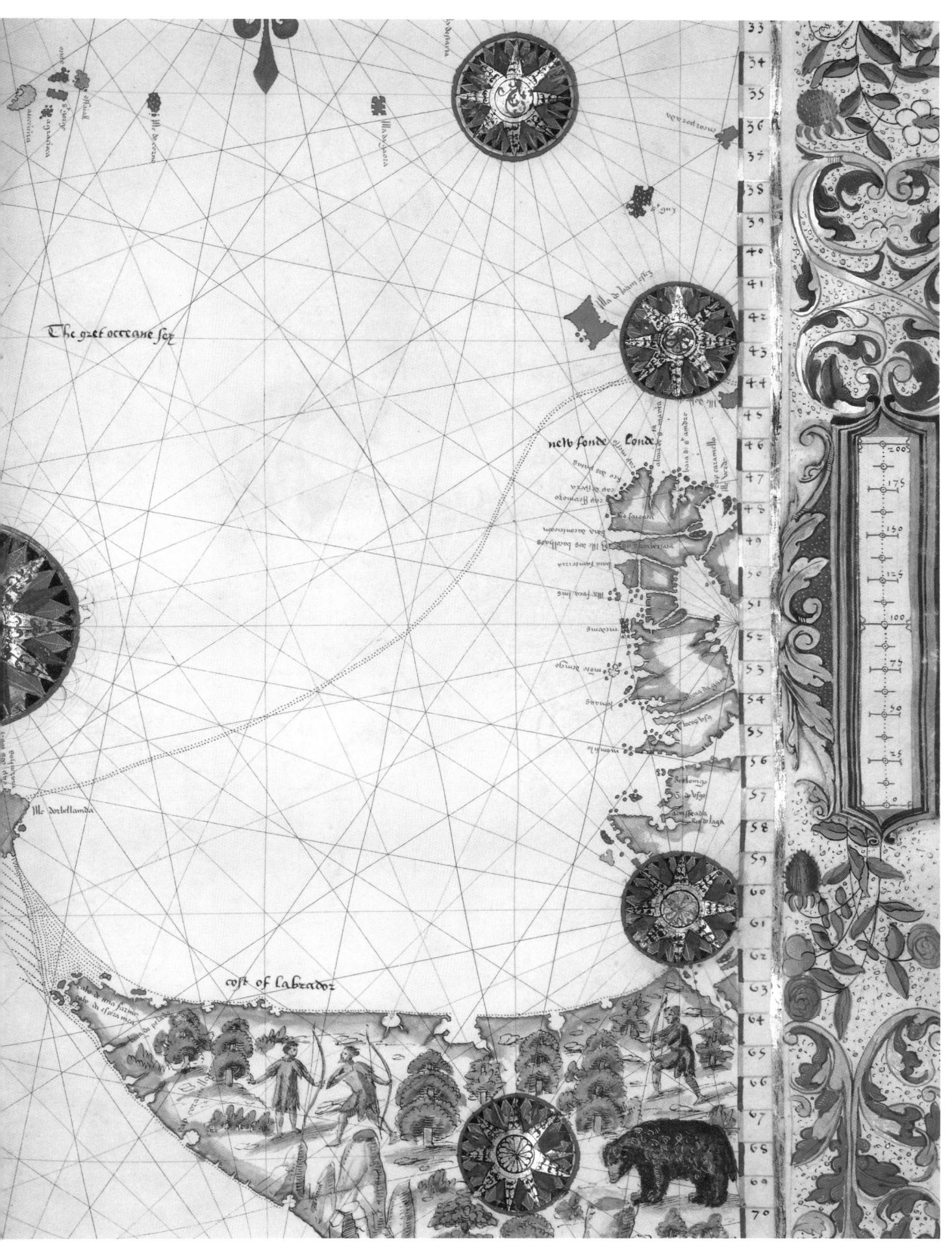

The gret occeane sey

nelb fonde londe

cost of labrador

Ille dozbellanda

The Dutch and Manhattan

The shape is familiar, but the streetscape is filled with farms in the earliest surviving map of New York. The Castello Plan – named after the Italian villa where it was discovered in 1900 – was compiled around 1660 by the surveyor Jacques Cortelyou for the then Dutch rulers of the city.

New York, ever a trading behemoth, began its life as New Amsterdam, part of the Dutch colony established after the English mariner Henry Hudson surveyed the river systems of the Hudson and Delaware in 1609. He came in search of the elusive Northwest Passage, a seaway falsely believed to provide a shortcut to Asia around the north of the American continent. What he found instead was a land rich in natural produce, in particular animal furs, which were in high demand in Europe.

As the area did not fall within the domain of the Dutch East India Company (see pages 116–17), independent traders came instead, such as Adriaen Block, who in 1614 became the first European to explore the Connecticut River. He found that the shells polished by the local Pequot tribes were highly valued by the Mohawks, who in turn had plentiful supplies of beaver, and so he set up a lucrative trade in European goods such as knives and glassware with the Pequot and secured piles of beaver pelts to sell back in the Netherlands.

More Dutch traders followed, and the fur trade became ever more profitable (over 52,000 pelts were shipped back to the Netherlands from 1626 to 1632). Finally, in 1621 the Dutch West India Company (Geoctroyeerde Westindische Compagnie, or WIC) was chartered, modelled on its eastern predecessor. As well as harassing Spanish shipping in the Caribbean and founding colonies on islands such as Curaçao, the WIC established a new North American base on Manhattan, which its director Peter Minuit bought from local Native American tribes in 1626 for 60 guilders-worth of trade goods.

The settlement, soon named New Amsterdam, began to prosper, reaching 300 inhabitants in 1630. A fort was constructed, and a street grid laid out, interspersed with large farms. One of these – at over 120 acres – was owned by the new director, Peter Stuyvesant, who supervised the colony from 1647. Yet New Amsterdam's future was already under threat. Its inhabitants did not enjoy full rights as Dutch citizens and resented Stuyvesant's dictatorial rule. They protested to the Netherlands government and received a city charter in 1652. Just then, however, war had broken out with England and the two sides patched up their differences long enough to agree to the building of a defensive timber wall between the East River and the Hudson.

This defensive line, along Wall Street, was never used. In 1664, Charles II of England, wishing to get his hands on both the fur trade and New Amsterdam's strategic location, announced its annexation and sent a fleet under Sir Richard Nicolls to seize it. Uncertain of the loyalty of his subjects, Stuyvesant surrendered without a shot. So it was that New Amsterdam became New York (named after Charles II's brother, the Duke of York). Although the Dutch briefly retook it in 1673, by 1674 the town was back in British hands, along with the rest of New Netherlands and the fur trade. The Castello Plan would be the blueprint for a British city, not a Dutch one.

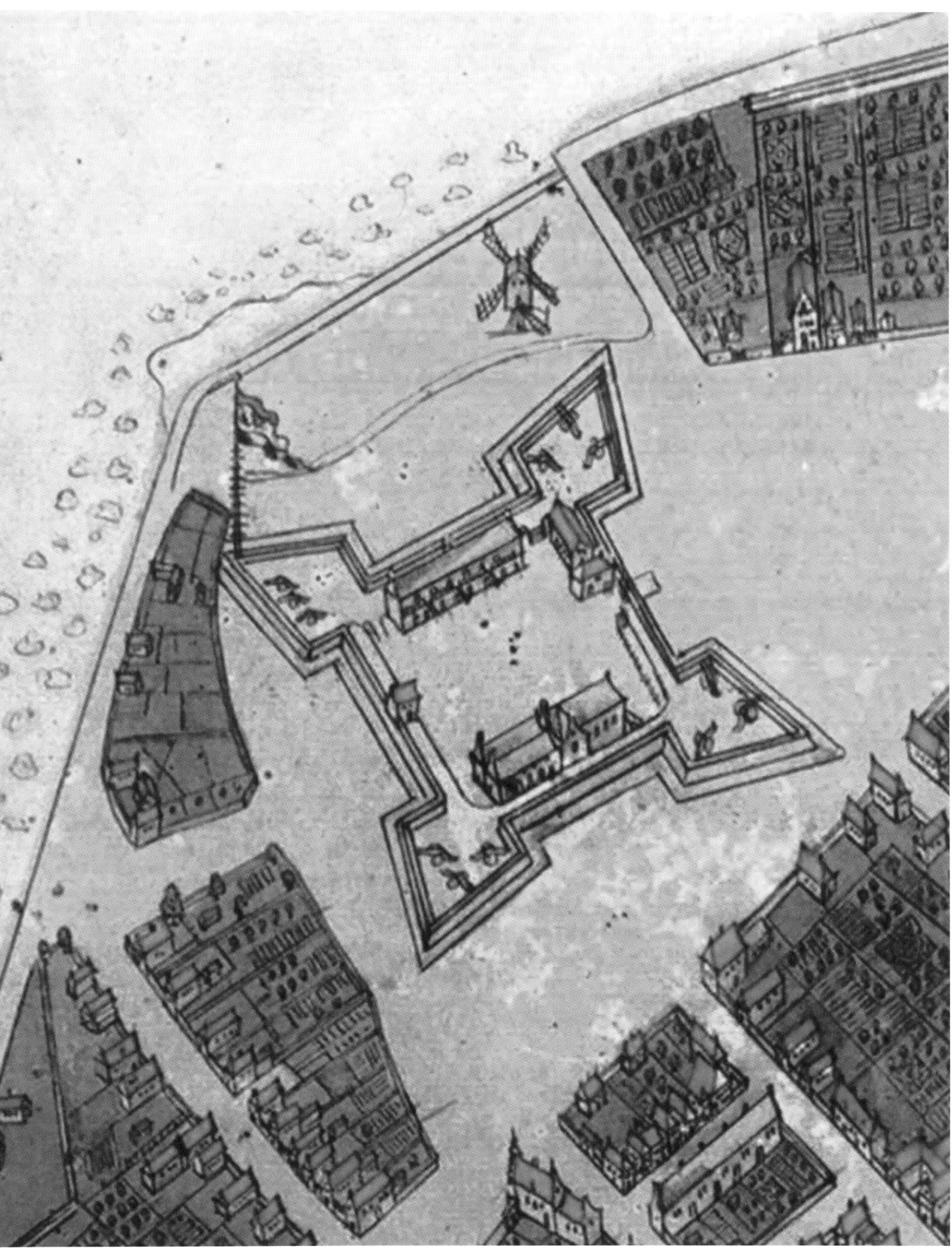

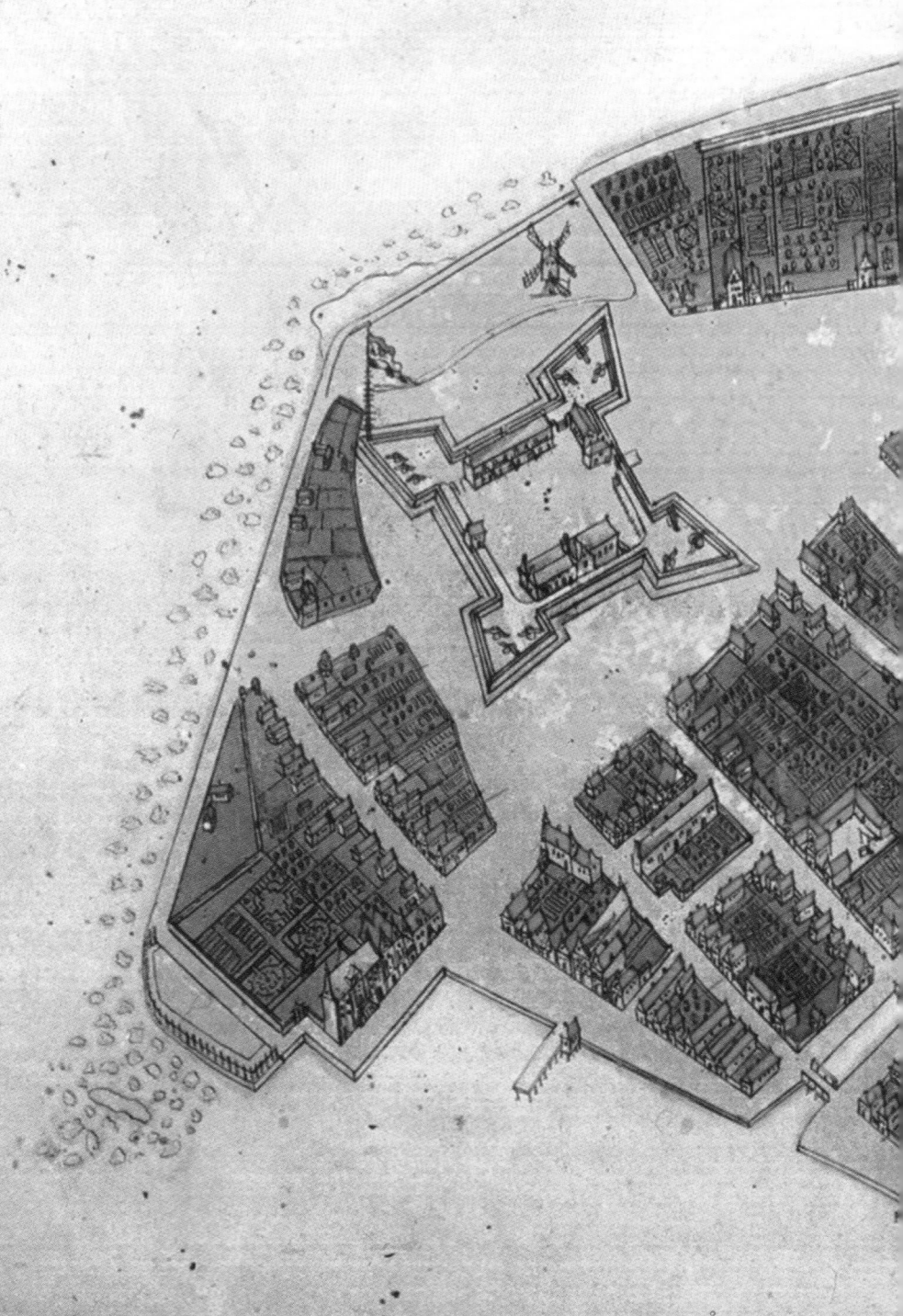

Needer Landt.

The Hudson's Bay Company and the Fur Trade

The engraved French chart from 1722 shows Hudson Bay in Canada. The land to the north is labelled as *Pays Inhabitable* ("Uninhabitable Country") and *Pays Inconnus* ("Unknown Countries"). By then, access to much of this land was indeed denied to the French trappers who had been chased out of one of the world's most profitable commercial enterprises, the trade in fur pelts from the Arctic north.

Most of Europe's fur-bearing animals had been hunted almost to extinction by the time a new vogue for hats in the 17th century created an upsurge in demand for felt, for which fur provides the raw material. Once again, the New World stepped in to fill the shortfall from the Old. When ships from southwest England started fishing the Newfoundland cod banks in the 17th century (see pages 92–5), they spent weeks ashore drying their catch, and discovered from local indigenous tribes that the wooded interior sustained a vast number of fur-bearing animals, in particular beavers. They began to trade these on a small scale in exchange for knives, kettles, beads and, occasionally, guns.

It was the French, though, who set up a proper industry first: from the moment that Samuel de Champlain established Quebec in 1608, fur helped support the infant colony of New France, regulated by a series of state companies beginning with the Compagnie des Cent-Associés in 1627. As the British established footholds in Canada, rivalry with the French became intense, particularly after the charter granted to Charles II's cousin Prince Rupert in 1670 for the Hudson's Bay Company, which gained a monopoly on all regions drained by waterways that flowed into Hudson Bay, a vast area of some 1.5 million square miles.

The company established factories at Rupert House and York House, where it collected beaver pelts for export. It avoided operating inland, however, and so was outflanked for the best furs by the French *voyageurs*, trappers who travelled upriver and dealt directly with local tribes. Even after New France was awarded to the British in 1763 as the spoils of victory in the Seven Years' War, the company was still threatened by the more agile Montreal-based North West Company (founded in 1779) which inherited much of the French network. Violent clashes erupted between the companies – such as a battle at Seven Oaks in 1816 in which 20 officers of the Hudson's Bay Company and its governor Robert Semple were killed – and finally, in 1821, they were forced to merge.

Still, the company yielded huge profits to its investors, helped by a rise in prices from 5 shillings a beaver pelt in 1713 to 16 shillings in 1763 (in part helped by the discovery in 1715 that the entire stock in French warehouses had been consumed by rodents). Others entered the market, including the Russians, who crossed from Siberia into Alaska and by 1812 were trading as far south as San Francisco, and the Americans themselves, who after the pioneering expedition of Lewis and Clark in 1803-04 began trapping for furs in the rugged lands around the Rocky Mountains.

The Hudson's Bay Company, though, fell on harder times after its monopoly was revoked in 1859, and the company lands were absorbed into the new Dominion of Canada ten years later. Over time it transformed itself into a land developer and then today's retailing company, finally selling off its fur trading division in 1987.

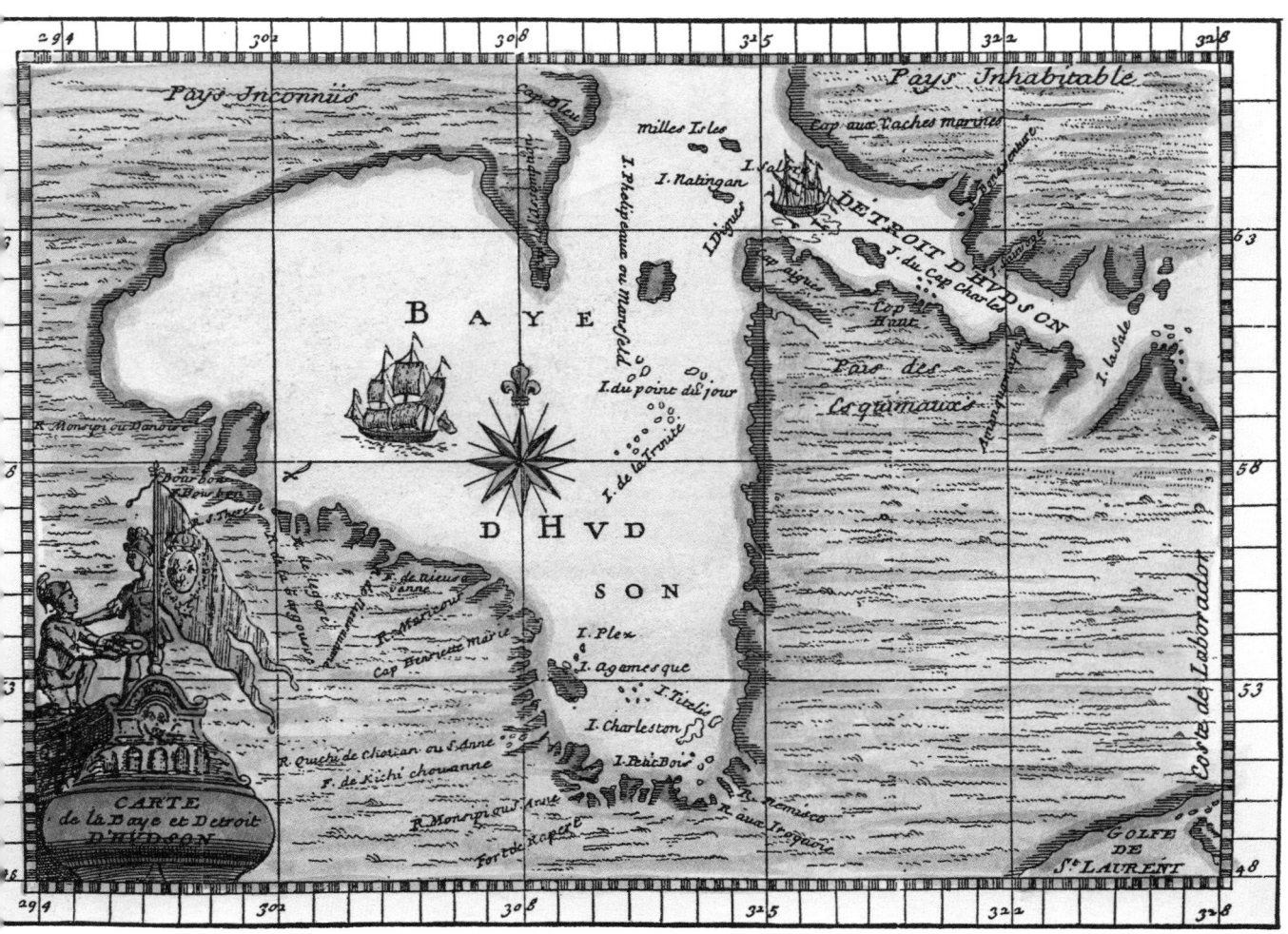

Pays Inconnuüs

Pays Inhabitable

milles Isles

Cap Blau

Cap aux Vaches marines

I. Salerio

I. Natingan

DETROIT D'HVDSON

I. Phelipeaux ou Mansfeld

I. du Cap Charles

I. Dignes

Cap Digne

Cap Hunt

B A Y E

Pays des

Cogumaux

I. du point du jour

I. la Sale

I. de la Trinité

D' H V D

S O N

I. Plex

R. Monsigi ou Danoire

I. Agamesque

R. Bourbon F. Bourbon

I. Titali

I. Charleston

I. de Rieus Vanne

R. Mat

I. Petit Bois

Cap Henriett Marie

R. Nemiseo

R. aux Iroquois

R. Ouebe de Chatian ou S. Anne

F. de Richelchouanne

GOLFE
DE
St LAURENT

R. Monsipi ou Anie

Fort de Rapell

CARTE
de la Baye et Detroit
D'HVDSON

Costes de Labrador

Trade and the Birth of the United States

The 1784 map by the Connecticut goldsmith and engraver Abel Buell was the very first published in the independent United States, which had emerged victorious and free in its struggle with Great Britain only the previous year. Buell proudly labels each of the 13 states which made up the new country, missing out only New York, which was engaged in a border dispute at its westward end with his native Connecticut and about which he did not therefore harbour fond feelings.

The storm which gave rise to American independence was brewed from tea, or rather its taxation. Although the colonies had been founded by a mixture of independent-minded religious refugees, fortune seekers and crown agents, they remained dependent on the mother country, and the largely agricultural produce which they exported – grain from the north and cotton from the southern states – travelled on British ships. By the 18th century it had begun to rankle that, British though they considered themselves to be, the colonists were second-class citizens who had the duty to pay taxes without the right to any say in government.

In 1767 the British government tightened its grip on American trade, passing the Townshend Acts, a series of measures that added duties on imports of paper, lead, glass and tea, and set up a new customs board in Boston to collect them. Although many of these dues were subsequently retracted, the impost on tea remained. Then, in 1773, after persistent lobbying by the British East India Company, whose profits were failing and debts mounting, a Tea Act was passed which authorised the shipment of 5,000 chests of tea to the Americas, duty-free, save for the threepence a pound still owed under the Townshend Acts.

The British government thought it had solved three problems at one stroke: it would still raise £1,750 in revenue, it would shake the grip of Dutch tea smugglers on the North American market (who had cornered over 80 per cent of it), and it would provide cut-price tea to a presumably grateful colonial market. It was a terrible mistake. The continued levying of the Townshend tariff inflamed sentiment, particularly in Boston, and this was fanned by the smugglers' allies.

When three East India Company tea ships, the *Dartmouth, Beaver* and *Eleanor* arrived in Boston Harbor, local leaders of the growing anti-British party urged their captains to refuse to pay the duty. After a heated public meeting on December 16, around 100 of the attendees slipped away and – many of them dressed in Native American costume – boarded the ships and dumped all 342 tea chests into the harbour waters.

The authorities' reaction was swift and harsh: they passed the Intolerable Acts to punish the colonists by closing Boston Harbor and suspending the colonial charter of Massachusetts. Yet these measures only solidified the belief of the colonists' leadership that compromise with Britain was no longer possible. Within the year the First Continental Congress had been established and on April 19, 1775, the first shots of the Revolutionary War were fired at Lexington and Concord. Eight long years of fighting later, the British were bested, and the United States of America had its independence. It was a lesson to Britain that trade, when used as a weapon, can backfire in the most alarming ways.

A
NEW and correct MAP
of the
UNITED STATES
of
North America
Layd down from the Latest Observations and
best Authorities agreeable to the PEACE of
1783
Humbly Inscribed to his Excellency the
Governor and Company
of the STATE of CONNECTICUT
By their
Most Obedient
and very humble servant
Abel Buell
NEWHAVEN Published according to Act of ASSEMBLY

THE ATLANTIC OCEAN

LAKE ONTARIO

NORTHERN IROQUOIS

PENSILVANIA

MASSACHUSETS

NEW JERSEY

CHESAPEAK

Meridian of Philadelphia

Longitude East from Philadelphia

English Miles 69½ to a Degree

South America and the Spanish

The 1592 map of South America by the Flemish engraver Theodore de Bry shows a slightly uncertain coastline, bulging at its tip to join the mythical southern continent still believed to lie there. De Bry delighted in tall tales from the New World, many of which he included in his multivolume *Grands Voyages*, to which this map acts as a companion.

Topping stories such as that of the explorer Hans Staden, who in 1553 persuaded the Tupinambá tribe not to eat him on the grounds that he was not Portuguese, but French (and therefore a possible ally), was the most fantastic narrative of all: that of the conquistador Francisco Pizarro. An adventurer and ne'er-do-well, Pizarro, with his ragamuffin band of around 160 armed Spaniards, had the good luck to gatecrash the borders of the Inca Empire in 1532, just as it was recovering from a civil war, and the ruthlessness to seize the Inca emperor Atahualpa when he granted them an audience at Cajamarca that November. Pizarro had been attracted by rumours of a gold-rich country called Birú, and the Inca Empire did not disappoint. Atahualpa paid his own weight in precious metal as a ransom, but Pizarro had him murdered nonetheless, and the Inca state collapsed into Spanish control.

As well as gold, South America also unlocked a trade in sugar, cochineal (a dye extracted from a cactus-eating insect), hardwood and hides that brought the Spanish more lasting wealth. More enduring than all of these, however, was the humble potato. An unassuming tuber with mildly toxic properties, it was grown on high slopes in the north of the Inca Empire and valued for its ability to withstand frost. Requiring very little tending, it also delivered a high calorific yield, twice that of rice per acre and far more than that of wheat.

Potatoes were brought by Spanish soldiers to the Philippines, and then west to Europe. They travelled across the Atlantic too, though probably not in the cargo hold of Sir Walter Raleigh, as legend has it. They were first described by the Swiss naturalist Gaspard Bauhin in 1596, and their novelty made them a dish of the rich, boosted by a reputation as an aphrodisiac. More generally, though, they were shunned. Their gnarled shape – allegedly like the hand of a leper – sparked rumours they caused leprosy, and their cultivation was banned in France from 1748 to 1772. Yet potatoes could be stored easily, and their underground tubers withstood the burning of other crops by warring armies, so they caught on. In France the pharmacist Antoine-Augustin Parmentier tasted them while imprisoned in Prussia (whose pragmatic ruler Frederick the Great had promoted their cultivation by the peasantry) and brought them back home. He vigorously promoted the potato in aristocratic circles, even serving them, it is said, at a dinner where Benjamin Franklin, then the American ambassador, was a guest.

It worked. Potatoes were legalised and Parmentier's name was immortalised in a dish of potato cubes fried in butter and herbs. Potatoes became a staple dish in many countries (with tragic results in Ireland, where it became the dominant crop and a blight from 1845-49 led to a million deaths). The reign of the one product of the Americas to be found in virtually every European household was a tale that de Bry would surely have relished.

d.gatos
l.sebeco
Costa braua
Cuba.
Davien.
Cariban
El cemi.
Antiochia
VRABA
La Culaca
Arma
PANAMA
Pina.
Quicare
S. Miguel
Cartago
Mapelo
P. de guera.
Cabo de baxas.
Neyua
Cally
P.o.R de peru
Popoian.
R. de S. Tiago.
Quito
Paſto
Los Quillac
S. Tiago
Insula S. Iacobi
ſiue pugna.
Coaque
Atauali
Carangui.
Aiai
Thomebāba.
rara vel ſctu
Tumbes
Tumbes
Los piedras.
R. d. la S. Olalla.
Trapicari
nape.
Tumbes Michaelis.
Tamboblāco
M.
C. Blanca.
Puchio
Loxa.
PERV PROVIN
Chilimazata.
ta
C. de la Enguila.
Chira
Caxamalca
CIA.
Payta
Motupe.
fuit regia
meio
Chimo vallis.
Guacha bāba.
Atabalipæ.
Truxillo
Turicarami
Guara
Vaicoda
a
Los Reyes.
Chintnos.
ontal
Lima vallis
Guamchuco
Lima
Caxamalaca
Tarama
Xaura
Curamba.
Callao Inſ
Piscabamba
Agouaca
Pacalcam
Chichan
Pachacama
Guamāga
Hacari
Arequipa
Cuzco
Ayrama.
Quilca
chiquana.
Canas.
Chuli.
Tiricacha Las
Plata.
Cuquito
Tacama Punta
Arica.
Potoſsi
Tarapaca.p
Tacamapunta

Suala Mons.

TERLICHICHIMICHI

LA FLORIDA

Golfo
Mexicano.

HISPANIA NOVA

MECHOACAN.

MEXICO.

IVCATAN

Costa
brava

PANAMA

PERV PROVIN
CIA

MARE

Circulus Æquinoctialis

P. de los Galopegos.

Chorographia nobilis & opu-
lentæ Peruanæ Provinciæ,
atque Brasiliæ, quas à decimo
ad quintum & quinquagesi-
mum feré gradum ultra Ae
quatorem in longitudinem
patere, diligenti observatione
deprehensum est: ex Aucto=
rum, qui eas Provincias per-
lustrarunt, scriptis recens à
Theodoro de Bry concinnata.

Cæsareæ Matis privilegio
ad quadriennium.
MDXCII.

MARE
Magellanicum siue
pacificu

PARANA

Chili.

Archipelago
minore

Hic Magellanus gigantes
uenit 10 pedum longitud
GIGANTVM REGIO

Estrecho de
Magellanes

Terra del fuo

AMERICAE PARS MAGIS COGNITA

SEPTENTRIO

ORIENTIOR

MAR DEL

OCCIDENS · ORIENS

MERIDIES

Solis

NORT

S.Paulo.

Tropicus Cancri

Hæc maris pars plena est Insulis,scopulis, breuibus
et puluinis valde insidiosis.

P.Sorrocha
Yocajouque siue maior
Lucaya.
Zagareo.
Bahata.

V.de plata.
Anegada
Boriquen
S.Ioh.Insel.
Laquillo
S.Crus
S.Lucia
hipe.
Guada
Buçar Diaues
Patigua
Tortuga
Margarita
Cubaca
Anguilla.
Baruada.
Antigua.
Deseada
Marigalente
Dominica.
Matinno.
S.Vincenta.
Baruodo
Granada
v.de S.B°.
P.de galea

P.Hondo
Costa de gente prata
Valle et clauter 450.Tasso
R.de bordon 400.
Gunma
Camari
Cariaco
Paria.
Auiapari
CARIBANA
Aoripana
Monte espeso
Ancon
Auiapari
R.de S.Vincente
Pincon
Rio dolce
R.Vita baxa
R.Verde
R.Salada
Aldea
de arpoled

Rio de las
Amazones.

R.da Madalena
Aiaurisama
PARGVANA
Maªrannion
flu.
Provincia
de Omagua
NOVA
Uratamban.
Maragnon flu.
B
Chicara
R.de Terroycori.
Para guate.
TISNADA
Chimos
Humos
R.Arboledai
R.Aoripana
Orellana.
Topeyos
R.de las
Maragno flu.
BRESILIA
AMAZONES R. de la

Monte pascual
R.de reges
Portus S.Lucia
D.rodolos sisratos
R.de Tenero
R.de baxos
R.das pescari
R.S.Andre
R.de faneiro
R.del estremo
Aldea.

Quitaaieno
V.y de Fernando
C.Negro
Ora
R.de S.Domingo
Ba.de conceiça
Porto Securo
R.das asretas.
Baia fermosa.
Ba.de S.Dominico
C.de S.Augustino.
Baia de todos
Sanctos.
Portus teales.
Porto Real ad quem Galli
mercatum nauigant.
Sinus S.Georgy
R.S.Elena.
C.da brolho.
R.S.londim
Ascension.
Baxos d'Abre ojo
B.d.Saluador.
Latrinidad.
S.Maria.

Tropicus Capricorni

OCEA

NVS ÆTHIO
PICVS

R.de Peti.
R.Parana
Asumption.
S.Anna
Mepenes.
El grand Rio de parana
Ningatas P.
Camechingones.
Ningatas.
R.de Xanaes
R.de Carcarae
S.Espirito
R.d.Carangomo.
R.de laplata
R.Carcarana
ACVTIA
Rio de la Plata
P.d.S.Vincti.
C.d.Cuenca
R.d.Cameça
B.das vollas.
R.dus patus.
B.d.Negros
Costa draha
B.dus ithus
C.S.Maria
C.Frio.
Ponta grossa
Punta de buen
abrigo
V.S.Catelina.
Tibiquiri
Promontorium diue virginis
Pieraliasdes.
V.de aque.
Hic repertus fluuius
aquæ dulcis in quo sste sunt
7.gemmarum inside.
B.das correntes.
P.de S.Helena.
Baia de baxos anegados.
Palmares.

CHICA
R.d.S.Mathia
Terra baxa
Baia sin fundo
Baretas blancas
Tres puntas
B.d.S.Mathia
Patagones
B.de Caballos
Arroças d'lobos
rium
delle ysllois
iteria
C.de crepusculo.
C.d.S.Domigo.
C.blanco
P.de S.Helena.
B.da Fondura
C.d.3.puntas.

Ex Geograph: calculo   tres gradus conficiũt
lxxx.leucas.gallicas,siue ccxl. miliaria italica
singuli ergo gradus fere xxvii.leue.gal.præcise
verò lxxx.mil. ital. comprehendunt.

The Portuguese and the Spice Trade

The Cantino planisphere, named after the agent of the Duke of Ferrara who smuggled it to Italy in 1502, contained precious intelligence. The unknown Portuguese mapmaker who drew it showed for the first time the coastline of Brazil. What he was unable to portray was the Spice Islands, the El Dorado of the east, which the Portuguese were only just beginning to access: the spot where they should be (the modern Moluccas and Banda Islands) is resolutely blank.

Spices were the oil of the Middle Ages, with the added allure that they were considered to possess medicinal properties, since cloves were valued for warding off the plague and pepper was believed to improve failing eyesight. Just like oil, they led westerners to meddle in the geopolitics of the east, trying to gain control of the trade routes and of the sources of the fabulously valuable commodities.

Nutmeg and mace could only be acquired in the Banda Islands; cloves, which grew solely on volcanic Ternate, Tidore and a few smaller specks in the Moluccas, could be bought at a comparatively low price by Chinese and Javanese merchants who then shipped their cargo to India. There, along with pepper from the Malabar Coast and cinnamon from Ceylon, they were taken by Arab merchants to Cairo and Constantinople, and then a portion sold to Venetian traders at a price between ten and 100 times the original cost in the Spice Islands. By the time it reached London in the 14th century, a pound of nutmeg was enough to buy a cow.

The Portuguese exploration of the west coast of Africa (see pages 78–9) was principally motivated by the desire to find an alternative route to the Spice Islands, bypassing the Muslim powers' grip on the trade. The Ottoman capture of Constantinople in 1453 made this more urgent, and so it must have been with some relief that the Portuguese court heard that Bartolomeu Dias had rounded the Cape of Good Hope in 1488, proving that sceptics who had quoted the Greco-Roman geographer Ptolemy to assert that a land mass would block that route were wrong.

The race to India was now on. Portuguese vessels explored the coast of east Africa, and in 1497 Vasco da Gama was dispatched with a tiny flotilla of three ships to bridge the gap over the Indian Ocean. On April 24, 1498 he set off from the coast of east Africa with a pilot supplied by the Sultan of Melinde (no doubt glad to get rid of him, as the Portuguese were violent and predatory guests). Out of sight of land for weeks, the crew developed scurvy, but on May 18 spotted the Malabar Coast.

Once in India, da Gama continued his undiplomatic ways, taking hostages and alienating the *zamorin*, the Hindu ruler of Calicut, by the ragbag collection of goods he presented as a gift, including a dozen pieces of striped cloth, four scarlet hoods, six hats and four strings of coral. With relations with both the *zamorin* and local Muslim traders – who saw that the Portuguese intended to encroach on their trade – deteriorating dramatically, da Gama departed, reaching Lisbon in September 1499. Although the ships brought back a small cargo of spice, the voyage had been a commercial failure. As a strategic proposition, however, it was a resounding success. The way to the east, and the spices, was open.

Da Gama's voyage would lead to the establishment of the *Estado da India* ("State of India"), a Portuguese empire of the East supervised by a viceroy based in Goa. In the map on page 115, the Dutch cartographer Johannes Baptista van Doetechum the Younger portrays the town in 1595, at the height of Portuguese power, with bustling wharfs and the palace of the viceroy ("As cazas do Vizorey") arrayed along the waterfront.

It took barely a decade for Portugal to establish a grip on southern India and then seize control of the Spice Islands themselves. Da Gama undertook a second

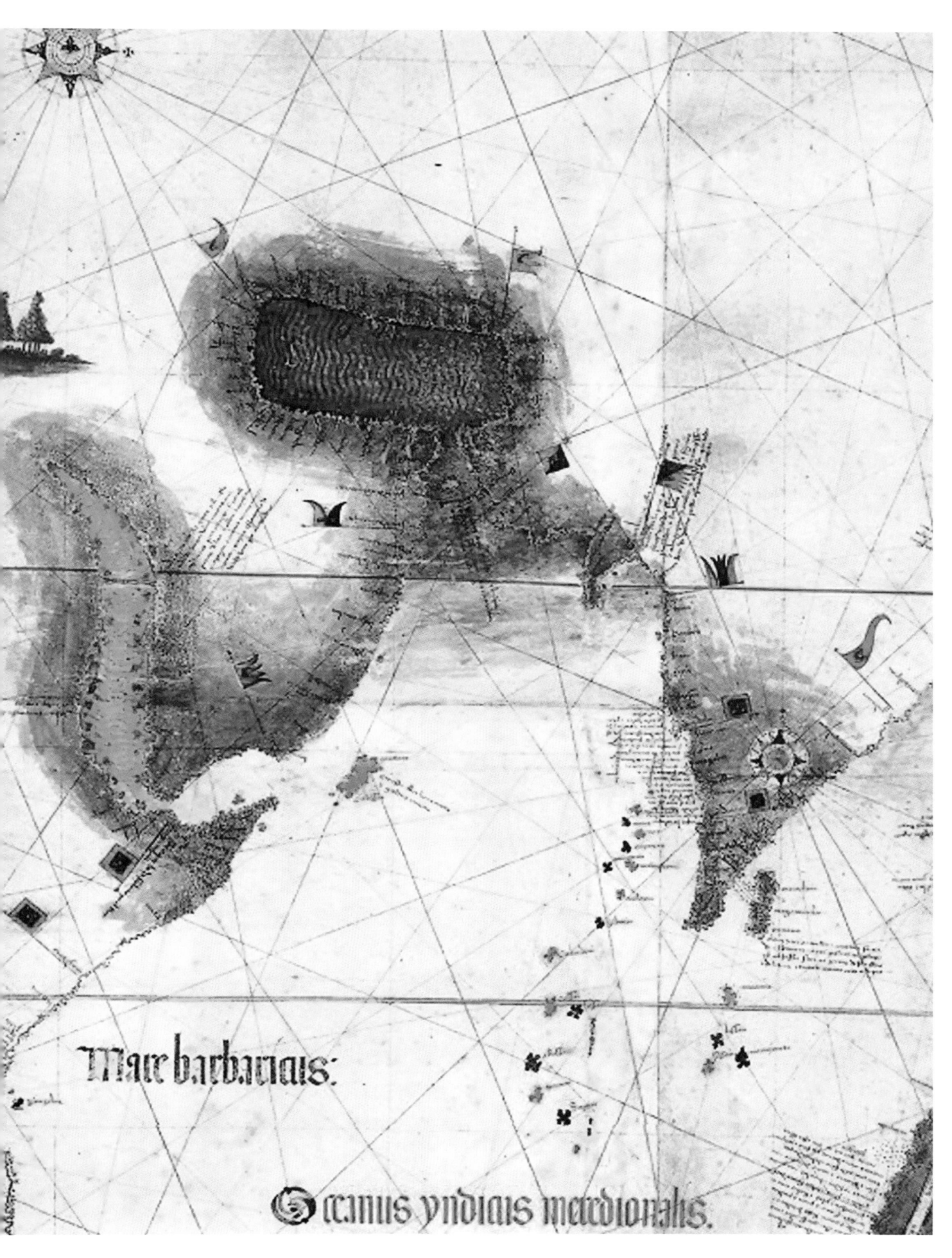

Mare barbaricus:

Occanus yndicus meridionalis.

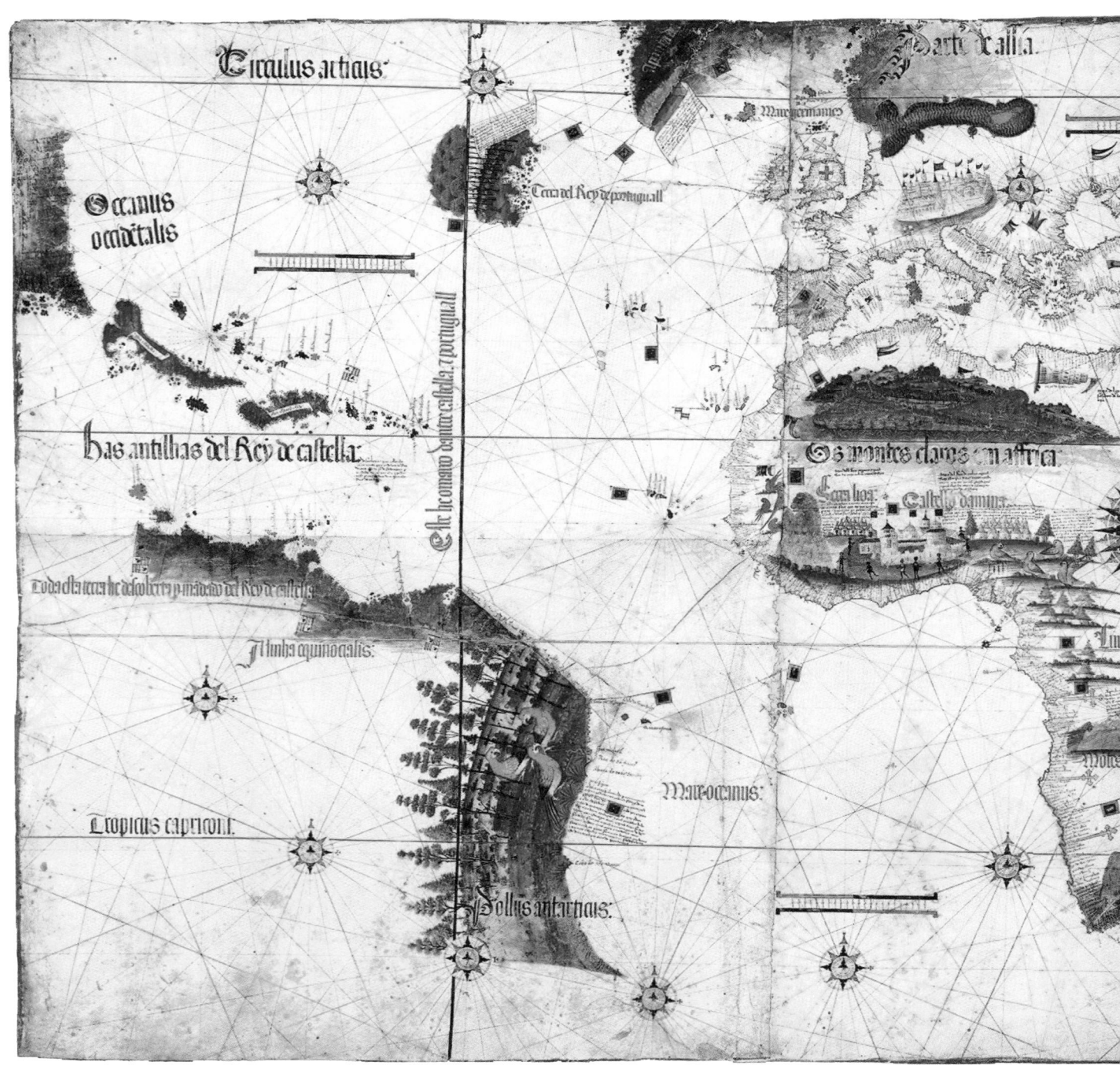

Circulus articus

Oceanus occidentalis

Terra del Rey de portugall

Parte de asia

Mare germanie

Has antillas del Rey de castella

Este he o marco entre castella e portugall

Os montes claros em affrica

Can hoa   Castello damina

Toda esta terra he descoberta por madado del Rey de castella

Linha equinoçialis

Tropicus capricorni

Mare occeanus

Pollus antarticus

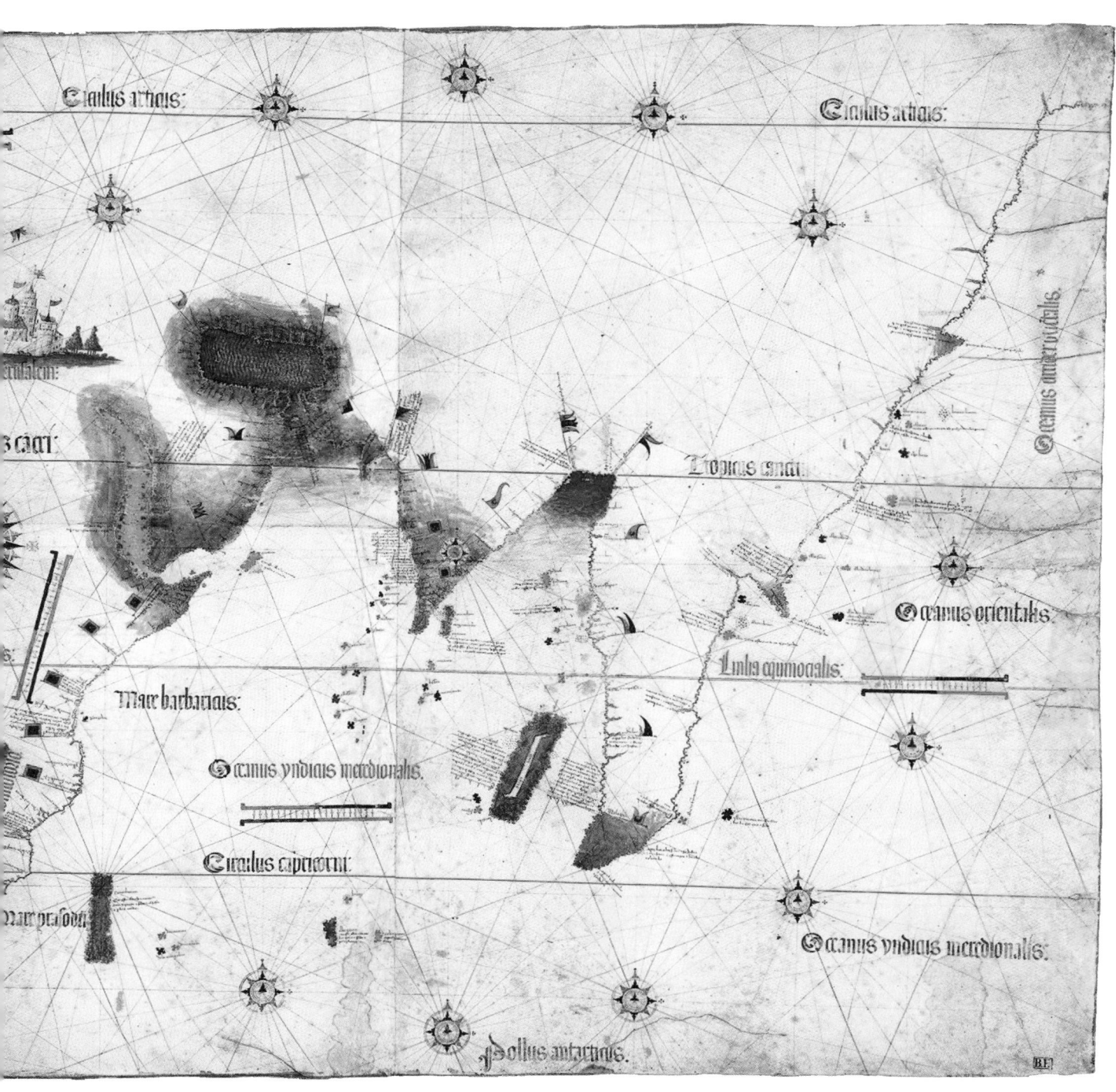

Circulus articus:
Circulus articus:

Oceanus amentudialis

occidentalem

s cancr:
Tropicus cancri.

Oceanus orientalis.

Linha equinoalis:

Mare barbaricus:

Oceanus yndicus meridionalis.

Oceanus yndicus meridionalis.

Circulus capricorni:

Mare pscodum

Pollus antarticus.

voyage in 1502. His abrasive conduct heightened by the lure of profit, this time he crushed an Arab fleet and made the *zamorin* sue for peace, returning with over 1,700 tons of pepper and 400 tons of cinnamon, cloves, mace and nutmeg.

By 1505 the Portuguese court had sent out its first viceroy, Francisco de Almeida, who systematically subdued the ports of Malabar and established a firm grip on the pepper and cinnamon trade. In 1509 he was succeeded by Afonso de Albuquerque, a ruthless and talented administrator and a naval tactician of genius. With an eye for the choke points of trade, in 1513 he tried unsuccessfully to capture Aden, which dominated the narrow Bab al Mandab channel, the entrance to the Red Sea. However, the assault on Malacca in 1511, where the local ruler Sultan Mahmud Shah was unpopular for his treatment of Hindus, was a resounding success. Now in control of the Strait of Malacca – between the Malay Peninsula and Sumatra – the Portuguese were in a position to strike even farther east.

In 1512 a flotilla led by António de Abreu and Francisco Serrão headed east towards the Spice Islands themselves. They reached the Bandas and Ternate, loading their vessels so heavily with nutmeg and cloves that one of them split apart. The Portuguese fleet also made the Sultan of Ternate an offer he could not refuse, which allowed them to establish a fort at Tolukko and to begin the domination of the Spice Islands through a chain of fortified posts.

With Portugal now in control of the entire chain of the spice trade, from the producing islands to the transhipment points in the Malay Peninsula and India, its wealth looked assured, especially when Spain sold its claim to the Spice Islands to Portugal for 350,000 ducats in 1529. Yet defending such a vast empire strained Portuguese resources, and the toll exacted by tropical disease and shipwrecks proved crippling. Over time Dutch sailors had to be called in to fill the shortfall, and they assiduously reported on what they had seen once home. Portugal so alienated the Ternatans – most notably by executing Sultan Hairun in 1570 – that a revolt erupted which led to the sacking of the fort on the island in 1575. The union of Portugal and Spain in 1580 privileged Spanish interests and, as the Dutch began to enter the Indian Ocean after the foundation of the VOC in 1602 (see pages 116–17), the Portuguese hold on the spice trade crumbled. The Dutch built a fort on Ternate in 1607 and by 1641 had captured Malacca. Spice, the glittering prize that da Gama and Albuquerque had won, had slipped from the Portuguese grasp.

d Vacas.

S. Paulo

A Trindade

N S da Luz

Forca

S. Andre

Sprital dos pobres

Pilour⁹ novo

Boticas

Rua dos ouriues

Pilourinho velho

Boticas

R. dos Carriçados

R. d aruore

R. do Açouge

Açouge

das Capllaens

S. Ant⁹

N.S. da Serra

A. mizericordia

Rua dos Jurradores

A. Rua dereita

Bº Ihs

N.S. da graça

Terr⁹ dos gallos

Terr⁹ de S. Ant⁹

O. Leilão

Caua

As 3. Igrejas

Inquisição

O. mandoui

Terr⁹ de Sabaio

A. cam⁹ra

A Se

S. Fran⁹

Vaz⁹ de S. Fran⁹

Caua

Os Contes

casas de archino

As naos d ormus

Terreiro do Vizorey

Spital del Rey

S. Mart⁹

O. tronco

As cazas do Vizorey

A. moeda

As cha gas

A. Ribeira grande

Bangasal

O. peso

O. terreiro

Ribª das gales

O. cays de Sª Caterª

Bazar grande

Alfandega

Champanas e cotias de gentios.

A.

'tNieuwe huys van
H. Bischoff

BATAVIA

Speelenburg

Koghallen

Ambon

Gaertens

Chinees Kerkhof

Nieuwe ge Plantu=

le witt

in Broock

Quartier

Quartier

Kaan

Assen

Craft

Maastenels sluys

Kryg't molen

Joosk

Iacatra

Vyffhoeck

Rodenburg

Pantier molen

Belvidere

Bolar

Rys Velden

Rys Velden

Sugker Riet
en Rys
Velden.

Van Hoorn

Stalmester

Noordwyck

Ryswyck

Briel

Buyten Wache

Nieuwe
Plantage

La

BA

Rynlandtsche Roeden van 12 voeten.

100   500   600   700   800   900   1000

The Dutch East India Company

Framed by a green sea of rice fields, the town of Batavia seems a fragile thing. Yet the fleet of ships approaching from the real sea on Dutch cartographer Jacob van Meurs's map reveals a different truth. The town hall enclosed within the settlement's wall formed the epicentre of one of the world's greatest and most ruthless trading empires, which by the 1680s – when this map was drafted – dominated much of southeast Asia and its lucrative spice trade.

From 1619 Batavia was the headquarters of the Vereenigde Oostindische Compagnie (VOC), the Dutch East India Company, affectionately known to its admirers as *Jan Compagnie*. The company drew its strength from a long-established mercantile tradition – the Dutch had begun to dominate the herring industry from the 1420s – and an inventiveness which had led them to pioneer an early form of futures market (selling the herring before it was even caught).

The Spanish annexation of Portugal in 1580, which made Portuguese colonies into enemy territory, offered the Dutch a chance to enter the Spice Islands (now named the Moluccas, part of modern-day Indonesia), the sole source of cloves and nutmeg, for which demand in Europe was sky-high. So, in 1595 Cornelis de Houtman led a fleet of four ships owned by the recently established "Company of the Far Regions" right into the heart of Portuguese-ruled Java. De Houtman's voyage yielded little profit – only a small cargo of pepper made it back to Amsterdam – but it highlighted the potential, and soon several Dutch fleets a year were heading east. In 1602 the government of the United Provinces (the independent Netherlands) stepped in to prevent disorderly competition and granted a 21-year monopoly on trade to the Spice Islands to a single company, the VOC.

Governed by the *Heeren XVII*, a board of 17 directors, the VOC sent its first ship to the Malay Archipelago in 1603, a voyage that yielded a huge return. With the Portuguese standing in the way of even greater profits, the *Heeren XVII* ordered their expulsion. VOC forces captured Ambon and Ternate in 1605, and from there a spider's web of Dutch forts spread across the East Indies, with a base at Jayakarta in western Java established in 1610, which by 1618 had become Batavia.

The Dutch East India Company now had free rein in the east, and its forceful director Jan Pieterszoon Coen had the entire native population of the clove-producing Banda Islands executed and replaced by slaves. The number of outbound VOC ships from the Netherlands surged to 151 in the 1620s, and the average annual value of their imports rose from 400 million pesos to over four times that amount 60 years later.

With their position assured, the Dutch muscled in on new areas – capturing Ceylon, the centre of the cinnamon trade, in 1637. Yet, over time, the VOC's powerful grip eventually weakened. The small size of the Netherlands meant that the Dutch were progressively overhauled in manpower, wealth and, most alarmingly, military power. The peace settlement after the Anglo-Dutch War of 1780-84 gave the English right of free trade in the Spice Islands for the first time, further damaging the VOC's liquidity. The outbreak of the French Revolutionary Wars delivered the final coup de grâce, and in 1799, virtually bankrupt and a decrepit shadow of its former self, the Dutch East India Company saw its monopoly cancelled. The company was dissolved; it was a pitiful end for the world's first global megacorporation. In its wake Batavia reverted from bustling trading hub to local administrative headquarters, only to rediscover its destiny in the 20th century as the Indonesian capital Jakarta.

The Portuguese
and the Japan Trade

The 18th-century Dutch edition of Jacques-Nicolas Bellin's plan of the Japanese city of Nagasaki shows a pattern of buildings around what had once been a prosperous international port. At its centre lies the tiny artificial island of Dejima, which by the mid-17th century had become Japan's sole conduit to the outside world.

The first Europeans to engage with Japan were the Portuguese, who came northwards from their Chinese bridgehead at Macao. The first landfall, though, was an accident, when three traders were forced ashore by a typhoon at Tanegashima island on the southern tip of the Japanese archipelago in 1543. They came at an opportune time, as relations between China and Japan had deteriorated, which led to an interruption of trade, and before long a regular flow of vessels was plying between Macao and Japan.

In 1550 King João III, who richly earned his nickname *O Colonizador* ("The Coloniser"), declared the burgeoning trade to be a royal monopoly. From then on one vessel a year set out from Macao (increasing to several after 1600) to profit from trading Chinese silk for Japanese lacquerware and silver in exchange for a licence costing tens of thousands of cruzados.

What the Portuguese brought above all was guns and the Gospel. Japan was in the midst of a civil war which dated back to the 1460s, and the *daimyo* (warlords) who fought in it were eager customers for the muskets which Portuguese merchants carried with them. As in the Americas, those merchants were accompanied by missionaries, who were led in Japan by the Jesuit priest Francis Xavier, who arrived in 1549. The Jesuits succeeded in converting sympathetic *daimyo*, notably Omura Sumitada, who allowed the establishment of a Portuguese settlement at Nagasaki in 1571 and granted them outright possession in 1580. So it was

there that the *Nanban-jin* ("southern barbarians") docked their ship each year, and a large Japanese Christian community emerged, nearly 215,000 strong by the early 1590s.

As the Japanese civil war wound to an end and the country approached reunification, its new rulers became unhappy with the growing foreign influence. In 1587 Toyotomi Hideyoshi ordered the expulsion of Christian missionaries, but the decree was ineffective. Once Tokugawa Ieyasu defeated the last of his rivals and established the Tokugawa shogunate in 1603, Japan's new rulers gradually strengthened central control. In 1634 Shogun Iemitsu ordered Portuguese merchants to be confined to Nagasaki, where Dejima island was constructed to house them safely offshore. In 1635 they issued the first of the Sakoku (or isolationist) edicts, effectively outlawing Christianity. The involvement of Christian samurai in the Shimabara rebellion of 1637-38 was the final straw, and in 1639 the Portuguese merchant community was expelled. When the authorities at Canton (now Guangzhou) in China sent an embassy to protest, 61 of its 74 members were beheaded. The Dutch, who were corralled in Dejima from 1641, wisely did not resist.

So, from then until 1853, when the US naval officer Commodore Perry sailed into Tokyo Bay to force the Japanese to open up trade at the barrel of a gun, the shogunate kept Japan isolated. A trickle of trade went through Dejima, where 20 Dutch merchants resided, and which Chinese trading junks were also allowed to visit. Yet, for the most part, Japan was closed, one of history's rare examples of a nation rejecting trade.

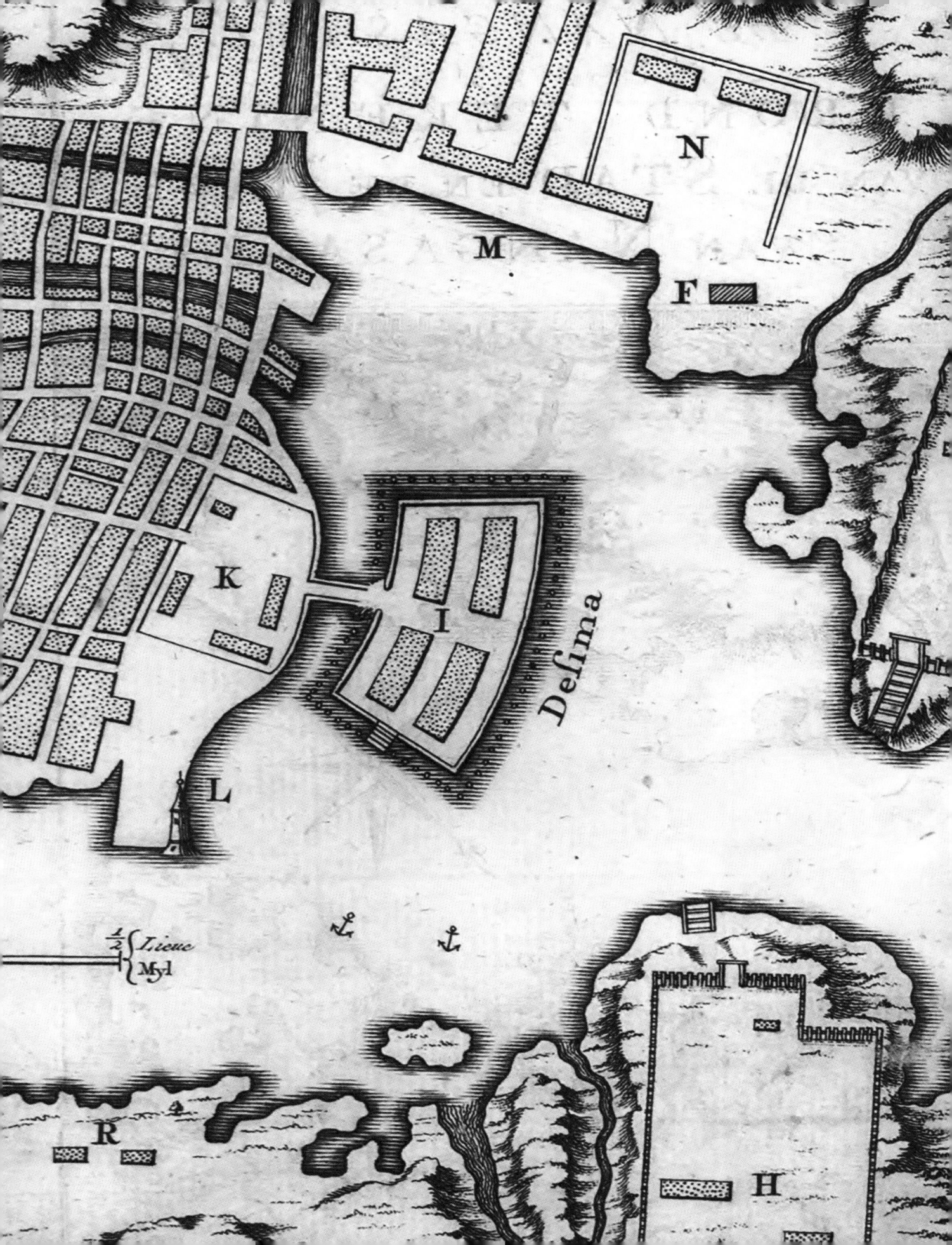

N

M

F

Defima

K

I

L

½ Lieue
Myl

R

H

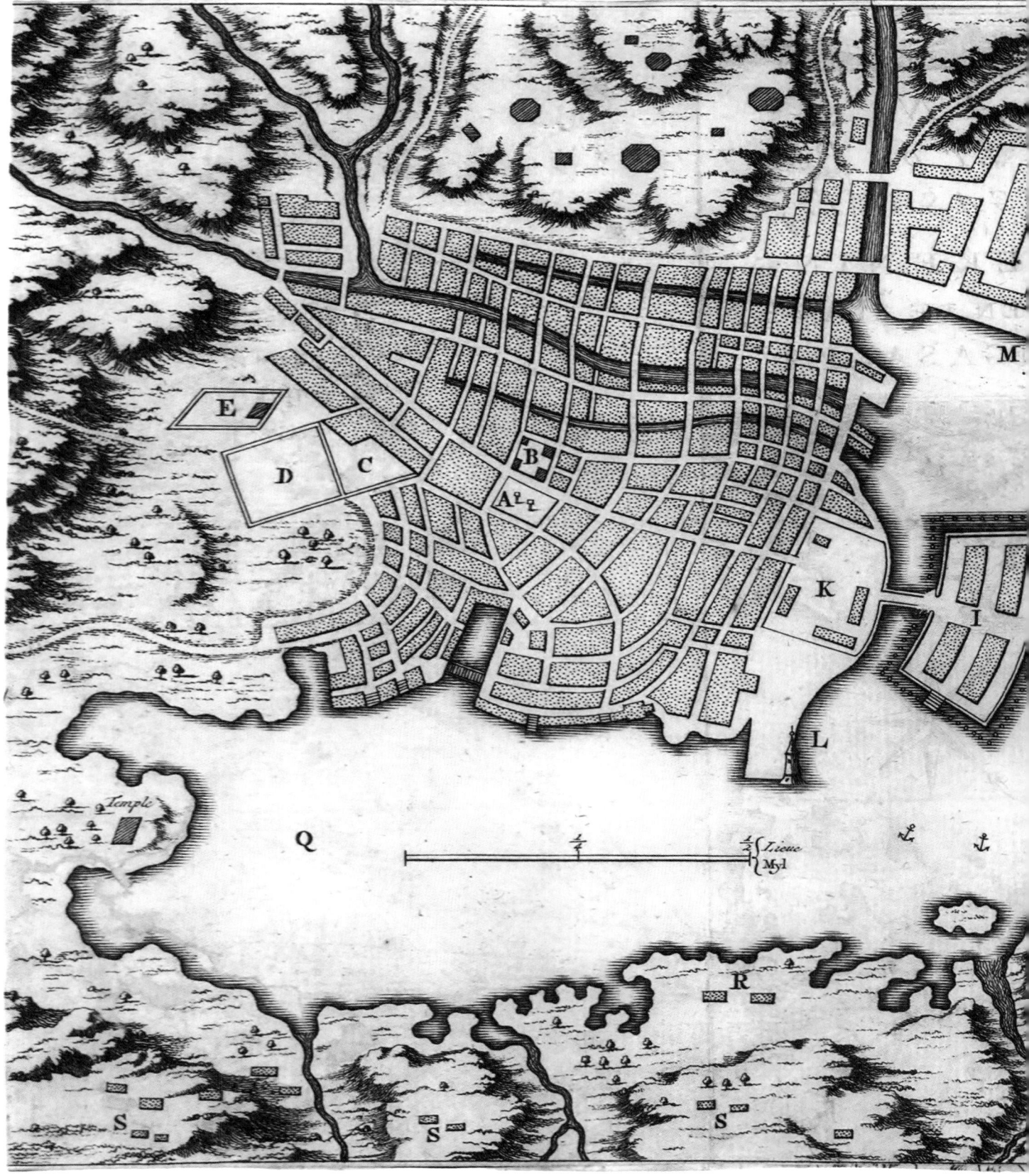

E

D C

B

A

M

K

I

L

Temple

Q

¼ | Lieue
My-l

R

S S S

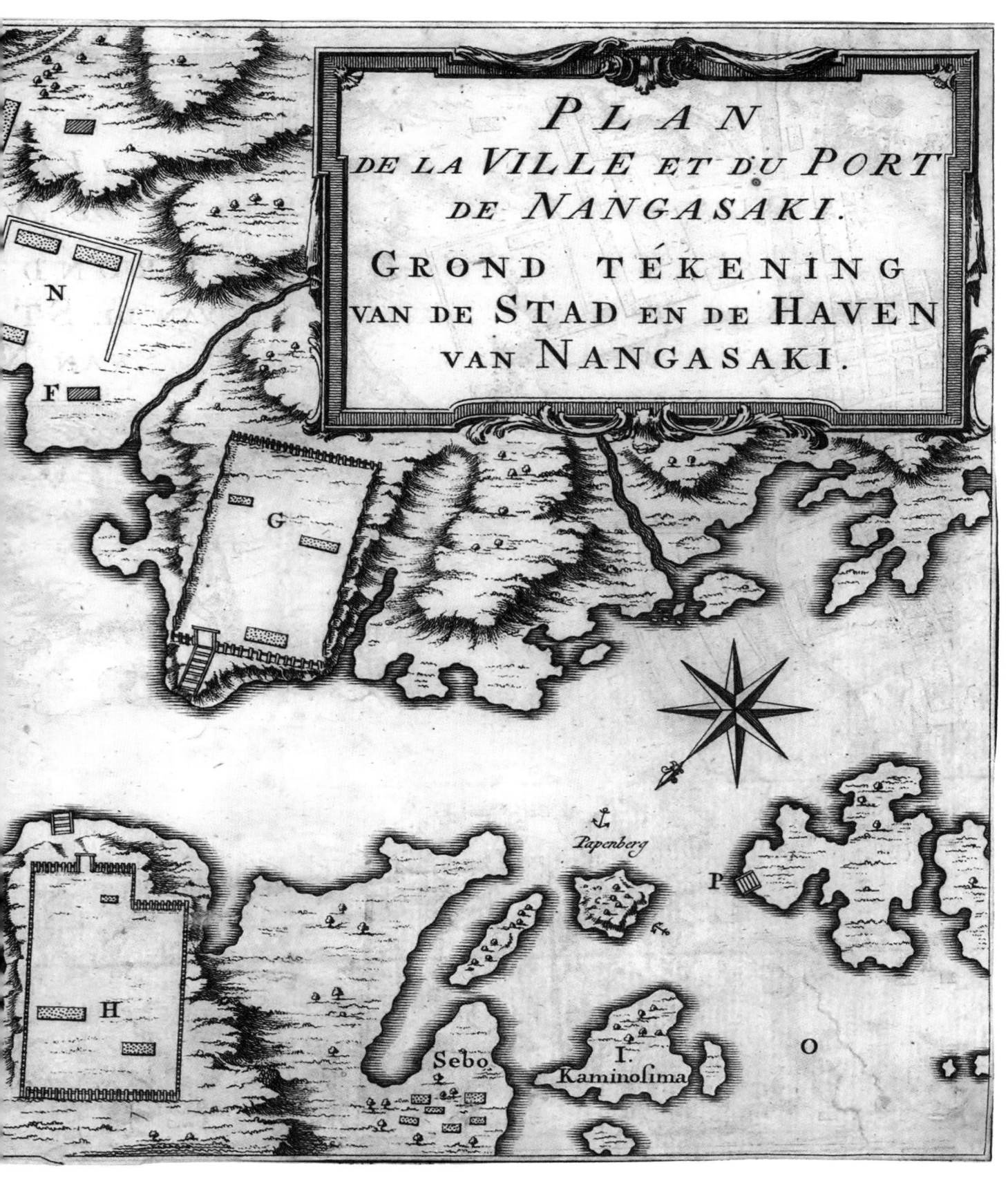

PLAN
DE LA VILLE ET DU PORT
DE NANGASAKI.

GROND TÉKENING
van de STAD en de HAVEN
van NANGASAKI.

N

F

G

H

Papenberg

P

Sebo

I.
Kaminosima

O

terra ouero Mare incognito

STRETTO DI ANNIAN

GOLFO DI CHENAN

Mare Cin

MANGI MARE EOO

Mare dell China

GIAPAN, ouero Cipangu
Isola

Portugal's China Trade

The Italian Dominican friar Ignazio Danti's spectacular map of China's eastern coastline comes from a series he painted in the 1560s and 1570s for the Palazzo Vecchio in Florence. An able mathematician and cosmographer who designed a number of armillary spheres (models of the solar system), Danti would have appreciated the growing geographical knowledge of the East brought by Portuguese exploration.

Portugal sought to establish links with Ming China almost as soon at its ships entered the Spice Islands. In 1517, four years after the first Portuguese vessel scouted the Chinese coast, Manuel I sent a formal embassy led by Fernão Pires de Andrade and Tomé Pires. After prolonged negotiations, Portuguese ships were allowed to dock at Canton (now Guangzhou), but the death in 1521 of the Zhengde emperor, who had been sympathetic to the Portuguese cause, and the presence at the court of the sultan of Malacca, whom the Portuguese had deposed (see pages 110–15) turned sentiment against them. Andrade and Pires were arrested and died in captivity, and Canton was closed to foreign trade until 1530.

Portugal had much to offer the Chinese, whose economy had an insatiable thirst for silver, and whose market also craved the spices which the Portuguese could now provide. The Portuguese *Estado da India* ("State of India") could ship pepper and cinnamon from India and cloves, nutmeg and sandalwood from the Spice Islands, as well as the silver – which had come from Mexico via Manila – that its traders sold in exchange for some of those goods in Japan.

The Chinese authorities allowed a small trading settlement to be established at Macao in 1557, in exchange for the payment of customs dues to the Ming government. Controls, though, were strict

and Portuguese sailors and merchants were not permitted to venture beyond a gate which blocked the isthmus linking Macao with the mainland. The port prospered and by 1585 had grown into a city with its own municipal council and provided a regular stopping point for the vessels which plied the Goa to Nagasaki trade, arriving in time for one of the great Canton silk fairs in June or January.

In both India and Japan the Portuguese used Christian missionaries to generate a constituency of converts sympathetic to their presence. In China, however, they faced far greater obstacles. In 1582 the Jesuits sent Matteo Ricci from Macao to proselytise mainland China. His approach was to learn as much as he could about Chinese culture, composing a Chinese–Portuguese dictionary and dressing in elite mandarin costume, but he was not permitted to proceed to the Imperial Palace in Beijing until 1601. Although Ricci became an adviser to the Wanli emperor and converted a number of high-ranking officials to Christianity, before his death in 1610, the numbers remained strictly limited.

As Portugal's hold on the east slackened, with the Portuguese expulsion from much of the Spice Islands in 1575, the increasing encroachment of the Dutch and the loss of Nagasaki in 1639, Macao became marooned as an outpost of a trading network that no longer existed. Although it continued in Portuguese hands, trade never returned to the levels which passed through its warehouses in the golden decades after 1557. Finally, in 1999 Macao was returned to Chinese control, which marked the end of the last vestige of the Portuguese empire in the East.

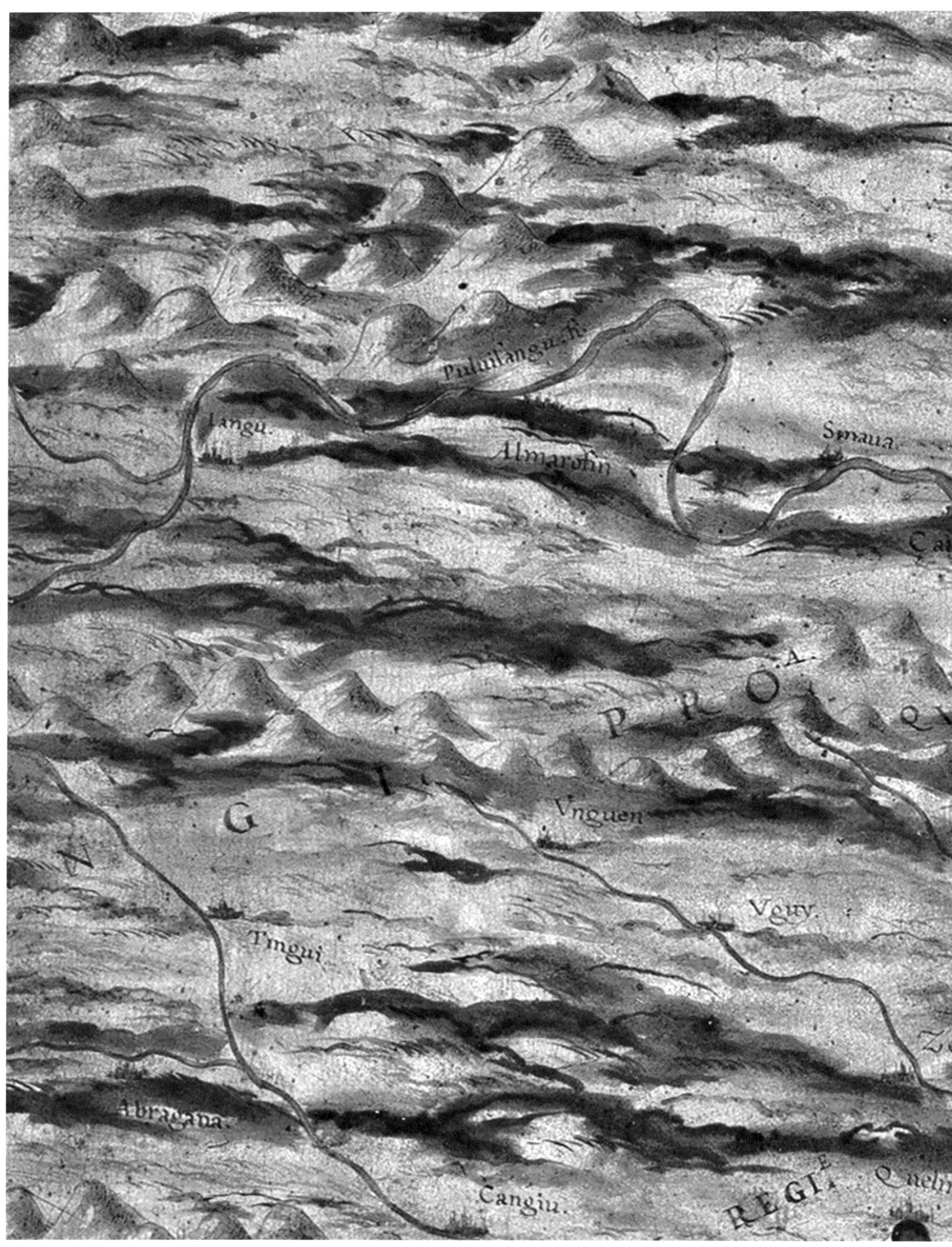

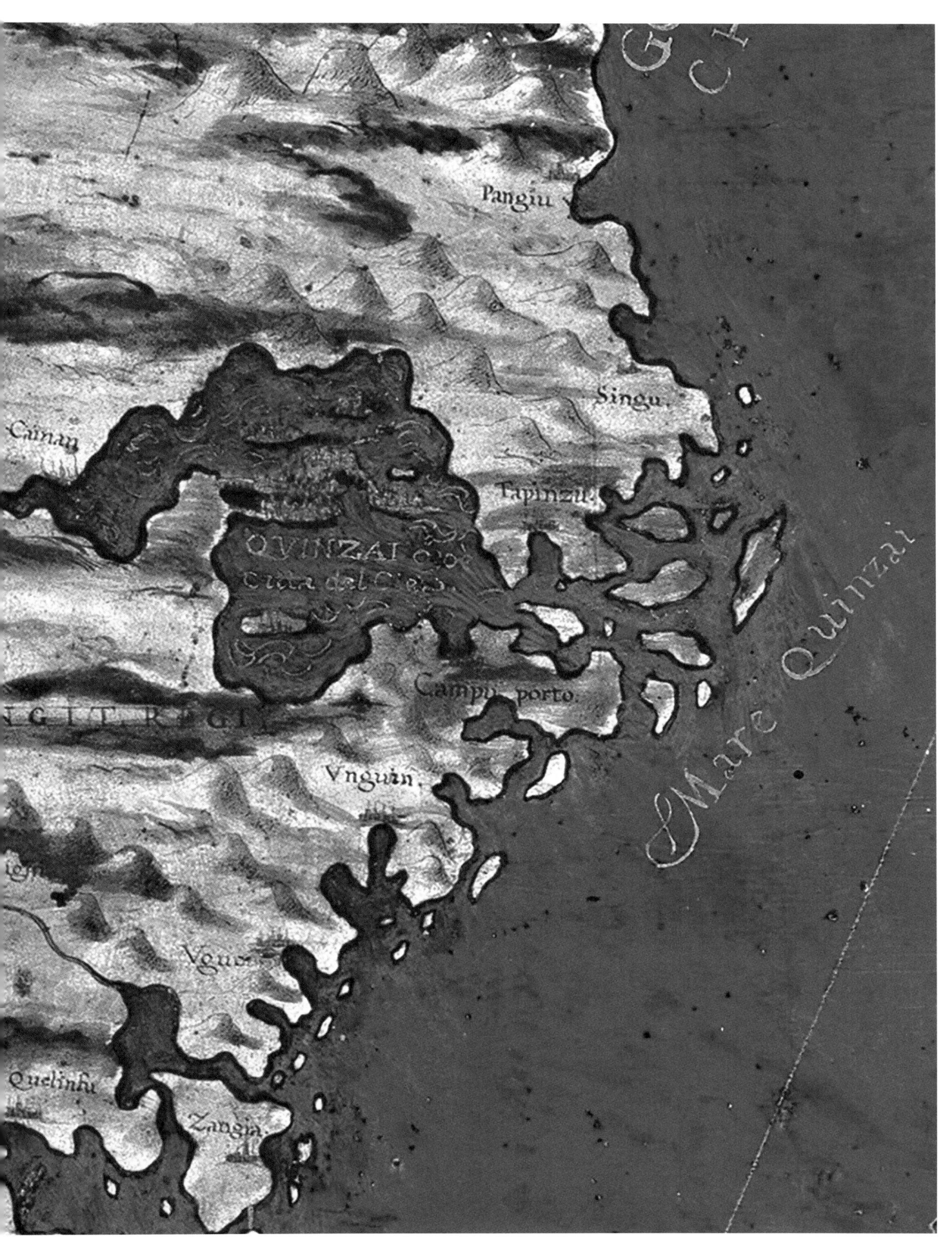

Pangiu

Singu.

Cainan

Tapinzu

QVINZAI cioe
Citta del Cielo

Campu porto.

GIT REGII

Vnguin

Mare Quinzai

Vgui

Quelinfu

Zangia

Sweden, Russia and North European Trade in the 16th Century

The map, a 1572 issue of a 1539 original by the Swedish cleric Olaus Magnus, is the first map to show Sweden in any detail. Its seascape is a riot of marine creatures both mythical and imaginary, while on the land leaping reindeer, hunters and trappers give a sense of the rich resources of the countries around the Baltic Sea.

Olaus, who had fled his native country by 1530, when the Reformation began to make Sweden uncomfortable for Catholic priests, would have had a sense of the geopolitics of the Baltic, whose shores (and trade routes) had become the subject of a bitter struggle for control between the Swedes, Danes, Poles and the up-and-coming power of Russia. The keys to controlling commerce were the Polish port of Danzig – through which grain, copper, lead and iron flowed – and southern Baltic ports such as Reval (modern Tallinn in Estonia) and Narva, which allowed access to the Russian interior and its rich trade in furs.

Sweden rose to the challenge, its greatness established by Gustavus Vasa (reigned 1523-60), and supported by the country's rich copper and iron ore deposits, which financed its growing army and bought imports of grain and salt. By 1561 Sweden had captured Reval and in 1581 took Narva, establishing a hegemony over the southern Baltic which lasted until it lost Reval in 1710.

By doing so they blocked the ambitions of the Grand Duchy of Muscovy, which under Ivan III (reigned 1462-1505) had consolidated Russia's previously fractious principalities and conquered the merchant republic of Novgorod in 1478. Further expansion eastwards into Kazan had created a trading network that stretched from the Black Sea almost to the Baltic and which exploited Russia's enormous natural resources, particularly furs such as sable and ermine, which were highly prized in the Ottoman Empire. Under Ivan IV (whose swing to erratic autocracy later in his reign gave him the nickname "the Terrible"), Russia took Narva in 1558, and at once merchants from all over Europe rushed there to access the Russian fur trade. Yet Russia's window on the Baltic remained open less than a quarter of a century, and instead it turned eastwards towards Siberia, where from the 1580s the Stroganov family and their Cossack fighters pushed Russian control eastwards as far as Okhotsk on the Pacific coast in the 1640s.

The one possible opening to the west offered by the arrival in 1553 of Richard Chancellor on a mission from the London-based Company of Merchant Adventurers (later the Muscovy Company) proved small consolation. Although Chancellor made his way to Moscow and was received by Ivan IV (no doubt with some trepidation, as the tsar was reputed to have nailed a hat to the head of a French ambassador who failed to doff it in his presence), the trade through Archangel which continued until 1649 was relatively small-scale. Russian furs, wax, timber and grain were loaded onto the company ships in return for cotton, weapons, wine and salt, but the English were soon overtaken by the Dutch, who in 1604 sent 17 ships to Archangel to their nine, and in 1698 the company's monopoly was revoked. It would not be until Peter the Great's victory against Sweden in the Great Northern War (1700-21) and the foundation in 1703 of St Petersburg, which became the new capital of the Russian Empire in 1712, that Russia would once again become a Baltic power.

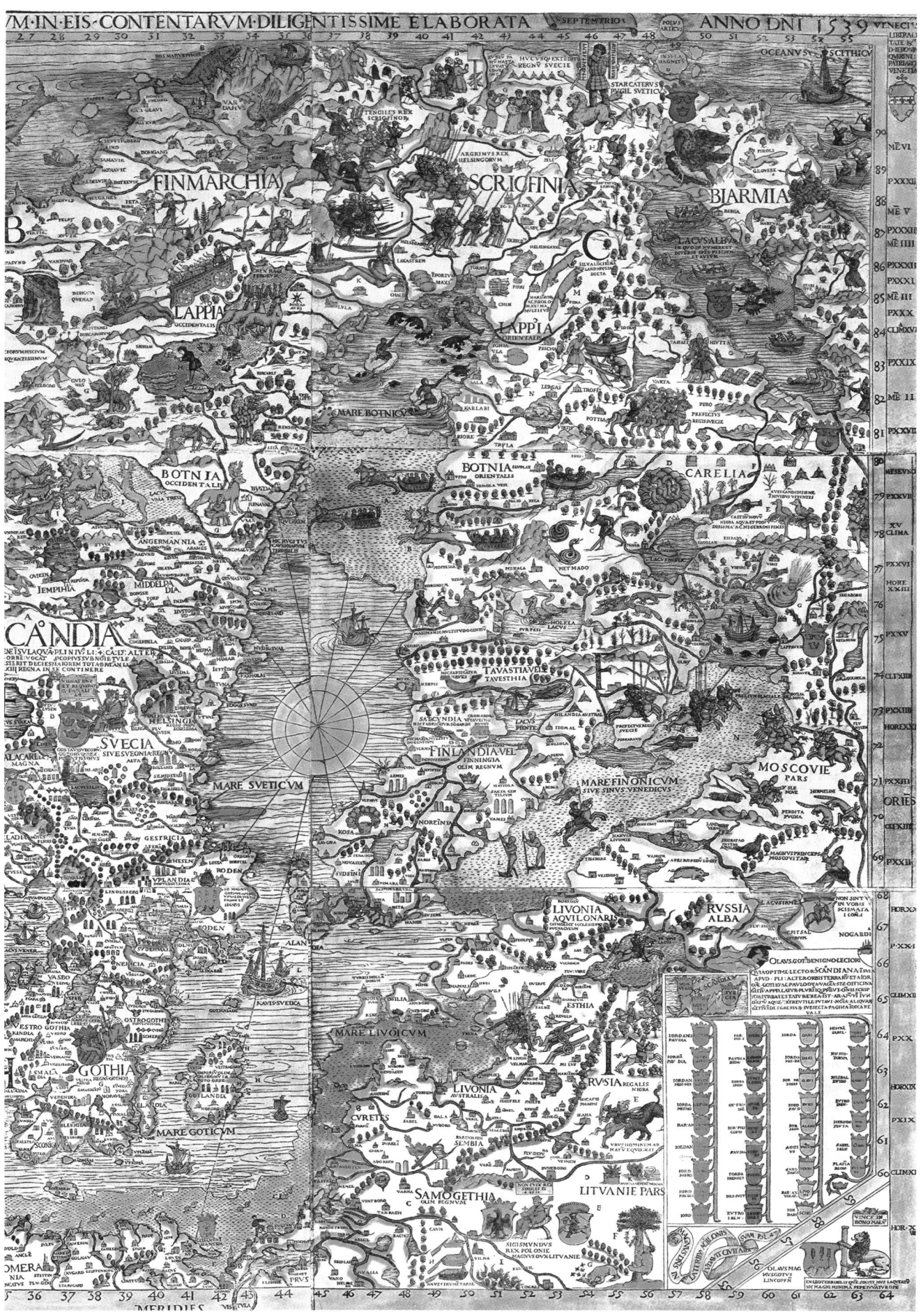

The British in India

James Rennell's 1782 map of Hindoostan marks a moment of transition for Britain's power in India. Its dominant position there had been achieved through a private organisation, the English East India Company. It was in its service that Rennell had made his career, beginning as a callow 14-year-old midshipman and rising to the rank of Surveyor General in 1764, a post he held for 13 years. It was also a body which had never really been intended to trade with India, let alone to conquer it.

Like so much in the Age of Exploration, the company's foundation was driven by spice. When the Dutch cornered the market in pepper in 1599, tripling its price, a group of merchants lobbied Elizabeth I to grant them a monopoly on trade from England to the Indies. Chartered in 1600, the East India Company delivered enormous returns to its investors, but the Dutch reacted violently, and the beheading of ten English merchants on Amboina (now Ambon) in 1623 led the company to retreat from the Spice Islands.

Fortunately, in 1609 it had had the foresight to get permission from the Mogul emperor Jahangir to establish a trading post at Surat in northwest India, from where a small-scale trade in cotton, saltpetre and indigo dye began. The company's directors set up further trading bases in Madras (1639) and Bombay (1668) – which had been acquired from the Portuguese as part of the dowry on Catherine of Braganza's marriage to Charles II – and finally Calcutta (1690).

Together with Surat, these became the presidencies, or main company headquarters in India, from which it profited mightily from the growing taste back home for Indian cotton chintzes and calicoes (both coloured fabrics). By 1720 around 15 per cent of British imports were from India, the lion's share brokered by the company. As the Mogul state weakened in the early 18th century, the company turned from coastal enclaves to the acquisition of territory inland. Their French rivals in *La compagnie française des Indes orientales* were driven out in the Carnatic Wars of the 1740s and 1750s, and the victory of Robert Clive over the nawab of Bengal and his French allies at Plassey in 1757 delivered all Bengal to them (and a huge fortune to Clive, who was accused of corruption on his return to Britain in 1760).

South India followed when the company's army, which by then was approaching 250,000 strong, overcame the kingdom of Mysore in 1799. Yet, commercially, the East India Company was showing strains. The cost of defending its new empire was crippling, even without the inefficiency and graft that plagued it. The Regulating Act (1773) and the India Act (1784) established a formal board which was responsible to parliament, depriving company shareholders of their direct say on policy, and in 1813 the company was stripped of its commercial monopoly.

Though wounded, the giant took time to fall. The Indian Mutiny in 1857 in which the sepoys (Indian soldiers in company service) almost expelled the British showed that the company risked losing control of India altogether. The next year it was deprived of any governmental role there at all, and direct rule from London was imposed. A ghost of the great trading enterprise it had once been, the East India Company was wound up in 1874. Britain remained in control of India until 1947, but its experiment in private imperialism was over.

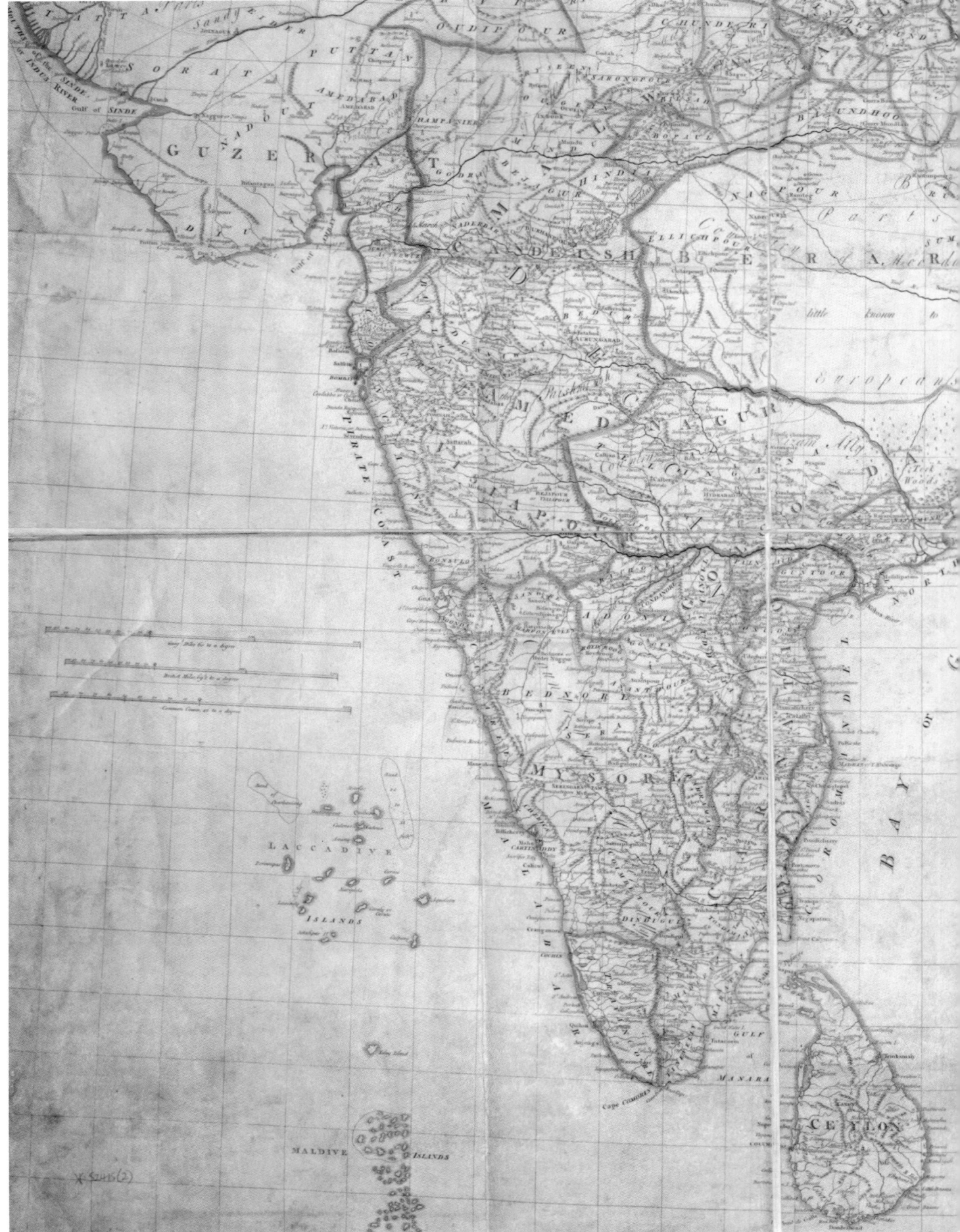

HINDOOSTAN
By J. Rennell F.R.S. 1782.

The Slave Trade

Shown overleaf, the Chevalier de Préfontaine's 1763 map of his sugar plantation in Cayenne, in French-controlled Guiana, presents an idealised view of the slave trade, with the cantonment for the slaves neatly placed at the northern periphery of an establishment that radiates harmony and order.

The realities of the trade were very different. The majority of enslaved Africans found themselves on sugar plantations in the Caribbean or mainland South America (see pp 138–9). There, life was brutal and most often short, dominated by backbreaking labour. They found themselves at the sharp end of a commerce with ancient roots: from the first civilisations there are records of slaves, and slavery formed a vital underpinning of the economy of the Roman Empire. Although European slavery had largely withered away by the late Middle Ages, Europe's commercial expansion in the Age of Exploration gave it a fillip. The maritime empires of Venice and Genoa came into contact with slave-holding societies in the Muslim world, and were more than happy to provide captives to feed it.

When the Portuguese began exploring the west coast of Africa, they came into contact with states in Senegambia that were accustomed to supplying slaves to the Arab world and which deftly refocused their trade towards the European newcomers in exchange for cloth, guns, beads and alcohol. Although the Portuguese used some African slaves on plantations in the region – with around 100,000 working in the sugar mills of São Tomé by the 17th century – the need for slaves soon multiplied.

Meanwhile in America, the Spanish found that the diseases they brought with them had decimated the potential workforce of Native Americans. By 1500, around 5,000 slaves were being brought across the Atlantic annually to work on plantations, but once the English, Dutch and French entered the trade, this number grew hugely. The first slaves were sold in Virginia in 1619 and before long had become crucial to the economies of the southern colonies of North America. Slavery became big business. The British slave traders became lords of the "triangular trade", which took trade goods to Africa, bought slaves there and sold them in America for rum, sugar and other plantation products for resale in Britain at a huge profit.

The conditions in which Africans crossed the Atlantic

were appalling. The "middle passage" meant being shackled below deck in damp and disease-ridden holds with barely enough nutrition to sustain life. Around 1.5 million died during the crossings, leaving 9.5 million to disembark into a life of slavery between 1519 and the 1860s. Over time the chorus calling for an end to this profitable, but immoral trade grew louder. Abolitionists used the voices of freed slaves such as Olaudah Equiano, whose 1789 autobiography *The Interesting Narrative* told of his harrowing experiences, to call for the trade's suspension. Finally, in 1807, the trade in slaves was abolished in the British Empire, but a million people remained enslaved on British-owned plantations, and were not freed until the Slavery Abolition Act came into force in 1834. The interests of the plantation owners were carefully safeguarded; under the guise of preparing them for freedom, former slaves in the West Indies were forced to works as "apprentices" for their former masters, a system whose iniquity generated such a storm of protest that it was terminated in 1838. Even then, the former slave owners could console themselves with the colossal sum of £20 million which they were paid in compensation for the loss of their "property", an amount equivalent to around two-fifths of the British state's income at the time and which was funded by a loan which the government only finally finished paying off in 2015.

The slave trade remained stubbornly persistent and United States vessels still plied it until the nation was torn apart by the Civil War and slavery was abolished there in 1865. In India, slavery was only abolished in the territories of the British East India Company by the India Slavery Act of 1843 and even then, lack of other opportunities in the tea-growing areas meant many workers were reduced to the condition of indentured labourers, which was little different from slavery. More than half a million were transported to the Caribbean to replace the former African slave workforces on the plantations there between 1838 and the ending of indentured labour in 1920. Sugar plantations continued to be worked by slave labour until Brazil finally outlawed slavery in 1888, and Mauritania, the last country in the world to do so, only made slavery illegal in 1981. Although the freedom of many former slaves was marred by poverty and the continued denial of their theoretical legal rights, and remnants of slavery survive in the guise of people trafficking, the trade itself is a rare example of one whose disappearance is positive.

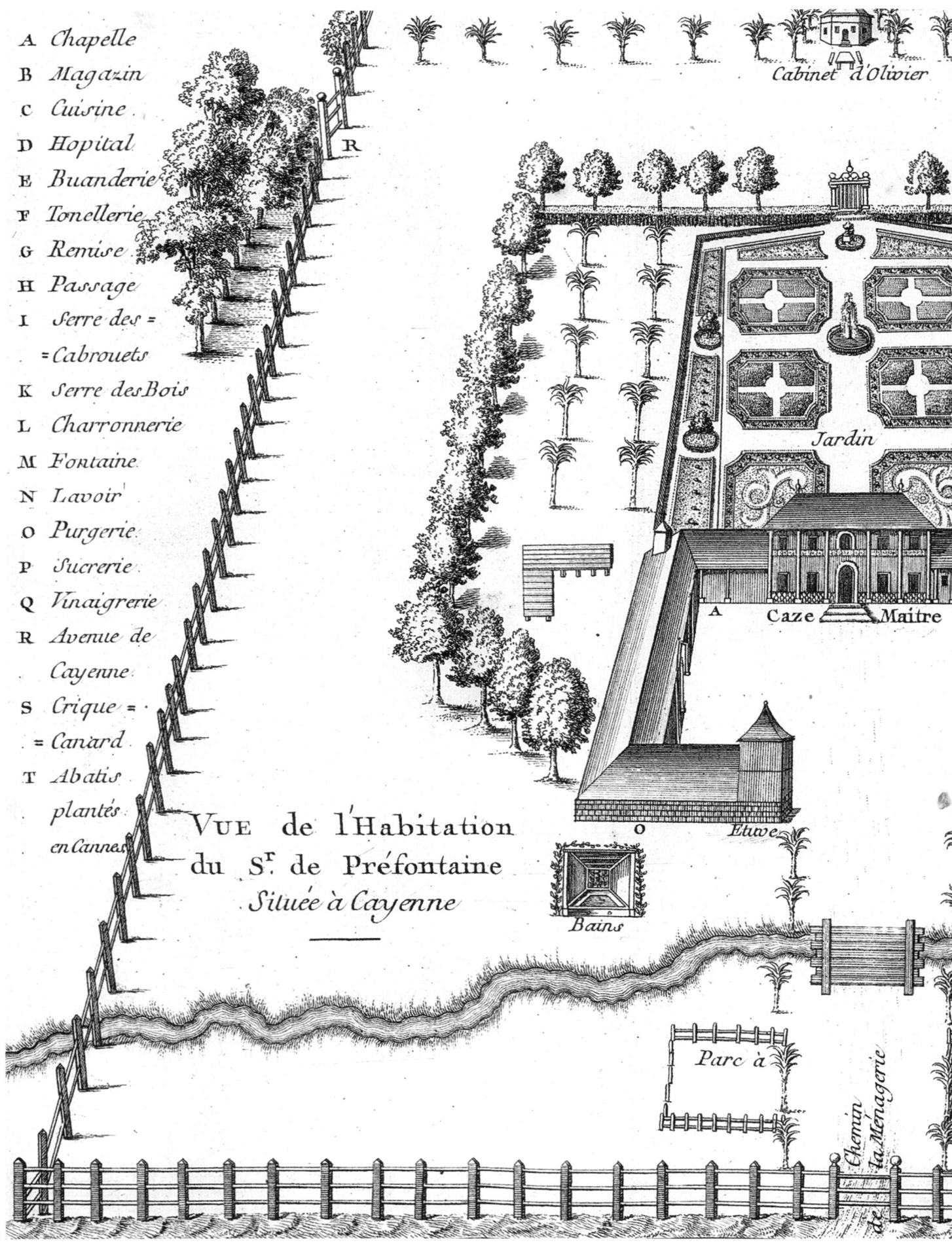

A Chapelle
B Magazin
C Cuisine
D Hopital
E Buanderie
F Tonellerie
G Remise
H Passage
I Serre des =
= Cabrouets
K Serre des Bois
L Charronnerie
M Fontaine
N Lavoir
O Purgerie
P Sucrerie
Q Vinaigrerie
R Avenue de
Cayenne
S Crique =
= Canard
T Abatis
plantés
en Cannes

R

Cabinet d'Olivier

Jardin

Caze Maitre

A

O

Etuve

Bains

VUE de l'Habitation
du Sr. de Préfontaine
Située à Cayenne

Parc à

Chemin de la Ménagerie

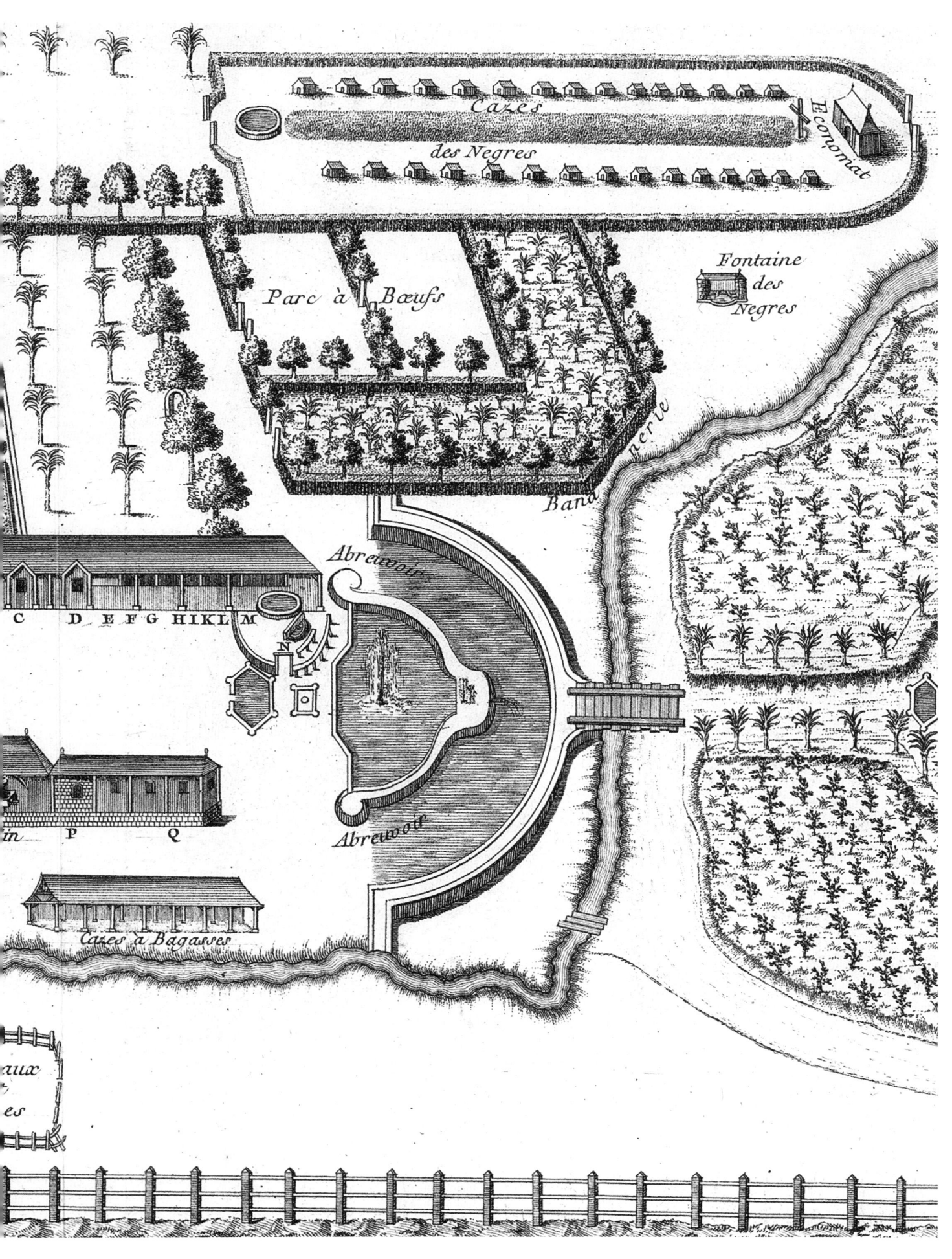

Cazes
des Negres

Economat

Fontaine
des
Negres

Parc à Bœufs

Bana...erie

C   D E F G H I K L M

N

...in   P   Q

Abreuvoir

Abreuvoir

Cazes à Bagasses

...aux
...es

The Sugar Trade

Amid the folds of northwest Jamaica's hills, the Scottish surveyor James Robertson's 1804 map of the island shows a stipple pattern of rectangles and villa-like triangles. These mark a dense concentration of the 830 sugar plantations and mills that were the engine of Jamaica's prosperity and the heart of a trade which had transformed the Caribbean.

Sugar is native to New Guinea and indigenous peoples had chewed the bark for its sweet taste since at least 8000BC. By the 5th century AD, a means had been found in Gupta India to boil the cane to a juice, and then condense it down and produce dried crystals that were easy to transport. From there sugar percolated through the Middle East via the Silk Road, becoming a staple of cooking in the Islamic world (and a handy addition to mollify tea's bitter taste once the beverage became popular around 1400).

Returning Crusaders brought sugar back to western Europe in the late 11th century and the Venetians, ever with an eye for a good deal, soon cornered the trade in the eastern Mediterranean. Yet sugar was a luxury, as valuable as spices such as cloves and nutmeg, and consumption was tiny. Only the development of more effective sugar presses around 1390 and the beginning of Europe's westward expansion – with sugar production beginning on Madeira in 1455 and the Canaries in the 1480s – began to make it more widely available.

Columbus changed everything. The Caribbean climate proved especially suitable for the growth of sugar cane, and Hispaniola produced its first crop in 1501, just nine years after its discovery. Sugar production in southern Europe and North Africa collapsed: once thriving cane fields in Spain withered, and the thriving sugar processing factories of Morocco crumbled to dust, as trading networks switched from the Mediterranean to the Atlantic.

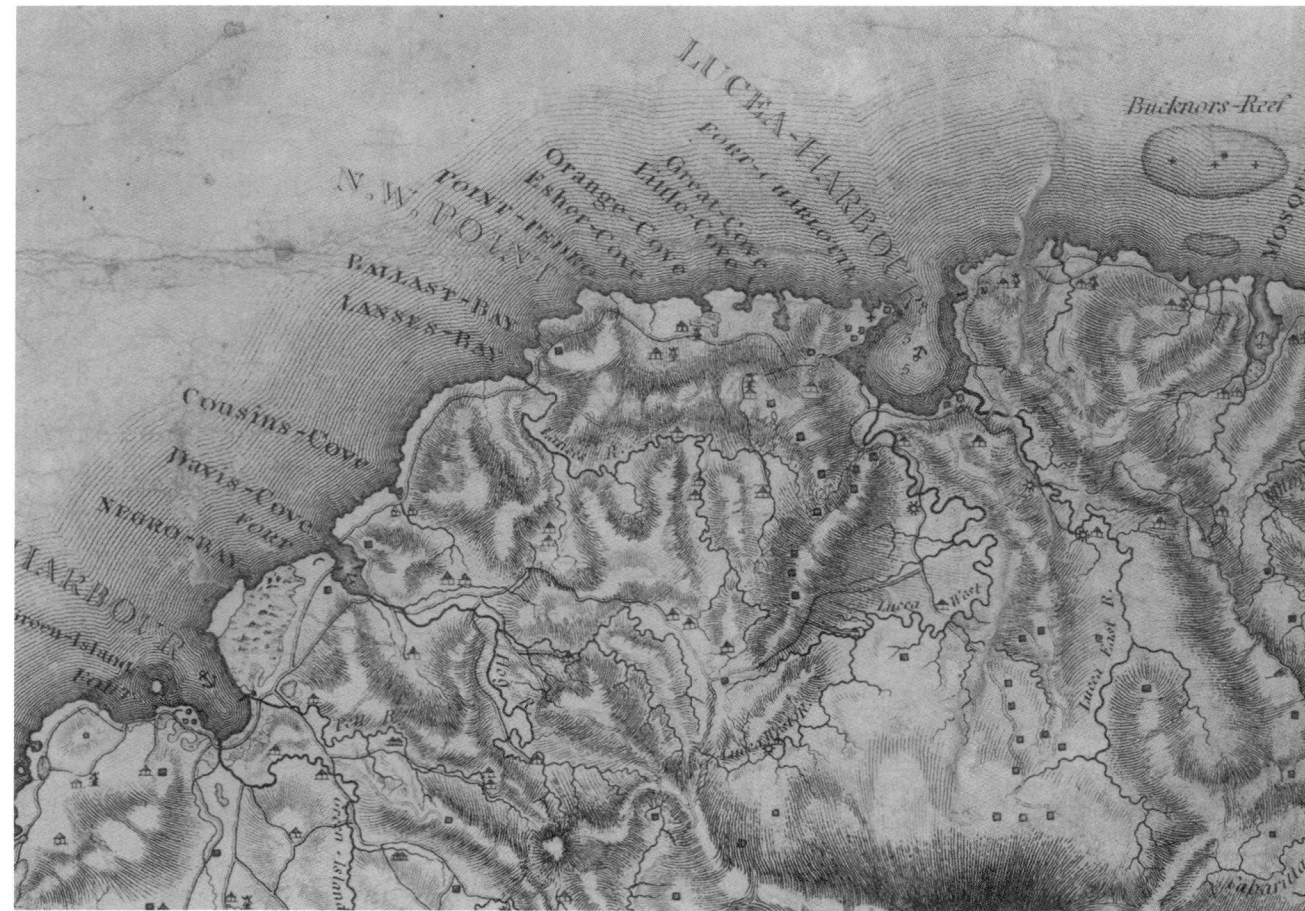

Plantations spread, and by the 18th century the Caribbean was supplying 90 per cent of Europe's consumption, which in Britain soared from barely a teaspoon a year in the Middle Ages to four pounds in 1700 and 36 pounds by 1850.

Sugar production spread farther, and Brazil was producing 14,000 tons of "white gold" annually in 1612, which led the Dutch East India Company to seize Pernambuco from the Portuguese in 1630 and run a profitable industry of their own until they lost the town again in 1654.

Sugar production was labour-intensive, and the workforce for the fields and mills was provided by huge numbers of African slaves. Of the 3.25 million carried across the Atlantic by British ships between 1662 and 1807, the vast majority were put to work on plantations, and two-thirds of those in the sugar fields. The sweetness of British tea and puddings and the riches of many of its merchants were founded on the sweat and blood of those slaves, and 19th-century abolitionists suggested that a boycott of sugar might bring slavery down.

Jamaica itself became the epicentre of Britain's sugar wealth after its seizure from Spain in 1655, and the exhaustion of Barbados's soil led to the collapse of the industry there. By the time James Robertson began his survey in 1796, it was well established, particularly in the west of the island, where it did not compete with coffee and rum for land. Even though a dip in prices led to the abandonment of 140 sugar estates between 1832 and 1847, the industry has endured. With average annual consumption at around 80 pounds per head in the United States, the world's taste for sugar is undiminished.

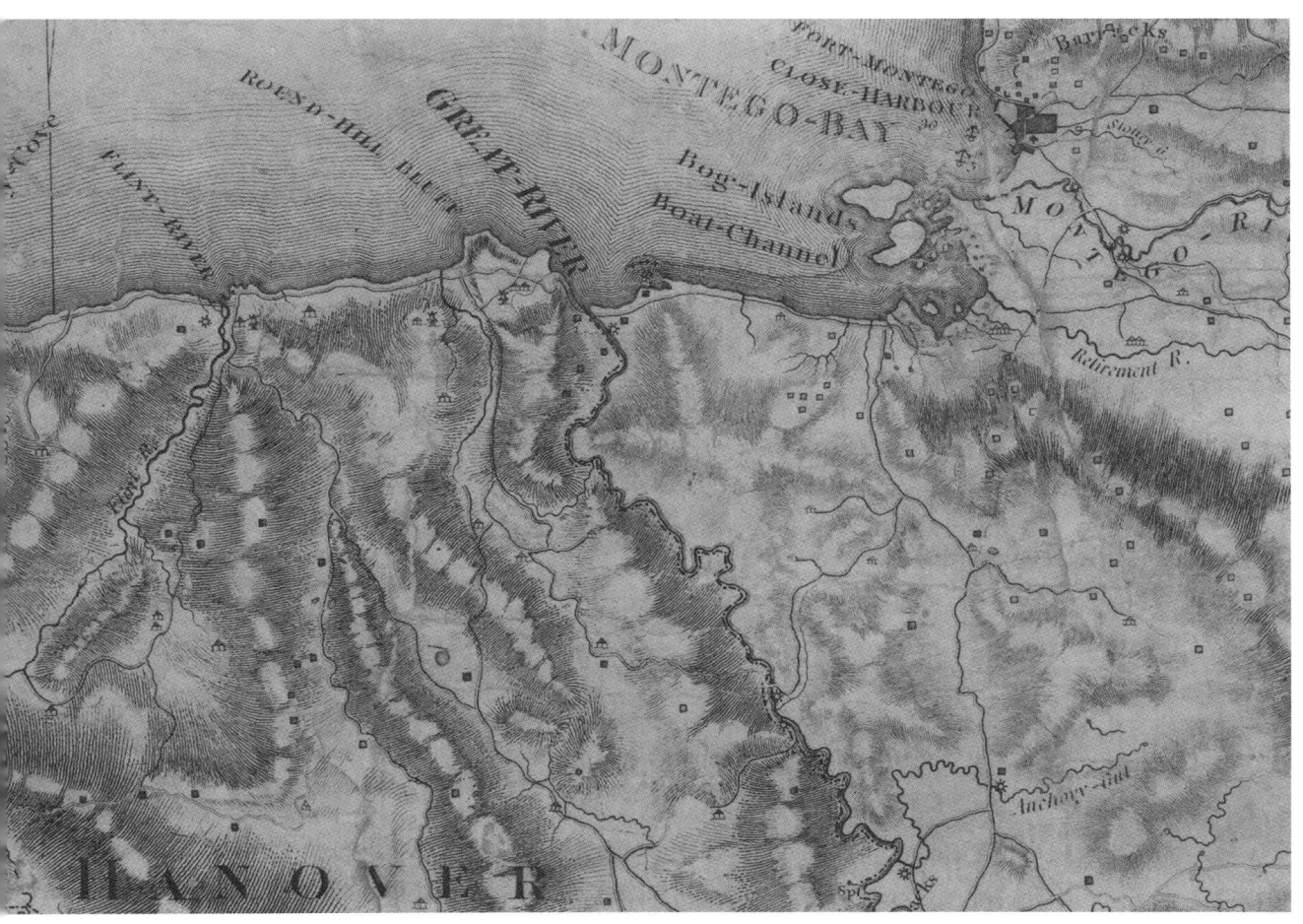

The Cotton Trade

The 1862 map by the American journalist and landscape architect Frederick Law Olmsted shows a dense network of cotton production, the vivid blue of the deepest concentration of plantations dominating the landscapes of Arkansas, Mississippi, Alabama and Georgia. Yet Olmsted's map was not intended as a celebration of "King Cotton", as the industry had become known, but as a condemnation of its pernicious influence in rendering the southern states poorer than they should be, with the profit from the labour of millions of slaves pouring into the hands of just 8,000 large plantation owners.

Cotton's ascent to becoming the world's main manufactured product during the Industrial Revolution was a long one. Varieties of the Gossypium plant from which cotton fibres are extracted were domesticated both in the Americas (from around 3000BC) and in the Old World, principally India (about 4000BC). Its fibres were teased out, made into thread and then woven into cloth in a labour-intensive process that produced light and durable cloth, a practice which spread throughout Asia.

Like so many other products of the East, cotton was brought to Europe by the Venetians, but its supply remained limited until the English East India Company established a base at Surat in India in 1609. Indian printed fabrics, or calicoes, rapidly became popular in England and by the late 17th century the East India Company was shipping 1.5 million bolts of cotton cloth a year, which represented around five-sixths of its total exports. By then, cotton had definitively dethroned spice as the king of trade.

It took around 100 days of labour to complete all the processes – ginning, carding, bailing and spinning – needed to transform raw cotton into cloth. It was only with the invention of the flying shuttle by John Kay in 1733, which doubled the number of shuttles weavers could manage, that the British cotton industry really took off. By 1765, it produced half a million pounds of finished cloth, and 16 million pounds in 1784, aided by the development of new machines, such as Richard Arkwright's water frame, which automated further parts of the cotton production process.

In 1790 America's cotton plantations began production, which had been made more economical by the employment of slave labour, and it soon supplanted India as Britain's main supplier. The British government became so concerned about this dependency that by the 1850s it once again sought alternative sources, including, ironically, a return to Indian cotton. It was well that it did so, for the outbreak of the Civil War in the United States in 1861 cut off the cotton supply. Indian shipments provided less than half the shortfall. Britain suffered a virtual cotton famine, and the price relative to wool tripled between 1860 and 1865, when the supply was restored at the end of the war.

The 1.2 million slaves who had laboured in the cotton industry were freed, though many of them simply became sharecroppers on their former plantations. Given that they had few economic prospects and suffered systematic discrimination and denial of the civil rights – notably that to vote – which they had in theory been granted, Olmsted's hope that the legacy of slavery would cease to blight the South went largely unfulfilled.

Even in the 21st century, the United States remains the world's third-largest source of raw cotton (after China and India) in an industry that produces around 25 million tons annually, and is worth around $30 billion. The cotton kingdom's borders are still wide indeed.

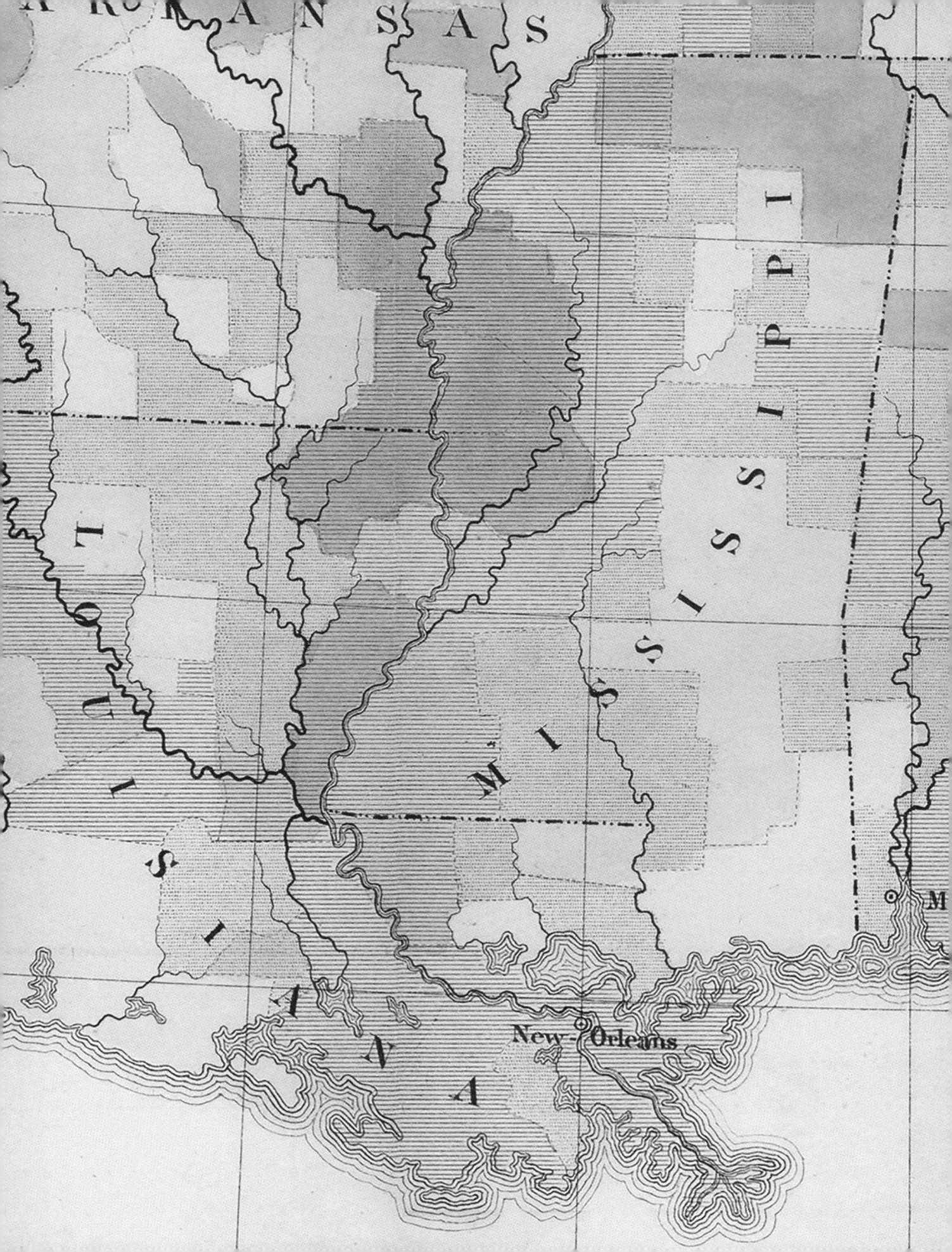

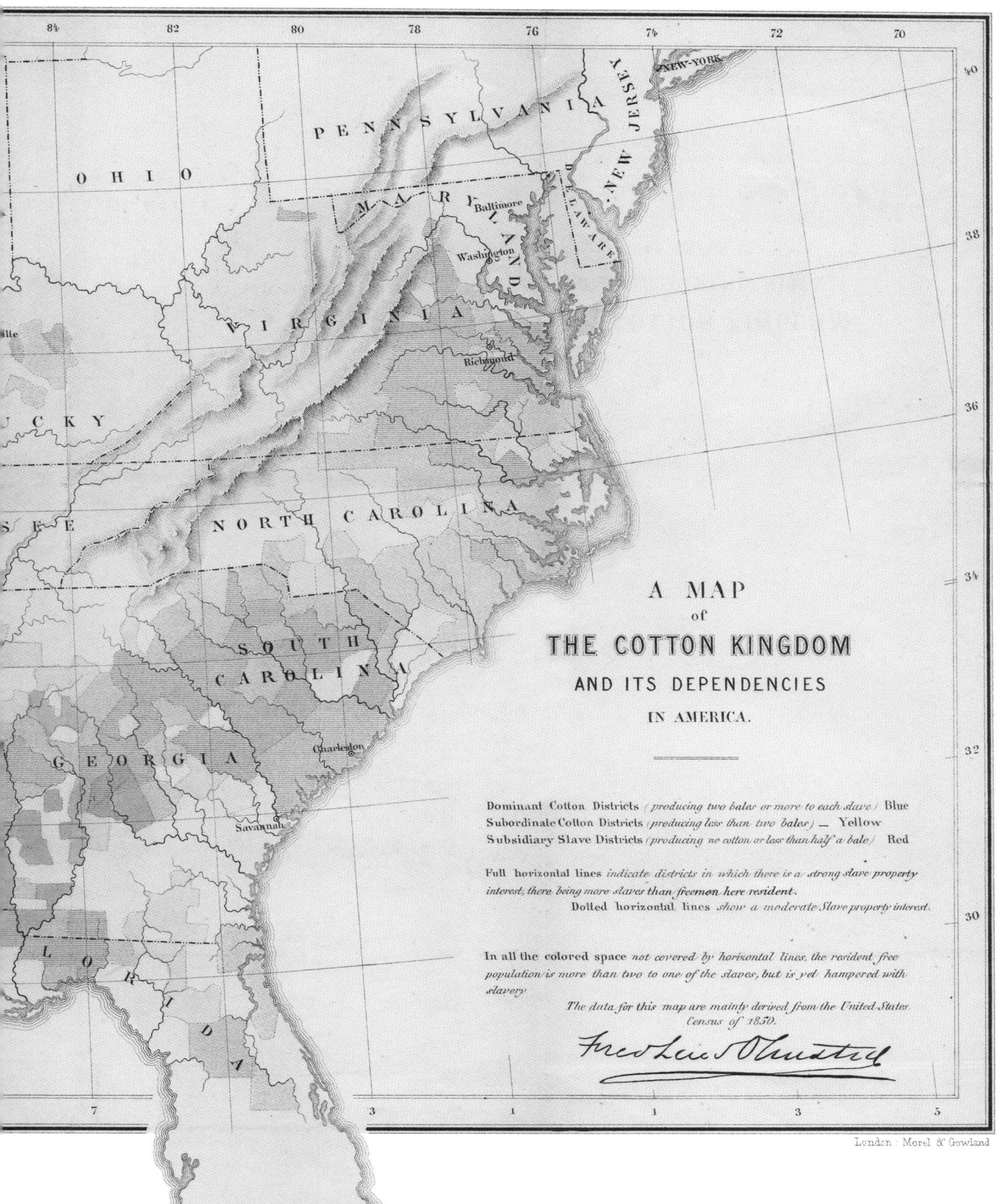

A MAP
of
THE COTTON KINGDOM
AND ITS DEPENDENCIES
IN AMERICA.

Dominant Cotton Districts *(producing two bales or more to each slave)* Blue
Subordinate Cotton Districts *(producing less than two bales)* — Yellow
Subsidiary Slave Districts *(producing no cotton or less than half a bale)* Red

Full horizontal lines *indicate districts in which there is a strong slave property interest, there being more slaves than freemen here resident.*
　　　　Dotted horizontal lines *show a moderate Slave property interest.*

In all the colored space *not covered by horizontal lines, the resident free population is more than two to one of the slaves, but is yet hampered with slavery*

The data for this map are mainly derived from the United States. Census of 1850.

Fred. Law Olmstead

London : Morel & Gowland

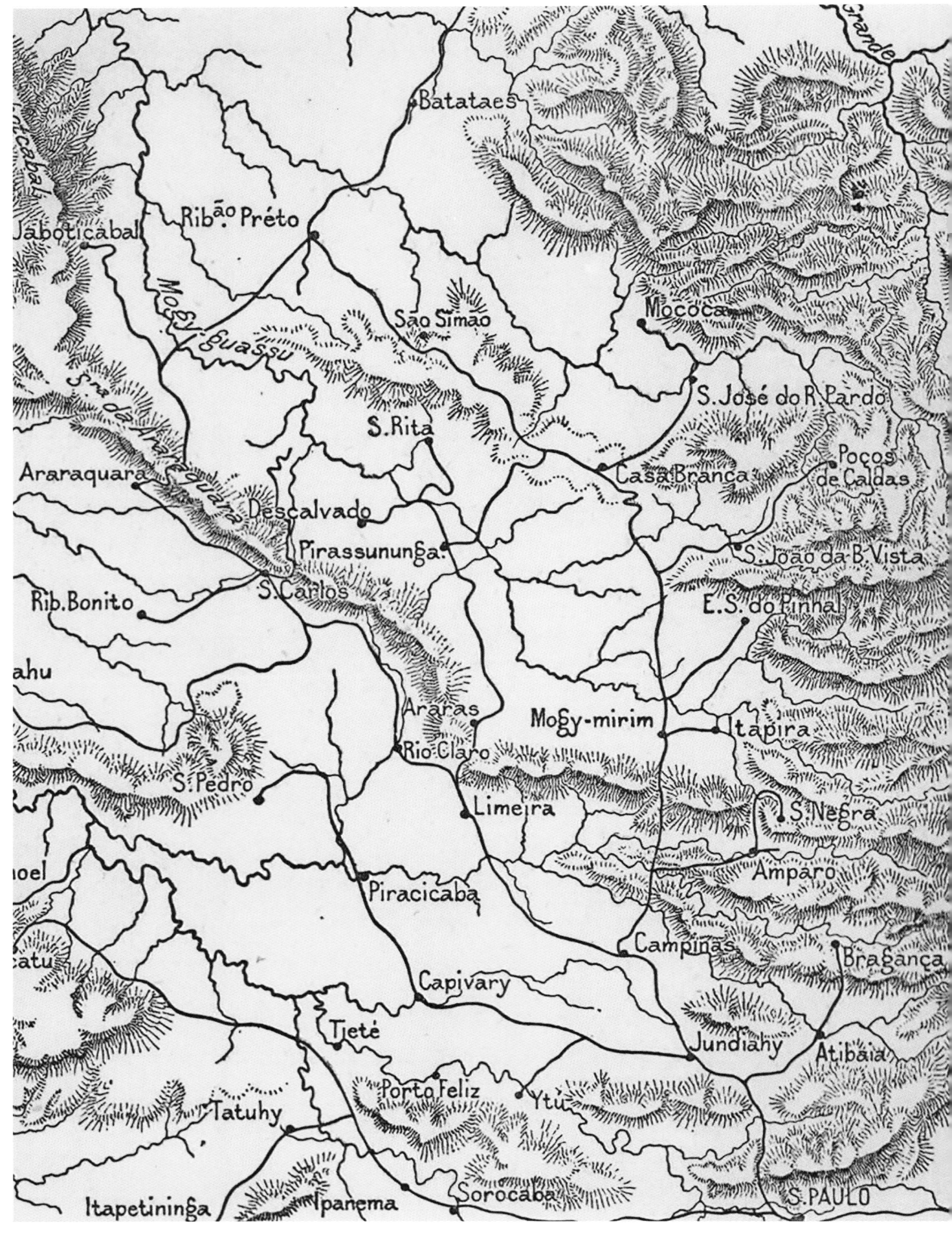

The Coffee Trade

The map, drawn up in 1885, shows coffee plantations north of São Paulo in Brazil. This area was the centre of an industry that brought enormous prosperity to the country, and by the 21st century made it the world's leading exporter, with almost one-third of a market worth $31 billion.

Although two billion cups of coffee are now consumed worldwide each day, the industry's origins were humble. One probably apocryphal story relates that a 9th-century Ethiopian goatherd named Kaldi noticed his flock became frisky when chewing on the berries of a particular bush. He tried one himself, and found its stimulant effect remarkable. Soon word of the wonder berry spread to local Sufi mystics, who used it to enhance their concentration in prolonged religious rituals. By about 1400 it had reached southern Arabia and the Yemeni city of Mocha, which would for centuries be the heart of the coffee trade.

The addition of boiling water to ground coffee beans created an infusion. So popular did this become in Arabia – encouraging the creation of coffeehouses, an avenue for secular socialisation and dissent that had previously been lacking – that in 1511 Khair Beg al-Mimar, the governor of Mecca, had bags of coffee burnt and banned the drink for 13 years. By now, though, coffee was unstoppable, reaching Constantinople in 1555, and from there spreading west to Europe. Another legend has it that it became fashionable in Vienna after the Ottomans lifted the siege of the city in 1683 and left bales of it behind in their abandoned baggage train.

The small coffeehouse that opened in London's Cornhill in 1652 spawned 3,000 imitators within a quarter of a century. They became the centre of social and financial life, giving rise to institutions such as Lloyd's and the Stock Exchange. Not everyone was pleased, and the 1674 *Women's Petition against Coffee* argued that it led husbands to neglect their wives for this "little base, black, thick, nasty stinking nauseous puddle".

Coffee could only be obtained in the markets at Mocha, and, by keeping the price high, the Yemenis caused agents of the English East India Company and its Dutch counterpart (the VOC) to try to secure plants to begin their own industries. The VOC managed to obtain one in 1616, but successive attempts to propagate it in Ceylon and Malabar had limited success until coffee was planted in Java in 1697. By the 1730s, the Dutch no longer needed Mocha coffee, and the French acquisition of plants in 1715, which they transported, first to Réunion and then to Martinique and Guiana, further undermined the Yemeni town, which soon relapsed into a backwater.

The Brazilian coffee industry began in dubious, yet romantic circumstances. A certain Francisco de Melo Palheta, who was sent in 1727 to resolve a border dispute with French Guiana, seduced the French governor of Cayenne's wife, who then gifted him a bouquet containing a coffee seedling. Soon coffee plantations were established throughout Rio de Janeiro, São Paulo and Minas Gerais provinces, their large slave labour force allowing the production of vast quantities at low price. When slavery was finally abolished in 1888, huge numbers of migrants flooded in to work in the industry, which allowed São Paulo to grow from a minnow to today's leviathan of 12 million people. For the Brazilians, coffee had proved a golden brew.

worlds greatest TEA drinkers. Their average annual consumption is over 9 lbs. per head

Dr. Johnson 1709-84 would drink 16 or more cups of TEA at a sitting

Ever since the 17th Century the have been great TEA drinke

TEA was first introduced into England in 1657

The custom of putting milk into TE first introduced into France in the

The British Navy drinks two tons of TEA every day

TEA is stored in Alpine hu to revive the stranded clir

Victor Hugo & Balzac were great TEA drinkers

Queen Catherine going from Portugal to London to marry Charles II took TEA with her to console her future loneliness

The Dutch first brought TEA to Europe in 1610

TEA is the favourite drink of North Africa

Picturesque boats car up the Nile into the

Bedouins say that a camel, a qu TEA are the three essentials of

Sahara Desert. No water to make TEA

Route of the famous TEA clippers

"TEA cleared my head and left me with no misapprehensions" Duke of Wellington

TEA is the chief d great markets of

TEA is s on the E

Equator

TEA is on the

ASCENSION I.

ANGOLA

ST. HELENA

SOUTH WEST

The China Tea Trade
and the Clippers

"Tea Revives the World" proclaims the banner on this lavish 1940 map of the tea trade by renowned British cartographer and graphic artist MacDonald Gill. The accompanying labels provide a wealth of information on the trade's history, but in the list of the main suppliers of the beverage, there is one glaring absentee: China, where it all began.

Tea cultivation and drinking originated there in the distant past, through probably not as long ago as 2727BC, when the legendary emperor Shennong is said to have discovered it after the wind blew leaves from a tea bush into a pot of boiling water. It was first mentioned in a Han dynasty document of 59BC, and by the time Lu Yu (733-804) wrote his classic *Cha Jing* (Manual of Tea) its drinking was a refined art, with prescribed rituals.

Knowledge of tea slowly filtered westwards and the first large-scale consignment was shipped to Europe by the Dutch East India Company in 1610. By the 1630s it was being drunk in Paris, and in 1658 was recorded in London as "the China Drink" or "Tcha". Yet, although it was fashionable, its spread was hampered by cost: in 1700 a pound of tea cost £3 in London, which kept the poorer classes from access to the brew. That changed with Britain's acquisition of empire and its involvement in the triangular trade that brought sugar and tobacco back to Europe on the same ships which transported the slaves to the plantations which produced them. Britain's trading prosperity would not have been possible without such massive involuntary migrations, which distorted the societies, both of departure and of destination, for many generations to come.

Ample supplies of sugar, in particular, and the new working patterns of the Industrial Revolution, meant consuming a quick-acting mild stimulant was a useful

fillip, and that tea, a bitter beverage in its original homelands, became a sugar-laden staple. Price proved the key, however. A new breed of sharp-bowed, sleek-hulled ships appeared in the 1840s. These clippers – first used in the opium trade – were then turned to the transport of tea. The *Oriental*, which arrived back in London from China in December 1850 after a passage of just 97 days, caused a sensation and set off a storm of competition to be the first to land the new season's tea and receive a bonus of £1 per ton offloaded. Tea, suddenly, was more plentiful. The tea races were furiously competitive and in the most renowned, in 1866, four clippers, the *Ariel, Fiery Cross, Taeping* and *Serica*, set off from Fuzhou and jostled all the way for leadership. Finally the *Taeping* pipped the *Ariel* to reach London's docks just 20 minutes ahead of its rival.

Scarcely had it begun than the opening of the Suez Canal in 1869 put an end to the golden age of the clipper, as steamships using it could transport back a load of tea in an unbeatable 60 days. When the *Cutty Sark*, the most famous tea clipper of all, entered service in 1870, their heyday was all but done. By then the tea trade was transformed in other ways too. The East India Company, concerned that silver was haemorrhaging into China to pay for the tea, promoted the consumption of opium (see pages 156–9), while an expedition led by the plant collector Robert Fortune in 1848 smuggled tea plants out of China. Soon it was being grown in Ceylon, and large-scale production in Assam in northeast India began in the 1880s. By the following decade more Indian tea was being exported to Britain than Chinese. As MacDonald Gill's map illustrates, the tea trade had gone global.

THE·WORLD

BARENTS SEA

KARA SEA

LAPLAND A bowl of TEA is passed round the family circle

Russians fill their TEAPOTS many times a day from their famous samovar, inside which water is heated round a vertical pipe containing live charcoal. They do not put milk or cream in, but prefer a slice of lemon or a small spoonful of jam; in some circles they break up their sugar and pop a small piece in before each mouthful of TEA

Ever since the 17th Century the Dutch have been great TEA drinkers

The custom of putting milk into TEA was first introduced into France in the 17th Century

"TEA tempers the spirits, calms and harmonises the mind, it arouses thought and prevents drowsiness, lightens and refreshes the body, and clears the perceptive faculties."
LU YU 780 A.D.

A.D. 1159 The Czar's first gift of TEA from China

TEA travels on two-humped camels from China to the U.S.S.R.

Lake Baikal

TEA is stored in Alpine huts to revive the stranded climber

Colchis swamps Russians are developing TEA plantations here and in neighbouring Georgia

MONGOLIA

Earliest credible mention of TEA A.D. 350

U. S.

The shaggy yak, cousin of our native cattle bears to Tibet the valued TEA bricks

The Emperor of China received TEA in gold boxes as tribute from Japan in the X century

BLACK SEA

TURKEY

SINKIANG

Here bricks made from TEA are used as money

PEKING

SYRIA

Through the Suez Canal come the ships bringing TEA to Europe from India, Ceylon & the Netherlands East Indies

Houseboats on the Indus

CHINESE

Lu Yu wrote The First TEA Book presenting skilful methods of making TEA & extolling its virtue

bitter drink of North Africa

ITALIAN LIBYA

IRAQ

AFGHANISTAN

Here churned TEA or bitter TEA boiled with a little red potash, aniseed & salt is popular

The Tibetans are an ancient TEA drinking nation They take TEA churned with butter & other ingredients and drink anything up to 80 cups a day

Here in 1825 Major Robert Bruce first discovered the TEA plant in India

Picturesque boats carry TEA up the Nile into the interior

INDIA is the largest supplier of TEA to the World

DELHI

Mt. Everest climbers carried TEA

DARJEELING

Mother Nature's TEA Garden, where the plant is indigenous: the largest TEA growing district in India, with 1,800 TEA gardens covering 500,000 acres

The Ships used to steam & boil the TEA leaves & then mould them into balls to be eaten with salt, oil, garlic and dried fish

TEA is the beverage of the fellaheen working on their farms in the ancient way

Bedouins say that a camel, a gun & TEA are the three essentials of life

CALCUTTA

The centre of India's TEA trade The first Assam TEA was sent from here to England in 1838

YELLOW

EAST CHINA SEA

SHANGHAI

FORMOSA

Newly married couples drink out of the same cup, a mixture of TEA leaves steeped in oil to ensure a happy union

BURMA

The people of Siam chew TEA for midday as they call it, with salt and other condiments

SUDAN

TEA is the chief drink in the great markets of the Sudan

Here are TEA plantations

The Nilgiris An important TEA growing area of Southern India. In this region lies the worlds highest TEA garden over 7,500 feet up

SIAM

HONG KONG

LUZON

BANGKOK

FRENCH INDO CHINA

CHINA SEA

MANILA

PHILIPPINE IS

MINDANAO

CAMEROONS

TEA is served to passengers on the Empire air routes

TEA is always drunk on the big game safaris

TEA is the drink of the Africans in the Reserves & in the markets

The first shipment of Ceylon TEA was sent to London in 1875 To-day CEYLON is the second largest supplier of TEA to the World

CELEBES SEA

BORNEO

BELGIAN CONGO

ANGOLA

NYASALAND

TEA is grown here

Equator

Worlds third largest TEA supplier

JAVA SEA

JAVA

ARAFURA SEA

SOUTH WEST AFRICA

NORTHERN RHODESIA

MOZAMBIQUE

MADAGASCAR

INDIAN

OCEAN

A cup of TEA greets Air travellers on arrival

AUSTRALIA

TEA is grown here

Tropic of Capricorn

TEA keeps the whaler's crew alert

Camels carry TEA to the stations in the back blocks

UNION OF SOUTH AFRICA

TEA is always served at 11 a.m. in South African offices

Miners on the gold fields have TEA served as usual

TEA is grown here

DURBAN

TEA is the favourite beverage of the Bantu

Sheep shearing

TEA is the drink in the gold

CAPE TOWN

PORT ELIZABETH

TEA was the drink of the original Dutch Settlers in South Africa

PERTH

seamen brought their voyage rope

SOUTHERN OCEAN

KERGUELEN

receives supplies of British warship

The Age of Steam

Arching across the Atlantic Ocean in a dense network and, from the west coast of the Americas, converging on Hawaii before linking to almost every major port of the Pacific, the routes shown on George Philip & Son's 1912 "Commercial Chart of the World" are the sinews of the Age of Steam.

For millennia, sail had been king of the waves, transporting passengers, goods and armies ever greater distances, its dominance seemingly unassailable. The harnessing of the Industrial Revolution's steam power to shipping at first seemed a gimmick and when, in 1807, the *Clermont* travelled the 150 miles from New York City to Albany under steam, the sail magnates barely raised an eyebrow. Early steamships were cumbersome paddle-driven affairs which consumed vast quantities of coal, leaving little room for cargo and struggling in heavy seas. The first steam-powered crossing of the Atlantic, by the *SS Sirius* in 1838, was an exciting novelty, but steam remained strictly marginal to world trade.

That began to change in the 1840s with the development of far more effective propeller screws and iron-hulled ships which could contain them (the force of their vibration had an unfortunate tendency to tear wooden vessels apart). The launch in 1843 of Isambard Kingdom Brunel's *SS Great Britain* was a harbinger of things to come: its crossing of the Atlantic in a mere 14 days – less than half the sailing ships' average – marked the true start of the Age of Steam.

Steamers were coal-hungry and earned their keep as passenger liners and mail ships. The bulk trade in cargo such as wheat and coal was still the domain of sail. The invention of a fuel-efficient compound engine in the 1860s finally allowed steam to outrun its wind-driven competition, and in 1866 the *Agamemnon* made the 8,500-mile trip from Liverpool to Mauritius without stopping once for fuel.

The network of steam routes pioneered by companies such as the Peninsular & Oriental Steam Navigation Company (P&O) – founded in 1840 – suddenly became a more viable commercial prospect. Already P&O had established routes to Egypt and India in the early 1840s, extending to Penang, Singapore, Hong Kong and Shanghai, and reaching Australia in 1852. Now the coal stations at hubs such as Singapore, Aden and Bermuda, and outposts such as Trincomalee in Ceylon and Fanning Island in Kiribati buzzed with ever more visitors (and their inhabitants had to endure the mariners' thirst for alcohol and female companionship). The steamships' holds were packed with bulk cargoes, whose price dropped in markets which had been hard to service: the price gap between the United States and Europe for textiles fell from 14% in 1870 to 3.6% in 1913.

Steamers such as the *Stirling Castle* were the aristocrats of the new age. Glasgow-built, the 4,800-ton vessel had a truly global career, beginning service with an Italian line in 1883 on the Genoa–Buenos Aires route, before taking a break to ferry British troops to the Sudan to put down the Mahdist revolt in 1885, and again in 1899, when it carried Russian soldiers to suppress the Boxer Uprising in China. The ship then ran between Palermo and New York for a further decade before a terrible storm damaged her off Morocco in 1910. The *Stirling Castle* limped into port with her cargo of horses and had to be scrapped. By then, as the map shows, her loss would barely have dented the vast international flotilla of trading steamships.

MAGNETIC PARALLELS AND MERIDIANS

VARIATION
of the Compass
(Isogonic Lines)
1912

World Cities

The map of Rio de Janeiro in 1867 – published by the brothers Eduardo and Henrique Laemmert – shows a city in the midst of rapid expansion, its street grid set to burst the bounds of the protective ring of *morros* (forts) around its rim. This growth – and the elevation of the Brazilian settlement into the elite rank of a new breed of global cities – was fuelled by trade through its port, here seen dotted with the *trapiches* (sugar mills), which processed one of its most lucrative products for the world market.

Rio de Janeiro, which took its name ("River of January") from the month in which the Portuguese landed at Guanabara Bay in 1502, was slow of gestation, with only 8000 inhabitants by the late 17th century. The development of the coffee and sugar industries in the surrounding region and the establishment there in 1808 of the Portuguese royal family – having fled Napoleon's occupation – gave the city an economic boost. English merchants and bankers settled in newly fashionable suburbs such as Praia do Flamengo and coffee, cotton, sugar and rubber flowed from the interior to Rio's port.

Trade did not benefit just the merchants, and the city was reborn, with oxcart traffic being banned from its main street in 1829, while in 1854 gas replaced oil for street lighting. The population soared, reaching 113,000 by 1821 (and eventually 3 million in the 1960s), spawning a new periphery of *favelas*, unregulated suburbs that the city authorities periodically tried to clear away. The increase was fuelled by immigration from less economically successful areas of Europe, most notably Italy, with 6,000 people a year settling in Rio in the late 1890s.

It was a phenomenon repeated elsewhere in other great port cities. The port of London swelled, from the building of West India Dock in 1800 to the opening of the Royal Albert Dock in 1880, taking advantage of Britain's status as an imperial power, with products pouring in from all over the empire (7 million tons of grain a year to Victoria Dock alone by the early 20th century). The city's population exploded from 1.4 million in 1815 to over 7 million a century later. In New York, similar growth took place, fuelled by mass immigration and a business-friendly environment: the city gradually toppled London for financial and trading pre-eminence, a transition symbolised by the sprouting of skyscrapers to create Manhattan's modern streetscape, beginning with the wedge-shaped Flatiron Building in 1902.

What trade gave, it could also take away. While Brazil prospered from its gold and coffee industries, the climate of uncertainty in the aftermath of the First World War, which eventually fed into the Great Depression, treated it unkindly. After the stock market crash in the United States in October 1929, a web of international indebtedness unwound as American banks called in loans, agricultural commodity prices crashed (that of Brazilian coffee by more than 50 per cent) and protectionist tariff barriers went up. Those countries like Brazil which were reliant on exporting primary commodities suffered badly. Mismanagement of the economy by military dictatorships, hyperinflation, and an overvalued currency undermined Brazil's economy and sapped Rio's attractiveness as a port of entry. Although Brazil, buoyed up by its abundant natural commodities, recovered, by the 21st century other cities had replaced Rio in the global pecking order of world trading cities. Cities such as Shanghai and Seoul grew as their governments' investment in modern technology brought factories to their hinterlands and made them new hubs of global trade. Just as for medieval London or Rio in its heyday, the true mark of a world city was the level of its international commerce.

Nheco

Morro da Gamboa

Morro da

Trapiche da Gamboa

Trapiche do Vapor

Morro Providencia
da Formiga

Fabrica de Seguros de Rohê

Fabrica de Vapores (Engenheiros)

Coberto

Morro de Paula Mattos

Morro do Lavradio

Morro da Saude

Ponte

Ponte

Comp. Ponte Brasileira de Paquetes a Vapor Trapiche da Saude

1ª Estação da Estrada de Ferro de P. 2ª

Morro do Senado

Campo da Tijuca

d'Acclamação

79.j

Trapiche de Damião
Trapiche do Vallongo

Deposito de Lenhas Fabrica de Vapor (Engenheiros)

Morro do Vallongo

Caes da Imperatriz

Trapiche da Pedra do Sal

Morro de
hereza

Praça da Constituição

Trapiche da Ordem

Trapiche do Cleto

Morro de
S. Antonio

Trapiche de Bustos

Morro de S. Bento

Arsenal da Marinha

Praia da Lapa

Arsenal de Guerra

Caes dos Mineiros

Fr. dos Mineiros

Morro do Castello

Largo do Paço

Praia de Sta. Luzia

Praia do Peixe

Vapor Ferr.

Praia de D. Manoel

Ponte das Barcas de Vapor de Nicterohy

ILHA DAS

Armazem da Marinha Ingleza

FORTALEZA

COBRAS

Arsenal da Marinha

DADE

R O.

Ponta do Vidal

Ponta da Ilha Chegar e Voltar

Ilha dos Ratos

Ponta de Callabouço

Imperialism and Trade

Thomas Collinson's 1845 map of Hong Kong shows the British colony in its infancy. An officer in the Royal Engineers on secondment to the Ordnance Survey, Collinson took two years to complete his task, and the map provided the first record of many modern Hong Kong place names such as Quarry Bay and Shek O (which appears as Shicko on the map).

Hong Kong was an icon of Britain's new imperial ambition. Earlier overseas ventures had been motivated by the interloper's desire to enter trading spheres previously dominated by Spain and Portugal, and physical occupation had been confined to regions where native peoples were unable to resist the implantation of colonies, such as North America and Australia, or to coastal enclaves in India and along the west African coast.

Yet as Britain's economy grew, so too did its military might and the chorus of merchants insisting that its trade must be protected at all costs. Opium, a highly addictive drug, had become popular in China, where the authorities banned it in 1729. Yet it offered a solution to the problem which had concerned the English East India Company: the flow of tea, porcelain and silk from China all had to be paid for in silver, as Britain produced little that the Chinese wanted.

Although not officially allowed to trade it abroad, the company simply sold Indian-grown opium to other trading houses, such as Jardine Matheson, one of whose founders James Matheson shipped it from 1822 to China via the newly established British port at Singapore. In 1834, the British sent a delegation under Lord William Napier to try to modify the system under which, since 1757, foreign merchants had been restricted to factories in Canton (now Guangzhou) and only allowed to trade through 13 *Hong* merchant houses. Napier's undiplomatic conduct rendered the mission a fiasco, and relations deteriorated still further in 1839, when, concerned at the rise in opium addiction, the Qing government ordered Imperial Commissioner Lin Zexu to crack down on its trade.

Lin had dealers publicly beheaded outside the Canton factories and blockaded them until the European traders agreed to hand over 20,000 chests of opium to be destroyed. As the crisis escalated, Captain Charles Elliot made for Canton with a flotilla of Royal Navy vessels and bombarded imperial junks blocking the river. The Chinese stood little chance in the First Opium War which now erupted, and in 1842 were forced to sign the Treaty of Nanking, opening up Canton, Shanghai, Foochow (now Fuzhou), Amoy (now Xiamen) and Ningbo as Treaty Ports, where British merchants could trade unhindered in addition to their rights in Hong Kong. A second Opium War broke out in 1856, and once again the Chinese were overwhelmed. The Treaty of Tientsin (1858), which ended its first phase, gave the British and other western powers access to even more ports.

The blueprint for an imperial trade policy that China had offered was pursued even more aggressively elsewhere, as European powers sought to secure mineral resources or simply to stop others from doing so. The Berlin Conference (1884-85), which determined that European countries could only claim land they had some form of control over, set off the Scramble for Africa, in which imperial powers carved up virtually the whole continent. Cecil Rhodes, operating under the guise of the British South Africa Company from 1889, pushed Britain's sphere of influence deep into southern Africa, motivated by glory as much as by the diamond fields there.

By then Hong Kong had been British for almost 50 years, the centrepiece of its eastern imperial policy. When finally it was handed back to China in 1997, the imperial age was truly over.

VICTORIA HARBOUR

West Tide

Chowr D

Chinsa tour

Kellet's Island

Causeway Bay

East Point

GREEN ISLAND

Belchers Bay

Sulphur Channel

West Point

Possession Point

Bank

MOUNT DAVIS

VICTORIA PEAK

The Happy Valley

Sandy Bay

WEST DIVISION

MOUNT GOUGH

Pokefulum

MOUNT KELLET

Tathowan Bay

H   O   N   G

Heong Kong

Waterfall Bay

ABERDEEN

Stauntons

Valley

Aberdeen Bay

Cumming Inlet

Tree Island

Deep Water Bay

Wext Rock

ABERDEEN ISLAND

MOUNT JOHNSTON

Middle   Island

George   Island

Round   Is

LAMMA   ISLAND

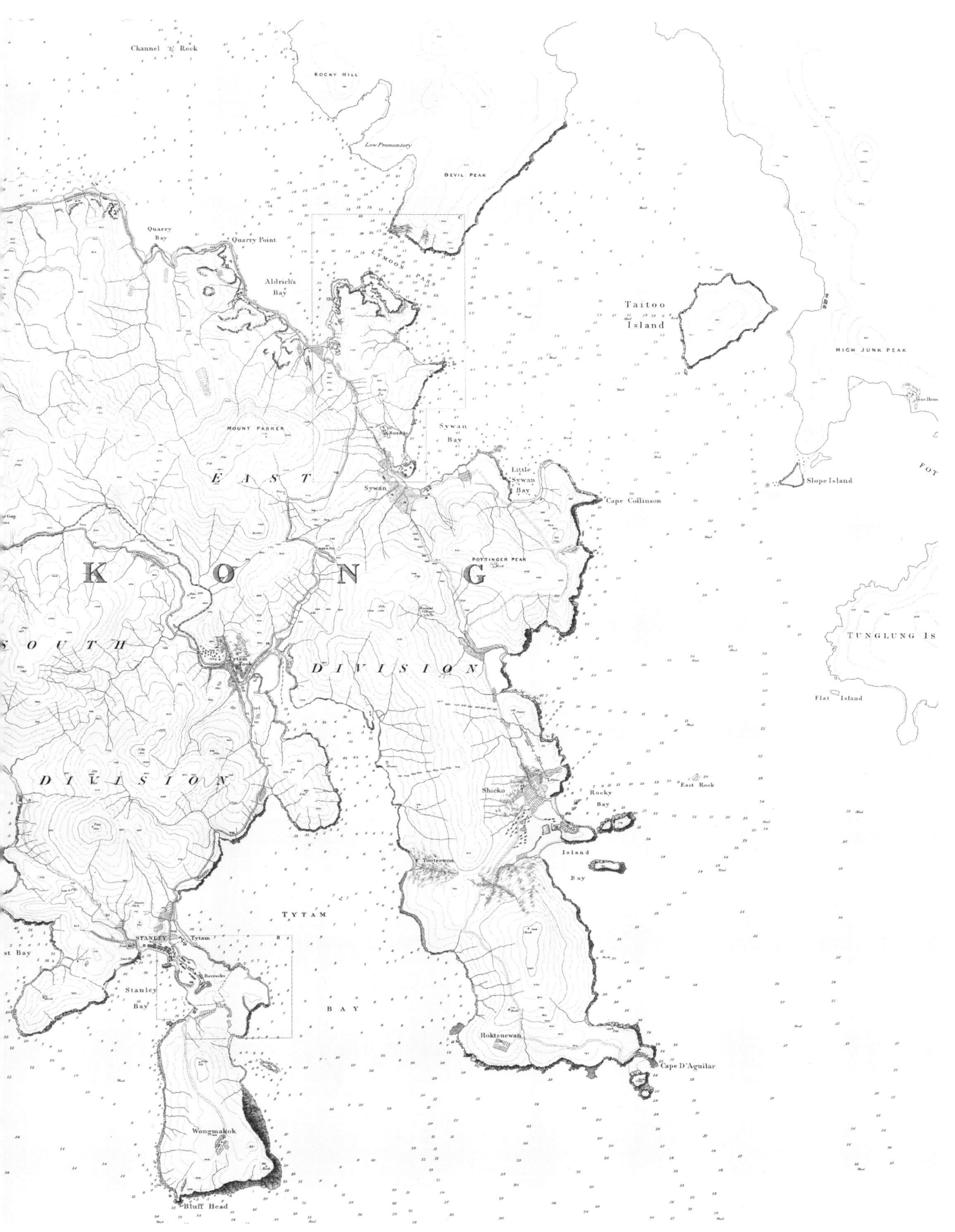

Channel Rock

ROCKY HILL

Low Promontory

DEVIL PEAK

Quarry
Bay

Quarry Point

Aldrich's
Bay

LY MOON
PASS

Taitoo
Island

HIGH JUNK PEAK

MOUNT PARKER

Barracks

Sywan
Bay

E A S T

Sywan

Little
Sywan
Bay

Cape Collinson

Slope Island

FOT

K O N G

POTTINGER PEAK

S O U T H

D I V I S I O N

Tytam
Hook

TUNGLUNG IS

Flat Island

D I V I S I O N

Shieko

Rocky
Bay

East Rock

Island

Tontewon

Bay

T Y T A M

STANLEY   Tytam

st Bay

Barracks

Stanley
Bay

B A Y

Hoktsuewan

Cape D'Aguilar

Wongmakok

Bluff Head

The Erie Canal

The 1832 cross section of the route of the Erie Canal shows its 363-mile route from Buffalo on the east coast of Lake Erie to the Hudson River at Albany in New York State. Made just seven years after the waterway's completion, the plan, with its steeply falling gradient mitigated by 83 locks, shows the engineering problems which needed to be overcome to resolve a serious trading problem.

Land transport was expensive, cripplingly so. In 1830, the price of transporting wheat by road, on rickety wagons, was 38 times that of ocean freight, and so by the time grain from the fertile Ohio valley completed the four-week journey to the New York port, it had already lost its competitive advantage against European-grown wheat. Canals, on which freight costs were a sixth of those on land, offered a solution.

There had been proposals for a canal to take grain to New York ever since the 1780s, but it was one drafted in 1808 by Jesse Hawley – who had strong feelings on the matter as he composed his plan from debtor's prison after an investment in a grain-growing project went sour – that reached the ears of DeWitt Clinton, the mayor of New York. The federal government had baulked at the cost of underwriting the bonds needed to back the project, but seeing its commercial benefits for the state, the bullish Clinton got the New York legislature to agree to fund it.

Construction started nine years later, but initially went at a crawl, as the height differential between the Hudson River and Lake Erie at either end was 550 feet, and cutting the necessary locks and viaducts was challenging and costly. When, after two years, only the first 15-mile section could be opened, sceptics derisively labelled the whole thing "Clinton's Folly".

Yet progress accelerated, and on October 26, 1825, the Erie Canal was inaugurated. A triumphant Clinton sailed its length aboard the *Seneca Chief* at the head of a flotilla of barges, and when he reached New York City, he emptied a keg of Lake Erie water into the ocean, proclaiming it the "wedding of the waters".

The effect on the grain trade was electric. In its opening year the canal carried 185,000 tons of cargo eastbound, and in 1834 it had to be enlarged to take deeper barges. By 1828 the tolls collected along the canal were sufficient to fund the entire federal government, and the bonanza continued as freight levels reached two million tons in 1852. The writing, though, was already on the wall, as the spread of railways offered an even cheaper way to freight grain and other bulky goods.

Although the canal still carried three-fifths of freight crossing New York State in 1866, the trade was becoming uneconomic, and in 1882 tolls had to be abolished. As a final effort to revive it, the New York legislature in 1903 funded a complete upgrade, but it was too late, and the Erie Canal slowly dwindled into commercial oblivion. Its construction had one long-lasting effect, however. It breathed life into New York, the trade it brought elevating the city to the financial capital of the United States, so that it eclipsed its long-time rival Philadelphia, and helping its population to quadruple between 1820 and 1850. Without Jesse Hawley's vision and DeWitt Clinton's persistence, the New York City we know today would not exist.

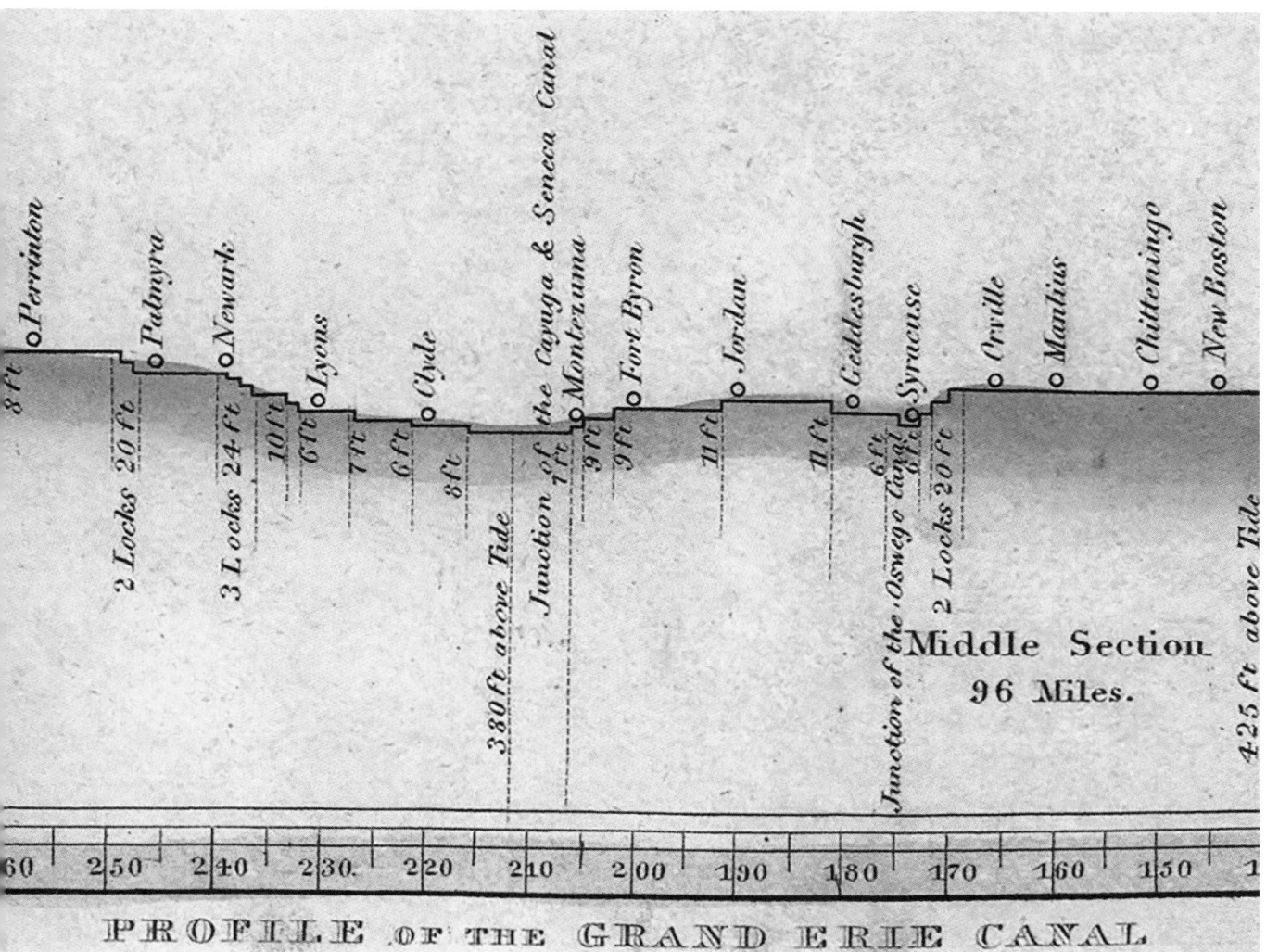

PROFILE OF THE GRAND ERIE CANAL

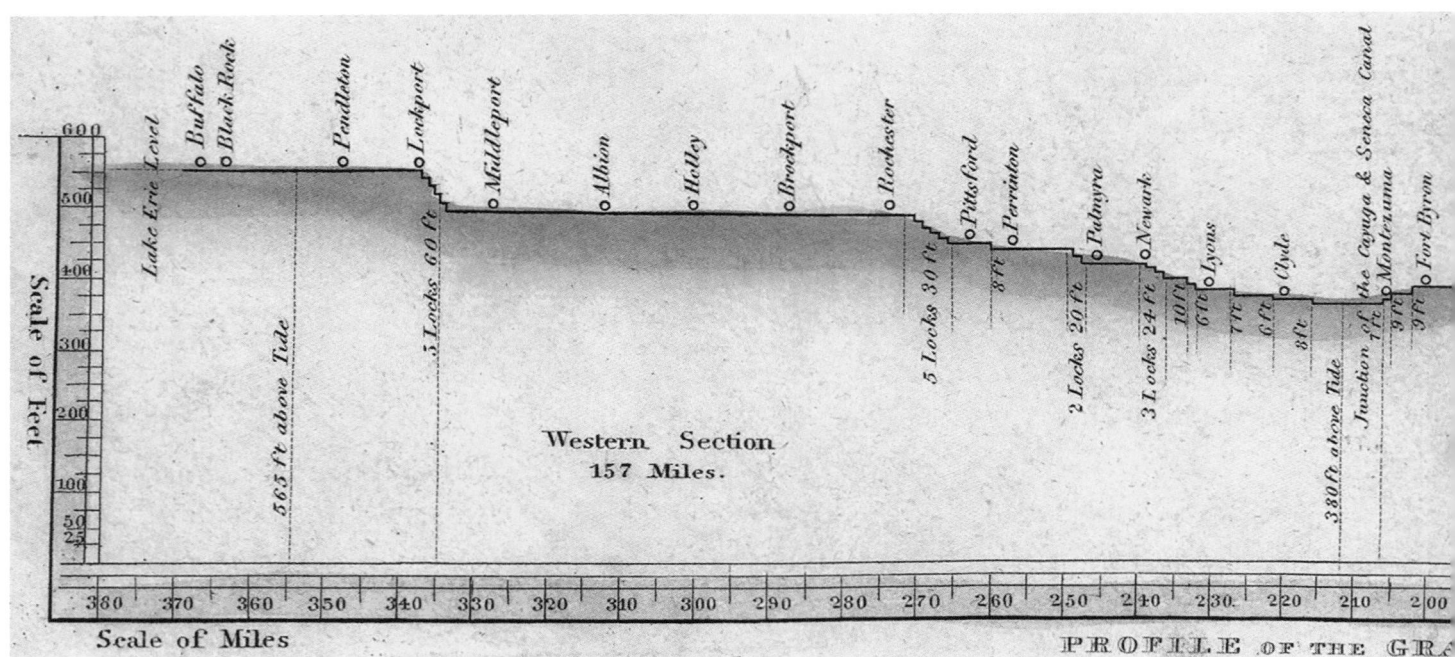

Scale of Feet

600
500
400
300
200
100
50
25

Lake Erie Level

○ *Buffalo*
○ *Black Rock*

○ *Pendleton*

○ *Lockport*

5 Locks 60 ft

○ *Middleport*

○ *Albion*

○ *Holley*

○ *Brockport*

○ *Rochester*

○ *Pittsford*

○ *Perrinton*

○ *Palmyra*

○ *Newark*

○ *Lyons*

○ *Clyde*

○ *Montezuma*

○ *Fort Byron*

Junction of the Cayuga & Seneca Canal

5 Locks 30 ft
8 ft

2 Locks 20 ft

3 Locks 24 ft
10 ft
6 ft
7 ft
6 ft
8 ft

7 ft
9 ft

565 ft above Tide

380 ft above Tide

Western Section
157 Miles.

Scale of Miles

380   370   360   350   340   330   320   310   300   290   280   270   260   250   240   230   220   210   200

PROFILE OF THE GR

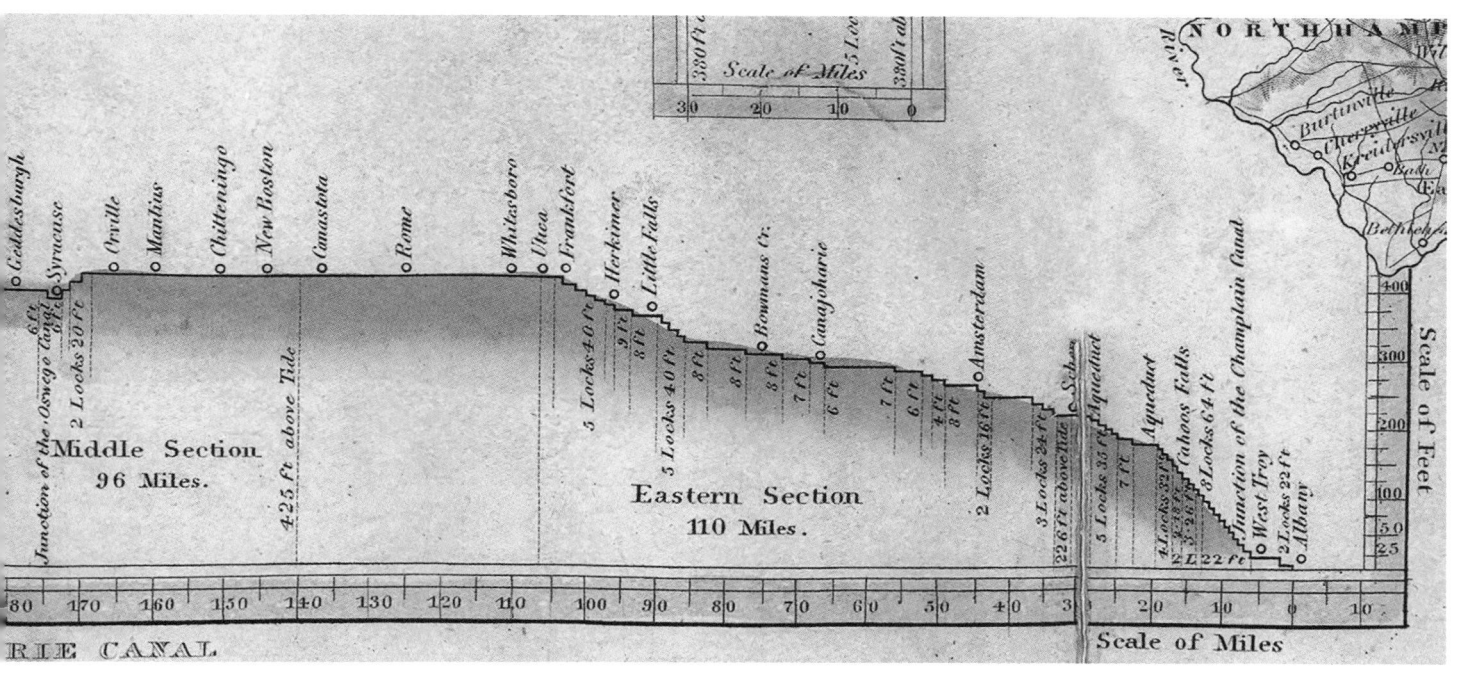

NORTHAMP...

Burtinville
Oteysville
Kreidersvill

Bethleh...

Geddesburgh
Syracuse
Orville
Manlius
Chittening
New Boston
Canastota
Rome
Whitesboro
Utica
Frankfort
Herkimer
Little Falls
Bowmans Cr.
Canojoharie
Amsterdam
Schen...
Aqueduct
Aqueduct
Cohoes Falls
Junction of the Champlain Canal
West Troy
Albany

Junction of the Oswego Canal
6 ft
2 Locks 20 ft
425 Ft above Tide

Middle Section
96 Miles.

5 Locks 40 ft
9 ft
8 ft
5 Locks 40 ft
8 ft
8 ft
8 ft
7 ft
6 ft
7 ft
6 ft
4 ft
3 ft
2 Locks 16 ft
3 Locks 24 ft
22 6 ft above tide
5 Locks 35 ft
7 ft
4 Locks 33 ft
3 Locks 64 ft
2 L 22 ft
2 Locks 22 Ft

Eastern Section
110 Miles.

Scale of Feet
400
300
200
100
50
25

80   170   160   150   140   130   120   110   100   90   80   70   60   50   40   3   20   10   0   10

RIE CANAL.

Scale of Miles

The Suez Canal

From Port Said in the north to Suez in the south, one of the world's great trading waterways traces a 120-mile course through evocatively named locations such as the Plains of Pelusium and the Bitter Lakes in this chart by the prolific London cartographer James Wyld II.

Published just five days after the canal's opening on November 17, 1869, Wyld's map charts the solution to a centuries-old problem: the extra burden imposed on trade by the need for ships travelling between Europe and the Indian Ocean to round the southern coast of Africa. It was not the first attempt to bridge the narrow gap across the Sinai Peninsula between the Mediterranean and the Red Sea. The Egyptian pharaoh Senusret III had ordered the digging of a connecting channel around 1850BC, but that had silted up in the Middle Ages. It was the rediscovery

of its dried-up bed by troops of Napoleon's Egypt expedition in 1799 that prompted the European powers to wonder if a new waterway could be dug.

A mistaken belief that there was a 30-foot difference in height between the seas retarded progress, and the British were sceptical about channelling all trade through a narrow chokepoint that, if in unfriendly hands, could throttle trade with its Indian possessions. A new survey in 1830 proved that there was no disparity in levels, but British reticence allowed the French to gain a head start and in 1854 the French diplomat Ferdinand de Lesseps obtained a 99-year franchise to build and operate a canal. The Egyptian khedive Sa'id Pasha received a 44 per cent stake in the Suez Canal Company and facilitated the 30,000-strong workforce of labourers needed to construct it.

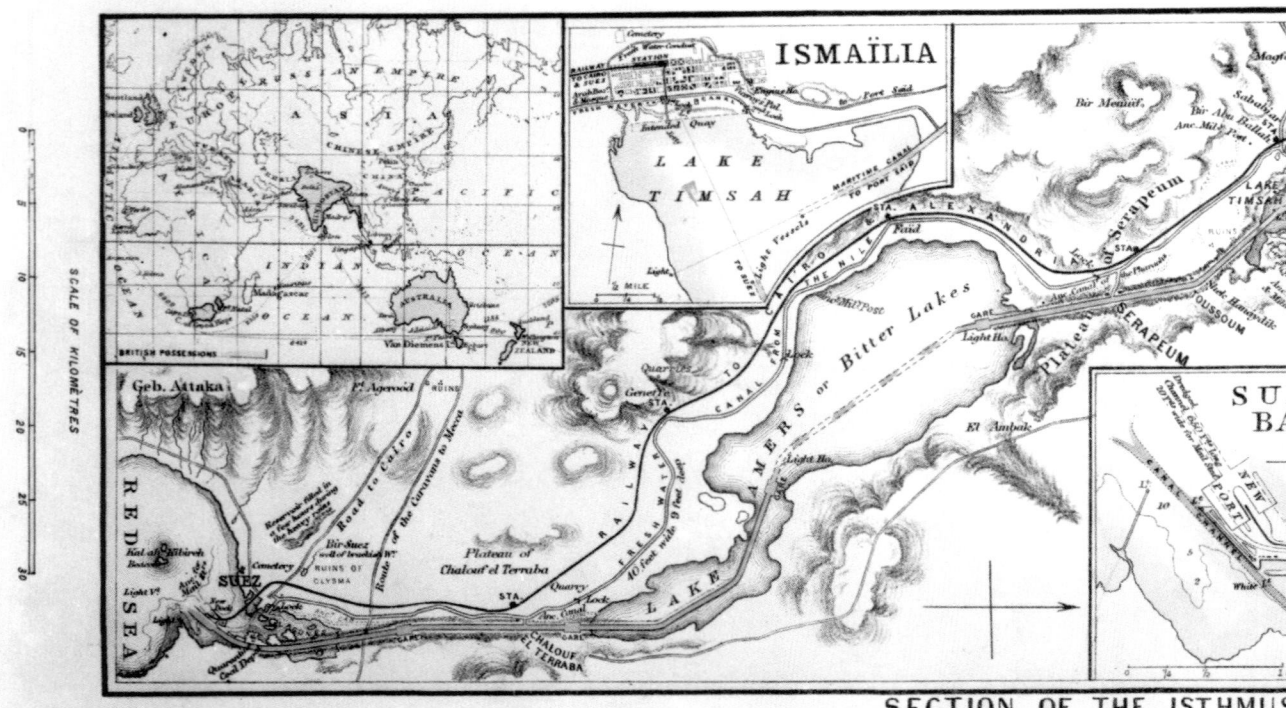

WYLD'S OFFICIAL MAP OF T

SECTION OF THE ISTHMUS

Finally, in late 1869 the work was complete. Amid great fanfare, the Khedive and invited European royalty enjoyed a son et lumière spectacular, before heading off in convoy down the canal, led by the French imperial yacht with Empress Eugénie on board. The effect on global trade was spectacular: at a stroke the sailing distance between London and Bombay fell from 11,500 to 6,200 miles and transport costs fell by 30 per cent. The canal accelerated the introduction of steamships, as sailing vessels had to be towed through it, and it made the development of European colonies in East Asia more attractive. Before long the French had drained the Mekong Delta in Vietnam and were exporting rice back to Europe, but the cost to the indigenous inhabitants was severe, as they were forced to work on large plantations and subject to ever more stringent colonial control.

Although world trade prospered, the Khedive did not enjoy its fruits. Extravagant Egyptian expenditure, encouraged by cynical European governments, outran income from the canal and in 1875 Sa'id Pasha's successor Ismail was forced to sell his share to the British government for £4 million. This toehold rapidly turned into outright control when, in response to anti-European riots in 1882, a British force bombarded Alexandria. This was followed by the declaration of a de facto British protectorate.

By 1888, the Canal was a neutral zone under British protection and remained so until President Nasser of Egypt nationalised it in 1956, prompting another Anglo-French expedition, this time ending in humiliating failure. A century after its opening, control over the Suez Canal remained one of world trade's greatest prizes.

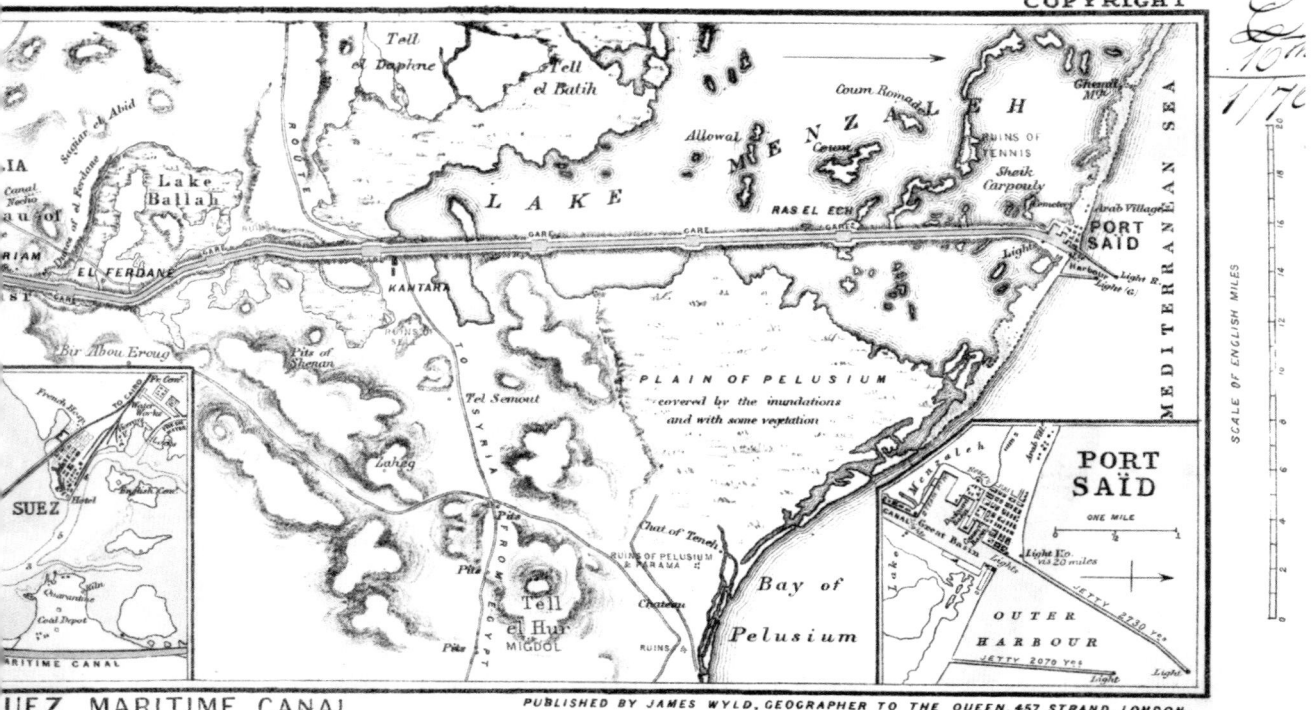

SUEZ MARITIME CANAL.

UEZ MARITIME CANAL.   PUBLISHED BY JAMES WYLD, GEOGRAPHER TO THE QUEEN, 457 STRAND, LONDON.

The Panama Canal

The map, drawn up by American cartographer Orville Whitmore Childs in 1851, shows a projected waterway cutting across Central America, making use of Lake Nicaragua and a navigable stretch of the River San Juan de Nicaragua to provide a means of avoiding vessels carrying cargo between the Atlantic and Pacific Oceans having to take the time-consuming and sometimes hazardous 8,000-mile detour around South America.

Almost since the conquistador Vasco Nuñez de Balboa first crossed the Isthmus of Panama in 1513, projects had been devised to ease the routes of the Spanish treasure ships across the two oceans, but a plan in 1529 came to nothing. The increasing economic power of the United States revived interest in creating a shortcut across Central America, which led to a diplomatic tussle with Britain over which

nation had the right to do so. The Clayton–Bulwer Treaty resolved the issue in 1850, by agreeing that whichever of them did so should not have exclusive control over it.

Yet despite a flurry of new schemes, including that mapped by Childs, no practical work was undertaken on the ground. Then, in 1878 an international commission awarded the right to build a canal to the French entrepreneur Ferdinand de Lesseps. Flush from his success in constructing the Suez Canal, he was in no mood to listen to naysayers such as Adolphe Godin de Lépinay – a qualified engineer – who warned that the isthmus was unsuitable for the building of a canal without locks (the method used in Suez). The result was disaster. Poor planning, humidity and tropical diseases wrought a terrible toll on the 40,000-strong workforce, and the inadequate

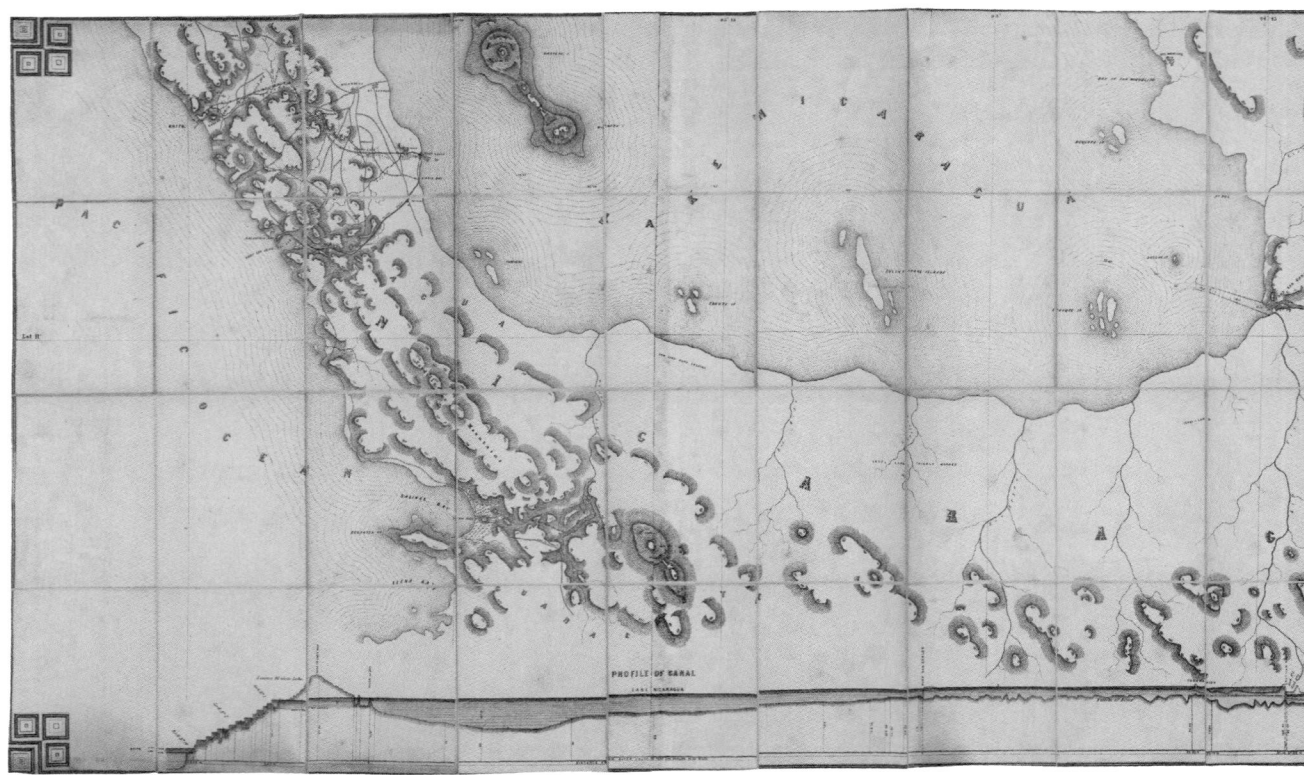

machinery, too light to make a dent in the heavy soils, slowed progress through the deep jungle to a crawl. Over 20,000 labourers died, a figure worsened by the habit in the company hospitals of placing the patients' beds in pans of water, in the belief this would stop insects crawling up them, but which in fact created ideal breeding grounds for malarial mosquitoes.

The company went bankrupt in 1889, which caused a major scandal in France and the discrediting of de Lesseps. The canal project lay fallow until in 1902 the US Congress authorised the acquisition of the French assets, and the signing of the Hay–Bunau-Varilla Treaty the following year with newly independent Panama gave the United States the right to build the canal and operate it in perpetuity. The route still had to be hacked through impenetrable jungle, but lessons had been learnt from the de Lesseps fiasco: the new canal was built with locks and its construction, between 1904 and 1914, cost a more modest 5,600 lives.

On August 15, 1914 the canal opened. The timing could have been better, as the outbreak of the First World War just a fortnight before soon caused global trade to congeal. Yet, once it was over, the canal and its owners prospered, despite periodic diplomatic tensions between the United States and Panama, whose rulers resented the inferior deal they had struck. Finally, in 1999 the United States passed full control of the canal back to Panama and today it is used by around 14,000 vessels a year. In all it yields around $1.8 billion in tolls, a far cry from the 36 cents paid by the American adventurer Richard Halliburton in 1928 as the price for swimming its length.

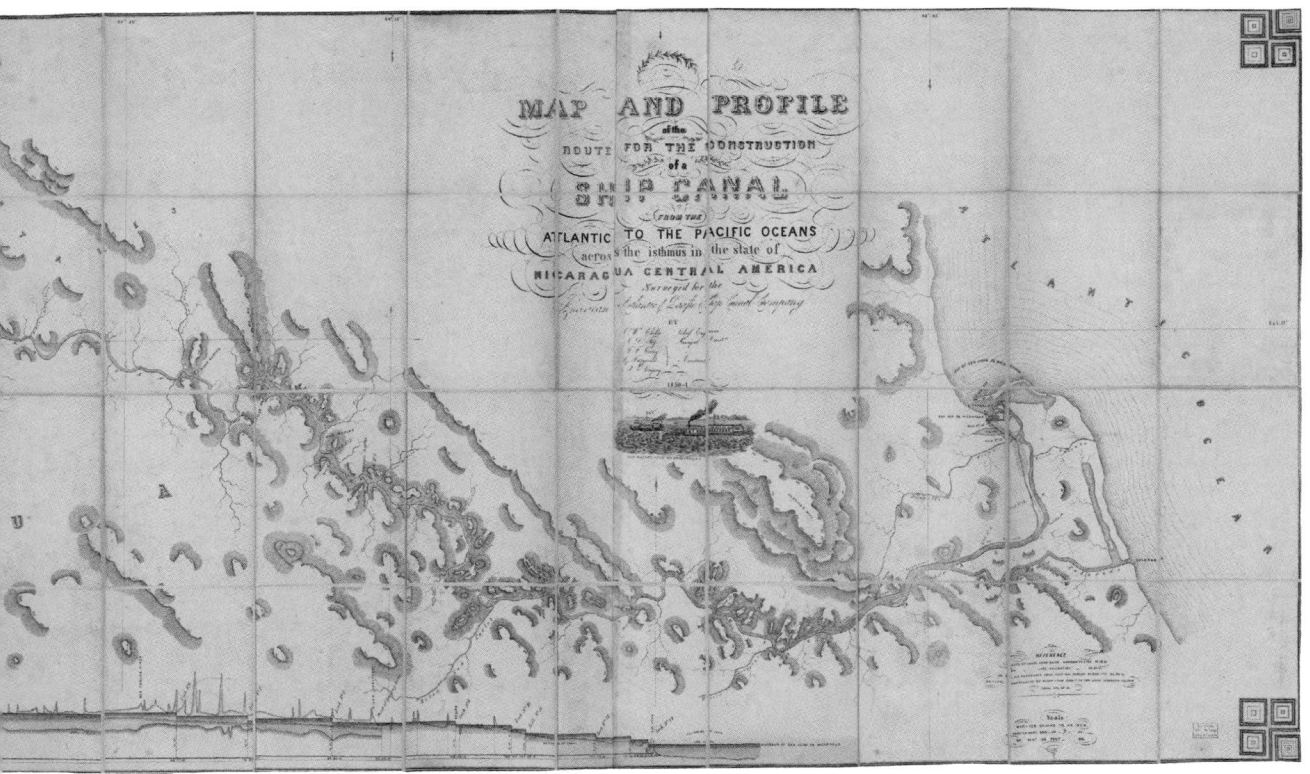

The US Transcontinental Railroad

Countries need to trade within themselves, and the transportation of goods and people across vast distances presented particular difficulties for growing nations such as the United States, which by the mid-19th century spanned a whole continent, a distance of over 2,000 miles. The New York cartographer Gaylord Watson's 1871 railroad map shows the moment a solution was found, as the thickening web of tracks in the east of the country was finally supplemented by a continuous transcontinental railroad.

Since the 1830s, there had been plans to join the established cities of the eastern seaboard with the infant territory of California. But the sheer scale of the project was too forbidding, involving pushing tracks across the endless vistas of the Great Plains and Californian deserts, and blasting a way through the Rocky Mountains and Sierra Nevada. The outbreak of the Civil War in 1861 further held back its commencement, but finally in July 1862 Abraham Lincoln signed the Pacific Railroad Act, establishing the route for the railroad and the terms under which the two successful bidders would build it.

The Union Pacific Company, which began from a railhead in Omaha, Nebraska, and the Central Pacific Company, which pushed eastwards from California, had hit on a mine more lucrative than the Gold Rush of 1849. The government paid each of them between $16,000 and $48,000 per mile of track (with the higher sum for mountainous terrain), while the actual cost was a mere $10,000 a mile. Both enterprises set up supply companies to carry out the work, siphoning money into the directors' and shareholders' pockets. The opportunities for embezzlement were on a colossal scale. The granting to the companies of all land within ten miles of the track on one side provided further possibilities for profit and led to persistent conflict with the Native American tribes whose territory had been summarily confiscated.

Ten thousand Chinese labourers were imported to accelerate the Central Pacific's progress, and by 1868 the two railroads had almost met. But then, reluctant to give up on this profitable game, the companies simply carried on, bypassing each other and proceeding along parallel lines. President Ulysses S Grant stepped in to stop the madness, and it was agreed that the two railroads should join at Promontory Point, Utah. So, on May 10, 1869, amid great fanfare, Dr Thomas Durant of the Union Pacific, and his Central Pacific counterpart Leland Stanford drove in a final, symbolic golden spike to unite the two networks.

The journey across the continent which had previously taken five long gruelling weeks by wagon train was now reduced to five days, and the electric telegraph that was laid alongside the tracks revolutionised communication between east and west. The system was not perfect; the first transcontinental service, which ran in May 1870 with luxury sleeping cars provided by George Pullman and its own onboard newspaper, still involved four changes of train, and it was not until 1872 that a true through service was established. Yet the first goods train, which bore a cargo of Japanese tea on May 11, 1869, the very day after the railroads joined, was a harbinger of great things. By 1880 the transcontinental railroad was carrying $50 million of freight a year, the Midwest had been opened up to grain cultivation on a vast scale, and new towns were springing up along the route – the heirs to the "hell on wheels" encampments of labourers, saloons and brothels which had accompanied the construction. Watson's map truly was a map of America's future.

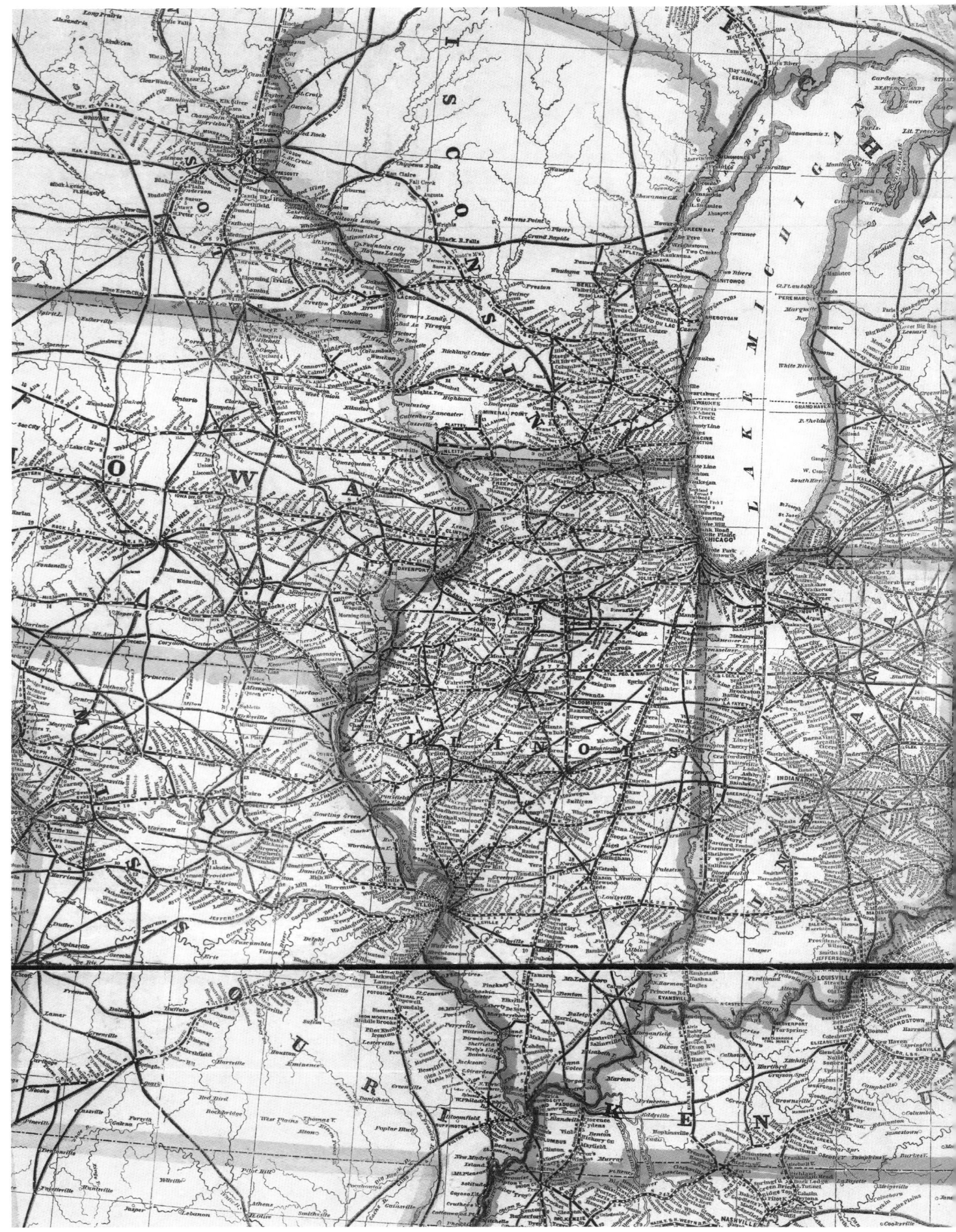

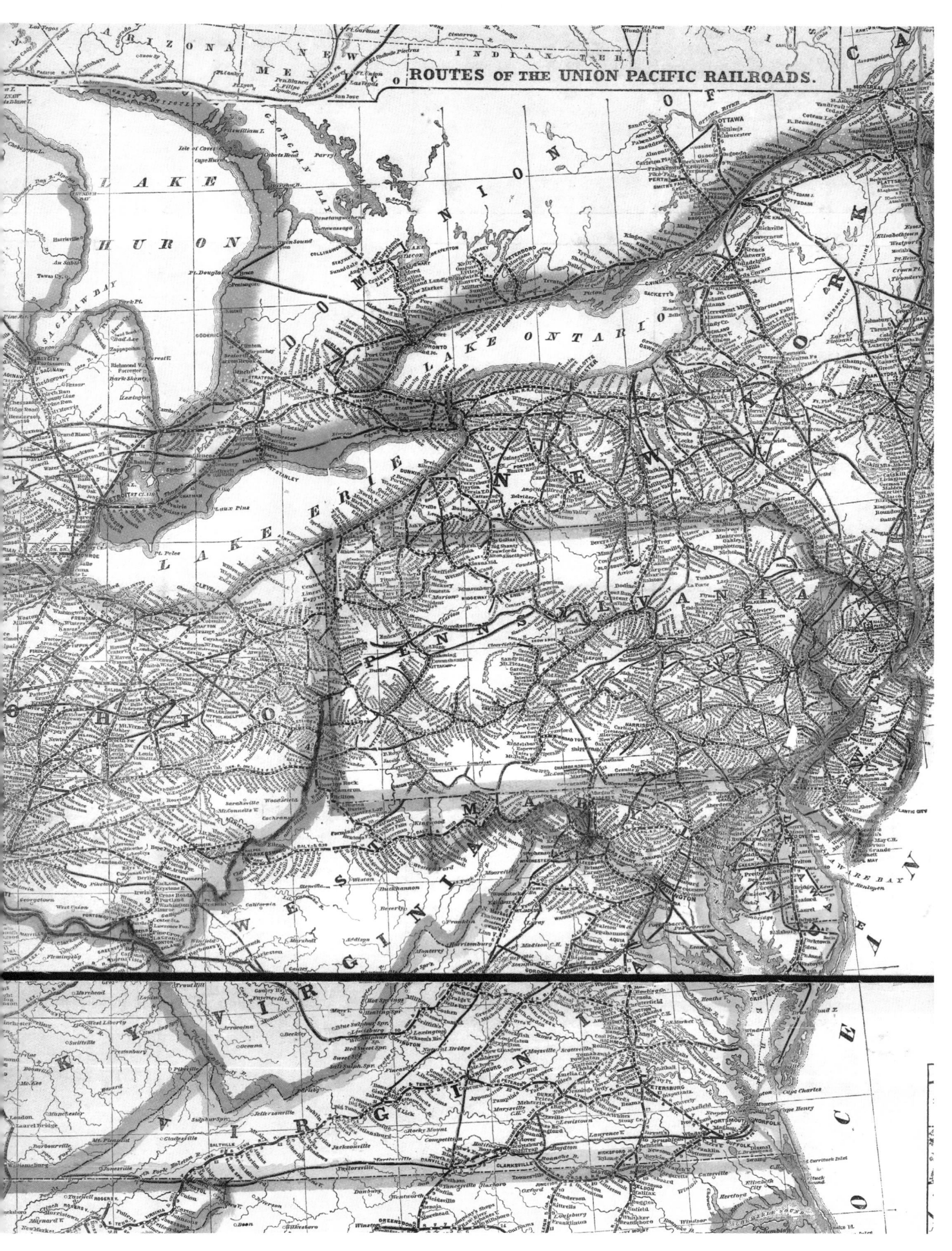

ROUTES OF THE UNION PACIFIC RAILROADS.

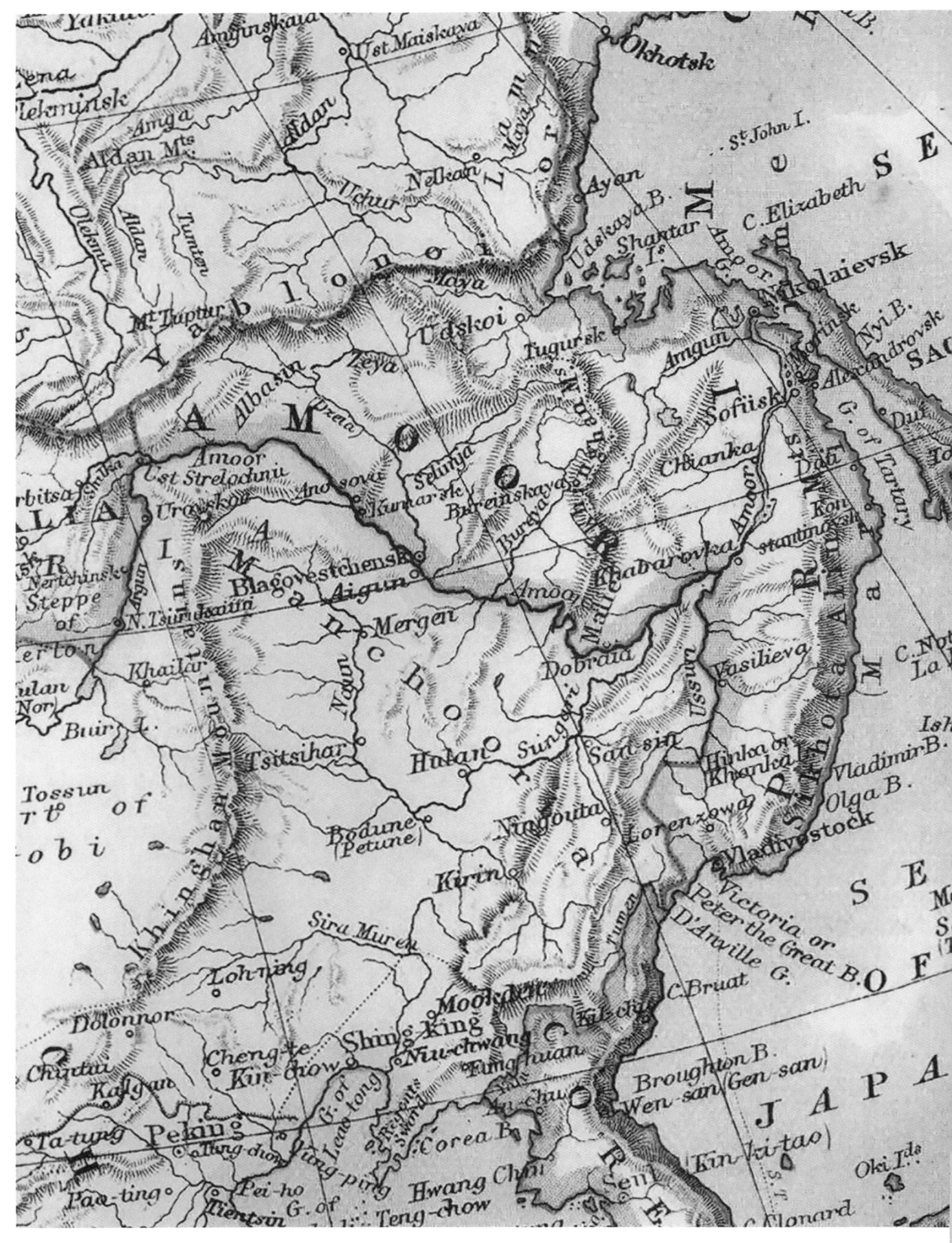

The Trans-Siberian Railway

The 1895 map by W & AK Johnston shows the vast sweep of "Russia in Asia", an area which posed a strategic problem for Russia. From the time that Russian adventurers, Cossacks and traders began to penetrate Siberia in the mid-16th century, Russian tsars had fretted about their ability to control this farthest reach of their growing empire.

A transcontinental railway seemed the obvious solution. However, Russia was no entrepreneur-friendly democracy like the United States, but an autocracy where individual initiative was treated with suspicion. Although a railway line was completed between Moscow and St Petersburg in 1851, further development was stifled by Tsar Nicholas I's insistence that all passengers be subject to a police check. The defeat in the Crimean War (1853-56) made the court realise that Russia had fallen far behind its European rivals, and the Chinese colonisation of Manchuria threatened to loosen Russia's hold on Siberia, but even so, little was done: the main Russian rail network did not even reach Orenburg on the southwest border of Siberia until 1877.

It took the genius of Sergei Witte, who rose from a humble position as a local railway administrator in Odessa to become director of the national network by 1889, to get the project started. With a talent for stroking the tsar's ego, in 1891 he appointed Prince Nicholas (who himself became tsar three years later) as the chairman of the Trans-Siberian railway committee.

With imperial patronage assured, construction began that summer, working westwards from Vladivostok – Russia's outpost on the Pacific, founded in 1860 – and east from Chelyabinsk. In western Siberia the work went smoothly, but east of Lake Baikal the surface was frozen until mid-July and then melted to create swamp-like conditions. In places the permafrost had to be dynamited and in the eastern sector large parts of track were swept away when the River Ussuri flooded, and had to be rebuilt.

Despite the nightmarish conditions, the 89,000-strong workforce proceeded steadily, the 13,500 convicts employed on the line encouraged by a two-year remission of sentence for each year they did so, and they laid down about 400 miles of track per year. The railway opened in stages, until the final section around Lake Baikal was completed in 1904. It had cost a staggering 855 million roubles, and even then a part had been built through China to save money, and so it was not until 1916 that a fully Russian transcontinental route operated.

The results were initially disappointing. Heavy incentives had to be offered to attract peasants to move to Siberia, and eventually four million did so. Strategically, the railway was a fiasco, its single track with passing loops woefully insufficient to transport troops to the east to face the Japanese in the Russo-Japanese War (1904-05) in which Russia suffered an ignominious defeat.

Yet, further development over the decades steadily improved the railway's capacity, until by 2018 it could carry 245,000 container loads a year. Passenger service proved more of a success, although the railway's strict adherence to Moscow time meant that by the time it approached Vladivostok, dinner was being served at 3am. For all its trials, the completion of the Trans-Siberian was a potent symbol that Russia was a single nation.

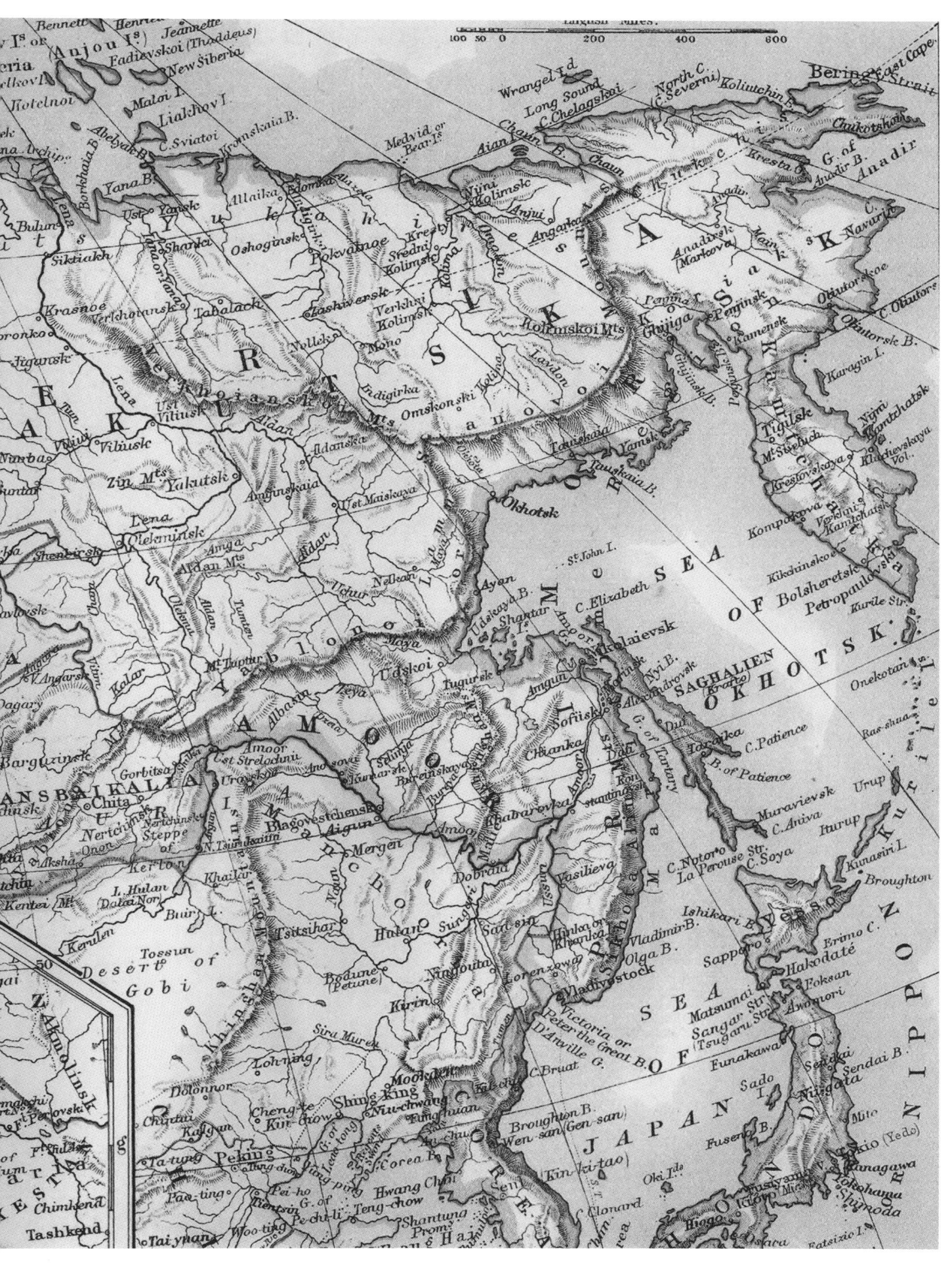

The Cape to Cairo Railway

The map, published in 1899, shows the projected route of a grand colonial project intended to link Britain's possessions in Egypt with those in southern Africa and provide a corridor both for trade and a statement of British imperial might.

The Cape to Cairo railway had originally been the brainchild of Edwin Arnold, the editor of *The Daily Telegraph*, who suggested it in a pamphlet in 1876. As his newspaper was the joint sponsor of Henry Morton Stanley's 1874 expedition to continue David Livingstone's quest for the source of the Nile, Arnold had both the interest and the political clout to push his idea.

Yet nothing was done. Britain's hold on southern Africa was still uncertain, and it took the intervention of one of the most ruthless and flamboyant champions of British imperialism to get it off the ground. Cecil Rhodes had been sent to South Africa as a 17-year-old to improve his sickly constitution. There, he transformed a £3,000 loan from his aunt into a business empire. In partnership with his brother, he bought up distressed diamond claims during an economic downturn, and by 1888, when he absorbed his main competitor and founded the De Beers company, he controlled the lion's share of the world's diamond supply and a fair share of its gold.

This, and a platform as the prime minister of Cape Colony from 1890, made Rhodes ideally placed to launch the Cape to Cairo project. In the late 1880s he began extending British control to the north by persuading or bullying local chieftains to sign agreements allowing mineral exploitation in their lands. In 1888 he achieved a major success in getting Lobenguela, the king of the Ndebele, to sign one such concession, after which miners flooded into his territory. Rhodes's British South Africa Company made further treaties and with the aid of thousands of company police established a de facto empire north of the Limpopo which in 1895 was formally renamed Rhodesia.

The first rail was laid on the Cape to Cairo track at Kimberley in 1889, and by October 1894 it had reached Mafeking (now Mahikeng) 225 miles away. But, then, Rhodes's disgrace after he sponsored an abortive attack on the independent Boer Republic of Transvaal in 1896 removed the railway's main backer. The diplomatic climate darkened too. In 1885 the Portuguese produced their "Pink Map" showing claims linking their colonies of Angola in the west with Mozambique in the east. In the 1890s, the French tried to launch another competing east–west line linking Senegal to Djibouti, which only foundered when their land grab was blocked by a confrontation with a British fleet at Fashoda on the Nile in 1897. King Leopold of Belgium's establishment of a personal fiefdom in the Congo in 1885, and the German annexation of Tanganyika in 1891, blocked progress northwards both to the east and the west.

By the time the British obtained German East Africa as a League of Nations mandate in 1922, enthusiasm for the Cape to Cairo project had waned. The economic carnage of the Great Depression, the Second World War and the decolonisation of the 1960s killed it off completely. Only slowly have the independent African countries built links to create a transcontinental network, with a Chinese-funded line linking Tanzania to Zambia completed in 1976. Gaps, though, remain, such as the sector between Sudan and Uganda, so the partial Cape to Cairo railway that exists today is very far from Cecil Rhodes's dream of a unified and British-controlled network.

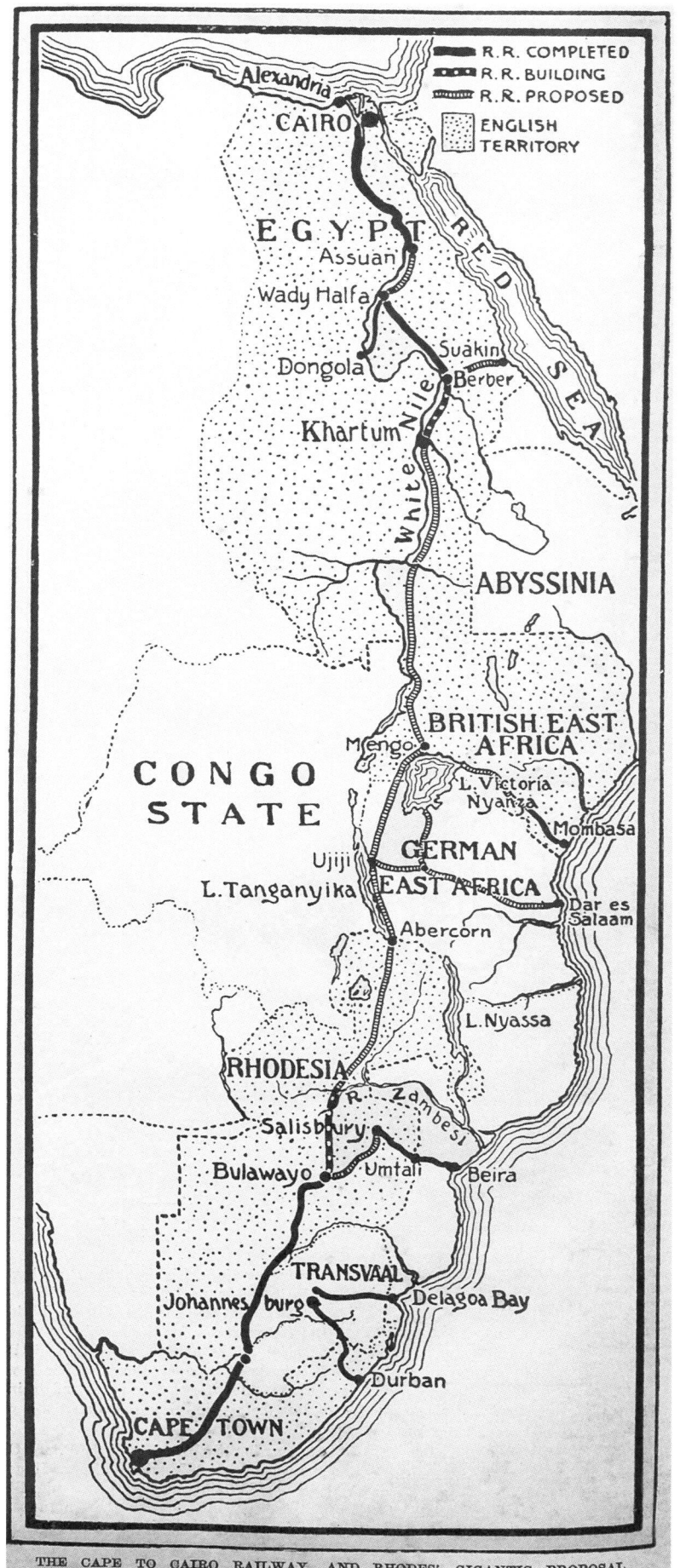

THE CAPE TO CAIRO RAILWAY, AND RHODES' GIGANTIC PROPOSAL.

Iceland

530 m.

Forge Is
450 m.

Shetland Is

Orkney Is

Quebec 2558 m.

Londonderry

BRITISH
ISLES

Ireland
Belfast
Dublin
Cork

John

Glasgow Leith
Edinburgh
SCOTLAND
Inverness Aberdeen

2270 m.

L. Man
ENGLAND
LONDON
Cardiff
Southampton
Ply.

Queenstown

Channel Is

Brest

St Nazaire
La Rochelle

Bordeaux

Santander
Coruña
Vigo
Saragossa
Oporto
Madrid

Lisbon

SPAIN

Seville
Cadiz
Tangier
Gibraltar

Madeira

Canary Is
(Spain)
Teneriffe Palmas

Rio de Oro

C. Blanco

St Louis

C. Verd
SENEGAL
Bathurst
Bissao
Bissagos Is
(Port.)

FRENCH
GUINEA

Los Is
SIERRA
LEONE

Freetown

Monrovia

C. Palmas

Trondhjem
Christiansund
Molde
Aalesund

Bergen
Stavanger
Christiansand

Drammen

North Sea

DENMARK

Kiel Rostock
Bremen
Hanover
Amsterdam
Rotterdam
Antwerp
Brussels
Cologne

Paris

Orleans
Loire
FRANCE Bern
SWITZERLAND
Lyons
Turin
Toulouse

Marseilles
Corsica
Barcelona

Valencia
Balearic Is

Medit

Oran
Algiers
Fez
ALGERIA
Saffi MOROCCO
Morocco
Mogador
Figig
El Golea

In Salah

TIMBUKTU

Niger

FRENCH SUDAN

S U D A N

Kuka
Ilo
Zungeru
NIGERIA
DAHOMEY
TOGO
Lagos
Whydah
Accra
GOLD COAST
Sekondi
IVORY COAST
Bassam
Kumasi
LIBERIA
Gr. Bassam
1440 m.
Fernando Po
Gulf of Guinea Bight of Biafra
RIO
St Thomas MUNI
Libreville

Annobon FRENCH CONGO

Umea

Gefle

Stockholm
Norrköping

Gottenburg
Karlskrona
Malmö
Copenhagen
Baltic Sea

GERMANY
Berlin
Leipzig
Prague
Munich
Vienna
AUSTRIA-HUNGARY
Buda-Pest
Trieste
Venice
Genoa

Rome
Naples
Sardinia

Palermo
Sicily
Messina

Tunis
TUNIS
Malta
Tripoli
Cabes
Bengazi
Ghadames

TRIPOLI

FEZZAN

Murzuk

S A H A R A

Sokoto

L. Chad

Massenya

Yola

DUALA
Kamerun

Welle
Ubanghi
Congo

CONGO STATE

Leopoldville

Loango

Fleöborg

FINLAND

Nikolaistad
Vasa

Abo

St Petersburg

Revel
Pskov

Riga

Memel
Königsberg
Danzig
Stettin
Warsaw
POLAND
Cracow
Lemberg Kiev

Belgrade
BOSNIA
SERVIA BULGARIA
Philippopolis
Adriatic Sea
Brindisi Salonica
Aegean Sea
GREECE
Athens
Smyrna

Crete

ASIA MINOR
TURKEY IN ASIA
Eregli

Cyprus

Beirut
Jaffa
Jerusalem
Damascus

Alexandria
P. Said
Cairo Suez

EGYPT

Siut

Aswân

Nile

Wady Halfa
Suakin

Dongola

Berber
Omdurman Massowah

Khartum
ANGLO-EGYPTIAN SUDAN
Kodok
(Fashoda)

ABYSSINIA

Addis
Abeba
Harar

L. Rudolf

UGANDA

Victoria
Nyanza

Coquilhatville

Ujiji

White
Sea

Archangel

Dwina

Ko

Vologda
Yaroslav

Moscow

R U S S I A

Nijni
Novgorod

Orel
Kursk

Saratov

Kharkov

Volga

Odessa
Rostov
Astrakhan

Galatz
Bukarest
Danube
ROUMANIA
Sebastopol
Novorossusk
Black Sea
Varna
Constantinople Poti
Scutari Trebizond Petrovsk
Batoum Tiflis
ARMENIA
Tabriz

Aleppo
Euphrates
Tigris

Bagd

Tel

A R A

Bahre

Basra
Kuweit

Medina

Jidda

Mecca

Aden

Jibuti Perim
Zeila Berber
BRI.
SOMALI

Kamaran I.

Gondar

Obiat

BRITISH
EAST AFRICA

Kismayu
Lamu
Mombasa

Baraw

Mog

ITALIAN

The Wool Trade

The 1907 Bartholomew map of global wool commerce shows the vast extent of one of the world's oldest trades, with red and blue colouring used to denote the distribution of flocks across all the inhabited continents.

Sheep are one of mankind's oldest companions and were first domesticated in Mesopotamia around 10,000BC. Their capacity to yield both meat and long hair which could be shorn, treated and processed into woollen cloth meant that wherever agriculture travelled to, shepherds did so too.

Some regions, though, were particularly adapted to pastoral farming and Britain acquired a reputation for the quality of its wool as early as Roman times. The spread of large monastic houses in the early Middle Ages meant that England developed a substantial wool industry exporting to the cloth towns of the Netherlands, Bruges, Ghent and Ypres, where the wool was manufactured into finished textiles (see pages 62–5). By 1300, around 40,000 sacks of raw English wool were being exported there a year and the tariff revenue it generated largely funded Edward I's wars against Scotland and Wales between 1277 and 1304. It is no accident that the seat in parliament of the Lord Chancellor, the chief law officer of England, is modelled on a woolsack.

Britain's baton as champion of the wool trade was already passing to Spain, whose merino sheep had a finer, softer fleece. By 1567, 40,000 sacks of it were already going to Bruges, but then a new threat appeared. Lighter, softer cotton garments from Egypt and India were soon in vogue in Europe, so much so that the small weavers who had supplanted the large monastic estates by the 17th century took muscular action to keep cotton off the market. In 1678 their lobbying almost secured a parliamentary bill to make the wearing of wool garments by all students and lawyers mandatory and in 1696 the first stages of a bill passed, levying a fine of £100 on anyone importing calicoes (printed cotton cloths). An economic downturn in 1719 led the weavers of Spitalfields, a hotbed of pre-industrial activism, to engage in months of rioting (including tearing the clothes off any passers-by presumptuous enough to wear cotton).

Finally in 1721, parliament passed a law making it a crime to wear cotton on pain of a swingeing fine of £5. As a result, with its competition removed, wool priced itself out of the market, and the search for economic alternatives helped fuel the labour-saving cotton machines of the Industrial Revolution. For wool, the route back was a slow one, aided by the expansion of European empires to include vast spaces suitable for pastoral farming in South America, South Africa, New Zealand and Australia. When the First Fleet set off for Australia in 1787, as well as its human cargo of over 750 convicts, it carried 29 fat-tailed sheep. These proved unsuitable for Australian conditions, but in 1797 a consignment of merino sheep reached the colony. These grandparents of the Australian flock generated over 100 million offspring by 1900 and laid the foundation for an industry which exported its first fleeces back to England in 1807, and which by 1950 made up over 56 per cent of all Australia's agricultural production. Just as it had been 12,000 years before, the wool trade remained a vibrant one.

BRITISH ISLES
showing
DISTRIBUTION OF SHEEP

English Miles

NUMBER OF SHEEP
PER SQUARE MILE

OVER 500
300 TO 500
200 TO 300
100 TO 200
50 TO 100
UNDER 50

UNITED STATES
showing
DISTRIBUTION OF SHEEP

English Miles

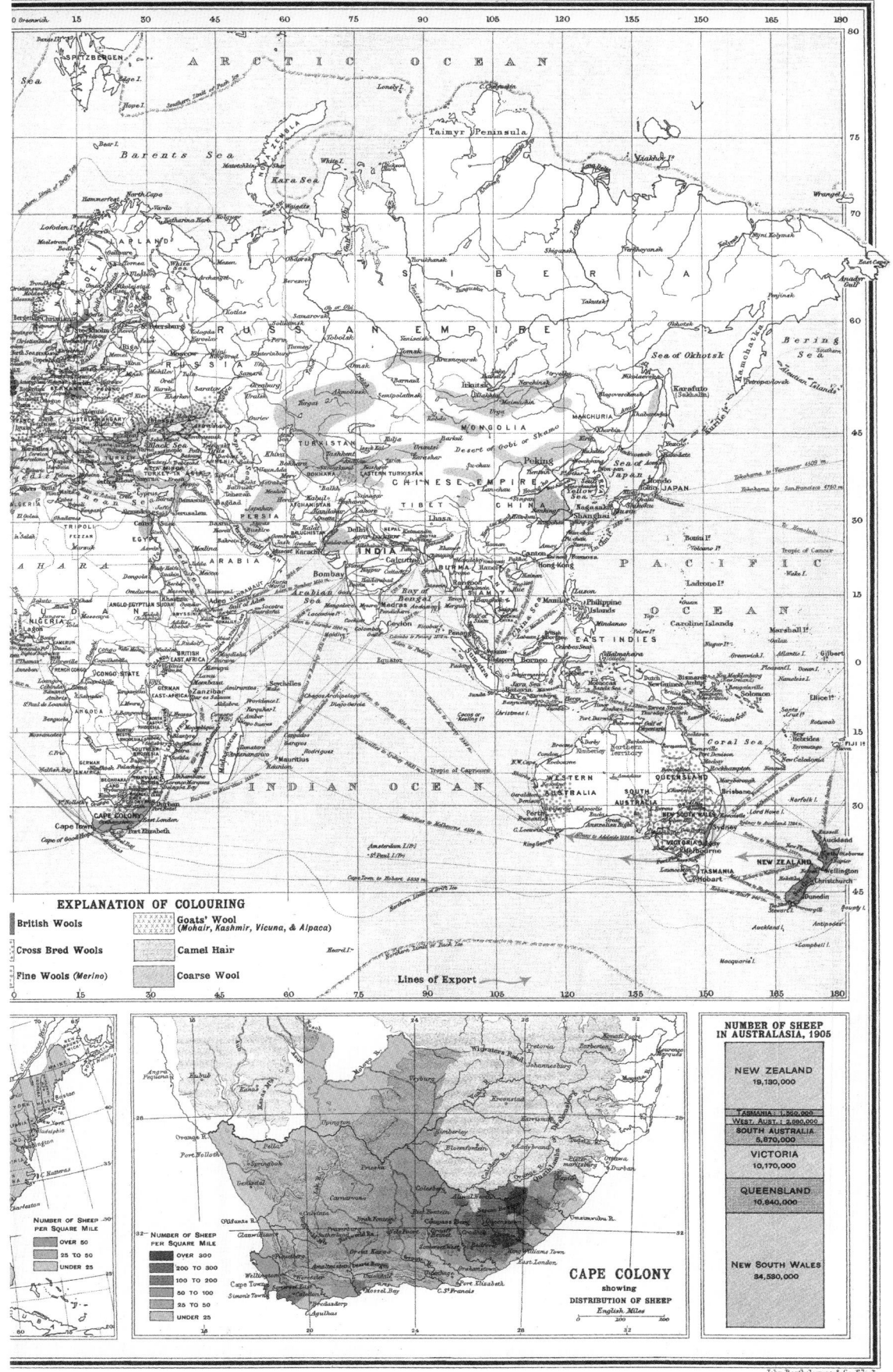

EXPLANATION OF COLOURING

▮ British Wools	▨ Goats' Wool (*Mohair, Kashmir, Vicuna, & Alpaca*)
▮ Cross Bred Wools	▢ Camel Hair
▮ Fine Wools (*Merino*)	▨ Coarse Wool

Lines of Export →

NUMBER OF SHEEP PER SQUARE MILE
- OVER 50
- 25 TO 50
- UNDER 25

NUMBER OF SHEEP PER SQUARE MILE
- OVER 300
- 200 TO 300
- 100 TO 200
- 50 TO 100
- 25 TO 50
- UNDER 25

CAPE COLONY
showing
DISTRIBUTION OF SHEEP
English Miles

NUMBER OF SHEEP IN AUSTRALASIA, 1905

NEW ZEALAND	19,130,000
TASMANIA : 1,560,000	
WEST. AUST. : 2,690,000	
SOUTH AUSTRALIA	5,870,000
VICTORIA	10,170,000
QUEENSLAND	16,640,000
NEW SOUTH WALES	34,530,000

John Bartholomew & Co. Edin.ᵣ

Refrigeration and the Meat Trade

Bartholomew's 1907 map of the meat trade indicates the principal exporters (mainly pork, mutton and beef) in red and the main importing countries in green. Although meat consumption that year was at its highest in Australia – a meat producer – at a champion 230 pounds per person annually, the British were chewing their way through a respectable 112 pounds, with other north European countries not far behind.

It was a trade that could not have existed a century earlier. Before the 1830s, perishable food had to be pickled, spiced or dried to preserve it for transportation or, for shorter distances, it could be moved on the hoof for slaughter. As populations grew during the Industrial Revolution (with that of England increasing from 5 million in 1700 to nearly 8 million in 1801, and then surging to 15 million in 1851), the growing cities could not be fed on local produce. The British partly filled the shortfall with imports from Ireland but it was not enough, and experiments with canning – which was used to ship some meat from Australia in the late 1860s – were both unappetising and small-scale.

Ice was the obvious solution, but it could not survive long voyages through the tropics, and even within the United States more than two-thirds of it melted on trips between the southern states and New England. Experimenting with various forms of insulation, the entrepreneurial Bostonian Frederic Tudor achieved such startling results that in 1833 he managed to ship ice to Calcutta. By the 1840s, the "Ice King" was sending chilled cargoes as far as Hong Kong.

Yet chilling was still inefficient and could not support large-scale meat exports. Primitive refrigerators had been developed around 1800 and refrigerated cars were introduced on American railroads in the 1840s to transport milk and butter. Scaling this up to shipping meat cargoes across continents proved challenging, but the development of ammonia-gas compression by the French scientist Charles Tellier in the 1860s provided the breakthrough. In 1877 the technique was used aboard the SS *Paraguay* to carry a cargo of mutton from Argentina to Le Havre, and two years later Tellier repeated the feat with a steamship called, appropriately, *Le Frigorifique*. Four years earlier, the US transportation magnate Timothy C Eastman had used somewhat more primitive equipment to send a first shipment of refrigerated beef to Britain. With a good eye for gastronomic diplomacy he had a consignment sent to Queen Victoria, who is said to have declared it "very good".

Australia sent its first shipment of mutton to Europe in 1876 aboard the *Northam*, but the refrigeration plant broke down and the meat was spoiled. It was not until 1880 that the *Strathleven* successfully brought a cargo of frozen beef and mutton to London, while New Zealand joined the burgeoning trade the following year.

Once established, the trade grew rapidly, and frozen imports to Britain reached 200,000 tons in 1900 and 347,000 tons a decade later. Argentina alone was shipping 253,000 tons of meat annually a year. As a result, by the end of the 19th century, the British were importing a third of their beef and mutton and half of their pork. Meat prices dropped sharply, and it became available for the first time to the urban poor. Ice had achieved great things.

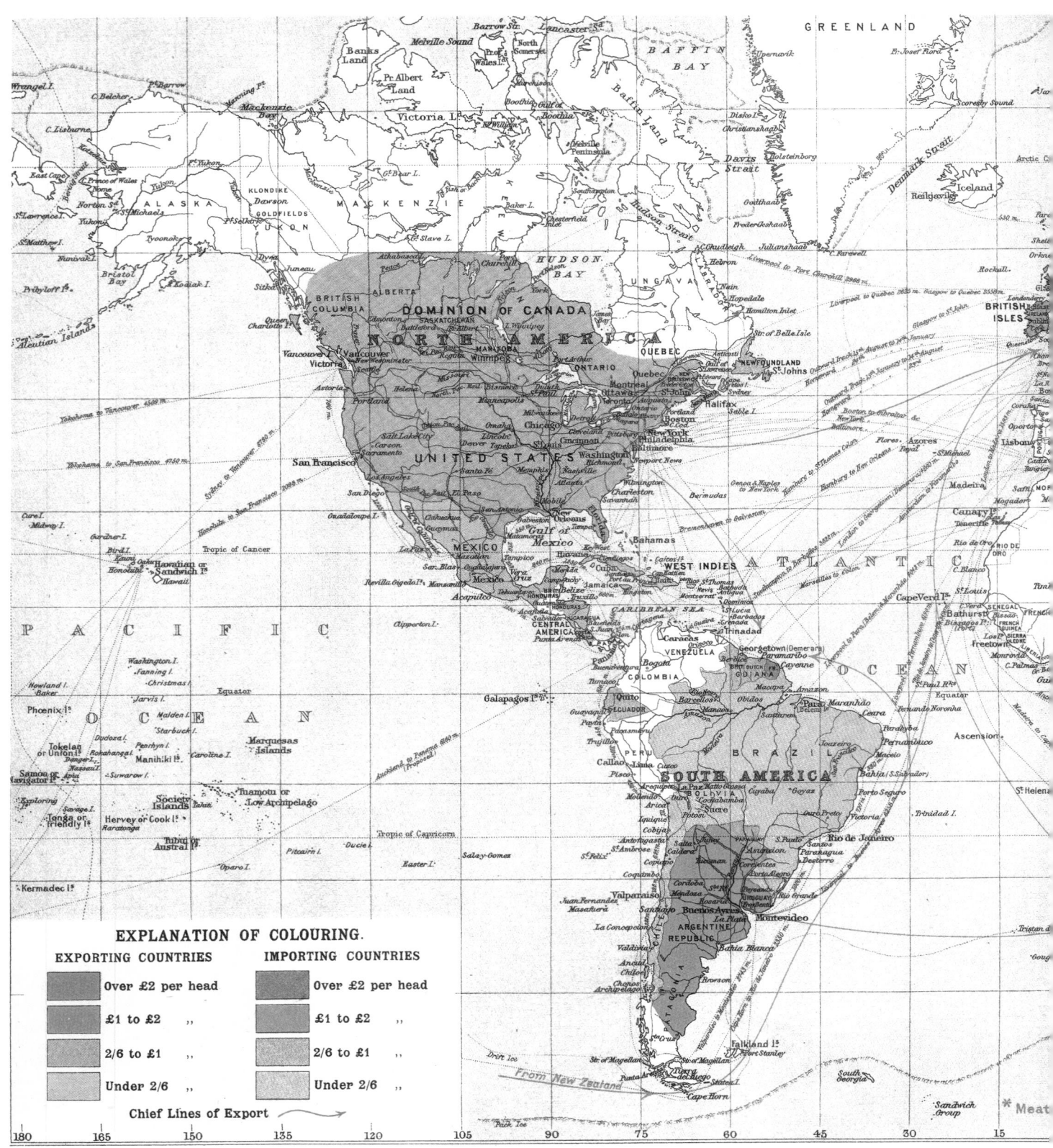

EXPLANATION OF COLOURING.

EXPORTING COUNTRIES	IMPORTING COUNTRIES
Over £2 per head	Over £2 per head
£1 to £2 ,,	£1 to £2 ,,
2/6 to £1 ,,	2/6 to £1 ,,
Under 2/6 ,,	Under 2/6 ,,

Chief Lines of Export ⟶

Cattle

The Coal Trade

The map of the coal trade in 1907 by the Edinburgh cartographic company John Bartholomew spatters the world in red to show its principal coal-exporting regions, a deep concentration in the United Kingdom more than outweighed by a sea of crimson in the United States and red ribbons in Australia, Russia, India and China, which show Britain's long-established dominance under threat from new competitors.

Despite Bartholomew's colour choice, coal was "black gold", a previously overlooked commodity which had come into its own during the Industrial Revolution. Used by the ancient Egyptians in powdered form for cosmetics and from at least the 4th century BC by Greeks and, later, by Romans for smelting in metallurgy, coal's ascent to become the lifeblood of industry was gradual. Britain was blessed with coal that was low in sulphur, which made it more suitable for domestic heating, but trade only began on a small scale in the 12th century with its movement within coal-producing areas in Scotland, the northeast of England and London, and the tiny beginnings of an export trade to English possessions in France in the 14th century.

This was all surface coal, or extracted from shallow shafts dug from the surface. A pioneering underground mine dug by Sir George Bruce of Carnock at Culross in Scotland in 1575 opened up new sources of coal, but there simply was not yet the demand to justify extensive deep mines. The steam age and the Industrial Revolution changed all that. Newcomen's engine in 1712, which pumped water from mine shafts, allowing them to penetrate deeper seams, and Watt's improved version in 1775,

which ultimately made steam the motor of industry, both needed coal to fuel them, while the growth in industries such as copper and iron smelting created an unprecedented thirst for coal.

In 1780 the annual average coal output from Britain was 6.25 million tons, which more than doubled to 16 million tons in 1815, and then reached 30 million by 1930. Already by 1800, Britain was producing around 90 per cent of world coal output and much of this was exported, providing a handy outbound cargo for ships which otherwise would have sailed empty, and allowing lower freight charges for return cargoes such as wheat or copper, which gave British carriers a huge competitive advantage.

At the hub of all this was Cardiff: its port, strategically sited near the heart of the vast South Wales coalfields, hosted more than 120 shipping companies in 1913, which between them exported more than 10 million tons of coal annually. Yet the worries of the Victorian economist William Jevons, whose 1865 report on "The Coal Question" fretted that the coal industry, the "alpha and omega" of British prosperity, would soon be outpaced by others, proved to be well founded. Australia began exporting coal on a small scale in 1801, and coal was found in Wyoming in 1842 and in Russia's Donetsk Basin in 1869. The establishment of the first coal-fired power station in London in 1882 created a new market for coal, and by 1900 the United States's production had reached 270 million tons. No longer the unchallenged coal king by the time of the map, Britain was already being forced to share black gold's bounty.

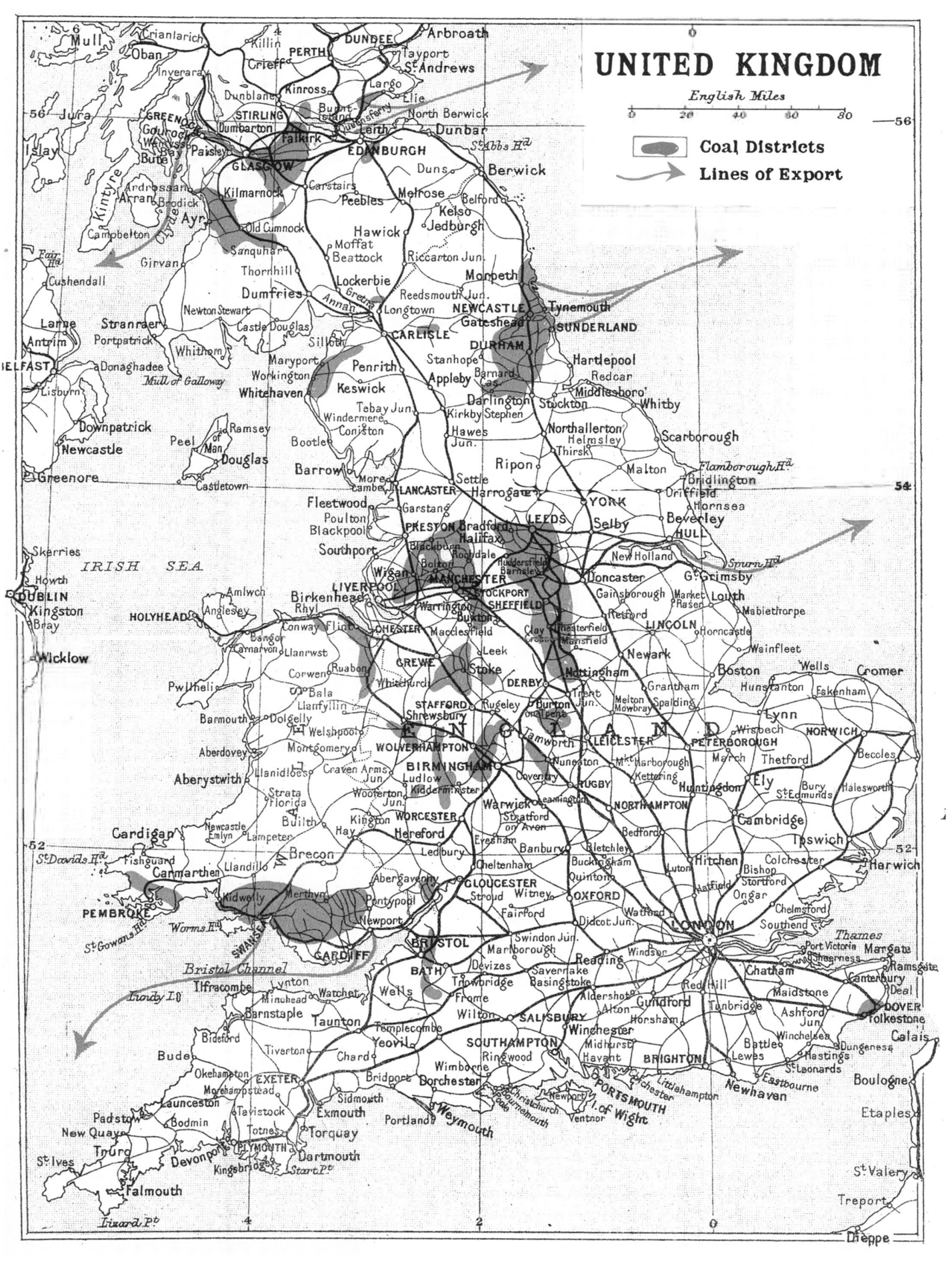

UNITED KINGDOM

English Miles

0   20   40   60   80

◯ **Coal Districts**

→ **Lines of Export**

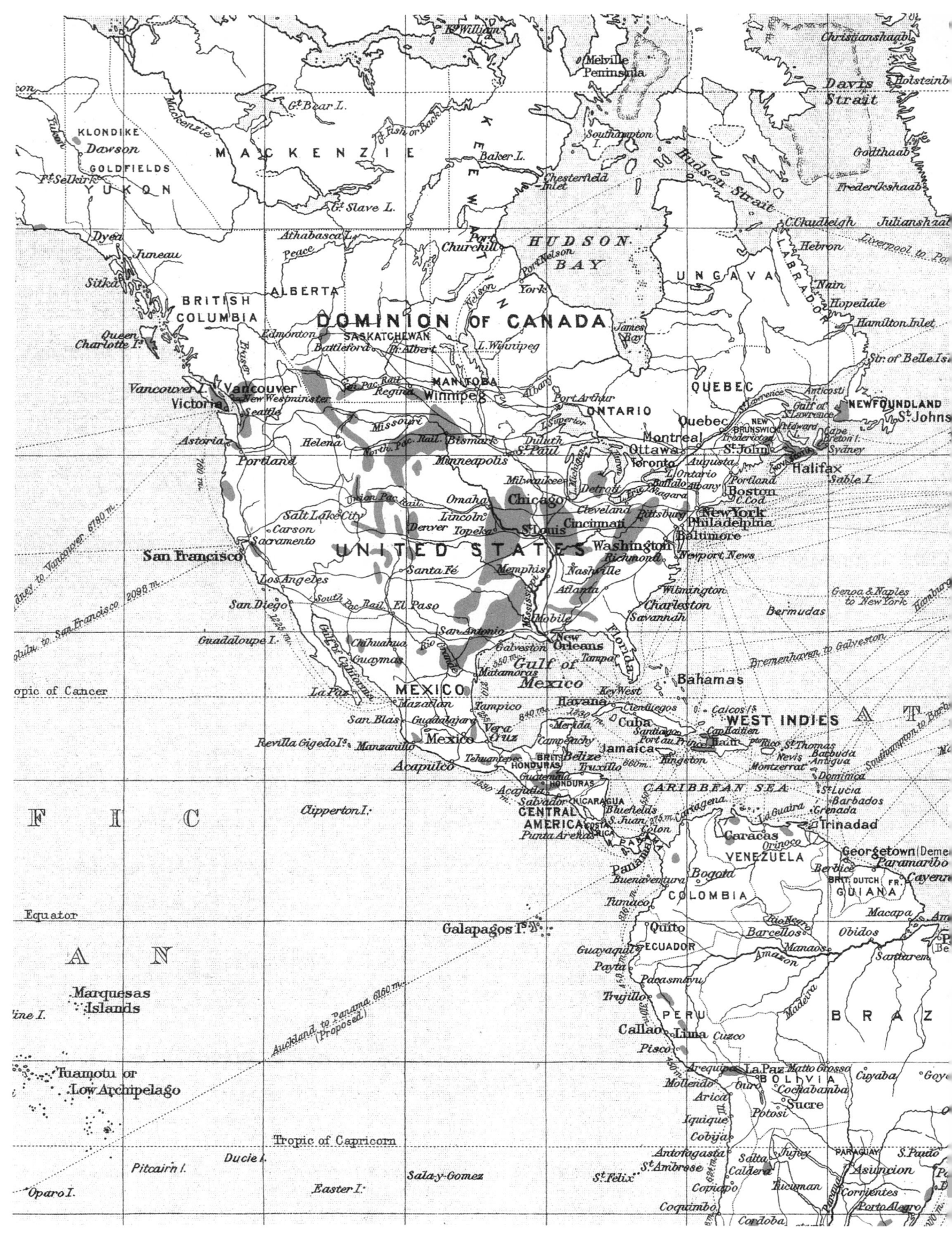

The Second Industrial Revolution

The diagram, from the 1907 Bartholomew *Atlas of the World's Commerce*, shows the gradual loss by the United Kingdom of its position as the world's premier trading nation. Although its share of total trade had slipped only slightly between 1885 and 1905, from 18 per cent to 15 (30 to 26 per cent, if Britain's colonial possessions are included), the rise of the United States' share from 9.3 to 10.5 per cent and that of Germany from 10 to 11.3 per cent showed that more nimble competitors were beginning to nip at its heels.

Britain had been the home of the Industrial Revolution, but it squandered its position as prime mover, both through the export of technology such as railway transport to Europe and the Americas and by its sluggish response to a new wave of innovation which constituted a second Industrial Revolution. The height of British self-satisfaction came at the Great Exhibition of 1851, a showcase for the country's industrial prowess, at which other nations were, rather grudgingly, permitted to show their own wares. Whilst Britain's efforts were undoubtedly impressive, too much attention was paid to showy exhibits such as the Koh-i-noor diamond, and too little to the Germans, who brought along a cast steel cannon designed by Alfred Krupp, or the Americans, whose McCormick reaper, Colt revolvers and pick-proof locks were ignored in the press in favour of sniping about the stuffed squirrel which formed part of their display.

In the chemical industry, although it was a British scientist, William Perkin, who invented the first synthetic dye in 1856 (by adding alcohol to aniline to produce deep-purple mauveine), it was German companies who exploited the discovery, developing further dyes such as alizarin. As a result, by 1914 Britain was a net importer of synthetic dyes, importing 1,550 tons a month from Germany. Similarly, although the open-hearth process – which enabled mass production of steel by reducing the energy needed by 70 per cent – was invented in England in 1861 by William Siemens, it was first put to industrial use in France in 1865. Soon steel plants in Germany and the United States were churning out ever-greater quantities of the raw material needed for bridges, railway lines and, in American cities, skyscrapers.

In industry after industry, Britain ceded its lead, and in crucial new ones it never gained a foothold. The first practical automobile was patented by a German, Karl Benz, in 1886, but the automotive future belonged to the Americans. Henry Ford founded the Ford Motor Company in 1903, and in 1908 unveiled the iconic Model T. Five years later he introduced the production line to his assembly plant, which reduced the time taken to put together a vehicle from 12.5 to 1.5 hours and allowed his company to sell some 15 million Model Ts before production ceased in 1927.

Britain's share of world trade slipped inexorably, until by 2011 it had reached 2.6 per cent of exports, roughly on a par with that of Belgium, and only just ahead of that of Canada. Like others before it, Britain had learnt that trading supremacy is an ephemeral thing.

COMMERCIAL GROWTH OF NATIONS

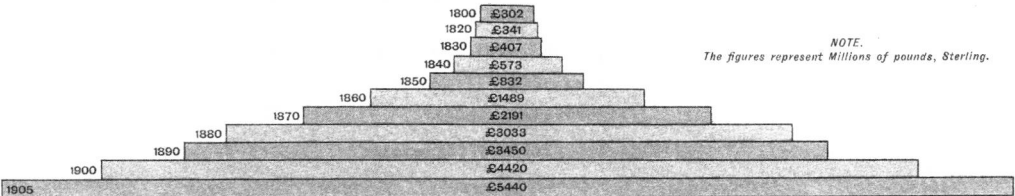

GROWTH OF THE WORLD'S TRADE IN THE NINETEENTH CENTURY

NOTE.
The figures represent Millions of pounds, Sterling.

PROPORTION OF THE WORLD'S TRADE
HELD BY DIFFERENT NATIONS IN 1885 AND 1905

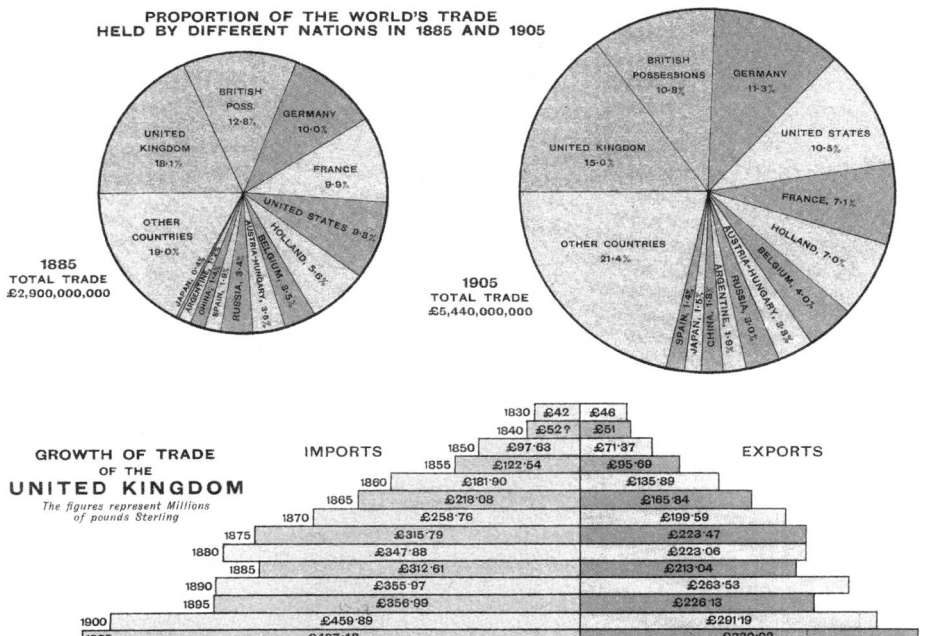

GROWTH OF TRADE
OF THE
UNITED KINGDOM
The figures represent Millions of pounds Sterling

IMPORTS   EXPORTS

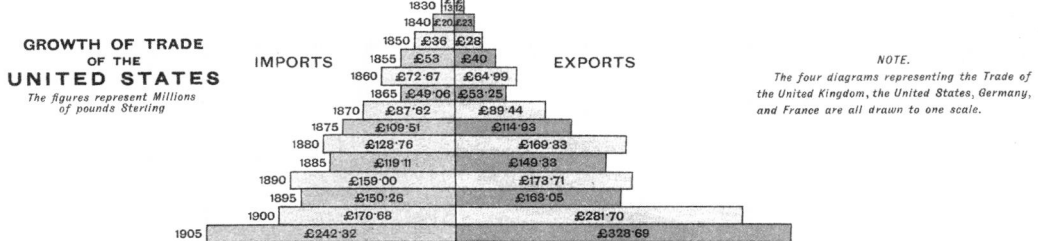

During the five years ending 1905, British commerce increased by nearly 9 per cent., but in the single year 1906, it has risen 10 per cent. (imports 7·4 per cent. and exports 13·6) the total value being nearly 899 millions sterling.

GROWTH OF TRADE
OF THE
UNITED STATES
The figures represent Millions of pounds Sterling

IMPORTS   EXPORTS

NOTE.
The four diagrams representing the Trade of the United Kingdom, the United States, Germany, and France are all drawn to one scale.

The exports of the United States exceeded those of the United Kingdom in 1901 and 1903, and also, according to the figures given in the *Board of Trade Journal*, in 1905, but in America, where 4·8665 dollars are taken as equivalent to a pound sterling this is not so reckoned in 1905. For the above figures 4·866 dollars have been taken as equivalent to one pound. During the eleven months of 1906 ending November, the increase over the corresponding period of 1905 is 10 per cent. for imports and 13 for exports, at which rates the total trade for the year will be nearly 638 millions.

GERMANY   **FRANCE**

IMPORTS   EXPORTS   IMPORTS   EXPORTS

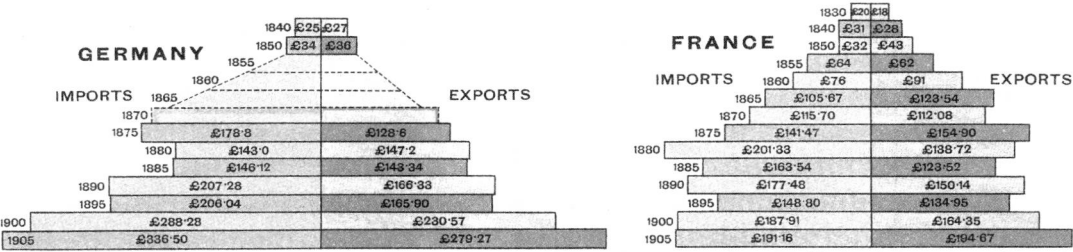

The figures for German trade are not exactly comparable before 1889 when the Hanseatic ports were incorporated into the Customs Union. The figures now available for nine months of 1906 show an increase of 14·7 per cent. over those of the corresponding period of 1905.

As a rule the imports into densely populated manufacturing countries exceed the exports, but in 1905 the exports from France exceeded the imports. The figures given for this year are from a French official report published in September 1906. For the eleven months ending November 1906, the increase of trade is 9·5 per cent. for imports, and 5 per cent. for exports compared to the corresponding period in 1905, and should the same rates have been maintained through December, the value of the year's trade will be nearly 414 millions.

LABRADOR

Ungava

PENINSULA

Larch R.

Lower Seal L.
Clearwater L.
Apish-a-gamish L.
Upper Seal L.
the Whale R.
Nitchiquan L.
River
Lake assini
Manouan Lake
Chicoutimi
Tadousac
L. St. John
St. Lewis
Saguenay

Apish-a-gami
Trail L.
Wauguash Lake
Erlandson Lake
Okkak
Nain

Michikamow Lake
Grand Lake
Melville Lake
Hamilton R.
Ashwanipi Lake
Fox Lake
Mouse R.
St. Marguerite
Manicouagan
Outardes
St. Margueride
Natashquan R.
Magpie
St. John
Mingan
C. Whittle

Port Manvers
Newark I.
Pangnertok
Ford Harbour
Zoar
Ukusiksalik
Davis Int.
Gull Is.
Hopedale
Kaipokok
C. Webuc
Byron Bay
White Bear I.
Eskimo Bay
Sandwich B.
Hamilton Inlet
Rocky Bay
St. Michaels B.
C. St. Lewis
Str. of Belle Isle
Forteau Bay
C. Bauld
Hare B.

2032
1815
1750
1535
1622
215
108
126

Kenamou Lake
Natashquan R.

White B.
Tilt Cove
C. St. John
Notre Dame B.
Twillingate
Fogo I.
C. Freels
Greenspond
Bonavista B.
C. Bonavista
Hearts Content

Anticosti I.
B. of Islands
C. Gaspé
C. St. George
GULF OF
St. LAWRENCE
Gaspé B.
220
Magdalen Is.
30
C. Ray
St. Paul
100
Fortune B.
Aspy B.
250
Newfoundland
St. John's
Avalon
C. Race

137

St. Lawrence
Matane
Father Pt.
Pasbebiac
Percé
Rimouski
Chaleurs B.
Fraserville
Dalhousie
St. Lawrence
Bathurst

Kamouraska
St. Joseph
St. Ignace
St. Thomas
Mt. Katahdin
St. John
Arthabaska
Richmond

Three Rivers
Quebec
U
e
l
è
b

New Brunswick
Chatham
Miramichi
Richibucto
Pr. Edward Island
Charlottetown
Georgetown
Sydney
Cape Breton Island
Cow Bay
C. Breton
Canso Gut

Montreal
Ogdensburg
White R.
Utica
Albany
Hampton
Conn.
Newark
N.J.
Wilmington
Delaware B. & R.
Chesapeake Bay
Hatteras

Maine
Bangor
Augusta
Bath
Calais
Eastport
Penobscot B.
Machias
Fredericton
Moncton
St. John
B. of Fundy
Windsor
Nova Scotia
Yarmouth
Machias B.
Annapolis

Buy Verte
Pictou
Parrsboro
Halifax
Sable I.
Sable I.

200
48
60
15
1428
1500

Richmond
Vermont
Montpelier
N.H.
Concord
Portland
Portsmouth
Newburyport
Gloucester
Salem
Mass.
Boston
Plymouth
C. Cod
Providence
New Bedford
Nantucket
Marthas Vineyard
Long I.
NEW YORK & Brooklyn
Sandy Hook

293
100
3
75
1340
1356

2600
1500
Philadelphia to Liverpool
1450

G U L F   S T R E A M

Bremen to Baltimore
New Orleans to Liverpool
New York to Lisbon

1625
740
2650
2800
2750
3450
2732
1240
1700
2920
2000
3700
3677
3022
2850
2875
2750
2690
2425
2382
Great Bank Newfoundland
Virginia
Southampton
2020
2600
Azores to France
Bermuda
Placentia B.
Fortune B.

A Smaller World

Bartholomew's 1907 map from *Atlas of the World's Commerce* shows a dense cluster of submarine telegraph cables stretching across from Europe to the eastern seaboard of North America. Less than 40 years old, this network had enabled a revolution in communications.

In the past, people and market information had travelled slowly, no more quickly than a courier on horseback, and often considerably less speedily, especially when an expanse of water intervened. In the 2nd century AD, at the height of the Roman Empire, the fastest overland journey from Antioch in the province of Syria to York in Britannia took five months, while the Polos spent four years travelling from Venice to the court of the Mongol Great Khan in northern China. Even in the Age of Exploration it took months for messages to pass from the court at Madrid to the Spanish colonies and months again for a reply to return, which rendered any attempt at close management of problems futile.

By the mid-19th century, the fastest passage by ship across the Atlantic still took ten days, which meant that information about market conditions, and contracts, was often stale by the time it arrived. The invention of the electric telegraph – which transmitted messages by means of electric pulses – offered some hope, particularly in the form popularised by the American Samuel Morse in 1838. In 1844 the first long-distance telegraph message ("What God Hath Wrought") was sent by Morse between Baltimore and Maryland. Soon attention turned to the maritime communication gap, with the successful laying of a cable across the English Channel in 1851 suggesting that the more ambitious span of the Atlantic might be bridged.

Cyrus Field's Atlantic Telegraph Company made several attempts in 1857 to lay a transatlantic line, but the huge weight of the cable (at 1.1 tons per nautical mile) meant it kept snapping, and it was only on August 5, 1858, that the last section was laid. Eleven days later, Queen Victoria sent a congratulatory telegram to US President James Buchanan celebrating "an additional link between the nations whose friendship is founded on their common interest and reciprocal esteem". It was fortunate she was not more loquacious, as the telegraph's technology permitted only one word to be sent every two minutes and so her entire message took 16 hours.

Disaster struck within three weeks, as the telegraph line degraded and stopped functioning. A new line was laid in the summer of 1866 by Isambard Kingdom Brunel's SS *Great Eastern*, the largest passenger ship of the age, and the last section was pulled ashore at Heart's Content, Newfoundland, in late July. Fortunately, advances in transmission technology meant that this new link could send eight words a minute, and the idea caught on. Additional cables were laid in 1873, 1874, 1880 and 1890, and the network soon extended globally, with submarine cables reaching India in 1870, linking Nagasaki in Japan to Shanghai in China in 1871 and joining Java to Darwin in northern Australia the same year.

The world was smaller and about to shrink further, as the telegram's reign was threatened by the telephone, patented by Alexander Graham Bell in 1876. The first transatlantic phone call did not take place until 1927, but when it did, the words of one of the callers were prophetic: "Distance doesn't mean anything any more." The world, indeed, was now a far smaller place.

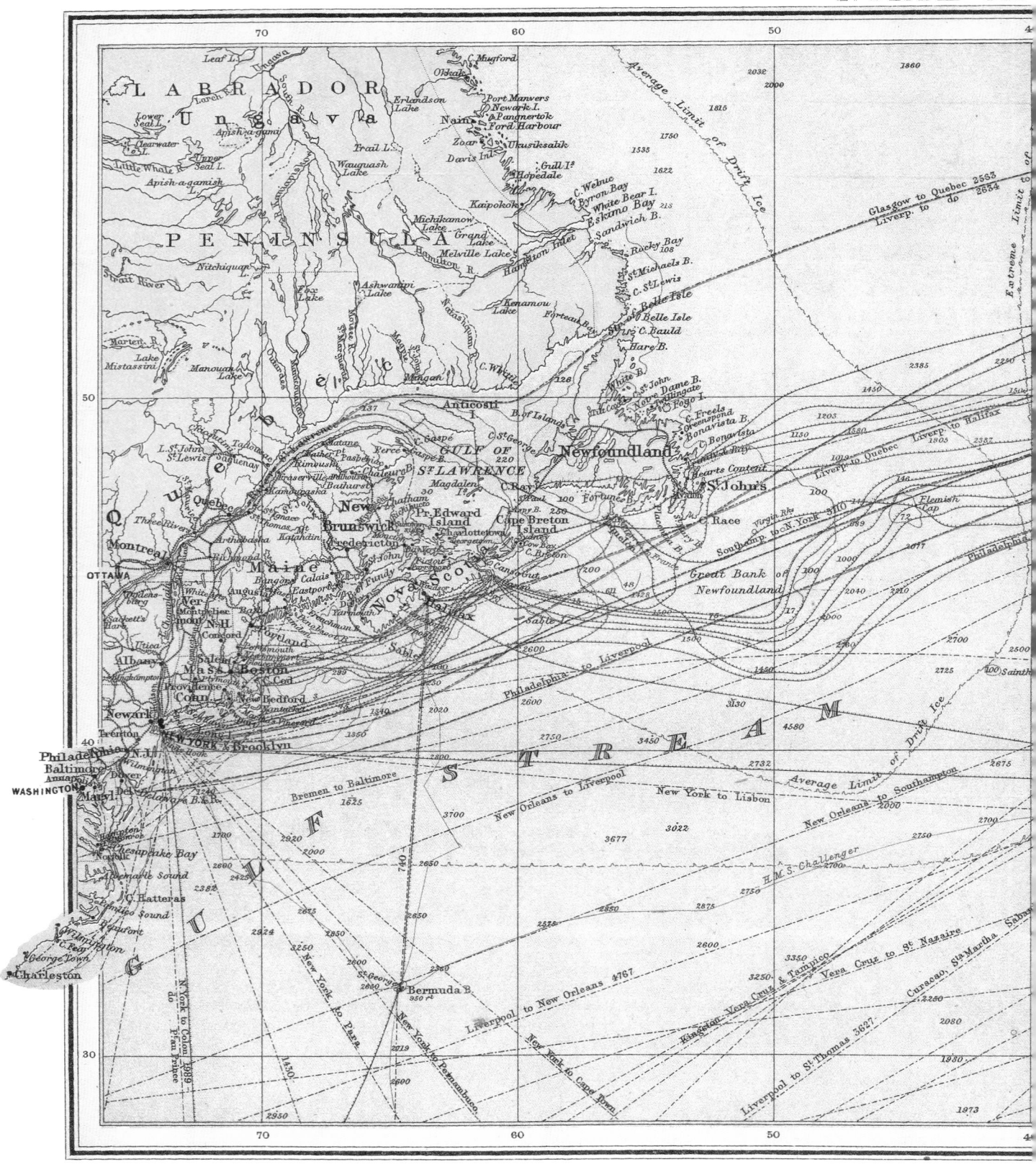

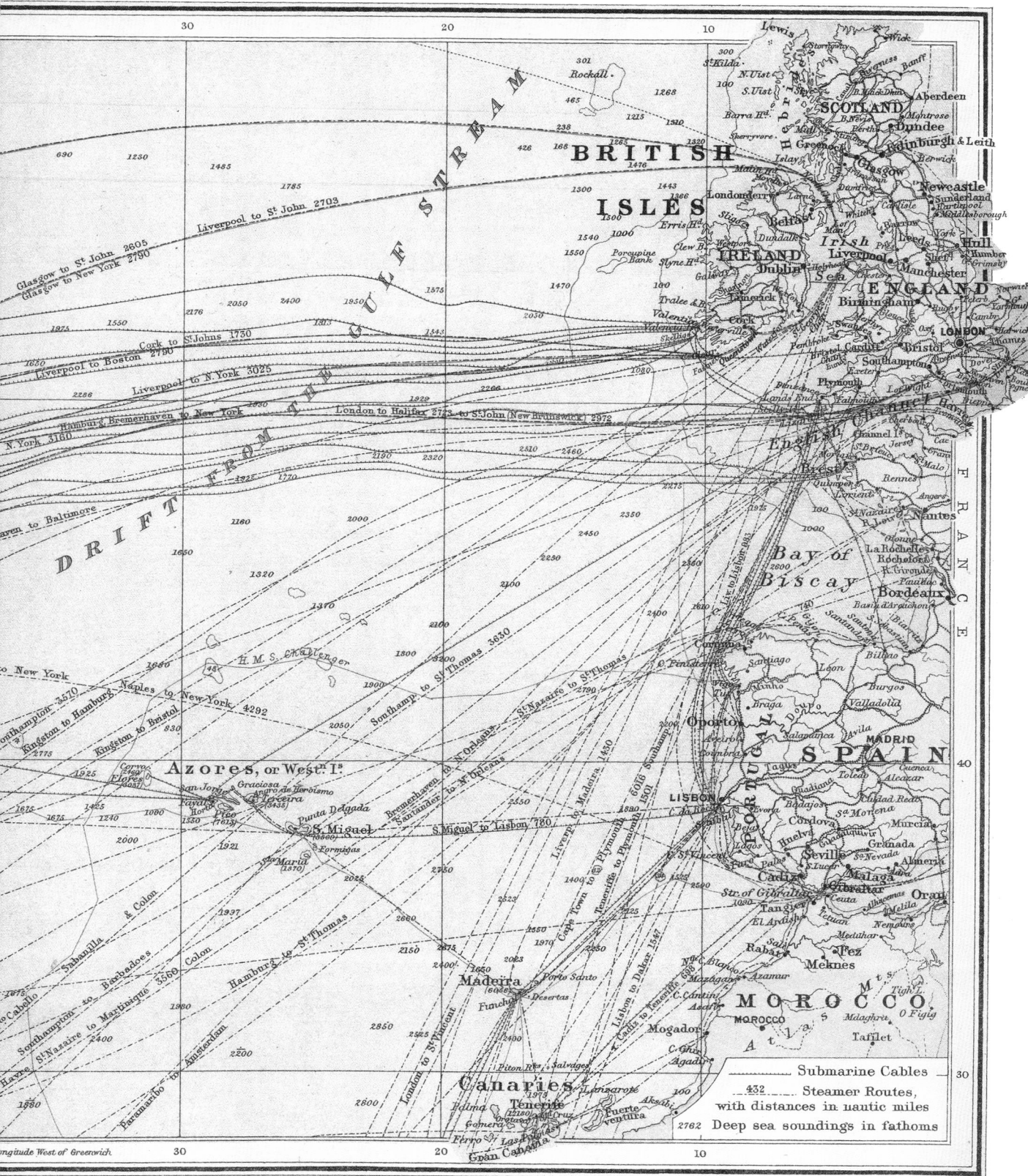

BRITISH ISLES

SCOTLAND

Lewis
Wick
St.Kilda
N.Uist
Aberdeen
N.Uist
Hebrides
Dundee
Edinburgh & Leith
Glasgow
Berwick
Newcastle
Sunderland
Hartlepool
Middlesborough
Londonderry
Carlisle
IRELAND
Belfast
York
Hull
Irish Sea
Liverpool
Manchester
Dublin
Grimsby
Leeds
ENGLAND
Birmingham
Limerick
Norwich
Tralee
Rugby
Yarmouth
Valentia
Cork
LONDON
Bristol
Cardiff
Harwich
Southampton
Exeter
Dover
Plymouth
Falmouth
Lands End

English Channel
Channel Is.
Brest
Jersey
Rennes
Nantes
FRANCE

Bay of Biscay
Bordeaux

Oporto
Santiago
Leon
Burgos
Valladolid
Braga
MADRID
SPAIN
LISBON
PORTUGAL
Evora
Badajos
Cordova
Toledo
Alcazar
Ciudad Real
Sa Morena
Murcia
Huelva
Granada
Seville
Almeria
Cadiz
Malaga
Gibraltar
Oran
Str. of Gibraltar
Ceuta
Tangier
Tetuan
Fez
Meknes
Rabat
MOROCCO
Mogador
Atlas Mts
Agadir

DRIFT FROM THE GULF STREAM

690   1230   1485   1785
Liverpool to St John 2703
Glasgow to St John 2605
Glasgow to New York 2750
Cork to St Johns 1730
Liverpool to Boston 2790
Liverpool to N.York 3025
N.York 3160
Hamburg, Bremerhaven to New York
London to Halifax 2723 to St John (New Brunswick) 2972

Azores, or West Is.
Corvo
Flores
San Jorge
Graciosa
Angra de Terceira
Fayal
Pico
Punta Delgada
Horta
S. Miguel
Formigas
Maria
S. Miguel to Lisbon 780
Bremerhaven to N.Orleans
Santander to N.Orleans

H.M.S. Challenger
Southamp. to St Thomas 3630
St. Nazaire to St Thomas
Cork Town

Madeira
Porto Santo
Desertas
Funchal
London to St Vincent
Hamburg to St Thomas

Canaries
Lanzarote
Palma
Tenerife
Gomera
Ferro
Gran Canaria
Fuerteventura
Sta Cruz
Las Palmas

	Submarine Cables
432	Steamer Routes, with distances in nautic miles
2762	Deep sea soundings in fathoms

Longitude West of Greenwich

John Bartholomew & Co., Edin�r.

Jan Mayen I.

North Cape

Vardö

Lofoden Is *Tromsö*

Katharin

Victoria Harb *Narvik*

Laplaud

Iceland

Trondhjem

Finland

Farae Is

Christiania

Stockholm *St Petersburg*

2635 m.

Edinburgh

Riga

Quebec

BRITISH
ISLES

Baltic Sea

Danzig RUSSI

Hamburg

Berlin

ool to St John

London

GERMANY

EUROPE

New York 3036 m.

Channel Is

Paris

Vienna

Odessa

St John

Havana 4744 m.

FRANCE

AUSTRIA-HUNGARY

3627 m.

Marseilles

Rome

Brindisi

TURKEY

Black Sea

Constantinople

Madrid

Azores Lisbon

SPAIN

Mediterranean Sea

ASIA MINOR

Gibraltar

Algiers

Malta

Cyprus

Damas

Fez ALGERIA

Port Said *Bassor*

Madeira

Morocco

TRIPOLI

Cairo *Suez*

Canary Is

MOROCCO

EGYPT

Ba

C

Aswan

Med

S a h a r a

Suakin

dl Is

SUDAN

athurst

SENEGAL *Niger*

Khartum

FRENCH SUDAN

Tariffs and Trade

The map from the 1907 Bartholomew *Atlas of the World's Commerce* illustrates a debate which had long bedevilled world trade: that between proponents of free trade and the advocates of protectionism, who argued that countries had a duty to preserve domestic industries by the levying of tariffs. A swathe of green marks the areas in the Americas and Russia where protectionism prevailed, while Europe remains, for the moment, a sea of low-tariff yellow.

Tariffs had not always been a tool of trade policy. In the ancient world, they were mainly deployed by governments which had fewer levers to extract additional income, and so customs inspections at the frontiers offered an obvious means to raise revenue; the tariff on goods entering the eastern borders of the Roman Empire was around 12.5 per cent. The advent of the era of classical economics in the 18th century – with works such as Adam Smith's *The Wealth of Nations* (1776) providing a clearer sense of how trade policy could influence national prosperity – gave rise to calls to use tariffs as a tool of government policy. In Britain, lobbying by powerful agricultural landowners led to the establishment in 1804 of a sliding scale of tariffs which imposed a 24-shilling-per-quarter levy if the grain price fell below 63 shillings a quarter, so assuring the profitability of domestic grain. In 1815 they secured the passing of the Corn Laws, which forbade grain imports completely when the price fell below 80 shillings. While the landowners enjoyed windfall profits, the poor suffered misery, as the price of bread soared, and the foundation of the Anti-Corn Law League in 1838 finally led to the repeal of the Corn Laws in 1846.

The argument was repeated elsewhere in Europe as cheap wheat from the New World flooded the market, which provoked the imposition of high tariffs in Germany in 1879. In the United States tariff levels seesawed, depending on the party in power, with the Republicans introducing the Fordney McCumber tariff of over 40 per cent in 1922. Governments increasingly fell prey to "nationalist economics", which contended that the preservation of a nation's industry and agricultural base must trump free trade.

In October 1929 disaster struck after the stock market crash in the United States destabilised its economy. Amid calls to preserve American interests, the Smoot-Hawley Tariff was passed in June 1930, imposing a punitive duty of 60 per cent on imports. Unsurprisingly, other governments reacted, with the Italians setting a retaliatory tariff of 100 per cent on American goods. A cascade of protectionist measures and countermeasures devastated world trade, and import levels declined by 68 per cent between 1929 and 1933. Industrial production fell by half in the United States, and unemployment soared – in Germany to 30 per cent – which contributed to a flight to political extremes and the rise of the Nazi party.

Seeing the damage that protectionism had wrought, the world turned back to free trade in the wake of the Second World War, with the foundation of the General Agreement on Tariffs and Trade in 1947 (and its eventual successor, the World Trade Organization, in 1995). Protectionist voices still clamoured for measures to preserve national industries or to retaliate against the dumping of cut-price products, but nobody could be in any doubt that a repeat of the tariff storm of the 1930s would be a catastrophe.

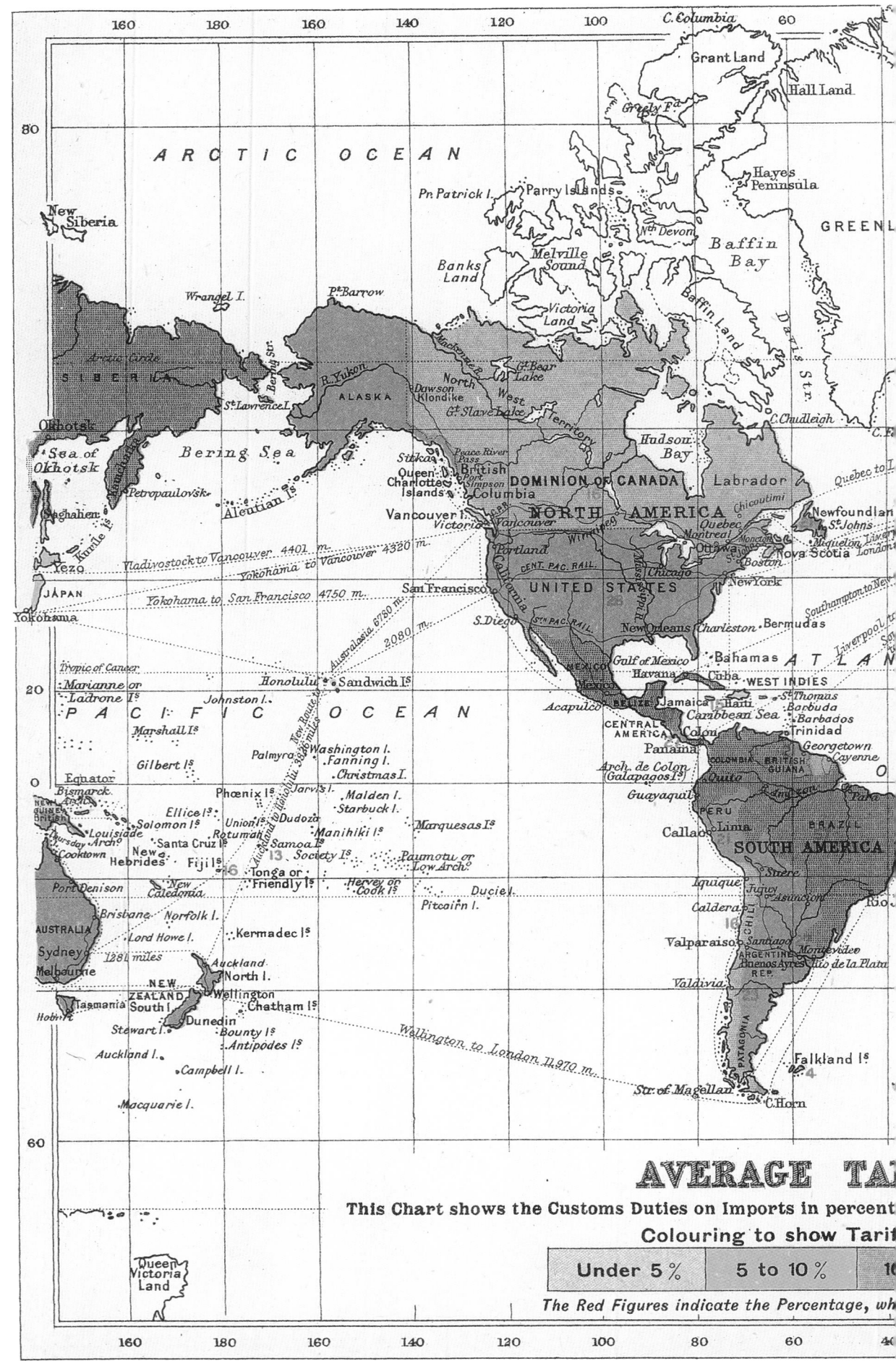

Coordinates (top): 160 180 160 140 120 100 C. Columbia 60

Arctic region: Grant Land, Hall Land, Greely Fd, Hayes Peninsula, GREENL[AND], Nth Devon, Parry Islands, Pn Patrick I., Baffin Bay, Banks Land, Melville Sound, Victoria Land, Baffin Land, Davis Str., C. Chudleigh

80 ARCTIC OCEAN

New Siberia, Wrangel I., P.t Barrow, Mackenzie, North West Territory, Gt Bear Lake, R. Yukon, Dawson Klondike, Gt Slave Lake, Hudson Bay, Labrador, Quebec to L., C. F[?], Newfoundland, St. John's, Miquelon, Liverp[ool]

Arctic Circle, SIBERIA, ALASKA, Peace River Pass, Port Simpson, British Columbia, DOMINION OF CANADA, NORTH AMERICA, Chicoutimi

Okhotsk, St Lawrence I., Sitka, Queen Charlotte Islands, Vancouver I., Victoria, Vancouver, Winnipeg, Quebec, Montreal, Ottawa, Moncton, Nova Scotia, London, Boston

Sea of Okhotsk, Bering Sea, Petropaulovsk, Aleutian Is., Portland, CENT. PAC. RAIL., Mississippi R., Chicago, New York

Saghalien, Kurile Is., Vladivostock to Vancouver 4401 m., Yokohama to Vancouver 4320 m., California R., UNITED STATES, Southampton to New[?], Liverpool to[?]

Yezo, JAPAN, Yokohama to San Francisco 4750 m., San Francisco, Sth PAC. RAIL., ATLAN[TIC]

Yokohama, Australasia 6780 m., 2080 m., S. Diego, New Orleans, Charleston, Bermudas

Tropic of Cancer, Marianne or Ladrone Is., Honolulu, Sandwich Is., Acapulco, MEXICO, Gulf of Mexico, Havana, Cuba, Bahamas, WEST INDIES

20 PACIFIC OCEAN

Marshall Is., New Route, Honolulu to Sandwich Is., Jamaica, Haiti, St Thomas, Barbuda, Barbados, Caribbean Sea, Trinidad, CENTRAL AMERICA, Colon, Panama, Georgetown, Cayenne

Gilbert Is., Palmyra, Washington I., Fanning I., Christmas I., Arch. de Colon (Galapagos Is.), COLOMBIA, BRITISH GUIANA

0 Equator Bismarck, NEW GUINEA BRITISH, Phoenix Is., Jarvis I., Malden I., Starbuck I., Guayaquil, Quito, Amazon R., Para

Louisiade Arch., Solomon Is., Ellice Is., Dudoza, Rotumah, Union Is., Samoa Is., Manihiki Is., Marquesas Is., Callao, Lima, PERU, BRAZIL

Cooktown, Thursday I., New Hebrides, Santa Cruz Is., Fiji Is., 13, Society Is., Paumotu or Low Arch., Sucre, SOUTH AMERICA

Port Denison, New Caledonia, 16, Tonga or Friendly Is., Hervey or Cook Is., Paumotu, Ducie I., Pitcairn I., Iquique, Jujuy, Asuncion

Brisbane, Norfolk I., Kermadec Is., Valdera[?], Rio

AUSTRALIA, Lord Howe I., Caldera

Sydney, 1281 miles, Valparaiso, Santiago, CHILI, Montevideo

Melbourne, New Zealand, Auckland North I., ARGENTINE REP., Buenos Ayres, Rio de la Plata

NEW ZEALAND South I., Wellington, Chatham Is., Valdivia

Hobart, Tasmania, Dunedin, Stewart I., Bounty Is., PATAGONIA

Auckland I., Antipodes Is., Wellington to London 11.270 m., Falkland Is.

Campbell I., Str. of Magellan, C. Horn

Macquarie I.

60 Queen Victoria Land

Title (bottom right):

AVERAGE TA[RIFF]

This Chart shows the Customs Duties on Imports in percent[ages]

Colouring to show Tarif[fs]

Under 5 %	5 to 10 %	10

The Red Figures indicate the Percentage, wh[...]

Coordinates (bottom): 160 180 160 140 120 100 80 60 40

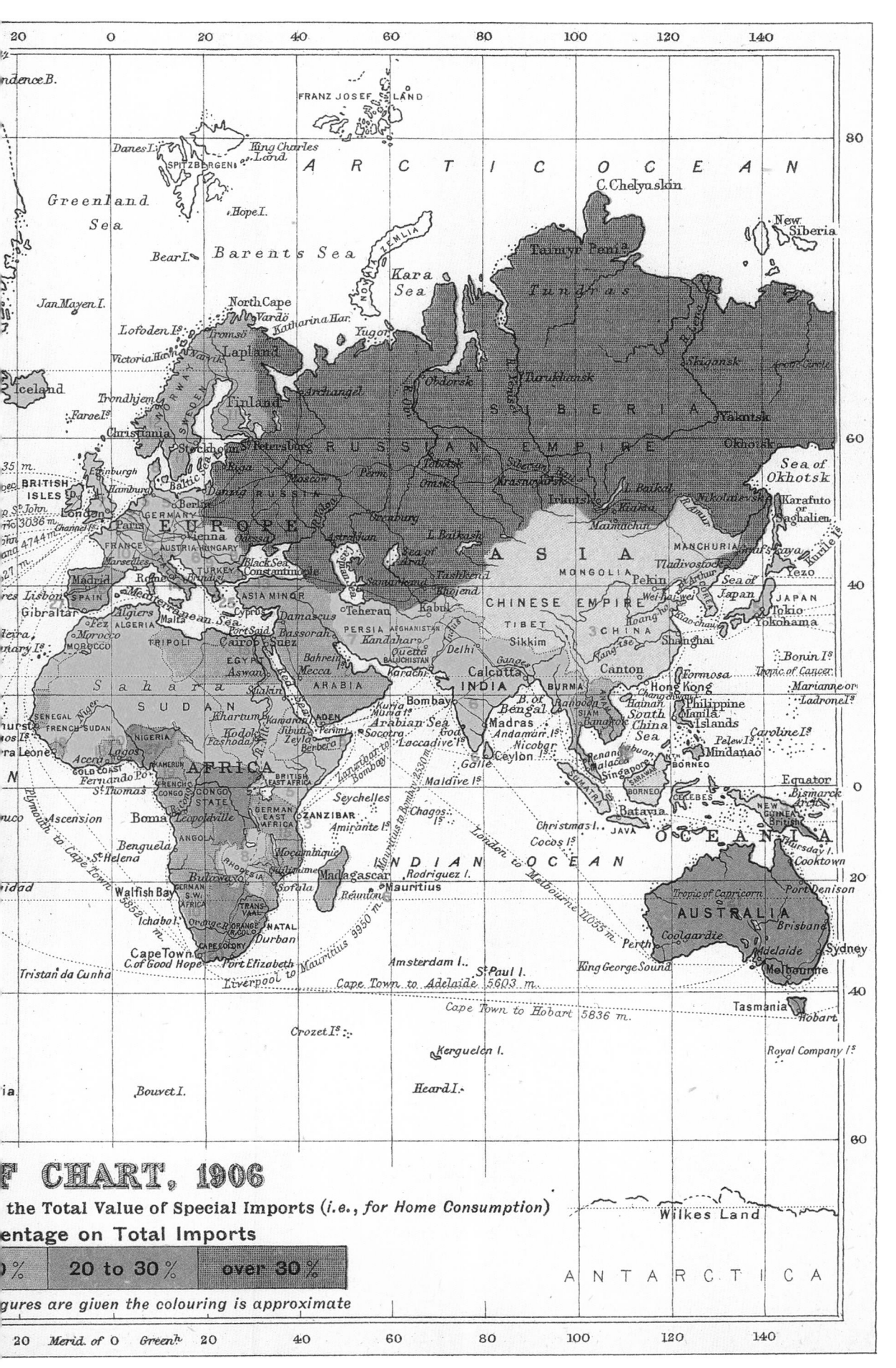

The map is image-dominant. Text elements within the map and legend:

Map labels (part of the illustration) and the legend at the bottom.

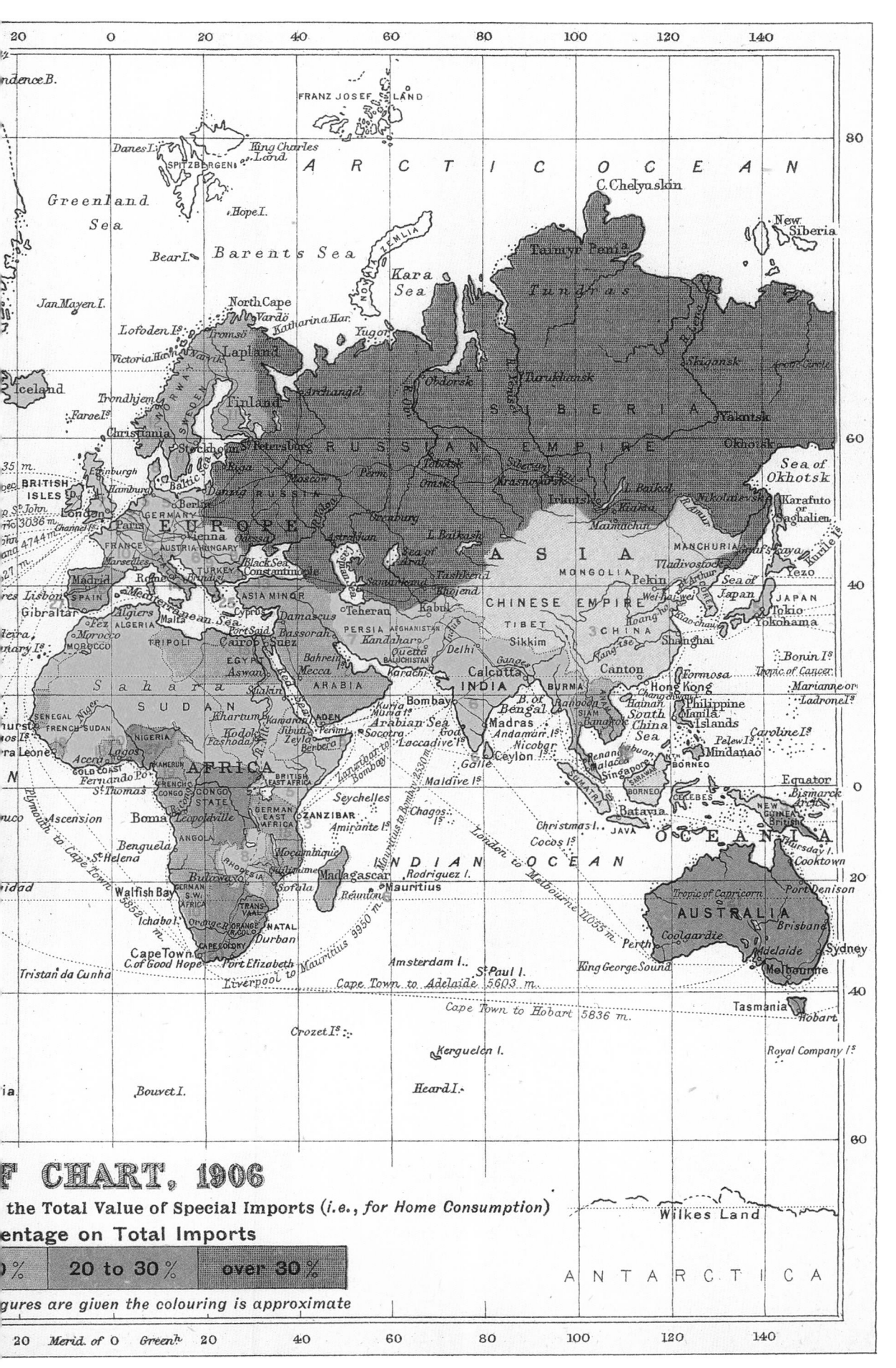

F CHART, 1906

the Total Value of Special Imports (*i.e.*, *for Home Consumption*)

entage on Total Imports

| 0 % | 20 to 30 % | over 30 % |

gures are given the colouring is approximate

The Oil Trade

The patchwork of yellow blocks shows the extent of Britain's North Sea Oil industry in 2016, a sector which provided a shot in the arm for the country's ailing economy in the 1970s and briefly pushed it into the ranks of the leading exporters of the world's most hotly contested trading commodity.

Oil was not always "black gold", and in the ancient world was put to far more prosaic uses such as caulking vessels with tar or, in Egypt, embalming mummies. As early, though, as 400BC, natural gas – one of oil's geological companions – had been discovered by the Chinese and transported in bamboo pipes for use as lighting fuel. By the Middle Ages, oil was being exploited in Azerbaijan, where it oozed up to the surface. Marco Polo saw it when he visited in the late 13th century, noting that it was not good to eat, but was useful for burning or for treating skin ailments. It was little touches like these, perfectly true, but seemingly outlandish back home in Venice, that led to his narrative being treated largely as fable.

The larger possibilities of the unprepossessing black slime only became apparent in 1846, when the Canadian geologist Abraham Gesner refined kerosene from coal and oil shale. The opportune discovery of oil at Titusville, Pennsylvania, by Edwin L Drake in 1859 created a ready supply of a commodity for which there was now a use, in domestic and industrial lamps. The industry soon spread to Ohio, where John D Rockefeller founded Standard Oil in 1865, and within 14 years had cornered 90 per cent of American's refining capacity. The rise of the automobile in the early 20th century then made petroleum, previously a waste product, the most profitable part of the oil industry.

The early 20th century was the era of oil giants: companies such as Standard itself, Royal Dutch Shell, formed in 1907, and the British-owned Anglo-Persian Oil Company, which found oil in modern Iran in 1908, and set off an oil boom in the Middle East. The Americans countered the British move into Persia by negotiating the right to prospect in Saudi Arabia in 1933, and by 1938 the Arabian American Oil Company had begun production there. Although the Saudi government profited through royalties, it chafed at the colonial attitudes of the oil company moguls and, in 1960, helped found the Organization of Petroleum Exporting Countries (Opec). This showed its muscle in 1973-74, when it imposed an oil embargo on western countries in retaliation for their support of Israel, quadrupling prices.

The preponderance of known oil reserves in the Middle East – at around 80 per cent of the world total – has created other problems. The only exit by ship from the Gulf, and for one-sixth of global oil production, goes via the two-mile-wide Strait of Hormuz, flanked on one side by Arab nations and on the other by Iran. With little love lost between them – Iran and Iraq fought a bloody war between 1980 and 1988 – instability in the region can cause oil prices to spike or oil supplies to plummet.

Large oil-consuming nations have reacted in various ways: some, such as the United States, investing in hydraulic fracturing (or "fracking") technology, which extracts crude oil from hard-to-access shale oil deposits; others in renewable technology such as wind power. For the time being though, oil remains black gold, the lubricant that keeps the world economy moving.

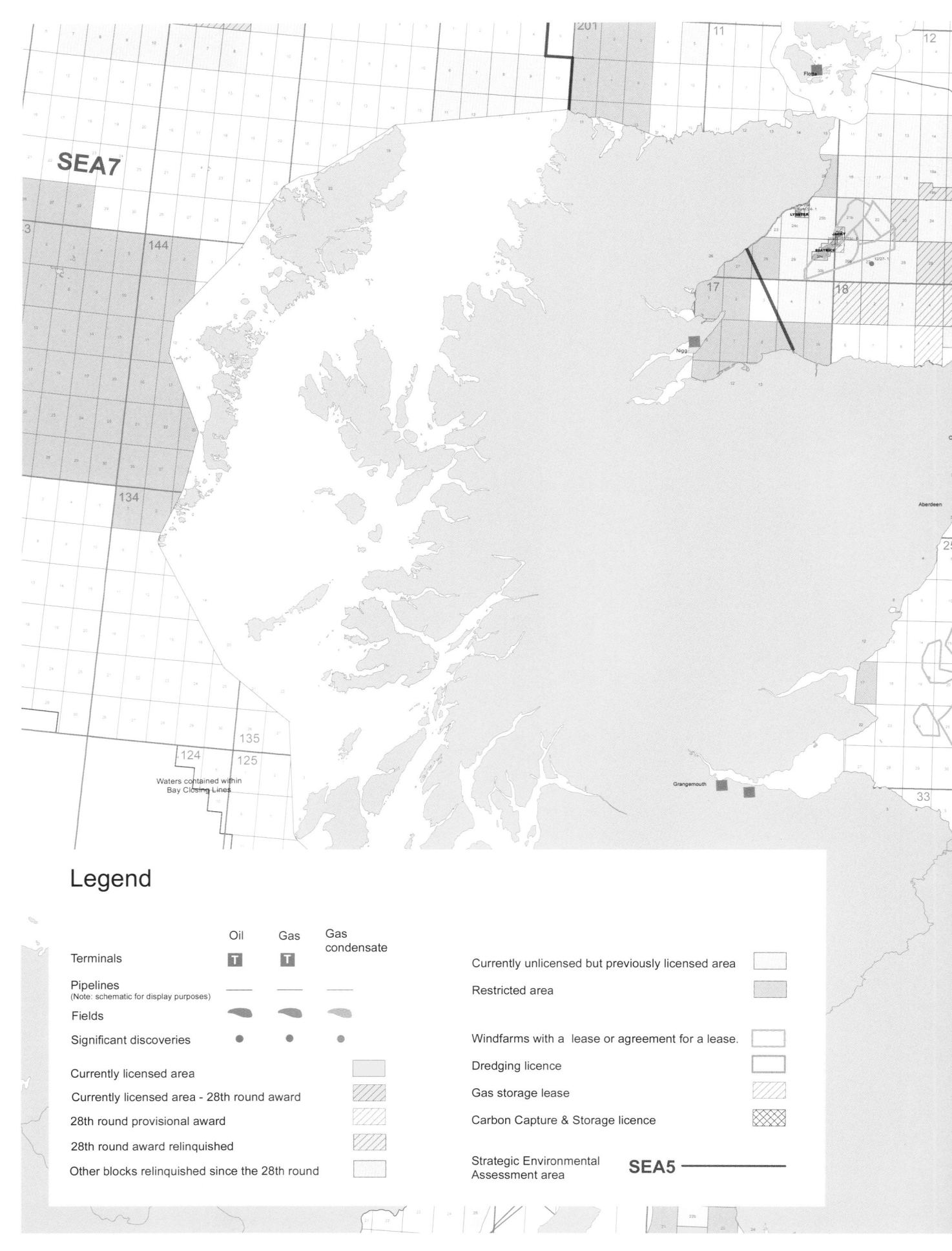

SEA7

SEA5

Legend

	Oil	Gas	Gas condensate
Terminals	T	T	
Pipelines (Note: schematic for display purposes)	—	—	—
Fields			
Significant discoveries	●	●	●

Currently licensed area

Currently licensed area - 28th round award

28th round provisional award

28th round award relinquished

Other blocks relinquished since the 28th round

Currently unlicensed but previously licensed area

Restricted area

Windfarms with a lease or agreement for a lease.

Dredging licence

Gas storage lease

Carbon Capture & Storage licence

Strategic Environmental Assessment area   SEA5 ——

Waters contained within Bay Closing Lines

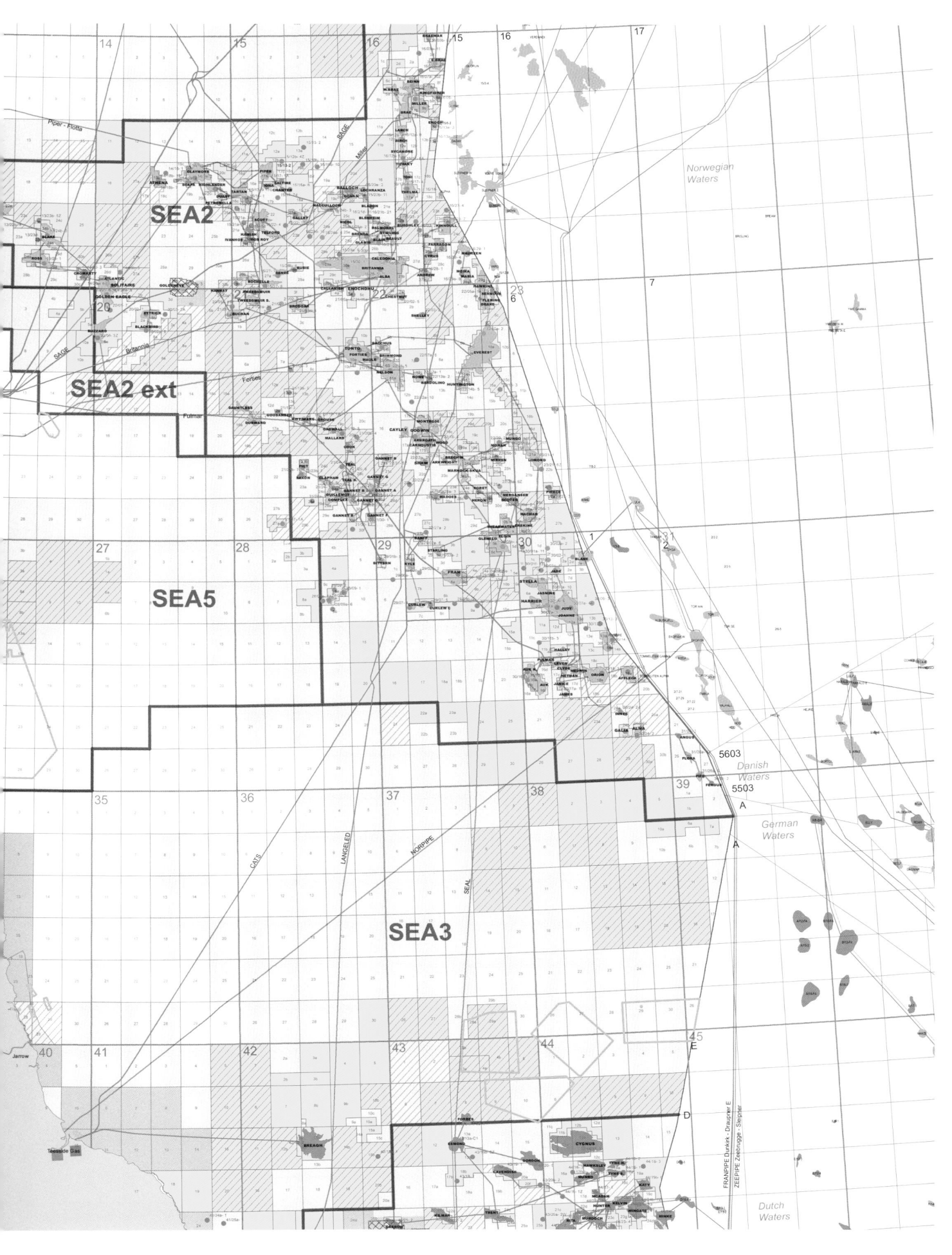

Electronics and the Internet

The map, produced by TeleGeography in 2018, shows the architecture of the internet, illustrating the top routes along which digital data flows. With large nodes in North America – the motherland of computer technology – and Europe, but expanding networks in India and China, it displays how information has become a global trade.

Information is the new gold, the possession and trading of which defines global success. The route, though, by which it became possible to transmit huge quantities of information in a fraction of a second was at first a slow one. IBM, for long the dominant force in the computer industry, was founded as the Computing-Tabulating-Recording Company in 1911, with a net income of just $800,000 in its first year. By 1980 had 340,000 employees, revenues of $26 billion and a seemingly unassailable lead in the business computing market.

Yet from then on technology advanced so quickly that competitors soon overtook it, including companies providing software, such as Microsoft (established in 1975), while the appearance of personal computers from 1974 brought computing power to the retail market for the first time. The power available to such users increased exponentially, from the then generous 4 kilobytes loaded on the TRS-80 in 1977 to the 16 gigabytes routinely available today, a more than 4-million-fold increase.

Building computers became big business, and a global tilt in trading towards China became apparent, as Foxconn opened its first factory in Shenzhen in southern China in 1988, and 20 years later had 400,000 employees assembling everything from iPhones (first launched in 2007) to laptops. The electronics revolution helped China to a global trading position it had not enjoyed since the heyday of the Silk Road, becoming the world's largest trading goods nation in 2013, with a market share of 11 per cent of global trade goods.

Without the ability to communicate, computers are but isolated, though powerful tools. It was connecting them that truly sparked an information revolution. Beginning in the 1960s, the US Department of Defense pioneered the ARPANET, which allowed multiple computers to communicate over a single network. In 1969 the first electronic message was sent between servers at UCLA and Stanford in California. Although that message ("login") was short, it crashed the fledgling system after the first two letters. By 1972 the system had become robust enough to support the first email utility, and in 1989 it took a leap forward when Tim Berners-Lee set out his proposals for what became the World Wide Web, using hyperlinks to navigate between pages and creating the internet we know today.

Within a decade the full potential of this was realised, with the appearance of e-commerce sites such as Amazon (founded in 1994) and eBay (1995). By the 21st century these began to overtake traditional retailers, with global online sales rising to around $4.1 trillion in 2020. Global internet capacity had risen unimaginably since its stuttering start in 1969, and by 2019 had reached 466 terabytes per second, enough to transmit every book ever written in an eighth of a second. With such power at their disposal, today's Marco Polos do their business at a keyboard, and todays Silk Roads are characterised not by camels and caravanserais, but by internet protocols and information hubs.

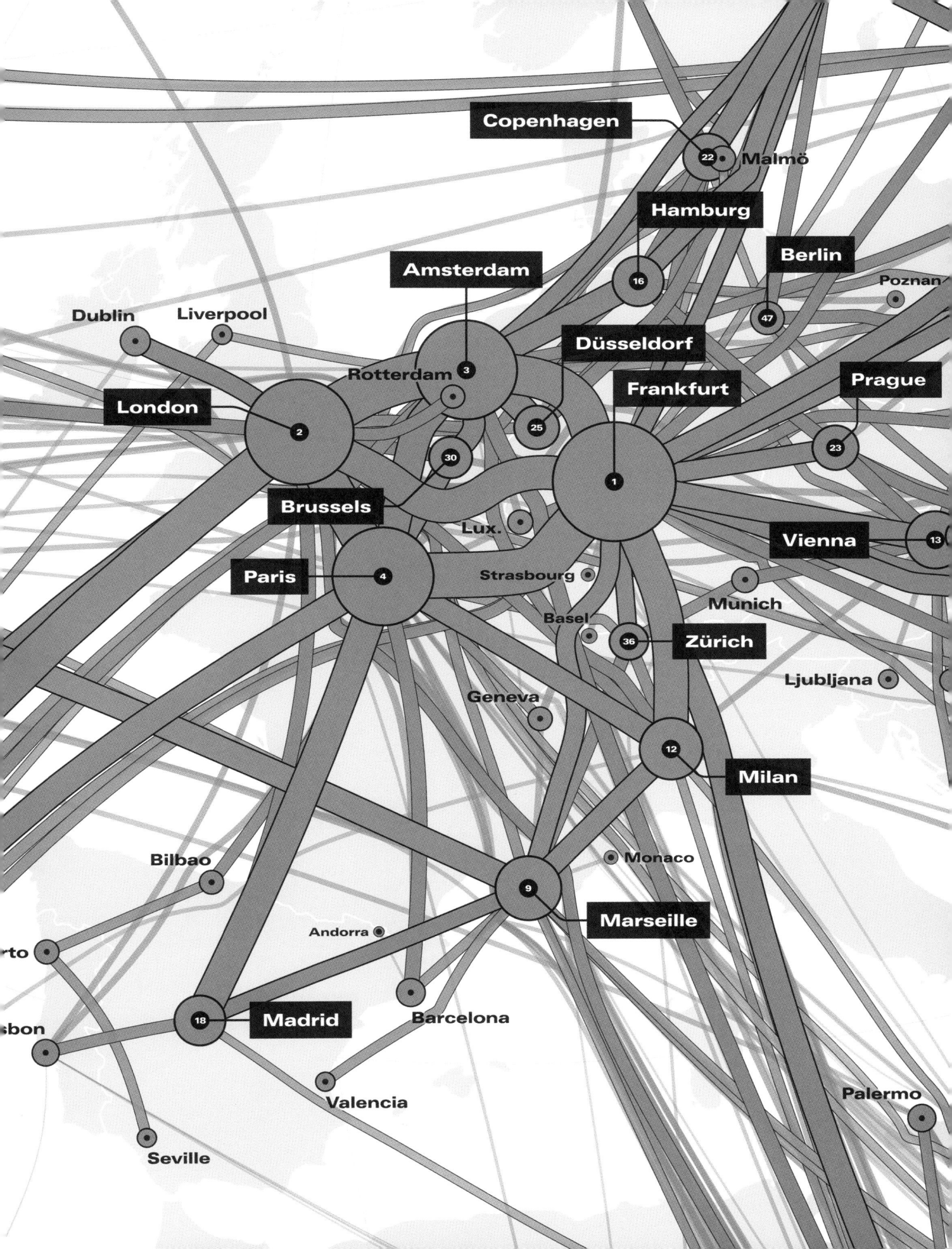

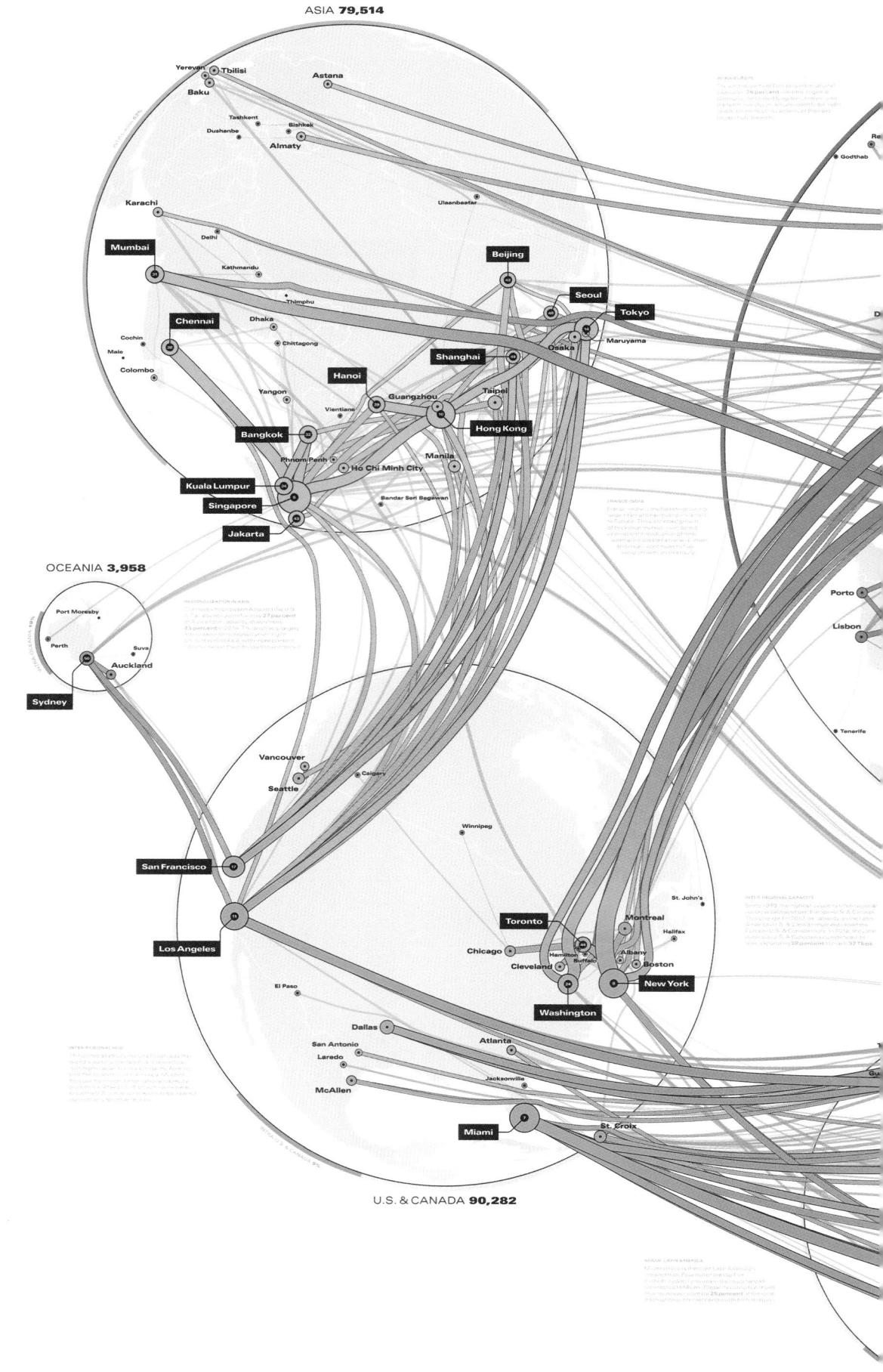

ASIA **79,514**

Yerevan
Tbilisi
Baku
Astana
Tashkent
Bishkek
Dushanbe
Almaty
Karachi
Ulaanbaatar
Mumbai
Delhi
Kathmandu
Beijing
Thimphu
Seoul
Chennai
Dhaka
Tokyo
Cochin
Chittagong
Osaka
Maruyama
Male
Shanghai
Colombo
Hanoi
Yangon
Guangzhou
Taipei
Vientiane
Bangkok
Hong Kong
Manila
Phnom Penh
Ho Chi Minh City
Kuala Lumpur
Bandar Seri Begawan
Singapore
Jakarta

OCEANIA **3,958**

Port Moresby
Perth
Suva
Auckland
Sydney

Vancouver
Seattle
Calgary
Winnipeg

San Francisco

St. John's
Toronto
Montreal
Halifax
Los Angeles
Chicago
Hamilton
Albany
Boston
Cleveland
Buffalo
New York

El Paso
Washington
Dallas
San Antonio
Atlanta
Laredo
Jacksonville
McAllen

Miami
St. Croix

U.S. & CANADA **90,282**

Re...
Godthab

Porto
Lisbon

Tenerife

Gu...

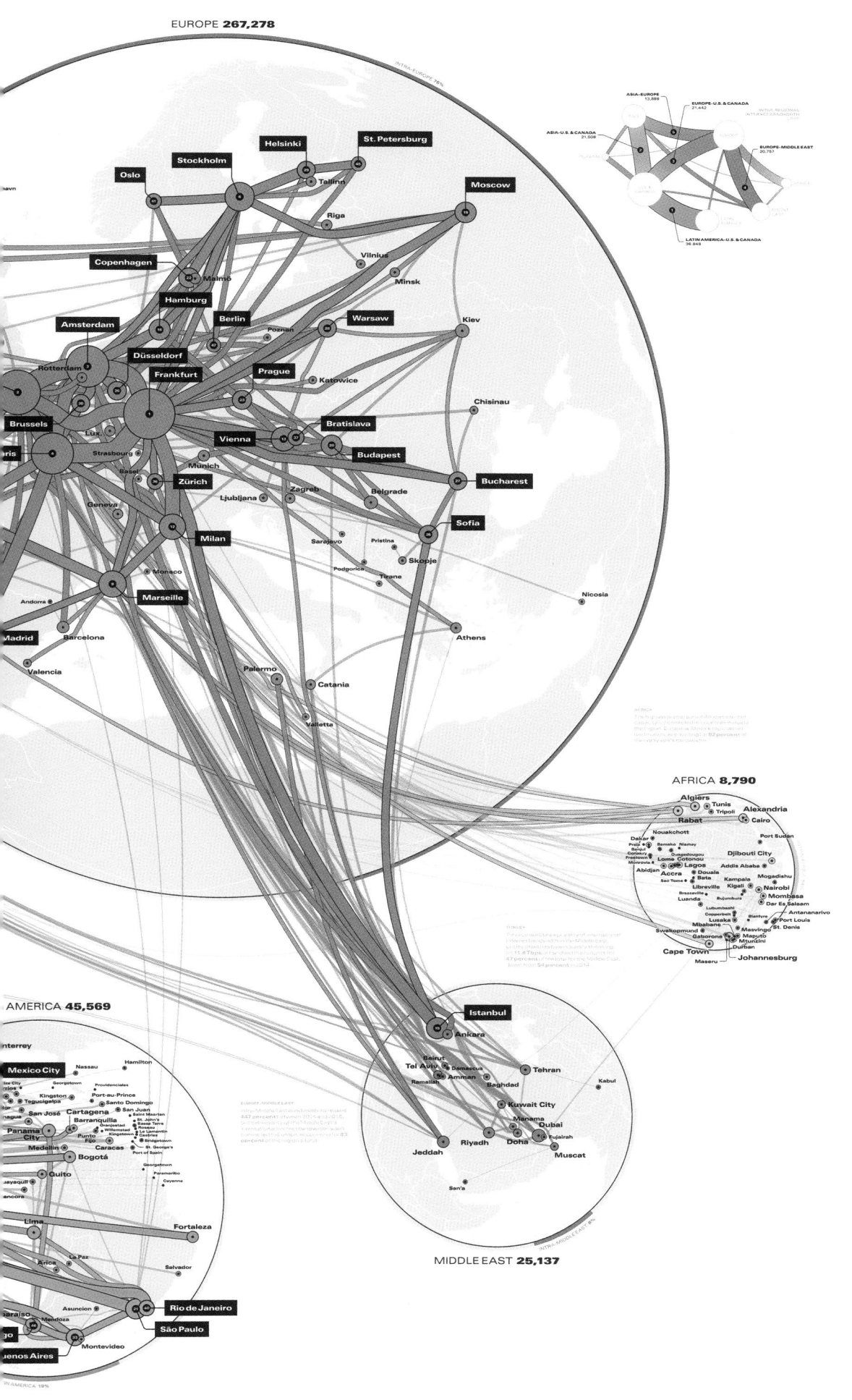

Banking and Finance

The map, from 2018, shows foreign reserves held by major countries. It is a measure both of the ability of nations to absorb external shocks and of their changing relative economic weight. The titan is China, with over $3 trillion in reserves, followed by Japan with more than $1 trillion, while Switzerland, long the repository for wealth seeking a discreet home, follows not far behind. The United States has a surprisingly modest $115 billion in reserves, a touch less than Indonesia.

How to measure and store wealth became an issue after its accumulation became possible with the appearance of the first cities in Mesopotamia in the 5th millennium BC. Enterprising merchants banded together to share their risk, such as the Egibi family in Babylonia around 600BC, who established joint ventures trading in commodities such as barley and timber.

Yet keeping wealth in such physical assets was risky, and the minting of the earliest coinage in Lydia (in western Asia Minor) around 600BC led to a financial revolution. The coin stood as a measure of value and could be transported far more easily than bushels of grain to pay a debt. In 363BC, the Greek orator Demosthenes recorded in a speech that bankers kept account books in which they balanced the amounts given out against those deposited, and by the time of the early Roman Empire *argentarii*, or moneychangers, were engaged in a lucrative trade, lending money to fund the extravagances of the senatorial class.

The emergence of mercantile republics in Italy (see pages 156–9) from the 11th century created even more demand for banking services. The first foreign exchange contract was struck in 1156 by two brothers from Genoa who wanted to change their own currency into bezants to make a payment in Constantinople. Great banking houses such as the Bardi and Peruzzi emerged, despite a Christian injunction against usury (or charging interest) which was made absolute in 1311. Royal houses throughout Europe came to them to raise finances for their campaigns, but were just as inclined to default, which led to the first

ever banking crisis in the 1340s, when Edward III of England refused to repay his loans. More nimble competitors such as the Medicis (founded in 1397) and the Fuggers of Augsburg, who made their first loan to an Austrian archduke in 1487, navigated the diplomatic storms better, but as governments grew more sophisticated and demanding, they could not supply their needs.

Trade and empire developed hand in hand as twin faces of power, and banking acted as the lubricant to their mutually beneficial arrangement. New forms of banking appeared in the imperial powers from the 16th century: in Seville to finance and invest the profits from Spain's colonial ventures in the Americas; in Istanbul under the auspices of Ottoman merchants; in Amsterdam to fund the spice-trading network the Dutch established in the 17th century; and, above all, in London, where successful merchants deposited their surplus cash with goldsmiths who in turn lent it out to other investors, turning a handy additional profit for both parties and laying the foundations for such leviathans as Barclays, whose forerunner bank dates back to 1690. Governments, too, entered the banking sphere, setting up their own central banks to print money and regulate the financial system, beginning with the Bank of England in 1694 (although the United States was a comparative laggard, its Federal Reserve only being approved in 1913).

Banking grew unimaginably more complex in the 19th and 20th centuries as banking dynasties like the Rothschilds gave way to financial megacorporations such as JP Morgan Chase, Mitsubishi and HSBC. The size of their businesses mushroomed beyond the dreams of those pioneer Babylonian traders, so that now $6.6 trillion is traded each day in foreign exchange transactions, and total foreign exchange reserves reached $11.3 trillion in February 2020. If financial derivatives, money on deposit, the value of property and company shares were tallied together with physical banknotes and coins, the amount of "money" in the world might well exceed a quadrillion dollars. It is as well that no one now need transport that amount in bushels of wheat.

EUROPE

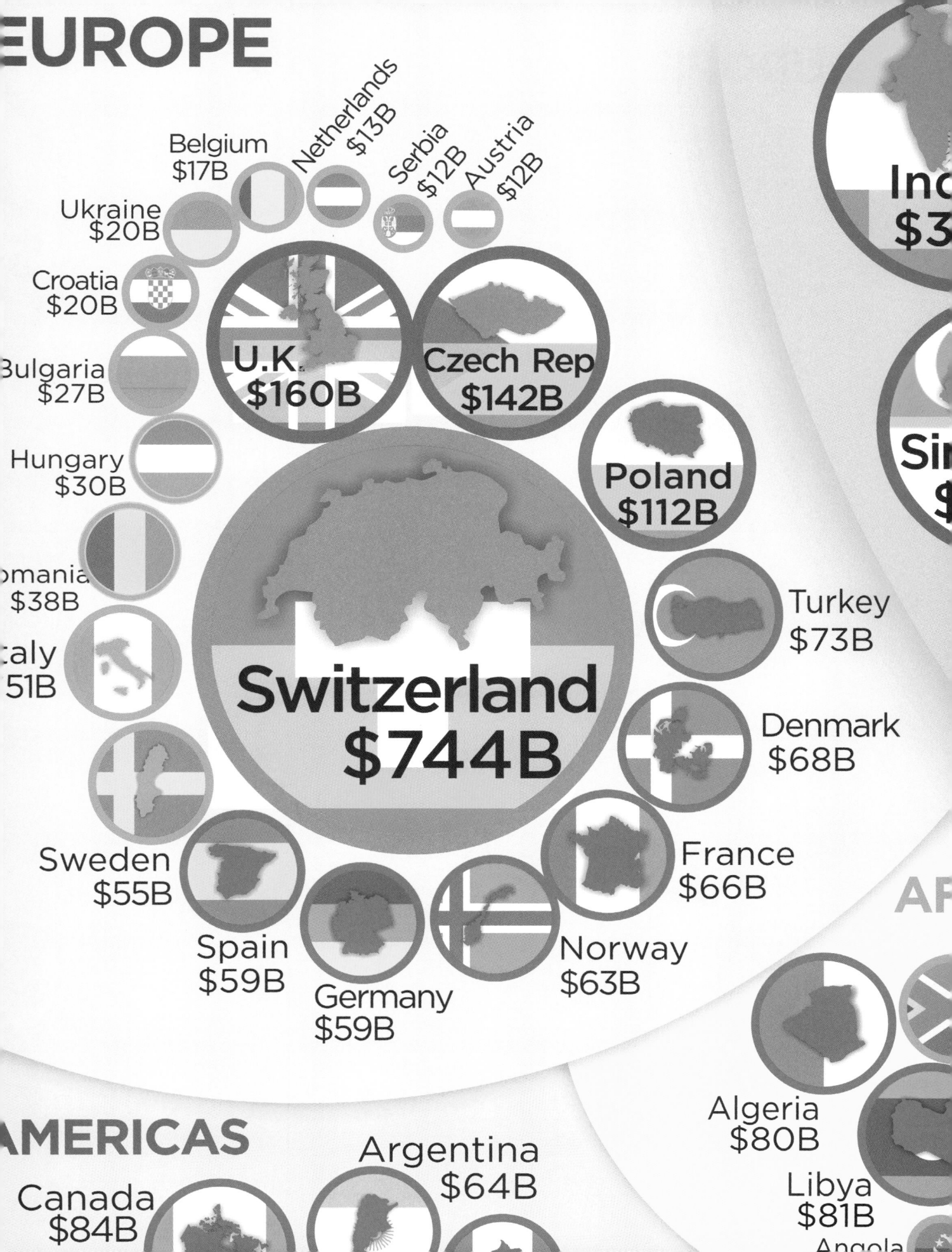

Belgium $17B

Netherlands $13B

Serbia $12B

Austria $12B

Ukraine $20B

Croatia $20B

Bulgaria $27B

Hungary $30B

Romania $38B

Italy $51B

Sweden $55B

U.K. $160B

Czech Rep $142B

Poland $112B

Switzerland $744B

Turkey $73B

Denmark $68B

France $66B

Norway $63B

Spain $59B

Germany $59B

India $3

Sin $

AMERICAS

Canada $84B

Argentina $64B

AF

Algeria $80B

Libya $81B

Angola

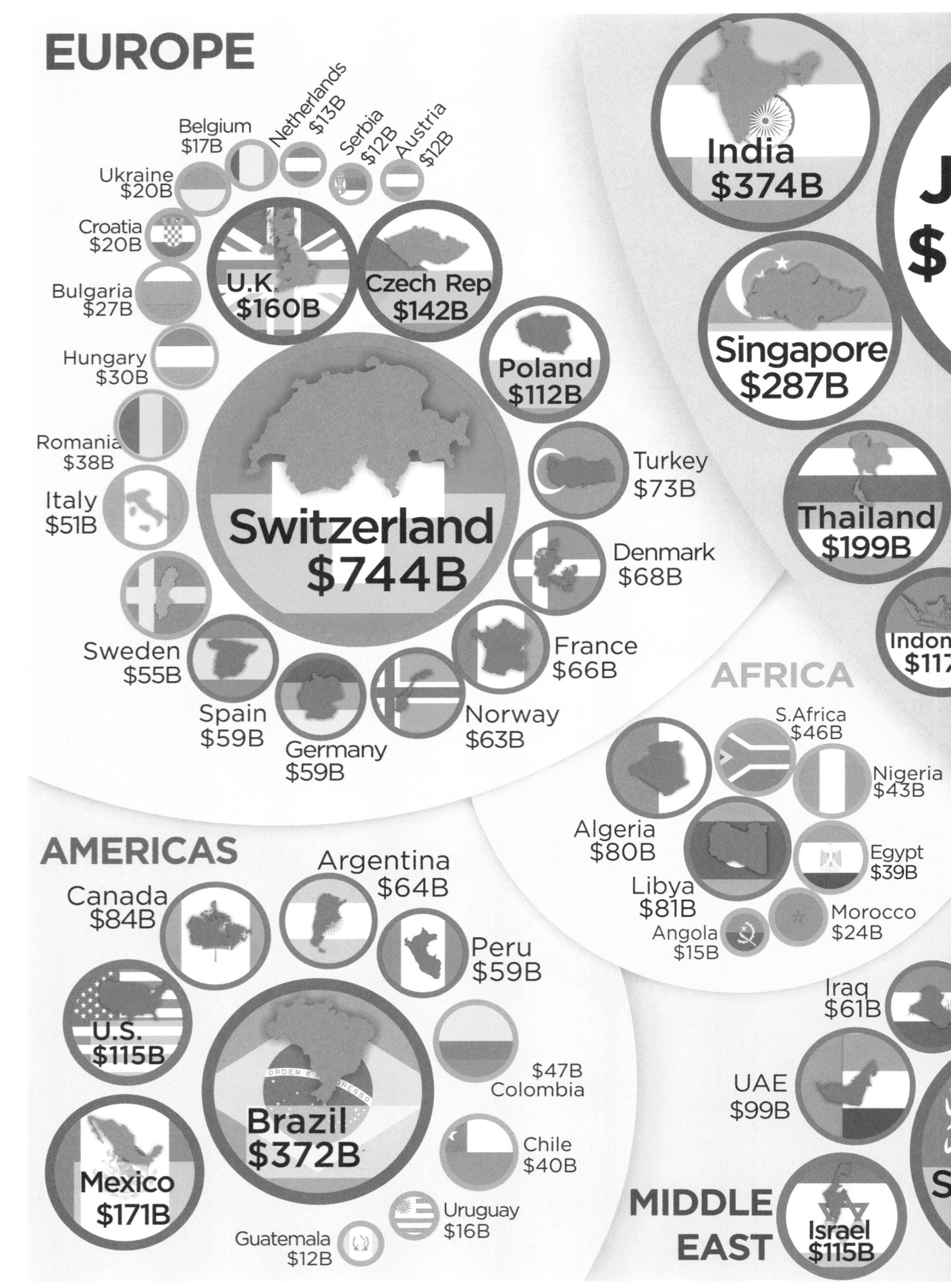

EUROPE

Belgium $17B
Netherlands $13B
Serbia $12B
Austria $12B
Ukraine $20B
Croatia $20B
U.K. $160B
Czech Rep $142B
Bulgaria $27B
Poland $112B
Hungary $30B
Turkey $73B
Romania $38B
Switzerland $744B
Italy $51B
Denmark $68B
Sweden $55B
France $66B
Spain $59B
Norway $63B
Germany $59B

AMERICAS

Canada $84B
Argentina $64B
Peru $59B
U.S. $115B
$47B Colombia
Brazil $372B
Chile $40B
Mexico $171B
Uruguay $16B
Guatemala $12B

India $374B
J $
Singapore $287B
Thailand $199B
Indon $117

AFRICA

S.Africa $46B
Nigeria $43B
Algeria $80B
Egypt $39B
Libya $81B
Morocco $24B
Angola $15B

Iraq $61B
UAE $99B
S
MIDDLE EAST
Israel $115B

ASIA

pan
24T

China
$3.09T

Taiwan
$462B

Hong Kong
$425B

S.Korea
$399B

Russia
$382B

ysia
0B

$71B
Philippines

Bangladesh
$31B

Macao
$20B

Kazakhstan
$17B

Cambodia
$13B

Lebanon
$41B

Kuwait
$37B

Qatar
$29B

Oman
$17B

i Arabia
496B

AUSTRALIA & OCEANIA

Australia
$51B

New
Zealand
$18B

**Total Country
Reserves***
($)

$1T

$100B

$50B

$10B

% of
World's
Reserves

Tourism and Trade

The map, from 1945, shows the routes flown by the British Overseas Airways Corporation, then the United Kingdom's flag carrier airline. Radiating from London, they lead disproportionately to Britain's colonial possessions, but they hint at an emerging Air Age, when travel for pleasure would soon become an enormous global industry.

For much of history, travel was largely a matter of necessity rather than choice, driven by famine or war, or undertaken by merchants along trade routes. The rich and the pious, though, did travel, whether aristocratic Romans relaxing in villas at Baiae along the Gulf of Naples, 6th-century Buddhist pilgrims in search of sacred texts in India, or Christian ones travelling to Jerusalem, as did St Helena, the mother of the Emperor Constantine in AD327. A few even went sightseeing, like Hadrian, who travelled in 130 with his imperial entourage to wonder at the Colossi of Memnon near Luxor, pharaonic statues which emitted a sound like the playing of a lyre.

Modern tourism was a creation of the 18th century, when aristocratic young Englishmen began to undertake the Grand Tour, in an effort to become imbued with a classical sensibility by visiting the major sites of Italy. Back home, spas like Bath came into fashion, and in 1793 Duke Friedrich Franz of Mecklenburg-Schwerin founded the first purpose-built seaside resort at Heiligendamm on the Baltic coast. Middle-class tourism arrived in 1841, when Thomas Cook chartered a train to transport clients from Leicester to Loughborough. In 1855 he organised his first excursion abroad, to Paris, followed by inaugural trips to America in 1866 and Palestine and Egypt in 1869. Despite being robbed in Jerusalem, the clients received good value for the £105 a head they paid for the trip. The gradual introduction of paid leave in the United Kingdom from 1871, and its legal enforcement in 1938, created new opportunities for leisure: within eight years, a million people a year were taking the train to Blackpool to enjoy a seaside break.

The growth of air travel in the 20th century revolutionised travel, with the first scheduled service between the forerunner of Heathrow airport and Paris beginning in 1919. Although progress was interrupted by the Second World War, in 1945, the same year as the map, a route opened up from London to Sydney, a gruelling nearly six-day trip for nine passengers that went via stops in Lydda, Karachi, Ceylon and Singapore. The invention of the jet engine during the Second World War allowed longer nonstop flights, and in 1958 Pan Am inaugurated the first transatlantic jet service from New York to Paris.

Air travel, and tourism, went from strength to strength, with the commencement of package holidays to the Mediterranean in the 1970s making foreign travel accessible to all. As a result, international tourist arrivals surged from 25 million in 1950 to 664 million in 1999 and then over a billion in 2012, with the busiest airports (Atlanta and Beijing) each handling over 100 million passengers. By 2015 the global travel and tourism industry was valued at $7.6 trillion, making up 10 per cent of global GDP (as opposed to 16 per cent for all manufacturing). Now, in contrast to all previous ages, travel itself is a more valuable trade than the goods carried by travellers. It is a phenomenon at which Marco Polo might truly have wondered.

Great Slave L.

Parry Is

Lat. 60° N.

C. Chelyuskin

Lukino

NORTH POLE

gnetic Pole

Ellesmere I.

Franz Josef
Land

R. Yenesei

GREENLAND

Nova
Zembla

R. Obi

Disko I.
Godhavn

80° N

Spitzbergen

Obdorsk

Bear I.

Tobolsk

Godthaab

Murmansk

Archangel

ose Bay

Bluie West One

Iceland

FINLAND

U

S

S

Reykjavik

SWEDEN

Leningrad

Kazalin

nder

Trondheim

Helsinki

wfoundland

Faroe Is

60° N.

Oslo

Stockholm

Moscow

Bergen

NORWAY

Tallinn

R. Volga

Christiansand

Riga

Edinburgh

Copenhagen

Memel

Astrakhan

Dublin

Danzig

Rostov

LONDON

GERMANY

Berlin

Warsaw

Baku

Amsterdam

Odessa

Brussels

Vienna

Batoum

CZECHOSLOVAKIA

Paris

AUSTRIA HUN.

Budapest

Bucharest

Sevastopol

FRANCE

RUMANIA

Varna

TURKEY

Belgrade

YUGO-SL.

Sofia

Istanbul

Venice

BULG.

Cetinge

Ankara

SYRIA

ITALY

ALB.

JORD.

Smyrna

Baghdad

Marseilles
Rome

Athens

Lagens

Naples

IRA

Azores

Espinho

Madrid

Lydda

Lisbon

PORTUGAL

SPAIN

Tunis

TRANS
JORDAN

Gibraltar

Malta

Cairo

Madeira o

Oran

Algiers

Casablanca

Benghazi

EGYPT

Ifni

MOROCCO

Lat. 30° N.

Las Palmas

Canary Is

ALGERIA

LIBYA

Port Sudan

RIO
DE
ORO

Tropic of Cancer

Wadi Halfa

ANGLO

Port Etienne

Mas

erde Is

FRENCH WEST AFRICA

EGYPTIAN

Sal

Kha

Dakar

Timbukto

L. Chad

El Fasher

SUDAN

Bathurst

GAMBIA

R. Niger

Kano

AFRICA

PORTUGUESE
GUINEA

NIGERIA

Fort Lamy

Konakri

Fort Archambault

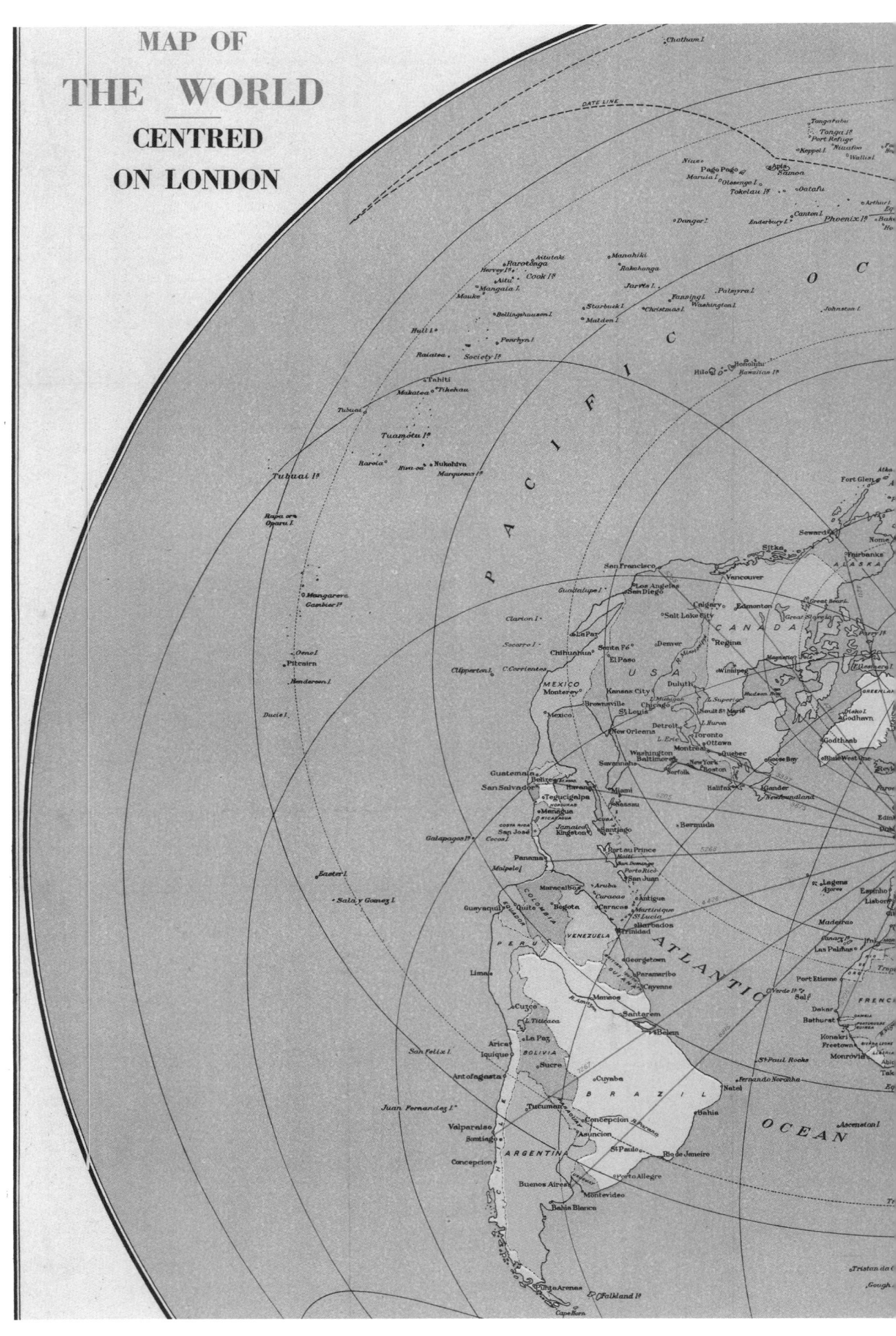

MAP OF
THE WORLD
CENTRED
ON LONDON

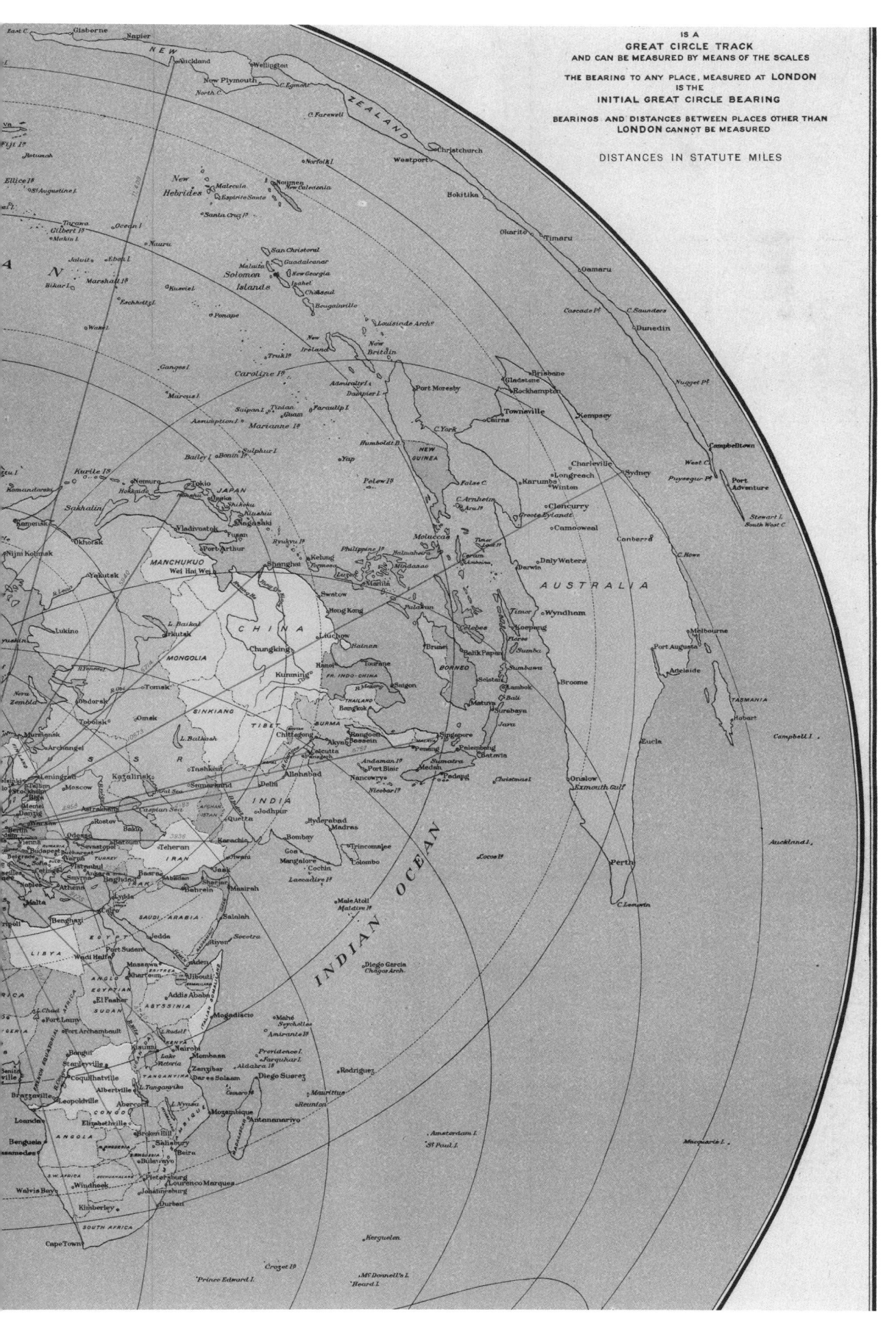

IS A
GREAT CIRCLE TRACK
AND CAN BE MEASURED BY MEANS OF THE SCALES

THE BEARING TO ANY PLACE, MEASURED AT LONDON
IS THE
INITIAL GREAT CIRCLE BEARING

BEARINGS AND DISTANCES BETWEEN PLACES OTHER THAN
LONDON CANNOT BE MEASURED

DISTANCES IN STATUTE MILES

Trade Blocs

The map, from *The Times Complete History of the World*, shows the development of the European Union from 1981, when the organisation (in its preceding form as the EEC) was made up of just ten members, to 2020, when it had 27.

The EU's growth shows the attraction of a modern solution to an age-old trading problem. Trade depends upon trust, that each party will receive goods of acceptable quality, will be paid the agreed sum and will have some recourse if these things do not occur. Within national jurisdictions, the growing power of governments from the 16th century provided a means of enforcement, but in contracts between merchants of different states this was not so easy. A partial solution was provided by the Hanseatic League (see pages 70–1), a group of Baltic trading towns which from 1210 agreed to a common set of laws to govern commerce.

This prototype of an international trade was far ahead of its time and, despite the evolution of the *Zollverein* or German customs union (founded in 1834) into a united state in 1871, the heyday of such organisations did not come until after the Second World War. It was clear that the economic and political reconstruction of a devastated continent could not come about through the untrammelled competition which had caused the disastrous conflict. So, right from its foundation by the Treaty of Rome in 1957, the European Economic Community worked to remove trade barriers between its members – abolishing tariffs in 1968 – and fostered a steady process of economic integration.

The French president Charles de Gaulle spoke in 1959 of his dream of a Europe stretching from "the Atlantic to the Urals". It was this political vision, and a far stronger secretariat in the shape of the European Commission – which acquired some quasi-executive powers – that set it apart from other regional trading groups such as ASEAN, founded in 1967 to bring together southeast Asian states, Mercosur, founded in 1991 as a South American grouping and Nafta, which bound Mexico, Canada and the United States in an uneasy partnership from 1994 to 2020.

When the Soviet Union collapsed in 1991, many of its satellite states sought membership of the European body, with eight of the ten nations which joined in 2004 being former communist countries. By then it had become the European Union and in 1993 had established the Single Market, in which goods – and, throughout much of it, people – could circulate freely with no customs dues and a set of common standards for goods. This trading nirvana attracted further members, until Croatia's adherence to the EU in 2013 made the number 28. Yet signs of deeper political integration troubled some, and a wave of populist politics which swept the continent in the wake of the global financial crisis of 2008, together with a surge in refugees fleeing to Europe to escape civil war in the Middle East from 2015, undermined support for the EU. This sentiment was particularly sharp in Britain, where entrenched political interests had always been sceptical of the European Union, and where a referendum in June 2016 delivered a narrow 52 to 48 per cent vote to end Britain's membership.

This "Brexit" vote resulted in the United Kingdom leaving in January 2020 and was a warning that trading networks, and organisations, can as easily break apart as grow.

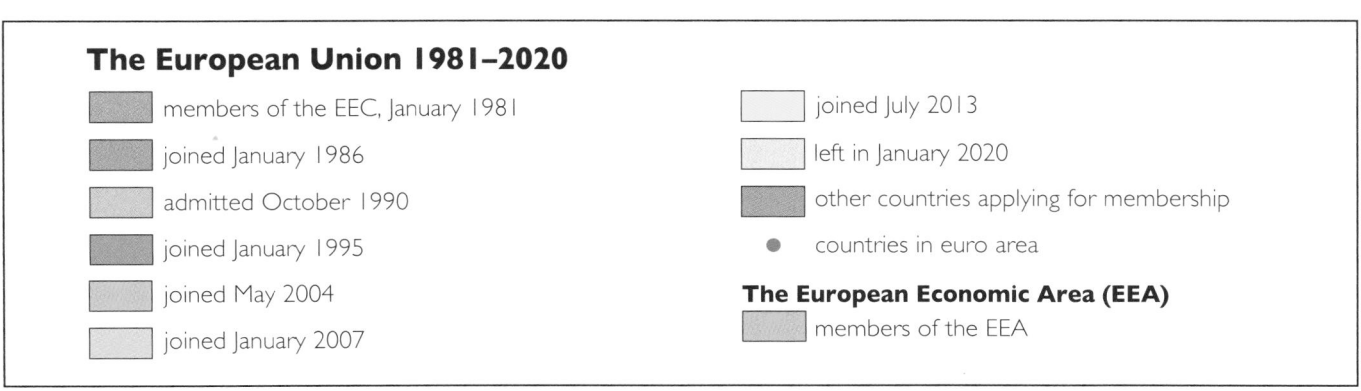

ICELAND
*EU membership
application withdrawn,
Mar. 2015*

ATLANTIC
OCEAN

*Norwegian
Sea*

N O R W A Y
S W E D E N
FINLAND

*Faeroe
Islands*

*North
Sea*

DENMARK

ESTONIA

LATVIA

LITHUANIA

RUSSIA

IRELAND

UNITED
KINGDOM

NETHER-
LANDS

BELGIUM

LUX.

GERMANY

POLAND

BELARUS

CZECHIA

SLOVAKIA

UKRAINE

MOLDOVA

*Bay of
Biscay*

FRANCE

LIECT.

SWITZ.

AUSTRIA

HUNGARY

SLOVENIA

ROMANIA

Black Sea

GEORGIA

ARMENIA

CROATIA

MONACO

ANDORRA

SAN
MARINO

I T A L Y

BOS.-
HERZ.

SERBIA

KOSOVO

BULGARIA

T U R K E Y
*customs union with EU
effective from 1 Jan. 1996;
application to EU recognised,
Feb. 2003*

PORTUGAL

S P A I N

Corsica

Balearic Is.

Sardinia

MONTENEGRO

N.
MAC.

ALBANIA

GREECE

SYRIA

IRAQ

GIBRALTAR

Sicily

Crete

CYPRUS

JORDAN

MALTA

Mediterranean Sea

MOROCCO

ALGERIA

TUNISIA

The European Union 1981–2020

- members of the EEC, January 1981
- joined January 1986
- admitted October 1990
- joined January 1995
- joined May 2004
- joined January 2007
- joined July 2013
- left in January 2020
- other countries applying for membership
- • countries in euro area

The European Economic Area (EEA)
- members of the EEA

Threats to World Trade

The map overleaf, created with data from the Johns Hopkins University Center for Systems Science and Engineering, shows the spread of the 2020 COVID-19 pandemic by late June, when almost every country in the world had been infected, with around 10 million confirmed cases recorded and almost 500,000 deaths. The pandemic's progress and its impact in economies shut down, lives lost and international commerce suspended, showed that, whatever the precautions made against the more predictable threats to world trade, unforeseeable events could prove even more damaging.

Those other threats, though, are very real, and have grown steadily since the 1990s, when the collapse of the communist bloc seemed to presage a new world order of political and economic stability. The explosive economic growth of China and its ascent to become the world's largest trading nation by 2013 threatened the United States' economic hegemony and led to a series of bad-tempered trading disputes,

culminating in June 2018 with the imposition of tariffs on Chinese technology such as robots, and Chinese retaliation against a range of American industrial goods, including automobiles.

The election of the Trump administration in November 2016 was part of a wave of populism which breached the established political consensus and brought nationalist and nativist leaders to power. A feeling that international trading bodies such as the WTO (World Trade Organization) had not protected American interests led Trump to withdraw support from its dispute resolution mechanism in 2019, which crippled the organisation's ability to operate. In Britain, longstanding scepticism about deeper European political integration led to a referendum vote in 2016 to withdraw from the European Union. Loss of access to the European Single Market is likely to complicate Britain's ability to trade with its largest markets and is a sign, along with the United States' pulling out of the Trans-Pacific Trade partnership (intended to remove trade barriers between Pacific nations) and its forced renegotiation of Nafta in 2017, that regional trade bodies are fracturing, to the possible detriment of all.

Some of the threats that have impinged on trade since ancient times are still present. Political instability makes access to some essential commodities difficult, such as the tantalum essential for the manufacture of mobile phones, 80 per cent of which is located in deposits in the war-ravaged Democratic Republic of Congo. The preponderance of oil reserves in the Middle East makes it too a perennial geopolitical flashpoint.

Yet there are also new shadows. Cybercrime and data fraud are enormous challenges. A single data breach may ruin an entire business, and a major hack may bring an economy to a virtual halt. By 2021, it is estimated that the total damage caused by cybercrime could reach $6 trillion, equivalent to the GDP of Japan. Global warming and climate change also threaten trade by changing the patterns of agricultural production and making crops unviable in some areas. The increase in extreme weather events damages infrastructure and the rise in sea levels may make some coastal areas (and, in the case of the Maldives, entire countries) uninhabitable.

In the face of such threats, the world trading system was vulnerable to a "black swan", an unpredictable event with a major impact for which it was unprepared. The COVID-19 pandemic proved to be just such a phenomenon, the need to lockdown entire economies presenting governments with a wholly unexpected series of problems. The total impact on world trade will take years to calculate, but, just as in the past, the human need to trade will rise to the challenge of repairing that damage.

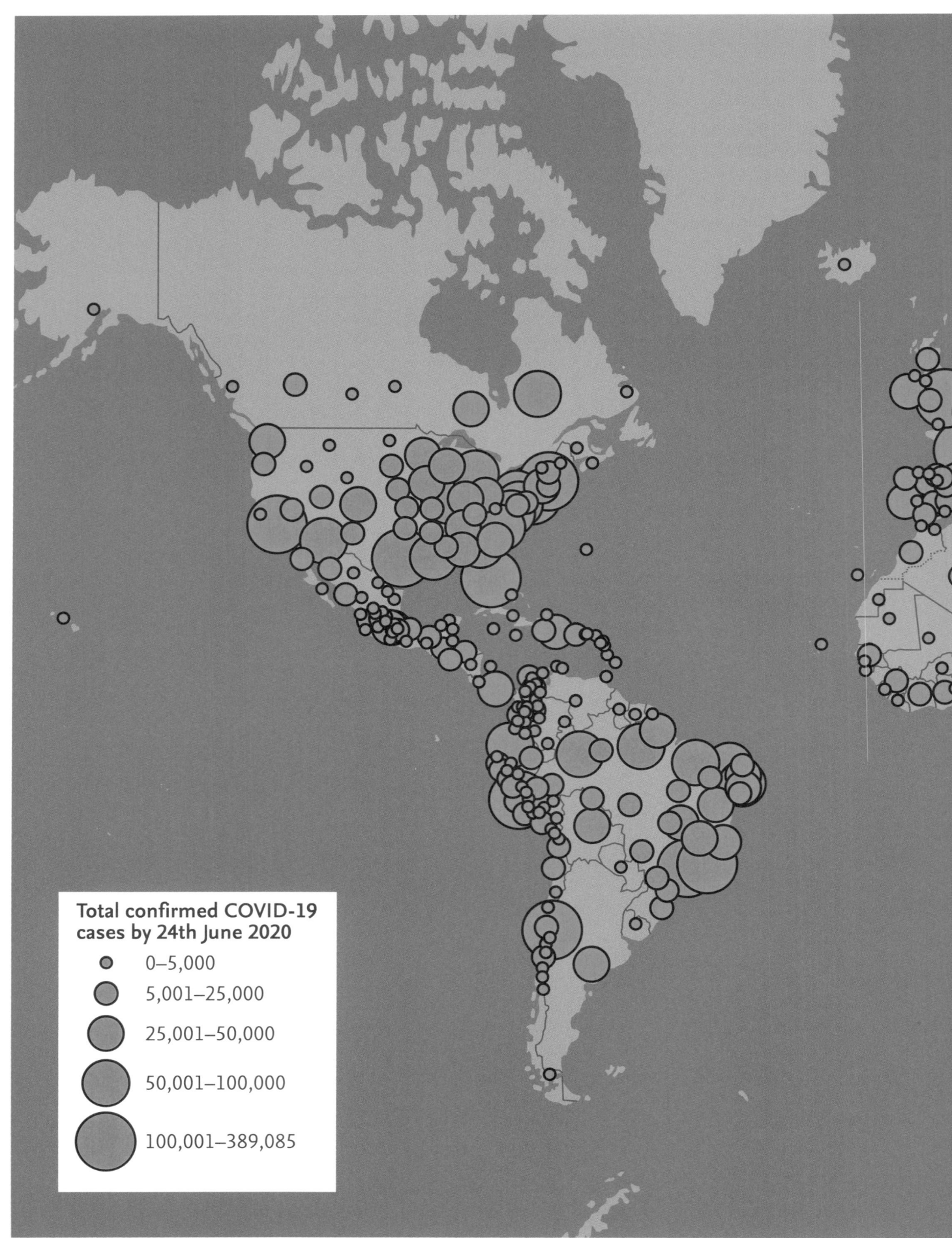

Total confirmed COVID-19
cases by 24th June 2020

- 0–5,000
- 5,001–25,000
- 25,001–50,000
- 50,001–100,000
- 100,001–389,085

Acknowledgements

While every effort has been made to trace the owner of copyright material reproduced herein and secure permission, the publishers would like to apologize for any omission and will be pleased to incorporate missing acknowledgements in any future edition of this book.

We are grateful to the following companies, organizations and individuals for supplying the historical maps included on these pages:

Front cover French chart of Hudson Bay, Canada, 1722. The Granger Collection / Alamy Stock Photo.

p7 Detail from Abraham Cresques's Catalan Atlas, 1375 / Bibliothèque Nationale, Paris, France. Bridgeman Images.

p8 James Wyld II's Official Map of the Suez Maritime Canal, 1869. Bridgeman Images.

p9 Map showing spread of COVID-19 pandemic, 2020. Data reproduced courtesy of Johns Hopkins University Center for Systems Science and Engineering.

p10 Çatalhöyük settlement plan, c. 6200BC / Anatolian Civilization Museum, Ankara, Turkey. Images & Stories / Alamy Stock Photo.

p12 Turin Papyrus, c. 1150BC. Zyzzy / Public domain.

p15–17 Map of Greek and Phoenician settlements in the Mediterranean basin, c. 550BC. From *Historical Atlas*, published 1923. Classic Image / Alamy Stock Photo.

p18 Late Babylonian map of the world, c. 600BC. World History Archive / Alamy Stock Photo.

p20 Burckhardt map of Petra, 1822. Gibson Green / Alamy Stock Photo.

pp23–5 Detail of Constantinople and the Middle East from the Peutinger map copy, c. 1265 / Bibliothèque Nationale, Paris, France. Bridgeman Images.

p26 Engraving of Abraham Ortelius's map of Asia with superimposed map of Europe, 1603 / Royal Geographical Society, London, UK. Bridgeman Images.

pp28, 30–1 City of Jerusalem and surrounding area from the Madaba mosaic map, c. 560 / Church of Saint George, Madaba, Jordan. Bridgeman Images.

pp33–5 Kaliningrad Oblast Map, 1979. By AO «Калининградский янтарный комбинат» - http://ambercombine.ru/, CC BY-SA 4.0, https://commons.wikimedia.org/w/index.php?curid=50342006.

pp36, 38–9 Petrus Bertius's 1623 map of the Carolingian Empire of Charlemagne. Public domain.

p41 Al-Istakhri's map of Iraq, c. 975. Granger / Bridgeman Images.

pp42–3 Al-Sharif al-Idrisi's *Charta Rogeriana*, 1154. Everett Collection Inc / Alamy Stock Photo.

p44 Hereford *Mappa Mundi*, c. 1300. Reproduced with permission from the Hereford Mappa Mundi Trust and the Dean and Chapter of Hereford Cathedral.

p47 Detail from Abraham Cresques's Catalan Atlas, 1375 / Bibliothèque Nationale, Paris, France. Bridgeman Images.

pp50–1 Stone map of China (Hua yi tu), 1136. Library of Congress, Geography and Map Division.

pp53–5 Fra Mauro's world map, 1459 / Palazzo Ducale, Venice, Italy. Alinari / Bridgeman Images.

pp58–9 Cristoforo de Grassi's copy of a 1481 painting commemorating the Battle of Otranto in 1481 in Genoa, 1597. De Agostini Picture Library / Bridgeman Images.

p60 Cristoforo Buondelmonti's map of Constantinople, c. 1420, from *Liber Insularum Cycladum* / British Library, London, UK. © British Library Board. All Rights Reserved / Bridgeman Images.

pp63–5 Frans Hogenberg's map of Bruges, 1572, from his *Civitates Orbis Terrarum*. © A. Dagli Orti / De Agostini Picture Library / Bridgeman Images.

pp68–9 Abraham and Jehuda Cresques's Catalan Atlas of the European continent with the Atlantic and the Mediterranean Sea, c. 1375. Bridgeman Images.

p70 Map of Northwest Europe and the North Atlantic Ocean from Abraham Ortelius's atlas, *Theatrum Orbis Terrarum*, 1570. Everett Collection Historical / Alamy Stock Photo.

p72 Map of coastline of Fujian Province and port of Changle, 1416, accompaniment to Ma Huan's *Overall Survey of the Ocean*. The Picture Art Collection / Alamy Stock Photo.

pp75–7 Martin Waldseemüller's *Universalis cosmographia*, 1507. Library of Congress, Geography and Map Division.

p78 Arnoldus Florentius van Langren's map of western Africa, 1594. Historical Picture Archive / Contributor / Getty Images.

pp81–3 Battista Agnese's world atlas, 1544. ART Collection / Alamy Stock Photo.

p85 Piri Reis's map of the world, 1513. WorldPhotos / Alamy Stock Photo.

p87 Replica of the front cover of the *Codex Mendoza*, 1541/ Museo Nacional de Antropología, Mexico City, Mexico. Ian Mursell/Mexicolore / Bridgeman Images.

pp88–9 George Anson's nautical chart of the Pacific Ocean depicting the trade routes used by Spanish Galleons from Mexico to the Philippines, 1743. The Picture Art Collection / Alamy Stock Photo.

p91 Baptista Boazio's map depicting Sir Francis Drake in Cartagena de Indias, 1589. The History Collection / Alamy Stock Photo.

pp 92, 94–5 Jean Rotz's chart of the western coast of Europe and the opposite coast of North America, from his *Boke of Idrographie*, 1542 / British Library, London, UK. © British Library Board. All Rights Reserved / Bridgeman Images.

pp97–9 Jacques Cortelyou's Castello Plan, c. 1660 / Biblioteca Medicea-Laurenziana, Florence, Italy. The Picture Art Collection / Alamy Stock Photo.

p101 French chart of Hudson Bay, Canada, 1722. The Granger Collection / Alamy Stock Photo.

pp102, 104–5 America's first national map by Abel Buell, 1784. Photo © Christie's Images / Bridgeman Images.

pp107–9 Theodore de Bry's map of South America, 1592 / Service Historique de la Marine, Vincennes, France. Bridgeman Images.

pp111–13 The Cantino planisphere, 1502. CPA Media Pte Ltd / Alamy Stock Photo.

p115 Johannes Baptista van Doetechum the Younger's map of Goa, 1595. The Stapleton Collection / Bridgeman Images.

p116 Jacob van Meurs's map of Batavia, 1682. ullstein bild / Contributor / Getty Images.

pp119–21 Jacques-Nicolas Bellin's plan of the city and port of Nagasaki, c. 1750. Library of Congress, Geography and Map Division.

pp122, 124–5 Ignazio Danti's map of China's eastern coastline, c. 1570. Pictures from History/Woodbury & Page / Bridgeman Images.

pp126, 128–9 Olaus Magnus's *Carta Marina*, 1572 (original 1539). World History Archive / Alamy Stock Photo.

pp130, 132–3 James Rennell's map of Hindoostan, 1782 / British Library, London, UK. © British Library Board. All Rights Reserved / Bridgeman Images.

pp136–7 "Plan of a Large Plantation, Cayenne (French Guiana), 1763", *Slavery Images: A Visual Record of the African Slave Trade and Slave Life in the Early African Diaspora*, accessed June 30, 2020, http://www.slaveryimages.org/s/slaveryimages/item/1332. Licensed under CC BY-NC 4.0.

pp138–9 James Robertson's map of Jamaica, 1804. Reproduced with the permission of the National Library of Scotland.

pp141–3 Frederick Law Olmsted's "Map of the Cotton Kingdom and its Dependencies in America", 1862. Cornell University – PJ Mode Collection of Persuasive Cartography.

p144 Map of coffee plantations north of São Paulo. Brazil, 1885. Antiqua Print Gallery / Alamy Stock Photo.

BOUND
FOR HELL

BOOK ONE

KENDRA LEIGH

Published by Evoke Publications

Cover Art by Kendra Leigh
Copy Editing by The Polished Pen
Formatting by Tugboat Design

ISBN: 978-1-910713-00-6

To M who is my rock
and
G who is my inspiration.

CHAPTER ONE

I blinked rapidly, attempting to alleviate the soreness of my dry, gritty eyes. I'd been staring at my computer screen for most of the afternoon. After posting on the news feed and updating the blog for Evoke Gallery's website, I spent the last few hours working on the photo editing for my forthcoming publication.

As a rule, I tended to have a balanced blend of self-satisfaction and self-doubt where my work was concerned, but today I felt utterly smug. My street photography was all about capturing the transient beauty of a moment in its rawest form. It was about demonstrating the distinction between cultures, at the same time identifying the common link between all of mankind: emotion—the thing which, in the end, rendered us all the same. Above all, the images I captured were intended to evoke some sort of memory or feeling to those who surveyed them.

The image on my screen in front of me achieved all those things. It had been taken on a sunny day in Central Park, and was of two homeless men. The first man was asleep on a park bench with his feet crossed at the ankles, arms folded across his chest, and an open copy of the *New York Post* covering his face to shield him from the midday sun. The second man was leaning over the first, taking full advantage of his oblivious state by helping himself to a sneaky peek of his newspaper.

I chuckled as I recalled the scene.

After stumbling upon the abandoned newspaper on a bench, man number one had settled down for an afternoon nap. I'd watched as, shortly after, he'd been joined by the second man, who had just salvaged a discarded, half-eaten bagel from a nearby garbage can and wandered over to enjoy his free meal next to his unacquainted companion. He'd appeared quite pleased with himself when he'd discovered that a free read was also on the agenda.

I'd captured the image right at this point, its title springing instantly to mind: *For pleasure has no relish unless we share it.* It was a quote from a book by Virginia Woolf and fitted the drama and unintended slapstick comedy of this image perfectly.

Man number two had been quietly scanning the open pages for a minute or two when something had gripped his attention. He'd leaned forward for a closer look, taking a bite of his lunch at exactly the same time. A large crumb had fallen with a thud directly onto the newspaper-covered face of the unsuspecting, sleeping man, waking him with a jolt. When he'd realized what was going on, he chased the man off, shaking his fist at him and shouting, "Buy your own goddamn paper, you thieving asshole!"

Ah, the irony! That was what I loved about my job; every image told a story—even though sometimes I was the only person who understood what it was.

My cell phone *bleeped*, alerting me to an incoming message. It was Jia. The text read: WHERE ARE YOU, BITCH?

Crap, I was late! Where the hell did time go? Swiftly putting my computer to sleep and grabbing my purse, I headed out through the showroom and into the gallery foyer to set the alarm.

Just as I was about to input the code there was a rapping on the glass door. I turned to see Jean-Paul standing on the doorstep with a bottle of wine and a hopeful, gagging-for-it look on his face.

"Any chance of a dance?" he asked when I opened the door.

Of course, I was under no illusion as to what he meant. A shimmy on the dance floor was not the kind of bump-and-grind Jean-Paul had in mind.

"Not tonight, Jean-Paul," I said, feeling slightly irked by his unannounced arrival. "I'm afraid I'm already late for a date." I tapped in the alarm code swiftly and pulled the door closed, locking it securely.

"A date?" he snapped, his brow furrowing.

"Yes, dinner with Jia. It's her birthday. Lose the frown," I said, poking the crease between his eyebrows and stepping onto the street. I frequently reminded him that it was in his best interests to keep all facial expressions to a minimum; his career as a male model would last longer.

"Where are you meeting?"

"Um, Eden," I answered cautiously.

"Mmm, I love Eden. I haven't eaten yet."

"Very subtle, Jean-Paul."

"So can I crash?" He batted his eyelashes.

A glance at my watch informed me there was no time to deliberate. I rolled my eyes, puffing air from my nostrils. "Come on, then. I don't expect she'll mind. You'll have to offer her the wine as a gift," I said, pointing to the bottle in his hand. "And hurry, will you? She's already after my blood."

The early spring evening was warm and perfect for a walk, and although we were only a few blocks away from the restaurant on 7th Avenue, in the Chelsea area of Manhattan, it was far enough and late enough for a cab. I left Jean-Paul the task of hailing one while I tapped out a quick text to Jia reassuring her that I was on my way, and forewarning her that Jean-Paul was in tow.

As the cab pulled out into traffic, I removed my compact from my purse to check my makeup and hair. Not having had time to return home and change, I was suddenly grateful for the wardrobe choice I'd made that morning. I was wearing an Alice and Olivia box-pleat, red leather skirt—short, but acceptably so—a white slim-fit blouse, and black Chrissie Morris Dafne ankle boots. I'd left my rich mahogany-brown hair loose to fall in long, tumbling curls around my shoulders, and my fully-loaded, brow-skimming fringe framed my square, angular-jawed face perfectly.

In my peripheral vision, I caught a glimpse of Jean-Paul's doting puppy-dog eyes watching as I applied a touch of nude gloss to my full lips. I turned to face him, his expression lustful to the point of near dribbling—almost as though he were hankering after a sugary doughnut he was observing me eat.

"Wassup?" I asked impatiently.

"You are. You're so damn fuckable, you make my cock ache. I want you tonight."

"We'll see," I said, turning to face the road ahead. "It's been a long day. I'm hungry and tired. Maybe some other time."

Eyes darkening, he turned to stare out the window, attempting to conceal the disappointment which immediately blanketed his face. His reaction infuriated me. I'd never been anything but honest with him about what this thing was between us. It was simple: friends with benefits. No dating, no calling, no strings, just the occasional fuck to scratch the itch, so to speak.

Jean-Paul was stunning; medium height, muscular, black hair, tanned skin and dark, bullet-black eyes. He was gentle and caring, but young at twenty-three, and new to the modeling profession. Although it wasn't usually my thing, I'd been helping to build his portfolio as well as his self-esteem. I wasn't aware of whether he ever actually looked in a mirror, but he seemed truly oblivious to the depth of his beauty. With his face and body, he would go a long way in his chosen career.

Yes, there was no denying Jean-Paul Debree was exceptionally desirable. He could have his pick of chicks with a snap of his fingers. But a relationship… with me? It was out of the question. As hot as he was, I didn't want a relationship with him or anyone else.

Having put my trust in somebody once before, I was certain it wasn't something I was eager to repeat. I'd been there, tried it, crashed and burned. I'd let my guard down when I should have known better and hadn't much liked the way it had made me feel. Sex was as much as I needed from a guy. I was only twenty-eight, for Christ's sake. The Jean-Pauls of this world came and went—quite literally, some of the time—and that suited me. But the second they got googly-eyed, they were gone.

The forlorn look on Jean-Paul's face told me that the time had come, and I was beginning to wish I hadn't said he could tag along.

"Sure you don't want me to drop you home?" I asked, ensuring my tightly-crossed fingers were well concealed beneath my knee.

Perking up instantly, he plastered a smile to his lips. "Fuck no, and pass up a night out with you?"

"Jean-Paul, this isn't a date. You know that, right?"

"Sure, Angel, no strings. I know." He looked away again, no doubt masking his disappointment.

The cab halted outside Eden—one of my favorite restaurants in all of New York. Not only was it a top Chelsea nighttime hot spot, it served fantastic food and had the added benefit of belonging to my younger brother, Adam. As I pushed open the door, I was greeted by the mouth-watering aromas of delicious cuisine, sounds of laughter and clinking glasses, and the ominous sight of Aaron—also my brother, and Adam's twin.

He was seated at the bar, uncouthly draped over a busty blonde—his usual type. Already pretty buzzed from the look of him, he cradled a glass of bourbon in one hand and the blonde's adequate thigh in the other.

My stomach roiled in protest, as it always did when I laid eyes on Aaron, especially when I hadn't taken countermeasures to nullify the effects. Although he was here most nights, Mondays weren't usually one of them, which was the very reason I'd suggested Eden for Jia's birthday.

A thick cloud of resentment seeped across the room toward me like a steadily advancing fog. He offered me a condescending nod before disregarding me completely and returning his attention to the blonde. I winced at his silent, uncompromising condemnation, the all too familiar feelings of worthlessness causing bile to rise from my stomach, tightening and searing my throat. I put my hand to my chest to rub away the discomfort.

Screw you! I slid into self-preservation mode and pushed my way through the crowded bar to the dining area, Jean-Paul close at my heels. As I rounded the corner, I practically ran straight into Adam.

"Hey, Sis." Reaching out, he gave my arm a squeeze. "Jia's waiting for you at your favorite table. I'll join you if I can persuade my staff to do the job they get fucking paid for." Evidently stressed out with some issue or other, he scooted off in the general direction of the kitchen.

Adam was very hands-on in the restaurant. He loved his job and had worked hard to make it a success. He was a natural restaurateur whose aim was to own a chain and follow in the footsteps of our maternal grandfather, who'd once owned a string of successful eateries throughout New York. He'd died a multi-millionaire from the combined sale of the diners the year the twins were born. My mother had inherited his estate, and we—the twins and I—had subsequently inherited some of that fortune following her tragic death two years later. Although my father was the main benefactor, a substantial amount had been held in trust until each of us had turned twenty-one.

Adam couldn't have been more different to his twin. Although they were almost identical to look at—broad shoulders with dark hair and green eyes—Adam was driven, with hopes, aspirations, and ideals of his own. An intrinsically reticent character, he had a propensity to keep to himself. The restaurant was his vocation, and for the time being, the only love in his life, and was aptly named. Adam had his Eden; his Eve would arrive soon enough.

Aaron, on the other hand, was more the extrovert. An A1 attention seeker and an A1 asshole. He didn't have a passion for anything other than spending his inheritance—usually on hard liquor and bimbos with dollar signs in their eyes. Instead of chasing dreams of his own, he'd tagged along in my father's footsteps by studying psychiatry at Columbia. Once he'd completed his residency training program, he would be granted board certification and automatically become partner in my father's private practice. The plate he'd been handed was undoubtedly gold-plated.

Even from across the room, I could feel the scorching heat of Jia's disgruntled glare, her rebuke unspoken, but no less devastating because of it. She had an uncanny knack of calling you out without so much as a word—just one piercing look of her daggers-drawn eyes would have most grown men peeing in their pants. She sat at a table with her girlfriend Charley on one side, a vacant seat—presumably for me—on the other, and her friends Kate and Laura, plus one more empty space opposite.

All but Jia smiled warmly as we approached. Jean-Paul hadn't met anyone other than Jia, so I introduced him to the others and motioned him to the empty chair beside Kate, grateful for the distance it would create between us. Jean-Paul hesitated before taking the seat, which seemed to delight Kate, who batted a thick layer of falsies in his direction.

Jia's eyes narrowed accusingly. "You're late, bitch."

Coming from Jia, *bitch* was a term of endearment and always expressed with a degree of affection.

"Sorry, my friend. I lost track of time. It has nothing to do with him," I added, mindful of the accusatory glare she shot in Jean-Paul's direction. "I just found him on the doorstep, like a stray cat soliciting a saucer of milk."

"Again?" She pulled a face of disgust. "The randy old tom."

"Happy birthday." I hugged her and she relaxed, flashing me a face-splitting grin. I was forgiven.

"I ordered for you both. You lost the right to choose for yourself thirty minutes ago," she declared triumphantly.

"Perfect, I trust you implicitly." And I did.

Jia Huang was probably the only person I trusted, or who came close to knowing me at all. As much as anyone could, she seemed to understand me, or at least respected me enough not to judge. She was my closest friend. We'd clicked the moment we met, almost seven years ago. To say I was in a pretty bad place at the time would be something of an understatement. Anxious, uncertain, withdrawn, and pretty fucked-up would be nearer to the truth. I'd moved into the city from my father's house in Brooklyn, and Jia had taken me under her wing—which when comparing her petite stature of five foot two to my tall one of five foot seven was quite comical to picture.

Jia was a classic Asian beauty. A Chinese American whose fiery personality was poles apart from her seemingly cute and delicate appearance and had caused many to fall prey to their erroneous first impressions. Some of those casualties would, at best, describe her as cold and intimidating, but many would go as far as hostile and positively ruthless. To me she was a pocket-rocket—my weapon of choice—and if I could choose anyone to be in my corner, it would definitely be her. She had a black belt in martial arts and a tongue to match. My advice? Don't judge a book.

Settling in my seat, I poured myself a glass of champagne from the bottle chilling in the ice bucket beside me. I took a sip, savoring the pleasant popping sensation of the exploding bubbles on my tongue, before permitting it to slide slowly down my throat, leaving a crisp, refreshing tang on my lips and a warm, fizzling effervescence in the pit of my stomach.

I think I felt him before I saw him—an inexplicable prickle of awareness tugging at my senses, causing me to scan the room to reveal the source. He was seated at a table opposite with one male companion and appeared to ignite the space around him with a surge of electrically-charged magnetism that was so intense I was baffled as to how I'd missed it.

One glance saw that he was supremely graceful, inherently powerful, and physically the most striking man I had ever seen. Impossibly beautiful. His perfectly sculpted face was accentuated with angular cheekbones, a strong masculine jaw line, perfectly straight nose, and full lips. His sexy tousled hair was dark blond with shades of gold and caramel reflecting warmly in the light, hair that was begging to be tugged and pulled. And his hypnotic eyes—a striking cornflower blue—bored into my soul from across the room.

He was watching me—no, assessing me—an unfathomable expression settling on his face, and I found myself desperately attempting to read it. My initial thought was we'd met somewhere before, maybe in challenging circumstances, and he was trying to place me. It would account for the trace of troubled perplexity, which appeared to cloud his expression. Quickly, I realized that couldn't possibly be, because I was sure if I'd laid eyes on that face before I would know; that exquisite face would be firmly etched in my mind forever.

Suddenly his expression softened, his vivid blue eyes narrowing sensuously to reveal a look of mystified wonder. He appeared cool and relaxed, making no attempt whatsoever to conceal his brazen and overt fascination with me.

My cheeks heated as I felt suddenly self-conscious and exposed under his steady scrutiny. Unable to hold his unceasing gaze any longer, I averted my eyes, refocusing on the stem of the fluted glass I held in my hand. I took a moment to compose myself, nodding at something Charley was saying. When I was ready, I allowed my gaze to flicker tentatively back to the face of the alluring stranger, who I was certain, by now, would have diverted his attention elsewhere.

I couldn't have been more wrong.

As our eyes locked once again, a nameless, but sexy-as-sin expression sizzled across his face, a flutter of amusement tugging at the edge of his lips. The tiniest, virtually imperceptible flicker of his eyebrow prompted his focus to dip to where my hand supported my glass, drawing my attention with it to discover what had tempted his eyes away from mine. My finger and thumb were lightly tracing the length of the long stem of my glass with slow, continuous strokes, up and down, and I immediately realized, albeit inadvertent, how sexual and highly suggestive the action was.

My cheeks heated again, and I released the glass, my hand fluttering to shield my face, as it often did when I was embarrassed. Fidgeting in my seat, I took a momentary interest in the conversation at the table before I dared to glimpse again, this time more furtively through the gaps of my splayed fingers. His eyes appeared to narrow, a transitory twitch of his brow conveying some unreadable emotion that was gone all too soon.

Damn this! I couldn't take cover behind my hand all night. I took a bolstering breath and came out from hiding, lifting the glass to my lips and taking a slow, sensual sip. I tried to fight the urge to look, but the intensity of his gaze was so enticing it seemed to lure me to him like magic—as though somehow we were bound by an undetectable wire yanking at my awareness. It was futile. Within seconds my eyes had betrayed me, connecting once again with his, and the invisible magnetic force crackled in the air between us. The stranger licked his lower lip as a slow, sexy hint of a smile settled onto his sensual lips. The action was so intoxicating I almost forgot to breathe.

Holy shit, if I was reading this right, the sexiest man alive was freaking hitting on me. Me!

Suddenly, his dinner companion seemed to drag him from his transfixed stupor, and his attention was momentarily drawn back to his conversation and a document they were perusing. I guessed it was some sort of business dinner, as their interaction presented as rather formal and professional.

In fact, it didn't take a trained observer to notice how effortlessly the stranger seemed to exude success, his power and authority practically flowing from his pores as though it were a near palpable thing. It clung to him like the impeccably suave and outrageously expensive black suit adorning his perfectly sculpted and athletically lean body. The entire package was mind-numbingly alluring.

At some unseen stage, my appetizer had arrived—a goat cheese soufflé with apple and walnut salad. It was delicious, but my appetite had vanished along with my capacity to string words together to form a sentence. Mercifully, the chatter seemed to be flowing freely around the table and Jean-Paul was happily engaged in what appeared to be flirtatious banter with Kate. My inattentiveness appeared to have gone undetected. Or so I'd hoped.

"Do you know him?" Jia asked, yanking me from my magical, bewitching exchange.

"Who?" I feigned ignorance and nibbled at my salad.

"Don't fuck with me, bitch. The Adonis, that's who. Shit, men are off the menu for me for the time being, but I, along with every other chick in this place, spotted him the second he arrived. With a face like that, he's pretty hard to miss."

Jia's sexual preference was as interchangeable as her favorite shoe designers. Like me, sex with no strings was usually the way she rolled—most found her too intimidating for anything more—but Charley seemed besotted with her, and before Jia even realized, she'd had fallen into a relationship with her. How long it would last, was anybody's guess.

"Yeah, okay, you got me," I conceded "He *is* kind of hard to ignore, and no, I don't know him. He's looking at me kind of funny though."

"Damn straight he is. Take a look around you, bitch. You've got every girl in here wondering what you have that they don't. Not that it's hard to figure."

"What? Why?" I scanned the room swiftly.

"Are you shittin' me?" She gaped at me open-mouthed and shook her head. "The second you walked in, the guy died and went to Heaven, bitch. He's gonna need some help to scrape his eyes up off the floor and pop the little beauties back in his goddamn, picture-perfect face."

A rush of unexpected excitement plowed through me—I hadn't misinterpreted the way he'd looked at me. It was a humble and surprising realization. I gathered my nerve to look again, discreetly peeking through my lashes, face angled down, and my hand flittering to my mouth to stroke my lower lip with my index finger—a vain attempt to mask my intrigue.

My gaze collided with his instantly. Intense and unmoving, it seemed I was the sole object of his attention, almost as if I were under a spotlight and as though the rest of the world had unobtrusively expired, He was the sole object of mine, both of us motionless, frozen in time.

There was certainly no ambiguity in his expression now; it was as plain and simple to read as the menu on the table. My insides heated and melted like chocolate as I observed a smoldering look sweep over his face. It was a look of pure want and raw desire, a yearning to covet me. Jia had been right. This hot-as-hell stranger wanted a piece of my ass. He was hot for me—and me for him. Christ, I was more than hot, I was on fucking fire.

All feelings of unease and inhibitions faded away, disappearing along with the empty appetizer plates. I felt powerless to break the connection, unable to tear my eyes away from his, as though somehow he'd cast his spell and bewitched me completely. The flesh between my thighs was suddenly slick with moisture—just the way he surveyed me was turning me on—and I began to squirm in my seat. I thought I saw the flickering of amusement at the corner of his mouth about to betray him, but it departed swiftly before I could be certain. His obscenely sexy mouth opened slightly, his tongue running delicately and subtly across his lips.

My heart thumped with rapid-fire, staccato beats against my chest as a main course of fillet steak was placed in front me. With knife and fork in hand, I began to pick absently at the food. Somehow I managed to nod and make the right noises at the appropriate times, answering yes and no in some semblance of communication with my friends, but my gaze barely left the face of the mysterious stranger across the room.

All I could think of was getting this man alone. Lewd images ran through my mind of me ripping the lavish clothes from his immaculately-toned body and having mind-blowing fuckery for as many hours as I could possibly muster before my heart gave way. The flesh at the apex of my thighs quivered in response to my amatory musings, and as I shifted uncomfortably, I became aware of my positively sodden panties.

Ridiculously aroused now, I watched as his fingers fluttered fluidly to his mouth, his thumb grazing over his lips. *God, those lips.* I hungered for a taste of him, to feel those fingers on my heated skin, on the flesh that was pulsing at the mere concept of them being there, stroking and delving.

Christ, I needed to calm down! I took a deep, steadying breath. My pulse rate had elevated to dizzying heights, and I was sure if I didn't get some release soon, I would either orgasm on the spot or spontaneously combust. I couldn't ever remember feeling so hot and needy. I squeezed my thighs together in a vain attempt to soothe the relentless throbbing.

Totally ineffective.

With no warning to my brain, my body suddenly stood, and excusing myself from the table, I began to walk in a trancelike state toward the stairs leading to the restrooms. It was as if someone else were controlling my movements—a helpless puppet functioning completely on impulse, without premeditation or rational thought. The stranger's gaze never strayed from mine, and as I passed, he pushed gracefully to his feet, mumbled something to his companion, and fell into step some distance behind me.

Deliberately slowly, I began to climb the stairs, lingering at the top to glimpse idly over my shoulder in time to see the stranger begin the ascent in pursuit. He moved with fluid poise, commanding attention from every angle of the room, but it may just as well have been empty. The stranger saw no one but me, and the realization sent a sharp stab of desire straight to my groin. I walked on, passing the entrance to a small, private function room and the restrooms, down the corridor and to the corner. There, I climbed a small flight of four steps leading to a short corridor, which I knew accommodated storage rooms, a laundry room, and an office.

I didn't stop to ensure the stranger was following me. I didn't need to. I could sense him with every nerve ending in my body. The sexual energy crackling between us was frenetic and damn near tangible.

As I reached the door to a small storage room I paused briefly, giving him time to draw nearer. When he was behind me, I pushed the door open, flicked the light switch to the side, and entered into a room heavy with the scent of fresh, clean linen. Tablecloths, napkins, towels, and various other freshly laundered items lined the wooden shelves bracketed to the walls and ran the perimeter of the room.

Taking a couple of cautious steps forward, I sensed him enter behind me, my chest rising and falling heavily in shortened gasps as I turned to look into the eyes of the sexiest man I'd ever laid eyes on. The striking oceans of blue were now dark like bullets, heavy with longing and lust. The scent of him—a sort of woody, spicy, almost leathery scent—filled the space around me, permeating my senses to sensual overload. The pulsing ache between my thighs gave me cause to wonder whether I might just go off at the mere proximity of him.

I nodded toward the door, silently instructing him to close it, and he responded instantly. The florescent light above us flickered uncertainly, as if the force of our attraction was somehow generating electrical interference. My heart hammered against my chest, blood pounding in my ears as a sudden surge of adrenaline pumped through my body violently. All thoughts of my safety, morality, and virtue had fled. I mean, I was no angel, but what I was about to do was way beyond sinful.

Suddenly, his mouth opened to speak. "I—"

I stepped forward into his space, dropping my purse, and swiftly placed my finger to his lips. "Shh," I whispered, shaking my head.

Then, in one fluid movement we connected, our mouths clamping together, tongues invading, dipping in and out as we tasted each other with unfathomable hunger. I reached up, fisting my hands into his hair, drawing him in closer still, as my senses devoured his scent.

Up close it was even more divine, the fragrance now more definitive: a subtle but expensive cologne mixed with his own clean, personal odor that simply oozed masculinity.

He guided me backwards and suddenly, I felt the shelves behind me, my foot reaching up to find a foothold for support. The action caused my legs to part, and he promptly took advantage, pushing back my thigh and entering the space between my legs, pressing his eager erection up against me. I felt the bulging throb of his cock through fabric rubbing against my already soaking sex, spurring me on as my arms reached out to both sides and up to gain a secure grip of the shelf.

His mouth continued to claim me, licking and tasting like a hungry animal, his hands moving to my blouse to begin unbuttoning, his dexterous fingers working furiously fast. Suddenly he broke the kiss, the lust in his eyes burning through my skin as they glided over my heaving, lace covered breasts. Reaching up, he yanked at the cup of my bra, a gasp of appreciation hissing through his lips as he perused the heavy swell of pink, jutting nipple. Using his finger and thumb, he began to roll over the pebbled pearl, tugging and pulling as his sumptuous mouth began a torturous nibbling and licking down my throat and neck until he reached my breast. Closing his mouth over my eager flesh, he sucked at the taut peak of my nipple, his tongue lapping and flicking as I threw my head back, gasping with the intense, soaring pleasure.

My subconscious yelled at me, implored me to stop, to see sense—I didn't know this man—but for some reason I felt at odds with that concept, as if something deep inside was telling me I needed this, needed him, and if I didn't take him, I'd regret it. As much as my head was telling me to fasten my goddamn shirt and get the hell out of there, I couldn't, because… it just felt right. And besides, I'd come way too far to turn back now, my body would never forgive me.

The stranger's hand dipped to the hem of my skirt and underneath to begin a sensuous ascent up and over my thighs, his fingers brushing over my panties drenched from readiness. He gasped in stunned appreciation and broke the kiss abruptly, pausing to look deep into my eyes. The lust in his was as riotous as that of a violent storm, the extent of his arousal as unequivocal as the difference between night and day. His gaze was awash with anticipation as it burned into mine, as if preparing for my reaction when he slid a finger under the fine lace to my slickness. This man I didn't know was making contact with the most intimate part of my body for the first time. My breathing stuttered and my body sang out and shunted forward, pressing my needy sex into his hand. He closed his eyes for a brief second, a low groan escaping his throat. I hadn't disappointed.

Gently, he slid a finger deep inside, and my trembling lips parted in unashamed pleasure as I attempted to control my breathing. As if the action had drawn his attention back to them, he claimed my already bruised lips, his tongue eagerly parting them to invade my mouth. He kissed me with his eyes open this time, his finger sliding inside me with ease, back and forth, in and out, rubbing my juices all over my sex and watching me with those perfect eyes, as if it was an essential requirement to observe how I responded.

Jesus Christ, his curiosity was so damn arousing. This absurdly handsome stranger seemed determined to know me intimately, without knowing me at all, and I seemed destined to let him. The muscles of my quivering sex clenched involuntarily around his eager finger as I began to move against him, the need to have him inside me becoming impossible to manage.

Out of my head with arousal, and unable to wait any longer, I reached down to where his gigantic erection strained for release against the luxurious fabric of his pants. Quickly, I began to unfasten them, popping the button and releasing the zipper to reach inside and free his throbbing cock. It fell impressively into the palm of my hand, taut and swollen and twitching with eagerness. Clasping him at the base, I squeezed the firm, aching mass into my fist. Taking my other hand, I ran my thumb over the pulsing crown until a sudden gush of hot pre-cum burst through the slit of the pounding head. A feral groan grated from his throat as I rubbed the fluid around the head and down the shaft. An overwhelming need to taste him had me bringing my thumb up to my mouth and sucking greedily.

Our eyes never strayed from each other's as he continued to slide his finger inside me, first one then two, pushing and thrusting harder and deeper, as he palmed my clitoris, rubbing and massaging as I shamelessly ground against him.

Waves of heat cascaded over me, the assault on my senses driving me closer to what was certain to be the most explosive orgasm I'd ever experienced. I could feel myself getting closer. He reached inside his jacket and retrieved a foil wrapper, ripping it open with his teeth and taking out the condom before rolling it down over his considerable length.

Grabbing both my wrists, he turned them so my hands could grip the shelves at either side of us, bracing me. Then running his hands down over my breasts, my thighs, and under my skirt, he slid them around and under my behind, lifting me. I wrapped my legs around his waist, the folded linen cushioning me from behind. His vivid blue eyes grew darker, his lips blood red with arousal, as he guided his slippery head toward my entrance.

I could feel his pulsing cock nudging against my clit at my slick opening, and his eyes were suddenly alight with warning and something else. An urgent question. He was silently seeking my permission. Without the slightest hesitation, I nodded my assent and suddenly he was sinking into me. I cried out with sheer pleasure as the full length of him pushed right into my aching core, filling and stretching me. The look in his eyes reflected the relief I felt at finally having this contact, as if the wait had somehow been eternal. He started to move, really move, rotating his hips and grinding into me, harsh, raw sounds from within coming with every punishing thrust. I moved with him, picking up the rhythm, accepting his length easily now. Our breathing increased with raspy, jerky gasps as the muscles in my entire body clenched and stiffened, preparing my body for climax.

He drove into me, deeper and harder, fucking me until we were both panting and groaning like wild, uncontrolled animals, and I could hold on no longer. My orgasm ripped through my body like a bolt of lightning striking at the very depths of my core and branching out to every hypersensitive nerve ending. My sex pulsed and quivered around his cock, the aftershocks and trembling vibrations of my climax bringing him with me, gasping and convulsing as he emptied himself inside me. We stifled each other's cries of release and pleasure with our mouths, licking and lapping as we rode out our combined ecstasy.

Finally, when it was over, we stilled, calming our ragged breathing as we came down from the high of our orgasms, and without breaking eye contact, he pulled out of me gently, leaving me to stand and regain my balance.

Abruptly, the spell seemed to break and the world crashed back down around us, reality rushing back into focus with stark, disbelieving clarity. The eye contact that had seemed like a constant necessity throughout our entire encounter suddenly disengaged as we busied ourselves rearranging clothes and fastening buttons. Swiftly, he removed the condom and after tying a knot at the end, placed it into his pocket and fastened his pants.

The silence was broken by the sound of a phone vibrating, and he reached inside his jacket to retrieve it, raising it to his ear to answer. Suddenly, my dignity was in tatters around me, my composure crumbling along with my morals, and I bolted for the door, scooping up my discarded purse as I scrambled for the door handle. I ran along the corridor, down the stairs and through the crowded bar, making my way toward the exit and the safety of the street. Just as I reached the door and pushed it open, I felt a sharp tug on my arm. I turned to find Jia glaring at me with dark, accusing eyes.

"Where have you been?" she said, following me outside.

"What?" I feigned innocence as I tried to catch my breath.

"You heard, bitch. Where have you been?"

"The bathroom, like I said."

"I followed you to the bathroom. You weren't there. So what, you've taken to throwing up in store cupboards now?"

"I wasn't throwing up," I laughed mirthlessly, desperately scouring the street for an empty cab. Spotting one, I signaled to him, the relief hitting me hard when he pulled in front of the flashy Executive SUV already parked at the curb.

"Your brother's restaurant is too fucking expensive to binge and purge, Angel, so where were you?"

"I did not throw up, Jia. Stop fussing." I winced at her accusation, the suggestion that I'd yielded to an old coping mechanism stung like a slap to the face. Besides, no-strings sex was the method I used to relieve the ache and fill the void these days. It was more fun and better for my curves, but even I had to admit that sex with a stranger in a storage room might just be taking the no-strings ethos a tad too far.

"Okay, ease up on the gas, bitch. I just saw Aaron the asshole at the bar earlier and—"

I glanced over Jia's shoulder, the sight of the stranger at the bottom of the stairs eclipsing the remainder of her sentence. His breathtaking features were clouded with concern as he talked into his phone, ducking and weaving as he tried to get a clear view of the table where Jean-Paul, Kate, and Laura were presumably still sitting. Holy shit, he was trying to find me. I needed to leave and quickly.

Jia followed my gaze, confusion fusing with shock-horror sliding onto her flawless face as she spotted him. Her eyes slid down the length of me—up and down—as she assessed my slightly disordered and crumpled state.

"Oh my fucking God, you didn't? What am I saying? Of course you did, you have an FFG to rival any I've ever seen," she said loudly, pointing out my blatant freshly-fucked-glow.

"What?" I said with palms up and the most innocent look I could muster plastered on my face. "A girl's gotta eat, friend!"

"Yeah, this I know, but it's customary to stick to the items on the menu."

We laughed simultaneously, my smile quickly fading as I glimpsed the stranger heading for the door.

"I take it you don't want to stick around for dessert, then?" she asked, eyeing my panic stricken face. Without waiting for an answer, she reached out and opened the cab door, urging me inside. "Go, get out of here. I'll make your excuses to the others, don't worry."

"Thank you, friend, I owe you. Make sure to divvy the tab and I'll sort it tomorrow, oh, and…" I nodded toward the approaching stranger "…you haven't seen me, right?"

She cocked her head to the side and raised an eyebrow. "You definitely owe me, bitch."

"This *I* know." I blew her a kiss. "Happy birthday, friend." I closed the door and the cab pulled out into the traffic.

Swiveling in my seat, I gazed out of the rear window just in time to see the stranger running out into the street, his arm raised in a wave, his lips moving like he was shouting something after me. Jia turned and feigning ignorance, ducked back inside the restaurant without a word.

Turning to face forwards, I settled into my seat. *What the hell had just happened? What in the hell had I just done?* Scorching hot, fuckety-fuckery with a complete stranger in a storage room, and neither one of us had even spoken. Not a single word.

My body flushed from head to toe as the reality of what I'd done settled into my conscience. I smoothed my hands down the length of my skirt, as though that would somehow alleviate my sense of disgrace. What kind of girl did something like that? What would he think of me? Hell, where was my self-respect, and when did I stop caring about my own safety? The guy could have been a psychopath. My actions were wicked—sinful.

As I sat questioning my sanity, berating myself for my lewd, self-indulgent behavior and waiting for the sense of shame to engulf me entirely, I found myself distracted by a sentiment far more potent. Beyond that shame was a warm, fuzzy glow I felt powerless to ignore. The thrilling shiver of excitement still burned within my core, the smoldering remnants of lust and desire like none I'd experienced before. I could sense the sparkle in my eyes and the corners of my mouth curling as the beginnings of a smile spread slowly across my swollen, tingling lips.

CHAPTER TWO

T he next morning I awoke with the same smile etched on my face as I'd fallen asleep with—smug but bashful. Almost, but not entirely blushing, I slowly recalled the details of my encounter with the stranger. Turning to lie on my back, I stretched and ran my fingertips down my body, over the swell of my breasts and the flat of my stomach, gingerly placing my hand between my legs to clasp my sex. The slight tenderness I felt was enough to verify the unquestionable realness of the previous night's events. It hadn't been a dream.

It had been the most sexually erotic experience of my life, an experience most people wouldn't even dare to conjure in a fantasy. Sex with a complete stranger, who'd beguiled me so completely that he'd conveyed his most sexual desires from right across the room, almost hypnotically. No words. No touch. Just pure, unmitigated, visual seduction.

As electrifying as it had been, I knew it was an experience I would not dare repeat. I had momentarily lost control, both physically and rationally. And that was something Angelica Lawson could not afford to do.

A smile spread across my face as I resolved that my decision to bolt the night before had been the right one. I had no idea who the stranger was, and that was the way I preferred it. It was more of a thrill if it remained a mystery. Hell, I could survive on solo-performance orgasms with just the memory alone. If I never saw him again—and I was confident I wouldn't—there would be no need for awkwardness or shame. I could just revel in the memory.

With that settled, I jumped out of bed and made a beeline for the kitchen to put on coffee. My open-plan, loft-like apartment was my pride and joy. Its southern exposure provided an abundance of light through huge windows and glass paneled doors, which led to a private terrace. It was a sun-drenched haven and the reason I fell in love with the place.

My bare feet padded across the dark walnut floors to the glass coffee table in the middle of the lounge where a huge glass bowl took pride of place.

"Good morning, Ponyo. And how are you this morning? Hungry, I expect."

Ponyo was my goldfish and the only animate being I would allow to share my personal living space. Roommates were only good for some people and I wasn't one of them. Jia had given her to me as a present two years earlier, and I'd named her after the character from one of my favorite Japanese animation films about a little girl who had turned into a fish.

Ponyo shimmied past excitedly, nuzzling up to my fingertip as I pressed it to the glass. No, I wasn't deluded. I was fully aware she was simply searching for food but took comfort in interpreting it as personal affection. I pinched a finger full of food and tossed it into the top of the bowl, smiling as she rushed to the surface to catch it.

After turning on the coffee machine, I made my way into the large limestone bathroom with its deep, egg-shaped soaking tub and huge walk in shower. I loaded my toothbrush and began to brush as I studied my reflection in the mirror.

It was gone.

My heart skidded to a dramatic halt, missing a beat as I stared at my bare neck where my diamond pendant should have been. I'd definitely worn it the night before. My hands flew to my chest and into my hair, furiously combing it through with my fingers, thinking maybe it had become tangled in my sleep. Abandoning my toothbrush, I raced back to the bedroom, yanking open the drawer to find the velvet box where I usually stored it, in hope that I'd put it away last night and just forgotten. *Please let it be here. Please, please, please.* The box was despairingly empty. Turning, I began to tear the sheets from the bed, rummaging through the comforter and pillows frantically. Nothing.

I stopped, froze, and drew in a deep breath. *And breathe.* Willing myself to calm down, I pressed my fingertips to my temple, trying to clear my head so that I could mentally retrace my steps. Then I sank to the floor on my hands and knees and began to crawl through the apartment, my eyes scanning every inch of its surface area, every space or gap it may possibly have fallen into. I checked surfaces, my purse, the clothes I'd worn the night before, even the passage between my front door and the elevator.

But it was hopeless. It was gone.

In utter despair, I sauntered aimlessly back to my room and perched on the edge of my bed. I picked up the velvet box from the floor at my feet and opened it. My fingers traced the sunken hollow where the weight and shape of the pendant had left an indentation in the pale blue, silk fabric. Burning tears filled my eyes, brimming over to trickle down my cheeks and splashing into the empty box, as my throat constricted to form a hard, painful lump.

The pendant had belonged to my mother, a gift from my grandparents on her eighteenth birthday. It was a beautiful heart-shaped locket, handcrafted in lustrous white gold and detailed with an abundance of small round-cut diamonds. I knew it weighed around 4.6 carats, and to someone else was worth around six, maybe seven thousand dollars. To me it was priceless—completely irreplaceable. It was the only keepsake I had to remember her by; there was nothing else, not even one solitary photograph.

My father had destroyed everything that reminded him of her the day she was killed in a tragic accident when I was just six years old.

On the morning of the day she'd died, I'd taken the pendant from its velvet box where my mom had kept it on a dresser in her room. I'd wanted her to wear it, but she'd said it was way too precious for everyday wear and was just for special occasions. So I'd squirreled it away, hiding it under my pillow until later when I could hold it up to the moonlight to watch it sparkle. I'd loved the way the light had reflected off the diamonds to create a mirage of twinkling images and shapes that danced around the room. I would imagine they were fairies fluttering their wings as they flew, soaring and twirling around the room, and scattering their fairy dust to turn everything into treasure.

I'd intended to put it back the next morning, but my mom hadn't returned home that day—or any day after that. So I'd kept it, tucking it away in a special hiding place with the hope that my father would never find it. If he had, he would have taken it from me, of that I had no doubt. And so every night, before I went to sleep, I would hold it up to sparkle in the moonlight and picture my mom dancing and laughing with the fairies.

After a while, without photographs to remind me, memories of my mom had faded, and the magical fairy-tale imagery faded with her. When I could no longer recall her face or her voice, I'd put the pendant away in its box beneath the floor of my closet, believing that the memories would return if I hid it away to rekindle its magic.

A childish fantasy.

It was only recently that I'd begun to wear it, just on the odd occasion. It had made me feel, in some way, connected to her again, made me feel special. And now it was gone.

I swiped at my tears angrily. Why hadn't I removed it before I got into bed as I usually did? The only reason I could possibly have overlooked it was if I wasn't wearing it. I hadn't thought to remove it because it was already gone.

In my mind I retraced my steps, vowing to search every inch of everywhere I'd stepped foot—my office, the gallery, the street, Eden— but my bet was that I'd lost it in the storage room in the midst of my sinful romp.

Checking my watch, I realized that it was already eight-thirty. I couldn't afford to wait until Eden's lunchtime rush on the off chance someone else found it, but I needed to wait until the staff were busy to avoid unwanted questions. Having to explain to someone why my pendant ended up tangled in the linen of a storage room would prove to be tricky, and not something I relished doing.

Carefully, I put the empty box away, and after showering and dressing in record time was out in the humid hustle and bustle of Manhattan by nine. I hurried down my tree-lined street and onto 7th Avenue to join the hordes of people already time pressured and rushing to reach their destinations. Office workers, street sellers, food vendors, and tourists alike, all absorbed in their own lives, but with the same objectives in mind: to dodge the crowds, the cars, and sea of yellow taxis to get to the place they needed to be.

Evoke Gallery was located only a few blocks away from my apartment in the Chelsea area of Manhattan, so it wasn't too long before I was able to leave the frenzy behind.

The front door was locked—unless by private appointment, the gallery didn't open to the public until midday—so I pumped my password into the security panel outside and pushed open the double glass doors. The front desk was empty. Alice, my receptionist, wouldn't arrive for at least a couple of hours yet, but the rich aroma of coffee drifting down the passage to the foyer told me Jia had already arrived.

It was Jia who'd encouraged me to take my love of photography more seriously. Nobody understood the value of capturing a moment within an image more than me. Sometimes a photograph could be the only link you had to a part of your past, the only thing to shape your memories and keep them alive. So from the moment I could afford my first camera, photography had become something of an obsession. Jia had convinced me I had a talent for it, and it turned out she was right.

A passionate hobby had turned into a promising career and eventually, using some of the money from my inheritance, I'd opened my own gallery. Jia had agreed to take on the role of curator and gallery manager. She was in her element and had played a huge part in making the gallery a massive success.

Jia possessed a discerning eye for photography. Although she wasn't a photographer herself, she had an innate ability to identify with our clients' needs, enabling us to offer a service which helped new and established collectors procure the images which best reflected their requirements.

Evoke was a small gallery, in comparison to the vast majority of others scattered in and around Chelsea, and showcased contemporary photography by emerging and mid-career artists. With Jia on board to manage running the gallery, attending to exhibitions, collection development, and so forth, it allowed me to devote my time to my own work.

My zest was for street photography, primarily in New York, but it had taken me to various parts of the country. I showcased my work frequently was a regular contributor to *The New Yorker* and *New York Times Magazine,* and on several occasions had worked voluntarily for a charity, documenting projects in Zambia.

I followed the smell of coffee through the glistening white foyer and down the hallway to the kitchen where Jia was already pouring me a cup.

"What's up with your face, bitch?" she said, observing my sullenness. "Last time I saw you, you looked like the cat that got the fucking cream. What happened? You decide it wasn't cream?" Her playful manner changed swiftly when she saw my bottom lip begin to tremble, her expression morphing to one of quiet concern. "What is it?"

As tears threatened again, I struggled to squeeze my response past the resurfacing lump in my throat. "I lost my pendant."

She arched a brow. "Bitch, please. Shit is going down all over the freaking world and you're having a meltdown because you misplaced a necklace?" Shaking her head in disgust, she strode off out of the kitchen and across the hall into the office to take a seat at her desk.

I picked up my mug of coffee and followed her out of the room, pausing to perch on the edge of her desk. "My mom's pendant."

"Oh. Shit, that's worth a fucking fortune." She placed a hand on my arm as she realized the precise significance of her words. "Do you know—?"

"Jia, really? You're actually going to ask me if I know where I lost it?"

She held her hands out, palms up, and shrugged helplessly.

"Well, actually," I conceded, "if I had to guess, Eden would probably be a safe bet. It may have come loose in the storage room when I… you know…"

Her eyes widened in utter dismay. "You fucked in a storage room?"

"I thought you'd figured that much already."

"Um, well, yeah. Stupid me. Like people fucking in restaurant storage rooms is a regular thing, right?"

"Okay, Jia, give it a rest," I pleaded. "I feel bad enough already without the promiscuity lecture."

She held her hands up again, this time in a fine-I'll-back-off-then gesture. The truth was I felt completely at odds with myself. My mood was all out of sync. One minute I was absorbed in the thrill of the warm, lingering buzz of my encounter with the mysterious stranger, and the next I was overwhelmed by the contradicting anguish of losing my mom's pendant.

"I need to go to Eden to look for it. Trouble is, I'm having a hard time coming up with a credible explanation if I'm caught rummaging around on my hands and knees in the storage room."

"You worry about this now? And what if you'd been caught in there last night? Tell me, what excuse did you have in mind as to why a complete stranger was bending you over the napkins, pounding your pert, pink ass?" She was pointing and wobbling her shoulders the way she did when she took the moral high ground.

I narrowed my eyes and shot her a caustic look.

"Just sayin', Angel. I mean, if you'd have crossed your legs for a couple of hours and waited until you at least got back to his place, all you would have to do is give the guy a call and say, 'Hey, it's me, can I come get my diamonds,' but no. This is what comes of a commitment-phobic quickie. I bet you didn't even take your panties off, did you?" She glared at me, hands on hips, waiting for me to verify her accusation. When I just shrugged, saying nothing, she shook her head. "I just hope it was worth it, that's all."

"No! Of course it wasn't," I spat. "I wouldn't trade that pendant for anything. It was all I had."

"I know this. Shit, I'm sorry," she said, cursing herself. "I am trying my best to be sympathetic, Angel."

"Really? That's sympathy?"

It was Jia's turn to shrug. "So I'm guessing the closet fuck wasn't all that great?"

I glared at her, but the corner of my mouth twitched. "Well, actually, it was the best sex I've ever had. Jeez, that guy was so hot my bits are still buzzing, and I'm not even joking."

"Get out!" she gushed, suddenly becoming interested. "Way to go, bitch. It's not like you to get high on sex."

"Ordinarily no. Since James, it's barely scratched the itch," I said, remembering my ex for a brief moment. "But this guy was something else. I can't explain it, but it was like I was drawn to him. Like I'd been put under some sort of spell and had no control over what I was doing. I just had to have him. It was the most surreal, yet erotic experience I've ever had."

Jia was smirking at me now. "I think I know what you mean, honey. When you fuck, you want to stay fucked, right?"

I grimaced at her choice of words, but said, "I suppose so, yeah."

"So, tell me about him. Who is he and where the hell did he come from?"

Head bowed in contrition and doing my best to avoid eye contact, I went to sit at my own desk.

"You don't know, do you? You didn't even ask the guy his freaking name?" She glared at me, astounded. "Jesus, Angel, what the hell?"

As if perfectly timed, the intercom buzzed at the front door, providing me with a moments reprieve from Jia's wrath.

She held up a single finger in warning that she hadn't finished with me and moved down the hall into the foyer to the front door. After a few seconds and some mumbling, she returned, hidden behind the largest bouquet of flowers I had ever seen. She set them down on my desk, and before I could reach out for the envelope, she'd seized it, ripped it open, and began to read.

"Well, that answers that question," she declared with a smug grin. "Your closet fuck goes by the name of Ethan Wilde."

Oh my God. How in the hell had he found me?

I snatched the card from her grasp in horror. "Stop with the closet fuck shit. It was a room—a storage room—but a room, nonetheless."

Jia shrugged. "What-evs."

I turned away to read the card.

Dear Miss Lawson,

Please accept my heartfelt apologies for neglecting to introduce myself last night—I'm afraid I was somewhat distracted.

I would dearly love the opportunity to make amends for my ill manners.
Dinner, perhaps?

In anticipation,
Ethan Wilde

Flushing, I looked up at Jia, who was now sporting a shit-eating grin. "How the hell does he know my name, or where to find me?"

She shrugged.

The office telephone began to ring and Jia picked up. "Evoke Gallery, Jia speaking."

I went back to studying the card. Ethan Wilde. Yes, it suited him. A sexy name for an incredibly sexy and wildly passionate man, if last night was anything to go by. And a very courteous, incredibly sexy man, if the card was anything to go by.

Jia grabbed my attention by poking me in the ribs, the combination of amusement and shock on her face telling me in no uncertain terms who the caller was.

"Yes, Mr. Wilde, I can confirm that a bouquet of flowers has arrived for Miss Lawson, and I will personally make sure she gets them ... Is she available to speak to?"

In horror, I shot up from my chair, shaking my head frantically, the mere thought of speaking to him sending my pulse rate hurtling through the roof.

"No, Mr. Wilde, I'm afraid she's otherwise engaged at the moment. Is there a message? Thank you, Mr. Wilde, I'll be sure to pass that on. Goodbye." She returned the phone to its cradle and stared at me in amazement.

"Well?" I gasped impatiently, releasing the breath I'd been holding.

"Oh. My. God. The guy has got the sexiest freaking accent. Why didn't you tell me he was English?"

"English?" It was my turn to stare, wide-eyed and mouth gaping. "He's English?"

"You're telling me you didn't notice? How could you not notice? What the fuck, Angel?"

Sitting down to absorb the information, I found myself desperately wishing I'd have listened to the conversation. God, I loved an English accent. "We didn't exactly spend much time chatting." An understatement if ever I'd heard one.

"Angel, you wouldn't need to. Hello would have been enough to pick up on that silky-as-fuck accent." She paused. "Fuck, did you even speak to him at all?"

"I don't remember… No… I don't think so. No," I finally admitted, my face flushing as I shrunk down in my seat, priming myself for another scolding.

Jia began to laugh. Just a chuckle at first, until I joined in, and then we were both laughing uncontrollably. "Un-freaking-believable!" She gasped, clutching her sides. "Only you, bitch. Only you."

We laughed until our sides hurt and tears coursed down our faces.

By eleven-thirty, I'd made my way over to Eden and was standing outside rehearsing what I might say if someone were to find me rifling through the linen in the storage room. When I couldn't think of anything even slightly plausible, I crossed my fingers and pushed open the door, hoping for the best.

The restaurant was quiet, the lunchtime hordes hadn't yet descended, but the noises coming from the kitchen told me they were deep in preparation for it. I spotted a waiter I knew vaguely; he hadn't been with Adam long. He was young and still learning the ropes. "Hi, Sam. Is Adam around?" I asked casually.

"Oh, Angel. Um, no. He had to pop out. I don't think he'll be very long, though. Did you want me to get you a coffee while you wait?"

"Oh, no, that's okay. I'm in a bit of a rush myself. I'll just catch up with him later." I turned as if to leave, and then, like something had just occurred to me, swiveled around and headed toward the stairs. "Bathroom," I said as way of an explanation.

As I began my ascent, he called after me. "Oh, um… I um… I hope I did the right thing, but last night there was this guy." He spoke as though he were asking a question. "He asked me if I knew who you were. I hope you don't mind, but I gave him one of your business cards—the ones Adam keeps behind the bar. When he pointed to where you were sitting and asked about the stunning brunette…" he flushed a deep shade of red "…I knew it could only be you he was talking about. I'm not in any trouble, am I?" he pleaded, anxiously.

I couldn't help but feel sorry for him and at least I now knew how the stranger—how Ethan Wilde—had found me. Not wanting to waste precious time by asking Sam questions, I told him it was fine and not to worry and then headed up the stairs.

When I reached the door to the bathroom, I stopped to ensure there was nobody around, took a deep breath to steady my nerves, and made a quick dash the hall to the storage room. I pushed open the door tentatively, flicked the light on, stepped inside, and closed the door behind me. The light flickered, as it had the night before, and the rush of clean smelling linen flooded my nostrils, taking me right back to the moment.

Relishing the memory, I closed my eyes as images of Ethan Wilde fucking me like a frenzied beast rushed into my mind, leaving me breathless and aching for a repeat performance. My nipples tingled, hardening against the lace fabric of my bra, and before I knew what I was doing, I'd reached inside to cup my breast. I tweaked my nipple hard, the action making me gasp with a thrilling pang that went straight to the heated flesh between my legs. Jeez, the mere memory of that man and what he'd done to me had me so turned on I was actually considering touching myself here—now. How fucking crazy was that? My eyes sprang open. "No!" I said aloud. "Get a grip. Remember why you're here." Placing my hand over my sex, I squeezed quickly, a feeble attempt to suppress the ache.

I searched the room high and low—the floor, under the shelves, on top of the shelves—I even shook out the tablecloths, taking care to fold them again before placing them back where they belonged. The pendant was nowhere to be found.

My heart sank as it had that morning when I first realized it was missing. I'd been counting on finding it here, convinced that I would. It had been my last scrap of hope, and now it was gone. Conscious of the fact that I had limited time, I admitted defeat and headed back down and out to the street, waving to Sam as he showed a couple to a nearby table.

When I was safely outside, I flagged a cab and reached for my cell to call Jia. I'd promised to update her as soon as I'd carried out the search. She did her best to boost my solemn mood, promising to help me search the apartment again, but deep down I knew our efforts would be futile. The probability and worst case scenario was that it had fallen off in the cab on my journey home. If that were true, by now it would either be a very extravagant gift for someone, or sold for cash before the day was out. The idea of either one was soul-destroying and beyond depressing.

In her attempts to cheer me up, Jia informed me that the gorgeous Mr. Wilde had called again to ensure I'd received my flowers. Despite the misery of losing the pendant, the shiver of excitement I felt on hearing his name was unmistakable, but melding with the thrill was the sound of warning bells. The man hadn't been far from my mind since the moment I'd laid eyes on him. He'd completely captivated me—too completely—and stirred feelings of desire inside me I didn't know I was capable of. The knowledge left me feeling uncontrolled and willfully wild, and that didn't sit comfortably. Desire led to need, and I didn't need anyone. I knew better than to go back for seconds with a man I really liked; I'd done that once with James, and it had ended badly. Despite my lust for him, and the images of the way he'd looked at me that I just couldn't get out of my mind—his assessing eyes raking over my heated skin as if he owned me, like he could easily go out of his mind if he didn't have me—I knew they were the very reasons I shouldn't pursue this any further.

No, it had been a cursory encounter and, although mind-blowing on the orgasmic Richter scale, was best kept that way. The trouble was, he knew where to find me, and from his actions so far, it seemed Mr. Wilde could be a very persistent man. I needed to decide how I would handle this and quickly. The flowers and calls had completely thrown me off balance; after all, I hadn't expected to hear from him again. I resolved to call him as soon as the opportunity arose. I'd thank him for the flowers and set him straight. There was no reason to prolong it, no need for apologies, or fancy dinners. Yes, definitely safer that way.

As the cab pulled up outside the gallery, my cell started to *buzz* with an incoming call. Thrusting a note into the driver's hand, I climbed out quickly, the bold, flashing three letter word—*DAD*—on the caller display, causing my belly to turn inside out with the familiar flutter of nerves. My father making contact with me was a rare occurrence, but when he did, I found that my body would usually respond in a certain way.

Nervous excitement combined with a smidgen of what—deep down—I knew was hopeless, childish optimism, anxiety, dread, and if I'm really honest, fear. It was a peculiar and confusing blend of emotions, and I preferred not to dwell on them or what lay beneath them. I fumbled nervously with the cell as I accepted the call.

"Hi, Dad," I answered with as much gusto as I could muster.

"Angelica, I need you to come by on Friday. Lunch. My office. I'll be free around two."

"Oh, okay, yeah, that would be great. It's good to hear from you. How are you?"

"I've no time to talk now. Don't be late." He hung up.

It was short and brusque, but standard. My father never had much to say—not to me, at least. I wondered briefly what he might want to see me about, a trace of anxiety curdling at my gut, but I promptly dismissed it. *There's nothing to be concerned about,* I told myself. It was good he wanted to see me. Wasn't it?

After reassuring myself for a moment longer, I pushed open the door to the gallery and walked through the foyer into the office, where Jia was busy at her computer. She looked up as I walked in. "Oh good, you look like you've perked up. Have you found it?"

"No such luck, but guess what? My dad called, he wants to have lunch on Friday."

"Okay." She paused, as if mentally editing before saying what was on her mind. "Did he say what he wanted?"

"No. Just lunch, he didn't have time to talk just now."

"Okay," she repeated. Her lips offered a slight smile, but her eyes exposed her doubts. She turned her attention back to her work, electing not to express them.

Although I valued Jia's opinion, I needed to stay positive. There was little point in spending the rest of the week worrying about why he wanted to see me, so I was grateful for her silence.

Just as I was settling down to some work, feeling somewhat behind schedule, my cell phone rang again. I glanced at it and sighed. I sure didn't have time for this.

"Hey, Jean-Paul." I glanced up at Jia helplessly. She chuckled and went back to work. "Sorry about last night, I don't know what happened. I think I was just tired and…"

"Oh, that's okay," he interjected, "Kate took care of me. Actually, that's why I'm calling, apart from finding out how you're feeling, of course. Only, I'm assuming Jia told you I left with Kate, and I didn't want you to think anything had happened between us. I wouldn't do that to you, Angel, especially with a friend of yours. I mean Kate's really hot, but…"

"Whoa, hold on just a minute, Jean-Paul. Firstly, no, Jia didn't mention anything about you leaving with Kate, and I suspect that's because she knows it's none of my damn business, and also because she understands that I am not in a relationship with you. And secondly, you are free to go home with anyone you choose, Jean-Paul, so if you would like to date Kate, I am absolutely fine with that. She is beautiful and clever and funny. You'd be great together. Call her."

There was a long pause. Jia's expression was set in an anticipatory grimace, her shoulders slumping into a crouch as if she were expecting a bomb to drop.

Finally, he spoke. "You make it sound like this is the best news you've had all day."

It probably was to be fair, but I didn't say that. "Jean-Paul, I'm just trying to be honest. You're a free agent. You can do whatever makes you happy, and I want you to be happy."

"Honest?" He laughed, but his tone was filled with scorn. "Like you're being honest about last night? You couldn't take your eyes off that guy, Angel. It was embarrassing. When you disappeared to the bathroom, he wasn't far behind you, and when you left, so did he. Want to explain?"

It was my turn to pause, stunned into silence from his unexpected and disproportionate response. By the time I found my voice I was livid. "No, Jean-Paul, I don't. I don't know how much clearer I can be. We are *not* an item, and I do *not* have to explain myself to you."

"You're a coldhearted bitch, is what you are. If clear is how you want it, get this: I'm falling for you, big time. I can't get you out of my head, and you just don't give a fuck. I've given you time and space, hoping one day you'll catch up, but all that concerns you is where your next fuck is coming from. I want more, Angel."

That stopped me in my tracks. I'd been afraid he was getting too keen, but I had no idea he'd developed feelings for me. Again, I was speechless.

"You don't give a shit do you?" he scoffed incredulously.

"Jean-Paul, I've obviously got this all wrong. In fact, I think we both have. I'm sorry, okay? I had no idea you felt like that. But you and me... it's just not... Look, if I've sent out the wrong signals, misled you in any way, it wasn't intentional." I paused. "I'm sorry."

"So, what are you saying?"

"I think you know what I'm saying. We should call it quits, JP. I'm really sorry."

"Yeah." His voice broke over his words. "Well, not as sorry as I am." He hung up.

For minutes I just sat in a state of shock, Jia staring at me, still poised for the imaginary bomb to explode. In my world, it already had.

"He just told me he was falling for me, for fuck's sake." I said it like the notion was utterly ludicrous. "I had no idea he felt that way. If I had, I would have backed off. I never wanted... I would never purposefully hurt him."

Jia nodded. "I know. I probably should have warned you."

"What do you mean?"

"Bitch, you must have seen the way he looks at you. It's tragic. The guy's crazy about you. He was doing his damnedest to get your attention last night. He flirted shamelessly with Kate, and you hardly even noticed he was there. He was seething when you disappeared. I reckon he left with Kate hoping I would tell you, just to see if he'd get a reaction."

Shit, how could I not have seen this coming? I shook my head.

Since my thing with James had ended, I'd steered clear of getting emotionally involved with anybody. I didn't do relationships. I did… arrangements… fun… sex. Usually with people I liked and could trust, but never with anyone who I thought was looking for more. I'd assumed Jean-Paul was a safe bet—a young, hot model with offers in reams. Obviously, I'd got it wrong.

Having knowledge of what it was like to hurt, I had absolutely no inclination to be the cause of someone else's pain. I should have spotted this coming, nipped it in the bud before it was too late. I hated being on bad terms with people, hated that he thought I was cold and heartless.

"Well, let that be a lesson to me. I really did not see it, Jia. Do you think I should call him back?"

"No. Don't beat yourself up. He's a big boy, he'll be fine, you'll see. I'll get Kate to call him. Now she *was* gagging for it…"

Jia was trying her best to cheer me up, but my mood had plummeted once again. I couldn't focus on work, so in the hope that I'd lost my pendant before my night had even started, I began another painstaking search. When I'd searched the gallery, my office, and the street outside, I asked Jia to call Eden on the remote chance that somebody had found it and handed it in. They hadn't.

When I'd awakened that morning with the memory of last night's sexual escapades, I'd been deliciously high but had come crashing down when I discovered that, of course, my pleasure had come at a price. I'd lost the only thing I'd ever had that connected me to my mom.

Then I'd received the largest bouquet of flowers I had ever seen, only to realize that the sender was far too hot to risk seeing again.

I'd nearly cracked a rib laughing with Jia when realizing I had the moral virtues of a total, closet-fucking hussy. Then came the daunting surprise of the lunch invitation from my father, and finally—for good measure—I'd been described as a coldhearted, thoughtless bitch.

Wow, I was feeling pretty battered from the erratic shifting of my emotions; they were giving me a bad case of whiplash.

Any hope I'd had of finding Mom's pendant had gradually diminished throughout the course of the day, and the thought of never laying eyes on it again had my heart breaking into tiny fragments.

As I lay in bed that night, I tried to visualize the light reflecting shapes, sparkling and glimmering in the moonlight, as they danced and soared around the walls of my room. But no matter how hard I tried, the walls were desolate and empty. The images had vanished. The magic had vanished—just like the memories of my mother's face, her voice, and the sound of her laugh.

My chest began to ache as a solitary tear tumbled on to my cheek, slid silently down my face, and melted into the pillow. Like everything else, it had vanished forever.

CHAPTER THREE

B y Friday I'd managed to evade several calls from the tenacious Mr. Wilde and hadn't yet gathered the courage to call him back. I needed to put the guy out of his misery, but for some reason I couldn't place, I couldn't quite bring myself to. I vowed to call later, when I returned from lunch. I would see how I felt then.

My father's private practice was located on Madison in Midtown Manhattan. I exited the elevator on the twelfth floor and turned left to the large set of double glass doors. The words etched over the top read: DR HARLEY LAWSON MD, PSYCHOTHERAPIST and PSYCHIATRIST.

A sudden wave of nausea curdled in my gut, the familiar onset of nerves and anxiety at what was in store for me far outweighing the vague rays of optimism. Doing my best to ignore the rate my pulse was pounding, I pushed open the doors into a wide reception area. The surroundings were clinical, all white with gray furnishings, and one-too-many ordinary looking ferns hanging around in pots and baskets. If the place was supposed to put you at ease, it didn't.

Audrey, my father's receptionist, was behind the desk and looked up as I approached, her reading glasses perched on the end of her nose. She was a gray-haired, portly woman who was a conscientious worker and incredibly loyal to my father. She'd worked for him for almost twenty years and although kindly, was also quite reserved and formal, choosing always to refer to me by my surname. I offered her the same courtesy when I said, "Hi, Mrs. White, my father's expecting me for lunch. I'm a little early."

"Oh, Miss Lawson, how nice to see you." She smiled warmly. "It's been such a long time. You look well."

"Thank you."

"I'll let your father know you're here." She glanced at the appointments page looking confused. "There doesn't appear to be anything in the diary, Miss Lawson. Are you sure the appointment is for today?"

"Yes, I'm certain." My heart sank. *Friday. Lunch. My office. Around two.*

"Oh, well I'm afraid he already had a lunch meeting, but I'm sure he'll manage to squeeze you in before his two fifteen arrives. Why don't you take a seat?"

Forcing a smile to help mask my disappointment, I nodded and took a seat on the plush leather sofa near the window overlooking the city. My watch read a quarter to two, so I settled in for a wait, replaying the phone conversation again in my head, trying to figure out how I'd managed to misinterpret it. *Friday. Lunch. My office. Around two.*

Audrey glanced up from her work several times, proffering apologetic smiles and offers of coffee, which I politely declined. I didn't actually think I could drink or eat anything now anyway, despite the fact I hadn't eaten all day.

At five past two the door to my father's office opened. Laughter drifted out into reception, followed by the muffled sound of two familiar voices. My father's deep, overbearing tones, I'd been expecting, but as my brain computed the familiarity of the second, I found my sense of disappointment and anxiety suddenly intensify.

My brother Aaron appeared in the doorway, but before emerging fully, he stopped to turn and shake my father's hand. My father clapped him on the back with his free hand. "Well done, Son. I'm proud of you. We'll do dinner next week. Make sure Adam's free. And thanks for the bourbon."

"No problem, Dad. I'll talk to you later," Aaron replied.

No problem, Dad. Smug bastard!

I glanced at my hands as I twisted them in my lap, berating myself for still allowing the way they froze me out to get to me. My father and brother had eaten lunch together, while I'd hung around in the waiting room like some insignificant piece of furniture, to discover why I'd been summoned. You would think I would be used to their indifference by now. Christ knows I'd suffered their cold, unresponsive disregard for me for as long as I could remember, but it still cut like a knife.

My father turned and went back inside his office without so much as a glance in my direction. Aaron raised his hand to bid farewell to Audrey, his noxious gaze catching me in the edge of his vision. I shrunk down in my seat trying to make myself as invisible as possible. As he turned to face me, his smile faded, only to be swiftly replaced with an arrogant smirk. He plunged his hands into his pockets and strode toward me with a superior swagger.

"What are *you* doing here?" he demanded.

The animosity seeping from him was palpable, and I couldn't help the way my lip instinctively curled at the edges in response.

"Nice to see you too, Aaron. Dad wants to see me. What's your excuse?"

"Dad *wants* to see you? Really? I find that hard to believe." His mouth twisted with wry amusement. "I suppose there's a first time for everything." He chuckled and glanced at his watch. "Well, I'd love to stick around and chew the fat, *Sister,* dear, but one, I don't have time, and two, I actually have a life. Laters."

He strode off confidently, kissing Audrey on the cheek as he passed and making her blush. They seemed very familiar with each other. Very different to the conventional way Audrey and I conducted our relationship. My heart sank further.

Audrey turned to me. "You can go in now, Miss Lawson."

"Thank you." I hesitated before adding, "Please, call me Angel."

She smiled but said nothing.

Feigning the most convincing smile I could muster, I stood and strode into the office, closing the door behind me.

Harley Lawson was a tall, well-built man, who—for his age at sixty-six—still looked in remarkably good shape. He was a handsome man with thick white hair, the only thing which betrayed his age. He'd been ten years my mother's senior.

"Hi, Dad." I forced the buoyancy into my tone.

"Oh, Angelica, you're here." His voice was laced with disinterest and irritation, as though I were an unwelcome gust of wind blown in from the street. "I'm running late, so I'll get straight to the point."

No shit. Like it's ever any different.

No matter how positive and amenable I tried to be, my father would blow it right out of the water within moments of being in my company. As the habitual sense of inadequacy curled tightly around me and the atmosphere grew thick with resentment, my brain felt like it was beginning to swell and throb. I resented him for resenting me— and he resented me, it seemed, merely for existing.

Unlike the cozy lunch with my brother, it was abundantly clear this was no social meeting. I'd been summoned for a purpose. I remained silent and waited for him to explain why.

"I received a call from an old friend. She's getting married tomorrow and she's been let down by her photographer. She asked me if you could step in. I said you would."

"Tomorrow?" I was horrified. "Dad, that's really short notice. I mean these things need a lot of organizing, time and structure. And a wedding? They're not really my thing, I'm not sure..." The look on his face halted me in my tracks.

With one raised eyebrow, lips pursed with agitation, he glowered at me from across his desk. And instantly I was right back there, six years old, puddle of spilled milk, heart pounding as I waited in trepidation for the scolding I knew would ensue.

"Angelica," he said, slowly. "Claudia Miller is a highly-respected businesswoman, who supports and contributes extensively to the charity. Without her fundraisers and personal financial backing, the charity would be nowhere near as successful as it is. I will not risk losing that support because you're too selfish to alter your weekend plans to facilitate somebody else's needs." His tone had risen progressively with the ferocity of his castigation.

My face burned with humiliation as I frantically searched for the right words to try and rationalize with him, to explain why his demand just wasn't feasible. All I could manage was a mouthful of garbled stuttering as I shook my head nervously. As usual, he'd rendered me wordless and unable to defend myself. My father recognized my weakened and vulnerable state in an instant and closed in for the kill. I squeezed my eyes shut, waiting for the surefire onslaught.

"Angelica, you are in an exceedingly privileged position which you do not deserve to be in." I'd heard it a million times. "Just remember that the money you squandered on that fanciful business of yours should have gone to your brothers. By rights, you shouldn't have a pot to piss in, so you will do this because I'm telling you to." Anger radiated from his body as he bellowed his disparaging words. "Do you really think that she would have left you so much as a dime if she'd have known? It's your fault, Angelica, remember that!"

The ferocity of his words had me physically recoiling, unable to bear the excruciating pain which they triggered in my chest. I tore my eyes away from the vile condemnation that burned from his, and once again found myself staring at my shoes. Always my damn shoes. Like if I stared hard enough they would magically transport me to another place far away from his toxic fury.

I struggled to fight back the threat of scorching tears and the urge to gag on the sob that was burning in my throat, knowing it was suicide to show him any signs of weakness.

Calmer, but just as forcefully, he took an envelope from his inside jacket pocket and slammed it on the desk with such aggression it caused me to flinch.

"Claudia's details—her address and telephone number—she is expecting your call. You will absorb the expenses. Do not, under any circumstances, accept payment for this job. It is my gift to her. You will be gracious, polite, and professional. Do not let me down again, Angelica." He cleared his throat, unbuttoned his jacket, and took a seat at his desk, turning his attention to his computer. I'd been dismissed.

Snatching up the envelope, I walked silently out of the office. Audrey, having clearly heard the commotion, didn't look up from her desk as I passed, graciously sparing me from further humiliation.

By the time I reached the elevator, the tears had escaped from the corners of my eyes and slid silently down my cheeks. The elevator was crowded, but nobody appeared to notice the distressed, lone female staring at the floor. The moment the door slid open, I hurtled down the passage and through the foyer. The floods had burst their banks, and I began to sob uncontrollably as I pushed through the revolving doors and out onto the street.

I didn't see the man until I ran straight into him. Oddly, he seemed to open his arms to catch me, as though he were expecting me to fall. Still attempting to conceal my emotional state, I glanced up timidly, to apologize for my clumsiness, and looked directly into the eyes of Ethan Wilde.

Astounded by his exquisite beauty, which my memory had in no way served justice, I felt my breath rush from my lungs and was momentarily riveted to the spot. His striking blue eyes were suddenly filled with concern and alarm, his strong arms encircling me, holding me as if he were expecting me to break. Our lips were only inches apart, and I could feel the warmth of his breath on my face, strangely comforting like that of a soothing balm. His woody, spicy scent was divine—insanely so. And the desire which radiated from his formidably lean frame seemed to permeate my body with such crackling heat, it aroused and awakened my inner senses to the extreme.

The noise of the city became muffled, like I was suddenly encased in a glass bubble and the usual raucous sounds outside were reduced to subtle, muted murmurs. Everything and everybody around me appeared to lose pace, moving robotically in slow motion. I'd entered his world again, captivated and completely consumed by the magnificent male specimen standing before me. I was aware of only him. Saw, felt, and smelled only him.

As he held me in his firm embrace, I felt suddenly mended, safe, and oddly protected—more so than I could ever remember feeling in my entire life. It was ludicrous and also disconcerting that this man—a virtual stranger—could bestow these wonderful but unfamiliar feelings upon me.

With graceful ease, he placed me back on my feet, but his strong hand remained protectively at my elbow. "Miss Lawson, are you alright? You seem distressed. Has somebody upset you?" His tone was heavy with concern, his voice smooth and sexy, the impeccable English accent dripping like slithers of silk from his perfect, full red lips.

It felt like an age passed before I finally found the words to answer. "I'm fine. Thank you. I'm so sorry. I walked right into you."

Seemingly unconvinced, he led me away from the crowd of people to a waiting SUV close by—a Cadillac Escalade, the one I'd seen parked outside Eden the other night, if memory served correctly. The vehicle was immaculate: shiny black bodywork with huge chromed aluminum wheels and tinted windows. It looked as if it cost a small fortune. An attractive man who looked around mid-thirties stood by the rear door, a driver perhaps. He was dressed smartly in a black suit and tie with a white dress shirt and began to open the door as we approached.

"Please, let us give you a ride somewhere. The gallery, perhaps." His strong hand urged me toward the open door of the car.

"No, I'm fine, really. I can walk."

"Nonsense, you're in no fit state." When I made no move to comply, he added, "At least let me buy you a coffee until you gather yourself.

You look like you could do with one."

Actually, he was right. I hadn't eaten all day. Reeling from the confrontation with my father, I was beginning to feel quite nauseous and dizzy. Ethan Wilde was probably the last man on Earth I wanted to stagger into in this ridiculously fragile state, but despite feeling mortified, I found myself nodding in assent.

Nodding once to the man by the open car door, he led me back into the flow of pedestrian traffic. We walked for a few minutes in silence, him guiding me protectively by my elbow through the crowd, until we came to a restaurant. On entering, we were greeted enthusiastically by the maître d` who led us through the crowded seating area and off to the side into a private booth. The walls were draped in lavish black and gold wallpaper, complimenting the luxurious black leather seating which curled around a mahogany table. The soft candlelight and soothing piano music playing in the background completed the warm and wonderfully romantic setting.

"Just coffee, please," Ethan said to the man who had shown us to our table.

"Of course, Mr. Wilde. And may I say how much of a pleasure it is to see you."

Ethan smiled in response and the man turned and walked away.

"A regular, huh?" I asked, managing a smile.

"Hmm, sort of," he answered distractedly. He seemed to be examining my features, and I wondered if he was trying to decide if I was how he remembered.

Flushing with shame, I suddenly recalled how he'd seen me last—shoved up against the shelves of a storage room with a look of orgasmic pleasure on my face. I blinked and glanced away shyly. God, what must he think of me? And now, here I was, a tragic mess with a blotchy, tear-stained face, who was so positively rude and ill-mannered I couldn't be bothered to return his calls.

Shit and double freaking shit!

"Oh, um… the flowers. Thank you. They were absolutely beautiful.

I've been meaning to call, but the last couple of days have been… well, kinda tricky. But that's no excuse. You must think I'm really rude. I apologize."

One corner of his sinful mouth turned into a sort of half smile as he searched my eyes. Seeming to ignore my apology, he asked, "Are you going to tell me what happened? Why were you so upset just now?"

Shocked by the sudden candid question, I found myself staring blankly at him. Considering this was only the second time we'd met, he sure didn't seem afraid to ask personal questions, and the forthright way in which he asked suggested he thought he had every damned right to know the answer.

A waiter arrived with our coffee, breaking the tension and providing me with a moment to compose myself. I swiped at my tear-stained face, as if I could wipe away the evidence of my prior despair in the hope that he'd believe he'd imagined it.

"I … It's a long story … You wouldn't be interested," I answered, attempting to sidestep the question. I reached into my purse for a tissue to finish the job, and as I was about to raise it to my face, he closed his hand over mine, removing the tissue gently from my hand.

"May I?" he asked.

After a beat, I nodded warily. Then to my utter astonishment, he reached out, dabbing softly at the delicate skin under my eyes and smoothing away the tear tracks. It was such an intimate gesture, carried out with such tenderness and compassion, that for a second I had the crazy, overwhelming urge to cradle my cheek against his hand.

"I wouldn't have asked if I wasn't interested," he persisted.

For some bizarre reason, I felt compelled to explain, at least in part. Under normal circumstances, I would have told whoever it was to mind their own damn business, but there was something about this guy that persuaded me to trust him. It wasn't like he was prying, he seemed genuinely concerned.

Averting my gaze shyly, I muttered, "I had a fight with my father."

He nodded, urging me to continue.

"He commissioned me to do some work at very short notice, tomorrow, in fact. Photography. I'm a photographer. But this you already know." I hesitated, wondering where in the hell I was supposed to start explaining. "I told him it just wasn't doable. He got angry, brought my mom into it—she died—an accident. He blames me. He hates me." I started to giggle nervously as I blurted it all out in a rush. "I'm sorry, this isn't making any sense. You don't want to hear any of this—"

"Why does he blame you?" He cut me off mid-sentence, blue eyes blazing as they tried to read into my soul.

Disengaging from the intensity of it, I gazed off vacantly into space as I considered how to answer. Then almost completely void of all emotion, I said, "Because I killed her."

He paused, searching my face, eyes narrowed as they continued to study. "You said it was an accident. Did you mean to kill her?"

"No!" The question horrified me. "It *was* an accident. I was six years old, I..."

"Then you didn't kill her, did you? So why do you believe you are culpable?"

Unable to comprehend that I was having this discussion with somebody I'd only just met, I could only gape in astonishment. I had never discussed my mother with anyone—ever. It was as though I'd been completely removed from reality. I needed to get a grip. "I'm sorry, do you mind if we talk about something else?"

A flash of something, regret, disappointment maybe, momentarily furrowed his brow. "If you'd prefer. I didn't mean to cause you further distress."

"No, it's fine. It's just that I don't usually... I'm not used to... Damn!" I cursed at my sudden inability to form a complete sentence. "God, I'm sorry. I don't usually struggle with the art of speaking. I seem to have lost all capacity to function properly."

He smiled widely, the most wonderful, captivating smile that started out in his eyes before making its way to his delectable mouth. The sexiest smile I'd ever encountered. And then he was laughing, and I was laughing with him.

"You're exquisite," he said as the laughter abated, head tilted slightly to the side as if contemplating me. "Even more so than I remembered. I've seen three very different and dramatic sides to you, already, Miss Lawson. All of them conflicting and at odds with each other—and all of them equally exquisite. You fascinate me."

I flushed slightly at his flattering comments. "Three sides?"

"Yes," he said. "You're exhilaratingly beautiful when you're relaxed and laughing in the spirit of the moment, yet delicately beautiful when sad and vulnerable." He paused, his awed expression changing to something much darker and more sensual. "And you're at your most beguiling and spellbinding when you're surrendering yourself to your most sensual and carnal desires. A woman who knows what she wants and is daring enough to explore her fantasies in order to satisfy her cravings is an enormous turn-on. Being part of that experience was the most erotic moment of my life. It drove me crazy when you came for me. You're the sexiest, most exciting woman I have ever met—or fucked, Miss Lawson."

Christ, say what's on your mind, why don't you? This man clearly had no problems communicating his feelings candidly. I gazed at him, utterly dumbfounded and burning with embarrassment.

"And so easily disconcerted, I see." A hint of amusement trickled over his luscious lips. "I wouldn't have figured *that* on Monday night. Yet another alluring trait, Miss Lawson. You're full of surprises. Quite simply irresistible."

"I'm just adjusting to your candidness, Mr. Wilde."

"Does it upset you?"

I paused, thinking about the question. "No." I answered honestly. Because if anything, I was finding his forthright approach a complete turn on. "But I've only met you once before and, until ten minutes ago, wasn't sure I'd ever lay eyes on you again."

"Did you hope that you would?"

"You ask a lot of questions." I smiled in my attempt at digression. "Let me ask you some."

"Go ahead." He sipped his coffee, casually unconcerned.

"Who the hell are you?"

Laughing, he reached out to shake my hand formally, his touch sending a current of vibrating sexual energy through my body. "Ethan Wilde, twenty-nine, born in New York. My parents are Richard and Veronica Wilde. I have one brother, Damon, twenty-six. One sister, Abby, twenty-two. I was educated and spent most of my early life in London, as you've probably guessed, and I've been back and forth between here and the UK ever since. I now live more or less permanently here in Manhattan. Next question."

"Do you always psychoanalyze and cross-examine the women you casually fuck in storage rooms?" *Wow, where the hell did that come from?*

A flicker of his brow hinted at surprise. "Well, now it's I who needs to adjust to your candidness, Miss Lawson. But in answer to your question, I've never fucked anybody—casually or otherwise—in a storage room before. Furthermore, until now, nobody's interested me enough to want to psychoanalyze them... if that's what I'm doing. You're a totally unique experience, Angelica."

I smiled a lazy smile as I absorbed this information. "Angel. I prefer Angel."

"Hmm, a very heavenly angel." He smiled approvingly. "Who were you dining with the other night?"

"I'm not finished with my questions."

"It's my turn," he insisted.

"My friend Jia—it was her birthday—and some other mutual friends."

"The man. Who was your male friend? The one you arrived with."

I paused. "Oh, Jean-Paul. Just a friend," I lied.

"He couldn't take his eyes off you."

"Really? I didn't notice." The truth.

"Are you available, Miss Lawson?"

"Available for what?"

"To see me. Only, I'd rather be aware of potential and unwanted complications now. I don't want anything standing in my way."

My heart hammered riotously. This man didn't waste any time, and my God was it arousing.

"I'm not in a relationship, if that's what you're asking."

"Good. Let me take you out to dinner, then."

Panic seemed to rush at me all at once. I wasn't sure I wanted to take this any further. Or I was sure that I did, and it was that which scared the shit out of me. He was intense, too sure of himself, and too damned hot. My instinct was to run.

"I can't. I'm sorry. I'm afraid I don't do the whole dating thing." Gathering my purse, I made to stand. "Thanks again for the flowers and the coffee, but it's getting late. I really have to go."

Ethan Wilde was clearly a man unfamiliar with being rebuffed, recoiling in his seat as if I'd hurled a personal insult. Suddenly his hand shot out, resting on my arm to halt me.

"I see, that's a shame. Please sit down, Angel, just for one more minute. I have something for you."

As he spoke he slid his hand inside his jacket pocket to retrieve something. It was a small, blue, velvet purse with a gold drawstring.

A gift?

"Look, like I said. Thank you for the flowers, they were lovely, but I really can't accept any more gifts from you."

He smiled. "It's not a gift."

Despite the instinct to flee, something else persuaded me to stay so I took my seat. Ethan handed me the purse, his eyes warm and kind, but wary under his hooded brow. Cautiously, I loosened the drawstring and tipped the contents onto the table.

It sparkled in the candlelight, reflecting like the glistening tears that had sprung—unbidden—to my eyes. There on the table lay my mother's diamond pendant.

For what seemed like an eternity, I gazed in disbelief at the priceless piece of treasure. I thought it was lost forever, yet here it was—my magic returned to me by this magical, mysterious man. Its enchanting beauty was reflected in the breathtaking face I now turned to gaze at. Ethan watched me, his eyes assessing, waiting for my reaction. The weight which lifted from my heart at that moment was physically alleviating, and the tears which brimmed under my lashes spilled over on to my cheeks. Ethan reached out, and with a feather-light touch, brushed them tenderly away with the tip of his thumb.

"What is it?" His voice was raw with concern. "I thought you'd be pleased to have it returned to you. It looks incredibly expensive."

"It's priceless," I sobbed through tears of joy. "You have no clue what this means to me. It was my mom's, the only part of her I had left. Where did you find it?"

"On the floor in our, um… storage room. The clasp must have worked lose. I took the liberty of having it repaired." He bowed his head, a playful smile teetering at the edge of his mouth. "I chased after you, but you left in rather a hurry. I thought it might be fun to track you down and return it. A bit like the glass slipper scenario—you being my Cinderella."

"And you, my Prince Charming," I said, enchanted by the analogy and overwhelmed with gratitude.

Immediately I felt foolish. He'd obviously put a lot of effort into finding me, and I hadn't exactly made it easy for him. In fact, I'd been completely ungracious. "You've gone to a lot of trouble to find me and return it. I'm so grateful, you will never know how much." I regretted it, as soon as it was out there.

"Then have dinner with me. I'd like to get to know you better, Angel. You intrigue me."

I shook my head. "It's not a good idea."

"Christ, Angel, I'm not asking you to marry me. I'm just asking you to dinner," he exclaimed, slightly impatiently.

"It's just that I don't usually…"

"What? Eat? Now you're going to tell me you don't eat?"

Whoa! Suddenly I felt so overwhelmed. This entire situation was so improbable, so illusory, it seemed out of control. I hated not being in control. I preferred to wake up every morning knowing exactly what to expect, to be in charge of my own destiny. I could either run for my life… or I could stick around to see what the world of Ethan Wilde had to offer me.

Before I could change my mind, I stood. "I'm really grateful you took the trouble to return my pendant, but I really need to get back to work."

Disappointment flooded his face, but was gone in seconds. "Of course. My apologies." A trace of exasperation now laced his voice. "I've taken up far too much of your time. Please, at least let me drive you."

For some reason I couldn't place, I felt a strange stab of regret instead of the relief I'd anticipated. I hadn't expected him to give up quite so easily, not when he'd been so determined a moment ago. Despite the huge part of me that wanted to flee, I found a much larger part not wanting to leave him, and before I knew, I'd accepted the ride eagerly.

He nodded to the maître d` as we made our way toward the door.

"Oh, the coffee," I said, suddenly remembering that we hadn't paid.

"Don't worry, it's taken care of," he replied, as he pushed open the door and led me out onto the street.

Like before, the SUV was waiting at the curb, and the attractive man by the opened rear door smiled widely as we approached. I wondered briefly about the extent of Mr. Wilde's power and wealth to require the constant use of a personal driver.

"Thank you, Jackson," Ethan said, acknowledging the driver.

Jackson nodded, first to Ethan and then to me, saying simply, "Miss Lawson."

I smiled back, as much in surprise at him knowing my name as in politeness. My unspoken question must have registered on my face, amusing both men.

"Miss Lawson, this is Jackson, my right hand man."

"Hello, Jackson." I turned to shake his hand.

"I'm very pleased to meet you, Miss Lawson," Jackson replied in a distinct London accent.

The two men exchanged a look I couldn't place, and I climbed into the vehicle. The scent of leather and luxury hit the second the door was opened. The interior was beyond lavish; wealth and opulence practically oozed from the materials that made up the large, airy space. The premium cream leather bench seat felt more like a plush and sumptuous sofa, while the darkened windows and dimly lit spotlights which shone from the ceiling, created a soft, almost romantic ambience. The furniture was finished in either matching leather or hardwood. There were windowsills with inlays on the doors, and the rich, thick piled carpet was complete with matching leather piping trim. In front of us were some rear facing jump seats, currently folded away, and there was an ice chest and what looked like a mini refrigerator. There was a folding, aircraft-like desk with a laptop and a pile of papers, a media system, and a stereo system—yes, beyond lavish.

Ethan settled in next to me.

"Wow," I muttered, my eyes still scanning our surroundings. "You like to travel in luxury."

His smile was modest. "I like to be able to work whilst I'm stuck in the unrelenting hindrance of Manhattan traffic. I like the look of the Cadillac Escalade and it serves the purpose. It's the CEO Executive Bentley Edition. It's like a mobile office and luxury limo in one."

"Mmm, I can see that."

Smiling again, he turned to address Jackson through the rearview mirror. "We'll take Miss Lawson back to her gallery, Jackson."

"Yes, boss," Jackson replied as he signaled to pull out into the traffic.

"Oh, yes," I said "It's—"

"Jackson knows where it is," Ethan interjected, his lip curling as he nodded once to Jackson.

Although only his eyes were visible, there was something about the way Jackson's eyes crinkled at the edges that told me he was somewhat amused.

"Is there something I should know?" I asked, curious to know what the wordless exchange between the two men was about.

"Jackson's just pleased I managed to track down my Cinderella is all." Chuckling, he shifted closer, our thighs practically touching.

The electric charge between us was instant and undeniable—a profound, enticing energy, which caused the hairs on my body to stand on end. His close proximity in this restricted space was so compelling it was practically too much for my body to endure, and impossible to ignore. He smelled divine, and I found myself closing my eyes and inhaling his aroma deep into my lungs. Static heat crackled between our almost touching thighs, causing a tingling wave of desire to ascend slowly up my inner thigh to the aching, quivering summit.

God, I could easily lose my mind with this man. I was a complete train wreck when I was around him. Ever so discreetly, I tried to inch away, a vain attempt to evade the compulsion to fling myself at him. Somehow, I needed to contain the desire which flared with such unexpected intensity inside me.

As though he could read my mind, he reached out and took my hand. "Do I make you feel uneasy, Angel?"

Jesus, understatement. I drew in a deep breath, trying to slow my ragged heartbeat and gather the nerve to look him in the eye. When I was ready, I turned to him, our gaze locking securely. "Yes," I breathed.

"Why?"

"I find your approach a little imperious, a bit bullish, perhaps."

"I'm a very busy man. I don't believe in wasting time, Angel. If I see something I want—in this case, *someone* I want—I do my damndest to attain her."

"Even if that *someone* doesn't want to be attained?"

"I don't believe that to be true."

"You're wrong."

"Am I?" he challenged.

I swallowed hard, hoping to suppress my desire enough to speak without my voice betraying me. "I told you. I don't do relationships."

He nodded once. "So what do you do?"

"I prefer casual affairs."

His eyes widened.

The car drew to a halt outside the gallery, and Jackson got out, moving around the car to wait with his back to my door. Ethan's gaze remained locked on to mine, the raw sexual tension between us sizzling against the strain of trying to deny it. He was right. I desired this man as much as he desired me, but I couldn't say that. I could barely breathe, never mind speak.

"I happen to believe I've taken rather a circuitous route in pursuing you, Miss Lawson. Perhaps, it would serve us both more effectively if I were all the more direct," he paused. "I want you, Angel. I want you so bad I can taste you. I want to fuck you like I did the other night, except for longer and harder. I've thought about nothing else since I watched that sweet orgasm rip through your absurdly beautiful body, and I won't be content until I'm inside you again. In fact, I think I'll go insane if you deny me. If a casual affair is the only way I get to do it, then so be it. Now, if that's imperious, then I guess I'm guilty as charged."

I was so aroused, I was afraid to move in case I went off. "Well," I gasped, "why didn't you just say?"

And so I entered the world of Ethan Wilde.

CHAPTER FOUR

J ia stared at me dumbstruck. It wasn't often she was lost for words; I made a mental note of the time, the date, and the reason for future reference.

"Fuck," was the first word out of her mouth. I'd given her the entire lowdown: the meeting with my dad, which led to me running straight into the path of Ethan Wilde, him returning my mom's pendant—Cinderella style—and finally, my agreeing to have dinner with him on Sunday.

She didn't know which bit to comment on first, but decided to start with my father.

"Fuck. The motherfucking son of a bitch. Who the hell does he think he is? One of these days—"

"Jia," I scolded, "he's still my father."

"You think?" she retaliated. "My father wouldn't treat a dog the way your father treats you."

Although I knew her words to be true, they still made me wince. Sitting down at my desk, I tucked into the sandwich she'd bought me. I was ravenous and pleased for once that she appeared to know my father better than I did.

"Here," she said when she'd presented it to me. "I knew the asshole wouldn't buy you lunch."

God bless her.

"And Mr. Freaking Wilde had better watch his attitude, as well, bitch, because I won't stand for any audacious bullshit. He hasn't met me yet. He sure doesn't want it to be an unpleasant experience."

I laughed. Jia had assumed the role of my protector at some point in our friendship, and although sometimes it could be a little excessive, it was also reassuring to know somebody had my back. It wasn't something I'd ever encountered before.

"I'd better give this Claudia Miller a call," I said, retrieving the envelope my father had given me from my purse and pulling out the details to read. "You have got to be kidding," I closed my eyes and put my head in my hands.

Jia raised an eyebrow. "Tell," she instructed.

"The Hamptons," I whined. "The goddamn, freaking gig is in the Hamptons." Reluctantly, I picked up the phone and began to dial Claudia Miller's number. "It could take almost two hours to drive out there. Fingers crossed it's an afternoon wedding," I said to Jia, who sat open mouthed and seething.

Fortunately, Claudia proved to be a genuinely pleasant and approachable woman, which came as a bit of a surprise since she was an associate of my father's. I had expected her to be, at best, lukewarm toward me.

We chatted for a while as I explained that my photography expertise and style wasn't usually of a traditional nature, and that I tended to have a more contemporary approach, focusing mostly on candid images rather than posed images. It turned out that it was exactly what she wanted. What's more, she'd apparently seen some of my work and had called my father to see if he could persuade me to drop everything at short notice to attend and photograph her wedding. This was a week ago and she had cancelled her initial photographer because my father had assured her that I would be there. She'd been waiting for my call ever since.

My father had known about this for a whole week. Deciding not to bother even trying to figure out why he would leave it until today to inform me about it, I spent the next few minutes making up some garbage reason as to why I'd left it so late to call.

We agreed that I would aim to arrive at the house by eleven-thirty. The wedding was scheduled for two o'clock, so it would give me time to prepare, assess the house and grounds, and more importantly capture the preparations in progress on film.

When I finished the call, I found my thoughts wandering back to Ethan Wilde, his forthright words resounding in my ears. As much as I'd criticized his approach, I'd been wildly turned on by it. By what he'd said, the way he'd said it, his accent, his smell—every goddamn thing about him.

Knowing I didn't have the time to be preoccupied, I called my brother Adam to make sure the car was available. Adam and I shared a black Volvo S60. Neither one of us went out of the city very often, so the use of a car full-time wasn't necessary; it was easier to flag a cab, use the subway or simply walk. I used the car the least, so it made sense to leave it at Adam's. After making a big deal about how considerate it was of Dad to pass on the work, he agreed to drop it by my apartment. I grunted and hung up.

Adam knew, deep down, that my father had never done anything for me, unless it had benefitted him in some way. He'd witnessed Dad's icy indifference toward me his whole life, but found it simpler to turn a blind eye. He was wrapped up in his own life; I didn't blame him really. No point in putting yourself on the wrong side of my father unless it was absolutely necessary.

I packed a selection of equipment, including my favorite Leica, Nikon, and Canon cameras and lenses and headed home exhausted.

My home welcomed me with its familiar ambiance, the feel and aromas warm and inviting. The sense of comfort and solace it offered felt as reassuring as the open arms of a loved one enfolding me into a soothing embrace—or so I imagined. Closing and bolting the door behind me, I felt an instant release. I was back in my bubble.

After a wonderfully hot bath in my luxurious soaking tub, with softly lit scented candles and oodles of bubbles, I began to relax. I dressed in just my fluffy deep crimson robe, poured a glass of red wine, and prepared the most wonderful pasta with tomatoes, peppers and chilies. It hadn't gone unnoticed that throughout the entire process, I'd yet again been immersed in thoughts of Ethan.

Jia broke me out of my delicious musings when she called, still convinced that I should just tell my father to "stick the job up his great big, fat, hairy ass." Her words. I laughed and told her I was fine and not to worry. I'd call her when I returned home from the wedding.

Wanting an early start to ensure I arrived in plenty of time, I decided to crash early. Having said goodnight to Ponyo, I was about to head for my bedroom when I found myself wandering over to the desk containing my laptop. I sat down, fired her up, and began a search on Ethan Wilde.

A couple of clicks brought me an image of his insanely handsome face. The pang of desire was immediate, shocking me to the core. I couldn't ever remember being this physically attracted to anyone in my life. He fascinated me and it was profoundly unnerving. I began to read.

Ethan Wilde, president and chief operating officer of Wilde Industries Inc. managed one of the largest privately-held commercial real estate portfolios in the United States and UK. It included office, industrial, retail, and residential properties. Hotels, gyms, restaurants, leisure complexes, casinos, golf courses—you name it. Wilde Industries was a massive chunk of it. His father, Richard Wilde, was the founder, chairman and chief executive officer of Wilde Industries, while his brother, Damon, ran the investment arm of the company. His sister, Abby, was studying business at Columbia, and the entire family, particularly his mother, Veronica, were active supporters of countless charitable causes.

"Oh my God," I breathed aloud. When he'd mentioned his parents' names, earlier today, it hadn't registered for one minute who they were.

I hadn't made the connection between him and Wilde Industries. Jeez this man was rich-rich-rich. The entire family were multi-billionaires on a tremendous scale with lots of fingers in copious amounts of pies. Their name was continually connected to new acquisitions, developments, re-developments, renovations; anything that was current, happening and cutting edge had the word Wilde written all over it.

There was a mountain of data on the Wildes. I could have read on all night, but suddenly I didn't want to be aware of it. Pushing the laptop away from me, I snapped it shut. My views and feelings for this man needed to derive from my own perceptions and gut instincts. I did not want it clouded by details and statistics interpreted, or misinterpreted, by the media.

With that in mind, I scurried off to bed, scolding myself for snooping at all. I was too damn nosy for my own good.

Just as I was about to set my morning alarm on my cell it *buzzed* in my hand, making me jump. It was a text message from an unknown sender. I opened it cautiously.

Until Sunday. Sleep well, Cinderella x

Jeez, it was him. My face flushed as I stared at the message in wonder, my stomach doing a strange and unfamiliar flip. Butterflies, excited butterflies, and then a wave of queasiness, nervous, panicky queasiness. Oh man, such a jumbled concoction of feelings. Shaking my head in bewilderment, I quickly typed a reply:

Like a baby, thanks to the return of my "glass slipper." Thanks again, Prince Charming ;)

Opting for the smiley-winky face in place of the kiss, to keep things light, I pressed send. Then I questioned whether it was too friendly, and then doubted whether I should have replied at all.

Eventually, exhausted, I fell into a deep but troubled sleep.

The corridor seemed as if it were never-ending as I ran faster than I thought my legs could possibly carry me. Both sides were lined with closed doors, every single one locked and bolted from the outside, leaving me no means of escape. The crashing, pounding noise of what sounded like hooves hurtled after me, drawing nearer with every terrifying stride. I took a chance and glimpsed over my shoulder, trying to gauge the distance between me and my pursuers.

The beasts were unusual—white with black spots, built like horses, but with abnormally large heads. One beast was crying inconsolably, but the other barked viciously, frothing at the mouth like that of a rabid dog. Suddenly, I felt agonizingly conflicted, uncertain whether I should stop and care for the crying beast, but at the same time, compelled to keep on running from the ferocious one.

My fear won out and I raced on, clutching my treasured glass slipper tightly to my chest, terrified of dropping it and losing it forever. My legs felt as if they might give way, my lungs burning painfully, my sides aching as I gasped urgently for breath. Just when I thought I could run no further, I stumbled upon an open door. I pushed it open and entered a room no larger than a closet, closing the door firmly behind me. With nowhere left to run to, I crouched down in the corner, folding my arms around my knees in a comforting hug.

The horror of being discovered closed around my battering heart, and despite my desperation to gulp in air and replenish my lungs, I was far too terrified to even draw breath. Too terrified to move or look, or do anything but remain silent and motionless in my tight little ball and stare down at my shoes—shiny, red patent shoes scuffed at the toes.

I awoke gasping for breath, my hair clinging to my fevered, sweat-soaked skin. *What the hell was all that about?* Fragments of the dream were familiar, particularly the red patent shoes and the spotted beasts; they'd manifested themselves within my dreams in some shape or form many times before. I never wished to dwell on their significance.

Sitting up, I swung my legs out of bed and rubbed my forehead, attempting to smooth out the furrow that had developed while I'd slept. The time on my cell said it was almost time to get up, so I disabled my alarm call and headed for the shower, desperate to wash away the confusion of my dream.

Needing fuel for my long drive, I ate breakfast on the terrace, the warmth from the sun and the pulsing energy from the city below helping to soothe the remnants of unease. Considering my disrupted sleep, I felt surprisingly refreshed and untroubled.

Deciding to drive in jeans, a T-shirt and sandals, so as not to wrinkle on the way. I packed my clothes and a small bag of toiletries in a tote bag to freshen up when I arrived.

The journey went off without hiccups, and I arrived in plenty of time, unhurried and relaxed by eleven-fifteen. A private driveway led to a stunning 1920's-built traditional estate set in around two and a half acres of idyllic, rustic seclusion. There were people milling about everywhere, delivery vans for flowers and catering trucks, people carrying lawn furniture and boxes of champagne. I found a place to park my car, and unraveling my long limbs, got out and stretched, breathing in the scent of a wonderful ocean breeze. A valet approached me, and after I explained who I was, he kindly unloaded my bags and led me through the open front door into a spacious hallway with a sweeping staircase.

Looking up, I saw an extremely attractive woman descending the stairs. She looked to be in her late forties, early fifties, slender and toned with fair skin and red, shoulder length hair.

"You must be Angelica." Claudia Miller reached the bottom of the stairs and shook my hand. "Please, come in. Thank you so much for slotting me in. I know you must have a really tight schedule." She smiled warmly and motioned for me to follow her down the hallway.

"Come, we'll find somewhere a little quieter."

I followed her into a large, elegant light-filled living room, impeccably furnished with an impressive stone fireplace and huge glass doors leading out to a covered porch. Outside was a large swimming pool surrounded by sprawling, immaculate lawns, and beyond that was a magnificent view of the Atlantic Ocean.

"What a fantastic place," I said, wandering over to the doors and looking out.

"Oh, thank you, we love it here. It's so peaceful and serene."

"Yes, it must wonderful to be surrounded by so much open space, so easy to breathe."

"Can I get you something cold to drink?" she asked, dragging me reluctantly from the view. "You must be thirsty after your long drive. Some homemade lemonade, perhaps?"

I accepted gratefully, my mouth watering in anticipation of the cold, citrusy fluid. I gazed around, taking in my surroundings while Claudia arranged for the lemonade, and then we sat down to talk.

Claudia Miller seemed sincere and unpretentious, and I warmed to her instantly. She explained that she was remarrying her ex-husband, Rob. Their marriage had apparently fallen apart four years earlier, when their only child, Alisha, had fallen into drink and drugs. They'd inevitably blamed each other for their conflicting parenting approach and overall inattentiveness throughout her childhood. The battle to get Alisha back on the straight and narrow had taken its toll on both, and they'd eventually gone their separate ways.

My father had been Alisha's therapist and had seen her through a difficult recovery and rehabilitation process. Needless to say, he was now right up there among the gods in the eyes of Claudia and Rob Miller. He'd brought their daughter back from the depraved world of drinking and drugs, and furthermore, unwittingly played a fundamental role in the restoration of their marriage. All hail to Dr. Harley Lawson.

I listened attentively as Claudia relayed her romantic anecdote, feigning pride and loyal adoration toward my father while struggling to resist the urge to stick my fingers down my throat. It was difficult to maintain, but I managed to cleverly conceal my false smile behind the glass of absurdly good lemonade.

My father specialized in the treatment of various mood and behavioral disorders. Among other things, his patients suffered with depression and anxiety, and most were drug and alcohol dependents. He was the founder of a charity which supported the recovery and rehabilitation of drug and alcohol addicts, and I discovered it was the Millers' unsolicited confrontation with their daughter's addiction that had subsequently inspired their involvement and financial assistance in the charity.

And now he had come to their rescue again. Ah, how it all becomes clear.

Claudia Miller would indeed be indebted to my father for a very long time. I had no doubt that my free-of-charge services would enable my father to benefit from the Millers' financial backing for some time to come.

At that moment, Rob walked in and Claudia introduced us. He was tall and thin with pointed features and smiled widely as he shook my hand. He was warm and friendly, like his former and future wife, and it wasn't hard to see that they were made for each other. Claudia beamed a smile as he sat down next to her, his eyes filled with affection as he took her hand and clasped it firmly in his.

We talked in detail about the way in which I would convey the story and atmosphere of the day through the pictures I would take. It was to be an informal event; they would walk down the aisle together and the ceremony would be brief. They said they preferred to see the day as a celebration of their love, more like renewing their vows, because they'd never really felt unmarried to each other. Today was simply about making it official.

So rather than a series of pre-determined poses, we agreed I would blend with the guests and focus on capturing images that evoked the real emotions of the day, with the emphasis on spontaneity, natural reactions, and momentary expressions of the couple and their guests.

When we were through, Claudia showed me upstairs to a guest room with adjoining bathroom so that I could freshen up and change. I dressed in a coral, floaty, knee-length dress with a wide-scooped neckline, long sheer sleeves, and nude, peep-toe platforms. I swept my hair into a whimsical, fairy-like updo and opted for pronounced, dramatic eyes, peachy cheeks, and nude, glossy lips. Finally, I retrieved the blue velvet purse from my bag and put on my mother's pendant, smiling widely at my reflection in the mirror.

Feeling refreshed and happy with the way I looked, I set out to survey my surroundings. The house and grounds were expansive with wraparound mahogany decks and views over the ocean. There was an infinity edge waterside pool with floating day beds and spa, and the immaculate lawns were filled with wisteria, perennials, and specimen trees.

The lawn which ran down the side of the house was set up with chairs in two sections, forming an aisle in the middle. Round tables with impressive flower arrangements were set out across the lawns at the back of the house next to the pool, and off to the side were long, narrow tables laden with luxurious, scrumptious looking food.

I wandered inside and found Rob drinking a cold beer in the kitchen. He was talking to a man I guessed was his brother, the similar height and features giving it away. After taking some natural shots of them sharing a private joke, I made my way upstairs to the master suite.

It was a large room with a private sitting room and fabulous views over the ocean. I was just in time to capture Claudia getting the final touches to her hair and makeup and then being helped into her dress: a simple ivory satin strapless gown. She looked elegant and refined.

I captured some shots of the bouquet and the wedding rings strategically placed on a glass table, making clever use of angles and reflective light.

Outside, the final touches were being made and the guests had started to arrive. I caught the facial expressions of *oohs* and *aahs*, the laughter, delight, and amusement on people's faces.

The sound of girly giggling coming from over near the pool house caught my attention and I sauntered over to check it out. The doors were slightly ajar, and as I approached, I heard the voice of a young woman telling her giddy companions to calm down and get dressed because the guests were arriving.

After tapping lightly on the door, I pushed it open. A young woman, around twenty-one, turned toward me, and on noting my camera, smiled widely. "Hi, you're Angelica, right?"

From her long, vivid red locks of hair tumbling effortlessly down her back, I determined swiftly that she had to be the daughter of Claudia and Rob Miller.

"And you must be Alisha? May I?" I said, asking permission to enter.

"Sure, come in." She nodded enthusiastically, tilting her head toward the heap of arms and legs in the center of the room. The limbs belonged to four other girls of a similar age, all of whom were dressed scantily in shorts and tees and seemed to be tangled up in a play-fight. "And this rabble here, are my frien—" The rest of her sentence came out garbled as she was whacked directly in the face with one of the countless huge, feathery cushions which adorned the room.

Laughing, she picked up a cushion and smashed it into the back of one of the other girls. Soon, everyone was hitting everyone else, screeching with hysterical laughter, and squealing with delight. And as feathers flew through the air, I snapped away, capturing the scene unfolding before me and preserving it forever.

As I moved around the room with my camera, dodging the girls as they fooled around, I found myself in complete awe of their merriment and the easy way in which they intermingled.

And then suddenly, I felt it—a terrific thud pounding full force into the center of my back. I froze in utter shock as the noise in the room promptly ceased, all movement suspended. And then slowly, cautiously, I turned to face my assailant. The petite frame that stood before me, wielding probably the largest cushion in the room, was strikingly pretty. She had collar-length, almost black hair, large eyes, and a tiny, slightly up-turned nose. She surveyed me with amiable defiance, stilled, and waited. I stood motionless, mouth gaping in shock, everyone's eyes upon me as they waited in consternation for my reaction.

Stooping, I gently lowered my camera to the floor, tucking it safely under a coffee table. As I straightened, I picked up a discarded cushion from the floor in front of me, and with pure devilment glinting in my eyes, and screeching like a woman possessed, I launched myself at her. Brandishing my weapon, I hurled it with all my might, knocking her to the ground. Peals of side-splitting laughter rang out as the battle recommenced.

Minutes later, we all lay on the floor in exhausted disarray, our laughter subsiding as our rapid breathing abated. I couldn't ever recall being part of such frivolous fun before. It was invigorating and liberating, and a total, utter pick-me-up.

Still lost in the giddiness of the moment, I became vaguely aware of one of the girls, a short, curvy blonde, jumping to her feet and smoothing down her clothes. "Oh crap. Abby, your brother," she said to the petite girl who had attacked me.

Abby pulled herself up to lean back on her elbows and looked toward the door, a huge grin spreading across her face. "Hey, Brother. How long have you been there?"

"Long enough."

The voice was a low, sensual growl and spoke in what was now a familiar, refined English accent. Leaning up against the doorjamb, head cocked to one side, hands deep in pockets and staring directly at me, stood the sexy-as-hell Ethan Wilde.

CHAPTER FIVE

He was dressed in a stylish, urbane suit, dark in color. It was slim-fitting and encased his formidably lean structure perfectly. There was no doubt he looked polished and cultured, and smolderingly sexy, the sight of him sending a powerful thud of desire straight to my sex. Judging from the amount of burning, flustered faces around the room, I wasn't the only one affected by him. The girl that I now knew to be Abby—and evidently Ethan's sister—gushed with admiration. She clearly idolized him.

Swiftly re-arranging my dress and hair, I bent to retrieve my camera, flashed the girls a cheeky smile, and made my way toward the door. Ethan's expression was unreadable, his impressive frame resolute as he stood in the doorway, completely blocking my exit, but making no attempt to budge. I looked up to meet his eyes, his delicious smile spreading seductively across his face.

"Cinders." He nodded his greeting.

"Charming," I responded, revising his designated pet name, unsure as to whether the title of prince was yet deserved. The jury was still out on that.

Unable or unwilling to suppress neither my good mood, nor the grin which had commandeered my face, I pushed past him through the door. Conscious of the nudging and whispering going on in the room behind me, I suspected the girls could sense my unease conflicting with Ethan's self-assured coolness. It wouldn't take a brain surgeon to work out there was history between us. What they couldn't know was what or how recent the history was. Nevertheless, I was consumed with the need to escape and quickly.

Once outside, I stopped to compose myself. Damn, it was such a small freaking world. So, Alisha was clearly a friend of Abby's, and Abby was Ethan's sister. But why was Ethan here, I wondered.

Angling my head to peer at him over my shoulder, I was once again captivated by his infinite beauty. His gaze penetrated mine, a deliberate smile playing at the corner of his mouth, his eyes scorching with a look of…What was it? Yearning. Yes. What I could see was pure, irrefutable hunger. I wasn't in any doubt, because I felt it too. And I wasn't sure how much longer I could control my appetite.

I pivoted on my heel, about to walk away, when suddenly, I felt as though the earth had fallen away from beneath my feet. Strolling toward me, not more than six feet away, was my father, arm in arm with a busty blonde almost half his age. I stopped dead in my tracks as we caught sight of each other, but as he drew level with me, he continued to pass, offering a barely perceptible nod, as though we were but mere acquaintances.

The public disparagement was as painful and humiliating as a slap in the face and left me feeling about six inches tall. My father's knack of making me feel worthless never failed to bewilder me, but as a rule it was something I endured in private. Today was different, and the rush of fury which raged through my blood in response took me by surprise. My nostrils flared in anger.

You fucking jerk! I imagined shouting after him. *You goddamn, ignorant, fucking jerk!* I could barely restrain the scorched curse from escaping my lips, but of course I did. Biting down on my tongue, I averted my flushed, humiliated face and stared down at my shoes.

Suddenly, I remembered Ethan and my mortification multiplied tenfold. He'd been watching me. Was he still? Had he witnessed my public degradation?

I glanced tentatively over my shoulder, praying he'd moved away. No such luck. His expression had changed, his brow creased in confusion, possibly even perturbed by the way my demeanor had altered during the very small but surreal exchange, which he'd indubitably surveyed. As if attempting to figure out exactly what he'd just witnessed, he glanced between me and my father's retreating back. I took the opportunity to flee, hurrying away to hide in among the guests.

Christ, it hadn't even entered my mind that my father would be present, which, in itself, was ridiculous considering how much the Millers must have felt they owed him. Of course he'd have an invitation to their wedding; after all, he'd contributed hugely to their reunion, hadn't he?

I tried to convince myself that Ethan probably hadn't even realized who my father was, and therefore wouldn't have noticed anything out of the ordinary. Vowing to put the whole thing out of my mind, I turned my focus to what I was there to do: work.

The next couple of hours were spent snapping away. The ceremony and speeches, though brief and unorthodox, had been very romantic. It was obvious a lot of thought had gone into the day, and I was confident that I'd captured its true essence. I'd taken some brilliant candid shots, and confident that Claudia would be thrilled with them, I gave myself a well-earned pat on the back.

Throughout the afternoon, I'd been mindful of repeatedly scanning the crowd for even the slightest glimpse of Ethan, noting that I'd been naturally drawn to whichever part of the grounds that might be. Of course, I'd also found myself instinctively searching the crowd for my father so I knew which areas to dodge. Fortunately, both had emulated my behavior. My father went to great lengths to elude me, while on the other hand, Ethan had been equally attentive of me, mingling politely with the crowd but his gaze never drifting far from mine.

Using every opportunity to survey him, I'd carefully positioned myself so I could zoom in with my camera, using groups of guests as convenient camouflage. I soaked him in, my eyes sliding over every mouthwatering, flawless inch of him. His was perfection personified—a work of art. A strutting, preening English peacock.

Each time our eyes locked, I shivered from the profound visceral effect of the connection. My heart pounded, my blood heated, and my insides yearned for the pleasure of the skillful touch which his raw, primal gaze silently promised.

Excitement and desire was building frantically inside me and suddenly, I was too hot, desperate for air and for space. I was about done with the photographs anyway and had been desperate to explore the grounds further. So in search of escape, I strolled down to the bottom of the gardens in the direction of the ocean.

A path of stepping stones led to an ornate iron gate with shrubs and small specimen trees on either side. Pushing through it found me at the top of a set of wooden steps leading down to a jetty and the beach. I'd caught a glimpse of the gate and what was beyond it from an upstairs window, so I'd kind of known what to expect. What I hadn't prepared for was the way in which the magnificent panorama would take my breath away.

My awed smile stretched lazily across my face as my gaze flitted over an endless private beach and miles of deep, blue ocean. I sauntered to the end of the wooden jetty, which, supported by rocks and boulders, ran straight through the wonderful sandy beach, projecting out into the ocean to form a dock.

When I reached the end, I kicked off my shoes, relishing the soothing effect from the sun-heated wood on my aching feet. I inched closer to the water until my feet grazed the edge of the wood, my toes curling slightly around the lip for balance, and stared out at the infinite horizon. Sucking in a deep, replenishing breath, I held it, closed my eyes, and breathed out slowly and steadily. The smell of the sea air was an instant energizer and wildly intoxicating.

The distant peals of laughter and chatter from the party dwindled away into insignificance. I could hear only the sound of the waves breaking gently against the shore and the harsh, high-pitched cries of hungry gulls.

Spreading my arms out to the sides, as though nailed to a cross, I spread my fingers wide to feel the soft caress of the breeze filter gently through the gaps. Tilting my face to the sun, I bathed in the glow, absorbing the warmth and comfort of the streaming rays of light on my skin. I closed my eyes again. The sense of peace and serenity was engrossing as I completely immersed myself in the freedom of my solitude.

I was so deeply absorbed and content in the moment that I neither saw nor heard the intruder approach. Suddenly, a voice broke through the silence, a voice I now recognized as Ethan's.

"I hope—"

I was so vehemently startled from my reverie that I virtually jumped out of my skin, losing my balance and almost falling into the water. His strong, competent arm reached out just in time, encircling my waist and pulling me back into the safety of his embrace. The heat from his breath grazed the skin on the back of my neck, and despite the warmth of the sun, an instant, tingling shiver cascaded down my spine. My nipples stiffened, jutting out suddenly like hard pearls through the sheer fabric of my dress.

Without thought, I stilled, savoring the unexpected physical contact, the safety of his arms, his woody, spicy scent—a smell so pungently sexy it was dizzying. The knowledge that it had become so easily and swiftly recognizable was somewhat unnerving. Then, leaning my head back slightly to rest on his shoulder, I slowly turned my face toward him. Our lips were now only millimeters apart. I could feel his breath on my face, taste him almost.

My eyes flickered up to meet his, impaling me with their vivid, striking blueness—as infinite and blue as the ocean before me. His gaze seemed to penetrate my soul so deeply that the desire and hope which flooded it was unmistakable. The rawness of his craving was near tangible and in poetic congruence with the intensity of mine.

My body quivered in response, my breath harsh against his lips, and as I exhaled, a soft, almost inaudible moan escaped from my throat. It was a subtle invitation, but more than enough to entice him. Ethan's mouth closed over mine. It was tentative at first—a soft, tender, gentle kiss igniting a burning, longing passion so great it snatched my breath away. His arms shifted from my waist to my hips, and slowly he turned me to face him, our kiss deepening, tongues licking and circling. He tasted delicious and my tongue dipped into his mouth greedily, hungering for more. I'd imagined this kiss so many times since our first encounter.

Instinctively, I ran my hands around the back of his neck and into his hair, pulling him closer, wanting to devour him. He responded eagerly, grasping me by my hips, his taut, rigid cock up against my abdomen making me gasp with anticipation and pure unadulterated want.

Suddenly, the sound of giggling disrupted the raging passion transpiring between us, and I pulled away, startled, breathless, and panting.

Two little girls around the ages of seven and nine had wandered off from the wedding party and were standing halfway between us and the steps from the garden. Both were visibly amused from our very public display of passion, attempting to stifle their chuckles behind cute, clenched fingers clamped firmly over their mouths. They nudged each other and ran off on to the beach, laughing and playing.

Returning my attention to Ethan, I noticed the sheepish grin which had spread across his wonderful face. Suddenly he looked quite boyish and youthful, seeming to relish in the pleasure of the moment. He stood with his hands in his pockets, smiling eyes glinting wickedly in the sunlight, peeping down at me through long thick lashes—a delightful combination of mischief and innocence.

"I don't know what it is you do to me, Miss Lawson, but I find it incredibly difficult to keep my wits about me when you're around. You do appear to incite the most unruly behavior from me."

God, that accent turned me on.

"Really, Mr. Wilde, I think you'll find that it is essentially you who instigates such wickedness. You are plainly awash with debauchery.

I'm merely an innocent casualty of your depravity."

Seemingly stunned by my bold retort, he began to laugh, poking me in the ribs teasingly and making me giggle.

The two little girls had dispensed with their shoes and socks and were splashing around at the water's edge, laughing playfully. It was wonderful to see them so liberated and unconcerned with the world, so uncomplicated and innocent. Eager to capture their spontaneity, I scooped up my camera and began to snap away.

"It's a pleasure to watch you work. You seem to revel in it," said Ethan, observing me with awed wonderment.

"I love my work, especially when it's like this—impulsive, unrehearsed. I tend to lose myself in it."

"I can see that. You have an amazing talent: the gift of observing a scene and capturing its story, almost before it unfolds. I'd love to see some of your work."

"You can view my webpage." I batted my eyelashes at him sassily before turning to look out at the ocean once more. Taking a deep breath, I filled my lungs, gulping greedily like it would be the last breath of air I would inhale for a while.

"You like it here, don't you?" His eyes narrowed pensively.

I nodded, closing my eyes against the warmth of the sun again. "It's so peaceful. It's the most relaxed I've felt in a long time. I'm certain I could just sit and gaze at the endless space forevermore and never tire of it."

Opening my eyes and sighing despondently, I slipped on my shoes, preparing to leave. "However, as much as I would love to stay and admire the view a while longer…" my gaze shimmied cheekily down the length of him to reinforce the double entendre "…I'm afraid I need to head back before—"

"May I drive you home?" he cut in before I had chance to finish.

"Oh. Well… I can't. I have my car with me."

"That's okay. I'll get one of my security team to drive it back for you."

"Security team?"

He shook his head dismissively, as though the detail wasn't important. "Are you ready to leave now?"

"No, not quite." I giggled, amused by his sudden zeal. "I need to speak with Claudia before I leave, and in any case, I haven't agreed to ride with you yet."

"No, but you will, Angel. You can't wait to be alone with me any more than I can wait to be inside you again. And I really don't think I can wait much longer. In fact, I might actually explode if you turn me down." His last words were spoken with an urgent, frantic need, and the effect was a catalyst for my rapidly mounting arousal.

The thought of declining Ethan's offer hadn't occurred to me for a second, and quite frankly wasn't even an option. I was desperate to be alone with him, he was right about that. The idea of spending the next couple of hours with him was a temptation beyond rejection.

Throwing caution to the wind, I responded in what I hoped was my most seductive voice. "Well, we can't have that, can we? I'll be ready in ten minutes."

Eager to be ready, I tracked down Claudia quickly to tell her I was done and about to leave. She tried to persuade me to stay and join the party, but I declined politely, telling her I had a long journey ahead and would call and arrange a meeting to go through the slides once they were ready. She thanked me again for responding at such short notice, and I rushed upstairs to the guest room to gather my things.

The prospect of spending some time alone with Ethan had me jittering with nervous excitement. He was the first man who'd had any real effect on me since James, and the mere memory of that whole episode of my life was almost enough to make me take off and never look back. Trust wouldn't come easy to me ever again, because being hurt wasn't something I cared to repeat. Casual sex was as far as I would normally allow it to go these days, but there was something about Ethan Wilde that drew me in, and I wanted—needed—to understand what it was.

After a last check around, I bent to fasten the zipper on my tote bag. Suddenly, I felt the vibes in the room change, and I knew without doubt he was behind me. I froze, the air around us charging with a sudden burst of electricity. An almost ethereal eeriness filled the room. His presence appeared to occupy all the available space around me, permeating my body to the core and invading my very soul. Ethan Wilde was proving to have an indefinable and profoundly potent effect on me. The knowledge, while making me vaguely uneasy, also had me feeling as horny as hell.

He approached slowly and with exhilarating silence, the magnetic force between us growing stronger with every nearing inch. I closed my eyes in gorgeous anticipation as I felt his lips glide across the back of my neck toward my ear. His warm breath on the sensitive spot below my lobe had me curving my neck to give him easier access, and he rewarded me with a gentle nibble to the delicate flesh.

He inhaled deeply. "God, you smell so fucking good."

The candor of his words hastened the rush of desire, prompting me to arch my back, pushing my backside toward him in search of his rigid bulge. He took me by the hips and pulled me backward against him, responding to my wordless request. And so that I could feel how hard he was, he tucked his swollen, pulsing hard-on between the curves of my butt. I gasped loudly and pushed myself into it, silently cursing the barrier of fabric which lay between us.

"I want you, Angel. Christ, I want you so bad, it's fucking painful." His voice rasped between hard, gusting breaths.

My sex clenched and ached with yearning, so desperate to feel his touch, but I needed to get a grip and remember where I was.

"We can't, Ethan, not here," I groaned, but my words contradicted my actions, because I was far too aroused to pull away.

Slowly, his hand slid slowly over my hip and down my thigh to the hem of my dress. "I need this, Angel. I need you to come for me right here, right now. Don't fight it, I beg you."

Oh God!

Goose bumps sprang to sheathe my body in a fine layer of hypersensitive nerve endings, causing my skin to tingle in glorious expectation. I'd gone too far. I needed this too.

I consented silently when I didn't protest, and with the faintest, featherlight touch, his eager fingers began their journey. His fingertips grazed gently over the sensitive skin of my inner thigh as they traveled from my knee to the edge of my lace panties. With every inch of their voyage, I became more aroused, my heart rate and breathing intensifying. His touch, only just detectable, gently stroked over the outside of my panties grazing my sex. My flesh pulsed and trembled in eager response. I'd never wanted a man's touch so much. My breasts ached with fullness, and groaning helplessly, I lifted my hands to them to soothe and massage.

"Oh yes, baby, play with your tits like that. Squeeze them, let me see you." His lips skimmed the side of my neck, my earlobe, his breathing becoming faster, heavier, with his growing arousal.

At last, a finger slid under the lace material to my pulsating, soaking wet flesh, the light massaging of my clitoris making me gasp and groan with pleasure.

"Oh, so ready, Angel." Ethan growled in my ear. "Your pussy is so wet and ready for me."

The sound of his voice and his lewd words revealing his appreciation and admiration pushed me to the edge, urging me to thrust against his hand in an invitation to enter my quivering slit. He didn't disappoint. His finger rubbed more firmly against my slick flesh and pushed inside me, opening me and stretching me. He slid in another, both fingers gliding effortlessly through my silky wetness. Unable to stop myself, I groaned loudly, my hips moving rhythmically to thrust against his expert fingers, and I could feel his satisfied smile against my cheek.

Reaching around and under my dress with his other hand, he began to rub the hypersensitive bud of my clit while continuing to finger-fuck me with the other. My climax was drawing closer, building with every delectable thrust, the height of ecstasy only seconds away. The pressure of his eager, throbbing cock pressing against my behind, coupled with the quickening of his fingers finished me off, and I exploded, coming into his hand violently and noisily.

At that moment, I heard footsteps approaching, and a deep, familiar voice, which seemed disturbingly close. "Ah, I'm looking for Angelica Lawson. The photographer?"

Shit, it was my father's voice and he was heading in my direction. I pushed Ethan away quickly toward the adjoining bathroom, my finger pressed tightly against my lips to silence him. He stared at me, startled and bewildered, a profusion of questions on the edge of his lips.

"Shh, please," I whispered with pleading eyes. He nodded once and ducked behind the bathroom door.

An unknown female voice answered my father's question. "You'll find her just along the corridor, the last door on the left, I think."

Still trembling from my explosive orgasm, I turned my attention quickly back to my tote bag. I was mortified, confounded by my inability to control myself when I was around Ethan Wilde. Yet again, I'd allowed myself to get carried away in the most conspicuous of places. Smoothing down my dress, I took a deep breath and glanced nervously toward the half-closed bathroom door to be certain that Ethan was sufficiently hidden. He was, and provided he didn't make a noise, I was confident my father wouldn't know he was there.

"Ah, there you are," my father boomed, entering the room without knocking. "Did I hear somebody back here with you? I thought I heard a noise."

I kept my head down to hide my burning red face. The mere thought of being caught by my father was too humiliating to even consider. Taking far longer than was necessary to fasten my bag, in an attempt to compose myself, I muttered quickly, "Oh, it was my toe—I stubbed my toe against the chair."

"Speak up, Angelica!" he hollered.

"Sorry, I stubbed my toe. You probably just heard me cry out."

"Always was clumsy." He shook his head with irritation. "I'm here to make sure that you're about to leave. Claudia mentioned she was going to ask you to stay. I'm trusting you remained professional and declined?"

"Yes, Dad, it's okay. I won't get in your way. I was just about to leave," I assured him bluntly.

"Good. Did you remember to tell her that the photographs were my gift to her and Rob?"

Opening my bag again, I pretended to rummage around for something I'd misplaced in the hope of keeping the conversation brief and avoiding eye contact. "We haven't discussed payment yet, but I'll be sure to make her aware when we meet to go over the proofs. She's a little busy today. I didn't feel it was appropriate to mention the invoice."

"No, well I was going to suggest that. Well, I'll leave you to it, then. Drive safely…"

The shock of his words and his apparent concern for my well-being caused me to bolt upright, my jaw dropping open in stunned amazement as I spun around to look at him.

Drive safely?

It was short lived.

"…See if you can contain your clumsiness for a couple of hours. You need to make sure you get that car back to Adam in one piece." Smirking, and apparently pleased with his parting shot, he turned to leave.

I glowered at his retreating back with embittered incredulity that this man would starve me of even the slightest bit of consideration.

Just as he was about to cross the threshold, he halted abruptly, paused for a second, and then turned ever so slowly to face me. My heart sank, my stomach turning inside out, as a look of wretched, blazing anger crept slowly up his neck to his face—as if something enraging had suddenly occurred to him. He stared at me with utter repugnance, as if I'd just knifed him savagely in the back, and for a second I was terrified he'd read my thoughts.

Glaring at my face, he strode purposefully toward me, his sudden haste and aggression, so dark and menacing it forced me to recoil as he drew closer. It was then I realized it wasn't my face he was focused on, it was my neck—my pendant—my mother's pendant.

I gasped in horrified realization as I became rudely conscience of my error. I'd completely forgotten I was wearing my pendant because I'd put it on that morning, foolishly unaware that my father would be attending. Instinctively, my hand raced to my neck to conceal it, but it was too late.

"What the hell ..?" he growled ferociously.

Suddenly, he reached out, grabbing my wrist and snatching it violently from my neck. His fingers closed tightly around the diamond pendant, and with a sadistic snarl, he ripped it brutally from my neck. I cried out loudly from the sudden searing pain as it sliced into my skin, watching in horror as the pendant tumbled to the floor, coming to rest under the edge of the bed.

As my father stooped to retrieve it, I suddenly became aware of Ethan. He stood on the threshold of the bathroom, a look of complete horror and fury instantly paling his complexion. His body shook, visibly vibrating with anger, and for one terrified moment, I thought he was about to launch himself at my father. I shook my head frantically, silently pleading with him to stay hidden as I mouthed the words *"No, please."*

My terrified expression stopped him dead in his tracks, but his uncertainty of how to react appeared to render him frozen. His eyes were filled with tumultuous conflict, torn between an innate need to retaliate to my father's vicious attack on me and doing what I was pleading with him to do—hide. Finally, but reluctantly, he withdrew back into the bathroom, his fury palpable but mercifully unobserved.

My father, having retrieved the pendant from under the bed, stood and glared at me, his face a bright, burning red of pure anger.

I mustn't cry. I mustn't cry.

His gaze flitted pitilessly over the wound on my neck where the chain had gouged into my skin—a scratch but deep enough to draw blood. "You have two minutes to get out of my fucking sight." Without another word he turned on his heel and stormed out of the room.

I gasped, greedily gulping the air I'd been withholding into my burning lungs. Red-hot, scorching tears seared my eyes, but I shook my head, blinking them away, refusing to succumb to my emotions and my father's vicious cruelty.

Suddenly, Ethan was standing before me. A combination of bewildered horror and devastating compassion etched into his face. He shook his head, as if desperately trying but unable to find the appropriate words to comfort me. For a second I wanted to hide my face in shame, horrified that he'd witnessed the ugliness of what should have been a private degradation and hating his resultant pity. But what I saw when I looked deeper was outrage at my indignity. His eyes glistened with angry, unshed tears as he raised his hand to gently wipe the trickle of blood dripping lightly down my neck. Then, cupping my chin, he leaned in and brushed a delicate, featherlight kiss across my lips. The gesture was so soothing and affectionate that for a moment the constant ache in my chest lifted and I felt nourished and strong.

In that moment, I'd never wanted or needed anybody more in my life. I pulled him to me, my mouth claiming his as I kissed him deeply. Without any hesitation, he responded hungrily, his tongue licking deep into my mouth as he pressed his lean body against me. His kiss was passionate and desperate, reassuring and curative, silently speaking all the words that for now he couldn't utter. Suddenly, he broke the kiss and looked down at me though sad, hooded eyes.

"Let's go." He took my hand and grabbing my bags led me out of the door.

I went with him without question, grateful that, for now at least, he hadn't questioned what had just happened. That he'd observed my father's contempt was enough without the shame of having to rationalize it. I was more than happy to forget it had ever happened and focus my attention on him. I would grieve for the loss of my mom's pendant, again, when I was alone.

As if by magic, Jackson was waiting for us outside next to the SUV. Disappointment flooded me, the mental image I'd conjured earlier—Ethan in the driver's seat of a sexy sports car offering me furtive glances, me having the opportunity to discreetly study his features, his strong hands gripping the steering wheel—disappearing in a puff of vapor… damn it!

Of course, I should have known that we would be driven, and that alone time wouldn't actually be *alone* time. But now I wasn't sure I could handle such proximity for such a lengthy journey without going out of my head with the need to touch him.

Jackson opened the rear door as we approached, nodding his greeting. Smiling in response, I did my best to conceal the fact that the poor man's presence frustrated me and climbed in, sliding along the bench seat to allow room for Ethan. The scent of luxury hit me once again and a faint fluttering of excitement heated my insides, as if I already associated the aroma with this outrageously sexy man.

Ethan spoke briefly to Jackson and another man, to whom he handed my car keys, and then slid into the seat next to me. As the vehicle slowly pulled away, Ethan turned to gaze at me. His pupils were dilated, dark and intense, simply oozing unmistakable lust and desire.

Just as I was wondering how the hell I was going to manage this torturous journey without fucking his brains out, Ethan reached out, pushing a button on the illuminated console built into the hardwood panel of the door.

Goddamn!

Much to my wildly delighted surprise, an electric privacy divider slid gently into place right behind Jackson and suddenly we were in total seclusion.

My heart began a battering rhythm against my chest, my skin

tingling and sex clenching as realization gradually dawned—what was an unlikely fantasy a few moments ago was now an imminent reality. We were alone.

"Oh." My voice was barely audible above the sound of blood pumping in my ears.

Ethan pulled me onto his lap to straddle him before the car had even left the grounds. For what seemed like an age, we gazed at each other with a mouthwatering craving, our breathing labored and heavy. Then, with a sudden urgency, his hands slithered up my parted thighs, pushing the delicate fabric of my dress up to my hips to reveal my panties. Lowering his chin, he angled his head downward before dragging his gaze from mine to fix on the spot where his hands gripped the tops of my thighs, both thumbs skimming the edge of lace.

The expression on his face was one of complete rapture, as if I were a long-awaited gift he was about to unwrap. The concept was unbearably arousing, and I groaned with aching want, my hips jerking involuntary toward him, begging for his touch.

"So eager, Angel." His voice was a mere whisper straining through the intensity of his longing.

At last, he slowly hooked a thumb under the delicate lace and gently tugged it to one side, exposing my soaking, pulsing flesh. A sharp gasp of appreciation hissed from his lips as he gazed down at my sex, his eyes wide with a look of deep veneration, as though it were the most wondrous sight ever to behold. His tongue snaked out, licking achingly slowly across his upper lip as he observed the action of his thumb stroking gently across the hot button of my clitoris.

"My God, you're so beautiful, Angel. Look at how wet you are for me." As he spoke, he placed the middle finger from his other hand at the entrance to my sex and began to rub in gentle circular motions, spreading my gushing juices around the opening of my body. "Soaking. Fucking. Wet."

By now, I'd reached a state of arousal I'd never encountered before. All traces of shyness and inhibitions forgotten, even under Ethan's close, blatant inspection of my most intimate parts. In fact, his patent, unashamed appreciation just made me hornier than ever, and I shunted forward, groaning with sinful pleasure. My body ached for him to enter me, my sex pulsing and quivering in needy anticipation.

"Please, Ethan," I implored him.

He smiled a dark, lazy, lust-filled smile. "Soon, Angel. I want to take my time. I want to savor every moment and every delicious part of you. You have the most beautiful pussy I've ever seen."

The directness of his remark and the way he spoke it, with such sincere adulation, almost sent me over the edge, and I thrust toward him again.

Groaning in response, he plunged a finger inside me, first one then two, angling them perfectly to reach the most sensitive zones. My sex quivered and clenched around him, drawing him in deeper as I shoved my hips forward to meet every decadent thrust. He continued to observe his own actions as he sunk his expert fingers inside me over and over, his arousal mounting with every driving inch. He looked up, his fervent gaze resting on my face to study my wanton pleasure.

"Oh my God, Angel, I need to taste you."

Oh Jesus, I wasn't sure if I could take this. I was already almost crazed with the burning desire to come. In one deft movement, he flipped me so I sat in his position and he was kneeling on the floor in front of me. Gripping my hips, he yanked my ass toward him and slid my panties off, pushing my knees apart to spread my legs wide open. He ran his hands smoothly up the sensitive skin of my inner thighs, pushing them wider as he reached the summit, his thumbs spreading my hot, swollen folds displaying me fully for his indulgence.

A shiver of exhilarating need slid silkily through my body as his eyes skimmed over me in blissful reverence. He knelt before me as though I were worthy of exaltation, of being worshipped like some supreme goddess.

When his eyes finally found mine, he slowly lowered his head between my legs until his mouth was only inches away from my soaking sex. He blew gently, the air, chilled against my dampness, sending a shockwave of electric currents racing through my nerve endings. Then, as if this gesture wasn't salaciously attentive enough, he proceeded to blow my mind when his nose dipped toward my trembling sex and inhaled deeply, breathing in my scent. "Oh yes." His voice was hoarse with pure desire. "Oh Christ, you smell so good."

God this man was going to drive me insane. Struggling to contain my mounting need, I gripped the seats at either side of me, digging my nails into the soft, plush leather as though I were clinging to life itself.

I cried out as his nose nudged against my clitoris, sending searing, painful pleasure right through the center of my core. "Oh my God, Ethan, please."

"What is it, Angel? Tell me what you want?"

"Taste me. Taste me, Ethan, I beg you." His tongue flicked against me once, twice—then again and again, hitting the swollen, pulsing spot every time. The building pleasure became a dull, sensual ache as my body screamed and trembled, craving the climax I knew would come. His tongue lapped at me, licking my throbbing flesh, sliding inside me, in and out, pushing me closer and closer to the edge of insanity.

I shoved my hands into his hair and thrust my pussy against his hungry mouth, urging him deeper. Swiftly, he caught me by my wrists, pinning them to my sides to prevent my intervention. This man knew what he wanted. He was in complete control and he would devour me at his own pace.

Just as I thought I was about to lose my mind with the need to come, he released one of my hands and inserted a finger inside me, moving it in and out rhythmically while lashing at me with his tongue. He licked and nibbled hungrily at my clitoris, driving me higher than I've ever been, until finally, I exploded, erupting like a violent volcano. My body jerked and convulsed as I pumped my hips, shamelessly grinding myself into his skillful mouth. I cried out in a voice I didn't recognize as my own, my body ragged and weary from the extreme, overwhelming sensations.

He gazed up into my eyes, watching as I struggled to control my shuddering body and lapping at me gently until the quaking tremors began to subside. "You're the most beautiful creature I've ever seen, Angel." His words whispered gently over my throbbing, sensitive flesh. "And when you come—when your body writhes with pleasure, basking so willingly in the pinnacle of sensation, you are utterly breathtaking. I've never wanted anybody more than I want you. God, you're making me fucking crazy."

Mindless with passion, I stared at him, breathless and wordless—unable to even form a sentence. I'd just experienced the most mind-blowing orgasm of my existence, and I still wanted more of this man.

Abruptly, he pushed to his knees and unfastened his pants, lowering them to release his magnificent, bulging cock. "I need to be inside you." He spoke with urgency as he retrieved a foil packet from his jacket lying strewn on the floor at his feet. Then, ripping it open, he rolled the condom down over his thick, throbbing shaft.

His strong hands moved under me to cup my buttocks, urging me closer to the edge of the seat. And then his lips were crashing into mine, claiming me ravenously as his tongue dipped into my mouth with long, deep, decadent licks.

"Taste it," he said, his voice ragged as he lost himself in the kiss. "I want you to know how sweet you taste. Sweeter than I ever dreamed you'd be."

Incited by his words, I licked and sucked at his tongue, greedily devouring the remnants of my arousal, both of us panting and groaning into each other's mouths. Lifting my arms, he tugged my dress over my head and tossed it aside then unhooked my bra and slid it down my arms. His eyes wandered appraisingly over my body.

I needed him inside me desperately. Reaching up, I took hold of his shirt, grasping it at collar height and viciously ripping it open. Buttons popped and scattered in various directions, his shirt falling away to fully expose the solid, flexing muscles of his chest and abs.

"Fuck me, Ethan," I pleaded.

"Oh, Christ, Angel," he growled, taking a firm grip of my butt to hold me in place.

Guiding his thick, hard cock toward my sodden entrance, he paused, his eyes gazing unyielding into mine before plunging deep inside me. I gasped helplessly, the overwhelming fullness seizing my breath, the burning sting of pleasure rippling through my core as he took me the whole length of his impressive cock.

We moved rhythmically, in time with each other, meeting thrust for thrust, lost in a world known only to us. Our bodies were a mass of earth-shattering sensations as we fucked with an almost feral, intrinsic need, wholly consuming each other in a helpless haze of desire.

He withdrew and in one fluid movement, flipped me over to enter from behind. The extent of his size as he thrust back into me was a whole new sensation from the altered position, and the way he lay across my back, burying his face into my neck, kissing and nibbling, was as if he were claiming me entirely.

A low rumble escaped his throat, raw and carnal, as he rocked into me. Reaching round to cup my breast, he tugged and squeezed my nipple, his other hand moving to massage my clitoris, every punishing thrust of his pounding cock sending scorching hot waves of pleasure through my body. My orgasm started to build again, gathering from somewhere deep within and bursting like liquid fire through my bloodstream, my muscles tensing and quivering as my whole body vibrated in pure ecstasy. And then sweet, sweet release rippled through my veins as my body went limp and crumpled beneath him.

Just as I felt my depleted body could take no more, he picked me up, moving to sit on the seat and positioning me so I straddled him again. Being cautious with my swollen, sensitive flesh, he pulled me gently down onto him, entering me again.

"I need to see you, Angel. I want to lose myself in your eyes when I spurt my hot come into your tight little pussy."

Although physically drained, I began to move again, my gaze penetrating those dark, lust-filled eyes, readily and eagerly responding to his needs and desires. Burrowing his hands into my hair, he pulled me down to kiss me, groaning and moaning into my mouth, his breathing hard and rasping as he sucked and nibbled my swollen lips. I rode him harder, thrusting against him, nailing him to the seat. Sweat poured from our reckless bodies as need and yearning powered through us.

My body began to quicken again, closer and higher, until finally, another orgasm ripped through my body, sending me spiraling into oblivion. Ethan's gaze never strayed from mine, and the sight of my shattering climax was his undoing. He came hard and fast, the tremors of his ecstasy powering through him like a raging storm. He pulsed and jerked inside me, a primal groan grating from his throat, his eyes widening then closing slowly as he finally found his release.

I collapsed on top of him, my body boneless and limp. Ethan nuzzled gently into my neck, with hot replenishing gasps. It was then that I became aware of the tears rolling silently down my cheeks.

Ethan cupped my face, his expression full of warmth and compassion as he pulled me gently toward him to kiss the salty tears away, his thumb brushing over my bruised and tender lips. "What have you done to me, Angel?"

My emotions were suddenly overwhelming, swamping me so completely that words became impossible. Our exchange had been beyond a physical release; it had been engulfed in a passion and a raw veneration I'd never experienced before. He held me for the longest time, stroking my hair and kissing me gently, my tears an endless cathartic deluge of crushed emotions.

From this moment on our lives would never be the same. Ethan and I had connected both physically and spiritually—to a degree I wasn't even aware was possible and wouldn't even begin to understand for a long time to come. I was drawn to this man in a way I couldn't comprehend, as though he were a missing part of me which I'd unwittingly been searching for. And for the first time in my entire existence, I began to breathe.

CHAPTER SIX

S atisfied at last with my chosen outfit, I stood back to gaze at my reflection in the glass of the huge, floor-to-ceiling mirror in my bedroom.

I'd selected a champagne-colored silhouette mini-dress with a strapless neckline. Over the top was a sleeveless, see-through overlay with a drop waist and full-feathered skirt giving the suggestive creation a classy twist of cheeky-chic. My hair was brushed into a tight chignon to the side of my neck, and metallic, smoky eyes teamed with nude, glossy lips finished my look. I felt sophisticated and sexy.

Nervous excitement about dinner with Ethan had built progressively throughout the course of the day, and I was practically fit to burst. Butterflies fluttered wildly in my tummy, and I was struck by the thought that I'd never been nervous in anticipation of a date before.

Along with more incredibly beautiful flowers, I'd received text messages steadily throughout the morning and afternoon.

The messages were simple but affective:

Good morning, Cinders x
I can still taste you x
Hope you're having a good day. Can't wait to see you x
Looking forward to tonight. Feel like a small child at Christmas x

The last one was so cute, and a complete mirror image of my own feelings, that it only served to exacerbate my already fraying nerves.

We'd arranged for him to collect me at seven o'clock, but when the time came, I rode the elevator down to the ground floor to meet him, not ready to relinquish any part of my sanctuary yet.

As the elevator door slid open, I saw him standing before me, head cocked to one side, hands in pockets. A sultry smile sashayed across his lips as his scorching hot eyes slithered appreciatively up and down my body, finally coming to rest on my lips. Then, as if asserting his right to touch me, he stepped forward laying his hands confidently on my waist and bowed his head to kiss me. The passion which crackled between us was immediate and intense, taking both of us by surprise.

"You are utterly dazzling, Miss Lawson."

"You're too kind, Mr. Wilde." My eyes flittered to the floor shyly.

Smiling sweetly, he offered me his arm. "Shall we?"

Jackson was waiting by the car, a warm smile settling on his face as we approached. "Good evening, Miss Lawson."

"Hello, Jackson, it's lovely to see you again." Flushing lightly, I wondered if he'd heard the frenzied commotion in the rear of the limo the day before. He nodded graciously as he opened the door and we slid into the back.

"If you're worried, the discretion barrier in the SUV also comes with soundproofing," Ethan whispered, biting his lip to curb a mischievous smile.

My cheeks heated again, not only because he'd read my thoughts, but because the memory of our debauched romp was clearly vivid in his thoughts too. It was as if the two of us were privy to a secret no one else would ever be aware of, and the knowledge seemed to reestablish the connection we'd kindled immediately. As if affirming the notion, Ethan took my hand, cradling it firmly in his lap, the demonstrative gesture coming so easily to him that it took me by surprise.

"Sorry," he said suddenly, catching my expression. "I'm afraid I find it incredibly difficult to be around you without touching you. Do you mind?"

Tactility wasn't something which came naturally to me. Other than sex, I had no real experience of physical contact, certainly not of a sentimental nature. But I felt strangely and completely at ease with this man, and the need and desire to touch him seemed not only innate, but essential. Suddenly, I realized that the nervous tension which had accumulated steadily over the course of the day had completely vanished.

As I gazed back at him waiting patiently for my answer, it was like I knew his face so well. His charming, boyish grin reminded me of the image I'd conjured when I'd received his text about the small boy at Christmas.

No, I didn't mind in the least.

I shook my head to answer his question. Then, glancing down at our intertwined fingers, I sighed and sat back in my seat to revel in the warmth of the contact.

The restaurant was in the heart of Manhattan's Upper East Side, between Park and Madison, and boasted delectable Parisian cuisine. Its setting was designed with a contemporary finish over neo-classical architecture, creating an elegant and vibrant ambience.

If my hunch was correct, the restaurant was almost definitely owned by the Wildes, because by the time we'd been seated at the most private table in the room, Ethan had been greeted by name on several occasions. People turned in their seats to stare after him; women, both accompanied and otherwise, batted eyelashes in the hope of attracting his attention. It seemed that Ethan Wilde could seduce a room by simply existing.

Ethan, however, seemed oblivious to it all, and apart from a brief glance at the menu, his eyes never left my face. He ordered for both of us, selecting both food and wine that would have been my exact favored choices. We chatted casually about random subjects for a short time while we waited for our drinks to arrive, and as every second passed, I warmed to him more and more.

My eyes flickered around the room. "Nice choice of restaurant," I said, attempting to take the conversation to a more personal level, but also intrigued as to whether I was right about it being part of the Wilde's portfolio.

"Yes, it has an excellent reputation. I wanted to ensure you enjoyed yourself." Okay, so he wasn't giving anything away yet.

"I see. Well, if I do—enjoy myself, that is—next time it will be my turn to choose the restaurant."

Clearly brightened by the prospect of a *next time*, he smiled wryly. "I'll look forward to it."

"You talk like it's in the bag. What if I have a completely miserable evening?"

"Oh, it's in the bag, Cinders, I can assure you."

Christ, he simply oozed poise and self-assurance and it pushed my buttons wildly. My mind began drifting to the way he'd looked at me on the journey home from the wedding, as he'd positioned himself between my legs, his sultry gaze admiring and appreciating my most intimate areas in silent veneration.

My sex clenched at the memory alone, and as I began to wriggle in my seat, I suddenly realized that my gaze was firmly fixed on his delectable mouth. *Holy shit, I'm just sitting here having dinner with the guy and I'm practically ready to go off.* Biting down on my lip sharply, I averted my eyes, scanning the room in an attempt to distract myself from my explicit thoughts.

He followed my gaze, seemingly curious as to why my attention had been diverted away from him, and for the first time seemed to notice the interest we drew from the other diners. "You appear to be the center of attention, Angel. Not that I can blame anyone for fixating on the most beautiful creature in the room. I'm having a hard time focusing on anything else myself."

Laughing once, I replied without thinking. "Yeah, they're probably wondering what the hell one of the most gorgeous, richest, powerful men in the country is doing having dinner with *me*."

The comment appeared to shock him and then I realized what I'd said. "Two things, Miss Lawson. Firstly, don't ever put yourself down to me again—you're beyond beautiful, embrace it. And secondly, how do *you* know how rich and powerful I am?"

Cringing inwardly, it dawned on me how my comment might be interpreted. Instinctively, my hand fluttered to my face, an attempt to conceal my heated cheeks, and as I peeked through the gaps in my fingers, I noted a look of wonderment flit briefly across his face. At that moment the waiter arrived, placing appetizers of duck confit on the table in front of us. The timing couldn't have been more perfect. I'd never been so grateful for the presence of a waiter, and I took full advantage of the brief break in conversation to compose myself.

"That's not why I agreed to have dinner with you," I said defensively when the waiter moved away.

"I didn't say it was," he laughed. "There's no shame in being curious, Angel. I'm flattered that you were intrigued enough to do some research. I certainly was. In fact, why don't we play a game? We could see which one of us really did their homework. I'll go first."

Smiling playfully, he launched into a full and accurate account of my life so far. In fact, as I nibbled my way through the delicious appetizer, he recounted the names of my brothers and their chosen professions; he knew my high school and details of my professional footpath. He even knew information about aspects of the gallery's incorporation and shareholder particulars. He'd certainly done his homework.

"Now, why don't you take a turn, and when you're done we'll have some fun filling in the blanks," he laughed, clearly pleased with himself.

For a second I stared at him dumbstruck. "Well, at least I had the good grace to show contrition for my snooping."

"Why be contrite? I'm not ashamed or sorry about the fact that you've beguiled me so completely, I'm prepared to go to great lengths to learn more. I was rather hoping it was a similar fascination which urged you to do the same. Or am I completely off the mark? Perhaps your interest was merely precautionary. A means to safeguard yourself from having dinner with a convicted murderer or something." His demeanor changed instantly, morphing from one of self-assuredness to one of self-doubt. "That wasn't the reason was it?"

In a cruel attempt to prolong his agony, I hesitated before answering, my expression as poker-faced as I could manage. Not having the heart to keep it up for long, I broke into a mischievous giggle, and instantly he relaxed, his eyes narrowing in playful rebuke as he began to laugh with me.

"Well, I admit curiosity did get the better of me," I confessed, "but only briefly. Just long enough to learn the very basic facts about Wilde Industries—but nothing of a personal nature. After all, the night we first met, you intrigued me sufficiently enough to trust my instincts, and we both know what that led to." I paused as his eyes darkened with the mention of that first encounter. "Anyway, where would the fun be in discovering more about you from a search engine? For one, you can't always believe what you read, and I'm certain there's more pleasure to be had in discovering the real Ethan Wilde from my own personal experiences. I know I've had lots of fun so far. It just might take a while longer than expected to fill in the blanks."

Mother of Christ, what in the hell was it was about this man that compelled me to be so outwardly flirtatious and abandon all measures of constraint? I wondered this only briefly, because frankly, I was enjoying myself far too much to care. Ethan raised an eyebrow and smiled a slow, dark, appreciative smile.

"Well answered, Miss Lawson. I'm sure you're right. Getting to know each other better promises to be very pleasing indeed. In fact, the longer I spend in your company, the more certain I am of it. And don't worry about the length of time it's going to take. The longer, the better, as far as I'm concerned. So, why don't we get started? I do believe it's your turn to go first."

"I do believe you're right, Mr. Wilde."

I was beyond eager to know more about this man, hungry for every tidbit he was willing to share. I hesitated, wondering where best to start then figured there was only one place: the beginning. "Tell me about England. Why did your family make the move to the UK, and when did you move back?"

My sudden zeal appeared to amuse him, his lip kinking into a wry smile. "We moved to London when I was six. My grandfather owned a whole heap of hotels and restaurants across the States and my father wanted to expand the business into the UK. Once there, he branched into commercial real estate; took the business to a whole new level. Sadly, when I was nineteen, my grandfather took fatally ill and my father was needed in the business here, so the family moved back to New York. He handed the UK reins over to me and came home to spin his magic in the States. I've spent the last ten years expanding the residential element of the UK business, plus the development of a chain of health clubs, spas, casinos, hotels, and bars. But then I'm afraid history began to repeat itself."

He paused briefly, waiting for the waiter to serve a main course of seared salmon with roasted chestnuts and caramelized apples before continuing. "My father needed emergency heart surgery six months ago." I grimaced, an expression of my sympathy and concern, but not wanting to interrupt while he was in the flow said nothing. "It was a hair-raising time, but fortunately, he's now on the mend. Providing he sticks to doctor's orders—a stress-free diet—he should make a full recovery. My mom is doing her best to force him into early retirement, so she's dragged him on an extended world trip to recuperate. It's the only way he's guaranteed to keep his feet up and stay away from the office. They've been gone a couple of months, somewhere in Thailand at the moment, I believe. Needless to say, I'm now needed here; so here I am. London and I had just about finished our love affair anyway. It's good to be home."

"Wow." I was genuinely shocked. "Becoming a successful industrial tycoon must be intrinsic to your bloodline. That's a hell of a young age to take on running an empire, much less expand it. I'm impressed."

"I had a good teacher," he laughed. "And yes, I suppose business runs in the blood."

"You're close to your family." It was a statement, not a question. I could tell from what I'd heard so far that I was right.

"Yes, I am."

"That was your sister, yesterday, in the pool house?"

"Abby, yes." His eyes lit up. "She's the baby of the family, although she hates it when I call her that. She thinks I'm somewhat over protective, says I still treat her like she's twelve or something." He smiled warmly and clearly adored his sister. "You looked like you were having fun hanging out with the girlies."

"Did I?" Blinking rapidly, I looked away, suddenly embarrassed that he'd witnessed me engaging in such juvenile frivolity. "I don't think I had much choice, really, I guess they took me by surprise. In fact, I was pretty much ambushed, so it was a matter of self-defense. Kill or be killed."

"I see. Well, I had lots of fun watching you. In fact, I enjoyed every moment. You look incredibly hot when you're in survival mode." His gaze took on that dark-eyed, smoldering look again, the one which distracted me so easily, but I was still hungry for information and, for the moment, reluctant to digress.

"So, how do you know Claudia?" I pushed on, ignoring the flattery.

"Abby is good friends with her daughter, Alisha. They've been friends since childhood. She's a good kid—Alisha—but she's had some problems, and I promised Mom and Dad that I'd take care of Abby while they're away."

I nodded, suddenly realizing why Ethan had been present at the wedding. He was safeguarding his sister.

"I can understand that. Claudia filled me in a little," I added, as way of explanation. I took a breath, before continuing. "Apparently, my father was Alisha's therapist. Although, I had no idea until yesterday. I guess Claudia assumed I'd already known, that my father might have mentioned it to me." I shook my head at the ridiculous notion.

"Ah. Yes, of course, that would make sense. I did wonder what connection your father had to the family." He paused, as if choosing his next words carefully. "I'm guessing you're not so close to your family?"

Instantly uneasy with the question, I glanced down at my plate. "My brother Adam," I said, nodding, and then felt rather foolish. I loved Adam, he was my brother, but you definitely would not describe our relationship as close. Not in the way Ethan was close to his family. "Although, mostly when we were kids," I added quickly.

Without looking up to meet Ethan's eyes, I could sense his gaze zeroing in on the side of my neck where my hair was pinned into a chignon. It had been a transparent and futile attempt to hide my bruised, grazed skin—the result of my father's aggressive outburst the day before. Humiliation burned through me once again, my hand instinctively fluttering to the spot.

Ethan's hand shot out, closing over mine and lowering it back to the table. Then taking my chin lightly between thumb and forefinger, he tilted my head slightly to examine my marred skin. Slowly, he ran the edge of his thumb gently down the side of my neck. It was a soothing, yet intimate gesture, and sent an instant surge of wonderful sensations tumbling down my spine. I closed my eyes to the exhilarating, responding shiver.

"Are you going to tell me what happened yesterday with your father?" he asked softly. "I haven't been able to shake it from my mind. I don't understand why he was so violent toward you. The way he spoke to—"

"It was nothing," I interjected quickly. "It was my fault, really. I shouldn't have worn the pendant—I shouldn't have even had the pendant. He had a right to be angry."

With narrowed eyes, he stared at me like I'd just committed an atrocity. "How can you say that? Nobody has the right to assault somebody like that, especially not their own daughter. I wanted to rip his fucking head off his shoulders." His voice had risen in anger, his face flushing furiously as he glanced around the room remembering where he was.

Despite feeling guarded about the events of yesterday, I was stunned by his reaction and found myself smiling with bashful gratitude. It felt nice having someone concerned for me, protective of me. It made me feel cherished.

"I'm not joking, Angel," he snapped. "You have no clue as to how much inner strength it took to hold myself back yesterday. The only thing stopping me was the look of absolute fear written all over your face. Why are you so afraid of him?" His eyes burned into mine, as if searching deep into my soul for the answers he was looking for.

Answers I knew I could not give him.

"Look, I'm sorry you had to witness that yesterday, but there really is no need to be concerned. It was bad enough he barged in on us once, let's not allow him to ruin tonight for us as well." My tone was dismissive, so I followed my words with a smile attempting to smooth the burn.

Cautious eyes assessed me from across the table and for a dreadful moment I worried that he wasn't going to let the matter drop. Finally, the tension seemed to melt away from the muscles in his face, but the resolution which replaced it was unmistakable.

"Very well, Angel. I can see you don't want to discuss this right now, but be certain of two things. Firstly—if he ever lays so much as a finger on you again, I won't be so easily subdued. I'll just kill the cowardly fucker. And second—your reluctance to open up to me simply just won't do. I want to spend time with you—a lot of time, with your permission. I don't understand how or why, but you've quickly become very precious to me, and I think you feel it too. I feel drawn to you, connected to you, and I like to take care of those I cherish. So I'll agree to leave it for now, but it's imperative you stop hiding from me, Angel. In fact, it's absolute law."

Oh crap.

Rigid and speechless, all I could do was stare at him, conflicting thoughts and emotions racing through my mind. He was right. I did feel it, and I was torn between being excited by it and being bone rigid terrified of it. Part of me wanted to run like hell, because deep down I knew that being with this man would mean exposing my inner demons. It would mean facing issues which I'd avoided all my life. And that would also mean exposing my heart.

In my lifelong struggle to fend off the pain of loneliness that came with rejection, I'd developed something of a thick skin, and emotionally I'd lived my life in solitude. Other than the fundamental role of pumping blood to my body, my heart served no purpose. It was cold like stone, lifeless and unused—but at least that way it was preserved. That way it wouldn't feel pain.

In fact, I'd spent so long building the almost impenetrable protective barrier around me, I wasn't sure I'd left a gap large enough to allow anybody in even if I wanted to. And if that were the case, it also meant there was no means of ever escaping my solitude.

And then Ethan had barged into my life, forceful and demanding, with a confidence beyond all realms of comprehension. He'd seemed to position himself, as if a relationship with me was a foregone conclusion. But I didn't feel bullied or repelled by his advances. Instead, I had a strange and overwhelming sense of relief and warmth, as if the tremendous weight I'd carried alone was almost too much to bear, and suddenly I'd been swooped up, supported, fortified—no longer alone.

Perhaps there were cracks in my protective barrier, after all—a chance to escape my solitude. The question was could I afford for Ethan to barge into my heart, the way he'd barged into my life? And if the answer was yes, would it remain intact or break altogether? Would he give me strength, or would he make me weak? Should I flee before I perish or stay and discover the answers to my questions?

Of course, I knew the answers, at least to the final question. I was compelled to see where this journey would take me. There was something about the way Ethan made me feel that I was helpless to ignore. And there was something else—one thing I was absolutely certain of—and that was the unmistakable sexual energy which raged, untamed and unconcluded, between us. This man only needed to glimpse in my direction for me to want to tear his clothes off and fuck him until we were both in danger of it killing us.

At that moment, I couldn't have been more turned on. Not even if Ethan were to stand butt-naked before me. Mind-blowing fuckery with this man, anywhere and everywhere, as often as my body could take it, was all I could think about.

Before I could avert them, I realized my thoughts must be beaming like beacons from my eyes, etched all over my goddamn transparent face.

Ethan leaned in toward me, his gaze coming to rest on my mouth, and gently tugged my lower lip out from between my teeth. "You dirty, dirty girl," he whispered sensually.

Mother of fucking Christ!

He'd seen through me as easily as looking through a freaking window.

"How do you know what I'm thinking?" I breathed.

Reaching out, he cradled my face lightly in his fingers. "Because we're the same, you and I. Connected in some way. I knew it from the moment I laid eyes on you. You invite me in, bewitching me with your magic, leaving me helpless and unable to resist. Like a moth to a flame. 'Thus hath the candle singed the moth.'"

"*The Merchant of Venice.*"

He smiled. "You see? The same. You'd just better see to it that you're not my undoing."

"Or you mine," I warned him. "I don't relish the idea of being burned alive."

Pulling my face close to his, he kissed me gently.

"Ahem." The waiter cleared his throat, embarrassed that he'd intruded on our intimate moment. "Is everything all right, sir?

Madame?" He nodded toward our barely eaten food.

We both looked down at our plates, Ethan's hand still resting on my face, and giggled. Food was the last thing on either of our minds.

"Shall we get out of here?" Ethan whispered.

Unable to prevent my budding smile from unfurling across my face, I nodded.

Ethan stood to pull out my chair and turned to the waiter saying, "Yes, everything was delightful, thank you. But if we don't satisfy our hunger soon, I fear we'll both starve to death."

I burst into laughter as he took me by the arm and guided me through the sea of captivated diners, leaving the poor, bewildered waiter dumbstruck and open-mouthed.

As usual, Jackson's timing was perfect and he was pulling up to the curb as we escaped on to the street, laughing playfully. Ethan stopped and pulled me into a tight embrace, his eyes cheery and relaxed as he leaned in and planted an ardent kiss firmly onto my lips.

"Mmm, you're too damned hot for me, Miss Lawson," he said with a wicked glint in his eye. "I think I need to put you on ice for a while, calm you down."

Taking my hand, we turned to find Jackson waiting patiently with the door open, an approving smile rippling over his handsome face.

"Hey, Jackson," Ethan greeted him. "Miss Lawson and I would like to go dancing."

Jackson's smile widened, clearly amused by his boss's playful mood. "Of course, boss."

The club was huge with several bars and seating areas full of black lacquer and shiny chrome, glass, and polished surfaces. It featured timeless, luxurious finishes, including Italian marble and plush black leather. The atmosphere was energetic and lively, but comfortable and intimate.

We were escorted to a booth in one of the quieter areas by a pretty, curvy brunette, who not only knew Ethan by name, but batted her eyelashes shamelessly in the hope of being noticed. I seethed—quietly. To my delight, Ethan seemed unaware and, apart from placing his arm around me in a silent statement that he was unavailable, made no attempt to acknowledge it.

After taking our order for champagne, the brunette tottered away, disappointed that her attempts to gain his attention had gone unheeded.

"One of yours?" I asked.

He turned to look at the departing brunette, a puzzled and distasteful expression crumpling his face.

"The club, not the girl," I clarified.

"I was going say. Yes, the club is one of ours."

"I take it the girl isn't your type."

"God no. Way too obvious. And… no, just no."

"Well, if obvious repels you so, what the hell am I doing here? I'd say unacquainted fuckety-fuckery in a storage room is as pretty damned obvious as it gets."

"Fuckety who?" he laughed. "And you weren't obvious. You were alluring, hypnotizing. You, Angel, are my type. You're quite unique. A rare diamond."

As usual, his perception of me mystified me beyond words. Calvin Harris and Ellie Goulding began to belt out, "I Need Your Love" and without warning, he stood, pulling me to my feet and headed for the dance floor.

We danced for what seemed like forever and until a fine sheen of sweat glistened on the surface of our skin, having frivolous, easy fun the way you'd expect to enjoy yourself with your closest friend on the dance floor. And then as the tunes became slower and the energy heated, we danced more intimately, more suggestively, our hands touching and stroking—dancing like lovers. And boy, this man could dance.

Eventually, thirst drove us back to our table, where we sipped ice-cold champagne, and I told Ethan all about Jia. How we'd met, how she'd encouraged me to take my love of photography seriously, and how that had led to the opening of the gallery.

"It sounds like she means a lot to you."

"Yes. She is fearsome, but yeah."

"It's good to have strong, reliable people around you."

I nodded. "So what's the story with Jackson? You guys seem to be able to communicate without speaking. You telepathic or something?"

He seemed amused by my whimsical notion. "Admittedly, we do get away with minimal discourse. The secret to having a great right-hand man is to ensure he's fluent in your unspoken language. When he knows what you need to do or where you need to go, almost before you do, is when you're certain he's the right man for the job. And Jackson's brilliant at his, which makes my life a whole lot easier."

"And what is his job? Other than driving you around on your dates?"

The way he narrowed his eyes knowingly implied he knew I was grilling him about his love life, and he wasn't giving much away.

"Well, as you rightly say, he drives me—not specifically on dates, I might add. He's head of my security team, and he's... *The Man*."

"The man?"

"When I met him he was working the door at one of my clubs in London, advancing quickly to head up security across all of my clubs. He intervened in a situation one night, when things got... tricky. He went the extra mile when he was required to, and he did it without question—instinctively. He's an inherent protector. My strong, reliable person, I suppose."

"He's your bodyguard?"

He laughed. "And a solid sounding board, as it goes. He gives some very good advice, but don't ever tell him I said so. It'll go to his head."

"You value him a lot. I like that."

"Jackson's a good person. He was brought up by his grandmother, no other family that I know of. Turns out he was subsidizing his salary from the club by taking part in illegal fights to keep a roof over their heads. She was old and sick and needed full-time care, and fighting was the only way he could afford it. I saw him fight a couple of times." He winced, like the experience had been a remarkable one. "Let's just say that everybody could benefit with somebody like Jackson on their side—intrepid, dependable, and tenacious. So I offered him a job. One he couldn't turn down. He and his grandmother became like family." He paused, looking suddenly sad. "She died just over eighteen months ago."

My heart did a flip as I gazed at his poignant expression, his sorrow as clearly discernable as the nose on his face. This man wore his heart on his sleeve, and that was something completely unfamiliar to me. I found it overwhelmingly endearing and without deliberation, I instinctively reached out for his hand.

He responded eagerly, enfolding my proffered hand in his, then with a tentative but hopeful expression, he tilted his chin down and looked up at me through long, thick lashes. "Now, tell me, Angel, did I succeed? Have you had a good time?"

"Are you kidding? I have had the best night."

He smiled broadly, openly relieved. "Good, because that means you get to choose what we do on our next date. See, I told you it was in the bag."

Pulling me closer, he hooked my knees over his thigh, positioning me so my legs hung down between his, his left hand just above my knee. With his other arm folded around my back, his fingers began to trace light circles at the nape of my neck, instantly igniting the glowing embers of our mutual desire. Shifting gently, they dipped into the hollow beneath my ear, before tracing across my jawline and round to caress my lips. I nuzzled into his touch, inhaling the scent of his skin, my lips parting to tug and nibble the tip of his thumb with my teeth. He inhaled sharply, his eyes growing large and dark.

With stealthy adeptness, he navigated his left hand upwards, sliding under the fine fabric of my dress and along my inner thigh, coming to an abrupt pause at the summit and the fine edge of silk. My blood heated and suddenly I was on fire for him, my nipples taut, sex thudding with an urgent need. Leaving mine briefly, his gaze scanned the room behind us, as if reassuring himself of our state of privacy. My back was turned to the rest of the room and the low, intimate light cast large dark shadows over our seated area, making us virtually undetectable.

As his eyes returned to mine, they were black as bullets, full of promise and desire. My breath caught as his fingers deftly slid inside my panties and entered me. My response seemed to incite him, his lips parting to release a hiss smoldering with passion as he sunk his fingers into me over and over, slowly and deliciously palming my clitoris in delectable circular movements.

"Oh God," I muttered, unable to stop myself from rocking gently against his hand.

He bit down on his lip, sucking it through his teeth, the gesture so erotic it just made me want it harder, and my muscles began to squeeze around his fingers, gripping him greedily. The expression on his face was one of uncontrolled lust, his breathing growing labored as he surveyed me yielding to his touch, my climax mounting higher and closer, my hips rocking forward to grind against his hand.

"That's it, Angel. I can feel your tight little pussy as it squeezes around my fingers. Come against my hand. Come for me now."

This lewd, intimate act in this most public of places, combined with his lascivious words pushed me over the edge, and I gave myself to the swirling orgasm shooting through my core. I leaned in, my forehead resting against his, attempting to smother my moans of pleasure. The tremors of my orgasm settled into a palliative simmer as he rubbed me gently, gradually bringing me down from my volcanic high. And as my body stilled, our mouths found each other's, our kisses hot and needy, tongues licking and invading.

"We need to leave." He broke the kiss, his voice urgent and heavy with arousal.

"Yes. Now," I urged him.

Smoothing my skirt and setting me on my feet, he grasped my hand and led me through the club toward the nearest exit. The club had become crowded with the lateness of the hour, the space more cramped, and as we drew level with the dance floor, people were standing shoulder to shoulder, making it impossible to walk side by side. Ethan kept a firm grip of my hand, taking the lead and using his body as a shield.

Suddenly, I felt a tug on my free arm, causing me to falter and lose direction. Releasing my grip on Ethan's hand, I glimpsed behind me just an arm pulled me into the crowd and further away from him.

"Hey guys, check it out. If it isn't the motherfucking ice queen herself." Jean-Paul tugged me aggressively toward him, his arms ensnaring me possessively against his body, face only inches from mine.

"Jean-Paul, what the hell?" Gripping his upper arms, I shoved with all my might, attempting to push him away and wriggle free.

His companions, three well-built men of a similar age, laughed and jeered, inflaming his drunken belligerence.

"Don't be fooled, guys, she might be one hot piece of tits and ass, but on the inside, she's cold enough to make your balls turn blue." He pushed his lips violently against my mouth, his arms increasing their grip as I thrashed my head from side to side to get away.

"Get off me, Jean-Paul!" I screamed in his face.

"Take your dirty fucking hands off my girl before I break your face apart, you piece of shit." Ethan stood inches apart from Jean-Paul, anger visibly emanating from him.

Jackson was standing right by his side. "Do as Mr. Wilde advises, asshole."

Jean-Paul glared at them both before turning eyes tinged with betrayal back to me. He released me suddenly, almost pushing me away. "You fucking bitch." His words were venomous, his vicious sneer equally so, as he turned it on Ethan. "*Your* girl? Ya think? Well, you can *fucking* have her. But if you think you'll get anything more than a *fuck* out of her, then you're deluded. That's all Angel knows about—she'll *fuck* you, she'll *fuck* with your head, and then she'll *fuck* you right off." His glare turned back to me, eyes filled with loathing skimming over me as if I were something nasty on the sole of his shoe. "You're a cheap fucking whore."

In that second, two security men appeared from nowhere, and without a word simply lifted him from the floor, nodded once at Ethan and Jackson, and manhandled him through the crowd and out of sight.

His three companions held their hands up in a gesture that said they weren't looking for trouble as they backed away from Ethan and Jackson and followed Jean-Paul out of the club.

Ethan grabbed my hand, pulling me to his side, his glare burning with red-hot, livid anger. "This time, *do not let go.*"

We travelled the journey to my apartment in silence, the atmosphere so notably chilled it was practically arctic. Ethan's body language spoke louder than words ever could as he sat at a marked distance, body angled away from me, staring out of the window. It was as if he couldn't bear to even look at me, let alone touch me, as though my very presence disgusted him. He was a far cry from the man who'd felt compelled to hold my hand in his lap, who, not less than twenty minutes ago, was having hard time tearing his gaze from mine. That man had been relaxed, boyish, and carefree. Now he oozed disregard, his posture perceptibly tense, his jaw muscles bunching, leg jittering uncontrollably. I could almost hear the cogs in his mind working as they turned over and over, trying to make sense of what had just happened.

What *had* just happened?

Mirroring his actions, I angled away from him, not wanting to invade his space or his thoughts, until I could work out what I was thinking myself.

Jean-Paul's parting shot rang in my ears. *You're a cheap fucking whore*. Was his hostility and aggression born out of scorn? A childish, throwaway comment because I'd rejected him, dented his pride. Or was he right? Was I a coldhearted prick tease—a whore? I couldn't erase the perfidious look on Jean-Paul's face from my mind—the look of a betrayed man. The idea that someone could believe I'd intentionally set out to hurt them was unthinkable. I would never knowingly inflict the pain and distress of rejection on anybody.

I glanced over at Ethan, trying to read him, wanting to understand what was running through his mind, but let's face it: This wasn't rocket science. Jean-Paul's inferences combined with the unacquainted storage room fuckery circumstances in which we met would only lead him to draw one conclusion. *Cheap fucking whore.*

Whatever this was we'd had going, it was gone. It was damaged beyond repair before it had even really begun. I should have listened to the warning bells telling me to back off, but instead now I had to endure the rejection that would come with Ethan realizing this was a grave mistake.

But something about the confrontation kept drifting back to me, lurking at the edge of my conscious, awaiting acknowledgement.

My girl. That's what he'd called me. *My girl.*

My chest tightened with a sudden sense of panic, the familiar feeling of loneliness crawling up my insides to grip me by the throat. I glanced at him again, and suddenly I knew.

I'd spent most of my life afraid. Afraid of getting close to someone and afraid of being alone. Afraid of remembering and of forgetting, of being strong, but also of being weak. Always afraid of something. I'd known this man barely a week, but when I was with him, I felt different—safe, somehow. Tonight I'd felt more comfortable in my own skin than I ever had. I'd been filled with hope and possibilities, no longer afraid.

Until now.

Because suddenly the thought of him disappearing from my life, of never seeing him again, unearthed a fear in me like nothing I'd ever known before.

CHAPTER SEVEN

Jackson drew to a halt outside my apartment block, got out, and waited patiently with his back to the car. Ethan and I had remained silent, neither of us uttering a word throughout the entire journey, and I was desperate to escape to the comfort and security of my apartment.

I wasn't really sure what he expected me to do. Whether I should just get out of the car, walk away and not look back, or if I should try and explain or at least be polite and say goodbye. Ethan appeared to be unaware that the car had even stopped, so I didn't expect any direction from him. Eventually, I took a breath and gathered the nerve to speak.

"Ethan… I'm so sorry about what happened back there. You shouldn't have had to witness that." I paused. "What Jean-Paul said—"

"*You* said you weren't involved with him." He cut me off, finally turning to face me, his eyes burning with some unfathomable emotion. "That was the guy you arrived at your brother's restaurant with the other night, wasn't it?"

"Yes, it was. But I'm not involved…"

"The guy's in fucking love with you, Angel. That's pretty involved in my book!" he shouted.

"No, he isn't. He just thinks he is. He's young and he's mistaken lust for love. It's a crush. I swear, I had no idea how he felt when you asked me about him the other day. It was only when we spoke—"

"Lust? So you *are* sleeping with him?" He paled suddenly, as if sickened by the thought.

"Ethan," I paused, searching for a way to make it sound better than it was.

He closed his eyes, waiting for the impact of what I had to say as though he were expecting a physical assault, and I realized I'd faltered a second too long. There was no way to dress this up.

"Yes, I've had sex with him," I admitted finally, a flickering of anger singeing the edges of my nerves as he shook his head with what I could only assume was disgust. I went on, regardless. "But I am *not* in a relationship with him and never have been. What's more, I have never knowingly given him the impression that a relationship between us was even likely. I made it perfectly clear that it was nothing more than a… mutually beneficial arrangement."

"A casual affair." He nodded resignedly as he threw my own words back at me.

"I know how this looks, particularly considering how we first met…" I took a breath, knowing I was digging my hole even deeper "…but Jean-Paul wasn't an affair of any kind. It was just sex, and not even great sex, if I'm honest. But I did warn you that that's how I do things; it's all I have to offer. And if liking sex is a crime, then I'm guilty, but I have not deliberately misled anyone. And I don't even know why I'm explaining myself to you. I hadn't even met you the last time I screwed him. I haven't cheated on you or him, and I won't be judged by either of you."

I took another breath in an attempt to calm my sudden fury. "Look, I'm a whole heap of trouble. You've probably noticed it has a tendency to follow me around. And you're not a man who has time for trouble. I understand that. I'd probably run a mile as well, if I were you."

Picking up my purse, I reached for the door, pausing briefly to take in his riotously conflicted expression. The emotions on his face were so disordered they were undecipherable, but one thing was certain beyond doubt. This man was unbearably beautiful, inside and out, and the urge to reach out and touch him was overwhelming. I bunched my hands into fists to restrain myself, my nails digging into the palms of my hand, my heart twisting as the pain of regret and misery engulfed me.

I swallowed it down and forced my words through the lump which had formed in my throat. "Just so that you know… this… this felt different. You are an amazing person, Mr. Ethan Wilde." I opened the door, stepped out of the car and walked away.

Back in the sanctuary of my home, I went straight to my room and undressed, tossing my dress into a plastic bag knowing I would never wear it again. Then needing to cleanse myself of the odious aftertaste the evening had left behind, I stood under a steaming hot shower, hoping to soothe the discomfort of humiliation and loss and failure, which lingered in my hair and on my skin. I scrubbed until I turned a bright shade of pink, then putting on a clean T-shirt and shorts, climbed into bed, longing for sleep to take me to oblivion and to silence my disordered mind.

My body thrummed from the beat of the music and the hypnotic flashing lights as I danced around and around. A feeling of happiness glowed inside me. I was having fun and it felt intoxicating, liberating. Somebody was holding my hand, strong fingers enveloping mine to make me feel warm and safe, and the weight of loneliness suddenly lifted. The crowd had gathered around, clapping and cheering, urging me to dance and be free.

Suddenly, the person released my hand and I lost control, spinning round and round until I fell into the crowd. But instead of cushioning my fall, the sea of onlookers parted and I began to tumble down and down, plummeting into a seemingly never ending void. Finally, I crashed to the ground, falling heavily into something small and soft.

When I looked down at what had broken my fall, I saw a small animal. It stared helplessly into my eyes, its limp body bloodied and bruised, sad eyes accusing me of cruelty and betrayal. The music had stopped, and the only sound disrupting the silence was the pounding of my heart and the whimpering cries of the wounded animal.

Distraught by what I'd done, I turned to the crowd for help, for somebody to tell me what to do. The crowd shook their heads in abhorrence, loathing and condemnation radiating from them as they turned and began to walk away.

"Please. Help me," I begged. But they were gone and I was alone.

I gazed remorsefully down at the animal, wanting desperately to ease its pain, to comfort it, so I leaned forward to gather it into my arms. That's when I noticed my shoes. My shiny, red patent shoes were covered in blood, and a surge of panic flooded through my veins.

The sound of approaching footsteps shattered the silence and my body began to tremble. I stared down at my shoes, fear and trepidation clawing their way up my back as I lowered, folding into a crouch, steeling myself for the impending horror.

Suddenly, a hand extended out to me and I knew it was an offer of kindness and affection, and if I took it, it would lead me to safety. It was the same hand as before, the one that had made me feel safe and warm while I'd danced. I took it eagerly and without hesitation, slowly raising my head to learn the identity of my savior—and stared straight into the eyes of Ethan Wilde.

I awoke startled and confused, my face sodden with tears as I tried to make some sense of the dream. Bolting upright in bed, I shook my head to dispel the noise still thudding in my head. At first it seemed muffled and distant—a fragment of my dream lingering in my mind—but instead of fading to nothing, it grew louder, a distinct and steady pounding, which resonated through the apartment. The thumping noise I'd assumed were footsteps in my dream was actually the sound of knocking. Somebody was knocking at my door and it was becoming louder and more urgent.

A glance at the clock informed me it was just after three in the morning, and the bubble of unease turned into fear. Flicking on the lamp and jumping out of bed, I quickly made my way through the apartment toward the front door, anxiety flooding my veins as my mind worked over who the hell it could be dropping by at such an ungodly hour. When I reached it, the knocking suddenly ceased. I froze on the spot, holding my breath to listen for any sign of movement on the other side. I startled as the tap came again, this time lighter, like whoever it was had finally abandoned all hope of it being answered.

Then suddenly an exhausted voice rasped from the other side of the door, barely audible and crushed with defeat. "Angel, please." It was a voice I recognized.

Before my mind had time to even process what my body was doing, I flung open the door. Ethan stood there, his pale face and red rimmed eyes etched with tiredness and worry, but all the more perfect for his imperfections.

My hair was still damp from the shower, my face wet with tears, and suddenly the confusion of my dream came rushing into focus: the distress and fear which had enveloped me completely, the proffered hand of promise which had vanquished those emotions at the mere touch of a fingertip. A chance of happiness, a chance of peace. Ethan was the one offering those possibilities. He was my fate—my destiny. And I knew from the desperate mix of hope and fear which burned in his eyes, that I was his.

"I'm so sorry," he breathed.

I flung myself into his arms which folded around me readily, his mouth clamping hungrily over mine to kiss me, to claim me, both of us desperate for the fulfillment we knew we'd gain only from each other.

Locked in a tight embrace, we moved inside, kicking the door closed behind us. As I pulled him into the hallway, Ethan lifted me, folding my legs around his waist, his mouth devouring mine as he pressed me up against the wall. His steely erection pushed into my hot bundle of nerves, the pressure on the seam of my shorts providing the perfect amount of friction as I tilted my pelvis toward him. He shifted, taking my weight again and headed for the only room with a light on: my bedroom.

When we reached the bed, he lowered me, gently placing me back on my feet, his fingers sliding under the hem of my T-shirt and lightly skimming my sides to pull it up and over my head. Discarding it, he trailed his fingers slowly back down the full length of my arms to gently cup my breasts. His gaze heated in awe as it settled on my heaving, tender breasts rising and falling in the palms of his hands as I hungrily drew in air. Lowering his head, he closed his mouth over my nipple and began to suck. He kissed each one in turn, nibbling and sucking, stroking and caressing, drawing on my taut, protruding nipples until the sharp thrill spiked directly to my pining sex. The sensation was devastatingly erotic, like a switch which led straight to an abundance of overwhelming pleasure and promise. The profound gratification of his mouth on my skin was not too dissimilar to the assuaging relief of ice against a scalding burn.

Ethan sighed, moaning with pleasure as he tasted me, licking and lapping, pulling and tugging on my hardened nipples. My breath snagged as his kisses moved lower over my abdomen, his tongue dipping sensually into my naval as he sank to his knees. Then hooking his thumbs into the waistband of my shorts, he slowly slid them down over my hips, taking my hand to steady me as I stepped out of them.

He leaned back on his haunches studying me, his eyes caressing every inch of my naked body until I could almost feel their soft, wispy touch absorbing each and every tiny detail.

I closed my eyes against the burning need to touch him, my nerves on fire, longing for the contact to soothe the mounting ache. Finally, he reached out, his featherlight touch trailing the same path as his gaze, stroking and touching, attending to every inch of sensitive skin until his gaze eventually reached the spot at the apex of my thighs.

I held my breath in anticipation of his touch, but it didn't arrive.

Instead his fingertip trail halted, the only contact remaining being the steady heat of his appraising gaze on my needy sex. Suddenly, he leaned forward, his face only a fraction of an inch from my wet, pulsing, yearning clit. Then, closing his eyes, he took in a deep, voracious breath, inhaling my scent into his lungs. He'd done this before, the act so shocking and yet so deeply erotic that I moaned loudly, swaying toward him, desperate for his touch.

But it never came. Instead, he stood gracefully and gently maneuvered me backward until the edge of the mattress grazed the backs of my thighs, causing me to sit. He took a couple of steps, his fingers working quickly to undo the buttons of his shirt before removing it and tossing it to the side. His pants followed, releasing his huge, steely erection from the confines of his boxer briefs.

It was the first time I had ever seen him completely naked, and the sight which stood before me was utterly breathtaking. I took in a sharp intake of breath as I gazed with admiration and downright longing at the finest architecture I had ever seen. This godlike creature was clearly no stranger to exercise, because his body was like that of an athlete, long and lean. His taut, defined muscles pulsed and flexed as he moved, displaying strength and power—a perfectly polished and truly honed machine.

Tiny particles of sweat beaded on the surface of the skin between my swollen breasts, my mouth salivating in ravenous anticipation. I'd never wanted anything so badly in my life.

I reached out my hand to him, coaxing him nearer. I needed to taste him. He moved without hesitation and when he was in reach, I grasped him by the hips and guided him toward me. Gently, I stroked my fingertips around the tip of his penis and down the length, admiring every inch of his impressive shaft as it twitched with pleasure against my touch. He responded eagerly, thrusting his hips forward slightly, hot breath hissing from his lips. I replayed the motion, this time paying close attention to the pressure as I guided the pad of my thumb over the pulsing veins flooding him with the blood that made him thicker and harder. I cupped his balls with my other hand, dragging my lower lip through my teeth in an attempt to control my appetite. My eyes followed the trail of my touch, worshipping him as his had worshipped me.

My touch became firmer, my thumb pressing against the crown and over the top, releasing a warm stream of silky fluid. Unable to resist any longer, I lowered my head and gently ran the tip of my tongue through the sticky wetness of his desire. Ethan groaned loudly, his response causing the muscles of my sex to clench violently and moisture to pool at my core. My tongue traced around the bulging head of his cock and then slowly down the hot, thickly-veined shaft. My thumb followed in pursuit, trailing over the same journey as my tongue, rubbing his erotic juices all over his meaty, pulsing penis.

"Oh God, Angel," he rasped, his voice a low growl.

I grasped him firmly at the base and closing my mouth over his hot, silken head began to suck and lick him into my mouth, my tongue twirling and my hand twisting him to the back of my throat. His groans became louder, his breathing more ragged, as my head bobbed up and down, working him, consuming him. His hands moved into my hair as he began to move with me, thrusting his hips back and forth as he drove himself deeper into my hungry mouth, my throat opening up to take his length.

"Christ, Angel, stop. I'm going to come if you don't stop."

I didn't—I couldn't.

Instead, his words drove me on. Hungry for him, desperate to claim him, I gripped his hips, sucking him deeper and faster, fucking him voraciously with my mouth. Suddenly, he cried out my name, his cock convulsing as he violently spurted into my mouth. I felt the hot, thick come hit the back of my throat as I swallowed, gently working him down and sucking every drop of him dry.

Pulling back, he pushed me down on the bed, his eyes on fire, skin feverishly hot and glazed with a fine sheen of sweat. He gazed down in wonder at his solid erection standing thick and proud, still as rapacious and virile as when I'd taken him into my mouth.

"Christ, woman, what the fuck are you doing to me?"

Quickly, he retrieved a condom from his discarded pants' pocket, tore it open and slid it down over his shockingly hard length. Pushing my legs apart, he settled between them, his fingers reaching and finding the soft, pink folds of my flesh. His eyes rolled with delicious reverence as he slid his fingers into my slick opening to spread the cream of my desire over my quivering flesh. I bucked toward him, desperate for the feel of him inside me.

"Your pussy is so fucking incredible, Angel." He took his cock in his other hand. "And my dick is so fucking hard for you, it's on fire."

And then he was towering above me, his strong arms on either side of my shoulders to bolster his formidable structure. He gazed into my eyes as he sunk into me, spreading me wide and filling me to the max. Relief flooded us both as we took the pleasure we so desperately needed, and my muscles clenched in rapturous appreciation around him, squeezing his rock-hard dick inside me. He responded with his eyes, dark and wild with lust, and pulling out to the tip and thrusting with his hips as he lunged back inside me.

"You are so beautiful, Angel. I want you like I've been starved of you. I've never needed anything before in my life like I need to be inside you." His voice was a low growl, primitive and possessive.

He moved against me, thrusting and pounding, hips gyrating, screwing me into the mattress. I picked up the rhythm, moving with him. "Then let me ride you, Ethan. Because I need this too. And I need you as deep as you can possibly go."

"Fuck," he hissed through clenched teeth as he shifted into a sitting position, and pulling me into his lap, swiftly reentered me.

The fullness was extraordinary, the sting of the depth exquisite, and I folded my legs around his waist in complete possession. My hands fisted into his hair, bringing him closer to kiss him, our tongues delving deep into each other's mouths devouring one another.

I used the grip of my legs around his waist to rock into him, bringing him deeper into my core, the sensation sending shrill, electrical spasms throughout my being. My body shuddered and clenched as I ground myself against his hot, rigid cock, rubbing it inside me to massage that soft sweet spot.

The immense pleasure building inside was overwhelming, and suddenly I was wild in my pursuit of blissful satisfaction. I pushed him down on the bed and hooked my feet underneath his knees, bracing myself. Then I took a firm grip of the headboard and really began to ride him, thrusting and writhing with abandonment on his solid stick of indulgence.

Ethan growled, a low guttural rumbling from deep within him as he arched his hips to meet my thrusts, burrowing deeper into me. He reached up, spreading his hands across my breasts, to knead and squeeze.

"Christ, you look so fucking hot," he rasped, his words hoarse as he struggled against his desire. "Ride me, Angel. Take what you need and ride me until I come. Squeeze every last drop out of me with your tight, sweet pussy."

His words were my ruin, driving me over the edge as I flung my head back, closing one hand over his to squeeze my breast. Reaching down between my legs with the other, his thumb began rubbing expertly over the hard nub of my clit.

A rush of heat sped through my veins as my body sang out its pleasure and an orgasmic tidal wave washed over me, bringing me soaring into sweet oblivion. I screamed out as I reached my crescendo, the violent convulsing of my muscles bringing him with me.

A primal groan escaped his throat as he pumped himself inside me, his body quaking with the assault of his orgasm. Gradually, he slowed as the tremors subsided and I collapsed in a sated heap beside him.

We lay with our limbs entwined, my head on his chest listening to his settling heartbeat, exhausted and sated and happy—deliriously happy.

I wasn't sure what had happened tonight, what thoughts had gone through Ethan's head, or what had driven him to turn up at my door in the middle of the night. All I knew was that, for whatever reason, we both needed each other and it had felt good and it had felt right. The whys and wherefores could wait for now.

"Angel?" Ethan's voice was a cautious whisper.

"Mmm hmm."

"May I stay with you tonight?"

My eyes flickered open. The idea of having someone else in my apartment, let alone sharing my bed, would usually make me uneasy. But again, something about being with Ethan felt right. It didn't feel like he was imposing on my space, but cushioning it. And I felt more relaxed than ever.

"Well, I'm not sure I can move, so I guess you'd better."

I could sense the smile turning the corners of his lips. He stroked his fingers through my hair and kissed my forehead. "There's just one thing before you sleep, Angel."

"What?" I whispered, already drifting off.

"Don't ever let go of my hand again."

I smiled sleepily against his chest and with his words echoing in my head, I drifted off into a peaceful slumber.

When I awoke, it was with an odd sense of calm, and though my sleep had been massively disrupted, I felt rested. I opened my eyes, my gaze falling immediately on the reason for my contentment. Ethan sat on the edge of the bed, unfortunately fully dressed, but still as sexy as hell. His smiley blue eyes stared down at me, and the sight was sunshine in itself.

"Good morning, Cinders." He reached out to brush the hair from my face.

"What are you doing?" I asked shyly, suddenly mindful of my sex and sleep ruffled state. "How long have you been watching me?"

"Not long, a few minutes. It's hard to tear myself away, you're so beautiful."

Frowning dubiously, I eyed his dressed and ready-to-go state, wondering what it meant for us. "Are you leaving?"

"I'm afraid so. I have to work," he paused. "Angel, there's something I need to explain. About last night."

Uncertain as to which part of last night he was referring to, or where this conversation was leading, I remained silent and waited for him to continue. He bit down on his lip nervously, like he wasn't quite sure how to say what was on his mind. My heart began to beat frantically as I realized just how afraid I was of what he was about to say. He cleared his throat.

"Last night, you assumed I was running away. I wasn't. I just needed to take a step back from—"

"I know," I interrupted. "It's fine, really, you don't need to explain. I mean if you've had a change of heart…"

"No, you don't understand. It wasn't you I was stepping away from. It was *my* feelings I needed to get a clearer view of. Thing is, I scared myself back there in the club last night. I was suddenly exposed to a whole host of emotions and feelings that I've never encountered before, and I don't know where the hell they came from. I've known you for all of two minutes, and yet last night, I felt that everything I had, everything I cherished, was hanging in the balance. It's as if I've been put under some sort of crazy spell or something. The level of protectiveness and possessiveness, and fear I felt of losing you, if only even for a second, scared the shit out of me."

My heart pumped loudly in my chest as the words I hadn't even realized I'd been longing to hear poured from his mouth.

"When I saw that guy with his arms around you, trying to kiss you…" He faltered, as if grasping for the right words. "I couldn't bear it, Angel. I didn't know what the word *jealous* meant until that moment. My first instinct—after wanting to kill him—was to blame you for the way I felt. I didn't understand, couldn't work out what had provoked such an intense reaction. It felt like I was losing the plot.

"But when I got home—taking the space I thought I needed to figure it out—all I could think about was how terrified I was of losing you; that I'd blown it. And the craziest thing is that you're not even mine to lose. You were right—what you said. I had no right to be angry." He paused again, the muscles in his jaw working furiously. He glanced down at his hands, took a breath, and looked me straight in the eye.

"I want to change that, Angel. I'm not pretending to understand the way I feel, but I can't ignore it. I know what you said about only being able to offer a casual affair, and I thought that would be enough, but it's not. I want you to be mine. I want to have the right to be afraid of losing you, the right to be jealous, and the right to be angry if some fucker puts his hands on you. I won't share you. I don't want a casual affair. I want you totally and exclusively." He took another breath. "So, if any part of you doesn't feel the same, if you don't want what I want, then please, you have to tell me now and I'll walk away. Because if I stay in your life any longer—I'm not sure I'll ever be able to leave."

Oh! I wanted to pinch myself, make sure I wasn't having one of my crazy dreams. Ethan had just laid it all on the line for me, and I had no idea how to respond. He was a natural at wearing his heart on his sleeve, but I knew nothing of feelings, let alone how to convey them. Perhaps, I could learn something from him. The only thing I was sure of was there was no way in hell I wanted him to walk away. Whatever it was he was feeling, I felt it too—so I needed to learn pretty damned fast. I took a breath, waded in, and did my best.

"Do you like paella?"

"Excuse me?" His brows rose.

Jumping out of bed, I strode across the room to grab my robe. I slipped it on and sauntered toward him, taking his mystified face in my hands to kiss him tenderly on the lips.

"An explicitly defined understanding for the word *exclusive* is imperative if we're to remain on the same page." I turned and walked to the bathroom, Ethan getting up to follow. "Just so you know where

I am—I'm thinking sole, undivided rights of intimacy, rejecting all others from a part or share of either one of us. I will be absolutely, completely, and entirely yours. And you, Mr. Wilde... will be absolutely, completely, and entirely mine."

Ethan leaned against the doorjamb, eyeing me in bemused wonder, his mouth a cool impassive line. I grabbed my toothbrush, loaded it with paste, and began to brush.

"I was thinking we could discuss it further over dinner. I'll cook. So, do you like paella or not?" I asked casually through a mouthful of minty froth. I rinsed, watching him cautiously through the mirror, trying to gauge his reaction to my rather clumsy attempt at expressing my feelings.

Still his expression remained blank.

At best, my effort to bare my soul had been nonchalant, while in reality I felt anything but. Suddenly, I was worried that my cool approach had disappointed him, or offended him, or even that it had been simply ineffectual. I really didn't want to mess this up. I took a deep breath and turned to face him.

"You're looking at me as if I'm crazy." His brow flickered almost imperceptibly, the faintest hint of a smile teasing the corner of his mouth. I tilted my chin to gather valor. "Well, I am. I'm crazy-scared this spell is going to break. You see, you're not the only one caught up in this... surreality. You have captivated *me*. And I don't begin to understand it either, but I sure as shit know I don't want it to end."

Wow, did I just say that?

I was overwhelmed with the intensity of my feelings for this man I barely knew, and even more astounded that I'd been able to communicate them. But I knew that the reason I'd been compelled to share was because I was safe in the knowledge that he felt them too.

A look of pure relief settled on his beautiful face, his eyes alight with wonder. Pushing off from the doorjamb he moved toward me, his mouth curling into a slow, sexy smile making me catch my breath. Then placing his hands on my hips, he pulled me into a tight embrace and kissed me. It was a tender lingering kiss, soft and enticing, licking gently against my tongue. The spark ignited instantly, stoking the slow burning embers deep down inside me. Suddenly, he stopped, his hot lips pulling away from mine.

"Christ, woman, you turn me on so goddamn much, I can't get enough of you. I really need to get a grip or you'll drive me insane."

"You've got a perfect grip, Charming. I'm just waiting to see what you're going to do with it."

His gaze darkened lustfully. "You're insatiable, Cinders. And this fairy tale is going to be truly fucking amazing, I just know it."

My stomach flipped with excited anticipation at his words. I knew it too.

Dragging his gaze reluctantly from mine, he glanced at his watch, sighing in utter exasperation. "Damn, I have to go. I have to get home, shower, and change. In twenty minutes I'll have an entire boardroom waiting for me."

"Go," I laughed, pushing him back toward the door.

"I'll call you later." He kissed me again before adding, "Paella sounds good. And your definition of exclusive—that sounds even better."

My smile broke into a grin as he blew me another kiss, turned, and was gone.

After dressing in workout gear, I spent the next couple of hours in the gym. My building had a fantastic range of services and amenities, including a modern fitness center and spa. I pounded the treadmill for thirty minutes, spent another ten on the crosstrainer, and then hit the weight machines. Each time I caught a glimpse of myself in a mirror, my cheeks were glowing with a radiance I'd never seen before, my lips set in a smug, sassy grin.

Just as I was finishing up, my cell rang. "Hey, you eaten breakfast yet?" Jia asked.

The gallery didn't open on Mondays and we often hung out over breakfast or lunch.

"No, I'm just finishing up in the gym."

"Good, I'll be there in thirty with coffee and bagels."

"Excellent, my friend. Oh, could you get me a shot of something sweet in my coffee? I'm in need of a sugar hit."

"Naturally. Laters." She hung up.

Precisely thirty minutes later, I'd showered, dressed, and was eagerly awaiting the arrival of Jia and breakfast—not necessarily in that order.

Despite my upbeat mood, I couldn't get the look on Jean-Paul's face and the vile things he'd said the night before out of my head. Deep down I hated that he thought I deserved such treatment, and although I was angry about the way he'd behaved, I had to take some responsibility for the way things had turned out. He'd begun to develop feelings for me, and I'd either been blind to them or ignorant. Either way, it was important to me that he knew I'd never set out to hurt him.

That decided, I picked up my cell and dialed his number. It rang out for several beats before switching to his message service. "It's Jean-Paul, leave a message."

I didn't.

Jean-Paul always answered his phone. *Boy, he really hated me.*

Two minutes later my cell *buzzed* and fully expecting it to be Jean-Paul returning my call, I was shocked to see Ethan's name on the caller display. My heart rammed into my chest wall as though it had been hurled at me, my body temperature soaring to what must surely be a dangerous level. Jeez, the impact this man was having on me was devastating.

I answered on the third ring. "Hello, Charming."

"Hello, Cinders." His raspy voice and sexy accent made my toes curl up in my shoes.

"I thought you were supposed to be working?"

"I am—supposed to be, that is. But for some unnamed reason, I don't appear to be able to concentrate."

God, his voice!

"And why would that be?"

"Because every time I blink, I see your beautiful face. It appears to be etched on the inside of my eyelids. And if I concentrate and close my eyes, I can smell your scent on my skin. Taste you on my lips... It's exquisite."

Christ, this man could even get to me from the other side of the city. My lips parted as I caught my breath, desire pooling at my core leaving a dull erotic ache. I shook my head to dispel the images his words had conjured to my mind.

"I see," I said with mock pragmatism. "Have you seen a doctor?"

"No. I was hoping the sound of your voice would take the edge off. Be enough to get me through the day, until get my hands on the real thing."

"And has it?"

"The tremors are subsiding a little, but I'm afraid I'll probably need a pretty big fix tonight."

"I'm sure that can be arranged. I wouldn't want you to suffer unnecessarily. Is six-thirty good for you?"

"The sooner the better, Cinders. I'll bring some wine. See you later."

"Bye, Ethan." I hung up.

Holy fuck, the guy had a serious sex voice. I was a mess. Heart hammering, palms sweating, if I'd stayed on the phone any longer I might actually need to consider changing my panties.

By the time Jia arrived, I'd managed to compose myself. We ate breakfast while I entertained her with tales from the previous couple of days. I told her all about Claudia and the wedding, the house and the beach. By the time I reached the part about Ethan showing up and the ride home, she raised her eyebrows warily.

"Jeez, you two just seem to keep bumping into each other. Bit of a coinkydink, don't you think?"

"I know it seems bizarre, but he had a legitimate reason for being there. He's not stalking me if that's what you're implying."

She held up the palms of her hands in a "you said it," sort of way.

"It just seems like fate keeps throwing us together, somehow. Perhaps it's divine intervention."

She burst into laughter. "You're crackin' my balls, bitch."

I got up to clear our plates. "I hate to be the one to break it to you, but you don't have any balls. Deal with it, my friend."

"Bullshit, I've got bigger balls than any guy I know," she continued to laugh. I had to laugh as well, in a metaphorical sense she was probably right.

When she eventually pulled herself together, I told her about the rest of my weekend. After enlightening her to Jean-Paul's outburst in the club, I had to physically lean in and push her chin up to close her mouth.

"Well, it seems like hearts are breaking all over the world for you at the moment, honey. I mean, I knew the poor kid had it bad, but he is *too* far gone. It's all freaking over for him."

"Christ, Jia, don't say that. I feel bad enough as it is. I thought you were getting Kate to call him, take the heat off a bit."

"I did. He apparently spent twenty minutes talking about you."

I raised my eyes skyward and told her about the remainder of the evening, and about what Ethan had said that morning about exclusivity. By the time I finished, she was looking at me with unexpected affection.

"Jeez, bitch, it sounds like you're falling for this guy. And him for you, in a big, big way."

I shook my head. "It's still early days."

"Yeah, so? Take it easy, but follow your heart. If it feels right, grab it with both hands. Don't wait until it slips away."

It wasn't like Jia to have a serious take on anything, which made what she'd said even more momentous. I gazed at her, the temptation to be openly honest about my feelings for the second time that day getting the better of me

"I'm scared," I told her.

She nodded. "I know. But that's a good thing. What you perceive as fear is actually some other emotion in disguise. It's a message. If it scares the shit out of you, it means it deserves some serious attention. Consider why it scares you. You're not afraid of giving this thing a go, because it's your choice whether you do or you don't. So why sweat it? It's losing it you're afraid of. You're scared of what it might mean if you take a chance on it and it slips away. And that means it's something worth sweating your ass off to keep. Don't cut your nose off, bitch."

"Very profound." I smiled at her, digesting her deep words of wisdom. Wise Jia made a valid point.

"I know, right." She looked at her watch. "Enough deep shit. I need shoes."

"Oh, no. You're kidding."

Jia had a weakness for shoes. Her petite stature had led to her spending most of her life in killer heels to compensate for it.

"It won't take long, I promise. It's just that I can't decide between two pairs. Help me decide?" she pleaded. "You owe me, bitch." Her expression quickly changed to a snarl.

Three hours, a couple of glasses of wine, two pairs of shoes for Jia—and one for me—later, I was back home. I'd collected groceries for dinner on the way and was in high spirits, excited for the evening ahead.

Pushing my fingertip up against the glass of Ponyo's bowl, I smiled as she nuzzled into it like a cat. Ah, the little things... As was my daily ritual, I leaned in, putting my face close to the glass, and told her about my day.

By the time I'd prepared the ingredients for our paella and freshened up, it had just turned six. I was wearing my new Giuseppe Zanotti strawberry pink peep-toe wedges with my black and white zigzagged skinny jeans and white T-shirt.

My cell rang and a wave of strange emotion at the prospect of it being Ethan hit me. I picked up, nervously. "Hello?" Oddly though, there was no reply. I checked the display to find the caller had withheld, so I hung up.

In an attempt to calm this alien feeling of nervous excitement lurching around in my belly, I poured myself a glass of wine and pushed open the large glass doors to the spacious terrace. In the day time, with a clear sky, it was a sun-worshipper's dream. In the evening it was cozy whatever time of year. The space was flanked with potted plants and small specimen shrubs, with warm, glowing lanterns placed at irregular intervals, some hanging, some freestanding. In the middle of the space was a cast iron fire pit which, when lit, provided wonderful, atmospheric lighting, while at the same time kept you lovely and toasty warm. Scattered around it were bean bags of various shapes and sizes, all of them covered with faux fur throws. In the corner stood a huge Brazilian hammock, perfect for a night of stargazing and easily big enough for two.

I loved this space, whatever the time of day or year. It was a snug and private sanctuary, which also provided an abundance of breathing space and complete escapism in the infinite sky above.

The evening had a slight chill, so I pulled on a black off-the-shoulder cashmere sweater. Then placing scented firestarters, made from all-natural pine cones in the bowl of the fire pit, I began to form a pyramid with kindling. I lit the wick and waited until it was fully ignited, the pleasant and familiar aroma of honeysuckle and jasmine floating into the air.

Placing the dome-shaped protective spark guard over the budding flame, I turned to look out at the breathtaking views of the New York City skyline. The position of the sun had shifted, the day ebbing steadily toward twilight. As if seeing it for the first time, I looked out across the city and saw a cocktail of vibrancy and color imbued with a sort of joie de vivre.

A profusion of sanguinity swept through me and suddenly I felt carefree and buoyant, as if only just realizing I was comfortable in my own skin. If I took Jia's advice and chilled out, this could be the beginning of a whole new chapter of my life. A chance to feel and be whole and belong.

So far, I'd traveled the road of life alone, convincing myself it was meant to be, that I was happy in my solitude. But this journey I was embarking on with Ethan seemed more and more like a passage I was destined to take.

Jia had been right on the button. And I refused to cut my nose off to spite my face. I was ready and willing to sweat my ass off for a chance at happiness with Ethan. Ready to embrace the unmistakable magic between us, to nurture it and watch it grow. I would allow myself to dream of life's endless possibilities, and for the first time ever—to hope.

CHAPTER EIGHT

My buzzer sounded, the sudden raucous noise startling me from my reverie and alerting me to Ethan's arrival. An insane combination of nerves and excitement prickled through my veins, bursting wildly into flames deep in the pit of my stomach.

When I opened the door and laid eyes on him, my knees went weak from the mere sight of the splendid specimen which stood before me. Did this man actually become more striking on a daily basis?

The top button of his pale blue dress shirt was undone, the cornflower blue tie, which matched his irises perfectly, pulled casually loose. His navy vest was fastened, encasing his impeccably toned, stunningly sexy body like a layer of skin. The finger of one hand hooked under the collar of his jacket slung over one shoulder, and in the other hand he carried a bottle of wine. I wanted to shove my hands into his mussed-up hair, I wanted to eat him—and then I wanted to fuck him.

When his gaze dipped to my mouth, I realized I was biting my lip voraciously as I eyed him. Then, as if he'd decided he wanted a taste of his own, he stepped inside, and with an urgent fervency, closed his mouth over mine. His soft, full lips were warm and mouthwateringly delicious as they consumed mine in a slow, seductive kiss, his woody, spicy scent filtering into my senses like a drug. The unrelenting flames spread through my body at an obdurate speed.

"Hi," I breathed, trying desperately not to pant like a dog in heat.

"Hi." His voice was silky smooth, like melted buttery caramel. "My God, you look amazing."

I look amazing? *Really?* Have you looked in a mirror recently? "Drink?" was about all I could manage until I pulled myself together properly.

"I'd love a glass of wine." He wiggled the bottle he was holding.

As I turned to go and fetch it, something suddenly occurred to me. "How did you get in here?" I'd been so absorbed in his deliciousness that I'd completely overlooked that his arrival hadn't been announced by the front desk.

He gazed at me with raised brows, like he was suddenly worried about the state of my mind. "You opened the door for me, Angel."

"Duh. I don't mean that. I mean the front desk didn't call up. Come to think of it, they didn't last night either."

An awkward look flittered across his face. "I um... I sort of have a pass."

Realization dawned. "You own the building." It wasn't a question. "Oh my god, how much property do you actually own?"

"Well, obviously there are works in progress to bear in mind, but currently, by today's figures around fifty-two million square feet. In New York, anyway. It's strange, but that's something people usually already know about me."

"Well, I'm not *people*. I told you, I prefer to get the facts firsthand. Details like that don't really matter to me anyway. It's you that interests me, not the assets you've procured."

"I'm glad to hear it. But I can offload the building if it makes you feel uneasy."

"God no, don't be ridiculous. It doesn't, although it's probably best Jia doesn't know. She already thinks there are some bizarre coincidences between us. I think she thinks you're some sort of creepy stalker." I laughed as his face fell. "Jokes! Don't fret—she's just generally mistrustful."

As he rolled his eyes in something I think was relief, I entered the kitchen area to grab a glass, pouring Ethan a glass of wine while he took in the space around him with surprising interest. It was then I realized that although he'd woken up that morning in this very apartment, he'd only actually seen the bedroom and bathroom.

"I love your place and what you've done with it. Wow, is this all your work?" he asked of the photographic art lining the walls.

"Yes," I answered, joining him and handing him the glass of wine.

"Tell me about them."

I smiled. I was proud of my work and it thrilled me that he was showing an interest. Other than Jia and gallery clients, nobody on a personal level really had.

"The Victoria Falls." I pointed to the one he appeared mesmerized by. "Or more locally known as *Mosi-oa-Tunya*. It means, 'Smoke that thunders.' Located on the Zambezi River, but this you probably know. I took the picture in the final minutes of the sunset."

"It's breathtaking. I'd love a copy."

"Sure. I have several of the falls taken from different angles, different weather conditions, different times of day." I walked back to the kitchen area to begin preparing our food while we talked.

"When was it taken?" Ethan continued.

"Last year. I spent some time volunteering for a charity out in Zambia. At the start of the project there were around two hundred children receiving a very basic education in a derelict farmhouse. The roof leaked and there was no access to clean water on site, not much in the way of furniture either. The charity raised enough to build a new school house. My job was to document the lives of the people and children in the village, the progress of the build, its effect on their lives, and so forth. Tell their stories through pictures."

"These are some of the children?" he asked, pointing to another picture further along the wall.

"Yes." I smiled at the memory.

The picture was a close up of a group of village children absorbed in the fantastic vista of a dwindling sunset. They stood huddled together, all facing in the same direction. None of the children were in the least bit mindful of me or the camera, too immersed in the final minutes of the fading day. Each face indicated a distinct and separate expression, and it was that which had fascinated me, because not one of them had manifested enough to reveal the thoughts behind them.

"The picture's called *Waiting*?" Ethan asked thoughtfully. "What?" he asked, glancing back at me. "What are they waiting for?"

I shrugged. "A new day. Hope. Rain, perhaps." It was all pure conjecture, of course. "I couldn't quite read their expressions enough to be sure what they were thinking, but it struck me that they seemed less enthralled by the beauty of the sunset and more concerned with the significance of the dying day. As though they were waiting for the possibilities a new day might bring."

He blinked, his expression steeped in deep contemplation and something resembling awe. "They're amazing. You're amazing."

Laughing, I pointed to another picture. The one of the two homeless men on a bench in Central Park—*For pleasure has no relish unless we share it*. When I told him the story behind it, he laughed until his sides appeared to hurt.

"Ah, something I recognize," he said, pointing to a picture of Gapstow Bridge.

The picture had been taken in the middle of fall, and I'd captured it in atmospheric light, the bridge curving gracefully over the narrow neck of the pond. There was a calmness surrounding it—something ethereal and moody.

"I've taken hundreds of pictures of Gapstow," I said, plating the paella. "I have this weird fixation with the place."

"Why's that?"

Picking up the two steaming plates, I walked toward him, pausing to look up at the picture. "Well, that's the odd thing. I'm not really sure. Something draws me to it. It's like I know it's significant to me, but I don't know why. So I take silly amounts of photos of it, hoping someday something will jog my memory. Grab the wine." I motioned to a freshly opened bottle on the breakfast bar and began to walk toward the terrace.

"Do you mind eating out here?" I asked him as we settled into seats around the fire pit.

"God no, this is fantastic," he said, glancing around.

The light had faded now, and the glow from the lanterns and the flames of the fire pit created warmth and intimacy.

My cell began to vibrate in my back pocket and retrieving it, I noticed again that it was an unknown caller. Not wanting to be rude, I rejected the call and tossed the phone to one side.

"Nothing important, I hope?" Ethan asked, his eyes narrowing.

I shook my head dismissing it, and we both began to eat.

"This is delicious, Angel. You're proving to be an extremely talented person. Not only are you a gifted photographer, but you have an amazing eye for design." He waved his hand, indicating the terrace. "On top of that you're a brilliant cook… and an incredible lover. You truly are a prize. I can see I'm going to have to keep a very *stringent* hold on you."

I felt the heat of my flushing cheeks immediately, both from his heartfelt compliments and the implication behind his warning. Whatever he meant, it sounded hot.

"You must have had somebody cook for you before." I knew nothing about Ethan's romantic connections and was eager to learn whatever tidbits he was willing to share.

"Nobody that wasn't my mother or paid handsomely to do so, no." He paused before adding, "Nobody special, anyway."

"I see. So does that mean that there was somebody special, but she just didn't cook for you?"

"Ah, now we get to the real question." The edges of his lips curled in amusement as he observed me flushing for the second time. "Don't be afraid to ask me questions, Angel. I've no intentions of holding back when it comes to getting to know you." He hesitated for a moment. "It means there's never been anybody special. I won't lie; I've had my fair share of transient relationships. I've even been a little unprincipled in my associations with women. But I've never been in love before, not even close."

Before what?

His voluntary confession and the unexpected relief I felt from the honesty of it took me back. Unsure of how to respond, I nodded and took a sip of my wine.

"And what about you, Angel?" Tilting his head to the side, he seemed to eye me warily. "Who, other than the buffoon last night, has dared to fall in love with you? And more importantly, who have you been in love with?"

I shrugged. "What does it even mean, love? No two people are the same. What feels like love to one person may not even impact on another. So, if everybody's interpretations of love differ, how do we really know that what we feel is the real thing? Love could be a mere extension of need, a fear of loneliness, or even a simple figment of our imagination conjured by desire."

My philosophy seemed to fascinate him, his gaze wandering off momentarily, as if what I'd said sparked a memory. "I recall once when Abby was about seventeen. She'd been dumped by a boy whom she believed she was in love with and cried relentlessly into my mother's lap for hours. My mom told her not to worry, there were plenty more fish in the sea—the usual bullshit. But Abby was convinced her heart was broken, because the boy had been 'the one' and when Mom asked her why she thought that, she said she didn't know. Mom shook her head and told her that there was no way he could be 'the one,' because if he was, she would know why. When Abby asked her how, she just said, 'Because when you find the one, the world will suddenly seem like a different place, a much brighter place. And you will know.'"

My heart missed a beat, the concept prodding me to recall my earlier thoughts when I'd looked out across the city. How everything had suddenly seemed much sharper and more colorful—brighter.

"No, then," I exclaimed in a rush.

Ethan frowned in confusion. "No, what?"

"I've never been in love before, either."

"But you thought you might have been at some point, am I right?"

It seemed Ethan had a propensity to see right through me. I would need to get used to that. He'd also warned me to be honest and open with him, forbidding me from hiding my thoughts and feelings. I couldn't promise I would bear my soul, but honesty was important to me too, and I guessed now was as good a time as any to start.

"James. Dr. James Foster." The words tumbled out of my mouth with an ease I wasn't expecting. He blinked, glancing away briefly, as though preparing himself for what he might hear. When he looked ready, I continued. "He was a surgeon—is a surgeon. Older than me by almost ten years. I met him at a charity auction I'd donated some of my work to; he was the buyer. We were seeing each other for about eight months. I trusted him. It turned out I shouldn't have." I took a deep breath and braced myself. I wasn't proud of what I was about to tell him.

"One day his wife came to see me at the gallery to ask that I leave her husband alone. I had no clue he was even married." I shook my head in shame. "She said she'd known about me for a few months and had hoped it would fizzle out, but that she feared he was falling for me and preparing to leave her. She said the only chance she had of saving her marriage was for me to convince him it was over and walk away. She pleaded with me to never reveal that she'd known about us." I took a breath and continued.

"Of course, I was angry. I felt hurt and deceived. He was the first person I'd ever put any trust in, the only person I'd ever even vaguely relied on, and he let me down. But I didn't really feel I had the right to be cut up about it. After all, he wasn't really mine to lose. He was hers. And I'll never forget that look on her face—the look of heartbreak and misery. I couldn't bear that I'd been partly to blame for it. So, I agreed. I arranged to see him straightaway and told him it was over. He persisted for some time with calls and texts, but I never saw him again."

I turned to look at Ethan, his expression unreadable. "I swear I didn't know. I would never have gone near him if I'd known, would never knowingly take another woman's man. Of course I realize it sounds crazy that I didn't know he was married, but we didn't see each other all that often; he worked long hours, so when we were together we spent all our time in..." He winced, and I revised my choice of words quickly. "...doors, we spent all our time indoors."

Bowing his head, his lip curved into a half smile, seemingly grateful that I'd spared him the finer details. Then for a fleeting moment, a shadow seemed to cross his face, as if perturbed over something I'd said. It vanished as quickly as it had appeared, his expression changing swiftly to a smile, as though dismissing whatever was on his mind.

He opened his mouth to speak, but paused before asking, "Did you ever tell him you loved him?"

"No," I answered without hesitation, "because I didn't. I cared for him, a lot, but when I was with him, I can assure you the world was not a brighter place. It was as grim as it always had been."

He narrowed his eyes in question at my choice of words, but then took my hand in his and kissed the back of my fingers with a brush of his lips.

"Thank you for telling me about him, for being honest. I'm not deluded. I realize you have a past, as does everyone, as do I. However, I can't pretend I don't hate the thought that anyone else has ever been near you, and I'm aware that seems ludicrous. But I can't help it. The sex..." he flinched "...I can just about handle—if I don't think about it. Knowing it wasn't anything special is what matters to me. I think I might be able to tolerate the fact that you existed before meeting me, if I can believe you've never been in love."

For some reason, his logic didn't appear ludicrous at all, but instead resonated with me, and before I could fathom how, I blurted, "I'm not even sure I did that much existing, if I'm honest."

"Christ, you probably think I'm some sort of crazy person. Maybe your friend Jia is right to be concerned. I know this is moving a bit swiftly, but I feel strangely compelled to tell you what I'm thinking."

I knew exactly what he meant. It felt good to talk, to open up and to feel a connection with someone. Crazy, yes, but good. My new found buoyancy seemed to spur my candor. "You're not crazy alone in this, Ethan. I feel it too. It's absurd, I know—some sort of whirlwind rollercoaster ride. But if we're both on board, both willing to take the journey, all we can do is sit back and see where it takes us."

He smiled widely, a look of relief relaxing his features. "I, for one, would definitely like to see where it takes us." He paused. "But first, we need to agree on terms."

"What do you mean? What terms?"

"This morning, you told me what your definition of exclusive is. And I liked it, but I feel it needs further discussion."

Tilting my head to the side in question, I waited for him to expand.

"Angel, I need to be sure you understand what the implications will be living by my definition of it."

Oh. This sounded pretty serious. Although I'd meant every word I'd said that morning, my intention had been merely to reassure him that I was on the same page as him—my clumsy way of agreeing to a relationship. It certainly wasn't a dictation of terms. I was stunned and vaguely wary about what I was about to hear, but strangely eager to hear it anyway.

"Okay, and what are those implications?"

"A question first. Please answer honestly," he instructed.

My brow furrowed, an indication that I was pissed he thought I might be anything other than honest. He raised his hand, as though I should hear him out before I passed judgment.

"Have you spoken to... Jean-Paul since last night?" He spoke the name through gritted teeth.

"No," I answered honestly.

"Have you attempted to speak to him? Or has he tried calling you?" His gaze flickered to my abandoned phone.

"That's another two questions."

"Angel..." His tone was serious, a caution.

Honesty was important to me too, and I had principles. I took a breath. "Yes." There was a flicker of anger in his eyes. I trudged on nonetheless. "I tried to call him this morning."

"Why?"

"It bothers me that he believes I misled him."

"Why do you care what he thinks?" He sounded outraged, his brow furrowing with uncertainty. "He must matter to you then?"

"No. Not in the way you're implying, anyway. I just don't like the thought of hurting somebody, and even less, that they may think I don't care that I did."

He shook his head with frustration. "You really need to learn not to worry about what other people think, Angel. From what you've said, you made it clear there wasn't going to be a relationship. So, therefore, any misinterpretations are his, and he has to deal with the fallout. Don't you agree?"

"I suppose, when you put it like that, yes."

"When you say you tried to call him, but didn't speak to him, I'm guessing he didn't answer. Did you leave a message?"

I shook my head indicating that I hadn't, but didn't trust myself to speak. I wasn't entirely sure how I felt about Ethan's commanding tone, but the way my nipples had pebbled hinted strongly that it was a turn-on.

"I don't want you to see him or speak to him again, Angel. I know it seems harsh, but I know how a guy thinks, and believe me, any attempt to contact him will seem like a come-on. People like him don't need an excuse to make a nuisance of themselves, so don't give him one. Don't answer his calls, and definitely do not make any attempt to call him. I want you to promise that if he tries to make contact you will tell me."

Okay, so evidently he was still pretty pissed about last night. I wasn't sure whether his instructions were born of a desire to protect me, or if they were fueled by jealousy and possessiveness, as he'd inferred this morning. Either way, for some reason I liked it. And my body definitely liked it. My nod of agreement appeared to placate him.

"Good. Nothing you can say will make him feel any better, anyway. He'll get over you in time. He'll have to. Any kind of apology or justification on your part will only prove to make *you* feel better. It's kinder if you just let it be."

"Okay, you have a point," I admitted, before adding cheekily, "Anything else?"

Wary eyes regarded me closely as he considered the question. "Are there others?"

"No," I snapped, but then realized I couldn't really blame him for wondering. Softening my tone, I repeated the answer. "No. Look, I realize you've not had the best impression of me so far, but I've never been dishonest. Other than James, my relationships have been casual. Entirely physical arrangements devoid of attachment or emotion. I've made no secret of that. But I'm no bed hopper."

"I wasn't suggesting you are." My assumption seemed to horrify him. "I told you, I can handle that you have a past. Just as long as everyone in it, stays in it. You belong to me now, Angel. I won't share you."

Whoosh! The speed at which this relationship was moving made me slightly off-balance, although I knew I was just as accountable for its intensity. I'd told him I was on board and I was, every bit as much as he was. And despite the ferocious intensity of his possessive nature and the candidness of his demands, my skin prickled with the kind of heat that could only be associated with being hugely turned-on. This strong, formidable, and usually completely composed man appeared to have a weak spot and it delighted me that I was it. I'd never felt like I truly belonged before, and now I belonged to him.

Astounded by the way my body reacted to him, I found myself unable to string a coherent sentence together, and instead only managed to mutter, "R... right."

By the dubiety on his face, my response hadn't convinced him that I'd completely understood "the implications." It drove him to explain further.

"It's essential that you make it instantly clear that you're unavailable to anyone who shows you even the vaguest interest. There can't be a repeat of last night, Angel. One, it'll drive me nuts and two, I'll probably end up killing someone. I had no idea that I was a jealous person until I saw that fucking scrote with his hands all over you." He spat the words with rancor. "What ties me up in knots is that *he* thought he had a right to put his hands on you, and I hated the way that felt—" His words and his fury suddenly melted away as his eyes narrowed on me desperately trying, but failing, to conceal my amusement behind my hands. "What?"

"Scrote?"

His beautiful face transformed into a smile. "Yes, scrote—*fucking* scrote. What of it?" He was laughing now and leaning toward me to nuzzle into my neck. I placed my finger on the edge of my lip in a pondering fashion.

"Mmm," I said.

"Mmm, what? What are you thinking?"

I turned to look him square in the eye, my face a somber mask. "I was just wondering what the female equivalent of a 'scrote' was, in order to explain with equal clarity that I expect you to behave in a comparable manner. I do not want to see every girl you come across hanging on your every word, and you're to make it blatantly clear that you are not available to those who do. Don't think I haven't noticed the attention you get, Mr. Wilde. You belong to me now and it just won't do to forget it."

"Fuck, you are damned hot when you're bossy, woman!"

"Funny, because there's an inferno coming off you,"

Without a glimmer of hesitation, his mouth locked firmly onto mine as we fell back onto the enormous bean bag and pulled the faux fur throw over our heads. The night had a chill in the air, but our bodies were warm from the heat of the fire pit, the wine, and the intense conversation. Beneath the fur it was cozy and snug, and when Ethan peeled me slowly out of my clothes, before wriggling out of his own, the heat quickly increased to boiling point.

His hands flowed gracefully over my earnest body, awakening every cell, every nerve, every tight nub of exhilarated flesh. Deepening the kiss, his tongue invaded my mouth in search of mine, lapping and claiming me, my sex clenching and pulsing in response to his persuasion.

In a deft move, he was on top of me, his knees pushing mine apart to spread me wide while his mouth began a hungry trail of kisses over the line of my jaw and down past the pulsing hollow at the base of my neck, until he finally reached my breasts.

His mouth circled the pink, puckered flesh of my nipple, his teeth grazing finely over the delicate skin, before appeasing it with a soft warm lick. With his hand paying close attention to the other breast, he massaged and tugged at my nipple, elongating the solid bud until my body arched toward him, the aching need for him to be inside me becoming unbearable.

I pushed my fingers into his hair and then smoothed them down his neck and over his strong shoulders. My fingertips brushed over a slight indentation in his left shoulder blade, the healed fibrous tissue of a scar. I didn't have time to give it much thought, too distracted by the pangs of need darting straight to my sex from Ethan's expert tending to my breasts.

His breath came in short, sharp gasps, his desperate need corresponding to mine. "Contraception," he blurted the word through the thickness of his desire.

"I'm on the pill. And I have regular checkups."

"Ditto—not the pill bit. I need to feel you, Angel. No barriers, just us. Do you trust me?" he asked.

"I trust you, Ethan."

"Oh God." He plunged into me. "You're mine, Angel." He stilled for a moment, allowing us both to adjust to the confinement of our unity. "You feel so perfect, so wet and warm and fucking right. My dick's been aching for the sensation of your snug, silken pussy all day long." He rocked into me steadily, pushing higher with each thrust—owning me.

"Yes, yours, Ethan. And you are mine. So show me. Fuck me until I'm certain you mean what you say. Until I know you belong solely to me."

My words seemed to goad him, the solid length of his cock sinking harder and deeper. "Oh Christ, Angel, you have no clue. No clue how much I want you. Open your legs wide, baby, and let me show you just how much."

He pushed my knees up toward my shoulders, and I folded my legs across his back tightly, bringing him in deeper with every thrust—owning him.

Still inside me, he sat back on his haunches, his hands sliding gently underneath my buttocks to tilt my pelvis. I placed my feet flat to take my weight, allowing me to sway toward his demanding thrusts. The position offered me the most erotic view of his magnificent penis sliding effortlessly inside me. Muscles rippled with the power of his momentum, his biceps bulging, abs and pecs taut and flexing, every lunge driving me closer to a core-trembling climax. The extent of his rigid cock filled me and stretched me, rubbing against the sensitive walls of my vagina with the perfect amount of friction. My body responded eagerly, my sex tightening and pulsing, delighting in every blissful plunge.

"I want to come inside you, Angel. I want to make you mine. I want to own you," Ethan gasped, fucking me harder and faster.

"Do it."

We came together, gasping each other's names like a prayer of worship and thanks. We surrendered willingly, giving up our bodies and souls to each other like a sacrificial offering, and we accepted willingly—gratefully and wholly claiming possession.

Later, Ethan carried me to bed and we made love until the early hours. Each time was like the first. Our bodies sang out with pleasure as we discovered each other again and again. With each climax came wonderment, a new revelation—and a silent solemn pledge. Until eventually, with our exhausted limbs entwined, we fell into a deep and sated sleep.

The next morning I awoke with my head on Ethan's chest, his arm surrounding me protectively. It felt wonderful, warm and secure, and a part of me was terrified to move or even breathe in case I woke him and broke the spell.

For the longest time, I watched him sleeping, mesmerized by the lines and angles of his chiseled features, enjoying the peacefulness of his gentle breathing, the calm and steady rise and fall of his chest. I'd never been this intimate, this comfortable with anyone. Never woken up in the morning tangled up in someone else's limbs. And I liked it. Actually, I loved it.

Eventually, I wriggled out of bed without waking him, put on my robe, and wandered to the kitchen to make coffee, pausing to wish Ponyo a good morning on the way. As usual, she brushed against the glass, up close to my finger, as I spoke to her gently.

Suddenly, I felt Ethan's arms around me. "What's this?" he asked, "I thought you promised I wouldn't have to share your affection."

I laughed. "Ethan, meet Ponyo. Ponyo, this is Ethan." I could have sworn her eyes widened in shock as she shot me a look that said, "And who the hell is Ethan?"

"Hello, Ponyo," he said, bending down to her vast glass bowl. As he did, I caught sight of the scar I'd detected beneath my fingertips last night. A single, diagonal slash about four inches long marred the perfect skin across his left shoulder blade. Instinctively, I reached out, my fingers lightly tracing the outline. "How did you get this?"

"Through carelessness." He paused briefly to stand. "Ponyo, you say? And where, might I ask, did you come across such a beautiful name?"

I grinned. "It's from one of the *Studio Ghibli* films." His puzzled expression implied he had no idea what I was talking about. "It's an animation about a goldfish named Ponyo, who is rescued by a young boy named Sosuke. They build up a wonderful friendship and go on an exciting, enchanted journey. Ponyo's father, a wizard, brings her back to their undersea home, but she misses her special friend, so she magically transforms herself into a little girl so that she can be with him. She goes…" Ethan's look of amused wonderment stopped me in my tracks, and I realized I was babbling incessantly. "Sorry, you didn't ask for her life story, did you?"

"No." He kissed me on the forehead. "But I should have known there would be something profound and meaningful behind it. You're a very passionate woman, Cinders."

Feeling slightly embarrassed about my outward show of gusto, I offered a non-committal shrug. I was hopelessly and ingenuously enthusiastic when it came to my beloved little fish and my love for the naiveté of animation. It was sometimes easy to forget that Ethan was a powerful business mogul, and although he shared my passion in the bedroom, I figured this was a passion he most certainly wouldn't partake in. I scuttled off to make coffee.

We carried our steaming hot mugs outside, glancing as we passed at the heap of tangled fur throws on the bean bag—evidence of our wild, hedonistic love making. Ethan folded his arms around me, clinching me into a tight embrace and kissing me gently. Sighing happily, he turned to look out at the New York skyline and the progressively mounting hustle and bustle of the streets below.

"Wow! It seems so vivid out there today. Everything looks razor sharp, defined. Brighter somehow…" He stopped abruptly in the middle of his sentence, his eyes wide with stunned surprise, as if a gust of wind had been hurled full force and without warning into his face. Goose bumps sprang to prickle the surface of his skin, causing his hairs to stand on end and his body to visibly shudder.

Neither of us spoke a word, but when Ethan reached out and touched my cheek in the most tender, loving way, we both knew. He knew and I knew—our lives would never be the same.

CHAPTER NINE

T
he days slipped into weeks, racing by as we floated through life in a hazy, dreamlike existence. Unless forced to be apart because of work commitments, we spent every moment together. We worked out in the gym, cooked, laughed, and talked. We watched TV and watched each other sleep. And most gloriously of all we had an abundance of wild and decadent sex. Sometimes we made gentle, tender love, and other times we indulged in unashamed debauchery—loving every single damn minute of it.

We ventured from my building only to work and buy groceries. It was as though the world outside just stopped turning when we were in each other's arms, everything and everyone ceasing to exist. I was yet to discover Ethan's apartment. He'd returned there out of necessity alone, for changes of clothes and personal items. We'd established a routine I was reluctant to tamper with, afraid that if I stepped out of the bubble that now comfortably encompassed Ethan, it would burst. We were both privately aware of this—Ethan had come to know me well—and we knew that if we were to avoid becoming reclusive, we needed to venture out of my comfort bubble.

"Jia asked if we would like to join her and Charley for drinks tomorrow night. I think she wants to check you out properly. She's been bugging me about it for weeks."

We sat cross-legged on the huge bean bag on the terrace, sharing a bottle of wine and feeding each other Chinese food with chopsticks.

Wonderful classical music played in the background, and the Friday night summer sky was clear and brightly lit with a myriad of twinkling stars.

For a second, I could swear I caught a glimmer of unease sweep across his beautiful features, but the expression faded before I could be certain. Popping a spicy prawn into my mouth, he smiled, dabbing at the edges of my mouth with a napkin.

"Yes, I think that's a wonderful idea," he replied. "I want to get to know the people who are important to you."

Well, that shouldn't take long.

"I'll warn you now, though, it could be a wild night. Jia can drink like a fish."

He grimaced.

"Damon and Abby are eager to meet you too. I suppose we can't shut the world out forever. Although, I'd much rather not share you with anyone at all." He paused. "I've almost forgotten what my apartment looks like. I thought we could go tomorrow. It seems a bit peculiar that you haven't even seen where I live."

"No, you're right, we should go. I'd love to see where you live."

Pleased with my response, he stood, offering me his hand and pulling me to my feet. He led me over to the huge hammock in the corner and we lay down, Ethan's arm around my shoulders, me snuggling into his neck and gazing up at the profusion of twinkling stars above us.

"It's beautiful," he proclaimed. "Like a sky full of diamonds."

The comment brought my mom's pendant instantly to mind, and my hand flittered to my throat, half expecting to find it there. My heart sank, as it always did, when I remembered I no longer had it in my possession. I blinked, eager to erase the image of twinkling diamond shapes forming in my mind.

Ethan kissed my forehead, his uncanny antennae reading me perfectly. "I'm going to buy you all the diamonds you deserve, Cinders."

I angled my face to look up at him. "Forever my Prince Charming, eh? Perhaps I will go to the ball one day after all."

"Damn straight, woman."

A few minutes passed in silence when Ethan suddenly asked, "Do you remember much about your mom?"

The question stopped me in my tracks, robbing me of breath for a moment like a sharp gust of wind. I couldn't recall having a detailed conversation with anyone about my mom—ever. In fact, I'd avoided it at all costs. But with Ethan, I realized I felt differently.

"No. I've lost count of the infinite hours I've spent trying to visualize her face. It's bizarre, but sometimes I think I can remember the way she smelled. Like I'll just catch a fleeting trace of a memory and then it's gone. And I can remember the way it felt when she held me against her chest and cuddled me in her lap, the steady, restful drumming of her heartbeat against my ear. It would send me off to sleep." I paused, shrugging. "But I can't remember what she looked like, no matter how hard I try."

A crease formed in the middle of Ethan's brows. "But surely you've got photographs?"

"Not one." I shook my head. "He got rid of everything."

"Your dad?" His tone was incredulous.

I nodded. "The only thing I had was the pendant. And now that's gone too."

"Why would he do that? Get rid of everything?"

Confusion reigned in his face. It resembled the permanent perplexed state I'd been trapped in for most of my life. "I don't really know. Maybe he just found any reminder of her too painful."

"It sounds like he didn't give a shit."

"No, that's not it," I shook my head, rejecting his theory. "If anything, he loved her too much."

"Hmm, pity he didn't give any thought to how that would affect his daughter."

"What do you mean?"

"Well, wiping out all traces of your mom might have helped him come to terms with her death, but what about you? You can't remember what your own mom looked like."

I was stunned to hear it put that way. Not once had I ever considered my father's actions to be selfish. I'd always deemed them to be the coping strategies of a broken-hearted man—wreckage I was responsible for. This concept was something of a revelation, and not one I was too keen on exploring. In fact, this whole subject wasn't one I wished to confront at all. Perhaps I'd been right in the first place; it was far easier to avoid it altogether.

Making one last attempt to justify my father's behavior in the hope he'd leave it alone and move on, I uttered, "He was angry, Ethan."

"What about? What was he angry about?"

"You know."

"No, Angel, I don't. You haven't told me anything about what happened or why your father treats you the way he does."

He had no intention of letting it drop and suddenly the instinct to flee was barging through my bones at a rampant rate. Clambering out of the hammock, I moved to make my way indoors, but before I could make any progress, Ethan reached out to grab my arm. "Don't run away, Angel." He pulled himself to his feet, shifting to hold me tightly at the tops of my arms.

"Leave it, Ethan." I tried to pull away. "You don't know what happened or what I did."

Tightening his hold, he held firmly to my gaze. "Then tell me. Tell me what you did. You have to talk about this sooner or later. You said when we first met that your father hated you because you killed your mom. What did you mean?"

The question was like a punch to the gut—too direct, too... invasive.

I stared at him for the longest time, my mouth dry and clamped shut. Even if I'd wanted to talk, it would have been physically impossible. The words were frozen in my chest, too large and foreboding to escape, and I knew if I tried they would choke me.

"Leave me alone, Ethan." I wrenched myself free and stomped

inside to busy myself in the kitchen.

As I banged around the kitchen putting dishes away, I glanced up through the open terrace doors. Ethan remained rooted to the spot I'd left him in when I'd stormed off indoors, his arms dangling limply by his sides, a look of grim abandonment and deep hurt etched into his beautiful features—hurt which I had inflicted.

I raised my hand to my chest to rub away the mounting tightness, and in that moment, I realized my heart was actually aching. Seeing the hurt in his eyes broke my heart, and I couldn't bear that I was the cause of his pain. After all, this wonderful man was the only person in the world who'd ever cared enough about me to ask these questions.

Turning away in shame, I walked quietly into my bedroom, closing the door behind me. Sitting on the edge of the bed, I pulled up my knees and hugged them to my chest. The doors of my closet had been left slightly ajar, and from where I sat, I had a clear view of the top shelf inside. Four or five minutes passed as I stared through the gap, slowly gathering my courage.

Finally, I climbed off the bed and walked into the closet, retrieving a shoebox from the shelf I'd been gaping at. Setting it down on the bed, I pulled on the red ribbon which bound it and removed the lid. Inside were a few mementoes from my childhood; there hadn't been much worth keeping. Most were pictures drawn by Adam at school, some birthday cards he'd made for me, and a handful of photographs of the twins when they were small.

At the bottom of the pile was a small envelope. I tugged it free and stared down at it in my hands, turning it over and over nervously between my fingers, palms clammy with apprehension. Glancing at the closed bedroom door, I warred with indecision, knowing with every painful beat of my heart that if I left this room with the envelope in my hands, the enigma of my past would begin to unravel and my rawness would be exposed.

Ethan would finally understand the reason why my father and Aaron hated me so much. He would know the reason why Adam, who had at least been human enough to show compassion for the guilt and burden I'd carried every day since… *that day*, now simply pitied me. But he'd also know that I cared enough about him to try and share my pain, and that way I could help erase the pain that I'd caused him.

Resolute in my decision, I stood and painstakingly made my way out of the bedroom and into the lounge. Ethan sat cross-legged on the sofa, his laptop resting on his knees. I sauntered over and stood beside him, waiting for him to acknowledge my presence.

"I have to work, Angel." His tone was woeful as he continued to tap away on the keys, refusing to meet my eyes.

Without a word, I carefully placed the envelope on his keyboard and went to sit on the sofa facing him. The tapping ceased, his eyes darting warily up at mine before looking back down to the envelope. "What is this?"

I folded my arms across my chest, one hand fluttering up to play nervously with the skin on my lips, the pain in my chest becoming tighter. "The answers. You said you wanted to understand."

Turning his attention back to the envelope, he paused for a beat before picking it up and turning back the flap to carefully remove the folded piece of paper. Inside was a newspaper article, the words of which were etched into my memory I'd read it so many times. Self-repulsion unfurled inside me, and although the feeling was familiar, it suddenly felt like I was about to lay bare the ugliness of a dirty, sinful secret for the entire world to see. One which had already branded me unworthy of love and barely even tolerated. With bated breath, I watched as Ethan began to read.

MOTHER DIES SAVING CHILD'S LIFE
By SAM COHEN
Published: November 21, 1990

A woman was killed after she was hit by a pickup truck and thrown into the air near to the 59th Street entrance of Central

Park in Manhattan. The incident happened shortly after 5:00 p.m. on Saturday.

The victim, Mrs. Felicity Lawson, 34, had apparently been coming from the direction of Central Park with her 6-year-old daughter.

Witnesses at the scene said that they didn't see what had caused the accident, but after hearing screams, they saw the mother of 3 fly through the air and fall behind a parked van at the curb.

It is thought that the child had run into the road and the woman had sped out after her, pushing her to safety. She had been struck full force by the oncoming vehicle, say police.

The driver, although too distraught at the scene, later confirmed that the child had ran out from between two cars and the mother had run after her. The driver swerved to miss the child and struck the woman. He was taken to New York Presbyterian Hospital with minor injuries.

Police sources say that alcohol did not play a role in the accident, and no charges were expected against the driver.

Lawson, of Brooklyn, New York, and her daughter were said to be regular visitors to the Park. Her husband and 2-year-old twin boys were not present at the scene. The child was uninjured and although traumatized, was said to be doing well. She was reunited with her father later. The woman died at the scene.

Ethan must have read the article through several times for the sheer length of time he gazed at it, no doubt attempting to absorb the magnitude of what he'd learned. The entire time I studied his face, seeking to gain the vaguest clue as to what he was thinking, but found nothing. His stoic countenance was completely unreadable. Finally, he re-folded the paper along the existing crease and placed it back in the envelope.

I waited a few seconds, but still he didn't speak, so I got to my feet, tentatively removing the envelope from his hands. "So, now do you see? I killed her." Pausing for a beat, I added, "I'm gonna go take a bath."

The deep, egg-shaped soaking tub was filled to the brim with bubbles. Lit candles lined the glass shelf above the tub and the soothing aromas of ylang-ylang, lavender, and lemon permeated the air. The classical music streamed from the bathroom speakers through the multi-room sound system, and the tension was slowly ebbing away.

Provided I continued to recite the script of one of my favorite Disney or Japanese animation movies word for word, or count backwards from one hundred on a continual, recurring cycle—as I often did to tune out of something emotionally testing—I would come through this night with my psyche intact.

To this day, I'd never dealt with my mother's death, what had happened, how I felt. I'd stored the myriad of suppressed memories and emotions somewhere in the back of my brain, like a slow releasing vat of poison slowly eroding my insides. I'd done it because I'd never felt truly strong enough to face them. But now I'd flipped the lid off that poison. And I'd done that because I'd had no choice, because my reticence was hurting the only person I truly cared for, and I couldn't bear that. Now, I wasn't sure if I'd done the right thing, and I felt a desperate need to slam that lid back on and shut it all away again.

Pushing the tips of my fingers into my ears, I took a deep breath to fill my lungs, held it, and slithered under the water. When the skin on my face and scalp had adjusted to the heat, I slowly removed my fingers from my ears and relaxed my arms out to the sides. Concentrating hard on slowing my heart rate, secure in the knowledge that my lungs were filled with all the oxygen I needed, I began to mentally zone out.

The silence and serenity of being completely immersed under water was surreally liberating. Although, I wasn't physically inhaling oxygen, the strange sense of calmness which washed over me as I controlled the need for it was as satisfying as the act of breathing itself. All of life's intrusions, even sound, melted and faded away, because I was locked into my own transcendent state. A blissful state, free from pain and worry. A state which offered an escape from the confinement of my tortured mind—a state I quietly craved.

When I could no longer hold my breath, I opened my eyes and exhaled, slowly allowing the confined air to escape and bubble to the surface in a long-flowing stream.

Suddenly, through blurred vision, I saw a shadow against the faintly-lit room, and then there was a figure looming above me and grasping me by the shoulders. I gasped as I was yanked to the surface, the shock and the force causing me to swallow a mouthful of water.

"Angel, what the fuck?" yelled Ethan, brushing the hair away from my stunned face.

I gagged, coughing and spluttering as the water cascaded down my wind pipe, choking me.

"What the fuck are you doing?" he screamed at me.

I stared at him, aghast, the remnants of my choking fit subsiding as I struggled to regain my breath, the music resonant and dramatic in the background. "Taking a bath?" I exclaimed between coughs.

"I thought…" Hesitating, he gripped me, pulling me to his chest and holding me there tightly.

Suddenly it dawned on me and I pulled away. "What? What did you think? That I was drowning?" I paused. "Or that I was drowning myself?"

"Whichever. Does it matter? You scared the living shit out of me."

"Yes, it matters. Do you really think I'm so damaged that I'd be capable of that?" The idea shocked me to the core.

"What were you *doing,* then?" he asked.

"I was blanking out—finding peace—shutting down." I said it like it was absolutely absurd that he didn't know.

Then I realized that my interpretation sounded, in some ways, very similar to what Ethan had feared I was doing—the end result just being very different. Some people sought their escape from a bottle. My idea of seeking oblivion took me dangerously close to unconsciousness, and anybody witnessing it would have the right to draw the same conclusion. In a nutshell, I realized, for the first time, that what I'd just done was freaking weird. Perhaps I was more fucked up than I thought I was.

"Are you for real?" he breathed.

The fear and confusion on Ethan's face said everything he couldn't, and the knowledge that I needed to face some daunting truths became a startling reality.

"Ethan. I know I have to deal with… my junk," I said quietly. "And I will try. Just give me time."

He stared at me for what seemed like a lifetime before leaning his forehead against mine. "Angel, you don't get it, do you? You're not alone anymore. You've got me to help deal with your junk. I want you to share your life with me, the good, the bad, and the fucking junk. You've made considerable progress tonight, whether you're aware of it or not. I'll give you all the time you need, as long as you agree to let me help carry the burden. It's been way too heavy for you alone, baby girl."

My heart physically ached for this man and the words he spoke with such compassion and sincerity. Words, until now, I didn't even know I'd yearned to hear. He was right. The onerous weight of my grief and guilt had been too overwhelming, too terrifying to bear on my own. But could I summon the courage to face the demons of my past with him by my side? I wasn't sure.

"God, Ethan, I'm so sorry for scaring you and for pushing you away before. I didn't mean to hurt you. It's just that I've never talked about all this, and I don't know where to begin. It's just… it's been so much easier just to leave things alone, and I guess I panicked. You don't understand how afraid—"

"It's okay, baby. I know how difficult this must be, and I do understand why you're afraid. I'm glad you shared what happened with me. But it's essential for *you* to understand something as well." His gentle touch belied his emphatic tone when he took my face in his hands. "It was an accident, Angel. What happened to your mom was a cruel and tragic accident. But you are not to blame, and it is wrong on every level that you've been allowed to believe you are."

I shook my head in protest. "But—"

He placed his finger on my lips. "No buts. It was *not* your fault."

My lip trembled beneath the touch of his finger, my body beginning to shiver, not only from the cooled water, but from the cathartic aftermath of sharing my burden.

"Holy fuck, you're turning blue, woman. Come on before you freeze to death."

Grabbing a large fluffy towel from the rail, he helped me to my feet and placed it around my shoulders, holding my hand to support my weight as I stepped out of the tub. Gently, he began to dab at my skin, moving the towel gradually over my body, lifting my arms and spreading my legs to reach every part of me, until eventually I was dry. Then, sitting me down on a chair, he knelt before me, lifting each foot in turn to dry the soles and in between my toes. Finally, he came around behind me to towel dry my hair.

"What's funny?" he asked, catching sight of my amused expression in the mirror. Abandoning the towel, he reached for my hairbrush and began to brush my hair like it was the most natural thing in the world to do.

"Nobody's done any of this stuff for me since my mom." The ease in which I spoke the words astounded even me.

"It strikes me your mom was the last person to do almost anything for you. That's all going change now, baby. I'm here and I'm going to look after you."

And I believed him. This gloriously beautiful man was all the strength I ever needed. The flood gates were open, yes, but I was glad because with this man by my side, I could take on anything. I was sure of it.

Hungry eyes shimmied over my naked body and suddenly he was pulling me into his arms. "You are so fucking sexy, Cinders. Your skin is all warm and soft from the hot, soapy water. Look…" he nodded at the mirror behind me "…your tight little ass has turned pink. Jesus, you make my dick go hard." He winced as he adjusted himself before squeezing my ass forcefully. "Get dressed or I'll have to fuck you, and I've got work to do."

With a sexy growl, he turned to leave the room, the sight of his all-masculine form stirring a need within and suddenly an overwhelming urge washed over me. Before I knew what I was doing, I'd picked up the discarded towel from the floor, twirled it into a spiraled rope and flicked him hard on the behind. The action made a loud thwacking noise, and I knew that the end of the towel had caught him perfectly, the image of a large, purple colored splotch right in the middle of his left butt cheek, forming in my mind.

He stopped dead, waited a few agonizing beats, and slowly began to turn at the waist to meet my gaze. Wide eyes and parted lips revealed an expression that flitted somewhere between disbelief and outrage.

Oh shit!

I swallowed hard. There was no doubt I was in trouble, but of what kind, I wasn't sure. Hitching a brow, I pursed my lips, trying my best to appear fearless and challenging—not easy when you're butt naked and vulnerable.

With knotted brows and narrowed eyes, he turned fully to face me, hands on his hips, head cocked to one side. "Did you just towel snap me, Miss Lawson?"

I raised my chin defiantly. "What if I did?"

Stunned by my brazenness, he continued to stare accusingly; the only evidence that he was fighting the need to smirk was the slight twitching of his lips. "Oh. She's not only foolishly audacious, but she has a sassy mouth besides."

Exhilarated panic flooded me, and suddenly I was torn between the urges to giggle, to scream, to flee, and to beg for forgiveness. I said and did nothing, just pushed my chin out in overstated obstinacy.

"Not so clever to begin a towel snapping war when you're butt naked, Miss Lawson." His eyes slid greedily and victoriously over my bare body.

I felt incredibly exposed. He was right. I was naked and defenseless. He was strong, mean-looking, and blocking my escape route. A look of exultance slid onto his perfect face, his lips twitching with a touch of smugness. Christ, he looked fucking sexy.

I glanced around the room, cautiously weighing my options. Ethan's eyes seemed to follow mine, moving between him, the open doorway, and my robe, which was discarded on the floor where I'd left it.

"What? You really think you have a hope in hell of escaping?" He shook his head, making a *tsk*ing noise.

Shrugging, I replied foolishly, "What? You think you have a hope in hell of stopping me?"

His eyes lit up with the challenge, a smoldering intensity settling on his sinful mouth as his tongue flicked out to run over his upper lip. My gaze shifted briefly to the bulge of his swollen cock straining beneath the fabric of his jeans, leaving me in no doubt as to the level of his aroused state. My mouth kinked into a wry smile.

"I'll tell you what I'm going to do," he said guilefully. "I'll give you to the count to three to make your escape, and then I'm coming after you. And when I catch you—which I will—I'm going to spank your pert, pink ass. And then… I'm going to fuck you… Hard."

Oh my fucking God!

A sudden rush of blood tore through my veins, pumping into my now swollen, jutting nipples and heating the flesh between my thighs to leave a delicious, rhythmical throb. Something on my face must have revealed the raw, visceral effect his words were having on me, and his attention shifted to my nakedness. He hitched a brow suggestively, nodding once toward my full, aching breasts, a slow, playful smile curling the corner of his mouth.

He licked his lips slowly. "One."

Oh my God, he was counting down! With no time to lose, I made a swift dash toward the door, dipping slightly to the left as I scurried past him to scoop up my robe from the floor. As I did, I felt a hard stinging slap catch me squarely on my right butt cheek. The sensation was indiscernible, a strange combination of pleasure and pain, but undeniably incendiary to my already smoldering desire. My response was immediate, the resulting electrifying tingle travelling a direct line to my damp, pulsating pussy. The shock of the impact and how it had affected me caused me to lose my grip on the robe, leaving me no choice but to abandon it.

"Two."

Reaching the bedroom, I glanced around frantically for sanctuary, for some place he couldn't see me or reach me—some place that didn't exist.

"Two and a half."

It was futile. There was nowhere to run to, nowhere to hide. Hopelessly, I turned to face the bathroom doorway, my arms out in front in combat pose, preparing to meet my adversary.

"Three." The voice which drifted through from the bathroom was deep and masterful, full of dark, exhilarating promise.

Suddenly, his strong, consummate frame filled the doorway— smoldering, sexy, and shirtless, wearing nothing but his low slung jeans. The wonderful scent of Ethan flooded my nostrils, the aroma manly and sexy, growing more intense with the heightening state of his arousal. It was his own special, personal scent which clung to his skin, stirring and rousing my senses until I was almost depraved with hunger for him. My heart hammered wildly against my chest.

"Not running, Miss Lawson?" he crooned. "But I was so looking forward to the chase. Surely, you don't give up so easily. A beast likes to stalk his prey, hunt her down before he strikes. Render her defenseless before taking her for his own decadent pleasure."

Holy fuck, I was beyond aroused. Practically panting with desire, I watched as he moved to a chest of drawers just inside the room, sliding the top one open and dipping his hand inside to remove a pair of silk stockings.

Oh, maybe he wants me to dress up—kinky.

But instead of offering the stockings to me, he began to draw them slowly through his hands, sliding the full length of their sheer, delicate softness steadily through his fingers.

"But maybe we can save the chase for another day. Because today, I can see you're leaning more toward submissive."

Submissive? What does he mean, submissive?

"I like that. I like that a lot. It will give *me* more time to feast." He licked his lips again in that slow sexy way of his. "Now, I think it's high time you learned a lesson. Get on the bed, Angel," he suddenly commanded.

I glanced at the bed, then back to him, suddenly nervous about what to expect. "Why? What are you going to do?" I asked breathlessly, excitement of the unknown bubbling away in the depths of my core.

His eyes narrowed. "Do you trust me, Angel?"

"Yes, of course. More than anyone—ever," I assured him.

"Good." He nodded. "Well, firstly you are going to learn to do as you're told and get on the bed. And then—after I've taught you a lesson—you are going to beg me to fuck you."

Jesus, I was so damned wet and aching with want that the temptation to clasp my fingers firmly over my sex to quell the building desire was overwhelming. Instead, I bit down on my lip.

"What do you mean, teach me a lesson?"

"Angel…" he shook his head "…stop with the questions. You really are not in a position to ask questions." He continued to slide the soft silk stockings through his fingers. "Now turn around so I can peruse your incredible ass. I need to be certain I spanked you hard enough."

I knew from the warm, strangely pleasant, glowing sensation that he had, and that there would be a perfect red handprint across my butt cheek as evidence. I did as I was told, and turned to face the bed.

There was a harsh sound of air hissing through pursed lips, an indication that he was satisfied with his aim. "Good. Now, on all fours, I want you to crawl slowly to the top of the bed."

I edged on to the foot of the bed, hands first and then on to my knees.

"Wait!"

Responding to the order instantly, I stilled, sensing him shifting so he stood at the foot of the bed.

"Slowly. I want you to crawl *very* slowly, so I can see your perfect, little pussy."

Mother of God.

My sex was on fire, thumping deliciously with the power of his words. I couldn't have been more turned on. Obeying his command, I began to make my way up the bed, creeping inch by inch, until I reached the pillows. The intensity of his gaze burned into my eager flesh, the sound of appreciative murmurs escaping his sinful lips.

"Stop," he ordered. "Now spread your legs wide. As wide as you can."

Complying quickly and willingly and with no inhibition, I shifted my knees apart, spreading myself wide open until my most intimate parts were on display and completely exposed for Ethan's pleasure.

"Oh, Angel," he gasped. "You respond so readily. Your quivering little pussy is glistening with the need to be fucked."

A low, involuntary moan squeezed from my throat, his lewd words alone sending me dangerously close to a powerful detonation. My sex ached almost painfully, desperate for his touch. Minutes seemed to pass, and then I felt him approach to the side of the bed.

Suddenly, he thrust two fingers inside me, my body jerking and crying out with the unexpected pleasure. I lunged backwards onto them, wanting them deeper and faster.

"Mmm, so wet, Angel. Always so fucking gorgeously wet," he crooned, removing his fingers and rubbing my juices all around my trembling slit. But then his touch was gone and a whimper of protest at the sudden loss of contact passed unbidden through my lips.

"You're so earnest, Angel. A dirty girl, who's dripping wet and desperate to be fucked."

I groaned loudly, certain I would go off if he continued to talk that way.

"Turnover," he demanded.

Doing as I was bid, I lay with my head on the pillow, my focus shifting to find him standing directly in my line of sight at the foot of the bed. Swiftly, he unfastened his pants, pushing them down over his hips and kicking them off to unveil his masterpiece. The size of his rock-solid cock never failed to amaze me, the thought of it pushing inside me, owning me, was enough to make me weep with pent up desire.

Eyes dark with lust and the need to be satisfied raked wickedly over my body. "Open... Your... Legs." The command was a calm, controlled instruction.

When I complied, he closed his eyes for a brief second, as if the sight was too much, his teeth biting down on his lower lip to gain control. Then in a wildly provocative gesture, he took his impressive cock in his hand and began to stroke gently up and down his stone shaft.

Oh fuck.

The vision of him standing there before me, his muscles flexing, my stockings draped from one hand and his bulging cock pulsing in the other, was a sight too erotic to behold. Unable to prevent the groan from grating loudly past my lips, I began to squirm, my hips moving in time to the rhythm of him stroking his cock.

"Do you want this, Angel?"

"Hell yes," I replied, my breathing becoming even more erratic by the second.

"I don't believe you."

"I swear to…"

"Shh." He put his finger to his lips to silence me.

"Hold your arms out to the sides and up." Quickly, he moved to the top of the bed, and using a stocking swiftly bound my wrist to the bar on the left side of the headboard. Then, shifting around the bed, repeated the process with the other to the right side.

Holy shit, this game was beyond exciting; being naughty was proving to be fun and damn well erotic.

Ethan moved back to the bottom of the bed to observe my defenseless, naked body, legs spread and wrists tethered, completely at his mercy. Smiling a slow victorious smile, he nodded toward the apex of my thighs. "Wider."

His masterful tone sent heated shock waves straight to my sex, my hips bucking impulsively toward him in response. If he didn't fuck me soon I would surely combust.

"God, you look fucking amazing, Angel. Your tits are full and erect; your beautiful pussy pounding and soaking wet. You're all trussed and bound and ready to be fucked."

Oh Christ, I couldn't stand it.

Licking his lips, he crept slowly on to the foot of the bed between my legs, his avid gaze fixed and unmoving on the focus of his desire at the summit. He inched closer, sidling stealthily toward my pulsating flesh with the voracious hunger of an animal stalking its prey. Finally he came to rest barely an inch away, my sex quivering and aching in anticipation of his greedy mouth. Suddenly, his eyes darted to mine, his tongue snaking out and lashing me once against my clit.

I groaned and arched up toward him, yearning for the connection. He pulled away.

"Uh uh. Keep … still."

Oh man, this was going to be torture. Beads of sweat sprang to the surface of my skin. My pulse pounded in the hollow of my throat, heartbeat reverberating in my ears. But I didn't move. Pleased with my response, he lowered his head again, his tongue darting out and hitting me directly on my sweet, tender spot. I cried out in utter relief at the long awaited connection, my coiled up buds of tormented nerve endings ready to burst open with the power of my release.

"I don't think you want it enough," he said, backing away again.

Desperation charged through my abandoned body. "No! I do. God, you don't know how much."

"Then let me hear it, baby. I want you to beg me. If you don't beg, then I'll leave you here bound to the bed and unable to touch yourself."

"Please, I beg you to do it." I wriggled again, wanting to thrust my hands into his hair and push his head down onto me, but the tightly wound stockings prevented any movement.

"Do what, Angel? What do you want me to do?" The torment continued, his tongue whipping out at my clit again, the flesh throbbing and pulsing in earnest imploration.

"I want you to lick me, Ethan," I pleaded.

"Lick what, Angel? I can't hear you."

Oh, you bastard. Payback will be hell for this.

I raised my head from the pillow to get a clear view of his face. "Lick my fucking pussy, Ethan. Now!"

And he did.

He licked it relentlessly, pushing his tongue inside me, hot and demanding, and then flicking across my clit. His fingers slid inside me, teasing and thrusting as I ground my hips against them, my muscles clenching tightly around his fingers as they fucked me, his tongue lapping and licking me in unison. Just as I was about to explode from a mind-blowing orgasm, he suddenly stopped and again his touch disappeared, leaving me bereft and desperate.

"No," I screamed. "No. Don't you fucking stop. Not now. Please, Ethan."

Moving so he was kneeling up between my legs, a wicked triumphant smile slid sinfully onto his lips. His stance was braced, strong and dominant as he gripped me by the hips and tilted my pelvis toward him. "Oh, baby, I'm going to bury my cock so far inside of you, you're going to be begging me to stop."

"Never," I hissed, almost crazy with desire. The challenge incited him, fueling his responding need, and with eyes on fire, he slammed into me.

"Oh my God," I screamed, "Yes, Ethan. Like that. Fuck me like that."

"Oh fuck." My words drove him wild, the struggle to maintain control evident in his straining jaw and clamped shut eyes. Swiftly, he gripped hold of my legs, pushing them up and wide, his fingers gripping my calves. "Oh fuck!" He thrashed with wild abandonment, driving into me as if his life depended on it, his skin suddenly slick with sweat.

"Come now, Angel. Come with me now."

A burning heat rushed like a tidal wave, racing through me as I came wildly and loudly, my orgasm rippling through my shuddering sex with eye-watering intensity. The sight of my ascension into an untamed, toe-curling climax was Ethan's undoing and his body convulsed, his cock twitching and jerking with his own violent release.

As our bodies eased back down, he reached out, releasing one hand and then the other from my restraints before collapsing by my side. We lay gasping to regain a steady breath, sated and basking in the aftermath of our lovemaking, our eyes locked in a mutual intimacy of what we'd shared.

"What the fuck have you done to me, Angel Lawson? Look at what you drive me to," he laughed. "Where the hell did that come from?"

"I don't know, but—I enjoyed the hell out of it," I confessed, laughing as well.

Suddenly I was boneless, my eyelids heavy with contented exhaustion. I curled onto my side, nestling into the cozy space of his neck between his ear and shoulder, our limbs entwined. Our breathing slowed as we drifted, and somewhere between consciousness and sleep, I could have sworn I heard Ethan say something.

Perhaps it was a dream, or a hopeful ideal summoned by the intensity of our lovemaking and the tender way in which Ethan had cared for me earlier. The words were a barely audible whisper, a soft resonating hum on the edge of my slumber. *I love you, Angel.* I fought with my conscious mind to make sense of it, but the fatigue was overwhelming, and with no strength left, I finally surrendered.

CHAPTER TEN

"**I** was thinking you might want to pack a few things to bring with you," Ethan said with a cautious smile.

We were preparing to go over to his place for the first time, and I had a feeling he was slightly nervous about it.

"Like what? And why?"

"Well, like your iPod, or laptop, maybe a book or film. You seem to have a fair collection there." He nodded to the narrow cabinet against the wall in the lounge where the faint outlines of about forty DVDs could just be seen through the smoke-tinted glass.

"Oh, I'm not sure you'd like any of those." I felt my face flush. "And you didn't explain why."

There was that wary look again.

"Well, I guess I'm making a few assumptions, but I was kind of hoping you would like to stay at my place for the weekend. I know we've spent all of our time here together these past few weeks, but…" He paused. "The thing is, baby, I need to have access to my home office. I'm going to need to spend more time there. I'm getting snowed under with work, and as much as I love it here with you… I mean, if it doesn't suit and you would rather stay here, then I understand. I guess we can't be in each other's pockets all the time," he laughed. "You'd probably be glad of some space anyway."

Oh. I felt my heart stumble, and the buoyancy I'd felt all morning, recalling the words I thought I'd heard last night, fell suddenly flat.

Although those three little words terrified the hell out of me, Christ, they'd felt good to hear. I wasn't even certain I'd actually heard him speak them, but I'd dared to consider that I might have. Throughout the morning, I'd allowed myself to believe they were the ramblings of a man falling in love as he'd succumbed to sleep, and not just my exhausted imagination.

Now I was seized with panic that the whole thing was a product of my deluded mind, a detached fragment of one of my bat-shit crazy dreams. It wasn't him confessing hidden feelings; it was him backing off, him wanting space. Maybe he saw me in a different light after finding out about my mom and was freaked out by the whole bathtub fiasco. Maybe my junk was just too fucked-up for him after all.

Forcing my lips to smile, I shrugged. "Sure, if you'd rather go to your place alone, I understand. You have to work. You're behind and it's my fault," I blurted out. "I should have realized. Shit, you can't be a successful, multi-billionaire businessman rolling around in the sack with me for weeks on end."

"That's not what I said, Angel. Why do you always assume the worst?"

Do I?

He took hold of my hands. "I love rolling around in the sack with you. But it's not all I love. I love simply being with you, even if we're doing different things. Just knowing that you're there next to me, curled up with a book, or in the next room is uplifting enough. Besides, I can't wait to show you my home. If you relax a little, you might actually find you like it."

The sound of his cell *buzzing* in his pocket suddenly distracted him. He took it out, frowning as he glanced at the display, before rejecting the call and pocketing the cell.

"Who was that?" I'd noticed him rejecting calls a lot recently.

"No one." He shook his head and continued. "The reason I asked you to bring some things with you was so you wouldn't get bored when I need to work. But like I said, that's on the assumption that you wouldn't rather be here. If I had my way, I'd have you stapled to my hip, but I was conscious that I haven't given you much space recently, and I don't want to be too demanding on your time."

The way my heart stuttered and began to beat again confirmed one thing for sure. I didn't want any damn space. "Actually, I quite like it when you're demanding." My voice was laced with seduction, heavy with the memory of the demands he'd made the previous night. The implication didn't go unnoticed.

"You're a dirty, dirty girl, Miss Lawson." Squeezing my ass tightly in his hands, he pulled me against his hard body. "You were so fucking hot last night, I swear to God…" As if the memory alone was too much, he closed his eyes and shook his head, his cock twitching and turning rigid against me. "No," he exclaimed, more to himself than to me, as he gripped my hips and pushed me back. "As much as I would like nothing more than to spend the day fucking the living daylights out of you, we have too much to do. Now," he said, kneeling to slide the cabinet door open, "let's choose a film for you."

"Wait!" *Oh crap.*

It was too late. Ethan's gaze moved gradually along the collection of DVDs, his face becoming more crumpled with confusion the deeper he went. The shelves were filled with Disney classics, Disney Pixar, and Studio Ghibli movies—everything from *Peter Pan* and *Pocahontas* to *The Incredibles* and *Whisper of the Heart*.

"I did say they probably wouldn't be to your taste." I cringed with embarrassment as I waited for him to peruse the whole stack.

"Wow," he said eventually. "Okay, well, unless you have a secret child you haven't told me about, I guess you're into cartoons." Glancing at me for verification, I noted the effort it was taking to prevent the laughter in his eyes from reaching his lips.

I thought briefly about going with the secret child idea. After all, a girl who's into Disney is hardly a major turn-on. But I suppose he had to see every side of the real me at some time, even the quirky side, so I guess I had no choice but to suck it up.

"No shit, Sherlock." Curling my lip into a cynical snarl, I knelt down beside him. "And what of it? Most other stuff is too damn serious and depressing. The world is full of grim reality without watching it for entertainment. Animation is a far safer bet. It's just bright, cheerful colors and illustrations brought to life." I shrugged. "I suffer from world-weariness and being forced to confront the evils of the world makes me sad—even if it is just a movie. For that reason, I prefer to indulge in the world of fantasy. So shoot me."

"I think it's sweet." Smiling widely, he reached out to tug my cheek, as if he thought I was cute or something.

As if. Screwing my face up in disgust, I brushed his hand away, watching as he turned to study the selection again. He bit down on his lip boyishly and threw me a sideways glance out of narrowed eyes, as if pondering whether to disclose something.

"You want to know a secret?" he asked, slightly abashed.

"What?"

"I've always secretly wanted to see *Finding Nemo*."

"No way!"

"God, do you have it?" he asked, excitedly scanning the shelves.

I gazed at him in wonderment. Could this guy be more made for me? Leaning forward, I kissed him on the cheek.

"What was that for?"

"Not only do you accept that your girlfriend's guilty pleasure is totally tragic, but you embrace it. Now that's what I call sweet."

His smile broadened. "I like the sound of that."

"What, that I'm totally tragic?"

He twisted his mouth wryly and hitched a brow. "Girlfriend, cheeky. *My* exquisitely beautiful, sexy, horny *girlfriend*." His expression morphed into that smoldering sexy look of his, his heated gaze sliding lustfully over my lips as he leaned in for a kiss.

I pulled back, shaking a finger at him. "I thought you didn't have time to spend the entire day fucking me senseless."

"I know, but it's so hard when you're just there looking like you do and saying the naughty things you say."

"You talk so much shit." I giggled and shook my head. "Now quit, before I submit and let you take me to bed." I watched his eyes gleam at the mention of the word *submit*. "Now you're the one being naughty." Punching his arm playfully, I pointed at the shelves. "Help me choose a movie."

After scanning the shelf for a few moments, he pulled one out, holding it up for approval. It was *Ponyo*.

"Mmm, good choice."

"Anything else?"

"No, I'll take my laptop, catch up with some emails."

"Okay. Good to go, then?"

"No, I haven't packed any other stuff yet."

"You don't need to. We're going shopping first. I want to buy everything you need to keep at my place so you can stay there whenever you choose."

"I need more than a toothbrush and a change of underwear, E," I objected. "I'll need makeup and a hairdryer and clothes and—"

"And we'll buy them." He paused. "What did you just call me?"

"Um... E." I blinked and pulled a face. "I don't know where it came from. Sorry, don't you like it?"

For a moment, he seemed to contemplate the question. "No, I love it," he beamed, pulling me to my feet. "Let's go."

Several exhausting hours later we were finally on our way to Ethan's apartment on Fifth Avenue. I thought Jia knew how to shop, but she had nothing on Ethan. Admittedly, it made it a whole lot easier when you had Jackson outside every store with the SUV, and Jackson to carry everything to the car, and Jackson to load the car. Ah, God bless Jackson.

Clothes, shoes, makeup, toiletries, purses, electrical—you name it, we bought it. Or Ethan did. Each time I tried to shove my card at an assistant he just pushed my hand away, looking vaguely affronted. It didn't sit comfortably with me to let him buy me everything. I was used to being self-sufficient; nobody had ever spoiled me in my life. But when I objected, he just said I'd better get used to it because he planned to spoil me rotten.

We rode the private elevator up from the basement parking, leaving Jackson to unload the car. Ethan held my hand protectively the entire climb to the top floor penthouse, a boyish smile—which had me practically melting—playing on his face.

The elevator opened into a private foyer where a beautiful, black marble vintage console table stood proudly against a white wall. Atop was a black statement vase teeming with white lilies, the sweet distinctive scent infusing the air. The foyer to the right opened into circular room where the walls were lined with loaded bookshelves. An armchair, sofa, and a small desk with a reading lamp made up a small but cozy library.

Turning left from the elevator was a pair of bold black iron studded doors with white frosted glass running from the top to the waist. Their style was almost medieval, like the fortified entrance to a prince's fortress. In this case, my aptly named, extremely sexy Prince Charming.

Ethan pushed on the heavy doors and motioned for me to lead the way. They opened up into a huge living room, the entire far wall a sheet of expansive glass, connecting the indoor with the outdoor, and giving the space a bright, airy feel. What felt like miles of ebony floor ran straight through the open-plan lounge, kitchen, and dining room, the walls, a stark white in contrast, continuing the distinctive black and white theme throughout.

I stepped into the room, eyes wide and jaw lax from wonderment as I took in the sprawling space. Every luxurious inch smacked of style and panache, and lots and lots of money.

There was a selection of super modern pieces of furniture, but the two which caught my eye were a pair of beautiful, snow white, petrie-style sofas adorned in zebra print cushions. They were strategically placed to capture the full advantage of a magnificent state-of-the-art fireplace. It had to be at least six-feet wide, open-fronted, and sunken into the wall. Although it wasn't lit, I could imagine the depth of heat it would throw into the room on a cold winter day. Abstract art with bold, black and white graphic designs stood out on white walls, adding to the clean lines and super minimalist look.

"Well, what do you think?" asked Ethan, grinning at my awed expression.

I shook my head. "I... I... Words fail me, Ethan."

He laughed.

"I suppose I'd gotten so used to you existing in my little bubble that I'd forgotten who you actually are."

His brows knitted together to crease his forehead. "What I am, not who I am, surely? I may be ludicrously rich, but I'm still just a person, Angel."

"You think?" His underrated self-perception amused me. "You've never been just a person. You're Ethan Wilde—powerful and influential. You have prominent, successful people shaking your hand, and glamorous, rich women falling at your feet. You have a chunk of everything, and everyone wants a chunk of you."

I noted his expression fall, a vague look of worriment clouding his features.

"I honestly felt like I lived in the lap of luxury, but this... This is stuff out of magazines, E. This, I want to photograph and then pack away like it's been assembled just for the photo shoot." Stealing a glance at his solemn face I suddenly realized he may be misinterpreting what I was saying. "Don't look so worried. I absolutely love it—I'd just forgotten is all."

When he released his shoulders and seemed to visibly relax, I wandered over to the kitchen, dark and dramatic with its bold black cabinetry and white countertops balanced out with a more neutral stone island, the color of moon-rock gray. Chrome lights hung from the ceiling and ran the length of the island, and chrome stools were pulled up against it. Off to the side was a small breakfast table with black and white dotted mademoiselle breakfast chairs and in the corner a white spiral staircase led to an upper floor. The whole space had a chic and tailored urban twist and was immaculately clean.

"The kitchen doesn't look like it's seen much in the way of cooking." I knew the depths of Ethan's culinary skills.

"It does actually. Mrs. Hall's a brilliant cook."

"Mrs. Hall?"

"My housekeeper. She often leaves me something delicious for dinner. She stocks up my freezer with homemade goodies and when she doesn't, I can pan-fry a steak." He was right. He made a mean steak. He grinned as I glanced around for Mrs. Hall. "She's here on Mondays and Thursdays."

I nodded and walked over to the spiral staircase. He motioned with his eyes, giving me the green light to go on up. The upstairs was equally spacious, but with only four very large areas: a chill-out area overlooking breathtaking views of New York, a game room with a full size snooker table, a gym, and a home cinema room. Each was as plush and luxurious as the last, and had me just as dumbstruck. At the far end was another staircase leading back down to the ground floor. It was direct access to the bedrooms—four of them, all with private bathrooms—a guest powder room, and a lavishly furnished office, which could also be reached off the hallway to the left of the main doors in the lounge.

Ethan's room was what I'd expected, given the luxury of the place so far. Glass filled one entire wall, and a white bed the size of New Jersey was covered in black satin sheets against the center of the wall facing it. There was a stunning, black velvet chaise lounge in the corner, with an elegant scrolling arm and gorgeous antique feet. On the opposite side was a floor-to-ceiling frosted glass wall, which concealed a polished, black and white bathroom suite with a fantastic infinity tub overlooking Manhattan.

Adjacent to this, was a walk-in closet the size of my entire bedroom. Actually, a walk-in closet wasn't the most accurate description, as it bared more resemblance to a full-on designer boutique.

Expensive designer suits, dress shirts, vests, and shoes hung on one side, with casual jeans, hoodies, sweaters, and T-shirts stocked neatly on shelves further down. Across from this was an identical space, which to my utter amazement was filled with my newly purchased wardrobe.

I gripped the edge of a dress, holding it out in questioning to Ethan.

"Jackson," he said, answering my silent query.

"Oh my God, is there any end to *The Man*. I didn't expect him to put them away, as well as unload the car and bring them up. In fact, I didn't expect him to do that." I pulled open a drawer, my face flushing a light shade of pink as I realized Jackson had also unpacked the vast array of lingerie I'd purchased with Ethan's approval.

Ethan laughed again. I seemed to be inducing bouts of hilarity a lot from him today.

Further exploration had me discovering my hairdryer and makeup, toiletries and jewelry. Seeing my personal effects lining the shelves, and in Ethan's personal space, suddenly invoked a feeling of belonging. I wouldn't have previously imagined feeling even near comfortable living anywhere other than in my apartment—my bubble. But now? Now, I was sure I could feel secure anywhere that encompassed Ethan.

It was utterly crazy. This man I'd known for a couple of months, if that, had helped me feel more at home in my own skin than I'd ever felt before. I gazed at him lovingly, wondering where the hell he'd been all my life, but silently thanking God he was finally here.

"You look like you could do with a drink," he said, checking his watch. "Why don't you check out the view while I pour us a glass of wine?"

I nodded enthusiastically.

Access to the vast terrace which looked out over Central Park could be gained from the lounge area and the bedroom. The space was private and pleasantly furnished, but lacked the coziness of my terrace. The view, however, was to die for.

"I could sit and look at this view all day," I exclaimed as he handed me a glass of wine. "The park is amazing from up here."

"We could go for a run through in the morning if you like."

"Yeah, I'd like that," I said, instantly warming to the idea.

"Well, I ran you a bath. I thought you could enjoy your glass of wine in comfort, get a feel for the place. I want you to feel at home here. You can take in a bit more of the view while you bathe."

"Thank you, that sounds wonderful."

His cell began to *buzz*. He scowled and quickly rejected the call. "I'll catch up with you in a little while. I have some calls to make." He kissed me on the forehead and began to make his way back inside.

As he reached the door, I called out, no longer able to ignore the troubled expression which crossed his face, as it had a few times recently when his cell rang.

"Is everything alright, Ethan?"

As he turned, his lips were smiling, but the contentment didn't appear to reach his eyes. "Sure." He nodded and disappeared inside.

A few minutes later, I made my way indoors, taking the route through the lounge, and as I reached the hallway, I could hear Ethan's voice coming from the direction of his office at the far end. I assumed he was talking on the phone, and although I couldn't make out what he was saying, his tone was unmistakably irked. Not wishing to pry, I stepped inside Ethan's bedroom suite, just in time to hear the click of the office door as he closed it firmly behind him.

After a long, hot soak, I dressed in my new skin-tight, black leather pants, sheer white blouse, black blazer, and ankle boots. I applied makeup—dramatic eyes and rosy red lips—and left my hair long and messy.

Ethan had taken a shower while I'd dressed, and just as I was applying the finishing touches, he emerged dressed in jeans, a light blue shirt, and navy blazer. He looked and smelled practically edible, and I was beginning to wish we hadn't agreed to meet with Jia and Charley.

We surveyed each other assiduously from across the room.

"Damn, you look so fucking hot. Do we have to go out?" His gaze slid over me hungrily. "I hate having to share you with the rest of the world."

"Ditto. But I'm afraid we're committed, yes."

"Just a couple of hours," he said, reluctantly, "and then I'm going to peel you out of those spray-on pants and fuck you hard. So unless you want to risk making-out in a storeroom again, you'd better make damn sure we're home."

Jeez, his lewd threat sent a pang of desire straight to the needy flesh at the summit of my thighs. The mere memory of our "closet fuck"—as Jia called it—was enough to drench me through. His eyes took on that heavy-lidded, sexy look, his mouth curling at the side provocatively as he accurately interpreted my thoughts.

"You are *such* a dirty girl."

I shrugged coyly. "It's all because of you, Mr. Wilde."

"Oh, now my cock is painfully hard." Rolling his eyes, he grabbed my hand to lead me out to the elevator. "Come on, let's go before I lose all manner of self-control."

The bar Jia had chosen was crowded and noisy, but luckily she and Charley had arrived already and managed to grab a table. I made the necessary introductions, and we ordered drinks. Jia was her usual confident, chatty self, but somewhat circumspect, as though she were quietly considering Ethan's intentions, the way a protective brother or father might.

Charley was sweet and reserved. She was petite, like Jia, but more of a Converse and Brothel Creeper kinda girl—a stark contrast to Jia in her killer heels. In Charley's words, wearing heels made her feel like a transvestite. She had short blond hair, a huge smile, and a friendly, bubbly personality.

It was important to me that Ethan and Jia get to know one another, even like each other, if possible. After all, apart from Ethan, Jia was the only person in the world who really cared about me. That said, I was under no illusion it would be an uncomplicated alliance. In the time I'd known her, Jia had assumed the role of my protector, to some extent, and over the last couple of months, I'd become mindful that Ethan now fulfilled that role. I'd put my trust in someone else, begun to lean on someone else, and although she was happy for me, I feared Jia felt somewhat redundant because of it.

Ethan, on the other hand, was used to having me entirely to himself. So far, we'd lived in a world where only he and I existed, and he'd made no secret of his disinclination to share me. Both of them were strong, dominant characters who would almost certainly view each other as competition.

About an hour in to the evening, Charley left the table to take a call on her cell. There'd already been a handful of subtle point-scoring comments on either side, but I'd purposefully chosen to ignore them, pretending not to notice or laughing them off. But while Charley was gone, I thought it would be a good opportunity to give Ethan and Jia a few moments alone to work through their rivalry. My friendship with Jia was entirely distinct and separate from the blossoming relationship I had with Ethan, and there was plenty of room in my life for both. But they needed to figure that out for themselves, so I excused myself and went to the restroom.

After I emerged from the stall, I spent an exaggerated amount of time washing my hands and applying gloss, eventually making my way slowly and tentatively back into the bar. The table Jia and Charley had chosen had a wooden partition separating it from the booth behind. The way it jutted out allowed me to approach unseen, and as I drew level with the empty booth behind, I could hear Ethan and

Jia deep in conversation. A quick glance toward the bar confirmed that Charley still hadn't returned and was engrossed in a discussion with the barman. Although, I knew the conversation wasn't intended for my ears, I suddenly couldn't help myself, and with the partition concealing my presence, I paused to listen.

"I'm just saying you need to be careful with her. She thinks she's made of stone, but she bruises like a fucking peach." Jia's words made me wince.

"I think you underestimate her. She's actually very strong. She's had to be." Ethan's tone was brusque at best.

"What, you think I don't know this? You've known her for all of two minutes and suddenly you think you know what makes her tick?"

"Yes, actually."

Although the time I'd known Jia far exceeded my relationship with Ethan, I'd disclosed things to him I'd never told anyone. Jia wouldn't know this, but I was certain Ethan wouldn't divulge my secrets.

"Well, you'd better," Jia went on, "because she sure as shit doesn't need more rejection in her life. And she definitely doesn't need building up to be let down by another sly fucking man. She doesn't give her trust to people easily. If you fuck it up, you'll break her. Don't say I didn't warn you. If you fuck with her, you fuck with me. And if you fuck with me, then I'll have you killed. Which means I go to jail, Angel's left with no one, and we all lose. Game over."

Wow, that was harsh.

"Back the fuck off, Jia. Angel has me now and I'll be the one who has her back. It was nice of you to stand in while I showed up, but I'm here and I'm not going anywhere."

"She doesn't need a bodyguard, you sanctimonious son-of-a..."

Jesus, I'd heard enough. I backed up out of earshot.

A tense but mutual appreciation of each other's roles in my life was what I'd been expecting, not a freaking pissing contest. Figuratively speaking, they were slapping their dicks on the table, albeit in Jia's case an imaginary one, to see whose was biggest. Between them, they were making me sound like a mistreated, abandoned puppy—damaged and defenseless. I didn't want either of them to know I'd eavesdropped on their conversation; it would mean even more conflict and that would only fuel the fire. But equally, I didn't relish the idea of being stuck here having to endure a shitload of awkward moments. We needed a distraction—something to lighten the tone of the evening—and I knew just the place. Feigning ignorance, I plastered on a smile and turned the corner.

CHAPTER ELEVEN

Paddy's Bar exuded authentic Irish ambience, which hit you immediately when you walked through the door. The style reflected medieval Ireland steeped in traditional art and pieces of architectural salvage, such as intricately carved edged tables with sturdy Gaelic timber tops. The place was full of character and characters alike, with the smell of real ales permeating the air, and the warm, friendly Irish accent resounding throughout.

It was run by Patrick, better known as Paddy, and Kathleen O'Connor, and their son, Dylan. Paddy spotted me as soon as I walked through the door, pushing through the crowd to greet me with a big bear hug. He was a well-built man in his late fifties, whose bulging beer belly provided clear supportive evidence of how well he tended his ale.

"Well ain't yer a sight for sore eyes?" he bellowed in his wonderful Irish accent. "Where 'av yer been, lassy? We've missed yer bonny face."

"Hey, Paddy, it's good to see you too," I said, squeezing him back. "I see this place is keeping you as busy as ever."

"It certainly is, me love. An' who might dis be?" He turned his attention to Ethan.

"Paddy, this is Ethan Wilde, my boyfriend." It was the first time I'd said that aloud, and I felt my cheeks heat with the innovation. "Ethan, this is Paddy and Kathleen, his wife," I said as a small, roundish woman came rushing toward us on the other side of the bar. Paddy smiled and nodded, as if it answered the unasked question of why they hadn't seen me in a while.

"Tis grand ter meet yer, Ethan. I 'op yer takin' good care o' dis bonny lassy," Kathleen said, shaking Ethan's hand and winking at me.

"She's my number one priority," he assured her, grinning my way.

"Oi'm glad to 'ear it. Now, wat 'ill yer have?"

We ordered our drinks and Kathleen rushed off to get them.

"Are ye walking de dog tonight?" Paddy asked with a throaty chuckle, pretending there was a dog snapping at his ankles, a look of mock fear on his round, red face. Of course, he was teasing; it was his way of enquiring whether Jia was with me.

Instantly realizing what he meant, Ethan began to laugh, and I punched him on the arm in playful rebuke.

"Yes, Jia's with us, and Charley. I think they went straight to the restroom."

"Ah, grand." His tone was insincere as he turned to Ethan. "She frightens de life out o' me, dat wan."

Ethan laughed again.

"Now stop it, the pair of you," I scolded, lightheartedly. "She'll hear you."

"And we definitely wouldn't want dat," Paddy said with feigned horror. He squeezed my arm, clapped Ethan on the back, and pointed toward the bar, motioning that he was needed. As he moved away, I felt somebody's arms reach around my waist and plant a kiss on my cheek. Ethan's face fell stony.

Twisting at the waist, I found Dylan with a beaming smile on his face. Similarly aged to me, at about twenty-eight, Dylan was broad shouldered and muscular with short, almost shaved blond hair and tattoos on both arms. He was seriously attractive, but not my type.

Moving around to my front, he took me by the hands and held them out to look at me. "You sure know how to brighten a place up, Angel cake."

As he pulled me in for a squeeze, I became painfully aware of

Ethan's displeasure. Being manhandled by another man was almost certainly a misdemeanor; he'd made that perfectly clear already, so I introduced him quickly.

"Hey, Dylan, it's good to see you. Let me introduce you to my boyfriend, Ethan Wilde."

For a second I could swear there was a fleeting glimpse of disappointment in Dylan's eyes, but it was too brief for me to be sure. He reached out to shake Ethan's hand, smiling politely. "Good to meet you, Ethan."

"Dylan." Ethan returned the gesture with a courteous nod, holding on to Dylan's hand a fraction too long.

Sensing an uncomfortable silence descending, I was relieved when I spotted Jia returning from the restroom with Charley. Dylan turned, immediately engaging them in conversation, he and Jia exchanging some mirthful banter about the last time she'd seen him.

Grateful for the interruption, I turned my full attention to Ethan. He snaked an arm around my waist, pulling me toward him in a possessive clinch and kissing me fully on the mouth. It was typical of Ethan to be openly affectionate, but there was little doubt that this was a public declaration for Dylan's benefit. Ethan was staking his claim, marking his territory. The gesture didn't go unnoticed by Jia who raised a quizzical eyebrow. I ignored her.

Dylan turned and began to walk toward the small stage at the back of the room, tapping me on the shoulder as he passed. "I'm on. Laters."

I held up a hand in a sort of wave, but said nothing.

Ethan glared at me.

"What?" I asked innocently.

Leaning in close to my ear so as not to be heard, he hitched a sardonic eyebrow. "Angel cake?"

I shrugged.

"How well do you know him?"

I shrugged again and knowing all too well it wasn't what Ethan meant, answered, "I've known him a while, maybe about eight years."

He tilted his head in warning. "You know what I mean, cheeky."

"No, Ethan. I haven't slept with him and have no intentions of doing so."

The muscles in his face relaxed, his chest rising with the inhalation of breath he'd been holding.

"I haven't slept with every good looking guy I've ever met you know."

"You think he's good looking?" His mouth set in a grim line, his nostrils flaring.

"Yes, Ethan," I shook my head, baffled by his sudden uncertainty. "But he's not my type, and before you ask, you…you are my type. And since you're unique, you have nothing to worry about."

Thankfully, my words seemed to appease him, his features relaxing into a smile just as Jia pulled on my sleeve and pointed to a recently vacated table at the edge of the room. Pushing through the increasingly busy bar, we reached the less crowded seating area where several people acknowledged me, either by shouting out a greeting or waving. As we settled at the table, Dylan hopped on the stage, guitar in hand.

"You seem very popular in here," Ethan said pointedly.

"Don't seem so surprised," said Jia with a smirk. "Angel's popular wherever she goes."

Ethan's reaction to Dylan hadn't gone unobserved, and if I knew Jia, she would use it as a stick to hit him with every chance she got. I shot her a warning look to quit her antics.

"This place has a lot of regular clients, that's all. People remember you."

"They remember you, that's for sure."

Dylan strummed on his guitar and smiling sweetly over at me, began to sing. "Please Stay," an Irish love song.

Jia and Charley burst into laughter, while Ethan sucked in his cheeks, not nearly so amused.

What the hell? I closed my eyes on a grimace.

"Is he always this fixated with you?" Ethan's jaw bunched as he spoke.

"No, of course not. It's a conspiracy to wind you up, Ethan. Don't play into their hands." I gave Jia an admonitory dig, but they continued to laugh.

Dylan sang beautifully. He was born and bred in America, so spoke with an American accent, but when he took to the stage to belt out the Irish classics, he adopted the same Irish twang his parents spoke with, and the crowd loved it.

Over the next twenty minutes or so, he sang his way through some of the favorites: "When Irish Eyes are Smiling," "It's a Long Way to Tipperary," "I've been a Wild Rover," and more. Then he started getting shouts from the crowd with requests for funny country Irish songs, which were hilarious and had the crowd in stitches of laughter. Even Ethan appeared to warm to him, enjoying the jovial interaction with the crowd, laughing and clapping along.

A song drew to a close and Dylan waited for the applause to subside. Then without warning, he turned in my direction and locked eyes with me. I knew instantly what was coming and began to shake my head furiously, mouthing the word "*No,*" over and over.

And then over the microphone, he addressed the crowd.

"Are you all thinking what I'm thinking?" he asked them. A few of the regular clients, who'd spotted me earlier, caught on to what he was suggesting and some whoops went up.

"Angel, Angel, our beautiful Angel. Take off your halo and lay it down on the table," Dylan said melodically.

The crowd began to laugh and chant my name.

"Then get your ass up here and sing us a naughty, naughty song."

Everyone's eyes were on me, people clapping and cheering, Jia's voice screaming, "Work it, bitch," ringing out above the noise.

Feeling cornered I looked to Ethan. At first, he seemed bewildered, unsure about what Dylan was asking me to do, but as realization dawned, his face broke into a beaming grin, and to my surprise he began to clap along with everyone else.

"You can sing?" he shouted to me over the crowd.

"No, not really. I've been known to have one too many and get up and make a fool of myself. That's a far cry from being able to sing!"

"Well, it looks like you're up from where I'm sitting. Let's hear it," he teased.

Oh crap! I looked around. There was no getting out of this. I'd been up on the O'Connors' stage countless times to sing, but I don't think I'd ever done it sober. I took a deep breath. *Okay, here goes.* Standing up, I removed my blazer and began to roll up my sleeves. The crowd cheered louder. I gazed down at Ethan's awed expression, wondering if he would feel the same way about me in a few minutes time. He was about to get a glimpse of yet another quirk of mine. Figuring I'd find out soon enough, I turned and made my way toward the stage, pausing halfway to accept a proffered shot of vodka from one of the regulars. I downed it in one go and took to the stage as the crowd stamped their feet, spurring me on.

Dylan handed me his guitar and bowed his head slightly, chuckling under his breath.

"You are *so* dead, Dylan O'Connor," I threatened.

He winked and left the stage.

I perched on the edge of his stool, hooking the heel of one boot behind the footrest so I could hitch a knee and support the guitar comfortably. The crowd quieted as I adjusted the microphone and cleared my throat. It felt croaky and someone passed me another shot of vodka. Nodding my thanks, I downed the liquid courage and glanced tentatively over at Ethan. He sat with his elbows on his knees, fingers intertwined to support his chin, his gorgeous, smiling face full of delighted expectancy.

Shit, why am I so nervous and what the hell am I going to sing? I glanced at the shot glass in my hand and inspiration suddenly hit. Closing my eyes, I clambered desperately through my memory for the words and the correct chord to an old favorite by Seamus Moore. My mind refreshed, I lowered the glass to the floor, strummed a note on the guitar, leaned in to the microphone, and in my best mock Irish accent, announced, "Dis is called de *Vodka Song*. Oi tink most of yer 'ill know it."

Everyone cheered and I began to sing.

I'd like to tell a story, and every word is true.

It's all about a substance, a very special brew.

Soon everyone was laughing and clapping, and as I got to the chorus, those who knew it joined in. By the time the song drew to a close the crowd was in raptures and it warmed my heart to see such a delighted reaction.

My eyes flickered through the crowd to find Ethan gazing back with mystified reverence, and I breathed a sigh of relief. I suddenly realized that I'd half expected him to be cringing with embarrassment, but what I saw oozing from his sparkling eyes and sexy smile could only be described as pride. He was proud of me. Had anybody ever been proud of me before?

The crowd spurred me on, chanting and cheering for another song, and as I stared across the room into those enchanting blue eyes, I suddenly knew the perfect piece. It was an acoustic version of a song by Sting, one of my favorite artists of all time, but one I'd only ever dared do justice in the privacy of my own apartment. I was straying from the usual Irish ditty or ballad that would normally be expected by the regular clients of Paddy's, but what the hell; tonight I felt uplifted.

Strumming a chord, I turned again toward my source of inspiration, the room quieting as I nodded once to Ethan in silent dedication and began to sing. His lips quirked into a beaming smile on hearing the first few lyrics of "An Englishman in New York," and although, strictly speaking, Ethan was a full-blooded American, I knew instantly that I'd chosen well.

When the song finished, I stood, took a bow, and made my way through the cheering crowd back to my seat. Ethan stood as I reached him, taking my face in his hands and drawing me to him to kiss me. My fingers curled around the lapels of his blazer, tugging him closer, eager to be consumed completely by this man who seemed to speak to me so deeply he awakened a sense of self-assurance I'd no idea I possessed. The crowd whooped again, delighted by our public display of affection.

"Is there any end to your talents, you beautiful, funny, sexy woman?" He kissed me again, his awed expression making my belly feel all warm and fuzzy inside.

"Ew! Get a room, you two!" Jia scolded.

Just then, I heard a slow, exaggerated clap of hands approaching from behind me, and Ethan's expression immediately twisted into one of anger. I turned quickly to see Jean-Paul standing before me, his face steeped in contempt and bitterness. It was obvious he'd been drinking heavily; his eyes were glazed, his speech slightly slurred and steeped in sarcasm.

"Quite the adoring couple these days, aren't we?"

"What do you want, Jean-Paul?" I asked, fearful of the scene that would almost definitely ensue.

Ethan pulled me to his side. "Whatever it is, he isn't getting it. If he knows what's good for him, he'll turn around and walk away."

Out of the corner of my eye, I noticed Jackson slowly and surreptitiously closing in from behind. I hadn't even realized he was in the bar. Ethan held a hand up to hold him off. Jean-Paul ignored them both.

"I just want to talk to you, Angel. It won't take long."

"No fucking way, asshole. Now are you going leave or—"

"You haven't been answering my calls, Angel. I just want to talk," Jean-Paul interjected as if he hadn't even noticed Ethan's presence.

Ethan shot me a sideways glance, the heat of his silent accusation searing my skin.

Ever since the night in the club when Jean-Paul grabbed me, I'd been receiving anonymous calls on my cell. I'd answered the first couple, but as nobody had spoken I'd given up, and although the calls had been relentless, I'd rejected every one. A part of me had suspected Jean-Paul was responsible, but as there was no evidence to prove it, I hadn't mentioned the calls to Ethan. I'd hoped that after a while, he'd get bored and stop, that if I ignored them for long enough the problem would right itself and disappear. Yet here it was, and multiplied. I decided to play dumb—damage limitation.

"What calls?" I asked.

Ethan's eyes narrowed suspiciously as he waited for Jean-Paul's response. Jia and Charley remained quiet, waiting for the drama to unfold, most likely intrigued as to how Ethan was going to handle the confrontation.

Jean-Paul cocked his head to one side and raised his brows. "Don't play games, Angel."

Ethan had heard enough. "The only one playing a game here is you, dickhead, and it's a dangerous fucking game. Now like I said, it might be in your best interest if you left."

"Or what," spat Jean-Paul, acknowledging Ethan for the first time.

Other people had begun to notice the commotion, and a concerned looking Dylan had begun to make his way toward me.

"Or fucking what?" Jean-Paul continued, taking a step closer. "You gonna hit me?"

Ethan stepped up into his face, fists balled at his sides, his powerful, menacing gait leaving no doubt of his intentions. "Hit you?" he shook his head. "I'll fucking kill you."

The threat, although uttered quietly, was loud enough for me to hear, and the impact on Jean-Paul was as intended. Backing down instantly, he stepped back out of Ethan's space, and then turning to look me in the eye, shook his head, pivoted, and walked away.

Dylan put his hand on my shoulder. "Angel? Is everything all right?"

"She'd be fine if everyone left her the fuck alone," Ethan snapped, clearly frustrated by everyone's interference. Then, as though realizing his reaction was rather harsh and unwarranted, added in a lighter tone, "Please accept my apologies for any disruptions. We're leaving now."

191

Dylan nodded. "No worries." He looked to me for verification that I was okay, and I smiled that I was.

Ethan snatched up my blazer and grabbing my hand, turned to Jia, his eyes blazing. "And you don't think she needs a bodyguard." It was more of a statement than a question, and without waiting for a response, added with sarcasm, "Goodnight, ladies, it's been an absolute pleasure."

I nodded to the girls and left the bar, sandwiched between the ever loyal and dedicated Jackson and his furious, possessive boss.

The minute the car was in motion, Ethan held out his hand to me. I was about to place my hand in his—relieved and grateful for the sweet gesture—when he made his request abundantly clear.

"Phone," he demanded.

Sighing in exasperation, I reached into my purse to retrieve it.

"And don't sigh, Angel. You are not in a position to sigh."

"I haven't technically done anything wrong."

"I'll be the judge of that." He began to scroll through the call history on my cell.

"Are you going to let me speak?"

"Shh," he held up his hand to hush me. I was clearly disrupting his close examination of my cell phone.

I sighed again.

Eyes daggered and brows raised, he glanced up from the phone. "Really?"

Suitably reprimanded, I turned away in time to catch a glimpse of Jackson watching me through the rearview mirror. He averted his gaze quickly, but not before I saw a trace of something in his eyes—a silent show of support, maybe.

Ethan took out his own cell and seconds later my cell *buzzed* in his hand. No ringtone though. With pursed lips, he shook his head. Great, now I looked guilty because I'd had it on silent. He placed both cells in his pocket as Jackson turned into the basement garage, and then without looking at me held his hand out to me again.

"Now I want your hand." It was a gentle demand.

With no eye contact, I was unsure yet as to how much trouble I was in. He was mad, there was no disputing it, and I found myself wondering if he had a right to be. I suppose I had promised to inform him if J.P. tried to get in touch and I'd broken that promise, but still. Although I hated the tension, I was pissed that he'd gone through my phone without giving me the chance to explain. With that in mind, I ignored his outstretched hand and turned my face to look out the window.

Jackson pulled up at the elevator and I climbed out quickly. Ethan joined me as the door slid open, both of us taking position at opposite ends of the car, the atmosphere thick with agitation. The entire ride up to the apartment was spent in silence, me with arms folded, Ethan with his hands deep in his pockets as he stared impassively at the elevator doors. Once we were inside the apartment he went directly to the kitchen, filled two glasses with wine and handed one to me.

As I took it from him, he jolted and reached into his pocket for my cell. It was vibrating with an incoming text message. Without a second's hesitation he began to open it to read it.

"Whoa…" I thrust out my hand to reach for it. "That is way out of bounds, you have no right. My call history is one thing, Ethan, but this is taking it too far. Give me the phone!"

His eyes shot to mine, glaring in silent rebuke. "You are *not* in a position, Angel."

Eyes darting back to the phone, he read the message, his stern expression dissolving as the corners of his mouth curved into a smug smile. He handed me the cell. The text was from Jia: Hope all ok. Ethan passed by the way—V. impressed x

I couldn't help but smirk either. Maybe Jia challenging Ethan earlier had been some kind of a test of his gallantry.

Ethan walked over to the huge glass wall and looked out over

Manhattan. Something about the way he stood, the way he worked his jaw muscles, and the way he drew in a deep preparatory breath had me holding my own.

"There are thirty-seven missed calls from an unknown caller and five accepted calls from an unknown in the past few weeks." His tone was measured, authoritative. "I'm assuming you had an inkling they were from him, yet you chose not to mention them to me as you promised you would. Do you wish to explain?"

Put like that it didn't sound too good, but I felt prickly and defensive by the way he was confronting me about it, addressing me as if I were an errant child. I stuck out my chin stubbornly. "No, not really, because I'm not sure I like your tone, Ethan. I don't have to explain anything to you."

"Yes you bloody well do, Angel." He turned to face me angrily. "But if you really believe that, then this is not what I thought it was."

I swallowed hard, suddenly realizing how what I'd said must have sounded like he didn't have a right to know. Now I'd given him reason to doubt us and that terrified me.

"I didn't mean it like that. I just meant that you don't tell me about every call you get and you spend half your day declining them."

His eyes widened in surprise. "That's different and you know it. I have all manner of people attempting to contact me for all manner of reasons, predominately business. If I took every call, I'd never be off the damn thing."

"You're right, I'm sorry." I suddenly felt unreasonable and extremely foolish to compare my phone activity to that of one of the largest business leaders in the country. "Look, I started getting these calls from an anon the day after the club. I answered the first few and no one was there, so after a while, I just started declining them. I thought he'd get bored."

"He?" He pinned me with his eyes.

"It was a figure of speech. I wasn't certain it was Jean-Paul. I know you asked me to tell you if he got in touch, and I promised I would, but

I wasn't sure it was him."

"Angel, the calls began the day after our last altercation. Of course they were from him."

"Then why didn't he speak, and why would he hide his number?"

"The guy's playing games with you, Angel. Probably hoping you'd get rattled by the calls, initially, and turn to him." The look on his face implied he couldn't believe I hadn't worked this out for myself.

"But that doesn't make any sense. Why make a shitload of shady calls to someone and then say, 'Hey, you didn't answer any of my calls... you know the ones where I hid my number so you wouldn't know it was me?' It just makes him look like... like a freak."

Ethan hitched a brow as though I'd just stated the obvious and turned back to the view, taking a sip of his wine. "It was intended to cause trouble between us."

"Oh, well, he's done a smokin' job, then," I said, wandering over to join him.

As I approached, I caught sight of his reflection in the glass and mindful that he was unaware of my gaze, I halted to study it. A distinct vulnerability glazed his eyes, his expression. Though hard to read, it seemed distant, brooding, as if lost in a concoction of fused emotions. Suddenly, his eyes seemed to regain focus and he started to speak.

"What troubles me greatly, Angel, is that you have an inclination to... disregard matters of significance. Trivialize them and sit on them in the hope they'll go away. Usually they don't. They burrow deep— fester—until finally you have no choice but to deal with them, because they come at you when you're least expecting it. Blindside the fuck out of you."

For a moment, I wondered if we were still talking about Jean-Paul, or if the conversation had taken a turn I'd somehow missed.

As if realizing he'd digressed, he turned to face me. "The fact of the matter is you *should* have told me about the calls regardless of who they were from. Anything which remotely threatens your safety, even if it's something that makes you feel vaguely uncomfortable, I need to know about it. And the very fact you didn't discuss it with me, when I've specifically requested that you do, pisses me right off and… just fucking hurts, frankly."

"God, Ethan, I'm sorry, I didn't think. I guess I'm just not used to having someone who gives a damn."

My response seemed to feather his features, his anger and frustration slowly disintegrating and softened by something much warmer. Stepping toward me, he took my hand in his.

"I know, but now you do. This is new to us both, Angel, and the truth is … well, giving a damn about someone is one thing, but the way I feel about you—it consumes me. If someone were to hurt you in any way, it would utterly annihilate me. And unfortunately, that, in itself, makes you a target."

My heart skipped a beat, warmed by the profoundness of his words, but at the same time, confused by what sounded like a warning. My expression must have reflected my puzzlement, spurring Ethan to expound.

"My father plans to make me CEO when he returns from his trip," he announced suddenly.

"Well that's fantastic news. Congratulations."

"Yes, it is, and thank you, but you have to remember, as do I, that there are people out there who would take great delight in destroying Wilde Industries, and with me at the helm that makes it personal. Having power and wealth comes with risk—but that I can handle. It's now that I have you that makes me feel vulnerable. Some people would use whatever means necessary to bring me down. What better way than through the most precious thing in my life."

Oh! I'd never actually considered that somebody might want to get at Ethan—even less that they might go through me to do it. I suppose I tended to forget just how extraordinarily powerful and wealthy he actually was. He watched as I absorbed what he said.

"I don't want to scare you, Angel. I just want you to be mindful is all. I guess this whole thing tonight has just made me sit up and listen.

I have enough concerns over your safety without that asshole stalking you."

"What? Stalking me? No, Ethan. I totally get your concerns with security overall, but Jean-Paul stalking me? That's just absurd."

"Angel, we've been pretty much holed up in your apartment since the night we saw him in the club. He was there then and he was there tonight. He's called you a total of forty-five times in the last few weeks to essentially listen to your goddamn voicemail, and you don't think he's stalking you?"

Put like that, it did seem a tad suspect. But Jean-Paul? "I just meant that the idea sounds ridiculous."

"But not beyond the realms of possibility. Not even in the fairy-tale land of Angelica Lawson."

"What's that supposed to mean?" I winced.

"Oh, it just worries me, Angel." He forced the words through gritted teeth. "You're just so determined to see the good in everyone you can't spot the phonies when they're staring you in the face. I accept that on this occasion the threat to you isn't because of me—it's because he's a sad obsessed dick—but it's a threat nonetheless. Ingenuousness can be a dangerous trait. Just be careful about who you trust. Never turn your back on anyone. People are never what they seem. I've learned that."

"I hope you've never doubted my integrity," I said, troubled by his cynicism.

"Oh, Angel…" He cupped my face in his hands and kissed me gently on the lips. "You just don't get it, do you?"

I wasn't sure I did. "Get what?"

He shook his head. "I… I need to work." Kissing me lightly on the tip of my nose, he strode over to the kitchen sink, pouring away what remained of his wine.

"Now? But it's late," I called after him as he walked toward the door in the direction of his office.

"I'll try not to be too long. Make yourself comfortable. Everything I have is yours."

"But you didn't answer my question. You do trust me, right?"

Coming to halt in the doorway, he paused for a few seconds before turning to look at me over his shoulder.

"Didn't you just hear me, Angel? *Everything* I have is yours. I'd trust you with my life. I hope you know you can do the same."

I smiled and nodded then watched as he disappeared down the hallway and out of sight.

CHAPTER TWELVE

I climbed into the enormous bed with my laptop, the night's absurd events and revelations still spinning around in my head like noisy, loose springs. This wasn't exactly how I'd envisaged spending my first night at Ethan's apartment. Besides his earlier promise to peel me out of my clothes, I was out of my comfort zone and feared that falling asleep without the familiarity of Ethan beside me would not be an easy feat.

Briefly, I wondered whether to go find him and drag him off to bed, but what happened with Jean-Paul had really rattled him, and something told me he'd be better left alone. He'd come to bed when he was ready, and besides, he had work to do. I decided to check my emails while I waited for him; it would take my mind off things, at least.

Most were junk, but one caught my eye. It was from Martha and Phil at the charity foundation in Zambia. They'd emailed a few weeks back asking if I was planning on joining them on their forthcoming project. I'd told them I wasn't sure I'd make it this year, that unfortunately other commitments were consuming most of my time. The truth was I wasn't sure I could bear to tear myself away from Ethan. It was a selfish reason and not one I cared to admit.

The email contained the trip details in case I'd changed my mind. They said they had enough volunteers, but there would always be room if I felt like a change of scenery, I was always welcome.

Tapping out a speedy response, I closed my laptop down and

snuggled into the luxurious, black satin sheets. To my surprise, I didn't feel uneasy as I'd expected, but quite the opposite; I couldn't have been more relaxed. Being surrounded by Ethan's belongings inside of his home was incredibly soothing. Although it was all new to me, it felt strangely familiar—cozy and homelike. His wonderful scent clung to the air, and his presence was perceptible throughout every square inch of his home. Although, I'd planned to wait up for Ethan, I felt my muscles relax and my eyelids grow heavy, and before I knew it, I was succumbing to sleep.

I walked through vast halls and rooms, each one adorned in black and white checkers, like that of a chessboard—a game. People stood around in groups, but all were either faceless or deliberately attempting to conceal their identity, turning their backs on me as I passed. My subconscious wagged a cautionary finger, but despite my unease, I kept on walking, because somehow I knew that I was there to find Ethan and that I was going in the right direction.

Suddenly someone thrust a guitar into my arms and told me to play. The people began to turn toward me and as I finally glimpsed their faces, I realized who they were. They were standing in a line—Jia and Charley, Dylan and his parents, my father and brothers, and then at the end of the line, Jean-Paul. But although I knew it was him, it didn't look like him. His features were odd and inhuman, like that of a dog. He smirked and nodded toward the others and when I looked, their faces were those of dogs too.

Suddenly, Ethan was there, frantically shaking his head at me, warning me not to turn my back on them, but his cell was ringing and he was moving further away from me. The crowd was getting louder, urging me to sing, and although I wanted to follow Ethan, their manner was so foreboding, so intimidating, I felt compelled to stay.

I looked down at the guitar in my arms and began to strum the chords. I strummed and strummed, but no sound came from the instrument and everyone began to jeer and laugh. My face burning with humiliation, I threw down the guitar and ran off in search of Ethan. I searched the endless rooms and infinite corridors, but Ethan was nowhere to be found. Panic was closing in, my chest tightening, lungs burning, and suddenly I couldn't breathe.

Just as I was about to pass out, I glimpsed a bathtub in the corner of the room and ran toward it, knowing what I needed to do. If I could immerse myself in the water, I could block out the noise of the jeering crowd. I would escape the fearsome, devious faces of the dogs and find peace—and finally, I would be able to breathe.

I climbed in and lay back into the warm water as it spilled up and over my face and body, completely immersing me in its welcoming, blissful silence. The relief was instant, the panic in my heart and searing pain in my lungs gradually ebbing away, as finally, freedom took me into the comfort of its arms and the darkness of peace descended.

Oblivion was almost mine when a sudden, dreadful thought occurred to me. My eyes flew open, the peace and tranquility fleeing from my body as fear gripped my heart in a vise-like fist. I fought to reach the surface of the water, frantically hoping my fears were unfounded, but as I stared down at my feet, the horror I dreaded became a frightening reality.

My shiny red shoes were sodden and ruined, and my father's voice bellowed my name. "Angelica! Angelica!"

"Angelica! Angelica! Baby, wake up."

Ethan shook me gently by the shoulders, dragging me wide eyed, disorientated, and breathless from the ravages of my dream. It took me a few moments, but slowly I began to remember where I was, my surroundings becoming discernible, the fog clearing and allowing me to focus as my gaze settled on Ethan's face. The relief of seeing his beautiful and familiar features was overwhelming, and as he pulled me into his arms, I knew he was the only person in the world that could chase away the nightmare and make me feel so secure and protected.

"What is it?" he asked me gently. "What did you dream about?"

I shook my head, reluctant to revisit my night terror.

"I'm so sorry, baby. I shouldn't have left you alone. Not on your first night here. It was stupid and selfish. This is not how I'd planned it. I've been a fool letting things get in the way and I'm so sorry." Cradling me in his arms, he showered the top of my head in soothing kisses.

"No, don't worry, its fine, E. It was just one of my crazy dreams. It's not your fault."

"You don't understand. I shouldn't have gotten mad at you earlier. People around us are determined to create a shit storm and I let it get to me—let them win. I took it out on you, but it won't happen again. I'm going to make it go away, baby. I promise, I'm going to make it go away."

I wasn't sure quite what he meant, but the real significance of his words ran much deeper than the wrangle with Jean-Paul, I was certain. Something else was troubling him, but the exhausting nightmare and intoxicating smell of his warm skin was having a profound effect on my ability to think. I angled my head to look at him, reaching up to close my mouth over his in a deep, demanding kiss.

The magic ignited the moment our mouths collided, both of us mindful that the only way to find shelter from the demons that chased us was to seek it through each other—through our bodies and the ecstasy we knew would come to soothe and heal in silent affirmation. And so we made gentle love until our bodies could take no more, and in a tangled mass of arms and legs, we fell into a deep, solacing sleep.

We awoke the next morning in a similar formation, our legs entwined, bodies engulfed protectively in each other's arms, as if afraid to let go. I knew from the way he breathed that he was awake and as reluctant as I was to disturb the magic which fused our bodies into one.

I looked up into his gorgeous, smiling face.

"Morning, Cinders," he greeted.

"Morning, Charming." I cuddled into him, inhaling his yumminess like the breath of life. "I could stay here like this for the entire day. Well, for my entire life, actually."

For a few a moments he didn't speak and I mentally kicked myself, wondering if the declaration had been too deep. Then he pulled himself up suddenly, swinging his legs out of bed.

"Well, as good as that sounds, Cinders, I think you'll remember you promised to accompany me on a run this morning."

I groaned. "Oh, you have to be kidding, that was yesterday. It always sounds like a good idea until the time actually comes around."

He'd disappeared into the walk-in closet while I was speaking, re-emerging with the new training shoes and training clothes that I'd picked out yesterday.

My cell *beeped* with an incoming message, and I grabbed it quickly from the bedside table. Ethan held out an outstretched palm in a silent demand for the phone.

"Seriously?" I asked, astonished.

He cocked a brow. "Seriously, Angel. Let me see."

For a brief moment I thought about refusing, irked by his demanding tone and mistrust. But I didn't want last night's events spilling into a new day and ruining it, and I definitely didn't want another fight. Frowning to ensure he knew I wasn't happy, I shoved it forcefully into his hand, carefully studying his expression as he read the message.

Ethan sighed and shook his head. "Mmm, I can see exactly how things are going to be." He handed the phone back.

"How what things are going to be?" Confused, I glanced down at the cell, my heart sinking as I read a message from Dylan.

Whoa. Who let the dogs out? If you ever need time out, Angel cake, the beer's on me x

The last thing I wanted was for the events of last night to spill over into our day and ruin the wonderful mood we'd both woken up in. I looked up at Ethan for any signs of how he was going to react.

He reached out to cup my face in his palm. "It would be foolish of me to expect other men to close their eyes to your beauty. What man wouldn't want to spend time with you or… want you in his bed?" A furrow appeared in his forehead as if the thought pained him. I opened my mouth to speak, but he pressed his finger to my lips, silencing me. "If you didn't belong to me, I would crave you inordinately, covet you, yearn to possess you." His finger left my lips, trailing down to my jaw, before reaching the nape of my neck in a possessive hold. "Fortunately, you do belong to me. And as long as everyone remembers you're off limits, and no one crosses the exceptionally fine line, there shouldn't be a problem." His lip curled up in a victorious smile as he threw my clothes and running shoes on the bed. "Put these on. You have five minutes." He strutted off toward the bathroom, grinning.

My face broke into a smile of my own, pleased that he'd managed to isolate last night's events by not allowing Dylan's message to agitate him, and amused at myself for finding his possessive, jealous streak so entirely hot. It felt good to belong to him and even better that he belonged to me. I bit down on my lip as I gazed lustfully after his gorgeous, edible, bare butt, disappearing into the bathroom.

It was a glorious morning and we pounded the paths of Central Park for almost an hour—far longer than I would have done had I been running alone. I was physically fit, but Ethan even more so, and I struggled to keep up with him. There was no doubt about it, having Ethan in my life would motivate me to push my physical boundaries in every sense of the word.

We finally collapsed on the grass, panting and sweating, and devoured the contents of our bottled water. The park was busy, people taking full advantage of a sunny Sunday morning. A mother pushed a dozing toddler in a stroller while she talked on her cell. Behind her trailed two older children, a boy about nine and a girl maybe a couple of years younger.

The boy snatched a rag doll from his sister's hand, extending his arm up in the air to hold it out of reach. He stuck his tongue out, tormenting her further. "Nah-nah."

"Give it back, gas-bag!" shrieked the girl, stretching up on tiptoes in an attempt to retrieve her doll.

"Come and get it, smelly diaper face. Stupid, dumb doll's gonna get it if you don't. Arrrh!" Making murderous gurgling noises, he held the doll above his head with both hands and began to stretch her.

"No! Nooo! Mommy, Billy's got my doll!" squealed the girl.

"Shh," the mom hissed, placing her hand over the mouthpiece of the phone. "Billy, give it back."

The boy pulled his face, shoving it back at the girl with enough force to push her over and pulled his tongue out again. "Crybaby."

They ran off pushing and shoving.

Ethan looked at me and laughed. "Smelly diaper face?"

"I know right. I would have kicked the little *gas-bag* in the balls if he was *my* brother."

Whistling air through pursed lips, he puckered his brow, feigning pain, then lay down on his side, propping himself up on one elbow.

"Did you fight with Damon and Abby when you were young?" I asked, moving to lie at a right angle to him, using his waist as a pillow to support my head.

"With Damon, yes. We're both incredibly competitive and equally bad losers. We'd usually end up settling our disputes with an arm wrestle or a fist fight."

"A fist fight? Really?"

"It was just playful, sibling rivalry. Nothing serious." He chuckled at my shocked expression. "I didn't torment him, but we would get into fights because he always wanted what I had and his philosophy was just to take it. The contention proved to be useful in our journey to adulthood though. It brought out the protector in us both. It's integral to human instinct to defend yourself, and even more to defend those you love. No one would get within a hairsbreadth of one without going through the other first. We're still the same now—with Abby too. She came along a little bit late to tease, so I was her protector from the moment she was born."

I smiled at the thought of him as a child and a teenager, defending his younger siblings.

"How about you and the twins?" he asked. "Were you their tormentor or their protector?"

I thought about the question for a moment and shook my head. "Neither really. I mean, *they* fought like cats and dogs constantly. They might look identical but their personalities are poles apart. Aaron was always the stronger one of the two, both mentally and physically. I suppose, if anything, I was the peacemaker. But my intervention wasn't usually very welcomed."

"How so?"

"Well, Aaron had a vicious temper, so fights between them usually ended up with something being upturned or broken. If my father found out, he would go nuts and I would usually get the blame, so I'd try my best to keep the peace. Aaron used to see it as me just trying to spoil his fun."

"Why would you get the blame, if it was the boys who were fighting?"

I screwed up my nose and shrugged. "I suppose with me being the oldest, I was expected to play the responsible role, so if it all went wrong it meant that I'd failed."

"Were you expected to take care of them?"

"They had a nanny when they were really young, and we usually had a housekeeper, although they never seemed to stick around for very long. By the time I was about twelve the housekeeper would leave when I returned from school, and I would take care of the boys until my father came home. Deep down I think Aaron purposefully timed his episodes so I would be caught letting things get out of control."

"What makes you think that?" he asked, his brows knitting together.

"Well, I remember this one time I was laying the table for dinner and re-heating the meal the housekeeper had left for us. The boys were playing in the garden with a ball when Aaron suddenly decided he didn't want to share anymore and pushed Adam to the ground. Adam ran inside with a grazed elbow, tears streaming down his face. While my back was turned cleaning up the wound on Adam's arm, the oven dish and its contents somehow ended up on the floor. My father came home as I was cleaning it up and went crazy. He started yelling at me, saying how useless I was and how I couldn't even be trusted to heat up the damn dinner. I was forbidden to eat with them for two weeks after that."

Ethan paled with incredulity. "Are you serious?"

I nodded. "Isolating me was his favored approach to discipline. He would just remove the place setting from the table to let me know I wasn't welcome. So I either just ate in my room or I'd wait until they were finished."

"Didn't the twins tell him what had happened? Didn't you?"

"Me? I knew better than to waste my breath. My father's verbal assaults could leave you bruised and battered for days. Aaron sniggered from the doorway, as usual, and Adam would always make himself scarce when my father went on one of his tirades against me. He didn't know how to handle it, so he did his best to ignore it."

He fell silent for a few beats before solemnly asking, "Why do you think Aaron had it in for you?"

"Oh, I don't suppose it's his fault either, really. He learned to point the finger from a very early age, my father drip feeding his poison until hatred for me became as natural as breathing. I was the selfish little bitch who had robbed him of his mother, and he took great joy in reminding me. Adam never played the blame game though, or at least not openly. I think he pitied me in some ways, maybe even thought it was enough that I endured my own guilt."

I glanced at Ethan's troubled expression.

"I can't believe they could be so cruel." He bit down on his lip as if he wanted to ask something but was afraid to.

"What?" I prompted.

"Did your father… Did he ever hit you?"

He hadn't been afraid to ask. He'd been afraid of the answer.

"No." I shook my head and looked off into the distance. "Sometimes I wonder if it would have been less painful if he had. Ostracism and the dreaded silent treatment can be a slow and prolonged form of torture. It's like being trapped in a cold, dark void where no one can hear you—the agony comes from never knowing when it will end."

I casually picked at a blade of grass, realizing how easy I was finding it to open up to Ethan. It felt good talking about this stuff, like assuaging a persistent ache. Ethan remained silent and I knew he was waiting for me to continue.

"I remember one particular time when I was fifteen—I don't recall what it was I'd done now or even if I ever did know—I just arrived home one day to a wall of silence. I was well acquainted with my father's reticence, he only ever really spoke to me when it was necessary, but these occasions were noticeably different. Not even a nod of acknowledgement, no eye contact, nothing. It was as if I just didn't exist. Aaron thought it was highly amusing and would always be eager to emulate my father's behavior, and Adam only dared speak to me when no one else was home. The silence lasted four months on that particular occasion, and then one evening, out of the blue, he told me I could set a place for myself at dinner."

When I looked, Ethan's face was flushed, his eyes slightly glazed and simmering with some unnamed emotion. Sitting bolt upright, he swiped at his eyes, his hands rubbing first over his face and then frantically through his hair. His reaction took me a moment to process, but then I realized what it was I'd seen in his eyes. He was appalled, sickened, disgusted by what I'd told him, and suddenly I felt so ashamed. I'd revealed a side of me which I hated. Given him a glimpse of the person my family saw when they looked at me—the sinner, the inadequate, unlovable runt, weak and contemptible, unworthy of even rudimentary acceptance. I was aware that my upbringing was… unorthodox. I only needed to look around me as I was growing up to know that. But to someone like Ethan, who'd been raised in a loving family unit, it would seem inconceivable. Was it any wonder he had no clue what to say? He'd most likely be turning in on himself with embarrassment.

"Hey, I don't know about you but I'm starving." I pushed swiftly to my feet, brushing the grass from my hands and the conversation aside to where it could easily be ignored.

He gazed up at me from his place on the grass, wordlessly gauging my expression. Finally, his eyes focused on the mock smile I was finding increasingly hard to maintain and seemed to arrive at the correct conclusion. The conversation was over.

"Yeah, me too," he said, accepting my outstretched hand, an offer to help him to his feet. "Do you like pancakes?" He put his arm around me and we began to walk.

"Are you kidding? I love pancakes. Do you have maple syrup?"

"Of course. And fresh berries."

"Then what are we waiting for," I laughed.

When we reached the apartment, I ran straight for the shower, leaving Ethan in the kitchen to start on the pancakes. I needed time to compose myself, cleanse my body and mind of the conversation which had seemed to sully the morning. Leave it behind, forget it. It was the first time I'd ever shared my shit with anyone, and it would teach me to leave it where it belonged. In my poisonous past.

When I finished, I dressed quickly in jeans and a top, and padded barefoot toward the kitchen, squeezing droplets of water from my hair with a towel.

Ethan had his back to me, unaware of my approach, and was slamming about in a rage, anger radiating from every pore of his body. As I came within a few feet of him, he seemed to lose it all together, and raising a bowl in the air, smashed it down violently into the sink.

"E, what are you doing? What's happened?" I gasped, stunned by the vehemence of his demeanor.

My presence startled him and he swung around to face me, his eyes dark, nostrils flared with seething rage. Seeming to war with himself, he opened his mouth to speak, but the words failed, as if they'd already begun to evaporate before he could form them. Instead, he just stared at me, his eyes dark and intense with emotion boring so deeply into mine that they seemed to reach inside my very soul.

Suddenly he moved, striding swiftly toward me and without a word, flung his arms around me, squeezing me so tight it stole the breath from my lungs.

"What is it?" I asked, fear gripping my heart with the frightening possibilities raging through my mind.

As if the physical contact with me offered sustenance, he relaxed his grip, his face angling to look down at me through glistening eyes. A profound sadness seemed to have engulfed him, a helpless, angry veil shrouding his usually poised mien. Then, as if to dispel the emotion that even impeded his speech, he shook his head and closed his eyes. As he did, a solitary, angry tear escaped from the corner of his eye and spilled on to his cheek.

"E, please tell me. What's wrong?" I pleaded.

When his voice finally emerged it was hoarse, barely above a whisper. "You."

Me? I was causing him this apparent agony?

"What have I done?"

"Oh, baby," he said, pulling me close again. "*You* haven't done anything. I just wish you could see that yourself. Life has dealt you a sack of shit and despite the cold, bitter bastards that have dragged you down and trampled all over your sweet, trusting soul, you've come through it a beautiful person, a beautiful angel—but…" His teeth clenched together, his jaw working furiously. "I think you're ignoring your broken bits."

Broken bits?

Jesus Christ, what had I done when I'd bared my soul today? I'd given Ethan a glimpse of the fragility that I'd spent most of my life trying to hide. He'd seen past the mask of bravado and indifference to the untold damage beyond—my broken bits. Had I revealed too much? Is that all he would see when he looked at me now, just an ugly, unlovable, fractured soul?

My throat felt tight and dry with self-loathing. "I'm sorry, I shouldn't have said anything."

"What? No! I'm glad you did. I want you to talk to me. That's my point. I think you've shrugged off the way you were treated for far too long. It pains me to think of my privileged, sheltered upbringing, when all the while you were suffering, ignored and alone."

"I don't want pity." I shrugged free from his hold.

"I don't feel pity. I feel sick to the depths of my core that they treated you so despicably. No one deserves the pain you've been forced to endure—no one. I can't help but feel like *I* have let you down, like I should have come into your life sooner, that if…"

"Whoa, Ethan, stop. That's ludicrous. It's all done now. I'm fine."

"No, Angel, you're not. Stuff like… that… what you told me before… doesn't occur in people's lives without causing damage, without leaving scars. Oh, you look fine on the outside, sure. You're physically fit and healthy. The smile on your beautiful lips even reaches your eyes, but what about the inside?" Placing his fingertip on the part of my chest covering my heart, he prodded gently. "What about the destruction in here? You can't ignore the tears on the inside, Angel."

"Ethan, what I told you today, I've never told anyone. And the reason I've never opened up about my past is because I've never felt strong enough to. But I've got you now and you're all the support I need. I believed you when you said you would help me carry my burden, and you do. The release is already having an effect. Today is evidence of that. Yes, I know there are cracks, broken bits even, but they will heal now that you're here and putting me back together. I feel more complete now than I ever have."

"Really?" His expression warmed instantly, his eyes alight at the sound of my words as he cupped my face tenderly in his hands. "Do you mean that? Because that's what I want. You're *my* broken angel, and I want to mend you and take away your pain. I want to give you all the love you've never had and always deserved…"

My limbs felt suddenly weak, a strange lightheadedness washing over me.

Love?

His sweet breath was warm on my face, his beautiful, full lips opening to form the words that terrified me, but at the same time longed to hear. I reached up and brushed my fingertips over them— needing to hear, to see, to feel the words emerge.

"… I love you, Angel," he whispered.

My knees buckled as I slumped against him and the tears began to fall. They streamed down my cheeks like a surging torrent from a broken dam that had been threatening to burst for a lifetime— unleashed and unstoppable.

Love.

Somebody *loved* me. Ethan loved me. And I loved him. More than words could possibly convey—I loved him.

But they were words I couldn't bring myself to utter. Words that were so huge and foreboding they were frozen upon my lips, unable to be spoken—because I was afraid. Afraid that to say them aloud or to feel them in my heart would dispel the magic and chase away the dream. And I was afraid, because I knew that if I loved him and lost him, I would surely die.

All I could do was sob. And Ethan kissed away the tears from my sodden cheeks and the unspoken words from my lips, and he knew. He knew from the way I kissed him back and from the way my body responded when he took me to bed and buried himself inside me, until my body sang out in pure, unashamed ecstasy. He knew—and he would wait until I was fully mended and no longer afraid.

212

CHAPTER THIRTEEN

S ometime later, I wandered back into the kitchen, busying myself
with clearing up the shattered dish in the kitchen sink and
making pancakes. Although I'd tried to reassure him, Ethan
had still looked slightly troubled from our earlier conversation in the
park and had disappeared into his office, saying he needed to make
some calls. I hadn't expected that hearing details of my childhood
would unsettle him the way it had and guessed he was having trouble
processing what I'd told him.

Ethan had an intrinsic need to protect those he cherished because
he'd been brought up in a world surrounded by love and support. The
fact that he'd been unable to protect me from my miserable childhood
made him feel like he'd failed me in some way—absurd as this was.

When he emerged he seemed more resolute and less anxious,
insisting that he'd work the rest of the day from his laptop, because he
didn't want to leave me alone. Realizing that any attempt to reassure
him that I was fine and he was being silly would be a complete waste
of breath, I curled up on the sofa to watch *Ponyo*. Although one of
my favorites, I found my attention wandering, switching between the
movie and the beautifully sculptured lines of Ethan's face. Gradually
his attention deviated from his work, becoming more and more
enthralled with the movie until eventually the laptop was abandoned
and we curled up together varying between being engrossed in the
movie and engrossed in each other.

"I loved it," he announced when the credits rolled. I laughed and punched him playfully on the arm, assuming he was humoring me. "No, seriously, I *really* loved it. But I probably should have stayed in the office. Between you and little Ponyo there, I haven't got a thing done. You're such a distraction."

"I'm sorry, baby. Look, why don't you spend a couple of hours in the office and I'll make us some dinner?"

He contemplated this for a few seconds and then said, "I've got a better idea. Why don't we open a bottle of wine, order in, and watch *Finding Nemo*? I made a little purchase of my own yesterday."

A beaming smile stretched across my face. "Really?"

"Really." His fingertips brushed a stray hair from my cheek. "I love it when you smile. My life's ambition is to make you smile and laugh as much as possible. And the best place to start is with *Finding Nemo*." Laughing, he pushed to his feet and went in search of menus.

We settled on Thai food and opened a bottle of wine while we waited for it to arrive. My phone *chimed* with an incoming message. Ethan had asked me to turn on the volume since the run-in with Jean-Paul, and although I hadn't heard anything from him, I was still slightly nervous to see who it was. Ethan's face dropped a little at the sound of the alert, and he put down the bottle he was un-corking while I read the display.

"It's Jia," I said with relief and opened the message.

Hey! You ok? You still locked away in Wilde's ivory tower?

"And what does Jia have to say?" Ethan smirked, picking up the bottle again.

Smiling, I hoisted myself up onto a stool at the kitchen island to read it to him.

"Ah, Jia, Jia, so funny," he said, his tone dripping with cynicism.

"Oh, don't take it the wrong way. She doesn't mean anything by it. She's just being a friend."

"You think?"

"Sure. What else?"

Ethan shrugged as if suddenly reluctant to elaborate.

"What's on your mind, E?"

"I just think you might want to tell her—that she's just a friend, I mean. Because somehow, I'm not sure that's the way she sees it."

"What do you mean?"

He smirked at me over the rim of his glass as he sipped his wine.

"What?" I asked again.

"She's in love with you, Angel."

"What? That's the biggest load of horse shit I ever heard!" I threw my head back and laughed hysterically.

"Fine, if you prefer to be in denial. But I'll bet you Charley wouldn't be so quick to refute the theory."

"You are joking, right?" The idea horrified me.

"I saw the way she looks at you. And so did Charley."

I shook my head in disbelief. "You're deluded."

He shrugged. "Okay, whatever you say. But I'm right."

"You're *so* wrong."

"I can't believe you haven't seen it. Having said that, the whole Jean-Paul thing was staring you in the face and you didn't see that either."

Suddenly, I felt irked. "Well, *I* can't believe you *have* seen it. Or you think you have. Your problem is you think everyone in my life is in love with me. First it's Jean-Paul, now Jia."

He hitched a justly brow. "Well, I was right about that dickhead. But don't worry, I see the two as very different. As long as she remembers her place, Jia's lust for you doesn't concern me."

"Why?" I asked confused, but relieved that he wasn't about to ask me to end my friendship with one of the few people I could trust.

"Because I don't see her as a threat."

"Why, because she's a woman? That's a brave assumption you make. For all you know, I might have a penchant for chicks as well? Maybe I like a change every now and then, something tender and sweeter." I pushed my chin out, testing him.

"There's no chance in hell of that," he scoffed confidently.

"You can't be certain."

"Yes, I can baby. You enjoy my cock far too much to have ever even considered it." With a smug smile, he moved slowly around the island toward me. "You like your meat solid and substantial. Hot, red-blooded, and plenty of it."

He was right. I did. And the very thought of his hot, pulsing cock had me instantly filled with heated desire, the flesh between my thighs as succulently moist as my watering mouth. Something in the darkness of my eyes must have betrayed my highly aroused state, because suddenly he smiled a knowing smile, yanked my knees apart, and stepped inside the space between them.

"See, you can't get enough of it, you dirty girl." Gripping my buttocks, he yanked me against his throbbing bulge, evidence that his arousal reflected mine. Its firm and substantial state never failed to take me by surprise, and I couldn't contain my natural urge to flex my hips against it.

"Christ, are you permanently hard?" I asked.

"Only when you're around." His hand fisted into my hair as he claimed my mouth, kissing me with a passion that had me thrusting my sex against the stiff seam of his jeans in search of some much needed friction.

I broke the kiss, my eyes slithering hungrily down his toned and sculpted chest and abs clad in a tight, shape hugging t-shirt, and down to his low slung jeans. I knew exactly what I wanted.

Slithering off the stool to the floor, I knelt with my back against the island, until my eyes were level with the denim fabric stretched over his mass of pulsing flesh. Then, placing my hands on his thighs, I slowly slid them upward, until my fingertips reached the protruding mound, pressing them against the rigidity and at the same time leaning in, my nose up against him. Closing my eyes, I breathed in deeply, inhaling the scent of his manliness through the barrier of material.

When my eyes opened, my gaze fluttered up to his face in time to capture his expression: the heat of lust darkening his eyes, his parted lips turning red with the rush of arousal. Swiftly, I unfastened his button and fly, yanking down his jeans and boxers enough to release his beautiful cock. It stood erect and proud, pounding veins snaking down the shaft and warm silky fluid oozing from the head. I licked my lips slowly.

"Ah Christ, Angel," he gasped. "What are you doing?"

Placing my hands gently on his hips, I guided him toward me, snaking my tongue out to lash at the throbbing, bulging head. He groaned.

"*My* cock," I purred, lashing out again. "You said I like *your* cock too much. I'm just reminding you that you belong to *me*."

Folding my lips over his hot, slick tip, my tongue circled the swollen rim then into the slit and down the shaft as I gently sucked in his taut, silken flesh, taking him right to the back of my throat. Ethan's whole body tensed and quivered, his hands reaching out to grip the edge of the island for balance.

Sheathing my teeth with my lips, I began to withdraw back up the shaft, my rigid tongue tracing a path until I reached the head. Then taking him in one hand, my fingers folding firmly and possessively around his width, I slid him out and circled my tongue around the rim, pushing my thumb firmly over the top to release another surge of hot, sticky pre-cum. He thrust his hips toward me, silently begging me for more. I pulled back and looked up into his avid, needy eyes smoldering with deep, dark yearning.

"You are mine, Ethan. Say it. Wholly and completely mine."

"I am yours, Angel. I am wholly and completely yours. Suck me like you own me, baby."

Without further hesitation, I took him back into my mouth and gripping him firmly at the base, I did as he asked. Opening my throat wide, I took him in as deep as I possibly could, sucking him greedily, my fisted hand sliding and twisting up and down his shaft. Breathless and gasping, Ethan gripped the island harder, his hips thrusting back and forth, fucking my ravenous mouth in his pursuit of ecstasy.

Suddenly, we heard the elevator door slide open and footsteps moving through the foyer toward the main door. Ethan froze. I froze, my mind frantically searching through who it could be, what I should do, and what we must look like. But I didn't move, and neither did Ethan. A moment later, I heard the foyer door open and then Jackson's voice.

"Boss, your food delivery has arrived."

It was then I realized that from Jackson's position in the doorway, I was completely out of view, and to all appearances, it would look like Ethan was completely alone in the kitchen. Ethan must have reached the same conclusion and after what seemed like minutes, but could only have been mere seconds, he reached down with one hand, fisting it into my hair. Holding me firmly, he pressed his hips forward, sliding his cock further into my mouth in silent encouragement.

Oh… My … God!

He cleared his throat. "Thank you, Jackson." Taking his lead, I began to move, sucking him harder and faster, picking up the pace to where I was moments before, his cock swelling and pulsing with his frantic need to orgasm. "Leave it… um… on the foyer table, would you?" His words came out stunted and breathless.

I sucked him even faster, even deeper, my head bobbing up and down wildly, my fisted hand squeezing and milking him toward climax. The whole crazy situation was absurdly erotic and I found myself uncontrollably turned on.

Silence for a second and then, "You alright, boss?" Jackson sounded concerned.

Ethan nodded, biting his bottom lip. "Yup… good," he mumbled.

Impelled by my libidinous quest for completion, I twisted him into my mouth, sucking hungrily, pumping him into me.

"Goodnight, Jackson," he blurted urgently.

"Goodnight, boss."

There was the sound of retreating footsteps, the elevator door closing, and then, "Ah, fuck, fuck, fuck!" Ethan cried out, a deep rasping noise emanating from his jerking, shuddering body. His cock pulsed, spurting a hot burst of come to the back of my throat, again and again. I swallowed, sucking every last drop of his erupting orgasm until he was dry.

When his body stopped trembling, I withdrew and tilted my chin to gaze wickedly up at him through heavy eyelids. I was so desperately turned on that my pussy was drenched and pounding almost painfully, desperate for release.

Ethan recognized the yearning in my eyes, his own passionate, fiery gaze filled with unspoken promise. I shuddered in anticipation of the satisfaction I knew would come. Suddenly, he pulled me to my feet, turning me around and tugging at my jeans and pants in one swift movement. I shrugged out of them quickly.

"Hold on, baby," he growled into my ear as he bent me over the island.

Acting immediately, I curled my fingers around the edge of the island as Ethan had done moments before. He thrust his hand between my thighs, urging them apart, his feet pushing against mine to spread them wider.

"Oh, Angel." His voice was hoarse with arousal. "I'm going to fuck you now, hard and deep. I want to feel your tight quivering pussy around my cock when you come, and I want to hear you scream for more."

"Yes, Ethan. Yes." I nodded frantically, knowing that it wouldn't take much for me to go off. I was so close already.

My body shuddered as I felt him place the head of his implacable, steely cock between the folds of my flesh and enter me in one deep thrust. I cried out with ecstatic pleasure, gasping as my sex clenched deliciously around him, his cock filling and spreading me as it stroked inside me over and over. He lunged into me, taking me closer to the edge with every wild, pounding thrust, his hips rotating, driving deeper.

He reached around, searching for my aching clit, and with one possessive graze of his fingertip, I erupted. My orgasm thundered through me, intense and burning and core deep as I screamed out his name incoherently. My muscles clenched and convulsed around his cock until finally I shattered into a million pieces, the searing intensity of my pleasure bringing him hurtling to another ferocious climax.

We stilled, breathless and panting, Ethan lying across my back, still swollen inside my slick, pulsating sex.

"Sweet Jesus, woman," he gasped for breath. "You're going to fucking kill me."

He began to laugh and soon we were both hysterical.

The food was delicious. We sat crossed-legged, feeding each other and laughing sporadically as we joked about Ethan literally being caught with his pants down.

He gazed at me with a sort of mystified admiration. "You never fail to take me completely by surprise, Miss Lawson. You seriously have me doing things I would never have imagined, even in my smuttiest of dreams."

"You have smutty dreams, Mr. Wilde?" I feigned shock. "Well really, I never would have guessed."

"I've experienced one or two, especially in the time I've known you, but I can absolutely assure you none of them featured me rendered powerless with my cock in your mouth while speaking to Jackson," he said, shaking his head and laughing. "You are super naughty and downright, utterly filthy—and actually, yes, in answer to your earlier question, you make me permanently and painfully hard."

"Are you complaining, Mr. Wilde?"

"No, I most certainly am not. I totally fucking love it."

"Good, so do I" I grinned sheepishly. "I never actually knew that sex could be this amazing."

"Really? You too, huh?"

I nodded. "It's bizarre really, but things are so unmistakably clear to me now."

"How so?"

Although I found it difficult to express my thoughts and feelings, I'd been a little uninhibited with sex in the past, and had always known that I'd been using it as a substitute for something else. Now I understood what.

"I think in the past, I've confused the physical act of sex with affection. Maybe saw it as a source of comfort in place of a hug. But a hug is only really satisfying if it's given by someone you have feelings for. Because affection is a genuine emotion which derives from a state of consciousness—a response of the mind and soul. Without it, sex is just... sex. But combine real emotion with the physical, sexual expression of it and the results are phenomenal. Unparalleled ecstasy, I'd say."

He reached out and stroked my cheek lovingly.

"You are so right. I couldn't have put it more precisely. It all makes perfect sense now." He smiled and looked off into the distance in contemplation of something. "Do you think the ecstasy feels the same for both us?" he asked thoughtfully. "I mean, do you think a woman's orgasm feels the same as a man's. Is it the same experience?"

I smiled and shrugged. "I have absolutely no idea. I think we go through life assuming it is, but I guess we'll never really know. I once read somewhere that, allegedly, Kate Bush meant to draw attention to men and women's minimal understanding of each other's roles in life when she wrote 'Running Up That Hill.' She sings about making a deal with God to swap places with someone in order to exchange experiences. I've often wondered whether she meant it in a sexual sense. It's a wonderful song—one of my all-time favorites."

Ethan grinned. "Me, too. I have Placebo's version on my iPod. But I'll admit I had no idea what it was about. What an amazing theory. It would be fantastic to trade experiences, to feel what you feel when you come for me."

Ethan's eyes darkened with the idea and my sex clenched in response, causing me to wriggle in my seat. He smiled a slow, lustful smile.

"You are utterly insatiable, Miss Lawson. Finish your dinner, watch the movie, and then maybe, just maybe—if you're very good—I'll take you to bed and bury my cock in you again." I squirmed again, unsure if I could wait that long. Leaning forward and sealing a warm passion-filled kiss on my mouth, he said with a wry smile, "Ready for the movie?"

I laughed and nodded.

Finding Nemo was amazing and went straight in my top ten of current favorites. When it was finished, Ethan scooped me up from the sofa and carried me to the bedroom, kissing my face with every step he took. As he laid me on the bed to begin the slow sensual process of undressing me, his cell rang out. Eyeing it warily, he snatched it up to answer it and instantly began to pace up and down—something I'd noticed he was inclined to do when he was tense.

"Alex... Yeah... Good... Everything is in place...? Did you reschedule Carter...? Good... No, don't bother forewarning them, we'll take the bastards by surprise... Okay, see you tomorrow—and sorry again about the short notice." He hung up but continued to stare at his phone.

"Is everything alright?"

He offered me a perfunctory nod, his eyes meeting mine tentatively. Unease moved across his face, his shoulders stiffening as if he were on the verge of telling me something that was bothering him, but needed to edit the words before he spoke them.

"Alex?" I prompted, feeling the need to assist. I'd heard him have conversations with Alex many times, so guessed the call was work related.

"Um, yeah. My right arm."

"Oh, I thought I was your right arm?" I pouted, feeling childishly envious of Alex and how valuable and indispensable he evidently was to Ethan.

"I meant purely in the business sense, of course," he assured me, moving to sit by my side and sweeping the hair from my face with a featherlight touch of his fingertips. "And you are far more than my right arm, baby. You are my entire reason for breathing."

God, what this man could do to me with his words. They seemed to reach out and caress my heart in a way that I never thought possible. My insides fizzed, an odd whirling sensation causing my breath to catch, like the giddy way you feel on a rollercoaster when you feel like you've left your stomach behind.

Before I could respond, he planted a chaste kiss on my lips and got up from the bed, his hand reaching round to the back of his neck to rub away the returning tension. He took a deep breath.

"Angel, I have to go to London," he blurted hastily. "There are some major hiccups which require my attention. The trip can't be avoided I'm afraid."

The announcement utterly floored me, my heart now reeling from the sudden plummet back down to Earth and landing with a bang. Attempting a quick recovery, I cleared my throat. "Oh, okay," I hesitated as a question formed. "When?"

It was his turn to hesitate, his jaw muscles tensing with a grimace. "Tomorrow."

"Tomorrow? For how long?"

My heart filled with dread. The idea of not being with him terrified me beyond imagination, and the realization of how much and how quickly I'd come to depend on him, both emotionally and physically, shocked me to the core.

"I'm not sure yet—a few days—maybe a week, not much more."

Oh my God, this got worse. My chest began to tighten like the start of a panic attack, a feeling I knew all too well. I had to get out.

I nodded. "Give me a second, will you? I need to use the bathroom."

Once safely inside the adjacent bathroom, I leaned against the vanity unit in front of the mirror, head bowed as I took in deep controlled breaths and began a count down from one hundred.

This is ridiculous, I told myself when I finished. *There are going to be occasions when you have to spend time apart. Christ, who's to say you're even going to stay together… Oh God, you're not helping. Breathe. It's just London for a few days—just a few thousand miles—Oh, God. Get a grip! He cannot see you like this. Oh my God, if he sees you like this, he will think you're a complete freak. Too needy; too dependent; too desperate. Get a fucking grip.*

I counted again and when I finally felt like I could hold it together, I splashed water on my face and made my way back to the bedroom.

Ethan was pacing up and down when I returned, his face creased with concern. "You okay?" Ethan asked, his words guarded as if he wasn't sure he wanted the answer.

"Sure." Trying my best to sound cool, I began to undress. "What time do you leave tomorrow?"

Ethan frowned, seemingly unconvinced by my poise. "Sometime in the afternoon."

"Haven't you arranged flights yet?"

"We have the private jet. I'm waiting for the flight schedule."

"You have a private jet? Of course you have a private jet—stupid." I said the last bit under my breath, cursing myself for my naivety.

We both finished undressing in contemplative silence and climbed into bed.

"Who's we?" I asked suddenly, pulling the sheets up to my chin.

"Sorry?"

"You said, '*We* have the private jet.'"

"Ah, yes, I was going talk to you about that. Well, I'll take Alex with me, obviously, but I've decided to take Simon instead of Jackson. I'm going to leave Jackson here. He'll chaperone you whilst I'm away. "

"Chaperone me? Why would *I* need Jackson to chaperone me?"

Sighing in frustration at my predicted protest, he held up his hand to stop me in my tracks. "Before you start, Angel, this is not up for negotiation. You've got some besotted prick out there who could turn out to be a total psycho, and I'm not taking any risks with your safety. I won't be here to protect you, so I want the next best thing—and that's Jackson."

His pointed glare suggested he fully anticipated a fight, but behind his uncompromising mask his wonderful chiseled features were tense and full of concern—for me. This time tomorrow we would be thousands of miles apart, how could I bear to fight with him.

"Well okay, then," I relented with ease, "if it makes you more comfortable. Although, I'm sure you're being way too over cautious."

Relief smoothed the worry lines as he let out a breath, clearly grateful to have escaped the predicted battle. Lying down on his side, he pulled me in close, tucking my body safely inside his, his lips brushing the top of my head with a gentle kiss.

"How can it be over cautious, baby? You're my entire reason for breathing, remember."

CHAPTER FOURTEEN

The next morning, I helped Ethan pack a few things for his trip. He didn't need much—he said he still had a closet full of stuff at his apartment in London.

Although I knew it was stupid, I couldn't help feeling almost resentful that he had a whole other life, another home in another country which I knew nothing about. I tried to console myself with the reality that, until this weekend, I hadn't even visited this one and it hadn't bothered me. But maybe that was the problem. I was only just getting a glimpse of Ethan's life, when suddenly he was being whisked away to one I'd probably never gain insight to.

Although I'd never openly admit it, I guess a part me—the naïve and childlike part who resided on planet Angelica—had thought we'd remain holed up in my apartment, like a pair of loved-up bunnies, forever. He was COO, soon to be CEO of Wilde Industries, for Christ sake.

Neither of us had spoken very much, both mentally preparing ourselves for the inevitable void that would be created by his departure. In my mind it was a huge, dark, and lonely crater, because it would be the first time we'd ever been apart. And I knew from the look of melancholy I glimpsed in his eyes when we exchanged meaningful glances that he felt the same.

Oh, we'd spent hours away from each other for work and such, but we'd fallen asleep and woken up in each other's arms every day, pretty much since the first week we'd met.

When we emerged from the bedroom suite there was a smell of cooking and a clanking of pots and pans coming from the direction of the kitchen. I turned to Ethan in alarm.

"It's Mrs. Hall," he explained, amused by my shocked expression.

We walked into the kitchen to find a petite woman in her mid-fifties with short brown hair, a round face, and a huge friendly smile.

"Good morning, Mr. Wilde, Miss Lawson." She nodded politely in my direction.

Oh, she knows my name?

I caught a trace of amusement on Ethan's face again.

"Mrs. Hall, allow me to formally introduce my girlfriend, Angelica Lawson." The pride in his voice made me smile. "She's the reason I've not been taking advantage of your remarkable culinary skills of late. Angel, this is Mrs. Hall."

Mrs. Hall wiped her hand on a towel and held it out to shake mine. "I'm very pleased to meet you, Miss Lawson. And please call me Anna. I'll get your eggs and toast as usual, Mr. Wilde. Now, what can I get you for breakfast?" she said, turning back to me.

"Oh. No, nothing, thank you. Just coffee—black please."

Ethan scowled at me. "You have to eat, Angel."

My insides were churning. There was no way I could eat a thing. Although Mrs. Hall seemed really pleasant and cheery, I found myself resenting her presence wanting to spend the short time we had alone. To me it wasn't the time for a cheery breakfast; to me it felt more like the last supper.

"I'm not hungry," I muttered in reply.

Mrs. Hall served us our breakfast and coffee at the dining table and wandered back to the kitchen. We usually ate at the island or on the floor at the coffee table. Why did everything feel so formal all of a sudden?

"I have some things I need to take care of at the office before I leave for London, so I'll take you home after breakfast," he said casually.

Oh great, it gets better. Foolishly, I'd been hoping we'd have a few hours, at least, before he left. My heart sank as I nodded and stared down into my cup.

Ethan ate in silence while I sipped my coffee, both of us exchanging meaningful glances, conveying words we somehow couldn't begin to express.

This morning he looked even more delicious than ever, and I wanted to sit and just gaze at him, like he was some glorious, breathtaking vista to feast my eyes upon. Dressed in an impeccably suave navy suit and vest, a crisp white shirt and vivid blue tie, which drew attention to the cornflower blue of his irises, he looked every bit the stylish, entrepreneurial billionaire—powerful, devastatingly handsome, and implausibly sexy. He moved with the grace of a gazelle, his scent—a combination of expensive cologne and his own personal male muskiness—causing my mouth to salivate with relish.

When he finished his breakfast, Mrs. Hall took away the plates and moved out of sight into another room. Ethan put his hand in his pocket and pulled out my cell and a set of keys. I'd been so preoccupied with Ethan and the looming London trip that I hadn't even missed my phone.

"I've put Jackson's number into your cell. I want you to call him fifteen minutes before you need to leave to go anywhere. And I mean anywhere, Angel. I also want you to call him if you're home and feel in the least bit worried about anything."

I screwed my face up. "Like what? E, you need to chill about this entire J.P. thing. I really don't think he's a threat, he's just a young man with a crush."

"J.P.?"

"Jean-Paul."

"I know who you mean. I just didn't realize you had a *pet* name for him."

"It's not a *pet* name—it's a convenient, truncated nickname. The two are entirely different."

"Like when you call me 'E,' you mean? That's just because you can't be bothered with the full-length version, not because you mean it in an endearing way?"

"No, in your case it's meant to convey affection, to signify intimacy. It's my special name for you."

He arched a brow and pursed his lips. "Not *entirely* different then?"

"You're being pedantic."

"I'm being pragmatic."

"Ethan, you have absolutely no worries on my part where Jean-Paul is concerned." I emphasized the words Jean-Paul.

He held my gaze for a moment, as if measuring my words, and then held out the keys to me. "These are your keys to this place. They include security keys for the elevator and such."

That took me by surprise. Giving someone their own key to your home meant something in my book.

"You're giving me my own keys to your apartment?" I couldn't keep the excitement out of my voice.

"If you would like to stay here at any time, even while I'm in London, that's fine—I'm okay with that. In fact, I'd really like it. I want you to feel at home here. Besides, Jackson is right downstairs if you were to need him. It would probably be more convenient."

Oh. Maybe it wasn't so much a romantic gesture, but more of a precautionary one.

"I see." I tried to hide my disappointment. "Well thanks, but I'm sure I'll be just fine at home."

The idea of having a bodyguard at my disposal was swiftly losing its appeal. In my opinion, Ethan was being melodramatic about the whole Jean-Paul-psycho-stalker issue, but I would turn a blind eye to his histrionics—for now.

"So, Jackson lives in the building?" I asked, realizing now where he'd popped up from so swiftly the previous night.

"Yes, he and Simon are on the floor below. All part of their remuneration. No point in having security if they're not on hand."

Glancing at his watch, he pushed to his feet. "I'm sorry, baby, I have to brush my teeth, and then we really must go."

The words I'd been dreading. I nodded reluctantly.

When we were settled in the back of the car, Ethan grabbed my hand and pulled me close to him. His expression was laced with unease, and I didn't want to add to his worries by expressing my misgivings about the keys, so I cuddled into him willingly.

"When this London trip is out of the way, things will be better, I promise," he said comfortingly. I wasn't quite sure what he meant by "things will be better," but took it to mean that the current problematic business issues would be resolved and he would feel less pressured. I suddenly felt guilty about being high-maintenance and sulky—realizing he could well do without it. I snuggled into him further.

"I would love to see where you work sometime," I said more cheerfully.

"Really?" He hesitated as if pondering an idea. "Well, why don't you come now? If you don't mind waiting around for me, that is. At least it will give us a bit longer before we have to say goodbye."

Music to my ears. I nodded enthusiastically.

The building was impressive, an original stone-built base with marble archways, pillars, and floors. A grand water feature dominated the center of the lobby, as well as being a striking centerpiece it served to humidify and chill the area. The rest of the structure was all glass and steel and ultra modern, with white interior walls and furniture and shiny marble floors.

Everybody who passed by was businesslike and immaculately dressed, to the point where I found myself silently thanking God for the clothing I'd selected that morning. I'd opted for a pair of classy wide-legged crepe pants in white with a gray soft cashmere sweater.

My long mahogany waves were pinned loosely to one side so they flowed elegantly down over one shoulder in a single twisted coil.

When the elevator opened up on the thirtieth floor, Ethan took my hand and guided me through an elaborate entrance with a set of frosted glass security doors. The words *Wilde Industries Incorporated*, were ornately engraved in stone over the top.

A spotlessly dressed, studious looking brunette sat behind a shiny, white reception area. She flushed pink at the sight of Ethan, beaming a warm, winning smile in his direction.

"Good morning, Mr. Wilde," she enthused.

"Morning, Emily," Ethan replied with a vague nod. She offered me a warm but curious smile as way of acknowledgement.

By the time we'd walked down the corridor to the space at the end, Ethan had been greeted with the same gushing courtesy numerous times.

The huge open space consisted of a number of entrances to other corridors verging off in various directions and several large offices with secretary desks outside, all of which were manned by attractive young males and females. Ethan's arrival and the simple fact that he was holding my hand seemed to be creating a lot of attention with a combination of pleasant surprise, inquisitiveness, and a shocked exchange of glances between the staff. Ethan squeezed my hand in silent reassurance.

The two largest offices, both with opaque glass walls and doors shielding their interiors from view, took up one entire side of the space. The doors to both were open, and Ethan led me to the one furthest away in the corner.

The corner room was vast with both exterior walls an expanse of glass overlooking the city. It was minimally designed with contemporary furnishings, clean geometric lines—and white. Everything was white. The leather chairs and sofas, the desk, the floor, everything.

"Oh, there you are," said a voice with a softly spoken English accent.

A stunning blonde with hair almost down to her waist emerged from one of the smaller offices across. She was impeccably dressed in a chocolate-brown pantsuit and entered the room perusing the paperwork in her hand.

"I was beginning to think you weren't coming. I have the itinerary… Oh," she said, stopping abruptly when she saw me. "Sorry, I didn't realize you were in a meeting."

"Oh, no, I'm not," Ethan quickly corrected her. "This is Angel. Angel, this is Alex."

My jaw suddenly lost all muscle function, my mouth falling lax in a state of utter shock. "Alex?"

Words seemed to fail me, absorbed in the shock that would have been less brutal if she'd been introduced as Fred Flintstone. The Alex I'd pictured in my mind's eye would probably have been more likened to Fred than the blond beauty that stood before me—given that I'd assumed Alex was a man.

I remember Jia had once said to me, "Never assume anything. It's the mother of all fuck ups." Turns out she was right. And it was my bad.

Alex stepped toward me, her hand held out, a warm smile on her very pretty mouth. And something acerbic and unfamiliar bubbled in the pit of my stomach.

"Oh, how lovely to meet you, at last. It's so nice to finally put a face to a name," she said sweetly.

Damn straight, I thought, shaking her hand politely, but still in too much shock to articulate. Ethan regarded me with a confused expression, probably wondering why I'd turned mute all of a sudden. Until it finally dawned on him, his eyes becoming wide with acute, abrupt awareness of my blatant misconception.

"Alex, could you give us a few minutes?" he said, quickly ushering her to the door.

"Of course." She smiled and left the room without question.

Ethan closed the door quietly behind her, but didn't turn around. He stood with his head slightly bowed, shoulders stiff, hands thrust deep in his pockets. I could picture the shrinking, cringing expression I knew would be etched on his face as he mentally kicked himself for not being more definitive when he'd mentioned Alex. He turned slowly.

I motioned toward the closed door, as if a beautiful blond vapor had been left behind in her wake. "I take it Alex—as in, your-right-arm-Alex—is short for what, Alexandra, Alexis?" I asked dryly.

Ethan blinked. "Alexandra, yes."

I nodded slowly, trying to contain the bubbling anxiety from spilling over into my voice. "And has Alexandra been shortened to Alex in an affectionate, endearing way, or just because you can't be bothered with the full length version?"

He rolled his eyes. "I have no idea. It's just the name she uses and the one I've always known her as. Look, I'm sorry, I just assumed that—"

"Never assume anything. It's the mother of all fuck ups," I interrupted. Jia would have been proud.

He seemed to recoil a little, stung by my words or their tone, or both. "Thank you for the advice, Angelica. I'll do my best to remember that."

"Is it a coincidence that she's English?"

"No." Rolling his eyes again, he said, "I brought her with me, along with Jackson."

"Wow. You were pretty damned accurate when you described her as your right arm then. She must mean an awful lot to you. I mean, we do have very efficient, educated, professional people here in the States, you know. But you obviously see her as indispensable, so I can only assume it's something more personal she provides you with, something over and above what you must pay an extortionate amount for."

"I thought you said that to assume is 'the mother of all fuck ups'?"

I raised my chin obstinately. "Say what you see is my motto."

"You're being pedantic."

"I'm being pragmatic."

He paused for a second. "You're being a sassy mouth."

I folded my arms in a show of obstinacy.

"*And* you're being jealous, Miss Lawson."

"Yes," I admitted way too quickly, surprising even myself.

The edge of his lip curled with a slight trace of amusement, his eyes narrowing in that way that implied he could eat me, all mean and sexy. And all of that—along with his quick, sharp retort—was enough to take the edge off my fury and make me melt like a slab of chocolate in the midday sun.

Stay focused, I told myself.

"Look, baby." His expression softened. He'd had my admission and was now changing tact. "Alex has been with me a long time. She's advanced within the company at a deserved rate, because she's proven herself to be shrewd, ambitious, competent, and above all, loyal. I need people like that around me in business, people I can trust. So when I find the best, I do whatever I can to keep them. But that comes in the form of a generous remuneration package and nothing else. I don't, I never have, and I never will screw the workforce."

Just then there was a tap at the door. It opened to reveal a tall, dark, extremely good-looking man, dressed in an expensive gray suit. Without waiting for an invitation, he came bustling into the office with a heap of excited energy.

"Hey, my man. I hear it's raining in London. I hope you packed your slicker." The man seemed completely at ease as he jested with Ethan.

Ethan beamed a smile at him as they clasped each other's hands and pulled each other into a man hug with a single pat on the back.

"Hey, Damon, I'm glad you're here. I want you to meet Angel."

Of course, Ethan's brother, Damon. It hadn't crossed my mind that he would be here too. The other large office next door would obviously be his. He turned to gape at me.

"Oh man, you said she was beautiful, but drop-dead-gorgeous, you did not mention." Moving toward me, he took me into a huge bear hug, the sudden outward display of affection taking me completely by surprise.

Ethan grinned and then arched a brow as Damon's hug became a prolonged embrace, nuzzling his face into my neck. "Oh, dude, she smells utterly divine too."

Damon was definitely a cheeky charmer who clearly thrived on winding Ethan up, and I couldn't help the giggle which bubbled to the surface of my lips.

Ethan glared at him. "Okay, Damon, I'll put this very simply. If you don't get your hands off my girl in the next three seconds, you won't be able to smell anything for a very long time."

"Okay, dude, chill your boots." He released me but held on to my hand, squeezing it playfully. "He never did learn to share."

I laughed, warming to him instantly. "It's a pleasure to finally meet you, Damon."

"The pleasure is entirely mine, Angel, I can assure you." He brought my hand to his lips and kissed my fingers lightly. "He's kept you to himself for far too long. It's about time I finally found out who's got my brother's blood pumping like a randy—"

"Have you got a death wish, Bro?" Ethan interjected quickly.

The door opened again, the beautiful, blond Alex imparting a harried look toward Ethan. "I'm sorry, but we really have to..."

"Yes, sorry, I'm right with you." He threw a pleading look my way trying to gauge if things were good between us. I smiled to reassure him all was forgiven—for now.

"Don't you worry about Angel. I'll look after her," Damon threatened, smirking at his brother.

Ethan scowled back, then using two fingers to point at his own eyes, he jabbed them in Damon's direction, indicating an "I'm watching you" warning. As he left the room he called over his shoulder to me. "Don't massage his ego. It's bursting at the seams as it is."

Damon laughed and gestured toward the plush leather sofas.

"Why don't you take a seat, Angel?" He strolled over to the open office door with his hands in his pockets and shouted to whoever might be listening. "Okay, let's get some coffee in here."

A disembodied voice replied hurriedly, "On its way, Mr. Wilde."

I smiled to myself, thinking how odd it was to hear someone other than Ethan addressed as Mr. Wilde. Although there were elements of similarities within their physical structures, such as their strong, chiseled jawline and their height and build, it was pretty much where their resemblance ended. Damon was dark haired and green eyed, as opposed to Ethan's fairer, blue eyed semblance of a god—okay, so I was biased. But the fact that Damon had an American accent made it even less obvious they were brothers.

It seemed their personalities were also very distinct. Ethan was quite reserved and enigmatic in his character. His intensity and assertive, forceful nature commanded your unwavering attention and was seriously, seriously hot.

Damon, on the other hand, appeared to be more easy going, but with attractive, vivacious qualities. He was a shameless tease, definitely no stranger to overt flattery and flirtatiousness and was evidently completely at ease being the center of attention. I suspected that where women were concerned—if he so desired—he would score every time, but perhaps a little too eagerly, making reckless, hasty decisions.

Ethan, in contrast, would be more of a cautious observer, selecting with thorough, careful judgment to ensure he was totally satisfied with his final choice.

Or at least, that's what I preferred to think.

Damon sat down across from me and propped the ankle of one leg on the opposite knee, a playful smile etched onto his mouth. A small, curvy blonde delivered our coffee, smiling sweetly at Damon. We both thanked her, and as she shimmied away, I couldn't help but notice how he did a double take of her wiggling ass as she disappeared out of view.

My mouth twitched at the corner as I tried to suppress my amusement. Something told me that, unlike his brother's assertion, maybe Damon wasn't completely opposed to screwing the workforce.

He looked at me, his expression suddenly ominously serious. "If you promise to tell me what you've done with my brother, and who the hell that jackass is posing as him, I'll tell the cops to go easy on you. Provided you haven't harmed him, you could get away with second-degree kidnapping. In New York State, I believe it's ranked as a class B felony—you could get as little as five years."

Furthermore, this guy was funny.

Throwing my head back, I laughed loudly. "I have no idea what you mean, Damon." I straightened my face to play along.

His smirk was back as he assessed my amiability. "Oh, come now, Angel. I know my brother, and my brother does not do *smitten*. That guy in there…" he hitched a thumb over his shoulder in the general direction Ethan had walked in "…has it written all over his strikingly handsome, runs-in-the-family face."

I laughed again. "Well, there you go, then. I'm not sure about the 'smitten' bit, but I surely wouldn't be able to find an imposter that could come anywhere near to doing justice to his striking good looks."

"Good point, Angel. A detail I appear to have overlooked." He paused. "Which mind-altering drugs have you been force feeding him, then?" We both laughed. "Okay, I know, enough already. But seriously, babe—that boy is hooked. Trust me."

I shook my head, smiling shyly.

"And you have the most incredible laugh, by the way."

The door opened and Ethan strode in.

Damon got to his feet, and as I followed suit, he leaned forward to peck me on the cheek.

"You have brightened my Monday morning beyond belief, Angel." He started walking backwards toward the door and Ethan. "If you're lonely and hungry while Bro's away, I'll bring you dinner."

Smiling, I raised my hand to bid him goodbye. He turned to Ethan and shook his hand.

"You are one lucky bastard, my man. Have a safe trip. We'll confer later, yeah? Laters, guys." He left the room closing the door behind him.

Walking over to Ethan, I laced my arms around his neck, planting a tender kiss on his wonderfully luscious mouth. It was difficult to stay mad at him. He closed his eyes and emitted a long deep audible breath.

"You taste so good…" he nuzzled into my neck just below my lobe and inhaled "…and smell so good." He shook his head, bringing him back to the present, and released me.

"Did Damon behave himself?"

"Yes, he was charming and very funny."

"Yes, I thought I heard you laughing. It was very distracting. Not too charming I hope?" He narrowed his eyes, half smirking, half accusing.

"I'm not sure. It was hard to see past his devastating good looks," I teased.

He spanked me on the ass sharply, sending a spark of burning exhilaration straight to my groin. "Don't even josh with me, Miss Lawson. Not when I'm about to leave you alone for the next few days. I'll never stay focused. And just so we're clear, dinner with my brother is out of the question. Not without me at any rate. In fact, it might be best if you don't go out at all, especially in the evenings."

I examined his expression. He wasn't joking.

"Because, of course, you won't be venturing out of your apartment other than to work, will you?" I said pointedly, raising my brows.

He shrugged.

"Can we remember that it is you who is venturing over three thousand miles with a disturbingly attractive blonde?"

We looked into each other's eyes, his reflecting the angst that I was sure flooded mine.

"I have to go," he muttered.

"I know."

"Jackson is waiting for you. He's fully briefed."

As I nodded reluctantly, he took me into a firm embrace, kissing me deeply and possessively, the warm taste of him on my lips as addictive as a drug. His mouth moved briefly to my neck, inhaling again, as if storing my scent to memory, and then he took my hand in his and we walked out of the office and silently down the corridor to the elevators. Ethan pressed the button and the door slid open immediately. His grip was firm on my hand, reluctant to let go, but I pulled it free and stepped inside, not wishing to prolong the agony of leaving him. I focused my attention on my shoes, afraid to look up at him through fear of exposing the wretchedness in my eyes.

The elevator was mercifully empty, and unable to refrain any longer, I looked up to meet his gaze. He stood with his hands in his pockets, his manner resolute and focused, his face a mask of stoicism. I gathered my poise, attempting to mirror the strength I saw in him, leaned forward and pressed the button for the lobby.

"Cinders." He nodded once.

A second's hesitation. "Charming."

The elevator door slid firmly closed, and I was alone.

My heart beat quickened as I felt my chest begin to tighten and my breathing grow shallow and arduous. The elevator jolted to a halt on the floor below and the door opened, allowing two men in business suits, deep in discussion, to get into the car. I moved silently into the corner and focused on my shoes.

The journey to the lobby took forever and when the door finally opened, I exited quickly, searching for the nearest restroom; I couldn't let Jackson see me like this. I needed a moment. Eventually, I found one and ran into the first available stall, locking the door behind me.

Get a freaking grip.

I was angry with myself. I was becoming far too emotionally attached, allowing things to progress to the point of becoming dependent even. It wasn't like me to behave in this way; I'd never needed anyone before. Foolishly, I'd let my guard down, allowing myself to fall too hard and too fast. But somehow it had crept up on me, and now I wasn't even sure how to turn back.

Get a grip.

I vowed to use this time apart from Ethan as a lesson. To prove I could still function alone—to detach myself to a safe distance.

I am strong. I am Angel Lawson. I don't need anyone in order to survive.

When I finally felt calm enough, I opened the door and made my way slowly through the busy foyer and outside to where Jackson was waiting by the car. He opened the door on my approach, smiling reassuringly. "Miss Lawson."

Managing a weak smile in response, I climbed in and got comfortable in the backseat. It felt strange sitting there alone, and I found myself reaching out into the empty space beside me, the weight of Ethan's absence lying heavy in my chest.

As the car waited to pull out into traffic, I looked up to see Ethan and Alex emerging from the revolving doors and head over to another car in front of ours. A man, whom I guessed must be Simon, opened the rear door smiling widely at the approaching couple, who I suddenly noticed looked strikingly well-matched. My heart lurched at the sight of the two of them together. He laughed at something she said, placing his hand on the small of her back and guiding her to the open door in the same intimate way he might touch me.

My heart filled with repulsive jealousy, the vile, caustic taste in my mouth making me sick to my stomach. It was an emotion I'd never really experienced before meeting Ethan, and never so powerfully as right now. Our car finally pulled out into traffic as I swallowed back the ascending bile and threat of invading tears. Suddenly Ethan looked up, as if the weight of my gaze had summoned him, a startled look of alarm disturbing his exquisite features—he hadn't been expecting to see me, probably presumed we'd be long gone by now.

"Where to, Miss Lawson?" Jackson asked, eyeing me in the rearview.

"Home, Jackson. Take me home."

I looked away quickly, and we were gone.

CHAPTER FIFTEEN

J ackson insisted on carrying the few items I'd taken to Ethan's up to my apartment, and when he'd done a quick check around— unnecessary, but apparently part of his brief from Ethan—he left, reminding me to call him if I needed to go anywhere.

For the next hour, I wandered around my home looking for something to distract me from the odd, unsettled feeling I had from being alone. My home had been practically the only place in the world where I'd felt completely comfortable, and in the past had even preferred to be alone. But since Ethan had stormed into my life like a vehement tornado, altering everything about it from what I did to how I thought, I felt suddenly lost and strangely inept without him.

Although deep down, there was nothing I would change about meeting Ethan, I couldn't help notice an element of resentment creeping into my mood. I hated that I was so entirely hooked on him, the craving and the panic and the ache caused by the sudden withdrawal felt like something akin to the pain of an addict desperate for a fix. I found myself blaming Ethan for it.

I made a conscious decision that while he was away in London, I would focus on all the things I'd allowed to slide recently. Catch up on the dull and dreary stuff, gain back some control of my life. It was torture for me to picture him somewhere else, with someone else, so I figured it would be easier to try not to think of him at all. I wouldn't call him. I'd allow him the space to concentrate on fixing whatever it was he needed to fix. When and if he had the time, he would call me. And so I pushed him as far from my mind as I could manage.

Feeling encouraged by my new-found resolve, I changed into shorts and T-shirt, and put on some music, setting the iPod to shuffle. Paramore's "Brick by Boring Brick" came on—one of my favorites— and I smiled to myself at how fitting the lyrics were. Keeping my feet on the ground sounded like good advice, Angel Lawson had spent enough time in her fairy-tale world with her head in the clouds. Time to remember who I was. I turned up the volume, flung open the terrace doors, and set about cleaning and tidying, dancing as I went.

Before long my mood lifted and I felt noticeably stronger.

When I finished my spring cleaning, I caught up on emails and confirmed a Friday lunch meeting with Claudia to go through her photographs. By the time I was done it was seven o'clock and my stomach was complaining, reminding me I hadn't eaten all day.

I used up things in the refrigerator for a sandwich and made a fruit salad, settling to eat in front of a rerun of *Friends*. When I finished, I rang Jia and we chatted about the gallery and an exhibition that had been arranged for the forthcoming Saturday, doing my best to steer the conversation away from Ethan each time she attempted to lead it in that direction.

When I hung up, I realized I was exhausted, so I took a quick shower and climbed into bed. Checking my phone for messages revealed my inbox to be empty, but I wasn't too surprised. I wasn't exactly sure of Ethan's flight schedule, but I was almost certain he was still in the air. Blocking it from my mind, I curled up in my suddenly, extremely large bed, eventually drifting off into a restless sleep.

My mind was a jumbled mass of confusion, the distress of being lost and disoriented creeping under my skin like a cold layer of ice. The dim, murky lighting was only just bright enough for me to make out the complex network of passages and pathways, but I didn't know how long I had left before the darkness closed in entirely.

Blocking the fear from my mind, I trudged on through the maze, the ground becoming dense and boggy underfoot, making it even trickier to navigate. Each time I reached what I thought was a clear opening, I found it blocked by a large mirror, forcing me to turn around and find another route. With each false turn I became more perplexed, unable to decipher which path I'd already tried.

After a while, I began to notice something odd about my reflections. Although the mirror images looked like me, they didn't appear to accurately replicate my actions. Their behavior was out of time with mine, their expressions totally contradicting the angst I felt inside when they smiled slyly back at me. The maze was full of imposters—deviously disguised and pretending to be me.

Suddenly, I felt so uncertain, so dreadfully insecure. I didn't know which of the reflections to trust, and if I couldn't rely on my own instincts—my reflections—how would I escape the imposing and oppressive confined enclosure which I'd found myself in.

As I stumbled around trying to find the way out, the feelings of suspicion and wariness intensified. Then out of the blue, I caught sight of Ethan, just a glimpse as he turned a corner. Filled with hope, I started after him, but by the time I reached the corner where he'd turned, he was rounding another one—out of reach and out of earshot.

Finally, I saw him about to walk through the exit to the clearing beyond, but he wasn't alone. His companion was tall and slender, long, blond hair tumbling down behind her. Ethan guided her safely toward the outlet, his hand resting intimately in the small of her back. I began to run to catch up, but it was useless. The mud dragged my feet down further with every step, pulling and grabbing at my shoes—my shiny, red patent shoes.

And Ethan was gone.

Over the next few days, I threw myself into my work as much I could manage. Jia and I worked hard preparing for the upcoming exhibition, and when I got home, I worked out in the gym until my muscles ached from exhaustion. I did everything I could to tire myself out in order to attain a peaceful night's sleep.

Jackson had ferried me the meager distance to the gallery and back every day. I hadn't called him, feeling the journey too negligible to bother him, but he was always there waiting when I emerged. I suspected Ethan had maybe anticipated my aversion to being chaperoned and had instructed him to wait around for me. I felt guilty about it—his boredom threshold must have been vast.

On Tuesday morning at eight-thirty I'd received a text message from Ethan. It said he hoped I was okay and explained that he would be in meetings all day but would try and call later. I replied telling him not to worry and to focus on his work. I was fine.

On Wednesday he called as I was preparing to leave for the gallery. When I saw his name on the caller display my heart hurtled into my mouth, the familiar fluttering of nervous excitement like fire in my belly. I didn't think I would ever get used to how he made me feel.

"Hey, baby," he breathed in his husky voice.

My legs turned instantly to Jell-O. "Hey, how's it going?" I asked.

"Oh, never mind all that. I'm sorry I've not had chance to call, are you okay?"

"It's fine, I'm fine." It wasn't fine, I hated it and missed him like crazy, but I wasn't about to tell him that. "I've been busy with the gallery. There's an exhibition this weekend, so I've barely noticed you gone." I hadn't meant to say that, but suddenly it was out there. I wanted to retract the words, but didn't know how to, and then the moment had passed. There was an awkward pause.

"How's Alex?" *What? Where did that come from?* I slapped my forehead with my palm. It was like someone else was controlling my mouth.

"Everything is fine here," he snapped. "Look, I'm about to go into a lunch meeting, and you and your sassy mouth are evidently busy."

"Yes, as you appear to have been since you left." I paused, waiting for him to respond. When he didn't, I added, "You looked good together, you and Alex—when I saw you getting into the car. You were... very attentive."

Where in the hell was all this coming from?

Although I'd done my very best to block out all conscious thoughts of Ethan in order to self-preserve, I realized that my subconscious had been working overtime without my knowledge. She hadn't run any of this shit by me, and now she was unrestrained and running amok.

"You're jealous," Ethan said after a beat.

No! Really? You think?

"I just don't like being made a fool," I snapped.

"The only person making a fool of you, is you, Angel. I've told you, you don't have anything to worry about with Alex. She's an excellent, trustworthy member of my team and that is all."

There was another awkward silence, and when I didn't respond, Ethan spoke again, but this time his tone was brimming with regret. "I have to go. Goodbye, Angelica."

Use of full version of name noted.

Trying to think past the finality in his voice, I scrambled through my mind for something to say, something to take the edge off this progressively crumbling situation. But I couldn't think of anything. My mind had gone blank, my psyche suddenly hijacked by a muddle of contrasting emotions.

"Goodbye, Ethan."

Desolation hit me full in the face the moment I hung up. My self-preservation techniques had clearly packed a bag and left on vacation, leaving me alone with this irrepressible insane jealousy. I'd lost all manner of control, allowing the separation and my insecurities to get the better of me. Figuratively speaking, I couldn't kick myself hard enough. I grabbed my purse and left for work.

When Jackson delivered me to the gallery on Friday, I informed him of my plans for lunch and we arranged for him to collect me in time for my meeting with Claudia at two o'clock.

Jia was busy making last minute arrangements for the exhibition opening, seeing to deliveries of champagne and white lily arrangements. The photographer who was showcasing had arrived in a fluster, and various other people milled around setting up the display under Jia's watchful, critical eye. The hustle and bustle gave me quite a buzz, and with my recent conscientious, focus-on-work attitude, I decided it was time to set a date for my own exhibition; I'd been promising collectors for months.

By the time I walked into the restaurant to meet Claudia, I was a little harried and glad to have been able escape the chaos. Claudia's vivid red hair was instantly discernable from across the room and I realized, by the just as vibrant but longer locks of her companion, that Alisha had also tagged along.

Both stood to welcome me as I approached, greeting me as though I were an old friend.

"How lovely to see you again, Angel," enthused Claudia, kissing the air on both sides of my face. "You look truly exquisite, such wonderful deportment and posture. I hear you made quite an impression on just about everyone at my wedding," she said animatedly as we took our places at the table.

"Oh?" I quizzed, confused as to what she meant. "I can't think why. What exactly did I do?"

"Judging by the attention you commanded, I dare say you just floated in and breathed, honey."

My brows knotted in confusion.

She shook her head. "Humble as well. No wonder I was bombarded with requests for your telephone number from every eligible bachelor in attendance."

"In her defense," Alisha intervened smugly, "it's hardly surprising she didn't notice anyone else. Ethan Wilde pretty much dominated her attention from the second he arrived, and given that he's, by far, the most eligible and hottest guy on the planet, you can't really blame her, can you?"

By now I was grinning, and they were watching me carefully, fishing for any tidbits of information. When I didn't offer any, they gazed at me pleadingly.

"Oh, come on, spill, we want the whole ball of wax," Alisha prompted. "It's not like it's a secret or anything, any damn fool could see that Ethan couldn't take his freaking eyes off you. I mean who can blame him, you're gorgeous. She's gorgeous, right?" She directed this to her mother. Claudia nodded wholeheartedly and Alisha gushed on. "You should have seen the way he stood watching her with his mouth open in the pool house. All smoldering and smoking hot for her. I mean his eyes were practically hopping across the floor and getting down and dirty with her all on their own. Everyone was so jealous. I mean he was hot for her. He was *so* freaking hot for you." She aimed the last part back at me.

Oh Boy, this girl could talk up a blue streak. When she finally came up for breath we all stared at each other for a long moment and then burst into laughter.

"Okay, okay," I said, deciding to toss them a scrap to keep them quiet but also swerve the subject as quickly as possible. "Let's just say I've seen quite a lot of Ethan since then and everything is going well." The last bit was forced through gritted teeth in the hope of concealing my uncertainty. Considering he was thousands of miles away and our last conversation hadn't been the most amicable, I wasn't exactly sure how it was going.

"Is that it?" they both asked simultaneously, sparking another fit of giggles.

"Jeez, nailing Jell-O to the wall would be easier. I mean, I got more out of Abby." Alisha started up again. "She says that Ethan can't get enough of you, and she's predicting wedding bells. She's been just busting to tell her mom about you, but Ethan won't let her, because apparently their mom's too nosy for her own good, and based on the fact that he's never shown any interest in a serious relationship before, he reckons she'd be likely to cut their world trip short just to get back and check you out, and seeing as though his dad needs to convalesce he doesn't want to risk it, so he's told her to keep it zipped."

"Do you breathe?" I asked, my eyes wide with shock.

She was like a freaking freight train. I was reeling. But Alisha's effusiveness was only partly to blame, because what really had my tail in a spin was that people I barely knew not only appeared to know a lot about what was going on in my private life, but were also freely discussing it. The knowledge was unnerving.

She clasped her hand over her mouth, her eyes darting from me to her mother in search of reassurance. "Have I said too much? I've said too much."

"Too much?" I asked with mock confusion. "Too much about what?"

A look of relief settled on her pretty pink cheeks, and I snatched the opportunity to change the subject. The last few days had been hell, trying to push all thoughts of Ethan from my mind. We hadn't spoken since our spat on Wednesday, and I was secretly quite worried about the extent of the damage I'd caused. The last thing I needed was a full on convo about him, about us.

After ordering salads and wine, I booted up the MacBook, both of them gushing with enthusiasm as I took them through the images of the wedding. Alisha fell instantly in love with the ones of the girly pillow fight in the pool house, requesting several large prints of the images to hang in there, as that's where she spent a lot of her time, especially, she said, when she had friends over.

"It has everything you need to be completely self-sufficient in there. It's like living alone really. I can totally look after myself," she said with pride.

Claudia rolled her eyes at me. "She thinks she can, but she's deluded. She thinks making herself a cup of coffee is being self-reliant."

I laughed as the two bantered back and forth, suspecting the pool house was some kind of compromise between the Millers and their daughter, a way of giving her the freedom she craved while at the same time allowing them to keep a watchful eye on her. Who could blame them when she'd gone off the rails once already? It was a smart move and I gave Claudia a knowing, but discreet wink.

Claudia selected the images which she wanted to enlarge and hang in various parts of their home. She wanted me to advise her and hang them as a surprise for a Christmas present. I told her I'd be delighted.

When she saw the ones of the two sisters on the beach splashing at the water's edge, she gasped with appreciation. The children, it turned out, were her goddaughters, and her eyes glimmered with affection when she saw them. "Their mother will adore these. I'd better have two copies made, one set in the largest print. They will make such a wonderful gift."

These very images evoked wonderful memories for me too. The sense of peace and serenity which had overwhelmed me on that beach as I'd gazed out at the infinite ocean was one I'd never forget. And then my encounter with Ethan, the emotions and sensations bombarding my mind and body with his words, his scent—his touch. The place rekindled all of those feelings and would remain special to me forever because of them.

"You are so lucky to live in such tranquility. I loved your house and the beach, all the free air. If you ever need a house sitter, look no further."

Suddenly Claudia's eyes lit up. "I've got a fantastic idea. We plan to go to our house in California in the fall and won't be back until Christmas. Why don't you spend some time at the house while we're gone? You can deliberate as much as you need about where to hang your works of art, and take advantage of the peace and quiet while you're there." She sounded quite excited. "It would be a personal thank you for all your hard work. I'd be delighted if you agreed."

I was utterly shell shocked. The house sitting remark had of course been a frivolous one, but I couldn't deny that the idea of spending some time away from the city in such serene surroundings really excited me.

"Oh, say yes," squealed Alisha. "If you like, you could stay in my pool house. The main house is so large when you're alone. Oh," she squealed again, "if you let me know when you're planning on arriving, I could sneak back early and we could have an absolute riot." Her eyes were wide with the thought of party time without the parents. Oh, to be twenty-one.

"Uh, not so fast, Alisha, you won't be sneaking off anywhere, and besides, Angel would be going for the peace and quiet, not to party."

I didn't know what to say. "I um…" I held my hands spread helplessly in front of me.

"Of course you will," Claudia blurted quickly, "I know your father, and I'd lay odds that he has no intention of reimbursing you for our 'wedding gift…'" she made air quotes with her fingers "…Please say yes, it's the least I can do."

I flushed with the accuracy of her insinuation. She read my expression and interpreted it exactly.

"Enough said. I won't take no for an answer. I'll let you have the code for the gate and alarms and the keys before we leave for California."

I smiled. "I'd love to, thank you. Escaping the city for a few days would be fantastic."

"Good, that's settled then." She clapped her hands together.

By the time Jackson dropped me home, I was feeling quite tipsy. I wasn't used to drinking alcohol with lunch and the wine had gone straight to my head. The effects had crushed all capacity to keep my thoughts and feelings at bay, and as a melancholic cloud descended, my thoughts inevitably strayed to Ethan. Although I'd tried my best to ignore my feelings, I'd missed him terribly and was angry that he hadn't called since our spat. In my mind, I had every right to be mad at him and didn't believe my behavior to be anymore unreasonable than his meltdown over Jean-Paul.

I dug out my cell in the hope that he'd called. He hadn't, but there was a message in my inbox received a couple of hours ago. My heart was in my shoes as I held my breath and opened it.

I expect you and your sassy mouth are busy—as am I—so I won't keep you. Just wanted to inform you that I'll probably be back sometime next week. I'm exhausted and plan an early night. You needn't reply. E.

The message was starched and formal—an insufficient gesture to placate me. In fact it was downright fucking rude and the impact was like a brutal punch in the gut. The separation, it seemed, had taken its toll. He seemed so cold and distant, a stark contrast to the man who'd held me close and kissed me, who'd taken away my fear with promises to mend me and… love me.

Perhaps it was too soon in the relationship to withstand such disjuncture. Maybe the space had exposed his true feelings, revealing that what he'd thought was true, deep-seated affection, was actually only confused, inflated emotions. He'd just gotten carried away in the frantic pace of our connection.

Maybe that's why he'd gone to London, to differentiate his feelings.

Or maybe I'd been right to be pissed about him being vague and somewhat misleading with regards to Alex. Oh, I didn't know what to think. My mind was steadily erupting, insane with the dreadful and endless probabilities that were going through his mind.

All I knew was that his behavior was positively insolent, and the more times I read the message the more unacceptable and offensive it became. If I was totally off the mark about Alex, then surely he would be attempting to assuage my concerns by facilitating trust, instead of being angry and dismissive.

After all, he could be up to who-knows-what with who-knows-who. And yet, thanks to Jackson, Ethan knew every move I'd made since he left town. Oh my God. How freaking stupid and naïve had I been? He would know where I'd been, who with, and for how long. Well not anymore. I wouldn't call on Jackson again, not even if my life depended on it.

I paced the floor of my apartment, frustrated and angry at myself and Ethan, each step and every passing second convincing me of my duped status. Fueled by alcohol and fury alike, and without even taking the time to consider what I was about to say or even what time of day it was in the U.K. I picked up my cell and dialed his number.

The phone rang out for what seemed like an eternity, eventually going to voicemail—I hadn't expected that. More questions raged through my head: Why hadn't he answered? Who was he with? Why was he ignoring me? I left a garbled and impulsive message.

"How dare you! I don't know who the hell you think you are but… Actually, you know what? It doesn't matter, forget it. Just forget the whole fucking thing!" I hung up.

Suddenly, I was filled with panic. What the hell had I done? Why had I allowed myself to become tangled up in a relationship when I knew better?

I had vowed that I would never become involved with anyone again after James. There were reasons why I'd never allowed anyone past the barrier I'd spent my life building—why sex was as much as I offered to a man—because everyone let you down in the end. But despite this, I'd fallen for the charms of a man I'd had no right to believe I would be anything other than a passing fancy to. I'd been foolish enough to think that someone would care for me, be loyal to me—would *love* me.

The walls were closing in around me, and for the first time my home—my bubble—could not console me. I needed to get out, and I needed a drink. Grabbing my purse and throwing my cell inside, I ran out of my apartment.

CHAPTER SIXTEEN

Twenty minutes later, I was propped on a stool at the bar in Paddy's, nursing a large glass of white wine. Not my usual tipple on a visit to Paddy's—that would normally be beer or vodka—but this wasn't a usual visit, and as I was topping up from earlier I didn't want to mix.

Mercifully, Paddy and Kathleen were nowhere to be seen, probably taking a break before the evening rush. Dylan appeared shortly after I arrived, his brow creasing into a quizzical frown when he saw I was drinking alone. I just shook my head in a "don't ask" motion. As much as I liked Dylan, I really wanted to be alone with my misery and my wine, but beggars couldn't be choosers, and I knew that if I didn't offer, Dylan wouldn't pry.

"Hey, Angel cake, what's up?" His handsome face was strewn with concern as he walked the length of the bar and leaned on the counter in front of me. "No guard dogs tonight? You were pretty much surrounded by them last time you were here."

"Hey, Dylan." I feigned a smile, inwardly wincing with the reminder of my last visit. "No. No guard dogs. Sorry about all that, Dylan. I hope your mom and dad weren't too pissed with me."

"No worries, Angel cake. They didn't even notice. Why the long face?"

And here I thought I was putting on a convincing performance.

"Oh, nothing major really. I've just gone and painted myself into a corner over something."

"Anything to do with the formidable Mr. Wilde?"

"No," I refuted a little too quickly. "Why do you say formidable, anyway? What do you know of him?" The question made me instantly suspicious, as I recalled, I'd only introduced Ethan to him by his first name.

"I know he's filthy rich."

"And?" *Like that makes him a bad person.*

"And usually money comes with power, influence, dominance, a penchant for control. He seemed very… possessive the other night."

Suddenly, I felt the need to defend Ethan from Dylan's critical assessment, finding it gratuitous and unwanted. The way I felt had nothing to do with the way Ethan was, or how much money he had. It had to do with me letting my guard down, taking my eye off the ball. It was my own fault I felt so wretched.

"It's nothing to do with him. It's to do with work—no biggie. I just needed some *me* time." I beamed a smile to take the edge off the warning for him to back off.

"Okay, well if you need to blow off steam, just holler." Taking the hint, he grabbed a bottle of wine and began to top up my glass. "On the house, Angel cake. Enjoy your *me* time, and don't sweat the small stuff too much." Suddenly his smile disappeared, his lip curling in distaste as he seemed to focus on something or someone over my left shoulder. "On second thoughts, maybe do."

Looking to see what had irked him, I turned to find a very contrite looking Jean-Paul walking toward me. His hands were shoved in his pockets, the action hoisting his shoulders up in a vain attempt at innocence.

Turning back to Dylan, I buried my face in my hands. "You have got to be kidding me."

"Afraid not. Do you want me to get rid of him?"

I considered this for a second, knowing how Ethan would take the news if I gave Jean-Paul the time of day. But only for a second, as I determined that, actually, Ethan could go to hell. I was no longer living by his rules. I decided to hear him out.

"No, it's okay. I'll deal with this."

"No worries. I'm right over here if you need me." He flashed Jean-Paul a warning look and moved down the bar to another customer.

"Hey," said Jean-Paul, arriving at my side.

I offered him a stern sideways glance. "Jean-Paul."

"Can I buy you a drink?"

I shrugged, and he leaned across the bar to shout in his order to one of the servers behind.

This—me being alone with my misery and my wine—wasn't working out too well, but the issue with Jean-Paul needed sorting out, once and for all.

"So what? You come to Paddy's regularly?" I asked.

He raised an eyebrow, a smirk forming at the corner of his mouth. "That's a pick-up line. You coming on to me?"

I scowled at him.

"Sorry. That was… inappropriate. I like this joint. It reminds me of you, since you're the one who introduced me to the place."

Another lapse of judgment on my part. My mistakes were biting me on the ass tonight that was for sure.

"So, I just wanted to apologize, Angel. What I said that night in the club and how I went off in here the other night, I screwed up. I was out of order. I'm sorry."

"You should be. You were an ass."

A few moments of silence passed, and I was just about thinking he might take the comment on the chin when his whole demeanor seemed to change, the smug arrogance returning to his eyes as they narrowed on me.

"So, you and this guy… Wilde. Are you in some sort of relationship, or is he just your latest fuck buddy?"

"It has nothing to fucking do with you," I snarled, glaring at him.

"I beg to differ, since I'm the one who got dumped to make way for him."

"Dumped?" I was incredulous. "You really are deluded, aren't you? For the last time, Jean-Paul, we were *not* in a relationship. It's pretty hard to dump somebody you're not officially seeing. I fucked you a few times—when I had nothing better to do." I spat the last part out without forethought, but I was so angry.

His eyes were blazing. "It was more than that and you know it. Or it was for me, and if you'd have given us a fucking chance, I could have convinced you we were good together. I could've made you happy."

The idea seemed preposterous. Me with Jean-Paul, together?

"We still can be, Angel. I can forgive you for Wilde, but you've got to stop fucking with my head."

It was then I realized with a startling reality that I wasn't dealing with a rational person. Feeling suddenly uneasy, I glanced down the bar to make sure Dylan was still around before deciding what tack to take. He was watching us closely and offered me a discreet nod to reassure me he had my back. Although it went against the grain, I concluded there was only one approach left, and that was brutal honesty.

"Me fucking with *your* head? Have you heard yourself? I'm not sure how much clearer I can make it, but it is never going to happen, Jean-Paul. Get over it and stay the fuck away from me."

"Oh, I see, so you think you've made a smart move holding out for Wilde? Yeah, for sure, I can see why you might think that. I mean the guy is loaded, right?"

Why was everyone harping on about Ethan's wealth tonight?

Jean-Paul's voice was considerably loud now and people began to pay attention. But the eyes and ears around us didn't seem to faze him as he continued with his crazed verbal onslaught.

"And for the first couple of months all was sweet, right, because Wilde was all about Angel. But where is he now? You're not in here drinking alone for nothing—he's not been around for days. Well, Angel? Where is Mr. Attentive-Money-Bags now? Not here with you. But *I* am."

Christ, Ethan was right; Jean-Paul had been watching me and the idea made my skin crawl. Suddenly I heard Dylan cough in an attempt to attract my attention, and as I looked his way he nodded toward the door.

A quick glance alerted me to the reason.

What in the hell was he doing here?

It was a question I would save for later, because seeing Jackson heading my way, looking dogged and determined, but professional as ever, was a surprising relief. I wasn't sure I liked the direction this exchange with Jean-Paul was taking, so if there was ever a good time to have a chaperone it was now. I waited until Jackson was practically behind him before continuing.

"Jean-Paul, have you been following me?"

A look of shame passed fleetingly over his face as he realized his slip of the tongue. Then slowly his expression changed, his gaze finding Jackson as he came up by my side, and recognition struck.

"Jackson." I acknowledged his presence, but my eyes never wavered from Jean-Paul's as I waited for his answer.

"Miss Lawson," Jackson nodded. "Your car is waiting, ma'am."

"Oh, I see. Wilde couldn't make it, so he sent his monkey." Jean-Paul sneered and turned to address Jackson. "Is she fucking you too?"

Without thinking, I lashed out, landing a hard slap across Jean-Paul's face. He recoiled instantly, his hand fluttering to his cheek where a blazing red hand print was beginning to form.

A ghost of a smile teetered on Jackson's face as Dylan rushed around from the other side of the bar, coming up beside me.

"I think you've said enough, you fucking asshole." I spat the words with vehemence. "This conversation's over."

Suddenly, anger exploded in his eyes. "It's over when I say it's—"

In one swift move Jackson had Jean-Paul's arm pinned up his back, his face screwing up in excruciating pain.

"Give me one moment, ma'am. I'm just going to take out the trash." Jackson's voice was calm and composed as he nodded graciously to Dylan.

"Be my guest." Dylan, half shocked, half amused proceeded to hold the door open while Jackson manhandled Jean-Paul with ease out to the street.

The confrontation had created a fair amount of attention, so I turned back to the bar to avoid the stares of other customers and looked down at my hand burning hot from the impact of colliding with Jean-Paul's face. I picked up my drink and downed it one gulp.

"You okay?" Dylan was back beside me.

I nodded. "Sorry. Again." I was having a hard time digesting what had just happened, my head full of questions. "I seem to bring trouble to your door of late."

Dylan smiled reassuringly. "No worries, Angel cake. You're welcome anytime. You should be able to drink in here without getting hassled. That asshole won't be getting in here again, I can assure you." He glanced once again over my shoulder. "I do believe your ride is here."

Jackson had indeed returned from dispensing with the trash and stood holding the door for me. Smiling gratefully at Dylan, I thanked him again and left.

After seeing me safely into the back of the car, Jackson walked around and got into the driver's seat. The blood had drained from my face and my hands were trembling. Shock took hold.

Jackson's eyes met mine through the rearview mirror. "Are you okay, Miss Lawson?" he asked kindly.

I nodded, smiling awkwardly. "Jackson. How did you know where I was?"

"I think you'd better check your cell phone, ma'am."

Puzzled by his instruction, I retrieved my cell from where I'd thrown it in anger to the bottom of my purse, my eyes widening in shock as I gazed at the display. I had eighteen missed calls and several messages—all from Ethan. I glanced back up at Jackson, who had his own cell now pressed to his ear, a sympathetic look on his face as he diverted his eyes away from mine to speak.

"I've got her, boss... Yes... There was an incident... Debree... That's correct, boss. I've taken care of it... She's a little shook up... Of course, I understand, one moment," Jackson turned in his seat and smiling gently, handed me his phone. "Mr. Wilde would like to speak with you."

I swallowed hard against the obstruction of my tongue, suddenly thick and pulsing from the reverberations of my pounding heart. Judging from the information on my cell, Ethan had been calling me virtually from the minute I'd left my apartment. He hadn't ignored my call; he'd just missed it.

Tentatively I took the phone from Jackson's hand and held it to my ear. Jackson smiled again, turned to face front, and set off into traffic, switching on the radio in front to afford me some privacy.

"H... Hello?"

"Angel, what the fuck?" Ethan growled, anger oozing down the phone line. "I don't know what game you're playing, or what fucking planet you're on, but I swear to God, if I could get my hands on you right now, I would spank your ass so fucking thoroughly you'd be hard pressed to sit for a week."

The severity of his tone took me by surprise, my face heating with the impact of his threat. I'd been expecting him to be cross, but jeez, he was livid. What I hadn't expected was the passion and blatant concern hidden behind the dominant tone of the admonishment and the influence it would have on my body. Rendered powerless to its effects, I found myself crossing my legs to ease the warm, quivering ache that had manifested at the intersection at the top of my thighs. My gaze fluttered to the rearview and Jackson, my flush deepening.

"I'm... sorry. I thought..."

"Right now I don't care what you thought, Angel. In fact, I think I can pretty much guess, and frankly I'm disappointed. I thought I meant more to you than that."

"You do," I yelled. "And hang on, don't turn this around on me. I had every reason to make judgment on the way you've behaved these past few days. You have known every move I've made until tonight while I've been completely in the dark. You've been secretive and elusive and cold and…"

"Stop, Angelica. I no longer wish to discuss this over the phone. We'll continue this conversation when I get home. In the meantime, my only concern is that you're okay. That fucker, Debree… Did he touch you, are you hurt?" His tone was softer, more anxious now.

"Not physically, no," I snapped.

"Well, that's a relief. We'll tend to your damaged ego when I return." I could almost hear him smirking.

"And when will that be, exactly?" I asked, unable to keep the cynicism out of my voice.

"I'll keep you informed. In the meantime, I would prefer it if you informed Jackson of every move you need to make."

"It appears I don't need to. How did Jackson know where to find me anyway?"

"*I* knew where to find you, Angel. If you don't play ball, I'll admit it makes it harder. But I'll always find you wherever you go. My only fear is that next time, it will be too late. I mean it, Angel. I warned you about Debree's obsession before I left. Perhaps now you'll trust that I know what's best for you. If you chose to defy me, the ramifications for Jackson will be substantial. His job is to protect you, and if you make it difficult, he will have failed in his duty. He's lucky I don't fire his ass over this fuck up as it is."

"What? No! It's not his fault. I'll never forgive you if you do that." I was horrified by his threat and suddenly mortified that my actions could have potentially cost Jackson his job.

"Well, I won't have to if you're a good girl and do as you're told, will I? I'm not taking any more risks with your safety. At least until I know the problem's been dealt with to my satisfaction."

"Argh, you're so infuriating. Why do you have to control everything?"

"Because I can, Angelica. And lower your voice, you're treading a fine line as it is. Consider yourself lucky I'm thousands of miles away, or you'd be receiving your punishment tonight. As it is, it will have to wait until I return."

What did he mean by that? I wondered, suddenly remembering his remark about spanking my ass. Oh, how humiliating would that be?

"Why? What do you mean? You're not serious about… spanking my ass?" I mumbled the last part under my breath, afraid of being overheard.

The line went quiet as if he were considering the idea. "No, Angelica. Not literally anyway. It's not something I'm really into. But take my word for it, when I return—I'm really going to let you have it. A spanking will be the least of your worries when I bend you over and fuck you good and hard."

Oh. His tone was menacing, but his voice had lowered, taking on a gravelly, husky quality. I squeezed my legs together even tighter, hoping to dull the increasing ache, afraid to speak in case my voice betrayed my state of arousal. I was so turned on by his words, I was practically panting.

"That's shut your sassy mouth, hasn't it?" His tone was now positively smug. I needed to find my voice and fast.

"Not really," I murmured, keeping my trembling voice low and sinking down in my seat out of sight of the rearview. "I thought you said it was supposed to be a punishment? If it's my sassy mouth you want to silence, maybe it's *that* you need to fuck. Although, I wouldn't consider that a punitive measure either. In fact, there's nothing I'd like more than for you to fuck my sassy mouth."

For once, it was his turn to be speechless, at least momentarily.

"Oh, Angelica." His voice was strained. "You never fail to amaze me. I should have known you would be a voracious little creature the moment we first met. You are the only person I've ever known that, even with thousands of miles between us, can affect me to the point where my dick is so painfully hard, I fear it might drive me insane. Right now the thought of fucking your mouth is almost too much to bear."

I triumphed over his words, silently rejoicing in the return of the Ethan I knew so well. The throbbing between my legs was growing intolerable and I was desperate to find some satisfaction, even pondering briefly if I might be forced to find my own release later when I got home. But I needed to keep it together for now.

"Well good," I muttered through dense desire. "Why don't you hold on to that thought, and when you finally return to me—your rightful place—we can work on bringing it to fruition. Maybe we could consider it my voluntary penance. After all, sinners must repent or go to Hell, right?"

"Quite right, Angelica. And Hell is no place for an angel. Especially, not *my* Angel." There was a brief pause as only the sound of our sexual tension crackled down the phone line, and then, "Angel?"

"Yes."

"You want to touch yourself, don't you?"

The suggestion robbed me of speech for a beat, stunned by how well he could read me, even when he couldn't see my expression. "Yes," I whispered finally.

"Hand the phone back to Jackson. In a few seconds, I'll ring your cell. Answer it immediately, do you understand?"

"Um... Yes."

"Are you sure? Only recently you seem to have had trouble complying with even basic requests."

"I understand, Ethan," I muttered petulantly.

"Good. Give the phone back now."

Shifting quickly across the space to the driver's compartment, I tapped Jackson on the shoulder and handed him the phone. He took it and spoke quietly into the mouthpiece. A moment later, the privacy divider slid into place. Christ, where the hell was Ethan going with this? What the hell did he have planned? I couldn't remember having used the divider since the delicious journey from Claudia's wedding.

My cell *buzzed*, startling me even though I was expecting it, my belly fizzing with a combination of apprehension and excitement that very soon my question would be answered. As instructed, I accepted the call without delay.

"Well done, Angelica. Now, are you wearing something with a waist band—a skirt or pants?"

Oh fuck. Now I knew where he was going with this. "Y… yes," I stuttered.

"Excellent. Now this is very important. You cannot utter a sound, Angel. Not even the slightest moan. The privacy shade is in place, you cannot be seen. But the aluminum divider is not, so you can still be heard—do you understand?"

Oh Jesus. "Yes."

"Good. I know you have insatiable appetite, Angel, and I can hear how turned on you are. So on this occasion, being as I can't be there to fuck your sassy mouth *or* your tight little pussy, I'm going to allow you to touch yourself, and I'm going to allow you to come against your own hand. But be mindful of this: This isn't simply for your pleasure, or indeed mine—it's because you need to learn a lesson. You behaved recklessly tonight when you fled without forethought, with no regard for your safety or my sanity. You need to learn how to control your impulsive behavior, Angelica, and you're going to start now. When you touch yourself, you're instinct to moan and to audibly express your pleasure will be overwhelming—but you *will* control it. Won't you, Angel?"

Oh my fucking… God.

I was so impossibly turned on, I could barely think past my pounding sex. I forced my answer out with as much composure as I could muster. "Yes." But I sounded more confident than I felt. Could I really do this? Bring myself to climax in the car with Jackson in earshot, and without making a sound? No! Maybe? Hell, yes—damn straight I could do it.

"Are you ready?"

"Yes."

"Good, ask Jackson to play the music."

Again, I did as instructed, and the second the request left my lips, I heard the first few wonderful tinkling sounds of piano keys. I recognized the piece instantly. The Belgian choir, Scala & Kolacny Brothers, singing an exquisite, specially produced arrangement of The Police's "Every Breath You Take." The pianists fingers glided effortlessly over the keys, the angelic voices of the choir caressing each word as if it would be their last. The message was unmistakable, a hauntingly seductive tale of obsession and possession—Ethan was staking his claim.

"How very apt."

"I thought so," he breathed darkly. "Reach down beneath your waistband, Angel, and slide your hand inside your panties."

"What? No, Ethan, I ca—"

"I don't think you're in a position to defy me, Angel. Now do as you're told. I'm not having you touching yourself when you're alone. Your body belongs to me and if you're going to come, it's going to be to my voice and my instruction. I want to be the one responsible for the way you feel when that orgasm rips through your quivering little pussy. Am I making myself clear?"

"Hell yes." I wasn't sure touch was necessary anymore; his words and the sound of his voice alone were enough to detonate my building arousal.

"That's more like it. Now reach inside. Tell me when your hand slips into your panties, but don't touch yourself. Not yet."

Astonished at what I was about to do, I slunk down further into my seat, unconvinced of the effectiveness of the fabric privacy shade, and gingerly pushed my hand down past the waistband of my pants and beneath the trim of my panties.

"Yes," I breathed almost inaudibly.

"Well done. Now I want you to feel how wet you are. Move your fingertips down and stroke them over your cleft."

Oh Jesus!

My fingers brushed through my strip of pubic hair and down to my soaking, pulsing cleft. "Yes."

"Are you very wet?"

"Yes."

"Of course you are, Angel. Just as I imagined you would be. You are dripping wet because that's the way I want you to be; it's the way I made you. Now place a finger between the folds, Angel. I want you to rub your sweet, delicious juice all over yourself. Rub it into your succulent clit, baby."

One brush of my fingertip was enough to make me gasp.

"Not a sound, Angel. Not even a whimper." His tone was heavy with his own desire. "God, I can almost smell your arousal from here, almost taste you. Do it again, rub your clit."

I did. The feeling was extraordinary. With the sound of Ethan's voice in my ear, it was almost as if he were touching me himself.

"Again, Angel. Slowly… round and round. Now… slide your finger inside. In and out—let your finger fuck you, baby. Do it for me."

His raw, lascivious sex words were driving me toward insanity at a dangerous speed. My skin burned like fire all over my body as I finger fucked myself, pumping my hips against my own hand with the tiniest of movements, and in complete and utter silence. I'd never realized, until now, how difficult it was to climax without making a sound. But climax I did. I came with the sweetest of orgasms, my muscles clenching around my finger as I almost choked on the effort to suppress my frenzied cries.

I hadn't emitted a single sound, but Ethan knew it was over.

"Better, Miss Lawson?" His voice was smooth like melted caramel to soothe and ease me down from my elated high.

"Yes, Mr. Wilde. Much better," I whispered, quietly struggling to control my breathing.

The line was silent for a few seconds, and then, "I miss you."

Oh God in Heaven. My Ethan Wilde was back. His words bore into my heart, instantly appeasing the dull physical pain caused by the unrest which had formed between us. Words I'd longed to hear since he'd left for London. I blinked away the tears that sprang unbidden to my eyes and swallowed past the lump in my throat. I didn't want to cry.

"And I miss you, Ethan. More than I ever thought possible."

I heard him relax, a heavy sigh of relief seeping down the phone line. Although the physical space between us remained, our combined divulgence had assuaged the strain the emotional gap had caused.

"I'll be home as soon as I can, baby. Please be a good girl. I'm not sure my heart can withstand much more."

"I will. Goodnight, E."

"Goodnight, my Angel."

CHAPTER SEVENTEEN

A banging head and a sore palm was what I awoke to the next day, both of which were an instant and unwelcome memory trigger of last night. I rubbed at the palm of my hand, wincing as I recalled the slapping noise it had made when it came into contact with Jean-Paul's face.

And then I remembered how the pain had dulled into insignificance when I'd been talked—no coerced—into committing a sinful and debauched act in the back of the SUV while Jackson had driven me home. I winced again. I would blame the alcohol and the adrenalin surge caused by the altercation with Jean-Paul—that and my domineering, impossible to defy, boyfriend.

My head thumped again. Fortunately, I wasn't due at the gallery until lunch time, so I swallowed a couple of Advil and took another hour to recover. Later, I went down to the gym in the lobby and did thirty minutes on the treadmill, and by the time Jackson collected me to take me to the gallery, I was feeling much better.

Despite my shameful behavior last night, I was confident that Jackson hadn't noticed a thing, and when he beamed a welcoming smile, I realized how much he was becoming a comforting and familiar sight. Until yesterday, we'd really only ever exchanged pleasantries, but the events in the bar last night had rendered us almost kindred spirits. We were both somewhat reliant on the formidable Mr. Ethan Wilde for our future satisfactions and fulfillments—albeit Jackson's interests being professional, and mine exceptionally private.

We had each incurred the wrath of Ethan last night, and as a result, were both able to identify with the other. On strict instruction, he'd carried out a full-security check of my apartment before assuring me that one of his team would be outside to keep an eye on my apartment all night. I'd protested, of course, but when I told him I thought that a round-the-clock guard was a tad extreme, he'd surprised me by proclaiming that I was Mr. Wilde's top priority, and where I was concerned, there was no such thing as being over cautious. The knowledge had warmed me from the inside out.

But it was nothing compared to the heat which coursed around my body on reading the message on my phone from Ethan.

Good morning, Cinders. I hope you slept well after your evening of reckless escapades and shameless self-indulgence. I couldn't sleep all night from the incessant and obscenely indecent thoughts of your perfect, sassy mouth and what I'd like to do to it. I can't wait to be inside you x

Excitement rushed through my body, my sex clenching in response to his words and his frisky mood. I was so relieved that our usual banter had resumed in place of the distant, awkward silence which had hung between us over previous days.

I tapped out a reply:

Good morning to you, Prince Charming. I'm afraid I'm also guilty of allowing explicit imagery to infiltrate my mind. And in my libidinous fantasies—you were inside me—several astonishing, breathtaking times x

His reply came instantly:

Oh, so I'm worthy of the title now, am I? Why am I not surprised by your wayward fantasies, Miss Lawson? You're such a dirty girl. I do hope you weren't tempted to touch yourself again? x

And if I was? x

You belong to me, Angelica. I can't bear the thought of you coming at the hands of anyone else, even your own—without permission.

Oh crap. No kiss—and full and proper use of my name. That meant he was mad. I replied hastily to put him out of his misery:

Relax, Charming, I'm saving myself for you and only you x

Good answer. What happened to my title? I have to go now, got a meeting in 2. Have a good day, baby, hope the exhibition goes well. Yours, E x

The jury is still out on your worthiness of the title. I'll let you know when the verdict's in. Enjoy your day, too. Equally yours, Angel x

Ah, the perfect start to my day.

At lunch time, I rocked up to the gallery with sandwiches and coffee for Jia and me.

"Oh, you read my fucking mind, bitch," was the first thing to spill from her lips when she saw me. She was stressed and it showed.

"Hello to you too, potty mouth. You're very welcome for your lunch. Don't be silly, you don't need to thank me."

She snarled at me with a mouthful of sandwich. "I thought I just did."

"Oh yes, sorry. I forgot to translate from Jia speak."

"Are you fucking with me? Since when did you become such a

tight-ass, prissy little bitch? You need to relax, girl."

"*Me* relax? *Really*? If you get any more wired, I'm gonna have to call in the bomb squad." I laughed.

She screwed up her nose and growled.

"Anyway…" I went on undeterred. "If you want to find out what happened to me last night, you'll have to be nice to me."

"Yuck and eww. I do not want a blow by blow account of your carnal gymnastics, thank you. And besides, I thought Ethan Almighty was out of town?"

"He is, and since when are you not interested in details? Oh, it doesn't matter, listen…" I launched into the Jean-Paul saga.

"Get the fuck outta here," she gasped when I finished. "What in hell's name is wrong with that crazy-assed motherfucker. He is showing real signs, bitch. You want to stay the fuck away from him, seriously."

"I'm trying to. Hopefully, Jackson saw him off for good this time. At least the calls have stopped since Ethan threatened him last week."

"Ah, not exactly," said Jia, tilting her mouth down at one side. "I was gonna mention it, but…"

"What, Jia? What were you going to mention?"

"Well, every morning there is a least a dozen hang ups on the answering machine."

"Well that can't be him. Why would he call here? I'm not at all likely to pick up here, especially in the evening."

"Um, I don't think he's expecting you to. The message on the machine is your voice, remember? I think just hearing your silvery tone is enough to satisfy whatever sick, vile thrill he's looking for."

She screwed up her nose again, this time in disgust as though she had a nasty taste in her mouth. I certainly had. The idea was unnerving.

I shook my head. "He always seemed so… normal."

"What? Nah, I had him down as a noodle-head freak from the get-go."

"And you didn't think to tell me? Jeez, thanks."

"Well, maybe not at first, but like you'd have listened anyway. It's nothing to do with me who you chose to screw."

Where was this sudden indifference about my sex life coming from? Usually she was up for every little tidbit of information I cared to throw her way. Ethan's intimations on the subject of Jia's feelings rang in my ears. *She's in love with you, Angel.* I shook my head to dismiss the concept from my mind. I refused to even go there.

I decided to change the subject.

"Right, any last minute details to attend to?"

The doors opened at six for the exhibition. The guests were by invitation only and there was a full turn out. Samuel Carter was a talented, aspiring artist, whose first showcase was attracting widespread interest. We'd hired waitstaff to keep the champagne and canapés flowing, which subsequently did its magic and kept the credit cards flowing. The exhibit opening was proving to be a resounding success.

I mingled with the guests, many of which were collectors who inquired as to when they could expect to see my next exhibit. I told them it would be very soon and to anticipate an invitation shortly— nothing like putting yourself under pressure. I spent some time with the press, commenting on the artist and his work, and how delighted Evoke was to present his first showcase. By eight-thirty, I was beat and Jia was still in her element, so I decided to leave her to it and called Jackson.

"I'm ready, Jackson," I told him wearily.

"I'm right outside. If you wait one moment I'll come in and get you."

"Oh, you're here already. There's no need. I'll just come out."

"If you don't mind, ma'am, I'd really prefer to come and get you."

Realizing he was probably just following orders, I agreed, although I had to admit, it did feel a bit suffocating. "As you wish, Jackson."

Within seconds he was at the door. I waved to Jia, but instead of waving back, she rushed over to me and gave me a hug. Like me, Jia was not in the least bit touchy-feely, which was probably the reason we were such good friends, so the sudden outward affection was completely unexpected.

"Hey seriously, watch your six, bitch. That guy is turning out to be a real creep."

"Don't worry, I'll be fine. I've got Jackson watching it for me." I smiled, though something about her words made me shudder inside. It took a lot to rattle Jia.

"How long have you been here?" I asked Jackson when he pulled out into traffic.

"Um, awhile."

I narrowed my eyes at him suspiciously. "You never left, did you?"

The reflection of his crinkled eyes in the rearview told me he was smiling in response.

"Jeez, you must have the patience of a saint," I said bemused. "I hope Ethan—Mr. Wilde, pays you well."

He smiled again, but didn't offer anything in way of verification.

The mention of Ethan's name brought him swirling to the forefront of my mind once again, causing a flurry of butterflies deep down in my belly. I dug out my cell in the hope that I'd have a message waiting, but there was nothing, and I couldn't help the feeling of disappointment which surfaced as a result. For a split second, I wondered about sending him a message, but hastily decided against it when I realized the time in London would be almost two in the morning.

The stark awareness was disheartening and I sighed heavily. It was tricky enough attempting to conduct a relationship thousands of miles apart, but living in different time zones made it even more testing. The sooner he was home the better.

Today had been an effective distraction, and I was so tired, I decided I'd bathe and go straight to bed. I'd been snacking on canapés most of the evening and wasn't at all hungry, so I could easily skip dinner without feeling guilty that I was under-nourishing my body. Besides, it would make the day go so much faster, and would be another step closer to Ethan's return.

Jackson parked the car and insisted on riding the elevator up to my apartment with me, so he could give it a quick once-over. I told him it wasn't necessary, that he was probably tired and should just get home, but as usual, he was impervious to my protests.

As the elevator drew to a halt and the door slid open, I began to rummage through my purse for my keys. Jackson exited first and began to walk toward my door. Without warning, he suddenly halted, causing me to plough into the back of him, his right arm shooting out to pull me in close behind him.

"Wait," he said in a harsh whisper.

"What?"

His finger rose precipitously to his lips to silence me as he nodded toward my door. It was slightly ajar.

What the...?

"Stay back." Jackson's tone was stern, his single hitched brow a warning to do as I was told. This stringent side of Jackson wasn't someone who'd take any crap. With one hand, he coaxed me to the side, pushing me flat to the wall. And with the other—he reached inside his jacket and withdrew a gun.

A gun? Oh shit.

Following his command, I flattened myself against the wall, my heart hammering wildly against my ribcage. Jackson moved stealthily forward, his gun pointing out in front of him as he surveyed the door casing and lock, presumably to establish if and how it had been forced. Slowly and silently, he pushed it open and stepped inside, rapidly scanning the open area before him to assess the threat of danger.

I watched nervously, holding my breath.

Suddenly his gaze froze, seeming to settle on a focal point near the kitchen. His eyes narrowed, squinting in bewilderment as he attempted to identify and fully absorb whatever had caught his attention.

"Shit," he growled quietly, his lip kinking into a wry snarl. A layer of sweat sprang to the surface of his skin, the beads glistening on the stubble of his upper lip. An expression I couldn't fathom moved across his face, his focus diverting to survey me closely as he weighed the situation.

"What is it?" I whispered, terrified by his reaction.

"Stay there," he ordered. "Don't move."

Then suddenly he was out of sight, moving off behind and to the right of the door, heading down the hallway toward the bedrooms. The seconds that ticked by seemed like hours, fear and trepidation escalating to beyond frantic with every nerve-racking moment, my mind racing with the worst imaginable ideas of what was happening. What had Jackson seen to cause his reaction? Why was he taking so long? What if someone was still in there? Should I go in and take a look? Jackson may need my help. But what if he'd been attacked, should I flee, or face the intruder?

Too afraid to wait any longer for my mind to make a clear decision, I gulped back my fear, and with my pulse racing and heart thumping out the rhythm of a drum, I began to inch my way steadily along the wall to the open door. My mouth and throat were dry with fear of the unknown, of what was awaiting me, but the idea of waiting out here alone was somehow more terrifying.

As I reached the entrance, I took a deep breath and moved cautiously into the doorway. As Jackson had done before me, I scanned the open-plan rooms. The drawers of my dresser were open, documents strewn on the floor, but I continued to search until my gaze fell upon the thing which had riveted Jackson so completely.

A large kitchen knife stood upright on the work surface of the breakfast bar. It had been stabbed with force, point down into a wooden chopping board, its sharp, stainless steel edge glinting in the spotlights shining down from above. Inching closer, my eyes followed the length of the blade down toward the tip, and that's when I noticed something shimmering in the cold, reflective steel—a luminous, vibrant orange.

"No!" I shook my head, my voice tearing from my lungs in a blood-curdling scream. "No!"

My hands flew into my hair, grasping at handfuls and pulling, tearing it from my scalp, as I struggled to take in the pitiful, heartbreaking sight before me.

My precious Ponyo.

Speared between the wooden board and the lethal point of the knife lay my loyal, lifeless friend.

Jackson was beside me in seconds pulling my head into his shoulder to shield me from the horror and my hands from my hair to protect me from myself. I gasped, howling and sobbing into his jacket, yanking him toward me as if the physical reality of him would erase the terror and revulsion of what would undoubtedly stay in my mind forever.

"Why?" I sobbed, my body shaking with unequivocal fear and disbelief. "Why? Who would do this?"

Taking me protectively under his arm, he guided me through the apartment to my bedroom, lowering me to sit on the edge of the bed. "Miss Lawson?" Crouching down in front of me, he folded my hands into my lap.

My tears halted abruptly, my eyes losing focus as I stared ahead in shock, not seeing him, not really hearing him.

"Miss Lawson?... Angel?" he said softly, his pale gray eyes searching mine.

The casual use of my first name stirred me from my trance, and I refocused on his face, frowning as if I'd only just become aware of his presence.

When he was sure he had my attention he spoke. "I have to go and secure the door, and remove... and tidy up."

Understanding what he meant, I nodded once, and he straightened moving off toward the door.

"Jackson?" I whispered hoarsely. He turned his head, looking over his shoulder toward me. "What will you do with her?"

"What would you like to do with her?" he asked gently.

I thought for a few seconds and then said, "I'd like to bury her."

He nodded and walked out of the door.

A disordered jumble of nauseating emotions seemed to swallow me up. I felt numb, confused, shocked, and horrified all at once. So many questions filled my head. Who? Why? When? How? Why? Why…? Why?

Sadness engulfed me for the loss of my tiny, orange friend. Most people would scoff at my grief, considering her to be *just a fish*. But she was *my* little fish—*my* little friend. And there had been times when she'd been the only one I'd had. I'd loved her, and now she was gone, taken in the cruelest of ways. I could not bear to think of her last moments, and guilt that she'd been a victim of such cruel barbarity that could only be aimed at me ripped through my heart. *Why*?

Jackson had returned and was forcing a glass into my hands. It was filled with amber liquid— bourbon, I thought. Jeez where the hell had he found that?

"Drink this."

I drank it down in one gulp, the caustic burn causing me to cough and shudder.

Jackson rolled his eyes. "I meant sip it."

I shrugged. "Sorry."

"It's… She's ready. I found a small box."

"Okay." I nodded. "Then I suppose we'd better go."

He hesitated for a beat, as if choosing his words carefully. "Are you sure you don't just want to… flush?"

I glared at him in horror, my eyes accusing him as if he'd just spat in my face.

"No." He shook his head. "Stupid. Just forget I said that."

"Central Park," I murmured.

His eyes almost popped out of his head. "Wh… Seriously? Now? Is that wise?" He was looking at his watch.

"It's not even properly dark yet. And besides, I've got you. Let's go." I got up and walked toward the door, stopping abruptly at the threshold. "You go first," I urged him.

Smiling kindly, he reached up to scratch his stubbly chin. "Yes, ma'am."

CHAPTER EIGHTEEN

T he fading twilight sky shimmered in reflection on the surface of the pond as I gazed down from Gapstow Bridge. Jackson waited at the end to give me space and privacy, his eyes darting about vigilantly.

I didn't look down at her mutilated body as I slid open the box, I knew it would be too much to bear. Instead, I closed my eyes and tipped, waiting for the sound of the small splash as her delicate body plunged through the surface and sank to the bottom of the pond. The water was the only place I could be certain she would be able to breathe. I knew that there she would find the peace, the silence, and the serenity that she deserved.

Jackson and I sat across from each other in a small two-seater booth, cradling mugs of strong, hot coffee. We were tucked away in the corner of some coffee shop, some place I didn't know where—the past couple of hours had passed in a blur.

"I need to inform the boss about what's happened," he said.

"Yes, I know. But it's the middle of the night in London. There's no point in waking him. It's not as though there's anything he can do when he's thousands of miles away. Let him sleep."

Jackson raised his brows and sighed. "As you wish, Miss Lawson. But don't underestimate the power of his capabilities. Mr. Wilde's influence can withstand a lot more than three and half thousand miles, trust me."

It was my turn to crease my brow as I responded on a grimace. "I daresay."

There was no doubt in my mind of the weight Ethan carried, despite which continent he was on, but I wasn't ready for the aftermath of tonight's goings on. Besides, what I needed from Ethan right now was his strong, solid arms to hold me and soothe me. And no matter his capabilities, I knew he couldn't manage that from the other side of the ocean that separated us.

"And really, Jackson, Angel will suffice, especially tonight. Ethan— Mr. Wilde isn't around to castigate, more's the pity." I said the last part, predominantly, to myself.

For a second he seemed to consider me as though wondering if he should divulge something. "Mr. Wilde. He's not as… impassive as you think he is."

"What do you mean?" I eyed him suspiciously. What did he know that I didn't? Quite a lot, I should think. "How do you know what I'm thinking?"

A shy smile ghosted his features, making his strong, handsome face even more becoming. I'd never really studied his face before. I usually only got to glimpse his eyes through the rearview mirror. They were smiley eyes, slightly crinkled at the edges in a charming and distinguished way. He sported a buzz cut and stubbly chin, which was longer than usual, probably evidence of the long day he'd had.

"Well, I don't know, but I'm guessing you're… noticing the distance between yourself and Mr. Wilde since he's been… unobtainable." He seemed to choose his words carefully, but I knew what he meant.

"A little," I murmured, feeling equally guarded.

"Mr. Wilde has been checking on your welfare almost hourly— during waking hours, anyway. He is anything but nonchalant when it comes to your happiness and well-being."

My mouth fell open in shock. Well, well. Talk about learning something new every day. My smile expressed my appreciation. His choice to divulge what must surely be a confidence to simply boost the depleting morale of a woman in mourning was gutsy in the least.

"Thank you, Jackson. You can rely on my complete discretion, of course." He nodded his own appreciation. "You think highly of him don't you? Ethan."

"Incredibly so," he responded ebulliently. "I was on a path of self-destruction when he took me on. I'd go as far as to say he saved me. I'll be forever indebted to him. He's the smartest, most compassionate person I've ever known. If he believes in somebody, he will go out on a limb for them every time."

There was a great ardor in the way he spoke about Ethan, his proclamation that he'd "saved" him ringing true for everything I knew about Ethan, in that his benevolence and aptitude for empathy were awe-inspiring.

"And what about Alex?" It was out there before I'd had time to compute what I was saying. I was venturing into deep, murky waters, knowing all too well the danger I could encounter, but I trudged on regardless. "He obviously believes in her too; he must to bring her all the way to New York. Will he go out on a limb for her?" I couldn't keep the animosity out of my voice.

For a second he regarded me thoughtfully. "On a professional level, yes, I don't doubt. A loyal, dependable workforce is crucial to Mr. Wilde. A man in his position—with his influence—needs people he can trust. He can trust Alex, and he recognizes the value of that."

The delivery of his words felt like a reprimand. He knew he hadn't told me anything I didn't already know, but something in his expression, in his eyes, said there was something else he thought I should hear. I waited patiently while his professional and intrinsic trait to be circumspect battled with what appeared to be a deep desire to put my mind at rest.

"If it's something else that's troubling you, Miss Lawson, I happen to know that Mr. Wilde's decision to take Simon with him in my place was a decision welcomed by both Alex and Simon. Trust me, Alex isn't a threat. It's not her you need to worry about."

"What do you mean?" I asked, dumbstruck.

"When Alex agreed to come out to New York to work for Mr. Wilde, he made her a promise that she could accompany him each time he went to London so she can visit with her family. And on this occasion, it will make for a good opportunity to introduce them to Simon—her new boyfriend." A mischievous smile played at the corner of his mouth.

My mouth dropped open in shock and utter relief. "You're kidding? Does he know? Mr. Wilde, I mean. Does he know?"

He shrugged. "It's not the type of thing he would concern himself with, Miss Lawson. Mr. Wilde's relationships with his staff are very professional. He's every bit the gentleman."

My God, I'd got it completely wrong. A weight suddenly lifted from my shoulders and I visibly relaxed.

"Feel better?" he asked, smiling.

"Yes." I also felt rather foolish and somewhat embarrassed. "What did you mean before, though? When you said it wasn't Alex I needed to worry about?"

"Did I?" He shook his head, frowning. "I simply meant you've no need to worry because she isn't a threat to you."

"Oh. Well good. Thank you, again. For sharing, I mean."

Picking up his mug, he finished his coffee in one gulp, a look of unease flickering across his face. He was worried he'd said too much, I could tell. Hoping to alleviate his discomfort, I steered the conversation in another direction.

"Shouldn't we inform the police? About tonight I mean."

"No. Not at this stage. Mr. Wilde will prefer to deal with this himself, of that I'm sure. Besides, the cops won't do anything anyway." He seemed quite adamant.

"Okay, you know best. Who do you think it was, Jackson?" Tears welled in my eyes as visions of my beloved Ponyo sprang unbidden to mind.

Eyes swarming with sympathy, he shrugged. "I'll do everything possible to find out, Miss Lawson—Angel. And when I do, I promise you the bastard will pay." The sincerity and passion in his pledge was instantly comforting.

"Thank you, Jackson. I was worried you might think I was... well, being melodramatic. But she meant a lot to me."

He looked incredulous. "Somebody broke into your place and killed your fish. It's sick. I love animals—fish, birds, anything really. It's mainly people *I* don't like—you and Mr. Wilde, and maybe a couple of others excluded of course."

Appreciating the sentiment, I offered him a half smile. "You think it was him, don't you? Jean-Paul Debree."

"It's not inconceivable. We certainly can't rule him out. But if it was him, he's more stupid than I thought. After the... warning he got last night. Well, frankly, it would surprise me."

"What happened last night? Did you... did you hit him?" I had a mental picture of Jean-Paul battered and bruised in the alleyway.

The corner of his mouth twitched in amusement. "No. That wasn't necessary. Besides, he was already nursing one extremely red handprint on his face."

I cringed. As much as I now despised the man, I didn't like the thought of him being physically hurt. On the other hand, if I discovered he was responsible for Ponyo's death, I'd kill the bastard myself.

Jackson glanced at his watch. "I think you should get some rest, ma'am."

Fear surged through my body like an electric current, my hairs standing up on the back of my neck at the mere thought of walking back into my apartment. Jackson noticed it immediately.

"What is it?"

"I don't... I'm not sure I can go back there. Not yet." The idea actually made me want to throw up. And then it made me want to sob my heart out. My home, my dependable haven, my protective bubble, no longer made me feel safe. I was afraid to go home.

"Don't worry. I've no intention of taking you back there tonight. Your safety's my top priority, remember? It would be more than my job's worth to even consider it."

My tightly coiled muscles unfurled, my spine visibly relaxing, making me realize just how tense I'd been.

Jackson must have caught a glimpse of my relief. "Mr. Wilde's place it is then?"

"Yes, I think that would be best."

Ethan's apartment seemed ridiculously large and empty without him. I wandered about as if seeing it for the first time, whilst Jackson did his usual security check.

"All clear, ma'am."

Why it made me feel so uneasy to be addressed as if I were royalty, I couldn't fathom. I nodded in acknowledgement, although I still couldn't shake the disquiet I felt about being alone. I needed to grow a pair and fast. It's not like I could ask him to stay. Jackson read me accurately, once again.

"Don't worry, ma'am. I've arranged for someone to stand guard outside. And the gray buttons you'll have noticed in every room are panic buttons. They're linked directly to my apartment one floor down. I can be here in seconds."

The man was a goddamn saint. I'd wondered what those buttons were for. A second later, I heard the arrival of the elevator, and there was a gentle tap at the double doors leading from the foyer. Jackson opened it and a broad-looking man in his thirties, with a kind face, nodded toward me. I nodded back.

"This is Carl. He's part of the security team. He'll be here for the rest of the night, just out there in the foyer. You can lock the doors when I leave. Thanks, Carl."

Jackson dismissed him and he moved off out of sight. Jeez, how many men did Ethan have working for him in this capacity?

"I'll be off now, Miss Lawson. Call me if you need anything, and use the buttons for an emergency." He turned to leave.

"Jackson," I called after him.

He turned back around, patiently waiting for instruction. His tired face was slightly pinched around his eyes, and suddenly I felt an unexpected wave of affection for him. Before I could stop myself, I strode with purpose toward him, stopping just within touching distance. Then leaning forward, I pecked him chastely on the cheek. He glanced at the floor, flushing slightly.

"Thank you, Jackson. For everything. I really don't know how I would have coped without you tonight. You really are the 'The Man' aren't you?"

He smiled widely at my use of his sobriquet. "It's no problem, ma'am. Just doing my job." With that he turned and left.

In that instance I understood what Ethan had meant when he'd said Jackson was brilliant at his job and always prepared to go the extra mile. He was right. The Man was strong and reliable, an exceptionally good man to have on your side.

Desperate to scrub away the vileness of the evening, I took the quickest shower in the history of man. Still feeling incredibly jumpy and nervous, I found myself almost creeping around the apartment, like if no one actually realized I was here it would somehow keep me safer. Paranoia had clearly overwhelmed me to the point where my ability to rationalize was virtually nonexistent.

For a while I curled up on Ethan's side of the bed. It was the closest I'd been to him in almost a week, and I could still detect his wonderful, woody scent in the air, on his sheets. I missed him terribly, my heart physically aching for his touch and for the way he made me feel when I was in his arms: warm and safe and cherished. My brooding inspired a fresh wave of tears to fill and scorch my eyes, but I blinked them away rapidly before my emotions won out and swallowed me up once again.

My eyes burned with the need to sleep, but I couldn't face Ethan's bed without him; it was too much of a reminder that he wasn't there. Craving his touch, I searched for something with his scent, finally opening the drawers in his room and pulling out one of his T-shirts, inhaling deeply as I tugged it over my head. Then grabbing the duvet from the bed, I padded into the living room where I lit the magnificent fire, threw some of the huge cushions on the floor, and curled up on the rug. Although it was a reasonably warm night, the violation of my home and my psyche had left me chilled to the bone.

The mesmerizing glow of the blazing fire drew in my awareness, the dancing flames licking and curling hypnotically as they billowed up from beneath white marble shingles. The room felt cozy and comforting, and within moments my eyes, gritty from fatigue and the heat of the blaze, grew heavy with the desperate desire to sleep.

But each time I gave in and closed my eyes, the vision would flash before my eyes again—the glint of the cold, steel blade and the heartrending reflection of shimmering golden-orange. Unable to contain my grief any longer, I wept silently and irrepressibly, until sleep engulfed me and guided me toward blissful oblivion.

A noise startled me, waking me abruptly from my slumber. Holding my breath, I strained my ears to the silence trying to determine whether it had derived from a dream or reality. As I was about to settle on the former, my senses were jolted again, this time to a distinct noise coming from the direction of the main double doors leading out to the foyer and the elevator. The sound of a key turning slowly in the lock. I froze, immobilized by fear, the gray button by the kitchen island seemingly light years away for all the good it would do me now. I willed myself to move, to act, but the noisy pounding of my heart obscured my ability to even think.

I squinted at the numbers on the digital clock illuminating from the kitchen—only one-thirty. It wouldn't be Jackson, and Carl, the guy on watch, didn't have a key.

A flood of adrenaline suddenly kick-started me into gear, instinct driving me to shift my position to gain full view of the doors. With wide, terrified eyes I held my breath and watched as the handle turned and the door swung open gently. Other than the light from the fire, the great room was in darkness, but the dim light from the foyer irradiated the background, outlining the dark shape of a figure in the doorway.

Fear crawled over my scalp and down my spine, terror clutching my heart and squeezing every last drop of oxygen from my bated breath. Unable to hold it any longer, I gasped as a sharp intake of air flooded my lungs, inflating them rapidly.

The figure in the doorway turned in my direction. Although I couldn't make out anything clearly—just a dark silhouette—something about the posture of the form before me, the contours and shape, the way it moved gracefully and lithely toward me, forced me to my feet. All the panic and trepidation that had been hurtling through my body only moments before vanished, and suddenly, I was racing toward the approaching figure and hurling myself into his open arms.

"Ethan!"

"Oh, Angel, baby."

Strong powerful arms surrounded my body as he scooped me up from the floor and crushed me against him. I folded my legs around his waist and took his face in my hands, stroking his stubbly chin and running my hands through his disheveled hair, needing to verify to myself that it was him, that he was truly there and not just a figment of my fevered dreams.

His scorching blue eyes searched mine, drinking in my features as lust and need consumed him. He pulled me to him, burying his face in my hair and inhaling deeply.

"Baby, I've missed you so much. I'm so sorry I wasn't here for you," he rasped, his voice hoarse with a mixture of passion and regret.

I tried to speak, but nothing would come out, and I was afraid that if it did, I would break and crumble with emotion. There was so much to say, but our craving for one another was too great to ignore. Finally, I whispered, "Kiss me, Ethan. Just kiss me."

Our mouths found each other's, seizing hold almost vise-like, desperate and ravenous for a taste of the desire that raged through our blood. Our tongues intertwined, frolicking and lapping as we invaded each other's mouths.

Slowly, he carried me over to the heap of cushions in front of the fire, drawn by the lure of the enticing, weaving flames, his lips never leaving mine. Gently placing me on my feet, his hands on my hips, he suddenly pulled away, straightening to stare down into my hungry eyes. His hands slid deftly under the hem of my T-shirt and trailed up my sides to lift it over my head, leaving me naked and trembling with need.

Tugging off his jacket, he threw it to the floor, following it quickly with his shirt, pants, and boxer briefs, until he was stood before me unsheathed and delicious. We stared at each other for a few seconds, engrossed in the glory and splendor of each other, and then we sank to the floor, entwined and united once again.

We lay naked on the rug, cocooned by the cushions and bathed in the warmth and glow of the fire. Ethan positioned his perfectly formed physique between my legs as we kissed with an almost obsessive longing, caressing and stroking each other's heated, sensitive skin. He nibbled and sucked at my lips, my ear, my neck, trailing eager kisses along my shoulder. I could feel his impatient and taut rigidity pressed firmly against my pubis, and I pushed my pelvis up toward him in ardent anticipation.

Ethan pushed himself up, supporting his weight on his sturdy, muscular arms, and looked down at me, his breath catching against the raw thickness of his desire. His striking blue eyes were pools of pure, lustful yearning, shimmering and incandescent from the flickering flames of the fire. I reached up to trace my fingers over his perfectly sculpted cheek bones and his strong, square jaw tense with zeal and readiness.

So consumed with longing for his touch, my breathing faltered, my body shuddering as I struggled to control it. My lips parted and I took a long, slow, steadying breath, filling my lungs to prime me, to fuel me, and almost inaudibly, I whispered, "Now."

Ethan groaned and plunged into me slowly and deliberately, filling and stretching me as my body acceded to the extent of him. I cried out with the sweet pleasure charging through the depths of my aching core. He withdrew slowly only to sink back into me, harder, deeper, the taut length of his cock stroking my tender spot to awaken my darkest, deepest pleasure. Gradually, he built up a rhythm, in and out, my hips moving, unwavering and persistent to meet his every driving thrust. Staring into each other's eyes was staring into each other's souls as we watched our inner turmoil unraveling, soothed and mollified by the throes of our passion.

"My Angel," he rasped, finally finding his voice.

I nodded eagerly.

"Say it." His tone was urgent and pleading.

"Yours, Ethan. I am your Angel."

My words drove him on as he pounded into me mercilessly, arching his neck to throw his head back, and crying out with a low guttural groan of torturous pleasure. "Mine. Mine. Mine."

The raw passion in his voice sent a swirling vortex of sweet, agonizing sensation rampaging through my body, exploding into a frenzied and untamed orgasm. Ethan drove on, nurturing my ecstasy until my clenching muscles squeezed and milked him to his own release. He pumped hot and thick inside me, his body shuddering and quaking with the violent extent of his climax. Finally, he collapsed, spent and exhausted by my side.

Without pause, he pulled me toward him protectively, my back to his front, enveloping me completely in a cosseted embrace, and for the first time in almost a week I felt whole and safe. My nerves unraveled and the dull, intense ache that seemed to weigh down my chest and encumber my lungs lifted. I could breathe again. It was the last thing I remembered thinking as I suddenly felt overwhelmed by fatigue, and unable to fight it any longer, I succumbed to inescapable sleep.

Droplets of icy water spattered into my face as the bundle of iridescent golden-orange plummeted into the water. The air around me was crisp and chilly, the scent of earthy autumn leaves adrift on the breeze.

I watched as the glinting orange hue faded, sinking to the bottom of the pond and out of sight. My chest felt heavy with sorrow and despair, my eyes burning with grief and unshed tears.

Suddenly, I saw something emerging from the water, swimming up to the surface to gulp the air greedily. A tiny little girl—no larger than the fish she once was—floated to the surface. She was smiling and waving, and I held my hand out for her to take.

Out of the silence came a small voice, a soft dainty whisper.

"Ponyo. Ponyo."

Looking out into the cold expanse in front of me, an eerie mist settled, and from the midst came a figure floating above the water. As the form drew nearer, I could see it was a woman with long mahogany-brown hair cascading down over her shoulders. She was dressed in a long, flowing white dress, which somehow fused with the cloud of suspended mist making it impossible to decipher where one ended and the other began.

I looked down toward her feet to try and understand how she was progressing along the water as she didn't appear to be walking—more drifting or gliding. I gasped in surprise as I gazed at the sharp burnished hue; the only varying shade of color in the now dense and impenetrable mist. Beautiful, shiny red shoes adorned her feet, perfectly polished and pristine in their condition.

My gaze shifted to find her face, still slightly obscured by the haziness, and as I watched her emerge fully into view, I saw a face I recognized as my own. The figure looked just like me.

"Ponyo, Ponyo."

She called out to the little girl-fish who swam toward her excitedly, and when she reached her they smiled at one another with love and joy. The woman with my face suddenly turned, diving gracefully into the water, and the pair began to swim around holding hands, plunging and leaping from the water like dolphins.

They began to swim away but stopped suddenly, turning back to proffer their outstretched hands for my acquiescence.

"Come with us. You'll be safe. You can breathe here."

The yearning to join them was overwhelming. I craved the freedom and the peace, and the capacity to finally breathe.

I shook my head slowly.

"I can't come with you. It's not my time."

The woman with my face smiled and nodded. Reluctant for them to leave, I held out my arm in front of me, trying to reach out to them, to touch them. Ponyo swam toward me, nuzzling into my fingertips for the last time. And then they were gone ...

"Angel, baby. Wake up. Wake up."

Tears flowed down my face as remnants of my dream lingered in my conscious mind, hating that the grief remained even with my eyes wide open. Suddenly, I became aware of Ethan cradling me in his arms and kissing away my tears.

"Oh, Ethan, you're here. Thank God."

"I'm here baby, don't worry. It was just a dream. You're exhausted and emotional. You need to try and sleep."

Turning in his arms, I reached out to grasp his face, pulling him into a deep tender kiss. He kissed me back, slowly and gently at first, until the spark of arousal ignited between us again, and he leaned up to deepen the kiss.

"I don't want to sleep. I want you. Make love to me, Ethan."

He responded instantly, sitting and pulling me into his lap so I was kneeling astride him, his hand reaching in between my legs to spread my folds and stroke my clitoris. The gentle touch of his expert fingers elicited a moan from deep within, my sex heating with instant sodden arousal.

Ethan closed his eyes, his lips parting as he hissed through his teeth in appreciation. "So responsive, Angel. So wet for me. I love that you're always so wet for me."

I moaned again as I moved gently against his caressing fingers.

"I'm always ready for you. Just the thought of you soaks me through."

His cock swelled and twitched in response, his eyes darkening with lust. I reached down and took the magnificent, pulsing length of him in my hand, gripping him firmly at the root before sliding back up the shaft, up and over the crown. A hot burst of lubricant escaped, and I rubbed my thumb through the silkiness, spreading it around the bulging head.

"Ahh," a low, rasping groan escaped from his throat and as his excitement grew, and my grip became firmer and faster, so did the rhythm of his fingers against my clit. Suddenly, he plunged two fingers inside me, rubbing and massaging the front wall of my vagina. I moved against them, moaning with the sensual pleasure, a languorous, swelling deluge building inside me.

Suddenly, his other hand closed over mine, halting my rhythmic tempo. "Stop. I don't want to come yet."

Withdrawing his fingers, he began to circle the opening, rubbing my arousal all over my sex, then dipping his fingers back in for more and out again, rubbing, in then out, in then out. It drove me wild as the gentle friction tantalized my hypersensitive nub of nerves over and over, merciless and unremitting, urging me dangerously close to the edge.

Without warning, his fingers left me, leaving me panting and bereft and desperate for the return of his touch. I didn't have to wait for long as his strong hands closed around my hips and lifted me, slowly guiding me on to his gorgeous, bulging penis.

I cried out as he filled me again, his eyes boring into me with wicked, carnal desire as he pulled me down onto him, climbing deeper and deeper inside me. My fingers gripped his strong biceps, running up and over his shoulders to graze the outline of his scar. Throwing my head back, I arched my back, thrusting my hips to drive him deeper, writhing against him like some wild, unhinged creature.

Ethan matched my tempo, his fingers digging into the skin of my hips almost painfully, but instead of hurting, it just incited me further.

"Fuck me, Ethan."

"Oh fuck. Oh fuck. Angel."

Every single muscle tightened and clenched as our excitement mounted and the dam finally burst. We came together, hard and brutal, soaring into some sweet forgotten universe, until all was still.

We remained joined like that for what seemed like eternity: Ethan buried deep inside me, both of us slick with sweat, boneless and complete. He stroked my hair, my shoulders, my back, until our ragged breathing slowed and returned to normal. Finally, Ethan lifted me gently and withdrew.

We lay as we had before, him nuzzling gently into my neck, pinning me to him in a possessive, crushing embrace, both of us exhausted and sated from our wild and necessary love-making. This is what we'd both needed to free ourselves and each other from the overwhelming angst and stress of the last few days. The wild, frantic sex and the close intimate proximity of lovers in need of reassurance.

I moved to gaze at him with heavy-lidded eyes, my lips parting slightly with words which wouldn't form.

"Shh," Ethan whispered, brushing his fingertips over them lightly. "Sleep now, baby. Sleep."

And I did. Only this time, I fell into a deep and blissful slumber.

CHAPTER NINETEEN

Something other than the intense, bright light and delicious smell of freshly made coffee roused me from sleep the next morning. I opened my eyes, curious as to what it was, only to find Ethan staring down at me from where he stood bare-chested and bare footed. Standing with hands on hips, his fingers grazed the waistband of his low slung jeans, the only item of clothing to adorn his perfectly toned body. His hair was tousled from sleep and sex, and his sensual, smoldering gaze told me it was more of the latter he was in need of. In short, he looked fucking hot and the muscles of my sex clenched deliciously, making me instantly want him inside me again.

I observed him silently as his eyes left mine and trickled slowly down the length of my naked body, coming to rest on the sweet spot between my legs. His gaze burned into the flesh there as he studied me, searing my skin and making me ache for his touch. A ravenous tongue peeked out to wet his lips and reveal his hunger as his eyes narrowed in a predatory gleam.

Suddenly, his eyes snapped closed, as if the vision before him was too overwhelming, and I couldn't help the way my mouth curled in victory at how easily I affected him. When he opened them, our eyes locked, and I bit down on my lip in mock shyness, knowing full well that the glint in my eye would betray me, because the flame that had begun to burn deep down inside was evident in every part of my body.

His lip skewed with slight amusement as he took a deep, slow breath giving depth to his words which rasped from his throat in a low gravelly voice. "Christ, you make me so fucking hard."

My gaze flickered down to the outline of his bulging cock restrained beneath the denim of his jeans and my smirk widened into a smile.

"So I see, Mr. Wilde."

Shaking his head, he leaned forward slightly, holding out his hands to pull me to my feet. When I was upright, he tilted my chin, gazing at me through scorching, blue eyes. He pressed his lips to mine, his hands folding around to cup my behind and pull me tightly against his substantial exuberance. I flexed my hips toward the pulsing bulge, pressing my bare sex against the harsh, abrasive fabric, causing him to groan.

"Oh! You are, in fact, practically bursting at the seams," I teased.

He groaned again and released me, bending nimbly to retrieve the T-Shirt I'd abandoned the night before.

"Quick, put this on before I eat you, or fuck you to death. As much as I want to bury my cock inside you again, we really do need to talk, baby. And when did you last eat?" he added, making his way over to the kitchen.

I pulled the shirt on reluctantly and went to sit on one of the island stools, crossing my legs in an attempt to quell my unshakeable desire. As much as part of me wanted to forget about the last few days and carry on from where we left off on the morning he went to London, I knew he was right. There was a lot we needed to say.

He poured me a cup of coffee as he arched a brow expectantly. "Well?"

"Oh, um, yesterday… lunchtime, I guess."

He frowned and shook his head. "I'll fix you something. What would you like?"

"Maybe just some fruit?" I suggested tentatively, not feeling the least bit hungry.

"Wrong answer."

"And toast?" I added with gusto.

With pursed lips he held out the flat of his hand, swaying it back and forth, as though I were verging on giving him the right answer.

"I really think that's all I could manage just now." I tried for leniency.

"We'll see how it goes, then," he conceded, heading toward the refrigerator.

Nodding gratefully, I looked down to gaze into my mug of steaming, black coffee. My insides flipped over, my heart sinking with the weight of lead as the events of yesterday hit me and wretched gloom descended once more.

My perfect Ponyo. My home—my sanctuary. The warm, heartfelt sentiment I usually felt for them both had been tarnished and sullied for a long time to come, I expected.

"Jackson briefed me last night," Ethan said cautiously, noting my melancholy. "I'll find the bastard who did this, Angel," he vowed.

I looked up to meet his eyes, his expression a confused mishmash of regret and anger.

"And if I discover it was that fucker, Debree. I swear to God…"

"Jackson thinks it's unlikely after the warning he gave him."

For some inane reason, I was finding it very hard to consider that Jean-Paul could be responsible for such a vile atrocity. The optimist in me was still naively hoping it was an unfortunate case of mistaken identity—some random person with an axe to grind just got the wrong place. Sometimes I was such a gullible bitch.

"You've discussed this with Jackson?" There was an edge to his tone.

"Yes, of course. Who else did I have?"

He recoiled, looking vaguely wounded.

"Ethan, I didn't mean…"

"No, it's fine, you're right. I should have been here. If I'd been here, then none of this would have happened."

"You can't know that." I shook my head at the absurdity.

"Of course I can. If I hadn't upset you by sending you that stupid message, you wouldn't have gone to Paddy's. That dickhead wouldn't have followed you. You wouldn't have had to fend him off yourself. Jackson wouldn't have antagonized him further, and Ponyo wouldn't be…"

His words faded as he took my right hand in his, tenderly kissing the palm. "How is your hand, by the way? Jackson tells me you have a mean right hook and you're not to be messed with. Is that an accurate appraisal, Miss Lawson?"

I shrugged.

"I'm sorry about Ponyo, baby. I know she meant a lot to you."

His tone was softer now, and I felt my mettle begin to dwindle. I blinked rapidly against the advancing tears, chastising myself inwardly for being so weak. I really needed to man up and grow a pair. Snatching my hand back, I began to pick at the fruit Ethan had prepared for me.

"She was just a fish," I said bluntly.

Seeming to accept my feigned indifference as my method of coping, he didn't comment. I needed to change the subject.

"Why didn't you let me know you were coming home?"

"I wanted to surprise you." He placed a plate of toast between us and sat down opposite me.

"Angel, I've hated every second we've been apart. I know I didn't handle things well. In truth, I didn't know how to handle the separation or the distance. And the other day, when I fucked up… Well, when you wouldn't answer your phone and Jackson couldn't find you, and I knew that psycho prick was stalking you… I've never been so terrified in all my life.

"All I knew was that I needed to return to you immediately, no matter the cost. And then when we landed and I received the messages from Jackson, I knew I'd made the right decision to cut loose and fly home. I just wish I'd got here a day or two earlier."

"What do you mean cut loose? Didn't you resolve the matter in London?"

For the first time since his return, I noted the strain around his eyes, the tension in his jaw, and I was filled with shame. I'd been so consumed by my own despair that I hadn't given any thought to the strain he'd been under, whatever the cause.

"What is it, E?" I asked.

As if to oust his concerns, he blinked and shook his head. "Nothing, everything's fine now. I did what I needed to and got the hell out. I spent a lot of money putting the right people in place. Hopefully this lot will do what I fucking pay them to do. If they can't cope, then I'll offload—sell the fucking lot. I've finished with London." His tone was littered with bitterness and resentment, causing me to wonder what could possibly have caused such an inflamed response.

"I hope you didn't return prematurely, particularly if it was because of me. I don't want to come between you and your work."

"You're not," he snapped. "If anything, it's coming between us, and I won't allow it. I won't allow anything to come between us. Everything was fine until *London*."

There it was again. He seemed to exude hostility. Toward what? A city? It didn't make any sense. I took hold of his hand, squeezing it tight.

"Okay, baby. You know best. Just don't make any impetuous decisions based on what happened while you were gone. It was bad timing, is all."

"No, it's not that. I've told you before. My love affair with London was over long ago. I don't want to spend half my life travelling back and forth anymore. I've got billions tied up in property in and around that fucking city. Hotels, casinos, leisure, you name it. I'd just rather sell and invest elsewhere, cut all ties with the fucking place. It's a noose around my…" He stopped abruptly and took a breath. "I'm sorry, I'm just ranting. Ignore me."

"I certainly won't. You can rant all you like." Getting up, I walked around the island to where he perched on a stool and placed my arms around his neck. I didn't know all that much about business, but I knew enough to know you didn't close down a lucrative empire because you hated the commute. Something else was eating him. "Are you sure there's nothing else worrying you? I mean you do seem incredibly angry at the city of London. If it's made you millions, it's done its job, hasn't it?"

"Exactly. It's done its job, now it's surplus to requirements. My heart is here—literally. And it's quite difficult to do a job conscientiously when one of your major organs is on another freaking continent."

I giggled at his drollness as he pulled me toward him and settled me between his legs.

"Come to think of it, this past week has been a complete out-of-body experience for me. My body's been working its butt off in London, whilst my heart and mind have been floating ethereally around New York with you."

We both laughed and I bit down on my lip wistfully, my eyes darkening to reveal lustful thoughts.

"What are you thinking, you dirty girl?" His eyes grew misty and heavy, mirroring mine.

"That you're right, of course. I mean, having your loving heart and dirty mind here with me is just incredible—but if your sexy butt, along with the rest of your exquisite, fuckable body is in London, well—what good is that to me? One is no good without the other, right? Why the hell should London get all the best bits? Sell, baby, sell—that's what I say. Screw London, I want you all to myself."

Ethan threw his head back and laughed, the worry lines smoothing out, his eyes sparkling with amusement. "That's what I love about you."

"What's that?" I asked. "My one track, mucky little mind?"

"Well, that and the fact that you always manage to make me smile. No matter how grim and hopeless a situation, you always succeed in finding a positive."

"Mmm, well, I've had lots of practice. Some would call it denial and say it's the wrong thing to do, that the problem just festers and multiplies. But it works for me. That and simple avoidance techniques.

In my experience, continuing to try and battle an unsavory situation only makes matters worse—so why revisit? If a situation causes any amount of discomfort, render your thoughts and feelings void, and shut the damn door."

"Is that what you were doing with me whilst I was in London? Shutting me out—pushing me away?"

His tone was more serious now. A trace of a smile remained on his lips, but the playful glint in his eyes had disappeared, replaced by... what? Apprehension? Fear, possibly.

God, is that how he felt? That I'd pushed him away? *Is* that what I'd done? Yes, I supposed it was. I dropped my arms from around his neck and guiltily cut my gaze to study my hands, which I clasped in his lap in front of me. He didn't release his hold on me.

"You must think I'm very cold," I muttered shamefully. "When I saw you from the car with Alex—"

"How many times do I have to tell you, Angel? I don't see Alex in that way."

I held the palm of my hand up to halt him, knowing I needed to try to explain.

"Let me finish. When I left you at the elevator, I was distraught. I felt like someone had robbed me of my heart and replaced it with a bag of stones and cement. The thought of being apart from you for several days, along with the distance that would be between us, opened up raw emotions I never thought it was possible to feel, or even knew existed." I glanced back at the ball of fingers I held in his lap, gathering strength to somehow explain the jumbled emotions that had been jostling around my unfathomable, disordered brain for days. "And then I saw you, laughing and touching her and you *looked* like you were where you wanted to be. Your outward behavior didn't reflect the way *I* felt, and it cut me to the core. I was jealous—and I hated it. So, yes. I guess I just tried to shut it out. Shut you out."

"Oh, baby, you have no idea. You have no clue what you mean to me, do you? Physical attraction swiftly dispelled by a quick roll in the sack, and at best mere fondness, is the extent of any feelings I've ever experienced before. Anything beyond that is alien to me too. I've never encountered the depth of emotion I feel now. Never, until you. You make me feel like you're the reason I exist."

My face heated. I felt incredibly humbled by the way his deep, heartfelt words slid effortlessly from his lips. He drew me closer and tucked my hair behind my ear, one hand clasping possessively around mine.

"I knew when you saw me outside with Alex that you'd misinterpreted what you'd seen. But I also knew that any attempts on my part to persuade you otherwise would have been futile. You needed to figure that out on your own. And to be honest, I thought I'd shown you enough of myself for you to do that." He was right. His ingenuousness had been a stark contrast to my reticence. I'd been quick to judge and my findings had been unmerited. "You have to remember that the face *you* see isn't the one I reveal to everyone else. It simply wouldn't do for the President and COO of Wilde Industries to be seen in bits, because he's not going to see his girlfriend for a few days, now would it?"

His brows lifted, his eyes suddenly alight with good humor, and the remaining tightness in my chest suddenly unfurled. Any doubt I'd had about his feelings for me vanished. All the murky confusion that had been running amok in my foolish, suspicious mind finally became lucid, and I was struck with a sudden sense of relief.

"And as for Alex," Ethan went on, "I'm pretty sure she only has eyes for—"

"Simon. I know," I interrupted hastily, mindful that it was only fair I came clean with what I knew. I blinked, looking up through my lashes contritely, hoping for a smooth ride.

His brows dipped as he eyed me suspiciously. "And what do you know about Alex and Simon?"

Whoops, maybe coming clean wasn't such a good idea after all. I twirled my hair around my fingers, aiming for innocence. "Um, well, only what Jackson told me—in confidence, of course. But you're clearly already aware of it, so…"

"Aware of what, Angelica?" His eyes narrowed even further, tilting his head to the side in what I hoped was feigned mistrust.

"Um. That they're a… an item."

His mouth set in a grim line, he looked cross. "My, you and Jackson have been busy haven't you? Tell me, what other idle gossip did the two of you find the time to entertain each other with?"

Oh crap. Why did I get the idea I'd just landed Jackson in a whole heap of shit?

"Gossip?" I stuttered. "We weren't gossiping. It just came up in conversation. He was just trying to make me feel better after what happened. He didn't do anything wrong, he was sweet—"

"Sweet? Now you think Jackson is *sweet*?" The word came out slowly and deliberately. "Is there anything else I should know?"

Christ, talk about digging myself a hole. Everything I said seemed to be making things ten times worse. Just as I was wondering how the hell I was going to turn this around, I caught the briefest glimpse of amusement flickering at the edge of his mouth, almost mocking me. It hovered for only a fraction of a second and then it was gone. But it was long enough for me to realize he was playing with me. The bastard. Well, two could play at that game.

Sliding on my best poker face, I looked him firmly in the eye, took a breath, and stood back out of his embrace. "Well, actually, there is something you should know. We're both really sorry, but Jackson and I have been having an affair. I'm pregnant with his baby and we plan to run off and get married."

His eyes widened in utter shock, his face draining of all color. Oh crap.

"Jokes!" I said quickly, and when he didn't respond, "Ethan, I'm joking."

Like a rabbit caught in the headlights of a car, I stood frozen while I waited for him to catch up and realize I was messing with him. As he did, his eyes grew dark and seductively ominous, their intensity causing me to back up, moving slowly out of reach to the other side of the island.

"You... Are... A... Naughty... Naughty... Girl," he hissed each word one by one as he stood and made his way toward me with dark intent. His eyes were scorching now, ablaze with excitement and wicked determination, and as if he'd thrown a match to fuel, suddenly I too was burning with an incendiary desire.

"The things I'm going to do to you when I get my hands on you, Angelica Lawson."

My heart thrashed against my chest, my sex suddenly thumping with the effect of his words, laden with dark menacing promise.

My gaze jerked around the room, and quickly realizing there was nowhere to hide, I blurted, "You're going to have to catch me first." Squealing loudly, I turned on my heel and fled. I raced through the apartment as fast as my legs would carry me, Ethan chasing closely behind, laughing hysterically.

When I reached the bedroom, I turned to slam the door behind me, but Ethan was too strong and too quick, and within seconds had forced it open. I turned again to make my escape, but he reached out, swiftly scooping me into his arms and whirling me around before flinging me onto the bed.

I scrambled backwards to get away from him, shrieking with a peculiar mixture of panic and exhilarated pleasure. Ethan crawled up the bed toward me, a look of wild, uncontrollable lust dominating his face.

"Oh, Angelica, what have you done?" he crooned.

He pounced on me as I wriggled helplessly, breathless from the chase and the unexpected wanton desire spreading through me like a forest fire. Straddling me, his strong thighs pinned my hips to the bed, one hand clasping my wrists, securing them above my head, rendering me powerless and completely at his mercy. With the other, he gripped my chin to still me. My stretched out position caused my T-shirt to ride up, completely exposing my nakedness.

"Such a wicked, naughty girl, Angelica," he teased in a salacious and depraved tone, eyes shining bright with immoral, sinful thoughts. He shook his head, making a *tsk*ing noise. "Now, what am I to do with such a badly-behaved girl? What kind of punishment is befitting for such cruel and provocative behavior?"

Electing to prey on his forgiving nature, I batted my lashes, pouting and feigning innocence. "I didn't mean it, baby. I'm sorry, I just couldn't help myself."

"'*I didn't mean it, baby. I'm sorry, I just couldn't help myself,*'" he repeated, mocking me. "Oh, but I think you did mean it. And don't *baby* me. You don't get around me that easily, Miss Lawson."

My chosen course of action was falling on deaf ears; I needed to change my tack. Bending my legs at the knees, and digging my heels into the bed, I began to buck violently beneath him. It was a sheer waste of energy and virtually ineffective as I barely dislodged him.

"I demand to be released, Mr. Wilde," I uttered daringly, changing direction again.

"You *demand*?" He threw his head back and laughed. "You're not in a position to do any such thing, Miss Lawson." He grinned down at me wickedly, his smoldering gaze sexy as hell. Arousal spiked through my body. God how I wanted him. I tried to move my hands so I could reach up and touch him, bring him toward me.

He shook his head, tightening his grip further. "Oh no. You're not going anywhere. In fact, I can see you need further restraining." In a beat, he gripped the hem of my T-shirt, dragging it up and over my head until it just covered my arms. He gathered the material together tightly in one hand, tethering my arms above me, leaving me bound and trussed and utterly defenseless.

When he was satisfied that he was in complete control, he shuffled further down my body to my thighs, gaining a firmer grip, and glanced down at my exposed sex. Suddenly, he thrust himself against me, the harsh seam of his jeans sending a surprising jolt of excitement right through every tiny nerve ending of my body. I gasped.

Pleased with my response he smiled cunningly. The fingers on his free hand began a trail across my lower lip, down my throat and collarbone and over the swell of my right breast to graze my nipple. My eyelids grew heavy with smoldering lust as a chill chased across the skin still tingling from his touch, and instantly my nipples were hard, protruding knots of need.

Ethan grunted in appreciation and leaned forward to take my mouth, but instead of kissing me as I'd expected, he nipped my lower lip once between his teeth. The action took me by surprise and the sharp sting sent an unexpected thrill to my sex, causing my chest to rise with the sudden intake of air I grappled for. Ethan's eyes grew darker still, his nostrils flaring with excitement. His tongue slid over my lip to soothe the loitering tingle, before pulling back to focus once again on my breasts.

Gently, he circled my nipple with his fingertip and then began to roll it between his fingers and thumb. He pulled, elongating it, pinching and squeezing until the sensation was almost painful, but very definitely pleasurable. I arched my back, pressing myself into his touch, wanting—no needing more. His fingers relaxed, releasing me, then sauntered down to the dip between my heaving breasts and up to exact the same blessed, blissful torture to the other nipple. I groaned, helpless to resist the pleasure my body craved.

"Damn, you're so aware, so receptive," Ethan muttered as he shifted uncomfortably, the extent of his own response making it difficult to maintain his position. I glanced down at his throbbing bulge and arched a brow in a "you can talk" gesture.

He yanked on the fabric surrounding my shackled wrists to tighten his grip, and with a wicked smile playing at the edge of his mouth, his fingers began to wander again.

They trickled down in between my ribcage to my navel, continuing on through my strip of pubic hair and halted suddenly. I gasped as the need for his journey to continue became more urgent than my next breath, my sex pulsing and clenched, aching for his touch. With a single finger he pushed gently into my pubic mound, just above the flesh that if he touched I knew would drive me wild. I closed my eyes and groaned, an almost inaudible, desperate plea escaping from my swelling, reddening lips. I sensed Ethan's smile as the tip of his finger brushed gently over my clit as a reward for my eagerness I knew I was failing miserably to hide.

I attempted to arch into his touch, but the weight and restriction of Ethan's thighs surrounding mine, keeping my legs pinned and tightly closed, prevented me from doing so. His finger paused above my clit so close I could feel my flesh vibrating gently beneath his fingertip as it quivered madly with need. He jabbed once, my clit responding so wildly I thought I might go off with the next touch, but it didn't come, and my eyes sprang open wide in accusation as they bore into Ethan's.

"Please, Ethan, what the fuck are you doing to me?" I begged.

A slow triumphant smile sidled leisurely onto his lips, his eyes closing briefly as if to savor his victory.

"Payback," he whispered.

This was fucking payback?

My head sunk back into the pillow, my eyes closing as I groaned in sheer frustration. "This is torture, not payback."

"Surely not, Angel. Torture is a sufferance with no release in sight. I'm merely making you wait for yours, and then you can appreciate it to its fullest extent. And next time you consider being a naughty girl, you'll remember this and you'll think twice. You've been extremely badly behaved recently. You're lucky I don't insist on that spanking we talked about the other day."

"You wouldn't," I hissed, not really sure how I felt about the threat.

Ethan raised an eyebrow. "Don't test me, Angel," he warned.

His tone heated my blood anew, and for fleeting moment I wondered whether to push him, see what he would do. He reached up to tug my lower lip out from beneath my teeth and smiled knowingly. He knew exactly how he affected me. Suddenly, he shifted onto his knees, lifting the weight from my thighs and thus releasing my legs.

"Spread your legs," he ordered. I obeyed and he moved to settle in between them. "That's better." Using his thighs as support, he pushed my knees up and wide, splaying my legs to expose my sex fully for his pleasure. "Now I can see your tight little pussy properly."

He spoke almost to himself, his gaze submerged in awe as it settled in the spot at the apex of my thighs. My wildly pulsating flesh was pink and swollen with need, wide open and exposed for his personal viewing— but I didn't have a trace of inhibition. I was used to the way Ethan loved to survey me, drinking in the sight of me as if I were a splendid vista. It just made me all the hornier.

"Fuck, Angel, you're drenched. Your pussy is soaking fucking wet for me." He glanced up with hooded eyes. "For me, Angel. It's all mine. Tell me."

"It's all yours, Ethan."

With a lust-filled smile he watched as his finger circled my opening, sliding the digit over the slit and through the silky fluid that was evidence of how impossibly aroused I was. "You're a dirty, dirty girl, Angel." He flicked it over the hard nub of my clit.

"It's all because of you," I cried out loudly, thrusting my hips forward, desperate for depth and friction. I was so close.

"I want to hear you, Angel. I want to hear your pleasure. I want to hear you moan when I fuck you with my fingers," he whispered.

Then slowly he sank two fingers inside me, and I released a slow, guttural groan of gratitude, moving my hips against him to meet his thrusts. His fingers slid against my slickness, rubbing and stretching me. I groaned and moaned with the almost unbearable pleasure, grinding my hips frantically and shamelessly toward him.

"Go faster, Ethan, deeper."

"I can't hear you, Angel, louder," he whispered.

"Faster, please, Ethan," I begged.

He shook his head. "I'm not sure you deserve it, Angel."

"I do. I'm sorry. I want it. I need it."

His eyes studied my expression as he teased me, his countenance morphing into a deep, needful, hungry yearning to reflect mine. Suddenly, he halted and withdrew his fingers.

"No," I shouted, my flesh trembling in protest, desperate for the return of his touch.

With eyes burning into mine, he released my arms, dragging the scrunched up material from where it bound me. Then, kneeling up, he swiftly undid the button and fly of his jeans, pushing them down to release his bulging erection. It sprang free, impressive and eager, and as he guided it toward my entrance, he paused—his dark lustful eyes finding mine.

"Beg," he mouthed.

Panting, helpless with wanting, I muttered, "Please, Ethan. I'm begging you. Fuck me, please."

His eyes closed in ecstasy as he sunk into me. "Argh, Angel, yes. That's what I want, baby. That's what I need."

My muscles clenched around him as I folded my legs around his back, linking them at the ankles to draw him deeper. We moved in unison, frantic and wild, Ethan pumping his hips as he pounded his cock into me, over and over. As my climax hurtled through my body, I began to shudder and jerk, every muscle in my body tensing, my pussy clenching around Ethan as I dragged him, spiraling into a sheet clawing orgasm.

Ethan rolled to the side and lay next me, both of us staring at the ceiling as we regained our breath, glowing in the heart-pounding warmth of our congruent state.

"Let that be a lesson to you, you naughty girl," he smirked jubilantly.

"You bastard," I muttered against heaving breaths. "You gorgeous, wonderful bastard."

Ethan laughed and turned his head to look at me. "You drive me insane, Angel. You needed to have a taste of what it feels like."

"You don't think I already know? You've been driving me out of my own mind since the moment I met you, and yet I can't get enough. I don't think I ever will."

"Good." He sounded smug. "That's just the way I like it. Come on, let's take a shower."

Leaving me no time to protest, he jumped to his feet, pulling me with him. I followed reluctantly as he led me into the bathroom and into the enormous walk in shower, switching on the water.

The steaming hot liquid cascaded down our bodies as he tugged me against his hard body, encasing me with his strong muscular arms and kissing me gently.

"A word of advice," he said, releasing my mouth. "Don't ever josh with me like that again."

Confused, I looked up into his eyes. "What the Jackson thing? Well, you didn't believe me, surely?" I asked, stunned.

"No, not really. But even hearing the words from your mouth was too much to bear. Even the tiniest thought of you being with someone else is just…" His eyes bore pleadingly into mine. "You can't ever leave me, Angelica."

I placed my finger to his lips to hush him as his expression switched from one of playful to anxious. "Shh, I'm not going anywhere."

Looking vaguely reassured, he nodded and hugged me to him tightly. Where had this come from? Attempting to lighten the mood, I changed the subject.

"You did know about Alex and Simon, right?"

Seeming more relaxed, he smiled and taking down the bodywash from the shelf, poured some into his palm and began to lather it over my body. "Not until we were in the air on the way to London, no, I had no idea. Otherwise, I would have told you, if only to put your mind at rest. But by the time the jet had left the runway, the sexual tension in there was pretty hard to ignore.

"I retired to my room as soon as we'd taken off, and left them to it. It was painful watching them trying to keep their hands off each other." Laughing as he recalled the instance, he continued to wash my arms and back as though it were the regular thing to do. It was as if my body was simply an extension of his, and the idea thrilled me. "They don't usually work together directly, so as long as they both stay focused in their work it's all that concerns me. Good luck to them."

Jackson was right; he had no interest whatsoever. The built-up tension in my muscles unfurled some more.

"Do they know you know?" I queried as he turned me around to wash my breasts and stomach.

He shook his head. "No, and I'd prefer it stayed that way. Acknowledging their relationship may incite them to relax and cavort openly. That will lend itself to distraction, which subsequently leads to error and misjudgment, neither of which is professional or something I wish to encourage. Besides, it's quite amusing watching them trying to hide it. They're useless at it."

"That's cruel," I scolded.

Fisting his hand into my hair, he pulled me to him, kissing me passionately. "What's cruel, baby, is you blowing my mind with unbearable images of you with somebody else." His soapy hand moved down to my buttocks and began to wash around and then underneath in my most intimate areas. I felt him harden against my belly. "You really can't do that to me ever again, Angel," he breathed.

"I'm sorry, but at least we're even. If you knew about Alex and Simon you could have put me out of my misery much sooner, and I wouldn't have had to endure picturing you with somebody else every minute of every day you were gone."

His face fell, his brow furrowing with concern as if he'd only just realized the anguish I must have felt and how easily it could have been avoided. Jealousy, it appeared, was an unfamiliar and unwelcome emotion for both of us.

"You're right, and I know now that's something I'll always regret. The idea of being with Alex was so ludicrous to me, I guess I thought you'd come to the same conclusion. But I'd no right to assume that, I'm sorry."

I nodded. "The mother of all—"

"Fuck ups, I know." He finished my sentence for me.

Squirting more soap into his hands, he lathered up and turning me around so that my back was to his front, he crouched to massage it into my legs. When he reached the summit, he washed me gently between my thighs, soaping my tender flesh like it was the most natural thing in the world. I felt the familiar excitement ignite in the core of my belly and bit down on my lip to stifle a moan.

He straightened, his fingers still tucked between my folds of flesh where his touch became more intimate, more methodical, stroking, exploring. I arched my neck to the side, inviting him in and he responded by sucking and nibbling my neck and shoulder, his kisses becoming more fervent, his erection more eager as it pressed firmly into my buttocks. I groaned.

"Oh Christ!" Suddenly he was pushing me up against the shower wall. I put my hands out to steady myself and in one swift movement, he pulled my hips back, shoved my legs apart, and entered me hard.

I gasped and pushed back, accepting his thrusts willingly. He eased himself out before sinking back into me with equal fervor. Uninhibited and zealous for his release, he lunged into me several more times, mumbling my name gutturally, his fingers digging into my hips almost painfully. With one last deep thrust, he stilled and exploded, spurting a hot stream vehemently inside me. His body jerked, convulsing as the remnants of his orgasm dissipated, his desire finally sated.

As he struggled to reclaim his poise, I smiled to myself, reveling in this newfound intoxicating knowledge. This man was greedy, and I was his indulgence. Slowly and gently, he withdrew and turned me to face him, taking my face in his hands and showering me with gratified kisses.

"Oh Christ," he said again. "I feel like I'm coming apart at the seams. I fear I may have to be caged like some wild animal when I'm around you, because if I carry on like this, I swear my fucking dick is going to fall off."

We both laughed contentedly.

"I'm sure I don't need to tell you just how catastrophic that would be, Mr. Wilde."

"No, Miss Lawson, you do not. It would be the end of the world as we know it."

CHAPTER TWENTY

By the time we finally dressed it was midafternoon and we were famished. It seemed the embers of our sex-hausted, sex haze refused to fade as we basked in the afterglow of our torrid lovemaking. The need to touch and kiss was unceasing, as though the days we'd spent apart had induced a perpetual, drug-like craving, which we were desperate, but unable to satiate.

"Let's go out and eat," Ethan suggested, closing the refrigerator door. "Mrs. Hall wasn't expecting me back quite so soon, so the cupboards are bare. Besides, I need to be somewhere I can't fuck you, or I may just end up killing us both."

"I could think of worse ways to die," I said, grinning.

"Yes, so could I. But dying from too much sex is not really how I saw today panning out."

"No, me neither. We could go to Eden. I haven't seen Adam in a while, and I'd like him to meet you."

Ethan narrowed his eyes as he mulled it over, that familiar, dark, sinful glint rekindling in his eyes.

"We could… and I would love to meet Adam… but wouldn't that be sort of defeating the object?"

"What do you mean?" I asked, confused.

"Going back to the scene of the crime? The storage room? I may be tempted to reenact the encounter."

It suddenly dawned on me what he meant. The memory of that

night came flooding back with the hot intensity it deserved. But it was fragmented, almost as though the experience had been a surreal fantasy.

"God, did we really do that?" I said, putting my hands to my face and flushing.

He nodded, gazing at me intently. "Oh yes, Angel. We really did."

Desire spiked through my body, my sex literally pulsing at the mere thought of reliving that night.

"Can you feel it?" Ethan said darkly.

"Oh yes," I answered, squirming.

"We need to get out of here. Anywhere that's public."

"I agree. I'm not sure my body can endure much more for one day."

Instantly, his gaze snapped back to mine, his lips pouting in protest. "I was thinking a couple of hours rest and get back to it, Angel."

I sniggered naughtily.

Just then there was a knock at the door, startling us both. Jackson entered, immaculate in his dark suit, as always. I smiled warmly at him.

The events of the past few days had engendered a rather comradely bond between us—at least they had for me. I realized that Jackson had been doing the job he was paid to do, but I also felt that he'd had a genuine desire to watch over me. He was an inherent protector, but considering he wasn't—by his own admission—much of a people person, it made me feel quite special.

"Miss Lawson. I hope you're feeling better today."

"Yes, thank you, Jackson."

Ethan frowned, observing the exchange, and a look of irritation crossed his face. "What is it, Jackson?"

"Damon and Abby are on their way up, boss."

Ethan closed his eyes and sighed heavily. "Fine, show them in when they arrive. And, Jackson, remain on standby. Miss Lawson and I will be going out shortly."

Jackson nodded and disappeared back into the foyer. I glanced back at Ethan, whose brow still crumpled his forehead. He was pouting.

"What's wrong?" I asked, puzzled by his reaction.

"What, apart from you batting your eyelashes at the workforce?" He snapped petulantly. "I wasn't expecting Damon and Abby, that's all. I wanted to spend time with you alone."

Bridging the small gap between us, I slid my arms around his waist. "Firstly, I wasn't batting my eyelashes, I was merely being polite and grateful to a man who I'm not sure I would have gotten through yesterday without."

He had the grace to look contrite.

"And secondly, you should be happy to see your brother and sister. You don't know how lucky you are to have them."

As if realizing he'd been churlish, he smiled and kissed me on the tip of my nose. "You're right. I'm sorry and I'm sorry. I just hate sharing you with anyone in any way, whatsoever."

"You're not. I'm entirely yours, I promise."

"Good." Tilting my chin, he kissed me deeply.

Suddenly there were voices coming from the foyer, and the steady din of bickering and banter alerted us to the arrival of Damon and Abby. The door flung open and their faces beamed at us across the room. As soon as Abby saw me, she turned to Damon and stuck out her tongue.

"See," she said haughtily as she raced across the room, hurling herself at Ethan and almost knocking him off his feet.

Ethan's eyes shone with affection for his sister. "Whoa, Sis, I was only gone a few days."

"I know, but I hate it when you go to London. I always worry you'll stay and I won't see you for months."

"Well, with any luck those days are over. I won't have to go again, for a while at least," he said, releasing her.

Abby turned to me and hugged me enthusiastically, the affectionate tactility taking me by surprise. "Angel, I'm so pleased you're here. I bet Damon a new pair of Christian Louboutins for the party that you would be." She turned and sneered at Damon, who was placing what looked like bags of groceries on the kitchen island. "You're even more beautiful than I remembered. No wonder Ethan thinks he's died and gone to Heaven," she giggled.

I flushed and glanced up at Ethan, who was smiling boyishly. He walked toward Damon and they bumped fists in that affectionate, brotherly-love way that was heartwarming to see.

"Good to see you back in one piece, Bro." Damon said to Ethan and turning to me, took my hand and lightly kissed my fingers.

"It appears my sister's perceptions are indeed spot-on for the second time today. You are by far the most beautiful woman I've seen since… well, since last time I saw you."

He beamed his big, cheeky smile and pulled me toward him, lifting me off my feet and swirling me around as though we were dancing.

"Put her down," growled Ethan, reaching for my hand and tugging me toward him. "Get your own, Damon, goddamn it. You always did want what's mine." He sounded petulant again.

Abby squealed with delight, her eyes widening in excitement. "Ah, Damon, did you see that? Ethan is *so* jealous. It is *so* cute. Mom and Dad are gonna be so *excited*." She said the last word in a sing-song voice.

"Abby," Ethan warned, "I've told you, Angel is my news to tell." The conversation with Alisha sprang instantly to mind. It appeared she was right about one thing, at least. Ethan suddenly seemed frustrated. "What are you guys doing here, anyway?"

I shot him a look, as did Abby.

"Don't be rude, Ethan," she scolded.

Ethan's jaw went slack with shock at his dressing-down, and he glanced at Damon seeking sibling support. Damon just laughed. Abby wandered over to the grocery bags and began to empty them, placing what looked liked wine, Italian meats and cheeses, fruit, and crusty bread on the island.

"As it happens, we brought you some nice food, because we know you got in late last night and knew that Mrs. Hall wouldn't have had chance to feed you yet," explained Abby.

"We were just going to go out to eat," said Ethan ungraciously, but noting my expression, quickly added, "But thanks for the thought."

Abby looked disappointed, and I suddenly felt sorry for her.

"Well, we could just eat here now, Ethan. Abby's been so kind, and it would be a shame to let the food go to waste," I urged him. "Besides it would be nice for us to get to know each other better. You will both stay and eat with us, won't you?"

Abby nodded, smiling enthusiastically. "You did promise we could come over this week to meet Angel properly." She fluttered her eyes pleadingly at Ethan.

"Very well," he sighed.

Abby squealed again and continued to unpack the food. I wandered into the kitchen to get plates and glasses, and Abby and I chatted while we arranged the food. Ethan poured the wine and we all sat down casually around the island to eat.

"I hope you're both free next Saturday, I'm having a party," said Damon.

"Oh, your birthday, of course," Ethan said, looking suddenly troubled.

"What's eating your face?" Damon asked, picking up on Ethan's changing demeanor.

Ethan shot him a look and shook his head. "Later." Beaming a smile, he added, "Yes, a birthday party sounds great. We'd love to." He looked to me for confirmation and I nodded.

"And I was wondering if you fancied a spa day, Angel, so we can indulge ourselves in some high-class pampering beforehand. What do you think?" Abby asked eagerly.

My eyes lit up. I loved a spa day. "Sounds fantastic."

She clapped her hands excitedly. "Damon's parties are the best," she enthused, launching into reminiscences of bygone parties.

I watched as Ethan unwound, making casual, relaxed conversation with his brother and sister. They laughed and joked, teasing each other with playful banter, and I marveled at how at ease they were with each other. They shared so many fun memories, and together they'd created an unbreakable bond, a love which ran so deep it was practically palpable. Shameful though it was, I couldn't help the pang of unbidden envy that crept up on me from behind.

Things had always been so strained with my brothers, our relationship permanently debilitated by the elephant in the room. I'd never discussed my mom with either one of them. Aaron frequently made flippant remarks to me about the absence of his mother, usually when he was feeling particularly cruel, but Adam had always avoided the subject altogether. What they understood about her life and her death would rely on whatever my father had chosen to tell them. All I knew was that their feelings toward me were constructed and influenced solely on the events surrounding her death.

Witnessing the warmth and closeness which came so easily to Ethan and his siblings made me realize what I'd missed out on. I found myself wondering how things might have been different if my mom had lived. Her tragic and untimely death meant that not only had we grown up without her, but that we'd been deprived of experiencing the kind of rapport I saw before me. I was to blame for that, for the lack of connection between us, the absence of love and mutual respect. I'd severed the bond between us when I'd ripped their mother from their lives. And now the only thing we shared was the ice-cold blood flowing through our veins. The knowledge saddened me deeply.

Ethan grasped my hand, tearing me from my deep pensive thoughts. I'd withdrawn into myself and it hadn't gone unnoticed.

"You okay, baby?" he asked tenderly.

I nodded, but seemingly unconvinced, he tugged me from my stool and arranged himself so I was perched on the edge of his in between his legs. He curled his arms around my waist, instantly dispelling the melancholy which had enveloped me only moments before. The gentle nuzzling into my neck, the strong, snug fit of his embrace assuaged the dull, empty void my thoughts had transported me to. I relished the intimacy, the feeling of being wanted and belonging. Despite the separation and the distance we'd endured, our reunion had brought us closer than ever, and as we stared longingly into each other's eyes, for those few brief, precious moments, we were alone—just the two of us.

Abby clapped her hands together excitedly, rousing us from our silent, intimate exchange.

Damon raised a brow and sneered. "Get a room you guys, seriously." He shook his head as if he couldn't quite believe what he was seeing. I flushed with embarrassment.

"Well, we've had rather a challenging week," Ethan offered as way of explanation for our indiscretion.

"Yeah, well I can see how three and a half thousand miles could be challenging, when it's evident you can't keep your hands off each other," Damon said dryly, making us all laugh.

"I need you to help me decide which dress to buy for the party," Abby said, retrieving her cell from her pocket and scrolling through some pictures. "I've narrowed it down to three. What do you think?"

Leaning across the island toward me she began to run through the possibilities. I shifted out of Ethan's embrace to see more clearly and noticed him exchange a look with Damon. They pushed to their feet and moved off toward the door in the direction of Ethan's office. As they were about to disappear, he turned to hold up his outstretched hand indicating that he would be back in five. Nodding, I turned my attention back to Abby and her party dresses.

Ten minutes later, we'd said our goodbyes to Abby and Damon and were alone again.

"Sorry that took so long," Ethan said, slipping his arms around me again.

"No, I enjoyed it. It was good to meet up with them. They are so lovely and you all have such a fabulous relationship."

"Really?" He seemed stunned by my inference. "Yes, I suppose we do. I don't really think about it. It's the way we've always been, I guess."

I nodded. "You're lucky."

His face fell as if it suddenly dawned that I hadn't been as fortunate.

"Well, look, before they arrived we were about to go Adam's. We can still go for drinks. What do you think?"

I screwed up my face. "Oh, we don't have to."

The idea was no longer very appealing. It would be a very different encounter to the one I'd just experienced, and if I was honest, after witnessing the way Ethan was with his siblings, I suddenly felt quite embarrassed about the way I was with mine. In comparison, we were virtual strangers.

"Come on. One quick drink," Ethan assured me.

I took a breath, accepting my inescapable fate and nodded. "Okay. One quick drink."

I think, on reflection, I'd been avoiding Eden ever since the fateful encounter with my father at Claudia's wedding. Both my father and Aaron frequented Adam's restaurant, and I didn't relish the thought of running into either of them.

When the SUV pulled up outside, I got the sudden urge to run. My heart was beating a rhythm against my chest and my palms had grown uncomfortably clammy. Classic symptoms of toxic-family syndrome.

"Wait," I said, just as Ethan opened the door to get out.

As he turned in question, his gaze drifted to my lap, his brow creasing with concern. He closed the door. "Why are you wringing your hands out like a drenched rag?"

My gaze followed his direction to where I'd unconsciously begun to twist my fingers. Stilling them promptly, I repositioned them out of sight and under my thighs, my attention turning to the window while I figured out what it was I wanted to say.

"Now you're biting your lip and nibbling on the imaginary loose skin that's never there. You do both of these things when you're either anxious about something or discussing your father. Talk to me."

"Do I?" I hadn't realized. Ethan arched a speculative brow, prodding me to answer. I sighed, feeling rushed into my thoughts. "I'm just not sure this is a good idea."

"Why on Earth not?"

"What if my father's here? Or Aaron?"

"Then I'll meet them as well. Two birds with one stone—or three in this case," he stated matter-of-factly.

"Oh, Ethan, it's not like it is with your family. I wasn't planning on introducing you to either of *them*. They don't give a crap what I do with my life, much less who I'm currently dating."

"Currently?" he echoed, looking offended.

"Oh, don't look at me like that, you know what I mean." I rolled my eyes.

The thought of introducing Ethan to my dad and Aaron was stomach churning. It just wasn't up there in my top one hundred billion things I was ever likely to want to do, and suddenly being presented with the idea that I might not have much choice scared the living shit out of me.

Ethan must have seen the angst in my face and his eyes softened. "Okay, baby, if that's how you want it." He paused for a second, a snarl taking shape at the corner of his mouth. "It's probably for the best anyway. I'd only end up telling the bastards what I think of them. The way they treat you makes me sick."

"Oh, no, you can't. You wouldn't, would you? They have their reasons for the way they behave. Please, promise me you won't say anything if we ever happen to bump into them. I can't risk pushing them further away. If my father knew I'd discussed private family stuff with you, he'd be furious with me." I couldn't keep the rising panic out of my voice.

"Okay, calm down. I'll respect your wishes, but for the life of me, I can't understand why you defend them."

"They're my family, E. What choice do I have?"

I could tell from the way his nostrils flared and the way he pushed a hand through his sexy, tousled hair that he was warring with himself. Wanting to support me, but struggling with the concept of having zero control over a situation, that left to him he would handle very differently.

"Angel, by your own admission, they don't give a crap. You have me now. You don't need the scraps they toss you just to keep you in line—to maintain the good doctor's public persona. Just fuck them off."

"And what happens if one day I don't have you? What will I do then if I just *fuck them off*? I'll lose Adam as well. He'll be forbidden to see me. I won't have anyone. I know it's not much, but I'll take what I can get and just keep on hoping that one day..." I paused, the words still forming in my head.

"One day, what?"

"One day, they just might forgive me."

Frustration raged through his eyes as he glared at me. "Angel—two things," he hissed, barely containing his annoyance. "First, you will *always* have me and it wounds me deeply that you doubt it. And second—" He ran a hand through his hair again, closing his eyes briefly in an attempt to compose himself. When he opened them, he spoke more calmly. "Second, you have to stop with the guilt complex. Your mother's death was an accident. If you can't rationalize what happened in your own mind, if you can't forgive *yourself*... there is no way in hell they ever will. They will always hold you accountable, because when you defend them, you justify how they've tried and convicted you. You accept culpability. By allowing them to treat you like shit infers you feel deserving, that it's okay for them to blame you. And it's *not fucking okay*." He spat the last few words through gritted teeth.

Jeez. What he said made a lot of sense, and if I was on the outside looking in, I could picture myself giving the same advice. But I wasn't, and it was so much trickier from within. I wished it were as easy as he made it sound. I wished I could just stop caring, walk away, and never look back. But the truth was—I just didn't dare. I was afraid, and I couldn't work out why.

Reaching out, I took his hand, bringing it to my lips to graze the backs of his fingers with a light kiss. "Okay—so here it is. First, I know I have you, and I don't doubt it for a second. But counting on someone isn't something I've any experience of. I've always been alone, Ethan—it's all I know. Being happy and part of something wonderful like this is unfamiliar to me. But I feel it now. I'm learning to embrace this. I'm learning to lean on you, really, I am. But I'm afraid. And I know you say it will never happen, but no one really knows what's around the corner, and if I lean too hard and one day, for whatever reason, you're not there to catch me—it will be a fall I won't have the strength to survive." He opened his mouth to speak, but I held up my hand to urge him to let me finish.

"And second, I hear what you're saying, I swear to you I do, and everything you say is true. But you need to give me time to decide for myself how I need to work through it. I know I'm clinging on to a fairy-tale ending, and I know that sooner or later I'll have to let go, and I will. Just have a little patience with me, please. I am trying."

The worry marring his perfect features softened as he nodded and squeezed my hand. "I just see your pain and the hell they put you through, and I hate it. I've told you before—Hell is no place for an angel, especially not my Angel. You're not alone now, baby, and I'll never let you fall. I love you too much. I know it will take time for you to believe that, and I will be patient. For as long as it takes."

Cupping his face, I leaned in to plant a soft kiss on his perfectly shaped, full lips. I yearned to reciprocate, to tell him what I knew he longed to hear. To relax and really embrace the feelings that had come to engulf my heart. I realized how hurtful it must be to hear me defend the people who had spent a lifetime condemning me, when I didn't have the courage to tell the only man I've ever cared about that… that I love him, too.

Damn my fucking insecurities to hell.

I gazed at the man I loved, hoping with all my heart that my eyes would tell him everything I was afraid to utter aloud. "You really are my Prince Charming, aren't you?" I whispered against his mouth.

He sighed heavily, and although I knew I hadn't iced his world in a crunchy, sugary coating, the warmth in his smile told me he'd seen enough to wait patiently for the rest.

Reaching out, he brushed the backs of his fingers lightly over my cheek. "And you're my dear sweet Cinderella."

The tension drained from my shoulders instantly, the anxiety from moments ago lifting as blissful serenity descended to envelope me once again. Ethan curled his arms around me, binding me to him in a strong, protective embrace, and I knew I was exactly where I belonged.

He was right. Hell was no place for an angel. The shackles of a hell bound existence had been way too oppressive. They'd blighted my life for far too long. Ethan had shown me a world where I could be free from the bondage of my sins, where I could love and be loved. A world where I could finally breathe. At long last, I was bound for salvation.

He turned to meet Jackson's gaze in the rear view mirror and nodded. "Take us home, Jackson."

The End

ACKNOWLEDGEMENTS

Immersing myself in the lives of my wonderful fictitious characters has been the most surreal yet liberating time of my life, and I have enjoyed every single second. However, I could not have done it so completely without the love and support of the two most important people in my life.

To my husband—my best friend, who has been a constant source of support, my inspiration for all things saucy, and a fantastic sounding board throughout the entire writing process. The journey from The End to pushing Publish and beyond could not have been made without you and my gratitude is immeasurable.

To my daughter, who was always my reason for living and became my reason for writing. Her wonderful imagination, writing skills, and self-belief encouraged me to believe in my own abilities and to finally pick up a pen (oh, okay, open the laptop) and begin the story of Angel and Ethan. Thank you, darling. Always believe in yourself and the sky's the limit.

To Max Dobson at the Polished Pen, whose early words of praise and incredible compliment put a massive smile on my face and were exactly what I needed to boost my confidence. You do a fantastic job of polishing! Thank you.

To James Ramsey for adding a final sparkle with your proofreading skills.

To Paula Radell, your support, advice, excitement and friendship throughout have been amazing. You're my right arm, and I am blessed to know you.

To all the bloggers who offered me their support and agreed to promote, read and review my debut. You make a huge difference to the world of independent publishing. Without you it would be a far steeper climb.

To E. L. James, who inspired so many to pick up a book and enter this world of erotic romance that now so few are willing to leave. You opened up a hunger for more, and a door to people like me who are eager to feed the starving throng of romance lovers.

And finally, thank you to all the readers who buy and read my book. Ethan and Angel have been such a huge part of my life for what seems like forever. I hope they make your hearts skip beats and that you fall in love with their story enough to travel beyond *Bound for Hell*. Their journey through *Bound for Salvation* will bring tears and tantrums, surprises, sassiness and sex. The road through *Bound for Nirvana* will be tumultuous, reveal secrets and unravel lies. But in the end it will be a journey you'll be glad you took. "Love conquers all".

ABOUT THE AUTHOR

Kendra Leigh fell in love with words and reading from a very young age. She was captivated when Enid Blyton whisked her away to the magical lands at the top of the faraway tree with Moon-face and the rest of the gang. Now, of course, she has more of a fondness for chocolate, cheese, and hot men in suits - not necessarily in that order. Kendra devotes her life to her devilishly handsome partner, scandalously beautiful daughter, and cute as hell Shih-Tzu. She believes in love at first sight, and as well as writing and reading, Kendra has a passion for great movies and brilliantly-written TV. Bound For Hell is her debut novel and book one of the Bound Trilogy.

You can contact Kendra Leigh at:

Email: Kendraleighwrites@outlook.com
www.kendraleighauthor.com
www.facebook.com/KendraLeighWrites
www.goodreads.com/author/show/10904742.Kendra_Leigh
www.amazon.com/Bound-Hell-Trilogy-Book-ebook/dp/B00QXD9Z72
www.amazon.co.uk/Bound-Hell-Trilogy-Book-ebook/dp/B00QXD9Z72
www.twitter.com/KLeighBooks

To receive heads-up alerts on upcoming releases, cover reveals, teasers and giveaways, please subscribe to my newsletter at www.kendraleighauthor.com.

If you enjoyed reading **Bound for Hell**, please consider leaving a rating and a review. Read on to see what happens for Angel and Ethan with the synopsis for book two in The Bound Trilogy, **Bound for Salvation**.

Bound for Salvation
Book Two in *The Bound Trilogy*
By Kendra Leigh

* * *

Savior or betrayer? Buried secrets lead to broken hearts...

Angel Lawson has spent her life alone and running from her past. After years of avoiding intimacy, she has finally found her soul mate in Ethan Wilde. Inch by inch, he's woven his way past her defenses, folding himself around her soul like a soothing blanket. Brick by brick, he's broken down the walls she built to protect her heart. For the first time in living memory she feels cherished and protected.

On the surface, Ethan is her savior – a man who has sworn to help heal her fragile heart, and release her tortured soul from a lifetime of guilt and shame.

But what lies lurking in the shadows of Ethan's past?

Pasts smothered and left to burn become toxic secrets. Secrets powerful enough to tear even the strongest love apart.

Is Ethan really her Prince Charming, her salvation? Or will he lead her right back to the start of her journey? Alone... and bound for Hell?

Bound for Salvation
Book 2 of The Bound Trilogy, by Kendra Leigh

Relentlessly sexy. Emotionally deep. Tangled, twisted, intricately woven love story with romance and suspense. For readers 18 and over due to explicit sexual content.

Printed in Great Britain
by Amazon

The Media Guide
2001

Edited by Paul Fisher

& Steve Peak

Researched by Emma Johnson

Elizabeth Butcher, Kate Fisher, Ben Hayes, Michael Howard, Joseph Piercy

Copyright 2000 The Guardian and Steve Peak
119 Farringdon Road, London EC1R 3ER

The ninth annual edition

A catalogue record for this book is available from the British Library: ISBN 1 84115 423-7

The right of Paul Fisher and Steve Peak to be identified as joint authors of this work has been asserted by them in accordance with the Copyright, Designs and Patents Act 1988.

Publisher: Mathew Clayton

Advertisement manager: Kassandra Farrington

Picture credits

22 Marjorie Scardino, Sean Smith
23 Conrad Black, Graham Turner
40 Piers Morgan, David Sillitoe
44 Rebekah Wade, The Guardian
45 Tony Blair, Martin Argles
49 Lord Steele, Murdo Macleod
53 Eve Pollard, The Guardian
55 James Brown, David Sillitoe
57 Lord Wakeham, Graham Turner
59 Larry Lamb, Don McPhee
59 Alastair Hetherington, Don Morley
59 Charles Wintour, The Guardian
64 Tim Bowdler, Johnston Press
174 Peter Rogers, ITC
174 Stuart Prebble, Tom Jenkins

178 Greg Dyke, Martin Godwin
182 Andrew Marr, Martin Argles
182 Patricia Hodgson, Martin Godwin
187 Gordon Brown, Martin Argles
189 Elisabeth Murdoch, Guardian
190 Kelvin McKenzie, Frank Baron
192 Cliff Richards, Paul Cox
195 Andy Kershaw, BBC
199 Walking With Dinosaurs, BBC
200 Gavyn Davies, Martin Godwin
201 Marks and Gran, Martin Argles
213 Charles Allen, The Guardian
261 Sara Cox, Graham Turner
261 Zoe Ball, Gill Flett
261 Helen Boaden, Sean Smith

261 James Boyle, Martin Argles
264 Chris Evans, David Sillitoe
305 Ali G, Channel 4
305 Gary Younge, Martin Argles
321 Chris Smith, Martin Argles
321 Stephen Byers, The Guardian
323 Peter Preston, The Guardian
326 Neil Hamilton, Martin Godwin
327 Lord Archer, Garry Weaser
339 Gary Lineker, BBC
379 Paul Foot, Eamonn McCabe
393 Wapping, Simon Grosset
401 Francis Chichester, The Guardian
405 Alexandra Palace, Garry Weaser

Printed in Great Britain by Bath Press

To order the **2002 MEDIA GUIDE**, phone Jem Marketing on 0870-727 4155

How can I advertise on Ask Jeeves?

Got a question?
Just type it in at www.ask.co.uk

www.ask.co.uk

CONTENTS AT A GLANCE   FULL CONTENTS OVERPAGE

THE INTERNET
                                                        MEDIA INDEX PAGE 494
12 THE INTERNET/INTRODUCTION
18 MAINSTREAM MEDIA ON THE WEB
24 SELECTED WEBSITES

PRESS
                                                        MEDIA INDEX PAGE 494
34 PRESS EVENTS: AUGUST 1999-JULY 2000
56 NATIONAL NEWSPAPERS
64 LOCAL AND REGIONAL NEWSPAPERS
108 MAGAZINES
132 LITERARY AGENTS/BOOK PUBLISHING
139 NEWS AGENCIES
146 PICTURE AGENCIES AND LIBRARIES/CUTTINGS AGENCIES
160 PUBLICATIONS ABOUT THE PRESS
164 PRESS SUPPORT ORGANISATIONS

BROADCASTING
                                                        MEDIA INDEX PAGE 494
174 BROADCAST EVENTS: AUGUST 1999-JULY 2000
196 TELEVISION
200 BBC TELEVISION
208 INDEPENDENT TELEVISION, CHANNELS 3, 4 & 5
227 DIGITAL TELEVISION
230 SATELLITE TELEVISION
236 CABLE TELEVISION
242 LOCAL TV/TELETEXT
244 TV AND RADIO NEWS AGENCIES
248 FILM LIBRARIES
251 INDEPENDENT TV PRODUCERS
260 BBC RADIO
264 INDEPENDENT RADIO
283 DIGITAL, CABLE AND SATELLITE RADIO
287 PUBLICATIONS ABOUT BROADCASTING
294 BROADCAST SUPPORT ORGANISATIONS

CROSS MEDIA
                                                        MEDIA INDEX PAGE 494
304 ETHNIC MEDIA   **348** AD & PR, MEDIA ANALYSTS
312 REPUBLIC OF IRELAND MEDIA   **359** HOW TO COMPLAIN TO THE MEDIA
320 DEPARTMENT FOR CULTURE   **360** MEDIA TRAINING AND EDUCATION
322 FREEDOM OF INFORMATION   **378** JOURNALISM AWARDS 2000
324 LAW AND THE MEDIA   **384** MURDOCH
326 LIBEL HEADLINES   **386** NEWS LEADS FOR 2001
339 SPORT AND THE MEDIA   **390** ANNIVERSARIES FOR 2001

OUTSIDE CONTACTS
406 UK FACTS AND FIGURES   **452** HOSPITALS
408 PARLIAMENT AND POLITICS   **456** THE SEA
415 E-GOVERNMENT   **459** BUSINESSES
417 QUANGOS   **465** CHARITIES/CONSUMERS
422 LOCAL & REGIONAL GOVERNMENT   **469** EDUCATION
428 EUROPEAN UNION   **471** RELIGION/SHOPPING
431 THE LEGAL SYSTEM/PRISONS   **475** TRAVEL
437 INTERNATIONAL   **479** WOMEN
441 DISASTERS AND EMERGENCIES   **481** THE WORKERS
443 THE MILITARY/INTELLIGENCE   **483** THINK TANKS
446 POLICE/FIRE/AMBULANCE   **484** ACTION

THE INTERNET

12 INTRODUCTION
Website index **15**; Mainstream media **18-23**; Selected sites **24-28**; Searching **30**

THE PRESS

34 EVENTS: August 1999-July 2000
Nationals **34-45**; English locals **46-48**; Scottish/NI papers **49-50**; Magazines **50-55**

56 NATIONAL NEWSPAPERS
Introduction/circualtions **56-59**; National dailies **60**; National Sundays **63**

64 LOCAL NEWSPAPERS
Intro **64**; Take-overs **66**; Owners **68-74**; Top dailies **75-76**; Top evenings **76-77**;
Top weeklies **78**; Top Sundays **79**; Top frees **81** INDEX TO LOCAL LISTINGS: **82**

108 MAGAZINES
Intro **108**; Owners **110-118**; Alternative magazines **119-122**; Listings **123-131**

132 LITERARY AGENTS AND BOOK PUBLISHING
Introduction **132**; Literary agents **133-135**; Publishers **136-138**

139 NEWS, PICTURE AND CUTTINGS AGENCIES
News **139-145**; Picture agencies and libraries **146-157**; Cuttings agencies **158-159**

160 PUBLICATIONS ABOUT THE PRESS
Press magazines **160-162**; Press yearbooks **162-164**

164 PRESS SUPPORT ORGANISATIONS

UK BROADCASTING

174 EVENTS: AUGUST 1999-JULY 2000
Free-to-air TV **174-183**; Pay TV **184-189**; Radio **190-195**

196 TELEVISION
Intro and audience shares **196-197**; Top programmes **198**

200 BBC TELEVISION
BBC: defence and attack **200**; BBC overview **202**; New management structure **203**;
BBC programming and broadcasting **204-206**; BBC commercial businesses **207**

208 INDEPENDENT TELEVISION
ITC **208**; Take-overs **211-213**; News at Ten **214**; Channel 3 companies **216-223**;
Channel 4 **224**; Sianel Pedwar S4C **225**; Channel 5 **225**

227 DIGITAL TELEVISION
Introduction **227**; Main contacts **228**; Digital channels **229**

230 SATELLITE TELEVISION
Introduction **230**; Sky listings **231**; Satellite channels **232-235**

236 CABLE TELEVISION
Introduction and audience figures **236-238**; Operators **238**; Cable channels **240-241**

242 LOCAL TV/TELETEXT
Local TV **242**; Teletext **243**

244 TV AND RADIO NEWS AGENCIES/FILM LIBRARIES
TV and radio news agencies **244-246**; Film libraries **248-250**

251 INDEPENDENT TV PRODUCERS

260 BBC RADIO
Introduction and radio bands **260-261**; BBC national and local radio **262-263**

264 INDEPENDENT RADIO
Intro and listening figures **264**; Franchises/owners **266-267**; Local stations **268-282**;
Digital radio **283-284**; Cable and satellite **285-286**; Additional service licence **286**

287 PUBLICATIONS ABOUT BROADCASTING
Broadcast magazines **287-291**; Broadcast yearbooks **292-293**

294 BROADCAST SUPPORT ORGANISATIONS

CROSS MEDIA

304 ETHNIC MEDIA
Introduction **304-305**; Ethnic press **306-310**; Ethnic broadcasting **311**

312 REPUBLIC OF IRELAND MEDIA
Nationals **313**; Locals **314**; Magazines **315**; TV and radio **316-318**; Contacts **319**

320 DEPARTMENT FOR CULTURE, MEDIA AND SPORT
Introduction **320**; Media white paper **321-322**; Freedom of information **322-323**

324 LAW AND THE MEDIA
Intro **324**; Libel headlines **326**; Insurance **332**; Law firms **332-338**; Publications **338**

339 SPORT AND THE MEDIA
Intro **339**; Sport and the web **342**; Sporting organisations **343-347**

348 AD, MEDIA & PR AGENCIES, MEDIA ANALYSTS
Intro, stats and quotes **348**; Charts and contacts **348**; Mags and yearbooks **352-353**;
Ad agencies **354**; Media agencies **356**; PR agencies **357**; Media analysts **358**

359 HOW TO COMPLAIN TO THE MEDIA

360 MEDIA TRAINING AND EDUCATION
Intro/contacts **360**; Press **365**; Broadcast **371**; Media studies **373**; Recruitment **377**

378 JOURNALISM AWARDS 2000
Press awards **306-307**; Broadcast awards **380-381**; Awards listings **382-383**

384 MURDOCH 1999-2000/NEWS LEADS/ANNIVERSARIES FOR 2001
Murdoch's year **384**; Next year **386-389**; 10, 15, 20 ... years ago **390-405**

THE STATE

406 UK FACTS AND FIGURES
Environment, populations **406**; Households, marriage **407**

408 PARLIAMENTS AND POLITICS
Scotland, Wales, Northern Ireland **408**; England **409-410**; UK action politics **411**

412 DEPARTMENTS OF STATE

415 E-GOVERNMENT
Introduction and websites **415**; Government phone lines **416**

417 QUANGOS
Intro and websites **417**; UK & English quangos **418-421**; Celtic quangos **421-422**

422 LOCAL AND REGIONAL GOVERNMENT
Intro and London mayoral elections **422-423**; Websites, regionalism, contacts **424**;
English two-tier councils **425-427**; English unitaries **427**; Celtic unitaries **427-428**

428 EUROPEAN UNION
Introduction and research **428-429**; Websites and other contacts **430**

431 THE LEGAL SYSTEM/PRISONS
Law officers, appeal/supreme courts **431**; Crown courts **432**; County and Scottish
courts, law centres **433**; Legal information, professional bodies **434**; Prisons **435-436**

437 INTERNATIONAL
Embassies **437-439**; Overseas territories **439**; The colonies, international bodies **440**

DISASTERS AND EMERGENCIES

441 INTRODUCTION

443 THE MILITARY
Organisation **443**; Ministry of Defence, armed forces **444**

444 INTELLIGENCE
Introduction **444**; MI5, MI6, GCHQ **445**

446 POLICE
Introduction **446**; Contacts, English police **447**; Celtic police **448**; Other bodies **449**

450 FIRE

451 AMBULANCES

452 HOSPITALS
England **452-454**; Scotland **455**; Wales, Northern Ireland and other organisations **455**

456 THE SEA
Introduction **456**; MCA, coastguards, lifeboats **457-458**

SOCIETY

459 BUSINESSES
Introduction, Companies House **459**; Websites, libraries **460**; Main contacts **461**;
Top companies **462-464**

465 CHARITIES
Introduction, co-ordinators **465-466**; Main charities **466**

467 CONSUMER WATCHDOGS
Regulatory bodies **467**; Ombudsmen, advisory committees **468**;
Advice and pressure groups **468**

469 EDUCATION
Websites, central bodies, unions **469**; Universities **470**

471 RELIGION
Anglican, Roman Catholic, other Christian **471-472**; Other religions **472**
Other religious bodies **472**

473 SHOPPING
Introduction, online shopping **473**; Large retailers, shopping centres **474**

475 TRAVEL
Travelling online **475**;
Trains **475-476**; Boats **476-477**; Planes **477-478**; Roads **479**

479 WOMEN

481 THE WORKERS
Introduction, employers and officials, trade unions and associations **481**;
Trade unions and associations, workers' action **482**

483 THINK TANKS

484 ACTION
Website directories **484**
Animals, farming & food **484-485**
Anti-capitalism **485**
Community action and work **485-486**
Drugs and addiction **486**
Education and family **486-487**
Environment and ecology **487-488**
Ethnic groups **489**
Health **489-490**
Telephone helplines **490-491**
History **491**
Housing **491**
International and human rights **491-492**
Roads and transport **492-493**
Science **493**
Sex **493**
War and peace **493**

Buy it...
Sell it...
Read it.

campaign
MEDIA BUSINESS
THE MAGAZINE FOR THE MEDIA SALES INDUSTRY   £2   A Haymarket publication   24 January 2000

Advertisers snap up USA Today's $1m front-page ad slot

by Jonah Bloom

It's only seven-eighths of an inch high, but the strip at the bottom of *USA Today* will cost clients more than $1 million a year for a once-a-week placement.

Since national newspapers moved away from splashing ads all over page one, the front-page ad has become something of a taboo.

But *USA Today* recently decided to offer a thin strip at the bottom of its front page.

The paper's senior vice-president, advertising, Carolyn Vesper Bivens, said: "For years advertisers have said if we decided to sell the space, they'd be interested."

The strip was snapped up within hours of being offered. Marriott, General Motors, NorthWest Airlines, AT&T and online superstore Value America, all bought the slot.

"We expect to make more than $5.2 billion from the first year," said Bivens.

USA Today has a daily circulation of 2.27 million.

Mediaventures in radio deal with Clear Channel

by Rachel Minter

Clear Channel is on the verge of signing a deal with the independent sales house Mediaventures, to back the development of in-store radio stations for Britain's shopping chains.

Mediaventures will initially develop independent radio stations for the retail market, but eventually it hopes to support the stations with a range of outdoor advertising sites, such as screens outside supermarkets. The sales house will also be looking to expand into other retail sectors.

Westside Broadcast Sales, the radio sales arm of Mediaventures, already sells airtime on Asda FM, which enjoys a potential audience of ten million shoppers every week. WBS will continue to sell airtime for the new retail radio stations.

Clive Reffell, consultant to Mediaventures, said that Clear Channel's investment stake in the new venture could not be confirmed. But he said the company's involvement would "give Mediaventures the financial clout and credibility to pitch to the agencies".

Reffell admitted that, as in-store radio operates outside of Rajar audience research, agencies still need to be persuaded of its worth.

"Commercial radio listeners don't have control. We need to establish the effectiveness of in-store radio, based on quantifiable research, and convince people that this is a very different kind of advertising," he said.

"Although sales can be recorded by a barcode to ascertain the link between a sale and the radio advertisement, part of the new venture will be to provide better evidence of success."

A media agency source said: "If in-store radio is presented to the agencies as part of a scheme to reach people via radio, big screens and maybe posters before they are about to spend money, then we might be more interested."

RBI display unit lures blue chips

by Lexie Goddard

Reed Business Information is offering display advertising across its 80-plus titles via a new centralised cross-selling scheme, designed to steal blue-chip clients from national newspapers.

The publisher will also incorporate its 80 websites into the initiative. This means its new Reed Business Display team could package deals involving a mixture of hard-copy display ads and banners on sites such as *New Scientist's Planet Science*, @Computer Weekly and the IT portal Totaljobs.com.

Reed Business Display is the brainchild of Sue Shmmin, business development manager, and Chris King, director of central sales and the man behind RBI's centralised inserts unit.

The inserts unit has quadrupled its ad revenue in four years, pulling in clients such as Microsoft and Royal Bank of Scotland.

King hopes to repeat the

Shmmin, King...new unit

formula, luring heavyweight clients away from the national press and management titles by persuading them RBI's titles reach a higher number of business people.

"The nationals have a falling readership and response levels are dropping, so advertisers are looking at new markets," he said.

"If Hewlett Packard wanted to advertise a laptop colour printer, 70 per cent of our readers run small to medium-sized enterprises. A company like Giroblank could reach corner-shop owners through *Independent Retail News* and hair salon owners through *Hairdressers' Journal*.

"Clients have been ringing up each month and asking if we could do this," he added.

"The revenue is limitless. The agencies think it's a great idea, they'll get a better price, one point of contact and we'll do the planning for them."

Two clients have already signed up: Action 2000 bought double-page spreads in 12 RBI magazines, while Intel took three consecutive right-hand pages in eight titles.

King is to appoint a senior sales manager to front the display unit and wants five senior sales executives with five to six years experience of selling to London agencies and blue-chip companies.

"We're looking for intellectual types," King said. "This is not a quick sell."

Ebookers.com...the company has bought 3,200 48-sheet sites

M&A wins monster net poster contract

by Jonah Bloom

Mills & Allen has landed the contract for the biggest British outdoor ad campaign booked by a web company.

Ebookers.com, the travel company, has bought 3,200 of M&A's 48-sheet sites for the campaign, as part of a £45 million pan-European marketing drive to boost sales.

Ian Chapman, national sales group head at M&A, who negotiated the sale, said the campaign would run across Europe, through M&A's parent JCDecaux.

"It's a huge campaign, the biggest in terms of volume and value we've seen from an internet company," he said. "It's running in France and Scandinavia as well as the UK." The campaign will run throughout January.

The negotiation was done with Ebookers.com's marketing officer Glenn Trouse, a former marketing director at Grey, and its marketing manager Lucy Smallbone, formerly of DMB&B.

Chapman said he first heard about the campaign from M&A's sister company Sky Sites. "Ebookers was talking to Sky Sites, whose portfolio fits very well with the target market. When it decided to roll out a pan-European campaign, it was logical to come to us," he said.

"Ebookers is likely to expand in Europe and we will obviously hope to do more work with it."

Only a few clients, such as fashion retailer Gap, book direct with M&A, but Ebookers marketing manager Jenny Evans said the company was "delighted with the deal" and had no "short-term plans to hire a media agency."

BBC Vegetarian Good Food to close

by Colin Grimshaw

BBC Worldwide is closing its monthly *BBC Vegetarian Good Food* magazine.

The February issue, which goes on sale on 27 January, will be the last.

The publishing director Seamus Geoghegan blamed the closure on the proliferation of information on meat-free cuisine.

He said: "Recipes and other information about vegetarian food are now widely available from other sources. It is common for people to eat meat-free meals at least some of the time but not to consider themselves vegetarians."

The title was launched in

BBC Vegetarian...its last

1992 — at the height of the vogue for vegetarianism — as a quarterly spin-off to *BBC Good Food*. Its ABC peaked at 83,691 in 1995 and has since been in decline. Its most recent ABC figure for the first half of last year was 65,181.

BBC Worldwide is trying to find alternative positions for the eight editorial staff but the ad sales staff, who cross-sold the title with *BBC Good Food*, are unaffected by the closure. A departmental reshuffle before Christmas cut the dedicated sales positions on the title.

Group ad director Justine Southall said: "We had a good base of small solus advertisers but bigger fmcg brands now have as many opportunities to talk to vegetarians. Our audience was too discrete."

THIS WEEK

Lights, camera, fellatio
Janice is letting a documentary team into your office: a recipe for disaster or a guaranteed PR coup? We talk to some recent victims p8,p28

Every Dog has his day
Classic FM's new sales director Simon 'Dogs' Daglish on why his radio brand isn't just for the pipe-and-slippers brigade p15

Emap On Air's habitat
Caught between the sofa shops and the cheap hi-fis is Emap's own music centre p27

Number one for jobs in media sales
Make that move with 11 pages of appointments p18

Two titles aimed at young girls set for spring launch

by Colin Grimshaw

Two magazines aimed at girls are to hit the newsstands in the next couple of months, amid rumours that IPC is also planning to launch a title in the market.

Buzz — aimed at 7- to 12-year-olds — will launch on 30 March from Practical Publications, owned by Highbury House. It will have a print run of 60-70,000 and a settledown target of 30-40,000.

The monthly will retail for £2.10 and promises to provide "clean and decent" coverage of fashion, pop, movies, computer games and pets, with puzzles and competitions. Boybands will feature on the cover but boyfriends and sex are off the agenda.

Managing director Andrew Hall said that advertising was not a priority and only two pages of the 52-page first issue are reserved for ads.

Egmont Fleetway, publisher of *Barbie*, is recruiting staff for "Project P". The title — for 7- to 11-year-old "tween" girls — will focus on hobbies and friendship, with some celebrity coverage.

Both titles aim to be slightly older and more aspirational than the market leader, BBC Worldwide's *Girl Talk*.

IPC is said to be seeking an ad manager to sell across *J17*, *Mizz* and a launch title, which is possibly aimed at the tween market.

The internet/introduction

Thirty years ago a brief message of L and O was passed between two computers in California for the first ever transmission of digitised letters. Hello!?. All of a sudden the internet holds a billion pages, two billion, four billion? Who knows? And why bother counting paper pages when gigabytes of words and pictures scroll down brightly lit screens from here to infinity?

The mind-numbing numbers grow exponentially in an echo of the redoubled power of each new generation of chips. Weighty statistics have spurred the questions about what it could all possibly mean away from geeky jokes and towards grandiose global paradoxes. Where journalists once struggled to find puns for the word chip which did not involve fish or old blocks or shoulders, the new journalistic clichés have been recalibrated. Today's technology news stories flip-flop between knowledge and pornography, the death of the book and the birth of a new image-based visual literacy, the electronic cottage and cyber terrorism, time-poor and information-rich, or a millennium bug which never hatched and instant millionaires who can barely spell. Free trade promises jostle against stories of I-love-you viruses with the conventional media telling us we must live in fear of global sabotage and in anticipation of the world-at-our-fingertips.

Each hyphenated stab at interpretation carries the burdens and expectations of an age that must digest contrasting tales of business opportunity or stock market collapse, individual empowerment or alienation. Online and it's one-nought, positive-negative, on-off, yes-no, right-wrong, black-white. The lists yield no shades of grey when binary logic seeps into working lives where constant change and instant redundancy have been rendered into unchallenged virtue. So, is the new orthodoxy unrestrictedfilth dot com or limitlesshope dot com?

Full stops go missing and words merge as clever marketeers rattle us along futuristic tracks with typographically ambiguous titles like ondigital ONDigital Ondigital On Digital OnDigital. The new TV station's switchboard operator said she writes it as a single small-lettered word, and then added that the logo has a big O and N with the magic digital word raised up. Who knows? Dead sub-editors roll in their graves, and what they never knew is that Off Analogue will soon be the new broadcasting order. Though the date isn't firm, we can be sure the mass media will be entirely digitised in less time than that first tentative, punning Hello was modulated into digits and then demodulated back into type. Thirty years on and every published syllable begins in a word processor, is electronically typeset and then recycled online, beautifully indexed on all the media sites listed throughout this book. We've already lived through that change and now wait for the bigger shifts which will follow when every radio and TV signal is digital. The media will mutate; radios will carry pictures, television sets will transform into computers and soon the mobile telephone will converge to do everything but change the nappies on the next generation of media consumers.

A few years forward - when hysteria becomes modern history - much of the hyperbole will spell dot con. For the moment, watch any commercial TV channel or open any newspaper and there's dot com advertising goading and intimidating us into new forms of shopping, banking and media consumption. The old media is adept at grabbing new money but this is a temporary bonanza, for advertising revenue leaks away. A recent conference - NetMedia was its shovelledtogethertitle - heard that online advertising in Europe will grow from £500 million to £3 billion over the next five years and to £17 billion globally. It was only five years back that Microsoft assigned the internet as "highest priority" and, with so much having altered since then, any such projection five years hence can hardly claim accuracy. No, the significance of these finger-in-the-wind figures is that they consider the world as a whole.

So too do the media owners who double up their fortunes chanting the mantra about

AN UPLIFTING NEW EXPERIENCE IN MARKETING, MEDIA, ADVERTISING AND DESIGN

technology-driven global competitiveness. If they entirely believe their rhetoric of inevitable digitised change, they are displaying signs of chronocentricity - the disease of conceit that one's own generation is poised uniquely on the cusp of history. We are on a continuum rather than at a cross roads and a revisionary historic dash might defuse the hype. Global competitiveness brought the bomb and, a decade before that, pre-war British education peddled the statistics of global imperialism. Our forebears imbibed propaganda of an empire built on the eighteenth century technology of accurate clocks used to determine longitude, the development that allowed an island nation to navigate its way to global domination. Later, the electronic telegraph bridged time and opened a way for fresh waves of telephone and information technology that eventually globalised finance and commerce.

In our own era and our own trade, Rupert Murdoch has had the visionary gleam and the entrepreneurial bottle to exploit technology and create the perfectly named News International empire. In straddling media categories and national borders, News International has rewritten parliamentary ownership legislation and rivals the power of many nation states. Yet now Murdoch must invest more millions into the web in an attempt to play catch-up with the likes of Time Warner and AOL. The biggest corporate marriage of all (Time Warner-AOL's market capitalisation is $235 billion against the BBC's annual £2.8 billion income) has united a content provider and content carrier to affect global media consumption and, once again, to shift - though not utterly alter - the commercial and political backdrop.

The bit of media churn closest to our interests is that Fourth Estate, the Media Guide's old publisher which was 42 per cent by the Guardian Media Group, has been sold to Murdoch's HarperCollins, or, in the commercially correct space-free manner, HarperCollins. Fourth Estate's founder, who remains as an employee of the new agglomeration, spells out the orthodoxy of sale. "Publishing is fast becoming a global enterprise," Victoria Barnsley says. "While the electronic revolution offers enormous opportunities for publishing, these developments can only be exploited world-wide." Globalisation's merging effects ripple through the UK corner of the global village with more changes to this Media Guide's listings than in any of the preceding eight annual editions. The standard-issue rhetoric justifying an annual publication like this gains more substance than usual and, as in every other bit of the old media, change is assimilated with an eye fixed toward an online future.

Every last section of the media must acknowledge the influence of the web and as we go to press we are only secure in the knowledge our browsable address book will slither out of date before the ink dries. It's a certainty there will be more web sites. Meanwhile more local paper groups might have merged, IPC's magazines might have been subsumed in Telewest's cable interests and the homogenisation of ITV will have moved forward.

The most significant recent British newspaper news item was the Hollinger Group's April 2000 announcement that the Telegraph is looking for partners in television, cable or telecommunications. Conrad Black's reasoning is the same as Victoria Barnsley, for he said the Telegraph needs to "unlock shareholder value" by following "the current trend to larger, consolidated multi-media entities". While not exactly erecting a For Sale notice, the Telegraph has formally admitted print is not enough. Whichever multimedia conglomerate eventually tucks in with the Telegraph, it will be a Time Warner-AOL deal written small and following exactly the same market logic that has had the newly christened 'content providers' bedding down with the cable, the telephone and the net businesses.

Global competitiveness is the main reason for a communications white paper which, in the autumn of 2000, prepares the way for legislation that wasn't even anticipated in Labour's 1997 election manifesto. Whereas the 1996 Broadcasting Act came from a single heritage department, the media's political importance is such that the next bill will be a converged effort assembled by the Culture Department in tandem with the Department of Trade. The government is answering a corporate clamour for an abandonment of ownership restrictions in the face of converging technologies. Once again, this is not as new as it sounds. The forces of convergence heard (and largely ignored) the arguments against cross-media ownership in 1991 when the Department of Trade commissioned an enquiry from John Sadler QC. He recommended the government "ensures the distinctions of advertisements from editorial copy [with] disclosure in advertisements of ownership links [and] disclosure in editorial content of newspapers of their owners' or associates' other media interests".

Sadler's reasonable proposition now has the ring of an outmoded peep from the liberal left. However, it's an easily acknowledged principle that too great a concentration of media ownership augers badly for independent news gathering. Listen to Michael Eisner, who led Disney's take-over of ABC TV in the US in the mid-nineties. "I would prefer ABC not to cover Disney," he ruled. "By and large, the way to avoid conflict of interests is to, as best you can, not to cover yourself." And that's the principled stand, disregarded by the cross-corporate puffery that has had Rupert Murdoch's Times and Sun denigrating the BBC with the purpose of boosting Rupert Murdoch's Sky.

The original intention of this introduction was merely to explain why the internet section has been brought to the front of the book. The Media Guide's first internet section was on page 216 of the 1997 edition and, though given a minor billing, that too carried an apocalyptic global tinge. It began: "Internet proponents claim that here is a medium which is as revolutionary as the invention of printing. They say that by enabling everybody with a computer, modem and phone line to publish to a global audience the Internet [it had a capital letter when the sentence was keyed in during 1996] is doing no less than alter media power balances. Disintermediation is the clumsy word for what happens in a publishing realm where there are

no controllers of information and where freedom of the press does not depend on owning a printing press." Since then the web's largest volume sites have moved into the hands of conglomerates. The name of the game has been appropriation rather than disintermediation and the changes have been swift. Every piece of the media has moved into the web to the extent that no media contact address is complete without a www dot appendage at the end of it. We're all internet proponents now.

Every media organisation in here which has a web site has that site listed under its entry and - paper being expensive - there's no point repeating those listings here. Instead this first section looks at what the mainstream media has been up to on the web and then lists useful sites which haven't been swept into one of the existing media categories. Likewise, the Outside Contacts section which begins on page 406 is peppered with web sites and netheads should go to:

SPORT SITES	**342**
POLITICS	**411**
E-GOVERMENT SITES	**415**
LOCAL GOVERNMENT	**424**
EUROPEAN UNION SITES	**430**
THE LAW	**434**
POLICE	**447**
EDUCATION	**469**
SHOPPING	**473**
TRAVEL	**475**
ACTION	**483-493**

The 1997 Media Guide began with a declaration that "If it's in the media, it's in the Media Guide". That slogan still stands, as does the invitation that if you find the book misses something out, please say. The email address is:

media.guide@guardian.co.uk

Otherwise write to:

The Media Guide 2002
The Guardian, 119 Farringdon Road, London EC1R 3ER

Register: www.mediatrader.co.uk

phone: 020 7439 7575

email: information@mediatrader.co.uk

MEDIATRADER
www.mediatrader.co.uk

The No.1 Platform for Media
Ideas, Opportunities and
Communication between
Buyers and Sellers
for all Media

Press

Outdoor

Ambient

Television

New Media

Digital

Radio

Cinema

What the mainstream media has done on the web

The Guardian

The Guardian was one of the first newspapers to produce a separate computer supplement with the launch of Computer Guardian in 1985. A decade later the newspaper went online, initially experimenting with the new medium and later developing a strategy to create a network of destination special-interest sites. Guardian Unlimited was born in January 1999 in close cooperation with the paper, providing a network of sites covering news, film, football, cricket, work and jobs. Later came Unlimited sites on education, books, shopping and money. The network was conceived as a way of migrating the Guardian's core audience to the net, attracting like-minded readers from other newspapers and stimulating new commercial opportunities (particularly as the web threatens the newspaper's reliance on classified job ads).

The contents of the morning paper make up only a small part of what is on a website but there is a close relationship with print-oriented staff, who contribute web-only comment, audio pieces and background coverage. Traffic on the network has more than doubled since the early days, and is now almost 17 million monthly page views, with more than a million unique users on the news site. Guardian Unlimited won five awards in 2000: online news service of the year in the British Press Awards; best use of new media by media owner in the Revolution Awards; best design of a newspaper online service in the US EPpy awards; and New Media Age awards for best media consumer site, and sponsorship and brand awareness.

The jobs site is at the heart of the commercial strategy, with banner ads, sponsorship and e-commerce as sources of revenue. The classified-ad strengths of the paper - the jobs-heavy media section, for instance - are a focus for future development: a media site goes live as this book goes to press. The Observer's former business editor Emily Bell heads a dozen journalists producing mediaguardian.co.uk, a business-to-business site which will remain closely integrated with the main paper.

www.guardianunlimited.co.uk/

News

The Guardian newspaper's main news website has the internet newspaper edition and gives breaking news, web-exclusive comment from Guardian writers, an archive and subject-specific reports. Listen to audio news, follow interactive graphics and interact with public figures - and other users - on the talk boards.

Jobs

Browse vacancies by job sector, or use the Career Manager to find suitable vacancies. There are listings of recruitment consultancies, employer profiles and course details. Also workunlimited.co.uk with jokes, interactive quizzes and psychometric tests, plus help with our guides to skills

Film

Breaking news, trailers, analysis, venues and the chance to give your own opinion in the Reader Reviews.

Books

This puts a web sensibility to Guardian and Observer literary content and has online essays from the London Review of Books, literary games and author profiles.

Football

Subscribe to the Fiver - a free tea-time e-mail service - and share your expertise on the site's talk boards. Coverage of news, stats for every club in the country and "more laughs than a night out with Stan Collymore".

Cricket

Run in conjunction with Wisden, the site combines cricket reporting, fixtures and results with opinion and talkboards to let you put your own spin on the game.

Money

A guide to personal finance with data tables to compare remortgage deals, find the best credit card or calculate the cost of moving home.

Education

Browse for jobs, search the education archive and share concerns with other site users on the talkboards. Also try www.Learn.co.uk, a joint venture between Guardian Media Group and Educational Interactive Solutions.

Shopping

Aimed at "anyone who's bought anything on the internet or contemplated doing so". Its directory of retailers offers objective advice, guidelines for online shoppers and a comparison-shopping engine.

Guardian Century

Go to www.guardiancentury.co.uk for an extended version of the millennium book. Read Guardian coverage from the year you were born.

AOL-Time Warner

Old and new media fused in a $350 billion deal when the America Online internet service provider (20 million customers) merged with Time Warner (CNN and 1 billion viewers/TV production/Time magazine plus over 30 more titles with 120 million readers/Warner Bros films). The world's biggest ever merger formed the world's third largest company behind Microsoft and General Electric. A week later the new monster swallowed EMI.

FIVE QUOTES ABOUT TIME WARNER-AOL

Steve Case, AOL founder: "This is an historic moment in which the new media has truly come of age. By joining forces with Time Warner, we will fundamentally change the way people get information, communicate with others, buy products and are entertained."

Gerald Levin, Time Warner chairman: "The digital revolution has already begun to create unprecedented and instantaneous access to every form of media and to unleash immense possibilities for economic growth, human understanding and creative expression. AOL-Time Warner will lead this transformation."

Guardian leader: "The merger of Time Warner with EMI barely a week after the former had been swallowed by AOL reflects the awesome speed of corporate realignments to meet the challenge of the web ... Multinationals appear to be the ones being empowered by the internet. They are busily buying each other up to become big enough in global terms to dominate the commerce of the internet."

George Monbiot: "The Time Warner-AOL consolidation could mark the beginning of the end not only of the residual freedoms of a consolidating press, but also of a brief but glorious flowering of internet democracy."

Granville Williams, Campaign for Press and Broadcasting Freedom: "All the recent mega-mergers ... are about ensuring market dominance. Consumers are told these deals will benefit them, but the consequences are programming shaped by commercial considerations, with a dire impact on journalism."

Barclay Brothers

The Barclay twins' Press Holdings invested £6 million in The New Media Group, a subsidiary which takes copy from Press Holdings' stable of Scottish titles and from Sunday Business. The brothers' editorial chief, Andrew Neil, explained the separate status of the company saying: "I believe that for e-commerce publishing, it has to be an entirely different company, not held back by the attitudes of what we call the legacy companies. It needs a new culture and different attitudes."

BBC

Bob Eggington, project director of BBC Online, spelled out the corporation's future when he said: "Within five years, more people will receive BBC programming via the internet than through television or radio." Eggington's role is leading 100 online journalists at Television Centre. Recent web milestones at the Beeb include: ads mooted for BBC Online; the Freebeeb.net internet access service; a sports web site launched to coincide with Euro 2000; expansion of the commercial Beeb.com, a site where viewers turn into users and where there is the associated business-babble of "leveraging the BBC's brand name to reassure customers they can buy safely through our websites". In January 2000 the BBC relaunched its defunct Listener magazine as an online revival nine years after its print demise. "The BBC had a wonderful brand in the Listener," Eggington said. "We expect magazine type publications to be a big thing in the UK in the next 12 months." In June, flushed with the success of News Online which got 89 million hits in May, the BBC launched a sports site with a staff of 70, including 45 journalists.

Capital Radio

At the end of 1999, Capital unveiled a £5.5 million plan to create Britain's top music web site. "It will be intelligent," the chief exec David Mansfield promised. "The site will be capable of understanding what types of music each user likes and invite them to listen to new music they are most likely to enjoy."

very good jobs

change is good   revolver.com

Channel 4

In a business-oriented digital version of Chris Tarrant's millionaire show, Channel 4 launched a site which declared: "Have you got a fantastic idea for a web site? Well, we've got £2 million to invest. We want you to tell us about it ... just click on the button below." In May 2000 C4 carried a webcast of sex scenes censored from a FilmFour production called The Idiots. "We believe the FilmFour audience is intelligent enough to make choices about what they watch," a C4 spokesman explained. "We disagree with the discrepancies that exist between what can be broadcast on television and seen on video and believe viewers should be allowed to make their own choices."

The Daily Mail and General Trust

DMGT announced a £20 million web investment with the promise the company would be as significant in new media as it is in the old. DMGT executives insisted the internet does not spell the death of the national press but said that the move of classified ads is a threat to regional papers.

Emap

In March 2000 Emap announced plans to spend £250 million on internet sites built around its 150 magazines. Its share price fell and a month later rumours - all of them denied - circulated about a possible £4 billion take-over of Emap by either Freeserve or Yahoo. The web navigation companies' interest in conventional media intensified when hi-tech shares lost a quarter of their value in Spring 2000. In May Emap announced a joint venture with Channel 4 to build a site combining the editorial contents produced by both companies concentrating on youth brands including Dawson's Creek, Hollyoaks, Smash Hits, Match and J17.

Ginger Media

An old term got a new global spin when Ginger Media Group and Ericson revealed plans for a UMTS (universal mobile telecommunication system) to transmit radio into mobile phones over the internet. Ginger shared its marketing vision of a technology allowing its Virgin Radio

station to be heard anywhere on the planet and a spokesman anticipated "third generation mobile phone networks which will transform the landscape of the radio industry and provide the stimulus for global consolidation into entertainment groups".

Granada

In April 2000 Granada announced the summer launch of full web access via the television with viewers entering the site via the G-Wizz home page on Granada, Tyne Tees and London Weekend. Access is subscription-free, with the pay back being a questionnaire about users' monthly spending habits. "This plays to the government agenda of getting over the e-divide," said Steve Morrison, Granada's chief executive. "Up to now, home internet access has been restricted to those who own computers and an estimated 70 per cent of UK homes are not yet online. We are offering anyone who has a TV and a phone the opportunity to get online."

The Guardian

See page 18

ITV

The Channel 3 companies have been slow off the Internet blocks. In June Carlton's chairman Jonathan Green said he expected ITV's website would gain strength through closer relationships between Channel 3 and digital TV interests. On Digital - which is jointly owned by Carlton and Granada - must have been somewhere in his mind. Further to the fore would have been the proposed merger of either Carlton or Granada with UN&M. "We believe in the consolidation of ITV," he said. "This is something that is going to help our industry." And - Green hopes - the future of ITV.com.

Johnston Press

The Newspaper Society revealed that 85 per cent of local papers are online and Johnston Press announced £10 million worth of new media plans. The local paper publisher intends expanding some 50 existing local web sites, extending free local internet service provision to entering new partnerships.

MARJORIE SCARDINO, PEARSON
"The internet is our business. It is what we have been doing with all our businesses. We have got what it takes to succeed in this business. We have some very strong brands, market scale, rich content and international reach. In five years 77 million students - 37 million of them in the US - will be connected to the internet at home."

News Corp

Rupert Murdoch: "Big will not beat small any more. It will be the fast beating the slow." In March 2000 News Corp announced a big £500 million European internet start-up strategy - with half the money to be spent in the UK. News Corp will split the investment with Softbank and Vivendi and channel funds through E*partners, a web division run by the former head of BSkyB, Mark Booth. "This offering is not just about capital," Booth said. "It is about a unique blend of experience, capital and assets. We offer unrivalled speed to a global market and we're very comfortable about what we can bring to the entrepreneur. This is like Christmas for British entrepreneurs." March 2000 also saw News International selling bun.com (the Sun's web site) to World Online for an undisclosed sum.

Pearson

In January 2000 Pearson raised £250 million to boost what the chief executive Marjorie Scardino called "our network of international business, investor and personal finance web sites". An early venture was a joint one with CBS for a European business news service aimed at the private investor.

Press Gazette

The Press Gazette launched its web site in March with a webcast of the British Press Awards. The Press Gazette editor Philippa Kennedy said: "Press Gazette Online offers a brilliant method of catering for the needs of new and existing readers. We expect it to become the industry's portal; a place to go not just for industry news but for ideas, contacts and interaction with other journalists."

Reed Elsevier

Christmas 1999 the magazine publishing group pledged £200 million investment in a bid to catch up with web schemes being mounted by every conceivable rival. A media analyst said Reed was "doing exactly what the market had hoped for". Three months later Reed said the internet investment would, in fact, be £750 million and its share price fell by 10 per cent.

Reuters

In February 2000 Reuters announced a £500 million plan to move its information business online. Peter Job, the chief executive, said: "You might almost say that the internet was invented for Reuters - it loves short expositions of things written clearly for the screen. The internet is changing the landscape of Reuters' potential customer base. We are no longer about hundreds of thousands of potential customers but tens of millions. The internet enables us to target individual retail investors which previously would have been uneconomical."

Scottish Media Group

In February 2000 SMG announced a £10 million internet investment programme to boost its Scottish interests and develop virginradio.com. Web launches were promised for the Autumn though shareholders were warned not to expect profits for at least five years. The SMG chief exec Andrew Flanagan said: "New internet companies are spending 70 to 80 per cent of their money on marketing. We have this enormous marketing clout."

Telegraph

At the end of April 2000 there was another step toward media convergence when Conrad Black - owner of Britain's biggest selling broadsheet - said his Hollinger Group needed to heed "the current trend to larger, consolidated multi-media entities". The financial-speak signalled the Telegraph's intention to strike a Time Warner-AOL style deal and find a buyer or merger partner to push the print dominated group into the merging arenas of the net and TV. The Electronic Telegraph - the UK's first online version of a national paper - celebrated its fifth birthday claiming a monthly readership of 75,000 for its 16 million pages.

Trinity Mirror

In Autumn 1999 Trinity Mirror launched www.wharf.co.uk as a web version of The Wharf weekly paper for Canary Wharf. Come the millennium, the company succumbed to the Spring 2000 internet fever with a three year plan to spend £150 million on national and local web sites on the back of its service provider ic24. It promised another 16 regional portals in the hope that most of the revenues will be from advertising. The share price fell.

United News and Media

In February 2000 UN&M announced a £270 million expenditure on a new media division to include LineOne which UN&M runs in tandem with British Telecom. "Our ambition is to be a major online player," said the UN&M boss Lord Hollick. Meanwhile his American CMP online media company was on target for a summer 2000 flotation.

Wall Street Journal

In February 2000 The Wall Street Journal went head to head with the FT and sought online business traffic by investing £36 million in a European online edition. Dow Jones (the owner of the Journal) plumped for a subscription service arguing this would protect the newspaper from being devalued by association with a free service.

CONRAD BLACK, TELEGRAPH

"AOL chief executive officer Steve Case told me the newspaper industry was 'somewhere between beleaguered and dying'. The high priests of the internet have been predicting the death of the newspaper, often with the affected indifference of the technological Darwinian. Anyone of consent age in a civilised place would have to be brain dead not to recognise the internet's power. Newspaper proprietors who fail to bridge the culture with internet developers and users are doomed to a precarious existence in a no-growth industry."

Selected websites

The next two pages of listings abandon the near completism which should rule elsewhere in the book and gives sites journalists might find useful but which aren't slotted in on later pages.

FREELANCES

www.tvnewsweb.com
A marketplace for freelance camera crew to sell their news footage.
www.journalism.co.uk
A marketplace for freelance journalists.

EVENTS AND NEWS

www.journalism.co.uk
Alternative news
www.ami@easynet.co.uk
Listings of future news events.
www.diarydates.com
Listings of business and leisure events.
www.mediainsider.com
News for PRs.
www.mediatel.co.uk
Media news and information database.
www.megastories.com
Global news site.
www.neravt.com/left
Environmental and financial news
www.newsnow.co.uk
An aggregation of UK news
www.pa.press.net

www.showbizwire.com
Trails the web for the top showbiz news stories
www.sportlist.com
UK sport TV listings.

OTHER SITES

www.aij-uk.com
Assoc of Independent Journalists with news reviews
www.altpress.org/newdir.htm
Alternative press index
www.andromedia.com
Andromedia web site.
www.annanova.com
Insider TV news.
www.aukmil.org.uk
Association of Media Librarians
www.bbc.co.uk
The most popular UK site.
www.bigbrother inside.com
Boycott Intel site.
www.bl.uk/collections/newspapers/sources.html
British Library link to UK newspapers.
www.cme.org
US Center for Media Education site.
www.communicationswhitepaper.gov.uk
For the latest on government media plans
www.cpgf.org.uk
Campaign for Press and Bradcasting Freedom site.
www.cybereditions.com/aldaily
Selection of articles from the world's broadsheets.

Journalists chasing the web £millions

Danny Kelly, former Q and NME editor, now boss of the 365 Corporation
Tim Jackson, former Financial Times and Indie foreign correspondent, now boss of QXL online auctions
Danny Bowers, former IRN financial editor made £6 million when he sold MoneyWorld
Jonathon Maitland, author of How To Make Your Million from the Internet. He began in January 2000 and his book is due out in January 2001. Check his progress on
www.howtomakeyourmillion.com

Guardian quote: "One City editor was offered a salary of £150,000 and shares worth around £250,000 by a US web site."
Richard Rivlin, former Financial Times journalist: "The mega deals on offer are something of a myth. We are talking about a salary which any national paper could match if they really wanted to and an options package of 100 per cent or 150 per cent of one year's pay. Maybe it gets better as you go up the food chain but it's not mega millions, which was really quite disheartening."

Work with us and make the web work for you

Some agencies offer web design, database management and e-commerce integration. Others boast WAP technology, streaming video or the latest in animation. A few enable you to manage your own site, writing, editing and publishing content from wherever. Occasionally they can manage the whole process, from design to installation, including ongoing management and support.

Then there's Red Snapper.

First we understand your business and communication objectives. And then we offer you all of the above.

Since you started reading this, the prime minister has resigned and Manchester United have sold their best striker.

What do you mean you didn't know?

The news never stops, so neither do we. When you want the very latest stories from the UK and across the world, visit Guardian Unlimited. Breaking news 24 hours a day, every day.

GuardianUnlimited.co.uk

www.culture.gov.uk
The Department of Culture's web site
www.dataprotection.gov.uk
UK data protection agency.
www.digitrends.net
New media marketing watch.
www.dti.gov.uk
The Department of Trade's web site
www.fair.org/media-beat
A campaign against corporate web dominance
www.freespeech.org
Internet TV resources
www.guilfin.org
Information network
www.henleycentre.com
Consumer trends
www.indymedia.org.uk
News of independent media
www.journalismnet.com/uk.html
Journalist's guide to the net with 3,000 links.
www.mediachannel.org
Resource listings and news
www.mediafilter.org
Free media
www.netfreedom.org
Cyber liberty campaigners
www.niss.ac.uk/
Bulletin board of internet -related events
www.ntk.co.uk
Weekly UK tech updates
www.theonion.com
US satire

www.piratetv.org
Pirate TV
www.press-freedom.org
The Reporters Sans Frontières site
www.privacy.org
Privacy International
www.profnet.com
PR service for journalists.
www.prwatch.org
Center for Media and Democracy site.
www.radio4all.org
Free radio
www.radiowaves.co.uk
Links to radio stations broadcasting on the net.
www.rawlinson.co.uk
Computer Assisted Reporting for journalists.
www.salon.com
Smart US mag covering culture and business
www.slashdot.org
"News for nerds"
www.slate.com
Microsoft owned cultural emag
www.spyinternactive
Parody interactive TV service
www.the-bullet.com
Insider TV news. "Ammunition for new media people."
www.videonetwork.org
Video activism
www.vlib.org/
The WWW virtual library
www.whitedot.org
Anti-TV site.

A new media life on the blower

In mid-2000 half the British population owned a mobile phone and market analysts predicted 60 per cent mobile usage by the end of the year. The mobile is thus set to become the most ubiquitous technology in the world with uses to extend way beyond saying Hi, I'm on a train. A new generation of mobiles will hook into every part of the electronic media, which is to say all media.

Wireless application protocol is the dull name which makes for the bright acronym describing mobile phones with web access and then, in about five years, digital TV.

The Orange WAP was on the market in time for Christmas 1999 and its media significance - certainly to print journalists - is that it offered access to ITN headlines rather than a newspaper's. Welcome to a new corner of an electronic arena dominated by snippets and gobbets with old-style journalists asking, once again, how to approach the net, how they'll have to change to survive and how intensified demands for brevity and speed will affect the skills of getting words onto paper. Meanwhile only half the world's population has made a phone call.

Be a Web design superhero
without having to wear your underwear
on the outside of your trousers.

MACROMEDIA FLASH™ 5 software is the Web design solution your heroes use. You can create anything from basic animation, menus and navigation systems to the most amazing feats of Web design ever attempted. Design in a familiar and intuitive user interface and then unlock the power of ActionScript to create remarkable Web experiences. And by using Macromedia Flash™ with FreeHand® and Generator™, you'll accelerate your workflow. Design like a superhero, but never, ever, dress like one.

For more information, including a free CD with product demos and trial versions call 0870 6500 1041. Upgrade to Macromedia Flash 5 for £99* and to Macromedia Flash 5/FreeHand 9 Studio for £179. To upgrade, call Macromedia 0800 169 8216 or Upgrades Unlimited on 020 8358 5855.

macromedia.com/uk

macromedia *what the web can be.*™

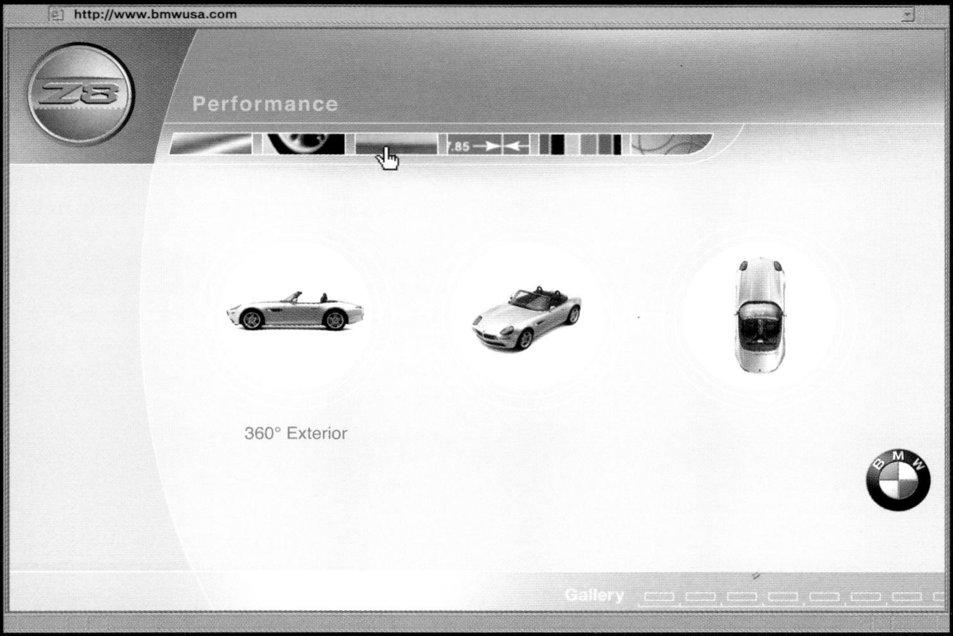

http://www.bmwusa.com

Performance

.85

360° Exterior

Gallery

Register or learn more about our seminar events by visiting www.macromedia.com/uk/events.
*Subject to VAT at 17.5% and a delivery charge of £8.95.

Internet searching

The internet's two main search services are: search engines which scan website pages to compile indexes; and directories, where human editors put the websites into useable categories. Search engines use programs to automatically crawl round all the web, reading as many pages on as many websites as possible, and then storing this data in an index. The engine consults its index for whatever words a person types and lists the results on screen. This is a good way of finding obscure information or carrying out in-depth research, but one can easily be overwhelmed by irrelevant references. The total number of indexable pages on all of internet has been estimated at just over a billion, with perhaps the same number of pages inaccessible. In mid-2000 Google was thought to be the biggest engine in action, with 560 million pages indexed. Google and Northern Light are the most popular engines, followed by AltaVista, HotBot and Infoseek.

Directories treat internet as more like a library of websites than a book of pages. The directories are run by humans, who filter the sites rather than the pages, arrange the sites with themes (like books on library shelves) and create a catalogue of brief comments about each site. They are the best places to begin searching, especially for general material. But in detailed research human, non-robotic editors can miss important sites that engines locate automatically. The most popular directory by far is Yahoo. Other useful ones

are LookSmart, Lycos, Open Directory, UK Index and UK Plus.

A compromise service is the metasearch engine, which approaches several search engines and directories with a query and presents the results in a single list. O these, Copernic, MetaCrawler and Metaplus are favourites.

But the former distinction that was made between directories and search engines is disappearing. Most of them are now hybrids, offering the other type of service as well as their own and they are collectively known as search sites. For simple searches, Yahoo and Google are often put forward as the sites, with Northern Light and HotBot recommended for approaching more advanced web-searching work. Other sites are known as portals, offering other services in the hope browsers will stay onsite and read the adverts. ISPs (internet service providers) like Freeserve and software companies such as Netscape and Microsoft also run portals.

AltaVista
www.altavista.co.uk
One of the most powerful and useful of search engines. A favourite with in-depth researchers because of its wide-ranging cove-rage, advanced search capabilities and many features. 350 million pages. Started 1995.

AOL Search
www.search.aol.com
Directory from the leading internet service provider AOL, mainly using Open Directory. Replaced AOL Netfind in late 1999.

Ask Jeeves
www.ask.co.uk
A simple child-friendlyentry points: just ask a question.

Debriefing
www.debriefing.com
A quality metasearch engine.

Excite
www.excite.co.uk
One of the more popular search services. Aimed at general searchers rather than specialists, it combines a 60 million page search engine with a directory of 5,000 sites, many of them UK. Owner of Magellan and Webcrawler.

FAST Search
www.alltheweb.com
One of the largest engines, with 340 million pages. Previously called All The Web; relaunched in 1999.

Go
www.go.com
An internet portal using the search capabilities of the former engine Infoseek, absorbed in 1999, plus a directory.

GOD (Global Online Directory)
www.god.co.uk
A well-known and interesting global directory, one of the first based in the UK.

Google
www.google.co.uk
The biggest search engine, with 560 million pages fully indexed and 500 million partially. It uses special methods to find high-quality sites for general searches, rather than advanced searches. Since mid-2000 Google has provided its engine as a supplement to Yahoo!. Run by Stanford University, USA, with UK version.

GoTo
www.goto.com
A simple search engine, where all you need is a word to initiate a search.

HotBot
www.hotbot.com
This user-friendly search engine is a favourite among serious researchers, with a wide variety of advanced search options almost equal to Northern Light. Includes directory services from Open Directory.

Inktomi
www.inktomi.com
Not a separate search engine, but a powerful index of over 200 million pages which provides enhanced services to some of the biggest engines.

LookSmart
www.looksmart.co.uk
A popular directory. Not only a stand-alone service, it provides directory results to MSN Search, Excite and other partners. American, with UK version.

Lycos
www.lycos.co.uk
Born as a search engine in 1994, Lycos became a directory in 1999, using Open Directory. Owner of engine HotBot. American, with UK version.

MetaCrawler
www.metacrawler.com
The vintage (1994) metasearch engine, often ranked as the best of its kind. Owned by Go2Net, the wideranging service provider whose name is also used.

Metaplus
www.metaplus.com/uk.html
A metasearch index of many UK directories, with links to as ;arge number of popular sites. American, with UK version.

Mirago
www.mirago.co.uk
A very UK-oriented search engine, aimed primarily at UK businesses and families.

MSN Search
http://search.msn.co.uk
Microsoft's Internet Explorer browser defaults to the MSN site, where this, its own engine is then made available.

Netscape Search
http://search.netscape.com
A well-used browser combining Netscape's own database and the Open Directory.

Northern Light
www.northernlight.com
Often ranked as the near-best of the advanced search engines, with its formidable database and innovatory features. Over 265 million pages, 6,900 full text sources. American.

Open Directory
http://dmoz.org
Formerly called NewHoo, this is one of the most interesting features of all Internet, being a community-based operation, run by over 12,000 volunteer editors. 800,000 sites. It powers Lycos and AOL Search.

Search.com
http://savvy.search.com
What was the metasearcher SavvySearch merged with Cnet's Search.com in 1999.

Search Engine Colossus
www.searchenginecolossus.com
Shows what search engines are in which country, with direct links onsite.

Searchengine.com / SearchUK
www.searchengine.com
The original SearchUK engine and directory, with 10 million pages and 700,000 sites, was rebuilt and relaunched as Searchengine.com in mid-2000.

Snap
www.snap.com
A new directory from NBC TV and Cnet, with search results from Inktomi in addition.

UK Directory
www.ukdirectory.co.uk
The nearest equivalent to a phone book of UK websites, listing names and sites online. So simple, so useful.

UK Index
www.ukindex.co.uk
Wide-ranging directory of UK sites.

UKMax
www.ukmax.com
Glossy UK searcher, owned by Hollinger Telegraph.

UK Plus
www.ukplus.co.uk
The largest home-brewed UK-specific directory, with a comprehensive UK service. Produced by Associated Newspapers (aka Daily Mail). Child-friendly.

Webcrawler
www.webcrawler.com
A simplified Excite, by another name. Easy to use for basic searches, but not for complicated ones.

Yahoo!
www.yahoo.co.uk
The oldest, biggest and most comprehensive directory, with 1.2 million sites. A good starting point for all types of search, especially simpler ones on a general topic. The innovative Yahoo is the most popular of all the search services. and is constantly expanding and improving. Launched in late 1994; now linked with Google. American, with UK version.

reverse takeovers

There's something you ought to know.

Business a.m., Scotland's new daily business and financial newspaper, is off to a flying start.

It's the first daily newspaper to launch in Scotland for 100 years and is proving to be a must read for the Scottish business community.

A unique paper, in a unique format. One that's already taken Europe by storm.

Business a.m. targets Scotland's 387,000* AB adults in full time employment, so including it in your advertising strategy will ensure that you reach more of the people you want to reach. And it'll allow you to speak directly to Scotland's decision makers.

Don't be left out. Call George Sandison, National Sales Manager, or Barry Henderson, Advertising Director, on 0131 330 0000.

They'll tell you everything you need to know.

*Source: NRS April 99–March 00.

Business a.m., 40 Torphichen Street, Edinburgh EH3 8JB. Tel: 0131 330 0000. Fax: 0131 330 0001.

www.businessam.co.uk

Now you know.

Scotland's new Business, Financial and Political Daily

National newspapers

INTRODUCTION **56**
FULL LISTINGS OF NATIONAL PAPERS **60-63**
THE NATIONALS AND THE INTERNET **18-23**

Stupid season

AUGUST 1999 "A fashion mistake," said the Telegraph. "A fashion icon," said the Times. They were talking about the wraparound sun glasses Prince William wore at a polo tournament in a month when the glare of front page coverage also focused on a successful driving test, a family holiday, a News of the World item speculating that he and Richard Branson's daughter might be an item and a Sun spread of Willie's fillies aka "girls with the right breeding for royal romance".

Tab vs tab

13 AUGUST The outraged Sunday Mirror accused the News of the World of trying to bribe Dennis Wise, its deputy news editor, into selling a weekly list of its news stories. Wise claimed he was offered £5,000 a week for the news list plus £3,000 for any stories that made a NoW splash. The dep ed wisely told his editor of the approach and an injunction was issued. NoW responded with a counter accusation and the row fizzled out with an exchange of letters rather than an entertaining court case.

Rogue Mail

16 AUGUST Janet Stansfield claimed she was bullied into resigning her Daily Mail ad sales job by "the corrosive and psychological battering" she received from the men in her department. An industrial tribunal ruled for a full hearing after which Stansfield said: "I was in tears nearly every day. I was working with four middle-aged men and there was me - a young blonde in her twenties. It was terrible. I just couldn't deal with it and in the end I just had to resign."

Price wars

18 AUGUST News Corporation's smaller than usual profits were blamed on "competitive price discounting". News Corp's chairman Rupert Murdoch said: "From a competitive perspective, the Sun continues its reign as leader in the tabloid market, with circulation exceeding that of its nearest competitor by 1.4 million copies a day." Two months later News Corp announced a Times price rise from 30p to 35p, then cancelled it in the face of Independent price cuts to 30p. Best estimates are that newspaper price cutting has cost the Times alone £50 million in lost revenue.

Widdecombe unfair

27 AUGUST The shadow home secretary Ann Widdecombe threatened to sue the Sunday Express claiming her £70,000 a year contract for a weekly column was broken without an agreed two month notice. Conservative head office - where the former Sunday Express editor Amanda Platell is now William Hague's press chief - scented a political plot saying that Platell's sacking had been due to her publishing gay tales about the cabinet minister Peter Mandelson. No Labour plot, exclaimed the Express. "The quality [of Widdecombe's copy] had gone down hill." All the normally loquacious ex-columnist would say was "The matter is in the hands of lawyers."

Diana and rats

SEPTEMBER James Hewitt, Princess Diana's former lover, became fixed in public consciousness as a love rat following his botched attempts to peddle his kiss-and-sell book to the Sunday Express or the Mail on Sunday. The MoS had upped the bidding to £600,000 when it changed its mind and thought the better of publishing a cache of 64 love letters. The Mail sued Hewitt for a return of the advance, Hewitt sued for breach of contract. Meanwhile Monsieur Romuald Rat and his snapper colleagues were absolved from blame in Princess Diana's death when judge Hervé Stéphan decided not to prosecute any of the paparazzi arrested two years earlier after the world's most famous car crash.

Indie losses ... and gains
2 SEPTEMBER The Independent News group slipped from profit when it posted a £2 million loss. Tony O'Reilly, whose global operation continued to prosper, pledged his continuing support for his ailing broadsheets, pointing to a rise in daily circulation to just over 225,000. What it lost in revenue the Independent gained in boardroom clout with two superannuated MPs - Paddy Ashdown and Kenneth Clarke - joining the board in October.

Mr Lobby
6 SEPTEMBER Peter Riddell, a Times political reporter, used a slot in the British Journalism Review to berate the way lobby correspondents must respond to their newsdesks' scandal driven agendas. He variously blamed broadsheet competition for dragging coverage from policy to personality and a "protect-my-back attitude" that has supposedly competitive journalists filing similar stories. "The real challenge to the position of lobby correspondents comes from the shift of power away from Westminster to the broadcasting studios, to European institutions, to the new devolved assemblies, to new semi-independent regulators and to the courts," Riddell wrote.

Guarding the Guardian
21 SEPTEMBER Guardian Media Group announced record profits for 1998 with the group overall making pre-tax profits of £68.2 million on a £412 million turnover. The GMG chairman Lord Gavron said GMG had net cash of £137 million and had spent £33 million on production upgrades. Lord Gavron figured in another news story when the Sunday Telegraph revealed he had donated over £500,000 to Labour's election campaign. "No other newspaper group, perhaps, would print criticism of its chairman," said a strap line over an article by Polly Toynbee. Having pointed out that Bob Gavron is the unpaid chairman of a trust - with none of the proprietorial powers of conventional owners - she worried about Gavron's ennoblement and wrote "To have a chairman who is soon to take the Labour whip ... makes many on this paper deeply uneasy ... I

do not believe Lord Gavron has done anything underhand but for the paper's sake it would have been better if he had refused a peerage."

Entrapment journalism
22 SEPTEMBER "Journalists should carefully examine their approaches to investigations where it involves no police until after the trap has been sprung and the story reported." So said Judge Timothy Perkins when the Earl of Hardwicke walked free from court after a sting engineered by News of the World journalist Mazher Mahmood. Though the aristo was found guilty of selling cocaine to the hack, the jury deemed journalistic deceit a worse sin than drug dealing and their "plea ... to exercise particular mercy" prompted the judge to hand out a suspended sentence to the earl and a public warning to journalists.

OTHER ENTRAPMENTS
Dec 97 William Straw (17 year old son of home secretary Jack) received a caution after supplying cannabis to The Mirror's Dawn Alford.
April 99 The Radio 2 DJ Johnnie Walker was suspended by the BBC after News of the World's Mazher Mahmood revealed a cocaine habit.
May '99 Tom Parker Bowles (son of Camilla) admitted cocaine usage to NoW's Nadia Cohen.
May 99 NoW at it again when the reporters Louise Oswald and Phil Taylor taped Lawrence Dallaglio boasting of cocaine and ecstacy usage. Dallagalio was fined £15,000, lost the captaincy, and then reinstated in the national team.
Richard Bacon of Blue Peter and the London's Burning actor John Alford are also victims of tabloid cocaine stings.

Alastair Hetherington dies
3 OCTOBER The Guardian editor between 1956 and 1975 died aged 79. He began his tenure as one of the few who opposed British aggression during Suez, fought off a merger with the Times in 1966 and finished his career as controller of BBC Scotland. Adam Raphael said: "Alastair was a good editor because he realised that once you got the right structure and the right people, the paper largely ran itself. I have no doubt that the success of today's Guardian owes much to his tolerant and open-minded leadership."

Mirror vs Mail

22 OCTOBER 1999 "I now look at the Mail first in the morning," said Piers Morgan, the Mirror editor. "I've never done that before." Both papers had been the only tabloids to show year on year circulation increases over the previous six months and both were chasing young women readers. The Mirror's pull out supplement M was credited with boosting Tuesday sales by 200,000. Its first issue had been met with a Mail spoiler also called M. Morgan said this move was "tacky and un-Mail" adding "we are no longer going head-to-head with the Sun but going after the Mail".

UN&M slump

23 OCTOBER United News and Media stood out as one of the media sector's worst performers with a performance lagging the FTSE share index by 46 per cent. With sales of the two Expresses and the Star down by 7 per cent, media analysts pointed out that parts of Lord Hollick's company might soon be up for grabs.

Insular papers

28 OCTOBER Ian Hargreaves, professor of journalism at the University of Wales, told an audience of PRs that foreign news no longer sells newspapers. Though this would hardly be a major concern at an Institute of Public Relations annual conference, Hargreaves said only the Telegraph had seen fit to splash the outbreak of war in the Balkans without any other trailers. "One broadsheet felt its readers need the distraction of a British fashion designer's current love affair [along with] coverage of the first war in Europe since 1945," Hargreaves said. Having dismissed this minor triumph of consumer PR, he blamed editors who paid too much attention to focus groups that reveal resistance to foreign news. Editors also copped the blame for insularity when the British Guild of Travel Writers complained of newspaper preference for soft holiday copy over "hard-hitting travel journalism". The traveller's oxymoron led to further agonising self examination. The guild pondered the difficulty of maintaining objectivity on a freebie and wondered whether a travel article boycott of repressive countries would do any good.

Sport slump

30 OCTOBER Sport Newspapers reported a £3.5 million loss which its proprietor, David Sullivan, blamed on a decline in Sunday newspapers and a £9 million management consultancy bill. Sullivan, who is reportedly worth £400 million, has made most of his money from porn.

Charles Wintour dies

4 NOVEMBER Charles Wintour, who edited the London Evening Standard for 17 years, died aged 82. "He essentially invented the modern Evening Standard - and, in doing so, influenced the development of papers far across Fleet Street," wrote the ex-Guardian editor Peter Preston. "He was one of the acknowledged masters of his trade."

Baron without a peerage

8 NOVEMBER The press baron Conrad Black began an action in the Canadian Supreme Court over what he said were illegal moves to prevent his becoming Lord Black of Havenwold. The Telegraph owner was miffed that Jean Chrétien, the Canadian prime minister, had advised the British government to block his nomination for the peerage. The judge said he'd rule on whether the case should proceed within six months.

Women in photos

29 NOVEMBER Women in Journalism published a four-week survey of 12,000 photos published by national papers.

NATIONAL PAPERS' SNAPS OF WOMEN
30% featured women
42% featured women celebrities
25% featured women professionals
14% featured women politicians
2% featured women in sport

"There are still more men than women in public life," said WiJ's Meg Carter. "The challenge in the face of declining newspaper readership is to update old-fashioned thinking. Readers may not expect their newspapers to do more than society, but they can expect to keep up with them."

Sun's thirtieth birthday

16 NOVEMBER Rupert Murdoch - who had recently bought the News of the World - brought out a revitalised Sun (pictured above) in 1969. He'd acquired the paper from IPC, which originally began it in 1964 from the wreckage of the old pro-Labour Daily Herald. On its relaunch under Murdoch (with a front page snap of Lady Leonora, an alleged girlfriend of Prince Charles), the Sun sold 850,000 copies to the Daily Mirror's 5 million. ABC figures for September 1999 showed the Sun's average daily circulation was 3,672,284 and the Mirror's 2,353,905.

Sport First first

19 NOVEMBER Sport First, Britain's most recently launched Sunday paper, recorded an October sale of over 100,000.

"Two editors, one paper ...

2 DECEMBER ...may the best woman win." Here is the cheesy subtitle for Scandal, also given a publisher's billing as a "bonkbuster for the chattering classes". Amanda Platell's novel got more coverage than most because a) she was editor of the Sunday Express for 38 issues until January 1999; b) she was the Sunday Mirror editor for six months; c) she's William Hague's press secretary and earns £100,000 a year. The book earned a four figure advance and she said she'd have made more money if she had gone on social security.

Who do you believe?

3 DECEMBER Gerald Kaufman MP released the second Daily Mail Monitor. Issue two of this catalogue of anti-Labour bias responded to the Mail's criticisms of issue one which had grizzled about the splash headline "Blair's U-turn on NHS drugs", a story on the north-south health divide and how computers would do away with post offices. "So who do you believe?" asked a Daily Mail headline.

Planet on Sunday

5 DECEMBER The flowering of a green newspaper whose first 64 page edition was unpolluted by ads and had features on homeopathy and hedgerows plus a spirit message from Princess Diana. It was first launched for one issue in 1996 and this time lasted a full six weeks until its nine staff came off the payroll and went "on holiday".

"A greedy corrupt liar"

22 DECEMBER This was the Guardian headline when a jury decided Neil Hamilton had taken Mohamed Al Fayed's cash for posing parliamentary questions. Hamilton's failed libel action against Al Fayed faced him with a £2 million legal bill which brought an end to a saga which started with cash-for-questions allegations first published in the Guardian in 1994. A month later Hamilton said that he had failed to raise cash for his promised libel appeal.

Star wars

23 DECEMBER The astrologer Jonathan Cainer decided to quit the Daily Mail for a move to the Express. The Mail had splashed out on TV ads promoting their star's millennium predictions and applied for an injunction forcing him to serve a period of notice. "I got bored of the Daily Mail's attitude," said Cainer. "I find them a bit 20th century." He moved to a higher plain at the Express on a reported £500,000 salary which makes him Britain's highest paid journalist.

photo: ....

/ CAMERA PRESS

TEL: (0)207-378-1300
FAX: (0)207-278-5126

LOOKING
FORWARD

21 Queen Elizabeth Street
London SE1 2PD

www.camerapress.com

Mirrorgate/Slickergate

17 JANUARY The "gate" headline cliché creaked open again when the Mirror editor Piers Morgan bought £20,000 worth of shares in Viglen Technology. He made his purchase the same day that his paper's City Slickers column had been written with an exclusive announcing Viglen was launching an internet division. The story ran the next day and - after the share price doubled from 188p to 355p - Morgan said he had been unaware of the Slickers' tip when he made his big purchase. His bosses at Trinity Mirror accepted his story and said that their editor's timing was "probably not right". However the City Slickers Anil Bhoyrul (who the Mirror had nominated as financial journalist of the year) and James Hipwell were fired for gross misconduct on 17 February with Mirror sources saying they "acted unacceptably" by trading in shares they were writing about. Another related sacking happened the same day when Andrew Laiker, Morgan's broker at Kyte Securities was ordered to leave his office. Meanwhile the PCC waited until 10 May for the chairman Lord Wakeham's declaration that: "It was a very bad case ... and ... Mr Morgan had fallen short of ... professional standards. It was a clear climate of slack. It was all gay abandon. These things just seemed to happen. I suspect it was more cavalier than anything else." The PCC was harsher on Messrs Bhoyrul and Hipwell and

Mirror editor Piers Morgan: the PCC said he "had fallen short of ... professional standards"

noted their combined total of 41 share purchases which preceded their tips. By June Morgan still hadn't replaced his Slickers, but word was out that he was offering the job to the Telegraph's Suzy Jagger : "Make sure you negotiate a whopping great salary with at least a year's notice," Bhoyrul and Hipwell advised in their Punch column. "After all, if you're going to sell out, you may as well do so at a good price."

Maxwell Senior resurfaces

9 JANUARY 2000 The ghost of Robert Maxwell emerged in a non-scandal involving Gordon Brown's purchase of a £130,000 flat in Westminster in 1992. The then shadow chancellor bought the flat from AGB Research, a firm which was owned by Maxwell and had Geoffrey Robinson (Brown's former ministerial ally, the News Statesman proprietor and money-lender to Peter Mandelson) as director. Friends and estate agents rallied round Brown to insist the careful and upright chancellor hadn't been tipped off or given a favourable price.

The business

6 FEBRUARY With sales rising to 70,000 Sunday Business doubled its price to £1. The two year old paper has prospered under the Barclay brothers and chief exec Andrew Neil promised an 80,000 breakeven circulation within a year.

Charles Schulz dies

13 FEBRUARY The creator of the Peanuts died the day his last cartoon strip was published. "Dear Friends," he wrote, "I've been fortunate to draw Charlie Brown and friends for almost 50 years. It has fulfilled my childhood ambition."

Aitken and money

13 MARCH The Press Complaints Commission said it would investigate Sunday Times payments estimated at £60,000 made to the former MP Jonathan Aitken - who had just served a seven months prison sentence for perjury - for serialising Pride and Prejudice. His book was published by HarperCollins which, like the Times, is also a Murdoch owned company. The PCC's code stipulates that payment for stories must not be made to convicted criminals but it rejected the complaint because fees paid went towards sorting out the bankrupted Aitken's debts.

Times and IoS redesigns

13 MARCH The Times - which had recently won the What the Papers Say newspaper of the year award - introduced a tabloid second section called Times 2. Over at the Independent on Sunday Janet Street-Porter, now six months into her editorship, launched a new look to include a blue-backed masthead, an A4 magazine and a new improved £1.10 price tag.

The Shayler affair

14 MARCH The Guardian and Observer challenged an Old Bailey court order to hand over emailed letters sent by the former MI5 agent David Shayler and alleging MI6 involvement in a plot to kill the Libyan leader Colonel Gadaffi. A Guardian leader said: "We will challenge this judgment. There ought, in a free country, to be a presumption that people can contact newspapers without the fear that their communications will be handed over to the police." Immediate backing came from the International Press Institute and the Society of Editors and the foreign secretary Robin Cook made a formal protest to the Home Office. The story then got an interdepartmental twist with a Whitehall source quoted as saying: "The Home Office has gone manic on this ... it's gone bloody crazy, the government should not be picking a war with the press." In May the Times carried a petition condemning the government for threatening press freedom by pursuing newspapers through the courts. Shayler's web site is: www.shayler.com

Campbell and the newspapers

15 MARCH Emerging shyly from his alias as "the official Downing Street spokesman" Alastair Campbell sanctioned the proposal that reporters could name him when they covered his daily 11am lobby briefings. A couple of weeks later Campbell fired off several letters and articles complaining of press unhealthiness and a general herd-like behaviour. In the Telegraph he wrote: "It was once media fashion - and still is abroad - to be hugely pro-Blair. The current fashion is broadly to dump on him, the more venomous the better. Failure, charlatan, phoney, liar, quisling, fascist, Hitler. Where do they go next?"

Anti German allegation ...

24 MARCH Conrad Black, the owner of the Telegraph, threatened to sue Sir Paul Lever for alleging his papers were biased against Germany. The British ambassador in Germany had said that foreign owned papers like Black's have an "underlying philosophy which is anti-European, and Germany is after all the biggest country in Europe". In an interview with the German daily paper Die Welt, Sir Paul also suggested the British press gave "a portrayal of Germany that is rather dominated by a vocabulary from the war and permeated by a feeling that somehow Britain is under threat". Sir Paul apologised and Black dropped his libel case.

... jingoistic papers

12 APRIL The European Commission criticised the British press for its consistent "jingoistic ... paranoid [and] distorted" reporting. An EU report also censured the Press Complaints Commission for failing to act and highlighted a Mirror story in February 2000 when a columnist wrote: "God forbid, had the Germans ever invaded, it's these same people [ie British officials implementing EU directives] ... who'd have happily shopped neighbours harbouring Jews." Several papers were singled out: the Daily Mail and Sunday Telegraph headed a list of anti-Euro mongers; and the Express was sneered at for suggesting Brussels wanted to ban the great British toilet.

publishing

digital

intellectual

property

film

media law

your guide

is

OLSWANG

Solicitors

90 Long Acre, London
WC2E 9TT, United Kingdom
T: +44 20 7208 8888
F: +44 20 7208 8800
E: olsmail@olswang.co.uk

www.olswang.co.uk

TV

defamation

e-commerce

internet

music

broadcasters

On the sick

28 MARCH An announcement that the Times editor Peter Stothard was to take leave to work on a "special project" got the rumour mill started with suggestions he'd been punished for coverage of the Tory chairman Michael Ashcroft's alleged links with money laundering and drug trafficking. The truth was that Stothard was being treated for leukaemia. His stand in is Ben Preston, son of the former Guardian editor Peter Preston.

PCC censures NoW

19 APRIL The Press Complaints Commission ruled that the News of the World had breached the editors' code of practice by publishing sexual details about Jacqueline Pirie, aka Coronation Street's Linda Sykes. Clause three of the code says "everyone is entitled to his or her private and family life, home, health and correspondence" and the PCC said this entitlement had been breached by a NoW exposé provided by Pirie's former lover. The judgement was important because it overrode the old excuse that Pirie had previously sought publicity and established a new benchmark which puts privacy ahead of kiss and sell.

Express centenary

24 APRIL The Express went home to its old Daily Express title in celebration of its hundredth birthday. "We decided to revert back to the Daily Express because that is how the paper is always referred to by readers, advertisers and retailers," said the editor Rosie Boycott. Several days earlier the paper won a legal battle when an appeal court judge, Lord Woolf, overturned a high court ruling which had sought to compel the Express journalist Rachel Baird to reveal who had given her documents about Elton John's finances.

Monthly sport

7 MAY The Observer launched Observer Sport Monthly, a glossy give-away sports mag which is also sold as a standalone title. Caroline Marland, managing director of Guardian Newspapers, said: "GNL has always been at the forefront of product innovation ... Our research has shown a major audience for this magazine."

End of price war

11 MAY Rupert Murdoch's News Corporation reaped a peace dividend when January-March profits rose 15 per cent. The end of the newspaper price war made its old media division the Murdoch empire's best performer.

Maxwell Junior resurfaces

12 MAY Kevin (son of Robert) Maxwell agreed to meet Department of Trade inspectors to answer questions about the collapse of his late father's Mirror Group Newspapers. "It was a bad collapse that was avoidable, and there will be heavy criticism of managers, of me and of professional advisers," Maxwell admitted. Maxwell is now chairman of the Telemonde telecommunications company in the US.

Northern Guardian

14 MAY The Guardian announced a regionalised edition produced in Manchester. Martin Wainwright, the editor, said: "There is real love and respect for the Guardian in the north of England in spite of times when we may have seemed in danger of becoming the absent friend. Recent appointments and the trainee scheme have ended that risk and the prospect of further reinforcement is tremendous. I can hear CP Scott tuning up his harp."

Sir Larry Lamb dies

19 MAY The Sun editor between 1969 and 1981 died aged 70. Rupert Murdoch appointed Sir Larry to run the moribund title he bought from IPC and a new populism (plus the introduction of page 3 girls) saw the circulation rise from 850,000 to 4 million. Murdoch said: "Larry Lamb towered above the editors of his generation. Through the pages of the Sun he helped reinvent popular journalism. To this day, his inspiration lives on within its pages."

Media death toll

24 MAY Kurt Schork, the Reuters correspondent, and Miguel Gil Moreno of Associated Press were killed in Sierra Leone. In the first half of 2000 17 journalists died in their work; it was 36 in 1999, 28 in 1998 and 26 in 1997.

Wade to edit NoW

23 MAY At 31 years old Rebekah Wade (above) became the youngest national newspaper editor when she took over from Phil Hall at the News of the World. The former Sun deputy arrived with a brief to keep circulation above 4 million and all eyes are on her to see how much she challenges a privacy-minded Press Complaints Commission and whether she changes the sex scandal formula. "Reporters will still be making their excuses and leaving," said a News International insider. At the beginning of June she showed herself thoroughly modern by breaking news of a rapprochement between the Queen and Camilla Parker-Bowles on www.newsoftheworld.co.uk. The next week it was business as usual when the PCC received a Palace complaint about the NoW's unauthorised snaps of Prince William. (Phil Hall switched to PR with a job supplied by Max Clifford.)

ITV backs Express take-over

1 JUNE The Independent Television Commission cleared the proposed change of ownership of UN&M's Express newspapers to Carlton or Granada in the event of either of their proposed mergers succeeding. Meanwhile the more important Competition Commission enquiry ground on.

Spat over snaps

9 JUNE A row over ways of publishing 18th birthday pictures of Prince William on 21 June led to the resignation of Prince Charles' press secretary Sandy Henny. She had agreed sole copyright to a Telegraph snapper, to the fury of the Mail and Times whose editors lobbied St James' Palace about the unfairness of a rival being able to print glossy pics while they had to make do with newsprint. The Palace promptly issued the pictures on a broader release. "Appalling, unprofessional," huffed Charles Moore, the Telegraph editor. "They have been weak and incompetent and have broken faith with us ... we had a clear agreement and they've broken it."

From press to PR

JULY Depite opposition from some in the civil service, the ex-Mirror journalist John Williams took over as the Robin Cook's chief spokesman at the Foreign Office.

POLITICO EX-HACKS

Alastair Campbell, ex-Mirror Tony Blair's spokesman

David Bradshaw, ex-Mirror Number 10 Downing Street speech writer

Sheree Dodd, ex-Mirror head of media relation at Department of Social Security

Lance Price, ex-BBC Labour HQ director of communications

Phil Murphy, ex-Yorkshire Post Downing Street press office

Sian Jarvis, ex-GMTV Department of Health press office

Mike Molloy, another ex-Mirror man, although one who continues to ply his original trade said: "We are in a world which is controlled, organised and manufactured by public relations." He told a debate organised by JICREG that there are three reasons why tabloids should not be trusted:

* public relations
* fantasy journalism which views newspapers as entertainment
* proprietors who conspire to obscure the truth

Blair family vs the press

Round 1

21 FEBRUARY 2000 The Press Complaints Commission upheld Tony and Cherie Blair's complaint against the Daily Sport for publishing a picture of their 15 year old son Euan kissing a girl. The PCC code of practice says newspapers must get parental permission before publishing shots of children under 16. The Sport's editor Tony Livesey had offered to settle the dispute in a penalty shoot-out with Blair's spokesman Alastair Campbell.

Round 2

3 MARCH In a row which went to the centre of the privacy debate, Cherie Blair successfully sought an injunction preventing the Mail on Sunday publishing her former nanny's account of life with the prime minister's family. Blair later dropped any claim for damages against the nanny, Ros Mark, and Tony B issued a statement saying: "We do not seek injunctions lightly and we will do whatever it takes to protect the legitimate privacy of our family life ... I have spoken to Ros, who remains a good friend of the family and who is deeply upset at what has happened. I know she's a good person who will not have intended any harm, and I'm only sorry that her good nature has been exploited by others."

Round 3

7 JULY Days after Blair had condemnded drunken youth, his oldest son Euan was arrested drunk in Leicester Square. The nationals were tipped off by the police but refrained from publishing and the Evening Standard splashed the story. The PCC said there could be no reporting restrictions because the boy was over 16, not in school and in a public place when he committed a criminal offence. The story could not have been reported if the proposed Youth and Criminal Evidence Act had been in force. Despite Blair's unlucky personal predicament

Tony Blair

highlighting the flimsiness of his public pronouncements, press and parliamentary criticism showed a muted understanding after the first bout of headlines.

Round 4

30 JULY Most Sunday papers published pictures of Leo Blair's christening in breach of the PCC code that pictures of children cannot be taken without the parents' consent. Blair lodged a complaint with the PCC and the Guardian commented: "By the crude standards of these matters, the newspapers behaved calmly over the drunken elder son episode. Some kind of payoff was was expected." The payoff came in Tuscany ...

Round

AUGUST ... and the entire Blair family trooped out for a photocall.

English local and regional newspapers

INTRODUCTION	**64**
TAKEOVERS	**66-67**
FULL LISTINGS OF REGIONAL PAPERS	**68-81**
FULL LISTINGS OF ENGLISH LOCALS	**83-102**
THE LOCALS AND THE INTERNET	**18-23**

Holy Trinity

13 AUGUST 1999 Trinity-Mirror's campaign to reform ownership rules intensified when it responded to Competition Commission demands that it sells Belfast titles in order to complete a merger with the Mirror Group. Trinity's half yearly report said: "The current competition regime allows overseas buyers and venture capitalists to acquire newspaper assets. This is unfair to existing owners."

Johnston's record results

1 SEPTEMBER Profits for the half year rose 3.9 per cent to £25.9 million on a £103 million turnover. The figure omitted interest payments and shares bought when Johnston acquired Portsmouth and Sunderland Newspapers.

Golden market

17 SEPTEMBER The Newspaper Society reminded its members that nearly half the population will be aged over 45 by 2020. An NS survey showed that over 45s whose children have left school are heavy users of the local press and issued the following statistics.

LOCALS AND THE OVER 45s

90% are readers of their local press

62% value local coverage

29% are more likely to read an evening paper

19% are more likely to read a local morning

12% are more likely to read a local paid-for weekly

Newscom profits

20 SEPTEMBER News Communication and Media showed a 10.3 per cent increase in full-year operating profits to £24.1 million. Having failed to buy Portsmouth and Sunderland Newspapers in May 1999, the chief executive John Dux said he was still seeking acquisitions to add to his roster of 70 titles.

Buyout bliss

8 OCTOBER Alec Davidson, a director of Northcliffe Newspapers, told a Newspaper Society meeting that two recent Competition Commission reports were "reasonably favourable" to the kind of "consolidations" he had been arguing for. Northcliffe Newspapers had recently bought Adscene's Central Independent Newspapers in Staffordshire without having to make a referral to the Commission.

Net network

15 OCTOBER Six regional newspaper groups climbed aboard the web bandwagon when they combined to establish internet classified advertising sites called Fish4cars (200k listings), Fish4homes (50,000 listings) and Fish4jobs. A £30 million investment aimed at staunching the flow of ad revenue away from the local press relies on Microsoft's British portal where user/readers can search the databases by post code or nationally. The investors publish some 80 per cent of the UK's local papers and are: Newsquest, Northcliffe, Trinity Mirror, Regional Independent Media and the Guardian Media Group.

Ageism = awful subbing

9 NOVEMBER The Lancaster Guardian's Danny Lockwood criticised the redundancy notices given to experienced old hands to accommodate new technology and new inexperienced journalists in the chase for younger readers. "The fact that decent sub-editors are as thin on the ground as rocking horse droppings pays testimony to how we have grievously mismanaged ... new technology. I think the subbing of our papers, particularly but not exclusively in the regional press, is little short of awful."

Metro mania

NOVEMBER The London Metro spawned a host of regional imitators with giveaway morning dailies handed out to commuters throughout the UK. With them came a host of stories about distribution battles on the buses and railway stations and then court cases disputing the right to use the Metro name. Print runs of these new papers are large: 350,000 in London; 100,000 in Scotland; 90,000 in Birmingham; 75,000 in Manchester. "Metros will change the face of newspapers," warned the Express' Chris Blackhurst in a lecture at Cardiff University. "I think that's the way newspapers are going to go as the markets are in decline. On the way to work I see people going out of their way to pick Metro up. These readers are the type of people who do not usually read a newspaper and whom every editor wants to attract."

METRO TITLES

title	owner	launch date
London Metro	Associated Newspapers	Mar 1999
Manchester Metro	Guardian Media Group	Nov 1999
Metro North West*	Associated Newspapers	Nov 1999
Metro West Midlands	Associated Newspapers	Dec 1999
Birmingham Metro	Trinity Mirror	Dec 1999
Metro Scotland	Associated Newspapers	Dec 1999
Metro (North East)**	Modern Times Group	Jan 2000
Metro (North East)	Associated Newspapers	Jan 2000

* Reborn as News North West after a court action

** Reborn as Morning News after a court action

In May 2000 Associated Newspapers and Trinity Mirror agreed to combine forces over the daily free metro paper with the former supplying national news and advertising with the latter supplying local copy.

Faked circulations

4 NOVEMBER Trinity-Mirror's three main Birmingham papers were revealed to have inflated circulation figures for the past six years. An internal audit by the new management uncovered "systematic" overstatement by between 10 per cent on Birmingham Post and 17 per cent on the Birmingham Evening Mail and Sunday Mercury. The company set aside £20 million to repay advertisers who had been overcharged. The papers were sold by Midland Independent Newspapers to the Mirror for £297 million in 1997 and Chris Oakley - the current Regional Independent Media chief exec who had been with MIN and stayed on for a while with the new owners - said: "Under no circumstance would I have taken any part in any action outside the ABC rules to inflate sales figures." On 12 January the Audit Bureau of Circulation said it would: review the frequency of ABC inspections; review the role of financial auditors; and consider mandatory training for accountants undertaking ABC audits. The report was scheduled for September 2000 and in May Simon Devitt, the departing ABC chief executive, said: "One of the problems with the regional press is that it doesn't appreciate the core values an ABC audit gives. Without it there would be complete anarchy."

Elliott: "Disgraceful pay"

10 NOVEMBER Geoff Elliott, editor of The News in Portsmouth for nine years and president of the Society of Editors, condemned the "disgraceful pay" of regional journalists. He compared salaries with teachers who "regardless of how good they are or what responsibilities they have" earn at least £23,500 by the age of 29. "I wonder how many people in this room edit newspapers and pay their staff anywhere near this figure? We are exploiting people ... and ... bring them into the job, saddle them with enormous debt because we can't afford to train them ourselves, pay them a poor wage - and are then surprised when they leave us."

"Mr Elliott, you're fired"

19 NOVEMBER Johnston Press sacked Geoff Elliott as editor of The News. Tim Bowdler, the chief exec and sacker in chief who had moved in six months earlier when Johnston bought The News' from the Storey family, acknowledged Elliott's success in editing one of the few evening papers to increase its circulation. So why was Elliott sacked? "As we look ahead we have to look at the management structure which is most appropriate to etc etc," Bowdler burbled. "The decision was not linked to anything Geoff said at the Society of Editors conference."

Tindle's predictions

24 JANUARY 2000 Sir Ray Tindle, the chairman of Tindle Newspapers, traded on his reputation as a trusty prophet of good news when, for the third year running, he struck a bullish note. He told the Newspaper Society: "My reading of all the signs suggests that the economy will hold up this year, revenue will rise, profits will be good, circulations will be steady and 2000 will be a great year for both large and small newspapers." He also predicted that the sales and consolidations would continue.

Local scoops national

18 MARCH Ray Bowyer, the disgruntled castaway who was the first to quit the BBC's Castaway 2000 project, hitched a ride away from Taransay in a boat hired by the Mirror. When he saw how the national tabloid was covering his story he did another runner and went local by telling his story to the Stornaway Gazette. Peter Urpeth, the Gazette's triumphant editor, said: "The Mirror had, apparently, offered Bowyer £5,000 for an exclusive, The same exclusive cost the Gazette a fiver, if you include the costs of a taxi rider, a ham roll and a lift to the ferry terminal."

NUJ/NS/BAJ and national pay

Media Monitoring Services revealed a recruitment crisis with an annual increase of media job small ads from two to three million column inches. The various professional bodies made their responses.

The National Union of Journalists' general secretary John Foster called for a revival of the national pay agreements which collapsed in the eighties when some Newspaper Society members decided to opt out of annual wage agreements. Delegates at the NUJ's annual conference voted for a minimum wage in excess of £10,000 and heard that one in 12 members was earning under £10,000 a year. The delegate for Birmingham and Coventry told of a Trinity-Mirror journalist on the Birmingham Post and Mail was earning £7,000 a year. Delegates also heard the average annual salary for a graduate is £19,500.

National pay CONTD.

The Newspaper Society conference heard that pay needed to be increased to stop young journalists going into new media. Liz Donaldson, of the Harlow College journalism centre, said: "The recruitment crisis is now so serious that anyone who cares about good journalism, the future of the industry and the bottom line for newspapers needs to sit up and do what they can to help solve it." She went on to criticise proprietors who paid so little that their trainees had to do second jobs. "Is this the sort of signal we should be sending out about the profession - that you must have two jobs to make ends meet? Is this the way to get 100 per cent commitment from a trainee?

The British Association of Journalists called for a minimum £8,000 a year salary for local paper trainees, rising by £1,000 a year until journalistts reach 30.

Ham 'n High treason

21 APRIL Talk of dumbing down at the Ham & High local paper got extra volume because of outrage expressed by Hampstead media luminaries like Liz Forgan and Desmond Wilcox. They complained of redundancies and didn't accept Eastern Counties' explanation that job losses were due to natural wastage.

Metro news

JUNE Guardian Media Group and Associated Newspapers resolved a legal tussle, with GMG keeping the right to call its morning freebie the Manchester Metro News. A week later Associated revealed plans for its own Manchester Metro and said that the London Metro had moved into profit. (Associate's paid-for London Evening Standard lost 3 per cent of sales in the first half of 2000.)

White paper lobbying

4 JULY "End unfair controls," was the Newspaper Society's main contribution to the autumn communications white paper. The Society pointed out that there is no justification for singling it out for specialist controls that handicap the traditional media but not the competitors.

Scottish and Northern Ireland papers

INTRODUCTION   **64**
FULL LISTINGS OF REGIONAL PAPERS   **68-81**
FULL LISTINGS OF SCOTTISH WELSH AND NI PAPERS   **102-107**

"Bitch journalism"

6 SEPTEMBER 1999 Lord Steel (above), the former Lib Dem leader and now presiding officer in the Scottish parliament, took the Daily Record to the Press Complaints Commission in protest at what he described as "bitch journalism". Scotland's largest tabloid newspaper had been critical of MSPs' pay, perks, 17 week annual holiday and the issuing of £7,000 worth of commemorative medals. The PCC found in favour of the Record with the PCC chairman, Lord Wakeham, commenting: "Fair comment may sometimes be tasteless or offensive, but newspapers are still entitled to make it." Eight months later Lord Wakeham used his platform at an awards dinner in Edinburgh to remind Scottish journalists that the PCC code demanded a balance between scrutiny in the public interest and responsibility. "You now have a particularly important role in scrutinising, in the public interest, the actions of a new parliament. It is an institution that was a long time in coming - some might argue it was a hundred years or so late - and now here it is inevitably proving a source of controversy."

Cassidy leaves Sunday Mail

24 SEPTEMBER Jim Cassidy, a successful editor of the Sunday Mail for eight years, resigned amid many rumours. Did he go voluntarily or did his new Trinity-Mirror bosses push? Was it because he was too close to Scottish Labour MPs? Was he at loggerheads with his editor-in-chief? Had he antagonised management with coverage of Rangers football club, particularly a photo of the party-loving Rangers PR man playing a bottle like an Orange marcher's flute? Gossip had it that management called this a bad commercial decision to which Cassidy's supposed reply was that he made editorial not commercial decisions.

The Moloney affair

28 SEPTEMBER Ed Moloney, the Northern Ireland editor of the Dublin based Sunday Tribune, won his battle to deny the police sight of his notes with an Ulster loyalist who had been accused of murder. Moloney, who had made it clear he would face jail rather than surrender his material, said: "This has the makings of a landmark decision. The lord chief justice has made quite clear that the police have to establish a case for needing to see journalistic material. They can't just wade in and assume they will automatically get it."

PROTECTING SOURCES

1988: Jeremy Warner of the Independent was fined £20,000 for refusing to give Department of Trade inspectors details about insider dealing.

1990: Bill Godwin, a graduate trainee on the Engineer magazine, was fined £5,000 and threatened with imprisonment. The European Convention of Human Rights said the government was in breach of its rights.

1992: Channel 4 and Box Productions were fined £75,000 for refusing to identify an informant who had given details of collusion between the RUC and loyalist assassins.

Barclay brothers

7 DECEMBER David and Frederick Barclay, the publicity-shy twins who own The Scotsman, made a rare venture into the limelight when they joined the Queen at the opening of their new £20 million offices in Edinburgh. A week later - and far to the south - the Channel Island of Sark reformed its land laws to allow the twins' four children to inherit their £60 million castle on the neighbouring island of Brecqhou.

Scotsman editor

3 FEBRUARY 2000 Alan Ruddock's two year tenure as Scotsman editor ended amidst rumour of his ousting due to Andrew Neil's over active interpretation of his role as editor-in-chief. Ruddock - who had commuted to the job from Ireland - was described by one staffer as "so laid back he was horizontal". Tim Luckhurst, the 37 year old deputy editor, took charge.

SMG profit surge

22 FEBRUARY Scottish Media Group announced pre-tax profits of £50 million on a £242 million turnover. SMG, which recently launched the Sunday Herald as part of its Herald range of titles, pledged to invest £10 million to capture a share of internet classified ad sales.

Independent buys Belfast Telegraph

17 MARCH Tony O'Reilly's Dublin based Independent News and Media Group paid Trinity Mirror £300 million for the Belfast Telegraph. Ulster Unionists, fearing a change of editorial policy in the 130 old paper, had tried to prevent the sale to a Republic of Ireland owner. INMG, which owns the London Independent and the Irish Independent in Dublin, made the bid after the Competition Commission ruled Trinity-Mirror's merger should force the sale.

Scotsman rival

MAY The September launch of an Edinburgh business paper got advanced publicity when its Swedish publisher recruited the Scotsman's crime reporter. Alert observers concluded the paper's remit would be wider than business. Meanwhile the Scotsman completed a revamp to attract readers from London-based nationals.

Magazines

INTRODUCTION	**108**
PUBLISHER LISTINGS	**110-118**
MAGAZINE LISTINGS	**119-131**
MAGAZINES AND THE NET	**19-22**

Diminishing consumption

AUGUST 1999 Sales of women's and men's monthlies fell in the first half of the year. Terry Mansfield, who has been managing director of National Magazines since 1982, gave his reasons for a general slump in sales. "The British magazine business is the most aggressive and the fastest-moving in the world. When we launched House Beautiful, for example, there were only seven titles in its category; now there are 28. There are also more newspaper supplements, more TV and radio stations, more internet opportunities. But there are still only 24 hours in a day - that can't be extended. So inevitably, you're seeing an over-supply of consumer titles, and slices are being cut out of every category."

Talked up

2 AUGUST The new New York based magazine Talk generated hundreds of British column inches on the strength of being edited by Tina Brown. The former editor of Tatler, Vanity Fair and the New Yorker produced a launch issue which had interviews with Hillary Clinton and George Bush Jnr but early interest didn't turn into high levels of continuing sales.

Sibyl trouble

20 SEPTEMBER Sibyl magazine became the latest of many left-leaning women's magazines to fall over when it failed to meet printer's bills. Its demise follows Spare Rib (1971-1993) and less politicised titles like Everywoman and Working Woman. The only magazine filling a potentially large market niche is the occasionally published Trouble and Strife. Gemma Mitchell, who had worked on Sibyl, said: "I recently bought a copy of Marie Claire and flicked through it: half was ads, and the features tended to be voyeuristic. If feminism has been main-streamed, why isn't it reflected in Marie Claire?"

The Guardian Guide to the Internet

A newly updated edition of this best selling guide.

How do you decide which is the best way to get online? The Guardian Guide to the Internet is the answer, it offers straightforward advice on all aspects of the internet from tips on buying computers to recommendations about how to surf around the Web. You'll find out about safeguarding financial transactions, designing your own website, what you can expect to find on the internet and what you might want to avoid.

£5.99 (p&p free)

Call the credit card hotline on 0870 7274155 or send the coupon below to: The Guardian Shop, JEM Marketing, Little Mead, Cranleigh, Surrey GU6 8ND.

The **Guardian** *free thinkers welcome*

- -

Please send me _____ copies of The Guardian Guide to the Internet. I enclose a crossed cheque value _____ payable to The Guardian. Or debit my Mastercard/Visa with the sum of £ _____

Card no: | | | | | | | | | | | | | | | | | | Expiry date: | | | | |

Name _____ Address _____

_____

Postcode _____ Signature _____

If you do not wish to receive details of any other services tick this box ☐
Please allow 28 days for delivery. Please photocopy this form if you do not wish to cut up the book.

TV listings

25 SEPTEMBER The BBC's Radio Times, whose circulation has halved to 1.4 million since the television listings market was deregulated in 1991, produced a redesign in response to the arrival of fresh competition from TV Choice. Since the market opened up to non-BBC and ITV publishers What's on TV has emerged as leader in a listings market which, despite no overall increase in circulation, has seen seven major launches and three failures.

TV LISTINGS MAGS
Total circulation 5 million

What's on TV	36%
Radio Times	28%
TV Times	17%
TV Quick	15%
TV & Satellite Week	4%

Cool recycler

11 OCTOBER Mark Leonard, who coined the "Cool Britannia" phrase, apologised for plagiarising a New Statesman article from an Observer article written by Anthony Browne and Richard Reeves. The 25 year old adviser to the foreign secretary claimed he'd relied on unsourced research notes. "It could have happened to anybody," he said. "It was very embarrassing, a cock up."

Religious spat

21 OCTOBER David Tolkington resigned as a Catholic Herald columnist saying the paper had gone to the right on birth control, ritual, theology, sex and gender. He thought the editor William Oddie, an Anglican convert, was abandoning a conciliatory line which had prevailed until Cardinal Hume's death. "People who come into the church at his age tend to be to the right of Attila the Hun," Father Tolkington said. Oddie retorted that the fault was in the defector's copy. "This is a problem all editors have when they try to do something about a column which has become dull." (Conrad Black, the Telegraph owner who is another convert to Catholicism from Anglicanism, owns 10 per cent of the Herald's shares and has a seat on the Catholic Herald board.)

Big apology

26 OCTOBER The Big Issue accepted undisclosed damages from the Observer plus an apology saying that a 1998 report on The Big Issue in Los Angeles was wrong in suggesting the magazine had muscled in on existing street mags and favoured celebrity interviews over homelessness issues.

GM spat

29 OCTOBER Richard Horton, editor of the Lancet since 1995, said he had been threatened by a Cambridge professor of immunology who warned him off publishing an article opposed to genetic modification. Professor Lachmann confirmed he had phoned Dr Horton to discuss "an error of judgment" but denied that he had questioned the Lancet editor's morality.

Total and partial collapses

1 NOVEMBER Emap closed its general sports magazine Total Sport after a troubled five year life. Blame was placed on the impossibility of running a monthly title in the face of so much competition from other media. Meanwhile the plethora of newish football titles recorded diminished sales with a 20 per cent fall in those aimed at the youth market. "There's no escaping the fact that football magazines are in decline," said Justyn Barnes, Man United magazine editor. "There's no single reason for the slump."

Trees a jolly good fellow

7 NOVEMBER Felix Dennis, founder of Dennis Publishing and a publisher who calls his business "tree killing", announced a £200 million plan to plant Britain's biggest forest in Warwickshire. Dennis started his career on Oz magazine and was jailed for obscenity in 1971. The Telegraph, which back then must have been loud in its condemnation, published an approving leader. "It takes a particular determination - and not one commonly seen - to wish to spend hundreds of millions of pounds on a creation whose full glory the planter is unlikely to be alive to enjoy." Meanwhile it was business as usual when Future bought four Dennis music mags and three web sites. Dennis kept its tree killing computer mags.

Crass lads

10 NOVEMBER The strapline declared "the rest of the world might think you have it easy, but some students prefer suicide to another term of cider, exams and Red Dwarf ..." Emap's FHM magazine editor and publisher wrote apologies to five families whose children had recently committed suicide. FHM's article had used specific suicides as case studies alongside an effectiveness rating for suicide methods and such lines as: "For maximum wall art effect use a shot gun like Ernest Hemingway, pulling the trigger by tugging on a piece of string." The Press Complaints Commission criticised the UK's best selling monthly magazine for a lack of sensitivity which treated real deaths "in a gratuitously humorous manner".

Pollard the mag-o-holic

15 NOVEMBER Eve Pollard (above), the Sunday Express editor until 1994, launched Wedding Day as Parkhill Publishing's second title after the summer launch of Aura, a title aimed at intelligent older women. "Everyone's promised that, haven't they," said Pollard. "But nobody's delivered. I feel there's no magazine for me and I'm a magazine-o-holic." The following August the venture appeared to have collapsed amidst complaints of her autocratic behaviour. Eve Pollard is 55.

Exclamatory rivals

16 NOVEMBER Hello!, whose grip on the text-light and snap-heavy celeb market has loosened, claimed a court victory over OK! A Hello! claim for malicious falsehood rested on the inaccurate estimates of sales figures that OK! had distributed. The tiffing continued when OK! objected to a post-courtroom Hello! press release which, it said, overestimated damages by more than £100,000! Earlier in the year OK! paid Mr and Mrs David Beckham £1 million for their wedding photos! In February 2000 OK! merged as market leader with ABC sales figures for July to December showing an OK! circulation 551,901 and with Hello! trailing on 495,349. What Hello! lacks in leadership, it made up for in moral tone when the publishing director Sally Cartwright said: "OK! have copied Hello! very extensively indeed! The only thing they haven't copied is our business ethics!!"

Informa buys FT and Emap mags

7 DECEMBER The Informa Group paid the Financial Times £13.5 million for seven FT Business magazines and 60 newsletters. Some 80 staff were involved and Informa said that despite the possibility of merging some overlapping titles, it had no redundancy plans. In November Informa paid Emap £28 million for a range of fishing, freight and finance titles.

IPC's collywobbles

16 DECEMBER The UK's largest magazine group announced a drop in pre-tax profits from £29.7 million to £10.5 million. IPC Magazines attributed the fall to marketing expenditure and the £55 million a year interest charges which followed the £869 million management buyout from Reed Elsevier in 1997. IPC said it hoped to float on the stock market in 2001, a year ahead of the target set during the buyout.

Cabal and the telly

JANUARY 2000 BBC2's Trouble Between the Covers profiled goings on at Cabal, the new publishing house which recently launched the lag mag Front and Real Homes. Within weeks of the broadcast Andy Sutcliffe, one of Cabal's founding partners, quit the company.

Emap's collywobbles
4 FEBRUARY Emap's Autumn euphoria when profits were up 17 per cent turned to Winter gloom. Its shares were temporarily suspended when the price fell by more than 20 per cent following news about poor results from its US publishing house. When trading resumed analysts maintained doubts about long term benefits from the 1998 purchase of Petersen, the Los Angeles publisher, for £720 million.

BBC mags into US
2 MARCH BBC Worldwide announced a £62 million US publishing venture to grow by acquisition and sell videos, books and magazines. The BBC is the third largest UK magazine publisher and wants to repeat its money spinning operations in areas such as food, nature, DIY, history and youth.

Internet mags
MARCH The latest set of ABC sales figures showed that web titles had bucked a downward trend in the magazine market and doubled their combined circulations in 1999. New titles continued to be launched with Internet Age - a fortnightly aimed at an estimated 16,000 web workers - from Forme Communications in January and then the UK debut of two glossy US imports called Red Herring and Business 2.0.

LM closes after legal defeat
15 MARCH LM (formerly Living Marxism) magazine ceased publication after ITN was awarded £375,000 for an LM libel about "The picture that fooled the world". This was LM's headline describing footage of emaciated Muslim prisoners, but the jury accepted that the camp was a prison and that the ITN pictures had not - as LM alleged - misrepresented the truth.

Motor Cycle crash
29 MARCH Emap's Motor Cycle News was caught lifting stories from the internet when uk.rec.motorcycles planted a fictitious story about new Honda bikes. "We wanted to see if they'd pass off internet gossip as pukka news," said uk.rec. Rob McDonnell, the old media editor, said his reporter hadn't checked his facts.

A thousand Eyes

21 APRIL Private Eye published its 1,000th issue with the Steve Bell cover cartoon above. Richard Ingram, the founding editor, had kindly words to say about his successor Ian Hislop. "Any magazine editor will be used to the cry "it's not as good as it was", but in the case of the Eye, the change is probably irrelevant. The Eye is much the same as it always has been, no better or worse. And still 40 years later there is nothing else like it. It has survived innumerable libel battles, it has overcome the resistance of WH Smith, and it has a circulation of more than 180,000. I would predict a bright future - so long, that is, as the editor resists the urge to turn it into a weekly." Private is unique among big-selling magazines in not relying on advertising revenue for survival.

Lad returns
26 APRIL Mike Soutar quit as editor of Maxim US in the States to retrun home and take charge of Loaded, Later and NME in his new role as managing director of IPC's music and sport

magazines. The former editor of FHM - whose exploitation of new-laddism boosted FHM's circulation from 60,000 to half a million - repeated the trick with Maxim in New York. He said: "In both the United States and the UK, men's general interest magazines are established as part of men's lives. Guys are simply not going to go back to reading specialist magazines about trout fishing and ferret breeding. The Holy Grail now, of course, is to be first to figure out where to guide that audience of men who are growing out of the twenty-something men's titles. IPC's Later, launched for that very purpose, has had a decent start but will take some developing - and I look forward to being involved in that."

IPC for sale - again

30 APRIL Magazines began a major flirtation with cable interests in merger negotiations where IPC began preparing for a possible £1.2 billion sale to Telewest. IPC was put up for sale by the Cinven venture capitalists which bought the magazine group (which includes Woman's Own, Marie Claire and Loaded) from Reed Elsevier for £650 million. Profits have been too low to venture an IPC stock market flotation and the owners followed the new consolidatory logic by wooing a buyer which is strong in TV programme making. Telewest - which had just merged with Flextech in a £2.26 billion deal - already offers multi-channel TV plus internet and telephone services. Emap followed Telewest into the purchasing arena but in June Sly Bailey, the IPC chief executive, said: "We have no intention of selling off any parts of our business. What we are in is building mode, absolutely not deconstruction mode."

Death of Life

5 MAY Life - once the foremost American photo-journalism magazine with an 8.5 million circulation during the forties and fifties - was folded after 66 years of publication. Despite having a 1.6 million circulation at closure, Time Warner deemed profits too small to justify continued publication. Life lives on as a website and its most famous photographs are on www.lifemag.com.

"Idiot savant"

15 MAY James Brown (above), the former Loaded editor, made £5 million on the strength of a promise when he floated his I Feel Good publishing company on the Alternative Investment Market. IFG's £10 million evaluation preceded the company's printing a word, though that changed with the launch of the Hotdog film mag. Felix Dennis, who owns 10 per cent of IFG and is its non-executive chairman, said: "I have never invested in someone else's company before. But James is a bit of an exception. The industry needs an idiot savant and he is close to genius. If we give him the backing, there is a strong possibility he could achieve a minor miracle within six months to a year."

Summer spree

JULY VNU bought Ziff Davies' European titles for £40 million, NatMags bought Prima and Best from Gruner and Jahr and there was a management buyout at Quantum (Press Gazette and Media Week) from P&O.

The nationals

There are 12 national dailies and 11 national Sundays. In the year since summer 1999 there have been no large openings or closures and - for another mark of stability - there was only one sacked editor when Phil Hall had to give way to Rebekah Wade at the News of the World. Compare this rate of editor-churn to the four editor's chairs that changed occupants last year and the eight in 1998.

Three of Fleet Street's finest editors died: Alastair Hetherington (Guardian editor from 1956 to 1975); Charles Wintour (Evening Standard editor from 1959 to 1976); and Larry Lamb (Sun editor from 1969 to 1981). The newspaper world has changed utterly since the prime of their working lives. The power of the unions has been broken by a rough mix of technology and government-backed proprietor power. The press has mutated into just one component of a broader media and entertainment industry where the big calculations have gone global. Synergy and convergence and market research have replaced older gut instincts based on know-thy-reader in a communications niche where - while they might still set the news agenda - newspapers are not bought by people who rely on them to tell them what's new. Or how to vote. In a nation where ideologies have converged into a free market consensus, newspaper readers look to their dailies and Sundays for a confirmation of style and their place in the socio-economic strata.

"Most Telegraph readers are unpolitical," declared the unswervingly Tory Charles Moore, who has edited the Daily Telegraph since 1995. He then went on to say that beliefs, behaviour,

NATIONAL NEWSPAPER CIRCULATIONS

DAILIES	JAN-JUN 00	JAN-JUN 99	CHANGE
1 Sun	3,563,803	3,730,466	-4.47%
2 Daily Mail	2,376,468	2,350,241	1.12%
3 Mirror	2,258,950	2,313,063	-2.34 %
4 Express	1,065,273	1,095,716	-2.78%
5 Daily Telegraph	1,033,680	1,044,740	-1.06%
6 Times	722,642	740,883	-2.46%
7 Daily Record	620,103	665,313	-6.80%
8 Daily Star	607,649	615,038	-1.20%
9 Financial Times	457,653	385,025	18.86%
10 Guardian	396,534	398,721	-0.55%
11 Independent	224,224	223,304	0.41%
12 Scotsman	84,716	79,925	5.99%
SUNDAYS			
1 News of the World	4,041,987	4,209,173	-3.97%
2 Mail on Sunday	2,297,915	2,279,430	0.81%
3 Sunday Mirror	1,939,513	1,981,059	-2.10%
4 Sunday People	1,538,991	1,643,310	-6.35%
5 Sunday Times	1,369,461	1,374,436	-0.36%
6 Sunday Express	977,791	1,003,287	-2.54%
7 Sunday Telegraph	811,408	816,653	-0.64%
8 Observer	415,004	404,859	2.51%
9 Independent on Sunday	248,564	250,034	-0.59%
10 Scotland on Sunday	105,277	120,644	-12.74%
11 Sunday Business	68,436	55,494	23.32%

Source: ABC July 2000

mannerisms and character are what people value in their newspaper. One could even argue that nationals have acquired a stronger character by allowing the Press Complaints Commission to take a tougher stance in its job of sitting between the scandalised and the scandal-seeking. Two examples: one is the way the PCC was swift to condemn both the Mail on Sunday and the Daily Sport for separate intrusions into the Blair's family privacy. The second is that Piers Morgan - the most newsworthy of the nationals' current editors - is under notice for good behaviour after the lenient way he was dealt with after the Mirror's share tipping scandal. There has been a slight cracking of the received wisdom that papers can only retain readers by chasing after the scandal which the public will buy - and then tell opinion pollsters it also wants privacy laws. Self-regulation via the PCC seems to be working and talk of a privacy law in the next communications white paper is almost non-existent.

After six years the price war seems to have ended, with News Corporation reaping a peace dividend when January to March 2000 profits rose. Here is good news for the rest of the newspaper business, for the estimated £50 million it cost the Times to achieve its 700,000 circulation chipped away at the prosperity of its broadsheet rivals. Meanwhile the rate of decline in circulation has diminished, which is testimony to a vigorous response where every paper delivers its readers more colour, more pages, more sections, more lifestyle, more sport, more columns, more features - more and more of everything except hard news. Readers now look to their newspapers for confirmation of style and the best paid journalist - if journalist is the word for a trader in medieval superstition - is the astrologer Jonathan Cainer who recently left the Mail for a £500,000 salary deal at the Express.

The Express celebrated its centenary and the Sun its 30th birthday under Murdoch. Here we can find some evidence of some long term decline rather than stability. The Sun, while still

The privacy-minded PCC chairman, Lord Wakeham, will keep a careful eye on the News of the World's latest editor Rebekah Wade

the soaraway red top with well over a million more daily sales than the Mirror, is 700,000 down from its 1988 circulation peak. The Express's move from right to soft centre under Lord Hollick's United News and Media ownership remains on its traditional gets-much-worse trajectory with sales hovering just above a million and the December 1999 ABC figures showing it sold less than the Telegraph for the first time. That is part of a larger story in a market of increasing educational standards and a redefinition of class stereotypes where daily broadsheet sales have risen from 500,000 in 1930 to 1.8 million in 1961, to 2.3 million in 1984 and nearly 2.8 million in 2000.

Over half the population still reads a national daily, and newspapers are embedded in the culture as portable, easy-to-store and accessible parts of normal day to day life. What a happy scene - there is time for mourning the dead and for birthday celebrations and job security (at least at the top), self-regulation, guaranteed production runs, general profitability, stable prices and circulations. Fleet Street's diaspora can gaze at a trim, if slightly creasing, navel.

This account of maturity omits mention of the web and the next mobile phone innovations which will soon be as ubiquitous as newsprint.

Orange introduced broadband internet capacity to mobile phones in time for Christmas 1999, and its media significance - certainly to print journalists - is that it offered access to ITN headlines rather than those from any newspaper. Welcome to a new corner of an electronic arena dominated by snippets and gobbets and fresh rounds of barely suppressed panic from old-style journalists asking, once again, how newspapers should approach the net, how they'll have to change to survive and how the intensified demands for brevity and speed will affect the skills of getting words onto paper. Those questions are being answered within new media departments on every newspaper where there is a new generation of web artistes in place led by the best young journalistic talent around. The demand is clear enough. On the Guardian - which sells 400,000 papers a day - the daily hit rate recorded by Guardian sites is 80,000 and rising, and that kind of alternative readership is the way ahead. Five years ago, web investment seemed a bit of a future-proofing sideline, stimulated by the realisation that online digital archives are cheap to run and that classified sales were bound to migrate to the net.

What began modestly now begins to define the structure of modern newspapers and propels newspaper groups toward thinking of themselves as national and international content providers. Newspaper executives turned a weather eye to the AOL-Time Warner deal in

HISTORIC NATIONAL NEWSPAPER CIRCULATIONS

DAILIES	1958	1968	1978	1988
Express	4,062,587	3,819,674	2,458,792	1,658,252
Financial Times	84,858	159,536	181,678	282,675
Guardian	177,962	274,638	283,494	454,038
Herald	1,513,217			
Independent				381,210
Daily Mail	2,104,932	2,067,468	1,973,580	1,775,695
Mirror	4,527,208	4,991,616	3,806,003	3,119,365
News Chronicle	1,255,233			
Record	523,748	721,796	770,589	
Sketch/Graphic	1,213,184	900,336		
Daily Star				990,110
Sun		1,037,577	3,960,076	4,182,848
Daily Telegraph		1,393,094	1,358,875	1,133,173
Times	248,338	408,300	295,863	443,462
Today				478,220

SUNDAYS	1958	1968	1978	1988
Empire News	2,155,132			
Mail on Sunday				1,926,047
NoW	6,716,258	6,161,138	4,919,905	5,287,190
Observer	642,588	878,266	712,712	735,826
The People	4,906,019	5,479,878	3,901,314	2,746,348
Reynolds News	356,676			
Sunday Dispatch	1,752,101			
Sunday Express	3,412,333	4,221,914	3,260,600	2,088,086
Sunday Graphic	933,214			
Sunday Mirror			3,865,926	2,866,007
Sunday Pictorial	5,378,189	5,076,344		
Sunday Sport				551,377
Sunday Telegraph		729,942	855,803	704,737
Sunday Times	813,924	1,450,694	1,399,073	1,338,623

Source: ABC

America and the biggest single recent British newspaper news item was the Telegraph's announcement at the end of April 2000 that it seeks partners in TV, cable or telecoms.

Back in Blighty a general election is pending but the proprietors will, for the most part, do what they did last time and back the likely winner in the knowledge that advice on which way to vote no longer sways readers as it once did. It's a sign of the times that party political public relations attracts as much coverage as anything so dreary as and unfashionable as policy. What will remain is a Euro-bashing jingoism which - according to a credible conspiracy theory - suits the interests of North American based proprietors who care most for a strong dollar prevailing over the possibility of a united European currency.

In an era when the main media ideology must look only to the bottom line, Rebekah Wade has a tough job. If she is to survive in post and be judged a success, she must keep the News of the World circulation above four million without getting too much censure from the PCC. "If I was a betting woman, I'd say the odds were pretty steep," she told the News International corporate newspaper. "But there *is* a chance, if we can get the package right." Wade shortened those odds over the short term with the rabble rousing paedophile coverage that began her editorship and she certainly faces a tougher commercial brief than that of any of the three war horses who died in the past year. While they all thrived on intense competition, they were more free to dictate a response to their markets. Larry Lamb was able surf an emerging political consensus to mould the Sun into a Daily Zeitgeist and his value to Rupert Murdoch was judged on more than circulation alone. Alastair Hetherington and Charles Wintour - who headed institutions that were at the core of their employer's organisations - were more free than any modern editor to invite judgement on quality ahead of quantity.

THREE FLEET STREET EDITORS WHO DIED IN 2000
Larry Lamb (pictured top), Sun editor from 1969 to 1981
Alastair Hetherington, Guardian editor from 1956 to 1975
Charles Wintour, Evening Standard editor from 1959 to 1976

NATIONAL DAILIES

Daily Express
245 Blackfriars Road, London SE1 9UX
Fax 020-76201654   Tel 020-7928 8000
E-mail newsdesk@dailyexpress.co.uk
Website: www.dailyexpress.co.uk
Editor: Rosie Boycott since April 1998
Advertising director: Richard Bogie
Founded: 1900.
Owner: United News and Media

Daily Mail
Northcliffe House, 2 Derry Street, Kensington, London
W8 5TT
Fax 020-7937 3251   Tel 020-7938 6000
News fax 020-7937 4463   Tel 020-7938 6372
Web site: www.dailymail.co.uk
Editor-in-chief: Paul Dacre since 1998, editor since
1992.
Advertising director: John Teal
Founded: 1896.
Owner: Daily Mail & General Trust

Daily Star
245 Blackfriars Road, London SE1 9UX
Fax 020-7620 1644   Tel 020-7928 8000
News fax 020-7620 1654   Tel 020-7922 7070
Editor: Peter Hill
Advertisement director: Richard Bogie
Founded: 1978.
Owner: United News and Media

Daily Telegraph
1 Canada Square, Canary Wharf, London E14 5DT
Fax 020-7538 6242   Tel 020-7538 5000
News fax 020-7513 2506   Tel 020-7538 6355
E-mail: name@telegraph.co.uk
Web site: www.telegraph.co.uk
Editor: Charles Moore, since 1995
Advertising director: Len Sanderson
Marketing director: Mark Dixon
Founded: 1855.
Owner: The Telegraph

Financial Times
Number One, Southwark Bridge, London SE1 9HL
Fax 020-7407 5700   Tel 020-7873 3000
Website: www.ft.com
Editor: Richard Lambert, since 1991
Advertisement director: David Walsh
Founded: 1888.
Owner: Pearson

The Guardian
119 Farringdon Road, London EC1R 3ER
Fax 020-7837 2114   Tel 020-7278 2332
Website: www.guardian.co.uk
Editor: Alan Rusbridger, since 1995
Advertisement director: Stuart Taylor
Founded: 1821
Owner: Guardian Media Group

Independent
1 Canada Square, Canary Wharf, London E14 5DL
Fax 020-7293 2435   Tel 020-7293 2000
E-mail name@independent.co.uk
Website: www.independent.co.uk
Editor: Simon Kelner since April 1998
Advertisement director: Guy Griffiths
Founded: 1986.
Owner: Independent Newspapers

The Mirror
1 Canada Square, Canary Wharf, London E14 5AP
Fax 020-7293 3843   Tel 020-7510 3000
News fax 020-7510 3409   Tel 020-7293 3831
Editor: Piers Morgan, since 1995
Trinity-Mirror advertising director: Mark Pritchett
Founded: 1903.
Owner: Trinity Mirror

The Sun
1 Virginia Street, Wapping, London E1 9BD
Fax 020-7488 3253   Tel 020-7782 4000
Website: www.thesun.co.uk
Editor: David Yelland, since June 1998
Advertising director: Ian Clarke
Founded: 1912 Daily Herald; in present form since '69.
Owner: News International

The Times
1 Pennington Street, Wapping, London E1 9XN
Fax 020-7488 3242   Tel 020-7782 5000
Website: www.the-times.co.uk
Acting editor: Ben Preston (while Peter Stothard, editor
since 1992 is on sick leave)
Advertising director: John Trickett
Founded: 1785.
Owner: News International

'Investing in Excellence in Art, Design & Media'

Study for Success

Falmouth College of Arts is a leading University Sector College specialising in art, design and media at undergraduate and postgraduate level.

The College offers the following one-year, full time, intensive, taught, postgraduate diplomas which prepare students for future careers in the media and creative industries:-

Broadcast Journalism

- Experience the challenges and opportunities which face the broadcast journalist, and train in our state-of-the-art radio and digital television studios. This BJTC accredited programme specialises in hard news and current affairs, and over 99% of graduates gain employment in the broadcast industry. The Jill Dando Bursary, donated by the BBC, is awarded annually to an outstanding applicant.

Broadcast Television

- Produce, direct, research and plan television programmes according to current professional practices, and acquire the skills which today's employers need. This programme is serviced by a purpose-built digital television studio complex and AVID editing suites, and is endorsed by the BBC, ITV and the industry training body, Skillset.

Creative Advertising

- Develop the portfolio you need for a creative career in advertising, and join our many graduates, now working as art directors and copywriters at leading agencies such as Saatchi & Saatchi, J Walter Thompson, Lowe Lintas and Leo Burnett. The programme is twinned with Ogilvy & Mather who provide on-going advice and sought-after work placements.

Professional Writing

- Focus on writing for new media, screenwriting and exploring creativity through writing in a multi-disciplinary environment, and contribute to the programme's lively online magazine, www.falmouth.ac.uk/bloc, which won the Guardian's Student Website of the Year Award in 1999. The Springboard Award, donated by the Jane and David Cornwell Charitable Trust, is awarded annually to an outstanding applicant.

For further information on these and other media opportunities at Falmouth College of Arts, please contact Admissions.

To reserve places on the College's Open Days, please contact Reception.

Falmouth College of Arts, Woodlane, Falmouth, Cornwall TR11 4RH. Telephone: 01326 211077.

A UNIVERSITY SECTOR COLLEGE

FALMOUTH *College of Arts*

How often have you thought, 'Where did the week go?'

The most time-efficient way of keeping up-to-date with world media is through the free weekly magazine – the **Editor**.

Amongst its 24 colour pages you'll discover how each week it **filters** global news and events.

We scour the newspapers and magazines of **the** world, tune into thousands of television and radio programmes, and log on to find the **best** of the net.

We then edit it all. Condensing the most compelling **bits**, and publishing them to provide you with a unique summary **of** planet earth this week.

Now, **the** Editor brings you an even more informed, more in-tune and wittier round up of the **world's** business, entertainment and sport. Providing an essential review of international **media.**

Fifteen minutes with the Editor will give you the low-down on the latest coups and tabloid scandals, bring you up-to-date with the week's 'simply must haves,' and fill you in on what's troubling parliament.

So, if like the majority of people these days, **you** find there are never enough hours in the day. And you really **don't** want life to pass you by, then all you **have** to do is pick up the Guardian this Friday.

You will be up-**to**-date with the world in just a little more time than it took you to get to the end of this ad**.**

NATIONAL SUNDAYS

Independent on Sunday
1 Canada Square, Canary Wharf, London E14 5DL
Fax 020-7293 2043   Tel 020-7293 2000
E-mail: sunday letters@independent.co.uk
Website: www.independent.co.uk
Editor: Janet Street-Porter since July 1999
Commercial director: Stephen Miron
Founded: 1990.
Owner: Independent Newspapers (UK)

Mail on Sunday
2 Derry Street, London W8 5TT
Fax 020-7937 3745   Tel 020-7938 6000
Tape Room Fax 020-7937 7896/3829
Editor: Peter Wright, since 1998
Advertising director: Sally de la Bedoyese
Founded: 1982.
Owner: Daily Mail & General Trust

News of the World
1 Virginia Street, Wapping, London E1 9XR
Fax 020-7782 4463   Tel 020-7782 4000
Editor: Rebekah Wade, since May 2000
Advertising director: Richard Webb
Founded: 1843.
Owner: News International

Observer
119 Farringdon Road, London EC1R 3ER
Fax 020-7713 4250   Tel 020-7278 2332
Editor: Roger Alton, since 1998
Advertising director: Stuart Taylor
Founded: 1791.
Owner: Guardian Media Group

The People
1 Canada Square, Canary Wharf, London E14 5AP.
News fax 020-7293 3810   Tel 020-7293 3201
Editor: Neil Wallis since January 1998
Trinity-Mirror advertising director: Mark Pritchett
Founded: 1881.
Owner: Trinity Mirror

Sunday Business
3 Waterhouse Square, Holborn Bars, 142 Holborn, London EC1N 2NP
Adv fax 020-7961 0103 Tel 020-7961 0000
Editorial fax: 020-7961 0102
E-mail: sundaybusiness@the-european.com
Editor: Jeff Randall, since 1998
Owner: Barclay Brothers

Sunday Express
245 Blackfriars Road, London SE1 9UX
Fax 020-7620 1654   Tel 020-7928 8000
Website: www.express.co.uk
Editor: Rosie Boycott since April 1998
Advertising director: Richard Bogie
Founded: 1900.
Owner: United News and Media

Sunday Mirror
1 Canada Square, Canary Wharf, London E14 5AP
Fax 020-7293 3405   Tel 020-7293 3000
News fax 020-7293 3939   Tel 020-7293 3601
Website: www.sundaymirror.co.uk
Editor: Colin Myler
Trinity-Mirror advertising director: Mark Pritchett
Founded: 1915 as Sunday Pictorial
Owner: Trinity Mirror

Sunday Sport
19 Great Ancoats Street, Manchester M60 4BT
Fax 0161-236 4535   Tel 0161-236 4466
E-mail: features@sport.demon.co.uk
Website: www.sundaysport.co.uk
Editor: Mark Harris
Advertising manager: Alan Pollock
Founded: 1986
Owner: Sport Newspapers (David Sullivan).

Sunday Telegraph
1 Canada Square, Canary Wharf, London E14 5DT
Fax 020-7538 6242   Tel 020-7538 5000
News fax 020-7513 2504   Tel 020-7538 7350
Editor: Dominic Lawson, since 1995
Advertising director: Len Sanderson
Founded: 1961
Owner: The Telegraph

Sunday Times
1 Pennington Street, London E1 9XW
Fax 020-7782 5658   Tel 020-7782 5000
Website: www.sunday-times.co.uk
Editor: John Witherow since 1994
Founded: 1822
Owner: News International

Local and regional papers

"Life is local," is a slogan buried in the Newspaper Society's excellent website which also carries the statistic that three-quarters of the UK workforce works within 10 miles of home, and 40 per cent within two miles. It adds strength to a Newspaper Society pitch to advertisers which says "regional [and regional is the preferred moniker when the locals want to aggrandise themselves] newspapers control the local information franchise .. and ... can deliver target audiences cost-effectively".

A more clunking bit of sloganising follows with the declaration that "media is moving from global to local" and a later assertion that "consolidation has left the industry in the hands of regional press specialists who have reinvested heavily in their core newspaper businesses". This may have been true when local ownership began moving into more local hands - such as Newsquest, Trinity and Johnston - from the mid nineties. However the sale of Newsquest to the giant American Gannett saw an important chunk of ownership moving away from local to global and to a proprietor, moreover, with a reputation for squeezing editorial resources.

The big-is-beautiful logic has had the current owners - backed in large part by City-based venture capital - spending around £4 billion on local press acquisitions since 1995 to create a market where the top 20 publishers account for

Tim Bowdler, chief executive of Johnston Press: "While the UK's regional press is subject to onerous constraints, foreign newspaper publishers are freely able to acquire newspapers in this country. Similarly, venture capitalists have been active buyers of regional papers, because they see the opportunity for a quick profit. It's their good fortune that regional publishers have been unable to compete on a level playing field."

four fifths of UK titles and over nine out of ten copy sales. Details are on the next page.

Tim Bowdler, the chief executive Johnston Press, wants a relaxation of "the special merger provisions to which regional newspaper publishers are subject" ie that owning more than one paid for title with a circulation over 50,000 triggers referral. Bowdler feels these rules constrain a home-grown group like his from competing equally with the likes of Gannett or, indeed, with venture capitalists such as the ones who funded the Newsquest management buyout and subsequently pushed through the sale to Gannett. "Virtually every other media sector, including other media, is subject only to general competition law," Bowdler says. "In a large number of cases, prior approval has extended to the statutory requirement for a full Competition Commission inquiry."

A new foreign competitor has arrived from Sweden with the Modern Times Group - aka Metro International - distributing decent quality daily give-aways in the metropolitan centres. Modern Times is pitched against Associated in Newcastle-on-Tyne and may well provide more competition for the Guardian Media Group and Associated in Manchester or Trinity and Associated in Birmingham. Once again the spectre of the frees arises to challenge the paid-fors. "Metros will change the face of newspapers," warned the Express' Chris Blackhurst in a lecture at Cardiff University. "I think that's the way newspapers are going to go as the markets are in decline. On the way to work I see people going out of their way to pick Metro up. These readers are the type of people who do not usually read a newspaper and whom every editor wants to attract."

The large sums of new money going into local papers over recent years have had two other effects. First is investment in the net and the second is the revival of the tradition that locals are seen as a good place to begin a career in journalism with more investment going into group training, usually of graduates, though sometimes direct entry straight after school. This hasn't disrupted the other old tradition which is that the majority of the 8,000 or so journalists who work on locals get "disgraceful pay". The quote marks are round a phrase by Geoff Elliott, spoken when the former editor of The News in Portsmouth told the Society of Editors that many teachers "regardless of how good they are or what responsibilities they have" earn at least £23,500 by the age of 29. "I wonder how many people in this room edit newspapers and pay their staff anywhere near this figure? We are exploiting people ... and ... bring them into the job, saddle them with enormous debt because we can't afford to train them ourselves, pay them a poor wage - and are then surprised when they leave us." Johnston Press sacked Elliott a fortnight later with his boss, Tim Bowdler, claiming: "The decision was not linked to anything Geoff said at the Society of Editors conference." Old traditions die hard.

A vigorous new web tradition is being established and this intro ends with a quote culled from the Newspaper Society's web site. "The industry has seen growing investment in electronic publishing ventures, including internet sites, audiotex, teletext and other electronic services, plus tie-ups with local radio and cable operators. The core business will remain newspaper-based for at least the next decade but with aggregate audiences increasingly swelled by new media businesses built on the back of the trusted newspaper brand."

LOCAL PAPER CHECK LIST

* There are more than 1,300 regional and local newspapers in the UK today, including 23 mornings (18 paid-for and 5 free), 74 evenings, 17 Sundays, around 530 paid-for weeklies, and 700 free newspapers.

* More than 40 million regional paid-for newspapers are sold and 28 million free newspapers delivered every week.

* The regional newspaper industry employs around 34,000 people. Nearly a quarter of these are editorial staff. The Newspaper Society claims that no other medium can come close to the regional press in matching the numbers of news and information gatherers and processors dedicated to reporting and opening up debate on local issues.

* British people are among the most avid newspaper readers in the world. 83 per cent of all British adults (38 million people) read a regional newspaper, compared with 71 per cent who read a national newspaper. Regional press has a high solus readership: 37 per cent of those who read a regional newspaper do not read a national daily.

The top 20 publishers now account for 78 per cent of all regional and local newspaper titles in the UK, and 94 per cent of the total weekly audited circulation.

* Regional press sales exceed £678 million a year. More than half (53 per cent) of regional newspapers in ABC membership increased sales in July-Dec 99, compared with 29 per cent four years before that. The weekly press (the largest sector) delivered the best performance with a total of 59 per cent showing increases and the rate of growth at +0.1 per cent. For the regional press overall, the seemingly relentless sales decline has slowed considerably (2.2 per cent four years ago to 1.8 per cent in 1999.)

* The local press is the second largest advertising medium in the UK, after television. Local and regional newspapers grossed £2,389 million in 1998 - 20 per cent of total UK ad spend. Magazines take 16 per cent (£1,918 million), national press 15 per cent (£1,793 million), posters 5 per cent (£563 million) and radio 3 per cent (£421 million). Ad revenue in the regional press was up 6.8 per cent in 1998. National display advertising in the regional press grew by 3.7 per cent to £247 million in 1998.

Source: Newspaper Society

Take-over times

Johnston buys P&SN

MAY 1999 Johnston Press paid £254 million to take over Portsmouth and Sunderland Newspapers. Johnston defeated other interest from Newsquest and Newscom and its chairman, Fred Johnston, said the purchase - which also includes titles in the north east - was the beginning of the consolidation of local paper ownership into four or five agglomerations.

Gannett buys Newsquest

JUNE Newsquest accepted a £904 million offer from Gannett. The US media group owns 74 papers including USA Today. Newsquest's management had led a buyout from Reed three years earlier.

Trinity Mirror merger

JULY Britain's biggest newspaper group emerged from the £1.5 billion merger of Trinity's local interests with the Mirror Group's national and local ones. The new company's roster of over 150 papers includes the Mirror in England, the People and the Sunday Mail and Sunday Record in Scotland and the Belfast Telegraph.

Denitz buys Adscene

JULY Denitz Investments bought the Adscene regional newspaper group for £75.4 million with a view to either a flotation or a trade sell off. In the event Denitz chose a sell off with sales of Central Independent, then Admag and then, the next February, the remainder of Adscene.

Northcliffe buys Admag

AUGUST Swift on the heels of Denitz' purchase of the Adscene group, Northcliffe paid £44.5 million for Central Independent Newspapers and Admag.

Northcliffe buys BUP

NOVEMBER Viscount Rothermere, aka Jonathan Harmsworth, the 30 year old inheritor of the Daily Mail group, made his first major acquisition in a bid valuing Bristol United Press at £121.5 million. The group, which includes the Western Daily Press and Bath Chronicle, was

already 24 per cent owned by the Daily Mail. Giles Clarke, a Bristol United non-executive director, resigned saying that he could not support a deal which entailed the loss of a local business' independence.

Newscom buys J&J

DECEMBER Newscom paid £16 million for the four titles owned by Jacob and Johnson. The deal secured Newscom the Hampshire Chronicle, a broadsheet founded in 1722, plus the Romsey Advertiser and two frees.

Johnston buys Tweeddale

DECEMBER Another family-owned group moved into a large consortium with the sale of Tweeddale Press to Johnston Press for an undisclosed sum. The group from Berwick was founded in 1808 and had been in the Smail family for eight generations and published the Southern Reporter, the Berwickshire News and the Berwick Advertiser.

Newscom up for grabs

DECEMBER The US group Gannett, publisher of USA Today made its first approach to buy Newscom via its UK subsidiary Newsquest. Newscom (formerly known as Southern Newspapers) rejected the bid within a week and Johnston Press showed an interest. The share price rose to give Newscom a market capitalisation of around £350 million. In March Trinity-Mirror announced itself as the third potential buyer.

THE MAIN DEALS

Johnston buys P&SN for £254m, May 1999
Gannett buys Newsquest for £904m, June
Trinity-Mirror merger - £1.5 billion, July
Denitz buys Adscene for £75.4m, July
Northcliffe buys Admag for £44.5m, August
Northcliffe buys BUP in £121.5m deal, November
Newscom buys Jacob and Johnson for £16m, December
Johnston buys Tweeddale, price undisclosed, December
Southnews buys Adscene for £52m, February 2000
Independent buys Belfast Telegraph for £300m, March
Gannett buys Newscom for £444m, May
Johnston buys part of Southnews, May
Gannett, GMG and Johnston line up to buy RIM

TOP 20 REGIONAL PRESS PUBLISHERS

GROUP NAME (1999 POSITION)	TITLES	WEEKLY CIRCULATION Jan-June 2000
1 Trinity-Mirror (1)	176	15,125,864
2 Newsquest Media Group (3)	204	10,187,211
3 Northcliffe Newspapers Group (2)	99	9,756,951
4 Johnston Press (4)	199	6,055,301
5 Associated Newspapers (2)	4	3,820,390
6 Regional Independent Media (6)	51	3,452,475
7 Southnews (10)	73	3,276,454
8 Guardian Media Group (7)	45	2,628,899
9 Eastern Counties Newspapers (8)	64	2,607,992
10 Midland News Association (11)	19	2,156,751
11 Independent Newspapers (19)	33	1,692,319
12 DC Thomson & Co (18)	3	1,427,663
13 Scottish Media (14)	3	1,310,962
14 Scotsman Publications (13)	6	1,300,406
15 Yattendon (Cambs. Newspapers) (16)	23	855,407
16 Kent Messenger Group (17)	21	762,967
17 Cumbrian Newspapers Group (-)	10	497,247
18 North Wales Newspapers (-)	12	472,725
19 Tindle Newspapers (-)	40	351,739
20 Clyde & Forth Press (-)	15	343,377

Source: The Newspaper Society, July 2000

Includes London Evening Standard, Daily Record, Sunday Post, Sunday Mail and the seven regional morning free titles.

Southnews buys Adscene

FEBRUARY 2000 Denitz' brief time as a local paper owner drew to a close when it sold the Adscene group of 16 paid-for and 17 free newspapers to Southnews. Greater London's predominant newspaper group paid £52 million for a stable of titles in London, Kent, Lincolnshire and Nottinghamshire. Gareth Clark, the Southnews chairman, said: "The deal will significantly strengthen our London operations whilst also providing us with a substantial presence in Kent."

Independent buys Belfast Telegraph

MARCH Tony O'Reilly's Dublin based Independent News and Media Group paid Trinity Mirror £300 million for the Belfast Telegraph. O'Reilly's group, which also owns the Independent in London and the Irish Independent in Dublin, made the bid following a Trinity Mirror merger which resulted in a Competition Commission ruling that forced the Belfast Telegraph sale. Ulster Unionists, fearing a change of editorial policy in the 130 year old paper, had tried to prevent the sale to a Republic of Ireland owner.

Gannnett buys Newscom

MAY Newsquest became publisher of the UK's most local papers with the £444 million purchase of Newscom. With nearly over 200 titles, Newsquest's 16 per cent British market share is only topped by Trinity-Mirror's 19 per cent. Gannett, Newsquest's owner since a £1.3 billion buyout in 1999, publishes 74 US dailies and owns 22 TV stations.

Johnston buys 14 Southnews titles

MAY Southnews sold 14 locals in Lincs and Notts to Johnston Press for £16.5 million. Southnews had only owned them since March, when it picked up the remainder of Adscene from Denitz.

Regional Independent Media: £650?

JULY Regional Independent Media, a buy-out from UN&M in 1998, was targetted for takeover by Gannett (aka Newsquest). RIM - which publishes the Yorkshire Post - then attracted the interest of Trinity Mirror, Johnston and the Guardian Media Group. The company is 50 per cent owned by the Candover venture capital firm.

LOCAL PAPER OWNERS

KEY CONTACT

Newspaper Society
Bloomsbury House, 74-77 Great Russell Street,
London WC1B 3DA
Fax 020-7631 5119   Tel 020-7636 7014
E-mail: ns@newspapersoc.org.uk
Website: www.newspapersoc.org.uk
Association for UK regional and local newspapers.
More details page 171

Adnews
Albert Chambers, Canal Street, Congleton CW12 4AA
Fax 01260-299324   Tel 01260-281012
E-mail: adnews.midlands@virgin.net
Website: www.adnews.co.uk
2 titles

Adscene Group
Newspaper House, Canterbury, Kent CT1 3YR
Fax 01227-470308   Tel 01227-767321
74 titles.
Taken over by Dentiz Investments in July 1999 and
then sold on to Southnews in February 2000.

Advertiser & Times (Hants)
62 Old Milton Road, New Milton, Hants BH25 6EH
Fax 01425 638635   Tel 01425-613384
E-mail: nma@globalnet.co.uk
Publishes New Milton Advertiser & Lymington Times.

Alpha Newspaper Group
56 Scotch Street, Armagh, N Ireland BT61 7DQ
Fax 028-37 527029   Tel 028-37 522639
Website: www.ulsternet-ni.co.uk
7 titles.

Anglia Advertiser
The Precinct, High Street, Great Yarmouth NR31 6RL
Fax 01493-652082   Tel 01493-601206
6 titles.

Angus County Press
Craig O'Loch Road, Forfar DD8 1BT
Fax 01307-466923   Tel 01307-464899
E-mail: anguspress@AOL.com
Publishes 12 papers.

Arbroath Herald
Burnside Drive, Arbroath DD11 1NS
Fax 01241-878789   Tel 01241-872274

Arran Banner Printing & Publishing
Brodick, Isle of Arran KA27 8AJ
                       Tel 01770-302142

Associated Newspapers
see Northcliffe Newspapers and Evening Standard

Banbridge Chronicle Press
14 Bridge Street, Banbridge, County Down BT32 3JS
Fax 018206-24397   Tel 018206-62322
E-mail: banbridgechronicle@btinternet.com

Barnsley Chronicle
47 Church Street, Barnsley, South Yorkshire S70 2AS
Fax 01226 734444   Tel 01226 734734
E-mail: editorial@barnsley-chronicle.co.uk
3 titles.

Baylis & Co
48 Bell Street, Maidenhead, Berkshire SL6 1HX
Fax 01628-419523   Tel 01628-798048
E-mail: news@maidenads.co.uk
Website: www.maidenhead-advertiser.co.uk

Bristol United Press
Temple Way, Bristol BS99 7HD
Fax 0117-934 3570   Tel 0117-934 3000
Web: www.epost.co.uk
E-mail: mail@epost.co.uk
10 titles. Now wholly owned by the Daily Mail and
General Trust.

Bute Newspapers
10 Castle Street, Rothsay, Bute PA20 9HB
Fax 01700-505159   Tel 01700-502931

CN Group
PO Box 7, Newspaper House, Dalston Road, Carlisle,
Cumbria CA2 5UA
Fax 01228-612601   Tel 01228-612600
E-mail: news@cumbrian-newspapers.co.uk
Website: www.cngroup.co.uk
9 titles.

Caledonian Newspaper Publishing
See SMG Publishing

Candover
See Regional Independent Media

Cambrian News
PO Box 4, Aberystwyth, Dyfed SY23 3WB
Fax 01970-624699   Tel 01970-615000
E-mail: edit@cambrian-news.co.uk
6 titles.

Cambridge Newspapers
Winship Road, Milton, Cambridge CB4 6PP
Fax 012334344157   Tel 01233-434434
E-mail: edit.camnews@dial.pipex.com
10 titles. A subsidiary of Yattendon Investment Trust.

Central Independent News
14b-14c Birmingham Road, Sutton Coldfield, West
Midlands B72 1QG
Fax 0121-355 0600   Tel 0121-355 6901
6 titles. The 3 best sellers are: Sutton Coldfield
Observer; Geat Barr Observer; Walsall Advertiser.

Champion Newspapers
166 Lord Street, Southport, Merseyside PR9 0QA
Fax 01704-531327   Tel 01704-392392
                       ISDN 01704-514309
E-mail: sales@champion.line.net
Website: www.championline.net
5 titles

Cheadle & Tean Times
18 Tape Street, Cheadle, Staffordshire ST10 1BD
Fax 01538-754465   Tel 01538-753162
3 titles.

Cheshire Newspapers
Brook Street, Leek, Staffs ST13 5JL
Fax 01538-386975   Tel 01538-399599
8 titles including the Courier series in Cheshire.

Chester Standard Newspapers
Linen Hall House, Stanley Street, Chester CH1 2LR
Fax 01244-351536   Tel 01244-351234
3 titles.

Chew Valley Gazette
5 South Parade, Chew Magna, Bristol BS40 8SH
Fax 01275-333067   Tel 01275-332266
E-mail: chewvalley.gazette@which.net

Chronicle Publications
102 Boothferry Road, Goole, Yorkshire DN14 6AE
Fax 01405-720003   Tel 01405-720110
E-mail: gooletimes@btinternet.com
Website: www.gooletimes.co.uk
Publishers of The Goole Times and Selby Post.

Clyde & Forth Press
Pitreavie Business Park, Dunfermline, KY11 8QS
Fax 01383-737040   Tel 01383-728201

Coates & Parker
36 Market Place, Warminster, Wiltshire BA12 9AN
Fax 01985-217680   Tel 01985-213030
Publishes the Warminster Journal.

The County Press
County Press Buildings, Bala, Gwynedd LL23 7PG
Fax 01678-521262   Tel 01678-520262
3 titles.

Courier Newspapers (Oxford)
2-4 Ock Street, Abingdon, Oxon OX14 5AH
Fax 01235-554465   Tel 01235-553444
E-mail: enquiries@courier-newspapers-oxford.co.uk
Website: www.courier-newspapers-oxford.co.uk
7 titles. The 3 best sellers are: The Oxford Journal;
Oxford Courier series; Reading's Thames Valley Weekly.

SR & VI Crane
see Newsquest Northeast

W Y Crichton & Co
2-4 Church St, Downpatrick, Co Down BT30 6EJ
Fax 028-44 614624   Tel 028-44 613711
E-mail: downr@sol.co.uk

D & J Croal
18 Market Street, Haddington, East Lothian EH41 3JL
Fax 01620-826143   Tel 01620-822451
E-mail: courier@croal.demon.co.uk
The 3 best sellers are: East Lothian Courier, Border
Telegraph, Peebleshire News.

Cumberland & Westmorland Herald
14 King Street, Penrith, Cumbria CA11 7AH
Fax 01768-890363   Tel 01768-862313
E-mail: cwherald@globalnet.co.uk

Derry Journal Co
Buncrana Road, Derry BT48 8AA
Fax 028-71 272218/272260   Tel 028-712 72200
E-mail: derryj@sol.co.uk
5 titles. The 3 best sellers are: Derry Journal (Friday);
Derry Journal (Tuesday); Donegal Democrat.

Dewsbury Reporter series
1 Market Street, Cleckheaton, W Yorks BD19 3RT
Fax 01274-851304   Tel 01274-874635
Publish Spenborough Guardian, Heckmandwike
Herald. Owned by RIM.

Dimbleby Newspaper Group
14 King Street, Richmond, Surrey TW9 1NF
Fax 020-8332 1899   Tel 020-8940 6030
E-mail: ad@dimbleby.oc.uk
Website: www.dimbleby.co.uk
11 editions.

Dumfriesshire Newspapers Group
96 High St, Annan Dumfriesshire DG12 6DW
Fax 01461-205659   Tel 01461-202078
The group publishes the Dumfries Courier, Annandale
Observer, Annandale Herald and Moffat News.

Dunfermline Press Group
Pitreavie Business Park, Dunfermline, Fife KY11 8QS
Fax 01383 737040   Tel 01383-728201
                     ISDN 01383-722827
E-mail: advertising@dunfermlinepress.co.uk

Dungannon Development Association
1 Savings Bank Street, Dungannon, County Tyrone
BT70 1DT
Fax 028-8772 4666   Tel 028-8772 5445

Eastern Counties Newspapers Group
Prospect House, Rouen Road, Norwich, NR1 1RE
Fax 01603-612930   Tel 01603-628311
E-mail: ecnmail@ecn.co.uk
Website: www.ecn.co.uk

Echo Newspaper series
Echo House, Jubilee Drive, Belton Park,
Loughborough, Leicestershire LE11 5TQ
Fax 01509-238363   Tel 01509-232632
E-mail: postmaster@echoweb.demon.co.uk
Website: www.loughborough-echo.co.uk
12 titles, the best seller is: Loughborough Echo.

Ellerman Investment (aka Barclay Bros)
20 St James's Street, London SW1A 1ES
Fax 020-7930 9131   Tel 020-7915 0915
6 titles. Ellerman Investment bought The Scotsman
Publications off Thomson Regional Newspapers for
£90 million in November 1995.

Ellesmere Press
The British School, Otley Street, Skipton BD23 1EW
Fax 01756-799766   Tel 01756-799765
E-mail: rufus@epltd.demon.co.uk
4 titles.

Eskdale & Liddesdale Newspapers
Commercial House, High Street, Langholm,
Dumfriesshire DG13 0JH
Fax 013873-80345   Tel 013873-80012
E-mail: langham.paper@iname.com

E&R Inglis
219 Argyll Street Dunoon, Argyll PA23 7QT
Fax 01369-703458   Tel 01369-703218
E-mail: info@dunoon-observer.co.uk
Website: www.dunoon-observer.co.uk
7 titles.

Forest of Dean Newspapers
Woodside Street, Cinderford, Glos GL14 2NN
Fax 01594-826213   Tel 01594-822126
E-mail: FODNews@Freenet.co.uk
The Forester, incorporating Dean Forest Guardian,
Dean Forest Mercury and the Lydney Observer.

Friday Ad Group
Old London Road, Sayers Common, West Sussex
BN6 9HS
Fax 0870-167 0168   Tel 0870-162 9999
E-mail: sales@friday-ad.co.uk
Website: www.friday-ad.co.uk
30 titles.

Galloway Gazette
71 Victoria Lane, Newton Stewart, Wigtownshire DG8 6PS
Fax 01671-403391   Tel 01671-402503
2 titles.

Gannett
see Newsquest

Garnett Dickinson Publishing
Eastwood, Fitzwilliam Road, Rotherham S65 1JU
Fax 01709-820588   Tel 01709-364721
E-mail: info@gdpublishing.co.uk
Website: www.gdprint.co.uk

Guardian Media Group
164 Deansgate, Manchester M60 2RD
Fax 0161-832 5351   Tel 0161-832 7200
Around 100 titles.
GMG's national titles are The Guardian and The
Observer. Its local papers are published by divisions in
Greater Manchester and Surrey and Berkshire.
Autotrader publishes regional editions in conjunction
with Hurst Publishing All ordinary shares of GMG are
owned by the Scott Trust and any dividends "shall be
devoted towards building up the reserves of the
company and expanding, improving and increasing the
circulation of its newspapers".

Guernsey Press Co
Braye Road, Guernsey, Channel Islands GY1 3BW
Fax 01481-240235   Tel 01481-240240
E-mail: gp@guernsey-press.com
Website: www.thisisguernsey.
2 titles, Guernsey Press, Globe.

GW McKane & Son
Reliance Works, 32-34 Station Street, Keswick,
Cumbria CA12 2HF
Fax 017687-71203   Tel 017687-72140
E-mail: smr@mortons.co.uk
1 title, the Keswick Reminder.

Hampshire Chronicle Group
57 High Street, Winchester, Hampshire SO23 9BY
Fax 01962-842313   Tel 01962-841772
E-mail: news@hampshirechronical.co.uk
Website: www.hampshirechronical.co.uk
Jacob and Johnson until purchase by Newscom in 1999

Hawick News
24 High Street, Hawick TD9 9EH
Fax 01450-370706   Tel 01450-372204

Heads (Congleton)
11 High Street, Congleton, Cheshire CW12 1BW
Fax 01260-280687   Tel 01260-273737
E-mail: jeremy-condliffe@compuserve.com
Website: www.beartown.co.uk
3 titles. Last independent paid-for weekly in Cheshire.

Heathrow Villager
260 Kingston Road, Staines, Middlesex TW18 1PG
Fax 01784-453196   Tel 01784-453196
Heathrow's only independent newspaper.

Herald Observer Newspapers
20 Church Green East, Redditch B98 8BP
Fax 01527-584371   Tel 01527-67714
E-mail: editorial@obsgraphics.demon.co.uk
10 titles.

Higgs Group (Henley Standard)
Caxton House, 1 Station Road, Henley-on-Thames,
Oxon RG9 1AD
Fax 01491-419401   Tel 01491-419400
E-mail: mail@higgsgroup.co.uk
Website: www.henley-on-thames.com

Hill Bros (Leek)
Cheshire Newspapers, Newspaper House, Brook
Street, Leek, Staffordshire ST13 5JL
Fax 01538-386975   Tel 01538-399599
12 titles including the paid for weekly Post Times series
in North Staffordshire.

John H Hirst & Co
see Dewsbury Reporter series

Hirst, Kidd & Rennie
172 Union Street, Oldham, Lancashire OL1 1EQ
Fax 0161-627 0905   Tel 0161-633 2121
E-mail: phirst@oldham-chronicle.co.uk
Website: www.oldham-chronicle.co.uk
Publishes 1 daily and 1 free weekly: Oldham Evening
Chronicle; Chronicle Weekend.

Edward Hodgett
4 Margaret Street, Newry, Co Down BT34 1DF
Fax 028-302 63157   Tel 028-302 67633

Holderness Newspapers
1 Seaside Road, Withernsea, E Yorkshire HU19 2DL
Fax 01964-615303   Tel 01964-612777
E-mail: news@holderness-gazette.co.uk
Website: www.holderness-gazette.co.uk
2 titles.

Home Counties Newspapers
63 Campfield Road, St Albans, Hertfordshire AL1 5HX
Fax 01727-837993   Tel 01727-866166
7 titles.In Jan 98 bought by the ECN group for £58
million, part of the CML division. Publishes The
Comet, The Herts Advertiser,Welwyn and Hatfield
Times, Welwyn Herald, Stevenage Herald, Business
Monthly and Hertfordshire Magazine.

Horley Publishing
76a Victoria Road, Horley, Surrey RH6 7PZ
Fax 01293-409653   Tel 01293-409649
E-mail: life.newspapers@talk21.com
2 titles

Independent Newspapers (Regionals)
Newspaper House, 2 Whalebone Lane South,
Dagenham, Essex RM8 1HB
Fax 020-8592 7407   Tel 020-8517 5577
43 titles. The 3 best sellers are: East London Advertiser;
Barking & Dagenham Post; Islington Gazette.

Irish News
113-117, Donegall Street, Belfast BT1 2GE
Fax 028-9033 7505   Tel 028-9032 2226
E-mail: newsdesk@irishnews.com
Website: www.irishnews.com

Isle of Wight County Press
Brannon House, 123 Pyle Street, Newport, Isle of
Wight PO30 1ST
Fax 01983-527204   Tel 01983-521333
E-mail: adman@iwcpress.demon.co.uk
Website: www.iwcp.co.uk
2 titles, 1 paid for weekly.

J&M Publishing
1181 Mid Street, Keith, Banff AB55 5BL
Fax 01542-886059   Tel 01542-886262
E-mail: ba@moray.com
Website: www.moray.com
3 titles.

Jacob & Johnson
see Hampshire Chronicle Group

Jersey Evening Post
PO Box 582, St Saviour, Jersey CI, JE4 8XQ
Fax 01534-611620   Tel 01534-611611
E-mail: editorial@jerseyeveningpost.com
Website: www.jerseyeveningpost.com

Johnston Press
53 Manor Place, Edinburgh EH3 7EG
Fax 0131-225 4580   Tel 0131-225 3361
E-mail: jpress@go-free.co.uk
Website: www.johnstonpress.co.uk
Britain's fourth largest local group by circulation and second largest by number of titles.

Kent Messenger
Messenger House, New Hythe Lane, Larkfield
Aylesford ME20 6SG
Fax 01622-719637   Tel 01622-717880
E-mail: kmgroup@kent-online.co.uk
Website: www.kent-online.co.uk
20 titles.

Kentish Times Newspapers
Roxby House, Station Road, Sidcup, Kent DA15 7EJ
Fax 020-8269 7171   Tel 020-8269 7000
Now owned by Independent Newspapers(UK). 17 titles, the three best sellers are: Gravesend Reporter, Dartford Times, Bromley & Beckenham Times.

Leigh Times Co
106 The Broadway, Leigh-on-Sea SS9 1AJ
Fax 01702-478710   Tel 01702-477666
5 titles

Lichfield Mercury
Graphic House, 17 Bird Street, Lichfield, Staffordshire WS13 6PX
Fax 01543-415814   Tel 01543-414414
E-mail: mercnews@aol.com
4 titles including the Lichfield Mercury, Rugeley Mercury and Cannock Mercury.

Local Publications (Bourne)
Newspaper House, 17 Abbey Road, Bourne, Lincolnshire PE10 9EF
Fax 01778-394087   Tel 01778-425876

Local Publications (Saffron Walden)
10 Emson Close, Saffron Walden, Essex CB10 1HL
Fax 01799-520561   Tel 01799 516161

Local Sunday Newspapers Group
22 Mill Street, Bedford MK40 3HD
Fax 01234-304404   Tel 01234-304403
E-mail: advertising@bos.demon.co.uk
7 editions.

Manchester Reporter Group
24 School Lane, Didsbury, Manchester M20 6RG
Fax 0161-434 9921   Tel 0161-446 2212
2 titles. South Manchester Reporter; Heatons & Reddish Reporter.

Metro International
Leconfield House, Curzon Street, London W1Y 7EB
Fax 020-7493 3229   Tel 020-7408 0230
E-mail: helle.kaiser@metrointernational.co.uk
Website: www.mtg.se
The Sweidsh group which launched giveaway Metro titles in the north east at the beginning of 2000.

Midland Independent Newspapers
28 Colmore Circus,Queensway, Birmingham B4 6AX
Fax 0121-233 3958   Tel 0121-236 3366
Website: www.go2birmingham.co.uk
30 titles.
Midland Independent was formed in 1991 and concentrates activites on local papers in the West and East Midlands. Now part of the Mirror Group.

Midland News Association
51-53 Queen Street, Wolverhampton, West Midlands WV1 1ES
Fax 01902-710106   Tel 01902-313131
E-mail: feedback@expressandstar.co.uk
Website: www.westmidlands.com
Holding company of Express & Star and Shropshire Newspapers. Publishes 2 evening titles, 7 paid weeklies and 14 free weekly titles. The two top sellers are the Express & Star and Shropshire Star.

Modern Times Group
see Metro International

Montrose Review Press
59 John Street, Montrose DD10 8QU
Fax 028-38 676232   Tel 028-38 672605
3 titles: Montrose Review, Mearns Leader, The Kincardineshire Observer.

Morning News
Bede House, All Saints Business Centre, Newcastle-upon-Tyne NE1 2EB
Fax 0191-229 9333   Tel 0191-229 9300
E-mail: linda.hardman@metronews.co.uk
Website: www.metronews.co.uk

Morton Newspapers Group
2 Esky Drive, Portadown, Craigavan BT63 5YY
Fax 01762-393940   Tel 01762-393939
25 titles led by East Antrim series; Ulster Star, Portadown Times. Owned by Scottish Radio Holdings.

Mortons of Horncastle
Newspaper House, Morton Way, Horncastle, Lincolnshire LN9 6JR
Fax 01507-527840   Tel 01507-523456
E-mail: admin@mortons.co.uk
Website: www.mortons.co.uk
6 titles.

Mourne Observer
The Roundabout, Castlewellan Road, Newcastle, Co Down BT33 0JX
Fax 028-437 24566   Tel 028-437 22666

NW Ireland Printing & Publishing Co
10 John St, Omagh, Co Tyrone, Ireland BT78 1DT
Fax 028- 82 242206   Tel 028- 82 243444
E-mail: editor@ulsterherald.com
Website: www.ulsterherald.com
4 titles: Ulster Herald, Derrypeople/Donegal News, Fermanagh Herald, Strabane Chronicle.

Nairnshire Telegraph Co
10 Leopold Street, Nairn IV12 4BG
Fax 01667-455277   Tel 01667-453258
E-mail: nairnshire.telegraph@btinternet.com

New Journal Enterprises
40 Camden Road, London NW1 9DR
Fax 020-7209 1322   Tel 020-7419 9000
E-mail: letters.cnj@cableinet.co.uk
2 titles

New Rutland Times
16b Mill Street, Oakham, Rutland LE15 6EA
Fax 01572-755599   Tel 01572-757722
E-mail: editorial@rutlandtimes.sagehost.co.uk

Newark Advertiser Co
Appletongate, Newark, Notts NG24 1JX
Fax 01636-681122   Tel 01636-681234
E-mail: post@newarkadvertiser.co.uk
Website: www.newarkadvertiser.co.uk

Newbury Weekly News (Printers)
Faraday Road, Newbury, Berkshire RG14 2DW
Fax 01635-522922   Tel 01635-564525
E-mail: editor@newburynews.co.uk
Website: www.newburynews.co.uk
3 titles, 1 paid for - the Newbury Weekly News.

Newscom
Newspaper House, Test Lane, Redbridge,
Southampton, Hampshire SO16 9JX
Fax 023-8042 4969   Tel 023-8042 4777
Website: www.dailyecho.co.uk
Bought by Newsquest/Gannett in May 2000.

Newsquest Media Group
Newspaper House, 34-44 London Road, Morden,
Surrey SM4 5BR
Fax 020-8646 3997   Tel 020-8640 8989
Website: www.newsquest.co.uk
Newsquest was formed by a management buyout of
Reed Regional Newspapers in November 1995 which
then bought Westminster Press from Pearson.
Flotation followed in 1997 and in July 1999 the
company was acquired by Gannett, the largest
newspaper company in the US.

Newsquest Northeast (The Clarion)
30 Queen Street, Redcar, Cleveland TS10 1BD
Fax 01642-477143   Tel 01642-480397
E-mail: mail@clarion1.freeserve.co.uk
Website: www.thisiseastcleveland.co.uk

Newtownards Chronicle
25 Frances St, Newtownards, Co Down BT23 3DT
Fax 028-91 820087   Tel 028-91 813333

Normanton Advertiser
4 West Street, Normanton, W Yorks WF6 2AP
Fax 01924-215327   Tel 01924-892117
E-mail: sales@normanton-advertiser.co.uk

North Devon Gazette & Advertiser
16 Tuly Street, Barnstaple, Devon EX31 1DH
Fax 01271-324608   Tel 01271-344303
E-mail: ndga@community-media.co.uk

North Edinburgh News
222 Crewe Road North, Edinburgh EH5 2NS
Fax 0131-467 3973   Tel 0131-467 3972
E-mail: mary@northednews.demon.co.uk

North Wales Newspapers
Mold Business Park, Wrexham Road, Mold, Flintshire
CH7 1XY
Fax 01352-700048   Tel 01352-707707
E-mail: nwnfd@netwales.co.uk
Website: www.nwn.co.uk
13 titles, top 3 sellers: Evening Leader, County Times,
Oswestry & Border Counties Advertiser.

Northcliffe Newspapers Group
31 John Street, London WC1N 2QB
Fax 020-7400 1207   Tel 020-7400 1100
Website: www.nng.co.uk
65 titles. Top 3 sellers: Aberdeen Press & Journal,
Leicester Mercury, Nottingham Evening Post.
Northcliffe Newspapers is part of the Daily Mail and
General Trust of which Associated Newspapers is the
overall management company. The group publishes the
Daily Mail and Mail on Sunday. In 2000 the company
acquired Bristol United Press.

Northern Newspaper Group
20 Railway Road, Coleraine, BT52 1PD
Fax 028-70 43606   Tel 028-70 43344
3 titles and 1 free. Coleraine Chronicle; Ballymena
Guardian; Northern Constitution.

Nuachtain News Group
301 Glen Road, Belfast, County Antrim BT11 8BU
Fax 028-9062 0602   Tel 028-9061 9000
E-mail: editor@belfast-news.ie
Website: www.belfast-news.ie
Publishes La, Andersonstown News and North Belfast
News

Nuneaton & District Newspapers
Newspaper House, 11-15 Newtown Road, Nuneaton,
Warwickshire CV11 4HR
Fax 024-7635 3481   Tel 024-7635 3534
E-mail: hen@btclick.com
3 titles.

Oban Times Group
Lochavullin Industrial Estate, Crannog, Oban PA34
5PY
Fax 01631-565470   Tel 01631-563058
E-mail: editor@obantimes.co.uk

Observer Newspapers (NI)
Ann Street, Dungannon, Co Tyrone BT70 1ET
Fax 028-87 727334   Tel 028-87 722557

The Orcadian
Hatston Industrial Estate, Kirkwall, Orkney KW15 1DW
Fax 01856-879001   Tel 01856-879000
E-mail: sales@orcadian.co.uk

Outlook Press
Castle Street, Rathfriland, Co Down BT34 5QR
Fax 028-406 31022   Tel 028-406 30202

PM Publications
The Messenger, 2 Kings Road, Haslemere, Surrey
GU27 2QA
Fax 01428-661658   Tel 01428-653999
E-mail: editor@the-messenger-newspaper.co.uk

John Penri Press
11 St Helens Road, Swansea SA1 4AL
Fax 01792-650647   Tel 01792-652092
2 titles.

W Peters & Son
16 High Street, Turriff, Aberdeenshire AB53 4DT
Fax 01888-563936   Tel 01888-563589
3 titles.

Portsmouth & Sunderland Newspapers
The News Centre, Hillsea, Portsmouth PO2 9TG
Fax: 023 9265 8011   Tel 023-9265 8040
19 titles.
Founded in 1873. The groups main activities are in
central, southern and north east England. Taken over by
Johnston Press for £254 million in May 1999.

Recorder (Wales)
Cambria House, Wyndham Street, Bridgend, Mid
Glamorgan CF31 1ED
Fax 01656-656894   Tel 01656-669330
E-mail: recorder@globalnet.co.uk
2 titles, both free. Bridgend & District Recorder.

Regional Independent Media Group
Wellington Street, Leeds, West Yorks LS1 1RF
Fax 0113-242 1814   Tel 0113-243 2701
Website: www.rim.co.uk
101 titles. Top 3 sellers: Yorkshire Post, Yorkshire
Evening Post, The Star, Sheffield. Formerly United
Provincial Newspapers until taken over by the Candover
venture capital group. It operates from centres in
Yorkshire and the North West.

Review & Advertiser Newspaper Group
Kinetic Business Centre, Theobald Street,
Borehamwood, Hertfordshire WD6 4PJ
                         Tel 020-8953 9119

Review Free Newspapers
The William Henry Building, Porters Wood, St Albans,
Hertfordshire AL3 6PQ
Fax 01727-852770   Tel 01727-834411
4 titles.

RIM Scotland
Sherwood Industrial Estate, Bonnyrigg, Midlothian
EH19 3LW
Fax 0131-663 6863   Tel 0131-663 4606
5 titles, the top three are: The Advertiser, East Lothian
News and Musselburgh News.

Ross Gazette
35 High St, Ross-on-Wye, Herefordshire HR9 5HE
Fax 01989-768023   Tel 01989-562007
E-mail: ross.gazette@internet-today.co.uk

SC Publishing Co
see Central Independent News

SMG Publishing
195 Albion Street, Glasgow G1 1QP
Fax 0141-552 1344   Tel 0141-552 6255
3 titles.
A company formed in 1992 by the management buyout
of The Herald and The Evening Times from Lonrho
and George Outram and Co. Now owned by Scottish
Newspapers. Formerly Caledonian Newspaper
Publishing.

Scotsman Publications
108 Holyrood Road, Edinburgh EH8 8AS
Fax: 0131-625 1515   Tel 0131-620 8620
Website: www.scotsman.com
4 titles.

Scottish and Universal Newspapers
40 Craigs, Stirling FK8 2DW
Fax 01786-459486   Tel 01786 459426
E-mail: marketing@s-un.co.uk
Website: www.inside-scotland.co.uk
            www.media-scotland.co.uk
33 titles, top 3 sellers: Ayrshire Post, Hamilton
Advertiser, Perthshire Advertiser.

Scottish County Press
see RIM Scotland

Scottish Daily Record & Sunday Mail
40 Anderston Quay, Glasgow G3 8DA
Fax 0141-242 3545   Tel 0141-248 7000
E-mail: editor@features.dailyrecord.co.uk
Website: www.record-mail.co.uk
Publisher of Scotland's best-selling daily and Sunday
newspapers. Also publishes The Glaswegian, Scotland's
largest free weekly newspaper, and a number of
magazine titles.

Scottish Media Group
195 Albion Street, Galsgow G1 1QP
Fax 0141-552 3050   Tel 0141-552 6255
E-mail: herald@scottishmedia.com
Website: www.the herald.co.uk
Owns Caledonian Magazines and Caledonian
Newspapers.

Scottish Provincial Press
13 Henderson Road, Inverness, Scotland IV1 1SP
Fax 01463-221251   Tel 01463-713700

Sheffield Mercury Newspaper (Baycro)
PO Box 70, Sheffield, South Yorkshire S8 0QA
                         Tel 0114-274 6555/6444
E-mail: sheffmerc@aol.com

The Shetland Times
Prince Alfred Street, Lerwick, Shetland ZE1 0EP
Fax 01595-694637   Tel 01595-693622
E-mail: editorial@shetland-times.co.uk
Website: www.shetland-times.co.uk
            www.shetlandtoday.co.uk

Slough Observer Group
Upton Court, Datchet Road, Slough, Berkshire SL3
7NR
Fax 01753-693895   Tel 01753-523355

G H Smith & Son
Market Place, Easingwold, York YO61 3AB
Fax 01347-822576   Tel 01347 821329
E-mail: ghsmith@globalnet.co.uk
Website: www.ghsmith.com

Southern Newspapers
See Newscom

Southnews
89-91 Eastworth Road, Chertsey, Surrey KT16 8DX
Fax 01932-573240   Tel 01932-566311
Website: www.southnews.co.uk
97 titles.
Formed in 1986 by Westminster Press and Reed
Regional Newspapers managers. Bought the Croydon
Advertiser for £12.95 million from Portsmouth and
Sunderland Newspapers in 1995. Later bought the
southern part of United Provincial and its most recent
acquisition was Adscene in 2000 for £52 million.

Southwark News
Unit J104, Tower Bridge Business Complex,
Clement's Road, London SE16 4DG
Fax 020-7237 1578   Tel 020-7231 5258
E-mail: newsdesk@southwarknews.co.uk

Spalding & South Lincs Herald
Riverside Key, Double St, Spalding, Lincs PE11 2AB
Fax 01775-713714   Tel 01775-768661

Spectator Newspapers
109 Main Street, Bangor, Co Down BT20 4AF
Fax 028- 91 271544   Tel 028- 91 270270
E-mail: spectator@dial.pipex.com
3 titles.

The St Ives Printing & Publishing Co
High Street, St Ives, Cornwall TR26 1RS
Fax 01736-795020   Tel 01736-795813
E-mail: times@echo.clara.net
2 titles

Star Publishing
6-8 Mill Street, Maidstone, Kent ME15 6XH
Fax 01622-675071   Tel 01622-678556
Website: www.starpublishing.co.uk

Star Newspapers (Camberley)
192 Victoria Road, Aldershot, Hants GU11 1JZ
Fax 01252-343042   Tel 01252-316311
E-mail: advertising@starnewspaper.co.uk

The Tamworth Herald Co
Ventura Park Road, Bitterscote, Tamworth,
Staffordshire B78 3LZ
Fax 01827-848511   Tel 01827-848610
E-mail: theherald@aol.com
3 titles, the best seller is the Tamworth Herald.

Teesdale Mercury
24 Market Place, Barnard Castle, County Durham
DL12 8NB
Fax 01833-638633   Tel 01833-637140
E-mail: sales@teesdalemercury.co.uk

DC Thomson & Co
2 Albert Square, Dundee, Tayside DD1 9QJ
Fax 01382-322214   Tel 01382-223131
E-mail: dct@dcthomson.co.uk
Website: www.dcthomson.co.uk
3 titles. Sunday Post, Dundee Courier & Adverrtiser,
Dundee Evening Telegraph.A family owned company
which also publishes the Beano and the Dandy.

Tindle Newspapers
114 West Street, Farnham, Surrey GU9 7HL
Fax 01252-723950   Tel 01252-723938
Website: www.tindlenews.co.uk
Over 100 titles. A family-owned company which
publishes in Surrey, Hampshire, Kent, Lancashire and
Wales. Best seller is the Farnham Herald.

Topper Newspapers
Maychalk House, 8 Musters Road, Notts NG2 7PL
Fax 0115-982 6565   Tel 0115-982 6974
Website: www.toppernewspapers.co.uk

Tri Media Publishing
2nd Floor, Paddington House, The Walks,
Basingstoke RG21 7LJ
                    Tel 01256-694120
E-mail: newbury@milestone.co.uk

Trident Midland Newspapers
Bridge Road, Coalville, Leicester LE67 3QP
Fax 01530-811361   Tel 01530-813101
E-mail: info@impartialreporter.com
4 titles. Top three sellers are the Ashby, Coalville and
Swadlincote Times.

Trinity-Mirror
Kingsfield Court, Chester Business Park, Chester,
Cheshire CH4 9RE
Fax 01244-687100   Tel 01244-687000
E-mail: trinity@trinity.plc.uk
Website: www.trinity.plc.uk
176 titles. The Liverpool Daily Post and Echo until 1985,
Trinity expanded by buying Argus Newspapers in
London and the home counties plus titles in Wales and
Scotland. It became the largest regional paper publisher
in Britain with the £327.5 million purchase, in 1995, of
the Thomson Regional Newspaper titles. In July 1999
Trinity merged with the Mirror Group in a £1.5 billion
deal that formed Trinity Mirror.

The Tweeddale Press Group
PO Box 10, 90 Marygate, Berwick Upon Tweed,
Northumberland TD15 1BW
Fax 01289-307377   Tel 01289-306677
E-mail: mail@tweeddalepress.co.uk
Website: www.tweeddalepress.co.uk
6 titles. The 3 best sellers are: Southern Reporter;
Berwick Advertiser; Hawick News. Part of Johnston
Press.

Tyrone Constitution Group
25-27 High Street, Omagh, Co Tyrone BT78 1BD
Fax 028-82 243549   Tel 028-82 242721
E-mail: editor@tyroneconstitution.com

United Advertising Publications
Link House, 25 West Street, Poole, Dorset BH15 1LL
Fax 01202-445245   Tel 01202-445000

United Provincial Newspapers
Sold by UNM to Candover and Southnews. See entries
for Regional Indpenedent Media and Southnews

West Highland Publishing Co
Broadford, Isle of Skye IV49 9AP
Fax 01471-822694   Tel 01471-822464
E-mail: newsdesk@whfp.co.uk
Website: www.whfp.co.uk
2 titles.

Westminster Press
see Newsquest

Wigtown Free Press
St Andrew Street, Stranraer, Wigtownshire DG9 7EB
Fax 01776-706695   Tel 01776-702551
E-mail: bill_henderson@btconnect.com

William Trimble
8-10 East Bridge Street, Enniskillen, N Ireland BT74
7BT
Fax 028-66 325047   Tel 028-66 324422
E-mail: info@impartialreporter.com
Website: www.impartialreporter.com
1 title. A family owned company since 1825.

Yattendon Investment Trust
see Cambridge Newspapers

TOP REGIONAL MORNINGS

TITLE	CIRCULATION Jan-June 2000	PER CENTAGE CHANGE	OWNER
1 Daily Record - Scotland	637,353	-5.8%	Trinity Mirror
2 The Herald - Scotland	100,603	-0.5%	Scottish Media Group
3 Press & Journal - Aberdeen	100,421	-3.9%	Northcliffe Newspapers Group
4 Courier & Advertiser - Dundee	93,406	-2.2%	DC Thomson
5 Eastern Daily Press - Norwich	76,664	-2.5%	Eastern Counties Newspapers
6 The Scotsman	75,757	-4.9%	Scotsman Publications
7 Yorkshire Post - Leeds	73,876	-2.6%	Regional Independent Media
8 Daily Post - Liverpool	70,019	-3.1%	Trinity Mirror
9 Northern Echo - Darlington	67,589	-3.9%	Newsquest Media Group
10 The Western Mail - Cardiff	57,131	-0.9%	Trinity Mirror
11 Western Daily Press - Bristol	56,977	-5.3%	Bristol United Press
12 Western Morning News - Plymouth	51,751	+0.1%	Northcliffe Newspapers Group
13 The Journal - Newcastle upon Tyne	51,458	-0.9%	Trinity Mirror
14 Irish News	50,353	+0.0%	Fitzpatrick Family
15 East Anglian Daily Times - Ipswich	45,029	-2.1%	Eastern Counties Newspapers
16 News Letter - Ulster	33,395	-1.4%	Century Newspapers
17 Paisley Daily Express	10,232	+12.8%	Trinity Mirror

Excludes Birmingham Post which currently has no ABC figure

Source: The Newspaper Society, July 2000

TOP REGIONAL MORNINGS

Courier & Advertiser
2 Albert Square, Dundee DD! 9QJ
Fax 01382-454590   Tel 01382-223131
E-mail: courier@dcthomson.co.uk
Website: www.dcthomson.co.uk/courier
Editor: Adrian Arthur
Owner: DC Thomson & Co

Daily Post
PO Box 48, Old Hall Street, Liverpool L69 3EB
Fax 0151-236 4682   Tel 0151-227 2000
E-mail: editor@dailypost.co.uk
Web: www.liverpool.com
Editor: Alastair Machray
Owner: Trinity Mirror

Daily Record
40 Anderston Quay, Glasgow, Strathclyde G3 8DA
Fax 0141-242 3340   Tel 0141-248 7000
E-mail editor@dailyrecord.co.uk
Editor-in-chief: Martin Clarke
Owner: Trinity Mirror

East Anglian Daily Times
Press House, 30 Lower Brook Street, Ipswich IP4 1AN
Fax 01473-211391   Tel 01473-230023
E-mail: EADT@ecn.co.uk
Website: www.suffolk.now.co.uk
Editor: Terry Hunt
Owner: Eastern Counties Newspapers

Eastern Daily Press
Prospect House, Rouen Road, Norwich, NR1 1RE
Fax 01603-612930   Tel 01603-628311
E-mail: edp@ecn.co.uk
Website: www.ecn.co.uk
Editor: Peter Franzen
Owner: Eastern Counties

The Herald
195 Albion Street, Glasgow G1 1QP
Fax 0141-552 2288   Tel 0141-552 6255
E-mail: herald@cims.co.uk
Website: www.theherald.co.uk
Editor: G McKechnie
Owner: Scottish Media Group

Irish News (Belfast)
113-117 Donegall Street, Belfast BT1 2GE
Fax 028-9033 7505   Tel 028-9032 2226
E-mail: newsdesk@irishnews.com
Web: www.irishnews.com
Editor: Noel Doran
Owner: Fitzpatrick family

The Journal
Thomson House, Groat Market, Newcastle upon Tyne NE1 1ED
Fax 0191-230 4144   Tel 0191-232 7500
Editor: Mark Dickinson

News Letter
Century Newspapers, 46-56 Boucher Crescent, Belfast, Co Antrim BT12 6QY
Fax 028-9066 4436   Tel 028-9068 0000
Editor: Geoff Martin

The Northern Echo
PO Box 14, Priestgate, Darlington DL1 1NF
Fax 01325-486234   Tel 01325-381313
E-mail: echo@nen.co.uk
Web: www.thisisthenortheast.co.uk
Editor: Peter Barron
Owner: Newsquest Media Group

Paisley Daily Express
Clyde & Forth Press, Pitreavie Business Park,
Queensferry Road, Dunfermline, Fife KY11 8QS
Fax 01383-737040   Tel 01383-728201
Editor: Fiona Howard

Press and Journal
Lang Stracht, Mastrick, Aberdeen AB15 6DF
Fax 01224-663575   Tel 01224-690222
E-mail: editor@pj.ajl.co.uk
Website: www.pressandjournal.co.uk
Editor: Derek Tucker
Owner: Northcliffe Newspaper Group

The Scotsman
108 Holyrood Road, Edinburgh H8 8AS
Fax 0131-625 1583   Tel 0131-620 8620
Website: www.scotsman.com
Editor: Tim Luckhurst
Owner: Scotsman Publications

Western Daily Press
Temple Way, Bristol Avon BS99 7HD
Fax 0117-934 3574   Tel 0117-9343000
Editor: Ian Beales
Owner: Bristol United Press

The Western Mail
Thomson House, Havelock Street, Cardiff CF10 1XR
Fax 029-2058 3652   Tel 029-2022 3333
E-mail: readers@wme.co.uk
Web: www.totalwales.com
Editor: Neil Fowler
Owner: Trinity Mirror

Western Morning News
17 Brest Road, Derriford Business Park, Plymouth
PL6 5AA
Fax 01752-765535   Tel 01752-765500
E-mail: wmnadmin@westcountrypublcations.co.uk
Website: www.westernmorningnews.co.uk
Editor: Barrie Williams
Owner: Northcliffe Newspapers Group

Yorkshire Post
Wellington Street, Leeds, West Yorks LS1 1RF
Fax 0113-244 3430   Tel 0113-243 2701
E-mail: yp.newsdesk@ypn.co.uk
Editor: Tony Watson
Owner: Regional Independent Media

TOP REGIONAL EVENINGS

Aberdeen Evening Express
PO Box 43, Mastrick Aberdeen AB15 6DF
Fax 01224-699575   Tel 01224-690222
E-mail: editor@ee.ajl.co.uk
Website: www.thisisnorthscotland.co.uk
Editor: Donald Martin   Owner: Northcliffe Newspapers

Belfast Telegraph
124-144 Royal Avenue, Belfast BT1 1EB
Fax 028-9055 4506   Tel 028-9026 4000
E-mail: editor@belfasttelegraph.co.uk
Websote: www.belfasttelegraph.co.uk
Editor: Edmund Curran   Owner: Trinity Mirror

Bristol Evening Post
Temple Way, Bristol BS99 7HD
Fax 0117-934 3575   Tel 0117-934 3000
E-mail: epost@bepp.co.uk
Website: www.thisisbristol.com
Editor: Mike Lowe   Owner: Northcliffe Newspapers

Coventry Evening Telegraph & The Pink
Corporation Street, Coventry, CV1 1FP
Fax 024-7663 1736   Tel 024-7663 3633
E-mail: editorial@go2coventry.co.uk
Website: www.go2coventry.co.uk
Editor: Alan Kirby   Owner: Trinity Mirror

Evening Chronicle
Thomson House, Groat Market, Newcastle NE1 1ED
Fax 0191-230 4144   Tel 0191-232 7500
E-mail: ec.news@ncjmedia.co.uk
Website: www.evening-chronicle.co.uk
Editor: Alison Hastings
Owner: Trinity Mirror

Evening News
20 North Bridge, Edinburgh, EH1 1YT
Fax 0131-225 7302   Tel 0131-225 2468
Editor: John McLellan
Owner: Scotsman Publications

Evening Standard
2 Derry Street, London W8 5EE
Fax 020-7937 3193   Tel 020-7938 6000
Website: www.thisis london.com
Editor: Max Hastings
Owner: Associated Newspapers

Evening Times
195 Albion Street, Glasgow G1 1QP
Fax 0141-553 1355   Tel 0141-552 6255
Editor: John Scott
Owner: Scottish Media Group

Express and Star
51-53 Queen Street, Wolverhampton WV1 1ES
Fax 01902-319721   Tel 01902-313131
E-mail: express and star.co.uk
Editor: Warren Wilson
Owner: Midland News Association

Hull Daily Mail & Sports Mail
Blundells Corner, Beverley Road, Hull HU3 1XS
Fax 01482-584353   Tel 01482-327111
E-mail: hdm@dial.pipex.com
Website: www.hulldailymail.co.uk
Editor: John Meehan

TOP 20 UK REGIONAL EVENINGS

TITLE	CIRCULATION Jan-June 2000	PER CENTAGE CHANGE	OWNER
1 Evening Standard - London	437,447	-2.8%	London Evening Standard
2 West Midlands Express & Star	183,759	-1.7%	Midland News Association
3 Manchester Evening News	173,179	-0.2%	Guardian Media Group
4 Liverpool Echo	155,920	-1.3%	Trinity Mirror
5 Belfast Telegraph	117,207	-5.9%	Trinity Mirror
6 Glasgow Evening Times	108,838	-6.6%	Scottish Media
7 Evening Chronicle - Newcastle u Tyne	107,511	-2.0%	Trinity Mirror
8 Leicester Mercury	102,640	-5.4%	Northcliffe Newspapers Group
9 Yorkshire Evening Post - Leeds	99,199	-1.4%	Regional Independent Media
10 The Sentinel - Stoke on Trent	89,772	-0.7%	Northcliffe Newspapers Group
11 Shropshire Star	87,629	-2.2%	Midland News Association
12 Sheffield Star	83,236	-2.0%	Regional Independent Media
13 Hull Daily Mail & Sports Mail	82,431	-2.6%	Northcliffe Newspapers Group
14 Coventry E'ning Telegraph & The Pink	80,250	-2.6%	Trinity Mirror
15 Bristol Evening Post	77,476	-2.4%	Bristol United Press
16 Evening News - Edinburgh	75,321	-6.7%	Scotsman Publications
17 South Wales Echo - Cardiff	70,973	-4.9%	Trinity Mirror
18 News & Sports Mail - Portsmouth	70,432	n/a	P'smouth & Sunderland N'papers
19 Evening Express - Aberdeen	65,607	-1.0%	Northcliffe Newspapers Group
20 South Wales Evening Post	63,922	+1.0%	Northcliffe Newspapers Group

Excludes Birmingham Evening Mail which currently has no ABC figure and Nottingham Evening Post which is independently audited

Source: The Newspaper Society

Leicester Mercury
St George Street, Leicester LE1 9FQ
Fax 0116-262 4687   Tel 0116-251 2512
E-mail: enquiries@leicestermercury.co.uk
Website: www.thisisleicester.co.uk
Editor: Nick Carter
Owner: Northcliffe Newspapers Group

Liverpool Echo
Old Hall Street, Liverpool L69 3EB
Fax 0151-236 4682   Tel 0151-227 2000
E-mail: editor@liverpoolecho.co.uk
Website: www.liverpool.com
Editor: Mark Dickinson Owner: Trinity Mirror

Manchester Evening News
164 Deansgate, Manchester M60 2RD
Fax 0161-832 5351   Tel 0161-832 7200
E-mail:
Website: www.manchesteronline.co.uk
Editor: Paul Horrocks
Owner: Guardian Media Group

Portsmouth News & Sports Mail
The News Centre, Hilsea, Portsmouth PO2 9SX
Fax 023-9266 4488   Tel 023-9266 4488
E-mail: newsdesk@thenews.co.uk
Web: www.thenews.co.uk
Editor: Geoff Elliott
Owner: Portsmouth & Sunderland Newspapers

The Sentinel
Sentinel House, Stoke-on-Trent, Staffs ST1 5SS
Fax 01782-280781   Tel 01782-289800
Editor: Sean Dooley

Shropshire Star
Ketley, Telford, Shropshire TF1 4HU
Fax 01952-254605   Tel 01952-242424
Editor: Andy Wright
Owner: Claverley Co

South Wales Echo
Thomson House, Havelock Street, Cardiff CF10 1XR
Fax 029-2058 3624   Tel 029-2022 3333
E-mail: letters@wme.co.uk
Web: www.totalwales.com
Editor: Robin Fletcher
Owner: Trinity Mirror

South Wales Evening Post
PO Box 14, Adelaide Street, Swansea SA1 1QT
Fax 01792-514197   Tel 01792-510000
Web: www.thisissouthwales.co.uk
Editor: George Edwards
Owner: Northcliffe Newspapers Group

The Star
York Street, Sheffield, South Yorks S1 1PU
Fax 0114-272 5978   Tel 0114-276 7676
Website: www.sheffweb.co.uk
Editor: Peter Charlton
Owner: Regional Independent Media

Yorkshire Evening Post
Wellington Street, Leeds, West Yorks LS1 1RF
Fax 0113-238 8536   Tel 0113-243 2701
E-mail: eped@tpn.co.uk
Editor: Neil Hodgkinson
Owner: Regional Independent Media

TOP 20 WEEKLIES

TITLE	CIRCULATION Jan-June 2000	PER CENTAGE CHANGE	OWNER
1 West Briton	50,616	+0.0%	Northcliffe Newspapers Group
2 Essex Chronicle	49,705	+0.0%	Northcliffe Newspapers Group
3 Kent Messenger	47,949	+5.7%	Kent Messenger Group
4 Surrey Advertiser	45,615	+0.3%	Guardian Media Group
5 Chester Chronicle	44,178	-0.3%	Trinity Mirror
6 Western Gazette	43,165	-2.1%	Bristol United Press
7 Derbyshire Times	41,939	-0.0%	Johnston Press
8 Hereford Times	41,164	+1.8%	Newsquest
9 Kent & Sussex Courier	40,464	-0.7%	Northcliffe Newspapers Group
10 Croydon Advertiser	40,147	+0.2%	Southnews
11 Chichester Observer	39,483	+12.4%	P'smouth & Sunderland N'papers
12 Barnsley Chronicle	39,463	-0.4%	Barnsley Chronicle
13 Isle of Wight County Press	39,401	+2.7%	Isle of Wight County Press
14 Cornish Guardian	37,992	+0.5%	Northcliffe Newspapers Group
15 Cumberland News	37,438	+0.9%	CN Group
16 South London Press (Fri)	36,210	-10.1%	Trinity Mirror
17 North Devon Journal	36,042	+1.8%	Northcliffe Newspapers Group
18 Warrington Guardian	35,317	+0.4	Newsquest
19 Guardian Series	34,731	+0.0%	Newsquest
20 Westmoreland Gazette	33,447	+1.0%	Newsquest

Excludes Birmingham Evening Mail which currently has no ABC figure and Nottingham Evening Post which is independently audited

Source: The Newspaper Society

TOP PAID-FOR WEEKLIES

Barnsley Chronicle
47 Church Street, Barnsley, Yorkshire S70 2AS
Fax 01226-734455   Tel 01226-734734
E-mail: ac@barnsley-chronicle.co.uk
Web: www.barnsley-chronicle.co.uk
Editor: Robert Cockroft
Owner: Barnsley Chronicle Holdings

Chester Chronicle
Commonhall Street, Chester CH1 2BJ
Fax 01244-322262   Tel 01244-340151
E-mail: newsroom@cheshirenews.co.uk
Web: www.cheshirenews.co.uk
Editor: Paul Chamberlain
Owner: Trinity Mirror

Chichester Observer
Unicorn House, 8 Eastgate Square, Chichester, West Sussex PO19 1JN
Fax 01243-3539307   Tel 01243-534123
Web: www.chiobserver.co.uk
Editor: Keith Newberry
Owner: Portsmouth & Sunderland Newspapers

Cornish Guardian
30 Fore Street, Bodmin, Cornwall PL31 2HQ
Fax 01208-72109   Tel 01208-78133
E-mail: cwncg@eurobell.co.uk
Web: www.thisiscornwall.co.uk
Editor: Alan Cooper
Owner: Northcliffe Newspapers Group

Croydon Advertiser series
19 Bartlett Street, South Croydon CR2 6TB
Fax 020-8763 6633 (ed) Tel 020-8763 6666
E-mail: edit@croydonadvertiser.co.uk
Editor: Malcolm Starbrook
Owner: South News

The Cumberland News
Newspaper House, Dalston Road, Carlisle CA2 5UA
Fax 01288-612640   Tel 01288-612600
E-mail: news@cumbrian-newspapers.co.uk
Website: www.cumberland-news.co.uk
Editor: Keith Sutton Owner: CN Group

Derbyshire Times
Station Road, Chesterfield, Derbyshire S41 7XD
Fax 01246-504580   Tel 01246-504500
Editor: Mike Wilson
Owner: Johnston Press

Essex Chronicle
Westway,Chelmsford, Essex CM1 3BE
Fax 01245-603353   Tel 01245-600700
E-mail: name@essexchronicle.demon.co.uk
Editor: Stuart Rawlins Owner: Northcliffe Newspapers

Guardian series
The Academy, Bridge Street, Warrington, Cheshire WA1 2RU
Fax 01925-434028   Tel 01925-434000
Owner: Newsquest Media Group

Hereford Times
Holmer Road, Hereford HR4 9UKJ
Fax 01432-343235   Tel 01432-274413
E-mail: stewartg@newsquestmidlands.co.uk
Editor: Stewart Gilbert

Isle of Wight County Press
Brannon House, 123 Pyle Street, Newport PO30 1ST
Fax 01983-527204   Tel 01983-521333
E-mail: adman@iowpress.demon.co.uk
Web: www.iwcp.co.uk
Editor: B Dennis

Kent Messenger
6 & 7 Middle Row, Maidstone, Kent ME14 1TG
Fax 01622-695666   Tel 01622-757227
E-mail: kmgroupcommercial@kentonline.co.uk
Web: www.kent-online.co.uk
Editor: Simon Irwin

Kent and Sussex Courier
Longfield Road, Tunbridge Wells TN2 3HL
Fax 01892-510400   Tel 01892-681000
E-mail: editor@ourier.co.uk
Web: www.thisiskentandeastsussex.co.uk
Editor: Martin Oxley

North Devon Journal
96 High Street, Barnstaple, Devon EX31 1HT
Fax 01271-323165   Tel 01271-343064
E-mail: editorial@northdevonjournal.co.uk
Web: www.thisisnorthdevon.co.uk
Managing editor: Andy Cooper

South London Press (Friday edition)
2-4 Leigham Court Road, London SW16 2PD
Fax 020-8769 1742   Tel 020-8769 4444
E-mail: robbowden@slp.co.uk
Web: www.slp.co.uk
Editor: Rob Bowden
Owner: Trinity-Mirror

Surrey Advertiser
Stoke Mill, Woking Road, Guildford GU1 1QA
Fax 01483-508930   Tel 01483-508900
E-mail: editorial@surreyad.co.uk
Web: www.surreyad.co.uk
Editor: Graham Collyer
Owner: Guardian Media Group

Warrington Guardian
138 Bridge Street, Warrington, Cheshire WA1 2RU
Fax 01925-434115   Tel 01925-434000
E-mail: webmaster@info-quest.com
Web: www.thisischeshire.co.uk
Editor: Jan Lever

West Briton
Harmsworth House, Lemon Quay, Truro, TR1 2LP
Fax 01872-265016   Tel 01872-271451
Web: www.thisiscornwall.co.uk
Editor: John Pearn

Western Gazette
Sherborne Road, Yeovil, Somerset BA21 4YA
Fax 01935-432266   Tel 01935-700500
E-mail: editor@westgaz.co.uk
Web: www.westgaz.co.uk
Editor: Martin Heal

Westmoreland Gazette
22 Stricklandgate, Kendal, Cumbria LA9 4NE
Fax 01539-723618   Tel 01539-720555
E-mail: kendal@westmorlandgaz.demon.co.uk
Website: www.thisisthelakedistrict.co.uk
Editor: Mike Glover

TOP PAID-FOR SUNDAYS

(CHART ON PAGE 80)

Scotland on Sunday
20 North Bridge, Edinburgh EH1 1YT
Fax 0131-220 2443   Tel 0131-225 2468
Website: www.scotsman.com
Editor: John McGurk
Owner: European Press Holdings

Sunday Herald
195 Albion Street, Glasgow G1 1QP
Fax 0141-302 7809   Tel 0141-552 6255
Website: www.sundayherald.com
Editor: Andrew Jispan
Owner: Scottish Media Newspapers

Sunday Independent
Burrington Way, Plymouth, Devon PL5 3LN
Fax 01752 206164   Tel 01752 206600
Editor: A Jenkins
Owner: Southern Newspapers

Sunday Life (Belfast)
124-144 Royal Avenue, Belfast BT1 1EB
Fax 028-9055 4507   Tel 028-9026 4300
E-mail: barnold@belfasttelegraph.co.uk
Editor: Martin Lindsay
Owner: Trinity Mirror

Sunday Mail
Anderston Quay, Glasgow G3 8DA
Fax 0141-242 3587   Tel 0141-248 7000
Website: www.record-mail.co.uk
Editor: Jim Cassidy
Owner: Mirror Group

Sunday Post
2 Albert Square, Dundee DD1 9QJ
Fax 01382-201064   Tel 01382-223131
E-mail: post@dcthomson.co.uk
Website: www.dcthomson.co.uk
Editor: Russell Reid
Owner: DC Thomson & Co

Sunday Sun
Thomson House, Groat Market, Newcastle NE1 1ED
Fax 0191-230 0238   Tel 0191-201 6330
E-mail: office@sundaysun.demon.co.uk
Website: www.sundaysun.co.uk
Editor: Peter Montellier
Owner: Trinity Mirror

Wales on Sunday
Havelock Street, Cardiff CF1 1XR
Fax 029-2058 3725   Tel 029-2058 3733
E-mail: wosmail@wme.co.uk
Website: www.totalwales.co.uk
Editor: Alan Edmunds
Owner: Trinity-Mirror

TOP PAID FOR SUNDAYS

TITLE	CIRCULATION	PER CENTAGE CHANGE	OWNER
1 Sunday Mail - Glasgow	759,567	n/a	Mirror Regional N'papers
2 Sunday Post - Dundee	684,567	-7.3%	DC Thomson & Co
3 Scotland on Sunday	109,273	-12.7%	Scotsman Publications
4 Sunday Sun - Newcastle upon Tyne	106,342	-5.8%	Trinity Mirror
5 Sunday Life - Belfast	94,768	-6.4%	Trinity Mirror
6 Sunday World, N Ireland edition	71,847	-1.2%	Sunday Newespapers
7 Wales on Sunday	66,239	+6.3%	Trinity Mirror
8 Sunday Herald - Glasgow	54,316	n/a	Scottish Media
9 Sunday Independent - Plymouth	34,705	-4.4%	Newscom

Excludes Sunday Mercury - Birmingham, which currently has no ABC figure

Source: The Newspaper Society

TOP UK REGIONAL FREE WEEKLIES RANKED BY DISTRIBUTION

TITLE	DISTRIBUTION	AVERAGE PAGINATION	AVERAGE % OF ADVERTISING
1 Manchester Metro News	300,088	90	55%
2 The Glaswegian	201,008	43	59 %
3 Nottingham & Long Eaton Topper	198,820	63	81%
4 Edinburgh Herald & Post	177,531	67	87%
5 Nottingham Recorder	176,004	58	80%
6 Southampton Advertiser	168,420	32	78%
7 Kingston Guardian	164,386	57	66%
8 Leeds Weekly News	158,471	58	76%
9 Bexley D'ford Gravesend N'ws Shopper	141,736	103	78 %
10 Wirral Globe	140,952	66	86%
11 Hendon Times	123,651	130	85%
12 Sheffield Weekly Gazette	122,346	41	69%
13 Barnet Press	120,218	78	82%
14 Aberdeen & District Independent	119,349	63	72%
15 Newcastle Herald & Post	118,656	28	62%
16 Croydon Post	113,037	89	87%
17 Croydon Guardian	112,865	52	71%
18 Leicester Mail	112,649	96	78%
19 Coventry Citizen	110,835	47	83%
20 Plymouth Extra	108,736	42	68%

Excludes Birmingham Evening Mail which currently has no ABC figure

Excludes Nottingham Evening Post which is independently audited

Source: The Newspaper Society

TOP FREE SUNDAYS

TITLE	DISTRIBUTION	AVERAGE PAGINATION	AVERAGE % ADVERTISING
1 Luton on Sunday	100,367	47	78%
2 Sunday Citizen - Milton Keynes	91,235	48	51%
3 Milton Keynes on Sunday	89,866	32	73%
4 Bedfordshire on Sunday - Borough	61,577	72	83%
5 Bedfordshire on Sunday - Mid Beds	47,569	73	83%
6 Bedfordshire on Sunday L Buzz	15,655	36	77%

Source: The Newspaper Society

TOP FREE WEEKLIES

Bexley Dartford Sidcup News Shopper
Mega House, Crest View, Orpington, Kent BR5 1BT
Fax 01689-875367   Tel 01689-836211
E-mail: aparkes@london.newsquest.co.uk
Website: www.thisislocallondon.co.uk
Editor: Andrew Parkes
Owner: Newsquest Media Group

Coventry Citizen
Corporation Street, Coventry CV1 1FP
Fax 024-7655 3820   Tel 024-7663 3633
Editor: Beverly Marun

Croydon Guardian
Guardian House, Sandiford Road, Sutton SM3 9RN
Fax 020-8770 2277   Tel 020-8644 4300
E-mail: cwarren@london.newsquest.co.uk
Website: www.thisislondon.co.uk
Editor: Claire Warren

Croydon Post
Brighton Road, South Croydon, Surrey CR2 6UB
                                    Tel 020-8763 6666
Editor: Malcolm Starbook
Owner: Southnews

Edinburgh Herald and Post
7 Newhaven Road, Edinburgh EH6 5QA
Fax 0131-556 5177   Tel 0131-243 3242
E-mail: edinhp@scotsman.com
Editor: Millind Kathatkar
Owner: Press Holdings

The Glaswegian
40 Anderston Quay, Glasgow G3 8DA
Fax 0141-242 3596   Tel 0141-242 3502
Editor: Liz Steele
Owner: Trinity-Mirror

Hendon & Finchley Times
124 Rickmansworth Road, Watford, Herts WD1 7JW
Fax 01923-235201   Tel 01923-242211
Owner: Newsquest Media Group

Kingston Guardian
Guardian House, Sandiford Road, Sutton SM3 9RN
Fax 020-8770 2277   Tel 020-8644 4300
E-mail: cwarren@london.newsquest.co.uk
Web: www.londonnews.co.uk
Editor: Claire Warren
Owner: Newsquest Media Group

Leeds Weekly News
PO Box 49, Wellington Street, Leeds LS1 1LW
Fax 0113-238 8484   Tel 0113-238 8769
Editor: Sheila Holmes

Leicester Mail
St George's Street, Leicester LE1 9FQ
Fax 0116-222 4669   Tel 0116-222 4600
Web: www.lleicestermercury.co.uk
Editor: Ian Amos

Metro
164 Deansgate, Manchester M60 2RD
Fax 0161-834 0556   Tel 0161-834 9677
E-mail: metro@mcr-eveing-news.co.uk
Editor: John Jeffay
Owner: Guardian Media Group

Newcastle Herald & Post
191 High Street, Gateshead, Tyne & Wear NE8 1AS
Fax 0191-490 0047   Tel 0191-477 3245
E-mail: cwarren@london.newsquest.co.uk
Web: www.londonnews.co.uk
Editor: Mel Maggit
Owner: Trinity Mirror

Nottingham Recorder
Castle Wharf House, Nottingham NG1 7EU
Fax 0115-964 4000   Tel 0115-948 2000
Editor: G Glen

Plymouth Extra
17 Brest Road, Derriford Business Park, Plymouth,
Devon PL6 5AA
Fax 01752-765515   Tel 01752-765500
Editor: Keith Scrivener

Sheffield Weekly Gazette
York Street, Sheffield, South Yorkshire S1 1PU
Fax 0114-272 5978   Tel 0114-276 7676
Editor: Peter Charlton

Southampton Advertiser
Test Lane, Redbridge, Hampshire SO16 9JX
Fax 023-8042 4545   Tel 023-8042 4444
E-mail: info@satton-echo.co.uk
Editor: Ian Murray

Wirral Globe
Catherine Street, Birkenhead CH41 6HW
Fax 0151-906 3049   Tel 0151-906 3000
E-mail: smorris@guardiangrp.co.uk
Web: www.thisiswirral.co.uk
Editor: Phil Fleming

TOP FREE SUNDAYS

Bedfordshire on Sunday - Borough
Local Sunday Newspapers, 22 Mill Street, Bedford
MK40 3HD
Fax 01234-304403   Tel 01234-300888

Bedfordshire on Sunday - L Buzzard
Local Sunday Newspapers, 22 Mill Street, Bedford
MK40 3HD
Fax 01234-304403   Tel 01234-300888

Bedfordshire on Sunday - Mid Beds
Local Sunday Newspapers, 22 Mill Street, Bedford
MK40 3HD
Fax 01234-304403   Tel 01234-300888

Luton on Sunday
Local Sunday Newspapers, 22 Mill Street, Bedford
MK40 3HD
Fax 01234-304403   Tel 01234-300888

Milton Keynes on Sunday
Local Sunday Newspapers, 22 Mill Street, Bedford
MK40 3HD
Fax 01234-304403   Tel 01234-300888
Editor: Andrew Kelly

Sunday Citizen
Napier House, Auckland Park, Bletchley, Milton
Keynes, Buckinghamshire MK1 1BU
Fax 01908-371112   Tel 01908-651300
Editor: Paul Brookman

LOCAL PAPER LISTINGS BY REGION

ENGLAND

BEDFORDSHIRE	**83**
BERKSHIRE	**83**
CITY OF BRISTOL	**83**
BUCKINGHAMSHIRE	**83**
CAMBRIDGESHIRE	**84**
CHANNEL ISLANDS	**84**
CHESHIRE	**84**
CORNWALL & SCILLY	**84**
CUMBRIA	**85**
DERBYSHIRE	**85**
DEVON	**86**
DORSET	**86**
DURHAM	**86**
ESSEX	**87**
GLOUCESTERSHIRE	**87**
HAMPSHIRE	**88**
HEREFORDSHIRE	**88**
HERTFORDSHIRE	**88**
ISLE OF MAN	**89**
ISLE OF WIGHT	**89**
KENT	**89**
LANCASHIRE	**90**
LEICESTERSHIRE	**90**
LINCOLNSHIRE	**91**
LIVERPOOL	**91**
LONDON - NORTH	**92**
LONDON - SOUTH	**93**
MANCHESTER	**94**
NORFOLK	**95**
NORTHAMPTONSHIRE	**95**
NORTHUMBERLAND	**95**
NOTTINGHAMSHIRE	**95**
OXFORDSHIRE	**96**
BATH & NE SOMERSET	**96**
SOMERSET	**96**
STAFFORDSHIRE	**97**
SUFFOLK	**97**
SURREY	**97**
EAST SUSSEX	**98**
WEST SUSSEX	**98**
TYNE & WEAR	**99**
WARWICKSHIRE	**99**
WEST MIDLANDS	**99**
WILTSHIRE	**100**
WORCESTERSHIRE	**100**
EAST YORKSHIRE	**100**
NORTH YORKSHIRE	**101**
SOUTH YORKSHIRE	**101**
WEST YORKSHIRE	**101**
YORK	**102**

SCOTLAND

CITY OF ABERDEEN	**102**
ABERDEENSHIRE	**102**
ANGUS	**102**
ARGYLL & BUTE	**102**
AYRSHIRE EAST	**103**
AYRSHIRE NORTH	**103**
AYRSHIRE SOUTH	**103**
BORDERS	**103**
DUMBARTON/CLYDE	**103**
DUMFRIES & GALLOWAY	**103**
DUNDEE	**103**
EDINBURGH	**103**
FALKIRK	**103**
FIFE	**104**
GLASGOW	**104**
HIGHLANDS	**104**
LANARKSHIRE NORTH	**104**
LANARKSHIRE SOUTH	**104**
EAST LOTHIAN	**104**
WEST LOTHIAN	**104**
MIDLOTHIAN	**105**
MORAY	**105**
ORKNEY ISLANDS	**105**
PERTHSHIRE & KINROSS	**105**
RENFREWSHIRE	**105**
SHETLAND ISLANDS	**105**
STIRLING	**105**
WESTERN ISLES	**105**

WALES

BLAENAU GWENT	**105**
CO. OF BRIDGEND	**105**
CO. OF CAERPHILLY	**105**
CARDIFF	**105**
CARMARTHENSHIRE	**105**
CEREDIGION	**105**
CO. OF CONWY	**105**
DENBIGHSHIRE	**105**
FLINTSHIRE	**106**
VALE OF GLAMORGAN	**106**
GWENT	**106**
GWYNNED	**106**
ISLE OF ANGLESEY	**106**
CO. OF MERTHYR	**106**
MONMOUTHSHIRE	**106**
NEATH/PORT TALBOT	**106**
CO. OF NEWPORT	**106**
PEMBROKESHIRE	**106**
POWYS	**106**
RHHONDDA CYNON	**106**
CO. OF SWANSEA	**106**
TORFAEN	**106**
CO. OF WREXHAM	**106**

N IRELAND

ANTRIM	**107**
ARMAGH	**107**
DERRY	**107**
COUNTY DOWN	**107**
FERMANAGH	**107**
TYRONE	**107**

By and large, for the sake of easier access, this list of locals uses old county boundaries. For the correct two-tier and unitary divisions, go to Local Government on pages 425-428

BEDFORDSHIRE

Ampthill & Flitwick Herald wf
Eastern Counties Newspapers
01234-364221
Bedford Times & Citizen series wf
Johnston Press
01234-363101
Bedford & Kempston Herald wf
Herald Newspapers
01234-364221
Bedfordshire On Sunday s
Local Sunday Newspapers
01234-306603
Biggleswade & Sandy Herald wf
Eastern Counties Newspapers
01234-364221
Biggleswade Chronicle w
Johnston Press
01767-313479
Dunstable Gazette w
Eastern Counties Newspapers
01582-21222
Leighton Buzzard Citizen wf
Johnston Press
01908-371133
Leighton Buzzard Herald wf
Eastern Counties Newspapers
01727-846866
Leighton Buzzard Observer w
Eastern Counties Newspapers
01525-370251
Luton Leader wf
Eastern Counties Newspapers
01582-870200
Luton News w
Eastern Counties Newspapers
01582-870200
Luton/Dunstable Herald & Post wf
Trinity Mirror
01582-700600

BERKSHIRE

The Advertiser wf
Newbury Weekly News
01635-524111
Ascot & Sunningdale Observer wf
Slough Observer
01753-523355
Berks & Bucks Observer w
Frank Lawrence
01753-523355
Bracknell & Ascot Times w
Berkshire Press
0118-957 5833
Bracknell & Wokingham News wf
Trinity Mirror
01344-56611
Bracknell & Wokingham Std wf
Guardian Media Group
0118-957 5833

Bracknell News w
Trinity Mirror
01344-56611
Crowthorne Sandhurst Newsweek w
Reading Newspaper Co
0118-950 3030
Crowthorne & Sandhurst Times w
Berkshire Press
0118-918 3000
Maidenhead Advertiser w
Baylis & Co
01628-798048
Newbury/Thatcham Chronicle wf
Trinity Mirror
01635-32771
Newbury Local Mart wf
Local Mart Publications
0118-950 3030
Newbury Weekly News w
Newbury Weekly News
01635-524111
Reading Chronicle w
Trinity Mirror
0118-950 3030
Reading Chronicle Midweek wf
Trinity Mirror
0118-950 3030
(Reading) Evening Post d
Guardian Media Group
0118 9575833
Reading Standard wf
Berkshire Press
0118 9575833
Sandhurst/Crowthorne Mail w
Guardian Media Group
01252-328221
Slough & Langley Observer w
Frank Lawrence
01753-523355
Slough,Langley Informer w
Southnews
01753-825111
Windsor/Slough wf
Southnews
01753-825111
Windsor & Maidenhead Obs wf
Frank Lawrence
01753-523355
Wokingham & Bracknell Times w
Guardian Media Group
0118- 957 5833
Wokingham News w
Reading Newspaper Co
01344-456611
Woodley Chronicle w
Reading Newspaper Co
0118-950 3030

CITY OF BRISTOL

Bath Adv wf
Southern Newspapers
01225-446800
Bristol Observer wf
Northcliffe
0117-934 3000
(Bristol) Western Daily Press d
Northcliffe
0117-934 3000
Clevedon Mercury wf
Northcliffe
01275-874248
Glos & Avon Gazette w
Newscon
01703-424424
Northavon Gazette w
Southern Newspapers
01453-544000
Portishead Admag wf
Southern Newspapers
01934-417921
Thornbury Gazette w
Southern Newspapers
01454-411459

BUCKINGHAMSHIRE

Buckingham Advertiser w
Johnston Press
01280-813434
Buckinghamshire Advertiser w
Southnews
020-8367 2345
Bucks Advertiser
Johnston Press
01296-318300
Bucks Examiner w
Southnews
01494-792626
Bucks Free Press w
Newsquest/Gannett
01494-521212
Bucks Herald
Johnston Press
01296-318300
(High Wycombe) Midweek w
Newsquest/Gannett
01494-755000
High Wycombe Leader wf
Southnews
01494-438071
Milton Keynes Citizen wf
Johnston Press
01908-371133
South Bucks Star wf
Newsquest/Gannett
01494-521212

d=daily, w=weekly, s=sunday, f=free

CAMBRIDGESHIRE

Cambridge Evening News d
Yattendon Investment Trust
01223-434434
Cambridge Weekly News wf
Yattendon Investment Trust
01223-434434
Cambs Times/March Adv w
Eastern Counties Newspaper Group
01603-628311
Cambs Town Crier wf
Johnston Press
01223-369966
Ely Standard w
Eastern Counties Newspaper Group
01353-667831
Ely Weekly News wf
Yattendon Investment Trust
01223-434434
Fenland Citizen wf
Johnston Press
01733-555111
Huntingdon Weekly News wf
Yattendon Investment Trust
01223-434434
Huntingdon Town Crier w
Peterborough Evening Telegraph
01733-555111
The Hunts Post wf
Eastern Counties Newspaper Group
01603-628311
Peterborough Citizen wf
Johnston Press
01733-555111
Peterborough Evening Telegraph d
East Midlands Newspapers
01733-555111
Peterborough Herald & Post wf
Midland Independent Newspapers
01733-318600
St Neots Weekly News wf
Yattendon Investment Trust
01223-434434
Wisbech Standard w
Eastern Counties Newspaper Group
01603-628311

CHANNEL ISLANDS

Guernsey Evening Press & Star d
The Guernsey Press Co
01481-45866
Guernsey Weekly Press w
Guernsey Press Co
01481-45866
Jersey Evening Post d
Jersey Evening Post
01534-611611
Jersey Weekly Post w
Jersey Evening Post
01534-611611

CHESHIRE

Bramhall & District Courier wf
Courier Group
01625-586140
Chester & District Standard wf
Chester Standard Newspapers
01244-351234
Chester Chronicle w
Trinity Mirror
01244-340151
Chester Mail wf
Trinity Mirror
01244-340151
Congleton Adnews wf
Adnews (Midlands)
01260-281012
Congleton Chronicle series w
Heads (Congleton)
01260-273737
Congleton Guardian wf
Newsquest/Gannett
01925-633033
Crewe & District Herald Post wf
Trinity Mirror
01244-340151
Crewe & Nantwich Guardian wf
Newsquest/Gannett
01925-633033
Crewe Chronicle w
Trinity Mirror
01244-340151
Didsbury & District Courier wf
Courier Group
01625-586140
Ellesmere Port Pioneer w
Trinity Mirror
01244-340151
Ellesmere Port Standard wf
Chester Standard Newspapers
0151-356 5500
High Peak Courier wf
United Provinicial Newspapers
01629-582432
Knutsford Express Advertiser wf
Guardian Media Group
0161-480 4491
Knutsford Guardian w
Newsquest/Gannett
01925-633033
Macclesfield Express Adv. w
Guardian Media Group
0161-480 4491
Macclesfield Messenger wf
Newsquest/Gannett
0161-477 4600
Macclesfield Times wf
Guardian Media Group
0161-480 4491
Middlewich Chronicle w
Chronicle Newspapers
01244-340151

Northwich Chronicle w
Trinity Mirror
01244-340151
Tameside Reporter w
Ashton Weekly Newspapers
0161-303 1910
Northwich Guardian w
Newsquest/Gannett
01925-633033
Northwich Herald & Post wf
Trinity Mirror
01244-340151
Poynton Times wf
Guardian Media Group
0161-480 4491
Runcorn Herald & Post wf
Trinity Mirror
01244-340151
Runcorn Weekly News w
Trinity Mirror
01244-340151
Runcorn World wf
Newsquest/Gannett
0151-424 7711
Sandbach Chronicle w
Heads (Congleton)
01260-273737
South Cheshire Mail wf
Chronicle Newspapers
01244-340151
South Wirral News wf
Trinity Mirror
01244-340151
Warrington Guardian w
Newsquest/Gannett
01925-633033
Warrington Mercury wf
Newsquest/Gannett
01925-434000
Widnes Weekly News w
Trinity Mirror
01244-340151
Widnes World wf
Newsquest/Gannett
0151-424 7711
Wilmslow Express Advertiser w
Guardian Media Group
01625-529333
Wilmslow Messenger wf
Newsquest/Gannett
020-8640 8989

CORNWALL & SCILLY

Bude & Stratton Post w
Cornish & Devon Post
01566-772424
Camelford & Delabole Post w
Cornish & Devon Post
01566-772424

Camborne & Redruth Packet wf
Tindle Newspapers
01326-213333
Cornish and Devon Post w
Tindle Newspapers
01566-772424
Cornish Guardian w
Northcliffe Newspapers Group
01208-78133
Cornish Times w
Tindle Newspapers
01579-342174
The Cornishman w
Northcliffe Newspapers Group
01736-362247
Falmouth Packet w
Packet Newspapers
01326-213333
Hayle Times w
St Ives Printing & Publishing Co
01736-795813
Helston & District Gazette wf
Packet Newspapers
01326-213333
Launceston Gazette wf
Tindle Newspapers
01566-772766
Liskeard Gazette wf
Tindle Newspapers
01579-47444
Mid Cornwall Advertiser wf
North Cornwall Advertiser
01208-815096
North Cornwall Advertiser wf
North Cornwall Advertiser
01208-815096
Packet Series w
Southern Newspapers
01326-213333
Penwith Pirate wf
Packet Newspapers
01326-370500
Redruth & Camborne Tinner
Packet Newspapers
01326-213333
St Austell, Newquay Packet wf
Southern Newspapers
01326-213333
St Ives Times & Echo w
St Ives Printing & Publishing
01736-795813
Truro Packet wf
Southern Newspapers
01326-213333
West Briton w
Northcliffe Newspapers Group
01872-271451

CUMBRIA
The Advertiser wf
CN Group
01229-821835
(Barrow) N West Evening Mail d
CN Group
01229-821835
(Carlisle) News & Star d
CN Group
01228-612600
Cumberland Herald w
Cumberland & Westmorland Herald
Newspapers
01768-862313
Cumberland News w
CN Group
01228-612600
Cumbrian Gazette wf
CN Group
01228-616100
Keswick Reminder w
G W McKane & Son
01768-772140
Lakeland Echo wf
United Provinicial Newspapers
01539-730630
Lakes Leader wf
Newsquest/Gannett
01539-720555
W Cumberland Times & Star w
CN Group
01900-601234
West Cumbrian Gazette wf
CN Group
01900-607607
Westmorland Gazette w
Newsquest/Gannett
01539-720555
Whitehaven News w
CN Group
01946-595100

DERBYSHIRE
Alfreton & Ripley Echo wf
Johnston Press
01246-504500
Alfreton Chad wf
Johnston Press
01623-456789
Ashboourne News Telegraph w
Yattendon Investment Trust
01283-512345
Belper Express wf
Northcliffe Newspapers Group
01332-291111
Belper News w
Johnston Press
01773-820971
Bolsover Advertiser wf
Derbyshire Times
01246-200144

Buxton Advertiser w
Johnston Press
01246-200144
Buxton Times wf
Derbyshire Times
01298-22118
Chesterfield Advertiser wf
Johnston Press
01246-202291
Chesterfield Express wf
North Derbyshire Newspapers
01246-234920
Chesterfield Gazette wf
Johnston Press
01246-200144
Derby Evening Telegraph d
Northcliffe Newspapers Group
01332-291111
Derby Express wf
Northcliffe Newspapers Group
01332-291111
Derby Journal wf
Journal Publishing
01332-202393
Derby Trader wf
Midland Independent Newspapers
01332-253999
Derbyshire Times w
Johnston Press
01246-200144
Dronfield Advertiser wf
Johnston Press
01246-202291
Eckington Leader wf
Johnston Press
01246-434343
Glossop Chronicle w
United Provinicial Newspapers
01457 865742
High Peak Courier wf
Johnston Press
01246-504500
Ilkeston Advertiser w
Johnston Press
0115-944 4411
Ilkeston Express wf
Northcliffe Newspapers Group
01332-291111
Matlock Mercury w
Johnston Press
01629-582432
Ripley & Heanor News w
Johnston Press
01773-742133
Swadlincote Times w
Trident Midland Newspapers
01530-813101

d=daily, w=weekly, s=sunday, f=free

DEVON

Axminster News wf
Eastern Counties Newspapers Group
01392-447766
Dartmouth Chron/S Hams Gazette w
Tindle Newspapers
01548-853101
Dawlish Gazette w
Tindle Newspapers
01626-864161
Dawlish Post wf
Devon & Cornwall Newspapers
01626-353555
East Devon News series wf
Eastern Counties Newspapers Group
01392-447766
(Exeter) Express & Echo d
Northcliffe Newspapers Group
01392-442211
Exeter Leader wf
Northcliffe Newspapers Group
01392-442211
(Exeter) Midweek Herald wf
Eastern Counties Newspapers Group
01392-447766
Exmouth Herald wf
Eastern Counties Newspapers Group
01392-447766
Exmouth Journal w
Eastern Counties Newspapers Group
01392-447766
Holsworthy Post w
Cornish & Devon Post
01566-772424
Honiton & Cullompton News wf
Eastern Counties Newspapers Group
01392-447766
Ivybridge Gazette w
Tindle Newspapers
01548-853101
Kingsbridge Gazette w
Tindle Newspapers
01548-853101
Mid-Devon Advertiser series w
Tindle Newspapers
01626-355566
Mid-Devon Express & Star wf
Southern Newspapers
01884-255977
Mid Devon Gazette w
Northcliffe Newspapers Group
01884-242500
Newton Abbot Weekender wf
Northcliffe Newspapers Group
01803-676000
North Devon Gazette & Adv wf
Eastern Counties Newspapers Group
01392-447766
North Devon Journal w
Northcliffe Newspapers Group
01271-343064

Okehampton Times w
Tavistock Newsapers
01822-613666
(Plymouth) Evening Herald d
Northcliffe Newspapers Group
01752-765500
Plymouth Extra wf
Northcliffe Newspapers Group
01752-765500
Plympton News wf
Tindle Newspapers
01548-853101
Pulmans Weekly News w
Northcliffe
0117-934 3000
Sidmouth Herald w
Eastern Counties Newspapers Group
01225 460556
South Devon & Plymouth Times w
Devon & Cornwall Newspapers
01803-862585
Sunday Independent w
West of England Newspapers
01752-206600
Tavistock Times Gazette w
Tindle Newspapers
01822-613666
Teignmouth News wf
Tindle Newspapers
01626-779494
Teignmouth Post w
Devon & Cornwall Newspapers
01626-353555
Torbay Weekender wf
Northcliffe Newspapers Group
01803-676000
(Torquay) Herald Express d
Northcliffe Newspapers Group
01803-676000
Totnes Times Series w
Tindle Newspapers
01803-862585
Western Morning News d
Northcliffe Newspapers Group
01752-765500

DORSET

Avon Adv (Hants & Dorset) wf
Southern Newspapers
01722-337466
Bournemouth/Christchurch/
Poole Advertiser wf
Southern Newspapers
01202-411411
(Bournemouth) The Daily Echo d
Southern Newspapers
01202-554601
Bridport News w
Southern Newspapers
01823-725000

Christchurch Advertiser wf
Advertiser Series
01202-554601
Dorset Evening Echo d
Southern Newspapers
01305-784804
Poole Advertiser wf
Advertiser Series
01202-554601
Stour Valley News wf
Southern Newspapers
01258-456067
Swanage & Wareham Adv wf
Southern Newspapers
01202-554601
Weymouth Advertiser wf
Southern Newspapers
01365-830930

DURHAM

Chester le Street Advertiser wf
Newsquest/Gannett
01325-381313
The Clarion wf
SR & VI Crane
01642-480397
Consett & Stanley Advertiser wf
Newsquest/Gannett
01325-381313
Darlington Advertiser wf
Newsquest/Gannett
01325-381313
Darlington & N Yorks Herald wf
Trinity Mirror
01642-245401
Darlington & Stockton Times w
Newsquest/Gannett
01325-381313
Durham Advertiser wf
Newsquest/Gannett
01325-381313
Darlington, Aycliffe & Sedgfield
Advertiser wf
Newsquest/Gannett
01325-381313
(Darlington) Northern Echo d
Newsquest/Gannett
01325-381313
Hartlepool Mail d
Johnston Press
01429-274441
Hartlepool Star wf
Johnston Press
0191-417 0050
Peterlee Star wf
Johnston Press
0191-417 0050
South Durham Herald wf
Trinity Mirror
01325-262000

Teesdale Mercury w
Teesdale Mercury
01833-637140
Wear Valley Advertiser wf
Newsquest/Gannett
01325-381313

ESSEX

(Basildon) Evening Echo d
Newsquest/Gannett
01268-522792
Basildon Standard Recorder wf
Newsquest/Gannett
01268-522792
Basildon Yellow Advertiser wf
United Provincial Newspapers
01268-522722
Braintree & Witham Times w
Newsquest/Gannett
01206-506000
Braintree & Witham Yellow Ad wf
United Provincial Newspapers
01268-522722
Brentwood Gazette w
Northcliffe Newspapers Group
01277-219222
Brentwood Weekly News wf
Newsquest/Gannett
01206-506000
Castlepoint Yellow Advertiser wf
United Provincial Newspapers
01268-522722
Castlepoint Recorder wf
Newsquest/Gannett
01268-522792
Chelmsford Weekly News wf
Newsquest/Gannett
01206-506000
Chelmsford Yellow Advertiser wf
United Provincial Newspapers
01268-522722
Clacton Coastal Express wf
Newsquest/Gannett
01255-221221
Clacton & Frinton Gazette w
Newsquest/Gannett
01206-506000
Colchester Evening Gazette d
Newsquest/Gannett
01206-506000
Colchester Express wf
Newsquest/Gannett
01206-506000
Colchester Yellow Adv wf
United Provincial Newspapers
01268-522722
Dunmow Broadcast wf
Eastern Counties Newspapers
01371-874537
Epping Forest Herald wf
Eastern Counties Newspapers
020-8478 4444

Epping Forest Independent wf
Newsquest/Gannett
020-8498 3400
Epping, Ongar & District Gazette w
Newsquest/Gannett
01992-572285
Epping Yellow Advertiser wf
United Provincial Newspapers
01268-522722
Essex Chronicle w
Northcliffe Newspapers Group
01245-60700
Essex County Standard w
Newsquest/Gannett
01206-506000
Essex Weekly News wf
Newsquest/Gannett
01206-506000
Frinton & Walton Gazette w
Newsquest/Gannett
01206-506000
Grays Herald wf
Eastern Counties Newspapers
01708-766044
Halstead Gazette&Advertiser w
Newsquest/Gannett
01206-506000
Harlow & Epping Herald wf
Eastern Counties Newspapers
020-8478 4444
Harlow Citizen wf
Newsquest/Gannett
020-8531 4141
Harlow/Epping Star wf
Yattendon Investment Trust
01992-586401
Harwich Standard w
Newsquest/Gannett
01206-506000
IlfordForest Recorder wf
Eastern Counties Newspapers
020-8478 4444
Loughton, Chigwell Gazette w
Newsquest
020-8531 4141
Maldon Standard w
Newsquest/Gannett
01206-506000
Rayleigh Recorder wf
Newsquest/Gannett
01268-522792
Rayleigh Times Group wf
Leigh Times Co
01702-77666
Redbridge Guardian w
Newsquest/Gannett
020-8498 3400
Saffron Walden Observer wf
Yattendon Investment Trust
01992-586401

Saffron Walden Reporter wf
Eastern Counties Newspapers
01799-525100
Saffron Walden Weekly News wf
Yattendon Investment Trust
01223-434434
Southend on Sunday w
Leigh Times
01702-77666
Southend Standard Recorder wf
Newsquest/Gannett
01268-522792
Southend Yellow Advertiser wf
United Provincial Newspapers
01268-522722
Thurrock Gazette wf
Newsquest/Gannett
01268-522792
Thurrock & Lakeside Recorder wf
Eastern Counties Newspapers
01708-766044
Thurrock, Lakeside, Grays Post w
Independent Newspapers
020-8517 5577
Thurrock Yellow Advertiser wf
United Provincial Newspapers
01268-522722
Walden Local wf
Local Publications
01799-516161
Waltham Abbey Gazette w
Newsquest/Gannett
020-8531 4141

GLOUCESTERSHIRE

Berkeley & Sharpness Gazette w
Newscom
01453-544000
Cheltenham News wf
Northcliffe Newspapers
01242-271900
(Dursley) The County Independent wf
Newscom
01453-544000
Forest of Dean Review wf
Tindle Newspapers
01594-841113
The Forester w
Forest of Dean Newspapers
01594-822126
Gloucester News wf
Northcliffe Newspapers Group
01452-419791
Gloucestershire Citizen d
Northcliffe Newspapers Group
01452-424442
Gloucestershire County Gazette w
Newscom
01453-544000
Gloucestershire Echo d
Northcliffe Newspapers Group
01242-271900

Stroud News & Journal w
Newscom
01453-544000
Tewkesbury Admag wf
Newsquest/Gannett
01684-292446
Wilts & Gloucester Standard w
Newscom
01285-642642

HAMPSHIRE

The Advertiser wf
Southern Newspapers
01329-280752
Aldershot Courier series wf
Guardian Media Group
01252-326755
Aldershot Mail w
Guardian Media Group
01252-328221
Aldershot News series w
Guardian Media Group
01252-328221
Alton Gazette w
Tindle Newspapers
01420-84446
Alton Herald w
Farnham Castle Newspapers
01420-82819
Alton Times & Mail wf
Tindle Newspapers
01252-716444
Andover Advertiser w
Newscom
01264-323456
Andover Advertiser Midweek w
Newscom
01264-323456
Arlesford & District Times wf
Gazette Newspapers
01256-461131
Avon Advertiser (Hants/Dorset) w
Southern Newspapers
01722-337466
Basingstoke & N Hants Gaz. w
Newscom
01256-461131
Basingstoke Observer wf
TriMedia Publishing
01256-694120
Bordon Herald w
Farnham Castle Newspapers
01252-725224
Bordon Times & Mail wf
Tindle Newspapers
01252-716444
Chronicle Advertiserr f
Newscom
01962-841772
Eastleigh Gazette Extra wf
Newscom
01962-867575

Fareham & Gosport Journal wf
Johnston Press
023-9266 4488
Farnborough Courier wf
Aldershot News
01252-326755
Farnborough Mail w
Aldershot News
01252-328221
Farnborough News w
Aldershot News
01252-328221
Fleet & District Courier wf
Aldershot News
01252-328221
Fleet Mail w
Aldershot News
01252-622448
Fleet News w
Aldershot News
01252-328221
The Forest Journal w
Salisbury Journal Newspapers
01722-412525
Hampshire Chronicle w
Newscom
01962-841772
Hart Courier Series wf
Guardian Media Group
01252-326755
Havant Journal wf
Portsmouth &Sunderland Newspapers
01722-412525
Liphook Times & Mail wf
Tindle Newspapers
01252-716444
Lymington Times w
Advertiser & Times
01425-613384
New Forest Post wf
Southern Newspapers
01590-671122
New Milton Advertiser w
Advertiser & Times
01425-613384
Petersfield Herald w
Farnham Castle Newspapers
01730-263005
Petersfield Mail wf
Tindle Newspapers
01252-899255
Petersfield & Bordon Post w
Johnson Press
01730-268021
(Portsmouth) The News d
Johnson Press
023-9266 4488
Portsmouth/Southsea Journal wf
Johnston Press
023-9266 4488

Romsey Advertiser w
Newscom
01962-841772
S Hants & W'chester Weekly News f
Newscom
01962-841772
Southampton Advertiser wf
Newscom
01703-424999
Southern Daily Echo d
Newscom
023-8042 4277
Surrey & Hants Star wf
Star Newspapers (Camberley)
01252-316311
Winchester Gazette Extra wf
Southern Newspapers
01256-461131
Yately & District Courier wf
Aldershot News
01252-326755
Yately Mail
01252-328221

HEREFORDSHIRE

Hereford & Leominster Jouranl wf
Midland News Association
01432-355353
Hereford Admag wf
Adscene/Southnews
01432-351544
Hereford Times w
Newsquest/Gannett
01432-274413
Ross Gazette w
Ross Gazette
01989-562007

HERTFORDSHIRE

Bishops Stortford Citizen wf
Newsquest/Gannett
020-8498 3400
Borehamwood Times wf
Newsquest/Gannett
0208-953 3391
Dacorum Independent w
01442-264464
Harpenden Advertiser wf
Eastern Counties Newspapers
01727-811555
Hemel Hempstead Express wf
Johnston Press
01442-213211
Hemel Hempstead Gazette w
Johnston Press
01442-213211
Herts & Essex Observer w
Yattendon Investment Trust
01992-586401
Herts Mercury w
Yattendon Investment Trust
01992-586401

Herts Star wf
Yattendon Investment Trust
01992-586401
Herts Advertiser wf
Eastern Counties Newspapers
01727-866166
Lea Valley Star wf
Yattendon Investment Trust
01992-586401
Potters Bar & Cuffley Press wf
Southnews
020-8203 5100
Potters Bar Times wf
Newsquest/Gannett
01923-242211
Royston & Buntingford Crow w
Eastern Counties Newspapers
01763-245241
Royston Weekly News wf
Yattendon Investment Trust
01223-434433
Saffron Walden Reporter wf
01799-525100
St Albans & Harpenden Observer wf
Newsquest/Gannett
01727-736000
St Albans /Harpenden Review wf
Review Free Group Newspapers
01727-834411
Star Classified
01992-586401
Stevenage Comet wf
Eastern Counties Newspapers
01462-422280
Stevenage/Letchworth Herald wf
Eastern Counties Newspapers
01462-422280
Watford Free Observer wf
Newsquest/Gannett
01923-242211
Welwyn & Hatfield Herald wf
Eastern Counties Newspapers
01707-327551
Welwyn & Hatfield Times w
Eastern Counties Newspapers
01707-327551
Welwyn Garden Review wf
Review Free Group Newspapers
01727-834411
West Herts & Watford Observer w
Newsquest/Gannett
01923-242211

ISLE OF MAN
Isle of Man Courier wf
Johnston Press
01624-623451
Isle of Man Examiner w
Johnston Press
01624-623451
Manx Independent w
Johnston Press
01624-623451

ISLE OF WIGHT
Isle of Wight County Press w
Isle of Wight County Press
01983-521333

KENT
Ashford & Tenterden Adscene wf
Adscene/Southnews
01227-767321
Ashford Extra wf
Kent Messenger
01233 626232
Canterbury Adscene wf
Adscene/Southnews
01227-767321
Canterbury Extra wf
Kent Messenger
01622-768181
County Border News wf
Tindle Newspapers
01959-564766
Dartford/Swanley Informer wf
Local Publications
01322-220791
Dartford Leaderwf
Fletcher Newspapers
01474-363363
Dartford Times w
Fletcher Newspapers
01474-363363
Dartford News Shopper wf
01689 836211
Dover/Deal/Sandwich Adscene wf
Adscene/Southnews
01227-767321
Dover Express w
Adscene/Southnews
01304-240660
Dover Mercury w
01622-240380
East Kent Gazette w
Adscene/Southnews
01795-475411
East Kent Mercury w
Kent Messenger
01622-717880
Edenbridge Chronicle wf
Chronicle Newspapers
01732-865455
Faversham News w
Kent Messenger
01622-717880
Faversham Times w
Adscene/Southnews
01795-536555
Folkestone & Hythe Adscene wf
Adscene/Southnews
01227-767321
Folkestone Extra wf
Kent Messenger
01622-717880

Folkestone Herald w
Adscene/Southnews
01303-850999
Gravesend & Dartford Extra wf
Kent Messenger
01622-717880
Gravesend Leader wf
Fletcher Newspapers
01474-363363
Gravesend Messenger
01622-717880
Gravesend Reporter w
Fletcher Newspapers
01474-363363
Herne Bay Gazette w
Kent Messenger
01622-717880
Herne Bay Times w
Adscene/Southnews
01227-771515
Hythe Herald w
Adscene/Southnews
01303-850999
Isle of Thanet Gazette w
Adscene/Southnews
01843-221313
Kent & Sussex Courier w
Northcliffe Newspapers Group
01892-526262
Kent Messenger w
Kent Messenger
01622-717880
Kent Today d
Kent Messenger
01622-717880
Kentish Express w
Kent Messenger
01622-717880
Kentish Gazette w
Kent Messenger
01622-717880
Maidstone Adscene wf
Adscene/Southnews
01227-767321
Maidstone Extra wf
Kent Messenger
01622-717880
Maidstone Star wf
Southern Newspapers
01622-678556
Medway & Disrict Adscene wf
Adscene/Southnews
01227-767321
Medway Extra wf
Kent Messenger
01622-717880
Medway News w
Adscene/Southnews
01634-841741
Medway Standard w
Adscene/Southnews
01634-841741

Romney Marsh Herald w
Adscene/Southnews
01303-850999
Sevenoaks Chronicle w
Northcliffe Newspapers Group
01892-526262
Sevenoaks News in Focus wf
Northcliffe Newspapers Group
01892-526262
Sevenoaks & Tonbridge Leader wf
Fletcher Newspapers
01474-363363
Sheerness Times Guardian w
Kent Messenger
01622-717880
Sheppey Gazette w
Adscene/Southnews
01795-475411
Sittingbourne Extra wf
Kent Messenger
01622-717880
Swanley Times w
01474 363363
Thanet Adscene wf
Adscene/Southnews
01227-767321
Thanet Extra wf
Kent Messenger
01622-717880
Thanet Times w
Adscene/Southnews
01843-221313
Tonbridge & District Friday-Ad wf
Friday Ad Group
01825-766000
Tunbridge Wells Adscene wf
Adscene/Southnews
01227-767321
Tunbridge Wells Extra wf
Kent Messenger
01622-717880
(Tunbridge Wells) News in Focus wf
Northcliffe Newspapers Group
01892-526262
Tunbridge Wells Friday-Ad wf
Friday Ad Group
01825-766000
Tunbridge Wells Leader wf
Fletcher Newspapers
01474-363363
Wealden Advertiser wf
01580-753235
Whitstable Gazette w
Kent Messenger Group
01622-717880

LANCASHIRE

Accrington Observer w
Guardian Media Group
01706-354321
Blackburn Citizen wf
Newsquest/Gannett
01254-678678

Blackpool Citizen wf
Newsquest/Gannett
01253-729081
(Blackpool) The Gazette d
United Provincial Newspapers
01253-400888
Burnley Citizen wf
Newsquest/Gannett
01282-452138
Burnley Express & News w
United Provincial Newspapers
01282-426161
Chorley Citizen
Newsquest/Gannett
01257-269011
Chorley Guardian w
United Provincial Newspapers
01257-264911
Clitheroe Advertiser & Times w
United Provincial Newspapers
01282-426161
Fleetwood Weekly News w
Tindle Newspapers
01253-772950
Fylde Extra wf
United Provincial Newspapers
01253-400888
Garstang Courier w
United Provincial Newspapers
01995-602494
The Garstang Guardian w
Lancaster & Morcambe Newspapers
01524-833111
Hyndburn Express wf
Guardian Media Group
01706-354321
Lancashire Evening Telegraph d
Newsquest/Gannett
01254-678678
Lancashire Evening Post d
United Provincial Newspapers
01772-254841
Lancaster/Morecambe Citizen wf
Newsquest/Gannett
01524-382121
Lancaster Guardian w
United Provincial Newspapers
01524-833111
Leyland Guardian
The Chorley Guardian
01257-264911
Longridge News w
United Provincial Newspapers
01772-783265
Lytham St Annes Express w
United Provincial Newspapers
01253-400888
The Morecambe Guardian w
Lancaster & Morecambe Newspapers
01524-833111
(Morecambe) The Visitor w
United Provincial Newspapers
01524-833111

Nelson Leader Series w
United Provincial Newspapers
01282-426161
Ormskirk Advertiser w
United Provincial Newspapers
01695-572501
Ormskirk Visiter wf
Trinity Mirror
01695-572501
Preston Citizen wf
Newsquest/Gannett
01772-824631
Preston Weekly Mail wf
United Provincial Newspapers
01257-254841
Rossendale Express wf
Guardian Media Group
01706-354321
Rossendale Free Press w
Guardian Media Group
01706-354321
Skelmersdale Advertiser w
Ormskirk Advertiser
01695-572501
Thornton Cleveleys News w
Tindle Newspapers
01253-772950
Todmorden News & Advertiser w
01422 260200

LEICESTERSHIRE

Ashby & Coalville Mail wf
Northcliffe Newspapers Group
0116-222 4600
Ashby Times w
Trident Midland Newspapers
01530-813101
Coalville/Ashby Echo wf
Echo Press
01509-232632
Coalville Leader wf
01530-813101
Coalville Times w
Trident Midland Newspapers
01530-813101
Harborough Mail w
Adscene/Southnews
01858-462626
Hinckley Herald & Journal wf
Midland Independent Newspapers
01455-891981
Hinckley Times w
Hinckley Times
01455-238383
Leicester Journal w
Journal Publishing Co
0116-233 3633
Leicester Mail wf
Northcliffe Newspapers Group
0116-222 4600
Leicester Mercury d
Northcliffe Newspapers Group
0116-251 2512

Long Eaton Advertiser w
Echo Press
01509-232632
Long Eaton Trader wf
Midland Independent Newspapers
0115-946 9909
Loughborough Echo w
Echo Press
01509-232632
Loughborough Herald & Post wf
Midland Independent Newspapers
0116-247 1000
Loughborough Mail wf
Northcliffe Newspapers Group
0116-222 4600
Market Harborough Herald wf
Midland Independent Newspapers
01604-614600
Melton Citizen wf
Johnston Press
01664-66666
NW Leicestershire Leader wf
Trident Midland Newspapers
01530-813101
Nu News w
Echo Press
01509-232632
Oadby & Wigston Mail wf
Northcliffe Newspapers Group
0116-222 4600
Rutland Times w
New Rutland Times
01572-757722
Shepshed Echo w
Echo Press
01509-232632

LINCOLNSHIRE

Alford Standard w
Lincolnshire Standard Group
01205-311433
Boston Standard w
Adscene/Southnews
01205-311433
Boston & Sleaford Target wf
Northcliffe Newspapers Group
01205-356262
Bourne Local w
Local Publications (Bourne)
01778-425876
Gainsborough Standard w
Adscene/Southnews
01205-311433
Gainsborough Target wf
Northcliffe Newspapers Group
01427-810148
Gainsborough Trader News w
Adscene/Southnews
01205-311433
Grantham & Melton Trader wf
Adscene/Southnews
02476-574433

Grantham Citizen wf
Adscene/Southnews
01476-562291
Grantham Journal w
Adscene/Southnews
01476-562291
Grimsby Evening Telegraph d
01472 360360
Grimsby Target wf
01472 360360
Horncastle News w
Mortons of Horncastle
01507-526868
Horncastle Standard Series w
Adscene/Southnews
01205 311433
Horncastle Target wf
Lincolnshire Publishing Co
01205-356262
Lincoln Chronicle w
Lincolnshire Standard Group
01205-311433
Lincolnshire Standard w
Lincolnshire Standard Group
01205-311433
Lincoln Target wf
Northcliffe Newspapers Group
01522-820000
Lincolnshire Evening Echo d
Northcliffe Newspapers Group
01522-820000
Lincolnshire Free Press w
Adscene/Southnews
01775-725021
Louth Leader w
Mortons of Horncastle
01507-606656
Louth Standard w
Adscene/Southnews
01205-311433
Louth Target wf
Northcliffe Newspapers Group
01205-356262
Mablethorpe & Sutton Leader w
Mortons of Horncastle
01507-606656
Mablethorpe & Sutton Standard s
Lincolnshire Standard Group
01205-311433
Market Rasen Mail w
Mortons of Horncastle
01673-844644
Rutland & Stamford Mercury w
Adscene/Southnews
01780-762255
Scunthorpe Evening Telegraph d
Northcliffe Newspapers Group
01724-273273
Scunthorpe Target wf
Northcliffe Newspapers Group
01724-273273

Scunthorpe Trader News wf
Adscene/Southnews
01427-615323
Skegness News w
Mortons of Horncastle
01754-768000
Skegness Standard w
Adscene/Southnews
01205-311433
Skegness Target wf
Lincolnshire Standard Group
01205 356262
Sleaford Standard w
Adscene/Southnews
01205-311433
Scunthorpe Trader News wf
Lincolnshire Standard Group
01205-311433
Spalding Guardian w
Adscene/Southnews
01775-725021
Spilsby Standard w
Lincolnshire Standard Group
01205-311433
Spilsby Target wf
Lincolnshire Publishing Co
01205-356262
Stamford Citizen wf
Adscene/Southnews
01780-762255
Stamford Herald wf
Midland Independent Newspapers
01733-318600
Woodhall Spa Target wf
Lincolnshire Publishing Co
01205-356262

LIVERPOOL AREA

Anfield & Walton Star wf
Trinity Mirror
0151-236 4422
Bebington News wf
Trinity Mirror
0151-647 7111
Birkenhead News wf
Trinity Mirror
0151-647 7111
Bootle Times wf
Trinity Mirror
0151-236 4422
Crosby Herald w
Trinity Mirror
0151-236 4422
Formby Times w
Trinity Mirror
0151-236 4422
Heswall News wf
Trinity Mirror
0151-647 7111
Hoylake/West Kirkby News wf
Trinity Mirror
0151-647 7111

Huyton & Raby Star wf
Trinity Mirror
0151-236 4422
(Liverpool) Daily Post d
Trinity Mirror
0151-227 2000
Liverpool Echo d
Trinity Mirror
0151-227 2000
Maghull Star wf
Trinity Mirror
0151-236 4422
Neston News wf
Trinity Mirror
0151-647 7111
Newton & Golborne Guardian w
Newsquest/Gannett
01925-633033
Prescot Reporter wf
Regional Independent Media
01744-22285
Skelmersdale Champion wf
Champion Newspapers
01704-392392
South Liverpool Merseymart wf
Trinity Mirror
0151-236 4422
Southport Champion wf
Champion Newspapers
01704-392392
(Southport) Midweek Visiter wf
Trinity Mirror
0151-236 4422
Southport Visiter wf
Trinity Mirror
0151-236 4422
St Helens Reporter wf
Regional Independent Media
01942-228000
St Helens Star wf
Newsquest/Gannett
01744-611861
Wallasey News wf
Trinity Mirror
0151-236 7320
West Derby Merseymart wf
Trinity Mirror
0151-227 2000
Wirral Globe wf
Newsquest/Gannett
0151-906 3000

LONDON - NORTH

Barking & Dagenham Advertiser wf
United Provincial Newspapers
01268-522722
Barking & Dagenham Express wf
Independent Newspapers
020-8517 5577
Barking & Dagenham Post w
Independent Newspapers
020-8517 5577

Barking & Dagenham Recorder wf
South Essex Recorders
020-8478 4444
Barnet & Finchley Press wf
Southnews
020-8364 0300
Barnet Advertiser wf
United Provincial Newspapers
020-8364 0300
Barnet Borough Times wf
Newsquest/Gannett
01923-242211
Brent & London Recorder wf
Tindle Newspapers
020-8450 5272
Brent Leader wf
Tindle Newspapers
020-8364 4040
Brentwood Recorder w
South Essex Recorders
01708-771500
Camden New Journal wf
New Journal Enterprises
020-7419 9000
Camden/St Pancras Chronicle w
Independent Newpapers
020-8340 6868
Chelsea News w
Adscene/Southnews
020-8741 1622
Chingford Guardian w
Newsquest/Gannett
020-8498 3400
City of London Dockland Times w
City of London & Dockland Times
020-7488 3888
City Post w
Adscene/Southnews
020-8741 1622
City of London Recorder w
Eastern Counties Newspapers
(Holdings)
020-8472 1421
City of Westminster Post wf
Adscene/Southnews
020-8741 1622
Docklands Express wf
Independent Newspapers
020-7790 8822
Docklands Recorder w
South Essex Recorders
020-8472 1421
Ealing & Acton Gazette w
Southnews
020-8579 3131
Ealing & London Recorder wf
Tindle Newspapers
020-8568 1313
Ealing & Southall Informer wf
United Provincial Newspapers
01784-433773

Ealing Leader wf
Southnews
020-8367 2345
East London Advertiser w
Independent Newspapers
020-7790 8822
Edgware & Mill Hill Times wf
Newsquest/Gannett
01923-242211
Enfield Advertiser wf
Southnews
020-8367 2345
Enfield Gazette series w
Southnews
020-8367 2345
Enfield Independent wf
Newsquest/Gannett
020-8498 3400
Evening Standard d
Associated Newspapers
020-7938 6000
Finchley & Hendon Advertisers
United Provincial Newspapers
020-8449 5577
Fulham Chronicle w
Adscene/Southnews
020-8741 1622
Greenford & Northolt Gazette w
Middlesex County Press
020-8579 3131
Hackney Echo wf
Newsquest/Gannett
020-7790 8822
Hackney Gazette w
Independent Newspapers (UK)
020-7254 6311
Hammersmith Chronicle w
Adscene/Southnews
020-8741 1622
Hammersmith/Fulham Post wf
Adscene/Southnews
020-8741 1622
Hammersmith Guardian wf
Tindle Newspapers
020-8962 6800
Hammersmith/Fulham Times wf
Southnews
020-7381 6262
Hampstead & Highgate Express
Home Counties Newspaper Holdings
020-7433 0000
Harefield Gazette w
Middlesex County Press
020-7381 6262
Haringey Advertiser wf
United Provincial Newspapers
020-8367 2345
Haringey Independent wf
Newsquest/Gannett
020-8531 4141
Haringey Weekly Herald wf
Independent Newspapers (UK)
020-8340 6868

Harrow Independent wf
Southnews
020-8424 0044
Harrow Informer wf
United Provincial Newspapers
01784-433773
Harrow Leader wf
Southnews
020-8427 4404
Harrow Observer w
Southnews
020-8427 4404
Hayes & Harlington Gazette w
Middlesex County Press
020-7381 6262
Hendon & Finchley Times wf
Newsquest/Gannett
020-8203 0411
Highbury and Islington Express w
020-7433 0000
Hornsey Journal w
Independent Newspapers (UK)
020-8340 6868
Hounslow Borough Chronicle w
Southnews
020-8542 4141
Hounslow/Chiswick Informer wf
United Provincial Newspapers
020-8943 5171
Hounslow Guardian
Newsquest
020-8640 8989
Hounslow Feltham Times w
Dimbleby & Sons
020-8940 6030
Hounslow & Isleworth Leader wf
Southnews
020-7381 6262
Ilford Herald wf
Eastern Counties Newspapers
020-8478 4444
Ilford Recorder w
Eastern Counties Newspapers
020-8478 4444
Ilford & Redbridge Post wf
Independent Newspapers
020-8517 5577
Ilford Yellow Advertiser
Southnews
020-8530 3641
Islington Chronicle wf
Independent Newspapers
020-8340 6868
Islington Gazette w
Independent Newspapers
020-8340 6868
Kensington & Chelsea Ind. wf
020-8752 0052
Kensington & Chelsea Mail w
Middlesex County Press
020-8579 3131

Kensington & Chelsea Post wf
Adscene/Southnews
020-8741 1622
Kensington News w
Adscene/Southnews
020-8741 1622
Kilburn & Brent Advertiser w
Independent Newspapers
020-8962 6800
Kilburn Times w
Independent Newspapers
020-8450 5272
Leyton Guardian w
Newsquest/Gannett
020-8498 3400
London Weekly Times wf
Southnews
020-8381 6262
London West End Extra w
New Journal Enterprises
020-7419 9000
Marylebone Mercury w
Adscene/Southnews
020-8741 1622
Notting Hill & Bayswater Ind. w
020-8752 0052
Paddington Mercury w
Adscene/Southnews
020-8741 1622
Paddington Times w
Independent Newspapers
020-8450 5272
Putney Chronicle w
Adscene/Southnews
020-8741 1622
Romford & Havering Post wf
Independent Newspapers
020-8517 5577
Romford Advertiser wf
United Provinicial Newspapers
020-8530 3641
Romford Recorder w
Home Counties Newspaper Holdings
01708-766044
Ruislip Informer wf
United Southern Publications
01895-451000
Southall Gazette w
Middlesex County Press
020-7381 6262
Stanmore Observer w
Middlesex County Press
020-7381 6262
Stratford & Newham Express wf
Independent Newspapers (UK)
020-7790 8822
Tottenham & Wood Green Journal w
Independent Newspapers
020-8340 6868
Uxbridge & Hillingdon Leader wf
Southnews
020-8367 2345

Uxbridge Gazette w
Southnews
01859-233133
Uxbridge Informer wf
United Provinicial Newspapers
01784-433773
Victoria & Pimlico Times wf
Southnews
020-8381 6262
Waltham Forest Guardian w
Newsquest/Gannett
020-8498 3400
Waltham Forest Independent wf
Newsquest/Gannett
020-8498 3400
Walthamstow Guardian w
Newsquest
0120-8498 3400
Wandsworth Comet
Newsquest
020-8640 8989
Wembley & Kenton Recorder wf
Tindle Newspapers
020-8568 0022
Wembley & Kingsbury Leader wf
Middlesex County Press
020-8427 4404
Westminster Mail w
Middlesex County Press
020-8579 3131
Westminster & Pimlico News
Southnews
020-8741 1622
Willesden & Brent Chronicle w
Independent Newspapers (UK)
020-8450 5272
Wood Green Herald wf
Independent Newspapers
020-8340 6868

LONDON - SOUTH
Barnes, Mortlake Times w
Dimbleby & Sons
020-8940 6030
Battersea News w
Dimbleby & Sons
020-88744226
Bexley Borough Mercury wf
Trinity Mirror
020-8769 4444
Bexley Leader wf
Fletcher Newspapers
020-8301 6663
Bexley News Shopper series wf
Newsquest/Gannett
01689-836211
Bexleyheath Mercury wf
Newsquest/Gannett
020-8692 1122
Bexleyheath/Welling Times w
Fletcher Newspapers
01474-363363

Biggin Hill News wf
Tindle Newspapers
01959-564766
Brentford, Chiswick Times
Dimbleby & Sons
020-8940 6030
Bromley, Beckenham Times w
Fletcher Newspapers
01474-363363
Bromley News wf
Tindle Newspapers
01959-564766
Bromley Leader wf
Fletcher Newspapers
01474 363363
Bromley News Shopper wf
Newsquest/Gannett
01689-836211
Chislehurst Times w
Kentish Times Newspapers
01474-363363
Croydon Advertiser series w
Southnews
020-8668 4111
Croydon Guardian wf
Newsquest/Gannett
020-8646 4300
Croydon Post wf
Southnews
020-8668 4111
Eltham & Greenwich Times w
Kentish Times Newspapers
01474-363363
Erith & Crayford Times
Kentish Times Newspapers
01474-363363
Greenwich Mercury wf
Trinity Mirror
020-8769 4444
Kingston Guardian series wf
Newsquest/Gannett
020-8646 6336
Kingston Informer wf
United Provincial Newspapers
020-8943 5171
Kingston, Surbiton Malden Times w
Dimbleby & Sons
020-8874 4226
Lewisham & Catford News wf
Trinity Mirror
01689-836211
Lewisham Mercury wf
Newsquest/Gannett
020-8769 4444
Lewisham News Shopper wf
Newsquest/Gannett
01689-836211
Newham Recorder w
Eastern Counties Newspapers
020-8472 1421

Newham Yellow Advertiser wf
United Provincial Newspapers
020-8530 2641
Orpington & Petts Wood Times
Kentish Times Newspapers
01474-363363
Putney & Wimbledon Times w
Dimbleby & Sons
020-8940 6030
Richmond Informer wf
United Provinicial Newspapers
020-8943 5171
Richmond/Twickenham Guardian wf
South London Guardian
020-8646 6336
Richmond/Twickenham Times w
Dimbleby & Sons
020-8940 6030
Sidcup & Bexley Mercury wf
Newsquest/Gannett
020-8692 1122
Sidcup & Blackfen Times w
Kentish Times Newspapers
01474-363363
South London Press w
Trinity Mirror
020-8769 4444
Southwark News w
Southwark News
020-7232 1639
Streatham Mercury wf
Trinity Mirror
020-8769 4444
Streatham Guardian wf
Newsquest/Gannett
020-8646 4300
Surrey Comet w
Newsquest/Gannett
020-8646 6336
Sutton Borough Guardian wf
Newsquest/Gannett
020-8646 6336
Teddington & Hampton Times w
Dimbleby & Sons
020-8940 6030
Wandsworth/Putney Guardian wf
Newsquest/Gannett
020-8646 6336
Wandsworth Borough News w
Dimbleby & Sons
020-8940 6030
Wimbledon Guardian wf
Newsquest/Gannett
020-8646 6336
Woolwich/Charlton Mercury wf
Newsquest/Gannett
020-8692 1122

MANCHESTER AREA
(Ashton) The Advertiser wf
Guardian Media Group
0161-339 7611
Blythe & Forsbrook Time w
01538-753162
Bolton Evening News d
Newsquest/Gannett
01204-522345
Bolton Journal wf
Newsquest/Gannett
01204-522345
Bury Journal/Messenger wf
Newsquest/Gannett
0161-764 9421
Bury Times w
Newsquest/Gannett
0161-764 9421
(Cheadle) District Advertiser wf
Guardian Media Group
0161-480 4491
Tameside Reporter w
Regional Independent Media
0161-303 1910
Hale, Altrincham Courier w
Courier Group
01625-586140
Heywood Advertiser w
Guardian Media Group
01706-354321
Leigh & Tyldesley Journal wf
Newsquest/Gannett
01942-672241
Leigh Reporter/Golborne Star wf
Regional Independent Media
01942-228000
Manchester Evening News d
Guardian Media Group
0161-832 7200
Manchester Metro News wf
Guardian Media Group
0161-834 9677
Middleton Guardian w
Guardian Media Group
01706-354321
Middleton/Moston Express wf
Guardian Media Group
01706-354321
Mossley Reporter w
Regional Independent Media
0161-303 1910
North Cheshire Herald w
Ashton Weekly Newspapers
0161-303 1910
(Oldham) The Advertiser wf
Guardian Media Group
0161-626 3663
(Oldham) Evening Chronicle d
Hirst, Kidd & Rennie
0161-633 2121
(Oldham) Chronicle Weekend wf
Hirst, Kidd & Rennie
0161-633 2121

(Prestwich) The Advertiser wf
Guardian Media Group
0161-789 5015
Prestwich Guide w
Newsquest/Gannett
0161-764 9421
Radcliffe Times w
Newsquest/Gannett
0161-764 9421
Reddish Reporter wf
South Manchester Reporter
0161-442 2584
Rochdale/Heywood Express wf
Guardian Media Group
01706-354321
Rochdale Observer w
Guardian Media Group
01706-354321
Sale & Altrincham Messenger wf
Newsquest/Gannett
0161-477 4600
(Sale & District) Courier w
Courier Group
01625-586140
Salford City Reporter wf
Guardian Media Group
0161-789 5015
South Manchester Express wf
Guardian Media Group
0161-480 4491
South Manchester Reporter wf
Mortons of Horncastle
0161-446 2212
Stalybridge Reporter w
United Provinicial Newspapers
0161-303 1910
(Stockport) Express Advertiser w
Guardian Media Group
0161-480 4491
Stockport Messenger wf
Newsquest/Gannett
0161-477 4600
Stockport Times wf
Guardian Media Group
0161-480 4491
Stretford Messenger wf
Newsquest/Gannett
0161-477 4600
Tameside Reporter w
United Provinicial Newspapers
0161-303 1910
Wigan Evening Post d
Regional Independent Media
01772 254841
Wigan Observer w
Regional Independent Media
01942-228000
Wigan Reporter wf
Regional Independent Media
01942-228000

NORFOLK
Dereham & Fakenham Times w
Eastern Counties Newspapers
01603-628311
Diss Express w
Johnston Press
01379 642264
Diss Mercury wf
Eastern Counties Newspapers
01603-628311
Great Yarmouth Advertiser wf
Anglia Advertiser
01493-601206
Great Yarmouth Mercury w
Eastern Counties Newspapers
01603-628311
Lynn News w
Johnston Press
01553-761188
Norfolk Citizen wf
Johnston Press
01553-761188
North Norfolk News w
Eastern Counties Newspapers
01603-628311
Norwich Advertiser wf
Eastern Counties Newspapers
01603-740222
(Norwich) Eastern Daily Press d
Eastern Counties Newspapers
01603-628311
(Norwich) Evening News d
Eastern Counties Newspapers
01603-628311
Thetford & Watton Times wf
Eastern Counties Newspapers
01603-628311
Wymondham Mercury wf
Eastern Counties Newspapers
01603-628311

NORTHAMPTONSHIRE
Brackley & Towcester Advertiser w
Central Counties Newspapers
01280-813434
Corby & District Citizen wf
Johnston Press
01536-506100
Corby Advertiser
01536 416777
Daventry Weekly Express w
Johnston Press
01327-703383
Kettering & Disrict Citizen wf
Johnston Press
01536-506100
Kettering Herald & Post wf
Midland Independent Newspapers
01604-614600
(Northampton) Chronicle & Echo d
Johnston Press
01604-231122

Northampton Mercury wf
01604-231122
Northamptonshire EveningTelegraphd
Johnston Press
01536-506100
Northants Herald & Post wf
Midland Independent Newspapers
01604-614600
Wellingborough Herald & Post wf
Midland Independent Newspapers
01604-614600
Wellingborough Citizen wf
Johnston Press
01536-506100

NORTHUMBERLAND
Berwick Advertiser w
Johnston Press
01289-306677
Berwick Gazette wf
Northeast Press
01289-308995
Hexham Courant w
CN Group
01434-602351
Morpeth Herald/Leader wf
Johnston Press
01665-602234
News Post Leader w
Northeast Press
01670-517171
Northumberland Gazette w
Johnston Press
01670-602234
Northumberland Herald & Post wf
Trinity Mirror
01670-517362

NOTTINGHAMSHIRE
Ashfield Chad wf
Johnston Press
01623-456789
Eastwood Advertiser w
Johnston Press
01773-760444
Hucknell & Bulwell Dispatch w
Johnston Press
0115-955 5577
Mansfield Chad w
Johnston Press
01623-456789
Mansfield Recorder wf
Northcliffe Newspapers Group
0115-948 2000
Mansfield & Sutton Observer wf
North Notts Newspapers
01623-465555
Mansfield Weekly Post wf
Northcliffe Newspapers Group
0115-948 2000

d=daily, w=weekly, s=sunday, f=free

Newark Advertiser ~Series w
Newark Advertiser Co
01636-681234
Newark Trader News wf
Adscene/Southnews
01606-640650
Nottingham Evening Post d
Northcliffe Newspapers Group
0115-948 2000
Nottingham/Trent Valley Journal wf
Journal Publishing Co
0115-958 8387
(Nottingam) Recorder wf
Nottingham Post Group
0115-948 2000
Nottingham Weekly Post wf
Northcliffe Newspapers Group
0115-948 2000
Retford & Worksop Times w
Northcliffe Newspapers Group
01777-702275
Retford & Bawtry Guardian wf
Johnston Press
01777-704242
Retford & Bawtry Trader wf
01777-704099
Sandiacre and Stapleford News w
Adscene/Southnews
0115-946 9909
(Worksop) Midweek Guardian wf
Johnston Press
01909-500500
Worksop Trader News wf
Adscene/Southnews
01909-483333

OXFORDSHIRE
Abingdon Herald w
Oxford & County Newspapers
01865-425262
Banbury Cake wf
Bailey Group
01295-256111
Banbury Citizen wf
Johnston Press
01295-264321
Banbury Guardian w
Johnston Press
01295-264321
Bicester Advertiser w
Newsquest/Gannett
01865-425262
Bicester Review wf
Johnston Press
01280-813434
Didcot Herald w
Oxford & County Newspapers
01865-425262
Henley Standard wf
01491-419400
Oxford Courier wf
Courier Newspapers (Oxford)
01235-553444

Oxford Guardian wf
Journal Pubishing Co
01926-888755
Oxford Journal wf
Courier Newspapers (Oxford)
01235-553444
Oxford Mail d
Newsquest/Gannett
01865-425262
Oxford Star wf
Newsquest/Gannett
01865-425262
Oxford Times w
Newsquest/Gannett
01865-244988
South Oxfordshire Courier wf
Courier Newspapers (Oxford)
01235-553444
Wantage & Grove Herald w
Oxford & County Newspapers
01865-425262
Witney & W Oxon Gazette w
Newsquest/Gannett
01865-425262

SHROPSHIRE
Bridgnorth Journal w
Midland News Association
01743-248248
Ludlow Advertiser w
Newsquest/Gannett
01584-872183
Ludlow Journal wf
Midland News Association
01743-248248
Newport & Market Drayton Ad w
Midland News Association
01743-248248
Oswestry Advertiser w
North Wales Newspapers
01691-655321
Shrewsbury Admag wf
Adscene/Southnews
01743-241414
Shrewsbury Chronicle w
Midland News Association
01743-248248
Shropshire Star d
Midland News Association
01743-248248
Telford Journal wf
Midland News Association
01743-248248
Whitchurch Herald w
Trinity Mirror
01244-340151

BATH & NE SOMERSET
Bath Chronicle d
Northcliffe
01225-322322
Bath & District Advertiser wf
Southern Newspapers
01225 446800
Bath Oberserver wf
Northcliffe
01225-322322

SOMERSET
Bridgwater Mercury w
Southern Newspapers
01823-365031
Bridgwater/Burnham Times wf
Northcliffe
01749-672430
Burnham & Highbridge News w
Southern Newspapers
01823-365031
Chard & Ilminster News w
Southern Newspapers
01460-63442
Clevedon Mercury wf
01275-874248
Mid-Somerset Gazette w
Northcliffe
01749-672430
Norton Radstock Advertiser wf
Southern Newspapers
01225-446800
Portishead Advertiser
01934 417921
Sedgemoor Express & Star
Southern Newspapers
01823-365031
Somerset & Avon Guardian w
Newsquest/Gannett
01225-322322
Somerset & Dorset News wf
Northcliffe
01935-700500
Somerset County Gazette w
Southern Newspapers
01823-725000
Somerset Standard w
Northcliffe
01225-322322
Taunton Express & Star
Newscom
01823-365151
(Taunton) Midweek Gazette wf
Newscom
01823-335361
Wellington Weekly News w
Northcliffe Newspapers Group
01823-664633
West Somerset Free Press w
Tindle Newspapers
01984-632731

West Somerset Trader wf
Tindle Newspapers
01984-632731
Western Gazette w
Northcliffe
01935-700500
Weston & Somerset Mercury w
Southern Newspapers
01934-414010
Weston & Worle News wf
Northcliffe
01275-874248
Weston-Super-Mare Admag wf
Southern Newspapers
01934-417921
Yeovil Express & Star wf
Southern Newspapers
01823-365031

STAFFORDSHIRE

Biddulph Chroicle w
Heads (Congleton)
01260-273737
Blythe & Forsbrook Times w
Cheadle & Tean Times
01538-753162
Brownhills Advertiser w
SC Publishing
01992-721234
Burntwood Mercury wf
Adscene/Southnews
01543-414414
Burton Advertiser wf
Yattendon Investment Trust
01283-512345
Burton Daily Mail d
Yattendon Investment Trust
01283-512345
Burton Trader wf
Midland Independent Newspapers
01283-512000
Cannock Chase Chronicle wf
Midland News Association
01543-506311
Cannock Mercury wf
Adscene/Southnews
01543-414414
Cheadle & Tean Times w
Cheadle & Tean Times
01538-753162
Cheadle & Post Times w
Hill Bros (Leek)
01538-750011
East Staffordshire Journal wf
Journal Publishing Co
01332-202532
Leek Post & Times w
Hill Bros (Leek)
01538-399599
Lichfield Chronicle wf
Midland News Association
01543-414455

Lichfield Mercury wf
Adscene/Southnews
01543-414414
Lichfield Trader wf
Midland Independent Newspapers
01543-258523
North Staffs Advertiser wf
Northcliffe Newspapers Group
01782-602502
Rugeley Mercury w
Adscene/Southnews
01543-414414
Stafford Chronicle wf
Midland News Association
01902-313131
Stafford Post wf
Newsquest/Gannett
01902-875800
Staffordshire Newsletter w
Yattendon Investment Trust
01785-257700
(Stoke) The Sentinel d
Northcliffe Newspaper Group
01782-602525
Tamworth Herald wf
Adscene/Southnews Co
01827-848586
Tamworth Post wf
Tamworth Herald
01827-848586
Uttoxeter Advertiser w
Yattendon Investment Trust
01283-512345
Uttoxeter Echo w
Cheadle & Tean Times
01889-562479
Uttoxeter Post & Times w
Hill Bros (Leek)
01538-399599

SUFFOLK

Beccles & Bungay Journal w
Eastern Counties Newspaper Group
01603-628311
Bury Citizen wf
Johnston Press
01284-768911
Bury Free Press w
Johnston Press
01284-768911
Bury St Edmunds Mercury wf
Eastern Counties Newspapers Group
01284-702636
East Suffolk Mercury
Eastern Counties Newspapers
01473-230023
Haverhill Echo w
Adscene/Southnews
01440-703456
Haverhill Weekly News wf
Yattendon Investment Trust
01223-434434

(Ipswich) E Anglian Daily Times d
Eastern Counties Newspapers
01473-230023
(Ipswich) Evening Star d
Eastern Counties Newspapers
01473-230023
Ipswich Advertiser wf
Anglia Advertiser
01473-611363
Lowestoft Journal w
Eastern Counties Newspapers
01603-628311
Mid Suffolk Advertiser wf
Anglia Advertiser
01473-611363
Newmarket Journal w
Johnston Press
01638-668441
Newmarket Weekly News wf
Yattendon Investment Trust
01223-434434
Suffolk Advertiser wf
Anglia Advertiser
01473-611363
Suffolk Free Press w
Johnston Press
01787-375271
Waveney Advertiser wf
Anglia Advertiser
01493-601206
West Suffolk Mercury wf
Eastern Counties Newspapers Group
01284-702588

SURREY

Addlestone & Byfleet Review wf
Guardian Media Group
01483-769991
Ash Mail
Aldershot News
01252-328221
Banstead Herald
Surrey & South London Newspapers
01737-732000
Camberley & District Courier wf
Guardian Media Group
01252-328221
Camberley Mail w
Guardian Media Group
01252-328221
Camberley News w
Guardian Media Group
01252-328221
Caterham Mirror wf
Trinity Mirror
01737-732000
Chobham & Windlesham News w
Surrey Advertiser
01483-755755
Cobham News & Mail w
Surrey Advertiser
01372-463553

County Border Times & Mail wf
Tindle Newspapers
01252-716444
County Border News wf
01959 564766
Cranleigh Times wf
Guardian Media Group
01483-579244
Dorking Advertiser w
Trinity Mirror
01737-732000
Epsom/Banstead Informer w
Southnews
020-8770 7171
Epsom & Ewell Herald wf
Trinity Mirror
01737-732000
Farnham Herald w
Tindle Newspapers
01252-725224
Farnham Mail w
Aldershot News
01252-328221
Godalming Times wf
Guardian Media Group
01483-579244
Guildford Times wf
Guardian Media Group
01483-579244
Haslemere Herald w
01252 725224
(Haslemere) Messenger wf
PM Publications
01428-653999
Horley and Gatwock Mirror w
Trinity Holdings
01737-732000
Leatherhead Advertiser w
Trinity Mirror
01737-732000
Liphook Times wf
Tindle Newspapers
01252-716444
Molesey News w
Surrey Advertiser
01372-463553
Reigate & Banstead Ind. wf
Johnston Press
01737-249372
Staines Informer wf
Southnews
01784-433773
Surrey & Hants News wf
Tindle Newspapers
01252-716444
Surrey Advertiser w
Guardian Media Group
01483-508700
Surrey Mirror w
Trinity Mirror
01737-732000

Walton & Hersham News & Mail w
Surrey Advertiser
01372-463553
Walton & Weybridge Informer wf
Southnews
01932-561111
Walton & Weybridge Leader wf
Southnews
01932-561111
Woking Informer wf
Southnews
01784-433773
Woking News & Mail w
Guardian Media Group
01483-755755
Woking Review wf
Guardian Media Group
01483-769991

EAST SUSSEX

Bexhill Adnews wf
Johnston Press
01424-854242
Bexhill Observer w
Johnston Press
01424-854242
(Brighton) Evening Argus d
Newsquest/Gannett
01273-544544
Brighton & Hove Leader wf
Newsquest/Gannett
01273-544544
Brighton Friday-Ad wf
Friday-Ad Group
01825-766000
Byfleet News and Mail w
Guardian Media Group
01483-755755
Eastbourne Advertiser wf
Johnston Press
01323-722091
Eastbourne Gazette w
Johnston Press
01323-722091
Eastbourne Herald w
Johnston Press
01323-722091
Hailsham Gazette w
Johnston Press
01323-722091
Hastings Observer w
Johnston Press
01424-854242
Hastings Friday-Ad wf
Friday-Ad Group
01825-766000
Hastings Ad News wf
Johnston Press
01424-854242
Horley and Gatwock Mirror w
Trinity Holdings
01737-732000

Rye & Battle Observer w
Johnston Press
01424-854242
Seaford Friday-Ad wf
Friday-Ad Group
01825-766000
Seaford Gazette w
Johnston Press
01323-722091
South Coast Leader wf
Newsquest/Gannett
01273-544544
Sussex Express & Herald w
Johnston Press
01273-480601
Uckfield Friday-Ad wf
Friday Ad Group
01825-766000

WEST SUSSEX

Bognor Chichester Journal wf
Johnston Press
01243-534143
Bognor Regis Observer wf
Portsmouth &Sunderland Newspapers
01243-534143
Burgess Hill Leader wf
Newsquest/Gannett
01273-54454
Crawley News
Trinity Mirror
01737-732000
Crawley News Extra
Trinity Mirror
01293-732000
Crawley Observer w
Johnston Press
01403-253371
Crawley Weekend Herald wf
Johnston Press
01293-562929
East Grinstead Courier w
Northcliffe Newspapers Group
01342-323652
East Grinstead Observer wf
Trinity Mirror
01737-732000
Haywards Heath Friday-Ad wf
Friday-Ad Group
01825-766000
Haywards Heath Leader wf
Newsquest/Gannett
01273-544544
Horsham Advertiser wf
Johnston Press
01403-253371
Lancing Herald w
TR Beckett
01903-230051
Littlehampton Guardian wf
Johnston Press
01903-209025

Littlehampton Gazette w
Johnston Press
01903-714135
Mid-Sussex Citizen
Johnston Press
01444-452201
Mid-Sussex Leader wf
Newsquest
01273-544544
Mid-Sussex Times
Johnston Press
01444-452201
Shoreham Herald w
Johnston Press
01903-230051
Steyning Herald w
TR Beckett
01903-230051
West Sussex County Times w
Johnston Press
01403-253371
West Sussex Gazette w
Johnston Press
01243 533660
Worthing Advertiser wf
Johnston Press
01903-230051
Worthing Guardian wf
Johnston Press
01903-209025
Worthing Herald w
Johnston Press
01903-230051

TYNE & WEAR

Gateshead Herald & Post f
Trinity
0191-477 3245
Morning Gazette df
Metro International
0191-229 3000
(Newcastle) Evening Chronicle d
Trinity PLC
0191-232 7500
(Newcastle) The Journal d
Trinity PLC
0191-232 7500
Newcastle Herald & Post wf
Trinity PLC
0191-477 3245
(Newcastle) Sunday Sun w
Trinity PLC
0191-232 7500
News Guardian w
Northeast Press
0191-251 8484
North Tyneside Herald & Post wf
Trinity
0191-477 3245
Seaham Star wf
Johnston Press
0191-417 0050

(S Shields) The Gazette d
Johnston Press
0191-455 4661
South Tyne Star wf
Johnston Press
0191-417 0050
S Tyneside Herald & Post wf
Trinity PLC
0191-477 3245
Sunderland Echo d
Johnston Press
0191-534 3011
Sunderland Star wf
Johnston Press
0191-417 0050
Washington Star wf
Johnston Press
0191-417 0050

WARWICKSHIRE

Atherstone Herald w
Tamworth Herald Co
01827-848586
Bedworth Echo w
Midland Independent Newspapers
024-7631 2785
Coleshill Herald w
Tamworth Herald Co
01827-848586
Kenilworth Weekly News w
Johnston Press
01926-888222
Leamington Review wf
Johnston Press
01926-888222
Leamington Spa Courier w
Johnston Press
01926-888222
Leamington Spa Observer wf
Herald Observer Newspapers
01926-451771
(Nuneaton) Heartland Evening News d
Nuneaton & Disrict Newspapers
024-7635 3534
Nuneaton Tribune wf
Midland Independent Newspapers
024-7635 1111
Rugby Advertiser w
Adscene/Southnews
01788-535363
Rugby Observer wf
Herald Observer Newspapers
01926-451771
Rugby Review wf
Adscene/Southnews
01788-535363
Stratford Gazette wf
Journal Publishing
01926-831338
Stratford Standard wf
Herald Observer Newspapers
01789-415717

Warwick Courier w
Central Counties Newspapers
01926-888222

WEST MIDLANDS

Aldridge Advertiser Weekly
01922-721234
(Birmingham) Evening Mail d
Midland Independent Newspapers
0121-236 3366
Birmingham Metronews wf
Midland Independent Newspapers
0121-234 5073
Birmingham News wf
Midland Independent Newspapers
0121-626 6600
The Birmingham Post d
Midland Independent Newspapers
0121-236 3366
(Birmingham) Sunday Mercury w
Midland Independent Newspapers
0121-236 3366
Bloxwich Advertiser w
SC Pubishing
01922-721234
Chase Post wf
Midland Independent Newspapers
01902-875800
The Chronicle wf
Midland News Association
01902-313131
Coventry & Warks. Journal wf
Journal Publishing Co
01926-335578
Coventry Citizen wf
Midland Independent Newspapers
024-7663 3633
Coventry Evening Telegraph d
Midland Independent Newspapers
024-7663 3633
Dudley Chronicle wf
Midland News Association
01384-355355
Dudley News wf
Newsquest/Gannett
01384-239461
The Express & Star d
Midland News Association
01902-313131
Falcon Lodge Observer w
SC Publishing
0121-355 6901
Great Barr Chronicle wf
Midland News Association
0121-553 7171
Great Barr Observer wf
Adscene/Southnews
0121-355 6901
Halesowen Chronicle wf
Midland News Association
01384-355355

Halesowen News wf
Newsquest/Gannett
01384-442466
Little Aston Observer w
SC Publishing
0121-355 6901
Sandwell Chronicle wf
Midland News Association
0121-553 7171
Solihull Journal wf
Journal Publishing Co
0121-693 5750
Solihull News wf
Midland Independent Newspapers
0121-705 8211
Solihull Times wf
Midland Independent Newspapers
0121-711 4777
Stourbridge Chronicle wf
Midland News Association
01384-355355
Stourbridge News wf
Newsquest/Gannett
01384-442466
Sutton Coldfield News wf
Midland Independent Newspapers
0121-626 6600
Sutton Coldfield Observer wf
Adscene/Southnews
0121-355 6901
Vesey Observer w
SC Publishing
0121-355 6901
Walmley Observer
SC Publishing
0121-355 6901
Walsall Advertiser wf
SC Publishing
0121-355 6901
Walsall Chronicle wf
Midland News Association
01922-444444
Walsall Observer wf
Midland Independent Newspapers
0121-236 3366
News of Willenhall, Wednesbury wf
Midland Independent Newspapers
01902-875800
Wolverhampton Chronicle wf
Midland News Association
01902-313131

WILTSHIRE

Amesbury Journal w
Salisbury Journal Newspapers
01722-412525
Calne Gazette & Herald w
Newsquest/Gannett
01793-528144
Chippenham Gazette & Herald w
Newsquest/Gannett
01793-528144

Chippenham News w
Newsquest/Gannett
01793-528144
Devizes Gazette & Herald w
Newsquest/Gannett
01793-528144
Devizes News wf
Southern Newspapers
01380-729001
Devizes Star wf
Newsquest/Gannett
01793-528144
Kennet Star wf
Newsquest/Gannett
01793-528144
Malmesbury Gazette w
Newsquest/Gannett
01793-528144
Marlborough Pewsey Gazette w
Newsquest/Gannett
01793-528144
North & West Wilts Star wf
Newsquest/Gannett
01793 528144
Salisbury Advertiser wf
Southern Newspapers
01722-412525
Salisbury Journal w
Southern Newspapers
01722-412525
Salisbury Times w
Southern Newspapers
01722-412525
(Swindon) Evening Advertiser d
Newsquest/Gannett
01793-528144
Swindon Star wf
Newsquest/Gannett
01793-528144
Trowbridge/Melksham Adv wf
Eastern Counties Newspapers Group
01225-760945
Warminster Journal w
Coates & Parker
01985-213030
West Wiltshire Advertiser wf
Eastern Counties Newspapers
01225-760945
Westbury/Warminster Adv wf
Eastern Counties Newspapers Group
01225-760945
Wiltshire Gazette & Herald w
Newsquest/Gannett
01793-528144
Wiltshire Star wf
Newsquest/Gannett
01793-528144
Wiltshire Times w
Newsquest/Gannett
01225-777292

WORCESTERSHIRE

Berrow's Worcester Journal wf
Newsquest/Gannett
01905-748200
Bromsgrove/Droitwich Ad wf
Newsquest/Gannett
01384-442466
B'grove/Droitwich Standard wf
Herald Observer Newspapers
01527-585588
Evesham Journal wf
Newsquest/Gannett
01386-442555
Kidderminster Chronicle wf
Midland News Association
01902-313131
Kidderminster Shuttle wf
Newsquest/Gannett
01905-748200
Kidderminster Why wf
Goodhead Publishing
01527-853625
Malvern Gazette w
Newsquest/Gannett
01905-748200
Redditch & Bromsgrove Jnl wf
Journal Publishing
0121-693 3740
Redditch Advertiser wf
Newsquest/Gannett
01384-442466
Redditch/Alcester Standard wf
Herald Observer Newspapers
01527 585588
(Worcester) Evening News d
Newsquest/Gannett
01905-748200
Worcester Why wf
Goodhead Publishing
01527-853625

EAST YORKSHIRE

Beverley Advertiser wf
Northcliffe Newspapers Group
01482-327111
Beverley Guardian wf
Johnston Press
01377-253213
Bridlington Free Press w
Johnston Press
01262-606606
Driffield Times w
Johnston Press
01377-253213
Goole HowdenThorne Courier wf
Johnston Press
01302-819111
Grimsby Evening Telegraph d
Northcliffe Newspapers Group
01472-360360
Grimsby Target wf
Northcliffe Newspapers Group
01472-360360

Haltemprice Advertiser wf
Northcliffe Newspapers Group
01482-327111
Holderness Advertiser wf
Northcliffe Newspapers Group
01482-327111
Holderness Gazette w
Holderness Newspapers
01964-614325
Hornsea Gazette w
Holderness Newspapers
01964-614325
Hull Advertiser series wf
Northcliffe Newspapers Group
01482-327111
Hull Daily Mail d
Northcliffe Newspapers Group
01428-327111

NORTH YORKSHIRE

Cleveland Clarion wf
SR & VI Crane
01642-480397
Craven Herald & Pioneer w
Newsquest/Gannett
01756-792577
Easingwold Weekly News w
GH Smith
01347-821329
East Cleveland Herald & Post wf
Trinity International
01642-245401
The Gazette & Herald
York & County Press
01904-653051
Harrogate Advertiser w
Regional Independent Media
01423-564321
Harrogate Herald wf
Regional Independent Media
01423-564321
Knaresborough Post
Regional Independent Media
01423-564321
(Middlesbrough) Evening Gazette d
Trinity Mirror
01642-245401
Middlesbrough Herald & Post wf
Trinity Mirror
01642-245401
North Yorkshire Advertiser wf
Newquest Media Group
01325-381313
North Yorkshire News wf
Regional Independent Media
01423-564321
North Yorkshire Star wf
Newsquest/Gannett
01325-381313
Northallerton Times w
Regional Independent Media
01423-564321

Pateley Bridge Herald w
Regional Independent Media
01423-564321
Ripon Gazette w
Regional Independent Media
01423-564321
Scarborough Evening News d
Johnston Press
01723-363636
(Scarborough) The Mercury w
Johnston Press
01723-363636
Selby Chronicle wf
Johnston Press
01924-375111
Selby Star wf
Newsquest/Gannett
01904-653051
Selby Times w
Johnston Press
01924-375111
Stockton Herald & Post wf
Trinity Mirror
01642-245401
Whitby Gazette w
Adscene/Southnews
01947-602836

SOUTH YORKSHIRE

Axholme Herald w
Northcliffe Newspapers Group
01427-874417
Barnsley Chronicle w
Barnsley Chronicle
01226-734734
Barnsley Independent wf
Barnsley Chronicle
01226-734734
Barnsley Star d
Sheffield Newspapers
0114-276 7676
Dearne Valley Weekender wf
Garnett Dickinson Publishing
01709-571111
Dinnington Guardian wf
Johnston Press
01909-550500
Dinnington Trader News wf
Adscene/Southnews
01909-565200
Doncaster Advertiser wf
Johnston Press
01302-819111
Doncaster Courier wf
Johnston Press
01302-819111
Doncaster Free Press w
Johnston Press
01302-819111
Doncaster Star d
Sheffield Newspapers
0114-276 7676

Epworth Bells Advertiser w
Adscene/Southnews
01205-311433
Goole, Thorne & Howden Courier wf
Johnston Press
01405-782404
Rotherham Advertiser w
Garnett Dickinson Publishing
01709-364721
Rotherham Star d
United News & Media
0114-276 7676
Sheffield Mercury w
Sheffield Mercury Newspapers
0114-274 6555
Sheffield Telegraph w
Regional Independent Media
0114-275 4896
(Sheffield) The Star d
Regional Independent Media
0114-276 7676
Sheffield Weekly Gazette wf
Regional Independent Media
0114-276 7676
South Yorkshire Times w
Johnston Press
01302-819111

WEST YORKSHIRE

Aire Valley Target w
Newsquest/Gannett
01274-729511
Batley News w
Regional Independent Media
01924-468282
Birstall News w
The Reporter
01924-468282
Bradford Star wf
Newsquest/Gannett
01274-729511
(Bradford) Telegraph & Argus d
Newsquest/Gannett
01274-729511
Brighouse Echo w
Johnston Press
01484-721911
Calderdale News wf
Johnston Press
01422-260200
Colne Valley Chronicle w
Express & Chronicle
01484-684011
Dewsbury Reporter w
Regional Independent Media
01924-468282
(Dewsbury) The Weekly Adv wf
Regional Independent Media
01924-468282
(Halifax) Evening Courier d
Johnston Press
01422-260200

Hebden Bridge Times w
Johnston Press
01422-842106
Hemsworth Express wf
Johnston Press
01924-375111
Holme Valley Express w
Express & Chronicle
01484-684011
Huddersfield Daily Examiner d
Trinity Mirror
01484-430000
Huddersfield District Chronicle w
Express & Chronicle
01484-684011
Huddersfield Weekly News wf
Trinity Mirror
01484-430000
Ilkley Gazette w
Newsquest/Gannett
01943-465555
Keighley News w
Newsquest/Gannett
01535-606611
Leeds Express wf
Johnston Press
01924-375111
Leeds Weekly News wf
Regional Independent Media
0113-243 2701
Mirfield Reporter w
The Reporter
01924-468282
Morley Advertiser w
Johnston Press
01924-375111
Morley Observer w
Regional Independent Media
01924-468282
Normanton Advertiser wf
Normanton Advertiser
01924-892117
Ossett & Horury Observer wf
Johnston Press
01924-375111
Pontefract Express w
Johnston Press
01924-375111
Pontefract Weekend Times wf
Johnston Press
01977-702151
Pudsey Times wf
Regional Independent Media
01423-564321
Spenborough Guardian w
Regional Independent Media
01274-874635
Todmorden News w
Johnston Press
01706-815231
Wakefield Express w
Johnston Press
01924-357111

Weekend Times wf
Yorkshire Weekly Newspapers
01977-702151
Wetherby News w
Regional Independent Media
01423-564321
Wharfe Valley Times wf
Regional Independent Media
01423-564321
Wharfedale Observer w
Newsquest/Gannett
01943-465555

YORK

York Advertiser wf
Adscene/Southnews
01904-639136
York Star wf
Newsquest/Gannett
01904-653051
Yorkshire Evening Post d
Regional Independent Media
0113-243 2701
Yorkshire Evening Press d
Newsquest/Gannett
01904-611488
Yorkshire Gazette & Herald w
Newsquest/Gannett
01904-611488
Yorkshire Post d
Regional Independent Media
0113-243 2701

SCOTLAND

CITY OF ABERDEEN

Aberdeen & District Independent wf
Aberdeen & District Independent
01224-618300
(Aberdeen) Evening Express d
Northcliffe Newspaper Group
01224-690222
Aberdeen Herald & Post wf
Northcliffe Newspaper Group
01224-690222
(Aberdeen) Press & Journal d
Northcliffe Newspaper Group
01224-690222
Deeside Piper w
Angus County Press
01467-25150
Donside Piper & Herlad w
Angus County Press
01307-464899

ABERDEENSHIRE

Banffshire Advertiser w
J & M Publishing
01542-832265
Banffshire Journal w
Scottish Provincial Press
01261-812551

Buchan Observer w
Eastern Counties Newspapers Group
01779-476373
Ellon & District Advertiser w
W Peters & Son
01888-563589
Ellon Times w
Eastern Counties Newspapers Group
01779-476373
Fraserburgh Herald w
Eastern Counties Newspapers Group
01346-513900
Huntly Express w
J & M Publishing
01466-476373
Inverurie Advertiser w
W Peters & Son
01888-563589
Inverurie Herald w
Angus County Press
01307-464899
Kincardineshire Observer w
Montrose Review Press
01674-672605
Mearns Leader w
Montrose Review Press
01569-762139
Turriff & District Advertiser w
W Peters & Son
01888-563589

ANGUS

Arbroath Herald w
The Herald Press
01241-872000
Brechin Advertiser w
Angus County Press
01356-622767
Forfar Dispatch w
Angus County Press
01307-464899
Kirriemuir Herald w
Angus County Press
01307-464899
Montrose/Brechin Review w
Montrose Review Press
01674-672605

ARGYLL & BUTE

The Buteman w
Bute Newspapers
01700-502931
Campbeltown Courier w
Oban Times
01586-554646
Dunoon Observer w
E & R Inglis
01369-703218
Helensburgh Advertiser w
Clyde & Forth Press
01436-673434

Oban Times w
Oban Times
01397-703003

AYRSHIRE EAST

Cumnock Chronicle w
Clyde & Forth Press
01290-421633
Kilmarnock Leader wf
Eastern Counties Newspapers
01292-611666
Kilmarnock Standard w
Trinity Mirror
01563-525113

AYRSHIRE NORTH

Ardrossan/Saltcoats Herald w
Clyde & Forth Press
01294-464321
Arran Banner w
Arran Banner Printing & Publishing
01770-302142
Clyde Weely News wf
Trinity Mirror
01389-742299
Garnock Valley Herald w
Clyde & Forth Press
01294-464321
Irvine Herald w
01294-278312
Irvine Times
Clyde & Forth Press
01294-73421
Largs Weekly News w
Clyde & Forth Press
01475-689009
North Ayrshire Leader wf
Eastern Counties Newspapers Group
01292-611666
North Ayrshire World wf
Trinity Mirror
01292-261111

AYRSHIRE SOUTH

Ayr Advertiser w
Clyde & Forth Press
01292-267631
Ayr Leader wf
Community Leader
01292-611666
Ayrshire Post w
Trinity Mirror
01292-262200
Ayrshire World wf
Trinity Mirror
01292-261111
Carrick Gazette w
01465-712688
Carrick Herald w
Clyde & Forth Press
01383-728201

Troon & Prestwick Times
Clyde & Forth Press
01383-728201

BORDERS

Berwickshire News w
Johnston Press
01289-306677
Berwickshire Advertiser
Johnston Press
01289-306677
Berwick & Borders Gazette wf
Johnston Press
01289-308995
Border Telegraph w
D & J Croal
01896-758399
Hawick News w
Hawick News
01450-372204
Peebles Times wf
Scottish County Press
0131-663 2404
Peeblesshire News w
D & J Croal
01896-758399
Selkirk Weekend Advertiser w
Johnston Press
01750-21969
Southern Reporter w
Johnston Press
01750-21581

DUMBARTON/C'BANK

Clydebank Post w
Clyde & Forth Press
0141-952 1345
Clyde Weekly News wf
01294- 222288
Dumbarton Lennox Herald w
Scottish & Universal
0141-353 3366
Dumbarton Reporter w
Clyde & Forth Press
01383-728201

DUMFRIES & GALLOWAY

Annandale Herald w
Dumfriesshire Newspapers Group
01461-202417
Annandale Observer w
Dumfriesshire Newspapers Group
01461-202417
Carrick Gazette w
The Galloway Gazette
01465-712688
Dumfries Courier wf
Dumfriesshire Newspapers Group
01461-202417
Dumfries & Galloway Standard w
Trinity Mirror
01387-255252

Eskdale & Liddesdale Ad. w
Eskdale & Liddesdale Newspapers
01387-380066
Galloway Gazette w
Galloway Gazette
01671-402503
Galloway News w
Trinity Mirror
0141-353 3366
Moffat News w
Dumfriesshire Newspapers Group
01461-202417
Stornoway Gazette w
Stornoway Gazette
01851-702687
Wigtown Free Press w
01776-702551

CITY OF DUNDEE

Broughty& Carnoustie Gazette w
The Herald Press
01241-872274
(Dundee) Courier & Advertiser d
DC Thomson
01382-223131
(Dundee) Evening Telegraph d
DC Thomson
01382-223131
(Dundee) The Sunday Post w
DC Thomson
01382-223131
(Dundee) Sporting Post w
DC Thomson
01382-223131

CITY OF EDINBURGH

Edinburgh Herald & Post wf
Barclay Bros/Ellerman
0131-620 8620
(Edinburgh) Evening News d
Barclay Bros/Ellerman
0131-620 8620
(E'burgh) Scotland on Sunday w
The Scotsman Publications
0131-620 8620
(Edinburgh) The Scotsman d
Barclay Bros/Ellerman
0131-620 8620
Lothian Times w
Scottish County Press
0131-663 2404

FALKIRK

Falkirk Advertiser wf
Johnston Press
01324 624959
Falkirk Herald w
Johnston Press
01324-624959

FIFE

Central Fife Times w
Dunfermline Press
01383-728201
Clyde Post wf
Clyde & Forth Press
01383-728201
Dunfermline Herald & Post wf
Barclay Bros/Ellerman
01383-621818
Dunfermline Press w
Dunfermline Press
01383-728201
East Fife Mail w
Johnston Press
01592-261451
Fife Advertiser wf
Johnston Press
01592-261451
Fife Free Press w
Johnston Press
01592-261451
Fife Herald w
Strachan & Livingston
01592-261451
Fife & Kinross Extra wf
Dunfermline Press
01383-728201
Fife Leader wf
01592-261451
Glenrothes Gazette w
01592-261451
Greenock Telegraph d
Clyde & Forth Press
01475-726511
St Andrews Citizen w
Johnston Press
01592-261451

CITY OF GLASGOW

Barrhead News w
Clyde & Forth Press
0141-889 8873
Bearsden Milngavie Courier w
Community Media
0141-427 7878
Cumbernauld Advertiser wf
Johnston Press
01324-624959
Cumbernauld News w
Johnston Press
01324-624959
East Kilbride News w
Trinity Mirror
01698-283200
East Kilbride World wf
Trinity Mirror
01698-283200
(Glasgow) Daily Record d
Scottish Daily Record and Sunday Mail
0141-248 7000

Glasgow East End Independent wf
East End Independent
0141-550 2220
(Glasgow) The Herald d
Caledonian Publishing
0141-552 6255
Glasgow South Extra wf
Eastern Counties Newspapers
0141-427 7878
(Glasgow) Sunday Mail w
Trinity Mirror
0141-248 7000
The Glaswegian wf
Trinity Mirror
0141-248 7000
Kirkintilloch Herald w
Johnston Press
0141-775 0040
Milngavie & Bearsden Herald w
Johnston Press
0141-775 0040
Rutherglen Reformer w
Trinity Mirror
0141-647 2271
Sunday Post
DC Thomspm w
01382-223131
Weekly News w
DC Thomspm w
01382-223131

HIGHLANDS

Caithness Courier w
Scottish Provincial Press
01955-602424
Fort William Extra wf
Oban Times
01397-703003
Inverness & Highland News w
Scottish Provincial Press
01463-710999
Inverness Courier w
01463-233059
Inverness Herald wf
01463-710999
John O'Groats Journal w
01955-602424
Lochaber News w
Preceding four Scottish Provincial Press
01463-710999
North Star w
01349-863248
Northern Times w
01408-633993
Ross-shire Herald wf
01463-710999
Ross-shire Journal w
01349-863436
Strathspey/Badenoch Herald w
Preceding five Scottish Provincial Press
01463-710999
West Highland Free Press w
West Highland Publishing
01471-822464

LANARKSHIRE NORTH

Airdrie & Coatbridge Advertiser w
Trinity Mirror
01236-748048
Airdrie & Coatbridge World wf
Trinity Mirror
01698-283200
Bellshill speaker w
D MacLeod
0141-775 0040
Carluke Gazette w
Johnston Press
01324-624959
Hamilton Advertiser w
Trinity Mirror
01698-283200
Hamilton People wf
Eastern Counties Newspapers
01698-261321
Hamilton World wf
Trinity Mirror
01698-283200
Lanarkshire People wf
Community Media
01698-261321
Lanarkshire World wf
Scottish & Universal
01698-283200
Motherwell People wf
Eastern Counties Newspapers
01698-261321
Motherwell Times w
Johnston Press
01698-264611
Wishaw Press w
Trinity Mirror
01698-283200
Wishaw World wf
Trinity Mirror
01698-283200

LANARKSHIRE SOUTH

Lanark Gazette w
Johnston Press
01324-624959

EAST LOTHIAN

East Lothian Courier w
D & J Croal
01620 822451
East Lothian News w
Scottish County Press
0131-663 2404
Musselburgh News w
Scottish County Press
0131-663 2404

WEST LOTHIAN

Linlithgow Gazette w
Johnston Press
01324-624959
Lothian World wf
Trinity Mirror
01506-633544

West Lothian Courier w
Trinity Mirror
01506-633544
West Lothian Herald wf
Scotsman Publications
01506-634400

MIDLOTHIAN
Midlothian Advertiser w
Scottish County Press
0131-663 2404

MORAY
Banffshire Herald w
J & M Publishing
01542-832265
Forres Gazette w
Scottish Provincial Press
01309-672615
Northern Scot w
Scottish Provincial Press
01463-710999

ORKNEY ISLANDS
The Orcadian w
The Orcadian
01856-879000

PERTHSHIRE & KINROSS
Blairgowrie Advertiser w
Trinity Mirror
0141-353 3366
Perth Shopper wf
Trinity Mirror
01738-626211
Perthshire Advertiser w
Trinity Mirror
01738-626211
Strathearn Herald w
Trinity Mirror
0141-353 3366

RENFREWSHIRE
Johnstone & Linwood Gazette w
Clyde & Forth Press
01383-728201
Paisley Daily Express d
Trinity Mirror
0141-353 3366
Paisley People wf
Clyde & Forth Press
0141-889 8873
Paisley & Renfrewshire News wf
Eastern Counties Newspapers
0141-427 7878
Renfrew & Erskine Gazette w
Clyde & Forth Press
0141-889 8873
Renfrewshire World wf
Trinity Mirror
0141-353 3366

SHETLAND ISLANDS
Shetland Times w
Shetland Times
01595-693622

STIRLING
Stirling & Alloa Shopper wf
Trinity Mirror
01786-451110
Stirling News wf
Dunfermline Press
01259-214416
Stirling Observer w
Trinity Mirror
01786-451110

WESTERN ISLES
Stornoway Gazette w
The Galloway Gazette
01851-702687

WALES

BLAENAU GWENT
Gwent Gazette w
Trinity Mirror
029-2058 3583
North Gwent Campaign wf
Regional Independent Media
029-2085 1100

COUNTY OF BRIDGEND
Bridgend Recorder wf
Recorder (Wales)
01656-669330
Bridgend & Ogwr Post wf
Trinity Mirror
029-2058 3583
Glamorgan Gazette w
Trinity Mirror
029-2058 3583

COUNTY OF CAERPHILLY
Blackwood & Risca News wf
01633-810000
Blackwood Campaign wf
029-2085 1100
Caerphilly Campaign wf
All three are Southern Newspapers
029-2085 1100

CARDIFF
(Cardiff) The Post wf
Trinity Mirror
029-2058 3583
(Cardiff) South Wales Echo d
Trinity Mirror
029-2058 3583
(Cardiff) Western Mail d
Trinity Mirror
029-2058 3583

Wales on Sunday
Trinity Mirror
029-2058 3583

CARMARTHENSHIRE
Burry Port Star
Northcliffe Newspapers Group
01792-510000
Carmarthen Citizen wf
Northcliffe Newspapers Group
01267-227222
Carmarthen Journal w
Northcliffe Newspapers Group
01792-510000
Llanelli Star w
Northcliffe Newspapers Group
01792-510000
South Wales Guardian w
Regional Independent Media
01269-592074

CEREDIGION
Cambrian News w
Cambrian News
01970-615000
Cardigan Advertiser w
Southern Newspapers
01239-612513

COUNTY OF CONWY
Abergele Visitor w
Trinity Mirror
01745-344444
Caernarfon Herald w
Trinity Mirror
01286-584321
Lladudno Advertiser wf
Trinity Mirror
01492-584321
(North Wales) The Pioneer wf
North Wales Newspapers
01352-707707
North Wales Weekly News w
Trinity Mirror
01492-584321

DENBIGHSHIRE
Corwen Times w
County Press
01678-520262
Denbighshire Free Press w
North Wales Newspapers
01745-813535
Rhyl/Prestatyn Journal wf
North Wales Newspapers
01352-707707
Rhyl & Prestatyn Visitor wf
Trinity Mirror
01745-344444

d=daily, w=weekly, s=sunday, f=free

FLINTSHIRE
The Chronicle
Trinity Mirror
01244-340151
Flintshire Herald & Post wf
01244-545504
Flintshire Leader wf
North Wales Newspapers
01352-707707

VALE OF GLAMORGAN
Barry& District News w
Southern Newspapers
01446-734349
Barry Gem wf
Tindle Newspapers
01446-774484
Cowbridge Gem wf
Tindle Newspapers
01446-774484
Glamorgan Gem wf
Tindle Newspapers
01446-774484
Llantwit Major Gem wf
Tindle Newspapers
01446-774484
Penarth Times w
Southern Newspapers
029-2070 7234
Vale Post wf
Trinity Mirror
029-2058 3583

GWENT
Blackwood & Risca News wf
Southern Newspapers
01633-810000

GWYNEDD
Anglesey Chronicle wf
North Wales Newspapers
01248-387400
Bangor Mail wf
Trinity Mirror
01248-362747
Y Cyfnod w
The County Press
01678-520262
Y Cymro w
North Wales Newspapers
01248-387400
Y Dydd
The County Press
01341-422547
Yr Herald w
Trinity Mirror
01286-671111
Merioneth Express w
The County Press
01678-520262
North Wales Chronicle wf
North Wales Newspapers
01248-387400

ISLE OF ANGLESEY
Bangor & Caernarfon Chronicle wf
Trinity Mirror
01248-387400
Holyhead Mail w
01286-671111

COUNTY OF MERTHYR
Merthyr Express w
029-2058 3583
Merthyr Campaign wf
Southern Newspapers
029-2085 1100
Merthyr Tydfil wf
Campaign Free Newspapers
029-2085 1100

MONMOUTHSHIRE
Abergavenny Chronicle w
Tindle Newspapers
01873-852187
Chepstow News wf
Southnews
01633-810000
Mon & Abergavenny News wf
Southnews
01633-810000
Monmouthshire Beacon w
Tindle Newspapers
01600-712142

NEATH/PORT TALOT
Neath & Port Talbot Guardian wf
Trinity Mirror
029-2058 3583

COUNTY OF NEWPORT
South Wales Argus d
Southern Newspapers
01633-810000
Newport Free Press wf
Southern Newspapers
01453-544000
Newport News wf
Southnews
01633-810000

PEMBROKESHIRE
County Echo &St Davids Chronicle w
County Echo Newspapers
01348-872179
Fishguard County Echo w
Tindle Newspapers
01348-874445
Narberth & Whitland Obs w
Tindle Newspapers
01834-843262
Western Telegraph w
Southnews
01437-763133
Tenby Observer w
Tindle Newspapers
01834-843262

POWYS
Heart of Wales Chronicle wf
01597-824151
Mid Wales Journal w
Midland News Association
01584-876311
(Welshpool) County Times w
North Wales Newspapers
01938-553354

RHONDDA CYNON TAFF
Cynon Valley Leader w
Trinity Mirror
01685-873136
Pontypridd Campaign wf
Southern Newspapers
029-2085 1100
Pontypridd Observer w
Trinity Mirror
029-2058 3583
Rhondda Campaign wf
Southnews
029-2085 1100
Rhondda Leader w
Trinity Mirror
029-2058 3583

COUNTY OF SWANSEA
South Wales Evening Post d
Northcliffe Newspapers Group
01792-510000
Swansea Herald of Wales wf
Northcliffe Newspapers Group
01792-510000
Y Tyst w
John Penry Press
01792-652542

TORFAEN
Cwmbran & Pontypool News wf
Southnews
01633-810000
Pontypool & District Press w
Southern Newspapers
01495-751133

COUNTY OF WREXHAM
(Wrexham) Evening Leader d
North Wales Newspapers
01978-355151
Wrexham Leader wf
North Wales Newspapers
01978-355151

N IRELAND

ANTRIM
Antrim Guardian w
Northern Newspapers
028-703 43344
Ballyclare Gazette w
028-37 522639
Ballymena Chronicle w
Observer Newspapers (NI)
028-87 722557
Ballymena Guardian w
Northern Newspapers
028-703 43344
Ballymena Times w
Morton Newspapers
028-25 653300
Ballymoney Times w
Morton Newspapers
028-706 66216
(Belfast) News Letter d
Trinity Mirror
028-9068 0000
Belfast Sunday Life w
Trinity Holdings
028-9033 0000
Belfast Telegraph d
Trinity Holdings
028-9026 4000
Castlereagh Star w
Morton Newspapers
028-9267 9111
East Antrim Guardian w
Northern Newspapers
028-703 43344
East Belfast Herald & Post wf
Trinity Mirror
028-9026 4060
East Belfast News wf
Trinity Mirror
028-90 680010
Larne Gazette w
Alpha Newspapers
028-37 522639
Larne Times w
Morton Newspapers
028-28 272303
Lisburn Echo wf
Morton Newspapers
028-92 601114
North Newtownabbey Post wf
Trinity Mirror
028-9026 4060
Portadown Times w
Morton Newspapers
028-38 339421
South Belfast Herald and Post wf
Trinity
028-9026 4060
Ulster Star w
Morton Newspapers
028-92 679111

ARMAGH
Armagh Down Observer w
Observer Newspapers (NI)
028-87 722557
Craigavon Echo wf
Morton Newspapers
028-38 350041
Lurgan Examiner w
Observer Newspapers (NI)
028-87 722557
Lurgan Mail w
Morton Newspapers
028-38 327777
Ulster Gazette w
Alpha Newspaper Group
028-37 522639

DERRY
Coleraine Chronicle w
Northern Newspaper Group
028-703 43344
Coleraine Leader w
Northern Newspaper Group
028-703 43344
Coleraine Times w
Morton Newspapers
028-703 55260
Derry Journal w
Trinity Mirror
028-7127 2200
Derry People & Donegal News w
NW Ireland Printing & Publishing Co
028-82 243444
(Londonderry) NW Echo wf
Morton Newspapers
028-713 42226
Londonderry Sentinel w
Morton Newspapers
028-777 48889
Mid-Ulster & S Derry Mail w
Morton Newspapers
028-79 762288
Mid-Ulster Echo wf
Morton Newspapers
028-79 761364
Mid-Ulster Observer w
Observer Newspapers (NI)
028-87 722557
Northern Constitution w
Northern Newspaper Group
028-703 43344

COUNTY DOWN
Armagh Down Observer w
Observer Newspapers (NI)
028-87 722557
Banbridge Chronicle w
Banbridge Chronicle w
028-406 62322
Banbridge Leader w
Morton Newspapers
028-406 62745

County Down Spectator w
Spectator Newspapers
028-91 270270
Down Recorder w
W Y Crichton & Co
028-44 613711
Dromore Leader w
Morton Newspapers
028-92 692217
Mourne Observer w
Mourne Observer
028-44 722666
Newtownards Chronicle w
028-91 813333
Newtownards Spectator w
Spectator Newspapers
028-91 270270
North Down Herald & Post wf
Trinity Mirror
028-9026 4060
The Outlook w
028-406 30202

FERMANAGH
Fermanagh Herald w
North West of Ireland Printing County
028-82 243444
Fermanagh News w
Observer Newspapers (NI)
028-87 722557
Impartial Reporter w
William Trimble
028-66 324422

TYRONE
(Dungannon) About Town wf
Dungannon Development Association
028-87 725445
Dungannon Observer w
Observer Newspapers (NI)
028-87 722557
Strabane Chronicle w
North West of Ireland Printing County
028-82 243444
Strabane Weekly News w
Tyrone Constitution Group
028-82 242721
Tyrone Constitution w
Tyrone Constitution Group
028-82 242721
Tyrone Courier w
Alpha Newspaper Group
028-87 722271
(Tyrone) The Democrat w
Observer Newspapers (NI)
028-87 722557
Tyrone Times w
Morton Newspapers
028-87 752801
Ulster Herald w
North West of Ireland Printing County
028-82 243444

d=daily, w=weekly, s=sunday, f=free

Magazines

Estimates of the number of magazines vary according to definition. Taking every last newsletter and alternative magazine into account, there are well over 10,000 titles in the UK, though a more conservative estimate comes from British Rate and Data (Brad) which lists 8,887 titles that take advertising. This is up from the 7,945 Brad listed in 1999, and the Audit Bureau of Circulation data says launches account for 4 per cent of growth in overall magazine sales and 7 per cent in value.

New is what sells. "New" is the word most likely to sell a magazine and hence appears on covers more often than other trusty temptations like "Princess Di" or "sex". A pair of notable new arrivals into the market during 1999 and 2000 are: one, the former Sunday Express editor Eve Pollard's Parkhill Publishing which inuagurated itself with the launch of Wedding Day; two, James Brown, the former Loaded editor, who started the I Feel Good publishing company and launched Hotdog film mag. IFG is backed by Felix Dennis, the founder of Dennis Publishing who - presumably to atone for being in the business of what he calls "tree killing" - announced plans to spend £200 million on planting Britain's biggest forest in South Warwickshire.

Despite all this activity, paid-for circulations have declined by nearly 40 per cent since 1995, with porn mags the hardest hit at 60 per cent down. That's a triumph for web porn. Magazine sales track general fashion and the consumer titles which have done best over the past five years deal in men's fashion, countryside, comics and teenage, motoring, computers and TV listings. The latter are likely to become vulnerable when web-based programme guides are directly accessible from TV sets.

Terry Mansfield, who has been managing director of National Magazines since 1982, explains the sales slump: "The British magazine business is the most aggressive and the fastest-moving in the world. When we launched House Beautiful, for example, there were only seven titles in its category; now there are 28. There are also more newspaper supplements, more TV and radio stations, more internet opportunities. But there are still only 24 hours in a day - that can't be extended. So inevitably, you're seeing an over-supply of consumer titles, and slices are being cut out of every category." We're also seeing much web activity by magazine publishers, notably at Future Publishing. A recent Periodical Publishers' Association survey of business magazine publishers had 84 per cent of them claiming to run some kind of a web site. Newsletters have been most immediately affected by the web, with the UK Newsletter Association adding "and Electronic Publishers" to its title and reporting an increase in online activity matched by a more or less correresponding decline in paper sales.

However the newsiest piece of news is IPC Magazine's likely sale, a move which reflects its current investors' uncertainty about the future of consumer magazines and echoes the AOL-Time Warner style of desire for economies of scale. The billion pound plus sale is being pushed by Cinven, the venture capitalist which has controlled IPC since it financed a management buyout from a forward looking Reed Elsevier in 1997. Cinven's list of likely buyers is long and includes cable interests at Telewest or web interests at Yahoo plus other magazine companies such as Emap in the UK, Hachette in France or Bertelsmann in Germany.

Of the magazines listed in Brad, 5,713 are business and professional magazines and the remaining 3,174 are consumer mags, which the Periodical Publishers Association defines as "providing people with leisure time information and entertainment". The PPA does the trade body thing of distinguishing what a Martian would find similar and its main definitions are in the box on the right. What is significant about the puff is that, rather than concentrate on recent history, most of the PPA bullishness is made on the basis of comparisons with a decade ago.

PPA DEFINITIONS

Consumer magazines

* Over the last ten years reader expenditure has risen 129 per cent (four times inflation), ad revenues by more than 30 per cent and the number of titles by 28 per cent.

* Since 1990 circulation has increased by 111 million copies or 9 per cent. Consumer expenditure has increased 129 per cent over a period when inflation increased by 29 per cent.

* Profit margins are back to a pre-recession level of more than 15 per cent, up from 6.5 per cent in 1991/2.

* Titles launched since 1993 account for 41 per cent of ABC mags ABC and 35 per cent of average issue circulation

Business information publishing

* Since 1990 business magazines have upped ad revenue by £384 million to £1,203 million which is an increase of over 50 per cent, the share of classified revenue has increased by 5 per cent to 35 per cent of total business magazine advertising revenue. The number of titles is up 39 per cent.

* Over the last ten years business magazines have become the focal point of an £8 billion business comms market.

* 95 per cent of business professionals read one or more publication regularly and 70 per cent of business professionals see them as essential reading.

* Business-to-business publishers produce a wide range of media products, using most of the distribution and delivery methods available and over half have extended their product range to include other media such as directories, contract publications, list rental, sponsored publications and advertorials. Around 50 per cent are organising exhibitions, conferences, award ceremonies and other events.

Customer magazines

* Customer magazines began in the 1980s. They are produced under contract for companies and mostly distributed free.

* The total value of the customer magazine sector is more than £250 million and since 1990 industry turnover has risen almost 300 per cent.

* The majority (70 per cent), are mailed with the remainder distributed through client outlets and a few are sold.

TOP MAGAZINES BY CIRCULATION

1 AA Magazine	4,246,863
2 Skyview	2,299,295
3 Cable Guide	2,067,752
4 Safeway Magazine	1,944,359
5 Boots Health & Beauty	1,909,500
6 What's on TV	1,741,156
7 Somerfield Magazine	1,413,900
8 Asda Magazine	1,363,354
9 Radio Times	1,334,908
10 The National Trust Magazine	1,319,122
11 Take a Break	1,218,915
12 Voila	1,200,000
13 Reader's Digest	1,131,273
14 Saga Magazine	1,019,629
15 TV Times	790,603
16 Debenhams	742,350
17 FHM	674,836
18 Woman	653,045
19 TV Quick	638,855
20 Birds	579,876
21 Bella	564,104
22 Woman's Own	552,916
23 IN2Film	525,500
24 That's Life	521,650
25 OK!	491,586
26 Chat	490,516
27 Woman's Weekly	483,722
28 Best	461,851
29 Cosmopolitan	460,970
30 Candis	450,443
31 Hello	436,523
32 Marie Claire	422,995
33 Prima	413,196
34 Sugar	395,952
35 Now	390,812
36 Good Housekeeping	384,541
37 People's Friend	383,149
38 Sainsbury's	382,161
39 National Geographic	378,976
40 Loaded	353,640
41 Top of the Pops	349,813
42 Motoring & Leisure	337,731
43 Official Playstation mag	337,186
44 Know Your Destiny	332,755
45 Auto Trader	326,388
46 Computeractive	325,751
47 My Weekly	324,216
48 BBC Gardeners' World	312,252
49 Yours	309,906
50 Maxim	304,663

Source: ABC, June 2000

MAGAZINE OWNERS

KEY CONTACT

Periodical Publishers Association
Queens House, 28 Kingsway, London WC2B 6JR
Fax 020-7404 4167   Tel 020-7404 4166
E-mail: info1@ppa.co.uk
Website: www.ppa.co.uk
The trade association for magazine publishers, representing nearly 200 companies generating 80 per cent of the industry's revenue.

Addax Media
Heritage House, Yalding Hill, Yalding, Kent ME18 6AL
Fax 01622-815222   Tel 01622-814999
E-mail: info@addaxmedia.co.uk
Website: www.addaxmedia.co.uk
Buisiness, leisure, transport magazines.

Advanstar Communications
Advanstar House, Park West, Sealand Road, Chester CH1 4RN
Tel 01244-378888
Website: www.advanstar.com
Science and medical.

Affinity Publishing
2nd Floor, 1-5 Clerkenwell Road, London EC1M 5PA
Fax 020-7251 5490   Tel 020-7251 5489

Aim Publications
Silver House, 31-35 Beak Street, London W1R 3LD
Fax 020-7734 5383   Tel 020-7440 3800
E-mail: info@aimpublications.co.uk
Bridal magazines.

Angel Business Communications
361-373 City Road, London EC1V 1PQ
Fax 020-7417 7500   Tel 020-7417 7400
E-mail: london@angelbcl.co.uk
Website: http://www.angelbc.co.uk
Electronics and packaging.

Asian Trade Publications
1 Silex Street, London SE1 0DW
Fax-020-7261 0055   Tel 020-7928 1234
E-mail: garavi@gujarat.co.uk
Trade and catering.

Aspen Publishing
Avon House, Avonmore Road, London W14 8TS
Fax 020-7906 2043   Tel 020-7906 2000
Customer magazines.

Attic Futura
17-18 Berners Street, London W1P 3DD
Fax 020-7323 1854   Tel 020-7664 6400
Youth and entertainment publisher.

Auto Trader
1 Francis Grove, London SW19 4DT
Fax 020-8879 0110   Tel 020-8946 1155
E-mail: ak80@dial.pipex.com
Website: http://www.autotrader.co.uk
Publishes the 13 regional editions of Auto Trader.
Owned 50 per cent by the Guardian Media Group.

Avia Press Associates
75 Elm Tree Road, Weston-super-Mare, BS24 8EL
Fax 01934-822400   Tel 01934-822524
E-mail: helicopter_international@compuserve.com
Website: www.helidata.rotor.com
Specialist publishers of rotary-wing/helicopter magazines with defence and civil content.

Axon Publishing
5th floor, 77-79 Farringdon Road, London EC1M 3JT
Fax 020-7242 1900   Tel 020-7242 0600
E-mail: axonpublish@compuserve.com

Ballantyne Ross
16 Hampden Gurney Street, London W1H 5AL
Fax 020-7724 2632   Tel 020-7724 5444
E-mail: info@ballantyneross.com
Website: www.ballantyneross.com
Business to business/trade publisher specialising in pharmaceutical/medical and information.

H Bauer Publishing
Shirley House, 25 Camden Road, London NW1 9LL
Fax 020-7241 8030   Tel 020-7241 8000
Women, TV and puzzles.

BBC Worldwide UK
Woodlands, 80 Wood Lane, London W12 0TT
Fax 020-8749 0538   Tel 020-8743 5588

BEAP- The Puzzle People
Keesing House, Stonecroft, 69 Station Road, Redhill, Surrey RH1 1DL
Fax 01737-767248   Tel 01737-769799
Publisher of quality puzzle magazines.

Bennett Publishing
2&3 The Centre, Weston-super-Mare BS23 1US
Tel 01934-622000
E-mail: propnews@btinternet.com
Website: www.propnews.co.uk
Property news.

Big Issue
236-240 Pentonville Road, London N1 9JY
Fax 020-7526 3201   Tel -020-7526 3200

Blackwell Publishers
108 Cowley Road, Oxford, Oxfordshire OX4 1JF
Fax 01865-791347   Tel 01865-791100
Website: http://www.blackwellpublishers.co.uk
Humanities and social science journals .

Blackwell Science
Osney Mead, Oxford, Oxfordshire OX2 0EL
Fax 01865-721205   Tel 01865-206206
Website: http://www.blackwell-science.com
Technical, medical, scientific and academic journals.

Blenheim Business Publications
See Miller Freeman

Bloomsbury House
49-55 London Road, Middlesex EN2 6DN
Tel 020-8342 2222
Weightwatchers.

BMJ Publishing Group
BMA Ho, Tavistock Square, London WC1H 9JR
Fax 020-7383 6556   Tel 020-7387 4499
Web: www.bmj.com
Publisher of the British Medical Journal and 28 other journals.

Bowker Saur
Windsor Court, East Grinstead House, East
Grinstead, W Sussex RH19 1XA
Fax 01342-336192   Tel 01342-326972
E-mail: marketing@bowker-saur.co.uk
Web: www.bowker.saur.co.uk
International journals.

BPL Business Publications
22 The Green, West Drayton UB7 7PQ
                    Tel 01895-421111
E-mail: mjones@bpl-business.com
Website: www.bpl-business.com
BPL publishes business-to-business magazines for the
IT sector and runs online services.

Brass Tacks Publishing
143 Charing Cross Road, London WC2H 0EE
Fax 020-7478 4701   Tel 020-7478 4700
E-mail: enquiries@brasstacks.co.uk
Customer magazines.

British European Associated Publishers
Stonecroft, 69 Station Road, Redhill, Surrey RH1 1DL
                    Tel 01737-769799
A VNU subsidiary which publishes puzzle magazines.

Builder Group
Exchange Tower, 2 Harbour Exchange Square,
London E14 9GE
Fax 020-7560-4014   Tel 020-7560 4000
French-owned construction and security magazines.

Business Magazine Group
Adams Way, Mansfield, Nottinghamshire NG18 5FP
                    Tel 01623-450500
Website: www.bmgroup.co.uk
Regional business.

Butterworths Tolley
2 Addiscombe Roads, Croydon, Surrey CR9 5AF
Fax 020-8686 3155   Tel 020-8686 9141
E:mail: customer-services@tolley.co.uk
Website: www.tolley.co.uk
A business publishing subsidiary of Reed Elsveir.

Cabal
374 Euston Road, London NW1 3BL
                    Tel 020-7554 5700
E-mail: cabalcomm.com
5 titles including Front and Pro Cycling.

Caledonian Magazines
6th Floor, 195 Albion Street, Glasgow G1 1QQ
Fax 0141-302 7799   Tel 0141-302 7700
E-mail: info@calmags.co.uk
7 consumer and business press titles.

Cambridge University Press
The Edinburgh Building, Shaftesbury Road,
Cambridge, Cambs CB2 2RU
Fax 01223-315052   Tel 01223-312393
E-mail: rsymons@cup.cam.ac.uk
Website: www.cup.cam.ac.uk
Publisher of over 150 academic journals.

Carnyx Group
3 Park Street South, Glasgow G3 6BG
Fax 0141-332 2012   Tel 0141-332 3255
E-mail: info@carnyx.com
Contract publishing business supplements.

Catholic Herald
Lambs Passage Bunhill Row, London EC1Y 8TQ
Fax 020-7256 9728   Tel 020-7588 3101
E-mail: catholic@atlas.co.uk
Intellectual Catholic broadsheet.

Centennial Publishing
2nd Floor, 1-5 Clerkenwell Road, London EC1M 5PA
Fax 020-7251 5490   Tel 020-7251 0777
E-mail: info@fengshui-magazine.co.uk
Website: www.fengshui-magazine.com

Centaur Communications
50 Poland Street, London W1V 4AX
Fax 020-7970 4521   Tel 020-7970 4000
Website: www.centaur.co.uk
Around 20 business titles.

Charterhouse Communications
4th Floor, Arnold House, 36-41 Holywell Lane, London
EC2A 3SF
Fax 020 7827 0567   Tel 020-7827 5454
Consumer finance.

Choice Magazine
39-41 Priestgate, Peterborough PE1 1FR
                    Tel 01733-555123
E-mail: fiona.cowan@bayardpresse.co.uk
"News and information for mature people."

Citrus Publishing
Vinery Court, 50 Banner Street, London EC1Y 8QE
Fax 020-7577 9344   Tel 020-7577 9300
E-mail: citrus@citruspublishing.com

Combined Service Publications
PO Box 4, 273 Farnborough Road, Farnborough,
Hampshire GU14 7LR
Fax 01252-517918   Tel 01252-515891
E-mail: csp@btconnect.com
Many British Army regimental journals.

Communications Team
Exmouth House, 3-11 Pine St, London EC1R 0JH
Fax 020-7923-5401   Tel 020-7923 5400
E-mail: info@communications-team.co.uk
Webste: www.publishing-team.co.uk
Customer magazines and corporate communications,
clients include: Barclays, Abbey National and Virgin.

Computer Wire
4th floor, 12 Sutton Row, London W1V 5FH
Fax 020-7439 1105   Tel 020-7208 4200
E-mail: marketing@computerwire.co.uk
Website: www.computerwire.com
IT business intelligence and publishes Busines Review.

Conde Nast Publications
Vogue House, Hanover Square, London W1R 0AD
Fax 020-7493 1345   Tel 020-7499 9080
Website: www.condenast.co.uk
The US-owned publisher of lifestyle magazines.

Consumers Association
2 Marylebone Road, London NW1 4DF
Fax 020-7740 7600   Tel 020-7770 7000
E-mail: which@which.net
Website:www.which.net
The campaigning body for consumers and a good place
to start any consumer feature. The Association
produces five magazines, including Which?

Croner Publications

Croner House, London Road, Kingston-upon-Thames, Surrey KT2 6SR
Fax 020-8547 2637   Tel 020-8547 3333
E-mail: info@croner.co.uk
Website: www.croner.co.uk
Publishes reference guides on technical and business topics. Owned by the Dutch company Wolters Kluwer.

Cross-Border Publishing

111-113 Great Titchfield Street, London W1P 7FQ
Fax 020-7637 3594   Tel 020-7637 3579
Website: www.irmag.com
Investor Relations Magazine and IR guide books.

Dalesman Publishing

Stable Courtyard, Broughton Hall, Skipton BD23 3AZ
Fax 01756-701326   Tel 01756-701381
E-mail: sales@dalesman.co.uk
Website: ww.dalesman.co.uk
Dalesman, Peak and Pennine Magazine.

Dennis Publishing

19 Bolsover Street, London W1P 7HJ
Fax 020-7636 5668   Tel 020-7631 1433
Publishes computer magazines and other consumer lifestyle titles.

Director Publications

116 Pall Mall, London SW1Y 5ED
                    Tel 020-7839 1233
E-mail: director-ed@iod.co.uk
Website: www.iod.co.uk
Publishes Director magazine for members of the Institute of Directors.

Distinctive Publishing

146 Cromwell Road, London SW7 4EF
                    Tel 020-7591 5809

DMG Business Media

Queensway House, 2 Queensway, Redhill, Surrey RH1 1QS
                    Tel 01737-768611
Website: www.dmg.co.uk/dmgbm/
Business and technical.

DMG Home Interest Magazines

Equitable House, Lyon Road, Harrow, Middlesex HA1 2EW
Fax 020-8515 2080   Tel 020-8515 2000
Website: www.dmg.co.uk

Dog World

Somerfield House, Wotton Road, Ashford, Kent TN23 6LW
Fax 01233-645669   Tel 01233-621877
E-mail: editorial@dogworld.co.uk

Economist Group

15 Regent Street, London SW1Y 4LR
Fax 020-7499 9767   Tel 020-7830 1000
Website: www.economist.com

Economist Newspaper

25 St James's Street, London SW1A 1HG
Fax 020-7930 3092   Tel 020-7830 7000
E-mail: letters@economist.com
Website: www.economist.com
Part of the Pearson Group.

Egmont Fleetway

25-31 Tavistock Place, London WC1H 9SU
Fax 020-7388 4154   Tel 020-7344 6400
A Danish-owned comic publisher with about 19 titles.

Elsevier Science Publishers

The Boulevard, Langford Lane, Kidlington, Oxon OX5 1GB
Fax 01865-843010   Tel 01865-843000
Website: www.elsevier.nl
Part of Reed Elsevier, Elsevier Science publishes over 400 scientific and technical journals for industry, science and academia.

Emap

1 Lincoln Court, Lincoln Road, Peterborough, Cambs PE1 2RF
Fax 01733-358081   Tel 01733-568900
E-mail: janetj@plc.emap.co.uk
Website: www.emap.co.uk
Emap has three publishing divisions, two in the UK and one in France. It also has a radio division and a publications distribution arm.

Emap Business Communications

33-39 Bowling Green Lane, London EC1R 0DA
Fax 020-7831 3540   Tel 020-7470 6200
Website: www.emap.com
Over 100 titles are published in the UK and Europe by eleven subsidiaries.

Architecture	020-7505 6600
Fashion	020-7520 1500
Freight	020-7505 6600
Cars	01733-467000
Local Govt/Finance	020-7505 8000
Media/Marketing	020-7505 8000
Business/Commercial fishing/	
Middle East	020-7470 6200
Trade/Retail	020-8277 5000

Emap Consumer Magazines

Mappin House, 4 Winsley Street, London W1N 7AR
Fax 020-7312 8950   Tel 020-7436 1515
Nearly 100 consumer titles are published from seven centres:

Bikes/Cars	01733-237111
Computers/Games	020-7972 6700
Photography/Gardens/Pets/Rail	
	01733-898100
Retirement	01733-555123
Health/Parenting/Lifestyle/Women	
	020-7437 9011
Music/Entertainment/Men's lifestyle	
	020-7436 1515
Country pursuits/Sport	
	01733-264666

European Magazines

IPC Kings Reach Tower, Stamford Street, London SE1 9LS
Fax 020-7261 5277   Tel 020-7261 5240
E-mail: marieclaire@ipc.co.uk
A subsidiary of IPC Magazines.

Faversham House Group
Faversham House, 232a Addington Road, Croydon,
Surrey CR2 8LE
Fax 020-8651 7117   Tel 020-8651 7100
E-mail: fhg@dial.pipex.com

Financial Times Business
see Informa Publishing Group

Findlay Publications
Franks Hall, Franks Lane, Horton Kirby, Kent DA4 9LL
Fax 01322-289577   Tel 01322-222222

Forme Communications
97-99 Upper Richmond Road, London SW15 2TG
Fax 020-8788 2276   Tel 020-8780 7800
E-mail: forme@forme.com

Frank Cass and Co
Newbury House, 890-900 Eastern Ave, Newbury
Park, Ilford, Essex IG2 7HH
Fax 020-8599 0984   Tel 020-8599 8866
E-mail: info@frankcass.co
Website: www.francass.com
Nearly 60 academic journals on international affairs,
politics, history, culture and military science.

Freedom House Publications
44a North Street, Chichester, W Sussex PO19 1NF
Tel 01243-533394
E-mail: sails@freedomhouse.co.uk
Website: boats-4sail.com

Freestyle Publications
Alexander House, Ling Road, Tower Park, Poole
BH12 4NZ
Tel 01202-735090
E-mail: admin@freepubs.co.uk
Website: www.freepubs.xo.uk
Specialist interest titles.

FT Media & Telecoms
Maple House, 149 Tottenham Court Road, London
W1P 9LL
Tel 020-7896 2700
Website: www.ftmedia.com

Future Publishing
30 Monmouth Street, Bath, BA1 2BW
Fax 01225-446019   Tel 01225-442244
Website: www.futurenet.co.uk
A pioneer of the cover mount freebie computer disc and
(with Classic CD) the sampler compact disc. Once
owned by Pearson but in 1998 bought back by a
consortium including the original owner.

GJ Palmer & Sons
c/o Church Times, 33 Upper Street, London N1 0PN
Tel 20-7359 4570
Website: www.churchtimes.co.uk
Publishers of Church Times, The Sign and Home
Words, Church Book & Desk Diary, other publications
and sales factoring.

Gramophone Publications
38-42 Hampton Road, Teddington, Middlesex TW11
0JE
Fax 020-8869 8400   Tel 020-8943 5000
E-mail: info@gramophone.co.uk
Publishes Gramophone and a series of specialist
quarterly classical music titles.

Granta Publications
2-3 Hanover Yard, Noel Road, London N1 8BE
Fax 020-7704 0474   Tel 020-7704 9776
E-mail: editorial@grantamag.co.uk
Website: www.granta.com
Publishes Granta the magazine of new writing and
Granta books.

Gruner and Jahr
197 March Wall, London E14 9SG
Fax 020-7519 5514   Tel 020-7519 5500
75% owned by Bertelsmann, G&J publishes 3 titles
including the science title Focus. Sold Best and Prima
to NatMags in July 2000.

GTI
The Barns, Preston Crowmarsh, Wallingford, Oxon
OX10 6SL
Tel 01491-826262
E-mail: gti@gti.co.uk
Website: www.drjob.co.uk

Harcourt Publisher
32 Jamestown Road, London NW1 7BY
Fax 020-7482 2293   Tel 020-7424 4200
Website: www.harcourt-international.com

Haymarket Group
174 Hammersmith Road, London W6 7JP
Fax 020-7413 4504   Tel 020-8943 5000
Website: www.haymarketpublishing.com
Publishes 40 of the leading business, medical and
consumer magazines, from offices at Lancaster Gate
and Teddington (both on the same phone number).

Hello!
Wellington House, 69-71 Upper Ground, London SE1
9PQ
Fax 020-7667 8742   Tel 020-7667 8740
E-mail: advertising@hello-magazine.co.uk

Hemming Group
32 Vauxhall Bridge Road, London SW1V 2SS
Fax 020-7233 5056   Tel 020-7973 6400
Website: www.hemming-group.co.uk

Highbury House Communications
1-3 Highbury Station Road, London N1 1SE
Fax 020-7704 0758   Tel 020-7226 2222
Website: www.hhc.co.uk
International publisher specialising in sport, leisure,
finance, travel and business magazines.

HMSO
see The Stationery Office

Ian Allan Publishing
Riverdene Business Park, Molesey Road, Hersham,
Surrey KT12 4RG
Fax 01932-266601   Tel 01932-266600
E-mail: info@ianallenpub.co.uk
Website: www.ianallanpub.co.uk
Publishes transport magazines, books and videos.

Icom Publications
Chancery House, St Nicholas Way, Sutton, Surrey
SM1 1JB
Tel 020-8642 1117
Website: www.icompub.com
International communications.

IDG Communications
99 Grays Inn Road, London WC1X 8UT
Fax 020-7405 0262   Tel 020-7831 9252
Website: www.digitmag.co.uk
Publisher of newspapers, magazines and books on IT,
including Macworld and Digit magazines.

I Feel Good
37 Farringdon Road, London EC1M 3JB
Fax 020-7691 4547   Tel 020-7691 8182
Website: www.hotdogmagazine.com
James Brown's new company.

Illustrated London News Group
20 Upper Ground, London SE1 9PF
Fax 020-7805 5911   Tel 020-7805 5555
Website: www.ilng.co.uk

IML Group
184 High Street, Tonbridge, Kent TN9 1BQ
Fax 01732-770049   Tel 01732-359990
E-mail: imlgroup@dial.pipex.com
Business to business, trade and technical publications.

Informa Publishing Group
69-77 Paul Street, London EC2A 4LQ
Fax 020-7553 1100   Tel 020-7553 1000
Website: www.informa.com
Recently acquired the newsletters, magazines, reports
and directories previously produced by Financial Times
Business. Other areas covered include pharmaceuticals,
law, freight, media, retail and insurance. Other services
include conference organising.

Informa Telecoms Group
Gilmoora House, 57-61 Mortimer Street, London
W1N 8JX
Fax 020-7453 5947   Tel 020-7453 2212
E-mail: mci@informa.com
Website: www.mobilecomms.com
Publisher of specialist magazines, newsletters and
reports for the telecomms industry.

Inside Communications
Isis Building, Thames Key, 193 Marsh Wall, London
E14 9SG
                         Tel 020-7772 8300
Website: www.insidecom.co.uk

Insider Group
43 Queensbury Street Lane, Edinburgh EH2 4PF
                         Tel 0131-535 5555
E-mail: editor@insider.co.uk
Corporate magazines and news letters.

Insight
15 Little Portland Street, London W1N 5DE
                         Tel 020-7580 6222
E-mail: LindseyRiley@insight-ltd.demon.co.uk
A subscription only trade publication specialising in the
footwear and leather market.

IPC Magazines
King's Reach Tower, Stamford Street, London SE1
9LS
                         Tel.020-7261 5000
Website: www.ipc.co.uk
Britain's largest publisher of consumer and leisure
magazines.

Jobson Publishing Corporation
Jobson House, Hill Rise, Richmond TW10 6UD
Fax 020-8332 6918   Tel 020-8332 6882
E-mail: emiddlebrook@jobson.com
Website: www.jobson.com
Publisher of optical magazines and special reports.

John Brown Publishing
The New Boathouse, 136-142Braley Road, London
W10 6SR
                         Tel 020-7565 3000
Website: www.johnbrowncontract.com
Viz, Fortean Times, customer magazines.

John Wiley & Sons
Baffins Lane, Chichester, Sussex PO19 1UD
Fax 01243-775878   Tel 01243-779777
E-mail: publicity@wiley.co.uk
Website: www.wiley.co.uk
Publishes 411 journals of all kinds.

Keesing (UK)
see BEAP

Killen International Partnership
34 Rose Street, London WC2E 9BS
                         Tel 020-7240 8295
Customer magazines.

The Lady
39-40 Bedford Street, London WC2E 9ER
Fax 020-7836 4620   Tel 020-7379 4717

The Lancet
84 Theobalds Road, London WC1X 8RR
Fax 020-7436 7570   Tel 020-7611 4100
E-mail: Clas.Advertising@ellsevier.co.uk
Website: www.thelancet.com

Law Society of England & Wales
113 Chancery Lane, London WC2A 1PL
Fax 020-7242 1309   Tel 020-7242 1222
E-mail: edit@punch.co.uk
Website: www.lawsociety.org.uk

Liberty Publishing
100 Brompton Road, London SW3 1ER
Fax: 020-7225 6725   Tel: 0171 225 6716
E-mail: adsales@punch.co.uk

Link House Magazines
Dingwall Avenue, Croydon, Surrey CR9 2TA
Fax 020-8760 0973   Tel 020-8686 2599
Website: www.linkhouse.co.uk

LLP/Informa Publishing Group
Sheepen Place, Colchester, CO3 3LP
Fax 01206-772771   Tel 01206-772277
E-mail: subscriptions@linforma.com
Website: www.informa.com
Commercial, legal and financial information and data
relatingt o shipping, maritime services, insurance,
freighting and transport, commodities and energy.

Loot
24-32 Kilburn High Road, Kilburn, London NW6 5TF
Fax 020-7625 7921   Tel 020-7625 0266
Website: www.loot.com
E-mail: freeads.london@loot.com
Regional mags where small ads get placed for nothing
and revenue comes from copy sales and business
advertisers. One of the slickest ideas since Caxton.

Macmillan Magazines
Porters South, 4 Crinan Street, London N1 9XW
Fax 020-7843 4640   Tel 020-7833 4000
Website: www.macmillanmags.com
Publishes 13 titles, mainly health service and scientific.

Manor Publishing
Manor Ho, Edison Road, Eastbourne BN23 6PT
Fax 01323-5090213   Tel 01323-507474
E-mail: manorgroup@mistral.co.uk
Trade mags.

Mark Allen Publishing
286a-288 Croxted Road, London SE24 9BY
Fax 020-8671 1722   Tel 020-8671 7521
E-mail: 1editor@markallen.com
Website: www.markallengroup.com
Mainly medical titles.

Marvel Comics
Panini House, Coach and Horses Passage, The
Pantiles, Tunbridge Wells, Kent TN2 5UJ
Fax 01892-545666   Tel 01892-500100
Website: www.panini.co.uk
13 titles. Part of the Panini sticker group.

Mature Tymes
The Wharf, 121 Schooner Way, Cardiff CF1 5EQ
          Tel 029-2046 8504
E-mail: sales@maturetymes.co.uk

Media Ventures Group
4 Ambassador Place, Altrincham, WA15 8DB
Fax 0161-608 0298   Tel 0161-608 0300

Mediamark Publishing
11 Kingsway, London WC2B 6PH
Fax 020-7212 9001   Tel 020-7212 9000
E-mail: info@mediamark.co.uk
Website: www.mediamark.co.uk
Work with clients to produce mags in print and on-line.

Metal Bulletin
Park Terrace, Worcester Park, Surrey KT4 7HY
Fax 020-8337 8943   Tel 020-7827 9977
E-mail: subscriptions@metalbulletin.plc.uk
Website: www.metalbulletin.co.uk

Miller Freeman
Marlowe House, 109 Station Road, Sidcup, Kent
DA15 7ET
Fax 020-8309 3606   Tel 020-8309 3666
E-mail: tdunne@unmf.com
Website: www.millerfreeman.co.uk
A subsidiary of United News and Media, Miller
Freeman specialises in business, trade and professional
magazines. Divisions include: Miller Freeman Business
Information Services (annual directories), and Miller
Freeman Entertainment.

Mining Journal
60 Worship Street, London EC2A 2HD
Fax 020-7216 6050   Tel 020-7216 6060
E-mail: editorial@mining-journal.com
Website: www.mining-journal.com

Miracle Publishing
1 York Street, London W1H 1PZ
Fax 020-7486 2002   Tel 020-7486 7007
E-mail: info@audience.ukcom
Website: www.audience.uk.com

AE Morgan
Stanley House, 9 West Street, Epsom KT18 7RL
Fax 01372-744493   Tel 01372-741411
E-mail: t.morgan@easynet.co.uk

National Geographic Society
16 The Pines, Broad Street, Guildford, Surrey GU3 3NX
Fax 01483-506331   Tel 01483-537111
Website: www.nationalgeographic.com

National Magazine Company
National Magazine House, 72 Broadwick Street,
London W1V 2BP
Fax 020-7437 6886   Tel 020-7439 5000
Website: www.natmags.co.uk
Titles include Country Living, Harpers&Queen, Esquire
and Cosmopolitan. Bought Prima and Best from G&J
in July 2000. Owned by the Hearst Corporation.

Needmarsh Publishing
71 Newcomen Street, London SE1 1YT
Fax 020-7378 6883   Tel 020-7403 0840
Website: www.rightstartmagazine.co.uk

New Crane Publishing
20 Upper Ground, London SE1 9PD
          Tel 020-7633 0266
E-mail: edit@newcrane.co.uk
Publishes Sainsbury's magazine.

New Internationalist
55 Rectory Road, Oxford OX4 1BW
Fax 01865-793152   Tel 01865-728181
E-mail: michaely@newint.org
Website: www.newint.org
Reports on world poverty and inequalities.

New Statesman
7th Floor, Victoria Station House, 191 Victoria Street,
London SW1E 5NE
Fax 020-7828 1881   Tel 020-7828 1232
E-mail: info@newstatesman.co.uk
Website: www.newstatsman.co.uk

Newhall Publications
Newhall Lane, Hoylake, Wirral, Merseyside CH47 4BQ
Fax 0151-632 5716   Tel 0151-632 3232
Website: www.candis.co.uk
Publishes Candis monthly mag for women.

Newsweek
18 Park Street London W1Y 4HH
Fax 020-7629 0050   Tel 020-7318 1600
Website: www.newsweek.com
National and international affairs, business, science and
the arts. Foreign language editions including Arabic.

Nexus Media/Nexus Special Interests
Nexus House, Azalea Drive, Swanley, Kent BR8 8HU
Fax 01322 667633   Tel 01322 660070
Website: www.nexusonline.com
Publisher and event organiser for industry, architecture,
lifestyle, business, education, horticulture, health, IT,
hobbies, crafts and puzzles.

Noble House Publishing
Silver House, 31-35 Beak Street, London W1R 3LD
Fax 020-7734 5383   Tel 020-7440 3800
E-mail: info@mobilechoiceuk.com
Mobile phone mag.

Nursery World
Admiral House, 66-68 East Smithfield, London E1W
1BX
Fax 020-7782 3398   Tel 020-7782 3000
Website: www.nursery-world.com

Oxford University Press
Great Clarendon Street, Oxford OX2 6DP
Fax 01865-556646   Tel 01865-556767
E-mail: jnl.info@oup.co.uk
Website: www.oup.co.uk
Publishes 170 academic journals.

Parkhill Publishing
100 Grays Inn Road, London WC1X 8AL
Fax 020-7269 7459   Tel 020-7269 7400

Parliamentry Communications
10 Little College Street, London SW1P 3SH
Fax 020-7976 0861   Tel 020-7878 1500
E-mail: subscriptions@parlicom.com
Publishers of The House Magazine, covering
government policies and parliament.

Paul Raymond Publications
2 Archer Street, London W1V 8JJ
Fax 020-7734 5030   Tel 020-7292 8000
Website: www.sexclub.co.uk
Britain's largest porn magazine publisher.

Personnel Publications
17 Britton Street, London EC1M 5TP
Fax 020-7426 0042   Tel 020-7426 0424
Professional financial journals.

Perspective Publishing
408 the Fruit and Wool Exchange, Brushfield Street,
London E1 6EP
Fax 020-7336 7637   Tel 020-7880 6200
Website: www.peoplemanagement.co.uk

Philip Allan Publishers
Market Place, Deddington, Oxon OX15 0SE
Fax: 01869 337590   Tel: 01869 338652
E-mail: sales@philipallan.co.uk
Website: www.philipallan.co.uk
Educational publishers and conference providers,
producing magazines, revision guides and conferences
for students, resource packs and one-day workshops for
teachers.

Phillips Business Information
3rd Floor, 19 Thomas Moore Street, London E1 9YW
Tel 020-7423 4500
E-mail: kbrody@phillipslid.co.uk
Website: www.the-phillips-group.com
Publisher of business newsletters in telecoms, IT, cable,
satellite, broadcast and new media markets.

Plain English Publishing Company
Pixmore Busines Centre, Pixmore Avenue,
Letchworth, Herts AG6 1JG
Fax 01462 486812   Tel 01462 486810
E-mail: admin@the-sticks.com
Website: www.the-sticks.com
Puboisher of The Sticks group magazine with editions
throughout the south totalling a monthly 280,000
circulation.

Police Review Publishing
1st Floor, 180 Wardour Street, London W1A 4YG
Fax 020-7405 7167   Tel 020-7851 9700
E-mail: fabiana.angelini@policereview.co.uk
Website: www.policereview.com
Publishes three magazines, training books and course
material.

Practical Publications
Suite C, 21 Heathmans Road, London SW6 4TJ
Tel 020-7384 3261

Premier Media Partners
1 Oxendon Street, London SW1Y 4EE
Fax 020-7839 4491   Tel 020-7925 2544
Website: www.premiermp,com
A client publishing agency.

Quantum Publishing
Quantum House, 19 Scarbrook Rd, Croydon CR9 1LX
Fax 020-8565 4444   Tel 020-8565 4200
Formed in 1989. In 1997 Quantum bought 13 Emap
titles including Press Gazette and Media Week.

Raven-Fox
Nestor House, Playhouse Yard, London EC4V 5EX
Fax 020-7779 8249   Tel 020-7779 8228
E-mail: rfmail@euromoneyplc.com

RCN Publishing
Nursing Standard House, 17-19 Peterborough Road,
Harrow HA1 2AX
Fax 020-8423 4302   Tel 020-8423 1066
E-mail: nursing.standard@rcn.org.uk
Website: www.nursing-standard.co.uk
Publishes the weekly Nursing Standard and a wide
range of journals for nurses in different specialties.

Reader's Digest Association
11 Westferry Circus, Canary Wharf, London E14 4HE
Fax 020-7715 8181   Tel 020-7715 8000
Website: www.readersdigest.co.uk

The Redan Company
1st Floor, Ramillies Building, 1-9 Hills Place, London
W1R 1AG
Fax 020-8563 1478   Tel 020-7434 1612
E-mail: sam@redan.co.uk

Redwood Publishing
7 St Martin's Place, London WC2N 4HA
Fax 020-7747 0701   Tel 020-7747 0700
Website: www.redwood-publishing.com
Redwood is a contract publisher, with clients including:
AA, BSkyB, Boots, BT, Dulux, Harvey Nichols,
Homebase, Marks & Spencer, PSION, Safeway, Volvo,
Yellow Pages.

Reed Business Information
Quadrant House, The Quadrant, Sutton, Surrey SM2
5AS
Fax 020-8652 3960   Tel 020-8652 3500
Website: www.reedbusiness.com
One of Britain's largest business publishers.

Reed Elsevier
25 Victoria Street, London SW1H 0EX
Fax 020-7227 5799   Tel 020-7222 8420
Website: www.reed-elsevier.com
In January 1993 Reed and the Dutch group Elsevier set up Reed Elsevier plc to create one of the world's biggest publishing companies employing over 25,000 people. The main UK magazine divisions (listed elsewhere in this section) are:
  Butterworth-Heinemann
  Elsevier Science Publishers
  IPC Magazines
  Reed Business Publishing

River Publishing
Victory House, Leicester Square, London WC2 7QH
                              Tel 020-7306 0304
Customer magazines.

Rodale Press
7-10 Chandos Street, London W1M 0AD
Fax 020-7299 6060   Tel 020-7291 6000

Romsey Publishing Company
4 The Courtyard, Denmark Street, Wokingham, Berkshire RG11 2AZ
                              Tel 01189-771677
UK travel and gardens, including The English Garden.

Rooster
49a Goldhawk Road, London W12 8QP
Fax 020-8743 0888   Tel 020-8743 8111
E-mail: info@hhpublishing.demon.co.uk
Contract publisher specialising in travel and technology.

Routledge
11 New Fetter Lane, London EC4P 4EE
Fax 020-7842 2298   Tel 020-7583 9855
Web: www.routledge.com/routledge.html

Saga Publishing
The Saga Building, Middleburg Square, Folkestone, Kent CT20 1AZ
Fax 01303-776699   Tel 01303-771523
E-mail: editor@saga.co.uk
Website: www.saga.co.uk/publishing/
Magazines for the over 50s.

Sage Publications
6 Bonhill Street, London EC2A 4PU
Fax 020-7374 8741   Tel 020-7374 0645
E-mail: market@sagepub.co.uk
Website: www.sagepub.co.uk/
An academic and professional publisher of social science books, journals and software.

Scholastic
Villiers House, Clarendon Avenue, Leamington Spa, Warwickshire CV32 5PR
Fax 01926-883331   Tel 01926-887799
Website: www.scholastic.co.uk

TG Scott
10 Savoy Street, London WC2E 7HR
Fax 020-7379 7118   Tel 020-7240 2032
E-mail: ian@tgscott.co.uk
Website: www.mcmscott.com
Specialist advertising sales company.

Shepherd Press
111 High Street, Burnham. Buckinghamshire SL1 7JZ
Fax 01628-664334   Tel 01628-604311
E-mail: publishing@shepherd.co.uk
Website: www.shepherd.co.uk
Publishers of international specialist aerospace and defence magazines.

The Spectator
56 Doughty Street, London WC1N 2LL
Fax 020-7242 0603   Tel 020-7405 1706
Website: www.spectator.co.uk

SPL
Berwick House, 8-10 Knoll Rise, Orpington, Kent BR6 0PS
Fax 01689-876438   Tel 01689-887200
E-mail: @splpublishing.co.uk
Security and cars.

The Stage Newspaper
Stage House, 47 Bermondsey Street, London SE1 3XT
Fax 020-7403 1418   Tel 020-7403 1818
E-mail: info@thestage.co.uk
Websites: www.thestage.co.uk
              www.showcall.co.uk

The Stationery Office
St Crispin's, Duke Street, Norwich NR3 1PD
Fax 01603-695607   Tel 01603-622211
Website: www.national-publishing.co.uk
To order material on credit card via phone, tel: 020-7873 9090.
HMSO was privatised in September 1996. A residual part of HMSO remains within the Cabinet Office putting legal material on the internet.
Website: www.hmso.gov.uk

Sterling Publishing Group
55-57 North Wharf Road, London W2 1XR
                              Tel 020-7915 9660
Website: www.sterlingpublications.co.uk
120 technical and business journals and directories.

Style Publishing
126 Great Portland Street, London W1N 5PH
Fax 020-7436 9957   Tel 020-7436 9766
E-mail: barnshaw@freeuk.com
Publishers of hair and beauty consumer and trade titles.

Summerhouse Publishing
St James' Yarn Mill, Whitefriars, Norwich NR3 1XU
Fax 01603-664410   Tel 01603-664242
E-mail: tj@summerho.demon.co.uk
Website: www.summerhouse-publishing.com
Part of the ECN Group, Summerhouse Publishing produce customer publications.

Sweet and Maxwell
100 Avenue Road, London NW3 3PF
Fax 020-7393 7010   Tel 020-7393 7000
E:mail: webmaster@smlawpub.co.uk
Website: www.smlawpub.co.uk
Legal publishing.

The Tablet Publishing Company
1 King St Cloisters, Clifton Walk. London W6 0QZ
Fax 020-8748 1550   Tel 020-8748 8484
Website: www.thetablet.co.uk

Taylor and Francis (Carfax)
11 New Fetter Lane, London EC4P 4EE
Fax 020-7842 2298   Tel 020-7583 9855
E-mail: info@tandf.co.uk
Website: www.tandf.co.uk
Publishes around 180 academic titles. One of the largest social science publishers.

DC Thomson and Co
2 Albert Square, Dundee, Tayside DD1 9QJ
Fax 01382-322214   Tel 01382-223131
Website: www.dcthomson.co.uk
A Scottish based, family owned company which produces more than 2 million magazines, comics and newspapers every year. Titles include, The Beano, The Dandy, The Scot's Magazine and The Sunday Post.

Thomson Corporation
1st Floor Quadrangle, 180 Wardour Street, London W1A 4YG
Fax 020-7734 0561   Tel 020-7437 9787
Website: www.thomcorp.com.uk
The magazine publishing subsidiary of the Thomson Corporation of Canada. Its main UK subsidiaries are:

Derwent Information
Janes Information Group
Primary Source Media
Routledge
Sweet and Maxwell
Thomson Financial Services
Westlaw

Time Life International
Brettenham House, Lancaster Place, London WC2E 7TL
Fax 020-7322 1005   Tel 020-7499 4080
Website: www.time.com
Publishes Time magazine

Titan Magazinel
Titan House, 144 Southwark Street, London SE1 0UP
Tel 020-7620 0200
E-mail: jfree@dircon.co.uk
Science fiction.

Time Out
Universal House, 251 Tottenham Court Road, London W1P 0AB
Fax 020-7813 6001   Tel 020-7813 3000
E-mail net@timeout.co.uk.
Website: www.timeout.co.uk

Times Supplements
Admiral House, 66-68 East Smithfield, London E1W 1BX
Fax 020-7782 3200   Tel 020-7782 3000
Website: www.tes.co.uk
A Murdoch-owned subsidiary of News International and publisher of the Times Educational Supplement, Times Higher Educational Supplement, Times Literary Supplement and Nursery World.

Timothy Benn Publishing
39 Earlham Street, London WC2H 9LD
Fax 020-7306 7101   Tel 020-7306 7000
E-mail: postmag@benn.co.uk
Website: www.tbp.co.uk
Trade titles insurance and photography.

TPD Publishing
Long Island Ho, 1-4 Warple Way, London W3 0RG
Fax 020-8600 9101   Tel 020-8600 9100
Website: www.tpd.co.uk
Contract publications for technology companies in any country, in any language, in print or online.

Trinity Publications
Tindal Bridge, Edward Street, Birmingham B1 2RA
Tel 0121-233 8712
Website: www.trinitypub.co.uk
Buying and selling.

United Advertising Publications
Link House, West Street, Poole, Dorset BH15 1LL
Fax 01202-445245   Tel 01202-445000

United News and Media
245 Blackfriars Road, London SE1 9UY
Fax 020-7921 5002   Tel 020-7921 5000
Website: www.unm.com
United News and Media (formerly United Newspapers) has a total of about 120 magazines in Britain, and roughly 150 abroad. Its main magazine subsidiaries are:

Benn Business Publishing
Miller Freeman

Unity Media
Quebec Square, Westerham, Kent TN16 1TD
Fax 01959-564390   Tel 01959-565690
Publishers of ten business and professional titles from Unity Business Press and five consumer motoring titles from Unity Consumer division.

VNU Business Publications
32-34 Broadwick Street, London W1A 2HG
Fax 020-7316 9003   Tel 020-7316 9000
Website: www.vnu.co.uk
One of the UK's largest magazine publishers.

Voice Communications Group
370 Coldharbour Lane, London SW9 8PL
Fax 020-7274 8994   Tel 020-7737 7377
E-mail: veeteeay@gn apc.org

Warners Group
West Street, Bourne, Lincolnshire PE10 9PH
Fax 01778-425688   Tel 01778-391000
Website: www.warners.co.uk
Caravans, motoring and roofing.

Which?
See Consumer Association

William Reed Publishing
Broadfield Park, Crawley, West Sussex RH11 9RT
Fax 01293-610322   Tel 01293-613400
Website:www.foodanddrink.co.uk

Yachting Press
196 Eastern Esplanade, Southend SS1 3AB
Fax 01702-588434   Tel 01702-582245
E-mail: YandY@compuserve.com

Ziff-Davis UK
International House, 1 St Katherine's Way, London E19 UN
Fax 020-7403 0668   Tel 020-7378 6800
Website: www.zdnet.co.uk
An American company - acquired by Willis Stein and Partners in December 1999, which is selling UK interests, most recently ten titles to VNU in July 2000.

ALTERNATIVE MAGS: LEFT

The majority of magazines are about TV, sex or shopping. This section lists the other mags which, for want of a better title, are the alternative ones and whose ideology extends beyond boosting circulations in order to sell more advertising.

Simon Regan, the founding editor of Scallywag magazine who died in August 2000, puts it like this: "My own definition of alternative media is that part [of the magazine business] not run by accountants and the all-pervading lawyers. For libel and nearly a dozen other gagging laws have always been the most formidable weapon. An alternative press is not so much anti-establishment but existing and acting independently from it. It should attempt to tell alternative truths, even if they are libellous, and sometimes especially if they are libellous. They say 'opinions are free: facts are sacred'. I feel it should be the opposite. Facts are, in modern journalism, often highly suspect. Eyewitness accounts of almost anything differ madly. But opinions should be considered sacred in any society which pretends it is free."

The Media Guide can't rely on mainstream sources to update this list so if you know of any titles which you think should be included here please send an email to:
media.guide@guardian.co.uk

The Agitator
HSG, PO Box 2474, London N8
Fax 020-8374 5027   Tel 020-8374 5027
E-mail: london@bigissue.com
Annual directory of alternative groups, centres, magazine and book shops. Price £2

Big Issue
236-240 Pentonville Road, London N1 9JY
Fax 020-7526 3201   Tel 020-7526 3200
E-mail: london@bigissue.com
Website: www.bigissue.com
Top-selling magazine, campaigning for the homeless, sold by the homeless. Weekly. Editor: Matthew Collin.

Black Flag
BM Hurricane, London WC1N 3XX
E-mail: blackflag@dircon.co.uk
Website: www.flag.blackened.net/blackflag/
Analysis of the revolutionary anarchist movement. 4pa.

CARF
BM Box 8784, London WC1N 3XX
Fax 0870-0525899   Tel 020-7837 1450
E-mail: info@carf.demon.co.uk
Website: www.carf.demon.co.uk
Voice of Campaign Against Racism and Fascism. 6pa.

Contemporary Review
14 Upper Mulgrave Rd, Cheam, Surrey SM2 7AZ
Fax 020-8241 7507   Tel 020-8643 4846
A liberal look at life. Founded 1866. Monthly.

Diva
116-134 Bayham St, London NW1 0BA
Fax 020-7284 0329   Tel 020-7482 2576
E-mail: diva@gaytimes.co.uk
Website: www.divamag.co.uk
Europe's leading lesbian magazine. Monthly. Editor: Gillian Rodgerson.

Do Or Die
6 Tilbury Place, Brighton BN2 6GY
E-mail: doordtp@yahoo.co.uk
Comprehensive Earth First! UK journal.

Earth First! Action Update
PO Box ITA, Newcastle upon Tyne NE99 ITA
Tel 0797-4791841
E-mail: actionupdate@gn.apc.org
Website: eco-action.org/efau
News and diary of the environmental direct action movement. Monthly.

Earth Matters
FoE, 26-28 Underwood St, London N1 7JQ
Fax 020-7490 0881   Tel 020-7490 1555
E-mail: lesley@foe.co.uk
Website: www.foe.co.uk
Friends of the Earth news, background and updates. 4pa. Editor: Lesley Smeardon; Deputy: Nicola Baird

Ecologist, The
Unit 18, Chelsea Wharf, 15 Lots Road, London SW10 0QJ
Fax 0120-7351 3617   Tel 020-7351 3578
E-mail: kate@theecologist.org
Website: www.theecologist.org
Green journal. 10pa. Editor: Zac Goldsmith.

Environmental Politics
Frank Cass, 900 Eastern Ave, Ilford IG2 7HH
Fax 020-8599 0984   Tel 020-8599 8866
E-mail: info@frankcass.com
Website: www.frankcass.com/
For an academic slant. 4pa.

Ethical Consumer
Unit 21, 41 Old Birley Street, Manchester M15 5RF
Fax 0161-226 6277   Tel 0161-226 2929
E-mail: ethicon@mcr1.poptel.org.uk
Website: www.ethicalconsumer.org
An alternative Which? 6pa. Editor: Rob Harrison.

Feminist Review
11 New Fetter Lane, London EC4P 4EE
Fax 020-7842 2373   Tel 020-7583 9855
E-mail: sophie.harrap@routledge.co.uk
Website: www.tandf.co.uk
"Contesting feminist orthodoxies". Published 3pa.

Festival Eye
BCM Box 2002, London WC1N 3XX
Tel 020-7794 1708
E-mail: festivaleye@stones.com
Website: www.festivaleye.com
Annual. News and forum for alternative festivals.

Fortnight
7 Lower Crescent, Belfast BT7 1NR
Fax 028-9023 2650   Tel 028-9023 2353
E-mail: mairtin@fortnite.dnet.co.uk
Website: www.fortnight.org.
Northern Ireland news. Monthly. Editor: John O'Farrell.

Free Press
8 Cynthia Street, London N1 9JF
Fax 020-7837 8868   Tel 020-7278 4430
E-mail: freepress@cpbf.demon.co.uk
The CPBF journal . 6pa. Editor: Granville Williams.

Freedom
84b Whitechapel High St, London E1 7QX
Fax 020-7377 9526   Tel 020-7247 9249
Website: www.tao.ca/~freedom
Anarchist commentary on current affairs. Founded
1886 (longest-running anarchist paper in UK). 24pa.

Gay Times
116-134 Bayham St, London NW1 0BA
Fax 020-7284 0329   Tel 020-7482 2576
E-mail: info@gaytimes.co.uk
Website: www.gaytimes.co.uk
Europe's biggest selling gay news and information
magazine. Monthly. Editor: Colin Richardson.

Green Anarchist
BCM 1715, London WC1N 3XX
Tel 0836-223646
E-mail: greenanarchist@hotmail.com
Website: www.lineone.net
Genetics, prisoners of war,animal liberation etc.

Green World
49 York Road, Aldershot, Hants GU11 3JQ
Fax 01252-330506   Tel 01252-330506
E-mail: greenworld@btinternet.com
Website: greenparty.org.uk/greenworld
News, action and networks of the Green Party.
Editor: Peter Barnett. 4pa.

In Balance
50 Parkway, Welwyn Garden City, Herts AL8 6HH
Fax 01707 395550   Tel 01707-339007
E-mail: vbrown@pintail.u-net.com
Website: www.inbalancemagazine.com
Quarterly. Holistic health and lifestyle magazine with a
source directory of courses, clinics and therapists.

International Journal of Human
Rights/International Peacekeeping
Frank Cass, 900 Eastern Ave, Ilford IG2 7HH
Fax 020-8599 0984   Tel 020-8599 8866
E-mail: info@frankcass.com
Website: www.frankcass.com/jnls/
Academic journals.

Irish Democrat
244 Grays Inn Rd, London WC1X 8JR
Tel 020-7833 3022
Views of Irish politics. Founded 1939. 6pa.

Jewish Socialist
BM 3725, London WC1N 3XX
E-mail: js@bardrose.dircon.co.uk
Debate, news and reviews. 4pa.

Labour Left Briefing
PO Box 2378, London E5 9QU
Fax 020-8985 6785   Tel 020-8985 6597
E-mail: llb@labournet.org.uk
Website: www.llb.labournet.org.uk
Independent voice for socialist ideas in the labour
movement. 10pa.

Labour Research
78 Blackfriars Rd, London SE1 8HF
Fax 020-7928 0621   Tel 020-7928 3649
E-mail: info@lrd.org.uk
Website: www.lrd.org.uk
Data and research from the independent Labour
Research Department. Formed 1917. Monthly.

Lobster
214 Westbourne Ave, Hull HU5 3JB
Tel 01482-447558
E-mail: robin@lobster.karoo.co.uk
Website: www.lobster-magazine.co.uk
Probes the clandestine state.2pa. Editor: Robin Ramsay.

Morning Star
787 Commercial Road, London E14 7HG
Fax 020-7538 5125   Tel 020-7538 5181
E-mail: morsta@geo2.poptel.org.uk
Website: www.poptel.org.uk/morning-star/
The former Communist Party newspaper, founded
1930. Daily. Editor: John Haylett.

New Ground
SERA, 11 Goodwin St, London N4 3HQ
Fax 020-7263 7424   Tel 020-7263 7389
E-mail: SERAoffice@aol.com
Magazine of SERA, the environment group affiliated to
the Labour Party. News, campaigns and features. 2pa.

New Humanist
Rationalist Press Association, 47 Theobalds Rd,
London WC1X 8SP
Fax 020-7430 1271   Tel 020-7430 1371
E-mail: jim.herrick@rationalist.org.uk
Quarterly.news on life from a humanist point of view.

New Internationalist
55 Rectory Rd, Oxford OX4 1BW
Fax 01865-793152   Tel 01865-728181
E-mail: michaeely@newint.org
Reports on world poverty and inequalities. Monthly.

New Left Review
6 Meard St, London W1V 3HR
Fax 020-7439 3869   Tel 020-7734 8830
E-mail: mail@newleftreview.org
Web: www.newleftreview.org
Political theory. 6pa.Editor: Perry Anderson.

New Statesman
191 Victoria Street, London SW1E 5NE
Fax 020-7828 1881   Tel 020-7828 1232
E-mail: info@newstatesman.co.uk
Website: www.newstatesman.co.uk
Britain's leading left of centre political magazine.
Founded 1913. Editor: Peter Wilby. Weekly.

News Line
BCM Box 747, London WC1N 3XX
Fax 020-7620 1221   Tel 020-7928 3218
Daily newspaper of the Trotskyite Workers
Revolutionary Party (with TV and sport).

New Times
6 Cynthia St, London N1 9JF
Fax 020-7278 4425   Tel 020-7278 4451
E-mail: newtimes@pop3.poptel.org.uk
Website: www.newtimes.org.uk
Magazine of the modernising left, published by
Democratic Left. Monthly. Editor: Keevin Davey

Nonviolent Action
5 Caledonian Road, London N1 9DY
Fax 020-7278 0444   Tel 020-7713 6540
E-mail: nva@gn.apc.org
News, listings, discussion, by and for British peace,
environmental etc. campaigners. 12pa.

Notes from the Borderland
BM Box 4769, LOndon WC1N 3XX
E-mail: larryohara@hotmail.com
Independent parapolitical research.

Organise!
84b Whitechapel High St, London E1 7QX.
Journal of the Anarchist Communist Federation. 2pa.

Pagan Dawn
Pagan Fed. BM Box 5896, London WC1N 3XX.
E-mail: kate@pagmedia.demon.co.uk
Pre-Christian beliefs as practised today.

Peace News
5 Caledonian Road, London N1 9DY
Fax 020-7278 0444   Tel 020-7278 3344
E-mail: peacenews@gn.apc.org
Website: www.gn.apc.org/peacenews
For nonviolent revolution. 4 x pa.

Pink Paper, The
72 Holloway Rd, London N7 8NZ
Fax 020-7957 0046   Tel 020-7296 6000
E-mail: editorial@pinkpaper.co.uk
Lesbian and gay news. Weekly.
Editor: Justin A Webb

Political Quarterly/Political Studies
Blackwell, 108 Cowley Road, Oxford OX4 1FH
Fax 01865-381381   Tel 01865-791100
E-mail: jnlinfo@blackwellpublishers.coluk
Website: www.blackwellpublishers.co.uk
Politics from many perspectives. 4pa. Also Politics(3pa).

Radical History Review
Cambridge University Press, Edinburgh Bldg,
Shaftesbury Rd, Cambridge CB2 2RU
Fax 01223-315052   Tel 01223-325757
Website: www.cup.cam ac.uk
Academic study of the past from a non-sectarian
perspective. 3pa. CUP also publishes British Journal of
Political Science (4pa). Editor: David Sanders

Radical Philosophy
75 Balfour Road, London N5 2HD
Fax 020-8704 6027   Tel 020-7226 2724
Website: www.radicalphilosophy.com
Journal of a socialist and feminist philosophy. 6pa.

Raven, The
84b Whitechapel High Street, London E1 7QX
    Tel 020-7247 9249
Website: www.tao.ca/~freedom
Anarchist discussion and analysis. 4pa.

Red Kite
Brynmadog, Gwernogle, Carmarthen SA32 7RN
Fax 01267-202471   Tel 01267-202375
E-mail: peterpolish@rdekite.net
Website: www.redkite.net/redkite
Independent radical magazine of Wales.

Red Pepper
1b Waterlow Road, London N19 5NJ
Fax 020-7263 9345   Tel 020-7281 7024
E-mail: redpepper@redpepper.org.uk
Website: www.redpepper.org.uk
Green left. national magazine. Monthly.

Resurgence
Ford House, Hartland, Bideford, Devon EX39 6EE
Fax 01237-441203   Tel 01237-441293
E-mail: ed@resurge.demon.co.uk
Website: www.resurgence.org
Ecology/spiritual mag. 6pa. Editor: Satish Kumar.

SchNews
PO Box 2600, Brighton, East Sussex BN2 2DX.
Fax 01273-685913   Tel 01273-685913
E-mail: schnews@brighton.co.uk
Website: www.schnews.org.uk/
Direct action alternative frontline. Weekly.

Scottish Workers Republic
1148 Argyle Street, Glasgow G3 8TE
Fax 0141-357 3690   Tel 0141-357 3690
E-mail: Donald@scotrepublic.freeserve.co.uk
Website: www.glaschu.freeserve.co.uk
Campaigning for an independent socialist Scotland.

Searchlight
37b New Cavendish Street, London W1M 8JR
Fax 020-7284 4410   Tel 020-7284 4040
E-mail: editor@searchlightmagazine.com
Website: www.searchlightmagazine.com
Research on the extreme right. Monthly.

Socialist, The
PO Box 24697, London E11 1YD
Fax 020-8988 8780   Tel 020-8988 8777
E-mail: editors@socialistparty.org.uk
Website: www.socialistparty.org.uk
The newspaper of the Socialist Party (known as Militant
Labour until early 1997). Weekly. Also the monthly
Socialism Today. Editor: Ken Smith.

Socialist Affairs
Socialist International, Maritime House, Old Town,
Clapham, London SW4 0JW
Fax 020-7720 4448   Tel 020-7627 4449
E-mail: secretariat@socialistinternational.org
Website: www.socialistinternational.org
Debates of the international movement. 4pa.

Socialist Appeal
PO Box 2266, London N1 7SQ
Fax 020-7251 1095   Tel 020-7251 1094
E-mail: socappeal@easynet.co.uk
Website: www.socialist.net
Marxist magazine. 12pa.Editor: Alan Woods.

Socialist Standard

52 Clapham High Street, London SW4 7UN
Fax 020-7720 3665   Tel 020-7622 3811
E-mail: spgb@worldsocialism.org
Website: www.worldsocialism.org/spgb
A Marxist monthly founded in 1904.

Socialist Worker

PO Box 82, London E3 3LH
Fax 020-7538 0140   Tel 020-7538 0828
E-mai: editorial@socialstworker.co.uk
Website: www.swp.org.uk
Socialist Workers Party's newspaper. Weekly. SWP also
publishes Socialist Review (monthly) and the more
theoretical International Socialism journal(4pa).

Sorted?

7 Rock Place, Brighton, East Sussex BN2 1PF
Fax 01273-620203   Tel 01273-683318
E-mail: sorted@nacro.org
Website: www.nacro.org/sorted/welcome.htm
Written by young people for young people.
Editor: Bee Bop.

Soundings

Lawrence & Wishart, 99a Wallis Rd, London E9
Fax 020-8533 7369   Tel 020-8533 2506
E-mail: soundings@l-w-bks.demon.co.uk
Website: www.l-w-bks.co.uk
"A journal of culture and politics". 3pa. Editors: Stuart
Hall, Doreen Massey, Michael Rustin.

The Spark Magazine

86-88 Colston Street, Bristol BS1 5BB
Fax 0117-914 3444   Tel 0117-914 3434
E-mail: john@spark.u-net.com.

Squall Download

Website: www.squall.co.uk

Statewatch

PO Box 1516, London N16 0EW.
Fax 020-8880 1727   Tel 020-8802 1882
E-mail: office@statewatch.org
Website: www.statewatch.org
Monitor of the state and civil liberties in the UK and
Europe. £15pa.

Tribune

308 Grays Inn Rd, London WC1X 8DY
Fax 020-7833 0385   Tel 020-7278 0911
E-mail: george@tribpub.demon.co.uk
Website: www.tribuneuk.co.uk
The "voice of the left". Launched 1937. Weekly.

Trouble and Strife

PO Box 8, Diss, Norfolk IP322 3XG
Feminist magazine. 2pa.

Undercurrents

16b Cherwell Street, Oxford OX4 1BG
Fax 01865-243562   Tel 01865-203662
E-mail: underc@gn.apc.org
Website: www.undercurrents.org
Radical news videos supporting environmental/social
justice campaigns and direct action.

Voice, The

370 Coldharbour Lane, London SW9 8PL
Fax 020-7274 8994   Tel 020-7737 7377
Weekly newspaper for the young blacks.

ALTERNATIVE MAGS: RIGHT

Candour

Forest House, Liss Forest, Liss, Hants GU33 7DD
                    Tel 01730-892109
Defending national sovereignty from international
monetary power. Founded 1953. Monthly.

The Flag

BCM Natdems, London WC1N 3XX
Fax 070-7122 6074   Tel 070-7122 6074
E-mail: natdems@netlink.co.uk
News of the rightwing National Democrats. Monthly.
Editor: Ian Anderson. Also publish Vanguard magazine
(4pa).

Freedom Today

Freedom Association, Room 222, Southbank House,
Black Prince Road, London SE1 7SJ
Fax 020-7463 2054   Tel 020-7793 4228
E-mail: 100703.2174@compuserve.com
Website: www.tfa.net
Exposure of official actions and attitudes which reduce
choices and freedoms. Editor: Alec Paris. 6pa.

Right Now

PO Box 2085, London W!A 5SX
Fax 020-8692 7099   Tel 020-8692 7099
E-mail: rightnow@compuserve.com
Website: www.right-now.org
Right-of-centre conservative comment. 4pa.
Editor: Derek Turner.

Salisbury Review

33 Canonbury Park South, London N1 2JW
Fax 020-7354 0383   Tel 020-7226 7791
E-mail: salisbury-review@easynet.co.uk
Website: www.easyweb.easynet.co.uk/~salisbury-review
Dry conservative thought, comment and analysis.
Editor: Roger Scruton. 4pa.

The Spectator

56 Doughty Street, London WC1N 2LL
Fax 020-7242 0603   Tel 020-7405 1706
E-mail: editor@spectator.co.uk
Website: www.spectator.co.uk
Best-known and most popular vehicle of centre-right
news and reviews. Founded 1828. Weekly. Editor: Boris
Johnson.

Third Way

PO Box 1243, London SW7 3PB
Fax 020-7373 3432   Tel 020-7373 3432
E-mail: thirdway@dircon.co.uk
Website: www.thirdway.org
"Voice of the Radical Centre", seeking alternatives to
capitalism and communism. 6pa. Also publishes:
ecological newsletter Mother Earth (4pa) and Counter
Culture (4pa).

MAG LISTINGS

19	020-7261 5000
100 Arrows/Crosswords/Word Search	01737-769799
20/20	020-8332 6882

A

AA Magazine	020-7747 0700
ABC Freight Guide	020-7439 4222
Accolade	020-7487 5155
Accountancy	020-7833 3291
Accountancy Age	020-7316 9000
Acorn User	01625-878888
Active Life	020-7906 2000
Aeroplane Monthly	020-7261 5000
Aerosol Review	020-8309 7000
African Affairs	01865-556767
African Review of Business	020-7834 7676
Air Forces Monthly	01780-755131
Air International	01780-755131
Air Mail	020-8994 8504
Air Navigation International	020-8652 3096
Air Pictorial	01424-720477
Aircraft Illustrated	01932-266600
Aircraft Technology	020-7828 4376
Airline Business	020-8652 3500
Airliners	01780-755131
Airports International	01892-839200
Airport Review	020-8700 3700
Airtrade	020-7505 3560
AJ Focus	020-7505 6600
Al Aalam Magazine	020-7608 3454
Al Hawadeth	020-8740 4500
Al Majalla	020-7831 8181
Al Wasat	020-7602 9988
Amar Deep	020-8840 3534
Amateur Gardening	01202 440840
Amateur Photographer	020-7261 5000
Amiga Format	01225-442244
Amenity Management	020-8943 5000
Amusement Business Europe	020-7439 4222
An Phoblacht (Sinn Fein/IRA)	028-9060 0279
Angler's Mail	020-7261 5000
Angling Plus	01733-264666
Angling Times	01733-264666
Animal Life/Action	01403-264181
Antique Interiors	020-7359 6011
Antiques & Art Ind	07000-765263
Antiques Diary	0118-940 2165
Antiques Trade Gazette	020-7930 7192
Apollo	020-7233 8906

Appropriate Technology	020-7436 9761
Arable Farming	020-8309 7000
Architectural Design	020-7262 5097
Architecture Today	020-7837 0143
Arena	020-7278 1578
Art Business Today	020-7381 6616
Art & Craft	01926-887799
Art Monthly	020-7240 0389
Art Quarterly	020-7225 4800
Art Review	020-7236 4880
ArtWork	01651-842429
Asda Magazine	0113-242 2228
Asian Electricity	01737-768611
Asian Review of Business &Tech.	020-7834 7676
Astronomy Now	01732-367542
Athletics Weekly	01733-264666
Attitude	020-7308 5090
Audience	020-7486 7007
Audio Visual	020-8565 4200
The Author	020-7373 6642
Auto Express	020-7631 1433
Automotive Digest	01733-467000
Automotive Marketing Review	01733-467000
Auto Trader	020-8543 8000
Autocar	020-8943 5000
The Automobile	01932-864212
Autosport	020-8943 5000
AutoTrade	01733-467000
AV Magazine	020-8565 4200
Axiom Magazine	020-7833 3399

B

B	020-7664 6500
Baby	020-7331 1000
Back Hill Reporter	020-7514 6500
The Band	01225-442244
The Banker	020-7896 2525
Baptist Times	01235-517670
Barbie	020-7344 6400
Bassist	01225-442244
BBC Gardener's World	020-8576 2000
BBC Good Food	020-8576 2000
BBC Good Homes	020-8576 2000
BBC Learning is Fun	020-8576 2000
BBC Match of the Day	020-8576 2000
BBC Music Magazine	020-8576 2000
BBC Toybox	020-8576 2000
BBC Wildlife	0117-9738402
Beano	01382-223131
Beautiful Homes	020-7261 5000
Bee World	029-2037 2409
Beekeeping & Development	01600-713648
Bella	020-7241 8000

Best	020-7439 5000
Best of Postman Pat	020-8653 1563
Best of Rosie & Jim	020-8653 1563
Best of Thomas The Tank Engine	020-8653 1563
Best of Tots TV	020-8653 1563
Better Satellite	020-7331 1000
Big!	020-7436 1515
The Big Issue	020-7526 3200
Bike	01733-237111
Billboard	020-7323 6686
Birmingham What's On	0121-626 6600
The Biochemist	020-7580 5530
Biologist	020-7581 8333
Bird Keeper	020-7261 5000
Bird Life	01767-680551
Bird Watching	01733-898100
Birds	01767-680551
Birdwatch	020-7704 9495
Bizarre	020-7565 3000
Bliss	020-7437 9011
Blue Pages	020-7878 1500
Blueprint	020-7906 2000
Blues & Soul	020-7402 6869
Boat Angler	01733-237111
The Bomb	01305-266360
Bonhams Auction Guide	020-7393 3900
Book & Magazine Collector	020-8579 1082
Books & Company	01386-593352
Books in the Media	01494-792269
Books in Wales	01970-624151
The Bookseller	020-7420 6000
Bowls International	01780-755131
Boxing News	020-7734 4784
Boys Toys	01202-735090
Boyz	020-7296 6000
Brand Strategy	020-7439 4222
Breakthru	01753-856433
Bride & Groom Magazine	020-7437 0796
Brides & Setting Up Home	020-7499 9080
British Archaeology	01904-671417
British Baker	020-8565 4200
British Birds	01767-640025
British Dental Journal	020-7935 0875
British Jeweller	020-7520 1500
British Journal of Community Nursing/Health Care Management/Hospital Medicine/Midwifery/Nursing/Practice Nursing	020-8671 7521
British Journal of Photography	020-7306 7000
British Medical Journal	020-7387 4499

British Printer 01732-364422
British Rate & Data (BRAD)
020-7505 8000
Broadcast 020-7505 8000
Budgerigar World 01604-624549
Building 020-7560 4000
Building Design 020-8309 7000
Building Homes 020-7560 4000
Building Services 020-7560 4000
Bunty 01382-223131
Burlington Magazine
020-7388 8157
Bus Fayre 01274-881640
Business Equipment Digest
01732-359990
Business and Technology
020-8652 3500
BusinessAfrica/Asia/China/Europe/
Latin America/Middle East/Russia
020-7830 1000
Business Franchise 020-8742 2828
Business Travel World
020-7470 6200
Butterfly Conservation
01206-322342
Buy a Boat 01243-533394
Buying Cameras 01733-898100
The Buzz 01232 331694

C

Cab Driver 020-7493 5267
Cabinet Maker 01732-364422
Cable Guide 020-7419 7300
Cable & Satellite Europe
020-7896 2700
Cable Television Engineering
0191-281 7094
CadCam 020-8277 5000
Cage & Aviary Birds 020-7261 5000
Cake Decorating 01225-442244
Cakes & Sugarcraft 01252-727572
Camcorder User 020-7331 1000
Campaign 020-8943 5000
The Campaigner 020-8846 9777
Camping & Caravanning
024-7669 4995
Canal & Riverboat 01372-741411
Candis 0151-632 3232
Canoeist 01235-847270
Car & Accessory Trader
020-8943 5000
Car Boot Calendar 0118-940 2165
Car Mechanics 01959 541444
Caravan Club Magazine
01342-326944
Caravan Life 01778-391000
Caravan Magazine 020-8686 2599
Caribbean Times 020-7702 8012
Caribbean World 020-7581 9009
Cars & Car Conversions
020-8686 2599

CarSport 01232 783200
The Cartoonist 020-7353 2828
Car World 01733-237111
Cash & Carry Management
020-8688 2696
Cat 020-8943 5000
The Cat 01403-221900
Catalyst 01869-338652
Caterer & Hotelkeeper
020-8652 3500
Catering Update 020-8652 3500
Catholic Herald 020-7588 3101
Cats 0161-236 0577
Caves & Caving 01524-262770
C B Radio Active 023-9261 3800
Celebrations in Cross Stitch
01225-442244
Centrepoint 020-8539 3876
Channel Business 01895-421111
Chat 020-7261 5000
Checkout 020-8652 3500
Checkout Fresh 020-8652 3243
Chemical Engineer 01788-578214
Chemist & Druggist 020-8309 7000
Chemistry in Britain 01223-420066
Chemistry Review 01869-338652
Chess 020-7388 2404
China Economic Review
020-7834 7676
China In Focus 01253-894582
Choice 01733-555123
Christian Family 01903-821082
Christian Socialist 020-7833 0666
Church Times 020-7359 4570
City Life 0161-839 1416
Civil Engineer International
020-7505 6600
Class 020-7247 1455
Classic & Sportscar 020-8943 5000
Classic Bike 01733-237111
Classic Boat 020-8686 2599
Classic Car Weekly 01733-237111
Classic CD 01225-442244
Classic Stitches 01382-223131
Club Mirror 020-8565 4200
Club On 020-7247 1100
Coach & Bus Week 01733-467000
Coarse Angling 020-7261 5000
Coat of Arms 0118-932 0210
Comagazine 01895-444055
Combat 0121-344 3737
Combat & Survival 01484-435011
Commercial Motor 020-8652 3500
Commercial Vehicle Manager
01733-467000
Common Cause 020-7281 4101
Communications Africa
020-7834 7676
Communications International
020-7505 8000

Communications Law
020-8686 9141
Community Care 020-8652 3500
Community Nurse 020-7843 3600
Community Pharmacy
020-7334 7333
Community Transport Magazine
0161-351 1475
Company 020-7439 5000
Computer Active 020-7316 9000
Computer Arts 01225-442244
Computer & Video Games
020-7972 6700
Computer Buyer/Shopper
020-7631 1433
Computer Music 01225-442244
Computer Success 020-8600 2000
Computer Video 020-7331 1000
Computer Weekly 020-8652 3500
Computing 020-7316 9000
Conde Nast Traveller
020-7499 9080
Conference and Incentive Travel
020-8943 5000
Construction News 020-7505 6600
Containerisation International
020-7505 3550
Contemporary Visual Arts
020-7740 1704
Contract Journal 020-8652 3500
Control & Instrumentation
020-8309 7000
Control Systems 01732-359990
Convenience Store 01293-613400
Cornish Banner 01726-843501
Corporate Money 020-7439 4222
Cosmopolitan 020-7439 5000
Counter Culture 020-7373 3432
Country Homes & Interiors
020-7261 5000
Country Life 020-7261 5000
Country Living 020-7439 5000
Country Music International
020-8261 2897
Country Music People
020-8692 1106
Country Sports 01206-263234
Country Walking 01733-264666
The Countryman 020-7261 2897
Countryside 01242-521381
Couples 020-8688 5670
CPRE Voice 020-7976 6433
Crafts 020-7278 7700
Craftsman Magazine
01377-255213
Creative Review 020-7439 4222
Creative Technology 020-7357 6161
Cricketer International
020-8699 1796
Crops 020-8652 3500
Cross Stitch 01225-442244

Cross Stitch Collection	01225-442244
Cross Stitcher	01225-442244
CTN	020-8565 4200
Cult Times	020-8875 1520
Current Archaeology	020-7435 7517
Cycle Sport	020-7261 5000
Cycle Touring & Campaigning	01483-417217
Cycling Plus	01225-442244
Cycling Weekly	020-7261 5000

D

Dairy Farmer	01473-241122
Dalton's Weekly	020-8949 6199
Dance & Dancers	020-7813 1049
Dance Express	01372-741411
Dance News	01483-428679
Dancing Times	020-7250 3006
Dandy	01382-223131
Darts World	020-8650 6580
Day by Day	020-8856 6249
Dazed & Confused	020-7336 0766
Deadpan	020-8579 5414
Dealer Principal	01733-467000
Debenhams	020-7565 3000
Decanter	020-7610 3929
Decor	020-8877 0077
Defence Helicopter	01628-604311
Defence Industry Digest	020-7242 2548
Defence Upgrades	020-8700 3700
Defence Weekly	020-8700 3700
Demon Dispatches	020-7251 6688
The Dentist	01483-304944
Design Engineering	020-8309 7000
Design Products & Applications	01732-359990
Design Week	020-7439 4222
The Devil	020-8994 7767
Diesel Car	01225-442244
Digital Photo FX	01733-898100
Diplomat	020-7837 5600
Disability Now	020-7619 7100
Disability Times	020-7233 7970
Disco International (DI)	01322-660070
Disney & Me	020-7344 6400
Diva	020-7482 2576
Diver Magazine	020-8943 4288
DIY Week	01732-364422
DJ	01322-660070
Docklands Recorder	020-8472 1421
The Doctor	020-8652 3500
Doctor Who Magazine	01892-500100
Document	01905-729000
Dog World	01233-621877
Dogs Today	01276-858880

Dorset Life	01929-551264
Drapers Record	020-7520 1500
The Drum	0141-332 3255
Druglink	020-7928 1211

E

Earth Matters	020-7490 1555
Early Music Today	020-7333 1744
Eastern Eye	020-7702 8012
e-business partner	01895-421111
The Ecologist	020-7351 3578
Economic Review	01869-338652
Economic Trends	020-7873 0011
The Economist	020-7830 7000
Edge	01225 442244
Ego	01872-272550
E-First	01458 441128
Electrical Contractor	020-7560 4000
Electrical Products	01732-359990
Electrical Review	020-8652 3113
Electrical Times	020-8652 3500
Electronic Engineering	020-8309 7000
Electronic Manufacture & Test	01732-359990
Electronic Product Design	01732-359990
Electronic Product Review	01322-277788
Electronic Showcase	01732-359990
Electronics	01702-554155
Electronics & Wireless World	020-8652 3500
Electronics Times	020-8309 7000
Electronics Weekly	020-8652 3500
Electronics World	020-8652 3500
Elle	020-7437 9011
Elle Decoration	020-7437 9011
Elvis Monthly	0116 2537271
Empire	020-7436 1515
Employee Benefits	020-7439 4222
Employer's Law	020-8652 4669
Enchanted Lands	020-8653 1563
Energy Management	020-8277 5000
The Engineer	020-8309 7000
Engineering	01564-771772
English Churchman	01227-781282
English Garden	01189-771677
English Review	01869-338652
Environmental Health News	020-7928 6006
ES Magazine (free)	020-7938 6000
Esquire	020-7439 5000
Essentials	020-7261 5000
Essential Playstation	01225-442244
Essex Countryside	01799-544 2000

Estate Agency News	01253-722142
Estates Gazette	020-7437 0141
Ethical Consumer	0161-226 2929
Euroguy	020-8348 9963
European Chemical News	020-8652 3153
European Pig and Poultry Fair	020-8309 7000
European Plastics News	0181 277 5000
Events In Scotland	0131-332 2433
Exchange & Mart	01202-445000
Exe	020-7439 4222
Executive Woman	020-8420 1210
Expert Systems & Applications	01732-359990

F

The Face	020-7689 9999
Fairplay International Shipping	020-8660 2811
Family Circle	020-7261 5000
Family Tree Magazine	01487-814050
Farmers Guardian	01772-203800
Farmers Weekly	020-8652 3500
Farming News	020-8309 7000
Fast Car	01689-874025
Fast Ford	01452-307181
Feel Good	020-791 7 5719
Feng Shui	020-7251 0777
FHM - For Him Magazine	020-7436 1515
The Field	020-7261 5000
Fiesta	01376-534534
Film Guide	020-7602 9790
Film Review	020-8875 1520
Financial Adviser	020-7896 2525
Financial Director	020-7316 9000
Fire Prevention	020-8236 9690
First	020-7439 1188
Fish Farming International	020-7470 6200
Fishing News International	020-7470 6200
The Flag (Nat Dem)	07071-226074
Fleet Car	01733-467000
Fleet Dealer	01733-467000
Fleet News	01733-467000
Flicks	020-7381 8811
Flight International	020-8652 3500
Flipside	01707-226929
Flying Angel News	020-7248 5202
Flying Saucer Review	01923-779018
Focus	020-7519 5783
Focus on Africa	020-7857 2716
Folk Roots	020-8340 9651
Food Illustrated	020-7565 3000
Food Manufacture	020-8309 7000

Food Manufacture Ingredients &	
Machine Survey	020-8309 7000
Food Processing	01732-359990
Food Service Management	
	020-8652 8389
Food & Travel	020-8332 9090
Food Worker	01707-260150
Football Monthly	020-7565 1493
For a Change	020-7828 6591
Fore!	01733-264666
Foreign Report	020-8700 3700
Forestry and British Timber	
	01732-364422
Fortnight	028-9023 2353
Fortune	020-7499 4080
Forum	020-7308 5090
Four Four Two	020-8943 5000
Franchise Magazine	01603-620301
Frank	020-7689 9999
Free Church Chron	01782-614407
Free Press	020-7278 4430
Freedom	020-7247 9249
Freelance Informer	020-8652 3500
Freemasonry Today	020-7486 3852
Fresh	01752-204470
Fresh Direction	020-7424 0400
The Friend	020-7387 7549
Front	020-7554 5700
Frontiers	01225-442244
Fun to Learn	020-8563 1563
Furnishing	020-8515 2000
Future Music	01225-442244
Future Net	01225-442244
FW	020-7520 1500

G

Games Today	020-7837 1212
Gamesmaster	01225-442244
Garavi Gujarat	020-7928 1234
The Garden/Garden Answers	
	01733-898100
Garden Trade News	020-8855 9201
Gardeners World (BBC)	
	020-8576 2000
Gardens Illustrated	01454-618905
Gatelodge	01132-428833
Gatwick News	01293-775000
Gay Times	020-7482 2576
Genealogists Magazine	
	020-7251 8799
General Practitioner	020-8943 5000
Geographical Magazine	
	020-7938 4011
Geography Review	01869-338652
Geoscientist	01225-445046
Geriatric Medicine	01732-464154
Girl About Town	020-7872 0033
Girl Talk	020-8576 2000
Global Transport	020-7467 9400
Go Organic	01737-222910

Going Wild In London	
	020-7261-0447
Golf Industry News	020-7477 7399
Golf Monthly	020-7261 5000
Golf Weekly	01733-264666
Golf World	01733-264666
Good Food (BBC)	020-8576 2000
Good Housekeeping	
	020-7439 5000
Good Times	020-7526 2400
Good Vibrations	01733-370777
Good Woodworking	
	01225-442244
The Gospel Magazine	
	01462-811204
GQ	020-7499 9080
GQ Active	020-7499 9080
Gramophone	020-8422 4562
Grand Prix Review	020-8943 5000
Granta	020-7704 9776
Grassroots Campaigner	
	01422-843785
The Great Outdoors	0141-302 7700
Green Futures	01223-568017
The Grocer	01293-613400
Ground Engineering	020-7505 6600
The Guardian Weekly	
	020-7713 4400
The Guide	020-8297 0809
Guiding	020-7834 6242
Guitarist	01225-442244
Guitar Techniques	01225-442244

H

Hair	020-7261 5000
Hairdressers' Journal	
	020-8652 3500
Ham Radio Today	01707-853300
Hansard	020-7873 0011
Harpers & Queen	020-7439 5000
Hazards Magazine	0114-276 5695
Headlight	020-8660 2811
Headlines	01442-233656
Health & Beauty Salon	
	020-8652 3500
Health & Fitness	01322-660070
Health Insurance	020-7505 8000
Health & Safety at Work	
	020-8686 9141
Health Club Management	
	01462-431385
Health Service Journal	
	020-7843 3600
Heat	020-7312 8902
Heavy Horse World	01243-811364
Helicopter International	
	01934-822524
Helidata News	01934-822524
Hello!	020-7667 8700
Here's Health	020-7437 9011
Heritage Scotland	0131-226 5922

Heritage Today	020-7973 3000
Hi-Fi Choice	020-7631 1433
High Life	020-7925 2544
Hindsight	01869-338652
Hip Hop Connection	
	01225-442244
History Today	020-7534 8000
History Workshop Journal	
	01865-556767
HN	020-7747 0700
Holyrood	020-7878 1500
Home & Country	020-7371 9300
Home Entertainment	
	020-7631 1433
Home & Family	020-7222 5533
Home Magic	020-7581 1371
Homebase Living	020-7747 0700
Homes & Antiques (BBC)	
	020-8576 2000
Home Furnishings	01732-364422
Homes & Gardens	020-7261 5000
Homes & Ideas	020-7261 5000
Homestyle	020-7928 5869
Horoscope	01202-881749
Horse	020-7261 5000
Horse Exchange	020-7261 5000
Horse & Hound	020-7261 5000
Horse Magazine	020-7261 5000
Horse & Pony	01733-264666
Horticulture Week	020-8943 5000
Hospital Doctor	020-8652 3500
Hospital Equipment & Supplies	
	01322-277788
Hot Shoe International	
	01622-687031
Hotel	01323-507474
Hotel & Restaurant Magazine	
	020-8681 2099
The House	020-7827 9929
House Magazine	020-7878 1500
House & Garden	020-7499 9080
House Beautiful	020-7439 5000
Housewares	01732-364422
Housing	020-7837 8727
Housing Today	020-7843 2275

I

I-D Magazine	020-7813 6170
IBM Computer Today	
	020-8652 3500
Ideal Home	020-7261 5000
The Idler	020-7691 0320
Illustrated London News	
	020-7805 5555
Image	01603-664242
Improve Your Coarse Fishing	
	01733-264666
Improve Your Sea Angling	
	01733-264666
In Balance	01707-339007
In-Store Marketing	020-7439 4222

Independent Retail News
020-8652 8754
Index on Censorship
020-7278 2313
India Weekly 020-7251 3290
Individual Homes 020-7439 4222
Industrial Exchange & Mart
01202-445000
Inside Cosmetics 020-8855 7777
Inside Eye 020-7439 4222
Inside Soap 020-7636 5095
Inspirations 020-7836 0519
Insurance Age 020-7505 8000
Intelligence & National Security
020-8599 8866
Intelligence Review 020-8700 3700
InterMedia 020-7388 0671
International 020-7896 2525
International Defense Review
020-8700 3700
International Express
020-7928 8000
International Food Ingredients
020-8309 7000
International Food Manufacture
020-8309 7000
International Freighting Weekly
020-7470 6200
International Money Marketing
020-7439 4222
International Police Review
020-7440 4700
International Risk Management
020-7505 8000
International Socialism
020-7538 5821
Internet 020-7477 7399
Internet Magazine 020-7477 7399
Internet Works 01225-442244
Interzone Science Fiction
01273-504710
Investment Fund Index (CD Rom)
020-7439 4222
Investor Relations 020-7637 3579
Investors Chronicle 020-7896 2525
Irish Post 020-8741-0649
Irish World 020-8453 7800
IT-Mag 020-7355 4489
IT Week 020-7316 9000

J
Jam 01865-268400
Jane's Defence Weekly
020-8700 3700
Jane's Review 020-8700 3700
Janomot Bengali Newsweekly
020-7377 6032
Japan Forum 01264-343062
Jazz Journal International
020-7608 1348

Jewish Chronicle 020-7415 1500
Jewish Quarterly 020-7629 5004
Jewish Telegraph 0161-740 9321
Jewish Tribune 020-8800 6688
The Job (The Met) 020-7230 1212
The Journalist 020-7278 7916
Journal of Wound Care
020-7874 0200
Junior 020-7630 5500
Just 17 020-7437 9011

K
Kerrang! 020-7436 1515
Kindred Spirit 01803-866 686
Kitchens, Bedrooms & Bathrooms
020-8515 2000
Knave 01376-534534
Kriss Kross 020-8846 9922

L
Labour Left Briefing 020-8985 6597
Labour Market Trends
020-7873 9090
Labour Research 020-7928 3649
The Lady 020-7379 4717
The Lancet 020-7436 4981
Land Rover Owner International
01733-237111
The Landworker 020-7828 7788
Law Society's Gazette
020-7242 1222
The Lawyer 020-7439 4222
Leather 01732-364422
Legal Action 020-7833 2931
Legal Business 020-7396 9292
Leisure Manager 01491-874800
Leisure Painter 01580-763315
Leisure Week 020-7439 4222
Level 01305-251263
Library Association Record
020-7636 7543
Lifeguard 01789-773994
Lifewatch 020-7722 3333
Light & Lighting 020-7560 4000
Linedancer 01704-501235
Line Up 01323-491739
The List 0131-558 1191
Literary Review 020-7437 9392
The Little Ship 020-7236 7729
Live & Kicking 020-8576 2000
Living 020-7261 5000
Lloyd's List International
01206-772277
Loaded 020-7261 5000
Lobster 01482-447558
Local Government Chronicle
020-7505 8000
Local Government News
020-8680 4200

Local Government Tenders
020-7505 8000
Local History Magazine
0115-9706473
Logisitic Europe 020-8943 5000
London Cyclist 020-7928 7220
London Gazette 020-7394 4580
London Hotel Mag 020-7373 7282
London Magazine 020-7925 2544
London Review of Books
020-7209 1141
London Theatre Guide
020-8545 8300
Londonzok 020-7221 6611
Looks 020-7437 9011
Loot 020-7625 0266

M
M Magazine 020-7439 5000
M & S Magazine 020-7747 0700
Mac Format 01225-442244
MacUser 020-7631 1433
MacWorld 020-7831 9252
Mad About Dogs 020-7240 2032
Madam 0131-662 4445
Magazine Guide 020-7689 3373
Magazine News 020-7404 4166
Mailout 01484-469009
Majesty 020-7436 4006
Making Music 01322-660070
Management Today 020-8943 5000
Manchester United Magazine
0161-872 1661
Manufacturing Chemist
020-8309 7000
Manga Max 020-7620 0200
Marie Claire 020-7261 5000
Marie Claire Health & Beauty
020-7261 5000
Marine Conservation
01989-566017
Marketeer 0141-332 3255
Marketing 020-8943 5000
Marketing Direct 020-8943 5000
Marketing Events 020-8943 5000
Marketing Week 020-7439 4222
Master Builder 020-7242 7583
Match 01733-264666
Materials Recycling Week
020-8277 5540
Maxim 020-7631 1433
Max Power 01733-237111
Mayfair 020-7734 9191
MBUK 01225-442244
M & E Design 020-8652 3115
Meat Trades Journal
020-8565 4200
Medeconomics 020-8943 5000
Media & Marketing Europe
020-7505 8000

Media, Culture & Society 020-7374 0645
Media International 020-8652 3500
Media Week 020-7565 4200
Medical Imprint 020-8943 5000
Melody Maker 020-7261 5000
Men Only 020-7734 9191
Men's Health 020-7291 6000
Men's Wear 020-7520 1500
Metal Bulletin 020-7827 9977
Metal Hammer 020-7631 1433
Metalworking Production 020-8309 7000
Methodist Recorder 020-7251 8414
Micro Computer Mart 0121-233 8712
Microwave Engineering Europe 0181 309 7000
Middle East Economic Digest 020-7470 6200
Middle East Electricity 01737-768611
Middle East International 020-7373 5228
Midweek Magazine 020-7636 3666
Milap Weekly 020-7385 8966
Mims UK 020-8943 5000
Mind Your Own Business 020-8771 3614
Mining Journal/Magazine 020-7216 6060
Ministry 020-7378 6528
MiniWorld 020-8686 2599
Minx 020-7437 9011
Missles And Rockets 020-8700 3700
The Mix 01225-442244
Mixmag 020-7436 1515
Mizz 020-7261 5000
Model Rail 01733-898100
Modern History Review 01869-338652
Mojo 020-7436 1515
Money Management 020-7896 2525
Money Marketing 020-7439 4222
Money Marketing Focus Surveys 020-7439 4222
Money Observer 020-7713 4188
Moneyextra 020-7917 5719
Moneywise 020-7715 8000
More! 020-7437 9011
Mother & Baby 020-7437 9011
Motor Cycle News 01536-411111
Motor Industry Management 01992-511521
Motor Ship 020-8652 3500
Motor Sport 020-8943 5000
Motor Trader 020-8652 3500
Motor Transport 020-8652 3500

Motorboat & Yachting 020-7261 5333
Motorcaravan Monthly 01778-393313
Motoring News 020-8943 5000
Mountain Bike Rider 020-7261 5000
Mountain Biker International 020-8686 2599
Mountain Bike UK 01225-442244
Movie Idols 020-8875 1520
Movie International 020-8574 2222
Moving Pictures International 020-7520 5200
Mslexia 0191-281 9772
MS London Magazine 020-7636 3322
Municipal Journal 020-7973 6400
Musclemag International 0121-327 7525
Museums Journal 020-7250 1834
Music Magazine 01733 370777
Music Week 020-7620 3636
Muzik 020-7261 5000

N
N64 01225-442244
National Trust Magazine 020-7222 9251
National Geographic 020-7365 0916
Natural World 020-7306 0304
Nature 020-7833 4000
Navy International 020-8700 3700
Navy News 023-9282 6040
Needlecraft 01225-442244
.net 01225 442244
the net 020-8943 5000
Network Week 020-7453 1300
Network World 020-7453 1300
New Christian Herald 01903-821082
New Civil Engineer 020-7505 6600
New Eden 020-7261 5000
New Ground 020-7263 7424
New Humanist 020-7430 1371
New Internationalist 01865-728181
New Law Journal 020-7400 2500
New Left Review 020-7734 8830
New MediaAge 020-7439 4222
New MediaFinance 020-7439 4222
New Musical Express 020-7261 5000
New Scientist 020-7331 2701
New Statesman 020-7828 1232
New Stitches 01227-750215
New Times 020-7278 4451
New Woman 020-7437 9011
Newsweek International 020-7318 1600
Nine to Five 020-7436 3331
Nineteen 020-7261 6390

Nintendo Magazine 020-7972 6700
Ninento Official Mag 020-7880 7415
NME 020-7261 5000
Noddy 020-8576 2000
Northamptonshire Image 01604-231122
Now 020-7261 7366
Nursery Choice 020-7713 7000
Nursery World 020-7782-3000
Nursing Standard 020-8423 1066
Nursing Times 020-7843 3600

O
O Magazine 020-8600 9100
Observer Life (free) 020-7278 2332
Occupational Health 020-8652 3500
Off-Licence News 01293-613400
Office Equipment News 01322-277788
The Official Playstation Magazine 01225-442244
Offshore Engineer 020-8277 5000
Offshore Financial Review 020-7896 2525
OK! 020-7308 5090
Old Glory 01780-763063
The Oldie 020-7734 2225
Omnia 020-7925 2544
On Digital 020-8600 9100
On Target 01787-376374
One Shots 020-7631 1433
Opera 020-7359 1037
Opera Now 020-7333 1740
Optician 020-8652 3198
Oral History 01206-873055
Orbit 020-8780 2266
Our Baby 020-7261 5000
Our Dogs 0161-236 2660
Outsourcing 01732-359990

P
Pacemaker Update 020-8943 5000
Packaging News 020-8565 4200
Packaging Magazine 01732-364422
Panel Building 01732-359990
Parent Talk 01460-30500
Parents 020-7437 9011
Parikiaki 020-7272 6777
Parkers Car Price Guide 020-7477 7306
Parliament Magazine 020-7878 1500
Parliamentary Monitor 020-7878 1500
PASS 020-8652 3500
PC Advisor 020-7831 3191
PC Answers/Format/Plus 01225-442244
PC Dealer/Week 020-7316 9000

PC Direct/Magazine	020-7316 9000	Police	020-8399 2224

PC Direct/Magazine 020-7316 9000
PC Gamer 01225-442244
PC Gaming World 020-7316 9000
PC Guide 01225-442244
PC Know How 020-7581 1371
PC Pro 020-7631 1433
PC Review 01225 442244
PC Magazine 020-7316 9000
PC Zone 020-7631 1433
Peace News 020-7278 3344
Pensions Age 020-7426 0424
Pensions Week 020-7463 3000
Pensions Management
020-7896 2525
Pensions World 020-7896 2525
Penthouse 020-7308 5090
People's Friend 01382-223131
Perfect Home 020-8515 2000
Performance Bike 01733-237111
Performance Chemicals
International 020-8652 8126
Period Living 020-7437 9011
Personal Computer World
020-7316 9000
Personnel Today 020-8652 3500
Pet Magic 01903-816600
Pet Product Marketing
01733-898100
Pet Reptile 01202-735090
Petroleum Economist
020-7831 5588
The PFI Report 020-7439 4222
Pharmacy Today 020-7334 7333
Pharmaceutical Journal
020-7735 9141
Photo Technique 020-7261 5000
The Photographer 01920-464011
Physics Review 01869-338652
Physics World 0117-929 7481
The Picture Business
020-8855 9201
Pig Farming 020-8309 7000
Pingu 020-8576 2000
Pink Paper 020-7296 6210
Plain Truth 020-8953 1633
Planet 01970-611255
Planet Playstation 01625-878888
Planned Savings 020-7505 8000
Planning 020-7413 4454
Plant Managers Journal
020-8652 3500
Plastics & Rubber Weekly
020-8277 5000
Play 01202-299900
Playdays 020-8576 2000
Playstation Plus 020-7972 6000
Playstation Power 01225-442244
Playstation Pro 01625-878888
Pocket Arrows/Crosswords/
Wordsearch 01737-769799
Pocket Kidz! 01737-769799

Police 020-8399 2224
Police Review 020-7393 7600
Policing Today 020-8700 3700
Politics Review 01869-338652
Popular Crafts 01322-660070
Popular Patchwork 01322-660070
Postgraduate Doctor
01243-576444
Pot Black 020-8959 3611
Poultry World 020-8652 3500
Powerstation 01202-299900
PR Week 020-7943 5000
Practical Boat Owner
020-7261 5000
Practical Caravan 020-8943 5000
Practical Classics 01733-237111
Everyday Practical Electronics
01202-881749
Practical Fishkeeping
01733-898100
Practical Householder
01322 660070
Practical Internet 01202-299900
Practical Parenting 020-7261 5000
Practical Photography
01733-898100
Practical Wireless 01202-659910
Practical Woodworking
01322-660070
Practice Nurse 020-8652 3123
The Practitioner 020-8309 7000
Precision Marketing 020-7439 4222
Prediction 020-8686 2599
Pregenancy & Birth 020-7437 9011
Premiere 020-7208 3563
Premises & Facilities Management
01732-359990
Pre Press World 01732-364422
Press Gazette 020-8565 4448
Pride 020-7228 3110
Prima 020-7439 5000
Prima - Baby 020-7519 5783
Prima- Christmas Traditions
020-7519 5783
Prima - Your Home 020-7519 5783
Prime Time Puzzles 01737-769799
Print Week 020-8943 5000
Printing World 01732-364422
Private Eye 020-7437 4017
Pro Cycling 020-7554 5700
Process Engineering
020-8309 7000
Processing 01732-359990
Production Journal 01442-233656
Production Solutions
020-7505 8000
Professional Engineering
01284-763277
Professional Nurse 020-7843 3600
Professional Printer 01892-538118

Promotions and Incentives
020-8943 5000
Property Direct 020-7560 4000
Property Week 020-7560 4000
Prospect 020-7255 1281
Prospect 0141-332 3255
Psychic News 01279-817050
The Psychologist 0116-254 9568
Psychology Review 01869-338652
Public Administration
01865-791100
Public Finance 020-7543 5728
Public Service & Local Govt
01959-565690
Public Treasurer 020-7505 8000
Publican 020-8565 4200
Publishing News 020-7692 2900
Pulse 020-8309 7000
Punch 020-7225 6716
Punjab Times 01332-372851
Puzzle Compendium
020-8846 9922
Puzzle Corner 01737-769799
Puzzle Corner Special
01737-769799
Puzzle Kids 01737-769799
Puzzle Monthly 01322-660070
Puzzle Mix Special 01737-769799
Puzzle World 01322-660070
Puzzler Collection/Puzzler
020-8846 9922

Q

Q 020-7436 1515
Quick and Easy Cross Stitch
01225-442244
Quizkids 01737-769799
Quizkids Special 01737-769799

R

Race and Class 020-7837 0041
Racing & Football Outlook
01635-578080
Radio Communication
01707-659015
Radio Control Models
01322-660070
Radio Magazine 01536-418558
Radio Modeller 01322-660070
Radio Times 020-8576 2000
Rail 01733-898100
Railway Gazette International
020-8652 3500
Railway Magazine 020-7261 5000
Rambling Today 01480-496130
The Raven 020-7247 9249
Readers Digest 020-7715 8000
Ready Steady Cook 020-7836 0519
Real Homes 020-7554 5700
Real Money 020-7426 0424
Record Collector 020-8579 1082

Red	020-7437 9011
Redline	01225-442244
Red Pepper	020-7281 7024
Regiment	01322-660070
Resident Abroad	020-7896 2525
Resurgence	01237-441293
Retail Jeweller	020-7520 1500
Retail Newsagent	020-7689 0600
Retail Technology	01895-421111
Retail Week	020-8277 5000
Review of Social Economy	
	01264-343062
The Review - Worldwide Insurance	
	020-7505 8000
Revolution	020-8943 5000
Revs	01733-237111
Rhythm	01225-442244
RIBA Interiors	020-7560 4000
RIBA Journal	020-7560 4000
Ride	01733-237111
Right Start	020-7403 0840
The Round Organ	01202-889669
Rugby News	020-7323 1944
Rugby World	020-7261 5000
Runners World	020-7291 6000
RUSI Journal	020-7930 5854

S

Safeway Magazine	020-7747 0700
Saga Magazine	01303-771527
Sailing Today	01225-442244
Sainsbury's: The Magazine	
	020-7633 0266
Salisbury Review	020-7226 7791
Satellite Times	0113-258 5008
Satellite Trader	020-7896 2700
Sayidaty	020-7831 8181
Scene	01702-435328
SchNews Magazine	01273-685913
Scots Law Times	0131-225 4879
Scots Magazine	01382-223131
Scottish Farmer	0141-302 7700
Scottish Field	0131-551 2942
Scottish Memories	0141-204 3104
Scouting	020-7584 7030
Screen Digest	020-7482 5842
Screen International	020-7505 8000
Sea Angler	01733-264666
Sea of Faith	015396-25321
Searchlight	020-7284 4040
Seatrade Review	01206-545121
Security Management Today	
	01689-874025
Select	020-7436 1515
Sen- Shop Equipment & Shop	
Fitting News	020-8277 5000
Sewing World	01684-594505
SFX	01225 442244
She	020-7439 5000
Shivers	020-8875 1520
Shoot!	020-7261 5000

Shooting & Conservation	
	01244-573000
Shooting Times	020-7261 5000
Shopping Centre	01293-613400
Short Wave Magazine	
	01202-659910
Shropshire Magazine	
	01743-362175
Sight & Sound	020-7255 1444
The Sign	01603-615995
The Singer	020-7333 1733
Skin Deep	01244 660044
Sky	020-7436 1515
Sky Digital TV Guide	020-7747 0700
Slimming	020-7437 9011
Smallholder	01453-544000
Smash Hits	020-7436 1515
SME Business	01895-421111
Soccer Stars	020-7261 5000
Social Housing	020-7700 4199
Socialism Today	020-8533 3311
Socialist Affairs	020-7627 4449
Socialist Standard	020-7622 3811
Socialist Worker	020-7538 0828
Sociology Review	01869-338652
Solicitors Journal	020-7242 2548
Somerfield Mag	020-7478 4700
Sorted?	01273-683318
Special Schools in Britain	
	020-7439 4222
The Spectator	020-7405 1706
Spectrum	020-7478 4700
Spirit	020-8533 6667
Sporting Gun	020-7261 5000
Sports Management	
	01462-431385
Sports Marketing	020-7439 4222
Spot	0181 576 2000
Spotlight	020-7437 7631
Stage, Screen & Radio	
	020-7437 8506
The Stage & Television Today	
	020-7403 1818
Star Trek	020-7620 0200
Starburst	020-8875 1520
Stargirl	01892-523767
Stars & Cars	020-8943 5000
Statewatch	020-8802 1882
Steam Railway	01733-898100
Steam World	01753-898100
Sticks, The	01462 486810
Stillwater Trout Angler	
	020-7261 5000
Storyland	020-8653 1563
Straight No Chaser	020-7613 1594
Strad, The	020-8863 2020
Streetwise	01737-769799
Structural Engineer	020-7235 4535
Subcon	020-8309 7000
Sunday Express Magazine (free)	
	020-7922 7297

Sunday Mirror Magazine (free)	
	020-7293 3000
Sunday Times Magazine (free)	
	020-7782 4000
SuperMarketing	020-8652 3500
Surrey County Magazine	
	01622-687031
The Surveyor	020-7973 6400
Sussex Life	01903-218719
Swarovski Magazine	
	020-7747 0700
Sweet FA	020-7284 0417

T

T3	01225-442244
The Tablet	020-8748 8484
Take a Break/Crossword/	
Look/Puzzle	020-7241 8000
The Taste	01780-763063
Tatler	020-7499 9080
Taxation	020-8686 9141
Technical Review Middle East	
	020-7834 7676
Teeny Weeny Families	
	01737-769799
Telegraph Magazine (free)	
	020-7538 5000
Teletubbies	020-8576 2000
Television (Reed)	020-8652 3500
Television (Royal TV Soc)	
	020-7430 1000
Television Business Internat	
	020-7896 2700
Television Europe	020-7520 5281
Television International	
	020-7520 5281
Televisual	020-7439 4222
That's Life!	020-7462 4700
Third Text	020-7372 0826
Third Way	020-7373 3432
The Thomas Cook Magazine	
	020-7747 0700
Timber For Architects	
	01732-364422
Timber Trades Journal	
	01732-364422
Time Life International	
	020-7499 4080
Time Out	020-7813 3000
Times Education Supplements	
	020-7782 3000
Times Literary Supplement	
	020-7782 3000
Titbits	020-7351 4995
Today's Golfer	01733-264666
Today's Runner	01733-264666
Top Of The Pops	020-8576 2000
Top Gear	020-8576 2000
Top Sante	020-7437 9011
Top Sante Health & Beauty	
	020-7938 3033

Total 64	01392-495155
Total Bike	01225-442244
Total Film	01225-442244
Total Football	01225-442244
Total Guitar	01225-442244
Total Production	01702-291292
Touch	020-7739 5727
Townswoman	01603-616005
Toybox	020-8576 2000
Toy Soldier & Model Figures	
	01403-711511
Toy Trader	01993-775545
Trade It	01202-445000
Trade Marks Journal	
	01633-811448
Traditional Homes	020-7437 9011
Trail	01733-264666
Training	020-8652 3500
Transit	01733-467000
Transport Retort	020-7388 8386
Travel Trade Gazette	
	020-8309 7000
Treasure Hunting	01376-521900
Trees	01342-712536
Trees are News	01342-712536
Tribune	020-7278 0911
Trout Fisherman	01733-264666
Trout & Salmon	01733-264666
Truck	020-8652 3500
Truck & Driver	020-8652 3500
TV & Satellite Week	020-7261 5000
TV Hits	020-7636 5095
TV Quick	020-7241 8000
TV Times	020-7261 5000
TV World	020-7505 8000
Tunnels and Tunnelling	
	020-8309 7000
Twinkle	01382 223131

U

UFO Times	01924-444049
UK press gazette	020-8565 4448
Ulster Nation	020-7373 3432
Ultimate PC	01392-495155
Uncut	020-7261 5000
Under Five Contact	020-7833 0991
Union Review	020-8462 7755
The Universe	0161-236 8856
Unlimited	0141-332 3255
Unmanned Vehicles	01628-664334
Untold	020-7729 8384
Update	020-8652 3500
Used Car Dealer	01733-467000
Utility Europe	020-8652 3500

V

Vanguard (Nat Dems)	
	07071-226074
Vanity Fair	020-7499 9080
Vegetarian, The	0161-928 0793

Vegetarian Good Food (BBC)	
	020-7576 2000
Veterinary Times	01733-325522
Vintage Motor Cycle	
	01283-540557
Viz	020-7565 3000
Vogue	020-7499 9080
The Voice	020-7737 7377
Volvo Magazine	020-7747 0700

W

Wanderlust	01753-620426
The War Cry	020-7332 0022
Water	020-7240 2032
Water Gardener	01233-621877
Waterways	01283-790447
Wax	0141-353 1118
Wedding Cakes	01252-727572
Wedding & Home	020-7261 5000
The Week	020-7229 0006
Weekly Law Digest	020-8686 9141
Weekly News	01382-223131
Weight Watchers	020-8342 2222
What Bike?	01733-237111
What Camcorder?	020-7331 1000
What Car?	020-8943 5000
What Digital Camera?	
	020-7261
5000What Hi-Fi?	020-8943 5000
What Investment?	020-7827 5454
What Mobile & Cellphone	
	020-7251 6688
What Mortgage?	020-7827 5454
What PC & Software?	
	020-7316 9000
What Plant?	020-7505 6600
What Satellite?	020-7331 1000
What to Buy for Business	
	020-8652 3500
What Video?	020-7331 1000
What's New in Building/Design	
/Electronics/Farming/Industry/	
Interiors/Process & Control	
	020-8309 7000
What's On TV	020-7261 5000
When Saturday Comes	
	020-7729 1110
Which Motorcaravan	
	01778-391000
Which?	020-7770 7000
Whisky Magazine	020-8563 2975
Wide World	01869-338652
Wild London	020-7261 0447
Wildfowl and Wetlands	
	01453 890333
Windows Expert	01625-878888
Wine	020-7549 2575
The Wire	020-7439 6422
Wisden Cricket Monthly	
	01483-570358

WM	029-2058 3583
Woman	020-7261 5000
Woman & Home	020-7261 5000
Woman Alive	01903-821082
Woman's Journal	020-7261 5000
Woman's Own	020-7261 5000
Woman's Realm	020-7261 5000
Woman's Weekly	020-7261 5000
Women & Golf	020-7261 5000
Women in General Practice	
	020-7843 3600
Wood Based Panels International	
	01732-364422
Woodworker	01322-660070
Woodworking News	
	01474-536535
Word Search	020-8846 9922
Workers' Health	0114-276 5695
Working Women	020-8947 3131
Works Management	
	01689-850156
World of Interiors	020-7499 9080
World Soccer	020-7261 5000
The World Today	020-7957 5700
World's Fair	0161-624 3687
Working Together	01522-544400
Writers News	01667-454441
Writers Newsletter	020-7723 8074
Writing Magazine	01667-454441

X

X Files Monthly	020-7620 0200
XL for Men	020-7436 1515
Xpose	020-8875 1520

Y

Yachting Monthly	020-7261 5000
Yachting World	020-7261 5000
You Magazine (free)	020-7938 6000
You & Your Wedding	
	020-7437 3493
The Young Dancer	01769-574929
Your Cat/Dog	01733-898100
Your Garden	01202 440840
Your Greatest Guide to Calories	
	020-7437 9011
Your Horse	01733-264666
Your Mortgage?	020-7833 5566
Yours	01733-555123

Z

Zest	020-7439 5000
Zipper	020-7482 2576
Zit	01273-773224
ZM	020-7439 5000

Book publishing

News about books last year concentrated on rich authors getting richer through transfers to new publishers and high advances. Amis transferred to Miramax for $1 million and Hornby signed on with Penguin Utd for £2 million. Meanwhile Liverpool FC's Michael Owen signed a £2 million three book deal and the Manchester United manager Alex Ferguson earned at least a million from his autobiography.

This year it was a publisher who hit real pay dirt when Peter Kindersley pocketed £100 million from the sale of Dorling Kindersley to the Pearson Group. His company - which was founded in 1974 and pioneered a book publishing approach of lavish production values for a mass market - had run into trouble when 10 million copies of its Star Wars book failed to sell over Christmas 1999. That, Kindersley maintained, wasn't the reason for the sale. Marjorie Scardino, the Pearson chief executive, had web business as much as print on her mind when she pushed ahead with the £311 million purchase. "The Dorling Kindersley imprint is one of the most respected in the world and its assets offer a unique potential in the online environment. We aim to invest in its brand and its content so that it has a great future both on and offline."

For the past year - as in the rest of the media - news of the net is what has made headlines. As online book ordering kept expanding, so too did such stories as publishers faking good reviews on amazon.com. "We have email reviews from all over the world," said an Amazon spokeswoman. "We even had God reviewing the Bible." That puts an almighty spin on disintermediation, the media studies jargon for what happens when there are no controllers of information.

There are two stories, both from the west coast of America, which show the way publishing could be going. In July 2000 Stephen King, the best-selling horror writer, started publishing his latest novel on the web with the request that

readers send him a dollar for every chapter they decide to download. King says that if more than 25 per cent of those who log on to it don't pay, he will stop writing and abandon the project. His web book is called The Plant and is on www.stephenking.com

In January 2000 the Microsoft founder Bill Gates declared his hopes of breaking the print habit hopes to break print habit in a deal with the book retailer Barnes and Noble to develop electronic books. Microsoft had just demonstrated the Reader software which "delivers an on-screen reading experience similar to print". Dick Brass, a Microsoft vice president, looked ahead to a rapid growth of e-books on hand-held computers and likened the announcement to the way the Model T Ford spurred the switch from horses to cars. "We've been predicting this will overtake print books in about ten years," Brass said. "Three to five years out we see a billion dollar market-place."

In May 2000 we heard that "Net wins 9 per cent of young readers" when an Arts Council funded survey concluded: "As many as 9 per cent of children use electronic sources exclusively for obtaining reference information. They don't use books for this purpose." However, reports of the death of the dead tree business are exaggerated, for the survey also identified reading books as the biggest single cultural pastime in Britain. Four out of five adults say they read books for pleasure for an average of five and a half hours a week, and for 15 per cent this rises to at least 11 hours a week. Fiction is the favourite for 60 per cent of adults and 70 per cent of children, though non-fiction takes over in popularity among older people.

* Most journalists have a book or two in them and the way to publication is via a literary agent rather than making direct contact with publishers. That's why agents are listed here with their addresses prior to a phone-only listing of book publishers.

LITERARY AGENTS

KEY CONTACT

Association of Authors' Agents
4th Floor, Haymarket House, 28/29 Haymarket,
London SW1Y 4SP
Fax 020-7396 0110   Tel 020-7396 6600
E-mail: illoyd@curtisbrown.co.uk
The Association of Authors' Agents maintains a code of
professional practice to which all members of the
Association commit themselves; holds regular
meetings to discuss matters of common professional
interest; and provides a vehicle for representing the
view of authors' agents in discussion of matters of
common interest with other professional bodies.

AM Heath & Co
79 St Martins Lane, London WC2N 4AA
Fax 020-7497 2561   Tel 020-7836 4271
Main authors: Anita Brookner, Graham Hancock,
Areas covered: Fiction, non-fiction, reference etc.

AP Watt
20 John Street, London WC1N 2DR
Fax 020-7831 2154   Tel 020-7405 6774
E-mail: apw@apwatt.co.uk
Main authors: Estates of PG Wodehouse and Robert
Graves, also Andrew O'Hagan, Graham Swift.
Areas covered: Commercial and literary fiction, non-
fiction, TV, film.

The Agency (London)
24 Pottery Lane, London W11 4LZ
Fax 020-7727 9037   Tel 020-7727 1346
E-mail: info@theagency.co.uk
Main authors: Jimmy McGovern, Alan Bleasdale
Areas covered: Film, TV and theatre.

Gillon Aitken Associates
29 Fernshaw Road, London SW10 0TG
Fax 020-7376 3594   Tel 020-7351 7561
E-mail: reception@aitkenassoc.demon.co.uk
Main authors: Pat Barker, Helen Fielding, Sebastian
Faulks, VS Naipaul.
Areas covered: Fiction and non-fiction.

Andrew Lownie
17 Sutherland Street, London SW1V 4JV
Fax 020-7828 7608   Tel 020-7828 1274
E-mail: lownie@globalnet.co.uk
Website: www.andrewlownie.co.uk
Main authors: Norma Major, Alan Whicker, Sir John
Mills, John Rae.
Areas covered: History, biography, current affairs,
UFOs, food & wine.

Andrew Mann
1 Old Compton Street, London W1V 5PH
Fax 020-7287 9264   Tel 020-7734 4751
E-mail: manscript@compuserve.com
Areas covered: Fiction, non-fiction, TV, radio, film.

Andrew Nurnberg Associates
Clerkenwell House, 45-47 Clerkenwell Green, London
EC1R 0QX
Fax 020-7417 8812   Tel 020-7417 8800
E-mail: anurnberg@nurnberg.co.uk
Areas covered: Fiction and non-fiction.

Barbara Levy
64 Greenhill, Hampstead High Street, London NW3
5TZ
Fax 020-7431 2063   Tel 020-7435 9046
Areas covered: General non-fiction and fiction, TV
presenters.

Blake Friedmann
122 Arlington Road, London NW1 7HP
Fax 020-7284 0442   Tel 020-7284 0408
E-mail: firstname@blakefriedmann.co.uk
Main authors: Gilbert Adair, Jane Asher, John Harvey,
Ken Hom, Glenn Meade, Joseph O'Connor, Michael
Ridpath
Areas covered: Commercial and literary fiction, wide
range of non-fiction. No juvenile, poetry, science fiction
or fantasy.

Campbell Thomson & McLaughlin
1 King's Mews, London WC1N 2JA
Fax 020-7242 2408   Tel 020-7242 0958
Areas covered: Most areas except academic and
childrens.No unsolicited scripts.

Capel & Land
29 Wardour Street, London W1V 3HB
Fax 020-7734 8101   Tel 020-7734 2414
Areas covered: Literary non-fiction, commercial fiction
and journalism.

Caroline Sheldon Literary Agency
71 Hillgate Place, London W8 7SS
Fax 01983-760206   Tel 020-7727 9102
Areas covered: Fiction, particularly women's and
children's books.

Cat Ledger Literary Agency
33 Percy Street, London W1P 9FG
Fax 020-7 631 4273   Tel 020-7436 5030

Charles Pick Consultancy
Flat 3, 3 Bryanston Place, London W1H 7FN
Fax 020-7724 5990   Tel 020-7402 8043
Main authors: Wilbur Smith, Deidre Purcell
Areas covered: Fiction, non-fiction especially human
rights and international relations.

Christine Green
40 Doughty Street, London WC1N 2LF
Fax 020-7405 3935   Tel 020-7831 4956
Areas covered: Fiction and general non-fiction, no sci-fi,
childrens or poetry.

Christopher Little
125 Moore Park Road, London SW6 4PS
Fax 020-7736 4490   Tel 0171 736 4455
E-mail: christopher@christopherlittle.net
Main authors: J K Rowling, Simon Singh, Michael
Cordy, Robert Mawson, Rebbecca Ray
Areas covered: Literary and commercial fiction and
non-fiction. No unsolicited submissions.

Curtis Brown
4th Floor, Haymarket House, 28/29 Haymarket, London SW1Y 4SP
Fax 020-7396 0110.   Tel 020-7396 6600
E-mail: cb@curtisbrown.co.uk
Areas covered: Literary and commercial fiction, wide range of non-fiction,TV, radio, film and theatre.

Darley Anderson
Estelle House, 11 Eustace Road, London SW6 1JB
Fax 020-7386 5571   Tel 020-7385 6652
E-mail: darleyanderson@virgin.net
Main authors: Paul Carson, Lee Child, Martina Cole, John Connolly, Lesley Pearse, Peter Sheridan, Joan Jonker, Adrian Plass, Peter Sheridan.
Areas covered: All types of commercial fiction and non-fiction, Irish novels, children's books.

David Higham Associates
5/8 Lower John Street, Golden Square, London W!R 4HA
Fax 020-7437 1072   Tel 020-7437 7888
Main authors: John le Carre, Stephen Fry, Anne Fine.
Areas covered: Commercial and literary fiction,non-fiction, children's books, film and tv.

Deborah Owen
78 Narrow Street, London E14 8BP
Fax 020-7538 4004   Tel 020-7987 5119
Main authors: Delia Smith, Amos Oz, Ellis Peters
No new authors at present.

Dinah Wiener
12 Cornwall Grove, Chiswick, London W4 2LB
Fax 020-8994 6044   Tel 020-8994 6011

Ed Victor
6 Bayley Street, Bedford Square, London WC1B 3HB
Fax 020-7304 4111   Tel 020-7304 4100
E-mail: edvicltd@dircon.co.uk
Main authors: Douglas Adams, Frederick Forsyth, Josephine Hart, Jack Higgins, Erica Jong, Kathy Lette, Erich Segal, Lisa St Aubin de Teran.
Areas covered: Fiction and non-fiction.

Edwards Fuglewicz
49 Great Ormond Street, London WC1N 3HZ
Fax 020-7405 6726   Tel 020-7405 6725
E-mail: efla@ftech.co.uk
Areas covered: Fiction (literary and quality commercial), non-fiction.

Faith Evans Associates
27 Park Avenue North, London N8 7RU
Fax 020-8340 9410   Tel 020-8340 9920

Felicity Bryan
2A North Parade, Banbury Road, Oxford OX2 6LX
Fax 01865-310055   Tel 01865 513816
Main authors: Karen Armstrong, Liza Cody, Angela Huth, John Julius Norwich, Iain Pears, Rosamunde Pilcher, Matt Ridley, Roy Strong
Areas covered: History, science, literary fiction.

Frances Kelly
111 Clifton Road, Kingston-upon-Thames Surrey KT2 6PL
Fax 020-8547 0051   Tel 020-8549 7830
Areas covered: Non-fiction

Futerman Associates
17 Deanhill Road, London SW14 7DQ
Fax 020-8286 4861   Tel 020-8286 4860
Main authors: Judy Upton, Joseph Miller, Peter King, Angela Meredith, Sally Becker, Brian Milton
Areas covered: Fiction with film potential, stage plays, screen plays, biography, show business.

Greene & Heaton
37 Goldhawk Road, London W12 8QQ
Fax 020-8749 0318   Tel 020-8749 0315

Gregory & Radice
3 Barb Mews, London W6 7PA
Fax 020-7610 4686   Tel 020-7610 4676
E-mail: info@gregoryradice.co.uk
Main authors:Minette Walters, Val McDermid, Mo Hayder, Sophie Hannah, Laura Wilson
Areas covered: Literary and commercial fiction, crime, thrillers, politics, non-fiction.

Intercontinental Literary Agency (Translation rights only)
5th Floor, the chambers, Chelsea Harbour, London SW10 0XF
Fax 020-8351 4809   Tel 020-8351 4763

Jane Conway Gordon
1 Old Compton Street, London W1V 5PH
Fax 020-7287 9264   Tel 020-7494 0148
Areas covered: Fiction and non-fiction, no poetry or science fiction.

Jane Judd Literary Agency
18 Belitha Villas, London N1 1PD
Fax 020-7607 0623   Tel 020-7607 0273
Areas covered: General fiction and non-fiction.

Jane Turnbull
13 Wendell Road, London W12 9RS
Fax 020-8749 6079   Tel 020-8743 9580

John Farquharson
4th Floor, Haymarket House, 28/29 Haymarket, London SW1Y 4SP
Fax 020-7396 0110   Tel 020-7396 6600
E-mail: cb@curtisbrown.co.uk

John Johnson
Clerkenwell House, 45-47 Clerkenwell Green, London EC1R 0HT
Fax 020-7251 2172   Tel 020-7 251 0125
E-mail: johnjohnson@btinternet.com

Jonathan Clowes
10 Iron Bridge House, Bridge Approach, London NW1 8BD
Fax 020-7722 7677   Tel 020-7722 7674
E-mail: jonathanclowes@aol.com
Areas covered: Mainly fiction.

Judith Chilcote
8 Wentworth Mansions, Keats Grove, London NW3 2RL
Fax 020-7794 7431   Tel 020-7794 3717
Main authors: Jane Alexander, Fiona Harold, Zita West.
Areas covered: Commecial fiction, sport, cinema, self-help, health, TV tie-ins.

Limelight Management
33 Newman Street, London W1P 3PD
Fax 020-7637 2529   Tel 020-7637 2538
E-mail: limelight.management@virgin.net
Areas covered: Non-fiction, food, wine, health, crafts.

Lisa Eveleigh
26a Rochester Square, London NW1 9SA
Fax 020-7485 6960   Tel 020-7267 5245
E-mail: eveleigh@dial.pipex.com
Areas covered: Literary and commercial fiction.

Lucas Alexander Whitley
14 Vernon Street, London W14 0RJ
Fax 020-7471 7910   Tel 020-7471 7900
E-mail: law@lawagency.co.uk
Areas covered: fiction, non-fiction, not poetry, short stories or children's books.No submissions via E-mail.

Lutyens & Rubinstein
231 Westbourne Park Road, London W11 1EB
Fax 020-7792 4833   Tel 020-7792 4855
E-mail: name@lutyensrubinstein.co.uk
Areas covered: Literary and commercial fiction, non-fiction. No sci-fi, fantasy, poetry or children's books.

MBA Literary Agency
62 Grafton Way, London W1P 5LD
Fax 020-7387 2042   Tel 020-7387 2076
E-mail: agent@mbalit.co.uk
Areas covered: Fiction, non-fiction.

Maggie Noach Literary Agency
22 Dorville Crescent, London W6 0HJ
Fax 020-8748 8057   Tel 020-8748 2926
E-mail: m-noach@dircon.co.uk
Areas covered: Literary fiction, travel writing, history, biography, children's books (7 upwards).

Maggie Pearlstine
31 Ashley Gardens, London SW1P 1QE
Fax 020-7834 5546   Tel 020-7828 4212
E-mail: post@pearlstine.co.uk
Main authors: John Biffen, Menzies Campbell, Uri Geller, Roy Hattersley, Lisa Jardine, Charles Kennedy, Mark Leonard, Raj Persaud, Robert Winston.
Areas covered: History, current affairs, biography, health and fiction. No unsolicited mss.

Margaret Hanbury
27 Walcot Square, London SE11 4UB
Fax 020-7793 0316   Tel 020-7735 7680
E-mail: mhanbury@mhanbury.demon.co.uk

Mark Paterson & Associates
10 Brook St., Wivenhoe, Colchester, Esex CO7 9DS
Fax 01206-822990   Tel 01206-225433
E-mail: info@markpaterson.co.uk
Main authors: Sigmund and Anna Freud, DW Winnicott, E Balint, W Bion
Areas covered: Psychoanalysis for professional market, some history and education.

The Marsh Agency
11-12 Dover Street, London W1X 3PH
Fax 020-7399 2801   Tel 020-7399 2800
E-mail: enquiries@marsh-agency.co.uk
Areas covered: Translation rights.

Mary Clemmey
6 Dunollie Road, London NW5 2XP
Fax 020-7267 1290   Tel 020-7267 1290
Main authors: Paul Gilroy, Sheila Kitzinger
Areas covered: High quality fiction/non-fiction with an international market.

Michelle Kass Associates
36-38 Glasshouse Street, London W!r 5RH
Fax 020-7734 3394   Tel 020-7439 1624

PFD
34-43 Russell Street, London WC2B5HA
Fax 020-7836 9539   Tel 020-7344 1000
E-mail: postmaster@pfd.co.uk
Areas covered: Most, no sci-fi or poetry.

Rogers, Coleridge & White
20 Powis Mews, London W11 1JN
Fax 020-7229 9084   Tel 020-7221 3717
Areas covered: Literary fiction and non-fiction but no unsolicited mss.

Rupert Crew
!a King's Mews, London WC1N 2JA
Fax 020-7831 7914   Tel 020-7242 8586
E-mail: rupertcrew@compuserve.com
Areas covered: General fiction and non-fiction. No plays, poetry, film or TV scripts.

Sheil Land Associates
43 Doughty Street, London WC1N 2LF
Fax 020-7831 2127   Tel 020-7405 9351
E-mail: info@sheilland.co.uk
Main authors: Peter Ackroyd, Melvyn Bragg, Catherine Cookson, Richard Mabey, Van Morrison, Tom Sharpe.
Areas covered: General commercial and literary fiction and non-fiction. Also theatre, film, radio and TV scripts.

Shelley Power Literary Agency
Le Montaud, 24220 Berbiquires, France
Fax 00 33 55329 6254   Tel 0033 55329 6252
E-mail: puissant@easynet.fr
Areas covered: Adult fiction, literary and commercial, general non-fiction. No poetry, scripts, plays.

Shirely Stewart Literary Agent
36 Brand Street, Greenwich, London SW10 8SR
Fax 020-7305 2175   Tel 020-8305 2175
Areas covered: Literary fiction and non-fiction. No drama, screenplays, poetry or children's mss.

Tanja Howarth
19 New Row, London WC2N 4LA
Fax 020-7379 0969   Tel 020-7240 5553
E-mail: tanja.howarth@vrgin.net
Main authors: Patricia Highsmith, Patrick Süskind, Peter Ustinov

Tessa Sayle Agency
11 Jubilee Place, London SW3 3TE
Fax 020-7823 3363   Tel 020-7823 3883
E-mail: rcalder@tessasayle.demon.co.uk
Areas covered: Fiction, crime, history, biography, travel.

Trevor, Lavinia
49a Goldhawk Road, London W12 8QP
Fax 020-8749 7377   Tel 020-8749 8481
Areas covered: Fiction, general non-fiction including popular science. No children's books, sci-fi or poetry.

Vanessa Holt
59 Crescent Road, Leigh-on-Sea, Essex SS9 2PF
Fax 01702-471890   Tel 01702-714698
Areas covered: Commercial fiction and non-fiction.

Watson, Little
Capo di Monte, Windmill Hill, London NW3 6RJ
Fax 020-7431 7225   Tel 020-7431 0770
E-mail: sugrazaman@watlit.demon.co.uk
Areas covered: Popular science, history, leisure.

William Morris Agency (UK)
Stratton House, 1 Stratton Street, London W1V 6HB
Fax 020-7355 8600   Tel 020-7355 8500

PUBLISHERS

A

AA Publishing 0990-448866
ABC-Clio 01865-311350
Absolute Press 01225-316013
Addison Wesley Longman
01279-623623
Age Concern Books
020-8679 8000
Aidan Ellis 01548-842755
Airlife Publishing 01743-235651
Allen Lane 020-7416 3121
Allison & Busby 020-7636 2942
Andersen Press 020-7840 8700
Andre Deutsch 020-7580 2746
Andromeda Oxford 01235-550296
Anness Publishing 020-7401 2077
Appletree Press 01232-243074
Arcadi Books 020-7436 9898
Arrow Books 020-7840 8400
Art Trade Press 01705-484943
Ashgate Publishing 01252-331551
Athlone Press 020-8458 0888
Atlantic Europe 01491-628188
Attic Press 021-321725
Aurum Press 020-7637 3225
Award Publications 020-7388 7800

B

Bantam 020-8579 2652
Barefoot Books 0117-932 8885
Barrie & Jenkins 020-7840 8400
Barry Rose (Law) 01243-775552
Batsford 020-7471 1100
Baylin Publications 0118-941 4468
BBC Books 020-8576 3017
Bedford Square Press
020-7713 6161
Belitha Press 020-7978 6330
Bellew Publishing 020-8673 5611
Berg Publishers 01865-245104
Berlitz 020-7518 8300
Bernard Babani 020-7603 2581
BFI Publishing 020-7255 1444
Bible Society 01793-418100
Billboard 020-7323 6686
A&C Black 020-7242 0946
Blackstaff Press 01232-668074
Blackstone Press 020-8740 2277
Blackwell 01865-791100
Blackwell Science 01865-206206
Blake Publishing 020-7381 0666
Blandford Press 020-7420 5555
Bloodaxe Books 01434-684855
Bloomsbury 020-7494 2111
Boatswain Press 01243-377977
Bodley Head 020-7840 8400
Booth-Clibborn 020-7637 4255
Bowker-Saur 01342-326972
Boxtree 020-7881 8000
BPP (Publishing) 020-7420 5555
Brassey's 020-7471 1100
Breedon Books 01332-384235

Brewin Books 01527-854228
Brilliant Publications 01525-222844
British Film Institute 020-7255 1444
British Museum Press
020-7323 1234
Broadcast Books 020-8769 3483
Brown, Son & Ferguson
0141-429 1234
Brown Wells and Jacobs
020-8771 5115
Burns & Oates 01892-510850
Butterworth 020-7400 2500
Butterworth-Heinemann
01865-310366
Butterworth Tolley 020-8686 9141

C

Calder Publications 020-7633 0599
Cambridge University Press
01223-312393
Canongate Books 0131-557 5111
Carcanet Press 020-7734 7338
Carlton Books 020-7734 7338
Cartermill Int. 01334-477660
Cassell 020-7420 5555
Catholic Truth 020-7640 0042
Cavendish 020-7278 8000
CBD Research 020-8650 7745
Chadwyck-Healey 01223-215512
Chambers Harrap 0131-556 5929
Chapman 0131-557 2207
Chatto & Windus 020-7840 8400
Child's Play 01793-616286
CHurst 020-7240 2666
Cicerone Press 015395-62069
Colin Smythe 01753-886000
Collins & Brown 020-7924 2575
Conran Octopus 020-7240 6961
Constable 020-8741 3663
Croner CCH 020-8547 3333
Corgi 020-8579 2652
Coronet 020-7873 6000
Countryside Books 01635-43816
Crescent Moon 01622-729593
Cressrelles 01684-540154
Croner 020-8547 3333
Crowood Press 01672-520320
CW Daniel Co. 01799-521909

D

Dalesman 01756-701381
Darton, Longman & Todd
020-8875 0155
David & Charles 01626-323200
David & Charles Children's
020-7616 7200
David Bennett 01727-855878
David Fulton 020-7405 5606
Dedalus 01487-832382
Demos 020-7353 4479
JM Dent & Sons 020-7240 3444
diehard 0131-229 7252
Dorling Kindersley 020-7836 5411
Doubleday 020-8579 2652

Dragonflair 01694-722504
Dref Wen 01222-617860
Dublar Scripts 01794-501377
Duncan Baird 020-7323 2229

E

East-West 020-8758 0999
Ebury Press 020-7840 8400
Edinburgh U Press 0131-650 4218
Educational Explorers
01734-873101
Egmont Children's 020-7761 3500
Element Books 01747-851339
Elliot Right Way 01737-832202
ELM Publications 01487-773238
Elsevier Science 01865-843000
Emap Media 020-7837 1212
Encyclopaedia Britannica
020-7862 4000
Epworth Press 01733-332202
Euromonitor 020-7251 8024
Europa 020-7580 8236
Evans Brothers 020-7935 7160
Everyman's Library 020-7539 7600
Exley Publications 01923-250505

F

Faber & Faber 020-7465 0045
Farming Press 01473-241122
Fernhurst Books 01903-882277
Flicks Books 01225 760756
Floris Books 0131-337 2372
Focal Press 01865-310533
Folens 01582-472788
Fontana 020-8741 7070
Fourth Estate 020-7727 8993
Frances Lincoln 020-284 4009
Frank Cass 020-8599 8866
Frederick Warne 020-7416 3000
Free Association 020-7388 3182
FT Management 020-7379 7383
Funfax 020-7836 5411

G

Gaia Books 020-7323 4010
Garnet Publishingg 01189-597847
Gay Men's Press 020-8348 9963
Geddes & Grosset 01555-665000
Gee & Son 01745-812020
Godsfield Press 01962-735633
George Philip 020-7581 9393
George Ronald 01865-841515
Gerald Duckworth 020-7434 4242
Giles de la Mare 020-7465 7607
GMP Publishers 01366-328101
Golden Cockerell 020-7405 7979
Gomer Press 01559-362371
Graham & Whiteside
020-8947 1011
Granta Publications 020-7704 9776
Green Books 01803-863843
Greenhill Books 020-8458 6314
Grub Street 020-7924 3966
Guinness 020-88914567

H

Hamish Hamilton	020-7416 3000
Hamlyn	020-7581 9393
Harcourt Publishers	020-7424 4200
Harlequin Mills & Boon	
	020-8288 2800
Harold Starke	01379-388334
HarperCollins	020-8741 7070
Harrap	0131-557 4571
Harvill	020-7704 8766
Haynes	01963-440635
Hawk Books	020-8969 8091
Hazar Publishing	020-8742 8578
Helicon Publishing	01865-204204
Heinemann	020-7840 8400
Hilmarton Manor	01249-760208
Hippopotamus	01373-466653
HMSO Books	020-7873 0011
Hobsons Publishing	01223-460366
Hodder Headline	020-7873 6000
Hollis Directories	020-8977 7711
How To Books	01865-793806
Hugo's Language	020-7836 5411
Hutchinson Books	020-7840 8400

I

Ian Allen	01932-266600
IB Tauris	020-7831 9060
In Print	01273-205599
Interactive Media Publications	
	020-7837 3345
IOP Publishing	0117-929 7481

J

JA Allen	01225-679388
James Clarke & Co	01223-350865
James Currey	01865-244111
James Nisbet	01462-438331
Jane's	020-8700 3700
Jarrold	01603-763300
Jessica Kingsley	020-7833 2307
John Donald	0131-556 6660
John Hunt	01962-736880
John Jones	01824-704856
John Murray	020-7493 4361
John Wiley & Sons	01243-779777
John Sherratt	0161-236 9963
Johnson Publications	
	020-7589 0589
Jonathan Cape	020-7840 8576
Jordan Publishing	0117-918 1232
Journeyman Press	020-8348 2724
J Whitaker & Sons	020-7420 6000

K

Karnak House	020-7243 3620
Kenilworth Press	0129-671 5101
Kenneth Mason	01243-377977
Kevin Mayhew	01449-737978
Kingfisher	020-7903 9999
Kluwer	020-8547 3333
Knockabout	020-8969 2945
Kogan Page	020-7278 0433
Kyle Cathie	020-7840 8400

L

Ladybird Books	020-7416 3000
Larousse	020-7903 9999
Laurence King	020-7831 6351
Lawrence & Wishart	020-8533 2506
Letts Educational	020-8740 2266
Libris	020-7482 2390
Lion Publishing	01865-747550
Little Brown	020-7911 8000
Liverpool UP	0151-794 2233
Lonely Planet	020-428 4800
Longman Group	01279-623623
Lund Humphries	020-8458 6314
Lutterworth Press	01223-350865

M

Macdonald Young Books	
	01273-722561
Macmillan Publisher	020-7881 8000
Magi Publications	020-7486 0925
Mainstream Publishing	
	0131-557 2959
Manchester UP	0161-273 5539
Mandarin	020-7840 8400
Mantra Publishing	020-8445 5123
Mansell Publishing	020-7420 5555
Marion Boyars	020-8788 9522
Marshall Publishing	020-7291 8222
Marshall Cavendish	020-7734 6710
Martin Dunitz	020-7482 2202
McGraw-Hill	01628-623432
Medici Society	020-8205 2500
Melrose Press	01353-646600
Mercat Press	0131-622 8222
Merehurst	020-8355 1480
Merlin Press	020-7836 3020
Merrell Holberton	020-7403 2047
Methuen	020-7840 8400
Methodist Publishing	
	01733-332202
Metro Publishing	020-7734 1411
Michelin	01923-415000
Michael Joseph	020-7416 3000
Michael O'Mara	020-7720 8643
Miller Freeman	01732-362666
Mills & Boon	020-8948 0444
Mitchell Beazley	020-7840 8400
MQ Publications	020-7490 7732

N

Nelson Thomas	01242-267100
Network Books	020-8576 3017
New Beacon Books	020-7272 4889
New Cavendish Books	
	020-7229 6765
New English Library	020-7876 6000
New Holland	020-7724 7773
New Theatre Publications	
	020-8651 4119
Nexus	01332-660070
Nicholas Brealey	020-7713 7455
Nick Hern Books	020-8749 4953
Northcote House	01752-202368
NTC Publications	01491-574671

O

Octagon Press	020-8348 9392
Octopus Publishing	020-7531 8400
Oleander Press	01223-244688
Omnibus Press	020-7434 0066
Oneworld Publications	
	01865-310597
Onlywomen Press	020-8960 7122
Open Gate Press	020-7431 4391
Open UP	01280-823388
Orion	020-7240 3444
Osprey	020-7225 9365
Oxford University Press	
	01865-556767

P

Paladin Books	020-8741 7070
Pan Books	020-7373 4997
Pandora Press	020-8741 7070
Parragon Books	01225 478888
Paternoster	01228-512512
Paul Chapman	020-7374 0645
Pavilion Books	020-7350 1230
Pavilion Publishing	01273-623222
PDQ Publishing	01865-820387
Pearson Education	01279-623623
Pen & Sword	01226-734222
Penguin Books	020-7416 3000
Pergamon Press	01865-310111
Peter Collins	020-8943 3386
Peter Halban	020-7437 9300
Peter Lowe	01865-858333
Phaidon Press	020-7843 1000
Piatkus Books	020-7631 0710
Picador	020-7373 6070
Philips	020-7225 9826
Piatkus	020-7631 0710
Piccadilly Press	020-7267 4492
Pipers' Ash	01249-720563
Pitkin Guides	01264 409200
Plexus	020-7622 2440
Pluto Press	020-8348 2724
Policy Press	0117-954 6800
Polity Press	01223-324315
Portland Press	020-7580 5530
Prion Books	020-7482 4248
Prism Press	01258-817164
Profile Books	020-7404 3001
Puffin	020-7416 3000
Pulp Books	020-7700 3409
Purple House	01865-511999

Q

Quadrille Publishing	020-7839 7117
Quartet Books	020-7636 3992
Quarto	020-7700 6700
Queen Anne Press	01582-715866
Quiller Press	020-7499 6529

R

Random House	020-7840 8400
Readers Digest	020-7715 8000
Readers Digest Children's	
	01225-463401
Reed Books	020-7581 9393
Reed Children's	020-7761 3500
Reed Educational	01865-314097
Reed Elsevier	020-7222 8420
Reed Information Services	
	01342-335832
Rivers Oram Press	020-7607 0823
Robert Hale	020-7251 2661
Robinson Publishing	
	020-7938 3830
Robson Books	020-700 7444
Rosendale Press	020-7834 1123
Roundhouse Publishing	
	01237-474474
Routledge	020-7583 9855
Royal National Institute for the blind	
	0345-023153
Ryland Peter & Small	
	020-7436 9090
Rushmere	01502-574515

S

Sage Publications	020-7374 0645
Saint Andrew Press	0131-225 5722
Salamander Books	020-7700 7799
Samuel French	020-7387 9373
SB Publications	01323-893498
Schofield & Sims	01484-607080
Scholastic	020-7421 9000
Science Museum Publications	
	020-7938 8136
SCM Press	020-7359 8033
Scottish Academic Press	
	0131-220 6061
Scottish Cultural Press	
	0131-555 5950
Scripture Union	01908-856000
Seafarer Books	01394-420789
Search Press	01892-510850
Secker & Warburg	020-7840 8400
Seren Books	01656-663081
Serif	020-8981 3990
Serpent's Tail	020-7354 1949
Severn House Publishers	
	020-8770 3930
Sheed & Ward	020-7702 9799
Sheldrake Press	020-8675 1767
Shepheard-Walwyn	020-7240 5992
Shire Publications	01844-344301
Sidgwick & Jackson	
	020-7373 6070
Sigma Press	01625-531035
Simon & Schuster	020-7316 9100
Skoob Books	020-7275 9811
Souvenir Press	020-7580 9307

Specialist Crafts	0116-251 0405
SPCK	020-7387 5282
Spellmount	01580-893730
Springer-Verlag	01483-418800
Stacey International	020-7221 7166
St Pauls	020-7828 5582
St Paul's Bibliographies	
	01962-864037
Stainer & Bell	020-8343 3303
Stanley Gibbons	01425-472363
Stanley Thornes	01242-228888
Stationery Office	0870-6005522
Sterling Publishing	
	020-7258 0066
Summersdale Publishers	
	01243-771107
Sunflower Books	020-7589 1862
Sussex Academic Press	
	01273-699533
Sutton Publishing	01453-731114
Sweet & Maxwell	020-7538 8686

T

Take That	01423-507545
Tamarind	020-8866 8808
Tate Gallery Publishing	
	020-7887 8869
Tarquin Publications	01379-384218
Taylor & Francis	020-7583 9855
Telegraph Books	020-7538 6826
Thames & Hudson	020-7845 5000
Thames Publishing	020-8969 3579
Thomas Nelson	01932-252211
Titan Books	020-7629 0200
Transworld Publishers	
	020-8579 2652
Treehouse Children's Books	
	01458-835757
Trentham Books	020-8348 2174
Trotman & Co	020-8486 1150
Two-Can Design	020-7684 4000
T&T Clarke	01223-350865

U

Unicorn Books	01892-833648
University of Exeter Press	
	01392-263066
University of Luton Press	
	01582-743297
University of Wales Press	
	029-2023 1919
Usborne Publishing	020-7430 2800

V

V&A Publications	020-7938 9663
Wentura	020-7416 3000
Verso	020-7437 3546
Victor Gollancz	020-7420 5555
Viking	020-7416 3000
Virago Press	020-7383 5150
Virgin Publishing	020-7386 3300
Virtue Books	01709-365005
Vision Paperbacks	020-7323 9757

W

W Foulsham	01753-526769
Walker Books	020-7793 0909
Warburg Institute	020-7862 8949
Ward Lock	020-7420 5555
Ward Lock Educational	
	01342-318980
Warner/Chappell Plays	
	020-8563 5888
Watts Publishing Group	
	020-7739 2929
Wayland Publishers	01273-722561
Websters International	
	020-7940 4700
Weidenfeld & Nicolson	
	020-7240 3444
WH Freeman	01256-332807
Which? Books	020-7830 6000
Whitaker & Sons	020-7420 6000
Whittet Books	01449-781877
Whurr Publishers	020-7359 5979
Wiley Europe	01243-779777
William Heinemann	020-7840 8400
Windrush Press	01608-652012
Writers & Readers	020-7226 3377
WW Norton	020-7323 1579
Womens Press	020-7251 3007
Woodhead Publishing	
	01223-891358
Wordsworth Editions	
	020-7706 8822
World International	01625-650011
Writers & Readers	020-7226 3377

X

The X Press	020-7729 1199

Y

Yale University Press	
	020-7431 4422

Z

Zed Books	020-7837 4014
Zoe Books	01962-851318

News agencies

KEY CONTACT

National Association of Press Agencies
41 Lansdowne Crescent, Leamington Spa,
Warwickshire CV32 4PR
Fax 01926-424760   Tel 01926-424181
Trade association for news and photographic agenies.

24/7 Media
Bradford Street, Birmingham, B12 0NS
Fax 0121-608 1171   Tel 0121-608 1166
News, pictures and features from West Midlands.

Advance Features
Stubbs Wood Cottage, Hammerwood, East
Grinstead, West Sussex RH19 3QE
Fax 01342-850480   Tel 01342-850480
Provides text, cartoons, crosswords and puzzles for
newspapers, magazines and TV.

AFI Research
The Ground Floor, 27 The Avenue, Newton Abbot,
Devon TQ12 2BZ
Fax 01626-335040   Tel 01626-335040
E-mail: info@afi-research.com
Website: www.afi-research.com
International research and consultancy in areas of
politics, defence, INS, history and biography.
Specializes in discreet info gathering for media and
corporate markets.

AFX News
13-17 Epworth Street, London EC2A 4DL
Fax 020-7490 3007   Tel 020-7253 2532
Website: www.afxnews.com
A joint venture of the AFP and the FT Group, AFX is
the fourth largest global financial news agency.

Agence France Presse
78 Fleet Street, London EC4Y 1HY
Fax 020-7353 8359   Tel 020-7353 7461
E-mail: london.bureau@afp.com
Website: www.afp.com
London office of the global news agency. Supplies
international news and pictures. The reporting network
covers 167 countries and uses the latest technologies.

Alert Communications
1 Stuart Road, Thornton Heath, Surrey CR7 8RA
                    Tel 020-8655 1750
                    07831-196693
E-mail: alert@cr78ra1uk.win-uk.net
Produces news and current affairs factuals, information
and educational features, often supported by fact sheets
and helplines.

AllScot News & Features Agency
PO Box 6, Haddington, East Lothian EH41 3NQ
Fax 01620-825079   Tel 01620-822578
E-mail 101324.2142@compuserve.com
Provides a full range of news agency services about
Scotland for UK and overseas media outlets.

Andes Press Agency
26 Padbury Court, London E2 7EH
Fax 020-7739 3159   Tel 020-7613 5417
                    Tel.020-7739 3159
E-mail: photos@andespress.demon.co.uk
Covers global social, religious, political, economic and
environmental, especially in Latin America.

Anglia Press Agency
91 Hythe Hill, Colchester, Essex CO1 2NU
Fax 01787-249001   Tel 01787-249001
Covers: Essex, Suffolk and Norfolk, news and pictures.

Anglo-Danish Press Agency
Grosvenor Works, Mount Pleasant Hill, London E5
9NE
Fax 020-8806 3236   Tel 020-8806 3232

ANSA
Essex House, 12-13 Essex Street, London WC2R
3AA
Fax 020-7240 5518   Tel 020-7240 5514
Website: www.ansa.it
The leading Italian news agency.

Associated Press (AP)
12 Norwich Street, London EC4A 1BP
Fax 020-7353 8118   Tel 020-7353 1515
Website: www.apweb.com
UK office of the American agency, owned by US media
companies. Supplies international news and picture
services to the UK media, and collects British material
for US and other clients. Also runs the AP-Dow Jones.

Australian Associated Press
12 Norwich Street, London EC4A 1QJ
Fax 020-7583 3563   Tel 020-7353 0153
E-mail: aaplondon@hotmail.com
Website: www.aap.com.au
Australia's only domestic news agency. Reports on
events in Britain and Europe of interest to Australia and
the South Pacific.

Bellis News Agency
Seabreezes, 14b Kenelm Road, Rhos-on-Sea,
Colwyn Bay LL28 4ED
Fax 01492-543226   Tel 01492-549503
E-mail: bellisd@aol.com
News reporters for most of north Wales .

Bloomberg News
City Gate House, 39-45 Finsbury Square, London
EC2A 1PQ
Fax 020-7392 6000   Tel 020-7330 7500
Website: www.bloomberg.com\uk
Business and financial news.

Bournemouth News & Picture Service
14 Lorne Park Road, Bournemouth BH1 1JN
Fax 01202-553875   Tel 01202-558833
Hants, Dorset, Wilts. News, features and photos.

Brian Unwin
16 Shearwater, Sunderland, Tyne-and-Wear SR6 7SF
Fax 0191-529 5022   Tel 0191-529 5012
E-mail: brian_unnwin@bigfoot.com
Website: www.welcome.to/Brian_Unwin

Central Office of Information (COI)
Hercules Road, London SE1 7DU
Fax 020-7928 5037   Tel 020-7928 2345
Website: www.coi.gov.uk/coi
The government press and publicity agency.

COI South East
Hercules Road, London SE1 7DU
Fax 020-7928 6974   Tel 020-7261 8795
COI Eastern
Three Crowns House, 72-80 Hills Road, Cambridge
CB2 1LL
Fax 01223-316121   Tel 01223-311867
COI West Midlands
Five Ways House, 4th floor, Islington Row,
Middleway, Edgbaston, Birmingham B15 1SL
Fax 0121-626 2041   Tel 0121-626 2023

COI East Midlands
Belgrave Centre, Talbot St, Nottingham NG1 5GG
Fax 0115-971 2791   Tel 0115-971 2780
COI North West
Piccadilly Plaza, Manchester M1 4BD
Fax 0161-236 9443   Tel 0161-952 4513
COI Plymouth
Mast House, Sheppards Wharf, 24 Sutton Road,
Plymouth PL4 0HJ
Fax 01752-227647   Tel 01752-635053
COI South West
The Pithay, Bristol BS1 2NQ
Fax 0117-945 6975   Tel 0117-945 6969
E-mail: bristol@coi.gov.uk
COI Yorkshire & Humberside
City House, New Station Street, Leeds, LS1 4JG
Fax 0113-283 6586   Tel 0113-283 6599

Bridge Information Systems
KR House, 78 Fleet Street, London EC4Y 1NB
Fax 020-7583 0519   Tel 020-7842 4000
Website: www.bridge.com
Bristol & West News Agency
80 Combe Avenue, Portishead, N Somerset BS20 6JT
Fax 01275-843899   Tel 01275-842053
Sports coverage of the region.
Canadian Press
12 Norwich Street, London EC4A 1EJ
Fax 020-7583 4238   Tel 020-7353 6355
The leading Canadian news agency.
Cassidy & Leigh (Southern News Service)
Exchange House, Hindhead, Surrey GU26 6AA
Fax 01428-606351   Tel 01428-607330
News and pictures: Surrey, Sussex, Hants and Kent.
Picture library, picture transmitter.
Caters News Agency
Suite 40, Queens Gate, 121 Suffolk Street,
Queensway, Birmingham B1 1LX
Fax 0121-616 2200   Tel 0121-616 1100
                     ISDN 0121-616 2014
E-mail: catersnews@aol.com
Covers: West Midlands and around, news, showbiz etc.
Cavendish Press
17-19 Whitworth Street, Manchester M1 5WG
Fax 0161-237 5353   Tel 0161-237 1066
                     ISDN 0161-236 1370
Website: www.cavendish-press.co.uk
Covers: North west England. News, features, pictures.
Central News Network
30a Newmarket Street, Falkirk, FK1 1JQ
Fax 01324-630515   Tel.01324-630505
Central Press Features
Temple Way, Bristol BS99 7HD
Fax 0117-934 3639   Tel 0117-934 3600
E-mail: mail@central-press.co.uk.
Website: www.central-press.co.uk
Features syndication worldwide. Specialists in TV
listings, crosswords, puzzles and motoring.

Central Press Lobby
House of Commons, London SW1A 0AA
Fax 020-7799 1026   Tel 020-7219 5287
Parliamentary reporting for regional press and TV.
Chapman & Page
Denegate House, Amber Hill, Boston,Lincs PE20 3RL
Tel 01205-290477
Syndications agency supplying regular weekly columns
and crosswords plus editorial to support ad features.
Chester News Service
Linen Hall House, Stanley Street, Chester CH1 2LR
Fax 01244-326075   Tel 01244-345562
Covers: Chester local courts, sport and features
Chester Press Bureaux
Riverside Ho, River Lane, Saltney, Chester CH4 8RQ
Fax 01244-678749   Tel 01244-678575
E-mail: chester.pb@virgin.net
Provides press agency, PR and contract publishing.
Cotswold & Swindon News Service
101 Bath Road, Swindon, Wilts SN1 4AX
Fax 01793-485462   Tel 01793-485461
E-mail: cotswin@stares.co.uk
Website: www.stares.co.uk
Specialist cover of magistates' and crown courts. Also
news and features. Accredited media trainer,
nationwide courses.
Coventry News Service
1st Floor, 3 Queen Victoria Road, Coventry CV1 3JS
Fax 024-7663 4906   Tel 024-7663 3777
E-mail: adent@clara.net
JW Crabtree & Son
43 Cheapside, Bradford, West Yorkshire BD1 4HP
Fax 01274-732937   Tel 01274-732937
Covers: Bradford area for sport and news.
Dee News Service
12 Chester Street, Mold, Clwyd CH7 1EG
Fax 01352-759009   Tel 01352-754016
Covers: NE Wales area including courts coverage.
Deutsche Presse Agentur
30 Old Queen Street, London SW1H 9HP
Fax 020-7233 3534   Tel 020-7233 2888
German news agency, owned by German media.

Devon News Agency
4 Clifton Road, Exeter, Devon EX1 2BR
Fax 01392-435248   Tel 01392-276338
Covers: Devon and Cornwall.

Dow Jones Newswires
10 Fleet Place, Limeburner Lane, London EC4M 7RB
Fax 020-7842 9361   Tel 020-7842 9900
E-mail: helen.donnellan@cor.dowjones.com
Website: www.dowjones.com
UK office of newswire service owned by Dow Jones &
Co, publishers of the Wall Street Journal. Supplies
international news affecting global financial markets.
Produced in co-operation with AP.

Dragon News & Picture Agency
21 Walter Road, Swansea, SA1 5NQ
Fax 01792-475264   Tel 01792-464800
E-mail: mail@dragon-pictures.com
Website: www.dragon-pictures.com
Covers: South and west Wales.

Dundee Press Agency
10 Victoria Road, Dundee DD1 1JN
Fax 01382-907790   Tel 01382-907700
Covering east and central Scotland.

Elliott News Service
1 Fisher Lane, Bingham, Nottingham NG13 8BQ
Fax 01949-836583   Tel 01949-836566

Essex News Service
121 High Street, Witham, Essex CM8 1BE
Fax 01376-521222   Tel 01376-521222
perfect@essexnews.freeserve.co.uk
Covering all news and features in Essex.

Extel Financial
see AFX News

Features International
Lydeard St Lawrence, Taunton, Somerset TA4 3PS
Fax 01984-623901   Tel 01984-623014
Syndicates internationally newspaper and magazine
features.

Ferrari Press Agency
1A Hurst Road, Sidcup, Kent DA15 9AE
Fax: 020-8302 6611   Tel 020-8302 6622
E-mail: ferraripress@compuserve.com
Covers: Kent, south London, Essex, Surrey and Sussex,
news, features and pictures.

First Features Syndicate
39 High Street, Battle, East Sussex.
Fax 01424-870877   Tel 01424-870877
E-mail: first.features@dial.pipex.com
Supplies all types of feature material to press and radio .

Fleet News Agency
Fleet House, 68a Stanfield Road, Bournemouth,
Dorset BH9 2NR
                    Tel 01202-515151
Covers: Bournemouth, Dorset and surrounding area.

Fleetline News Service
1a Bedford Road, London N2 9DB
Fax 020-8444 2313   Tel 020-8444 9183
Covers: London and Home Counties.

Fourth Estate Press Agency
12 North Campbell Avenue, Glasgow G62 7AA
                    Tel 0141-956 1540
Covers: Glasgow and west of Scotland.

Fowlers Press Agency
11 Village Way, London SE21 7AN
Fax 020-7236 8136   Tel 020-7248 6858
Nationwide bankruptcy and liquidation service.

Frank Ryan News Service
Cargenriggs, Islesteps, Dumfries DG2 8ES
Fax 01387-251121   Tel 01387-253700
E-mail: smeddum@btinternet.com
Covers: South west Scotland - news, features, PR,
photography.

Freemans Press Agency
Raleigh House, 1 Mill Road, Barnstaple EX31 1JQ
Fax 01271-344922   Tel 01271-324000
Covers: News features, PR and pix all SW England.

Front Page News Agency
1st Floor, 67 High Street, Bidford-on-Avon,
Warwickshire B50 4BQ
Fax 01789-490286   Tel 01789-778590
Covers: True life features in the UK.

Gemini News Service
9 White Lion Street, London N1 9PD
Fax 020-7278 0345   Tel 020-7278 1111
E-mail: alexw@panoslondonorg.uk
International news and feature service.

Gloucestershire News Service
26 Westgate Street, Gloucester GL1 2NG
Fax 01452-300581   Tel 01452-522270
E-mail: glosnews@cwcom.net
Local news and sports coverage.

Great North News & Features
Woody Glen, How Mill, Carlisle, Cumbria CA4 9JY
Fax 01228-70381   Tel 01228-670381
E-mail: gnorthnews@aol.com
News from the northern Lake District to southern
Scotland and coverage of Carlisle courts.

Great Scot International
Camerons, Midton Road, Howwood PA9 1AG
Fax 01505-702333   Tel 01505-705656
E-mail: great.scot@glasgow.almac.co.uk
Newspaper, magazine, TV, radio, books. They have
Scottish experts and international medicine specialists.
Close to Glasgow Airport,

Guardian/Observer News Services
119 Farringdon Road, London EC1R 3ER
Fax 020-7837 1192   Tel 020-7278 2332
International syndication services of news and features
from the Guardian and Observer. Most national daily
and Sunday newspapers have similar syndication
operations; contact via their main switchboards.
See also London News Service and Solo Syndication,
below.

Hayter's Sports Agency
146-148 Clerkenwell Road, London EC1R 5DG
Fax 020-7837 2420   Tel 020-7837 7171
E-mail: sport@hayters.com
Website: www.hayters.co.uk
Sports reporting, features, statistics and event support.

Hill's Welsh Press
58 Lower Cathedral Road, Cardiff CF1 8LT
Fax 029-2022 4947   Tel 029-2022 7606
A news and photographic agency specialising in news,
sport, features, PR. Mac facilities.

Hopkinson News & Feature Service
22 Hallfield Road, Bradford BD1 3RQ
Fax 01274-725565   Tel 01274-725565
Yorkshire and Humberside.

Hull News & Pictures
Room 115, Hull Microfirms Centre, 266-290
Wincolmlee, Hull HU2 0PZ
Fax 01482-210267   Tel 01482-210267
E-mail: hull@hullnews.karoo.co.uk
East Yorkshire and north Lincolnshire.

INS News Group
145 Wharfedale Road, Winnersh Triangle, Winnersh,
Reading, Berks RG41 5RB
Fax 01118-922 9404   Tel 0118-944 0600
E-mail: newsdesk@insnews.co.uk
24 hour coverage of the home counties and the south
west.

Inter-Continental Features
48 Southerton Road, London W6 0PH
Fax 020-8741 3819   Tel 020-8748 9722
Agents for syndicated cartoons and features.

Islamic Republic News Agency (IRNA)
3rd Floor, 390 High Road, Wembley, Middx HA9 6AS
Fax 020-8900 0705   Tel 020-8903 1630
E-mail: payam@irna.co.uk
Website: www.irna.com
News and photo agency.

Jarrolds Press Agency
68 High Street, Ipswich, Suffolk IP1 3QJ
Fax 01473-218447   Tel 01473-219193
Covers: Suffolk and surrounding area and football
coverage.

Jenkins Group
186 High Street, Rochester, Kent ME1 1EY
Fax 01634-830930   Tel 01634-830888
Covers Kent for news features.

Jiji Press
International Press Centre, 76 Shoe Lane, London
EC4A 3JB
Fax 020-7583 8353   Tel 020-7936 2847
E-mail: jijildn2@ma.kew.net
Japanese news agency.

John Connor Press Associates
57a High Street, Lewes, East Sussex BN7 1XE
Fax 01273-486852   Tel 01273-486851
E-mail: newsdesk@jcpa.freeserve.co.uk
Website: www.jcpa.freeserve.co.uk
News, pictures and features from East and West
Sussex.

Kett's News Service
53 Christchurch Road, Norwich, Norfolk, NR2 3NE
Fax 01603-508055   Tel 01603-508055
Covers news and features in Norfolk and Suffolk.

Kuwait News Agency
150 Southampton Row, London WC1B 5AL.
Fax 020-7278 6232   Tel 020-7278 5445

Kyodo News
Suites 119-130, NW Wing, Bush House, Aldwych,
London WC2B 4PJ
Fax 020-7438 4512   Tel 020-7438 4501
Website: www.kyodo.co.jp
Japanese news agency that covers UK and Scandinavia.

Lakeland Press Agency
Birch Garth, Beemire, Birthwaite Road, Windermere,
Cumbria LA23 1DW
Fax 015394-45128   Tel 015394-45127
Covers: Lake District.

Leicester News Service
Third Floor, 1c Conduit Street, Leicester LE2 0JN
Fax 0116-255 6565   Tel 0116-255 5055
Covers: Leicestershire, Rutland.

London At Large
36 Aybrook Street, London W1M 3JL
Fax 020-7224 4452   Tel 020-7224 4464
E-mail: newsbreaks@londonatlarge.com
A forward planning press agency specialsing in arts and
entertainment.

M & Y News Agency
65a Osborne Road, Southsea, Hants PO5 3LS
Fax 023-9229 1709   Tel 023-9282 0311
Covers: Hants, West Sussex, IoW, Dorset. Specialists in
sport, particularly soccer and cricket.

Masons News Service
Chesterton Mill, French's Road, Cambridge CB4 3NP
Fax 01223-361508   Tel 01223-366996
E-mail: masons.news@dial.pipex.com
News, photographs and TV packages from eastern
England for national and international news outlets.

Mercury Press Agency
The Cotton Exchange, Old Hall St. Liverpool L3 9LQ
Fax 0151-236 2180   Tel 0151-236 6707
E-mail: mercury@livpool.u-net.com
Covers: north west of England and north Wales, with
news, features and pictures.

MAPA
Second Star on the Right, Land of Green Ginger, Hull
HU1 2EA
Fax 01482-589926   Tel 01482-589900
E-mail: Group@MAPA.demon.co.uk
Formerly Mike Ackroyd Press Agency. Covers Hull area
sport. Produces local publications.

National News Press Agency
109 Clifton Street, London EC2A 4LD
Fax 020-7684 3030   Tel 020-7684 3000
E-mail: national.news@dial.pipex.com
Court and general news and features in London and the
south east. Picture syndication to 25 countries.

New Zealand Press Association
12 Norwich Street, London EC4A 1EJ
Fax 020-7583 3563   Tel 020-7353 5430
E-mail: kippyb@hotmail.com
The co-operatively owned national news agency.

Newsflash Scotland
Viewfield Chambers, Viewfield Place, Stirling FK8 1NQ
Fax 01786-446145   Tel 01786-477310
E-mail: newsflash@dial.pipex.com
3 Grosvenor Street, Edinburgh EH12 5ED
Fax 0131-225 9009   Tel 0131-226 5858
E-mail: newsflashed@dial.pipex.com
Scotland's leading news, features and picture agency.

Press Association
PA News Centre, 292 Vauxhall Bridge Road,
London SW1V 1AE
Fax 020-7963 7192   Tel 020-7963 7000/7146
Pictures: 020-7963 7155
Teletext: 020-7963 7241
Marketing: 020-7963 7511
Website: www.pressassociation.press.net
The Press Association is the national news agency of
the UK and the Republic of Ireland. Its shareholders
include Trinity-Mirror, UN&M, News International
and the Daily Mail and General Trust. Operating 24
hours a day, 365 days a year, PA is the UK's leading
supplier of news and sports editorial, photographs,
weather and listings to the print, broadcast and
electronic media.
PA maintains a news library of over 15 million
cuttings and a photo library of over 6 million pictures.

PA Belfast
Queen's Buildings, 10 Royal Avenue, Belfast, BT1
1DB
Fax 028-9043 9246   Tel 028-9024 5008
E-mail: deric@pa.press.net
PA Birmingham
1st Floor, Charles House, 148/149 Great Charles
Street, Birmingham B3 3HT
Fax 0121-212 3350   Tel 0121-212 3225
PA Bristol
3rd Floor, 66 Queens Road, Clifton, Bristol BS81RE
Fax 0117-922 0493   Tel 0117-922 0560

PA Cardiff
11 Brynawelon Road, Cardiff CF2 6QR3
Fax 029-207 64213   Tel 029-207 64211
PA Dublin
41 Silchester Road, Glenageary, Dublin
Fax 00 353 1 28 04221   Tel 00 353 1 28 00936
PA East Anglia
3 Edieham Cottages, Angle Lane, Shepreth,
Royston SG8 6QJ
Fax 01763 262638   Tel 01763 262638
PA Exeter
143 Sweetbriar Lane, Exeter Devon EX1 3AP
Fax 01392 431166   Tel 01392 431166
PA Glasgow
124 Portman Street, Kinning Park, Glasgow G41
1EJ
Fax 0141-429 1596   Tel 0141-429 0037
PA Liverpool
PO Box 48, Old Hall Street, Liverpool L69 3EB
Fax 0151-472 2411   Tel 0151-472 2548
PA News - Leeds
PA NewsCentre, Central Park, New Lane, Leeds
LS11 5DZ
Fax 0113-244 0758   Tel 0113-234 4411
PA Manchester
5th Floor, 33 Piccadilly, Manchester M1 1LQ
Fax 0161-228 7331   Tel 0161-228 7717
PA Southampton
11 Wembley Way, Fair Oak, Hampshire SO5 7JN
Fax 023- 806 92015   Tel 023- 806 92015

News Team International
Albany House, Hurst Street, Birmingham B5 4BD
Fax 0121-666 6370   Tel 0121-346 5511
Website: www.newsteam.co.uk
News, pictures and features from West Midlands and
Manchester areas. Syndicates for Midland Independent
Newspapers, Manchester Evening News and others.
North Scot Press Agency
18 Adelphi, Aberdeen AB11 5BL
Fax 01224-212163   Tel 01224-212141
News, features and picture coverage of Grampian and
North of Scotland.
North Wales Press Agency
157 High Street, Prestatyn, Denbighshire LL19 9AY
Fax 01745-855534   Tel 01745-852262
North West News & Sports Agency
148 Meols Parade, Meols, Merseyside CH47 6AN
Fax 0151-632 5484   Tel 0151-632 5261
Covers: Wirral and Birkenhead, mainly court and sport.
Northants Press Agency
28 Hunter Street, Northampton, Northants NN1 3QD
Fax 01604-638008   Tel 01604-638811
E-mail: steve.scoles@northantspress.co.uk
Northants and sourrounding counties. News, features,
TV and digital picture desk. Corporate communication
and design.

Northern Ireland Information Service
Block B, Castle Buildings, Stormont, Belfast BT4 3SG
Fax 028-9052 8473   Tel 028-9052 0700
11 Millbank, London SW1P 4QE
Fax 020-7210 0254   Tel 020-7210 3000
Website: www.nio.gov.uk
Government information service.
Nottingham News Service
8 Musters Road, West Bridgford, Nottingham NG3
7PL
Fax 0115-982 2568   Tel 0115-982 1697
Novosti
See Russian Information Agency
Orbit News Service
1 Froghall Lane, Warrington, Cheshire WA2 7JJ
                              Tel 01925-631592
E-mail: orbit@cwcom.net
Website: www.orbit.news.mcmail.com
News and picture service in Cheshire and South
Manchester.
Page One
11 West Avenue,West Bridgford, Nottingham NG2 7NL
Fax 0115-981 3133   Tel 0115-981 8880
E-mail: news@pageonemedia.com
E-mail: pictures@pageonemedia.com
Website: www.pageonemedia.com
Central and east Midlands. Features, news, photos,
online photo library, tv filming and editing facilities.

Parliamentary & EU News Service
19 Douglas Street, London SW1P 4PA
Fax 020-7821 9352   Tel 020-7233 8283
E-mail: pnspublications@btinternet.com
News on Parliament and the EU.

Press Agency (Gatwick)
1a Sunview Valley, Peacehaven, Sussex BN10 8PJ
Fax 01273-589112   Tel 01273-583103
Covers: Gatwick Airport and surrounding area.

Press Gang News
137 Endlesham Road, London SW12 8JN
Fax 020-8673 3205   Tel 020-8673 4229
News, features, and investigations for London and

Press Team Scotland
Unit 53 Fountain Business Centre, Ellis Street,
Coatbridge ML5 3AA
Fax 01236-440066   Tel 01236-440077
Covers: Gatwick Airport and surrounding area.

Quicksilver Media
St George Street, Leicester LE1 9FQ
Fax 0116-251 2151   Tel 0116-253 0022
E-mail: news@quicksilvermedia.co.uk
Provides national and international news, sport. and
pictures to 33 regional papers. UK News has reciprocal
arangements with subscriber newspapers, giving it
access to the work of hundreds of journalists. It also has
lobby journalists based at the House of Commons.

Raymonds Press Agency
Gower Street, Derby DE1 1SD
Fax 01332-386036   Tel 01332-340404
E-mail: ako@raymonds.demon.co.uk
Covers: Central and east Midlands. One of the largest
regional agencies. Provides news, sport, photo and
feature coverage.

Reuters
See TV and Radio News Agencies

Russian Information Agency - Novosti
3 Rosary Gardens, London SW7 4NW
Fax 020-7244 7875   Tel 020-7370 1162/3002
E-mail: ria@novosti.co.uk
Website: www.rian.ru
Russian news and information service/photo library.

SNS
15 Fitzroy Place, Glasgow G3 7RW
Fax 0141-221 3595   Tel 0141-221 3602
E-mail: info@snspix.com
Sport and corporate photos.

Samuels News & Photo Service
71 Stafford Road, Uttoxeter, Staffs ST14 8DW
Fax 01889-567181   Tel 01889-566996

Saudi Press Agency
18 Cavendish Square, London W1M 0AQ
Fax 020-7495 5074   Tel 020-7495 0418/9

Scarborough News/Ridings Press Agency
19 Hall Garth Lane, Scarborough YO13 9JA
Fax 01723-865054   Tel 01723-863395
News, features, rural, sport and PR.

Scase News Service
Congham, Kings Lynn, Norfolk PE32 1DR
Fax 01485-600672   Tel 01485-600650
E-mail: news@scase.co.uk
Website: www.scase.co.uk
Covers: East Anglia and specialises in news, royal news
and features.

Scottish Office Information Directorate
St Andrews House, Edinburgh EH1 1DG
Fax 0131-244 1721   Tel 0131-244 2709
Website: www.scotland.gov.uk
Government information service.

Scottish News Agency
99 Ferry Road, Edinburgh EH6 4ET
Fax 0131-478 7327   Tel 0131 478 7711
E-mail: scotnews@sol.co.uk
10 FVictoria Road, Dundee DD1 1JN
Fax 01382-907700   Tel 01382-907790
Scottish news and sports pictures.

Seven Day Press
132 West Nile Street, Glasgow G1 2RQ
Fax 0141-572 0265   Tel 0141-572 0060
E-mail: daypress@aol.com
Sports agency based in Scotland. News and features
and covers every senior football game.

Shrewsbury Press Service
1a Victorian Arcade, Hills Lane, Shrewsbury, Salop
SY1 1PS
Fax 01743-247701   Tel 01743-352710
Covers: Shropshire.

Sirius Media Services
Green Farm, Harleston, Stowmarket, Suffolk IP14 3HW
Fax 01449-736894   Tel 01449-736889
E-mail: grnfarm@globalnet.co.uk
Provides a range of editorial features, particularly
crosswords, puzzles and quizzes.

Smith Davis Press
8 Westport Road, Stoke-on-Trent, Staffs ST6 4AW
Fax 01782-812428   Tel 01782-812311
E-mail: smith-davis@smith-davis.co.uk
Provides press agency, PR and contract pubishing
services.

Solent News & Photo Agency
21 Castle Way, Southampton SO14 2BW
Fax 023-8023 2983   Tel 023-8022 3217
Covers: Hants, IoW, Wilts and Dorset.

Solo
49-53 Kensington High Street, London W8 5ED
Fax 020-7938 3165   Tel 020-7376 2166
E-mail: solosyndicationltd@btinternet.com
Features and news from Associated Newspapers, The
European, News Limited of Australia. Also archive
library of three million photos including 12,000
Spanish images.

Somerset News Service
43-44 High Street, Taunton, Somerset TA1 3PW
Fax 01823-332862   Tel 01823-331789
Covers: Somerset, south west. News and digital pictures
with mobile transmission. Also PR and research.

South Bedfordshire News Agency
134 Marsh Road, Luton, Beds LU3 2NL
Fax 01582-493486   Tel 01582-572222
E-mail: south.b@virgin.net
Covers: Herts, Beds and Bucks.

South Coast Press Agency
22 St Peters Road, Bournemouth, Dorset BH1 2LE
Fax 01202-554937   Tel 01202-290199
Covers: Dorset and surrounding counties.

South West News Service
Media Centre, Emma-Chris Way, Abbeywood Office
Park, Filton, Bristol BS34 7JU
Fax 0117-906 6501   Tel 0117-906 6500
E-mail: news@swns.com
Website: www.swns.com
Covers: West Country and South Wales.

South Yorkshire Sport
6 Sharman Walk, Apperknowle, sheffield S18 4BJ
Fax 01246-414767   Tel 01246-414767
E-mail: nicksportl@aol.com
Sports, news and features in the south Yorkshire
region. Written and broadcast, specialises in football.

Space Press
Bridge House, Blackden Lane, Goostrey, Cheshire
CW4 8PZ
Fax 01477-535756   Tel 01477-534440/
                     01477-533403 (24 hours)
E-mail: scoop2001@aol.com.uk
Covers: Cheshire & surrounding counties, news,
features, photos.

Spanish News Agency (EFE)
299 Oxford Street, 6th Floor, London W1R 1LA
Fax 020-7493 7314   Tel 020-7493 7313
E-mail: agenciaefe@btconnect.com
The news agency for Spain and Latin America.

Steve Hill Agency
12 Steep Hill, Lincoln LN2 1LT
Fax 01522 569571   Tel 01522 569595
Covers: Lincolnshire & surrounding counties, news,
features, photos.

Stewart Bonney News Agency
17 St Peter's Wharf, Newcastle-on-Tyne NE6 1TZ
Fax 0191-275 2609   Tel 0191-275 2600
E-mail: www.photography@stevehill.u-net.com
St Peter's Wharf, Newcastle-upon-Tyne NE6 1TZ
North east England, supplying news, features, photos.

Strand News Service
226 The Strand, London WC2R 1BA
Fax 020-7936 2689   Tel 020-7353 1300
General coverage.

Tass/Itar
320 Regent Street, London W1R 5AB
Fax 020-7580 5547   Tel 020-7580 5543
London office of the Russian news agency.

Teespress Agencies
15 Baker Street, Middlesbrough, Teeside TS1 2LF
Fax 01642-880744   Tel 01642-880733
Covers: Teesside, North Yorkshire, South Durham.

Tim Wood Agency
11 Village Way, Dulwich, London SE21 7AN
Fax 020-7236 8136   Tel 020-7248 6858
Covers: London courts, including Old Bailey.

Torbay News Agency
45 Lymington Road, Torquay, Devon TQ1 4BG
Fax. 01803-214557   Tel 01803-214555
Covers: Torbay and south Devon.

United Press International (UPI)
2 Greenwich View, Millharbour, London E14 9NN
Fax 020-7538 1051   Tel 020-7675 9967
Covers: Middle East, business, sport, features, news and
political events.

Two-Ten News Network
210 Old Street, London EC1V 9UN
Fax 020-7490 1255   Tel 020-7490 8111
E-mail: info@twoten.press.net
Website: www.twoten.press.net
Transmits news and feature stories direct onto
journalists' screens in 220 newsrooms around the UK.

Wales News Service
Womanby Street, Cardiff CF1 2UD
Fax 029-2066 4181   Tel 029-2066 6366
Covers: Wales and the West.

Warwickshire News & Picture Agency
41 Lansdowne Crescent, Leamington Spa,
Warwickshire CV32 4PR
Fax 01926-424760   Tel 01926-424181
Covers: Warwickshire and West Midlands.
Features, investigations and photographic services.

Watson's Press Agency
103 Adelaide Street, Blackpool, Lancs FY1 4LU
Fax 01253-623996   Tel 01253-623996
Covers: Lancashire and South Cumbria.The agency
specialises in local news, sport and feature work.

Welsh Office - Information Division
Cathays Park, Cardiff CF1 3NQ
Fax 029-2082 5508   Tel 029-2082 5648
E-mail: webmaster@wales.gov.uk
Website: www.wales.gov.uk
Government communications agency.

Wessex News & Features Agency
108 High Street, Hungerford, Berkshire RG17 0NB
Fax 01488-684463   Tel 01488-686810
E-mail: news@britishnews.co.uk
           features@britishnews.co.uk
Website: www.britishnews.co.uk
News, features, photos covering England and Scotland.

West Riding News & Sports Service
Field House, Wellington Road, Dewsbury, West
Yorkshire WF13 1HF
Fax 01924-437564   Tel 01924-437555
Supplies news and features from Huddersfield, Halifax
and Dewsbury. Specialises in soccer and rugby league.

Xinhua News Agency of China
8 Swiss Terrace, Belsize Road, London NW6 4RR
Fax 020-7722 8512   Tel 020-7586 8437
E-mail: xinhua@easynet.co.uk
Covers: foreign and domestic affairs.

Yaffa Newspaper Service
Suite 305-7, 29 Gt Pulteney Street, London W1R 3DD
Fax 020-7439 7318   Tel 020-7437 5133
E-mail: john@yaffa.co.uk
UK representatives of US syndication King Features.

Picture agencies and libraries

KEY CONTACTS

British Association of Picture Libraries and Agencies (BAPLA)
18 Vine Hill, London EC1R 5DX
Fax 020-7713 1211   Tel: 020-7713 1780
E-mail: bapla@bapla.demon.co.uk
Website: www.bapla.org.uk
BAPLA is the trade association representing 350 picture libraries and agencies and provides a referral service for image research. Publishes the industry magazine Light Box, and an annual directory. BAPLA assesses many industry issues including copyright clearance, ethics, pricing, marketing and technology.

British Institute of Professional Photography
Fox Talbot House, Amwell End, Ware, Herts SG12 9HN
Fax 01920-487056   Tel 01920-464011
E-mail: bipp@compuserve.com
Website: www.bipp.com
Founded in 1901, this is the UK's qualifying body for professional photographers. It publishes the magazine The Photographer ten times a year., and the annual Directory of Professional Photography with details of over 3,000 members.

Council of Photographic News Agencies
Oak Trees, Burrows Lane, Guildford, Surrey GU5 9QF
Fax 01483-203378   Tel 01483-203378
Represents UK's 6 largest press agencies/photo libraries.

Picture Research Association
5a AlvanleyGardens, London NW6 1JD
Fax 020-7431 9887   Tel 020-7431 9886
                        01883-730123
E-mail: pra@pictures.demon.co.uk
Professional body for all those involved in supplying visual material to all forms of the media. It promotes professional standards and provides a forum for the exchange of information. It publishes a quarterly magazine, monthly newsletter and Freelance Register.

Picture Researchers Handbook
by Hilary & Mary Evans; Pira International
Fax 01372-377526   Tel 01872-802074
The standard reference book to picture sources

Ace Photo Agency
Satellite House, 2 Salisbury Road, Wimbledon, London SW19 4EZ
Fax 020-8944 9940   Tel 020-8944 9944
E-mail: info@acestock.com
Website: www.acestock.com
A wide-ranging colour photo library with material on many subjects.

Action Images
Image House, Station Road, London N17 9LR
Fax 020-8267 2035   Tel 020-8885 3000
E-mail: reception@actionimagescom
Website: www.actionimages.com
Sports pictures with UK and international coverage.

Action Plus
54 -58 Tanner Street, London SE1 3PH
Fax 020-7403 1526   Tel 020-7403 1558
E-mail: info@actionplus.co.uk
Sports library covering over 300 professional and amateur sports worldwide.

Adams Picture Library
156 New Cavendish Street, London W1M 7FJ
Fax 020-7436 7131   Tel 020-7636 1468
E-mail: cadams52@hotmail.com
Contains the work of more than 500 photographers.

The Advertising Archives
45 Lyndale Avenue, London NW2 2QB
Fax 020-7794 6584   Tel 020-7435 6540
E-mail: library@advertarchives.force9.co.uk
Website: www.advertising archives.co.uk
Collection of US and British press ads and magazine covers. Official UK agents for Saturday Evening Post artwork including Norman Rockwell cover illustrations.

Aerofilms
Gate Studios, Station Road, Borehamwood, Herts WD6 1EJ
Fax 020-8207 5433   Tel 020-8207 0666
E-mail: library@aerofilms.com
Aerial photography with library, 1.75 million images, dating back to 1919.

AKG London
5 Melbray Mews, 158 Hurlingham Road, London SW6 3NS
Fax 020-7610 6125   Tel 020-7610 6103
Website: www.akg-london.co.uk
London representative of the large Berlin picture library AKG and the Erich Lessing Archive of Fine Art and Culture, Vienna. Specialists in arts and history.

Alan Jones Photos
10 Pelwood Road, Camber, E Sussex TN31 7RU
                        Tel 01797-225448
Covers: Sussex and Kent. Has ISDN facilities.

Allsport (UK)
3 Greenlea Park, London SW19 2JD
Fax 020-8648 5240   Tel 020-8685 1010
E-mail: lmartin@allsport.co.uk
Website: www.allsport.com
The world's largest specialist sports library, represented in 27 countries. Has over six million images, dating from 1880.

Alpha Photographic Press Agency
63 Gee Street, London EC1V 3RS
Fax 020-7250 1149   Tel 020-7608 2796
E-mail: alphapress@compuserve.com
International photo feature agency and picture library
specialising in celebrities.

Andes Press Agency
26 Padbury Court, London E2 7EH
Fax 020-7739 3159   Tel 020-7613 5417
E-mail: photos@andespress.demon.co.uk
Covers social, religious, political, economic and
environmental issues around the world, especially in
Latin America.

Apex Photo Agency
Priests Court, Main Road, Exminster, Exeter EX6 8AP
Fax 01392-824155   Tel 01392-824024
E-mail: apex@apex-photos.co.uk
Website: www.apex-photos.co.uk

Aquarius Picture Library
PO Box 5, Hastings, East Sussex TN34 1HR
Fax 01424-717704   Tel 01424-721196
E-mail: aquarius.lib@clara.net
Over 1 million film stills, current and archival, dating
back to silent days. Also TV, vintage pop, some opera
and ballet.

Ardea London
35 Brodrick Road, London SW17 7DX
Fax 020-8672 8787   Tel 020-8672 2067
E- mail: ardea@ardea.co.uk
Wildlife, pets and the environment, worldwide.

Assignments Photographers
1Quaker Court, School Road, Norwich, NR10 4QL
Fax 01603-754767   Tel 01603-754254
ISDN: 01603-754466
E-mail: assignments@paston.co.uk
East Anglia based, corporate design and editorial.

Associated Sports Photography/Headline
21 Green Walk, Leicester LE3 6SE
Fax 0116-231 1123   Tel 0116-232 0310
E-mail: headline/asp@dial.pipex.xom
Website: www.sporting-heroes.net
National and international coverage. Has ISDN
facilities on 0116-232 5900.

ATP
1st Floor, Maverdine Chambers, 26 Westgate Street,
Gloucester GL1 2NG
Fax 01452-330966   Tel 01452-330966
                      07775-556610
E-mail: atpphoto@aol.com
News, sport and feature pictures on digital and film in
Gloucestershire and surrounding counties.

Australia Pictures
38 Carmac Road, Twickenham TW2 6NU
Fax 020-8898 0150   Tel 020-8898 0150
All aspects of Australia (travel, culture, underwater,
tourism). Also Africa, Middle East, Asia.

Autograph
5/25 Scrutton Street, London EC2A 4LP
Fax 020-7729 9400   Tel 020-7739 1777
E-mail: info@auto.demon.co.uk
Website: www.autograph-abp.co.uk

Barnaby's Picture Library
19 Rathbone Street, London W1P 1AF
Fax 020-7637 4317   Tel 020-7636 6128
E-mail: barnabyspicturelibrary@ukbusiness.com
Webs: www.ukbusiness.com/barnabyspicturelibrary/
A library of over 4 million colour transparencies, b/w
prints. The coverage is worldwide and historic.

Barnardo's Film & Photographic Archive
Tanners Lane, Barkingside, Essex IG6 1QG
Fax 020-8550 0429   Tel 020-8550 8822
500,000 photos dating from 1871, film from 1905,
covering the work of the UK's largest children's charity.

Barratts Photopress
63 Gee Street, London EC1V 3RS
Fax 020-7250 1149   Tel 020-7336 0632
E-mail: alphapress@compuserve.com
Has ISDN facilities.

BBC News Stills
Rm B250, TV Centre, Wood Lane, London W12 7RJ
Fax 020-8576 7020   Tel 020-8576 0690
E-mail: picture.desk@bbc.co.uk
Stills covering a wide range of news, stock subjects,
personalities and locations. Many images are held
digitally and ISDN facilities are available.

BBC Photograph Library
Rm B116, TV Centre, Wood Lane, London W12 7RJ
Fax 020-8746 0353   Tel 020-8225 7193
Programme stills, mainly comedy, drama and light
entertainment dating back to 1924,

Beken Maritime Services
16 Birmingham Road, Cowes, Isle of Wight PO31 7BH
Fax 01983-291059   Tel 01983-297311
E-mail: beken@beken.co.uk
Website: www.beken.co.uk
Sailing and boating form 1888 to the present day. Old
and new pictures of yachts, liners, tallships, racing etc.

The Bridgeman Art Library
17-19 Garway Road, London W2 4PH
Fax 020-7792 8509   Tel 020-7727 4065
E-mail: info@bridgeman.co.uk
Website: www.bridgeman.co.uk
A specialist source of the world's finest paintings,
drawings, manuscripts, sculpture, antiques and
antiquities; catalogue, research service, web catalogue.

British Film Institute
21 Stephen Street, London W1P 2LN
Fax 020-7323 9260   Tel 020-7957 4797
E-mail: istills.films@bfi.org.uk
Website: www.bfi.org.uk
Holds 7 million pictures recording the history of
cinematography and includes, film, TV and portraits.

British Library Reproductions
British Library, 96 Euston Road, London NW1 2DB
Fax 020-7412 7771   Tel 020-7412 7614
E-mail: bl-repro@bl.uk
Website: portico.bl.uk/repro/
12 million books and 5 million other items can be
photographed to order. A 'browsable' picture library
service is now available.

Bruce Coleman Collection
16 Chiltern Business Village, Arundel Road, Uxbridge, Middlesex UB8 2SN
Fax 01895-467959   Tel 01895-467990
E-mail: ilibrary@brucecoleman.co.uk
Website: www.brucecoleman.co.uk
Specialists in wildlife and travel. Free catalogue.

Bulletin International Video Library
5-8 Hardwick Street, London EC1R4RG
Fax 020-7278 6349   Tel 020-7278 6070
E-mail: info@bulletin-intl.com
Website: www.bulletin.com
Recent stock footage of industry, commerce, medicine, leisure, locations; mainly UK, Europe and Asia.

Calyx Multimedia
41 Churchward Avenue, Swindon SN2 1NJ
Fax: 01793-513640   Tel 01793-520131
E-mail: calyx@compuserve.com
Covers: Wiltshire + M4 corridor. Pics, features, PR.

Camera Press
21 Queen Elizabeth Street, London SE1 2PD
Fax 020-7278 5126   Tel 020-7378 1300
Website: www.camerapress.com
Long-established picture agency. Subjects include royals, celebrities, travel. Photographers include Karsh, Lichfield, Snowdon and Beaton. Has ISDN facilities.

Capital Pictures
49-51 Central Street, London EC1V 8AB
Fax 020-7253 1414   Tel 020-7253 1122
E-mail: post@capital pictures.demon.co.uk
Specialises in celebrity and personality photos. Also an extensive film stills collection.

Centrepix
20 Coleshill Road, Water, Orton B46 1SH
Fax 0121-608 6777   Tel 0121-608 6777/6888

Cephas Picture Library
157 Walton Road, East Molesey, Surrey KT8 0DX
Fax 020-8224 8095   Tel 020-8979 8647
E-mail: mickrock@cephas.co.uk
Website: www.cephas.co.uk
Wine and vineyards of the world, spirits, beers and ciders, 100,000+ images. Also food and drink archive.

Christian Aid Photo Library
PO Box 100, London SE1 7RT
Fax 020-7620 0719   Tel 020-7523 2235
E-mail: jcabon@christian-aid.org
Website: www.christian-aid.org.uk
Social pictures on community programmes in Africa, Asia and Latin America.

Collections
13 Woodberry Crescent, London N10 1PJ
Fax 020-8883 9215   Tel 020-8883 0083
E-mail: collections@btinternet.com
Website: www.btinternet.com/~collections
The life and landscape of the British Isles and Ireland, including the familiar, the obscure and the curious.

Colorific!
Innovation Centre, 225 Marsh Wall, London E14 9FX
Fax 020-7538 3555   Tel 020-7515 3000
E-mail: colorific@visualgroup.com
Specialises in celebrity images/portraiture, news, reportage and travel features. Historic archive from the 1940s and film stills.

Colorsport
44 St Peters Street, London N1 8JT
Fax 020-7226 4328   Tel 020-7359 2714
E-mail: c-sporthq@aol.com
Extensive library of sport photos, including football and cricket history. All other sports date from late 1960s to the present. Has ISDN facilities.

Comstock
21 Chelsea Wharf, 15 Lots Road, London SW10 0QJ
Fax 020-7352 8414   Tel 020-7351 4448
                                        00800-266786 25
E-mail: info@comstock.co.uk
Website: www.comstock.co.uk
General library with over 5 million pictures. Free catalogues and CD-Roms. Digital and transparencies, rights protected and royalty free picturesavailable.

David Hoffman Photo Library
21 Norman Grove, London E3 5EG
Fax 020-8980 2041   Tel 020-8981 5041
E-mail: lib@hoffmanphotos.demon.co.uk
Website: www.hoffmanphotos.demon.co.uk
Social issues. Policing, drugs, riots, protest, housing, environmental issues. Range of images from UK, Europe, US, Americas and Thailand. General files cover topical issues with many specialist files.

David King Collection
90 St Pauls Road, London N1 2QP
Fax 020-7354 8264   Tel 020-7226 0149
Photos, posters and ephemera covering political/cultural history of Russia, USSR, China, Spanish civil war. Communist leaders. Gulag. Collection of Stalinist falsifications. 250,000 images.

David Williams Picture Library
50 Burlington Avenue, Glasgow G12 0LH
Fax 0141-337 3031   Tel 0141-339 7823
Specialist Collections of Scotland and Iceland. Smaller collections of Faroe Islands, France, Spain, Canary Islands, Czech Republic, Hungary, Portugal and Western USA. Commissions undertaken, catalogue.

Dobson Photo Agency
26 Franklin Street, Scarborough, North Yorkshire YO12 7JU
Fax 01723-363661   Tel 01723-363661
E-mail: pix@dobsonagency.co.uk
Website: www.dobsonagency.co.uk
Covers: Yorkshire coast. Press and PR photographers, broadcast video and 40 year picture library

Ecoscene
The Oasts, Headley Lane, Passfield, Liphook, Hants GU30 7RX
Fax 01428-751057   Tel 01428-751056
E-mail: sally@ecoscene.com
Website: www.ecoscene.com
80,000 images on the environment, natural history, industry, energy, conservation and recycling.

Eminent Management & Production
The Old Truman Brewery, 91 Brick Lane, London E1 6QL
Fax 020-7247 4712   Tel 020-7247 4750
Website: www.eminentmanagement.co.uk
Organisation of photoshoots and management of fifteen photographers of celebrities.

Empics Sports Photo Agency
26 Musters Road, W Bridgford, Nottingham NG2 7PL
Fax 0115-840 4445   Tel 0115-840 4444
E-mail info@empics.co.uk
Website: www.empics.co.uk
International sports photo agency. covering major sports events. Online access to over 350,000 images. ISDN facilities.

Environmental Investigation Agency Photo Library
2nd Floor, 69-85 Old Street, London EC1V 9AX
Fax 020-7490 0436   Tel 020-7490 7040
E-mail: info@eia-international.org
Website: www.eia-international.org
Library following the charity's campaigns. Most pictures cover endangered subjects (wild birds, rhinos, whales, tigers, elephants, forests and wildlife trade).

Environmental Images
23c Woodstock Road, London N4 3ET
Fax 020-7263 0168   Tel 020-7263 6608
E-mail: environmentalimages@compuserve.com
Website: www.environmentalimages.com
Specialises in environmental issues. From road protests to climate change. 60,000 colour images.

ffotograff
10 Kyveilog Street, Cardiff CF11 9JA
Fax 029-2022 9326   Tel 029-2023 6879
E-mail ffotograff@easynet.co.uk
Website: www.
cf.ac.uk/ccin/main/buscomm/ffotogra/ffoto1.html
Photolibrary, specialising in travel, exploration and the arts and covering the Middle, Far East, and Wales. ISDN

Forest Life Picture Library
231 Corstorphine Road, Edinburgh EH12 7AT
Fax 0131-314 6285   Tel 0131-314 6411
E-mail: n.campbell@forestry.gov.uk
Official image bank of the Forestry Commission. It has comprehensive coverage of tree species, forests, woodland landscapes, timber production and a collection of wildlife and recreation images.

Format Photographers
19 Arlington Way, London EC1R 1UY
Fax 020-7833 0381   Tel 020-7833 0292
E-mail: format@formatphotogs.demon.co.uk
Social documentary library and agency. Includes: education, health, disability, religion and women. UK and abroad. Archive from 70's. Colour and b/w.

Francis Frith Collection
Frith's Barn, Teffont, Salisbury, Wiltshire SP3 5QP
Fax 01722-716881   Tel 01722-716376
E-mail: sales@francisfrith.com
Website: www.francisfrith.com
4,000 British towns and villages taken between 1860 and 1970. Has ISDN facilities.

Frank Spooner Pictures
16-16a Baldwins Gardens, London EC1N 7US
Fax 020-7632 5828   Tel 020-7632 5800
Large general photo library representing Gamma (Paris), for current international material and Roger Viollet for historic. Has ISDN facilities.

Gaze International
39-41 North Road, London N7 9DP
Fax 020-7697 8334   Tel 020-7697 8333
E-mail: info@gaze.co.uk
Website: www.gaze.co.uk
Picture library covers all aspects of gay, lesbian and transgender life and culture for editorial, reportage, features, ad campaigns and health promotions.

GeoScience Features Picture Library
6 Orchard Drive, Wye, Kent TN25 5AU
Fax 01233-812707   Tel 01233-812707
E-mail: gsf@geoscience.demon.co.uk
Website: www.geoscience.co.uk
Specialist source of worldwide earth sciences and natural history. Over 330,000 pictures.

Greenpeace UK
Canonbury Villas, London N1 2PN
Fax 020-7865 8200   Tel 020-7865 8294
Emaiil: photolibrary@uk.greenpeace.org
Website: www.greenpeace.org/gpimages
Holds approximately 60,000 photos of campaigns and environmental issues.

Greg Evans International Photo Library
6 Station Parade, Sunningdale, Ascot, Berks SL5 0EP
Fax 020-7637 1439   Tel 020-7636 8238
E-mail: greg@gregevans.net
Website: www.gregevans.net
Comprehensive colour photo library.

Guardian/Observer Photo Service
119 Farringdon Road, London EC1R 3ER
Fax 020-7837 1192   Tel 020-7713 4423
International syndication service for all Guardian pictures and for the pre-1989 Observer archive library. Has ISDN facilities.

Hulton-Getty
21-31 Woodfield Road, London NW9 2BA
Fax 020-7266 3154   Tel 020-7266 2662
E-mail: info@getty-images.com
Website: www.hultongetty.com
The Hulton Getty Picture Collection is part of Getty Images. It is one of the world's greatest picture libraries, covering nearly all topics and periods. The overall archive holds more than 50 special collections, including Picture Post, Keystone, Fox, Central Press, Evening Standard and Ernst Haas.

Hutchison Picture Library
118b Holland Park Avenue, London W11 4UA
Fax 020-7792 0259   Tel 020-7229 2743
E-mail: library@hutchinsonpic.demon.co.uk
Over 600,000 worldwide documentary colour transparencies. Subjects include: agriculture, energy, families, industry, landscape, transport and weather.

The Image Bank
17 Conway Street, London W1P 6EE
Fax 020-7391 9111   Tel 020-7312 0300
E-mail: tiblon@theimagebank.com
Webste: www.imagebank.co.uk
The world's largest source for the full range of contemporary and archive photography, illustration and film footage

Image Bank, Manchester
4 Jordan Street, Manchester M15 4PY
Fax 0161-236 8723   Tel 0161-236 9226
Image Bank, Scotland
57 Melville Street Street, Edinburgh EH3 7HL
Fax 0131-225 1660   Tel 0131-225 1770
Image Bank, Ireland
11 Upper Mount Street, Dublin 2
Fax 3531-676 0873   Tel 3531-676 0872
E-mail: tiblon@theimagebank.com
Website: www.imagebank.co.uk

ICCE Photo Library
Burcott House, Wing, Leighton Buzzard LU7 0JW
Fax 01296-688245   Tel 01296-688245
E-mail: icceplib@aol.com
Founded by the International Centre for Conservation Education. specialises in wildlife, habitats, conservation and environmental issues worldwide;.
Illustrated London News Picture Library
20 Upper Ground, London SE1 9PF
Fax 020-7805 5905   Tel 020-7805 5585
E-mail: iln.pictures@seacontainers.com
News images from 1842 onwards. Covers all aspects of history; industrial, social and political.
Images of Africa Photobank
11 The Windings, Lichfield, Staffs WS13 7EX
Fax 01543-417154   Tel 01543-262898
E-mail: info@imagesofafrica.co.uk
Website: www.imagesof africa.co.uk
Wide range of subjects covering 14 African countries from Egypt to South Africa. Excellent on wildlife, habitat, national parks, tourism and traditional peoples.
Impact Photos
26-27 Great Sutton Street, London EC1V 0DX
Fax 020-7608 0114   Tel 020-7251 5091
E-mail: library@impactphotos.demon.co.uk
Worldwide images covering all aspects of daily life.
Imperial War Museum
Photograph Archive, All Saints Annex, Austral Street, London SE11 4SL
Fax 020-7416 5355   Tel 020-7416 5333/5338
E-mail: photos@iwm.org.uk
Website: www.iwm.org.uk
National archive of more than six million photos dealing with 20th century warfare, especially the two world wars.
In-Focus
Sitwell Centre, Scarborough, N Yorks YO12 5EX
Fax 01723-503749   Tel 01723 501904
E-mail: picdesk@in-focus.co.uk
Web: www.in-focus.co.uk
Sport, politics, royals and celebrities. 50,000 images.
Insight ACR
10 Lambs Conduit Passage, London WC1R 4RH
Fax 020-7419 7777   Tel 020-7419 0171
E-mail: solutions@insight-visual.com
Website: www.insight-visual.com
Represents photographers working in the advertising, corporate and commercial sectors. Specialist areas include people, reportage, landscape and cars.

Insport International
Home Farm Cottage, Church Lane, Church Langton, Market Harborough LE16 7SX
Fax 01858-545492   Tel 01858-545492
E-mail: INSPORT@compuserve.com
Website: www.indport-pics.co.uk
Picture agency and library covering sporting events.
ITN Archive
200 Grays Inn Road, London WC1X 8XZ
Fax 020-7430 4453   Tel 020-7430 4480
E-mail: archive.sales@itn.co.uk
Website: www.itnarchive.com
Material that spans the century from the ITN and Reuters archives and the historic French Pathé library.
ITV Sport Archive
London Television Centre, Upper Ground, London SE1 9LT
Fax 020-7827 7634   Tel 020-7261 3064
E-mail: iitvsportarchive@lnn-tv.co.uk
Contains approximately 55,000 tapes of sports events shown on the ITV network from the 1960s to the present.
Janine Wiedel Photolibrary
8 South Croxted Road, London SE21 8BB
Fax 020-8761 1502   Tel 020-8761 1502
The photojournalist's coverage of contemporary society.
John Frost Historical Newspaper Service
8 Monks Avenue, New Barnet , Herts EN5 1DB
Fax 020-8440 3159   Tel 020-8440 3159
Over 65,000 British and overseas newspapers, and 100,000 cuttings, relating to outstanding events from 1640 to the present.
Julian Cotton Photo Library
see Powerstock Zefa
Katz Pictures
Zetland House, 5-25 Scrutton Street, London EC2A 4HJ
Fax 020-7613 1274   Tel 020-7377 5888
E-mail: katzpictures@katzpictures.com
Website: www.katzpictures.com
International photo agency and library covering many topics, including personalities, news and current affairs.
Kevin Fitzpatrick Photography
40 Woodville Drive, Sale, Cheshire M33 6NF
Fax 0161-962 9441   Tel 0161-969 2709
E-mail: fitzpix-munch@zoom.co.uk
Covering the northwest from south Manchester. News, features, library and wire facilities.

THE DEFINITIVE NEWSREEL ARCHIVE

AND

TV-am news

BRITISH MOVIETONEWS LIMITED
DENHAM MEDIA PARK, DENHAM, ENGLAND   UB9 5HQ
PHONE: 44 (0)1895 833071   FAX: 44 (0)1895 834893
EMAIL: library@mtone.co.uk   WEBSITE: www.movietone.com

Kobal Collection
4th Floor, 184 Drummond Street, London NW1 3HP
Fax 020-7383 0044   Tel 020-7383 0011
Collection of 1 million movie images including portraits and scene stills in colour and b&w, from 1895 to the present.

Lebrecht Collection
58b Carlton Hill, London NW8 0ES
Fax 020-7625 5341   Tel 020-7625 5341
E-mail: pictures@lebrechtmusiccollection.co.uk
Website: www.lebrechtmusiccollection.co.uk
Images of classical music, painting, photographs from early antiquity to post minimalism.

London Metropolitan Archives
40 Northampton Road, London EC1R 0HB
Fax 020-7833 9136   Tel 020-7332 3820
E-mail: ima@ms.corpotlondon.gov.uk
Half a million photos covering the history and topography of the London area. Run by the Corporation of London.

MacQuitty International Collection
7 Elm Lodge, Stevenage Road, London SW6 6NZ
Fax 020-7385 5606   Tel 020-7385 5606
E-mail: miranda.macquitty@btinternet.com
Library of 250,000 photos on social life and culture in over seventy countries dating back to the 1920s. Also some archive film.

Magnum Photos
5 Old Street, London EC1V 9HL
Fax 020-7608 0020   Tel 020-7490 1771
E-mail: magnum@magnumphotos.co.uk
Website: www.magnumphotos.com
International agency and library for leading photo-journalists. Over one million photos cover all aspects of C20 life from the 1936 Spanish Civil War onwards.

Mary Evans Picture Library
59 Tranquil Vale, London SE3 0BS
Fax 020-8852 7211   Tel 020-8318 0034
E-mail: lib@mepl.co.uk
Website: www.mepl.co.uk
Historical pictures, visual documentation of major events and decorative material for design purposes, includes prints, engravings and ephemera.

McKenzie Heritage Picture Archive
Unit 226, Station House, 49 Greenwich High Road, London SE10 8JL
Fax 020-8469 2000   Tel 020-8469 2000
E-mail: info@mckenziehpa.com
Website: www.mckenziehpa.com
Specialises in generic images of African, Caribbean and Asian communities in Britain and abroad.

Military Picture Library
28a Station Road, Aldershot, Hants GU11 1HT
Fax 01252 350546   Tel 01252-350547
E-mail: info@mpli.co.uk
Website: www.mpl1.co.uk

Mirror Syndication International
1 Canada Square, Canary Wharf, London E14 5AP
Fax 020-7293 2712   Tel 020-7266 1133
E-mail: desk@mirrorpix-com
Website: www.mirpix.com

Monitor Syndication
17 Old Street, Clerkenwell, London EC1V 9HL
Fax 020-7250 0966   Tel 020-7253 7071
Picture agency/large library specialising in personalities from 1959. Also personality file 1870-1930, music hall, theatre; file on Lotus cars and personalities from 1964.

Motoring Picture Library
John Montagu Building, Beaulieu, Brockenhurst, Hampshire SO42 7ZN
Fax 01590-612655   Tel 01590-614656
E-mail: nmmt@compuserve.com
Nearly 1,000,000 motoring related images.

Museum of London Picture Library
London Wall, London EC2Y 5HN
Fax 020-7600 1058   Tel 020-7814 5604/5605
E-mail: picturelib@museumoflondon.org.uk
Website: www.museumoflondon.org.uk
London views and life illustrated through paintings, drawings, historic photographs and exhibitions.

National Maritime Museum
Park Row, Greenwich, London SE10 9NF
Fax 020-8312 6533   Tel 020-8312 6631/6704
Website: www.nmm.ac.uk
Photos and other visual material covering all maritime topics as well as the Greenwich sites. CD rom available.

National Monuments Record
National Monuments Record Centre, Kemble Drive, Swindon, Wilts SN2 2GZ
Fax 01793-414606   Tel 01793-414600
E-mail info@rchme.co.uk
Website: www.english-heritage.co.uk
English Heritage's collection of aerial photos, pictures of historic buildings, and archaeological sites.

National Museum of Photography
See: Science and Society Picture Library

National Railway Museum
Leeman Road, York, North Yorks YO26 4XJ
Fax 01904-611112   Tel 01904-621261
E-mail: nrm@nmsi.ac.uk
Website: www.nrm.org.uk
4.5 million images relating to all aspects of railway life.

National Remote Sensing Centre
Arthur Street, Barwell, Leicestershire LE9 8GZ
Fax 01455-841785   Tel 01455-849227
E-mail: data-services@nrsc.co.uk
Website: www.nrsc.co.uk
UK's largest archive of satellite and aerial photography.

Neil Setchfield Travel Picture Library
Croft Street, Surrey Quays, London SE8 5DW
Fax 020-7394 9246   Tel 020-7394 9246
E-mail: neil@setchfield.com
Website: www.setchfield.com
Images of major cities and travel destinations of the world, including a comprehensive collection of London.

Network Photographers
4 Nile Street, London N1 7RF
Fax 020-7490 3643   Tel 020-7490 3633
E-mail: ilibrary@networkphotographers.xom
Website: www.networkphotographer.com
Group of photojournalists which represents Rapho (Paris) and Bilderberg (Hamburg). Has a library which includes social documentary, travel and feature stories.

Novosti Photo Library
3 Rosary Gardens, London SW7 4NW
Fax 020-7244 7875   Tel 020-7370 1873
E-mail: photos@novosti.demon.co.uk
Website: www.rian.ru
Russian photo agency with archive and current material.

Nunn Syndication Library
193 Fleet Street, London EC4A 2AH
Fax 020-7405 7688   Tel 020-7242 5544
E-mail: enquiries@nunn-syndication.com
Website: www.nunn-syndication.com
British and European royal families and celebrities.

Olympic Television Archive Bureau
Axis Centre, Burlington Lane, London W4 2TH
Fax 020-8233 5354   Tel 020-8233 5353
E-mail: jsieck@imgworld.com
Website: www.otab.com
Archive library of Olympic sporting history.

PA News Photo Library
PA NewsCentre, 292 Vauxhall Bridge Road, London SW1V 1AE
Fax 020-7963 7066   Tel 020-7963 7000
E-mail: photo-sales@pa.press.net
Over five million news sport and entertainment pictures from the 1890s to the present day.

Pacemaker Press International
787 Lisburn Road, Belfast, N Ireland BT9 7EX
Fax 028-9068 2111   Tel 028-9066 3191
All Ireland, covering news, sport, politics, current affairs and PR. Picture library.

Panos Pictures
1 Chapel Court, Borough High St, London SE1 1HH
Fax 020-7357 0094   Tel 020-7234 0010
E-mail: pics@panos.co.uk
Website: www.panos.co.uk
Documentary library specialising in Third World and Eastern European photography.

Parachute Pictures
1 Castelnau, Barnes, London SW13 9RP
                          Tel 020-8748 1445
E-mail: info@parachute.co.uk
Website: www.parachute.co.uk
Specialist Third World photo and documentary footage library with coverage of narcotics, human rights, children at risk, development issues and World music.

Pearson Television Stills Library
Teddington Studios, Broom Road, Teddington, Middlesex TW11 9NT
Fax 020-8614 2250   Tel 020-8781 2789
E-mail: stills.library@pearsontv.com
Website: www.pearsontvarchive.com
Library stores and sells around 1 million programmes stills from Thames, Grundy and Alomo productions. Archive research, duplication and private sales.

Photofusion
17A Electric Lane, London SW9 8LA
Fax 020-7738 5509   Tel 0171 738 5774
E-mail: library@photofusion.org
Website: www.photofusion.org
All aspects of contemporary life in Britain, particularly social issues. Photographers available for commission.

Photonews Scotland
36 Washington Street, Glasgow G3 8AZ
Fax 0141-572 1019   Tel 0141-248 4888
Picture, news and feature agency. Has ISDN facilities.

Picture House Photography
West Leam, Station Road, Baildon, W Yorks BD17 6HS
Fax 01274-531058   Tel 01274-531058
E-mail: wilkinson@picture-house.freeserve.co.uk

Pictor International
30-31 Lyme Street, London NW1 0EE
Fax 020-7267 1396   Tel 020-7482 0478
E-mail: info@london.pictor.co.uk
Website: www.pictor.com
International library with a collection of contemporary and creative stock photography.

Popperfoto
The Old Mill, Overstone, Northampton NN6 0AB
Fax 01604-670635   Tel 01604-670670
E-mail: Popperfoto@msn.com
Website: www.popperfoto.com
One of Britain's leading picture libraries, home to over 13 million images covering 150 years of photographic history. Collections include photos from Reuters, HG Ponting, AFP and Bob Thomas Sports Photography.

Powerstock Zefa
Unit G10, 59 Chilton Street, London E2 6EA
Fax 020-7729 7476   Tel 020-7729 7473
E-mail: info@powerstockzefa.com
Web: www.powerstockzefa.com
Lifestyle, business, finance and industry images.

The Press Features Syndicate
9 Paradise Close, Eastbourne, Sussex BN20 8BT
                          Tel 01323-728760
International photo-feature agency and picture library.

Professional Sport
18-19 Shaftesbury Quay, Hertford SG14 1KF
Fax 01992-505020   ISDN 01992-505000
E-mail: pictures@prosport.co.uk
Website: www.prosport.co.uk

Public Record Office Image Library
Ruskin Avenue, Kew, Surrey TW9 4DU
Fax 020-8392 5266   Tel 020-8392 5225
E-mail: image-library@pro.gov.uk
Website: www.pro.gov.uk/imagelibrary/
Historical images, wartime posters, Victorian photos, politics, royalty, transport and more from the National Archive. Free brochure and CD rom

RAF Museum
Grahame Park Way, Hendon, London NW9 5LL
Fax 020-8200 1751   Tel 020-8205 2266
E-mail: rafmus@dircon.co.uk
Website: www.rafmuseum.org.uk
Archive of military aviation. Written requests only.

Retrograph Nostalgia Archive
164 Kensington Park Road, London W11 2ER
Fax 020-7229 3395   Tel 020-7727 9378
E-mail: retropixl@aol.com
Website: www.Retrograph.com
Specialist picture library/design source of worldwide nostalgia.Posters, labels, magazine advertising (1860-1960). RetroTravel has worldwide travel/tourism images (1900-1960).

Rex Features
18 Vine Hill, London EC1R 5DZ
Fax 020-7696 0974   Tel 020-7278 7294
E-mail: rex@rexfeatures.com
Large international picture agency and photo library, strong on news, personalities and features. Represents over 1,500 photographers. Several million images covering news, personalities and features. Also handles some newspaper and magazine syndication. Features and organic library.

Robert Harding Picture Library
58-59 Great Marlborough St, London W1V 1DD
Fax 020-7631 1070   Tel 020-7478 4000
E-mail: info@robertharding.com
Website: www.robertharding.com
Over 2 million photos on all topics. Full E-commerce website, free registration and downloads for comps.

Royal Geographical Society Picture Library
1 Kensington Gore, London SW7 2AR
Fax 020-7591 3061   Tel 020-7591 3060
E-mail: pictures@rgs.org
Website: www.rgs.org/picturelibrary
Archive specialising in geographical and explorational activity from 1830 to the present day (including moving footage). For commercial and academic use.

Royal Photographic Society Picture Library
The Octagon, Milsom Street, Bath BA1 1DN
Fax 01225-469880   Tel 01225-462841
E-mail: piclib@collection.rps.org
Website: www.rpspictures.com
Over 250,000 images from the history of photography.Subject areas include: travel, portraits,war, landscapes, still-lifes and architecture. The RPS also arranges many exhibitions, lectures, seminars and workshops.

RSPCA Photolibrary
Causeway, Horsham, West Sussex RH12 1HG
Fax 01403-241048   Tel 01403-223150
E-mail: photolibrary@rspca.org.uk
Animal welfare, wildlife and natural history.

Sally and Richard Greenhill
357 Liverpool Road, London N1 1NL
Fax 020-7607 7151   Tel 020-7607 8549
E-mail: library.greenhill@shadow.org.uk
Website: www.shadow.org.uk/photoLibrary
Social documentary photos from cardle to grave, also China 1971 to present.

Science Photo Library
327-329 Harrow Road, London W9 3RB
Fax 020-7286 8668   Tel 020-7432 1100
E-mail: info@sciencephoto.com
Website: www.sciencephoto.com
Specialises in pictures of science, technology, earth, space and nature. Over 120,000 images.

Science and Society Picture Library
Exhibition Road, London SW7 2DD
Fax 020-7942 4401   Tel 020-7942 4400
E-mail: piclib@nmsi.ac.uk
Website: www.nmsi.ac.uk/piclib
Pictures from the collections of three major museums: the Science Museum, York's National Railway Museum and Bradford's National Museum of Photography, Film and Television. The latter's stock includes important collections (Frith, Fox Talbot, Sutcliffe, Herschel, Daily Herald Archive, etc).

Scottish Highland Photo Library
Croft Roy, Crammond Brae Tain, Ross-shire, Scotland IV19 1JG
Fax 01862-892298   Tel 01862-892298
E-mail: shpl@call.co.uk
Website: www.cali.co.uk/freeway/shpl
Images of the Highlands and Islands of Scotland.

Scottish Media Newspapers Picture Library
195 Albion Street, Glasgow G1 1QP
Fax 0141-553 2642   Tel 0141 553 3209
E-mail: iwatson@cims.co.uk
6 million Scottish photos from 1900 onwards,.

SIN
Unit 4, 2 Somerset Road, London N17 9EJ
Fax 020-8808 1821   Tel 020-8808 8660
E-mail: 101457.1516@compuserve.com
Website: www.sin-photo.co.uk
Rock and pop, and youth culture.

Skyscan Photolibrary
Oak House, Toddington, Cheltenham, Glos GL54 5BY
Fax 01242-621343   Tel 01242-621357
E-mail: info@skyscan.co.uk
Website: www.skyscan.co.uk
Collection of 'balloon's-eye' views of Britain, now extended to cover aircraft, international air to ground photography, aerial sports, in fact anything aerial.

SOA Photo Agency
87 York Street, London W1H 1DU
Fax 020-7258 0188   Tel 020-7258 0202
E-mail: info@soaphotoagency.com
Website: www.soaphotoagency.com
Specialising in funny photos, avant garde images and imagery from and about Germany.

Sport & General Press Agency
63 Gee Street, London EC1V 3RS
Fax 020-7250 1149   Tel 020-7336 0632
E-mail: alphapress@compuserve.com
One of Britain's oldest press photo libraries, specialising in sport, also general news stock. Allied to London News Service.

Sporting Pictures (UK)
7A Lambs Conduit Passage, London WC1R 4RG
Fax 020-7831 7991   Tel 020-7405 4500
E-mail: photos@sportingpictures.demon.co.uk
Website: www.sportingpictures.com
International library of over 3 million pictures

Sportsphoto
20 Clifton Street, Scarborough, N Yorks YO12 7SR
Fax 01723-500117   Tel 01723-367264
E-mail: stewart@sportsphoto.co.uk
Website: www.sportsphoto.co.uk
Established agency covering sport, entertainment, politicians and royals at national and international level.

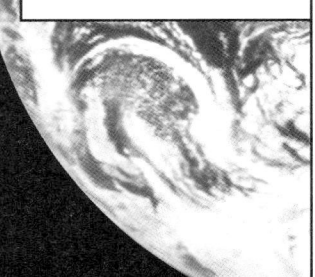

Steve Hill Photography
12 Steep Hill, Lincoln LN2 1LT
Fax 01522-569571   Tel 01522-569595
E-mail: www.photography@stevehill.u-net.com
Lincolnshire-based national and international
photographic service with ISDN facilities.

Stewart Ferguson Photography
11 Moredun Vale Grove, Edinburgh EH17 7QZ
Fax 0131-664 6614   Tel 0131-664 6614
Press and features covering all Scotland.

Still Moving Picture Co
67a Logie Green Road, Edinburgh EH7 4HF
Fax 0131-557 9699   Tel 0131-557 9697
E-mail: stillmovingpictures@compuserve.com
Website: www.stillmovingpictures.com
250,000 images of Scotland including Scottish Tourist
Board's collection. Free CD rom browser.

Still Pictures Whole Earth Photo Library
199 Shooters Hill Road, London SE3 8UL
Fax 020-8858 2049   Tel 020-8858 8307
E-mail: stillpictures@stillpic.demon.co.uk
Website: www.stillpictures.com
Key source on people and the environment, the Third
World and nature. Includes industry and agriculture.

Swift Imagery
The Old Farmhouse, Hexworthy, Yelverton, Devon
PL20 6SD
E-mail: swift@eurobell.co.uk
Worldwide travel, social documentary and lifestyle.

Sygma
12 Regent's Wharf, All Saints Street, London N1 9RL
Fax 020-7713 8770   Tel 020-7841 9696
E-mail: london@sygmaltd.demon.co.uk
Website: www.sygma-london.co.uk
London office of the large French photographic agency,
specialising in news, featues, showbusiness and
personalities. Sygma has access to the historical
archives of L'illustration and Keystone Paris.

Syndicated Features
PO Box 33, Edenbridge, Kent TN8 5PB
Fax 01342-850244   Tel 01342-850313
E-mail: admin@topfoto.co.uk
Website: www.topfoto.co.uk
A weekly general and showbiz features service available
by post or internet.

Topham Picturepoint
PO Box 33, Edenbridge, Kent TN8 5PB
Fax 01342-850244   Tel 01342-850313
E-mail: admin@topfoto.co.uk
Website: www.topfoto.co.uk
General agency and library, with over seven million
pictures. Includes UPI'scollection from 1932-1970.

Travel Ink Photo & Feature Library
The Old Coach House, 14 High Street, Goring-on-
Thames, Berkshire RG8 9AR
Fax 01491-875558   Tel 01491-873011
E-mail: info@travel-ink.co.uk
Website: www.travel-ink.co.uk
All aspects of travel images and information.
Worldwide coverage. From classic picture postcard
material to cultures, lifestyles and realism.

Tropix
156 Meols Parade, Meols, Wirral CH47 6AN
Fax 0151-632 1698   Tel 0151-632 1698
E-mail: tropixphoto@talk21.com
Website: www.merseyworld.com/tropix/
Positive images of developing nations. Also collection of
Liverpool and NW England.

TWI Archive
Axis Centre, Burlington Lane, London W4 2TH
Fax 020-8233 5301   Tel 020-8233 5300
E-mail: twiarchive@imgworld.com
Website: www.twiarchive.com
Sports images as well as historic scenic and cultural
stockshots from around the globe.

United Northern Photographers
2-4 Lower Green, Baildon, Bradford BD17 7NE
Fax 01274 425555   Tel 01274 412222
E-mail: picturedesk@unp.co.uk
Website: www.photodrone.com
Providing ditorial/reportage photography for national
press and PR firms.

Universal Pictorial Press & Agency
29-31 Saffron Hill, London EC1N 8SW
Fax 020-7421 6006   Tel 020-7421 6000
Archive for British and international personalities from
1944 to the present. Digital archive with ISDN facilities.

Waterways Photo Library
39 Manor Court Road, London W7 3EJ
Fax 020-8567 0605   Tel 020-8840 1659
E-mail: watphot39@aol.com
Britain's inland waterways, architecture, boats, holidays.

Wellcome Centre for Medical Science
210 Euston Road, London NW1 2BE
Fax 020-7611 8577   Tel 020-7611 8588
E-mail: photolib@wellcome.ac.uk
Website: www.wellcome.ac.uk
Over 150,000 images covering the history of medicine
and human culture, from ancient times to the present.

Wessex Photos
108 High Street, Hungerford, Berkshire RG17 0NB
Fax 01488-684463   Tel 01488-686810
E-mail: pictures@britishnews.co.uk
Website: www.britishnews.co.uk
Photos for newspapers, magazines and PR.

Windrush Photos
99 Noahs Ark, Kemsing, Kent TN15 6PD
Fax 01732-763285   Tel 01732-763486
Extensive wildlife and landscape collection, specialising
in birds, worldwide coverage.

Woodfall Wild Images
17 Bull Lane, Denbigh, Denbighshire LL16 3SN
Fax 01745-814581   Tel 01745-815903
E-mail: wwimages@btinternet.com
Website: www.woodfall.com
Landscape, environment, conservation, agriculture and
wildlife collection with worldwide coverage.

Cuttings agencies

The Newspaper Licensing Agency gathers copyright revenue from organisations that copy and fax newspaper articles. Some charities and schools are exempted.

The NLA was launched in January 1996 by a number of national newspapers including the Guardian and in October 1997 News International joined other newspaper publishers as members. "NI's participation means that companies and other organisations will be able to buy a single licence covering all national newspapers," said Guy MacNaughton, the NLA managing director.

The NLA represents the publications listed below and has granted photocopying licences to the agencies opposite:

KEY CONTACT

Newspaper Licensing Agency
Lonsdale Gardens, Tunbridge Wells, Kent TN1 1NL
Fax 01892-525275   Tel 01892-525274
Licensing   Tel 01892-525273
E-mail: copy@nla.co.uk
Website: www.nla.co.uk
National newspapers: Daily Mail, Mail on Sunday, Evening Standard, Express, Sunday Express, Daily Star, Financial Times, Mirror, Sunday Mirror, People, Daily Telegraph, Sunday Telegraph, Independent, Independent on Sunday, Guardian, Observer, Times, Sunday Times, Sun, NoW
Other publications: The European, Press & Journal (Aberdeen), International Herald Tribune, The Scotsman, Scotland on Sunday, Daily Record, Sunday Mail, The Sunday Mercury (Birmingham), The Birmingham Post, Birmingham Evening Mail, The Coventry Evening Telegraph, Grimsby Evening Telegraph, The Sentinel (Stoke), Hull Daily Mail, Leicester Mercury, Western Morning News, South Wales Evening Post, Nottingham Evening Post, Derby Evening Telegraph, Scunthorpe Evening Telegraph, Yorkshire Post, Yorkshire Evening Post, The Star (Sheffield, Barnsley, Doncaster, Rotherham editions), Manchester Evening News, Sunday Business, Western Gazette, Evening Post (Bristol), Western Daily Press, Lancashire Evening Post.

CUTTINGS AGENCIES

A-Line-Aberdeen
86 Hilton Drive, Aberdeen AB24 4NL
Fax 01224 276010   Tel 01224 484661
E-mail: info@a-line.co.uk
Specialist in oil and gas service only.

AC NielsenMMS
Tey House, Market Hill, Royston, Herts SG8 9JN
Fax 01763-245151   Tel 01763-248828
E-mail: sales@marketmovements.com
Website: www.marketmovements.com
Specialist monitoring for financial services companies.

CIS Information Services
73 Farringdon Road, London EC1M 3JQ
Fax 020-7242 5887   Tel 020-7242 5886
E-mail: cisinfo@compuserve.com
Website: www.cisclip.com

Clipability
Chapel Allerton Centre, 108 Harrogate Road, Leeds LS7 4NY
Fax 0113-268 7981   Tel 0113-269 3290
E-mail: info@clipability.co.uk
Website: www.clipability.co.uk

Clipserver.com
Newsserver House, Singer Street, London EC2A 4BQ
Fax 020-7959 1201   Tel 020-7959 1200
E-mail: info@clipserver.com
Website: www.clipserver.com

Cutting It Fine
Unit 24, River Road Business Park, Barking, Essex IG11 0EA
Fax 020-8591 5866   Tel 020-8507 0999
E-mail: info@cuttingitfine.com
A celebrity and personalities press cuttings service.

Durrants Press Cuttings
Discovery House, 28-42 Banner Street, London EC1Y 8QE
Fax 020-7674 0222   Tel 020-7674 0200
E-mail: contact@durrants.co.uk
Website: www.durrants.co.uk
Media monitoring - press cuttings (high speed national, regional consumer and trade service) broadcast service.

Energy Data Services
200 Great Dover Street, London SE1 4WU
Fax 020-7407 0765   Tel 020-7407 0764
E-mail: edsnews@hubcom.com

Entertainment Press Cuttings Agency
Unit 7, Lloyds Wharf, Mill Street, London SE1 2BD
Fax 020-7237 3388   020-7237 1712

Financial Times Information
89 Worship Street, London EC2A 2BE
Fax 020-7377 6103   020-7377 1742

House of Cuttings
Media House, 66 Sayes Court Road, Orpington, Kent
BR5 2PQ
Fax 01689-810050   Tel 01689-817000
E-mail: alison@hocl.com
Website: www.hocl.com
National, regional, consumer and trade press cuttings.

JHA Research Consultancy
9 Parkwood Road, London SW19 7AQ
Fax 020-8287 3492   Tel 020-8241 3355
E-mail: jharcscon@msn.com

International Press Cuttings Bureaux
224-236 Walworth Road, London SE17 1JE Road,
London SW19 7AQ
Fax 020-701 4489   Tel 020-7708 2113
E-mail: ipcb2000@aol.com

McCallum Media Monitor
Tower House, 10 Possil Road, Glasgow G4 9SY
Fax 0141-333 1811   Tel 0141-333 1822
E-mail: press_clips@cqm.co.uk
Website: www.press-cuttings.com
Website: www.press-clips.com

Media Shadowfax Europe
10 Barley Mow Passage, London W4 4PH
Fax 020-8994 9888   Tel 020-8994 6477
Music press cuttings agency.

NewsIndex
151 Farringdon Road, London EC1R 3AF
Fax 020-7833 4747   Tel 020-7833 866
E-mail: inquiries@newsindex.co.uk
Tailored summaries and press cuttings by fax/e-mail
from 6.30 am.

Paperclip Partnership
Unit 9, The Ashway Centre, Elm Crescent, Kingston-
upon-Thames, Surrey KT9 6HH
Fax 020-8547 1646   Tel 020-8549 4857
E-mail: paperclip.partnership@btinterrnet.com

Precise Press Cuttings
200 Great Dover Street, London SE1 4WU
Fax 020-7378 6565   Tel 020-7357 0808
E-mail: info@precise-press.co.uk
Website: www.precise-press.co.uk

Press Cutting Partnership
5 Hillgate Street, London W8 7SP
Fax 020-7727 8558   Tel 020-7229 7796
Fashion and home furnishing press cuttings.

Press Data Bureau
7 Easter Road, Edinburgh EH7 5AN
Fax 0131-656 7201   Tel 0131-656 7200
E-mail: info@pres-data.com
Website: www.press-data.com

Press Express
53-56 Great Sutton Street, London EC1V 0DE
Fax 020-7251 1412   Tel 020-7689 0123
E-mail: press.express@romeike.com
Website: www.press-select.co.uk
National dailies, key regionals, internationals and
business mags delivered by 7am seven days a week.

Press Select
1st Floor, Chaucer House, White Hart Yard, London
SE1 1NX
Fax 020-7403 4371   Tel 020-7278 4433
E-mail: info@press-select.co.uk
Website: www.press-select.co.uk
IT and telecommunications press cuttings.

PressScan
18 Picardy Place, Edinburgh EH1 3JT
Fax 0131-557 8737   Tel 0131-557 9020
E-mail: press.scan1@virgin.net

Romeike & Curtice
Hale House, 290-296 Green Lanes, London N13 5TP
Fax 020-8882 6716   Tel 020-8882 0155
E-mail: sales@romeike & Curtice
Website: www.romeike.com
Covers a comprehensive range of consumer and trade
titles.

Smith Willis Communications
The Bond, 18-20 Fazeley Street, Birmingham B5 5SE
Fax 0121-608 0073   Tel 0121-608 0077

Strata Matrix
23-25 North Parade, Aberystwyth, Ceredigion, Dyfed
SY23 2JN
Fax 01970-612774   Tel 01970-625552
E-mail: swyddfa@stratamatrix.co.uk
Website: www.sofres.com

Tellex Monitors
PA News Centre, 292 Vauxhall Bridge Road, London
SW1V 1AE
Fax 020-7963 7622   Tel 020-7963 7618
E-mail: kamran.sepehri@tellex.press.net

Publications about the press

PRESS MAGAZINES

The Author
84 Drayton Gardens, London SW10 9SB
Fax: 020-7373 5768   Tel 020-7373 6642
E-mail: authorsoc@writers.org.uk
Website: www.writers.org.uk/society
Publisher: Society of Authors
Editor: Derek Parker
Quarterly news magazine. £7 non-members.

The Bookseller
12 Dyott Street, London WC1A 1DF
Fax 020-7420 6013   Tel 020-7420 6000
Publisher: Whitaker Publishers
E-mail: letters.to.editor@bookseller.co.uk
Website: www.theBookseller.com
Editor: Nicholas Clee
The trade paper of the book industry. It publishes two
annual guides -Spring Books and Autumn Books - with
details of forthcoming titles. £2.50. Editor: Louis Baum.

Books in the Media
12 Dyott Street, London WC1A 1DF
Fax 020-7836 2909   Tel 020-7420 6178
Publisher: Whitaker Publishers
E-mail: t.holmon@whitaker.co.uk
Editor: Tom Holmon
£2.50. Weekly newsletter keeping bookshops and
libraries informed of books appearing in the media.

British Journalism Review
University of Luton Press, University of Luton, LU1 3AJ
Fax 01582-743298   Tel 01582-743297
E-mail: ulp@luton.ac.uk
Publisher: University of Luton Press
Editor: Geoffrey Goodman
Scholarly quarterly for discussion of media topics.

British Printer
Sovereign Way, Tonbridge, Kent TN9 1RW
Fax 01732-377362   Tel 01732-364422
E-mail: rhayes@unmf.com
Website: www.dotprint.com
Publisher: Miller Freeman
Editor: Rod Hayes.
Monthly news and features from the printing industry.

Comagazine
Tavistock Road, West Drayton, Middx UB7 7QE
Fax 01895-433602   Tel 01895-433600
Website: www.comag.co.uk
On-line business to business moonthly.

Communications Law
2 Addiscombe Road, Croydon, Surrey CR9 5AF
Fax 020-8686 3155   Tel 020-8686 9141
E-mail: Rajni_Boswell@tolley.co.uk
Publisher: Butterworth Tolley
6xpa. Journal of computer, media and telecomms law.

Financial Times Newsletters
See Informa Publishing Group

Free Press
8 Cynthia Street, London N1 9JF
Fax 020-8837 8868   Tel 020-7278 4430
E-mail: freepress@cpbf.demon.co.uk
Website: www.cpbf.demon.co.uk
Publisher: CPBF
Editor: Granville Williams.
Journal of the Campaign for Press and Broadcasting
Freedom, with analysis of monoply media ownership
and control, and other issues. 6x pa.

Freelance Market News
7 Dale Street, Manchester M1 1JB
Fax 0161-228 3533   Tel 0161-228 2362
E-mail: fmn@writersbureau.com
Website: www.writersbureau.com
Editor: Angela Cox
£29 for 11 issues. Newsletter with details of markets for
the work of freelance writers. Editor: Angela Cox.

Headlines
7 Sovereign Park, Cleveland Way, Hemel Hempstead,
Herts HP2 7DA
Fax 01442-219641   Tel 01442-233656
E-mail: gary@cullumpublishing.co.uk
Website: www.newstech.co.uk
Aimed mainly at the advertising industry, covering all
the regional and local papers.

Index on Censorship
33 Islington High Street, London N1 9LH
Fax 020-7278 1878   Tel 020-7278 2313
E-mail: contact@indexoncensorship.org
Website: www.indexoncensorship.org
Editor: Judith Vidal-Hall
International magazine for free speech, with interviews,
reportage and debates on the important issues of the
day. Paperback format. 6x pa.

Informa Publishing Group
69-77 Paul Street, London EC2A 4LQ
Fax 020-7553 1100   Tel 020-7553 1000
Website: www.informa.com
Recently acquired the media-related newsletters,
magazines, reports and directories previously produced
by Financial Times Business.

Journalism Studies
PO Box 25, Abingdon, Oxfordshire OX14 3UE
Fax 01235-401550   Tel 01235-401000
E-mail: enquiries@tandf.co.uk
Website: www.tandf.co.uk/journals
Publisher: Routledge Journals/Taylor & Francis
Quarterly, academic journal published in cooperation
with the European Journalism Training Association.

The Journalist
314 Grays Inn Road, London WC1X 8DP
Fax 020-7837 8143   Tel 020-7278 7916
E-mail: acorn.house@nuj.org.uk
Publisher: National Union of Journalists
For NUJ members. 6x pa.

Journalist's Handbook
1/4 Galt House, 31 Bank Street, Irvine KA12 0LL
Fax 01294-311322   Tel 01294-311322
E-mail: jh@carrickmedia.demon.co.uk
Publisher: Carrick Media
Quarterly journal with articles and a contacts list.
Editor: Fiona MacDonald.

Magazine News
Queens House, 28 Kingsway, London WC2B 6JR
Fax 020-7404 4167   Tel 020-7404 4166
Website: www.ppa.co.uk
Publisher: Periodical Publishers Association
Mainly for advertisers and agencies. 5x pa.

Media Lawyer
3 Broom Close, Broughton in Furness, Cumbria LA20 6JG
Fax 01229-716621   Tel 01229-716622
A newsletter for editors, reporters, media lawyers, trainers, and all concerned with media law. Bi-monthly. £36 pa.

Media Week
Quantum House, 19 Scarbrook Road, Croydon, Surrey CR9 1LX
Fax 020-8565 4394   Tel 020-8565 4200
E-mail: mweeked@qpp.co.uk
Website: www.mediaweek.co.uk
Editor: Patrick Barrett
Weekly. News on advertising. £1.85.

New Media Age
50 Poland Street, London W1V 4AX
Fax 020-7943 8168   Tel 020-7970 4000
E-mail: nma.info@centaur.co.uk
Website: www.nma.co.uk
Editor: Mike Butcher.
£2.95. Business weekly for advertising, marketing and e-commerce.

New Media Investor
50 Poland Street, London W1V 4AX
Fax 020-79743 8168   Tel 020-7970 4000
E-mail: jamesw@centaur.co.uk
Website: www.nma.co.uk
Specialist fortnightly newsletter for investment opportunities in digital media.

Newsline
11 Angel Gate, City Road, London EC1V 2SD
Fax 020-7689 0500   Tel 020-7689 0600
E-mail: publishing@newtrade.co.uk
Website: www.worldofmagazines.co.uk
Publisher: Newtrade Publishing
Editor: Mike Stanton
Monthly magazine for members of the National Federation of Retail Newsagents.

PrePress News
93-99 Upper Richmond Road, London SW15 2TG
Fax 020-8788 2302   Tel 020-8780 7800
E-mail: prepressnews@forme.com
Website: www.forme.com
Publisher: Forme Communications
Editor: Bryan Denyer
News. reviews and features relating to print production.

Press Gazette
19 Scarbrook Road, Croydon, Surrey CR9 1LX
Fax 020-8565 4395   Tel 020-8565 4200
E-mail: pged@qpp.co.uk
Website: www.pressgazette.co.uk
Publisher: Quantum Publishing
Editor: Philippa Kennedy.
£1.90. The old UK Press Gazette. A weekly paper for all journalists with a concentration on newspapers and magazines, plus coverage of television and radio.

PrintWeek
174 Hammersmith Road, London W6 7JP
Fax 020-8267 4455   Tel 020-8267 4397
E-mail: printweek@haynet.com
Publisher: Haymarket
The UK's largest circulation printing industry weekly, covering all sectors of the trade. Editor: Jo Francis.

Printing Industries
11 Bedford Row, London WC1R 4DX
Fax 020-7405 7784   Tel 020-7915 8300
E-mail: info@bpif.org.uk
Website: www.bpif.org.uk
Publisher: British Printing Industries Federation
The printers management journal (also known as Pi), published 10x pa.

Printing World
Sovereign Way, Tonbridge, Kent TN9 1RW
Fax 01732-377552   Tel 01732-364422
E-mail: printing.world@unmf.com
Website: www.dotprint.com
Publisher: Miller Freeman Publishers
Weekly covering all aspects of the printing industry and its personalities. Editor: Terry Ulrick. £2.75.

Private Eye
6 Carlisle Street, London W1V 5RG
Fax 020-7437 0705   Tel 020-7437 4017
E-mail: strobes@private-eye.co.uk
Website: www.private-eye.co.uk
Publisher: Pressdram
Fortnightly for journalists. It is one of the few mags which does not depend on ads to survive.

Production Journal
7 Sovereign Park, Cleveland Way, Hemel Hempstead, Herts HP2 7DA
Fax 01442-219641   Tel 01442-233656
E-mail: gary@cullumpublishing.co.uk
Website: www.newstech.co.uk
Newspaper Society monthly since 1958, reviewing newspaper and news media technology.

Professional Printer
Clanricarde Road, Tunbridge Wells, Kent TN1 1PJ
Fax 01892-518028   Tel 01892-538118
E-mail: iop@globalprint.com
Website: www.globalprint.com/uk/iop
Publisher: Institute of Printing
Journal of news and articles. Published 6x pa.

Publishing
111 Upper Richmond Road, London SW15 2TJ
Fax 020-8788 2302   Tel 020-8780 7800
E-mail: forme@forme.com
Publisher: Forme Communications
Editor: Lyndsey Reynolds.
£4.95. Management monthly on issues affecting the newspaper, book and catalogue market.

Publishing News
39 Store Street, London WC1E 7DB
Fax 020-7419 2111   Tel 020-7692 2900
E-mail: mailbox@publishingnews.co.uk
Editor: Rodney Burbeck
The weekly newspaper of the book trade.

Retail Newsagent
11 Angel Gate, City Road, London EC1V 2SD
Fax 020-7689 0500   Tel 020-7689 0600
E-mail: publishing@newtrade.co.uk
Publisher: Newtrade Publishing
Editor: Alexander DesForges
£1.10. Weekly magazine with news, comment and information on the newstrade.

Spokesman
20 Cardigan Road, London E3 5HU
Fax 020-8981 3779   Tel 020-8981 3779
E-mail: spokesman@cwcom.net
Website: www.spokesman.mcmail.com
Quarterly report on media and policy. £120 pa.

TMB Weekly
Islington Business Centre, 14-22 Coleman Fields, London N1 7AE
Fax 020-7688 6637   Tel 020-7688 6638
E-mail: tmb@dircon.co.uk
Publisher: Duvan
Weekly faxed newsletter. Now owned by Duvan.

The Week
5-11 Westbourne Grove, London W2 4UA
Fax 020-7229 0049   Tel 020-7229 0006
E-mail: admin.theweek@dennis.co.uk
Publisher: Dennis Publishing
Editor: John Connell
Weekly. £1.50. A digest of British and foreign press.

Writers News
PO Box 4, Nairn IV12 4HU
Fax 01667-454401   Tel 01667-454441
Publisher: Yorkshire Post Newspapers
Editor: Derek Hudson
Subscription monthly for all writers and would-be writers. also publishes quarterly Writing Magazine.

Writers' Newsletter
430 Edgware Road, London W2 1EH
Fax 020-7706 2413   Tel 020-7723 8074
E-mail: postie@wggb.demon.co.uk
Website: www.writers.org.uk/guild
Publisher: Writers' Guild of Great Britain
Editor: Tom Green
News from the writers' trade union. 6x pa.

PRESS YEARBOOKS

Benn's Media
Riverbank House, Angel Lane, Tonbridge, Kent TN9 1SE
Fax 01732-367301   Tel 01732-377591
E-mail: bennsmedia@unmf.com
Website: www.mfinfo.com
Publisher: Miller Freeman Information Services
Contact: Craig Curtis
3 vols £310, 2 vols £290, 1 vol £145.
Benn's has the most comprehensive listings of the general media directories. It comes in three volumes, covering the UK, Europe and the rest of the world.

The Circulation Report
Islington Business Centre, 14-22 Coleman Fields, London N1 7AE
Fax 020-7688 6637   Tel 020-7688 6638
E-mail: tmb@dircon.co.uk
Publisher: Duvan
Editor: Alan Macfarlane
£145, bi-annual. Also available on disc. Circulation and vital statistics of newstrade magazines.

Directory of Book Publishers, Distributors & Wholesalers
272 Vauxhall Bridge Road, London SW1V 1BA
Fax 020-7834 8812   Tel 020-7834 5477
E-mail: mail@booksellers.org.uk
Website: www.booksellers.org.uk
Publisher: Booksellers Association.
Editor: Sydney Davies
£55. Annual list of UK and Irish book publishers, wholesalers, distributors, sales agents etc.

Directory of Publishing
Wellington House, 125 Strand, London WC2R 0BB
Fax 020-7240 8531   Tel 020-7420 5555
E-mail: vhiggs@continuumboooks.com
Publisher: Continuum
Editor: Verona Higgs
£65. The definitive guide to the book publishing business, with all main publishers, organisations and agencies detailedin the UK and the Commonwealth.

Encyclopedia of the World Press
310 Regent Street, London W1R 5AJ
Fax 020-7636 6982   Tel 020-7636 6627
E-mail: press@fitzroydearborn.deon.co.uk
Web: www.fitzroydearborn.com/london/press.htm
Publisher: Fitzroy Dearborn
Due out in 2001. An illustrated, 2 million word history of the press in 180 countries, its sponsors include the Newspaper Society, the NPA, the World Association of Newspapers and the Freedom Forum. The deadline for entries is the end of 2000.

Freelance Directory
134 Grays Inn Road, London WC1X 8DP
Fax 020-7278 1812   Tel.020-7278 7916
E-mail: nuj@mcr1.poptel.org.uk
Publisher: National Union of Journalists
Editor: Don Mackglew
£35, inc p&p. Biennial directory of 1,200 freelance reporters, photographers, broadcasters, editors, subs, cartoonists and illustrators.

Freelance Photographer's Market Handbook

Focus House, 497 Green Lanes, London N13 4BP
Fax 020-8886 5174   Tel 020-8882 3315
Website: www.thebfp.com
Publisher: Bureau of Freelance Photographers
Editors: John Tracy, Stewart Gibson
£13.95. How to find markets for photographs, mainly with magazines.

IPO Directory

PO Box 30, Weatherby, West Yorkshire LS23 7YA
Fax 01937-541083   Tel 020-7261 8527
E-mail: nds@coi.gov.uk
Publisher: Central Office of Information
Editor: Phil Perry
£13. The official directory of the information and press officers in government departments and public corporations. Bi-annual.

Institute of Printing Handbook

The Mews, Hill House, Clanricarde Road, Tunbridge Wells, Kent TN1 1PJ
Fax 01892-518028   Tel 01892-538118
E-mail: iop@globalprint.com
Website: www.globalprint.com/uk/iop
Editor: Victoria Willan
Technical articles about printing and related industries with a listing of the names and addresses of IOP members. £100 or free to members.

MDB Magazine Directory

33-39 Bowling Green Lane, London EC1R 0DA
Fax 020-7505 8201   Tel 020-7505 8000
E-mail: andrewn@brad.co.uk
Publisher: Emap
Contact: Alan Macfarlane
£17.50 Biannual ad-oriented directory of magazines for sale in British newsagents.

Media Disc

34 Germain Street, Chesham, Bucks HP5 1SJ
Fax 01494-797217   Tel 01494-797200
E-mail: mediadisc@mediainfo.co.uk
Editor: Nick Elliot
Dial up media info on 15,000 titles and contacts. Label and check list service. Subs £200/month.

The Media Guide

Media Relations, Communications Group, Open University, Walton Hall, Milton Keynes MK7 6AA
Fax 01908-652247   Tel 01908-653343/653256
E-mail: press-office@open.ac.uk
Website: www.open.ac.uk
A guide for the media to the expertise of Open University academics.

The Media Guide

You're here.

Media Pocket Book

Farm Road, Henley on Thames, Oxon RG9 1EJ
Fax 01491-418600   Tel 01491 411000
E-mail: info@ntc.co.uk
Publisher: NTC Publications
Editor: Jeff Curtis
£26. Statistical data for all UK media.

National Small Press Centre Handbook

NSPC, BM Bozo, London WC1N 3XX
£12. How to self-publish, from bar codes to distributors.

New Media Companies 21st edition

6-14 Underwood Street, London N1 7JQ
Fax 020-7324 2312   Tel 020-7324 2346
E-mail: bcater@waterlow.com
Website: www.newmediainfo.com
Publisher: Waterlow Publishing
Contact: Bethan Cater
£149 for CD-ROM, print or web format. Lists over 16,000 companies that are active in the multimedia industry worldwide with contact details, description of company, company to company relationships, areas of interest etc.

New Media Titles 21st edition

6-14 Underwood Street, London N1 7JQ
Fax 020-7324 2312   Tel 020-7324 2346
E-mail: bcater@waterlow.com
Website: www.newmediainfo.com
Publisher: Waterlow Publishing
Contact: Bethan Cater
£149 for CD-ROM, print or web format. Comprehensive listing of CD-ROM and DVD titles. Over 32,000 listings in the 2!st edition. Also full contact details and other information on over 3,600 multimedia publishers worldwide, including those active in the DVD sector.

Pims Media Directories

Mildmay Avenue, London N1 4RS
Fax 020-7354 7053   Tel 020-7354 7000
E-mail: prservices@pims.co.uk
Publisher: Pims UK
Editor: Steve Reed
Pims produces a range of detailed, loose-leaf guides to editorial media contacts, all regularly updated, aimed mainly at the public relations sector. Titles include: UK Media Directory (£365 pa), A-Z Towns Directory (£250) USA Directory (£215), European Directory(£205).

PR Newswire Europe Directories

Communications House, 210 Old Street, London EC1V 9UN
Fax 020-7490 1255   Tel 020-7490 8111
E-mail: info@prnewswire.co.uk
Publisher: PR Newswire Europe
Contact: Jason Logan
UK Media - 6 issues pa - £325
UK Media Town by Town - 2 issues pa - £195
European Media - 2 issues pa - £610

Printing Trades Directory

Riverbank House, Angel Lane, Tonbridge,Kent TN9 1SE
Fax 01732-367301   Tel 01732-362666
E-mail: pleegood@unmf.com
Publisher: Miller Freeman
£123. Listing more than 7,300 print related companies (printers, manufacturers and suppliers).

Studies in Newspaper & Periodical History

3 Henrietta Street, London WC2E 8LU
Fax 020-7379 0609   Tel 020-7240 0856
Publisher: Greenwood Publishing
Scholarly look at press history. Formerly published as the Journal of Newspaper and Periodical History.

UK Press Directory - Newspapers
32 South Road, Saffron Walden, Essex CB11 3DN
Fax 01799-502664   Tel 01799 502665
E-mail: showell@ukmd.demon.co.uk
Publisher: Simon Howell
£155 for UK Vol 1, £155 for UK Vol 2, £90 for Republic
of Ireland. Financial profiles, rankings and maps of the
140 leading newspaper publishers in the UK (Vol 1),
100 leading UK subsidiary companies (Vol 2); 40
leading newspaper publishers in the Republic of
Ireland. Also publishes The UK Press Directory -
Consumer Magazines and the UK Press Directory -
Business Magazines.

Ulrich's International Periodicals Directory
Windsor Court, East Grinstead House, East
Grinstead, West Sussex RH19 1XA
Fax 01342-336192   Tel 01342-326972
E-mail: customer.services@bowker-saur.co.uk
Website: www.bowker-saur.co.uk
Publisher: Bowker-Saur
A five volume £395 American guide to the world's
periodicals, detailing approx 200,000 titles.

Willings Press Guide
Harlequin House, 7 High Street, Teddington,
Middlesex, TW11 8EL
Fax 020-8977 1133   Tel 020-8977 7711
E-mail: orders@hollis-pr.co.uk
Website: www.hollis-pr.co.uk
Publisher: Hollis Directories
Contact: John Chambers
Two vols £225. Alphabetical list detailing over 50,000
entries on newspapers and periodicals worldwide.
Available on web or CD for £275/£323.13 inc VAT. CD +
2 vols is £342.50 inc VAT.

Writers' & Artists' Yearbook
35 Bedford Row, London W1CR 4JH
Fax 020-7404 7706   Tel 020-7404 5613
E-mail: writers&artists@acblack.co.uk
Publisher: A & C Black
Contact: Christine Robinson
£12.99.A long-established handbook, mainly for
writers and authors.

Writer's Handbook
25 Eccleston Place, London SW1W 9NF
Fax 020-7881 8001   Tel 020-7881 8000
Website: www.macmillan.co.uk
Publisher: Macmillan
Contact: Claire Robinson.£12.99. A comprehensive
guide covering publishers, publications, broadcasting,
agents, services, prizes, etc.

Press support organisations

MAIN TRADE UNIONS

British Association of Journalists
700 members
Chartered Institute of Journalists
1,500 members
Graphical, Paper and Media Union
200,000 members
National Union of Journalists
29,000 members
Society of Authors
6,000 members

MAIN TRADE ASSOCIATIONS

Newspaper Publishers Association
National papers
Newspaper Society
Local papers
Periodical Publishers Association
Magazines
Scottish Daily Newspaper Society
Scottish dailies and Sundays
Scottish Newspapers Publishers' Association
Scottish regional and local papers

ABC
See Audit Bureau of Circulations

Amalgamated Engineering & Electrical Union (AEEU)
Hayes Court, West Common Road, Bromley, Kent
BR2 7AU
Fax 020-8315 8234   Tel 020-8462 7755
E-mail: j.steed@headoffice.aeeu.org.uk
Website: www.aeeu.org.uk
Formed from the merger of the Amalgamated
Engineering Union and the Electrical, Electronic,
Telecommunications and Plumbing Union. It has
members in newspaper production and broadcasting
and publishes quarterly newspaper Contact.

Advance Media Information
226 Strand, London WC2R 1BA
Fax 020-8 286 2482   Tel 020-8 549 0799
E-mail: ami@easynet.co.uk
Web site: www.amiplan.com
AMI supplies Britain's major news organisations with
a daily-updated list of future events, with access to
extensive background information.

Amnesty International Journalists' Network
99-119 Rosebery Avenue, London EC1R 4RE
Fax 020-7833 1510   Tel 020-7814 6200
E-mail: journos@amnesty.org.uk
Website: www.amnesty.org.uk
Campaigns on behalf of media workers who have been
imprisoned, tortured or threatened with death. Holds
meetings and publishes a quarterly newsletter.

Article 19, The Global Campaign for Free Expression
33 Islington High Street, London N1 9LH
Fax 020-7713 1356   Tel 020-7278 9292
E-mail: info@article19.org
Website: www.article19.org
International human rights organisation campaigning for the right to freedom of expression and information. Promotes improved legal standards for freedom of expression and defends victims of censorship. Publishes twice yearly report and a range of country and theme reports, with emphasis on media freedom.

Association of American Correspondents in London
AP, 12 Norwich Street, London EC4A 1BP
Fax 020-7936 2229   Tel 020-7353 1515
The association represents a broad spectrum of 200 American and Canadian journalists. It was founded in 1919 and holds regular lunches.

Association of British Science Writers
23 Savile Row, London W1X 2NB
Fax 020-7973 3051   Tel 020-7439 1205
E-mail: absw@absw.demon.co.uk
Its aim is to improve standards of science journalism. The association organises meetings with scientists and policy makers, and arranges visits. It publishes a monthly newsletter The Science Reporter.

Association of European Journalists, British Section
20 Cardigan Road, London E3 5HU
                        Tel 020-8981 4691
E-mail: spokesman@cwcom.net
Website: reportingeurope.cwc.net
The association is a network of journalists in all media and exists to improve access to information in Europe. There are 27 national sections and (according to the executive secretary Kevin d'Arcy) "the British section concentrates on private lunches with leading Europeans".

Association of Illustrators
81 Leonard Street, London EC2A 4QS
Fax 020-7613 4417   Tel 020-7613 4328
E-mail: info@a-o-illustrators.demon.co.uk
Website: www.aoi.co.uk
Professional association promoting British illustration and supporting illustrators through membership services. Also campaigns and lobbies. Publishes guides and bi-monthly journal.

Association of Investigative Journalists
Cedar House, 72 Holloway Road, London N7 8NZ
Fax 08700 882845   Tel 0709-121 6085
Website: www.aij-uk.com

Association of Little Presses
25 St Benedict's Close, Church Lane, London SW17 9NX
E-mail: asslp@geocities.com
Website: www.geocities.com/Athens/Oracle/7911
Represents 200 members producing books and magazines on all topics, especially poetry. Publishes newsletter, magazine, Poetry and LittlePress Information bulletins and annual catalogue; organises bookfairs. Does NOT publish any creative writing.

Association of Newspaper & Magazine Wholesalers
Celcon House, 6th Floor, 289-293 High Holborn, London WC1V 7HZ
Fax 020-7405 1128   Tel 020-7242 3458
E-mail: enquiries@anmw.co.uk
Website: www.anmw.co.uk

Association of Photographers
81 Leonard Street, London EC2A 4QS
Fax 020-7739 8707   Tel 020-7739 6669
E-mail: info@aophoto.co.uk
Website: www.aophoto.co.uk
Trade association for professional fashion, advertising, design and editorial photographers. Publishes monthly magazine Image. Holds annual awards and runs own gallery at address above.

Association of Publishing Agencies (APA)
Queen's House, 55-56 Lincoln's Inn Fields, London WC2A 3LJ
Fax 020-7404 4166   Tel 020-7404 4167
E-mail: info@apa.co.uk
Website: www.apa.co.uk
Trade body for customer magazine industry, providing research, training, events and marketing support. It aims to promote awareness of customer magazines as a marketing medium and to act as a central source of information. Affiliated to the PPA.

Association of UK Media Librarians
PO Box 14254, London SE1 9WL
                        Tel 020-7813 6105
Website: www.aukml.org.uk
A network of information professionals keeping pace with technological developments. Publishes quarterly journal Deadline.

Audit Bureau of Circulations (ABC)
Saxon House, 211 High Street, Berkhamsted, Herts HP4 1AD
Fax 01442-879301   Tel 01442-870800
E-mail abcpost@abc.org.uk
Website: www.abc.org.uk
Auditing body for the publishing industry, providing certified circulation data for newspapers, exhibitions and magazines. Also runs Verified Free Distribution, checking distribution claims of publishers of free newspapers. Figures are available via the Internet:

Authors' Licensing & Collecting Society
Marlborough Court, 14-18 Holborn, London EC1 2LE
Fax 020-7395 0660   Tel 020-7395 0600
E-mail alcs@alcs.co.uk
Website: www.alcs.co.uk
Collects and distributes royalties to writers (books, television, radio and film) and campaigns for collective rights schemes.

Birmingham Press Club
100 Hagley Road, Edgbaston, Birmingham B16 8LT
E-mail: andrew@birminghampressclub.co.uk
The world's oldest press club founded in Birmingham in 1865 has nearly 500 members. Visiting press welcome.

Book Trust
Book House, 45 East Hill, London SW18 2QZ
Fax 020-8516 2978   Tel 020-8516 2977
Website: www.booktrust.org.uk
The Book Trust organises and promotes literary prizes, including the Booker Prize and the Orange Prize for fiction, runs Children's Book Week and a Book Information Service. Publishes author profiles and guides to book selection.

British Association of Communicators in Business
42 Borough High Street, London SE1 1XW
Fax 020-7378 7140   Tel 020-7378 7139
E-mail: enquiries@bacb.org
Webste: www.bacb.org.uk
Formerly the BAIE, the association is for editors of in-house journals. It publishes Crucible 10x pa, the quarterly magazine Communicators in Business and the Editors' Handbook. It runs training programmes and organises an annual convention and awards.

British Association of Journalists
88 Fleet Street, London EC4Y 1PJ
Fax 020-7353 2310   Tel 020-7353 3003
A small non-TUC trade union set up as a rival to the National Union of Journalists in 1992 by some Mirror Group journalists and the former NUJ general secretary Steve Turner. It has over 700 members.

British Association of Picture Libraries and Agencies (BAPLA)
18 Vine Hill, London EC1R 5DX
Fax 020-7713 1211   Tel 020-7713 1780
E-mail: bapla@bapla.demon.co.uk
Webste: www.bapla.org.uk
BAPLA is the trade association that represents 350 libraries. BAPLA provides a referral service for image research. Publishes the industry magazine 'Light Box' and annual directory. As well as valuable work in copyright, BAPLA assesses many industry issues for both picture users and libraries, including copyright clearance, ethics, pricing, marketing and technology.

British Copyright Council
Copyright House, 29 Berners Street, London W1P 4AA
Fax 020-7306 4069   Tel 020-7306 4069
Liaison committee for the organisations representing owners of copyright in literary, musical and artistic works. Not an advice service, but will try to answer written queries. Publishes two guides to the law.

British Guild of Travel Writers
Hangersley Hill, Ringwood, Hampshire BH24 3JN
                          Tel 01425-470946
E-mail: adeleevans@compuserve.com
Association of writers, authors, broadcasters and photographers specialising in travel. Publishes monthly internal newsletter, Globetrotter, and annual yearbook with details of 170 members.

British Institute of Professional Photography
Fox Talbot House, Amwell End, Ware, Herts SG12 9HN
Fax 01920-487056   Tel 01920-464011
E-mail: bipp@compuserve.com
Website: www.bipp.com

Founded in 1901, this is the UK's qualifying body for professional photographers. It publishes the magazine The Photographer ten times a year., and the annual Directory of Professional Photography with details of over 3,000 members.

British Printing Industries' Federation
11 Bedford Row, London WC1R 4DX
Fax 020-7405 7784   Tel 020-7242 6904
E-mail: info@bpif.org.uk
Website: www.bpif.org.uk
The BPIF is the business support organisation for employers in the printing, packaging and graphic communications industry. Based in London and with six regional business centres around the country, the BPIF represents more than 3000 member companies. Publishes: Printing Industries (monthly), surveys, Directions (quarterly economic digest) and books.

British Society of Magazine Editors
c/o Gill Branston & Associates, 137 Hale Lane
Edgware Middx HA8 9QP
Fax 020-8959 2137   Tel 020-8906 4664
E-mail: bsme@cix.compulink.co.uk
Professional association for magazine editors and senior editorial staff. The Society organises annual editorial awards and industry forums.

Bureau of Freelance Photographers
497 Green Lanes, London N13 4BP
Fax 020-8886 5174   Tel 020-8882 3315
E-mail: info@thebfp.com
Website: www.thebfp.com
Gives advice and market information to freelance photographers supplying publishing markets (magazines, newspapers, books, picture agencies, etc). Publishes monthly Market Newsletter and annual Freelance Photographers Market Handbook. Annual membership £40.

Campaign for Freedom of Information
Suite 102, 16 Baldwin Gardens, London EC1N 7RJ
Fax 020-7831 7461   Tel 020-7831 7477
E-mail: admin@cfoi.demon.co.uk
Website: www.cfoi.org.uk
The campaign is pressing for a Freedom of Information Act which would create a general right of access to official records subject to exemptions protecting information whose disclosure would cause real harm to essential interests such as defence, law enforcement and privacy. Campaigns for a public interest defence under the Official Secrets Act. It also seeks disclosure in the private sector on issues of public interest. Publishes briefings and other publications.

Campaign for Press and Broadcasting Freedom
8 Cynthia Street, London N1 9JF
Fax 020-7837 8868   Tel 020-7278 4430
E-mail: freepress@cpbf.org.uk
Website: www.cpbf.org.uk
Campaigns for a democratic, diverse and accountable media, accessible to all. The CPBF opposes monopoly ownership of the press and seeks a Right of Reply. It organises events and publishes 6x pa journal Free Press, occasional pamphlets and the Media Catalogue of mail order books and postcards.

Cartoon Art Trust
7 Brunswick Centre, Bernard Street, London WC1N
1AF
Fax 020-7278 4234   Tel 020-7278 7172
E-mail: skp@escape.u-net.com
Website: www.cartooncentre.org.uk
Aims to preserve and promote the art of cartooning.
Runs an appeal to establish a national museum of
cartoon art and is building up a library of cartoon
material. Publishes quarterly newsletter and exhibition
catalogues. They run the Cartoon Art Trust Awards
which are given in November every year.

Cartoonists' Club of Great Britain
46 Strawberry Vale, Twickenham, Middlesex TW1 4SE
Fax 020-8891 5946   Tel 020-8892 3621
E-mail: terry@cartoonology.com
The Club is a social one for professional cartoonists. It
meets on the first Tuesday of every month at The
Cartoonist pub, Shoe Lane, London EC4, publishes the
monthly magazine Jester and holds regular exhibitions.

Central Criminal Court Journalists' Association
Press Room, Old Bailey, London EC4N 7EH
Fax 020-7248 0133   Tel 020-7248 3277
Represents media interests in court coverage.

Chartered Institute of Journalists
2 Dock Offices, Surrey Quays Road, London SE16
2XU
Fax 020-7232 2302   Tel 020-7252 1187
E-mail: memberservices@ioj.co.uk
Website: www.ioj.co.uk
Certificated independent trade union concerned with
preserving standards and protecting the pay and
conditions of its members. It publishes The Journal.

Chartered Society of Designers
1st Floor, 32-38 Saffron Hill, London EC1N 8SG
Fax 020-7831 6277   Tel 020-7831 9777
E-mail: csd@csd.org.uk
Main professional body for designers in all fields,
setting and maintaining standards. Organises events,
seminars and awards and publishes a newsletter.

Children's Express (UK)
Exmouth House, 3-11 Pine Street, London, EC1R 0JH
Fax 020-7278 7722   Tel 020-7833 2577
E-mail: enquiries@childrensexpress.btinternet.com
Website: www.childrens-express.org
A charitable organisation which gives children aged
between 8 -18 years the opportunity to learn journalism
skills, such as reporting and interviewing. Part news
agency and part youth club. Bureaux in London, Belfast,
Newcastle, Birmingham, Sheffield and Plymouth.

Commonwealth Journalists' Association
17 Nottingham Street, London W1M 3RD
Fax 020-7486 3822   Tel 020-7486 3844
Fosters interest in Commonwealth affairs, undertakes
training of journalists in Commonwealth countries and
defends journalists' rights where these are threatened.
Publishes newsletter 3x pa and holds international
conferences every 3 years.

Commonwealth Press Union
17 Fleet Street, London EC4Y 1AA
Fax 020-7583 6868   Tel 020-7583 7733
E-mail: cpu@cpu.org.uk
Website: www.cpu.org.uk
Association of Commonwealth newspapers, news
agencies and periodicals, upholding the ideals and
values of the Commonwealth. Activities include press
freedom monitoring and extensive training
programmes throughout the Commonwealth,
fellowhsips , biennial conferences. Publishes CPU
News, bi-monthly.

Copyright Licensing Agency
90 Tottenham Court Road, London W1P 0LP
Fax 020-7631 5500   Tel 020-7631 5555
E-mail cla@cla.co.uk
Website: www.cla.co.uk
Non-profit company looking after the interests of
copyright owners in copying from periodicals and
books. Collects copying fees and pays them to authors
(via Authors Licensing and Collecting Society, 020-7255
2034) and publishers (via Publishers Licensing Society,
020-7829 8486).

Council of Photographic News Agencies
Boswague Cottage, Boswague, Tregony, Cornwall
TR2 5ST
Fax 01872-501393   Tel 01872-501393
Represents the UK's six largest press agencies/photo
libraries.

Cricket Writers' Club
2 Bobble Court, Little Rissington, Glos GL54 2ND
                               Tel 07831-837437
E-mail: derekhodgson@compuserve.com
Secretary: Derek Hodgson
Represents most cricket writers in newspapers,
magazines, TV and radio.

Critics' Circle
c/o Stage Newspaper, 47 Bermondsey Street,
London SE1 3XT
Fax 020-7357 9287   Tel 020-7403 1818 x148
Organisation of professional critics in theatre, film,
music, dance and visual arts.

Defence, Press & Broadcasting Advisory Committee
Room 2235, Main Building, Ministry of Defence,
London SW1A 2HB
Fax 020-7218 5857   Tel 020-7218 2206
Aka the D-Notice Committee. The Defence, Press and
Broadcasting Advisory Committee oversees the
voluntary code which operates between the media and
those government departments with responsibilities for
national security. The vehicle for this is the DA Notice
system, where "advisory notices" are issued to the
media at editor level describing sensitive areas.

Directory & Database Publishers' Assoc.
PO Box 23034, London W6 0RJ
                               Tel 020-8846 9707
E-mail: RosemaryPettit@msn.com
Website: www.directory-publisher.co.uk
The DPA was established in 1970 for directory and
database publishers.

Edinburgh International Book Festival
137 Dundee Street, Edinburgh EH11 1BG
Fax 0131-228 4333   Tel 0131-228 5444
E-mail: admin@edbookfest.co.uk
Website: www.edbookfest.co.uk
Organises the annual festival, described by the
Guardian as Europe's happiest and largest. 11-27
August 2001.

Edinburgh Press Club
19 Rutland Street, Edinburgh EH1 2AE
No fax.   Tel 0131-229 2800
Social club for the media in the Edinburgh area. Runs
Festival of Journalism during the Edinburgh
International Festival.

EETPU
See Amalgamated and Electrical Union

Electronic Media Round Table
26 Rosebery Avenue, London EC1R 4SX
Fax 020-7837 8901   Tel 020-7837 3345
E-mail eps@epsltd.demon.co.uk
Independent and informal grouping of publishers,
hardware and software manufacturers, developers,
integrators, distributors, retailers and other companies
and individuals interested in promoting closer working
relationships for all forms of electronic publishing
activity.

European Society for News Design
28 Holden Road, London N12 8HT
Fax 020-8992 6964   Tel 020-8445 1262
For anyone - not just designers - interested in design in
newspapers and magazines, looking at all aspects of the
subject.

Federation of Entertainment Unions
1 Highfield, Twyford, Hants SO21 1QR
Fax 01962-713288   Tel 01962-713134
E-mail: harris@interalpha.co.uk
Collective body of trade unions, representing the
interests of 140,000 members in the broadcasting and
entertainment industries. The unions are: BECTU,
Equity, Musicians Union, NUJ, Writers Guild and the
AEEU. It provides liaison, lobbying and co-ordination
services on issues of common concern.

Financial Journalists' Group
51 Gresham Street, London, EC2V 7HQ
Fax 020-7696 8996   Tel 020-7216 7411
E-mail: financialjournalistsgroup@compuserve.com
Aims to improve the quality of financial journalism by
holding group briefings to reporters to help expand
their knowledge on a variety of financial topics.
Contact - Suzanne Moore

Fleet Street Motoring Group
Elmleigh, Old Perry Street, Chislehurst, Kent BR7 6PP
Fax 020-8300 5694   Tel 020-8300 2140
E-mail: fsmg@bakerdowning.demon.co.uk
Association of motoring correspondents.

Football Writers' Association
6 Chase Lane, Barkingside, Ilford, Essex IG6 1BH
Fax 020-8554 2455   Tel 020-8554 2455
Represents members' interests and liaises with football
bodies to improve working conditions at football
grounds. Since 1948 selects the Footballer of the Year.

Foreign Press Association in London
11 Carlton House Terrace, London SW1Y 5AJ
Fax 020-7925 0469   Tel 020-7930 0445
E-mail: secretariat@foreign-press.org.uk
Website: www.foreign-press.org.uk
Founded 1888. Helps London-based foreign
correspondents in their professional work, providing
extensive facilities and assistance at its headquarters.
Arranges briefings and social events. Publishes
newsletter and members list.

Freedom Forum European Centre
Stanhope House Stanhope Place, London W2 2HH
Fax 020-7262 4631   Tel 020-7262 5003
E-mail: freedomforumeurope@compuserve.com
Website: www.freedomforum.org
Provides a forum for debate about the media. Holds
discussions and talks on topical media issues and
photojournalism exhibitions. Has a news library.

Graphical, Paper and Media Union
Keys House, 63-67 Bromham Road, Bedford MK40
2AG.
Fax 01234-270580   Tel 01234-351521
E-mail general@gpmu.org.uk
Website: www.gpmu.org.uk
GPMU is the trade union for the printing, paper and
allied trades industry. Membership covers managerial,
administrative, clerical and production workers in
printing, publishing, papermaking, advertising and
information tchnology. Represents, and negotiates on
behalf of, its 200,000 members in advertising
agencies, art studios, newspapers, general print,
publishing, ink and papermaking and numerous
specialist industries. Provides legal and educational
services, pubishes GPMU Journal free to members ten
times a year.

Guild of Food Writers
48 Crabtree Lane, London SW6 6LW
Fax 020-7610 0299   Tel 020-7610 0299
E-mail: ckthomas@gfw.co.uk
Website: www.gfw.co.uk
Professional association of food broadcasters and
writers. Established in 1984 it has over 300 members.

Independent Publishers' Guild
PO Box 93, Royston, Hertfordshire SG8 5GH
                          Tel 01763-247014
E-mail: sheila@ipg.uk.com
Website: www.ipg.uk.com

INK
170 Portobello Road, London W11 2EB
                          Tel 020-7221 8137
E-mail: ink@pro-net.co.uk
Website: www.ink.uk.com
The trade association for alternative periodicals.

Institute of Journalists
See Chartered Institute of Journalists

Institute of Printing
The Mews, Hill House, Clanricarde Road, Tunbridge
Wells, Kent TN1 1PJ
Fax 01892-518028   Tel 01892-538118
E-mail: IOP@Globalprint.com
Website: www.globalprint.com/uk/iop
The professional body for the printing industry.

International Association of Women Sports Photographers
Wayside, White Lodge Lane, Baslow, via Bakewell, Derbyshire DE45 1RQ
Fax 01246-582227   Tel 01246-582376
E-mail: g.langsley@virgin.net
Aims to attract women into the profession, help beginners and raise standards. Produces videos, books, posters, calendars and exhibitions.

International Federation of the Periodical Press (FIPP)
Queens House, 55/56 Lincoln's Inn Fields, London WC2A 3LJ
Fax 020-7404 4170   Tel 020-7404 4169
E-mail: info@fipp.com
Website: www.fipp.com
FIPP fosters formal and informal alliances between publishers to exploit successful publishing ideas, marketing initiatives and technological opportunities. Publishes quarterly Magazine World, holds biennial FIPP World Congress.

JICNARS
See National Readership Surveys

JICREG
Bloomsbury House, 74-77 Great Russell Street, London WC1B 3DA
Fax 020-7436 3873   Tel 020-7636 7014
E-mail: steve@jicreg.co.uk
Website: www.jicreg.co.uk
JICREG provides readership information on regional and local newspapers with area flexibility, enabling the readership of papers or schedules to be established within any marketing or catchment area.

Library Association
7 Ridgmount Street, London WC1E 7AE
Fax 020-7255 0501   Tel 020-7255 0500
E-mail info@la-hq.org.uk
Website: www.la-hq.org.uk
Professional body for librarians which awards chartership status, sets standards and lobbies government. It works for freedom of access to information and against censorship and library cuts. Publishes monthly magazine Library Association Record.

LIRE Media Group
BM LIRE, London WC1N 3XX
Fax 020-7267 8106   Tel 020-7267 8003
E-mail: media@easynet.co.uk
A voluntary media group set up to promote critical journalism and research media issues. Organises media conferences, publishes reports and a newsletter Eyewitness.

London Press Club
c/o Freedom Forum, European Centre, Stanhope House, Stanhope Place, London W2 2HH
Fax 020-7363 4631   Tel 020-7402 2566
E-mail: lpressclub@aol.com
Club for journalists and media in general which makes three annual awards: Scoop of the Year; Edgar Wallace Trophy for outstanding writing; Freedom Award to the journalist or organisaiton doing the most for fredom of the press. Also runs seminars and lectures.

Media Research Group
7-11 Herbrand Street, London WC1N 1EX
Fax 020-7915 2165   Tel 020-7580 6690
Website: www.mccann.co.uk
Provides forum for debating issues relating to media planning and research. Holds bi-annual conference.

Media Resource Service
Novartis Foundation, 41 Portland Place, London W1N 4BN
Fax 020-7637 2127   Tel 020-7580 0100/631 1634
E-mail mrs@novartisfound.org.uk
Web: www.novartisfound.org.uk/
This service gives journalists free and independent access to experts in medicine, science and technology. It is run by the the Novartis Foundation. A twice yearly newsletter contains news of the MRS and the world of science communication.

Media Society
56 Roseneath Road, London SW11 6AQ
Fax 020-7223 5631   Tel 020-7223 5631
Forum for discussing issues pertinent to the media. Membership includes editors, journalists, pr, media lawyers, MPs and academics. Also submits evidence to appropriate select committees, commissions and enquiries.

Medical Journalists' Association
101 Cambridge Gardens, Ladbroke Grove, London W10 6JE
Fax 020-8968 7910   Tel 020-8960 4382
The MJA aims to improve understanding between health and medical journalists and the health and medical professions. The Association organises awards and social events and publishes directory of members and newsletter.

National Artists' Association
Studio 234, Cable Street Studios, 566 Cable Street, London E1W 3HB
Fax 020-7790 6630   Tel 020-7790 6696
E-mail: naa@gn.apc.org
It aims to bring improvements in the economic position, working conditions, rights and porfessional status of visual artists in the UK.

National Association of Press Agencies
41 Lansdowne Crescent, Leamington Spa, Warwickshire CV32 4PR
Fax 01926-424760   Tel 01926-424181
Trade association for news and photographic agencies. A free handbook is available.

National Federation of Retail Newsagents
Yeoman House, Sekforde Street, London EC1R 0HD
Fax 020-7250 0927   Tel 020-7253 4225
E-mail: info@nfrn.org.uk
Website: www.nfrn.org.uk
Represents 23,000 independent retail newsagents in the UK and Ireland. It publishes the weekly journal Retail Newsagent and has 10 regional offices

National Association of Press Agencies
41 Lansdowne Crescent, Leamington Spa, Warwickshire CV32 4PR
Fax 01926-424760   Tel 01926-424181
Trade association for news and photographic agenies. A free handbook is available.

oneworld.net

connect to a better world

National Printing Skills Centre
Grafton Place, Leicester LE1 3WL
Fax 0116-251 2368   Tel 0116-251 2367
E-mail: post@npsc.co.uk
Website: www.npsc.co.uk
Regular courses and individual courses for learning
pre-press, press and post-press skills.

National Small Press Centre
BM Bozo, London WC1N 3XX
                    Tel 01234-211606
A self-funding independent organisation for self-
publishers. It organises exhibitions, courses and
workshops; runs a consultancy service, has a reference
library and a collecion of samples.

National Union of Journalists
Acorn House, 314-320 Grays Inn Road, London
WC1X 8DP
Fax 020-7837 8143   Tel 020-7278 7916
E-mail: acorn.house@nuj.org.uk
Website: www.nuj.org.uk
The leading trade union representing all editorial
sectors of the media, including photographers and
freelancers. Membership totals 29,000, including
1,800 student journalists. It provides many services for
members, including legal. Campaigns for journalists'
rights and freedom of information, and against
censorship. Publishes: the prominent and widely read
bi-monthly magazine The Journalist; bi-monthly
bulletin Freelance, with news for freelancers; Freelance
Directory; Freelance Fees Guide; Careers in Journalism
guide booklet; comprehensive annual report; the NUJ
Code of Conduct; and much other material. Holds
conferences, seminars and training sessions.

Newspaper Library (British Library)
Colindale Avenue, London NW9 5HE
Fax 020-7412 7379   Tel 020-7412 7353
E-mail newspaper@bl.uk
Website: www.bl.uk/collections/newspaper
The national collection of UK newspapers, plus a large
overseas holding. Open Monday-Saturday, 10am-
4.45pm, admission free but only to persons over 18.
Arrive before 4pm and take proof of identity.

Newspaper Press Fund
35 Wathen Road, Dorking, Surrey RH4 1JY
Fax 01306-888212   Tel 01306-887511
A charity set up in 1864 to assist member journalists
and their dependants in need. Life membership is £50.

Newspaper Publishers' Association
34 Southwark Bridge Road, London SE1 9EU
Fax 020-7928 2067   Tel 020-7207 2200
Trade association for the eight publishers of national
newspapers. It promotes good relations with the
advertising industry and opposes government restraints
on the press.

Newspapers in Education
Manchester Evening News
164 Deansgate, Manchester M60 2RD
Fax 0161-839 0968   Tel 0161-211 2591
E-mail: name@mcn-evening-news.co.uk
Website: www.manchesteronline.co.uk
NIE provides resources for teachers to help pupils
become competent and confident writers and readers.

Newspaper Society
Bloomsbury House, 74-77 Great Russell Street,
London WC1B 3DA
Fax 020-7631 5119   Tel 020-7636 7014
E-mail: ns@newspapersoc.org.uk
Website: www.newspapersoc.org.uk
Association for the publishers of UK regional and local
newspapers. Its work is split into two broad areas:
marketing and lobbying. (Current priorities include
lobbying on press freedom issues and media ownership
regulations, and launching a £3 million generic
marketing campaign aimed at growing the industry's
share of national advertising.) Editorial services include
handling Royal Rota passes and press passes for major
sporting events and high profile court cases. The
Society also acts as gatekeeper to the UK press card
scheme. Publishes Production Journal, monthly and
Headlines, 6x a year. Runs a series of conferences and
seminars each year.
Director: David Newell
Marketing director: Chris Stanley
Head of legal: Santha Rasaiah
Head of employment: Sandy Park
Head of communications: Lynne Gardiner
Head of finance: Chris Welch

Paper Federation of Great Britain
Papermakers House, Rivenhall Road, Westlea,
Swindon, Wilts SN5 7BD
Fax 01793-886182   Tel 01793-889600
E-mail: fedn@paper.org.uk
Website: www.paper.org.uk
The employers federation for all sectors of the paper
industry. Runs the Pulp and Paper Information Centre,
supplying data to the media.

Paper Industry Technical Association
5 Frecheville Court, Bury, Lancashire BL9 0UF
Fax 0161-764 5353   Tel 0161-764 5858
E-mail: info@pita.co.uk
Website: www.pita.co.uk
For people interested in the technology of the paper
industry. Publishes: Paper Technology.

Parliamentary Press Gallery/Lobby Journalists
House of Commons, London SW1A 0AA
                    Tel 020-7219 4700

PEN
152-156 Kentish Town Road, London NW1 9QB
Fax 020-7267 9304   Tel 020-7267 9444
E-mail: enquiries@pen.org.guk
Website: www.pen.org.uk
English centre of the international association for
published writers, with over 130 centres in 100
countries. Fights for freedom of expression and against
censorship, and helps imprisoned writers worldwide.
Makes annual awards, holds regular meetings and
publishes newsletter. PEN stands for Poets,
Playwrights, Editors, Essayists and Novelists.

Periodical Publishers' Association
Queens House, 28 Kingsway, London WC2B 6JR
Fax 020-7404 4167   Tel 020-7404 4166
E-mail: info1@ppa.co.uk
Website: www.ppa.co.uk
The trade association for magazine publishers, representing nearly 200 companies generating 80 per cent of the industry's revenue. Lobbies on behalf of members, and organises conferences, seminars and awards. Produces many publications, including the journal Magazine News, annual Magazine Handbook with key data on the industry, and industry overviews. The PPA provides secretariats for the Association of Publishing Agencies (customer magazines), the International Federation of the Periodical Press (FIPP) UK Newsletter Publishers' Association and the British Society of Magazine Editors (BSME).

Periodicals Training Council
55/56 Queen's House, Lincoln's Inn Fields, London WC2A 3LJ
Fax 020-7404 4167   Tel 020-7404 4168
E-mail: training@ppa.co.uk
Website: www.ppa.co
The PTC is the training arm of the Periodical Publishers Association. It aims to enhance the performance of the UK magazine industry and act as a focus for training.

Picture Research Association
2 Culver Drive, Oxted, Surrey RH8 9HP
Fax 01883-730144   Tel 01883-730123
E-mail: pra@lippmann.co.uk
Website: www.pictures.demon.co.uk
Professional body for those involved in visual material for the media. Gives advice to members, organises meetings, quarterly magazine, monthly newsletter and Freelance Register.

Pira International
Randalls Road, Leatherhead, Surrey KT22 7RU
Fax 01372-802238   Tel 01372-802000
E-mail marionc@pira.co.uk
Website: www.pira.co.uk
Pira International is a provider of technical management information for the packaging, paper and board, printing, publishing and new media industries worldwide. It provides consultancy, testing, information and market intelligence services and organises a wide range of international conferences and training events for these industries. Pira is also a leading business-to-business publisher.

Press Complaints Commission
1 Salisbury Square, London EC4Y 8JB
Fax 020-7353 8355   Tel 020-73531248
E-mail: pcc@pcc.org.uk
Website: www.pcc.org.uk
For complainants about the contents and conduct of newspapers and magazines. Upholds a Code of Practice and advises editors on journalistic ethics.

Press Standards Board of Finance
Olympic House, 142 Queen Street, Glasgow G1 3BU
Fax 0141-248 2362   Tel 0141-221 3957
Co-ordinates and finances self-regulation in the newspaper and magazine publishing industry.

PressWise Trust
38 Easton Business Centre, Felix Road, Bristol BS5 0HE
Fax 0117-941 5848   Tel 0117-941 5889
E-mail: pw@presswise.org.uk
Website: www.presswise.org.uk
Non-profit making organisation promoting high standards of journalism and aiming to empower those ordinary people who become victims of unfair media intrusion and inaccurate or irresponsible reporting. Also provides media training and briefings on current media policy issues. Appointed to a European forum on the Information Society.

Publishers' Association
1 Kingsway, London WC2B 6XF
Fax 020-7836 4543   Tel 020-7565 7474
E-mail: mail@publishers.org.uk
Website: www.publishers.org.uk
Trade association for UK book publishers which produces many of its own publications.

Publishers' Publicity Circle
48 Crabtree Lane, London SW6 6LW
Fax 020-7385 3708   Tel 020-7385 3708
E-mail: ppc-@lineone.net
Provides a forum for book publicists to meet and share information. Monthly meetings with members of the media. Publishes directory and monthly newsletter.

St Bride Printing Library
St Bride Institute, Bride Lane, Fleet Street, London EC4Y 8EE
Fax 020-7583 7073   Tel 020-7353 4660
A unique public reference library covering all aspects of printing, with an extensive historical collection including artefacts, archive material, photographs and patents. The collection is strong on newspaper history and is housed in atmospheric surroundings just off Fleet Street. Hours: 9.30am-5.30pm, Monday-Friday.

Scottish Book Trust
Scottish Book Centre, 137 Dundee Street, Edinburgh EH11 1BG
Fax 0131-228 4293   Tel 0131-229 3663
E-mail: scottish book.trust@dial.pipex.com
Website: www.scottishbooktrust.com
Publishes directories of authors, literary guides, resources for schools and parents. Organises readership campaigns, operates a Book Information Service and adminsters the Fidler and Scottish Writer of the Year literary prizes and the Writers in Scotland scheme.

Scottish Daily Newspaper Society
48 Palmerston Place, Edinburgh EH12 5DE
Fax 0131-220 4344   Tel 0131-220 4353
E-mail: info@sdns.org.uk

Scottish Newspaper Publishers Association
48 Palmerston Place, Edinburgh EH12 5DE
Fax 0131-220 4344   Tel 0131-220 4353
E-mail: info@snpa.org.uk
Website: www.snpa.org.uk

Scottish Print Employers Federation
48 Palmerston Place, Edinburgh EH12 5DE
Fax 0131-220 4344   Tel 0131-220 4353
E-mail: info@spef.org.uk
Website: www.spef.org.uk

Scottish Publishers' Association
137 Dundee Street, Edinburgh EH11 1BG
Fax 0131-228 3220   Tel 0131-228 6866
E-mail: enquiries@scottishbooks.org
Website: www.scottishbooks.org
Trade association working for 68 Scottish publishers.
Publishes Directory of Publishing in Scotland
(annually) and new books lists. Provides training,
advice, marketing and promotion services to members.

Society of Authors
84 Drayton Gardens, London SW10 9SB
Fax 020-7373 5768   Tel 020-7373 6642
E-mail: authorsoc@writers.org.uk
Website: www.writers.org.uk/society/html
An independent trade union, which was founded in
1884, to promote the interests of authors and to defend
their rights. The Society gives a personal service to
writers, with wide range of facilities including advice on
contracts. It arranges conferences, meetings and social
events. It publishes a quarterly journal, The Author,
plus numerous guides and has over 6,000 members.

Society of Freelance Editors and
Proofreaders
Mermaid House, 1 Mermaid Court, London SE1 1HR
Fax 020-7407 1193   Tel 020-7403 5141
E-mail: admin@sfep.demon.co.uk
Website: www.sfep.org.uk
Professional body representing editors, especially
freelances, and working to improve editorial standards
by providing training, information and advice.
Publishes newsletter, directory and other publications.

Society of Indexers
Globe Centre, Penistone Road, Sheffield S6 3AE
Fax 0114-281 3061   Tel 0114-281 3060
E-mail: admin@socind.demon.co.uk
Website: www.socind.demon.co.uk
Publishes quarterly newsletter, twice-yearly journal The
Indexer.. Provides open learning course.

Society of Typographic Designers
Chapelfield Cottage, Randwick, Stroud, Gloucester
GL6 6HS
Fax 01453-759311   Tel 01453-759311
Promotes high standards of typographic design.

Society of Women Writers & Journalists
110 Whitehall Road, Chingford, London E4 6DW
                         Tel 020-8529 0886
E-mail: swwriters@aol.com
Founded 1894. Encourages literary achievement and
the upholding of professional standards. Organises
competitions, social events and monthly meetings.
Publishes magazine The Woman Writer 4x pa.

Sports Writers Association of Gt Britain
c/o English Sports Council, 16 Upper Woburn Place,
London WC1H 0QP
Fax 020-7383 0273   Tel 020-7273 1555
Founded 1948 for sports journalists. Now has over 500
members. Makes awards for the Sportsman,
Sportswoman and Sports Team of the Year. Organises
the British Sports Journalism Awards and Sports
Photographer of the Year Awards in conjunction with
the English Sports Council. It appoints the Olympic
press attache for the British media.

Talking Newspaper Association
Heathfield, East Sussex TN21 8DB
Fax 01435-865422   Tel 01435-866102
E-mail: info@tnauk.org.uk
A registered charity that provides 200 national
newspapers and magazines on audio cassette,
computer disk and E-mail for blind, visually impaired
and disabled people. There are over 530 local groups,
providing two million tapes of over 900 newspapers
and magazines for 200,000 visually impaired people.

Teenage Magazine Arbitration Panel
PPA 28 Kingsway, London WC2B 6JR
                         Tel 020-7404 4166
Website: www.ppa.co.uk
The TMAP considers complaints about the editorial
content of a sexual nature in magazines which have
more than 25 per cent of readers who are young women
under the age of 15.

UK Newsletter and Electronic Publishers
Association
79-89 Lots Road, London SW10 0RN
Fax 020-7393 7810   Tel 020-7393 7460
E-mail: uk.nepa@btinternet.com
UK NEPA helps newsletter and electronic subscription
publishers. Regular meetings, bulletins, and an annual
conference. Free legal and business advice to members.

Women in Publishing
Information Officer, Publishers Association, 1
Kingsway, Floor 3, London WC2B 6XF
Website: www.cyberiacafe.net/wip/
Publishes monthly newsletter, surveys and Women in
Publishing Directory.

Women Writers Network
c/o 23 Prospect Road, London NW2 2JU
Helps women writers further their professional
development by providing a forum for exchanging
information and giving support. Holds monthly
meetings, and publishes monthly newsletter and
annual directory of members.

Worshipful Company of Stationers &
Newspaper Makers
Stationers' Hall, Ave Maria Lane, London EC4M 7DD
Fax 020-7489 1975   Tel 020-7248 2934
E-mail: clerk@stationers.demon.co.uk
City livery company for stationers, printers, publishers,
booksellers, paper makers and packagers.

Writers' Guild of Great Britain
430 Edgware Road, London W2 1EH
Fax 020-7706 2413   Tel 020-7723 8074
E-mail: postie@wggb.demon.co.uk
Website: www.writers.org.uk/guild
Trade union representing writers in film, TV, radio,
theatre and books. Has scored many successes in
improving terms and conditions. Holds regular
meetings and publishes bi-monthly Writers' Newsletter.

Young Newspaper Executives' Association
Newspaper Society, 74-77 Great Russell Street,
London WC1B 3DA
Fax 020-7631 5119   Tel 020-7636 7014
E-mail: ns@newspapersoc.org.uk
Website: www.newspapersoc.org.uk
Focal point for newspaper managers aged under 40.

Free-to-air TV

TV INTRODUCTION	**196-199**
BBC ATTACKERS AND DEFENDERS	**200-201**
THE NEW BBC LISTINGS	**202-207**
ITV/CHANNEL 3 LISTINGS	**208-210**
ITV MERGERS	**211-213**
NEWS AT TEN	**214**
INDEPENDENT TV LISTINGS	**216-225**

"About half the population is not interested in paying more for their TV service."

Peter Rogers, ITC chief executive

"There are people who have never paid for extra television before. We are beginning to convert middle England to pay-TV."

Stuart Prebble, ONdigital chief executive

£22m BBC consultancy fees

7 AUGUST 1999 A Channel 4 documentary confirmed that the BBC was spending an annual £22 million on consultancy fees. The figure was teased out of Christopher Bland, the BBC chairman, who said 1 per cent of the £2.2 billion collected on licence fees went on outfits like McKinsey, KPMG and PA Consulting. "There was a lack of belief amongst governors that senior management was really up to it," said the former head of BBC Worldwide, James Arnold-Baker. "And then came a whole era of second guessing for our consultants."

Eyre's views and move

27 AUGUST "Public service broadcasting will soon be dead," the ITV chief executive Richard Eyre declared at the annual MacTagggart lecture. "In the long run, regulation as a sort of conscience rule book won't exist. What will replace it? You and me." Until Greg Dyke's appointment as BBC director general, Eyre had wanted to replace John Birt in the BBC's top job. He only had to wait until October 2000 for a job move when joined Pearson - Greg Dyke's former employer. Eyre's role as boss of Pearson TV gave him the non-public service brief of targetting Channel 5.

Wonderful BBC2

SEPTEMBER Nicky Campbell - a man previously more famous for his career move from being a Radio 1 DJ to presenting ITV's Wheel of Fortune - started a brief stint as a Newsnight presenter. All part of the search for accessibility.

BBC1's schedule and gripes

SEPTEMBER The BBC1 controller Peter Salmon announced a £195 million autumn schedule to include French and Saunders Let Them Eat Cake, Walking With Dinosaurs and the promotion of the Royle Family from BBC2. Salmon defended the proposal for an extra £24 digital licence fee and said: "BBC1 can still offer the public what the commercial sector can't or won't produce." He also attacked commercial channels for poaching the likes of Martin Bashir, Des Lynam, Harry Enfield and Noel Edmonds. The comedians Frank Skinner and David Baddiel plus the political editor John Sergeant were to continue the exodus of BBC star names to ITV. At the end of the month Salmon told the Edinburgh TV Festival that his channel would need his £585 million budget increased by £100 million in order to make better comedy and drama.

GOOD
MORNING
TELEVISION

For 26 million viewers*

* Average Monthly reach January - June 2000. Source BARB

Fantasy wage demand

1 SEPTEMBER The comedian Frank Skinner had his comically high demand for a £20 million two-year contract rejected by the BBC. The same day his partner David Baddiel announced a £5.5 million deal with Sky for a sit-com about therapy.

Devil's Advocate

2 SEPTEMBER Radio 4's Today presenter John Humphrys (who later made the news as one of the nation's older fathers-to-be) published the Devil's Advocate, a book which criticised dumber news coverage. He described the Panorama interview with Louise Woodward (the au pair who was convicted in the US of killing a child in her care) as "pure soap". He said BBC1's Six O'clock News had "gone softer and opted for an agenda dominated by social issues with a consumerist angle".

Ford flees Flack

7 SEPTEMBER Half an hour before the 11am BBC news bulletin Anna Ford had to dash for cover when an intruder broke into the White City newsroom, picked up a table and smashed it through a plate glass window. The break in - for which an undergraduate called Nigel Flack was charged - stoked fears for the safety of TV journalists following Jill Dando's murder and death threats to Tony Hall, the chief executive of BBC News.

New DG's money

19 SEPTEMBER Greg Dyke, who was soon to replace John Birt as BBC director general, cut his links with his old employer at Pearson by cashing in £800,000 worth of share options. That came in addition to £768,000 pay in the year preceding his departure. With the £7 million he got when LWT was taken over by Granada in 1994 plus a new annual salary of £400,000, he can afford the kind of spokesman who commented: "Greg is not short of cash - if he was worried about money, he wouldn't be doing the BBC job. He's doing it for the challenge and the honour." In October Dyke resigned from the Manchester United board and in January 2000 he was forced to sell £6 million

worth of Granada shares. "Bizarre," commented Simon Jenkins in the Times. "As long as he has a financial incentive in ITV's success, he will have an incentive in the BBC's public service commitment to the high ground. For as long as the BBC sticks to the high ground, ITV will sweep up the populist game of audience-chasing."

BBC World merges with News 24

20 SEPTEMBER The John Birt vision for a global cable and satellite news empire underwent a corporate refocus when 50 jobs and several programmes went from BBC World. The international news channel merged with the News 24 domestic news service with scaled down plans for half-hourly news bulletins from April 2000.

Old news: did ITN leak?

28 SEPTEMBER Norman Lamont's biography included a passage where the former chancellor wrote that in the 1990 Tory leadership campaign an ITN executive had polled Tory MPs and passed its results to Tory head office. The Times led on the story and identified Dame Sue Tinson as the leaky ITN associate editor. Dame Sue, who was ennobled by John Major and was close to Margaret Thatcher, used an ITN spokesman to say: "Sue Tinson has categorically denied today's unsubstantiated report in the Times. The story is based on pure speculation."

Monster hit

19 OCTOBER Walking With Dinosaurs became the most watched science programme when it recorded audience figures of 18.9 million. Good news for a beleaguered corporation which, in September, had endured an all time low peak viewing audience of below 30 per cent when rivals broadcast the England vs Poland game and Who Wants to be a Millionaire? at the same time.

New news: ITN plans

NOVEMBER In two separate deals ITN was poised to replace Sky News as the UK news provider for Reuters TV and to launch a 24 hour news channel in conjunction with NTL.

From flow charts to informality

1 NOVEMBER The consensus view of the change in director generals was that harsh managerialism would give way to a softly softly approach. Sir John Birt's £50,000 farewell bash at Hampton Court Palace was timed to coincide with Greg Dyke's arrival as his deputy director general until 1 April 2000. On the day when power at the top started to be handed over, Birt and Dyke paid each other compliments and announced a restructuring of BBC Broadcast, the corporation's buying and scheduling department.

Speed kills

8 NOVEMBER A transport select committee told the BBC to stop encouraging young men to drive dangerously. "The media as a whole has portrayed driving in an irresponsible manner," MPs said. "Many programmes feature car cases and, whether openly or implicitly, suggest there is virtue in driving too quickly." The committee's report singled out BBC2's Top Gear for "macho posturing" and an obsession with acceleration and speed.

Free licences to over 75s

9 NOVEMBER Chancellor Gordon Brown's budget announced a free TV licence to pensioners aged over 75, a concession to 3 million households with a £300 million cost which the government said it would reimburse. Older viewers comprise over 20 per cent of the BBC's audience and are the most loyal segment of the BBC's market.

Investigative Beeb

10 NOVEMBER Donal MacIntyre was moved to a BBC safe house following death threats from football hooligans. The MacIntyre Undercover documentary identified specific attacks on the police plus drug dealing and links to right wing groups like Combat 18. MacIntyre had spent a year making covert recordings and police praised his work saying it had uncovered "some interesting legal nuggets". MacIntyre's populist approach to investigative journalism spawned Channel 4's commissioning of a me-too show and jealousy from Panorama employees who

compared their £100,000 per programme budgets with MacIntyre's £350,000 budgets. In March 2000 a Panorama programme about the nuclear industry was watched by a new low of 10 per cent of the viewing audience. "Down the pan-orama," declared a Sun headline. In April MacIntyre quit in a row over money. "We offered Donal a healthy contract to do a four-part investigation. His agent asked for double [and] we decided not to meet the demands," said a BBC spokeswoman.

Ground Force

DECEMBER "We're not supposed to have any secrets," Nelson Mandela said to his wife Graça Michel when he returned home to find that his garden had had a Ground Force makeover. South Africa's former president had kept a small garden when imprisoned at Robben Island for 27 years. "The sense of being a custodian of this small patch of earth offered a small taste of freedom," Mandela wrote in his memoirs. His new TV garden included a pergola, a pond, slate paving and a patch of bedding plants. "He seemed delighted," said the Ground Force presenter Alan Titchmarsh. "But rather poignantly, he said that he just hoped he had enough time to enjoy it."

News revamp

8 DECEMBER A cornerstone of the John Birt regime crumbled when the recently (and resentfully) engineered unification of television and radio newsgathering was abandoned. The abandonment of Birt's bi-media scheme saw the appointment of separate TV and radio news bosses.

C4 bags Friends and ER

16 DECEMBER Channel 4 won broadcasting rights for Friends and ER in a £124 million deal with Warner Brothers. Sky dropped out of a bidding contest which secured Channel 4 a three year deal, beginning in 2001, TV and terrestrial rights and first refusal on other Warner shows. The deal was followed by confirmation of plans for Channel 4's launch of the E4 subscription entertainment channel by the end of 2000.

Granada/Radio Rental deal

17 DECEMBER The TV rental business of Granada and Radio Rentals were merged into a £1 billion joint venture to create Box Clever, a chain of 900 shops to compete with Dixons and Comet. The trade secretary Stephen Byers cleared the deal the following April on condition that the new company freezes rental charges for five years.

Letting the cameras in

JANUARY 2000 A BBC2 programme called Trouble Between the Covers looked at life at the Cabal publishing house. It found a troubled life and within weeks of the broadcast Andy Sutcliffe, one of the founders, quit the company.

---

15 MINUTES OF FAME … YEARS OF REGRET
Those who have regretted letting TV in
… and what happened afterwards …

Cabal … founder quit new publishing house

Royal Opera House … Jeremy Isaac's management style held up for ridicule

Live TV… Kelvin MacKenzie, Janet Street-Porter and David Montgomery all left the TV business

Graham Taylor … C4 turned Taylor's "Do I not like that?" into a catch phrase and Taylor lost his job as England manager

Bath rugby club … A titan of a club filmed as it turned into a turkey

The Independent … Rosie Boycott's departure to the Express

More BBC defectors

18 JANUARY ITV signed deals with the comedians Frank Skinner and David Baddiel and with the political reporter John Sergeant. The names made big by BBC will appear on ITV as Baddiel and Skinner Unplanned. Of the Sergeant defection, the ITV controller of news said: "We are delighted. This man pushes all the right political buttons."

Paxman's Scottish discontent

27 JANUARY Jeremy Paxman's dislike of a regionalised Scottish ending for Newsnight - introduced in October 1999 to coincide with Scottish devolution - earned him a ticking off after BBC Scotland executives complained to their London bosses. The Scots complained of Paxman's hostility and accused him of deliberately messing up the 11pm handover. "The thing was cooked up as a way of buying off the demand for a Scottish Six O'Clock News," Paxman said. "The sooner it is dead and buried the better." Two years earlier he'd said Scotland was an English colony ridiculously over-represented at Westminster and, talking of the number of Scots in the Labour government, he'd commented. "It feels a little like living under the Raj."

Bye bye Birt …

... hello Greg Dyke

28 JANUARY Sir John Birt left his director general's post two months ahead of schedule with news of a very generous £370k "farewell package" and that he was hawking a book round the publishing world containing his insights and experience on how to be a good manager. Some useful tips to wannabe chief executive officer material are that it's OK to sack 4,000 members of staff, fine to spend tens of millions on management consultants, sound practice to reduce income tax by working as a full time freelance and smart to write Armani suits off against tax. A Guardian leader asked: "Can theories of management be extracted from the utterly, gloriously anomalous BBC? The more its structure and values resemble those of a commercial organisation, the less likely it is to serve public interest. Birt … leaves the BBC every bit as peculiar (and peculiarly managed) as the organisation he took over from Sir Michael Checkland in 1992. Long may it remain so. Odd in its governance, in its relationship with the state, in its weight in cultural life and journalism, it has to remain gloriously odd in its people. Without them there would no be programmes worth watching or listening to."

BROADCAST

THE UK'S ONLY WEEKLY NEWSPAPER FOR THE BROADCAST INDUSTRY

NOW INCLUDES 3 FREE SUPPLEMENTS:
- B+ on the art and craft of programme making and post production, monthly
- Broadband on the new opportunities for content providers and distributors in the digital age
- Broadcast International on international production, acquisition and distribution

SUBSCRIPTIONS TEL: +44 (0)1858 438847 please quote ref 1002
ADVERTISING TEL: +44 (0)20 7505 8011

No to Lockerbie broadcast

4 FEBRUARY Scottish judges refused the BBC's application to break a British precedent and allow camers into the courtroom to televise the trial of the Libyans accused of the Lockerbie bombing. The trial was in the Hague and though trial footage was to be broadcast direct from the Netherlands to families of the victims of the 1988 terrorist attack, the pictures were denied a wider circulation.

Bakewell quits

16 FEBRUARY Joan Bakewell resigned from the Heart of the Matter religious debate programme in protest at financial cuts and increasingly late scheduling. She said she wasn't trying to attack the BBC and would continue working on non-religious programmes such as BBC2's One Foot in the Past.

Licence fee up £3

21 FEBRUARY An inflation-plus-1.5 per cent rise bought the BBC licence fee up to £104. In announcing the increase, the culture secretary Chris Smith set two conditions: that the BBC makes a commercial income and that it makes bureaucratic savings to the point where "each extra £1 the BBC receives from the licence fee ... is expected to generate almost the equivalent through self-help". Smith - who described the corporation as "hitherto too much the judge and jury in its own cause"- announced a review of the BBC's governors. What Smith described as "tough love" was a disappointment within a corporation which had lobbied for £700 million a year rise and got £200 million and had demands for a £24 digital supplement turned down.

Talent spotting

9 MARCH The BBC Talent Campaign began a search for 40 new people with no previous broadcasting experience by inviting outsiders to report for the Holiday programme, star in a comedy show or win a year's training on Radio 1. The scheme got the backing of professional performers who will give master classes and was promoted by the Guardian, Odeon Cinemas and WH Smith.

Gormenghast and other dramas

FEBRUARY Despite a £6 million budget and lavish puffing in the Radio Times, the dramatisation of Mervyn Peake's gothic trilogy attracted audiences of around 2.5 million. The BBC quoted a new script when it commented that it was less concerned with ratings than with broadcasting challenging TV.

DRAMA HITS
BBC

Pride and Prejudice: 1995, 11.3m watched the final episode

Wives and Daughters: 1999, an average 7.95m viewers/episode

Vanity Fair 1998, nearly 7m viewers

ITV

Oliver Twist: 1999, an average 8m viewers/episode

Brideshead Revisited: a TV triumph of the 80s

Moll Flanders: 1996, 13m viewers max

DRAMA MISSES
BBC

Gormenghast: 2000, down to 2.5m viewers

Rhodes: 1996, £10m for under 5m viewers

Nostromo: 1997, under 3m viewers

ITV

Hornblower: £12m for 6m viewers

Video on demand

27 MARCH BBC Worldwide concluded a deal to provide a TV series for the Yes Television video-on-demand service. Yes TV includes British Telecom among its backers and was pledged to begin marketing a broadband television service to six million households from summer 2000.

News 24

28 MARCH The culture secretary Chris Smith delayed his review of News 24 until after the next election. The move went back on Smith's suggestion - made when he raised the licence fee - that a review of the channel's £55 million annual budget was imminent. Sky, which was being loud in its complaints that News 24 competes directly with Sky News, said: "We are very surprised given that it was stated the review would be a priority."

Fewer managers = better programmes

3 APRIL Greg Dyke began his clear out of Birt style management culture by announcing a cut back in bureaucratic costs from a quarter of the BBC income to 15 per cent. The savings included a dismantling of the BBC's internal market and trimming on chauffeurs and other management perks. A Guardian leader said: "Greg Dyke must be one of the few executives in the world who can announce up to a thousand redundancies - and hear his own staff cheer."

Invasion of privacy

6 APRIL The court of appeal upheld a judgement that the BBC's Watchdog programme had been guilty of invading the privacy of Dixons the electrical retailer. Watchdog had made clandestine film of sales transactions which it suspected were passing off second hand goods as new. They found no such wrong doing and the film was not broadcast.

Dyke fingers Smith

13 APRIL Greg Dyke told the Voice of the Listener and Viewer annual conference that the BBC is the best judge of good TV. His speech was a direct challenge to the culture secretary Chris Smith who had recently commented that the BBC is "too much the judge and jury in its own cause" and that it should make more "humdingers" such as Walking With Dinosaurs. Dyke said: "Well Chris, as we all know, it's not a minister's job to tell us what programmes we should and shouldn't be commissioning and showing. First, because politicians watch very little television, so who are they to judge? And second, because the BBC's independence has been jealously guarded over many years and will be equally guarded over my time as director general."

New money

23 APRIL Rows about the tenor of the BBC2's current affairs coverage crystallised around suggestions that the sober-sided Money Programme was to be replaced by a more "accessible" alternative to compete with more popular business shows like Trouble at the Top and Working Lunch.

Channel 4 sale plans

1 MAY News emerged of government plans to privatise Channel 4 as part of the broadcasting and communications bill due before the next parliament. The sale would raise around £2 billion and C4's chairman Vanni Treves, a Labour supporter, is on record as opposing any such move. In the 1999 annual report he wrote: "Channel 4's responsibility is to satisfy the full range of viewers' interests. That is what increasingly distinguishes us from the other commercial broadcasters, old and new, and it is that distinction which leaves us in no doubt that privatisation would be a disaster both for the channel and for the viewer." Treves' chief executive Michael Jackson, an ex-BBC man who is driving a highly commercial strategy at C4, took the same line during a lecture to the Royal Television Society where he also questioned the impartiality of BBC governors. Three weeks later C4 admitted it may seek stock market money for some of its commercial operations such as FilmFour and the proposed E4 digital entertainment channel.

BBC sport vs ITV quiz show

2 MAY The BBC won an odd ratings battle when its broadcast of the world snooker finals went up against ITV's celebrity edition of Who Wants to be a Millionaire? While 4 million saw Mark Williams win the snooker, 12.8 million watched Carol Vorderman and Kirsty Young being quizzed by Chris Tarrant. However, the snooker proved sufficient attraction that Who Wants to be a Millionaire? reached nowhere near its 18 million peak viewing figure.

BBC quiz shows

5 MAY The new BBC boss Greg Dyke revealed his populist credentials by commissioning a clutch of quiz and game shows fronted by celebrities like Anthea Turner, Ulrika Johnson, Terry Wogan, Gaby Roslin, Vinny Jones and Sir Michael Caine. The last two were mooted for a show called The Heist where four people who have never met must collaborate to crack security systems and organise fictional robberies at banks, art galleries and stately homes.

Royle family

8 MAY The Royle Family missed out on its expected Golden Rose award at the Montreux TV festival after judges were shown an ineligible programme first broadcast in 1998. Granada, which makes the programme for the BBC, said: "They've shot themselves in the foot with a 12-bore. It's a complete cock-up."

Royal family

12 MAY "How dare the BBC snub the Queen Mother?" demanded a querulous Daily Mail headline when it learned that plans for live coverage of a hundredth birthday parade on 19 July had been scrapped. The BBC decided the Royal's latest happy family spectacular wouldn't attract enough viewers and, in a burst of Mail-style patriotism, ITV took the option on showing the centennial bash. It proved a good decision when the mid-July birthday pageant - broadcast without ads - attracted 3.5 million viewers. The BBC got into another royal tangle when it pulled an 18th birthday programme about Prince William for fear it was too critical. "The BBC's move is craven," said the writer Anthony Holden.

Marr to BBC

19 MAY The Observer columnist Andrew Marr, 40 (above), replaced Robin Oakley, nearly 60, as the BBC's political editor. Oakley's unwilling early departure to make way for a younger face was taken as a sign that Greg Dyke's new regime was gearing up to fight for viewers during the next general election.

Jackpot

8 JUNE Who Wants to be a Millionaire? finally created a millionaire with the announcement that the show's joint owner, Avesco, made a £1.9 million profit last year. It has been screened in 26 countries with options granted in 60 more and CD-ROMs plus books have further enriched Avesco and the Celador production company.

Dyke's deputy to ITC

12 JUNE Patricia Hodgson (above) quit her job as BBC director of public policy to become the Independent Television Commission chief executive. Her move was a boost to ITV consolidators for she is known to support the formation of larger TV groups.

"No one sets out to make a bummer"

21 JUNE For a third year in succession, the BBC governors' annual report said standards were "simply too variable" and "the average quality of programmes was "still not good enough". Greg Dyke found his honeymoon period as the new director general was over and promised "fundamental changes". He said: "No one sets out to make a bummer. BBC1 had some outstanding programmes last year, more than previous years, but what we need to do is to spread them across the year." Embarrassment was added to discomfort when news of the BBC's autumn spread of programmes leaked on the news website annanova.com. The schedule includes a new series of One Foot in the Grave and a History of Britain fronted by Simon Schama.

Broadloid TV news

7 JULY A BBC/ITC sponsored survey by Westminster University looked at 700 evening news bulletins from 1975-1999 and found a "tabloid shift" with only the BBC's Nine o'Clock News and Channel 4 News maintaining a broadsheet approach. The survey conclusions were:

"There has undoubtedly been a shift towards a more tabloid domestic agenda."

"The rise in sport and consumer stories, combined with the decline in political stories ... could lead to the gradual marginalisation of serious and foreign reporting."

"We are not wholly optimistic that ten years from now television news will have maintained its current balanced and diversified approach."

"British television news, once the backbone of an informed British electorate, has been heading inexorably downmarket."

Richard Tait, ITN's editor in chief, responded by criticising the way headline writers emphasised the report's "tabloid" conclusions and ignored its praise for "a remarkably robust and broadly serious approach to television news" Tait said: "If the only language for evaluating the changes which are already beginning to affect the way we make and deliver news is a crude division between broadsheet and tabloid, what hope is there for an intelligent and well-informed discussion?"

Big Brother

18 JULY The first episode of Channel 4's Big Brother, the show which gripped vast numbers of viewers throughout the summer. Wooed by fame and a £70,000 prize, over 40,000 people volunteered to sequester themselves as objects of national voyeurism. It was loved by many, loathed by a few. Jonathan Freedland wrote in the Guardian: "Big Brother is utterly a product of its time. We have got used to men and women making public what were once private emotions and this lot are merely getting in on the act. It's striking that not a single minute of Big Brother has shown a discussion of what we used to call public affairs: there is not a word about politics. It is all about relationships with each other, past loves or themselves."

England vs Germany: BBC vs ITV

23 JUNE When the BBC and ITV went head-to-head and broadcast the same live Euro 2000 football match, the gap between old TV rivals narrowed by a shade. The BBC - under Gary Lineker - got 11.8 million viewers compared with Des Lynam's ITV lads attracting 6.1 million. In the 1966 World Cup final (until Euro 2000, the last competitive match where England beat Germany) 17.5 million watched the BBC and 6.3 million watched ITV. For the 1998 World Cup final the figures were 15.6 million and 6.6 million respectively.

For more on sport and the media, tune in to page 339.

Dyke's "fundamental changes"

10 JULY The changes Greg Dyke promised when the BBC governors delivered their annual report in June were revealed as plans to cut 1,100 BBC management jobs and to make ten heads of department compete for three new senior positions. Dyke said resulting savings of £750 million would increase the proportion of programme spending in the overall budget from 76 to 85 per cent. Chris Smith, the culture secretary, told the New Statesman magazine: "Under Greg Dyke the BBC has begun to get its house in order. Some of the measures that Greg has announced will produce substantial efficiency savings, but he hasn't got near the £1 billion of savings I am looking for."

Call for single regulator

27 JULY In anticipation of the autumn communications white paper, Oftel gave its support for a single regulator covering telecomunications and media. The telecoms watchdog wants the Independent Television Commission to be wound up and for the BBC to be bought under the control of a combined regulatory body, already known as Ofcom. David Edmonds, head of existing telecoms regulation at Oftel, said: "We should start from scratch. The government needs to decide what it wants from regulation of the communications industry and then build a [new] agency. There is a strong case to have economic and content regulation sitting side by side within the same organisation."

Pay TV: satellite, cable and digital

DIGITAL TV INTRODUCTION	**227**
DIGITAL TV LISTINGS	**228-229**
SATELLITE INTRODUCTION	**230**
SATELLITE LISTINGS	**232-235**
CABLE INTRODUCTION	**236**
CABLE LISTINGS	**238-241**
TV AND THE INTERNET	**19-23**

"There are people who have never paid for extra television before. We are beginning to convert middle England to pay-TV."

Stuart Prebble, ONdigital chief executive

"About half the population is not interested in paying more for their TV service."

Peter Rogers, ITC chief executive

BBC's digital result

5 AUGUST 1999 The Davies report, commissioned by the government to decide the BBC's role in digital broadcasting, came up with the following recommendations:

* a £24 digital supplement on the licence fee
* no ads or subscription on core BBC services
* Partial privatisation of BBC Worldwide and Resources
* More transparent BBC accounting

Commercial broadcasters declared the £24 supplement a "digital poll tax" which breached European rules on state aid. Their lobbying campaign culminated in December when MPs rejected Gavyn Davies' main suggestions with the further comment that the BBC had failed to argue its case for an expanded digital role, that News 24 was an extravagance and that the BBC should not sell off BBC Worldwide or BBC Resources.

In January 2000 Sky intensified its threat to go to Europe and take action against any digital levy and on 21 February 2000 any faint BBC hopes for a digital supplement were dashed when the licence was raised by £3.

Sky's digital result

11 AUGUST Sky revealed its gamble to provide free set-top digital decoders had attracted nearly two million customers and that its analogue transmission would be switched off in 2001. Sky's share price climbed despite full year results to July of a £388 loss compared to the £270 million in the previous year. This confirmed that future-earning possibilities rather than immediate profits are what drives technology-based shares upwards. Later in the month Sky boosted its £13 a month starter package by including Sky Cinema in an offer designed to head off the challenge of digital cable and ONdigital. The move followed a fall off in the numbers of cable customers taking Sky's premium movie channels and the success of Cable and Wireless in finding new customers since it introduced digital cable to Manchester in July 1999.

Telewest completes London purchase

25 AUGUST Telewest continued a consolidation of the cable TV business with the £428 million purchase of the half of Cable London which it didn't already own. The stake was sold by NTL and gave Telewest a broadcasting franchise to 6.1 million north and east London homes.

Sky boss hits earth

29 AUGUST Tony Ball, the head of Sky, accused mainstream broadcasters of a lack of understanding. Speaking at the Edinburgh TV Festival he said the BBC's News 24 - which costs three times as much to run as Sky News - is a subsidised "me-too" rival and that ITV companies fail to differentiate themselves by picking off market niches. He also admitted that, despite his earlier warnings, Sky's digital service had been undamaged by the possibility of a digital supplement to the licence fee. This supplement, as it turned out, was not granted

C4 pay-TV

30 AUGUST Channel 4 announced plans for E4, a pay television entertainment channel to be carried by cable, satellite and terrestrial broadcasters. It would compete with Sky One though Michael Jackson, the C4 chief executive, anticipated more UK programming and promised to announce a firm decision by Christmas 1999.

Management exoduses

2 SEPTEMBER ONdigital lost its commercial director Jim Ratcliffe and its programming director Ashley Faull only six weeks after the chief executive Stephen Grabiner had quit to join Sky - and then changed his mind and joined Apax venture capitalists. This coincided with management turmoil at Sky which saw its chief executive Mark Booth depart in June to be followed by another executive, Ian West, in mid August.

Pay TV regulation

17 SEPTEMBER The Independent Television Commission ruled Sky had breached the programme code by broadcasting a live performance of the former Take That star Robbie Williams miming oral sex. The ITC also criticised the same broadcast for the cross-corporate puffery that gave undue prominence to the Sun newspaper - another Murdoch product. The ITC also announced plans for rules to govern the behaviour of digital interactive broadcasts.

Digital governance

18 SEPTEMBER The culture secretary Chris Smith reaffirmed the government's commitment to digital broadcasting by announcing both a digital deadline and a broadcasting act in the next parliament. In a lecture to the Royal Television Society Smith challenged the TV and telecomms bigwigs to push for a switch from analogue to digital by 2010 and that they should offer, as incentive, internet access to every home with a phone and a TV. He stressed that a final switchover date will not be set until at least 95 per cent of the country has digital TV. He also spoke of the BBC, saying: "What public service means is changing. But it needs a redefinition rather than a requiem. That doesn't mean abandoning the concept altogether."

Open e-tail channel

12 OCTOBER Open went live to offer interactive television shopping and banking. The £375 million joint venture between Sky, British Telecom, HSBC bank and Matsushita intends to convert the "lean forward" technology of home computing into the cheaper and more widely accepted "lean back" television way of attaining a fully wired world. "The idea of sitting on the sofa to do the weekly shop after a hard day's work rather than rushing around the supermarket is appealing," commented the Henley Centre. Within two months Open had processed 128,000 orders and generated £1 million worth of sales and in the Christmas rush it recorded weekly totals of £1 million in online orders. City analysts predicted profits within four years and immediately valued the venture at £1.4 billion.

ITV pay-TV

24 OCTOBER ITV made a de facto announcement of its pay-TV intentions when it advertised for an executive to overhaul ITV2 and a clutch of new channels for children, sport and drama. These will carry an overall ITV brand rather than the current practice of identifying channels according to the whether programmes come from Carlton or Granada.

Telewest's live services ...

21 OCTOBER At the launch of its Midland digital services, Telewest promised 150 digital TV and radio channels, cheap phone calls, home shopping and banking, internet access and a decoder box to link TVs and PCs into home-based multimedia hubs. The cable company, which is backed by Microsoft, trailed Cable & Wireless into the digital arena but was ahead of NTL its other main cable competitor.

... death of Live TV

21 OCTOBER Trinity Mirror dumped Live TV onto NTL after a four-year pioneering run into TV sleaze and trivia. The gimmicks were many, the audience few and where Live led, Channels 4 and 5 followed. A Guardian leader commented: "They thought they had spotted a gap in the market. They failed to foresee that Channel 4 would, in time, come trundling into that gap, or that Channel 5 would one day emerge as the spiritual home of the Lad, male or female. Their clothes, you might say, have been stolen. Still, the people who gave us topless darts can hardly complain about that."

Charity channel

4 NOVEMBER The Media Trust announced the Community Channel for people who work in community and voluntary organisations. It will begin broadcasting on digital terrestrial, digital cable and digital satellite from 1 May 2000 using three years of transponder capacity, a Sky donation worth £1.8 million.

Size does matter

13 NOVEMBER The trade secretary Stephen Byers referred two pay-TV mergers - those of NTL-Cable & Wireless and Sky-Vivendi - to the Competition Commission. The referrals stimulated predictable howls of rage. NTL-CWC - which announced an £18.7 billion marriage in July 1999 (with NTL also said to be planning to bid for the third cable big hitter Telewest) - said the government had bowed to pressure from Sky and pointed out their union would only hold 20 per cent of the UK market by revenue and 25 per cent by subscriber numbers. The ITC backed the NTL-CWC deal but opposed that of

Sky and Vivendi. The objection to Vivendi - the largest private employer in France which has built a 24.4 per cent stake in Sky - is that a joint venture with Sky would bring "unrivalled power" to buy up sporting events. Sky - still smarting from the Competition Commission's decision to block its purchase of ManUnited - complained of "victimisation" and "erratic treatment". Conspiracy theorists held that Sky dissembled and Murdoch wanted the Commission to block the deal for fear that Sky would become a football for French interests. See Sky and Vivendi, 18 April.

Spy TV

Just who is the Digital TV Revolution overthrowing?

10 DECEMBER The anti-TV author David Burke published a book which countered commercial brouhaha by pointing out that interactive TV poses real threats to privacy and democracy. Rather than follow the dogma that interactivity is a synonym for choice, Burke argues the opposite and in Spy TV wrote of a "cycle of stimulus, response and measurement used on lab rats in psychological experiments". He fears the tailoring of ads to psychographic profiles and political campaigns where interactive telly will be akin to "being in a focus group four hours a day, every day of your life".

Two NTL deals

15 DECEMBER One: NTL bought into the BBC's sports archive in an arrangement which will see it developing regular nostalgia programming on Premium TV. Two: NTL continued its European expansion with the £2.3 billion purchase of the Swiss based Cablecom.

Jobs TV

27 DECEMBER The chancellor Gordon Brown (right) announced the Jobs TV channel. "In 1909 Britain created the first labour exchange in the world," he said. "Today Britain must use the most modern technology to match the jobs without workers to workers without jobs."

Intellygence: Pace

JANUARY 2000 Pace and the Sky subsidiary NDS unveiled the prototype XTV set-top box in the hope it would be subsidised by the other broadcasters. By the end of 2001 the box will channel particular ads to particular households, and store video games and shopping catalogues. Unprompted, it will interact with viewing habits by, for example, recording films with favourite actors or automatically recording the final episode of a four part TV series.

Intellygence: Microsoft

7 JANUARY 2000 NTL announced plans to adopt Microsoft's operating system as the platform for its next generation of digital television. NTL/Microsoft services will include participation in games shows and access to web browsers and email. This NTL contract was early justification for Microsoft's TV-and-computers strategy and one clear way it will generate return on the £2 billion cable investment made during 1999. Among Microsoft's shareholdings are 29 per cent of Telewest and 5 per cent of NTL.

Sky and the OFT

11 JANUARY The Office of Fair Trading began an investigation of Sky's dominance of pay-TV and in particular the charges that Sky levies on other broadcasters for its channels. Sky said it hoped the OFT review would result in the relaxation of "outdated" programme supply regulations.

Telewest/Flextech merger

27 JANUARY Telewest, Britain's second-largest cable operator, merged with the pay-TV Flextech group with the purchase of £2.26 billion worth of shares. The deal united Flextech's 13 pay-TV channels (including Bravo, Living and UK Gold) with a Telewest cable network that runs past 4.6 million homes. The Observer's Emily Bell commented: "Telly Flex is neither the largest nor most dynamic pairing one might have wished for - it's hardly Sky and BT - but it has the ingredients of what future media businesses will be about: a vast array of content (and not simply television) poured into the home via more fibre and high-speed modems than you could shake a mouse mat at." On conclusion of the take-over-cum-merger Flextech shares had more than more than doubled in value from just a year before and its chief executive Adam Singer (despite running the smaller company) engineered an arrangement where the Telewest chief executive Tony Illsley reported to him. It was an uncomfortable relationship that couldn't last for long and, in April, Illsley quit with a £6 million pay off.

Christians fined

2 FEBRUARY The Independent Television Commission fined the Christian Channel £20,000 for broadcasting a half-hour advertisement-cum-TV programme where Morris Cerullo, an American evangelist, attacked homosexuality, abortion and the "demonic forces" that dominate British media. The heavenly cable channel said its committed Christian viewers wouldn't have been offended but the terrestrially based ITC insisted the Christian Channel had breached clear rules forbidding any form of televised political broadcasting.

New Broadcasting Act

3 FEBRUARY The culture secretary Chris Smith announced publication of an autumn white paper suggesting the overhauling of broadcasting and telecomms regulations in ways that allow the British media to compete in a global digital market. Smith began a balancing act where he will have to reconcile his promises of a lighter regulatory touch with a protection of broad consumer interests. Meanwhile rumour had it that the trade secretary Stephen Byers wanted to diminish the culture department's regulatory remit and bring together all communications businesses under a single regulator answerable to the DTI.

Sky and phone TV

8 FEBRUARY While its cable competitors consolidated, Sky took the convergence of communications a step further by announcing two joint ventures to deliver pay-TV and multi-media information across telephone networks. The first arrangement was with Kingston Communications, the Hull telephone company which runs a local TV service with 60 TV channels and high speed internet access. The second was with Vodafone, to allow mobile phone users to access sports results, team news, audio commentaries and statistics. The deals are part of Sky's £250 million new media investment which also includes sky.com, sky-sports.com and an interactive sports shop.

Gains and losses

11 JANUARY "There are people who have never paid for extra television before. We are beginning to convert middle England to pay-television," said the ONdigital boss Stuart Prebble, in the middle of announcing a 34 per cent sales rise in the previous three months. His celebration that middle England is being persuaded to buy dearly what it once got for very little was only slightly tempered by ONdigital's £148 million losses in the year to September 1999. These, however, were in line with the business plan laid down by ONdigital owners Carlton and Granada and the pay-for-it TV people look forward to increasing their subscriber base to 2 million and breaking even

by 2002. In March 2000 Telewest posted a £520 million loss incurred by its rapid expansion into digital TV along with the launch of a services for high speed internet, interactive TV and email.

Guardian TV

3 MARCH The Guardian Media Group and Sky made unlikely commercial partners when each negotiated a 20 per cent stake in the Artsworld pay TV channel led by the former Channel 4 boss Jeremy Isaacs. The channel will compete with the Daily Mail backed Performance cable channel and the BBC/Flextech UK Arena. GMG, which sold its 15 per cent stake in GMTV in January. At the time GMG also had a share of Endemol - the producer of Changing Rooms, Ground Force and Ready Steady Cook - but this was sold in summer 2000.

Digital scepticism

28 MARCH "Impractical" said the Independent Television Commission, when it reviewed government plans to switch the entire population to digital TV by 2010. Peter Rogers, the ITC chief executive, said "I don't think we will get there unless we can find a way to persuade the people who are only interested in free-to-air channels to switch to digital. That is a very serious challenge and we are not yet on course."

No to Yes

16 APRIL Yes Television, the company with big plans to provide interactivity and video on demand down phone lines, cancelled its listing on the London stock exchange. There were several reasons for delaying the expected £600 million market debut: one, the share issue coincided with a sudden lack of confidence in new tech stock market investments; two, NTL wobbled on an agreement to provide Yes video on demand over its network; three, another phone operator, Kingston Communications in Hull went public with its anger over the way Yes had "overhyped" their business relationship; and four, Yes had also fallen out with British Telecom, after criticising the type of technology being deployed on the British Telecom broadband network.

Sky and Vivendi

18 APRIL The Competition Commission cleared Vivendi's bulk purchase of Sky shares saying it was not against the public interest in sports and film acquisition or for pay TV subscription technology. Vivendi representatives replaced Pearson and Granada on the Sky board where the shareholding is: News Corp 40 per cent; other investors 35.5 per cent; and Vivendi 24.5 per cent. The French media group built its stake in Sky after the breakdown of merger talks between Sky and the French pay-TV group Canal Plus.

Murdoch E quits family business

28 APRIL Elisabeth Murdoch (above) resigned as Sky's network chief saying she wanted to give birth to her third baby and her second independent TV production company. "The true story is that this is a lifestyle change as much as an opportunity," she declared. The other story is that she was miffed that her younger brother Lachlan, 28, was ahead in the race of being the sibling most likely to succeed their father.

Digital waste

16 MAY Researchers from Oxford University said that by 2010 set-top decoders will cause 500,000 tonnes of extra carbon emissions each year. The boffins claimed that decoders left on for 24 hours a day consume 25W when they could be designed to use 1W.

Microsoft and Telewest

26 MAY As regulatory barriers erected by the European Commission looked set to thwart Microsoft's purchase of a 30 per cent stake in the cable company Telewest, several other buyers emerged. They include MediaOne, Deutsche Telecom and Telfonika. Microsoft was due to respond to EC competition officials by 4 July to allay fears that it might inhibit technological development by forcing its software on emerging interactive TV and cable internet services.

Radio into pay-TV

26 MAY GWR announced plans to launch a pay-TV channel version of its Classic FM radio station via the Daily Mail and General Trust's Performance arts TV station. DMGT owns 18.8 per cent of GWR and the pair have also agreed to develop internet portals where DMGT owns local papers.

ONdigital pay TV

19 JUNE In a move to make pay TV pay him more money, John Egan - ONdigital's former director of operations and strategy - threatened to take his ex-employers to an industrial tribunal. Egan claims he was only awarded half of a promised £100,000 bonus.

Microsoft not a UK TV player

7 JULY The European Commission thwarted Microsoft's bid to seize joint control of Telewest and thus impose its software standards on British interactive TV. The commission said: "[This ends] the possibility of Microsoft exercising decisive influence over the British broadband cable industry."

Sky goes for 7m pay-TV viewers

26 JULY Tony Ball, the BSkyB chief executive, announced a target for 7 million subscribers for its digital satellite service by 2003. It already had 3.8 million digital subscribers and Sky's ambitious plans gave a spur to government plans to end all analogue TV transmission within the decade. A couple of days earlier Sky took control of Open, the interactive TV supplier, in a deal that valued the business at £1.1 billion.

Radio

BBC RADIO INTRODUCTION **260-261**
BBC RADIO LISTINGS **262-263**
INDEPENDENT RADIO INTRODUCTION **264-265**
INDEPENDENT RADIO LISTINGS **266-282**
DIGITAL AND SATELLITE RADIO **283-286**

Record fine

6 SEPTEMBER 1999 Oxygen FM (Oxford), the first radio station for students, got a £20,000 Radio Authority fine and had its eight year licence shortened by two years. The unprecedented punishment was for the fabricated tapes Oxygen sent to the Radio Authority in its attempt to convince the industry watchdog it was fulfilling licence requirements to broadcast discussion, science and arts programmes.

Capital restaurant debacle

15 OCTOBER Capital Radio lost £35 million when it sold the My Kinda Town Latin American restaurant chain. The failed attempt at diversification beyond radio began in 1996 when Capital was led by Richard Eyre - the restless chief executive who has since taken his business acumen first to ITV network and then on to Pearson TV.

Digital radio

15 NOVEMBER A new era in commercial radio broadcasting began when Digital One started transmission of five of the multiplex's ten digital stations. Crystal clear reception - on radio sets costing around £500 - came from two new stations called Planet Rock (Bowie, the Doors etc) and Core (Britney Spears, Steps etc) plus Talk Radio, Virgin Radio and Classic FM. They joined the BBC's five channels which were already transmitted digitally - but only to about 3,000 digital radio users. GWR, which runs Classic FM and owns 63 per cent of Digital One, estimates that nearly a half of British households will own a digital radio by 2008. All that is for an uncertain digital future on the radio. With no digital TV-style giveaways of reception equipment, market reaction was tepid. An analyst at West LB Panmure said: "Unless these organisations are going to give away radios, it's not going to be a massive take up."

Talk

21 OCTOBER The Wireless Group bought the Independent Radio Group for £21.4 million. Kelvin McKenzie (left), who bought Talk Radio for £25 million in 1998, thus added Scot FM and another half dozen stations to a radio empire valued at nearly £100 million. In November the Rajar figures revealed Talk's shift from speech to sport had lost it 400,00 listeners. In April 2000 McKenzie disclosed plans to float the Wireless Group on the stock market at a valuation between £170 million and £200 million to make the former Sun editor a millionaire 14 times over.

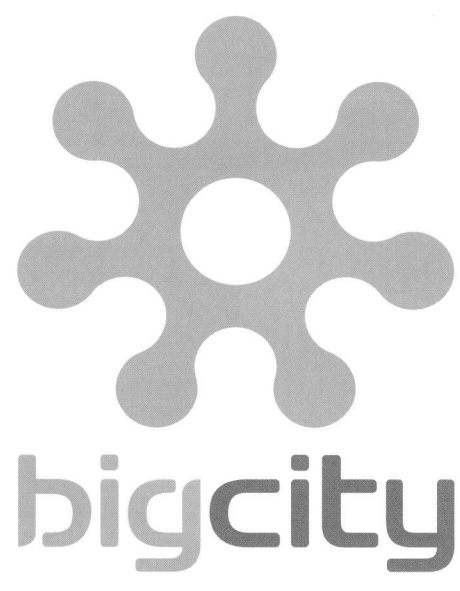

bigcity

8 radio stations, 2 million 15-34 year old listeners, 1 brand.

Alastair Cooke

17 DECEMBER 1999 Alastair Cooke's weekly Letter From America on Radio 4 was cancelled for the first time in 31 years. The 92-year-old Cooke - who began as a broadcaster half a century ago - had recovered sufficiently from bronchitis to resume transmission a week later.

Look, no radio

CHRISTMAS 1999 Despite getting no airplay from Radio 1 and 2, Capital and Virgin, Sir Cliff Richards' Millennium Prayer sold well enough to be top of the pop charts. Angry Cliff fans met outside the BBC, and the Christian station Premier Radio plugged the song hard. Sir Cliff (pictured above), who describes himself as "Britain's only radical pop star, said: "I thought I ought to start looking for my own radio station."

WEIRD NO 1s

Two Little Boys, Rolf Harris, 1969

Chirpy Chirpy Cheep Cheep, Middle of the Road, 1971

Ernie, Benny Hill, 1971

Shadduppa Your Face, Joe Dolce, 1981

Lord's Prayer/Auld Lang Syne, Sir Cliff, 1999

New Radio Authority boss

1 JANUARY 2000 Richard Hooper began a five year tenure as Radio Authority chairman. The ex-BBC producer, who led the net forerunner Prestel, got praise from the culture secretary Chris Smith: "Richard has a strong background and knowledge of the broadcast media industry. As a founder member of the Radio Authority, he is well placed to steer it in the coming years."

Talk Sport

JANUARY Plain old Talk Radio relaunched itself as talkSPORT, aimed at males aged between 25 and 44. Though the Radio Authority sanctioned change occurred with MacKenzie admitting an insufficient sports content - it beat the BBC to the punch by securing live rights for the Mike Tyson vs Julius Francis heavyweight fight in January 2000.

Curb on yob radio

4 FEBRUARY The Radio Authority began a public consultation into undisciplined local radio stations. This followed two record £50,000 fines on the Xfm station in London for discussing bestiality in a breakfast show and on Hallam FM in Sheffield for a "gratuitous description of paedophilia and the condoning and encouragement of rape" during a late-night phone-in show. The well-established DJ Simon Yates said: "There are too many desperate middle-aged disc jockeys working on tiny local radio stations trying to draw attention to themselves, like a seven-year old boy using rude words at the breakfast table."

BBC radio edges ahead

9 FEBRUARY Rajar audience figures revealed a growing market where commercial radio stations continued to lose audience share. Between October and December the BBC captured 51.3 per cent of the audience (up by 1%) and the advertising stations fell from 47.8 per cent to 46.7 per cent. Speech based output from Radio 4, Five Live and Talk Sport all attracted extra listeners.

Cakes and water

13 MARCH The wheels fell off the Radio 1 Road Show - seaside radio frolicking begun from a caravan in Newquay by Alan Freeman in 1973. In its place came the citified One Big Day. The former Radio 1 controller Matthew Bannister had never been a fan of the road show format. "There was lots of sexism and patronising on air," he said. "There was a lot of throwing cream cakes and water over women." In place of cakes and water, the radio audience was promised video screens and headline acts.

Capture your youth! In November, **POP2000** at the NEC will be bursting with the latest in pop talent, from SClub7 and Atomic Kitten to Billie Piper and Keith Duffy. The first total teen-based exhibition in the UK, POP2000 focuses on what's hot with today's teens, from music and fashion to technology and games. Aimed at 8-18 year olds, POP2000 is the ultimate chance to reach the whole youth market, giving you a unique opportunity to **develop your brand.**

popworld.com™ PRESENTS

POP 2000

the nec
birmingham

NOVEMBER 17-18-19 2000

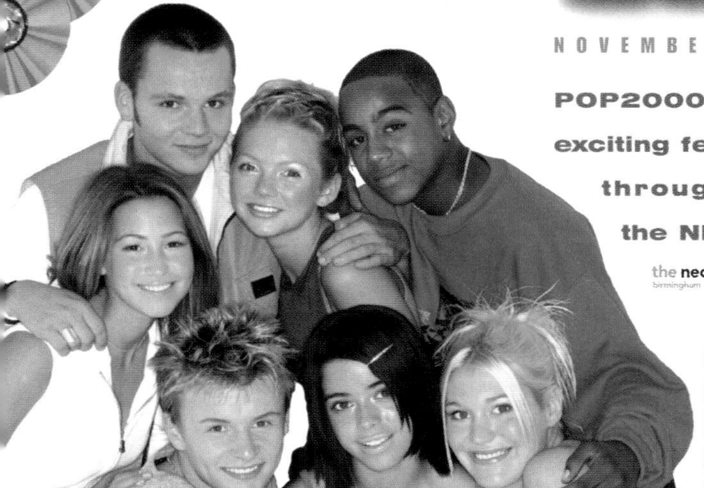

POP2000 is organised into 5 exciting feature areas spread throughout three halls of the NEC.

the nec group birmingham · MUSIC INNOVATIONS · gem

5 major feature areas

- POP PERFORMANCE STAGE
- POP FASHION RUNWAY
- POP MUSIC ON-LINE
- POP RECORDING STUDIO
- POP PLAY

or sponsorship and marketing call Georgina Capp @ Music Innovations on 0171 801 1976
or stand inquiries call Beverley Channell at The Nec on 0121 767 2117 Fax: 0121 767 3535

0121 767 2117

96·4 FM BRMB · TOWER RECORDS·VIDEO·BOOKS · Polaroid i-zone Instant Pocket Camera · GIVENCHY OBLIQUE

Should you stay, or should you go?

Second London multiplex

8 APRIL 2000 Kelvin MacKenzie and Chris Evans fronted the successful Switchmedia bid for London's second digital multiplex licence. They beat off a rival Guardian/GWR bid with plans to digitally broadcast Jazz FM, Saga Radio (easy listening), a Virgin soul station and a Ministry of Sound dance station. "Everything will be digital from photography to television to radio," MacKenzie said. "I've heard all the arguments against digital radio but then I heard all the arguments against digital in TV and that is rocking."

Good Virgin, bad Virgin

11 APRIL The Radio Authority renewed Virgin's national broadcasting licence "following its commitment to a digital simulcast service". A month later the authority fined Virgin £75,000 as punishment for Chris Evans' open support of Ken Livingstone during the London mayoral election. The boy got off lightly, with the Radio Authority commenting: "Since the broadcast was carried on national as well as a local station, the authority could have fined Virgin Radio up to 5 per cent of qualifying revenue (ie revenue gained from advertising and sponsorship), that is to say around £1 million."

Capital buys Border radio

19 APRIL Capital beat off Scottish Radio Holdings to gain control of Border, with a 32 per cent shareholding which valued the company at £151 million. Capital immediately confirmed the sale of Border's TV interests to Granada for £50.5 million and retained Border's three Century radio stations. After the acquisition setback Scottish Radio insisted it was still on the acquisition trail.

Radio 5 Live boss

25 APRIL The eight month search for a new Radio 5 Live boss ended with an in-house appointment when Bob Shennan moved into the job from head of BBC Sport. "Bob loves radio," enthused Jenny Abramsky, the BBC's director of radio. "I am really pleased that someone who has nurtured Radio 5 Live will be taking the network into the future."

BBC "connecting England"

12 MAY The BBC launched a five year plan to boost its 39 local stations by promising no more station mergers and an increase in local content. "Localness is the key," said Andy Griffee, the controller of BBC English regions. "Gone are the days of merging local radio stations and instead we're looking to provide more local services."

Kershaw booted out

24 MAY A middle-aged consensus had it that Radio 1's quest for teeny boppers led to Andy Kershaw (above) getting the sack. Kershaw's 15 year DJ-ing stint at Radio 1 gave him a genuine authority for introducing British audiences to a wide variety of musicians including Youssou N'Dour, Nusrat Fateh and Nirvana. "It is essential Radio 1 keeps moving and keeps changing," said the Radio 1 controller Andy Parfitt. "Heads should roll," said Ian Anderson, the editor of f-Roots magazine. "Andy is the kind of broadcaster the BBC should be cultivating: he manages to enthuse and inform, educate and entertain from a strong position of knowledge, experience and good judgment."

What the papers said

25 (and 24) MAY Radio 4's Charlotte Green got her script muddled when she read the previous day's headlines during the Today programme's round up of the day's papers. "It's just one of those things," said a Radio 4 spokesman.

Television: introduction

British TV splits into four categories. The BBC is publicly funded via an annual licence fee that raised a total of £2.3 billion in 1999. It is broadcast nationally with regional variations on BBC1 (which spent £752 million in 1998 and £823 million in 1999) and BBC2 (£406 million 1998, £421 million 1999). The commercial stations pulled in £2.725 billion worth of advertising split between ITV (aka Channel 3), which is broadcast regionally on 16 stations plus Channel 4 (£590 million in advertising in 1999), Channel 5 (£187 million) and S4C in Wales (£9 million). Then comes satellite and cable which are funded by £2 billion worth of subscriptions and advertising sales spread over more than 200 TV channels which, mostly, are broadcast nationally. Then there is digital where the potential is for up to 36 digital terrestrial, over 150 digital satellite and up to 400 digital cable channels.

Everybody wants a slice of digital action, with the BBC alone reporting a £208 million digital expenditure for 1999. All this is underwritten by a government which has set the analogue-to-digital deadline to 2010, by when - more than likely - there will be internet access to every home with a telephone and a television. As communications methods converge, so the number and type of TV channels increases and with it the competition for a fixed number of consumers and a challenge to the government-led public service assumptions that have determined most of British broadcasting history.

"What public service means is changing," says the culture secretary Chris Smith. "But it needs a redefinition rather than a requiem. That doesn't mean abandoning the concept altogether." Smith - who has been one of the more publicity-shy government ministers - will reappear in the limelight when his department and the Department of Trade produce their joint communications white paper in autumn 2000. One likely change is an homogenisation of the regulatory diversity where the Independent Television Commission licenses digital and terrestrial commercial TV, the Broadcasting Standards Commission inspects the content of all TV and radio, the BBC governors ensure that the BBC "fulfils its obligations" and the Office of Fair Trading covers the pricing of broadcast

Television sex

The past year has seen liberals watching sex on TV and - like the illiberal Mary Whitehouse before them - saying enough is enough.

Polly Toynbee used her Radio Times column to tell the BBC to stop "sexy freak shows" and said BBC2's Adult Lives used the "language of the porn business". "If serious subjects don't get big audiences," she wrote, "then the BBC should decide that high ratings don't matter or admit that analytical documentaries are a thing of the past and stop pretending with crowd pleasing stuff like this."

In May 2000 Jonathan Freedland listed the soft porn he'd seen in a week: C4's Secret Life of a Victorian Pornographer; Anna Karenina billed as "heroine or harlot"; ITV's Pleasure Island about sex and tourism; a BBC trailer with a girl saying she'd sold sex for a packet of cigarettes; Eurotrash; Ali G; Chris Evans; and a host of suggestive ads. "It's back to the dolly-bird culture of the 70s with none of the self-imposed restraint," Freedland wrote in the Guardian. "Does any of this matter? Shouldn't we all lighten up and rejoice in a once-puritanical nation that has learned to let its hair down and delight in the beauty of the human form? This is the chief argument of the new pornographers - but it is a trap designed especially to catch liberals ... The greatest crime of the pornographers is theft. They are stealing what should be a private, even spiritual part of human experience and turning it into a commodity. If they prevail, they will have proved that there is nothing that cannot be sold; even desire, that part of us which lives as long as the human heart."

SHARE OF TOTAL AUDIENCE

CHANNEL	'99-00	'98-99	'97-98
BBC 1	28.20%	29.00%	30.40%
BBC 2	10.80%	11.20%	11.30%
Channel 4	10.00%	9.90%	10.00%
Channel 5	5.60%	4.60%	3.20%
Sky	5.20%	5.00%	5.30%
Central	4.50%	4.70%	4.80%
Granada TV	3.80%	3.90%	3.90%
Yorkshire	3.20%	3.40%	3.40%
Carlton	2.70%	3.00%	2.90%
Meridian	2.40%	2.50%	2.50%
HTV	2.20%	2.30%	2.40%
LWT	1.90%	2.00%	2.00%
Scottish	1.80%	2.00%	2.10%
Anglia	1.80%	1.90%	1.90%
GMTV	1.60%	1.60%	1.70%
Sky One	1.60%		
Tyne Tees	1.50%	1.60%	1.70%
Ulster	1.00%	1.00%	1.00%
UK Gold	0.90%	0.80%	0.60%
Sky Sports 1	0.90%		
Westcountry	0.80%	0.80%	0.90%
Sky Premier	0.80%		
Cartoon N'work	0.80%	0.80%	0.80%
Nickelodeon	0.70%	0.70%	0.70%
Grampian	0.60%	0.60%	0.60%
Sky Sports 2	0.60%		
Living	0.50%	0.60%	0.40%
Border	0.50%	0.50%	0.50%
Sky Moviemax	0.50%		
MTV	0.40%	0.40%	0.30%
Sky News	0.40%		
Disney Channel	0.40%	0.30%	0.30%

SHARE OF TOTAL AUDIENCE CONT.

CHANNEL	'99-00	'98-99	'97-98
ZEE TV Europe	0.30%	0.20%	0.10%
Granada Plus	0.30%	0.20%	0.20%
Discovery	0.30%	0.30%	0.30%
S4C Wales	0.30%	0.30%	0.40%
Eurosport	0.30%	0.30%	0.30%
VH-1	0.30%	0.30%	0.20%
Bravo	0.20%	0.30%	0.30%
Challenge TV	0.20%	0.20%	0.20%
Discovery Home	0.20%	0.20%	0.10%
QVC	0.20%	0.20%	0.10%
Sci-Fi Channel	0.20%	0.20%	0.10%
Sky Sports 3	0.20%		
The Box	0.20%	0.10%	0.10%
Paramount	0.20%	0.10%	0.10%
Trouble	0.20%	0.10%	
TNT	0.10%	0.20%	0.10%
BBC News 24	0.10%	0.10%	
Channel TV	0.10%	0.10%	0.10%
CNN	0.10%	0.10%	0.10%
Fox Kids Netw'k	0.10%	0.10%	0.10%
Live TV	0.10%	0.10%	0.10%
Network 2	0.10%	0.10%	0.10%
Animal Planet	0.10%		
History Channel	0.10%		
RTE 1	0.10%	0.10%	0.10%
RTE 2	0.10%		
UK Horizons	0.10%	0.10%	
ITV 2	0.10%		
Nick Jr	0.10%		
Sky Box Office	0.10%		
Sky Cinema	0.10%		
UK Style	0.10%		

VIEWERS' FAVOURITE

ITV 41%
BBC1 30%

A BBC spokesman said:
"The ITC survey of viewers' favourite channels asked viewers what they thought rather than what they did."

SHARE OF TOTAL TELEVISION AUDIENCE

BBC 39%
ITV 30.4%

Channel 4 10.0%
Cable 9.8%
Channel 5 5.6%
Sky 5.2%

In the chart above, point size stands for 1 per cent of audience share. The figures for 1999 were:
BBC 40.2%; ITV 32.9%; C4 9.9%; C5 5.6%; Sky 5.2%

Source for all charts: ITC, June 2000

TOP 20 PROGRAMMES OF 1999

TITLE	AUDIENCE OF MILLIONS	DATE OF TRANSMISSION	SOURCE	TYPE
1 **Coronation Street**	19.82	Sun Mar 7	Granada	soap
2 **Who Wants ... Millionaire?**	19.21	Sun Mar 7	ITV	game show
3 **Coronation Street**	19.03	Mon Jan 4	Granada	soap
4 **Coronation Street**	18.22	Wed Jan 13	Granada	soap
5 **Heartbeat**	17.01	Sun Feb 28	Yorkshire	family drama
6 **Touch of Frost**	16.85	Sun Mar 21	Yorkshire	crime drama
7 **Coronation Street**	16.75	Fri Jan 8	Granada	soap
8 **Who Wants ... Millionaire?**	16.24	Tues Mar 16	ITV	game show
9 **Who Wants ... Millionaire?**	16.05	Thurs Mar 11	ITV	game show
10 **Who Wants ... Millionaire?**	16.01	Wed Jan 13	ITV	game show
11 **East Enders**	15.72	Thurs Jan 7	BBC1	soap
12 **Man U v B Munich**	15.62	Wed May 26	ITV Sport	football
13 **Coronation Street**	15.50	Sat Dec 25	Granada	soap
14 **Who Wants ...Millionaire?**	15.41	Fri Jan 8	ITV	game show
15 **East Enders**	15.40	Mon Oct 25	BBC1	soap
16 **East Enders**	15.38	Tues Jan 26	BBC1	soap
17 **Walking with Dinosaurs**	15.00	Mon Oct 4	BBC1	documentary
18 **England v Scotland**	14.60	Wed Nov 17	ITV Sport	football
19 **East Enders**	14.39	Sun Sep 5	BBC1	soap
20 **Vicar of Dibley**	14.37	Mon Dec 27	BBC1	sitcom

Source: Royal Television Society

transmissions. They could well give way to a single regulator which has already been christened Ofcom and will liaise more easily with the OFT, the Competition Commission and parliament.

Pre-white paper in the summer of 2000 there was the sound of lobbying. Contradictory noises from within the BBC say that it should no longer be chasing ratings or that it should have more freedom to dabble in commercialism. There's greater unanimity among ITV companies which want to coalesce into units where a single company is allowed to have more than 15 per cent of audience and 25 per cent of advertising in one area. They also want an end to their £400 million a year licence payments and (for a favourite phrase of deregulators) a more level playing field to compete with Sky - which thrives on much money from relatively few subscribers and has inflated costs to the point where it is paying £360 million a year for live football.

Each extra choice creates more expense and confusion. Free marketeers point to the triumph of technology in providing choice but that raises old questions put by the drama critic Clive Barnes who, in the 1980s, said: "Television is the first truly democratic culture - the first culture available to everybody and entirely governed by what people want. The most terrifying thing is what people do want." It's certainly terrifying to a cultural elite nurtured on Reithian ideals of informed entertainment. Perceptions of Quality in Television Production, a recent report by Cambridge University, asked when more choice equals less choice and concluded: "Government regulation has imposed competition on the television industry which has led to ratings-driven production companies all fighting for the middle ground. The pressures on budgets have also grown increasingly through the tendering of licences and franchises and the advent of Channel 5 as a low-budget channel."

Dumbing down is the cliché for it and an Observer survey clothed assertion in statistics when it logged the extent to which current affairs, documentaries and drama have been edged out by chat shows, quizzes and docu-soaps. The study found that since 1980 the amount of light TV has risen from 17 per cent to 33 per cent over the past two decades while serious programmes have fallen from 44 per cent to 29 per cent.

"I find television very educational," said Groucho Marx. "Every time someone switches it

Walking With Dinosaurs was a BBC triumph, yet it was only 17th in the 1999 ABC viewer ratings and this in a year when BBC1 recorded its lowest ever audience figure of 28.3 per cent. There was nothing from the BBC in the top ten and little - to quote the Royal Television Society - "to justify the Corporation's pretensions as a convenor of the whole nation for shared amusement and talking points".

on I go into another room and read a book." TV might have worked like this on Groucho Marx but it doesn't have the same effect on the British TV audience. Yet another survey - this one by the Organisation for Economic Co-operation and Development - linked high television watching with low levels of literacy. It found that British citizens top an international list of those who tune in for more than two hours a day with six out of ten saying they watch for more than two hours a day. Britain is 13th in a league table of adults who say they read a book at least once a month, and scores poorly in overall comparisons of literacy. Patrick Werquin, the OECD functionary who wrote the report, made the obvious conclusion. "Watching a lot of television goes against literacy. If you are watching TV, you are not reading a book."

Quality ahead of ratings

Rumours of an entertainment-only BBC1 aside - the BBC says it is returning to its Reithian roots of informing as well as entertaining. Walking With Dinosaurs is a case in point. Executives promised to take more risks - Beeb talk for fewer docusoaps - and promised not to sideline current affairs programmes to late evenings. The BBC pledged Question Time would be broadcast no later than 10.30pm and Everyman and Omnibus no later than 10.40pm. The TV adaptation of Mervyn Peake's Gormenghast bombed and a spokeswoman said: "If you're going to use something as crude and blunt as numbers as a barometer, you're not doing it justice. We're concerned about something more visceral." The same script was used when the Welsh political programme The Point failed to register in the ratings when it was watched by fewer than the 2,500 people necessary to trigger the counting mechanism. A spokesman said: "This is public service broadcasting and we're not in a ratings war."

BBC Television

Defending the Beeb

In August 1999 a Guardian/ICM poll exposed public criticism of its programmes, opposition to increased licence fees and support for the BBC exploiting advertising and sponsorship.

POINTS OF VIEW

	YES	NO
better over last 5 years?	8%	45%
digital supplement?	35%	58%
higher licence?	17%	79%
BBC adverts?	65%	30%
sponsored programmes?	77%	17%

Source: Guardian/ICM, August 1999

A Guardian leader said: "Our poll will delight the BBC's detractors and leave the corporation close to despair ... Loyalty to the BBC was once a general, almost unthinking response across the country. Not any more. There is more diversity now, and a lot less deference. To maintain its place in the world, to convince its political paymasters that it is worth the money it is asking for, the BBC needs public respect and loyalty."

In December a National Consumer Council poll revealed that 60 per cent of viewers felt they were not getting good value for the licence fee and the NCC said the BBC might not survive the digital age unless it was made more accountable to consumers. Meanwhile a BBC poll of licence payers generated 5,378 questionnaires where 86 per cent of respondents believed it Very Important that the BBC maintains its current breadth of programming. Sir Christopher Bland, the BBC chairman, said: "In the week beginning 6 November, a week in which you could have watched The River, Ivan the Terrible, Walking With Dinosaurs, The Cops, Real Women, How Do You Want Me? And the League of Gentlemen on BBC Television, or listened to a new Nicholas Nickleby or the original Under Milk Wood on BBC Radio, ITV's peak time offerings included nine episodes of Coronation Street, five of Emmerdale and Who Wants to be a Millionaire? stripped across every night of the week. But no peak-time science, no religion, no mid evening news, no current affairs."

In May 2000 BBC2 broadcast Peter Taylor's trilogy of programmes about Northern Ireland and a Guardian leader commented. "The entire series took five years to make. It was never going to reach a mass audience (though many serious newspapers and magazines would be pleased to reach its audience of 1.5 million). It involved thousands of hours of research, a hundred hours of filming and, in Peter Taylor's case, a lifetime of contacts and reading. It is no coincidence that the other outstanding documentary series of the past five years, Norma Percy's The Death of Yugoslavia, was also commissioned by the BBC. Every time a Murdoch tabloid sneers at the BBC, remember these two series. There is still such a thing as serious television journalism in this country and it appears to be increasingly pointless to expect it any more from ITV. There was some small irony that the last episode of Mr Taylor's series coincided with the ITC asking whether public service broadcasting can be sustained - or is even needed - any longer on commercial channels."

Gavyn Davies led the working party into the BBC's future: "There is no public outcry against the concept of the licence fee. Indeed, in all the evidence received by my panel, almost no one argued that advertising on the BBC would be good for broadcasting in this country."

Attacking the Beeb

Backbiting

Dawn Airey, Channel 5 director of programmes
"The fact is that BBC1 at the moment is failing to deliver the high-audience quality drama and comedy that the licence payer is entitled to expect. Repeat comedies ... fail to reach the five million audience mark which should represent the minimum entry level for BBC1 peak."
(Airey was being tipped as a future BBC1 controller.)

Alasdair Milne, former BBC director general
"The BBC has huge problems. Its main competitive channel, BBC1, is in a mess. Comedy is non-existent and there is no contemporary drama worth talking about. Most of the decent programmes it shows are repeats."
(In 1987 Milne became the only BBC director general to be fired since the war.)

Michael Grade, former head of Channel 4
"John Birt was so sure that he was right that anyone who challenged his ideas became not just a sceptic but an enemy. The place for enemies was outer darkness, into which some of the most talented and experienced BBC staff were cast. Whatever he put into the BBC, he sure as hell took the fun out of working there."
(Grade had been tipped for Birt's job.)

Hand biting

The first episode of the Starting Out sit-com in September 2000 coincided with its writers, Laurence Marks and Maurice Gran (pictured below) - who have earned millions from writing shows like Birds of a Feather and Love Hurts - attacking the "scared, low-brow BBC". Gran (right) said: "BBC1 is now the most mimsy and restrictive of all the networks." Marks added his two penn'orth: "I'm disenchanted with the fact that show business, which is why we came into this industry, has disappeared under John Birt. But Greg [Dyke] may bring show business back into television."

BBC overview

BBC MAIN OFFICES

BBC Corporate HQ & BBC Broadcast
BBC Broadcasting House, Portland Place, London
W1A 1AA
Tel 020-7580 4468
Website: www.bbc.co.uk
The hub of the BBC and the HQ for BBC Radio

BBC News, BBC Production, BBC Broadcast - Network Television
BBC Television Centre, Wood Lane, London W12 7RJ
Tel 020-8743 8000
The HQ for BBC News and Television Divisions

BBC World Service
Bush House, London WC2B 4PH
Tel 020-7240 3456
HQ of the BBC's World Service

BBC Worldwide
Woodlands, 80 Wood Lane, London W12 0TT
Tel 020-8743 3200
Headquarters of BBC commercial activities.

BBC White City
201 Wood Lane, London W12 7TS
Tel 020-8743 8000
The HQ of BBC Resources Ltd

BBC Written Archives
Caversham Park, Reading, Berkshire, RG4 8TZ
Tel 01734-472742

BBC PRESS OFFICES

The main BBC press office is at Television Centre and is the first point of call for press enquiries. Its opening hours are 8.00am to midnight on weekdays, and 10am to 11pm at the weekend.

Main press office	020-8576 1865
World Service	020-7557 2941
News	020-8576 7726
Resources	020-8752 4047
Worldwide:	020-8433 2339

BBC REGULATION

The BBC is a corporation established by Royal Charter. This sets out its public obligations and establishes the Governors as supervisors of BBC management and trustees for the public interest. The standards and services required of the BBC are set out in an agreement between the BBC and Government, which recognises the BBC's editorial independence. The 12 Governors are appointed by the Crown on advice from ministers. They are independent men and women with a range of experience and interests. The Governors are the trustees for the public interest in the BBC - ensuring that the organisation is properly accountable while maintaining its independence. Exercising their authority on behalf of the public, the Governors hold management to account. The Governors are committed to keeping in touch with the views of BBC audiences. They undertake a range of activities to help them achieve this including: public consultations; obtaining independent advice about BBC programmes; and audience research and public events.

BBC BOARD OF GOVERNORS
Chairman: Sir Christopher Bland (to 31.3.03)
Vice-Chair: Baroness Young of Old Scone (leaving before the end of 2000)
National governor for Scotland: Sir Robert Smith (31.07.03)
National governor for Northern Ireland: Prof. Fabian Monds CBE (31.07.03)
National governor for Wales: Roger Spencer Jones OBE (31.12.01)
ENGLISH NATIONAL FORUM
Chair: Ranjit Sondhi (31.7.02)
Dame Pauline Neville-Jones DCMG (31.12.01)
Baroness Hogg (08.02.04)
Adrian White CBE (31.10.00)
Sir Richard Eyre CBE (31.10.00)
Tony Young (31.7.02)
Heather Rabbatts (31.1.04)

EXECUTIVE COMMITTEE

The Director-General is the BBC's chief executive and editor-in-chief. The governors appoint the director-general and, with him, the most senior management. Day to day management is the responsibility of the executive committee led by the DG. In April 2000 Greg Dyke, the new director general, introduced a new management structure, putting stronger emphasis on programmes.

BBC operations are now run by the directors of nine programming and broadcasting divisions and six professional services, and by the chief executives of the BBC's two commercial businesses.

BBC EXECUTIVE COMMITTEE
Director-General: Greg Dyke
Director, drama, entertainment and children's: Alan Yentob
Director, television: Mark Thompson
Director, finance, property and business affairs: John Smith
Chief executive, BBC Resources Ltd: Margaret Salmon
Director, distribution and technology: Philip Langsdale
Director, human resources and internal communications: Gareth Jones
Director, public policy: Caroline Thomson
Director, BBC News: Tony Hall
Chief executive, BBC Worldwide Ltd: Rupert Gavin
Director, strategy: Carolyn Fairbairn
Director, BBC World Service: Mark Byford
Director, marketing and communications: Matthew Bannister
Director, radio: Jenny Abramsky
Director, new media: Ashley Highfield
Director, sport: Richard Sambrook (currently acting director until an appointment is made)
Joint Directors, factual and learning: Michael Stevenson and Lorraine Heggessey
Director, nations and regions: Pat Loughrey

Greg Dyke, the new BBC director general. In Spring 2000, his management shakeout emphasised programme making, with a new structure comprising: nine programming and broadcasting divisions; six professional services; and two commercial businesses.

THE BBC'S NEW MANAGEMENT STRUCTURE

PROGRAMMING AND BROADCASTING
Television
News
Nations and regions
Drama, entertainment and children's
Factual and learning
Sports
World Service
New media
Radio ... see Radio section, pages 262-263

COMMERCIAL BUSINESSES
BBC Worldwide
BBC Resources

PROFESSIONAL SERVICES
Marketing and communications
Distribution and technology
Public policy
Human resources/internal communications
Finance, property and business affairs
Strategy

BBC programming and broadcasting

Television

Responsible for the network television (BBC1 BBC2, BBC Choice), for commissioning in most genres, for broadcasting and presentation services and for supporting other television channel operations across the BBC.

News

Responsible for the BBC's national and international news and current affairs programmes on television, radio and online services at home and abroad, including specialist services such as BBC News 24, News Online and BBC World.

Nations and regions

Responsible for programmes and services on all media for audiences in Scotland, Wales, Northern Ireland and the English regions.

Drama, entertainment and children

The Drama, Entertainment and Children's Division is responsible for the production of drama, film and entertainment and for commissioning and producing children's programming and services.

Factual and learning

Produces specialist factual output and features. It also commissions and produces education programming and runs specialist education services.

Sports

Responsibile for all sport output and for running specialist services such as Sports Online.

World Service

Reaches 151 million listeners around the world with a huge range of programmes from authoritative news coverage to sport and the arts. BBC World Service can now be heard on FM in 110 of the world's capital cities.

New media

Leads new media developments across the BBC, bringing together online and interactive TV departments and new developments.

Radio

Responsible for BBC network radio - Radios 1, 2, 3, 4 and Radio 5 Live - and for music production. From the end of 2000 the Asian network will be included in this division.

BBC TELEVISION

Television Centre, Wood Lane, London W12 7RJ
Tel 020-8743 8000
Over 17,000 hours of television programmes are broadcast each year on BBC1 and BBC2. The great majority of programmes are commissioned in-house but the BBC has a statutory obligation to ensure that 25 per cent of its network television programmes are made by independent producers and, further, that a significant proportion are made in the regions outside London.

Director of television: Mark Thompson
Entertainment genre commissioner: Danielle Lux
Arts genre commissioner: Roly Keating
Drama genre commissioner: tba
Controller, BBC1: Peter Salmon
Controller, BBC2: Jane Root
Head of programming, BBC Choice: Stuart Murphy
Controller, press & publicity: Sally Osman
Head, television press & publicity: Vanda Rumney

BBC NEWS

Television Centre, Wood Lane, London W12 7RJ
Tel 020-8743 8000
Press Office: Tel 020-8576 7726
BBC News is the biggest newsgathering operation in the world, with journalists reporting for BBC World Service radio and BBC World television as well as the BBC's UK radio and television outlets. BBC News has more than 55 bureaux around the world, more than 200 specialist correspondents and employs some 2,000 journalists in total. There are four specialist units: world affairs; economics and business; politics; and social affairs.

Director, news: Tony Hall
Deputy director: Richard Sambrook
Asst director: Mark Damazer
Controller, finance: Peter Phillips
Controller, personnel: Lesley Hopkins
Head of current affairs: Peter Horrocks
Head of political programming: Francesca Unsworth
Head of radio news: Steve Mitchell
Head of new media: Richard Deverell
Head of TV news: Roger Mosey
Head of newsgathering: Adrian Van Klaveren
Executive editor radio daily current affairs: Anne Koch

BBC NATIONS AND REGIONS

Broadcasting House. Portland Place, London W1A 1AA

Tel 020-7580 4468
Press office: Tel 020-7765 2797
Director: Pat Loughrey
Financial controller: Sue Timmins
Head of press and publicity: Tim Brassell
Secretary, Regional Broadcasting: Moyra Tourlamain

BBC Scotland

Broadcasting House, Queen Margaret Drive, Glasgow G12 8DG

Tel 0141-339 8844
Controller, Scotland: John McCormick
Head of broadcast: Ken MacQuarrie
Head of production: Colin Cameron
Head of drama: Barbara McKissack
Head of news and current affairs: Blair Jenkins
Head of resources: Andy Davy

BBC Wales

Broadcasting House, Llandaff, Cardiff CF5 2YQ
Tel: 029 2032 2000
website: www.bbc.co.uk/wales

Controller, BBC Wales: Menna Richards
Head of programmes (English): Clare Hudson
Head of programmes (Welsh): Keith Jones
Head of news & current affairs: Aled Eirug
Head of marketing & communications: tbc
Head of public Affairs: Manon Williams
Head of personnel: Keith Rawlings
Head of finance & business affairs: Gareth Powell
Editor, Radio Wales: TBA
Editor, Radio Cymru: Aled Glynne Davies
Editor, BBC Choice Wales: Nick Evans
Head of drama: Matthew Robinson
Head of sport: Arthur Emyr
Head of factual: Adrain Davies
Head of arts: Paul Islwyn
Head of music: David Jackson
Musical director, BBC National Orchestra of Wales: David Murray

BBC Northern Ireland

Broadcasting House, Ormeau Avenue, Belfast BT2 8HQ

Tel 028-9033 8000
Controller: Anna Carragher
Head of news & current affairs: Andrew Colman
Head of factual and learning: tba
Head of entertainment and events: tba
Head of drama: Robert Cooper
Editor Foyle: Ana Leddy
Head of finance: Crawford MacLean
Head of human resources: Liz Torrans
Head of marketing: Peter Johnston
Head of public affairs: Rosemary Kelly
Head of resources: Stephen Beckett

NATIONS AND REGIONS: TV

BBC National & Regional Broadcasting (HQ)
Portland Place, London W1A 1AA
Tel 020-7580 4468

BBC Birmingham (English Regions HQ)
BBC, Pebble Mill, Birmingham B5 7QQ
Fax 0121-432 8364   Tel 0121-432 8888
Daily news programme: Midlands Today

BBC Nottingham
BBC, London Road, Nottingham NG2 4UU
Fax 0115-955 0501   Tel 0115-955 0500
Daily news programme: East Midlands Today

BBC Norwich
St Catherine's Close, All Saint's Green, Norwich, Norfolk NR13ND
Fax 01603-667865   Tel 01603-619331
Daily news programme: Look East

BBC Bristol
Whiteladies Road, Bristol BS8 2LR
Tel 0117-973 2211
Daily news programme: News West

BBC Elstree
Clarendon Road, Borehamwood, Herts WD6 1JF
Fax 020-8228 8092   Tel 020-8953 6100
Daily news programme: Newsroom South East

BBC Southampton
Havelock Road, Southampton, Hants SO14 7PU
Fax 023-8033 9931   Tel 023-8022 6201
Daily news progamme: South Today

BBC Plymouth
Broadcasting House, Seymour Road, Mannamead, Plymouth, Devon PL3 5BD
Fax 01752-234595   Tel 01752-229201
Daily news programme: Spotlight

BBC Manchester
PO Box 27, Oxford Road, Manchester M60 1SJ
Fax 0161-244 4999   Tel 0161-200 2020
Daily news programme: North West Tonight

BBC Leeds
Woodhouse Lane, Leeds, LS2 9PN
Fax 0113-243 9387   Tel 0113-244 1188
Daily news programme: Look North

BBC Newcastle
Barrack Road, Newcastle-upon-Tyne NE99 2NE
Fax 0191-221 0112   Tel 0191-232 1313
Daily news programme: Look North.

SCOTLAND
BBC Glasgow (National HQ)
Queen Margaret Drive, Glasgow G12 8DG
Fax 0141-334 0614   Tel 0141-338 2000
Daily news programme: Reporting Scotland

WALES
BBC Cardiff (National HQ)
Llantrisant Road, Llandaff, Cardiff CF5 2YQ
Fax 029-203 22576   Tel 029-203 22000
Daily news programme: Wales Today

NORTHERN IRELAND
BBC Belfast (National HQ)
Ormeau Avenue, Belfast BT2 8HQ
Fax 028-9033 8800   Tel 028-9033 8000
Daily news programme: Newsline 6.30

BBC SPORT

Television Centre, Wood Lane, London, W12 7RJ
Tel 020 8225 9900
Website: www.bbc.co.uk/sport

BBC Sport is a multimedia division providing live sport action, highlights, commentary and interactive text information across television, radio and online from a broad portfolio of sports rights bigger than all other terrestrial broadcasters in the UK put together. Currently BBC Sport creates nearly 5,000 hours of sport a year and the BBC shows a regular commitment to multi-sport output with around 100 editions of its weekend programme, Grandstand, a year. The BBC Sport Online site launched in the summer of 2000 is one of the most popular websites in Europe.

BBC NEW MEDIA

Television Centre, Wood Lane, London, W12 7RJ
Tel 020 8225 9900

Leads new media developments across the BBC, bringing together online and interactive TV departments and new developments.

BBC WORLD SERVICE

Bush House, The Strand, London WC2B 4PH.
Tel 020-7240 3456
Publicity Office: 020-7557 2941

The BBC World Service brings a world of news, information and entertainment. For more than six decades BBC World Service has earned a reputation for broadcasting excellence and high standards of journalistic integrity and impartiality. As the world's most trusted - and freely available - source of news and analysis World Service output is equally valued in media-rich societies and countries where news is far from free. Broadcasts are funded through the Foreign and Commonwealth office by a Parliamentary Grant in Aid. Operating under the BBC's Royal Charter, World Service has full editorial and managerial independence from commercial or political pressures.

Chief executive: Mark Byford
Deputy chief executive: Caroline Thompson
Director, news and programme commissioning: Bob Jobbins
Director, World Service regions: Andrew Taussig
Controller, resources and technology: Chris Gill
Controller, personnel: Lesley Granger
Finance and commercial director: Andrew Hind

FACTUAL AND LEARNING

Television Centre, Wood Lane, London, W12 7RJ
Tel 020 8225 9900

Produces specialist factual output and features. It also commissions and produces education programming and runs specialist education services.

Directors: Lorraine Heggessey and Michael Stevenson
Chief operating officer: Gary Marvin
Controller, documentaries and investigations: Jeremy Gibson
Controller, factual commissioning: Nicola Moody
Controller, specialist factual: Glenwyn Benson
Controller, leisure and factual entertainment: Anne Morrison
Controller of BBC Knowledge: Liz Cleaver
Controller, children's education: Frank Flynn
Controller, adult learning: Fiona Chesterton

DRAMA, ENT, CHILDREN'S

Television Centre, Wood Lane, London, W12 7RJ
Tel 020 8225 9900

The Drama, Entertainment and Children's Division is responsible for the production of drama, film and entertainment and for commissioning and producing children's programming and services.

Director: Alan Yentob
Controller, programme acquisitions: Sophie Turner Laing
Controller, daytime: Jane Lush
Controller of entertainment: Paul Jackson
Controller, entertainment commissioning: Danielle Lux
Head of entertainment and features Manchester: Wayne Garvie
Drama commissioner: tbc
Head of drama serials: Jane Tranter
Head of drama series: Mal Young
Head of film and single drama: David Thompson
Head of fictionlab: Richard Fell
Head of comedy: Geoffrey Perkins
Head of entertainment: Jon Plowman
Head of light entertainment: David Young

BBC RADIO

See pages 262-263

BBC commerical businesses

BBC WORLDWIDE

Woodlands, 80 Wood Lane, London W12 OTT
Fax 020-8749 0538   Tel 020-8433 2000
Press office: Tel 020-8433 2339
Website: www.bbcworldwide.com
Online programme catalogue:
www.bbcworldwidetv.com

BBC Worldwide Limited is the BBC's commercial
media business. Operating at arm's length from the
rest of the Corporation, its task is to realise the commercial value of BBC programmes and services, selling programmes to overseas broadcasters, operating
commercial channels in joint ventures with others
and publishing magazines, books, videos and CDs.
It was formed in May 1994 to encompass cable and
satellite channels, international programme distribution, internet and interactive activity and publishing.
A family of six themed channels under the UKTV
umbrella - UK Gold, UK Gold 2, UK Drama, UK
Horizons, UK Style and UK Play - reaches 27 million
homes and is established as the second largest block
of cable and satellite channels in Britain. A further
joint venture with Discovery was signed in March
1998. BBC Worldwide has also formed 3 major partnerships in North America. These are with independent merchant bank Veronis Suhler, Granada Media,
and Alliance Atlantis. BBC Worldwide is also a 20
per cent shareholder in UK TV, an entertainment
subscription channel in Australia, along with Pearson
and Foxtel.

Chief executive: Rupert Gavin
**Managing director, UK region & deputy chief execu-
tive:** Peter Teague
Managing director EMEIA: Mark Young
President and CEO, BBC Worldwide Americas: Peter
Phippen
Managing director, Asia/Pacific region: David Vine
**Director, GMBD (global marketing and brand devel-
opment):** Jeff Taylor
Finance director: David King
Director of international TV: Mike Phillips
Director, new ventures & strategy: Jeremy Mayhew
Managing director, BBC World: Patrick Cross
Managing director, internet & interactive: Drew Kaza
Director, business affairs: Sarah Cooper
Director, human resources: Bob McCall
Director of technology: Gary Richards
Director of communications: Janie Ironside-Wood
Director, joint ventures, Olga Edridge
General manager, BBC America: Paul Lee
Vice president, programming, BBC America: Liz
Barron
Chief operating officer, BBC sales company (US):
Candace Carlisle

BBC RESOURCES

BBC Resources Directorate
201 Wood Lane, London W12 7TS
      Tel 020-8752 5252
Press Office: Tel 020-8752 4047

BBC Resources was divided into two enterprises in the
summer of 1998: BBC Resources Limited - a wholly
owned subsidiary of the BBC, trading with both BBC
and independent customers - and Production Services,
which concentrated almost exclusively on BBC
activities. Most of the broadcast facilities were
transferred into the company, including the main
studios, outside broadcast fleet, post production
facilities and graphic design capability. In October 2000
BBC Resources was restructured. Parts of its
Production Services Division were devolved to other
parts of the BBC, leaving Radio Resources and
Production Services England within the division. BBC
Resources Limited now comprises London Studios,
Outside Broadcasts (including OBs in Scotland and
Wales) and Post Production and Graphic Design. It also
continues to manage its businesses in Manchester,
Birmingham and Bristol and the interactive design
business in Belfast. In its first full year of trading as a
wholly owned subsidiary (April 1999 to March 2000)
BBC Resources Ltd's annual turnover was £330 million.
In 2000 Secretary of State approval was sought for
setting up a new BBC owned subsidiary, BBC
Technology Limited, combining staff from Resources
Technology and IT services across the BBC to offer
broadcast, internet and desktop technology services.

Chief executive: Margaret Salmon
Commercial director: David Green
Financial director: Stephen Killick
Director of human resources: Rob Murdoch
Company secretary/legal advisor: Rakesh Nath

Independent TV/ITC

The Independent Television Commission "ensures fair and effective competition in the provision of television services", a grand remit derived from the 1990 and 1996 Broadcasting Acts. Much of that could change if the Communications Bill comes before the 2000/2001 parliament with recommendations to subsume the ITC within a larger regulatory body. For the moment, however, the ITC is responsible for licensing non-BBC television in Britain as shown in the chart below.

ITC licensed TV channels:

TYPE	NUMBER
Channel 3 regional	15
Channel 3 national	
breakfast	1
Channel 4	1
Channel 5	1
Digital terrestrial	3
Digital programme service	18
Digital additional	1
Restricted services	6
Public teletext	1
Other	1
Commercial additional	2
Satellite	250
Licensable programme	
(cable)	87
Local delivery (15 years)	40
Local delivery (5 years)	38
Prescribed diffusion	115

The ITC is a regulator as well as a licensor and in essence its job is to limit the independence of independent broadcasters and maintain a some kind of a public service with the following requirements.

National and international news
Three programmes each weekday of 20 minutes (lunch), 15 minutes (early evening) and half an hour in peak time

Current affairs
One and a half hours weekly average

Children
Ten hours weekly average

Religion
Two hours weekly average

Regional
Varies from franchise to franchise.

ITC Head Office

33 Foley Street, London W1P 7LB
Fax 020-7306 7800   Tel 020-7255 3000
E-mail: publicaffairs@itc.org.uk
Website: www.itc.org.uk
Chief executive: Peter Rogers
Director of economic regulation: Sheila Cassells
Director of programmes & cable: Sarah Thane
Deputy director - programmes: Marion Bowman
Deputy director - cable: Anthony Hewitt
Director of advertising and sponsorship: Stephen Locke
Deputy director - advertising and sponsorship: Ian Blair
Director of public affairs & regions: Richard Peel
Director of engineering: Gary Tonge
Secretary and director of administration: Michael Redley

ITC commission members

Chairman: Sir Robin Biggam, chairman of the Fairey Group.
Alastair Balls, Chief exec of International Centre for Life.
Sir Michael Checkland, a trustee of Reuters and chairman of the Higher Education Council for England. Former non-executive director of Nynex Cablecoms and former director general of the BBC.
Jude Goffe, venture capitalist and non-executive director of Moorfields Eye Hospital.
Maria Moloney, member for Northern Ireland. Director of the Northern Ireland Transport Holding Company.
Professor Derec Llwyd Morgan, member for Wales. Vice Chancellor and principal of the University of Wales. Former member of the BBC's General Advisory Council and the Broadcasting Council, Wales.
Dr Michael Shea, member for Scotland. Writer, broadcaster and visiting professor of personal and corporate communications at the University of Strathclyde.

ITC National and regional offices:

London HQ	020-7255 3000
Northern Ireland	028-9024 8733
Scotland	0141-226 4436
Wales	029-2038 4541
West of England	0117-915 4171
East of England	01603-623533
Midlands - Nottingham	0115-952 7333
North East England	0114-276 9091
North West England	0161-834 2707
S of England, Winchester	01962-883950
S of England, Plymouth	01752-663031

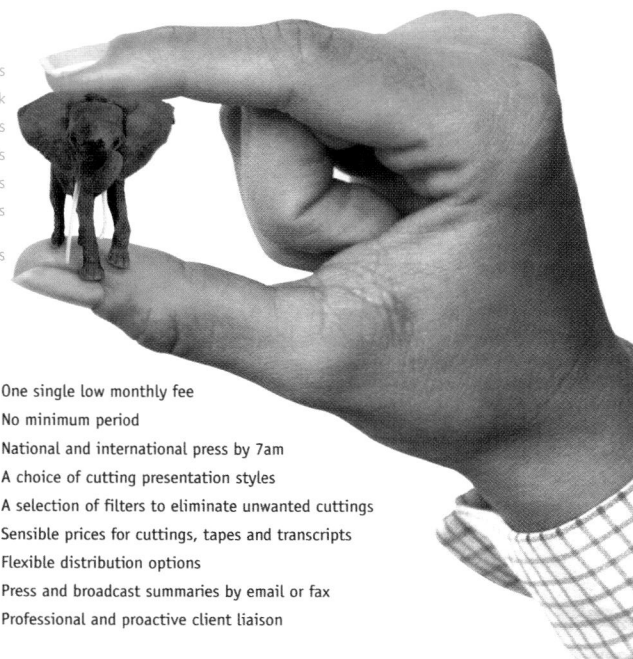

Channel 3 introduction

Channel 3/Independent Television/ITV consists of 15 regional licensees and the GMTV national breakfast station. They divide the UK into 14 regions, all but one of which has a Channel 3 company controlling broadcasting rights. The exception is London which is split between Carlton on weekdays and LWT at weekends.

Channel 3 licensees must produce or commission 65 per cent of programmes. The majority of TV production is co-ordinated in a Byzantine arrangement focussed on ITV Network Centre, a subsidiary owned by the ITV companies to commission programmes shown across the network. C3 news is also produced at Network Centre. Independent Television News has a weekly output of some 30 hours, and also supplies C4 and C5 news.

The delicately wrapped package assembled at the beginning of the nineties to hold British commercial TV together started splitting at the seams in November 1999 when Carlton and UN&M announced their intention to merge. Their prize was a 35 per cent grip on a Channel 3 advertising market worth nearly £2 billion a year and there were two barriers. One, legislation restricting access to more than 15 per cent of the TV audience or 25 per cent of TV advertising. Two, Granadas' intention to scotch the deal. As this book went to press in summer 2000, Granada appeared to have triumphed with the £1.8 billion take over of UN&M.

ITV Network Centre
200 Grays Inn Road, London WC1X 8HF
Fax 020-7843 8158   Tel 020-7843 8000
Council of ITV Association chairman: Leslie Hill
Chief executive: Richard Eyre
Children's programmes: Nigel Pickard
Drama: Nick Elliot
Entertainment: Claudia Rosencrantz
Documentary/factual: Grant Mansfield
Head of sport production: Brian Barwick
News/current affairs, religion: Steve Anderson

ITN
200 Grays Inn Road, London WC1X 8XZ
Fax 020-7430 4016   Tel 020-7833 3000
Press office   Tel 020-7430 4700
Website: www.itn.co.uk
ITN prodcues ITV News, C4 News and Channel 5 News.

CHANNEL 3
(Listings pp216 - 223)

UNITED NEWS AND MEDIA
Anglia on-air since October 1959. 1991 winning licence bid: £17.8 million.
Meridian on-air since 1993. 1991 winning licence bid: £36.52 million. January 1994 taken over by UN&M, with Anglia, in £292 million bid.
HTV on-air since March 1968. 1991 winning licence bid: £20.53 million. June 1997 taken over by UN&M for £372 million.

CARLTON COMMUNICATIONS
Central on-air since January 1982. 1991 licence bid: £2,000.
Carlton on-air since January 1993. 1991 licence bid: £43.17 million. In 1994 Carlton took over Central in £758 million bid.
Westcountry on-air since January 1993. 1991 licence bid: £7.82 million. In 1996 Carlton took over Westcountry for £85 million.

GRANADA GROUP
Granada on-air since 1956. 1991 licence bid: £9m.
LWT on-air since August 1968. 1991 licence bid £7.58m. February 1994 Granada took over LWT for £765m.
Tyne Tees on-air since Jaunary 1959. 1991 licence bid: £15.06m.
Yorkshire on-air since July 1968. 1991 licence bid: £37.7 million. In 1992 Yorkshire took over Tyne Tees in £30.4 million bid. August 1997 Granada took over Yorkshire-Tyne Tees in £711 million bid.

SMG
Scottish TV on-air since August 1957. 1991 licence bid: £2,000.
Grampian on-air since September 1961. 1991 licence bid: £9million. June 1997 Scottish Media Group tookover Grampian.

BORDER
Border on-air since September 1961. 1991 licence bid: £52,000. In April 2000 bought by Granada.

ULSTER
Ulster on-air since October 1959. 1991 licence bid: £1.03 million.

CTV
Channel on-air since September 1962. 1991 licence bid: £1,000.

GMTV
GMTV (Sunrise) on-air since January 1993. 1991 licence bid: £34.61 million.

Take over times

SMG's GMTV take-over attempt
2 SEPTEMBER 1999 The Scottish Media Group sought to increase its 20 per cent holding in the GMTV breakfast TV company. The move came as GMTV had just started moving into profit having had a reduction in licence payments which have totalled £300 million since it came on air in 1993. In January 2000 SMG bought the Guardian Media Group's 15 per cent GMTV holding for £5.6 million with a further £500,000 assumed in loan stock. In addition to SMG's 35 per cent, Disney and Granada each have over 20 per cent stakes in GMTV.

Granada attacks SMG's plans
24 NOVEMBER Granada, which owns nearly a quarter of Scottish Media Group, attacked SMG's plans to buy Chris Evans' Ginger Group for upwards of £200 million. There were suggestions that SMG wanted Ginger - which owns Virgin's London FM radio station - as a way of increasing its holdings to the point that a Granada bid for SMG would be thwarted by regulatory difficulties.

Carlton United
26 NOVEMBER Michael Green's Carlton and Lord Hollick's United News and Media proposed a "merger of equals" into a six channel monolith. In February the Competition Commission began an investigation. The deal raised two competitive concerns: first, a joint share of TV advertising exceeding levels defined by the 1990 and 1996 Broadcasting Acts; second, the domination of ITV programme production. A Guardian leader said: "The danger now is that in the ITV companies' dash to sell in the globalised market, their fragmented regional output - the reason why they were created in 15 original units in the first place - will become homogenised, except where local business imperatives dictate otherwise. The government must resist this trend at all costs; not just because it contradicts its own passion for evolution, but also because it would erode powerful creative forces that could otherwise be harnessed in everyone's interests."

UNITED NEWS & MEDIA, CARLTON AND GRANADA SHARE OF TOTAL TV AUDIENCE

AUDIENCE SHARE	12 MONTHS TO 31.3.00
UNM	
Meridian	2.4%
Anglia	1.8%
HTV	2.2%
Channel 5	2.8%
TOTAL UNM	9.2%
CARLTON	
Carlton	2.7%
Central	4.2%
Westcountry	0.8%
TOTAL CARLTON	7.7%
GRANADA	
Granada	3.8%
LWT	1.9%
Yorkshire	3.2%
Tyne Tees	1.5%
Granada Plus	0.3%
TOTAL GRANADA	10.7%
Other ITV (inc GMTV)	5.9%
BBC	39.1%
Channel 4	10.0%
Channel 5	5.6%
Other sat/cab	13.5%

Source: ITC

Granada's speculative bids
7 JANUARY 2000 Granada announced it was considering a bid for either Carlton or United News and Media, a move intended to provoke a full Competition Commission enquiry in the proposed Carlton-United merger. "We are very serious about both options," said Granada's chief executive Charles Allen. "What we decide to do depends on how the rules are drafted."

Granada abroad
7 FEBRUARY Granada added to its list of overseas production companies in the US and Germany with the purchase of a 9.1 per cent stake in Australia's Seven Network for £56 million. The company is Australia's largest TV producer and is most famous for making the Home and Away soap.

Take over times

Battle for Border TV

MARCH Scottish Radio Holdings put in a £116 million bid for the Carlisle based Border Television which also owns a clutch of radio stations. In April Capital Radio upped the bid to £146 million and won the backing of a quarter of Border's shareholders. As the Capital deal came to fruition, Granada entered the fray by offering to buy Border's television interests for £50.5 million. The final deal had Capital gaining control of Border with a 32 per cent shareholding which valued the company at £151 million. Then Capital immediately confirmed the sale of Border's TV interests to Granada.

Pearson/CLT ufa merger

7 APRIL A Euro TV monster emerged from the £4 billion unification of the Pearson's 160 programmes with the Luxembourg based broadcaster CLT ufa's 22 TV and 18 radio channels. Pearson produces Neighbours and The Bill and the merger marked the end of Pearson as the last major programme maker not to be owned by a broadcaster. Pearson holds 22 per cent of the new company with Bertelsmann and Groupe Bruxelles Lambert each holding another 30 per cent. The Pearson boss Marjorie Scardino said: "This deal creates great value that we could not create alone. It puts Pearson TV at the heart of one of Europe's most extensive and popular broadcasting networks."

Channel 5

8 APRIL Channel 5's shareholding structure underwent two changes in the space of a week. The Pearson/CLT ufa merger created a combined 65 per cent stake in Channel 5. Then United News and Media announced the sale of its 35 per cent Channel 5 stake in a bid to win regulatory approval for its planned merger with Carlton. Several independent producers showed interest and Richard Eyre, chief exec of Pearson TV, said: "There is a stand off between broadcaster and producers. Broadcasters need great content but are wary of the process of being asked, and producers see their route to market governed by gatekeepers."

ITC to change rules

12 MAY The Independent Television Commission signalled its readiness to raise the total permitted advertising share for ITV franchisees to above the current 25 per cent. In bending to the merger mania between Carlton, United News and Media and Granada, the ITC said it was still concerned to maintain a regional bias and had, indeed, mounted a public consultation as part of its contribution to the government's proposed communications bill. Maybe - if the government uses the bill to abolish the ITC in favour of a combined TV and telecomms regulator - the report could be a swan song.

Granada split

17 MAY Granada disclosed plans for a separate stock market listing of its media division in mid-July. The announcement of a discrete £6 billion media empire came amidst details of a £17.5 million merger with the Compass Hospitality catering group. Granada's chairman Gerry Robinson said: "It will give us a pure media play in the forthcoming bids for United or Carlton and give shareholders a clearer choice." In January 2000 Granada had announced it was considering a bid for either Carlton or United News and Media, a move intended to provoke a full Competition Commission enquiry into the proposed Carlton-United merger. The deal was duly referred to the Competition Commission in January 2000. Statements in support of the £8.3 billion merger said that Carlton and UN&M's empire building was founded on the need to create a global media enterprise; the sub-text was a more parochial desire to build a bi-polar British independent TV with Granada as the power in the north. Outsiders to the deal were more sceptical saying that in a world of mergers between America Online and Time Warner and Pearson and Bertelsmann a UN&M/Carlton combination would still be a relative tiddler and that the moment ITV became a single channel would be the moment it was snapped up by a global media shark.

Byers' pronouncement

14 JULY Stephen Byers, the trade and industry secretary, cleared the way for a consolidation of ITV companies by relaxing rules over shares of television advertising. Byers made the following statement: "The UK media scene has changed radically since the 1990s. It is important we allow ITV to develop in a way which allows it to compete efffectively in an increasingly diverse market." That meant he gave his approval to the merger of United News and Media with Carlton but only on condition that the new grouping sold off Meridian in the south of England. The condition opened the way for Granada to mount its promised takeover bid for United News and Media which immediately put a for sale sign over its television franchises Meridian, Anglia and HTV.

Granada and Carlton move for UN&M

JULY By the end of July Granada looked most likely to secure the deal it had been chasing since 1999 with the imminent purchase of United News and Media's Meridian and Anglia with Carlton picking up HTV.

HAPPINESS IS RUNNING TV STATIONS
Charles Allen, the chairman of Granada Media, who has emerged as the most powerful man in British commercial television

Dissenting voice

George Wedell, secretary to the Independent Television Authority (the ITC's forerunner) between 1961-1964, wrote this letter to the Times on 20 July 2000:

"It is the ultimate irony that a Labour government has agreed that various major terrestrial ITV companies can merge.

In the 1950s and 1960s much effort went into the design of an independent television system (followed a decade later by Channel 4) intended to ensure the continuation of the socio-cultural mission of broadcasting in this country conceived by Lord Reith.

Independent television was created as a regionally based federal system to complement the national television service provided by the BBC. The dominant role of the Independent Television Authority was enshrined in successive television acts in order to reinforce the responsibility of independent television to inform, educate and entertain its audience.

Advertising interests persuaded the Conservative government in the 1980s that this remarkable concordat should be abandoned. In the 1990s commercial ITV contractors persuaded governments that consolidation was imperative for survival. It is no such thing. Global competition brings no benefits to the viewers: it merely enhances the profits of the contractors. Independent TV was designed as a public service. Those who have competed for the regional contracts have done so on this clear understanding. Viewers will not forgive a government surrending this fundamental principle."

News At Ten

In March 1999 News At Ten was replaced by a 6.30 bulletin, an 11pm news top up and the weekly Tonight. A year later the prime minister Tony Blair repeated his hope that ITV would restore News at Ten to its former slot and later that month the Commons' media select committee issued a report which, to nobody's surprise, repeated what it had been saying all along. "This is a test case for the ITC," its chairman Gerald Kaufman said. "It is there to regulate commercial television, not to assist the ITV companies in maximising their commercial revenues."

The ITC had originally promised its review of ITV news in March 2000 but held off a decision until May. The ITC director of programmes Sarah Thane said: "I'm not sure if we can order ITV to put News At Ten back. What I can tell you is that if they don't meet our conditions, we will tell them to go and fix it." The trusty Trevor McDonald - who had acquiesced in the axing of the show that made him famous - weighed in with a call to end the debate. After hinting that he had opposed the alteration to a 30-year-old schedule he said: "We cannot keep looking over our shoulders at how things used to be."

Others did look back to how things used to be. Jackie Ashley, a former ITN political correspondent, said. "Since News At Ten disappeared, the stuffing has gone out of the organisation," His former bosses didn't see it like that; although the ITV's news audience dropped by 13 per cent, its overall audience share rose from 38 to 39 per cent, the latter figure including a disproportionate number of 16-34 year olds. Consequently advertising revenues rose by an estimated £70 million.

NOP polls said that 68 per cent of people miss News at Ten and rumour had it that a forward looking Greg Dyke might make an early mark by switching the BBC's Nine o'Clock News to a 10 pm slot. The Press Gazette commented: "The BBC's first natural born killer DG must also be tempted by the chance to claw back market share, matching ITV with three hours of prime-time entertainment. How can he resist?"

The ITC duly reported in May, but didn't make a pronouncement on bringing ITV News back to its old slot. That decision was postponed a month and a temporarily relieved ITV bosses promised to boost flagging viewing figures for its regional news magazine programmes, to invest an extra £21 million in programming during the run up to the 11pm news and to reintorduce News at Ten during election time. "We are not convinced their proposals will deliver the necessary required improvements," said ITC chairman Sir Robin Biggam. And finally on 22 June the ITC told the ITV to bring forward its 11pm news bulletin to an earlier time slot - but without saying when.

ITV chiefs, convinced the regulator has no power to regulate for ratings, moved to force a judicial review. A Guardian leader said: "ITV, understandably from its won commercial point of view, wants to run its own show. But it is not an ordinary commercial company. It has public service obligations which are part of its raison d'être. If it wants to be free, then it could switch its activities to one of the hundreds of digital channels now becoming available ... ITV should drop its threat to fight its corner in the courts and, for once, make news itself by admitting it has got this one wrong."

In mid July the ITC outlined its demands in a legally binding directive suggesting 10.30 might be negotiated as a compromise. ITV executives decided unanimously to continue seeking a judicial review. Both sides said they were confident of their legal position: the ITC has never lost a judicial review but ITV lawyers maintain the regulator has no power to dictate the timing of its news programme. In late August, Greg Dyke confirmed the BBC wanted to shift its news broadcast from 9pm to 10pm. ITV - in the hope of defusing the 11pm legal row - responded by saying it would move its 6.30 news to 7pm or 7.30pm

One thing is more certain and that is the truth of Gerald Kaufman's observation a year earlier that here is a test case for the ITC. A court case would throw its powers into sharp relief at a crucial time for its own future and the future of broadcasting in general.

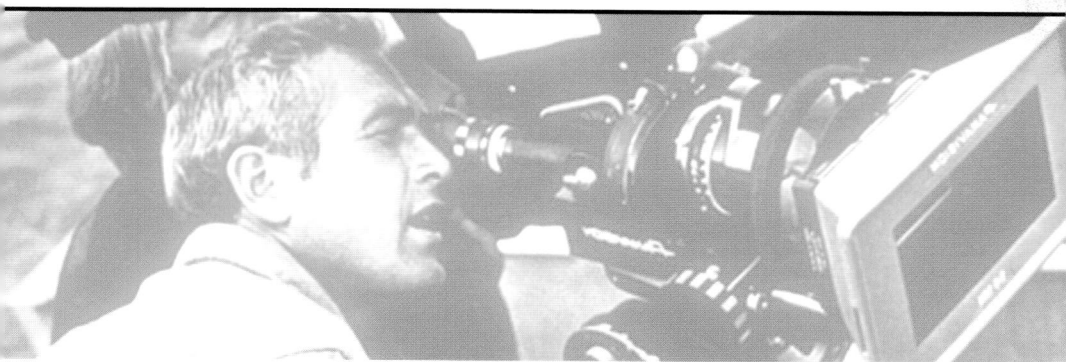

Become a film and television programme maker

If you're an active broadcast professional or a recent media/arts graduate then London Guildhall University's new MA in Audio Visual Production has been designed with you in mind. The course aims to open up career opportunities in the AV industry at large.

The course is based on a commitment to high level film-making across a range of genres. An agreed programme of independent study focused on specific film projects will complement a core programme of creative research. This core programme includes: scriptwriting; directing; producing; editing; camera, sound and experimental film making.

For further information, and a course application pack,
please contact:

Course Enquiries

Tel:	**020 7320 1616**
Fax:	**020 7320 1163**
email:	**enqs@lgu.ac.uk**
web:	**www.lgu.ac.uk**

LONDON GUILDHALL
UNIVERSITY

Advancing Learning and Equal Opportunities

Channel 3 companies

Anglia Television

Anglia House, Norwich, Norfolk NR1 3JG
Fax 01603-631032   Tel 01603-615151
E-mail: angliatv@angliatv.co.uk
Website: www.angliatv.com
London office: 48 Leicester Square, WC2H 7FB
Fax 020-7493 7677   Tel 020-7389 8555
Regional newsrooms:

Norwich	01603-753400
Cambridge	01223-467076
Chelmsford	01245-357676
Ipswich	01473-226157
Luton	01582-729666
Milton Keynes	01908-691660
Northampton	01604-624343
Peterborough	01733-269440

Covers: East of England.
Owner: United News and Media
Regional news programme: Anglia News East/West.
1993-2002 licence fee: £17.8 million pa.

ITC 1999 Performance Review: "Anglia Television celebrated its 40th year broadcasting to the east of England in 1999 and the general quality of its local output remained high, with more new programmes than in its previous three years. Particularly welcome was the introduction of new social action material known as Partnership Programming. Arts output, an area of criticism in past years, improved overall but stand-alone arts series deserved a better spread throughout the year. Light entertainment programmes, having made some progress in 1998, failed to capture viewers' attention. In the ITV network service, Anglia refreshed Sunday mornings with a new year-round religious magazine programme while its documentaries, talk shows and dramas performed well."

Chairman: David McCall.
Managing director: Graham Creelman
Director of programmes: Malcolm Allsop
Controller of news: Guy Adams
Controller of press and regional affairs: Bob Ledwidge

Border Television

The Television Centre, Carlisle, Cumbria CA1 3NT
Fax 01228-541384   Tel 01228-525101
Website: www.border-tv.com
Newsroom: 01228-829229
Covers: Scottish borders, Lake District and the Isle of Man. Also has local radio involvement.
Owner: Border Television; largest shareholder Cumbrian Newspapers Group (18 per cent).
Regional news programme: Look Around, Border News.
1993-2002 licence fee: £52,000 pa.

ITC 1999 Performance Review: "Border Television provided a high standard of service in 1999 and offered a good mix of programmes combining high production values with obvious regional interest. Of special note were the strengthened regional news service, a ground breaking documentary series, special coverage of political developments north of the border and enhanced sports coverage. Border increased its close identification with this diverse region and carried out an extensive capital investment programme in Carlisle and Edinburgh."

Chairman: James Graham
Chief executive: Paul Corley
Managing director: Peter Brownlow
Controller of programmes: Neil Robinson
Head of news: Ian Proniewicz

CARLTON COMMUNICATIONS

Carlton is the largest commercial terrestrial broadcaster in the UK, holding the ITV licences for London weekday, the Midlands and the south west. Together they reach 38 per cent of the population and account for 34 per cent of ITV advertising revenue. The group comprises two principal businesses - the Carlton Media Group and the Technicolour Group.

Carlton produces almost 3,000 hours of television programmes a year through Carlton Productions, Action Time and Planet 24. Carlton Studios is based in Nottingham, while Carlton 021 is the leading commercial operator of outside broadcast in Europe. Carlton has a library of 18,000 hours of TV programmes and over 2,000 films which it sells to over 100 countries. ONdigital - which is 50 per cent Carlton owned - carries Carlton shows including the Food Network and Cinema channels.

Carlton Communications HQ
25 Knightsbridge, London SW1X 7RZ
Fax 020-7663 6300   Tel 020-7663 6363
Chairman: Michael Green
Chief executive: Steven Cain
Finance director: Bernard Cragg
Executive director: Nigel Walmsley

Carlton Television
101 St Martins Lane, London WC2N 4AZ
Fax 020-7240 4171   Tel 020-7240 4000
E-mail: dutyoffice@carltontv.co.uk
Website: www.carltontv.co.uk

ITC 1999 Performance Review: "Carlton significantly increased its regional factual programmes in 1999 following the decision to end the drama series London Bridge. These covered a wide range of topics, some familiar such as gardening and antiques and others which added greater diversity to the schedule such as a series on scientific developments. Overall, Carlton delivered a high quality and varied service to the London region. All programmes were well produced but the audiences for some were adversely affected by the wider changes in ITV in which some regional slots moved to 5.30pm and 11.30pm. The amount of programmes supplied to the network increased and included some very high quality productions."

Carlton Television
Covers: London area, from 0600 Monday to 1715 Friday
Owner: Carlton Communications (100 per cent)
Chairman: Nigel Walmsley
Chief executive: Clive Jones
Director of programmes: Steve Hewlett
Chief executive, Carlton sales: Martin Bowley
Finance director: Mike Green
Controller business affairs: Martin Baker
Controller of regional & public affairs: Hardeep Kalsi
Legal affairs: Don Christopher

Carlton Productions
35-38 Portman Square, London W1H 0NU
Fax 020-7486 1132   Tel 020-7486 6688
Carlton Studios, Lenton Lane, Notts NG7 2NA
Fax 0115-964 5552   Tel 0115-986 3322
Website: www.carltontv.co.uk
Carlton Productions makes regional and network programmes for Carlton Broadcasting and Central Broadcasting.
Director of programmes: Andy Allan
Director of drama and co-production: Jonathan Powell
Entertainment and comedy: John Bishop
Factual programmes: Steve Clark
Children's programmes: Michael Forte
Network affairs: Claire Lummis
Finance director: Martin McCausland
Community programmes unit: Peter Lowe
Commissioning & network business affairs: Tom Betts
Production executive, Carlton Films: William Turner

Carlton Broadcasting
Upper Ground, London SE1 9LT
Fax 020-7827-7500   Tel 020-7620 1620
Central House, Broad Street, Birmingham B1 2JP
Fax 0121-643 4897   Tel 0121-643 9898
Controller of broadcasting: Coleena Reid
Finance director: Ian Hughes
Promotions: Jim Stokoe
Acquisitions: George McGhee
Presentation, Carlton Broadcasting: Wendy Chapman
Presentation, Central Broadcasting: David Burge

Carlton Studios
Lenton Lane, Nottingham NG7 2NA
Fax 0115-9645552   Tel 0115-9863322
Studios and related services.
Managing director: Ian Squires
Director of operations: Paul Flanaghan
Production controller: John Revill

Carlton 021
12-13, Gravelly Hill Industrial Estate, Gravelly Hill, Birmingham B24 8HZ
Fax 0121-327 7021   Tel 0121-327 2021
Carlton's outside broadcasting service.
Managing director: Ed Everest
Business manager: Mike McGowan
Head of operations: Rob Hollier
Chief engineer: John Fisher

Central Broadcasting

Gas Street, Birmingham B1 2JT
Fax 0121-634 4240   Tel 0121-643 9898
                      Press office 0115-986 3322
Website: www.carlton.com

Carlton Studios

Lenton Lane, Nottingham NG7 2NA
Fax 0115-964 5552   Tel 0115-986 3322
Unit 9, Windrush Court, Abingdon Business Park,
Abingdon OX14 1SA
Fax 01235-524024   Tel 01235-554123
Covers: English Midlands
Owner: Carlton Communications
Regional news programme: Central News East/ South/
West.
1993-2002 licence fee: £2,000 pa.

ITC 1999 Performance Review: "Major changes to the
programme serrvce for the East, West and South
Midlands happened in 1999. The Central name was
mostly erased from Midlands screens in favour of
rebranding as Carlton. While this did not affect
programme content, which remained strongly focused
on the region, the ITC regreted the decision to drop a
separate regional identity. The regional service was of
high standard overall and featured 11 new series. There
were improvements in a number of areas, such as
current affairs and multicultural output.
Disappointingly, Central experimented only on Fridays
with regional programming in the newly designed
5.30pm weekly slots. Central's supply of programmes to
the ITV network was much reduced but Midlands
facilities were used in the production of prgrammes for
other services."

Chairman: Nigel Walmsley
Managing director: Ian Squires
Finance director: Ian Hughes
News and operations: Laurie Upshon
Promotions: Mike Villiers-Stuart
Regional programmes: Duncan Rycroft
Regional affairs: Kevin Johnson
Sport: Gary Newbon
Technical director: Mike Snalam
Controller of broadcasting: Coleena Reid

Channel Television

Television Centre, La Pouquelaye, St Helier, Jersey,
Channel Islands JE1 3ZD
Fax 01534-816817   Tel 01534-816816
E-mail: newsroom@channeltv.co.uk
Website: www.channeltv.co.uk
Regional newsrooms:
    Guernsey   01481-41877
    Jersey   01534-816688
Covers: Channel Islands
Owner: Channel Islands Communications (TV), whose
largest shareholders are Lapwing Investments (29.9 per
cent) and 3i Capital Jersey (6.6 per cent).
Regional news programme: Channel Report
1993-2002 licence fee: £1,000 pa.

ITC 1999 Performance Review: "Against the trend in
ITV, the regional service provided by Channel
Television generally prospered in 1999. More viewers
switched to the weekday news magazine Channel
Report which remained at 6.00 pm, while, for the first
time, some regional factual programmes were
scheduled around peak time to good effct. Channel
delivered its most ambitious ever outside broadcast,
with two and a half-hours of recorded coverage from the
Island games on the Swedish island of Gotland. It also
introduced a new animated logo and on-screen image,
and finally ceased having continuity presenters in
vision."

Chairman: Tom Scott
Chief executive: John Henwood
Managing director, licensee: Michael Lucas
Head of programmes: Karen Rankine
Head of resources & transmission: Tim Ringsdore
Head of sales: Gordon de Ste Croix
Financial director: Charles Day

GMTV

London Television Centre, Upper Ground, London SE1 9TT
Fax 020-7827 7001   Tel 020-7827 7000
GMTV took over the ITV network breakfast-time service from TV-am in January 1993. Weekday programmes cover news, topical interviews, live reports, entertainment and lifestyle. Children's programming is provided at the weekend. The Sunday Programme from 0700 to 0800 deals with the week's political issues. In January 1999 GMTV launched its digital service, GMTV2 which broadcasts news, children's and lifestyle programmes seven mornings a week.
Covers: National, breakfast time from 0600-0925 daily.
Owners: Walt Disney (25 per cent), Granada Media (25 per cent), Scottish Media (25 per cent), Carlton (25 per cent)
1993-2002 licence fee: £20 million pa.
News programme: News Hour.

Chairman: Charles Allen
Commercial director: Simon Davey
Managing director: Christopher Stoddart
Sales and marketing: Clive Crouch
Controller of resources: Rhian Jones
Editor: Martin Frizell
Deputy editor: Malcolm Douglas
Director of programmes: Peter McHugh
Head of programme presentation: Helen McMurray
Mananging editor: John Scammell
Press and publicity: Sue Brealey
Training and personnel manager: Stephanie Edwards

Grampian Television

Queen's Cross, Aberdeen, Grampian AB15 4XJ
Fax 01224-846800   Tel 01224-846560
Website: www.scottishmediagroup.co.uk
Other production studios:
Seaforth House, 54 Seaforth Road, Stornoway HS1 2SD
Fax 01851-706406   Tel 01851-704433
Regional newsrooms:
  Inverness   01463-242624
  Dundee   01382-591000
Covers: North Scotland
Owner: Scottish Media Group
Regional news programme: North Tonight.
1993-2002 licence fee: £720,000 pa.index-linked

ITC 1999 Performance Review:
"Certain aspects of Grampian's regional service caused concern in 1999. A lack of genuine regional interest was an issue in some programmes, though not in news and current affairs, which provided thorough coverage of the Scottish Parliament elections. In peak-time when most viewers are able to view, there was insufficient non-news programmes of genuine regional interest with a particular north Scotland focus. The decision not to transmit a hogmanay programme from the region on the eve of the Millennium was difficult to comprehend. Although more new programmes were transmitted than in 1998, the best of these were either co-productions or had a pan-Scottish flavour rather than programmes made exclusively for and about the north Scottish region. These concerns have now been discussed with the senior management of Grampian and Scottish Media Group and the ITC received assurances that they are being urgently addressed. The ITC will continue to monitor the service to check that satisfactory progress is made."

Chairman: Calum Macleod
Controller: Derrick Thomson
Head of news & currrent affairs: Henry Eagles
Technical manager: A J Macdonald
Production resources manager: Avril Shannon
Press and PR: Bert Ovenstone

Granada Television

The Granada Group has four businesses in restaurants, hotels, rental and media. Granada Media Group controls Granada Television, LWT, Yorkshire and Tyne Tees and owns 50 oer cent of ONdigital. Granada TV is the ITV's biggest programme supplier.

Granada Television
Quay Street, Manchester M60 9EA
Fax 0161-827 2029   Tel 0161-832 7211
London office:
TV Centre, Upper Ground, London SE1 9LT
Fax 020-7261 3307(press)
Tel 020-7620 1620
Website: www.granadatv.co.uk
Regional newsrooms:
Blackburn	01254-690099
Chester	01244-313966
Lancaster	01524-60688
Liverpool	0151-709 9393
Manchester	0161-832 7211

Covers: North-west England.
Owner: Granada Group
Regional news programme: Granada Tonight.
1993-2002 licence fee: £9 million pa.

ITC 1999 Performance Review: "Granada performed strongly throughout the year at both regional and network levels. Areas of concern highlighted in last year's review were addressed successfully, notably by a significant increase in the contribution made by independent producers to the regional service. The move of the main regional newsroom from Liverpool to Manchester strengthened the service, particularly the quality of daytime bulletins. However, Liverpool remained an important source of regional programmes. In a year of transition for the ITV network, Granada's programming provided points of familiarity, as well as some of the most challenging new work, such as the award-winning documentary chronicling the impact of Alzheimer's disease Malcolm and Barbara: A Love Story."

Chairman: Charles Allen
Chief executive: Steve Morrison
MD, Granada TV: Brenda Smith
Joint MDs, Granada Productions: Jules Burns, Andrea Wonfor
Commercial director: Paul Taylor
Chief executive (sales): Mick Desmond
Director of programmes: Simon Shaps
Sales director: Mick Desmond
Controller of comedy: Andy Harries
Controller of entertainment: Duncan Gray
Head of factual programmes: Charles Tremayne
Controller of lifestyle: James Hunt
Head of regional programmes: Sue Woodward
Director of public affairs: Chris Hopson

HTV

HTV Wales
Television Centre, Culverhouse Cross, Cardiff CF5 6XJ
Fax 029-2059 7183   Tel 029-2059 0590
Website: www.htv.co.uk

HTV West
TV Centre, Bath Road, Bristol, BS4 3HG
Fax 0117-972 2400   Tel 01179-972 2722
E-mail: htv@htv.co.uk
Website: www.htv.co.uk
Regional newsrooms:
Cardiff	029-2059 0754
Carmarthen	01267-236806
Colwyn Bay	01492-534555
Newtown	01686-623381

Covers: Wales and Bristol, Gloucestershire, Somerset and Wiltshire plus parts of Devon and Dorset
Regional news programme: HTV News
1993-2002 licence fee: £2.09 million pa and 7% qualifying revenue

ITC 1999 Performance Review: "Both HTV Wales nd HTV West demonstrated considerable evidence of high quality across their separate outputs in 1999 and introduced improvements promised the previous year when the company's licence from the ITC was renewed. These included a strengthening of news and current affairs in Wales to reflect devolution and the changing structure of government; and a new drama series based in Wales, which was a bold and, for the most part, successful initiative. A previous weakness in regional children's programming on HTV Wales was also addressed. HTV West established a new community unit and its regional news service as a whole was excellent, including sensitive coverage of the Paddington rail crash. HTV West also continued to be strong in regional factual programming and to supply high quality children's and wildlife programming to the network. The main disappointment in the year was the impact of the new network schedule on the audiences for some regional programmes that fell significantly."

HTV
Managing director: John Cresswell

HTV Wales
Chairman: Gerald Davies
Managing director: Menna Richards
Light entertainment: Emlyn Penny Jones
Programme planning: Sian Thomas
Press and PR: Mansel Jones

HTV West
Chairman: Louis Sherwood
Managing director: Jeremy Payne
Press and PR: Richard Lister

London Weekend Television (LWT)

London Television Centre, Upper Ground, London SE1 9LT
Fax 020-7261 1290   Tel 020-7620 1620
Newsroom (LNN)   Tel 020-7827 7700
Website: www.lwt.co.uk
Covers: London area, from 1715 Friday until 0600 Monday.
Owner: Granada Group, whose largest shareholder is SG Warburg. LWT splits into LWT Productions, LNN, the London News Network (a joint news gathering and production venture between LWT and Carlton TV), and The London Studios which has production facilities for hire to independent producers and the corporate sector.
Regional news programme: London Today, provided by LNN.
1993-2002 licence fee: £7.59 million pa.

ITC 1999 Performance Review: "LWT's performance in 1999 was again marked by a high quality and diverse regional service as well as an impressive supply of popular programmes to the ITV Network. The company provided strong news output and a range of other well-made regional programmes across the weekend. Ease of access to the latter was affected by the limited number of good regular slots, chiefly as a result of demands by the Network for sport and other programmes. As a weekend-only licensee, the company largely avoided the upheavals brought about by the new ITV weekday peaktime schedule, although its regional service on Friday evenings did not escape difficulties. A number of regional series returned from the previous years, but new programmes also appeared, including programmes produced by The Lab, LWT's new programmes making unit. Overall the service complied with the licence conditions."

Chairman: Charles Allen
Chief executive: Steve Morrison
Managing director: Laim Hamilton
Director of programmes: Marcus Plantin
Chairman of LNN: Clive Jones
Managing director of The London Studios: Brenda Smith
Public affairs: Chris Hopson
Controller of entertainment & comedy: Nigel Lythgoe
Controller of drama: Jo Wright
Controller of arts: Melvyn Bragg
Controller of factual: James Allen

Meridian Broadcasting

Television Centre, Northam, Southampton SO14 0PZ
Fax 023-8033 5050   Tel 023-8022 2555
Website: www.meridian.tv.co.uk
London office: Ludgate House, 245 Blackfriars Road, London SE1 9UY
Fax 020-7579 4435   Tel 020-7579 4400
Regional centres:
   New Hythe, Kent   01622-882244
   Newbury, Berks   01635-522322
Covers: South and south-east England
Owner: United News & Media (76 per cent), Carlton Communications (20 per cent). Meridian took over its region from TVS in January 1993.
1993-2002 licence fee: £36.52 million pa.

ITC 1999 Performance Review: "Meridian enjoyed a successful year in terms of network production. Not only did it win more commissions, it also significantly increased the number of programmes produced in Southampton for the network. Although the changes to ITV's network schedule had a significant impact on the audiences to some regional programmes, Meridian's commitment to its regional service remained as strong as in previous years and standards overall were high. A wide-range of attractive regional programmes were shown, news presentation was modernised and improvements were evident in several areas such as current affairs, although there were still shortcomings in some social action programming."

Chariman: Bill Cotton
Managing director: Mary McAnally
Controller of corporate & commercial affairs: Martin Morall
Director of public affairs: Simon Albury
Director of finance: Tim Ricketts
Director of broadcasting: Richard Platt
Controller of news: Andy Cooper
Personnel: Peter Ashwood

Scottish Television

Cowcaddens, Glasgow G2 3PR
Fax 0141-300 3030   Tel 0141-300 3000
Website: www.scottishmediagroup.co.uk
London: 20 Lincoln's Inn Field, London WC2A 3ED
Fax 020-7446 7010   Tel 020-7446 7000
Scottish Television continues to achieve the highest
audience share of all broadcasters in Central Scotland at
35.5 per cent, remaining above the ITV national average
and with a lead over its nearest challenger, BBC1.
Covers: Central Scotland and south-west Highlands.
Owner: Flextech (5.95 per cent), Flextech Investments
(13.90 per cent), Scottish Daily Record/Sunday Mail
(19.81 per cent), Chase Nominees (5.38 per cent), FMR
Corp (4.94%).
Regional news programme: Scotland Today.
1993-2002 licence fee: £2,000 pa.

ITC 1999 Performance Review: "The handling of
national events in the devolution process placed all
Scottish media under the spotlight. Scottish Television
approached the challenge by committing significant
resources to enhancing its news and current affairs
service. Throughout the year, Scottish attracted criticism
over its internal restructuring and its corporate
commitment to the licence area. However, its licence
requirements were met with a broadly satisfactory
range of local output. New factual programming offered
strong regional appeal and efforts were made to serve
viewers' interest by marking Scottish calendar events.
The year culminated at hogmanay with Scottish opting
out of the network schedule to provide programmes of
regional interest including coverage from Edinburgh.
Apart from a small shortfall in Gaelic programmes, the
service complied with licence conditions. However,
there were significant problems with Scottish's supply
of programme data to the ITC, which must be rectified
by 2000."

Chairman: Don Cruickshank
Chief executive: Andrew Flanagan
FinanceDirector: Gary Hughes
Managing director of broadcasting: Donald Emslie
Corporate affairs director: Callum Spreng
Head of news: Paul McKinney
Head of factual programmes & sport: Denis Mooney
Human resources director: Gerry Stevenson

Tyne Tees Television

City Road, Newcastle-upon-Tyne NE1 2AL
Fax 0191-261 2302   Tel 0191-261 0181
E-mail: tttv.regional.affairs@gmg.co.uk
Covers: North East England and North Yorkshire.
Owner: Granada Media Group since 1997
Regional news programmes: North East Tonight.
1999-2009 licence fee: £11 million pa.

ITC 1999 Performance Review: "Tyne Tees maintained
high quality regional programming in 1999 building
on the strengths of well-established series as well as
offering a diverse range of new programmes. Progress
was made in entertainment and sport while Tyne Tees
maintained its impressive record in single factual
programmes, which were well received by viewers.
Regional news and the sub-regional news service were
consistently of high quality. The company's network
performance, however, was below expectations and
Tyne Tees needs to maintain its efforts to win network
commissions in 2000 and beyond."

Chairman: Charles Allan
Managing director: Margaret Fay
Director of broadcasting: Graeme Thompson
Managing editor - news: Graham Marples
Editor, current affairs & features: Jane Bolesworth
Head of young people's programmes: Lesley Oakden
Head of network features: Malcolm Wright
Head of sport: Roger Tames
Head of regional affairs: Norma Hope
Personnel manager: Lynda Wadge

UTV (Ulster Television)

Havelock House, Ormeau Road, Belfast BT7 1EB
Fax 028-9024 6695   Tel 028-9032 8122
E-mail: info@utv.live.com
Website: www.utvlive.com
Covers: Northern Ireland.
Owner: Ulster Television. No single holding over 6%
Regional news programme: UTV Live at Six.
1993-2002 licence fee: £1.03 million pa.

ITC 1999 **Review:** "1999 was an eventful year for UTV.
Its new licence came into force, under the terms of
which it committed itself to an extra 150 hours per year
of regional programming; the company underwent
significant restructuring; and changes at network level
enforced a reappraisal of its regional programming, the
bulk of which it continued to broadcast in peak-time.
There was welcome progress in terms of network
commissions, with agreement for two single
programmes and a short series."

Chairman: John McGuckian
Managing director: Desmond Smyth
General manager: John McCann
Controller of programming: Alan Bremner
Operatioons manager: Robert McCourt
Personnel: Mariead Regan

Westcountry Television

Langage Science Park, Plymouth PL7 5BQ
Fax 01752-333444   Tel 01752-333333
E-mail: info@westcountry.co.uk
Covers: Cornwall, Devon, west Dorset, south Somerset
Owner: Carlton Communications
Regional news programme: Westcountry Live.
1993-2002 licence fee: £7.82 million pa.

ITC 1999 **Review:** "TVin south west England went
through fundamental change in 1999. Not only were
there new formats or slots for some regional
programmes, but Westcountry Television adopted the
name of its parent company and became known as
Carlton. The loss of a familiar and carefully nurtured
regional brand was a matter of regret to the ITC.
Westcountry provided a regional service of generally
high quality, though to a lesser extent than last year.
Westcountry's well regarded news service was
restructured following changes to the schedule and
more news than in past years was shown in daytime.

Chairman: Clive Jones
Managing director: Mark Haskell
Director of programmes: Jane McCloskey
Controller, operations & engineering: Mark Chaplin
Controller of news: Brad Higgins
Controller of features & programme development:
CarolineRighton
Controller of public affairs: Mark Clare

Yorkshire Television

Kirkstall Road, Leeds, West Yorks LS3 1JS
Fax 0113-244 5107   Tel 0113-243 8283
Covers: Yorkshire, Humberside, Derbyshire, Notts, Lincs.
Owner: Granada Plc .
Regional news programme: Calendar.
1993-2002 licence fee: £37.7 million pa.

ITC 1999 **Performance Review:** "Yorkshire Television
won important commissions for ITV network
programmes in 1999 with particular succeses in
drama, children's and factual programmes. The
number of hours of programmes commisssioned was
slightly lower than the previous year but many
submissions still awaited a decision at the year end.
Overall, work on network programming and
programming for other outlets such as Channel 4 was
greater than for several years. The year was a difficult
one for the regional programmes service mainly as a
rresult of the ITV Network's revision of the weekday
peak-time schedule. Regional news programmes
narrowly remained first choice for most viewers.
However. a substantial drop in viewers for the early
evening magazine programme 'Tonight', which was
brought forward an hour to 5.30pm, was of particular
concern because this formed a substantial part of
Yorkshire's regional output. The licensee was not
persuaded that a move to a more diverse format at
different times would improve matters and thought it
might even reduce audiences. However the ITC will
wish to return to this issue if audiences do not show
marked improvement across the regional, non-news
schedule."

Chairman: Charles Allen
Managing director: Richard Gregory
Documentaries and current affairs: Chris Bryer
Entertainment: David Reynolds
Drama: Keith Richardson
News: Clare Morrow
Director of group corporate affairs: Chris Hopson
Director of programmes: John Whiston

Channel 4

Channel 4 began in 1982 as a minority station by design. Where the BBC must provide something for everybody and ITV must deliver ratings and profits to shareholders, Channel 4's duty was to deliver innovation, diversity and originality. With programmes like Ibiza Uncovered and anything with Denise Van Outen, the stern young thing has turned into something far more popularity-seeking. In 2000 C4 screened the first TV ejaculation - though not the penis it came from - in a documentary about porn. Though it hasn't yet commented on this bit of footage filmed in 1972, the ITC was impressed at C4's 1999 output and praised Queer as Folk, Divorce Iranian Style, cricket and the discovery of Ali G.

So gone is the worthiness of the 80s. "Am I alone in thinking the pursuit of demographics - in particular young, lager-drinking, upwardly mobile men - has led to a sapping of Channel 4's originality?" asked the worthy Michael Jackson in 1996. Four years on and Jackson, now firmly installed as Channel 4 boss, speaks somewhat differently. "I think a lot of the barriers between high and low culture, the serious and the trivial, have been crossed," he reasons. "We've gone through a period of change when we've had to work out what Channel 4 is for. That's inevitably been a bumpy ride."

Not so bumpy that Channel 4 doesn't turn in a decent profit on the £600 million advertising revenue it gathers for a 10 per cent audience share. A turn around for a station which used to be called Channel 4 per cent and for years was saddled by a weird deal whereby payments from ITV companies in the event of its commercial failure were reversed when it became a success. Over £400 million was leached away from it by this arrangement and the final £66 million payment was made early 1999. Channel 4 is, therefore, in fine shape for the privatisation now rumoured and the soon-to-be launched E4 digital entertainment channel, where the slogan is "Friday night every night".

Channel 4
124 Horseferry Road, London SW1P 2TX
Fax 020-7306 8366   Tel 020-7396 4444
E-mail Channel4.co.uk
Website: www.channel4.com

ITC 1999 Performance Review: "Channel 4 had a good year. Education programmes developed clearer educational purposes, always with back up material. There was more sustained coverage of politics. More multicultural programmes were broadcast with better scheduling and a better reflection of multiculturalism across the output generally. However the scheduling of foreign language films and the religious content of ostensibly religious programmes hardly improved. Progress in film investment and production outside London was satisfactory. Channel 4 News was relaunched with a brighter set and new presentation style but the strong journalistic values were maintained, and a half-hour peak-time bulletin was introduced at the weekends. Good documentaries looking at children in trouble were made. "Life skills" and health topics were tackled some directly and some indirectly as in the adult literacy story line in Brookside."

Chairman: Vanni Treves
Deputy chairman: Barry Cox
Chief executive: Michael Jackson
Managing director: David Scott
Director & general manager: Frank McGettigan
Director of strategy & development: David Brook
Commercial director: Andy Barnes
Director of finance and business affairs: Janet Walker
Director of programmes: Tim Gardam
Head of programmes (nat. & regional): Stuart Cosgrove
Head of corporate affairs: Sue Robertson
Chief executive Film 4: Paul Webster
Head of drama & animation: Gub Neal
Commissioning editor, sport: Mark Sharman
Commissioning editor, schools: Paul Ashton
Commissioning editor, youth: Andi Peters
Commissioning editor, arts: Janey Walker
Commissioning editor, documentaries: Peter Dale
Independent film & video: Adam Barker
Commissioning editor, multicultural: Yasmin Anwar
Religion & features: Janice Hadlow
Head of science, & education: Sara Ramsden
Head of news and current affairs: David Lloyd
Head of entertainment: Kevin Lygo
Commissioning editor of current affairs: Dorothy Byrne
Entertainment: Caroline Leddy, Graham Smith
Commissioning editor, animation: Claire Kitson
Commissioning editor, features: Liz Warner
Controller of marketing: Polly Cochrane

Sianel Pedwar Cymru S4C

S4C/Sianel Pedwar Cymru/Channel 4 Wales is a public service broadcaster which is regulated by the S4C Authority, whose members are appointed by the Department of Culture. Its direct funding by the Treasury dates back to an appeasement of Welsh Nationalist demands that the Welsh language got a share of the airwaves regardless of a low demand. It broadcasts an average of 34 hours per week in Welsh, 10 hours provided by the BBC, and carries over 70 per cent of C4's output, mostly rescheduled around the commitment to broadcast peak time Welsh language programmes.

S4C (Sianel Pedwar Cymru)
Parc Busnes ty Glas, Llanishen, Cardiff CF4 5DU
Fax 029-2075 1457   Tel 029-2074 1458
E-mail: s4c@s4c.co.uk
Website: www.s4c.co.uk
Chairman: Elan Closs Stephens
Chief executive: Huw Jones
Director of production: Huw Eirug
Director of corporate affairs: Iona Jones
Secretary and director of policy: Steve Martin
Head of corporate press and PR: David Meredith
Director of commercial operations: Wyn Innes
Commissioning editors:
  Factual programming: Cenwyn Edwards
  Drama: Angharad Jones
  Children's programmes: Meirion Davies
  Entertainment: Huw Chiswell
  Music consultant: Richard Elfyn Jones

Channel 5

Channel 5 exists because advertisers had demanded an alternative to the Channel 3 monopoly and it is more about choice for advertisers than for viewers. Still, it dishes up enough of what people want to have reached its launch target of 5 per cent of viewers and with it an annual advertising revenue approaching £200 million. The station has moved into profit for the first time and has overcome transmission difficulties to the extent that it now reaches nearly 20 million British homes, or over 80 per cent of the population. Another first was poaching the Australian soap Home and Away from ITV in a five year deal costing around £40 million. In March 2000, a month short of its third birthday, Channel 5 was valued at £1 billion when three of its founding shareholders bought out the stake held by Warburg Pincus, the US venture capitalist. United News and Media and the Luxembourg based CLT-ufa each paid £61 million to raise their shareholding from 29 per cent to 35 per cent and Pearson chipped in £51 million to raise its stake from 24 per cent to 29.25 per cent. Big money for a small station.

Channel 5 Broadcasting
22 Longacre, London WC2E 9LY
Fax 020-7550 5554   Tel 020-7550 5555
Website: www.channel5.co.uk
Value of ITC bid: £22,002,000
Shareholders: United News & Media, CLT ufa, Pearson Television, Warburg Pincus
ITC 1999 Performance Review: "The overriding impression remains that entertainment shows suffer from low budgets and low quality, while some material has sailed close to the wind in terms of compliance. Late at night UK Raw relied overmuch on sexual themes and side-show freaks which, at times, were at the very limit of acceptability."

Chairman: Remy Sautter
Chief executive: David Elstein
Director of finance: Damien Harte
Director of legal & business affairs: Colin Campbell
Director of sales: Nick Milligan
Director of marketing & communication: Jim Hytner
Director of programmes: Dawn Airey
Controller, current affairs/documentaries: Chris Shaw
Controller, drama: Corinne Hollingworth
Controller, arts and features : Michael Atwell
Controller, entertainment: Alan Nixon
Controller, sport: Robert Charles
Controller, children's: Nick Wilson
Controller, programme planning: Ashley Hill
Controller, acquisitions: Jeff Ford

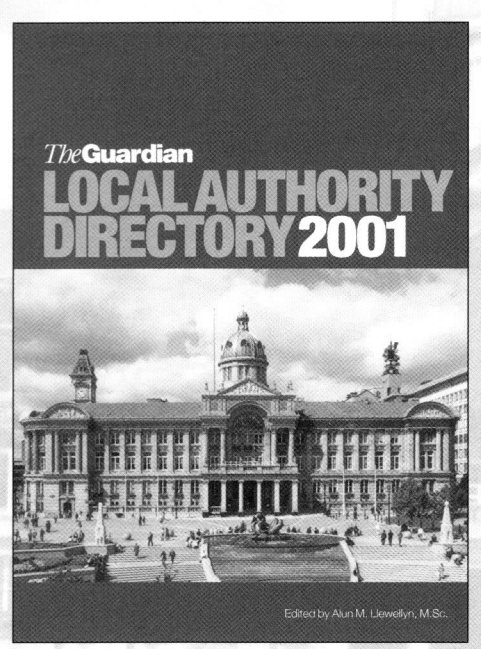

Digital television

Digital TV began in September 1998 with the BBC's digital broadcast of BBC1, BBC2, BBC News 24 and BBC Choice. Sky went digital in the October and ONdigital (which is jointly owned by Carlton and Granada) in the November. By spring 1999 the two big cable companies NTL and CWC had begun broadcasting their digital offerings and all this while John Birt was basing his tenure as BBC director general around a digital rush. Worship at the digital altar was Birt's main justification for his Trotsky-like regime of constant revolution and his reputation may well rest on whether or not history judges his enthusiastic embrace of all things digital to have been a success. Meanwhile the digital union of Granada's Gerry Robinson with Carlton's Michael Green presaged their moves toward a further amalgamation of ITV interests.

The advantages of digital TV are clear. For consumers, a technology superior to analogue transmission means clearer pictures on wider screens which show more channels. Media owners are grabbing opportunities to sell more product via the interactivity which is speeding the convergence of computers and TV sets. That convergence spurs mergers to take advantage of economies of scale, a process which is happening throughout the media. The perceived advantages of scale are to be seen in the ONdigital union and the more recent merger of the pay-TV company Flextech with Telewest, the other big cable company.

The government benefits too and could get £8 billion from selling today's analogue television frequencies to tomorrow's mobile telephone operators. Digital governance will be at the heart of the communications white paper which is expected in autumn 2000. When the culture secretary Chris Smith announced a broadcasting act for the next parliament, it was tantamount to announcing a relaxation of ownership restrictions and the next year will see intensive lobbying about the details. The future, of course, is uncertain but Chris Smith will frame new legislation in anticipation of internet access to every home with a phone and a television set and he has announced 2010 as a digital deadline, with the proviso that, by then, at least 95 per cent of the country will have converted their TVs. "Impractical," was the opinion of Peter Rogers, chief executive of the Independent Television Commission. "I don't think we will get there unless we can find a way to persuade the people who are only interested in free-to-air channels to switch to digital. That is a very serious challenge and we are not yet on course."

Commerce has already done much to persuade people to make the switch. Between them, ONdigital and Sky have invested about half a billion pounds supplying free set top boxes to attract nearly four million digital TV customers. With that kind of expenditure, it's small wonder Sky, Carlton and Granada lobbied hard against a suggestion that there should be a £24 digital supplement on the BBC licence fee. They called it a "digital poll tax", pointing out that it would breach European rules on state aid, and in January 2000 Sky - taking advantage of the European Union so despised by its owner - threatened to take action through European courts. On 21 February 2000 any faint BBC hopes for a digital supplement were dashed when the licence was raised by £3.

While digital TV makes for the sharpest pictures, the sharpest commercial exploitation of TV and all the interactivity that will sail with new forms of TV programming is going to be through cable. "Our digital services are more than just TV," said the Cable and Wireless chief executive Greg Clarke. "With a single connection, customers will get the TV of their choice, best value telephony and access to the world's most sophisticated interactive services including high speed internet through the TV. The internet already accounts for 20 per cent of our local call traffic. CWC will exploit this high demand via the television using its fibre optic broadband network, bringing services direct to the TV screen, for the first time opening internet to a mass market."

DIGITAL TV CONTACTS

BBC Digital TV
Television Centre, Wood Lane, London W12 7RJ
Tel 020-8743 8000
BBC Choice, BBC News 24, BBC Online, BBC Learning and Digital Radio

British Interactive Broadcasting
BIB (Platform) Company, 47 Cannon Street, London EC4M 5SQ
Tel 020-7332 7083
Owners: BSkyB (32.5 per cent), British Telecom (32.5 per cent), Midland bank (20 per cent), Matsushita (15 per cent)
Interactive services providing advertising and information.

British Sky Broadcasting
See Sky Digital

Cable and Wireless
Caxton Way, Watford Business Park, Watford, Herts WD1 8XH
Tel 020-7528 2000
C&W is developing a range of interactive TV services and on 1 July 1999 announced 130 channels. It has made deals with Barclays Bank, British Airways, Littlewoods/Granada Home Shopping, ITN, Associated New Media, Flextech Interactive, Bloomberg, Emap Online, Emap Radio, Scoot, PA Sporting Life, Uproar, Loot, Live TV, Manchester Evening News and ABC Connect. As of July further deals were possible with Discovery Networks Europe, Nickelodeon, QVC, What Car and First Call.

The Cartoon Network
16 Great Marlborough Street, London W1B 1AF
Fax 020-7693 1001   Tel 020-7478 1000
Holds an ITC Digital Programmes Service Licence.

DIGITAL: terrestrial/satellite/cable

DIGITAL TERRESTRIAL
Channels: Up to 36

Cost: Programmes free from most existing terrestrial broadcasters but some subscription set top boxes cost something over £200

Suppliers: BBC, ITV, On Digital/BDB

DIGITAL SATELLITE
Channels: 150+

Cost: Subscription plus a new dish

Supplier: BSkyB

DIGITAL CABLE
Channels: 100-400

Cost: Probably the same as for existing cable

Supplier: CWC, Telewest/Flextech

Digital 3 and 4 Ltd
Unit 4, 56 Norwich Road, Wymondham, Norfolk NR18 0NT
Fax 01953-601196   Tel 01953-608040
E-mail: d3and4@btinternet.com

FilmFour
124 Horseferry Road, London SW1P 2TX
Fax 020-7306 8366   Tel 020-7396 4444
Website: www.filmfour.com
Holds an ITC Digital Programmes Service Licence.

Flextech (Telewest)
160 Great Portland Street, London W1N 5TB
Fax 020-7299 6000   Tel 020-7299 5000
Website: www.flextech.co.uk
The content division of Telewest.
See under Telewest in Franchised Cable section.

GMTV2
The London Television Centre, Upper Ground, London SE19TT
Fax 020-7827 7001   Tel 020-7827 7000
Website: www.gmtv.co.uk
Holds an ITC Digital Programmes Service Licence.

Granada Sky Broadcasting (DTT)
Franciscan Court, 16 Hatfields, London SE1 8DJ
Fax 020-7578 4035   Tel 020-7578 4001
Website: www.gsb.co.uk
Holds an ITC Digital Programmes Service Licence.

Home Shopping Channel - Shop!
Atlantic Pavilion, Albert Dock, Liverpool L70 1AD
Fax 0151-242 6159   Tel 0151-242 6440
Website: www.shop-tv.co.uk
A joint venture between Littlewoods Retail and Granada. It broadcasts 24 hours a day on digital terrestrial, cable and satellite tv. Shop! also has a transactional website and interactive tv shopping services.

ITV2
200 Gray's Inn Road, London WC1X 8HF
Fax 020-7843 8432   Tel 020-7843 8000
Website: www.itv2.co.uk
Holds an ITC Digital Programmes Service Licence.

Microsoft
Endeavour House, 189 Shaftesbury Avenue, London WC2H 8JB
Fax 020-7632 5555   Tel 020-7632 5500
E-mail: Sharonba@microsoft.com
Website: www.microsoft.com/tv

NTL
CableTel House, 1 Lakeside Road, Farnborough, Hampshire GU14 6XP
Crawley Court, Winchester Hampshire SO21 2QA
Fax 01252 402100   Tel 01252-402000
NTL is both a cable operator and the provider of conventional transmission services for independent television. It aims to grow further via TV-based interactive services.

DIGITAL CHANNELS

B
BBC Knowledge
020-7765 5965

C
Carlton Select/Food/Cinema
020-7725 4600
Carlton Kids/World
020-7725 4600
Cartoon Network
020-7478 1000

F
Film Four
020-7396 4444
First ONdigital Champions
020-7819 8000

G
Games
020-7819 8000
Granada Breeze/Granada Plus/Men
& Motors
020-7578 4001
GMTV2
020-7827 7000

H
Havering Community Channel
01923-435000
Hellenic Television
020-8292 7037

H
Homechoice
01707-362592

I
IRIE TV Network
General entertainment
020-8985 0307
Interactive Channel
01923-435000
International Shopping
0115-912 2655
ITV2
020-7843 8000

L
Learning Channel
Educational programmes
0191-515 2452
Leicester Community Channel
0115-912240
Live TV Local Network
Local programming
020-7293 3900
Local Channel (Tellywest)
Local programming
01772-902902
Local 8
Local Peterborough/Norwich
01923-435000

M
MTV (UK)
020-7284 7797

S
Sky One/Sky Premier/Sky Movie
Max/Sky Sports 1/Sky Sports 2/Sky
Sports 3
020-7705 3000
S2
0141-300 3109
S4C2
029-2074 7441
Shop!
0151-235 2055

T
TeleG
029-2040 5600
TV-You
028-9032 8122

U
UK Horizons/UK Play/UK Style/UK
Channel Management
020-7765 1959
UK Gold
020-7765 1959

ONdigital
346 Queenstown Road, London SW8 4NE
Fax 020-7819 8100   Tel 020-7819 8000
Website: www.ondigital.co.uk
Owners: Carlton (50 per cent), Granada (50 per cent)
Primary channels: Carlton Food Network, Cartoon
Network, Breeze, Men and Motors Plus, Euro Sport,
Carlton Cinema, Carlton Kids, Home Shopping
Channel Sky One UK Gold, UK Play UK Style UK
Horizons, Carlton Select, Carlton World
Premium channels: Sky Sports 1, Sky Sports 3, Sky
Premier, Sky Movieman
Free-to-view digital channels: BBC1, BBC2, BBC
Choice, BBC News 24, C4, C5, Teletext, ITV, ITV2
ONdigital was the first company to provide digital pay
television through an ordinary aerial. It provides a
choice of pay channels from programme makers such
as BBC/Flextech, BSkyB and their own shareholders,
Carlton and Granada. It also carries an exclusive
channel - First ONdigital - that is used to show one-off
special events, such as pop concerts and sports. It is in
the process of adding new interactive services such as
email, games and Pay Per View, with an ordinary aerial.
Chief executive: Stuart Prebble

SDN
The Media Centre, Culverhouse Cross, Cardiff CF5 6XJ
Fax 029 2040 5625   Tel 029-2040 5600
Owners: United News and Media, NTL and S4C
Multiplex A and broadcasting S4C's digital output.

Select TV Cable
27-35 Mortimer Street, London W1N 7RJ
Fax 020-7725 4700   Tel 020-7725 4600
Website: www.cfn.co.uk
Holds an ITC Digital Programmes Service Licence.

Sky Digital
BSkyB, Grant Way, Isleworth TW7 5QD
Fax 020-7705 3030   Tel 020-7705 3000
Website: www.sky.com
Holds an ITC Digital Programmes Service Licence.

Satellite TV/Sky

Satellite is synonymous with Sky and Sky is synonymous with the aggressive face of new technology - all risk and innovation and constant change and commercial iconoclasm - ever since it began broadcasting from a pirate satellite in Luxembourg on 5 February, 1988. Rupert Murdoch's vision was such that he bet his whole company on Sky's success when, in the early nineties, he made huge losses yet still bought the competition at British Satellite Broadcasting and then upped the ante to outbid all rivals to buy the rights to broadcast live First Division football.

Football has, in Murdoch's phrase, been the "battering ram" which has breached old citadels. Sky precipitated the change in football's organisation when the top clubs broke away to form a Premiership which could keep its hands on all the new money flowing into the game. The decade-and-a-bit-old Sky was following tradition when, in May 2000, it paid £1.1 billion for up to 66 live Premiership games a season for three years from 2001. Meanwhile, following US patterns of media companies investing in the sport teams they broadcast, Sky spent further millions in accumulating 10 per cent shares of Chelsea, Leeds, Manchester United, Manchester City and 5 per cent of Sunderland.

The company has also led in digital TV, and its gamble of providing free set-top digital decoders paid off by attracting two million customers and boosting share prices. Its digital operation has 200 channels and a third share in BIB, the interactive TV company. In January 2000 Sky's subsidiary NDS unveiled the XTV set-top box which, by the end 2001, will direct particular ads to particular households, store video games and shopping catalogues and - unprompted - interact with viewing habits by, for example, recording films with favourite actors. Sky is also making a £250 million new media investment which includes www.sky.com/sports, an interactive sports shop and a couple of joint ventures to deliver pay-TV and multi-media information across telephone networks. One is with Kingston Communications, the Hull phone company which runs a local TV service with 60 TV channels and high speed internet access.

The second is with Vodafone, to allow mobile phone users to access sports results, team news, audio commentaries and statistics.

Though Sky controls the majority of pay TV revenue, it is still a relative tiddler in terms of viewing figures and has made a stack of money from a relatively small viewing audience - a 0.2 per cent increase over last year with Sky TV's 5.2 per cent share lining up against the BBC's 39 per cent. However, Sky's significance is always boosted through Murdoch's 30 per cent ownership of a British press where the Sunday Times, Times and Sun maintain a drizzle of propaganda against a BBC which Murdoch says is "a self-appointed elite who hate anything changing in Britain". Sky campaigned successfully against a digital levy for the BBC and the biggest current beef is that the BBC's News 24 competes unfairly with Sky News.

The Murdoch stance on Europe is more complex than the straightforward hostility toward the BBC. On the one hand his papers are against a single currency and on the other he is busy working towards a single European TV market. Recent forays into Italy and France were rebuffed after the breakdown of merger talks with Canal in Italy and later the French pay-TV group Canal Plus. However, in December 1999, Sky took a 24 per cent stake in Germany's biggest TV company, Kirch, to gain satellite access to a far larger market than the UK. The corporate deals are not entirely one-way traffic for, in April 2000, the Competition Commission cleared Vivendi's purchase of a quarter stake in Sky. Thus French TV executives have replaced Pearson and Granada on a Sky board where Murdoch's News International only has 14 per cent more shares than Vivendi.

Sky's next ten years look less assured. For the first time in over a decade it looks behind the pace in the media merger game and seems positively small when lined up against global players like Time/AOL and ABC/Disney. Despite the move into interactive TV and phone-based media, new competition will come from cable - a transmission technique superior to satellite and the focus of American investment.

BSkyB
6 Centaurs Business Park, Grant Way, Isleworth,
Middlesex TW7 5QD
Fax 020-7705 3030   Tel 0870-240 3000
Website www.sky.com
Ownership: News International 37.57%, Vivendi,
23.13% , Public 39.30%
Wholly owned channels: Sky One, Sky Sports One, Sky
Sports Two, Sky Sports Three, Sky Sports Extra, Sky
Spoirts.com TV, Sky News, Sky Premier, Sky Cinema,
Sky MovieMax, Sky Box Office, Sky Travel, .tv]
Board of directors
Chairman: Rupert Murdoch
Executive directors: Tony Ball, Martin Stewart
Non-executive directors: Phillip Bowman, David
DeVoe, Lesllie Hinton, Allan Leighton, Dieter Hahn,
Eric Licoys, Martin Pompadour, Arthur Siskind, Lord St
John of Fawsley, John Thornton, Morton Topfer.
Company secretary: David Gromley
Alternate directors: Richard Linford, Jay Itzkowitz,
Elisabeth Murdoch
Executives
Chief executive and MD: Tony Ball
Chief financial officer: Martin Stewart
General manager: Richard Freudenstein
Director, new media: John Swingewood
Director sales and distribution: Jon Florsheim
Head of legal and business affairs: Deanna Bates
Director, corporate communications: Julian Eccles
Director, sales: Peter Shea
Director, marketing: Scott Menneer

SKY JOINT VENTURES

National Geographic
Grant Way, Isleworth, Middlesex TW7 5QD
                Tel 020-7941 5450
Ownership 50%
National Geographic Channel is available in 48 million
homes, 56 countries and 9 languages, and in Europe
the channel is available in over 16.8 million homes, 30
countries and 8 languages. It shows factual
programmes on wildlife, adventure, exploration, world
cultures and natural phenomena, all from National
Geographic Television's library.
Adventure One
National Geographic, Grant Way, Isleworth, Middlesex
TW7 5QD
                Tel 020-7941 5450
Ownership 50%
Adventure is a digital only channel by National
Geographic launched in December 1999 with an 18
hours a day adventure schedule.
The History Channel
Grant Way, Isleworth, Middlesex TW7 5QD
                Tel 020-7941 5180
Ownership 50%
Went digital in 1998 and has a weekly analogue output
of 56 hours. Its website has articles by historians, a
history search engine and interactive functions.

Nickelodeon
15-18 Rathbone Place, London W1P 1DF
                Tel 020-7472 1131
Ownership 50%
Cable and satellite channel for children.
Nick Jr
15-18 Rathbone Place, London W1P 1DF
                Tel 020-7472 1131
Ownership 50%
For young children, launched on Sky Digital in 1999.
Granada Plus
Franciscan Court, 16 Hatfields, London SE1 8D
                Tel 020-7578 4040
Economic interest: 49.5%
Old shows, many from Granada Television and LWT
and distributed on satellite, cable, ONdigital and Sky.
Granada Men & Motors
Franciscan Court, 16 Hatfields, London SE1 8D
                Tel 020-7578 4040
Economic interest: 49.5%
Men's lifestyle magazine channel.
Granada Breeze
Economic interest: 49.5%
Franciscan Court, 16 Hatfields, London SE1 8D
                Tel 020-7578 4040
Economic interest: 49.5%
Programme with sex for thirtysomething women.
Paramount Comedy Channel
3-5 Rathbone Place, London W1P 1DA
                Tel 020-7399 7700
Ownership 25%
UK and US comedy programmes.
QVC - The Shopping Channel
Marcopolo House, Chelsea Bridge, 346 Queenstown
Road, London SW8 4NQ
                Tel: 020-7705 5600
Ownership 20%
24 hour channel with 17 hours of live programming
each day with a net turnover of £140 million in 1998.
Music Choice
Sentinel House, 16 Harcourt St, London W1H 2AU
                Tel 020-7298 8800
Ownership 20%
44 music channels of all sorts available 24 hours a day
without ads or DJs to 3 million people across Europe.
MUTV
274 Deansgate, Manchester M3 4JB
                Tel 0161-834 1111
Ownership 33.33%
Fottie news, phone-ins, classic games and live matches.
Sky News Australia
                Tel 0061 2 9 451 8200
Ownership 33.33%
Australian produced pay-tv news channel, with
Australia's Nine and Seven networks and distributed by
Foxtel and Optus Vision.
Open
34-35 Farringdon Street, London EC4A 4HJ
                Tel 020-732 7000
Interactive services on digital satellite including e-
mailing through TV, shopping, and entertainment.

SATELLITE CHANNELS

3+
Scandinavian entertainment
01895-433338
18 Plus Movies
Adult pay per view porn
020-7705 3000

A

Ace TV
Entertainment
020-8947 8841
Adult Channel
Porn
020-8581 7000
Adventure One
Documentary programing
020-7941 5073
Africa Independent TV
News, drama, soaps, sport
020-7233 7965
Al-Mustakillah TV
News and current affairs
020-8838 2884
Al-Rashad
Oriental & western cultures
020-7266 2114
Animal Planet
020-7462 3600
Anjuman
Urdu programming
020-7436 7774
Apna TV Asian entertainment and radio
020-7359 6464
Arab News Network
020-7323 9920
Artsworld
Arts programming
020-7491 7000
Asia 1 TV
Programmes in Punjabi
0121-507 1666
Asianet
Asian programmes
020-7566 9000
Asian Music Channel
Asian entertainment in English
0116-2335579
Asset Television
12 hour black family channel
020-8554 7766
Atomic TV
Music video entertainment
01622-357000
Auction Channel
Auction sales
020-8788 4429

B

B4U
Indian-Hindi films
020-8963 8778
BBC Prime
General entertainment
020-8576 2308
BBC World
News and information
020-8576 2308
BET International
Jazz
020-8814 2357
Babylon Blue Porn
Porn and sport
020-7287 6623
Bangla TV
Bengali speaking service
020-8514 8693
Bar Channel
General entertainment
020-7705 3000
Barker Service
Sky promotional
020-7705 3000
Best Direct TV
24 hour home shopping
020-8868 4355
Bloomberg Info TV
Financial news
020-7330 7500
The Box
Interactive music
020-7376 2000
Bravo
Films
020-7299 5000
Business Information Channel
01273-628728

C

C7TV
General entertainment
020-8977 1222
CNBC
Business programming
020-7653 9300
CNE
News from China, Hong Kong & Taiwan
020-7610 3880
CNN International
International news
020-7637 6700
CTV
Culturrally orientated documentary programming
01268-454748
Call TV
Telesales/telemarketing
070-0078 1808

Caribbean One TV
AfroCaribbea entertainment
020-8656 7244
Carlton Food Network
Cookery & lifestyle
020-7725 4600
Carlton Select
Entertainment
020-7725 4600
Cartoon Network
020-7478 1000
Challenge TV
Interactive
020-7299 5000
Channale Pakeeza
Asian programming
0141-248 2495
Channel East
Asian subscription channel
020-8573 4000
Channel 4
General entertainment
020-7396 4444
Channel 5
General entertainment
020-7550 5655
Christian Channel Europe
Christian programming
0191-495 2244
Christian Channel Shopping
Christian programming
0191-495 2244
Christian Children's Channel
Christian programming
0191-495 2244
Christian Communication Net
Christian programming
028-9485 3997
Christian Music Channel
Christian programming
0191-495 2244
Crime Channel
Fact and fiction
020-7573 4580

D

Discovery Channel
Documentaries
020-7462 3600
Discovery Civilization
History
020-7462 3600
Discovery Homr and Leisure
Educational
020-7462 3600
Discovery Italy,Africa, Russia
Factual programmes
020-7462 3600
Discovery Sci-Trek
Science, technology and paranormal
020-7462 3600
Discovery Travel and adventure
Documentaries
020-7462 3600
Disney Channel
Family entertainment
020-8222 1000

E

E! Entertainment TV
Light entertainment
020-7328 8808
E Music
Music
020-8741 2200
EIN
Infomercials
020-7927 8427
East-West
South Asian news & entertainment
020-8905 5355
Ecology Channel
Films
01565-750999
Eternal Word UK
Catholic programming
01721- 752625
European Film channel
Films
01565-750999
European Network Broadcasting
Christian programming
020-7917 2731

F

Fantastic TV
Children's programming
020-7328 8808
FilmFour
Feature films
020-7396 4444
Fox Kids
020-7554 9000
Fox Kids Poland
020-7554 9000
Fox Kids Scandinavia
020-7554 9000
Fresco channel
Cultural channel for EU states
01565-750999
Front Row
Films and sport
020-7551 5950

G

Global Net News Channel
News
020-7320 6534
Goodlife TV
Porn
020-7287 6623
Gospel channel
01249-446210
Granada Breeze
020-7578 4040
Granada Men + Motors
020-7578 4040
Granada Plus
020-7578 4040
Gurjari
Urdu programming
020-7436 7774

H

HBO
Entertainment for Poland
020-7972 7310
HSN/Screenshop
Shopping channel
160 Great Portland Street, London W1N 5TB
HVC
Action and horror films
020-8581 7000
Hallmark Entertainment Network
Horror films
020-7439 0633
Healix
Medical educational
0118-981 6666
Health Zone
Health porgramming
020-7689 5226
History Channel
Historical documentaries
020-7941 5225
Home Shopping Network
020-7499 1511

I

Ideal World
Home shopping
01733-777310
Indus Television
Multiracial entertainment
020-7722 2922
Inspiration Network
Christian programming
020-7491 2008
Intershop
Home shopping
01628-421517
Invention Shop Channel
Home shopping
01732-866356

J

JSTV
Entertainment
020-7426 7330

SATELLITE CHANNELS

K
KTTV
Christian programming
020-8896 3736
K.W.T.V.
Punjabi, Hindi and Urdu programming
0161-881 8665
Kanal 5
Entertainment for Sweden
020-8814 7500
Khalsa World Television
Punjabi, Hindu and Urdu
0161-881 8665

L
Landscape Channel
Classical music
01424-830900
Lashkara
Urdu programming
020-7436 7774
Life
Lifestyle channel
020-7491 7000
Living
Daytime mangazine
020-7299 5000
London Community Television
Local interest
020-7231 9939

M
JSTV
Entertainment
020-7426 7330
M4U
Indian music channel
020-8963 8778
MBC
General Arabic entertainment
020-7501 1111
MTV Networks
Music video channels
020-7284 7777
MUTV
Manchester United Football TV
0161-834 1111
Midnight Blue
Porn channel
020-7328 8808
Minaj Broadcast International
Afro-centric entertainment
020-7491 2393
Mine channel
Afro-Caribbean
07050-122288

The Money Channel
Financial programmes
020-7488 4862
Music Asia
Hindi and Indian music
020-8839 4010
Music Box Channel
Light entertainment
020-7328 8808
Muslim TV Ahmadiyya
020-8870 8517

N
NBC Channels
News and entertainment
020-7352 9205
Namaste
Asian programming
020-8507 8292
National Geographic Channel
Documentaries
020-8847 4319
Nickleodeon
Children's programming
020-7462 1000
Nickleodeon Scandinavia
Scandinavian children's programming
020-7478 5200
Novashop One/Two
Home shopping
020-7465 1234

O
Open
Advertising and info
020-7332 7000

P
Pakistini Channel
Urdu programming
020-8838 6300
Paramount Channel
Entertainment
020-7399 7700
Penthouse Channel
Porn
020-8581 7000
Performance
The performing arts
020-7927 8808
Phoenix
Chinese news and entertainment
020-7610 3880
Playboy TV
Porn
020-8581 7000
Pop Culture Channel
Films
01565-750999

Q
Q24
Home shopping
020-7465 1234
QVC Deutschland
German language home shopping
020-7705 5600
QVC Shopping Channel
020-7705 5600
Quantum Home Shopping
020-7465 1234
QuesTV
Male programming
10 Bourlet Close, London W1P 7PJ

R
Racing Channel
020-7253 2232
Rainbow Television
Gay entertainment
020-7328 7790
Rapture TV
Infotainment
020-7836 5259
Reality Channel
Films
01565-750999
Reality Television
Documentaries
020-7328 8808
Relationships Channel
Relationship counselling
020-7732 3521
Revival Channel
Christian
0191-495 2244
Romantica
Polish soap opera
020-7328 8808

S

S4C2
General entertainment in Farsi
029-2074 7441
Satellite Information Services
Racing information
020-7253 2232
Scene One
Listings and entertainment
020-7299 5000
Sci-Fi Channel Europe
020-7805 6100
Sell-a-Vision Shopping
Home shopping
020-7465 1234
Setanta Sport
Sports service for pubs
020-7930 8926
Shop!
Teleshopping
0151-242 6085
Shop America
Home shopping
01535-272424
Show Time
Feature films
020-7478 6900
Sima TV
Entertainment in Farsi
020-8959 3611
Simply Money
Personal finance
020-7692 1150
Sky channels
Entertainment, sports etc
020-7705 3000
Sony Entertainment
Live educational & business
020-7534 7575
Studio Universal
Theatrical films
020-8250 1651
Style
Women's programmes
020-7478 6900
Supershop
020-7465 1243

T

.tv
About computers
020-7599 8398
TCC Nordic
Children's programming
020-7299 5000
TNT
General entertainment
020-7478 1000
T.V
Tamil television
020-8428 9211

TV Danmark1
Light entertainment
020-8814 7500
TV Land
Middle Eastern entertainment
020-7478 6900
TV Shop
01895-431747
TV3 Denmark
Entertainment for Denmark
01895-433338
TV3 Norway
Entertainment for Norway
01895-433338
TV3 Sweden
Entertainment for Sweden
01895-433338
TVBS Europe
Chinese programmes
020-8614 8300
TV Travel Shop
Holiday channel
020-7691 6132
Television X
Soft porn
020-7308 6010
Tell Sell:
Home shopping
01784-898109
Travel Channel
Travel and exploration
020-7636 5401
Travel
Polish service
020-7636 5401
Trouble
Programming for teenagers
020-7299 5000
Turner Classic Movies
Films
020-7478 1000

U

U!
General information
01535-727424
U Direct Films
Filmed entertainment
020-7242 7770
UK Arena (BBC/Flextech)
Arts, drama, music
020-7299 5000
UK Gold (BBC/Flextech)
Classic British programmes
020-7299 5000
UK Gold Classics (BBC/Flextech)
Complementary service to UK Gold
020-7299 5000
UK Horizons (BBC/Flextech)
Educational/science
020-7299 5000

UK Play(BBC/Flextech)
Music/comedy for 15-34 year olds
020-7299 5000
UK Style (BBC/Flextech)
Lifestyle
020-7299 5000
University of Plymouth
Educational and business
01752-233640

V

VH1
Music
020-7284 7491
VT4
Entertainment for Benelux
01707-664555

W

What's in Store
020-7465 1234
Wholesale Shopping Channel
Teleshopping
01753-534828
Williams Worldwide Television
Home shopping
020-7734 7010
Wizja channels
Polish channels
01622-357000
Worship Channel Europe
Christian programming
0191-495 2244

X

X1
German language programming
020-7323 4747

Z

Zee TV
Asian programming
020-8839 4009
ZTV
01895-433338

Cable TV

For all the digging up of British streets, cable only passes just over a half of British households and of these, only a fraction over a quarter choose to buy cable. However, 36 per cent of homes which are able to, use cable for phones and internet and this is building up enough custom to start generating a payback on the £10 billion or so that has been spent on rewiring Britain.

The picture of cable suppliers has become clearer with - in order of the number of homes passed - Cable & Wireless Communications (CWC), Telewest, and NTL having bought up a host of their rivals. The mergers continue and - pending Competition Commission approval - NTL-CWC will become the cable market leader if their £18.7 billion marriage gets approval.

Telewest has been even busier in maintaining the merger trend. In August 1999 it continued the moves to consolidation with the £428 million purchase of the half of Cable London which it didn't already own. Then in January 2000 Telewest combined with the pay-TV Flextech group by purchasing £2.26 billion worth of Flextech shares. The deal united Flextech's 13 pay-TV channels (including Bravo, Living and UK Gold) with a Telewest cable network that runs past 4.44 million homes. At the end of June UnitedGlobalCom, an American telecommunications group took a 25 per cent share in Telewest in a complex deal where Telewest shares owned by Liberty Media, a subsidiary of AT&T, were sold to strengthen an UnitedGlobalCom/AT&T global alliance.

In July the European Commission stopped Microsoft securing a 30 per cent stake in Telewest. However it will remain a big presence in the cable market because NTL will adopt a Microsoft operating system as the platform for its next generation of digital television. NTL/ Microsoft services will include participation in games shows and access to web browsers and email. This NTL contract was early justification for Microsoft's telly-as-well-as-computers strategy and one clear way it will generate return on a £2 billion cable investment made in 1999.

The state of cable

	2000	1999
Number of franchises	137	137
Homes passed	12.446m	12.145m
Homes connected (TV &/or phone)	4.669m	4,239m
Homes connected (TV)	3.281m	2.971m

Source: ITC, June 2000

Top cable operators

	HOMES CONNECTED	HOMES PASSED
Telewest	1,140,835	4,444,556
CWC	926,328	4,042,589
NTL	1,158,620	3,630,964

Source: ITC June 2000

CABLE OPERATORS

Independent Television Commission licences for cable operators fall into two groups. Franchised Cable Systems or the Multiple Systems Operators (MSOs) are the first and they are dominated by Telewest, CWC and NTL. They have exclusive rights for the licensee to provide multi-channel TV over a large scale purpose-built cable system for 15 years. The licence also allows for telephone services to be supplied and this has proved a major stimulant to growth.

The second group is the Unfranchised Cable Systems and these are the cable operators which have been allotted a restricted channel capacity that predates the current franchising arrangement. Unfranchised cable systems operators don't have exclusive rights, are subject to shorter term licences and liable to be superseded by a franchised Multiple Systems Operator system.

CABLE AND SATELLITE AUDIENCE FIGURES

CHANNEL	AUDIENCE	CHANNEL	AUDIENCE	CHANNEL	AUDIENCE
QVC	3,280,625			Sky Premiere	835,630
TV Travel Shop	3,163,915	Granada Plus	1,629,799	Fox Kids	820,884
BBC News 24	3,014,124	Travel Channel	1,677,102	Disney	812,539
Channel Guide	2,953,692	Rapture	1,663,388	Sky Moviemax	810,168
Sky 1	2,873,800	Dsicovery	1,638,367	Sky Cinema	792,997
BBC Parliament	2,584 575	CNN	1,562,973	CNBC	742,000
UK Gold	2,373,799	History Channel	1,529,673	Vision	723,016
Sky News	2,321,121	Performance	1,511,436	Animal Planet	714,579
Cartoon N'work	2,292,047	Challenge TV	1,506,022	TV5	667,814
Living	2,274,315	Bloomberg Info	1,379,222	Christian Ch.	638,669
TNT	2,104,978	Carlton Food	1,372,788	Asianet	427,813
VH1	2,064,390	Bravo	1,365,551	Euronews	259,678
The Box	1,950,429	Carlton Cinema	1,362,590	Tara TV	228,643
UK Horizons	1,877,385	Trouble	1,327,885	Landscape	209,790
Discovery	1,837,846	Granada Breeze	1,281,221	Bet on Jazz	126,780
Eurosport	1,789,654	UK Style	1,197,216	C1 Liverpool	101,594
ITV2	1,789,428	Nat.Geographic	1,108,617	ZEE TV	53,413
Paramount	1,782,377	UK Arena	1,051,716	Namaste	44,533
Nickelodeon	1,781,825	UK Play	990,648	TVX	34,169
Sci-Fi	1,732,696	Sky Sports 3	957,607	Adult Channel	28,221
MTV	1,705,355	Sky Sports 1	939,911	Sky Travel	17,865
Granada Men	1,700,625	Sky Sports 2	853,583	Sony TV	17,563

Source: ITC June 2000

FRANCHISED CABLE

Atlantic Telecom Group
Holburn House, 475-485 Union Street, Aberdeen
AB11 6DP
Fax 01224-454011   Tel 01224-454000
Website: www.atlantic.co.uk
Franchises: Aberdeen

Cable & Telecoms (C&T)
IPO Mercer, Taylor Jaynson Garnet, Carmelite, 50
Victoria Embankment, London EC4Y 0DX
     Tel 020-7353 1234
Franchises: Carlisle, Central Cumbria, South Cumbria, Ayr, Northumberland, Dumfries, Galloway
Subsidiaries: Cumbria Cable & Telecoms, South Cumbria Cable & Telecoms, Ayrshire Cable & Telecoms, Northumberland Cable & Telecoms.
Owner: US Cable Corporation

Cable & Wireless Communications (CWC)
Watford Business Park, Watford WD1 8XH
     Tel 01923-435000
Website: www.cwcom.co.uk
Franchises: E Lancs, Bolton, Totton/Hythe, Chichester, Bognor Regis, Folkestone, Dartford, Dover, Eastbourne, Hastings, Brighton, Hove, Shoreham, Worthing, Bournemouth, Poole, Christchurch, Portsmouth, Winchester, Southampton, Eastleigh, Chilterns, North Surrey, Derby, N Yorks & S Co Durham, Bury, Rochdale,

Oldham, Wearside, Stoke-on-Trent, Macclesfield, Leeds, the Wirral, NE Cheshire, Newcastle-under-Lyme, Stockport, Manchester, Norwich, Great Yarmouth, Whittlesey, March, Wisbech, Harrow, Thamesmead, Epping Forest, S Herts, London Boroughs of: Bromley, Waltham Forest, Wandsworth, `Lambeth, Southwark, Newham, Tower Hamlets, Kensington, Chelsea, Hammersmith, Fulham, Ealing, Havering, London E

The Convergence Group (Convergence)
Martlet Heights, The Martlets, Burgess Hill, West Sussex RH15 9NJ
Fax 01444-250555   Tel 01444-250550
E-mail: tonyb@convergenceholdings.com
Website: www.convergenceholdings.com
Franchises: East Grinstead, Haywards Heath, mid Sussex, Yeovil
Owner: Convergence Group

Eurobell
Eurobell House, Churchill Court, Manor Royal, Crawley RH10 2PN
Fax 01293-400440   Tel 01293-400444
Website: www.eurobell.com
Franchises: Gatwick, Crawley, Horley, Tunbridge Wells, Sevenoaks, Tonbridge, Exeter, Plymouth, Torbay, Totnes, Newton Abbot.
Subsidiaries: Eurobell (South West), Eurobell (Sussex), Eurobell (West Kent).
Owner: Deutsche Telekom AG

Isle of Wight Cable & Telephone Co
EuroCable Communications Network, 2nd Floor, East Wing, Auckland House, New Zealand Avenue, Walton-on-Thames, Surrey KT12 1PL
Tel 01932-881884
Metro Cable Television (Metro)
Unit 12, 23 Park Royal Road, London NW10 7JH
Tel 020-8961 6776
NTL Group
NTL House, Bartley Wood Business Park, Bartley Way, Hook, Hampshire RG27 9XA
Tel 01256 752000
Website: www.ntl.com
Franchises: Glasgow, Paisley, Renfrew, Beasden, Milngavie, Inverclyde, South Glamorgan, Mid Glamorgan, Gwent, Glyncorrwg, Newport, Pontypool, Guildford, Woking, Camberley, Aldershot, Farnham, Fleet, south Bedford, Hertfordshire, Hampshire, Huddersfield, Northern Ireland.
Subsidiaries: CableTel Herts & Beds/Glasgow/Kirklees/ Northern Ireland/South Wales/Surrey.
Owner: NTL Inc USA
The third largest franchise holder.
Telewest Communications (Telewest)
Genesis Business Park, Albert Drive, Woking, Surrey GU21 5RW
Fax 01483-750901   Tel 01483-750900
Website: www.telewest.co.uk
Franchises: North Kent, south Essex, Merton, Sutton, Kingston, Richmond, Croydon, Newcastle, Gateshead, Tyneside, the Black Country, Telford, Liverpool, Southport, Blackpool and Fylde, St Helens, Knowsley, central Lancashire,Wigan, Falkirk, Livingston, Edinburgh, Lothian, Fife, Dundee, Perth, Motherwell, Dumbarton, Falkirk, Cumbernauld, Glenrothes, Kirkcaldy, Taunton, Bridgewater, Bristol, Bath and area, Cheltenham, Gloucester, Worcester.
Subsidiaries: Telewest Communications: (London South), (Midlands), (North East), (North West), (Scotland), (South East), (South West), Cable Corporation.
Owners: Principal shareholders are TeleCommunications Inc and US West Inc (29.8 per cent each), Cox Comms (10 per cent), SBC Comms (10 per cent. Remainder is public.
Flextech
160 Great Portland Street, London W1N 5TB
Fax 020-7299 6000   Tel 020-7299 5000
Chief executive: Adam Singer
Vice president, strategy & communications: John Murray
Chief executive, content division: Mark Luiz
Managing director, tv & broadcast: Jane Lighting
Managing director, business & commercial: Mike Smallwood
MD, broadband content: David Docherty
Managing director of Interactive: Ashley Highfield
Flextech is the content division of Telewest, the integrated digital media group. Its core business is the supply of entertainment, information and interactive content and services to the UK multi-channel television and online markets.

Other Flextech investments include: Scottish Media Groyup, 18.2%, Home Shopping Network Direct: 63%
Kindernet CV: 31%
Flextech has involvement with Bravo, Challenge TV, Living, Scene One, Screenshop, Trouble, UK Drama, UK Gold, UK Horizons, UK Play, UK Style.

UNFRANCHISED CABLE

Atlantic Telecom Group
475-485 Union Street, Aberdeen AB11 6DB
Tel 01244-646644
Kingston upon Hull
Ayrshire Cable & Telecoms
Metro Cable TV, Unit 12, 23 Park Royal Road, London NW10 7JH
Tel 020-8961 6776
Irvine
CDA Communications
Black Horse House, Bentalls, Basildon SS14 3BX
Tel 01268-450450
Ashford, Basildon, Brighton, Burnley, Canterbury, Chatham, Eastbourne, Faversham, Hastings, Herne Bay, Thanet, Lewes, Salford, Sittingbourne, The Wirral.
Cablecom Investments
Adjacent building 422, Dudley Street, RAF Lakenheath, Brandon IP27 9NX
Alconbury, Burnley, Lakenheath, Mildenhall, Upper Heyford.
Harris of Saltcoats
104-106 Dockhead Street, Saltcoats KA21 5EL
Tel 01294-64330
Largs, Saltcoats.
Gwyneth May Evans
1 West End, Dolrheoyn, Tanygrisiau, Blaenau Ffestiniog, Gwynedd LL41 3SR
Tel 01766-830721
Blaenau Ffestiniog
Metro South Wales
NTL House, Bartley Wood Business Park, Hook, Hampshire RG27 9XA
Tel 01256-752000
South Wales.
NTL Group
NTL House, Bartley Wood Business Park, Hook, Hampshire RG27 9XA
Tel 01256-752000
Washington, The Barbican, Brackla
Tawd Valley Cable
82 Sandy Lane, Skelmersdale, Lancashire WN8 8LQ
Fax 01695-51315   Tel 01695-51000
Skelmersdale.
A Thomson (Relay)
1 Park Lane, Beith, Ayrshire KA15 2FG
Fax 01505-503030   Tel 01505 503441
E-mail: glee40@compuserve.com
Beith, Kilbirnie
West Wales Aerials
97 Rhosmean Street, Llandeilo, Dyfed
Tel 01558-823 2781

CABLE CHANNELS

A
ATM
0161-627 1207
Adam and Eve Channel
Soft porn
020-8889 4243
Afro-Caribbean Channel
020-8802 4576
Airport Television
01753-579660
Alpha Channel
020-7610 5260
Andover Now
01264 401402
Arcade channels
01772-902909
Arsenal
020-7704 4000

B
BET on Jazz
020-8814 2357
BVTV*
020-8884 0467
Boro TV
Live football
01483-880800
Bradford Festival News
01274-727488
BIB Advertising & information
020-7332 7000

C
Cable 17
News /info south London
020-8251 5151
Cable 17
Local to Worcester area
01772-902909
Calderdale TV
01422-253100
Cambridge Interactive TV
01223-567200
The Channel Guide
01992-500016
Channel One
Liverpool
0151-472 2700
Channel 7
Grimsby
01469-515151
Channel 10
01224-402000
Christian Channel London
0191-4952244

E
Education Channel
01254-292182

Education & Training Channel
0191-515 2452
Epping Forest Community Channel
01923-435000

F
Festival Revue
Live performances from Edinburgh
0131-662 8600
The Food Channel
01384-395654

H
Havering Community Channel
01923-435000
Hellenic Television
020-8292 7037
Homechoice
01707-362592

I
IRIE TV Network
General entertainment
020-8985 0307
Interactive Channel
01923-435000
International Shopping
0115-912 2655

L
Learning Channel
Educational programmes
0191-515 2452
Leicester Community Channel
0115-912240
Live TV Local Network
Local programming
020-7293 3900
Local Channel (Tellywest)
Local programming
01772-902902
Local 8
Local Peterborough/Norwich
01923-435000
London Community TV
020-7231 9939

M
M Factory
Student programming
020-7911 5000
Metrovision
020-7935 4400

N
NCTV
Brighton & Northern
01923-435000
Natural Health
01384-395654
Network 021

Local - Birmingham
0121-628 1234
Nimrooz Persian channel
020-8748 6676

O
ON TV Local - Hampshire
01252-402000

P
Persian TV
Previews cable prorammes
020-8731 9333
Preview Channel
0113-239 2255

R
Redbridge Community Channel
01923-435000
Ridings TV
01274-778733
Royal Opera House Channel
020-7240 1200

S
SLCTV
Local Sheffield
0114-281 2661
Silverstone TV
01327-857271
Swindon Local
01252-402000

T
Take One
Film and event, pay-per-view
01252-402000
Tawd Valley Cable
01695-51000
TellyWest Avon area ·
01772-902909
Tower Hamlets
01923-435000

V
Videotron Channel
01923-435000
Vision Channel
01793-511244
Vision Rams
01332-667553

W
Waltham Forest
01923-435000

Y
YCTV-Youth Cable Television
020-8964 4646
Yes Television
020-7462 5600

CABLE AREAS

A
Aberdeen area:
Aberdeen Cable (Devanha)
01224-649444
Andover: Cablevision (IVS)
01264-334607
Avon:
United Artists (TeleWest)
01454-612290

B
Bedfordshire: south, Luton:
Cablevision Beds (CableTel)
01582-401044
Birmingham, Solihull:
Birmingham Cable (Comcast)
0121-628 1234
Bolton:
Cable and Wireless
0161-946 0388
Bradford:
Yorkshire Cable
01274-828282
Brighton, Hove, Worthing,
Shoreham:
Cable and Wireless
01273-880000
Burton-upon-Trent, Swadlincote,
Ashby-de-la-Zouch
LCL Cable
0800 952 2222

C
Cambridge, Ely, Newmarket,
Huntingdon:
Cambridge Cable (Comcast)
01223-567200
Coventry:
Coventry Cable (Devanha)
024-7650 5345

D
Derby:
Cable and Wireless
01332-200002
Dundee, Perth area:
United Artists (TeleWest)
01382-322220

E
Edinburgh:
United Artists (TeleWest)
0131-539 0002

G
Gatwick, Crawley:
Eurobell
01293-400444
Glasgow area:

CableTel
0141-221 7040
Guildford, W Surrey, E Hants:
CableTel
01483-254000

H
Hampshire: east, Portsmouth,
Gosport:
Cable and Wireless
01705-266555
Harlow, Bishops Stortford, Stansted:
Anglia Cable (Comcast)
01279-867000
Hertfordshire: south:
Jones Cable
01923-464000
Hertfordshire: west:
Telecential
01442-230444
Hinckley, BosworthLCL Cable
0800 952 2222

L
Lancashire: Merseyside:
Cable North West (SBC)
01772-832888
Lancashire: east:
Cable and Wireless
0161-946 0388
Leeds: Jones Cable
0113-293 2000
Leicester, Loughborough: LCL Cable
0800 952 2222
Lichfield, Burntwood, Rugeley
LCL Cable
0800 952 2222
LONDON
East End:
Cable and Wireless
020-7363 2000
Barnet, Brent, Ealing, Fulham,
Greenwich, Harrow, Kensington,
Lambeth, Lewisham, Southwark:
Cable and Wireless
020-8244 1234
Bromley:
Cable and Wireless
020-8446 9966
Camden, Enfield, Hackney, Haringey,
Islington:
Cable London (Comcast/TeleWest)
020-7911 0911
Croydon to Richmond:
United Artists (TeleWest)
020-8760 0222
Hillingdon, Hounslow:
Middx Cable (Gen Cable)
01753-810810
Westminster Cable (BT)
020-7935 4400

M
Motherwell, Hamilton, East Kilbride:
United Artists (TeleWest)
01698-322332

N
Northampton: Telecential
01604-643619
Northern Ireland CableTel N Ireland
01483-254000
Norwich: Cable (Cable and Wireless)
01603-787892
Notts, Grimsby, Lincoln, Mansfield:
Diamond Cable
0115-952 2240

P
Peterborough:
Cable and Wireless
01733-371717

S
Southampton, Eastleigh:
Cable and Wireless
023-8031 5000
Surrey: north, north east:
Cable and Wireless
01372-360844
Swansea, Neath, Port Talbot:
CableTel
029-2045 6644
Swindon: Swindon Cable (Telecential)
01793-480483

T
Tamworth, north Warwicks and
Meriden
Tamworth Cable (LCL)
0800 952 2222
Thames Valley, Basingstoke,
Wycombe:
Telecential
01734-756868
Tyneside:
United Artists (TeleWest)
0191-420 2000

W
Windsor, Slough, Maidenhead,
Heathrow:
Windsor TV (Gen Cable)
01753-810810
Wolverhampton, Dudley, Telford:
Cable Midlands (SBC)
01384-838483

Local TV: Restricted Service Licences

Restricted Services Licences were introduced by the 1996 Broadcasting Act and the first RSL to go live was TV12 which began in the Isle of Wight in October 1998. It was followed by Lanarkshire Television, the Oxford Channel and MATV in Leicester. Derry's TVC9 and Edinburgh's Channel 6 began in September 1999. More services are due for Bath, Cardiff, Hertford, Portsmouth, Chichester, Perth, Dundee and Aberdeen.

The way it works is that unused analogue frequencies are leased for broadcasts to a particular establishment or other defined location or even for a particular event. These new licences are available in two forms: the RSL L, such as taken out by TV12, is a renewable four year licence whereas the RSL E covers a maximum 56 day festival or sporting event.

The licensing process has two stages. An application to the Independent Television Commission must be covered by a fee to cover initial frequency planning work. If a potential frequency is identified, a further payment covers national and international frequency clearing work. Applicants successfully completing this stage are granted a licence upon payment of the ITC licence fee and the Wireless Telegraphy Act fee. If the frequency remains available, an RSL holder may reapply for a further two year licence at the end of the initial term, although this is open to competition.

KEY CONTACT

Local Independent Television Network
c/o Community Media Association, 15 Paternoster Row, Sheffield S1 2BX
Fax 0114-279 8976   Tel 0114-279 5219
E-mail: cma@commedia.org.uk
Website: www.litn.org.uk
LITN is an association of local TVstations who are operating under Restricted Service Licences or are applying for a licence. LITN is developing work in policy and regulation, promotion, businesss development and support. It is administered by the Community Media Association.

Lanarkshire Television
Hartwood Village, Shotts, Lancashire ML7 4LA
Tel 01591-82287
E-mail: lanarkshire@btinternet.com
Covers: Hamilton, Motherwell, East Kilbride
Contact: John MacKenzie

MATV
MPK House, 233 Belgrave Gate, Leicester LE1 3HT
Fax 0116-253 8900   Tel 0116-253 2288
E-mail: mbc.matv@technocom.com
Website: www.matv.co.uk
Owner: V Popat, H Popat, S M Majithia
Chairman: Ashwin Mistry
Managing director: Vinod Popat
Programme controller: Nilesh Thanki

MSTV
164 Deansgate, Manchester M60 2RD
Tel 0161-211 2366
Covers: Manchester
Owner: Manchester Student Television
Contact: Philip Reevell

Oxford Channel
270 Woodstock Road, Oxford OX2 7NW
Fax 01865-553355   Tel 01865-570000
E-mail: admin@oxfordchannel.com
Website: www.oxfordchannel.com
Owner: Oxford Broadcasting Ltd
Chairman: Frank Harding
Managing directors: Deborah Cackler/Thomas Harding

TV12
The Medina Centre, Fairlee Road, Newport, Isle of Wight PO30 2EW
Fax 01983-521660   Tel 01983-524745
E-mail: pault@tv12.co.uk
Website: www.tv12.co.uk
Covers: Isle of Wight and Solent region/Chichester
Chairman: Graham Benson
Managing director: Paul Meade
Station manager: Paul Topping
TV12 broadcasts a local mix of entertainment, current affairs, sports, weather and news 24 hours a day.

TVC9
Foyle Arts Centre, Lawrence Hill, Derry BT48 7NJ
Fax 01504-289901   Tel 01504-289900
E-mail: paulb@tvc9com/
Website: www.tvc9.com
Covers: Greater Londonderry
Owner: Derry Media Access, Honeybee Enterprises, VFG Finance
Chairman: Robert Gavin
Chief executive: Paul Boyle
Sales and marketing: Paudrig O'Dwyer
Finance director: John Ward

Teletext

Teletext is written copy broadcast on TV sets. All the main television companies operate a teletext service with bulletins on news, sport, travel, weather and entertainment. The BBC and Channels 3, 4 and 5 provide subtitling for people with hearing difficulties. About a half of all households have teletext decoders and the weekly audience is over 20 million.

The main teletext services are: Ceefax on BBC; Teletext Ltd on ITV; Simple Active on Channel 4; Data Broadcasting International (DBI) which uses spare capacity within the Channel 3 signal to provide commercial services; Sky Text from Sky; and 5 text which uses spare capacity on the Channel 5 signal and is a service licensed by the ITC to Sky Five Limited for ten years.

Ceefax is an in-house BBC operation which has recently merged with BBC News Online. Its editorial extends beyond text related to BBC TV programming and has recently expanded with local news, sport, weather, travel and TV listings for each of the BBC's 13 regions.

Teletext Ltd is an ITC-licensed consortium which is 75 per cent owned by the Daily Mail and General Trust. Simple Active has an ITV licence to use spare capacity within the Channel 4 signal to transmit "data packages for provision to a range of professional and consumer markets, with sub-licensing of some capacity to other users". Simple Active shares a senior management with DBI, which has another ITC licensee which "uses spare capacity within the Channel 3 signal and provides commercial services to subscription and to closed user groups". Sky Text has been available on Sky channels since 1992 and the latest Teletext arrival, 5 text, went live in autumn 1997 carrying news, sport, TV listings, weather, travel and advertising.

Ceefax (BBC teletext)
Room 7540, BBC Television Centre, Wood Lane, London W12 7RJ
Fax 020-8749 6734   Tel 020-8576 1801
E-mail: ceefax@bbc.co.uk
Editor: Paul Brannan

Data Broadcasting International
Allen House, Station Road, Egham, Surrey TW20 9NT
Fax: 01784-738734   Tel: 01784-477534
Website: www.databroadcasting.co.uk
Commercial additional service Channel 3 teletext. Uses spare capacity within the Channel 3 signal, operated by sub-licensees and closed user groups.
Chairman: Justin Cadbury
Managing director: Peter Mason

Sky Five Text Limited (5 text)
96-97 Wilton Road, London SW1V 1DW
Fax 020-7599 8975   Tel: 020-7599 8904
Email: 5text@5text.co.uk
The ten year licence to provide an additional service using spare capacity on the Channel 5 signal was awarded in July 1997 to Sky Five Text. The name on Channel 5 is 5 text. The service includes news, sport, television listings, weather, travel and advertising.
Chairman: Damien Harte
General manager: David Klein

Sky Text
BSkyB, West Cross House, Grant Way, Isleworth, Middlesex TW7 5QD
    Tel 020-7705 3000

SimpleActive
Allen House, Station Road, Egham, Surrey TW20 9NT
Fax: 01784-477722   Tel: 01784-477711
Website: www.databroadcasting.co.uk
SimpleActive has a licence to use spare capacity within C4 (and S4C in Wales) and provides data packages to various professional and consumer markets.
Chairman: Justin Cadbury
Managing director: Peter Mason

Teletext (ITV teletext)
101 Farm Lane, London SW6 1QJ
Fax 020-7386 5002   Tel 020-7386 5000
E-mail: dutyed@teletext.co.uk
Website: www.teletext.co.uk
Managing director: Mike Stewart
Editorial director: Graham Lovelace
ITC 1998 Performance Review: "At the end of 1998 22 million viewers wre using the service at least once a week compared to 13 million when the service began. Complaints were at a negligible level. A range of services were introduced during the year, notably in the city and finance section and in sport.

TV and radio news agencies

AA Roadwatch
Fanum House, The Broadway, Stanmore HA7 4DF
Fax 020-8420 8732   Tel 020-8420 8602
E-mail: lynn.healey@theaa.com
Trafffic and travel information provider to commercial radio, television, new media and on-line services.

ABC News Intercontinental
3 Queen Caroline Street, London W6 9PE
Fax 020-8222 5021   Tel 020-8222 5500
London office of the American news network.

APTN - Associated Press Television News
32 Oval Road, Camden Lock, London NW1 7DZ
Fax 020-7413 8311   Tel 020-7482 7400
E-mail: aptninfo@ap.org
Website: www.aptn.com
APTN is the international television arm of The Associated Press. APTN's operations include: a broad selection of specialised television services - the main news service; a specialised broadcst service; customised coverage for the Middle East; a productions division; weekly and daily entertainment news; an extensive video library; a current affairs programme, sports news and 83 bureaux in 67 countries.

BBC Parliament
160 Great Portland Street, London W1N 5TB
Fax 020-7299 5300   Tel 020-7299 5000
E-mail: viewer_tpc@flextech.co.uk
Website: www.parlchan.co.uk
Provides unedited live coverage of daily proceedings in the House of Commons and recorded coverage of the Lords, Parliamentary committees, business statements, the European Union and Question Time. Now run by the BBC, the channel was created by the British Cable Industry.

Bloomberg Television
39-45 Finsbury Square, London EC2A 1PQ
Fax 020-7392 6000   Tel 020-7330 7500
Website: www.bloomberg.com/uk
Covers business and financial news stories with multiscreen format. Broadcasts ten channels around the world in eight languages. Available on cable, satellite and Sky Digital.

CBS News
68 Knightsbridge, London SW1X 7LL
Fax 020-7581 4431   Tel 020-7581 4801
London office of the American news network.

CNN International
19-22 Rathbone Place, London W1P 1DF
Fax 020-7637 6738   Tel 020-7637 6700
Website: www.cnn.com
Cable News Network International, a wholly owned subsidiary of Time Warner Inc., is the world's only global network. Distributing 24-hour news via 15 satellites CNN and CNNI are seen by 224 million households in more than 210 countries. and territories world-wide, and have 36 international bureaux and nearly 700 affiliated TV stations around the world.

FSN-Feature Story Productions
40-44 Newman Street, London W1P 3PA
Fax 020-7436 9138   Tel 020-7580 4160
E-mail: london.bureau@featurestory.co.uk
Provides customised on-air coverage for radio and TV networks worldwide, including Global TV News, South African Broadasting Corporation, Channel News Asia, Asia News International, Radio New Zealand and National Public Radio.

FT Business News
50 Lisson Street, London NW1 5DF
Fax 020-7723 6132   Tel 020-7402 1011
Business and personal finance news for commercial radio from Unique Broadcasting, FT and ABC Radio.

IRN - Independent Radio News
200 Gray's Inn Road, London WC1X 8X2
Fax 020-7430 4092   Tel 020-7430 4090
News desk   Tel 020-7430 4814
E mail: news@irn.co.uk
Website: wttp://www.irn.co.uk
IRN is Britain's main radio news agency, supplying bulletins and services to over 90 per cent of the commercial radio stations. The news is provided to IRN by ITN, using the resources of ITN at its headquarters in 200 Grays Inn Road. IRN is effectively a commissioning agency acting on behalf of its customers. Its owners are the main radio groups.

ITN
200 Grays Inn Road, London WC1X 8XZ
Fax 020-7833 3000   Tel 020-7833 3000
Press office   Tel 020-7430 4700
E-mail: press.office@itn.co.uk
Website: www.itn.co.uk
ITN produces the daily news programmes for three competing British TV channels: ITV, Channel 4 and Channel 5. Other output includes radio news bulletins, documentaries, educational programmes, Internet websites and archive clips. ITN is also responsible for Euronews, a news channel in six languages which is seen in 43 countries. Founded in 1955 as the news department of ITV, ITN is now owned by a consortium comprising Carlton Communications, the Granada Group, Daily Mail & General Trust, UNM and Reuters.

The big news on radio.

240 Stations – 27 million listeners.

Source: Rajar

London News Network

London Television Centre, Upper Ground, London
SE1 9LT
Fax 020-7827 7710   Tel 020-7827 7700
Website: www.lnn-tv.co.uk
Jointly set up and run by the London ITV companies
Carlton and LWT to provide their local news. Began in
January 1992. Also supplies news to GMTV.

Lucas Media

72 New Bond Street, London W1Y 9DD
Fax 0870-707 0870   Tel 0870-707 0870
E-mail: go@Lucas-Media.com
Website: www.UKBroadcastNews.com
UK national and international news information
provider. Entertainment and current affairs for radio.

Metro Networks

29th Floor, Centre Point, London WC1A 1DD
Fax 020-7312 1320   Tel 020-7312 1300
E-mail: admin@metronetworks.co.uk
Website: www.metronetworks.co.uk
UK national and international news and travel news
provider for UK radio stations.

News Direct

200 Grays Inn Road, London WC1X 8XZ
Fax 020-7312 8470   Tel 020-7973 1152
Providing a 24-hour rolling news and information
service for London with news, traffic, weather, sport,
entertainment, city and headlines every 20 minutes.

NBC News Worldwide

8 Bedford Avenue, London WC1B 3AP
Fax 020-8600 6601   Tel 020-8600 6600
E-mail: nhaw@nbc.com
London office of the American network.

Parliamentary Channel

See BBC Parliament

Reuters

85 Fleet Street, London EC4P 4AJ
Fax 020-7542 4970   Tel 020-7250 1122
E-mail: rtv@reuters.com
Website: www.reuters.com
The Reuters Television network of more than 70
bureaux around the world provides broadcasters with a
fast, reliable news service. The Reuters Television World
News Service (WNS) delivers news feeds, news flashes,
live coverage and in-depth features via satellite to more
than 200 broadcasters plus their networks and affiliates
in 85 countries 24 hours a day. Reuters is an
independent public company, founded in 1851.

Sportsmedia Broadcasting

Number 47, Canalot Studios, 222 Kensal Road,
London W10 5BN
Fax 020-8960 6999   Tel 020-8962 9000
E-mail: jonny.gould@sportsmedia.co.uk
UK national and international sports news provider for
INR and ILR.

TV News London

Southbank House, Black Prince Road, Albert
Embankment, London SE1 7SJ
Fax 020-7793 4144   Tel 020-7793 4013
E-mail: roz@tvnews.ftech.co.uk
London news agency supplying stories about events in
the capital to regional broadcasting companies. Started
in 1992.

Unique's Business News/Unique's Entertainment News

50 Lisson Street, London NW1 5DF
Fax 020-7723 6132   Tel 020-7402 1011
E-mail: anna.burles@unique.com
Website: www.unique.co.uk
Financial and entertainment news for commercial
radio. Europe's largest independent producer of radio,
originating programming for all 5 BBC networks, the
BBC World Service and over 200 commercial radio
stations worldwide. It also provides multi-media
content to new media platforms.

Worldwide Television News (WTN)

See APTN

WRN (World Radio Network)

Wyvil Court, 10 Wyvil Road, London SW8 2TG
Fax 020-7896 9007   Tel 020-7896 9000
E-mail: online@wrn.org
Website: www.wrn.org
WRN operates a 24 hour-a-day network with news,
current affairs and feature programmes from 28 of the
world's public service broadcasters. WRN has three
language streams: English, German and Mulit-lingual,
for listeners across Europe, Africa, the Middle East,
Asia, the Pacific and North America. WRN 's European
English-language stream is available live via the
Internet and is also transmitted on DAB in both
London and Warsaw.

x-trax

5-13 Leeke Street, London WC1X 9HX
Fax 020-7923 5001   Tel 020 7923 5000
E-mail: info@x-trax.com
Website: www.x-trax.com
Provider of weekly entertainment features to stations
throughout the UK and Ireland. Also provides a
monthly show preparation/industry magazine.

onair

online

► **on**ward

► **control**the**power**

Market Tiers 4DC is the UK's leading radio and online agency... developing client campaigns across editorial and commercial areas... **providing media owners with programming and content**

commercialservices | promotions • sponsorship • advertising

editorialservices | interviews and webchats • webcasts & outside broadcasts audio/video features • competitions • media tours • fax-wires & e-wires • e-marketing QSheet magazine

To find out more, call **020 7253 8888** or email **inbox@markettiers4dc.com**

www.markettiers4dc.com

 **market**tiers**4DC**

Film libraries

KEY CONTACTS

Researcher's Guide to British Film and TV Collections
British Universities Film and Video Council, 77 Well Street, London W1P 3RE
Fax 020-7393 1555   Tel: 020-7393 1500
E-mail: ask@buvfc.ac.uk
Website: www.bufvc.ac.uk

FOCAL International: Federation of Commercial Audio Visual Libraries
Pentax House, South Hill Avenue, Northolt Road, South Harrow HA2 0DU
Fax 020-8423 5853   Tel 020-8933 4826
E-mail: info@focalint.org
Website: www.focalint.org
FOCAL is the international trade association for audio visual libraries, researchers and producers. It promotes the use of library footage, stills and sound in programming and holds regular seminars and meetings. Covers copyright, research, marketing and technology.

A19 Film and Video
21 Foyle Street, Sunderland, SR1 1LE
Fax 0191-565 6288   Tel 0191-565 5709
Documentary, current affairs and arts programming.

Archive Film Agency
21 Lidgett Park Avenue, Leeds LS8 1EU
Fax 0113-266 2454   Tel 0113-266 2454
Specialists in early newsreel, documentary, fiction. With a current stock shot library covering the world.

Archive Films
17 Conway Street, London W1Y6EE
Fax 020-7391 9123   Tel 020-7312 0300
E-mail: info@imagebank.co.uk
Website: www.imagebank.co.uk
30,000 hours of historical entertainment footage including silent films, feature films, newsreels and documentaries.

BBC Worldwide Television Library Sales
Woodlands, 80 Wood Lane, London W12 0TT
Fax 020-8433 2939   Tel 020-8576 2861
E-mail: ukls@bbcfootage.com
The BBC has Britain's largest library of film and videotape, with over 400 million feet of film.

Beulah
66 Rochester Way, Crowborough, Sussex TN6 2DU
Fax 01892-652413   Tel 01892-652413
E-mail: beulah@enterprise.net
Website: www.homepages.enterprise.net/beulah
Films and stills library of transport and social history.

British Film Institute
21 Stephen Street, London W1P 2LN
Fax 020-7436 7950   Tel 020-7255 1444
E-mail: helpdesk@bfi.org.uk
Website: www.bfi.org.uk
300,000 titles. BFI Collections also handles sales from the 7 million images in Stills, Posters and Designs.

British Movietone News
North Orbital Road, Denham, Middlesex UB9 5HQ
Fax 01895-834893   Tel 01895-833071
E-mail: library@mtone.co.uk
Website: www.movietone.com
1929-79 newsreel, including the Look at Life collection.

British Pathe
4th Floor, 60 Charlotte Street, London W1P 2AX
Fax 020-7436 3232   Tel 020-7323 0407
E-mail: pathe@enterprise.net
Website: www.britishpathe.com
50m feet of historical film footage from 1895 to 1970.

Carlton International Media
35-38 Portman Square, London W1H 0NU
Fax 020-7486 1707   Tel 020-7224 3339
E-mail: enquiries@carltonint.co.uk
Website: www.carltonint.co.uk
The Carlton International library of over 20,000 hours of film and television programming includes the Carlton Film Collection which is a selection of 1500 classic feature films, spanning over 60 years of European cinema from the Rank, Korda, Romulus, ITC and Rohauer film libraries.

Central Office of Information Footage File
4th Floor, 184-192 Drummond Street, London NW1 3HP
Fax 020-7383 2333   Tel 020-7383 2288
E-mail: research@film-images.com
40,000 Crown Copyright titles from the government's News and Information archives spanning over 75 years of British industrial, political, social and sporting history.

Channel 4 Clip Library
Channel 4 International, 124 Horseferry Road, London SW1P 2TX
Fax 020-7306 8363   Tel 020-7306 8490
E-mail: caustin@channel4.co.uk
Website: www.channel4.com

East Anglian Film Archive
University of East Anglia, Norwich NR4 7TJ
Fax 01603-458553   Tel 01603-592664
E-mail: eafa@uea.ac.uk
Web: www.uea.ac.uk/eafa/
Non-profit archive of moving images relating to Beds, Cambs, Essex, Herts, Norfolk and Suffolk from 1896 to the present.

Educational & Television Films
247a Upper Street, London N1 1RU
Fax 020-7226 8016   Tel 020-7226 2298
E-mail: zoe@etvltd.demon.co.uk
Website: www.etvltd.demon.co.uk
Documentary and factual films from the Soviet Union, Eastern Europe, China, Vietnam, Cuba, the British Labour movement and the Spanish Civil War.

Energy Film
101 Bayham Street, London NW1 0AG
Fax 020-7544 3400   Tel 020-7544 3410
E-mail: energy@getty-images.com
Website: www.energyfilm.com
Leading supplier of licensable cinematography with a large collection of footage spanning 100 years and just about every subject imaginable.

Environmental Investigation Agency
69-85 Old Street, London EC1 9HX
Fax 020-7490 0436   Tel 020-7490 7040
E-mail: info@eia-international.org
Website: www.eia-international.org
Film dedicated to exposing the illegal international trade in wildlife as well as trade in ozone depleting substances and illegal timber.

Film Research
177-183 Regent Street, London W1R 8LA
Fax 020-7734 8017   Tel 020-7734 1525
E-mail: frps@aol.com.
Provides a research service for footage for all media purposes.

GMTV Library Sales
The London Television Centre, Upper Ground, London SE1 9TT
Fax 020-7827 7043   Tel 020-7827 7363
E-mail: librarysales@gmtv.co.uk
Website: www.gmtv.co.uk
UK and worldwide news, showbiz, fashion and feature items and stockshots from October 1992 to present day.

Huntley Film Archives
78 Mildmay Park, London N1 4PR
Fax 020-7241 4929   Tel 020-7923 0990
E-mail: films@huntleyarchives.com
Website: www.huntleyarchives.com
Adverts, animation, art, dance, education, fashion, features, food, geography, history, industry, media, medicine, music, nature, personalities, places, royalty, science, social history, sport, stills, transport, war.

Image Bank Film
17 Conway Street, London W1P 6EE
Fax 020-7391 9123   Tel 020-7312 0300
E-mail: london@theimagebank.com
Website: www.imagebank.co.uk
The largest source of film imagery in the world with footage available from 75 offices worldwide.

Imperial War Museum Film & Video Archive
Lambeth Road, London SE1 6HZ
Fax 020-7416 5299   Tel 020-7416 5291
E-mail: film@iwm.org.uk
Holds material covering all aspects of conflict from the Boer War to Bosnia. Totals 120 million feet of film and 6,000 hours of videotape.

Index Stock Shots
12 Charlotte Mews, London W1P 1LN
Fax 020-7436 8737   Tel 020-7631 0134
E-mail: index@msn.com
Website: www.index-stockshots.com
Contemporary stock footage on 35mm film and tape, including aerials, cities, landmarks. Archival footage of Grand Prix racing, aviation, industry etc.

IVN Entertainment
500 Chiswick High Road, London W4 5RG
Fax 020-8956 2339   Tel 020-8956 2454
E-mail: bobburgis@aol.com
Website: www.ivn.com
Travel, including Reader's Digest and Lonely Planet footage. Free loan of BITC VHS.

ITN Archive
200 Grays Inn Road, London WC1X 8XZ
Fax 020-7430 4453   Tel 020-7430 4480
E-mail: archive.sales@itn.co.uk
Website: www.itnarchive.com
Material spanning the century from the ITN and Reuters television archives in the UK and the historic French Pathé library.

ITV
The ITV companies have libraries of material:

Anglia	01603-615151
Central	0121-643 9898
Channel Four	020-7396 4444
Granada	0161-827 2207
HTV	029-2059 0590
LWT	020-7620 1620
Meridian	023-8022 2555
Scottish	0141-300 3000
Ulster	028-9032 8122
Yorkshire - Tyne Tees	0113-243 8283

The London Film Archive
78 Mildmay Park, London N1 4PR
Fax 020-7241 4929   Tel 020-7923 4074
London images from 1895 to the present day, including streets, landmarks, housing, education and the arts.

London Stockshots Library
London News Network, London TV Centre, Upper
Ground, London SE1 9LT
Fax 020-7827 7579   Tel 020-7827 7784
E-mail: library@lnn-tv.co.uk
Website: www.lnn-tv.co.uk
LNN library of London region coverage during the
nineties.

North West Film Archive
The Manchester Metropolitan University, Minshull
House, 47-49 Chorlton Street, Manchester M1 3EU
Fax 0161-247 3098   Tel 0161-247 3097
E-mail: n.w.filmarchive@mmu.ac.uk
Website: www.nwfa.mmu.ac.uk
Documentary collection about life in the North West
region dating from 1896 to the present. Contact the
commercial access assistant for enquiries.

Nova Productions
11a Winholme, Armthorpe, Doncaster DN3 3AF
Fax 0870-1257917   Tel 01302-833422
E-mail: nova@sms.genie.co.uk
Production company with a social documentary archive
of shopping, transport and ways of life. Also runs the
Doncaster Film & Video Archive.

Oxford Scientific Films
Lower Road, Long Hanborough, Oxon OX8 8LL
Fax 01993-882808   Tel 01993-881881
E-mail: enquiries@osf.uk.com
Website: www.osf.uk.com
Natural history films, commercials, non-broadcast film
and extensive stills and footage resources.

Pearson Television International Archive
1 Stephen Street, London W1P 1PJ
Fax 020-7691 6080   Tel 020-7691 6733
E-mail: archive@pearsontv.com
Website: www.pearsontvarchive.com
The programme archive dates back to mid-fifties and
includes Thames, Grundy, ACI, Alomo and All
American productions with total of 15,000 hours of
programming.

Polygram Film and Television Library
See Carlton International Media

Reuters Television
85 Fleet Street, London EC4P 4AJ
                          Tel 020-7250 1122
TV news archive with over 26,000 hours of material.

Ronald Grant Archive
The Master's House, The Old Lambeth Workhouse, 2
Dugord Way, off Renfrew Road, London SE11 4TH
Fax 020-7840 2299   Tel 020-7840 2200
E-mail: martin@cinemamuseum.org.uk
Images of cinema and film from 1896 to present day.

RSPB Moving Images
61 Great Titchfield Street, London W1P 7FL
Fax 020-7580 2242   Tel 0230-7636 1818
E-mail: mail@rspblibrary.com
Website: www.rspblibrary.com
Natural history collection with British and international
birds. Also stock footage of landscapes and British
countryside.

Scottish Film & Television Archive
1 Bowmont Gardens, Glasgow G12 9LR
Fax 0141-377 7413   Tel 0141-337 7400

Sky News Library Sales
Grant Way, Isleworth TW7 5QD
Fax 020-7705 3201   Tel 020-7705 2872/3132
E-mail: libsales@bskyb.com
Website: www.sky.com/skynewssales/
Sky News, current affairs and entertainment footage
from 1989. Held on-site, available 24 hours a day.

Sports Video Library
see TWI Archive

TWI Archive
TWI, Axis Centre, Burlington Lane, London W4 2TH
Fax 020-8233 5301   Tel 020-8233 5500
E-mail: twiarchive@imgworld.com
Website: www.twiarchive.com
Video library of TWI sports programming.

Universal International Television
5-7 Mandeville Place, London W1M 5LB
Fax 020-7307 7501   Tel 020-7307 7500
The ATV/ITV libraries from 1955-1981.

Wales Film & Television Archive
Unit 1, Science Park, Cefn Llan, Aberystwyth SY23 3AH
Fax 01970-626008   Tel 01970-626007
E-mail: wftva@sgrin.co.uk
Website: www.sgrin.co.uk
The collection affects Welsh life in a variety of film
genres (documentary, drama, home movies, enimation
etc) from 1898 to the presnt day.

Wessex Film & Sound Archive
Sussex Street, Winchester, Hants SO23 8TH
Fax 01962-878681   Tel 01962-847742
E-mail: sadedm@hants.gov.uk
Website: www.hants.gov.uk/record-office/film.htmc
Documentary film and sound archive collections from
central southern England, particularly Hampshire.

Independent TV producers

There are around 1,500 independent TV producers of whom just over 1,100 are members of Pact - the Producers' Alliance for Cinema and Television. Between them they generate over £1 billion worth of programmes a year for a concentration of wealth that has been dependent on three factors: the rise of satellite and then digital TV; legislation from 1988 compelling terrestrial broadcasters to commission at least a quarter of their schedules from outside; and the establishment of Channel 4 as a TV publisher in 1982.

Peter Bazalgette, the creative director of Endemol Entertainment (a company co-owned by the Guardian until it sold its stake for £26 million in August 2000), feels independents are threatened by recent media turmoil. "Independent producers had a glorious history from the inception of Channel 4, via the 25 per cent production quota, to a position of creative dominance," he wrote in the Guardian in May 2000. "But, according to a number of wishful thinkers, it's all coming to an end. Several large indies are losing their status after being bought by broadcasters. A single ITV in England would no longer need a network centre with outside commissions. And the BBC is reviving in-house production at the expense of peddlers outside the city walls. Meanwhile, we're told, the new media maelstrom will sweep away such old-fashioned nostrums as the 1988 quota." In anticipation of communications reform, Bazalgette talked of preserving intellectual property within a new unspecified framework.

FIRST RUN HOURS (1998)

CHANNEL	HOURS
Satellite	4,913 hours
Channel 4	2,536 hours
ITV	1,055 hours
Channel 5	950 hours
BBC2	765 hours
BBC1	730 hours

Source DGA/BARB

KEY CONTACT

Pact
45 Mortimer Street, London W1N 7TD
Fax 020-7331 6700
Tel 020-7331 6000
E-mail: enquiries@pact.co.uk
Website: www.pact.co.uk

123 Productions	020-7263 4199
1A Productions	01360-620855
2.4 Media	01562-822099
3BM Television	020-7439 2664
3Di TV Software	0113-294 4343
400 Company	020-8746 1400
421 Productions	01524-842421

A

A19 Film & Video	0191-565 5709
A38 Films	01822 833955
AAA Productions	01622-880855
Aardman Animation	0117-984 8485
Abbey Films	01865-725015
About Face Media	028-9089 4555
Absolutely Productions	
	020-7930 3113
Acacia Productions	020-8341 9392
Achievement Concepts	
	01584-890893
Action Time (North)	0161-236 8999
Adams Wooding TV	01453-885700
Addictive Television	020-7700 0333

Adval	01243-578000
Afro Wisdom Films	020-7490 8386
After Image	020-7737 7300
Agenda Television	01554-880810
Agran Barton TV	020-7351 7070
Ailsa Productionns	0141-331 1005
Aimimage Productions	
	020-7916 3734
Airforce Television	01622-661800
Alan Torjussen	029-2062 4669
Alcibiades	020-89688873
Alfalfa Entertainments	
	020-7284 3275
Alhambra Films	01505 874111
Alibi Communications	
020-7845 0400	
Alive Productions	020-7384 2243
Amirani Films	020-7625 5551
Andrea Florence	020-7794 3787
Angel Express	020-8878 8563
angel eye film & tv	020-7437 0082
Angel Films	020-7704 9008

Animation Partnership	
	020-7636 3300
Annalogue	020-8743 3630
Antelope	020-7209 0099
Antelope South	01273-648800
Antena Productions	029-2031 2000
Antidote	01225-722262
Antonine Films	0141-221 6555
Apex TV	01223-872900
Approaching Fish	020-8960 6616
Apt Film & TV	020-7284 1695
Arcadia Films	020-7235 5935
Arcadian Productions	
	01430-430100
Ardent Productions	01276-700800
Aries Productions	01372-457724
Ark Productions	020-8788 8762
Armadillo Films	020-7439 0400
Around the World Productions	
	028-9068 2421
Artificial Eye	020-7240 5353
ASD Films	020-7253 0439
Aspect Television	029-2041 4100

Asylum Pictures	0131-270 5069
At It Productions	020-7323 6922
Atlantic Eye	020-7403 8528
Atlantic Productions	020-7371 3200
Attaboy TV	020-7564 6715
Augustus Films	020-8737 0405
Attic Productions	01423-504386
Atticus TV	020-8876 0406
Automatic Pictures	01752-201555
Available Light	0117-929 1311
Avalon TV	020-7598 7280
AVC Media	01224-248007
Avie Littler Assoc	020-7794 2742
Avonbridge Film	0131-478 4439
AVP Films	01773-828902

B

B&T Productions	020-7254 7737
Baby Films	020-7482 6467
Backbone Productions	
	020-7281 0445
Baker Tilly	020-7413 5100
Bamboo Film & TV	020-7916 9353
Bangaw Cyf	029-2059 0225
Bard Entertainments	
	020-7787 2777
Bare Faced Productions	
	020-8671 1139
Barraclough Carey	020-7258 6800
Bazal	020-7462 9000
Beach, The	020-7437 6957
Beach House	020-7689 0927
Beckett Communications	
	020-8669 8730
Beckmann Productions	
	01624-816585
Beeley Productions	0117-973 0200
Bell TV	01206-240192
Berwick Universal Pictures	
	020-7923 1998
Besom Productions	028-7137 0303
Best Productions	020-7373 2218
Beyond International	
	020-7636 9611
Beyond the Frame	020-7631 4441
BFI Production	020-7255 1444
BFM Productions	0121-248 3903
Big Bear Films	020-7229 5982
Big Events Co	020-8946 0056
Big Eye Film & TV	0161-832 6111
Big Idea Productions	
	020-7224 5100
Big Issue Film Unit	020-7526 3200
Big Strand	020-8876 7047
Big Table Film Co, The	
	020-7720 9349
Big Talk Productions	
	020-7255 1131
Bird & Bird	020-7415 6000
Bitcom International	01483-574545
Black Bear	0131-447 7448

Black Coral	020-8520 4569
Black Pudding Productions	
	020-7385 5561
Blackbird Productions	
	020-7352 4882
Blackwatch Productions	
	0141-341 0044
Blakeway Productions	
	020-8743 2040
Blast! Films	020-7267 4260
Blenheim TV Films	01491-614288
Blow By Blow Productions	
	01522-754901
Blue Heaven Productions	
	020-7436 5552
Blue Horizon	020-7434 2467
Bob Godfrey Films	020-7278 5711
Bounds Away	01892-521373
Bour Productions	020-8995 1308
Brainstorm Films	01736-732063
Branded Film	020-7706 7206
Breathing Canyon	020-7708 2931
Brechin Productions	
	020-8614 2893
Brenda Rowe Productions	
	0117-973 0390
Brian Waddell Productions	
	028-9042 7646
Bright Thoughts Co	01934-642732
Brighter Pictures	020-7733 7333
Britt Allcroft Group, The	
	023-8033 1661
British Pathe	020-7323 0407
British Screen	020-7323 9080
Britt Allcroft Company	
	023-8033 1661
Broad Productions	01505-843700
Broadbent Partnership	
	0141-332 2042
Bronco Films	0141-287 6817
Bronson Knight	020-7734 7042
Brook Lapping Productions	
	020-7428 3100
Brookside Productions	
	0151-722 9122
Buena Vista	020-8222 2578
Buffalo Pictures	020-7439 0401
Bumper Films	01934-418961
Burning Gold	0117-924 0905
Burrill Productions	020-7384 1122
Buxton Raven	020-7296 0012
BW Productions	020-7935 9788

C

Cactus Television	020-7465 6232
Cafe Productions	020-7460 4700
Caledonia, Sterne & Wyld	
	0141-353 3153
Callister Commuications	
	01846-673717
Cambrensis	029-2025 7075

Cambridge Film & TV	
	01223-236007
Cambridge Video	01223-553416
Canopus Communications	
	020-8858 3001
Canvasback Productions	
	020-8940 6710
Carey Films	0113-250 6411
Carey Street Productions	
	020-7586 7753
Carnival Films	020-8968 1818
Carol Gould	020-7266 1953
Case TV	020-7296 0010
Castle Haven Digital	01557-870366
Catalist Films	0141-942 5621
Catalyst TV	020-7603 7030
Catherine Bailey	020-7483 2681
Cause n Effect PH	020-7253 7371
CBTV	01434-602867
Celador Productions	
	020-7240 8101
Celtic Films	020-7637 7651
Celtic Productions	029-2075 2532
Central Reservation	0141-243 2123
Century Films	020-7378 6106
Chameleon Television	
	0113-244 4486
Channel X	020-7387 3874
Chapter One	020-8324 2744
Chariot Productions	0191-230 4449
Charlotte Metcalf Productions	
	020-7371 2389
Chatsworth	020-7734 4302
Cheeky Ideas	01923-859692
Cheerful Scout	020-7287 0076
Cheerleader Productions	
	0171 258 6800
Cheriton Enterprises	
	01963-350113
Children's Film/TV Foundation	
	020-8953 0844
Children's Film Unit	020-8785 0350
Childsplay Productions	
	020-7328 1429
Chistera Productions	
	028-9061 5573
Choi & Co	01904-470787
Christmas TV & Film Co	
	020-7733 0110
Christopher Swann Assocs	
	020-8749 9056
Christopher Sykes Production	
	020-8563 1790
Chrysalis Sport	020-7284 2288
Chrysalis Television	020-7465 6353
Chrysalis Visual Entertainment	
	020-7221 2213
Cicada Films	020-7266 4646
Cinar Europe	020-7591 7500
Cinecam Productions	
	01638-500888

Cinecontact	020-7323 0618
Cinecosse	01358-722150
Cinema Verity	020-7460 2777
Cinesite(Europe)	020-7973 4000
Cinnabar Films	020-8348 0918
City Broadcasting	01565-634083
Clanvisions	028-9042 1232
Clark	020-7388 7700
Class Productions	01462-742914
Claverdon Films	020-7702 8700
Clear Definition	020-7636 0366
Cogent Pictures	020-7616 9062
Coleridge	01752-761138
Columbia Pictues	020-7533 1000
Comedy House	020-7304 0047
Comedy Unit, The	0141 305 6666
Common Features	0191-261 8808
Communicopia	01273-384900
Company Television	020-7380 3900
Compulsive Viewing	020-7729 4560
Contrast Films	020-8472 5001
Convergence Productions	
	020-8993 3666
Coolbeans Films	0966-432809
Cool Crew Company	
	01292-267281
Cornerstone Films	020-7223 4850
Cosgrove Hall Films	0161-882 2500
Cottonwood Films	020-7385 4323
Couch Potato TV	020-8960 5676
Counterpoint Films	020-7700 4933
Countrywide Films	023-8023 0286
Courtyard Productions	
	01732-700324
Cowboy Films	020-7287 3808
Creation Company, The	
	020-7586 7012
Creation Video	0800 7312945
Creative Alliance	020-7637 2927
Creative Film Productions	
	020-8447 8187
Creative Law	01732-460592
Crewed Up	0161-442 0603
Crinkle Cut Motion Pictures	
	0191-284 4073
Criss Cross	0117-929 2011
Croc Productions	01799-522848
Cronk Dromgoole	020-7287 4441
Crossing the Line Films	
	353 1 287 2622
Cruickshank Cazenove	
	020-7735 2933
Cruisin Pictures	01225-336653
Crystal Media	0131-240 0988
CSV Media (Midlands)	
	0121-683 1800
CTVC	020-8950 4426
Cultural Partnerships	
	020-7254 8217
Cunliffe & Franklyn	01243-532531

Curious Productions	
	020-8299 2957
Curtis & Freud	020-7221 9434
Cutting Edge	020-8780 1476
Cyrus Productions	01491-638349

D

Dai Films	01570-471368
Dakota Films	020-7287 4329
Dan Films	020-7916 4771
Dark Horse Productions	
	01874-665435
Darlow Smithson Productions	
	020-7482 7027
Dashwood Productions	
	01308-420672
Dave Knowles Films	023-8084 2190
Davenhall	01565-653369
David Hickman	020-8995 8016
Dawkins Associates	01622-741900
Day-Lewis Productions	
	01278-671334
Deco Films & TV	020-8748 0448
Deep Water	0410-095581
Demaine Associates	
	020-7376 1739
Denham Productions	
	01752-345444
Dennis Woolf Productions	
	0161-442 8175
Desmond Wilcox	020-8743 7728
Devlin Morris Productions	
	0131-226 7728
Diamond Time	020-8203 3303
Dibb Directions	020-8748 1579
Diplomat Films	0161-929 1603
Direct TV	01865-437878
Disckit	020-8964 2077
Disruptive Element Films	
	0114-268 1350
Diva Pictures	020-8758 8432
Diverse Production	020-7603 4567
DLD Films	01707-664063
DLT Entertainment	020-7631 1184
DNA Films	020-7637 4111
Domaine	01737-766100
Domestic Films	0151-280 1634
Domino Films	01727-750153
Done & Dusted	07000-708708
Double Band Films	028-9024 3331
Double E Productions	
	01769-850583
Double Exposure	020-7490 2499
Double Take	020-8788 5743
Double-Band Films	028-9024 3331
Douglas Chirnside	020-7287 7027
DOX Productions	020-7602 3094
Dragon TV	01625-572544
Drama House	020-7586 1000
Dramatic Productions	
	0118-975 0754

Dreamchaser	020-8960 9555
Duchess Productions	
	020-7637 1684

E

Eagle & Eagle	020-8995 1884
Eagles Productions	0141-639 4217
East Wind Films	01603-628728
ECM Productions	020-7727 5752
Ecosse Films	020-7371 0290
Eden Productions	020-7794 1533
Edinburgh Film & Video	
	01968-672131
Educational Broadcasting	
	020-7765 5023
EFS TV Production	020-8950 8394
Eight Syndicate	020-8883 9929
Electric Sky	01273-384208
Element Films	01747-851448
Element Productions	
	0117-973 8799
Elephant Productions	
	01932-562611
Elgin Productions	020-7243 0660
Elstree Production Co	
	01932-572680
Emme Productions	020-7602 2595
Endboard Productions	
	0121-429 9779
Endemol	020-7462 9000
Endor Productions	020-8985 6459
English & Pockett	020-7287 1155
Enterchoice	020-7373 6796
Entertainment Film Production	
	020-7439 1606
Eo teilifis	353 91 553500
Eolas	01851-705638
Eon Productions	020-7493 7953
Eos Media	0161-428 7220
Epicflow Films	020-8452 8170
Ernst & Young	020-7931 4822
Esta's TV Company	020-8741 2843
Euphoria Films	020-7713 1961
EuroArt Media	020-7221 4162
Evans Woolfe	020-7388 7700
Excalibur Productions	
	01422-843871
Excelsior Group Productions	
	01737-812673
Extreme Film & TV	028-9188 8900
Eye Eye	020-7485 6924
Eye Film & TV	01379-870083
Eye to Eye TV	020-7281 5300

F

Fabulous Fruits	0131-446 0222
Faction Films	020-7690 4446
Fair Game Films	020-7286 8602
Fairline	0141-331 0077
Fairwater Films	029-2057 8488
Farnham Film	01252-710313

Fat Pictures	020-7267 9535
Feature Films	01202-736666
Feelgood Fiction	020-8746 2535
Feline Films	01225-461138
Festival Film & TV	020-8297 9999
Fflic	029-2040 9000
Figment Films	020-7287 3209
Fillum	028-9031 4826
Film Company, The	020-7586 3686
Film Education	020-7976 2291
Film Form Productions	
	020-7794 6967
Film & General Productions	
	020-7235 4495
Film Master Film	39 6 5925926
Film Video Multimedia	
	0973-251391
FilmFair Animation	020-8960 6415
Filmhouse	020-7734 7743
FilmNOVA	0191-402 0017
Films Of Record	020-7286 0333
Filmsmith	020-8332 0706
Filmworks	020-8741 5631
Final Draft Films	020-7386 7010
Finetake Productions	
	020-7359 5786
First Circle Films	020-7221 3737
First Day Productions	
	020-8692 8691
First Freedom Productions	
	020-7916 9355
First Take Films	01603-756879
Firstmile	0468-050145
Flagrant Films	020-7938 3246
Flame Television	020-7713 6868
Flashback Television	
	020-7490 8996
Flat Dog Films	020-7228 0880
Flatiron Films	020-7494 1800
Flipside Films	020-8788 2102
Flying Brick Films	020-7249 7440
Flying Elephant	020-8230 6920
Flying Fox Films	028-9024 4811
Flying Pictures	020-8758 8624
Focus Films	020-7435 9004
Focus International TV	
	020-7493 8801
Folio Productions	020-7258 6800
Footprint Films	07002-366877
Footstep Productions	
	020-7836 9990
Forged Films	0131-667 0230
Forget About It Films	
	029-2021 5369
Forward Films/Altogether Now	
	020-8881 9006
Foundation TV	01622-691111
Foundry Productions	
	020-7793 9976
Fountain TV	020-8900 1188
Fragile Films	020-7287 6200

Frances Anderson	0121-693 3505
Franklyn Films	01243-776625
Frantic Productions	020-8866 2430
Free Spirit Films	0117-908 3934
Freedom TV	020-7734 1555
Freeform Productions	
	020-7407 5008
Freelance Film Partners	
	020-7328 8202
Freeway Films	020-7937 9114
Friction Films	020-7586 2986
Friday Productions	020-7730 0608
Front Page Films	020-7736 4534
Frontier Films	353 1 497 7077
Frontrunner Films	020-7436 5373
Fugitive Group	020-7242 6969
Fuji International	020-7734 8888
Fulcrum Productions	
	020-7253 0353
Fulmar West TV & Film	
	029-2045 5000

G

GM Partnership, The	
	0161-929 8339
GM Productions	0141-357 5066
Gabriel Films	0141-287 9524
Gabriel Productions	01225-311194
Gabriela Productions	
	020-8993 3158
Gael Media	353 91-592 888
Gainsborough Productions	
	01753-651700
Galafilm	1 514 273 4252
Gauvain Productions	
	01508 532682
Geestor Productions	
	020-8985 7726
Genisis Media Group	
	029-2062 4669
Geofilms	01235-537400
Getzels/Gordon	01865-512556
Gimlet Productions	020-7350 2878
Ginger	020-7663 2000
Give It Loads	020-7602 8304
Glasgow Film & Video Workshop	
	0141-553 2620
Glasgow Film Office	0141-287 0424
Glasshead	020-8995 1344
Global Arts	020-8731 6811
Global Productions	0117-946 6110
Global Sports Productions	
	020-7610 6444
glowinthedark	020-7254 1150
GMTV	020-7827 7000
GNU Productions	020-7267 3399
Golden Square Pics	.020-7446 0080
Goldhawk Media	01494-729777
Goldhawk Universal	020-7494 2277
Gordon Getzels	01865-512556
Gorilla Entertainment	
	020-7792 9364

Gosh! Films	0141-353 0456
Grade Company, The	
	020-7409 1925
Granite Film & TV	020-7354 3232
Grant Naylor Productions	
	01932-572175
Grant Thornton	020-7728 2343
Graphite Film & TV	020-8994 6617
Grasshopper Productions	
	020-7229 1181
Green House Productions	
	020-8780 5960
Green Inc Productions	
	028-9057 3000
Green Room	020-7267 0950
Green Umbrella	0117-973 1729
Greenlit Productions	
	020-7287 3545
Greenpoint Films	020-7357 9924
Gruber Films	020-7436 3413
Gwynhelek Productions	
	01736-762132

H

Halo Productions	020-7379 7398
Hamilton TV	01298-79424
Hand Pict Productions	
	0131-558 1543
Hanrahan TV Productions	
	01789-450182
Hanson TV	020-7371 8431
Harbottle & Lewis	020-7667 5000
Harbour Film & TV	0131-228 1562
Harcourt Films	020-7267 0882
Hart Ryan Productions	
	020-7403 6363
Hartswood Films	020-8607 8736
Harvest Films	0117-904 3158
Hasan Shah Films	020-7722 2419
Hat Trick Productions	
	020-7434 2451
HD Thames	020-7437 2737
HEADflicks	020-7494 2329
Heartland Films	020-8444 4264
Heavy Entertainment	
	020-8960 9001
Helen Langridge Associates	
	020-7299 1000
Hewland International	
	020-7916 2266
Hexagon Productions	
	020-7437 1552
Hibbert Ralph Entertainment	
	020-7240 5787
Highflyer Productions	
	01653-658599
Hightimes Prods	01798-813264
Hindi Picture	020-8374 4333
Hit Entertainment	020-7224 1717
HLA	020-7299 1000

Hobson's Production Co
020-8742 7118
Hollyoaks Productions
0151-722 9122
Hollywood Reporter, The
020-7822 8300
Holmes Associates 020-7813 4333
Home Productions 0141-881 3119
Horrod & Harris 020-7430 1014
Horsepower Productions
020-7287 7322
Hot Property Films 020-7323 9466
Hot Shot Films 028-9031 3332
Hothouse 020-7385 7324
Hourglass Pictures 020-8540 8786
Huge Films 020-7603 5567
Hungry Horse Pictures
020-7734 7979
Hunter Productions 0141-943 2226
Hutchins Film Co 020-7636 2104
Huw Brian Williams 029-2084 4044
Hyphen Films 020-7734 0632

I

Icon Entertainment 020-7494 8100
Icon Films 0117-924 8535
Ideal World Productions
0141-353 3222
Ignition Films 0117-958 3087
Illuminations Films 020-7288 8400
Images of War 020-7267 9198
Imag Entertainment 020-8560 2071
Imagicians 020-7287 5211
Imago Productions 01603-727600
INCA 020-8748 9600
Independent Image 020-7292 4300
Index Entertainment 020-7240 9494
Indigo Television 020-7486 4443
Infactuation Productions
020-7359 9196
Infonation 020-7270 6062
Initial 020-7462 9000
INP 020-7229 1265
Inside Broadcast 020-7689 8899
Insight Films 020-7252 5328
Interesting Television
01926-844044
Intermedia Film 0115-955 6909
International Films 01732-874784
International Media Produuctions
0191-245 1000
International News Productions
020-7229 1265
Invincible Films 020-8237 1150
InVision Productions
020-7371 2123
IPH 020-7207 2965
IPTV 0131-659 6566
Iron Bridge/No Cake
020-8444 9574
Iron Productions 020-8570 7026

Ishbel Maclean 01786-823220
Isis Productions 020-8748 3042
IWT TV 020-7460 1106

J

J & M Entertainment
020-7723 6544
Jane Balfour Films 020-7267 5392
Jane Walmsley Productions
020-7290 2676
January Films 0141-287 9509
Jay TV 0191-201 2131
Jeito Films 020-7287 7244
Jelly Wall 020-7403 9470
Jeremy Isaacs Productions
020-7240 9920
Jerusalem 020-7410 7038
Jezebel Films 020-7689 0491
Jim Henson Productions
020-7428 4000
John Adams TV 01453-885700
John Cary Studios 020-7637 4760
John Gau Productions
020-7938 1398
John Lawrence Enterprises
0780-822 8067
Jumping Jack Animation
01453-883994
Juniper 020-7722 7111
Just Television 020-7404 6744

K

Kai Productions 020-8673 4550
Karen Hamilton 020-7254 0849
Kelnat 020-8582 1960
Kennedy Mellor 020-7483 3241
Keo Films 020-7490 3580
Kestrel Film Company
020-8788 6244
Keystone (Ealing) 020-8993 7441
Kilroy Television 020-8228 7444
King Fisher Productions
020-8932 8882
King Rollo Films 01404-45218
Kingfisher TV Productions
0115-964 5262
Kingsfire Services 020-7584 1664
KPA TV 0121-248 3900
Kudos Productions 020-7580 8686
Kugelblitz 020-7688 1711

L

La Plante Productions
020-7734 6767
Lambent Productions
020-7609 3881
Landmark Productions
01962-734227
Landseer Film & TV 020-7485 7333
Last Ditch TV 01986-892549
Laurel Productions 020-7267 9399

Leading Ladies Film Co
020-7229 5529
Learning Media 020-8332 9984
Lee-Wright Productions
01494 446429
Left Handed Pictures
020-7735 2933
Legacy Films 020-8341 1911
Leila Films 020-8291 6339
Leisure Time Midlands
01564-742520
Leisure Time Productions
020-7837 8777
Leman Productions 0131-447 1082
Liba Productions 020-8904 8136
LIBRA TV 0161-225 3530
Like Minds 0121-523 1212
Lilyville Productions 020-7371 5940
Limited Company Limited
020-7439 4277
Lindley Stone 020-7267 5870
Link Entertainment 020-8996 4800
Lion TV 020-8735 4000
Lionsgate Media 020-8614 2931
Little Bird 353 1 661 4245
Little Dancer Films 020-8653 9343
Lluniau Lliw Cyf 029-2025 5630
LMI Pictures 020-7439 8282
Local Television Co 023-8081 4928
Lodestar Productions
020-7287 3302
Lomond TV 0141-429 6768
London Film & Video Dev.
020-7383 7755
London Post 020-7439 9080
London Weekend TV
020-7261 3030
Longbow Productions
01822-610210
Longeye 020-7624 5444
Loose Arrangement Film & TV
020-8995 5833
Loose Moose 020-7287 3821
Loud Mouse Productions
020-7371 9429
Louise Panton Productions
020-7284 2870
Lucas Media 0870-707 0870
Lucky World Productions
020-8883 3900
Lunchtime Productions
020-8959 3545
Lusia Films 0171436 3050
Lust For Life 020-7372 7105

M

MASC Productions 020-8769 2286
MacHeath Productions
01952-201212

MacIntyre & Co   020-7242 0242
Macmillan Media   028-9068 3800
Magic Lantern Productions
                         020-7738 9911
Magic Stone   0141-569 1489
Maiden's Voyage   0117-924 7063
Makar Productions   0131-226 7077
Making Waves Film & TV
                         020-7917 2871
Malachite Productions
                         01790-763538
Mallory Films   028-4483 0160
Malone Gill Productions
                         020-7460 4683
Man Alive Group   020-8743 7431
Man-Made   020-7736 7110
March Hare Productions
                         01884-820877
Mark 4 Film & TV   01932-227675
Mark Patterson & Associates
                         01895-673610
Martin Gates Productions
                         020-7580 8440
Martin Pope Productions
                         020-7734 6911
MASC Productions   020-8769 2286
Masterbond Films   020-8342 9914
Maverick Television   0121-771 1812
Maya Vision   020-7836 1113
Mayfair Entertainment
                         020-7304 7932
Mayfair Productions   020-7491 4585
MBC Midlands   0121-233 9944
MBC North   0161-827 2073
MBS Productions   020-7793 4179
McConnell Film Assoc
                         0141-337 1414
McDougall Craig   020-7222 7504
Media Circus   020-7287 2223
Media Europe   020-8449 1128
Media Mermaid   0191-221 2400
Media Pictures   01746-781068
Meditel Productions 020-7613 5266
Memoir Film Productions
                         0191-265 2215
Mental Health Media
                         020-7700 8131
Mentorn Barraclough Carey
                         020-7258 6800
Mentorn Midlands   0121-233 9944
Mentorn International
                         020-7258 6800
Merlin Films   0191-414 7995
Mersey Television   0151-722 9122
Metamedia Productions
                         020-7287 6690
Michael Cole Productions
                         020-8994 4821
Michael Hurll TV   020-7371 5354
Michaelides & Bednash
                         020-7468 1168

Middlemarch Films 020-7371 4596
Midlantic Films Inc UK
                         020-8455 4481
Migrant Media   020-7254 9701
Mike Mansfield TV   020-7580 2581
Milestone Pictures   01635-581166
Millar Movies   020-7370 1830
Minerva Picture Co   020-7439 4220
Mintai   029-2048 9813
Miramax Hal Films 020-7535 8300
MirrorTel Productions
                         020-7293 2593
Mirus Production   020-8740 5505
MJW Productions   020-7713 0400
ML International Pictures
                         020-7460 6465
MNE TV   0141-353 3135
Mogul TV   01344-622140
Molotov Productions
                         020-7263 1083
Momentum Video   020-7729 3536
Monogram Productions
                         020-7734 9873
Moondance Films & TV
                         020-7323 6458
Moondog Productions
                         028-9057 2500
Moonstone Films   020-8998 6016
Mosaic Films   01594-530708
Mostly Movies   020-7633 9400
Move A Mountain   020-8743 3017
Move On Up   01381-600777
Moving Still Productions
                         353 1 670 9275
Multi Media Arts   0151-476 6050
Music Box   020-7478 7300
Music Mall   020-7534 1444
Music on Earth   020-8998 5675
Muso   020-7240 1140
Mutual Films   01788-555000
Myrddin Productions
                         01379-641640

N

Naked Ape   0117-973 2775
Naked Film   0131-332 6364
Nautilus Films   020-8348 6683
NCTV   01224-248007
Nebraska Productions
                         020-8444 5317
Nelvana Enterprises 020-7287 2770
Network Five TV   01902-640014
Never Summer Productions
                         07071-222171
New Media TV   01904-621331
New Street Productions
                         0121-248 2425
NFH   020-7584 8385
Nicholas Claxton Productions
                         020-8956 2261

Nick Patten Productions
                         0121-693 7117
NMTV   01904-621331
Nobles Gate   020-8743 6921
Noel Gay Motion Picture Co
                         020-8600 5200
NoHo Digital   020-7299 3434
Nomad Rush   01582-605222
North South Productions
                         020-7388 0351
North West One Films
                         020-7493 8600
Northern Exposure TV Co
                         0161-839 9394
Northlight Productions
                         01224-646460
Northridge Entertainment
                         020-8455 7125
Northstar TV   0161-428 6900
Notre Dame Films   020-7727 3572
Nova Inc Fim & TV   0151-474 9176
NVC Arts   020-7388 3833

O

Oasis Media   020-7450 9050
Objective Productions
                         020-8348 5899
Ocicat   020-8995 8991
Octagon Pictures   020-7834 0088
October Films   020-7916 7198
Octopus   020-7531 8469
Oil Factory   020-7837 0007
Old Street Films   01865-722357
ON TV   01235-537400
One Lung Productions
                         0973- 109768
One Way Film   020-7978 6788
Open Door Productions
                         020-7636 9355
Open Media   020-7603 9029
Open Mike Productions
                         020-7434 4004
Open Mind   020-7437 0624
Optic Nerve   020-8856 2642
Optomen TV   020-7967 1234
Opus TV   029- 2022 3456
OR Media   020-8987 1000
Orlando TV Productions
                         01608-683218
Orpheus Productions
                         020-8892 3172
Otmoor Productions
                         01865-331445
Out of the Blue   020-8288 9198
Outsider TV Production
                         020-8740 9285
Oxford Scientific Films
                         01993-881881
Oxford Television Company
                         020-7483 3637
Oxymoron Films   020-7437 5905

P

Pacific 1	020-7437 5905
Pagnamenta Assoc	020-7727 9960
Pagoda Film & TV	020-7534 3500
Paladin Pictures	020-8740 1811
Palimpsest Productions	020-7584 6254
Palindrome Productions	020-7262 7484
Palm Pictures	020-7229 3000
Pandora Productions	020-7287 0130
Panache Pictures	020-8809 7465
Panoptican Pictures	020-7729 7352
Parachute Pictures	020-8748 1445
Parallax Pictures	020-7836 1478
Parallel Pictures	020-8758 8603
Parker Mead	020-8579 1082
Parkside Productions	01268 472242
Partners in Production	020-7490 5046
Passion Pictures	020-7323 9933
Pathe Productions	020-7323 5151
Pathway Productions	0131-447 3531
Paul Berriff Productions	01482-641158
Paul Trijbits Productions	020-7439 4343
Pauline Muirhead Productions	0131-476 9598
PDP	01465-871219
Peakviewing Productions	01452 863217
Pearson TV	020-7691 6991
Pelicula Films	0141-287 9522
Peninsula Films	020-8964 2304
Penumbra Productions	020-7328 4550
Pepper's Ghost	020-8546 4900
Performance Films	01494-670505
Periwinkle Productions	01489-572009
Perx Productions	0113-274 2379
Peter Sasdy Productions	020-8783 1147
Peter Williams TV	01622-684545
Photoplay Productions	020-7722 2500
Picasso Pictures	020-7437 9888
Pictorial Heroes	0141-550 0875
Picture Factory	020-8347 9233
Picture House Productions	0117-973 8859
Picture House TV CO	020-8740 0074
Picture Palace Films	020-7586 8763
Picture Perfect	0131-331 1604
Picture This Independent Film	0117-972 1002

Picturehead	01962-622672
Pierrot Productions	020-8858 0846
Pilgrim Films	0191-230 3930
Pillarbox Productions	020-7700 0505
Pilot Film & TV Productions	020-8960 2771
Pioneer Productions	020-8748 0888
Pipedream Pictures	020-8830 3727
Pirate Productions	0141-337 1333
Pizazz Pictures	020-7434 3581
Planet 24	020-7345 2424
Planet Wild	0151-288 8000
Platinum Film & TV	020-7916 9091
Point Sound & Vision	020-7616 8100
Pola Jones Film	020-7439 1165
Polkadot Productions	020-7831 4002
Polygram Film	020-7307 1300
Pomegranate Pictures	020-7935 3400
Poorhouse Productions	020-7439 2637
Popular Films	020-7419 0722
Portman Entertainment	020-7468 3440
Portobello Pictures	020-7379 5566
Poseidon Productions	020-7734 4441
Pozzitive	020-7734 3258
Precise Media	0161-233 5000
Presence Films	020-7636 8477
Presentable Productions	029-2057 5729
Pressure Cooker	020-7722 9314
Princess	020-7243 5100
Principal Media	020-7928 9882
Producers Productions	020-7636 4226
Projector Productions	020-7434 1110
Prominent Features	020-7497 1100
Prospect Pictures	020-7636 1234
Pueblo Productions	020-8969 2134
Pukka Films	020-7437 4220
Pulse Productions	020-7794 1514
Puppetoon Productions	020-7636 2000
Purple Frog	01273-735475

Q

Quadrant Broadcast	029-2023 7333
Quadriga	020-8614 2339
Quadrillion	01628-487522
Quality Time TV	01672-540281
Quanta	01666 826366
Quicksilver Films	020-7603 8339
Quintessence Films	01626-770750
Quirky Film & TV	01753-651700

R

Radius Film Productions	020-7482 3261
Ragdoll Productions	01753-631800
Raging Star Films	0131-661 1894
RAP	01625-501332
Raphael Associates	020-7265 1620
Rapid Eye Movies	020-7613 0010
Rapido TV	020-7440 5700
Raw Charm	029-2064 1511
Raw Nerve Productions	028-7126 0562
Rawle Partnership	01702-353359
RDF Television	020-7313 6700
Real Life Productions	0113-234 7271
Real World Pictures	020-7978 1178
Really Animated Productions	01625-612459
Recorded Picture Co	020-7636 2251
Red Balloo	0191-232 7810
Red Door Productions	020-7637 3220
Red Galaxy Pictures	020-7622 2230
Red Green and Blue Company	020-8746 0616
Red Kite	0131-558 3003
Red Production Co	0161-798 9644
Redwave Films	020-7753 7200
Redweather Productions	0117-941 5854
Reel Life Television	020-7713 1585
Reel Scoop	0141-632 3345
Regent Productions	020-8789 5350
Reiner Moritz Associates	020-7439 2637
Remote Films	020-7738 2727
Renegade Films	020-7637 0957
Renaissance Films	020-7287 5190
Resource Base	023-8023 6806
Revolution Films	020-7242 0372
Richard Butler	020-7247 6555
Richmond Films & TV	020-7734 9313
Richmond Light Horse	020-7937 9315
Rishi Films	020-8960 1647
Riverchild Films	020-7636 1122
Rivercourt Productions	020-8748 4518
Riverfront Pictures	020-7481 2939
RM Associates	020-7439 2637
Roberts & Wykeham Films	020-7602 4897
Rock Sound films	020-8746 1566
Rocket Pictures	020-8741 9090
Roger Bolton Productions	020-7713 6868
Rohan-Asher Media	020-8968 1696

Rooftop Productions
020-7523 2403
Rose Bay Film Productions
020-8600 5200
Rosetta Pictures 020-7647 5900
Rosso Productions 01843-823992
Rough Sea Productions
0410 064632
RPM Arts 0141-778 1633
RS Productions 0191-259 1184
Rugby Vision Cyffro 01222 666800

S

Safe and Sound Productions
01789-450182
Safir Films 020-8423 0763
Sally Head Productions
020-8607 8730
Salsa Rock Productions
01932 856102
Salt Island Productions
028-9057 3000
Samba Films 020-8674 0141
Samuelson Productions
020-7439 4900
Sands Films 020-7231 2209
Sankofa Film & Video
020-7692 0393
SATV 0131-558 8148
Saunders & French Productions
020-7344 1010
Scala Productions 020-7734 7060
Science Pictures 01462-421110
Scope Productions 0141-332 7720
Scorer Associates 0117-946 6838
Scottish Screen 0141-302 1700
Scottish Television Enterprises
0141-300 3538
Screen First 01825-712034
Screen Partners 020-7247 3444
Screen Resource 01865-744451
Screen Ventures 020-7580 7448
ScreenAge Pictures 020-7835 1511
Screenbase Media 0131-652 4000
Screenhouse Productions
0113-239 2292
Second Sight 0121-603 7175
Secret Garden 01993-831904
September Films 020-7494 1884
Serendipity Picture Company
0117-929 0417
Seven Dials Films 020-8348 2047
Seventh Art Productions
01273-777678
Severn Pictures 01886-884745
SFTV 01844-202027
Shaker Films 020-8968 4278
Sharp Image Productions
020-8674 2901
Shattered Images 020-8946 9865

Shearman Productions
0117-946 6503
Shed Productions 020-7359 7655
Sheffield Independent Film
0114-249 2204
Sherbet 020-7636 6435
Shipleys 020-7312 0000
Shooting Partners 020-8941 1000
Showplay 020-7371 3234
Sigma Films 0141-339 1241
Signals 01206-560255
Siguy Films 020-7437 2890
Simkins Partnership 020-7631 1050
Siriol mm 029-2048 8400
Skyline Films 020-8354 2236
Skyline Productions 0131-557 4580
Skyscraper Films 020-7625 6465
Smith & Watson Productions
01803-863033
Smoke & Mirrors 020-7468 1003
SOI Film & TV 020-7267 4373
Solid Productions 020-7267 9479
Somethin Else 020-7613 3211
Songbird 020-7249 1477
Soul Purpose Productions
020-7625 1625
South West Media Development
0117-927 3226
Southern Star 020-7636 9421
Speakeasy Productions
01738-828524
Specific Films 020-7580 7476
Spike Island 0117-929 7299
Spire Films 01865-371979
Spirit Films 020-7734 6642
Spitfire Films 020-7792 3666
Split Screen 029-2059 0231
Sprocketeers 0131-554 4539
St Elmo Films 020-8741 7007
St Pancras Films 020-7385 2094
Stampede 020-7729 7174
Starlock Pictures 020-7734 0535
Stephinson TV 01457-820820
Steve Boulton 0161-338 3560
Stirling Film 028-9033 3848
Stockbridge Films 07771-921234
Stone City Films 020-7240 8789
Stories 020-7813 3323
Storm TV 0161-236 6006
Storyline 0191-232 2050
Straight Forward Productions
028-9042 6298
Straight TV 0161-228 2228
Strawberry Productions
020-8994 4494
Stray Cat Motion Pictures
0141-338 6662
Streetwise TV 020-7470 8825
Studio Arts TV 01665-721722
Suffolk Films 01986-875875

Suitcase Productions
1-212 647 8300
Sundog Media 01752 265562
Sunstone Films 020-7485 2884
Supervision 020-8251 9500
Susan Young 020-7928 7977
SVC Screen Entertainment
020-7460 6060
Swing Productions 020-7272 5007

T

Take 3 Video Video & Film
020-7434 4311
Takeaway Media 020-7267 0166
Talent Television 020-7434 1677
Talisman Films 020-7603 7474
Talkback 020-7323 9777
Tall Order Productions
01562-700707
Tall Stories 020-7357 8050
Tandem Television 020-7465 6365
Tangent Films 020-8749 5549
Tango Films 020-7289 7694
Tapecraft Productions
01502-711166
Taylored Productions
0141-334 1462
TC TV 01962-714359
Telemagination 020-7434 1551
Television Company, The
020-7837 0789
Television Junction 0121-248 4466
Television Sport & Leisure
020-7820 0700
Teliesyn 029-2030 0876
Tell-A-Vision TV 0131-556 3743
Tell-Tale Productions
020-8324 2308
Tempest Films 020-8340 0877
Tern Television Productions
01224-211123
Terra Firma Film Productions
020-7261 0885
Testimony Films 0117-925 8589
That 70's Co 020-8614 2579
Third Eye Productions
020-8940 9062
Third Man Productions
01752-331404
Thura Film 020-8735 0828
Tidy Productions 029-2049 2481
Tiger Aspect 020-7434 0672
Tiger Lily Films 020-7580 0633
Tigervision 020-7383 2267
Tigress Productions 020-7434 4411
Tilling Productions 01895-824022
Tilt Films 020-7502 7085
Titanic 01268-531905
TNTV 020-7722 8200
Toledo 020-7291 8050
Tomboy Films 020-7436 3324

Tonic Films	020-7689 5226
Tonic Pictures	020-7229 2512
Top Left	0141-357 3657
Topical TV	023-8071 2233
Touch Productions	01747-828030
Track 29	0141-424 1124
Trans World International	
	020-8233 5400
TransAtlantic Films	020-8735 0505
Treasure Trove Pictures	
	020-8686 3493
Tricky Pictures	020-8567 1412
Tricorn Associates	020-8995 3898
Triffic Films	01908-261234
Trijbits Productions	020-7439 4343
Triple Echo Productions	
	01503-272428
True Corner Productions	
	0151-281 0741
True TV and Film	0141-554 1196
True Visions Productions	
	020-8742 7852
Try Again	01225-862705
Tullstar Productions	01786-825587
Tumble Hill Productions	
	029-2059 4044
Turn On Television	020-7729 2611
Turnround	01242-224360
TV 6	020-7610 0266
TV21	020-7258 6800
TVF	020-7837 3000
TVF International	020-7359 8997
Twelfth House	020-7439 1210
Twentieth Century Fox	
	020-7437 7766
Twenty Twenty Television	
	020-7284 2020
Two Four Productions	
	01752-345424
Two Sides TV	020-7439 9882
TY FFILM	029-2038 7556
Tyro Films & TV	020-8943 4697

U

Uden Associates	020-7351 1255
Ugly Duckling Productions	
	0802-774100
Umbrella Entertainment	
	020-7267 8834
Umbrella Pictures	020-7385 4323
Umbrella Productions	
	0141-429 1750
Unhooked Prods	020-8208 0947
Unicorn Organisation	
	020-7229 5131
Union Pictures	020-7287 5110
United Artists	020-8563 4155
United Artists Films	020-7333 8877

United Broadcasting	
	020-7389 8654
Universal Pictures	020-8563 4153
Upfront Televsion	020-7836 7702
Uptown Films	020-7833 1153
Urban tv	020-7267 8003

V

Vanguard Films	01789-267672
Ventura Productions	
	01564-794320
Vera Productions	020-7436 6116
Vibrant Productions	0161-291 0123
Vicarious Productions	
	020-7622 9307
Victor Film Co	020-7494 4477
Victoria Real	01273-702007
Video Assignments	020-8343 2513
Video Visuals	020-7384 2243
Visage Productions	01753-783500
Visible Ink TV	01968-661291
Visible Jazz	020-7403 9333
Visionworks	028-9024 1241
Viva Films	020-8444 5064
Viz	01383-412811
Vobavision	01903-217567
Volcano Films	020-7424 0146
Vortex TV	020-7485 5326
Voyager Television	01865-408102

W

Wall to Wall Television	
	020-7485 7424
Wark, Clements & Co	
	0141-429 1750
Warner Brothers	020-7984 6250
Warner Sisters Film	020-8960 3550
Watchmaker Productions	
	020-7465 6000
Watchword	020-7381 2168
Water Productions	01442-872062
Watermark Films	020-7439 2274
Weigall Productions	020-7229 5725
West Highland Animation	
	01877-384671
Westway Film Production	
	028-7130 8383
Whitby Davison	020-8579 3811
White Magic	07000 784707
Whitehorse Films	020-7586 8940
Whitehouse & Co	020-8964 8035
Wide Eye Pictures	020-7636 1918
Wild Dream Films	029-2066 6311
Wildcard Film and Television	
	01752 262968
Wild Dream Films	029-2066 6311
Wild Films	020-8540 7107
Wild Rover Productions	
	028-9050 0980

Wildcard Film & TV	01752-262968
Wildcat Films	01434 381067
Wildflower Productions	
	020-7234 0330
Wildtrack TV	0151-330 2081
Winchester Entertainment	
	020-7851 6500
Windfall Films	020-7637 2666
Wire Productions	020-7436 2266
Wishbone Productions	
	020-7350 2219
Wobbly Picture Productions	
	020-8870 6369
Women Now Films	020-8830 5156
Women's Ind. Cinema House	
	0151-707 0539
Woodchester Productions	
	01453-872098
Working Title Films	020-7307 3000
World of Wonder	020-7737 2222
World's End Productions	
	020-7792 9800
World Productions	020-7240 1444
World Television	0117-930 4099
World Wide Group	020-7434 1121
WorldWide Entertainment News	
	020-7258 6800
Worldmark Productions	
	020-7792 9800
Wrench & Franks	020-7250 3026
Writers Republic	020-7613 4705

X

Xanadu Productions	
	020-7404 2225
Xanthe Film & TV	0131-667 9960
XL Entertainment	07000 953953
XYTV	0113-237 1199

Y

YI Productions	0191-281 2256
Yoda Productions	01306-889352
Yorkshire-Tyne Tees TV	
	0113-243 8283

Z

Zanzibar Film Productions	
	01425-472892
ZCZ Films	020-7284 0521
Zebra Productions	0117-970 6026
ZEF Productions	01273-384210
Zenith Ent.	020-7224 2440
Zenith North	0191-261 0077
Zephyr Films	020-7221 8318
Zin Zan Productions	0118-950 3816
Zingaru Productionns	
	01483-273920
ZKK	020-7482 5885

Radio: Introduction & BBC

Radio is the most popular form of broadcasting until 4pm each day and the average person spends more time listening to the radio than reading newspapers and magazines. The typical British household owns six radio sets and annual sales of radios are around 12 million.

To date some 20,000 digital radios have been sold and here is one of the next great hardware opportunities. That's a story for later. Little used digital services aside, most British people can receive 15 radio stations, six from the BBC and nine from commercial radio. London, listeners can tune into 24 services, of which six are from the BBC. British radio is divided between 242 local and regional commercial stations, and the licence-funded BBC which runs five national networks and 38 local stations serving England and national regional radio services in Scotland, Wales and Northern Ireland, including Welsh and Gaelic language stations.

The 1998 Media Guide said: "The consensus within the BBC is that its overall market share will eventually settle at 30 per cent, and so reach rather than share has become the measure BBC executives adhere to." That quality over quantity rhetoric is the story in BBC Television now, while in radio the talk of managing decline has diminished. BBC Radio happiness comes from comparing the 1999 and 2000 listening figures for the quarter to the end of March: they show that the BBC is no longer bracing itself for the psychological break point of holding less than half the radio audience and that every BBC radio station - with the exception of Radio 4 - grew its listenership. And Radio 4 which - arguably - had dumbed down under James Boyle's stewardship may well boost its ratings under Helen Boaden, whose appointment as Radio 4 boss was the first major one made under the Greg Dyke regime.

Jenny Abramsky, whose appointment as BBC director of radio at the end of 1998 signalled an end of BBC Radio's dominance by TV voices, is running a happier organisation. The traumatic move to west London from Portland Place is now complete and Abramsky is achieving what she set out to do by repairing the divide between programme commissioners and producers. Demographics are on her side too for the change in the BBC's fortunes is largely down to a middle aged baby boom generation demanding something more than DJ-babble punctuating drums and bass. The over 45s are turning to BBC stations rather than a youth obsessed commercial sector and Radio 2 shows the way ahead with continued expansion relying on a forty-and-fifty something diet of "popular music with lyrics people can remember".

Eventually digital radio will change the radio picture. Indeed, radios will carry pictures and display text, but for the moment a metaphorical radio picture revisits the old rather than running away with the new. Listen to Jason Bryant, Talk Sport's new development director, who says: "Older listeners like a more grown up style of presentation," he says. "They want quality news and information, not inane banter, or lists of who's shagging who around the world. There's no doubt that there's a strong market opportunity among the 45-plus age group. Commercial radio doesn't serve that audience."

RADIO BANDS

		MHz88-90.2	90.2-92.4	92.4-94.6	94.9 London	95.1	95.8	97.3	97.6-99.8
FM	Radio 2	Radio 3	Radio 4	GLR	GMR	CapitalFM	London News	Radio 1
	Light music	Classical	Talk	Pop/talk	All talk	Pop	News	Pop/rock

		194m	206m	1332/1413	1341	247m	261m	275/285	290m
		1548kHz	1458kH	1305kHz	873kHz	1215kH	1152kHz	1089/1053kHz	1035kHz
AM	Capital Gold	Sunrise	Premier	Radio Ulster	Virgin	LBC	Talk Radio	Country
	Oldies/sport	Asian	Christian	General	Pop/rock	Talk/news	Talk/news	C&W

Radio 1 and Radio 4 arrivals and departures

Radio 1: Cox for Ball

"She wants to spend more time as Mrs Zoe Cook rather than Ms Zoe Ball," said a Radio 1 spokesperson when the star DJ announced her intention to stop being Radio 1's top DJ and start a family. By the time Mrs/Ms Cook/Ball left Radio 1 in March 2000 her breakfast show had attracted record listening figures of over 7 million, eclipsing her publicity-crazed mentor Chris Evans over at Virgin Radio. She was replaced by Sara Cox, a 24 year old presenter who early in her career had also followed Zoe (plus Evans as well) onto the Channel 4 Big Breakfast Show. "I know it's going to be hard," Sara said. "Zoe knows that better than anyone. She will be the first person I ring if I have any problems."

IN: Sara Cox

OUT: Zoe Ball

Radio 4: Boaden for Boyle

"I will have to fall on my sword," said James Boyle, the Radio 4 controller, when asked what he would do if his 1998 Radio 4 revamp failed to work. In October 1999 the Radio 4 audience hit a new low and fell to below 8 million. In January 2000 Boyle fell on his sword and resigned - reportedly after a personality clash with the BBC director of radio Jenny Abramsky. Boyle's more popular replacement is Helen Boaden whose current affairs background gained her support among resentful BBC insiders. The Today presenter John Humphrys said: "She doesn't speak from some theory dreamed up God knows where. She understands the medium and, crucially, knows how much good radio costs."

IN: Helen Boaden

OUT: James Boyle

100 London			102.2				
102.-Manchester	100.7 Midlands	100-101.9	100.4	105.4		105.8 London/SE	106.2 London
KissFM	Heart	Classic FM	JazzFM	Melody		Virgin	Heart
Dance	Adult pop	Classical	Jazz/blues	Light music		Pop/rock	Adult pop

330/433m			417/1500m (lw)		463m	
909/693kHz	882kHz	810kHz	720/198kHz		648kHz	
Radio 5 Live	Radio Wales	Radio Scotland	Radio 4		World Service	
News/sport	General	General	Talk/general		General	

BBC NATIONAL RADIO

BBC Radio HQ
Broadcasting House, Portland Place, London W1A 1AA
Publicity office: 020-7765 4990
Director of radio: Jenny Abramsky
Managing Editor, digital radio: Glyn Jones

Radio 1
Broadcasting House, Portland Place, London W1A 1AA
Publicity office: 020-7765 4575
Controller, Radio 1: Andy Parfitt
Managing editor: Ian Parkinson

Radio 2
Broadcasting House, Portland Place, London W1A 1AA
Publicity office: 020-7765 4330
Controller, Radio 2: Jim Moir
Managing editor: Lesley Douglas

Radio 3
Broadcasting House, Portland Place, London W1A 1AA
Publicity office: 020-7765 2722
Controller, Radio 3: Roger Wright
Managing editor: Brian Barfield

Radio 4
Broadcasting House, Portland Place, London W1A 1AA
Publicity office: 020-7765 5337
Controller, Radio 4: Helen Boaden
Managing editor: Wendy Pilmer

Radio 5 Live
Television Centre, Wood Lane, London W12 7RJ
Publicity office: 020-8576 1694
Controller, Radio 5 Live: Bob Shennan
Controller, radio sports rights and deputy controller, Radio 5 Live: Mike Lewis

BBC LOCAL RADIO: SOUTH

BBC Radio Bristol
PO Box 194, Bristol BS99 7QT
Tel 0117-974 1111

BBC Radio Cornwall
Phoenix Wharf, Truro, Cornwall TR1 1UA
Tel 01872-275421

BBC Radio Devon
Seymour Road, Mannamead, Plymouth PL3 5BD
Fax 01752-234599   Tel 01752-260323

BBC Radio Gloucestershire
London Road, Gloucester GL1 1SW
Tel 01452-308585

BBC GLR 94.9 (London)
35c Marylebone High Street, London W1A 4LG
Tel 020-7224 2424

BBC Radio Guernsey
Commerce House, Les Banques, St Peter Port, Guernsey GY1 2HS
Tel 01481-728977

BBC Radio Jersey
18 Parade Road, St Helier, Jersey JE2 3PL
Tel 01534-870000

BBC Radio Kent
Sun Pier, Chatham, Kent ME4 4EZ
Tel 01634 830505

BBC Radio Solent
Havelock Road, Southampton SO1 7PW
Tel 023-8063 1311

BBC Somerset Sound
14-15 Paul Street, Taunton TA1 3PF
Tel 01823-252437

Southern Counties Radio (Sussex & Surrey)
Broadcasting House, Guildford GU2 5AP
Tel 01483-306306

BBC Thames Valley (Oxon & Berkshire)
PO Box 952, Oxford OX2 7YL
PO Box 954, Slough SL1 1BA
PO Box 1044, Reading RG30 1PL
Tel 01645-311444

Wiltshire Sound
Broadcasting House, Prospect Place, Swindon, Wilts SN1 3RW
Tel 01793-513626

LOCAL RADIO: MID/EAST

BBC Asian Network
Epic House, Charles Street, Leicester LE1 3SH
Tel 0116-251 6688
Pebble Mill Road, Birmingham B5 7SD
Tel 0121-414 8484

BBC Radio Cambridgeshire
Broadcasting House, 96 Hills Road, Cambridge CB2 1LD
Tel 01223-259696

BBC Radio Derby
PO Box 269, Derby DE1 3HL
Tel 01332-361111

BBC Radio Essex
198 New London Road, Essex CM2 9XB
Tel 01245-616000

BBC Hereford & Worcestershire
Hylton Road, Worcester WR2 5WW
Tel 01905-748485

BBC Radio Leicester
Epic House, Charles Street, Leicester LE1 3SH
Tel 01162 516688

BBC Radio Lincolnshire
PO Box 219, Newport, Lincoln LN1 3XY
Tel 01522-511411

BBC Radio Norfolk
Norfolk Tower, Surrey Street, Norwich NR1 3PA
Tel 01603-617411

BBC Radio Northampton
PO Box 1107, Abington Street, Northampton NN1 2BH
Tel 01604-239100

BBC Radio Nottingham
York House, Mansfield Road, Nottingham NG1 3JB
Tel 0115-955 0500

BBC Radio Shropshire
2-4 Boscobel Drive, Shrewsbury, Shropshire SY1 3TT
Tel 01743-248484
BBC Radio Stoke
Cheapside, Hanley, Stoke-on-Trent, Staffs ST1 1JJ
Tel 01782-208080
BBC Radio Suffolk
St Matthews Street, Ipswich, Suffolk IP1 3EP
Tel 01473-250000
BBC Three Counties Radio (Beds, Herts & Bucks)
PO Box 3CR, Hastings Street, Luton LU1 5XL
Tel 01582-637400
BBC Radio WM (West Midlands)
PO Box 206, Birmingham B5 7QQ
Tel 0121-414 8484

BBC LOCAL RADIO: NORTH

BBC Radio Cleveland
PO Box 95FM, Broadcasting House, Newport Road, Middlesbrough, TS1 5DG
Tel 01642-225211
BBC Radio Cumbria
Annetwell Street, Carlisle, Cumbria CA3 8BB
Tel 01228-592444
BBC GMR Talk (Manchester)
PO Box 951, Oxford Road, Manchester M60 1SD
Tel 0161-244 3002
BBC Radio Humberside
9 Chapel Street, Hull, N Humberside HU1 3NU
Tel 01482-323232
BBC Radio Lancashire
26 Darwen Street, Blackburn, Lancs BB2 2EA
Tel 01254-262411
BBC Radio Leeds
Broadcasting House, Woodhouse Lane, Leeds, West Yorks LS2 9PN
Tel 0113-244 2131
BBC Radio Merseyside
55 Paradise Street, Liverpool L1 3BP
Tel 0151-708 5500
BBC Radio Newcastle
Barrack Road, Newcastle-upon-Tyne NE99 1RN
Tel 0191-232 4141
BBC Radio Sheffield
Ashdell Grove, 60 Westbourne Rd, Sheffield S10 2QU
Tel 0114-268 6185
BBC Radio York
20 Bootham Row, York YO3 7BR
Tel 01904-641351

WALES, SCOTLAND, NI

BBC Radio Wales
Cardiff CF5 2YQ
Tel 029-2057 2888
BBC Radio Cymru
Broadcasting House, Llantrisant Road, Llandaff, Cardiff CF5 2YQ
Tel 029-2057 2888

BBC Radio Scotland
Broadcasting House, Queen Margaret Drive, Glasgow G12 8DG
Fax 0141-334 0614   Tel 0141-339 8844
BBC Radio Nan Gaidheal
7 Culduthel Road, Inverness IV2 4AD
Tel 01463-720720
BBC Radio Ulster
Broadcasting House, Ormeau Avenue, Belfast BT2 8HQ
Tel 028-9033 8000
BBC Radio Foyle
8 Northland Road, Londonderry, Northern Ireland BT48 7NE
Tel 028-9026 2244

INTERNATIONAL RADIO

The BBC World Service brings a world of news, information and entertainment. For more than six decades BBC World Service has earned a reputation for broadcasting excellence and high standards of journalistic integrity and impartiality. As the world's most trusted - and freely available - source of news and analysis World Service output is equally valued in media-rich societies and countries where news is far from free.

Broadcasts are funded through the Foreign and Commonwealth office by a Parliamentary Grant in Aid. Operating under the BBC's Royal Charter, World Service has full editorial and managerial independence from commercial or political pressures.

BBC World Service - HQ
Bush House, The Strand, London WC2B 4PH.
Publicity Office: 020-7557 2941
Chief executive: Mark Byford
Deputy chief executive: Caroline Thompson
Director, news and programme commissioning: Bob Jobbins
Director, World Service regions: Andrew Taussig
Controller, resources and technology: Chris Gill
Controller, personnel: Lesley Granger
Finance and commercial director: Andrew Hind

BBC Monitoring
Caversham Park, Reading, Berks RG4 8TZ
Fax 01734 463823   Tel 01734 469289
BBC Monitoring reports on foreign broadcasts to the BBC and the government. This information is also sold.
Director: Andrew Hills

Independent radio

Local independent radio is overseen by the Radio Authority (the auditory equivalent of the Independent Television Commission) which was set up by the 1990 Broadcasting Act to grant licenses and monitor content. The Act allowed for three national licenses - Classic FM, Talk Radio and Virgin - and these, plus a lighter regulatory touch which was lightened further by the 1996 Broadcasting Act, have ensured ad-funded radio's prosperity.

The nineties was commercial radio's decade. It secured its current 5 per cent plus share of the national advertising spend and looked set to outstrip BBC Radio's overall listening figures. This decade begins with a reversal, for Rajar figures show that its audience share has fallen from 47.5 to 47.1 per cent of the listening audience and the signs are that an ageing audience will intensify the downward trend unless commercial radio stops relying on schlock pop.

All of a sudden commercial radio doesn't seem quite so flavoursome. The former BBC DJ Simon Bates put it well when he said: "There are too many desperate middle-aged disc jockeys working on tiny local radio stations trying to

Evans the radio

With Channel 4's decision to take TFI Friday off the air, Chris Evans faded as a television presence. He remained ubiquitous on the radio ...

INTERNET RADIO AUGUST 1999 Ginger Media went into partnership with Ericsson to produce third generation mobile phones so people can hear the man's Virgin Radio station anywhere on the planet.

FAKE SPICE NOVEMBER Evans stepped out with the former Spice Girl Geri Halliwell. The romance soon fizzled but was the brief encounter love? "We didn't put this out," one of them said. "We knew it would be seen as a PR stunt."

MILLIONAIRE DECEMBER Evans trumped Chris Tarrant's millionaire TV show by being the first broadcaster to give a quiz show victor £1 million. Virgin Radio had lost nearly a million listeners in the six months to September 1999.

MULTI-MILLIONAIRE JANUARY 2000 Evans, already worth an estimated £30 million, pocketed a further £75 million when he sold his Ginger Media Group to the Scottish Media Group for £225 million. He said he'd still wake at 4am to present his ailing Virgin breakfast show.

REDDISM MARCH Evans made an on-air donation of £100,000 to Ken Livingstone's mayor of London campaign, then doubled it when Labour's Frank Dobson said his Mum had told him to steer clear of redheads. The Radio Authority saw red and fined Virgin £75,000 "for a serious breach of the rules requiring due impartiality".

DIGITAL RADIO APRIL Evans' 10 per cent in Switchdigital gave him a further stake in the future when the Radio Authority awarded it London's second digital multiplex licence.

draw attention to themselves, like a seven-year old boy using rude words at the breakfast table." The Radio Authority imposed two record £50,000 fines on the Xfm London station for discussing bestiality in a breakfast show and on Hallam FM in Sheffield for a "gratuitous description of paedophilia and the condoning and encouragement of rape", and in February 2000 the Radio Authority began a public consultation into yobbish local radio stations.

American inspired attempts at commercial diversification haven't worked well, with Capital abandoning its restaurant venture and - having failed in his bid to buy the Daily Star - nothing more from Chris Evans about going into print. The future for the commercial operators is technological with increasing investment in the web revealing their hope that the plethora of digital stations will enable them to repeat last decade's trick and continue a fragmentation of the radio audience. Typical of recent deal making are the plans of GWR to launch a pay-TV channel version of Classic FM with Daily Mail and General Trust's Performance arts TV and to develop internet portals where DMGT owns local papers.

On the broader commercial front the commercial operators continue lobbying against the imposition of a controlling government hand and - at least until the communications white paper - the culture secretary Chris Smith faces both ways. Sometimes he says: "My preference - and that of the government - is for deregulation where possible." On other occasions he says: "It is questionable whether the free market can fairly determine radio output ... [and] complete deregulation runs the risk that too much effort will be spent on a mainstream audience rather than broadcasters seeking different niches."

KEY CONTACT

Radio Authority
Holbrook House, 14 Great Queen St, Holborn, London WC2B 5DG.
Fax 020-7405 7062   Tel 020-7430 2724
Chairman: Richard Hooper
Deputy chairman: David Witherow
Chief executive: Tony Stoller
Director of development and deputy chief exec: David Vick
Director of finance: Neil Romain
Director of programming and advertising: Martin Campbell
Director of engineering: Mark Thomas
Chief press officer: Julie McCatty
Director of legal affairs and secretary to the authority: Eve Salamon

RADIO LISTENING FIGURES TO MID-2000

'99 figures in ( )	WEEKLY REACH		AVERAGE HOURS PER LISTENER		SHARE OF LISTENING	
ALL RADIO	43.35m	(42.63)	24	(22.4)	100%	(100%)
ALL BBC	31.34m	(30.50)	16.9	(15.8)	51.0%	(50.3%)
BBC Radio 1	11.31m	(10.84m)	9.1	(8.7)	9.9%	(9.8%)
BBC Radio 2	10.59m	(9.67m)	13.1	(12.7)	3.3%	(12.8%)
BBC Radio 3	2.14m	(2.27m)	6.6	(5.8)	1.4%	(1.4%)
BBC Radio 4	9.05m	(9.47m)	12.5	(11.6)	10.9%	(11.4%)
BBC Radio 5 Live	6.18m	(5.83m)	7.4	(6.8)	4.4%	(4.2%)
BBC Local/regional	10.68m	(10.20)	10.9	(9.9)	11.2%	(10.6%)
ALL COMMERCIAL	31.76m	(31.48m)	15.4	(14.4)	47.1%	(47.5%)
All national commercial	11.93m	(12.34m)	7.4	(7.3)	8.5%	(9.4%)
Atlantic 252	1.67m	(2.28m)	4.5	(4.3)	7%	(1.0%)
Classic FM	6.25m	(6.03m)	7.3	(6.6)	4.4%	(4.3%)
Talk Radio	2.37m	(2.32m)	6.0	(7.3)	1.4%	(1.8%)
Virgin Radio	3.31m	(3.52m)	6.3	(6.5)	2.0%	(2.4%)
All local commercial	27.06m	(26.37m)	14.8	(13.8)	38.6%	(38.1%)

Source: Rajar, March 2000

NATIONAL FRANCHISES

Until 1992 the only national radio channels belonged to the BBC. The Broadcasting Act changed all that and gave the Radio Authority power to issue licenses for three new Independent National Radio (INR) networks. Only INR1 could be on an FM frequency and the other two had to be on AM. The Act also said that INR1 should concentrate "wholly or mainly, in the broadcasting of music which ... is not pop music" and that the first AM service could offer any programming that did not duplicate INR1. INR3 would have to be primarily speech-based. Hence the arrivals of Classic FM, Virgin 1215 and Talk Radio (now talkSPORT).

Classic FM - INR1
PO Box 2834, London W1A 5NT
Fax 020-7344 2700   Tel 020-7343 9000
E-mail: enquiries@classicfm.com
Website: www.classicfm.com
Parent company: GWR Group
Starting date: 7.9.92
Dial: 100-102 FM
Area: national
Popular classical music, news.

talkSPORT - INR2
18 Hatfields, London SE1 8DJ
Fax 020-7959 7802   Tel 020-7959 7900
Website: www.talksport.net
Parent company: The Wireless Group
Starting date: 14.2.95
Dial: 1053/1089 kHz AM

Virgin 1215 - INR3
1 Golden Square, London W1R 4DJ.
Fax 020-7434 1197   Tel 020-7434 1215
E-mail: reception@ginger.com
Website: www.virginradio.co.uk
Parent company: SMG Plc
Starting date: 30.4.93
Dial: 1215

Atlantic 252
74 Newman Street, London W1P 3LA
Fax 020-7637 3925   Tel 020-7637 5252
E-mail: programming@atlantic252.com
Website: www.atlantic252.com
Atlantic 252 broadcasts from Southern Ireland beyond the fontiers policed by the Radio Authority but is effectively a national station with an audience in two-thirds of the UK.
Parent company: CLT UFA
Starting date: 1.9.89
Dial: 252 kHz LW

MAIN OWNERS

Border Radio Holdings
see Scottish Radio Holdings

Capital Radio
30 Leicester Square, London WC2H 7LA
Fax 020-7766 6100   Tel 020-7766 6000
E-mail: info@capitalradio.co.uk
Website: www.capitalfm.com
                www.capitalradio.plc.uk
Subsidiaries: BRMB Radio, Capital Radio London, Capital Gold Network, Century Radio Group, Fox FM, Invicta Radio, Ocean FM, Power FM, Red Dragon Radio, Southern FM, Sun FM, Xfm, Life Digital Radio, Capital Radio Digital Limited.
Stations: BRMB-FM, Capital FM, Capital Gold,Invicta FM, OceanFM, PowerFM, S Coast Radio, Southern FM, Sun FM Sunderland.

Chrysalis Radio
Chrysalis Building, Bramley Road, London W10 6SP
Fax 020-7221 6455   Tel 020-7221 2213
Website: www.heartfm.co.uk or www.galaxyfm.co.uk
Stations: Heart 106.2 FM, 100.7 Heart FM, Galaxy 101 FM, Galaxy 102 FM, Galaxy 102.2 FM, Galaxy 105 FM, Galaxy 105-106 FM

DMG Radio
Northcliffe House, 2 Derry Street, London W8 5TT
Fax 020-7938 6752   Tel 020-7938 6790
E-mail: dmgradio@dmgt.co.uk
Website: www.dmgt.co.uk
Stations: Breeze 1359/1431/1521 AM, Essex FM, Mercury FM97.5/102.7, Mercuty FM 96.2/101.6, Mercury FM 96.6, Ten 17 FM, Vibe FM.

Emap Performance
Mappin House, 4 Winsley Street, London W1N 7AR
Fax 020-7312 8227   Tel 020-7436 1515
Website: www.planetemap.com
                www.emap.com
Shares: Owns over 50% of Radio City, 19% of East Anglian Radio and 10% of Essex Radio.
Stations: Aire FM, Radio City 96.7, Hallam FM, Piccadilly Key 103, Kiss 100, Magic, Manchester's Magic 1152, Metro Radio, 97.4 Rock FM, TFM, Viking FM.

GWR Group
PO Box 2345, 382 Westlea, Swindon, Wiltshire SN5 7HF
Fax 0118-928 4310   Tel 0118-928 4313
E-mail: reception@gwrgroup.musicradi.com
Website: www.gwrgroup.musicradio.com
Stations: 2CR FM, 2-Ten FM, Beacon, Broadland 102, Chiltern FM, Classic FM, Classic Gold Amber (Norfolk/Suffolk), Classic Gold (666/954, 774-Gloucestershire, 792/828, 936/1161, 1152, 1260, 1332, 1359, 1431/1485, 1557), Classic Gold GEM, Classic WABC, Gemini FM, GWR FM, 102.7 Hereward FM, FM 103-Horizon, Lantern FM, 105.4 FM Leicester

Sound, Mercia FM, Northants 96, Orchard FM, 97 FM Plymouth Sound, Q103 FM, RAM FM, Severn Sound FM, SGR Colchester, SGR FM, 96 Trent FM, Wyvern FM, Now Digital (Wolverhampton).

Independent Radio Group
see The Wireless Group

Lincs FM plc
Witham Park, Waterside South, Lincoln LN5 7JN
Fax 01522-549911   Tel 01522-549900
E-mail: enquiries@lincsfm.co.uk
Stations: Lincs FM, Trax FM, Rutland Radio, Fosseway Radio, Ridings FM.

Local Radio Company
Cross Keys House, 22 Queen Street, Salisbury SP1 1EY
Fax 01722-335032   Tel 01722-415188
E-mail: tlrc@dial.pipex.com
Stations: 107.5 Cat FM, Isle of Wight Radio, The NRG, Spire FM, Vale FM, Victory 107.4, Wessex FM, Win 107.2

Marcher Radio Group
The Studios, Mold Road, Wrexham LL11 4AF
Fax 01978 759701   Tel 01978-415188
E-mail: info@mfmradio.co.uk
Website: www.mfmradio.co.uk
Stations: The Buzz 97.1, Champion FM 103, Coast FM, Marcher Gold, MFM 103.4

Minster Sound Radio
PO Box 123, Dunnington, York YO1 5ZX
Fax 01904-488878   Tel 01904-488888
E-mail: mail@minsterfm.co.uk
Website: www.minsterfm.co.uk
Stations: Home 107.9, Minster FM, Yorkshire Coast Radio,

Murfin Music International
Old Smithy, Post Office Lane, Kempsey, Worcester WR5 3NS
Fax 01905 820015   Tel 01905 820659
E-mail: old.smithy@virgin.net
Website: www.capitalradio.co.uk
Stations: Classic Gold 954/1530, Kix 96, Radio Maldwyn, Sunshine 855.

Radio Investments
Cross Keys House, 22 Queen Street, Salisbury SP1 1EY
Fax 01722-335032   Tel 01722-415188
E-mail: radio.investments@dial.pipex.com
Stations: Alpha 103.2, Central FM, 97.2 Stray FM, Minster Radio Sound.

Radio Services
Cross Keys House, 22 Queen Street, Salisbury SP1 1EY
Fax 01722-335032   Tel 01722-415188
E-mail: radio.services@dial.pipex.com
Stations: 107.8 Arrow FM, Nepture Radio, Quay West Radio, Sovereign Radio, 107.8 FM Thames Radio.

Scottish Radio Holdings
Clydebank Business Park, Clydebank, Glasgow G81 2RX
Fax 0141-565 2322   Tel 0141-565 2202
E-mail: radio@srh.co.uk
Website: www.srh.org.uk
Stations: Radio Borders, Clyde 1 FM, Clyde 2, Cool FM, Downtown Radio, Forth FM/AM, Moray Firth, Northsound 1/2, South West sound, Tay AM/FM, West sound AM, West FM, Score Digital.

SMG
Cowcaddens, Glasgow G2 3PR
Fax 0141-300 3030   Tel 0141-300 3300
E-mail: jane.wilson@smg.plc.uk
Website: www.smg.plc.uk
Stations: Virgin 105.8, Virgin 1215.

Sunrise Radio Group
Sunrise House, Merrick Road, Southall, Middlesex UB2 4AU
Fax 020-8813 9800   Tel 020-8574 6666
E-mail: radio@sunriseradio.com
Website: www.sunriseradio.com
Stations: Sunrise Radio London, Sunrise FM Yorkshire

Tindle Radio
Weavers Yard, 6 West Street, Farnham, Surrey GU9 7DN
Fax 01252 734007   Tel 01252 735667
E-mail: wendy.craig@internet-today.co.uk
Stations: Channel 103, Dream 100, Island FM, The Beach

UKRD Group
Dolphin House, North Street, Guildford, Surrey GU1 4AA
Fax 01483 531612   Tel 01483-300964
                          01483-306156
Website: www.ukrd.com
Stations: Active FM, Clan FM, County Sound, Delta FM, The Eagle, The Falcon, KL FM, Pirate FM, The Revolution, Star FM.

The Wireless Group
18 Hatfields, London SE1 8DJ
Fax 020-7959 7801   Tel 020-7959 7800
Stations: talkSPORT, Big AM, Imagine FM, The Pulse, 96.3 QFM, Scot FM, Signal Radio, The Wave and Swansea Sound, The Wave (Blackpool), 96.3 QFM, Scot FM, Wish FM (Wigan), 107.2 Wire FM, Wave 102 FM (Dundee).

LOCAL RADIO STATIONS

107.7 WFM
11 Beaconsfiled Road, Weston-Super-Mare,
Somerset BS23 1YE
Fax 01934 629922   Tel 01934 624455
E-mail: name@107.7wfm.com
Website: www.107.7wfm.com

107.8 Arrow FM
Priory Meadow Centre, Hastings, E Sussex, TN34 1PJ
Fax 01424-422622   Tel 01424-461177
E-mail: info@arrowfm.co.uk
Web: www.arrowfm.co.uk
Start date: 10.4.98   **Area:** Hastings

2CR FM
5 Southcote Road, Bournemouth, Dorset BH1 3LR
Fax 01202-255244   Tel 01202-259259
Website: www.2crfm.co.uk
Parent company: GWR Group
Starting date: 15.9.80   **Area:** Dorset, west Hampshire
Dial: 102.3 MHz (2CR FM) 828 kHz (Classic Gold)

2-Ten FM
PO Box 2020, Reading, Berks RG31 7FG
Fax 0118-928 8433   Tel 0118-945 4400
E-mail: musicmix@2tenfm.musicradio.com
Website: www.2-TENFM.co.uk
Parent company: GWR Group   **Starting date:** 8.3.76
Area: Reading, Basingstoke, Andover
Dial: 97.0 & 102.9 FM, 103.4 FM

96.7 FM
PO Box 77, 18 Blackfriars Street, King's Lynn, Norfolk
PE30 1NN
Fax 01553-767200   Tel 01553-772777
E-mail: klfmradio.co.uk
Area: west Norfolk

Active 107.5 FM
7 Western Road, Romford, Essex, RM1 3LD
Fax 01708-730383   Tel 01708-731643
E-mail: sales@activefm.co.uk
Web: www.activefm.co.uk
Starting date: 18.5.98
Area: East London, west Essex.

96.3 Aire FM
51 Burley Road, Leeds, West Yorkshire LS3 1LR
Fax 0113-283 5501   Tel 0113-283 5500
E-mail: airefm@airefm.co.uk
Website: www.airefm.co.uk
Parent company: Emap
Starting date: 1.9.81
Area: Leeds   **Dial:** 96.3 MHz

Alpha 103.2
11 Woodland Road, Darlington DL3 7BJ
Fax 01325-255551   Tel 01325-255552
E-mail: admin@alpharadio.demon.co.uk
Area: Darlington and Newton Aycliffe.
Dial: 103.2 FM

Amber Classic Gold
47-49 Colgate, Norwich NR3 1DB
Fax 01603-666353   Tel 01603-630621
Parent company: GWR Group
Starting date: 24.9.95
Area: Great Yarmouth & Norwich   **Dial:** 1152 KHz

Argyll FM
27-29 Longrow, Campbelltown, Argyll PA28 6ED
Fax 01586 551888   Tel 01586 551800
Starting date: 11.99
Area: Kintyre, Islay, Jura

Asian Sound
Globe House, Southall Street, Manchester M3 1LG
Fax 0161-288 9000   Tel 0161-288 1000
E-mail: asiansound@aol.com
Area: East Lancashire   **Dial:** 1377, 963 AM

B97 Chiltern FM
55 Goldington Road, Bedford MK40 3LT
Fax 01234-218580   Tel 01234-272400
E-mail: studio@b97fm.musicradio.com
Parent company: GWR Group
Area: Bedfordshire, Hertfordshire, Cambridgeshire
Dial: 96.9 FM

Bath FM
Station House, Ashley Avenue, Lower Weston, Bath
BA1 3DS
Fax 01225 471681   Tel 01225 471571
Starting date: 15 11.99
Area: Bath
Dial: 107.9 FM

The Bay
PO Box 969, George's Quay, Lancaster LA1 3LD
Fax 01524-848787   Tel 01524-848747
E-mail: thebay.co.uk
Starting date: 1.3.93
Policy: classic hits, local news, community information
Area: North Lancashire & south Cumbria.
Dial: 96.9, 102.3 & 103.2 FM

BCR FM
33 Manor Road, Brisgwater, Somerset TA6 4RJ
Fax 01278-444211   Tel 01278-444211
E-mail: studio@bcrfm.co.uk
Starting date: autumn 2000
Area: Bridgwater

The Beach
PO Box 103.4 Lowestoft, Suffolk NR32 2TL
Fax 07000 001036   Tel 07000 001035
E-mail: 103.4@thebeach.co.uk
Website: www.thebeach.co.uk
Parent company: Tindle Radio
Starting date: 29.9.96
Area: Great Yarmouth & Lowestoft   **Dial:** 103.4 FM

Beacon FM/WABC Classic Gold
267 Tettenhall Road, Wolverhampton WV6 0DQ
Fax 01902-461299   Tel 01902-461300
Parent company: GWR Group
Starting date: 12.4.76; Shrewsbury & Telford 14.7.87
Area: Wolverhampton & Black Country, Shrewsbury &
Telford
Dial: 97.2 & 103.1 MHz/990&1017 AM

FM 102 The Bear
Guard House Studios, Banbury Road, Stratford upon
Avon, Warwicks CV37 7HX
Fax 01789-263102   Tel 01789-262636
Parent company: Independent
Starting date: 24.5.96
Area: Stratford upon Avon and surroundings.
Dial: 102.0 FM

Beat 106
Four Winds Pavilion, Pacific Quay, Glasgow G51 1EB
Fax 0141-566 6110   Tel 0141-566 6106
Starting date: 10.99
Area: Central Scotland
Dial: 105.7 MHz, 106.1 MHz
Big
Forster Square, Bradford, West Yorkshire BD1 5NE
Fax 01274-203130   Tel 01274-203040
Parent company: The Wireless Group
Starting date: 1.5.89
Area: Bradford, Halifax, Huddersfield
Dial: 1278 MHz, 1530 MHz
Big
Stoke Road, Stoke on Trent ST4 2SR
Fax 01782-744110   Tel 01782-747047
Parent company: The Wireless Group
Starting date: 5.9.83
Area: Stoke on Trent
Dial: 1170 kHz
Big
4th Floor, Quay West Trafford Park, Manchester M17 1FL
Fax 0161-607 0443   Tel 0161-607 0420
Parent company: The Wireless Group
Starting date: 20.6.94
Area: Manchester
Dial: 1458 kHz
Breeze
Clifftown Road, Southend-on-Sea, Essex SS1 1SX
Fax 01702-333686   Tel 01702-333711
E-mail: studios@breeze.co.uk
Website: www.breeze.co.uk
Parent company: DME Radio
Starting date: 16.7.89
Dial: 1431 kHz (Southend), 1359 kHz (Chelmsford)
Breeze 1521
Radio Mercury, The Stanley Centre, Kelvin Way, Crawley, W Sussex RH10 2SE
Fax 01293-565663   Tel 01293-519161
Parent company: DMG Radio
Starting date: 4.5.92
Area: Reigate & Crawley
106.3 Bridge FM
25 Wyndham Street, Bridgend, CF31 1EB
Fax 01656-673611   Tel 01656-647777
Starting date: 1.5.00
Area: Bridgend
96.4 FM BRMB
Nine Brindleyplace, Broad Street, Birmingham B1 2DJ
Fax 0121-245 5245   Tel 0121-245 5000
E-mail: @brmb.co.uk
Parent company: Capital Radio
Starting date: 19.2.74
Area: Birmingham.   **Dial:** 96.4 FM
Bristol's 107.3 The Eagle
The Bristol Evening Post Building, Temple Way, Bristol
Parent company: UKRD
Starting date: 26.11.99
Area: Bristol

Broadland
47 Colegate, Norwich, Norfolk NR3 1DB
Fax 01603-666252   Tel 01603-630621
E-mail: sales@broadland102.co.uk
Website: www.broadland102.co.uk
Parent company: GWR Group
Starting date: 1.10.84 **Area:** Norwich/Great Yarmouth.
Dial: 102.4 MHz, 1152kHz
The Buzz
Media House, Claughton Rd, Birkenhead CH41 6EY
Fax 051-647 5427   Tel 0151-650 1700
E-mail: info@the buzz971.co.uk
Website: www.thebuzz971.co.uk
Parent company: Marcher Radio Group
Starting date: 31.3.89
Area: The Wirral
Dial: 97.1 MHz
Cambridge Red Radio
PO Box 492, Cambridge CB1 2BW
Fax 01223 577686   Tel 01223 722300
E-mail: (9name)@redradio.co.uk
Website: www.redradio.co.uk
Parent company: UKRD
Starting date: 20.03.98
Area: Cambridge
Dial: 107.9 MHz
Capital FM/Capital Gold
30 Leicester Square, London WC2H 7LA
Fax 020-7766 6100   Tel 020-7766 6000
Parent company: Capital Radio
Starting date: 16.10.73 (FM), 28.11.88 (Gold)
Area: London.
Dial: 95.8 MHz (Capital FM), 1548 kHz (Capital Gold)
Capital Gold, Birmingham
Nine Brindleyplace, Broad Street, Birmingham B1 2DJ
Fax 0121-245 5245   Tel 0121-245 5000
Website: www.brmb.co.uk
Area: Birmingham   **Dial:** 1152 AM
Capital Gold, Brighton
Radio Ho, Franklin Road, Portslade BN41 2SS
Fax 01273-430098   Tel 01273-430111
E-mail: info@southernradio.co.uk
Parent company: Capital Radio
Starting date: 29.8.83 (Brighton), 10.3.91 (Portsmouth & Southampton)
Area: Brighton, Southampton, Portsmouth
Dial: 1323 kHz (Brighton), 1170, 1557 kHz (Portsmouth, Southampton)
Capital Gold
West Canal Wharf, Cardiff CF10 5XL
Fax 029-2038 4014   Tel 029-2023 7878
E-mail: mail@reddragonfm.co.uk
Website: www.capitalgold.com
Parent company: Capital Radio
Starting date: 15.7.90
Dial: 1359 kHz (Cardiff), 1305 kHz (Newport)

107.5 Cat FM
Regent Arcade, Cheltenham, Glos, GL50 1JZ
Fax 01242-699 666   Tel 01242-699 555
E-mail: catfm@netcomuk.co.uk
Web: www.catfm.co.uk
Parent company: TLRC
Start date: Sept 1998
Area: Cheltenham, Tewkesbury

Q97.2 Causeway Coast Radio
24 Clafin Road, Coleraine BT52 2NU
Fax 028-70 326666   Tel 028-70 359100
Starting date: 26.1.00
Area: Coleraine
Dial: 97.2 MHz

Central FM
201-203 High Street, Falkirk FK1 1DU
Fax 01324-611168   Tel 01324-611164
Starting date: 4.6.90
Area: Stirling an Falkirk.   Dial: 103.1 MHz

Centre FM
5-6 Aldergate, Tamworth, Staffs B79 7DJ
Fax 0870-000 1024   Tel 01827 318000
E-mail: centrefm@centrefm.co.uk
Website: www.centrefm.co.uk
Starting date: 01.06.98
Area: SE Staffordshire   Dial: 101.6 MHz, 102.4 MHz

Century 105
Century Ho, Waterfront Quay, Salford Quays,
Manchester M5 2XXW
Fax 0161-400 1105   Tel 0161-400 0105
Parent company: Capital Radio
Starting date: 8.9.98
Area: North west
Dial: 105.4 MHz

Century 106
City Link, Nottingham NG2 4NG
Fax 0115-910 6107   Tel 0115-910 6100
Parent company: Capital Radio
Starting date: 23.9.97
Area: East midlands
Dial: 106 MHz

Century Radio
Century Ho, PO Box 100, Gateshead NE8 2YX
Fax 0191-477 15600   Tel 0191-477 6666
E-mail: reception@centurynortheast.com
Parent company: Border Media
Starting date: 1.9.94
Area: North East
Dial: 100.7, 101.8 & 96.2 MHz

Ceredigion
Alexandra Road, Aberystwyth, Dyfed SY23 1LF
Fax 01970-627206   Tel 01970-627999
Starting date: 14.12.92
Area: Ceredigion.
Dial: 103.3 & 96.6 MHz, 97.4FM

CFM
PO Box 964, Carlisle, Cumbria CA1 3NG
Fax 01228-818444   Tel 01228-818964
E-mail: traffic@cfmradio.com
Starting date: 14.4.93
Area: Carlisle.
Dial: 96.4 Penrith, 102.2 Whitehaven

Champion FM
Llys-y-Dderwen, Parc Menai, Bangor LL57 4BN
Fax 01248 671971   Tel 01248 671888
Website: www.championfm.co.uk
Parent company: Marcher
Starting date: 11.12.98
Area: Caernarfon
Dial: 103 MHz

Channel 103 FM
6 Tunnel Street, St Helier, Jersey JE2 4LU
Fax 01534-887799   Tel 01534-888103
E-mail: radio@103fm.itl.net
Website: www.103fm.itl.net
Starting date: 25.10.92
Area: Jersey.   Dial: 103.7 MHz

Channel Travel Radio
PO Box 2000, Folkestone, Kent CT18 8XY
Fax 01303 283874   Tel 01303-283873
Starting date: 1.10.95
Area: along the M20 towards Folkestone & the Kent
Channel ports

107.7 Chelmer FM
Cater House, High Street, Chelmsford, CM1 1AL
Fax 01245 259558   Tel 01245 259400
E-mail: mail@chelmerfm.co.uk
Website: www.chelmerfm.co.uk
Parent company: Mid-Essex Radio
Starting date: 18.10.98
Area: Chelmsford   Dial: 107.7 MHz

Chiltern FM/ClassicGold 792 & 828
Chiltern Road, Dunstable, Beds LU6 1HQ
Fax 01582-676241   Tel 01582-676200
Parent company: GWR Group
Starting date: 15.10.81 (Chiltern FM); 15.7.90 (Classic
Gold)   Area: Bedford, Luton.
Dial: 97.6 MHz Chiltern FM, 792 & 828 kHz Gold

Choice FM
291-299 Borough High Street, London SE1 1JG
Fax 020-7378 3911   Tel 020-7378 3969
Website: www.choicefm.net
Starting date: 31.3.90
Area: Brixton.
Dial: 96.9 MHz, 107.1

Choice 107.1
291-299 Borough High Street, London SE1 1JG
Fax 020-8348 1044   Tel 020-8348 1033
Website: www.choicefm.net
Starting date: 3.5.00
Area: North London
Dial: 107.1 MHz,

City Beat 96.7
46 Stranmills Embankment, Belfast BT9 5DF
Fax 028-9020 0023   Tel 028-9020 5967
E-mail: citybeat96.7@dnet-co.uk
Parent company: UKRD
Starting date: 6.9.90
Area: Belfast   Dial: 96.7 MHz

Clan FM
Radio House, Rowantree Avenue, Newhouse, ML1 5RX
Fax 01698-733318   Tel 01698-733107
E-mail: clanfm@aol.com
Starting date: 11.99   **Area:** North Lanarkshire

Classic Gold 828
5 Southcote Road, Bournemouth, BH1 3LR
Fax 01202-255244   Tel 01202-259259
Website; www.classicgold828.co.uk
Parent company: GWR Group
Area: Dorset, west Hampshire   **Dial:** 828

Classic Gold 1260
PO Box 2020, Watershed, Bristol BS99 7SN
Fax: 0117-984 3202   Tel 0117-984 3200
E-mail: reception@classicgold.musicradio.com
Parent company: GWR Group
Starting date: 25.11.88
Dial: 1260 kHz (Bristol), 936 kHz (west Wilts), 1161 kHz (Swindon)

Classic Gold 1332
PO Box 225, Queensgate, Peterborough PE1 1XL
Fax 01733-281445   Tel 01733-460460
E-mail: tima@musicradio.com
Parent company: GWR Group
Starting date: 14.4.92
Area: Peterborough.
Dial: 1332 kHz

Classic Gold 1359
Hertford Place, Coventry CV1 3TT
Fax 024-7686 8202   Tel 024-7686 8200
E-mail: mercia@musicradio.com
Parent company: GWR
Area: Coventry, Warwickshire

Classic Gold 1431
PO Box 2020, Reading, Berks RG31 7FG
Fax 0118-928 8483   Tel 0118-945 4400
E-mail: musicmix@twotenfm.musicradio.com
Website: www.2-tenfm.co.uk
Parent company: GWR Group
Starting date: 8.3.76
Area: Reading.
Dial: 1431 kHz

Classic Gold Gem
29-31 Castle Gate, Nottingham NG1 7AP
Fax 0115-912 9333   Tel 0115-952 7000
E-mail: @musicradio.com
Parent company: GWR Group
Starting date: 4.10.88
Area: Nottingham and Derby.
Dial: 999 & 945 kHz

Clyde 1/Clyde 2
Clydebank Business Park, Glasgow G81 2RX
Fax 0141-565 2265   Tel 0141-565 2200
E-mail: clydenews@srh.co.uk
Website: www.clydeonline.co.uk
Parent company: Scottish Radio
Starting date: 31.12.73
Dial: Clyde 1, 102.5 MHz (Glasgow), 97.0 MHz (Vale of Leven), 103.3 MHz (Firth of Clyde). Clyde 2, 1152 kHz

Coast FM
Media Hse, 41 Conwy Road, Colwyn Bay LL28 5AB
Fax 01492 535248   Tel 01492 533733
Website: www.coastfm.co.uk
Parent company: Emap   **Starting date:** 27.08.93
Area: North Wales Coast   **Dial:** 96.3 MHz

Connect FM
Unit 1, Robinson Close, Kettering NN16 8PU
Fax 01536-517390   Tel 01536-412413
Website: www.connectfm.co.uk
Parent company: HUb Trans Communications
Starting date: 6.4.90
Area: Kettering, Corby, Wellingborough, Rushden
Dial: 97.2, 107.4 FM

Cool FM
PO Box 974, Belfast BT1 1RT
Fax 028-91814974   Tel 028-9181 7181
E-mail: music@coolfm.co.uk
Website: www.coolfm.co.uk
Starting date: 7.2.90
Area: Belfast.
Dial: 97.4 MHz

County Sound Radio 1476AM
Dolphin House, North Street, Guildford GU1 4AA
Fax 01483-531612   Tel 01483-300964
E-mail: eagle@countysound.co.uk
Website: www.ukrd.com
Parent company: UKRD Group
Starting date: 4.9.95**Area:** W Surrey and NE Hampshire
Dial: 1476 KHz

106 CTFM
16 Lower Bridge Street, Canterbury, Kent CT1 2HQ
Fax 01277-785106   Tel 01277-789106
E-mail: reception@ctfm.co.uk
Website: www.ctfm.co.uk
Starting date: 21.9.97
Area: Canterbury, Whitstable, Herne Bay

Delta FM 97.1/102
65 Weyhill, Haslemere, Surrey GU27 1HN
Fax 01428-658971   Tel 01428-651971
E-mail: delta@ukrd.com
Website: www.ukrd.com
Parent company: UKRD Group
Starting date: 9.5.96
Area: Haslemere
Dial: 97.1 MHz, 102 MHz

Downtown Radio
Newtownards, Co Down, Northern Ireland BT23 4ES
Fax 028-9181 8913   Tel 028-9181 5555
E-mail: programmes@downtown.co.uk
Website: www.downtown.co.uk
Parent company: Scottish RadioHoldings
Starting date: 16.3.76
Dial: 1026 kHz (Belfast), 102.4 MHz (mid Antrim), 96.4 MHz (north), 96.6 MHz (west), 103.1 MHz South Down

Dream 100 FM
Northgate Hse, St Peters Street, Colchester CO1 1HT
Fax 01206-715102   Tel 01206-764466
E-mail: info@dream100.com
Website: www.dream100.com
Parent company: Tindle Radio
Starting date: 7.10.90
Area: Tendring
Dial: 100.2 FM

107.9 Dune FM
The Power Station, Victoria Way, Southport PR8 1RR
Fax 01704-502540   Tel 01704-502500
E-mail: name@dunefm.co.uk
Website: www.dunefm.co.uk
Starting date: 12.10. 97
Area: North Merseyside and west Lancashire
Dial: 107.9 fm

96.4 The Eagle
Dolphin House, North Street, Guildford GU1 4AA
Fax 01483-531612   Tel 01483-300964
E-mail: eagle@countysound.co.uk
Website: www.ukrd.com
Parent company: UKRD Group
Starting date: 4.1.96
Area: W Surrey and NE Hampshire
Dial: 96.4 MHz

107.3 The Eagle
Bristol Evening Post Building, Temple Way, Brostil
BS99 7HD
Fax 0117-925 0941   Tel 01117-910 6600
E-mail: eagle@bepp.co.uk
Website: www.1073eagle.co.uk
Parent company: UKRD Group
Starting date: 26.11.99
Area: Bristol
Dial: 107.3 MHz

107.9 The Eagle
Radio House, Sturton Street, Cambridge CB1 2QF
Fax 01223-577686   Tel 01223-722300
Parent company: UKRD Group
Starting date: 23.3.98
Area: Cambridge
Dial: 107.9 MHz

eleven SEVENTY AM
PO Box 1170, High Wycombe, Bucks HP13 6YT
Fax 01494 447272   Tel 01494 446611
E-mail: info@elevenseventy.co.uk
Starting date: 31.12.93
Area: High Wycombe.
Dial: 1170 kHz

Essex FM
Clifftown Road, Southend, Essex SS1 1SX
Fax 01702-345224   Tel 01702-333711
E-mail: studios@essexradio.co.uk
Website: www.essexfm.com
Parent company: DMG Radio
Starting date: 12.9.81
Dial: 96.3 MHz (Southend), 102.6 MHz (Chelmsford)

FM 107 The Falcon
Brunel Mall, London Road, Stroud, Glos GL5 2BP
Fax 01453 757107   Tel 01453 767369
E-mail: info@thefalcon.org
Website: www.thefalcon
Parent company: UKRD
Starting date: 28.11.98
Area: S Gloucestershire
Dial: 107.2 MHz, 107.9 MHz

FLR 107.3
Astra House, Arklow Road, New Cross, SE14 6BB
Fax: 020-8691 9193   Tel 020-8691 9202
E-mail: flr1073@global.co.uk
Web: www.ukrd.com/flr
Start date: Autumn 1998
Area: Lewisham

FM 103 Horizon
Broadcast Centre, Crownhill, 14 Vincent Avenue,
Milton Keynes, Bucks MK8 0AB
Fax 01908-564063   Tel 01908-269111
E-mail: morning crew@fm103.musicradio.com
Website: www.mkweb.co.uk
Parent company: GWR
Starting date: 1989
Area: Milton Keynes   Dial: 103.3

Forth FM/Forth AM
Forth House, Forth Street, Edinburgh EH1 3LF
Fax 0131-558 3277   Tel 0131-556 9255
Parent company: Scottish Radio Holdings
Starting date: 22.1.75
Area: Edinburgh, Lothian & Fife
Dial: 97.3/97.6, 102.2 FM, 1548 AM

Fosseway Radio
Suite 1, 1 Castle Street, Hinckley, Leicestershire, LE10
1DA
Fax 01455-616888   Tel 01455-614151
E-mail: enquiries@fossewayradio.co.uk
Web: www.fossewayradio.co.uk
Start date: 11.98
Area: Hinckley and SW Leicestershire
Dial: 107.9 FM

FOX FM
Brush House, Pony Road, Oxford OX4 2XR
Fax 01865-871036   Tel 01865-871000
E-mail: fox@foxfm.co.uk
Starting date: 15.9.89
Area: Oxford, Banbury.   Dial: 102.6 & 97.4 MHz

Fresh AM
Gargrave Road, Skipton, N Yorks BD23 1yd
Fax 01756 799711   Tel 01756 799771
E-mail: info@freshradio.co.uk
Starting date: 4.5.97
Area: Yorkshire Dales   Dial: 1413 KHz

Galaxy 101
Millennium House, 26 Baldwin Street, Bristol BS1 1SE
Fax 0117-901 4666   Tel 0117-901 0101
E-mail: FirstinitialSurname@Galaxy101.co.uk
Website: www.galaxy101.co.uk
Parent company: Chrysalis Group
Starting date: 10.95
Area: South Wales and the West
Dial: 101 MHz & 97.2 MHz

Galaxy 102
127-129 Portland Street, Manchester M1 6ED
Fax 0161-228 1020   Tel 0161-228 0102
E-mail: mail@galaxy102.co.uk
Website: www.galaxy102.co.uk
Parent company: Chrysalis Group
Starting date: 16.10.94
Area: Greater Manchester.
Dial: 102 MHz
Galaxy 102.2
1 The Square, Broad Street, Birmingham B15 1AS
Fax 0121-695 0055   Tel 0121-695 0000
Website: www.galaxy1022.co.uk
Starting date: 1.1.99
Area: Birmingham.   **Dial:** 102.2 MHz
Galaxy 105
Joseph's Well, West Gate, Leeds LS3 1AB
Fax 0113-213 1055   Tel 0113-213 0105
Parent company: Chrysalis Group
Starting date: 14.2.97
Area: Yorkshire
Dial: 105 MHz
Galaxy 105-106
Kingfisher Way, Silverlink Business Park, Tyne & Wear
NE28 9ND
Fax 0191-206 8080   Tel 01191-206 8000
Parent company: Chrysalis Group
Starting date: 1.6.99
Area: North east England
Dial: 105 3, 105.6, 106.4 MHz
Gemini FM/Westword Radio
Hawthorn House, Exeter Business Park, Exeter,
Devon EX1 3QS
Fax: 01392-444433   Tel 01392-444444
Parent company: GWR Group
Starting date: 1.1.95
Area: Exeter, east Devon and Torbay.
Dial: 96.4/97.0/103 Mhz, 666/954 kHz
GWR FM
PO Box 2000, Bristol, Avon BS99 7SN
Fax 0117-984 3202   Tel 0117-984 3200
E-mail: reception@gwrfm.musicradio.com
Website: www.gwrfm.musicradio.com
Parent company: GWR Group
Starting date: 27.10.81 (Bristol), 22.5.87 (Bath)
Dial: 96.3 MHz (Bristol), 103.0 MHz (Bath)
GWR FM Wiltshire
PO Box 2000, Swindon SN4 7EX
Fax 01793-842602   Tel 01793-842600
Parent company: GWR Group
Starting date: 12.10.82
Dial: 97.2 MHz (Swindon), 102.2 MHz (west Wilts),
96.5 MHz (Marlborough)
Hallam FM
900 Herries Road, Sheffield S6 1RH
Fax 0114-285 3159   Tel 0114-285 3333
E-mail: programmes@hallamfm.co.uk
Website: www.hallamfm.co.uk
Parent company: EMAP
Starting date: 1.10.74
Dial: 97.4 MHz (Sheffield), 102.9 MHz (Barnsley),
103.4 MHz (Doncaster)

100.7 Heart FM/Galaxy 102.2
1 The Square, 111 Broad Street, Birmingham B15 1AS
Fax 0121-696 1007   Tel 0121-695 0000
E-mail: heartfm@heart.co.uk
Parent company: Chrysalis
Policy: Soft adult contemporary music
Starting date: 7.9.94
Area: West midlands, Warwickshire
Dial: 100.7 MHz
Heart 106.2 FM
Chrysalis Building, Bramley Road, London W10 6SP
Fax 020-7470 1095   Tel 020-7468 1062
Website: www.heart1062.co.uk
Parent company: Chrysalis Group
Starting date: summer 1995
Area: Greater London. **Dial:** 106.2 MHz
Heartland FM
Lower Oakfield, Pitlochry, Perthshire PH16 5HQ
Fax 01796-474007   Tel 01796-474040
Some Gaelic and mixed language output.
Starting date: 21.3.92
Area: Pitlochry and Aberfldy.
Dial: 97.5 MHz
HertBeat FM
PO Box 299, Hertford SG14 3XN
Fax 01992-505362   Tel 01992-505362
E-mail: info@hertbeat.oom
Starting date: 3.3.01
Area: Hertford
Dial: 106.9 MHz
102.7 Hereward FM
PO Box 225, Queensgate, Peterborough,
Cambridgeshire PE1 1XJ
Fax 01733-281445   Tel 01733-460460
Parent company: GWR Group
Starting date: 20.7.80
Area: Peterborough
Dial: 102.7 MHz
Home 107.9
The Old Stableblock, Brewery Drive, Lockwood Park,
Huddersfield, HD1 3UR
Fax 01484-311107   Tel 01484-321107
Parent company: Minster Sound Radio
Start date: 1.3.98
Area: Huddersfield   **Dial:** 107.9 FM
Iamgine FM
Regent House, Heaton Lane, Stockport SK4 1BX
Fax 0161-285 1010   Tel 0161-285 4545
Parent company: The Wireless Group
Starting date: 17.2.90
Area: Stockport   **Dial:** 96.4 MHz
Invicta FM/Capital Gold
Radio House, John Wilson Business Park, Whitstable,
Kent CT5 3QX
Fax 01227-774450   Tel 01227-772004
E-mail: info@invictaradio.co.uk
Parent company: Capital Radio
Starting date: Invicta FM: 1.10.84, Capital Gold 27.3.89
Dial: Invicta FM 103.1 MHz (Maidstone & Medway),
102.8 MHz (Canterbury), 95.9 MHz (Thanet), 97.0
MHz (Dover), 96.1 MHz (Ashford). Capital Gold 1242
kHz (west Kent), 603 kHz (east Kent)

Island FM
12 Westerbrook, St Sampsons, Guernsey GY2 4QQ
Fax 01481-249676   Tel 01481-242000
E-mail: name@islandfm.guernsey.net
Website: www.islandfm.guernsey.net
Parent company: Tindle Radio
Starting date: 15.10.92
Dial: 104.7 MHz (Guernsey), 93.7 MHz (Alderney)

Isle of Wight Radio
Dodnor Park, Newport, Isle of Wight PO30 5XE
Fax 01983-822109   Tel 01983-822557
E-mail: admin@iwradio.co.uk
Website: www.iwradio.co.uk
Starting date: 15.4.90
Area: Isle of Wight   Dial: 107 & 102 MHz

Isles FM
PO Box 333, Stornaway, Isle of Lewis HS1 2PU
Fax 01851 703322   Tel 01851 703333
E-mail: islesfm@radiolink.net
Website: www.listen.to/islesfm
Starting date: 7.3.98
Area: Western Isle   Dial: 103 MHz

Jazz FM
World Trade Centre, Exchange Quay, Manchester M5 3EJ
Fax 0161-877 1005   Tel 0161-877 1004
E-mail: jazzfminfo@jazzfm.com
Website: www.jazzfm.com
Parent company: Jazz FM
Starting date: 1.9.94
Area: North west   Dial: 100.4 MHz

Jazz FM 102.2
26 Castlereagh Street, London W1H 6DJ
Fax 020-7723 9742   Tel 020-7706 4100
E-mail: info@jazzfm.com
Website: www.jazzfm.com
Parent company: Golden Rose Communications.
Starting date: 4.3.90
Area: Greater London.   Dial: 102.2 MHz

Juice
27 Fleet STreet, Liverpool, L1 4AR
Fax 0151-707 3109   Tel 0151-707 3107
E-mail: imail@juiceliverpool.com
Start date: 27.3.98
Area: 107.6 FM
Dial: 107.6 FM

KCR FM
PO Box 106, Prescot, Merseyside L35 0RN
                       Tel 07808-179999
Parent company: Knowsley Community Radio
Starting date: 2001
Area: Knowsley

107.6 Kestrel FM
2nd Floor, Paddington House, The Walks Shopping Centre, Basingstoke, RG21 7LJ
Fax 01256-694111   Tel 01256-694000
Start date: 18.5.98
Area: Basingstoke

Kick FM
The Studios, 42 Bone Lane, Newbury, Berkshire RG14 5SD
Fax 01635-841010-   Tel 01635-841600
Parent company: Fusion Radio Group
Starting date: 25.5.00
Area: Newbury
Dial: 105.6 MHz

Kingdom FM
Haig House, Haig Business Park, Markinch, Fife KY7 6AQ
Fax 01592-757788   Tel 01592-753753
E-mail: kingsomfm@aol.com
Parent company: Kingdom fm
Starting date: 5.10.98
Area: Fife
Dial: 95.2, 96.1 MHz

Kiss 100 FM
Kiss House, 80 Holloway Road, London N7 8JG
Fax 020-7700 3979   Tel 020-7700 6100
Website: www.kiss100.com
Parent company: Emap
Starting date: 1.9.90
Area: Greater London.
Dial: 100 MHz

Kix 96
Watch Close, Spon Street, Coventry CB1 3LN
E-mail: kix96@aol.com
Fax: 024-7655 1744   Tel 024-7652 5656
Website: www.indiscrete/kix96
Starting date: 28.8.90
Area: Coventry. Dial: 96.2 MHz

KL-FM
18 Blackfriars Street, Kings Lynn, Norfolk PE30 1NN
Fax 01553-766453   Tel 01553-772777
Website: www.ukrd.com
Parent company: Dawe Media
Starting date: 1.7.92
Area: Kings Lynn.
Dial: 96.7 MHz

Lantern FM
2b Lauder Lane, Roundswell Commercial Park, Barnstaple EX31 3TA
Fax 01271-340345   Tel 01271-340340
Starting date: 19.10.92
Area: North Devon.
Dial: 96.2 MHz

LBC 1152AM
200 Gray's Inn Road, London WC1X 8XZ
Fax 020-7312 8565   Tel 020-7973 1152
Website: www.lbc.co.uk
Britain's first commercal station, Relaunched in its current format in July 1996, the station provides 24 hour news and comment for London with phone-ins.
Parent company: London News Radio
Starting date: July 1996
Area: Greater London
Dial: 1152 am

Leicester Sound
Granville House, Granville Road, Leicester LE1 7RW
Fax 0116-256 1303   Tel 0116-256 1300
E-mail: leicestersound@musicradio.com
Parent company: GWR Group
Starting date: 7.9.84
Area: Leicester.
Dial: 105.4 MHz

Liberty Radio 963+972AM
Trevor House, 100 Brompton Road, London SW3 1ER
Fax 020-7893 8965   Tel 020-7893 8966
E-mail: liberty963@aol.com
Parent company: owned by the Universal Church of the Kingdom of God
Starting date: 3.7.95
Area: Greater London
Dial: 963 + 972 AM

Lincs FM
Witham Park, Waterside South, Lincoln LN5 7JN
Fax 01522-549911   Tel 01522-549900
E-mail: enquiries@lincsfm.co.uk
Starting date: 1.3.92
Area: Lincolnshire, Newark.

Lite FM
5 Church Stree, Peterborough PE1 1XB
Fax 01733 898107   Tel 01733 898107
E-mail: admin@litefm.co.uk
Website: www.litefm.co.uk
Starting date: 24.7.99
Area: Peterborough
Dial: 106.8 MHz

Lochbroom FM
Mill Street, Radio House, Ullapool, Rossshire IV26 2UN
Fax 01854-613132   Tel 01854-613131
E-mail: radio@lochbroomfm.co.uk
Website: www.lochbroomfm.co.uk
Starting date: 5.97
Area: north west coast - Scotland
Dial: 102.2 MHz

London Greek Radio
Florentia Village, Vale Road, London N4 1TD
Fax 020-8800 8005   Tel 020-8800 8001
E-mail: sales@lgr.co.uk
Website: www.lgr.co.uk
Music, news and info for Greek speaking listeners
Starting date: 13.11.89
Area: Haringey.
Dial: 103.3 MHz

London Turkish Radio
185b High Road, Wood Green London N22 6BA
Fax 020-8881 5151   Tel 020-8881 0606
E-mail: ltr1584am@aol.com
Music for the Turkish community
Starting date: summer 1995
Area: north London, Haringey.
Dial: 1584 kHz

Magic AM
900 Herries Road, Sheffield S6 1RH
Fax 0114-285 3159   Tel 0114-285 2121
E-mail: programmes@magicam.co.uk
Website:www.magicam.co.uk
Parent company: EMAP
Starting date: 12.2.97
Dial: 990 kHz, 1305 kHz, 1548 kHz

Magic 105.4
The Network Building, 97 Tottenham Court Road, London W1P 9HF
Fax 020-7504 7001   Tel 020-7504 7000
Starting date: 9.7.90
Area: Greater London.
Dial: 105.4 MHz

Magic 828
PO Box 2000, 51 Burley Road, Leeds LS3 1LR
Fax 0113 283 5501   Tel 0113 283 5500
E-mail: magic@magic828.com
Website: www.magic828.com
Parent company: Emap
Starting date: 17.7.90
Area: Leeds, west Yorkshire
Dial: 828 kHz

Magic 999
PO Box 974, Preston, Lancs PR11XS
Fax 01772 201917   Tel 01772 556301
Starting date: 5.10.82
Area: Preston, Blackpool
Dial: 97.4 MHz

Magic 1152
Newcastle-upon-Tyne NE99 1BB
Fax 0191-488 9222   Tel 0191-420 3040
Parent company: Emap Radio
Starting date: 8.4.89
Area: Tyne & Wear, Northumberland & Durham
Dial: 1152AM

Magic 1152 Manchester
Castle Quay, Castlefield, Manchester M15 4PR
Fax 0161-661 1152   Tel 0161-288 5000
Website: key103fm.com
Parent company: Emap Radio
Starting date: 2.4.99
Area: Manchester
Dial: 1152 kHz

Magic 1161
Commercial Road, Hull HU1 2SG
Fax 08456-382967   Tel 01482-325141
E-mail: magic1161.co.uk
Parent company: Emap Radio
Starting date: 13.9.93
Dial: 1161 kHz

Magic 1548
8-10 Stanley Street, Liverpool L1 6AF
Fax 0151-471 0330   Tel 0151-227 5100
Website: www.radiocity967.com
Parent company: Emap
Starting date: 21.10.74
Area: Merseyside
Dial: 1548 kHz

Magic 1170
Radio House, Yales Crescent, Thornaby, Stockton on Tees TS17 6AA
Fax 01642-868288   Tel 01642-888222
Parent company: Emap
Starting date: 8.4.89
Area: Teeside
Dial: 1170 kHz

Radio Maldwyn
Studios, The Park, Newtown, Powys SY16 2NZ
Fax 01686-623666   Tel 01686-623555
E-mail: radio.maldwyn@ukonline.co.uk
Starting date: 1.7.93
Area: Montgomeryshire.   **Dial**: 756 kHz

Mansfield 103.2
the Media Suite, Brunts Business Centre, Mansfield, Nottinghamshire NG18 2AH
Fax 01623-660606   Tel 01623-646666
Starting date: 1.2.99
Area: Mansfield
Dial: 103.2 MHz

Manx Radio
PO Box 1368, Broadcasting House, Douglas, Isle of Man IM99 1SW
Fax 01624-682604   Tel 01624-682600
E-mail: postbox@manxradio.com
Website: www.manxradio.com
Starting date: 5.6.64   **Area**: Isle of Man.

Marcher Coast FM
The Studios, 41 Conway Road, Colwyn Bay, Conway
Fax 01492-535248   Tel 01492-533733
E-mail: info@coastfm.co.uk
Website: www.coastfm.co.uk
Area: North Wales

Marcher Gold
The Studios, Mold Road, Wrexham LL11 4AF
Fax 01978-759701   Tel 01978-752202
E-mail: mfm.radio@ukonline.co.uk
Website: www.marchergold.co.uk
Parent company: Marcher Radio Group
Starting date: 5.9.83
Area: Wrexham, Chester, Deeside, north Shropshire
Dial: 1260 AM/MW

Mercia FM/Classic Gold 1359
Hertford Place, Coventry, W Midlands CV1 3TT
Fax 02476-86 8202   Tel 0247-686 8200
E-mail: reception@merciafm.musicradio.com
Parent company: GWR
Starting date: 7.3.94 (Mercia Classic Gold), 23.5.80 (Mercia FM)
Area: Coventry, Warwickshire.
Dial: 1359 kHz Mercia Classic Gold, 97.0 & 102.9 Hz Mercia FM

Mercury FM
1 East Street, Tonbridge, Kent TN9 1AR
Fax 01732-369201   Tel 01732-369200
E-mail: radio@mercuryfm.co.uk
Website: www.mercuryfm.co.uk
Starting date: 8.7.95
Area: Tonbridge, Tunbridge Wells and Sevenoaks
Dial: 96.2 Hz (south), 101.6 MHz (north)

Mercury FM
9 Christopher Place, Shopping Centre, St Albans, Herts AL3 5DQ
Fax 01727-834456   Tel 01727-831966
E-mail: information@mercuryfm.co.uk
Parent company: DMG (south east)
Starting date: 24.10.94
Area: St Albans, Hemel, Watford   **Dial**: 96.6 FM

Metro FM
Newcastle-upon-Tyne NE99 1BB
Fax 0191-488 9222   Tel 0191-420 0971
E-mail: enquiries@metrofm.co.uk
Website: www.metrofm.co.uk
Parent company: Emap Radio
Starting date: 15.7.74
Areas: Tyne & Wear, Northumberland & Durham
Dial: 97.1 MHz (Tyne & Wear)103.2 MHz (Tyne Valleyo, 102.6 Alnwick, Hexham.

MFM
The Studios, Mold Road, Wrexham LL11 4AF
Fax 01978-759701   Tel 01978-752202
E-mail: contact@mfmradio.co.uk
Website: www.mfmradio.co.uk
Starting date: 31.8.89
Area: Wrexham, Chester, Deeside and Wirral
Dial: 97.1 & 103.4 MHz

Millennium Radio
Harrow Manor Way, Thamesmead, London SE2 9XH
Fax 020-8312 1930   Tel 020-8311 3112
E-mail: mfmsales@106.8fm.co.uk
Starting date: 18.3.90
Area: Thamesmead   **Dial**: 106.8 MHz

Minster FM
PO Box 123, Dunnington, York YO19 5ZX
Fax 01904-481088   Tel 01904-488888
E-mail: @minsterfm.co.uk
Starting date: 4.7.92
Area: York.
Dial: 104.7 & 102.3 MHz

Mix 96
Friars Square Studios, 11 Bourbon Street, Aylesbury, Bucks HP20 2PZ
Fax 01296-398988   Tel 01296-399396
E-mail: mix@mix96.demon.co.uk
Website: www.mix96.demon.co.uk
Starting date: 15.4.94
Area: Aylesbury Vale, Thame, Tring, Leighton Buzzard
Dial: 96.2 MHz

Moray Firth
Scorguie Place, Inverness IV3 8UJ
Fax 01463-243224   Tel 01463-224433
E-mail: mfr@mfr.co.uk
Starting date: 23.2.82
Area: Inverness
Dial: 97.4 & 96.6 MHz, 1107 kHz

NECR
Town House, Kintore, Inverurie, Aberdeenshire AB51 0US
Fax 01467 632969   Tel 01467 6329090
E-mail: airefm@airefm.co.uk
Starting date: 6.6.94
Area: Inverurie   **Dial**: 102.6 MHz

Neptune Radio 96.4 & 106.8FM
PO Box 1068, Dover CT16 1GB
Fax 01304-212717   Tel 01304-202505
E-mail: mail@neptuneradio.co.uk
Website: www.neptuneradio.co.uk
Starting date: 29.9.97
Area: Dover & Folkestone
Dial: 106.8 MHz Dover, 96.4 MHz Folkestone

Nevis Radio
Inverlochy, Fort William PH33 6LU
Fax 01397 701007   Tel 01397-700007
E-mail: studio@nevisradio.co.uk
Website: www.nevisradio.co.uk
Starting date: 1.8.94
Area: Fort William
Dial: 96.6 & 102.3 MHz

News Direct 97.3FM
200 Grays Inn Road, London WC1X 8XZ
Fax 020-7312 8503   Tel 020-7973 1152
Website: www.newsdirect.co.uk
Providing a 24-hour rolling news and information
service for London with news, traffic, weather, sport,
entertainment, city and headlines every 20 minutes..
Parent company: London News Radio
Starting date: December 1996
Area: Greater London
Dial: 97.3FM

Northants 96
19-21 St Edmunds Road, Northampton NN1 5DY
Fax 01604-795601   Tel 01604-795600
E-mail: reception@northants96.musicradio.com
Parent company: GWR Group
Starting date: 1.10.86
Area: Northampton
Dial: 96.6 MHz, 1557 AM

NorthSound One/Two
45 Kings Gate, Aberdeen, Grampian AB15 4EL
Fax 01224-400003   Tel 01224-337000
E-mail: northsound@srh.co.uk
Parent company: Scottish Radio Holdings
Starting date: 27.7.81
Area: Aberdeen. Dial: 96.9, 97.6, 103 MHz (One),1035
kHz (Two)

The NRG
The Quadrant Centre Studio, Bournemouth BH1 2AD
Fax 01202 318110   Tel 01202 318100
E-mail: name@todaysmusic.co.uk
Website: www.todaysmusic.co.uk
Starting date: 26.6.99
Area: Bournemouth and Poole
Dial: 107.6 MHz

107 Oak FM
7 Waldron Court, Prince William Road,
Loughborough, Leics LE11 5GD
Fax 01509 246107   Tel 011509 211711
E-mail: info @oakfm.co.uk
Website: www.oakfm.com
Starting date: 14.2.99
Area: Loughborough
Dial: 107 MHz

Oban FM
132 George Street, Oban PA34 5NT
Fax 01631-570530   Tel 01631-570057
E-mail: us@oban-fm.freeserve.co.uk
Parent company: Oban FM Community Radio
Starting date: 1.7.96
Area: Oban, Lorn and the Isles

Ocean FM
Radio House, Whittle Avenue, Segensworth West,
Fareham PO15 5SH
Fax 01489-589453   Tel 01489-589911
E-mail: info@oceanradio.co.uk
Website: www.powerfm.com
Parent company: Capital Radio
Starting date: 12.10.86
Area: Portsmouth, Soton and Winchester
Dial: 96.7, 97.5 MHz

Orchard FM
Haygrove House, Taunton, Somerset TA3 7BT
Fax 01823-321044   Tel 01823-338448
E-mail: orchard@orchardfm.co.uk
Website: www.orchardfm.co.uk
Starting date: 26.11.89
Area: Somerset
Dial: 96.5, 97.1, 102.6 MHz

Oxygen 107.9
Suite 41, Westgate Centre, Oxford OX1 1PD
Fax 01865-726161   Tel 01865-724442
Parent company: Fusion Radio Group
Starting date: 14.2.97
Area: Oxford
Dial: 107.9 MHz

Paisley
26 Lady Lane, Paisley, Renfrewshire PA1 2LG
Fax 0141-887 0963   Tel 0141-887 9630
Start date: 1.9.92
Area: Paisley

Peak 107 FM
Radio House, Foxwood Road, Chesterfield, S41 9RF
Fax 01246-269933   Tel 01246-269107
E-mail: info@peak107.co.uk
Web: www.peak107.co.uk
Start date: 7.10.98
Area: Chesterfield, north Derbyshire

Piccadilly Key 103
Castle Quay, Castlefield, Manchester M15 4PR
Fax 0161-288 5001   Tel 0161-288 5000
Website: www.clickmanchester.com
Parent company: Emap Perrformance
Starting date: 3.9.88
Area: Manchester
Dial: 103MHz

Pirate FM 102
Wilson Way, Redruth, Cornwall TR15 3XX
Fax 01209 314345   Tel 01209-314400
E-mail: piratefm102.co.uk
Website: www.piratefm102.co.uk
Parent company: UKRD Group
Starting date: 3.4.92
Area: Cornwall, W Devon, Isles of Scilly
Dial: 102.2 MHz (east Cornwall, west Devon), 102.8
(west Cornwall, Isle of Scilly)

Plymouth Sound AM/FM
Earls Acre, Plymouth, Devon PL3 4HX
Fax 01752-670730   Tel 01752-227272
E-mail: plymouthsound@virgin.net
Starting date: 19.5.75
Area: Plymouth
Dial: 1152 kHz (AM), 97.0, 96.6 MHz (FM)

Power FM
Radio House, Whittle Avenue, Segensworth,
Fareham, Hampshire PO15 5SH
Fax 01489-589453   Tel 01489-589911
E-mail: info@oceanradio.co.uk
Parent company: Capital Radio
Starting date: 4.12.88
Area: Portsmouth, Southampton and Winchester
Dial: 103.2 MHz

Premier Christian Radio
Glen House, Stag Place, London SW1E 5AG
Fax 020-7233 6706   Tel 020-7316 1300
Parent company: London Christian Radio
Starting date: 10.6.95

The Pulse (FM) Classic Gold (AM)
Forster Square, Bradford, W Yorkshire BD1 5NE
Fax 01274-203130   Tel 01274-203040
E-mail: general@pulse.co.uk
Parent company: The Wireless Group
Starting date: 31.8.91
Area: Bradford, Halifax, Huddersfield
Dial: 97.5 FM Bradford, 102.5 FM Huddersfield &
Halifax, 1278 AM Bradford, 1530 AM Huddersfield &
Halifax

96.3 QFM
26 Lady Lane, Paisley, Strathclyde PA1 2LG
Fax 0141-887 0963   Tel 0141-887 9630
E-mail: colin.kelly@9-fm.com
Starting date: 1.9.92
Area: Paisley. Dial: 96.3 MHz

Q97.2 FM
24 Cloyfin Road, Coleraine, Londonderry BT52 2NU
Fax 028-7032 6666   Tel 028-7035 9100
E-mail: sales@q97-fm.com
Website: www.q97-fm.com
Starting date: 26.1.00
Area: Coleraine, Causeway coast
Dial: 97.2 MHz

Q102.9 FM
Old Waterside Railway Station, Duke Street,
Waterside, Londonderry BT47 6DH
Fax 028-7131 1177   Tel 028-7131 1000
E-mail: q102@iol.ie.
Website: www.q102-fm.com
Starting date: 21.10.93
Area: Londonderry, north west
Dial: 102.9 MHz

Q103 FM
PO Box 103, Vision Park, Chivers Way, Histon,
Cambridge CB4 9WW
Fax 01223-235161   Tel 01223-235255
E-mail: reception@Q103.musicradio.com
Parent company: GWR Group
Area: Cambridge, Newmarket

Quay West Radio
Harbour Studios, The Esplanade, Watchet, Somerset
TA23 0AJ
Fax 01984-634811   Tel 01984-634900
Area: west Somerset and Exmoor
Dial: 102.4 FM

Radio Borders
Tweedside Park, Galashiels, Borders TD1 3TD
Fax 01896-759494   Tel 01896-759444
E-mail: dannygallagher@srh.co.uk
Website: www.radioborders.co.uk
Parent company: Scottish Radio Holdings
Starting date: 22.1.90
Area: Scottish Borders, north Numberland
Dial: 96.8, 97.5, 103.1 & 103.4 MHz

Ram FM
35-36 Irongate, Derby DE1 3GA
Fax 01332-851199   Tel 01332-205599
Starting date: 3.3.78
Area: Derby
Dial: 102.8 MHz

Radio XL 1296 AM
KMS House, Bradford St, Birmingham B12 0JD
Fax 0121-753 3111   Tel 0121-753 5353
For the Asian community in the West Midlands
Starting date: 30.5.95
Area: Birmingham
Dial: 1296 kHz

Real Radio
PO Box 6105, Ty-Nant Court, Cardiff CF15 8YF
Tel 02920-231863
E-mail: info@realradiofm.co.uk
Website: www.realradiofm.co.uk
Parent company: GMG Radio
Starting date: Autumn 2000
Area: South Wales

Red Dragon FM
Radio House, West Canal Wharf, Cardiff CK10 5XL
Fax 029-2038 4014   Tel 029-2038 4041
E-mail: mail@reddragonfm.co.uk
Website: www.reddragonfm.co.uk
Parent company: Capital Radio
Starting date: 11.4.80 (Cardiff), 13.6.83 (Newport)
Area: south east Wales
Dial: 103.2 MHz (Cardiff), 97.4 (MHz (Newport)

Revolution
PO Box 962, Oldham, Lancs OL1 1FE
Fax 0161-665 0555   Tel 0161-628 8787
Starting date: 9.99
Area: Oldham, Rochdale, east Greater Manchester

Ridings FM
2 Thornes Office Park, Monkton Road, Wakefield WF2
7AN
Fax 01924 367133   Tel 01924 367177
Starting date: 3.10.99
Area: Wakefield
Dial: 106.8 MHz

RITZ 1035
33-35 Wembley Hill Road, Wembley, Middlx HA9 8RT
Fax 020-8733 1393   Tel 020-8733 1300
E-mail: studio@ritz1035.com
Website: www.ritz1035.com
Starting date: 1.9.94
Area: Greater London
Dial: 1035 kHz

RNA FM
Arbroath Informary, Rosemount Road, Arbroath,
Angus DD11 2AT
Fax 01241-439664   Tel 01241-879660
E-mail: rna@dkserv.demon.co.uk
Start date: 25.11.98
Area: Arbroath, Carnoustie

Rock FM
St Pauls Square, Preston, Lancashire PR1 1XS
Fax 01772-201917   Tel 01772-556301
Website: www.rockfm.co.uk
Parent company: Emap
Starting date: 1.6.90
Area: Blackpool, Preston
Dial: 97.4 MHz

Rutland Radio
40 Melton Road, Oakham, Rutland, LE15 6AY
Fax 01572-757744   Tel 01572-757868
E-mail: enquiries@rutlandradio.co.uk
Start date: 13.12. 1998
Area: Rutland and Stamford
Dial: 107.2 & 97.4 FM

Sabras Sound
63 Melton Road, Leicester LE4 6PN
Fax 0116-266 7776   Tel 0116-261 0666
24 hour music, news and info service to Asian
communities.
Starting date: 7.9.95
Area: Leicester, Nottingham, Derby and the east
Midlands
Dial: 1260 kHz

Scot FM
Number 1 Shed, Albert Quay, Leith EH6 7DN
Fax 0131-625 8401   Tel 0131-625 8400
E-mail: jaclark@scot-fm.com
Starting date: 16.9.94
Policy: Speech and adult contemporary music
Area: Central Scotland
Dial: 100.3 & 101.1 MHz

Severn Sound FM
Bridge Studios, Eastgate Centre, Gloucester GL1 1SS
Fax 01452-313213   Tel 01452-313200
E-mail: reception@severnfm.musicradio.com
Parent company: GWR Group
Starting date: 23.10.80
Area: Gloucester and Cheltenham
Dial: 102.4 & 103 MHz (Severn Sound),
774 kHz (Classic Gold)

SGR FM
Radio House, Alpha Business Park, Whitehouse
Road, Ipswich, Suffolk IP1 5LT
Fax 01473-741200   Tel 01473-461000
Website: www.sgrfm.co.uk
Parent company: GWR
Starting date: 6.11.82
Area: Bury St Edmunds
Dial: 96.4 MHz,

SGR Colchester
9 Whitewell Road, Colchester CO2 7DE
Fax 01206-561199   Tel 01206-575859
E-mail: prog.col@sgrfm.co.uk
Website: www.sgrfm.co.uk
Parent company: GWR Group
Starting date: 17.10.83
Area: Colchester **Dial:** 96.1 MHz

SIBC
Market Street, Lerwick, Shetland ZE1 0JN
Fax 01595-695696   Tel 01595-695299
E-mail: info@sibc.co.uk
Website: www.sibc.co.uk
Parent company: Shetland Islands Broadcasting Co
Starting date: 26.11.87
Area: Shetland Islands
Dial: 96.2 MHz

Signal 1
Stoke Road, Stoke on Trent ST4 2SR
Fax 01782-744110   Tel 01782-747047
Parent company: The Wireless Group
Starting date: 5.9.83
Area: Stoke on Trent
Dial: 96.9 MHz

Silk FM
Radio House, Bridge Street, Macclesfield, Cheshire,
SK11 6DJ
Fax 01625-269010   Tel 01625-268000
E-mail: mail@silkfm.com
Web: www.silkfm.com
Start date: 25.5.98
Area: Macclesfield   **Dial:** 106.9 FM

107 SouthCity FM
City Studios, Marsh Lane, Southampton SO14 3ST
Fax 02380 220060   Tel 02380 220020
E-mail: info@southcityfm.co.uk
Website: www.southcityfm.co.uk
Starting date: 5.9.99
Area: Southampton   **Dial:** 106.9 MHz

South Hams Radio
South Hams Business Park, Churchstow TQ7 3QR
Fax 01548 857345   Tel 01548 854595
Starting date: 1.12.99
Area: South Hams

South West Sound
Campbell House, Bankend Road, Dumfries DG1 4TH
Fax 01387-265629   Tel 01387-250999
E-mail: all@westsoundfm.netscapeonline.co.uk
Parent company: West Sound Radio
Starting date: 21.5.91
Area: Dumfries and Galloway
Dial: 97 FM, 96.5 FM, 103 FM

Southern FM
Radio Ho, Franklin Road, Portslade BN41 2SS
Fax 01273-430098   Tel 01273-430111
E-mail: info@southernradio.co.uk
Website: www.southernfm.com
Parent company: Capital Radio
Starting date: 29.8.83 (Brighton), 12.2.88 (Eastbourne)
Area: Brighton, Newhaven, Eastbourne and Hastings
Dial: 103.5 MHz (Brighton), 96.9 MHz (Newhaven),
102.4 MHz (Eastbourne), 102.0 MHz (Hastings)

Sovereign Radio
14 St Mary's Walk, Hailsham, East Sussex BN27 1AF
Fax 01323 440643   Tel 01323 442700
E-mail: info@1075sovereignradio.co.uk
Parent company: Radio Services
Starting date: 17.11.97
Area: Eastbourne
Dial: 107.5 MHz

Spectrum Radio
204-206 Queens Town Road, London SW8 3NR
Fax 020-7627 3409   Tel 020-7627 4433
E-mail: Spectrum@spectrum558am.co.uk
Website: www.spectrum558am.co.uk
Music, news and information for ethnic communities
Starting date: 25.6.90
Area: London   **Dial**: 558 kHz

Spire FM
City Hall Studios, Malthouse Lane, Salisbury, Wiltshire
SP2 7QQ
Fax 01722-416688   Tel 01722-416644
E-mail: admin@spirefm.co.uk
Website: www.spirefm.co.uk
Parent company: Local Radio Company
Starting date: 20.9.92
Area: Salisbury
Dial: 102.0 MHz

Spirit FM
Dukes Court, Bognor Road, Chichester, West Sussex
PO19 2FX
Fax 01243-786464   Tel 01243-773600
E-mail: info@spiritfm.net
Website: www.spiritfm.net
Starting date: 21.4.96
Area: Chichester & Bognor Regis
Dial: 96.6 MHz & 102.3 MHz

Star FM
Observatory Shopping Centre, Slough, Berks SL1
1LH
Fax 01753-512277   Tel 01753-551066
E-mail: onair@1066starfm.co.uk
Website: www.ukrd.com
Starting date: 21.5.93
Area: Windsor, Slough, Maidenhead
Dial: 106.6 MHz

97.2 Stray FM
PO Box 972, Station Parade, Harrogate HG1 5YF
Fax 01423-522922   Tel 01423-522972
E-mail: mail@972strayfm.co.uk
Parent company: Radio Investments + GWR Group
Starting date: 4.7.94
Area: Harrogate
Dial: 97.2 FM

Sun FM
PO Box 1034, Sunderland SR5 2YL
Fax 0191-548 7171   Tel 0191-548 1034
E-mail: mail@sun-fm.com
Website: www.sun-fm.com
Music, local news, sport and information.
Parent company: Capital Radio
Area: Sunderland, Washington, South tyneside and Co
Durham.
Dial: 103.4MHz

Sunrise Radio
Sunrise House, Merrick Road, Southall, Middlesex
UB2 4AU
Fax 020-8813 9800   Tel 020-8574 6666
Music, news and information for the Asian community
Parent company: Sunrise Radio
Starting date: 5.11.89
Area: Greater London and SE England
Dial: 1458 AM

Sunrise FM
30 Chapel Street, Little Germany, Bradford BD1 5DN
Fax 01274-728534   Tel 01274-735043
E-mail: sunrisefm@hotmail.com
Website: sunrisefm.com
Music, news and information for the Asian community
Starting date: 9.12.89
Area: Bradford
Dial: 103.2 MHz

Sunshine 855
Sunshine House, Waterside, Ludlow, Shropshire SY8
1PE
Fax 01584-875900   Tel 01584-873795
Starting date: 18.10.92
Area: Ludlow, south Shropshire
Dial: 855 kHz

Surf 107.7
PO Box 107, Brighton, BN1 1QG
Fax 01273-273107   Tel 01273-386107
E-mail: info@surf107.co.uk
Web: www.surf107.co.uk
Start date: 27.3.98
Area: Brighton
Dial: 107.2 FM

Swansea Sound (1170) Sound Wave 964
Victoria Road, Gowerton, Swansea, West Glamorgan
SA4 3AB
Fax 01792-511171   Tel 01792-511170
E-mail: sales@swanseasound.co.uk
Website: www.swanseasound.co.uk
Some Welsh language broadcasting
Parent company: The Radio Partnership
Starting date: 30.9.74
Area: Swansea   **Dial**: 96.4 MHz, 1170 kHz

Tay FM/Radio Tay AM
6 North Isla Street, Dundee, Tayside DD3 7JQ
Fax 01382-423252   Tel 01382-200800
E-mail: tayfm@srh.co.uk and tayam@srh.co.uk
Parent company: Scottish Radio Holdings
Starting date: 17.10.80 Radio Tay AM, 9.1.95 Tay FM
Area: Dundee, Perth
Dial: 102.8 MHz (Dundee), 96.4 MHz (Perth) Tay FM/
1161 kHz (Dundee), 1584 kHz (Perth), Radio Tay AM

107.4 Telford FM
PO Box 1074, Telford TF3 3WG
Fax 01952 280010   Tel 01952 280011
Starting date: 3.5.99
Area: Telford   Dial: 107.4 MHz

Ten 17
Latton Bush Centre, Harlow, Essex CM18 7BL
Fax 01279-445289   Tel 01279-431017
E-mail: studios@mercuryfm.co.uk
Website: www.mercuryfm.co.uk
Parent company: DMG Radio
Starting date: 1.5.93
Area: Harlow.   Dial: 101.7 MHz

TFM
Yale Crescent, Stockton-on-Tees, TS17 6AA
Fax 01642-868288   Tel 01642-888222
E-mail: radio@tfm.ace.co.uk
Website: www.yourteesvalley.com
Parent company: Emap Radio
Starting date: 24.6.75
Area: Teesside.
Dial: 96.6 MHz

107.8 FM Thames Radio
Brentham House, 45 c High Street, Kingston, Surrey KT1 4DG
Fax 020 8288 1312   Tel 020 8288 1300
E-mail: mail@thamesradio.co.uk
Website: www.thamesradio.co.uk
Starting date: 1.3.97
Area: SW London, N Surrey
Dial: 107.8 FM

TLR
Imperial House, 2-14 High Street, Margate, Kent CT9 1DH
Fax 01843 299666   Tel 01843 220222
E-mail: reception@tlrfm.co.uk
Website: www.tlrfm.co.uk
Starting date: 17.1.98
Area: Thanet
Dial: 107.2MHz

Tower FM
The Mill, Brownlow Way, Bolton BL1 2RA
Fax 01204 534065   Tel 01204 387000
E-mail: info@towerfm.co.uk
Website: www.towerfm.co.uk
Starting date: 20.3.99
Area: Bolton, Bury   Dial: 107.4 MHz

Trax FM
PO Box 444, Worksop, Notts, S80 1GP
Fax 01909-500445   Tel 01909-500611
E-mail: enquiries@traxfm.co.uk
Parent company: Lincs FM
Start date: 22.11.98
Area: Bassetlaw, Doncaster   Dial: 107.9 FM

Trax FM
PO Box 444, Doncaster DN3 3GB
Fax 01302-326104   Tel 01302-341166
E-mail: enquiries@traxfm.co.uk
Parent company: Lincs FM
Start date: 5.9.99
Area: Doncaster   Dial: 107.1 MHz

96 Trent FM
29 Castle Gate, Nottingham NG1 7AP
Fax 0115-912 9302   Tel 0115-952 7000
E-mail: admin@trentfm.musicradio.com
Parent company: GWR Group
Starting date: 3.7.75
Area: Nottingham, Mansfield
Dial: 96.2 MHz

97.4 Vale FM
Longmead, Shaftesbury, Dorset SP7 8QQ
Fax 01747 855722   Tel 01747 855711
E-mail: studio@valefm.co.uk
Website: www.valefm.co.uk
Parent company: Vale FM
Starting date: 25.6.95
Area: N Dorset, S Somerset, W Wiltshire
Dial: 97.4 MHz

Valleys Radio
Festival Park, Victoria, Ebbw Vale NP23 8XW
Fax 01495-300710   Tel 01495-301116
Parent company: Wireless Group
Starting date: 23.11.96
Area: Heads of south Wales valleys.
Dial: 999 & 1116MW

Vibe FM
Reflection House, The Anderson Centre, Olding Road, Bury St Edmunds IP33 3TA
Fax 01284-718839   Tel 01284-718800
E-mail: studios@vibefm.co.uk
Website: www.vibefm.co.uk
Parent company: DMG Radio
Starting date: 22.11.97
Area: East of England
Dial: 106.4 MHz(Suffolk), 105.6 MHz(Cambridge), 106.1 MHz(Norwich), 107.7 MHz(Peterborough)

Radio Victory
Media House, Tipner Wharf, Twyford Avenue, Portsmouth PO2 8PE
Fax 023-9263 9933   Tel 023-9263 9922
E-mail: info@radiovictory.co.uk
Starting date: soon
Area: Portsmouth
Dial: 107.4 MHz

Viking FM
Commercial Road, Hull, HU1 2SG
Fax 08456-382967   Tel 01482-325141
E-mail: stuart.baldwin@vikingfm.co.uk
Website: www.vikingfm.co.uk
Parent company: Emap Radio
Starting date: 17.4.84
Area: Yorkshire-Lincolnshire
Dial: 96.9 MHz

Virgin Radio London
1 Golden Square, London W1R 4DJ
Fax 020-7434 1197   Tel 020-7434 1215
E-mail: reception@ginger.com
Website: www.virginradio.co.uk
Parent company: SMG Plc
Starting date: 30.4.93
Area: National radio
Dial: 1215 AM nationwide, 105.8 FM London/south east

Wave 102
8 South Tay Street, Dundee DD1 1PA
Fax 01382 900999   Tel 01382 901000
Parent company: The Wireless Group
Starting date: 30.8.99
Area: Dundee   Dial: 102 MHz

Wave 105.2
PO Box 105, Fareham, Hampshire PO15 5TF
Fax 01489-481100   Tel 01489-481050
E-mail: studio@wave105.com
Website: www.wave105.com
Starting date: 14.6.98
Area: Solent region
Dial: 105.2 FM

The Wave
965 Mowbray Drive, Blackpool, Lancs FY3 7JR
Fax 01253-301965   Tel 01253-304965
E-mail: sales@thewavefm.co.uk
Website: www.thewave.co.uk
Starting date: 25.5.92
Area: Blackpool and the Fylde coast
Dial: 96.5 MHz

96.4 FM The Wave
PO Box 964, Victoria Road, Gowerton SA4 3AB
Fax 01792 511965   Tel 01792 511964
E-mail: info@athewave.co.uk
Website: www.thewave.co.uk
Starting date: 30.9.96
Area: Swansea
Dial: 96.4 MHz

Wessex FM
Radio House, Trinity Street, Dorchester, Dorset DT1
1DJ
Fax 01305-250052   Tel 01305-250333
E-mail: admin@wessexfm.co.uk
Website: www.wessexfm.co.uk
Starting date: 4.9.93
Area: Dorset
Dial: 97.2 MHz & 96.0 MHz

West FM
54a Holmston Road, Ayr KA7 3BE
Fax 01292-283665   Tel 01292-283662
E-mail: westfm@srh.co.uk
Website: www.west-fm.co.uk
Starting date: 1.1.97
Area: Ayrshire, Arran, the Cumbraes
Dial: 96.7 FM

West Sound
54a Holmston Road, Ayr KA7 3BE
Fax 01292-283662   Tel 01292-283662
E-mail: westsound@srh.co.uk
Web: www.west-sound.co.uk
Starting date: 16.10.81
Area: Ayrshire, Arran, the Cumbraes
Dial: 1035 AM

Win 107.2
PO Box 1072, The Brooks, Winchester, Hants SO23
8FT
Fax 01962 841079   Tel 01962 841071
E-mail: info@win1072.com
Website: www.win1072.com
Starting date: 9.99
Area: Winchester, central Hampshire
Dial: 107.2 MHz

107.2 Wire FM
Warrington Business Park, Long Lane, Warrington,
WA2 8TX
Fax 01925 657705   Tel 01925-445545
E-mail: mail@wirefm.com
Web: www.wirefm.com
Start date: Sept 1998
Area: Warrington

Wish 102.4
Orrell Lodge, Orrell Road, Orrell, Wigan WN5 8HJ
Fax 01942-777694   Tel 01942-761024
E-mail: general@wishfm.net
Parent company: Wireless Group
Starting date: 1.4.97
Area: Wigan, St Helens, Skelmersdale
Dial: 102.4 MHz

107.7 The Wolf
10th Floor, Mander House, Wolverhampton WV1 3NB
Fax 01902-571079   Tel 01902-571070
E-mail: studio@thewolf.co.uk
Website: www.thewolf.co.uk
Starting date: 7.10.97
Area: Wolverhampton   Dial: 107.7 MHz

Wyvern FM
5 Barbourne Terrace, Worcester WR1 3JZ
Fax 01905-746637   Tel 01905-612212
Area: Hereford, Worcester, Kidderminster
Dial: 97.6 Mhz (Hereford), 102.8 MHz (Worcester),
96.7 Mhz (Kidderminster)

X-Cel FM
46 Camel Road, Littleport, Cambridgeshire CB6 1EW
Fax 01353 865105   Tel 01353 865102
E-mail: (name)@xcelfm.co.uk
Website: www.xcelfm.co.uk
Starting date: 3.10.99
Area: Fenland
Dial: 107.1, 107.5 MHz

Xfm
PO Box 1049, London WC2H 7XX
Fax 020-7766 6601   Tel 020-7766 6600
Starting date: 9.97
Area: Greater London   Dial: 104.9 MHz

Yorkshire Coast Radio
PO Box 962, Scarborough, N Yorks YO12 5YX
Fax 01723-501050   Tel 01723-500962
E-mail: name@yorkshirecoastradio.co.uk
Starting date: 7.11.93
Area: Scarborough
Dial: 96.2 MHz

Digital, cable and satellite radio

Both the BBC and the Radio Authority have been talking up digital radio since the mid nineties. Despite a mass of digital channels, consumer take-up has been small, with few digital sets sold and no peep from broadcasters about repeating digital TV's trick of stimulating the market by giving away receivers.

The BBC has spent some £20 million (too much according to BBC chairman Christopher Bland in June 2000) on digital radio broadcasts since September 1995 and the Radio Authority is giving out digital radio frequencies at a rate of one a month. Sixteen had been handed out by summer 2000 with the big regional territories due to be allocated from autumn 2000, by which time the communications white paper will start redefining the radio market according to digital imperatives.

The talk is all about the future possibilities offered by increased bandwidth and Talk Sport's major shareholder, Kelvin McKenzie, has grown rich on such talk. His Wireless Group was part of the Switchmedia Group which won London's second digital multiplex licence then floated itself successfully on the stock exchange. "The market is beginning to value bandwidth after having discounted it before," McKenzie says. "It's all part of the convergence taking place around all media companies. Everything will be digital from photography to television to radio. I've heard all the arguments against digital radio but then I heard all the arguments against digital TV and that is rocking." He admits he's in a long game though. "We are at the beginning of things changing now [but] I'll be astonished if there is a sizeable audience for digital radio for about five to seven years. At the moment it is more a business than a consumer dynamic."

And the business dynamic sees Carphone Warehouse as a 5 per cent shareholder in Switchmedia. Welcome to the world of teldio or raynet or whatever the new boxes get called when they are boosted by new uses backed by a government committed to switch off radio's existing analogue frequencies to free them for mobile telephones and the like.

Radio and the web

Radio is the old medium least likely to be affected by the web's battle for the consumer eyeballs that currently read print and watch TV. Listening is something to be done alongside web surfing, and radio channels are accessed simply over the net as well. "Radio is a natural bedfellow of the dot.com user," says Talk Sport's Jason Bryant and Rajar reports that 11 per cent of 15 to 24 year old men have visited a radio web site and that a quarter tune into radio via the web. The Rajar survey also found that radio listeners are more likely to be netheads.

The point about digital radio is that it is far more than just superior audio and that it is likely to spur further changes into internet radio. The possibilities are summarised by Simon Cole of the independent radio producer Unique Broadcasting. "Radio has an opportunity to be part of the converging multi-content future," Cole says in finest tech-speak. "Those manufacturers making big grey boxes to plug into hi-fis at £400 so you get slightly better reception for Classic FM are wasting their time. No one is going to pay so much for that. But if you can plug a receiver for your PC to a device you can carry around in your pocket, that's different."

Virgin Radio has led the way in making the first links between radio and the web and has many listeners regularly visiting a site begun in 1996. The BBC entered the fray late but has now appointed a web manager for each of its five national stations. At the end of 1999, Capital Radio announced a £5.5 million plan to create Britain's top music web site. "It will be intelligent," the chief exec David Mansfield promised. "The site will be capable of understanding what types of music each user likes and invite them to listen to new music they are most likely to enjoy." Radio 1 was the first BBC station to make a significant web investment and it paid off with a six-fold increase in access.

DIGITAL RADIO CONTACTS

Capital Radio Digital
30 Leicester Square, London WC2H 7LA
Fax 020-7766 6100   Tel 020 7766 6000
Air date: October 2000
Eight services broadcasting 24 hours a day due on air
31.10.00 in Cardiff and Newport: Red Dragon; Capital
Gold; The Storm; Dance Radio; Adult Contemporary;
Xfm; BBC Radio Wales; BBC Radio Cymru.

CE Digital
30 Leicester Square, London WC2H 7LA
Fax 020-7766 6100   Tel 020 7766 6000
Air date: summer 2000
Seven services for Birmingham: BRMB; Capital Gold;
Xfm; Magic; Radio XL; Kiss 100; BBC Radio WM. Nine
programmes for Greater London: Capital FM; Capital
Gold; Kiss !00; Magic; News Direct; Xfm; Sunrise
Radio; LBC; Capital Radio. Six programmes for
Manchester: Kiss 100; Big AM; The Lounge; Xfm;
Asian Sound Radio; BBC GMR.

Digital One
Classic FM, 7 Swallow Place, London W1R 7AA
                    Tel 020 7518 2620
E-mail: info@digitalone.co.uk
Website: www.ukdigitalradio.com
Air date: 15.11.99
Ten programme services, mostly 24 hours a day:
Classic FM; Virgin Radio; talkSPORT; Planet Rock;
Core; Life; Oneword; Primetime Radio; new services to
come: finance and business news and Rolling News.

Emap Digital
Mappin House, 4 Winsley Street, London W1N 7AR
Fax 020-7312 8227   Tel 020-7436 1515
Air date: May 2001: Eight programmes for Leeds: Aire
FM; Classic Gold; Kiss; Magic 828; Ridings FM; Xfm;
Adult contemporary; BBC Radio Leeds.
Air date: February 2001: Eight programmes for
Liverpool: Radio City; Magic; Kiss; MFM; Marcher
Gold; Xfm; BBC Radio Merseyside.
Air date: October 2000: Eight programmes for South

Yorkshire: Hallam FM; Magic; Kiss; Trax FM; Classic
Gold; Xfm; Adult contemporary; BBC Radio Sheffield.
Air date: June 2001: Eight programmes for Teesside:
Classic Gold; Adult contemporary; Hot AC; Kiss; Magic;
96.6 TFM; Xfm; BBC Radio Cleveland.
Air date: November 2000: Eight programmes for Tyne
& Wear: Metro FM; Magic; Kiss; Adult contemporary;
Cool Continuous Country; Classic Gold; Xfm; BBC
Radio Newcastle.

Now Digital
GWR digital, PO Box 2269, London W!A 5UQ
Fax 020-7911 7302   Tel: 020 7911 7300
E-mail: reception@digital.musicradio.com
Website: www.gwrgroup.musicradio.com
Air date: January 2001: Nine programmes for Bristol
and Bath: GWR FM; Classic Gold; The Storm; Urban
service; Xfm; The Rhythm; Melodic easy listening; @
Bristol; BBC Radio Bristol: Nine programmes for
Wolverhampton, Shrewsbury and Telford: Beacon FM;
Classic Gold; The Storm; Xfm; Sunrise; WCR; BBC
Radio WM; BBC Radio Shropshire.

Score Digital
Clydebank Business Park, Glasgow G81 2RX
Fax 0141-565 2318   Tel: 0141-565 2347
E-mail: scoredigital@srh.co.uk
Websiite: www.scoredigital.co.uk
Air date: October 2000: Eight programmes for
Edinburgh: Forth FM; Forth AM; AHR; 3C; Sunrise
Radio; Xfm; The Storm; Saga Radio; BBC Radio
Scotland.
Air date: May 2000:Eight programmes for Glasgow:
Clyde 1; Clyde 2; 3C; Sunrise Radio; 96.3 Qfm; Xfm;
Kiss 100; BBC Radio Scotland.

Switchdigital
18 Hatfields, London SE1 8DJ
Fax 020-7959 7819   Tel: 020-7959 7869
E-mail: info@switchdigital.com
Websiite: www.switchdigital.com
Air date: summer 2000: Nine programmes for Greater
London: classic soul; adult contemporary; speech and
music; classic rock and sport; easy listening; jazz; chart
hits/club dance; traffic and travel; BBC London Live.

The technology of digital radio

A conventional FM/AM transmitter sends radio waves into the air, modifying them in a way which directly mimics the original sounds sent by the radio studio. Radios interpret this modulation and reproduce the original electronic mimicry of a microphone or other sound source to drive a speaker. Instead of using electronic circuits to mimic sounds directly, digital radio translates sounds into a rapid sequence of binary digits. These are converted back to analogue prior to hitting the radio speakers. The older methods of transmission are prone to distortion and interference, whereas digital radio listeners will either get a clear signal or nothing at all. The advantage to listeners, once they have invested in decoders, is reception quality to match a CD. Digital broadcasting principles are like digital TV, where multiplexing combines the signals of several broadcasters into a single stream on a single-frequency channel. There is no longer a direct one-to-one relationship between a programme service and a frequency.

CABLE RADIO

BCB (Bradford Community Broadcasting)
2 Forster Square, Bradford, West Yorkshire BD1 1DQ
Fax 01274-771680   Tel 01274-771677
E-mail: info@bcb.yorks.com
Website: www.bcb.yorks.com
Community radio for Bradford. Special event RSL broadcaster. Broadcasts full time from website. Radio production skills training.
Area: Bradford
Dial: 104 FM on the Yorkshire Cable Network 106.6 FM or 1566 AM during RSL broadcasts.

Cable 103.9
PO Box 103 Portslade, East Sussex
Fax 01273-411835   Tel 01273-418181
Local radio for Worthing and Brighton.
Parent company: Cable Radio
Starting date: 31.3.00
Dial: 103.9 MHz

Cable Radio Milton Keynes
14 Vincent Avenue, Crownhill, Milton Keynes MK8 0AB
Fax 01908-564893   Tel 01908-265266
E-mail: crmkfm@mail.com
Community radio for Milton Keynes on 89.8 FM
Starting date: 3.79
Area: Milton Keynes

Classic Gold
Hawthorn House, Exeter Business Park, Exeter EX1 3QS
Fax 01392-444433   Tel 01392-444444
Starting date: 1.1.95
Dial: 99.6 MHz on Eurobell South West

CN
72-74 Brewer Street, London W1R 3PH
Fax 020-7287 3777   Tel 020-7494 9400
Website: www.coppernob.com
Parent company: Coppernob
Starting date: July 2000

Forth FM
Forth House, Forth Street, Edinburgh EH1 3LF
Fax 0131-558 3277   Tel 0131-556 9255
Website: www.forthonline.co.uk
Pop
Starting date: 22.1.75
Dial: 97.3 FM, 1548 AM

Gemini FM
Hawthorn House, Exeter Business Park, Exeter, EX1 3QS
Fax 01392-444433   Tel 01392 444444
Start date: 1.1.95
Area: Eurobell South West Network
Dial: 99.6 FM on Eurobell South West Network

Music Choice Europe
16 Harcourt Street, London W1H 2AU
Fax 020-7724 0404   Tel 020-7724 9494
E-mail: sales@musicchoice.co.uk
Website: www.musicchoice.co.uk

Radio City
Singleton Hospital, Sketty Lane, Swansea SA2 8QA
Tel 01792-205666 x 5264
Website: www.radiocityswansea.com
E-mail: radiocity@zoom.co.uk
Starting date: 31.12.66

Radio Phoenix
Nidum Studio Centre, Neath General Hospital, Neath SA11 2LQ
Tel 01639-762029/762333
Starting date: 25.3.88
Area: Neath & Port Talbot

Radio Verulam
PO Box 396, St. Albans, Herts, AL3 6NE
Tel 01442 398099
Start date: 24.2.96
Area: West Herts

Town FM
PO Box 1072, London N9 0WQ
Fax 020-8373 1074   Tel 020-8373 1073
Community radio for North London
Starting date: 28.6.97
Dial: Cable London Channel 48 and 107.1 hook up

SATELLITE RADIO

ASDA FM (National in-store radio)
5 Springbank, Astley, Manchester N29 7BR
Fax 01942-884397   Tel 01942-889100
E-mail: emedia@hampson.co.uk
Website: www.hampson.co.uk

Asian Sound Radio
Globe House, Southall Street, Manchester M3 1LG
Fax 061-288 9000   Tel 0161-288 1000
E-mail: asiansound@aol.com
Asian community radio.
Starting date: 3.6.98
Dial: Transponder 26 of the Astra 1B satellite

Bloomberg News Radio
City Gate House, 39-45 Finsbury Square, London EC2A 1PQ
Fax 020-7392 6100   Tel 020-7330 7575
Dial: Astra 1B, transponder 31

CMR
PO Box 42, Alton, Hampshire GU32 4YU
Fax 01252-724312   Tel 01252-724891
E-mail: cmr@cix.co.uk
Website: www.countrymusic.org.uk

Costcutter Radio
PO Box 123, York YO1 5ZX
Fax 01904 488811   Tel 01904 488888
E-mail: costcutter@minsterfm.co.uk
Supermarket service.
Dial: Astra 10876.5 MHz

Cross Rhythms
PO Box 1110, Stoke-on-Trent ST4 8JR
Fax 01782 641121   Tel 01782 642444
E-mail: admin@crossrhythms.co.uk
Christian music and teaching.
Dial: Astra 1B 7.38 MHz

FEM FM/BHS Radio
29-30 Windmill Street, London W1P 1HG
Fax 020-7692 0201   Tel 020-7692 0200
Music, news etc for women.
Dial: Eutelsat TX46- 12588.56 Digital

Heart 106.2
The Chrysalis Building, 13 Bramley Road, London
W10 6SP
Fax 020-7470 1095   Tel 020-7468 1064
Website: www.heart1062.co.uk

Homebase FM
29-30 Windmill Street, London SW8 3NR
Fax 020-7692 0201   Tel 020-7692 0200
Music and information for the home improver
Dial: Eutelsat TX46 12589.64 Digital

MBC FM
204-206 Queentown Road, London SW8
Fax 020-7501 1025   Tel 020-7501 1000
E-mail: 100635.1314@compuserve.com

Music Choice Europe
Sentinel House, 16 Harcourt Stret, London W1H 2AU
Fax 020-7724 0404   Tel 020-7298 8800
Website: www.musicchoice.co.uk
Subscriber music service.

Oneword
Landseer House, 19 Charing Cross Road, London
WC2H 0ES
Fax 020-7930 9460   Tel 020-7976 3030
Plays, books, comedy and reviews

Premier Christian Radio
PO Box 13000, London SW1E 5PP
Fax 020-7233 6706   Tel 020-7316 1300

Radio Caroline
426 Archway Road, London N6 4JH
Fax 020-8340 3075   Tel 020-8340 3831
E-mail: mail@radiocaroline.co.uk
Website: www.radiocaroline.co.uk
Original 60s pirate now playing rock, rock and roll and
country music legally.
Dial: Astra 1c, transponder 35

Student Broadcast Network
109x Regents Park Road, Primrose Hill, London NW1
8UR
Fax 020-7691 4666   Tel 020-7691 4555
E-mail: info@sbn.co.uk
Website: www.sbn.co.uk
Provides national sales and support services to student
radio stations across the UK. Programmes include the
national student radio chart show and the best student-
produced shows.
Dial: Astra 1c, transponder 15

Sunrise Radio
Sunrise Road, Southall, Middlesex UB2 4AU
Fax 020-813 9800   Tel 020-8574 6666
Asian community radio
Dial: Astra 2 5850 SW

Tamil Radio and Television (TRT)
727 London Road, Thornton Heath, Surrey CR7 6AU
Fax 020-8683 2645   Tel 020-8689 7503
Website: www.trt.com
Tamil language community radio

TilesFM
29-30 Windmill Street, London W1P 1HG
Fax 020-7692 0201   Tel 020-7692 0200
Music and news for Tiles stores.
Dial: Astra 1c, transponder 33

Total Rock Radio
4 Fulham High Street, London SW6 3LQ
                        Tel 020-7731 6696
Rock and metal music, news and interviews.

UCB (United Christian Broadcasters)
Hanchurch Christian Centre, Hanchurch Lane, Stoke-
on-Trent ST4 8RY
Fax 01782-641121   Tel 01782-642000
E-mail: ucb@ucb.co.uk
Website: www.ucb.co.uk
Starting date: 4.93

Virgin Radio
1 Golden Square, London W!R 4DJ
Fax 020-7434 1197   Tel 020-7434 1215
Starting date: 30.4.93
Rock

World Radio Network
Wyvil Court, Wyvil Road, London SW8 2TG
Fax 020-7896 9007   Tel 020-7896 9000
Website: www.wrn.org
News from over 20 international public sector
broadcasters.
Dial: Astra 1B, 11.538 GHz

Youth fm
Manor Lane Studios, Oare, Berkshire RG18 9SE
Fax 01635-202800   Tel 01635-202700
Youth culture.
Starting date: 31.12.99

ADDITIONAL SERVICE LICENCE

Focus FM
18 Howard Way, Cromwell Business Park, Newport
Pagnell, Buckinghamshire MK16 9QS
Fax 01980-217327   Tel 01908-218200
E-mail: dannyw@cmt.co.uk
Website: www.cmt.co.uk
Differential Correction data to be used by global
positioning system receivers.
Dial: 99.9-101.9 MHz

Publications about broadcasting

BROADCAST MAGAZINES

Airflash
15 Paternoster Row, Sheffield S1 2BX
Fax 0114-279 8976   Tel 0114-279 5219
E-mail cma@commedia.org.uk
Website: www.commedia.org.uk
Publisher: Community Media Association
Editor: Haydn Suckling
£1.00. Quarterly journal about community media.
Ariel
Room 123, Henry Wood House, 3 and 6 Langham
Place, London W1A 1AA
Fax 020-7765 3646   Tel 020-7765 3623
E-mail: ariel.access@bbc.co.uk
Publisher: BBC
Editor: Robin Reynolds
Internal weekly BBC staff magazine. £50 pa to non-staff
Asia Image
6 Bell Yard, London WC2A 2JR
Fax 020-7520 5226   Tel 020-7520 5244
E-mail: france@asiai.com.sg
Website: www.ai-interactive.com
Publisher: Cahners
Editor: France Lee
Monthly magazine for people in Asian TV.
Audio Media
1 Station Road, St Ives, Cambs PE27 5BH
Fax 01480-461550   Tel 01480-461555
E-mail: mail@audiomedia.com
Website: www.audiomedia.com
Publisher: IMAS Publishing
£3.80. A monthly for audio professionals in recording,
broadcast, post-production, live sound and multi-media.
AV Magazine
Quantum House, 19 Scarbrook Road, Croydon CR9
1LX
Fax 020-8565 4282   Tel 020-8565 4224
E-mail: peterl@app.co.uk
Publisher: Quantum
Editor: Peter Lloyd
£3.90. Monthly news on the audio-visual business.
BBC On Air
Bush House, Strand, London WC2B 4PH
Fax 020-7240 4899   Tel 020-7557 2875
E-mail: on.air.magazine@bbc.co.uk
Website: www.bbc.co.uk/worldservice/onair
Publisher: BBC World Service
£2. Monthly programme guide to the BBC World
Service radio, and BBC World and BBC Prime TV.
Better Satellite
57 Rochester Place, London NW1 9JU
Fax 020-7331 1241   Tel 020-7331 1000
E-mail: bettersat@aol.com
Website: www.bettersat.com
Publisher: WV Publications
Editor: Alex Lane
£2.75. Quarterly for consumers of satellite products.

Books in the Media
15-Up, East Street, Lewins Yard, Chesham, Bucks
HP5 1HQ
Fax 01494-784850   Tel 01494-792269
E-mail: 100615.1643@compuserve.com
Publisher: Bookwatch.
£107 p.a. members, £112 non-members. Weekly
resource newsletter keeping bookshops and libraries
informed of books appearing in the media. Bookwatch
carries out book-related research for newspapers, TV
and radio.
Braille Radio/TV Times
100 Bridge Street, Peterborough, Cambs PE1 1DY
Fax 01733-358356   Tel 01733-358100
Website: www.rnib.org.uk
Publisher: Royal National Institute for the Blind.
Radio Times: 24p UK discount, 63p UK cost. TV Times:
42p UK discount, £1.30 UK cost.
British Journal of Photography
39 Earlham Street, London WC2H 9LD
Fax 020-7306 7112   Tel 020-7306 7000
E-mail: jt@benn.co.uk
Website: www.bjphoto.co.uk
Publisher: Timothy Benn Publishing
Editor: Jon Tarrant
£1.50. The leading weekly professional photographic
magazine which was established 1854.
Broadcast
33-39 Bowling Green Lane, London EC1R 0DA
Fax 020-7505 8050   Tel 020-7505 8014
E-mail bcasted@media.emap.co.uk
Publisher: Emap Media.
£2.40. The leading weekly newspaper on the TV and
radio industry, with news, features and comments.
Emap also publishes: Production Solutions, covering
key technological areas of production; Screen
International for the international film business and
Production Guide.
Cable Guide
172 Tottenham Court Road, London W1P 0JJ
Fax 020-7419 7299   Tel 020-7419 7300
Publisher: Cable Guide
Editor: Robin Jarossi
£3.25 monthly. Monthly cable listings magazine with
editorial coverage of film, drama and sports events.
Cable & Satellite Europe
149 Tottenham Court Road, London W1P 9LL
Fax 020-7896 2256   Tel 020-7453 2300
Website: www.media.ft.com
Publisher: FT Media & Telecommunications
£99. The journal of satellite and cable comms.
Cable & Satellite International
2 Queensway, Redhill, Surrey RH1 1QS
Fax 01737-855470   Tel 01737-768611
E-mail: jarmitage@cmg.co.uk
Web: www.cscinet.co.uk
£75 pa, ten issues a year. Mag for management with
purchasing power working in cable and satellite.

Commonwealth Broadcaster
17 Fleet Street, London EC4Y 1AA
Fax 020-7583 5549   Tel 020-7583 5500
E-mail: cba@cba.org.uk
Website: www.cba.org.uk
The magazine of the Commonwealth Broadcasting Association.

Convergence
University of Luton Press, 75 Castle Street, Luton, Beds LU1 3AJ
Fax 01582-743298   Tel 01582-743297
E-mail: convergence@luton.ac.uk
Quarterly. Journal on new media tech and research.

Creation
3 St Peters Street, London N1 8JD
Fax 020-7226 8586   Tel 020-7226 8585
E-mail: jameshamilton@mdi-uk.com
Publisher: Media Directories International
£2.95. monthly. Mag for people in film/TV/new media.

Crosstalk
PO Box 124, Westcliff on Sea, Essex SS0 0QU
Fax 01702-305121   Tel 01702-348369
E-mail: office@caclb.org.uk
Website: www.CACLB.org.uk
Publisher: CACLB
Editor: Jeff Bonser
Quarterly bulletin about churches and broadcasting.

Cuts Magazine
48 Carnaby Street, London W1V 1PF
Fax 020-7437 3259   Tel 020-7437 0801
E-mail: CUTS@compuserve.com
Website: www.demon.co.uk/interactive/cuts/
Publisher: Sound & Vision Publishing.
Editor: George Jarrett
£35 p.a. European TV and film production monthly.

Eyepiece
Primrose Street, Cambridge CB4 3EH
Fax 01223-569220   Tel 01223-561222
E-mail: ffilm+video@studio22ten.demon.co.uk
Publisher: Guild of British Camera Technicians
Editors: Kerry Anne Burrows, Charles Hewitt
£3.50, 6x pa. Magazine for film and TV people featuring location reports, equipment reviews and interviews.

Financial Times Business
Maple House, 149 Tottenham Court Road, London W1P 9LL
Fax 020-7896 2256   Tel 020-7896 2072
Website: www.media.ft.com
Publisher: FT Media & Telecoms Publishing.
Produces the following newsletters: Asia-Pacific Telecoms Analyst; Mobile Communications; Music & Copyright; New Media Markets; Screen Finance; Telecom Markets and related management reports.

Free Press
8 Cynthia Street, London N1 9JF
Fax 020-8837 8868   Tel 020-7278 4430
E-mail: freepress@cpbf.demon.co.uk
Publisher: Campaign for Press and Broadcasting Freedom.
Editor: Granville Williams
£1 non-members. Free members news magazines. Published six times a year.

Historical Journal of Film, Radio and Television
PO Box 25, Abingdon, Oxfordshire OX14 3UE
Fax 01235-401550   Tel 01235-401000
E-mail: enquiries@carfax.co.uk
Website: www.tandf.co.uk/journals
Publisher: Carfax Publishing/Taylor & Francis
Editor: David Culbert
Institutional rate: £322; personal rate: £112. Quarterly academic journal.

HotShoe International
Datateam Publishing, London Road, Maidstone, Kent ME16 8LY
Fax 01622 757646   Tel 01622-687031
E-mail: hotshoe@datateam.co.uk
Website: www.datateamc.o.uk
Publisher: Datateam Publishing
Editor: Chris Townsend
£2.95. bi-monthly. Magazine for the upper echelons of creative professional photography.

Image
81 Leonard Street, London EC2A 4QS
Fax 020-7739 8707   Tel 020-7739 6669
E-mail: jackiek@aophoto.co.uk
Website: www.aophoto.co.uk
Publisher: Association of Photographers.
£2.00. High quality, monthly photography magazine, with news, reviews, events and ads. Also published is The Awards Book, an annual of top advertising and editorial photography.

Image Technology
63-71 Victoria House, Vernon Place, London WC1B 4DA
Fax 020-7405 3560   Tel 020-7242 8400
E-mail: movimage@bksts.demon.co.uk
Website: www.bksts.demon.co.uk
Publisher: BKSTS.
Monthly technical journal for members of the British Kinematograph Sound and TV Society. Also publishes Cinema Technology.

Information World Review
Woodside, Hinksey Hill, Oxford OX1 5BE
Fax 01865-736354   Tel 01865-388000
E-mail: iwr@learned.co.uk
Website: www.iwr.vnu.co.uk
Publisher: Learned Information.
Monthly newspaper on the information industry, for users and producers of electronic information services.

InterMedia
3rd Floor, Westcott House, 35 Portland Place, London W1N 3AG
Fax 020-7323 9623   Tel 020-7323 9622
E-mail: martin@iicom.org
Website: www.iicom.org/
Publisher: International Inst of Communications
Discussion journal covering issues affecting international telecommunications, broadcasting and media. 6x pa.

International Broadcast Engineer
2 Queensway, Redhill, Surrey RH1 1QS
Fax 01737-855478   Tel 01737-768611
E-mail: 100553.151@compuserve.com
Website: www.dmg.co.uk
Publisher: DMG Business Media
Looking at broadcast technology, for senior engineering and operational staff. 9x pa.

Journal of Educational Media
PO Box 25, Abingdon, Oxfordshire OX14 3UE
Fax 01235-401550   Tel 01235-401000
E-mail: enquiries@carfax.co.uk
Website: www.tandf.co.uk/journals
Publisher: Taylor & Francis
Editor: Ian White
Academic journal providing forum for discussing developments in TV and related media in education.

Kagan World Media
524 Fulham Road, London SW6 5NR
Fax 020-7371 8715   Tel 020-7371 8880
E-mail: kwmresearch@kagan.com
Website: www.kagan.com
Kagan is an international company specialising in analysis of the media and communications industries. It publishes a range of Europe-oriented monthly newsletters, covering topics around TV, cable, video and radio, and special reports.

Line Up
27 Old Gloucester Street, London WC1N 3XX
Fax 01905-381725   Tel 01323-491739
E-mail: hugh.robjohns@cwcom.net
Publisher: Institute of Broadcast Sound.
Journal mixing technical information, news and articles by practitioners in broadcast sound. 6x pa.

Media, Culture & Society
6 Bonhill Street, London EC2A 4PU
Fax 020-7374 8741   Tel 020-7374 0645
E-mail: market@sagepub.co.uk
Website: www.sagepub.co.uk
Publisher: Sage Publications.
6x pa, £47 individual sub, £259 for institution. An international forum for presentation of media research within political, economic, cultural and historic context.

Media Education Journal
c/o Scottish Screen, 2nd floor, 249 West George Street, Glasgow G2 4QE
Fax 0141-302 1711   Tel 0141-302 1700
E-mail: info@scottishscreen.com
Website: www.scottishscreen.com
Publisher: Association for Media Education in Scotland.
2x pa. Media theory, and ideas for teaching from primary one to adult. Also teaching packs.

Media Week
Quantum House, 19 Scarbrook Road, Croydon CR9 1LX
Fax 020-8565 4394   Tel 020-8565 4200
E-mail: mweeked@qpp.co.uk
Website: www.mediaweek.co.uk
Publisher: Quantum
Editor: Patrick Barrett
£1.85. Weekly magazine linking media and advertising .

Middle East Broadcast & Satellite
Chancery House, St Nicholas Way, Sutton , Surrey SM1 1JB
Fax 020-8642 1941   Tel 020-86421117
E-mail: farah@icompub.com
Website: www.icompub.com
Publisher: Icom Publications Ltd.
£65. 9x.pa magazine on satellite and broadcast in the Middle East & S Asia. Also publishes Middle East Communications.

Moving Pictures International
34-35 Newman Street, London W1P 3PD
Fax 020-7636 7379   Tel 020-7637 0651
E-mail: mopix@compuserve.com
Website: www.filmfestivals.com
Publisher: Moving Pictures International
Monthly coverage of the international film, televsion and video industry.

Off-Air
5 Market Place, London W1N 7AH
Fax 020-7255 2020   Tel 020-7255 2010
E-mail: info@radioacademy.org
Website: www.radioacademy.org
Publisher: The Radio Academy.
Monthly journal of the Radio Academy.

The Pact Magazine
3 St Peters Street, London N1 8JD
Fax 020-7226 8586   Tel 020-7226 8585
E-mail: Godfreyo@mdi-uk.com
Website: www.pact.co.uk
Publisher: Media Directories International
Members magazine for the Producers Alliance for Cinema and Television.

The Photographer
Fox Talbot House, Amwell End, Ware, Herts SG12 9HN
Fax 01920-487056   Tel 01920-464011
E-mail: bipp@compuserve.com
Website: www.bipp.com
Publisher: British Institute of Professional Photography.
Editor: Steve Bavister
£3.25, free to members. 10 issues p.a. The British Institute of Professional Photography's journal of professional images and imaging technology.

Post Update
3 St Peters Street, London N1 8JD
Fax 020-7226 8586   Tel 020-7226 8585
E-mail: rebeccah@mdi-uk.com
Publisher: Media Directories International
£3.50. monthly. The European post-production magazine, features regular, detailed product reviews and technology updates.

Production Solutions
33-39 Bowling Green Lane, London, EC1R 0DA
Fax 020-7505 8076   Tel 020-7505 8000
E-mail: catherinew@media.emap.co.uk
Monthly magazine aimed at people working in television, production and film. Covers new technology, film issues, training and features a buyers guide to technology. Cover price £5.00.

The Radio Magazine
25 High Street, Rothwell, Northants NN14 6AD
Fax 01536-418539   Tel 01536-418558
E-mail: editor@theradiomagazine.co.uk
Website: www.theradiomagazine.co.uk
Publisher: Goldcrest Broadcasting.
Editor: Howard Rose
£80. p.a.Weekly, glossy on the radio world.

Radio Review
PO Box 46, Romford, Essex RM7 8AY
Editor: Geoff Baldwin
Newsletter about pirate stations etc. Trial 6 issues for
£7.80, or free sample by sending medium SAE.

Radio Times
Woodlands, 80 Wood Lane, London W12 0TT
Fax 020-8433 3923   Tel 020-8576 2000
E-mail: radio.times@bbc.co.uk
Website: www.radiotimes.com
Publisher: BBC Worldwide
Editor: Sue Robinson
Weekly, 79p. The BBC's money-spinning listings mag.

Satellite TV Europe
531-3 Kings Road, London SW10 0TZ
Fax 020-7352 4883   Tel 020-7351 3612
E-mail: stv1@compuserve.com
Website: www.satellite-tv.co.uk
Publisher: Millenium Consumer Magazines
£2.50. Monthly.
Satellite TV listings.

Satellite Times
The Stable Block, West Hill Grange, North Road,
Horsforth, Leeds LS18 5HG
Fax 0113-258 9745   Tel 0113-258 5008
E-mail: stimes@cix.co.uk
Publisher: Everpage
£2.30. Monthly listings for satellite, cable and digital TV.

Screen Digest
Lymehouse Studios, 38 Georgiana Street, London
NW1 0EB
Fax 020-7580 0060   Tel 020-7482 5842
E-mail: editorial@screendigest.com
Website: www.screendigest.com
Publisher: Screen Digest.
Editor: David Fisher
£325 p.a. Monthly round-up of news, research and stats
on film, video, multimedia and TV aimed at executives.

Screen International
33 Bowling Green Lane, London EC1R 0DA
Fax 020-7505 8117   Tel 020-7505 8080
E-mail: screeninternational@compuserve.com
Website: www.screendaily.com
Publisher: Emap Media
International editor: Colin Brown
£2.50. Weekly on the international cinema business.

Short Wave Magazine
Arrowsmith Court, Broadstone, Dorset BH18 8PW
Fax 01202-659950   Tel 01202-659910
E-mail: kevin@pwpublishing.ltd.uk
Website: www.publishing.ltd.uk
Publisher: PW Publishing.
Editor: Kevin Nice
£2.99. Monthly for enthusiasts of all types of listening.

Shots
33 Bowling Green Lane, London EC1R 0DA
Fax 020-7505 8490   Tel 020-7505 8487
E-mail: info@shots.net
Website: www.shots.net
Publisher: Emap Media
Editor: Lyndy Stout
£467.50 + VAT. Bi-monthly video mag on DVD, with
advertising, music promos and post production.

Sight & Sound
21 Stephen Street, London W1P 1PL
Fax 020-7436 2327   Tel 020-7255 1444
Publisher: British Film Institute.
E-mail s&s@bfi.org.uk
Website: www.bfi.org.uk/sightandsound/
Editor: Nick James
£2.95. Leading monthly covering the film world.

The Stage (incorporating Television Today)
47 Bermondsey Street, London SE1 3XT
Fax 020-7357 9287   Tel 020-7403 1818
E-mail: info@thestage.co.uk
Website: www.showcall.co.uk
Editor: Brian Attwood
90p. Weekly newspaper of the entertainment industry -
theatre, dance, opera, TV and radio. The publishers also
produce Showcall, a light entertainment directory.

Stage, Screen & Radio
111 Wardour Street, London W1V 4AY
Fax 020-7437 8268   Tel 020-7437 8506
E-mail: info@bectu.org.uk
Website: www.bectu.org.uk
Publisher: BECTU.
£2, free to members. 10x p.a. Journal of the largest trade
union in film and broadcasting.

Television
100 Grays Inn Road, London WC1X 8AL
Fax 020-7430 0924   Tel 020-7430 1000
E-mail: ipublications@arts.org.uk
Website: www.rts.org.uk
Publisher: Royal Television Society
Editor: Peter Fiddick
10x pa, £80 pa. Covers all aspects of the TV industry.

Television
Quadrant House, Sutton, Surrey SM2 5AS
Fax 020-8652 8111   Tel 020-8652 8120
E-mail: tessa.winford@rbi.co.uk
Publisher: Reed Business Information
Editor: John Reddihough
£2.80. Specialist monthly. Technical news and features
for the TV/video servicing engineer.

Television Asia
6 Bell Yard, London WC2A 2JR
Fax 020-7520 5226   Tel 020-7520 5244
E-mail: will@tvasia.com.sg
Publisher: Cahners Publishing
Editor: William Lawrence
Monthly glossy magazine looking at the TV business
across Asia.

Television Europe
Tel 020-7520 5281
E-mail: KateMcKean@rbi.co.uk
Editor: Kate McKean
Monthly, free. Trade magazine aimed at senior TV executives, buyers, producers and distributors.

Television International
Tel 020-7520 5281
E-mail: KateMcKean@rbi.co.uk
Editor: Kate McKean
4 issues per year - Natpe, LA Screenings, MipTV, MipCom. Trade magazine aimed at TV executives, buyers, producers and distributors. .

Televisual
49-50 Poland Street, London W1V 4AX
Fax 020-7970 6733   Tel 020-7970 6666
E-mail: televisual@centaur.co.uk
Publisher: Centaur Communications
Editor: Mundy Ellis
£2.95. Monthly business magazine for independent producers, facility providers and the TV industry.

TV Quick
Shirley House, 25-27 Camden Road, London NW1 9LL
Fax 020-7241 8066   Tel 020-7241 8000
Publisher: H Bauer Publishing
62p. Weekly TV listings geared to women's interests.

TV & Satellite Week
Kings Reach Tower, Stamford Street, London SE1 9LS
Fax 020-7261 7525   Tel 020-7261 7534
E-mail: TVandSatweek@ipc.co.uk
Website: www.unmissabletv.com
Publisher: IIPC Media.
80p. Weekly consumers guide.

TV Times
Kings Reach Tower, Stamford Street, London SE1 9LS
Fax 020-7261 7777   Tel 020-7261 5000
E-mail: tvtimes@ipc.co.uk
Website: www.ipc.co.uk
Publisher: IPC Magazines.
Weekly details of television programmes. Sales of the TV Times have now been overtaken by What's On TV, operating out of the same offices.

TV Zone
9 Blades Court, Deodar Road, London SW15 2NU
Fax 020-8875 1588   Tel 020-8875 1520
E-mail: tvzone@visimag.com
Website: www.visimag.com
Publisher: Visual Imagination
£2.99. Longest running magazine dedicated to cult television. Monthly plus 4 quarterly specials with an emphasis on science fiction and fantasy.

UK Radio Guide & Directory
Crown House, 25 High Street, Rothwell, Northants NN14 6AD
Fax 01536-418539   Tel 01536-418558
radiomazine-goldcrestbroadcasting@btinternet.com
Website: www.theradiomagazine.co.uk
Publisher: Goldcrest Broadcasting.
Editor: Paul Boon
£20. 6 monthly. Radio audience update on Rajar participating stations, plus industry directory.

Vertigo
20 Goodge Place, London W1P 1FN
Fax: 020-7631 1040   Tel 020-7436 3050
E-mail: vertigo.insia@lineone.net
Editor: Kimberley Cooper
£3.75, bi-annual. Vertigo gives independent film, video and television works outside the mainstream the attention they deserve.

Viewfinder
77 Well Street, London W1P 3RE
Fax 020-7393 1555   Tel 020-7393 1500
E-mail: ask@bufvc.ac.uk
Website: www.bufvc.ac.uk/
Publisher: British Universities Film & Video Council
News and features published three times a year by the British Universities Film/Video Council, which exists to promote the production, study and use of film, TV and related media for higher education and research.

Voice of the Listener & Viewer
101 Kings Drive, Gravesend, Kent DA12 5BQ
Fax 01474-351112   Tel 01474-352835
E-mail: vlv@btinternet.com
Website: www.vlv.org.uk
Publisher: Voice of the Listener and Viewer.
Quarterly newsletter of the independent watchdog, which bills itself as "the citizen's voice in broadcasting and the only consumer body speaking for listeners and viewers on the full range of broadcasting issues".

What Satellite TV
57-59 Rochester Place, London NW1 9JU
Fax 020-7331 1241   Tel 020-7331 1000
E-mail: wwhatsat@aol.com
Website: www.wotsat.com
Publisher: WV Publications
Editor: Geoff Bains
£2.99. Monthly consumer magazine with news on "the equipment to buy and the programmes to watch".

What's on TV
See TV Times

World Media
BBC Monitoring, Caversham Park, Reading, Berks RG4 8TZ
Fax 0118-946 3823   Tel 0118-946 9289
E-mail: marketing@mon.bbc.co.uk
Website: www.monitor.bbc.co.uk
Weekly, also available via Internet, containing news of the international broadcasting scene, reporting on satellite, cable and terrestrial radio and TV. Annual subscription £410.

Zerb
Church Barn, Harberton, Totnes, Devon TQ9 7SQ
Fax 01803-868444   Tel 01803-868652
E-mail: 100701.1712@compuserve.com
Web: www.easyweb.easynet.co.uk/~guildtvc
Publisher: Guild of TV Cameramen.
£7.50 pa. Twice a year. Features relevant to the craft and business of TV cameramen.

BROADCAST YEARBOOKS

BAPLA Directory of Picture Libraries
18 Vine Hill, London EC1R 5DZ
Fax 020-7713 1211   Tel 020-7713 1780
E-mail: enquiries@bapla.org.uk
Website: www.bapla.org.uk
Contact: Linda Royles
£20. Full details of all BAPLA members, a description of their stock, a subject index and hints for library users.

Benn's Media
Riverbank House, Angel Lane, Tonbridge, Kent TN9 1SE
Fax 01732-367301   Tel 01732-377591
E-mail: bennsmedia@unmf.com
Website: www.mfinfo.com
Publisher: Miller Freeman Information Services
Contact: Craig Curtis
3 vols £310, 2 vols £290, 1 vol £145. Benn's has the most comprehensive listings amongst the general media directories. It comes in three volumes, covering the UK, Europe and the rest of the world.

BFI Film and Television Handbook
21 Stephen Street, London W1P 2LN
Fax 020-7436 7950   Tel 020-7255 1444
E-mail: helpdesk@bfi.org.uk
Website: www.bfi.org.uk
Editor: Eddie Dyja
£20. Combines hundreds of film and broadcasting facts and figures with a directory of contacts and addresses.

Blue Book of British Broadcasting 2000
Tellex Monitors Limited, PA News Centre, 292 Vauxhall Bridge Road, London SW1E 1AE
Fax 020-7963 7628   Tel 020-7963 7616
E-mail: publications@tellex.press.net
Entries for all UK broadcasters with details of key personnel.

Bowkers Complete Video Directory
Bowker-Saur, Windsor Court, East Grinstead House, East Grinstead, West Sussex RH19 1XA
Fax 01342-336192   Tel 01342-326972
E-mail: customer.service@bowker-saur.co.uk
Website: www.bowker-saur.co.uk
£210, four vols. Info covering over 107,000 video titles.

Cable & Satellite Yearbook
Maple House, 149 Tottenham Court Road, London W1P 9LL
Fax 020-7896 2749   Tel 020-7453 2300
E-mail: info@ftmedia.com
Website: www.media.ft.com
Publisher: FT Media & Telecoms
£295 for yearbook, £295 for TV Business International. Both on CD £595. Also published is: TV Business International, with the world's TV stations and prices.

Commonwealth Broadcasters' Directory
17 Fleet Street, London EC4Y 1AA
Fax 020-7583 5549   Tel 020-7583 5550
E-mail: cba@cba.org.uk
Website: www.cba.org.uk
Publisher: Commonwealth Broadcasting Assocation
£25 non-members, UK; £28 non-members, Europe.

Directors' Guild Directory
15-19 Great Titchfield Street, London W1P 7FB
Fax 020-7436 8646   Tel 020-7436 8626
E mail: guild@dggb.co.uk
Website: www.dggb.co.uk
Publisher: Directors Guild of Great Britain
£25. Published every two years.

Directory of International Film & Festivals
11 Portland Place, London W1N 4EJ
Fax 020-7389 3041   Tel 020-7389 3065
E-mail: paul.howson@britcounc.org
Website: www.britfilms.com
Publisher: British Council
£11

International Satellite Directory
24 River Gardens, Purley, Reading RG8 8BX
Fax 0118-9414468   Tel 07836-582785
E-mail: vincentbay@hotmail.com
Website: www.baylin.com
Publisher: Baylin Publications
Editor: Silvano Payne
£173. US technical manual and guide to satellites.

Kays UK Production Manual
Pinewood Studios, Pinewood Road, Iver Heath, Bucks SL0 0NH
Fax 01753-656844   Tel 01753-651171
E-mail: info@kays.co.uk
Website: www.kays.co.uk
Publisher: Kays Publishing
£70. With its Crew Directory, this is one of the most comprehensive and reliable manuals of people and organisations in the production side of the film, TV and broadcast industry. Contains 15,000 names and addresses in over 250 classifications. Also available is its European equivalent the European Production Manual (£85), plus the Art Diary (£35) listing the art business.

Kemps Film, TV & Video Yearbook
6 Bell Yard, London WC2A 2JR
Fax 020-7520 5237   Tel 020-7520 5233
E-mail: sara@variety.demon.co.uk
Website: www.kftv.com
Publisher: Variety Media Publications
Editor: Sara Tyler
£44 UK; £97 International. Kemps provide comprehensive information to the film, TV and commercial industries. Contains 35,000 companies from 56 countries, shown under 200 classifications. The data is also available on labels, print out or floppy disc.

The Knowledge
E-mail: knowledge@unmf.com
Website: www.theknowledgeonline.com
Publisher: Miller Freeman Information Services
Book £95; CD rom £95; book and CD £120. The leading guide to the products and services of the UK film, TV and video industry. Over 15,600 listings of companies and freelance crew. Also industry information, charts and maps. Book includes portable version in A-Z format for use on location.

Multimedia and CD-ROM Directory
6-14 Underwood Street, London N1 7JQ
Fax 020-7324 2312 Tel 020-7324 2345
E-mail: gbuecker@waterlow.com
Website: www.newmediainfo.com
Publisher: Waterlow Publishing
Contact: Gesche Beucker
Vol 1. Media Companies - £149
Vol 2. Media Titles - £149;
both £249

The Production Guide
33-39 Bowling Green Lane, London EC1R 0DA
Fax 020-7505 8293 Tel 020-7505 8000
Publisher: Emap Media
Contact: Martha Hawkins
£65. Details of technical contacts, services and equipment.

Programme News
6-7 Cross Street, London EC1N 8UA
Fax 020-7430 1089 Tel 020-7405 4455
E-mail: info@profilegroup.co.uk
Website: www.profilegroup.co.uk
Publisher: The Profile Group
From £574 p.a. with monthly bulletins. An information service in directory format. Independent broadcast listings. The UK industry guide for advance broadcast planning.

Radio Academy Directory
5 Market Place, London W1N 7AH
Fax 020-7255 2029 Tel 020-7255 2010
E-mail: info@radioacademy.org
Website: www.radioacademy.org
Publisher: The Radio Academy.
Annual directory/listings guide of the radio industry's leading professional society.

Radio Advertising Handbook
77 Shaftesbury Avenue, London W1V 7AD
020-7306 2505 Tel 020-7306 2500
E-mail: rab@rab.co.uk
Website: www.rab.co.uk
Publisher: Radio Advertising Bureau
Free. Handbook of radio advertising, providing an overview of the commercial radio industry, with masses of data and listings information.

Radio Authority Pocket Guide
Holbrook House, 14 Great Queen Street, London WC2B 5DG
Fax 020-7405 7062 Tel 020-7430 2724
E-mail: info@radioauthority.org.uk
Website: www.radioauthority.org.uk
Publisher: Radio Authority
Free. Annual reference book listing all independent radio stations and other radio related organisations.

Radio Listener's Guide
PO Box 151 Abingdon, Oxon OX13 5DP
Tel 01865-820387
E-mail: clive@radioguide.demon.co.uk
Publisher: PDQ Publishing
Editor: Clive Woodyear
£4.95. Pocket guide to UK radio stations, and an invaluable aid to those trying to find their way around the radio dial.

Royal Television Society Directory
100 Grays Inn Road, London WC1X 8AL
Fax 020-7430 0924 Tel 020-7430 1000
E-mail: publications@rts.org.uk
Website: www.rts.org.uk
Publisher Radio Television Society
Editor: Sue Griffith
£10. Guide to the society, listing full membership details.

Television Business International Yearbook
Informa Media Group, Newlands House, 40 Berners Street, London W1P 3AA
Fax 020-7453 2352 Tel 020-7453 2334
E-mail: tony.cribb@informa.com
Website: www.informamedia.com
Publisher: Informa Media Group
£295. Directory listing all key terrestrial broadcasters worldwide.

University of Manchester Broadcasting Symposia
75 Castle Street, Luton LU1 3AJ
Fax 01582-743298 Tel 01582-743297
E-mail: ulp@luton.ac.uk
Publisher: University of Luton Press
£14.95
Each year all sides of the broadcasting industry meet for a symposium organised by the University of Manchester. The proceedings are published in book form. The latest publication is Youth and the Media.

The White Book
The White Book
Tel 01932-572622
£50. The key international production directory.

Who's Who in Digital, Cable & Satellite TV
Phillips Business Information, 3rd Floor, 19 Thomas More Street, London E1 9YW
Fax 020-7504 3526 Tel 020-7423 4572
E-mail: pgreen@the-phillips-group.com
Website: www.cabletoday.com
Publisher: Philips Business Information
Published in January and July, the Who's Who contains in excess of 1,400 business contacts for this industry.
Single edition: £57, 1 year's subscription: £97.

World Radio & TV Handbook
50-51 Bedford Row, London WC1R 4LR
Fax 020-7242 9136 Tel 020-7822 8300
E-mail: bevans@bpicomm.com
Website: www.billboard.com
£21.50. World broadcasting stations, by frequency, time and language.

Broadcast support organisations

All-Party Media Group
9 Old Queen Street, London SW1H 9JA
Fax 020-7222 4189   Tel 020-7222 4179
Cross party forum of 100 MPs and peers with an interest in media issues.

AMARC
15 Paternoster Row, Sheffield, Yorkshire S1 2BX
Fax 0114-279 8976   Tel 0114-221 0592
E-mail: europe@amarc.org
Website: www.amarc.org
AMARC, the World Association of Community Radio Broadcasters, is a world-wide network of local radios which operate for social purposes and are independent of governments and large media corporations.

Amnesty International: Journalists' Network
202 Mansfield Road, Nottingham NG1 3HX
Fax 0115-924 5055   Tel 0115-924 5100
E-mail: nottm@amnesty.org.uk
This division of Amnesty International campaigns on behalf of media workers who have disappeared, been imprisoned, tortured or threatened with death. It holds meetings and publishes a quarterly newsletter.

Amsat-UK
40 Downsview, Small Dole, West Sussex BN5 9YB
Fax 01273-492927   Tel 01273-495733
E-mail: g6ziu@amsat.org
Website: www.amsat.org
National society specialising in amateur radio satellite matters. Publishes Oscar News 6x pa.

Article 19, The Global Campaign for Free Expression
Lancaster House, 33 Islington High Street, Islington London N1 9LH
Fax 020-7713 1356   Tel 020-7278 9292
E-mail: info@article19.org
Website: www.article19.org
International human rights organisation campaigning for the right to freedom of expression and information. The organisation promotes improved legal standards for freedom of expression and defends victims of censorship. It publishes newsletters plus country and theme reports, with emphasis on media freedom.

Aslib
Staple Hall, Stone House Court, London EC3A 7PB
Fax 020-7903 0011   Tel 020-7903 0000
E-mail: members@aslib.com
Website: www.aslib.com/aslib/
The Association for Information Management is the leading corporate membership information management association. It gives advice on information sources and strategy. There is also a network of special interest groups.

Association of Broadcasting Doctors
Sindalthorpe House, Ely, Cambridge CB7 4SG
Fax 01353-688451   Tel 01353-688456
E-mail: abd@soundplanltd.netscapeonline.co.uk
Represents practising doctors who also broadcast, providing training, data and media liaison.

Association of Smallscale Scottish Broadcasters
Struan House, The Square, Aberfeldy, Perthshire PH15 2DD
Fax 01887 820038   Tel 01887 820956
E-mail: wwright@sol.co.uk
For those interested in small-scale radio and TV broadcasting, RSLs and workshops in Scotland.

Audio Visual Association
156 High Street, Bushey, Hertfordshire WD2 3DD
Fax 020-8950 7560   Tel 020-8950 5959
Special interest group of the British Institute of Professional Photography representing people working to sub-broadcast standard in audio visual and multi-media. The association evolves with new technical developments.

Bafta
see British Academy of Film and Television Arts

Barb
See Broadcast Audience Research Board

British Academy of Film and Television Arts
195 Piccadilly, London W1V 0LN
Fax 020-7734 1792   Tel 020-7734 0022
BAFTA North   Tel 0151-283 3726
BAFTA Scotland   Tel 0141-302 1770
BAFTA Wales   Tel 029-2022 3898
Website: www.bafta.org
BAFTA was formed in 1947 and promotes high creative standards in film and television production, and encourages experiment and research. It organises awards ceremonies for film, television, children's films and programmes and interactive entertainment and has an extensive programme of seminars, lectures etc. It has 3000 members and provides screenings and previews and publishes a monthly newsletter. It also offers a range of educational and training initiatives.

British Academy of Composers and Songwriters
25-27 Berners Street, London W1P 3DB
Fax 020-7636 2212   Tel 020-7636 2929
E-mail: info@britishacademy.com
Website: www.britishacademy.com
Represents the interest of songwriters and composers across all genres, providing advice on professional and legal matters. It administers the Ivor Novello awards. and publishes a quarterly magazine, The Works.

British Amateur Television Club
Church Road, Harby, Notts NG23 7ED
Fax 01522-703348   Tel 01522-703348
E-mail: secretary@batc.org.uk
Website: www.batc.org.uk
Founded in 1948 to inform, instruct, co-ordinate and represent the activities of television enthusiasts in the UK and worldwide. Publishes quarterly technical magazine CQ-TV

British Board of Film Classification
3 Soho Square, London W1V 6HD
Fax 020-7287 0141   Tel 020-7439 7961
E-mail: webmaster@bbfc.co.uk
Website: www.bbfc.co.uk
Classifies films and videos for sale or rent.
   U (Universal)
   Uc (Universal particularly for young children, video only)
   PG (Parental Guidance)
   12 (age 12 and over only)
   15 (age 15 and over only)
   18 (age 18 and over only)
   R18 (over 18 and applies principally to videos only available through licensed sex shops)

British Film Commission
10 Little Portland Street, London W1N 5DF
Fax 020-7224 1013   Tel 020-7224 5000
E-mail: info@bfc.co.uk
Website: www.bfc.co.uk
Bath Film Office	01225-477711
Central England Screen Commission	
	0121-643 9309
East Midlands Office	0115-910 5564
Eastern Screen	01603-767077
Edinburgh Film Focus	0131-622 7337
Glasgow Film Office	0141-287 0424
Herts Film Link	01923-495051
Isle of Man Film Commission	
	01624-685864
Lancashire Film Office	01772-434400
Liverpool Film Office	0151-291 9191
London Film Commission	
	020-7387 8787
Manchester Office	0161-238 4537
Mid Wales Film Com	01970-617995
N Ireland Film Commission	
	028-9023 2444
Northern Screen	0191-233 9234
N Wales Film Comm	01248 354103
Scotttish Highlands and Islands	
	01463-710221
Scottish Screen	0141-302 1700
S Wales Film Comm	029-2059 0240
Southern Screen Commission	
	01273-384211
SW Film Commission , south office	
	01752 841199
SW Film Commission , north ofice	
	01752 841199
SW Scotland Screen Commission	
	01387-263666
Yorkshire Screen	01142-799115

Founded in 1991, the BFC is part of the Film Council, funded through the Department of Culture. Its remit is to promote the UK as an international production centre and provide support to those filming in the UK. The BFC produces Check Book, a UK production guide for overseas film-makers. It participates in trade events abroad and helps foreign film makers in the UK. It works with the UK Film Commission Network.

British Film Institute
21 Stephen Street, London W1P 2LN
Fax 020-7436 0439   Tel 020-7255 1444
Website: www.bfi.org.uk.
The Brtish Film Institute is about the world of film and television. Its three main departments are: bfi Education, comprising the bfi National Library, bfi Publishing and Sight and Sound magazine, as well as bfi Education Projects, which encourages life-long learning about the moving image; bfi Exhibition, which runs the National Film Theatre on London's South Bank and the annual London Film Festival, and supports local cinemas and film festivals UK-wide; and bfi Collections, which preserves the UK's moving image heritage and promotes access to it through a variety of means, including film, video and DVD releases and touring exhibitions. The bfi also runs the bfi London IMAX Cinema at Waterloo, featuring the UK's largest screen.

British Interactive Multimedia Association
5-6 Clipstone Street, London W1P 7EB
Fax 020-7436 8251   Tel 020-7436 8250
E-mail: enquiries@bima.co.uk
The trade body for the multimedia industry. Publishes directory of members and newsletter. Meets ten times a year.

British Internet Publishers' Alliance
c/o Frank Rogers, Telegraph Group, 1 Canada Square, Canary Wharf, London E14 5AP

British Kinematograph, Sound and Television Society (BKSTS)
63 Victoria House, Vernon Place, London WC1B 4DA
Fax 020-7405 3560   Tel 020-7242 8400
E-mail: movimage@bksts.demon.co.uk
Website: www.bksts.com
BKSTS was founded in 1931 and is the only European society covering all technical aspects of film, television, sound and associated industries. It plays a leading role in the development and implementation of technical standards. The main aim is to keep members abreast of the continually changing technlogy in the industry and its implications. The society achieves this through its journals, Cinema Technology and Image Technology (10x pa) and by holding seminars and conferences. Many training courses are held.

British Library National Sound Archive
96 Euston Road, London NW1 2DB
Fax 020-7412 7441   Tel 020-7412 7440
E-mail: nsa@bl.uk
Website: www.bl.uk/collections/sound-archive
The national collection of sound recordings, covering all topics since the 1890s. Provides library, information, listening and transcription services. Publishes newsletter Playback and range of print and audio titles.

British Radio andElectronic Equipment Manufacturers' Association
Landseer House, 19 Charing Cross Road, London WC2H 0ES
Fax 020-7839 4613   Tel 020-7930 3206
E-mail: name@brema.org.uk
Trade association for consumer electronics manufacturers.

British Screen Advisory Council
19 Cavendish Square, London W1M 9AB
Fax 020-7287 1123   Tel 020-7287 1111
E-mail: bsac@bsacouncil.co.uk.
Independent, industry funded, advisory body to
government and policy makers at national and
European level. It provides a forum for the audiovisual
industry to discuss major issues. It commissions
research and organises conferences and seminars.

British Screen Finance
14 -17 Wells Mews, London W1P 3FL
Fax 020-7323 0092   Tel 020-7323 9080
E-mail: info@britishscreen.co.uk
A private company partly financed by grants through
the Department of Culture, Media and Sport and by
lottery money through the Arts Council of England.
Provides investment in development and production of
feature films aimed at the commercial cinema
marketplace. Manages the European Co-production
Fund and the Greenlight Fund.

British Society of Cinematographers
11 Croft Road, Gerrards Cross, Bucks SL9 9AE
Fax 01753-891486   Tel 01753-888052
E-mail: BritCinematographers@compuserve.com
Society of motion picture cinematographers. Arranges
technical meetings, social events, film shows etc.
Publishes directory biennially.

Broadcasters Audience Research Board (Barb)
2nd Floor, 18 Dering Street, London W1R 9AF
Fax 020-7529 5530   Tel 020-7529 5531
Website: www.barb.co.uk
Barb provides information to all elements of the TV
industry, broadcasters, advertising/media buying
agencies and advertisers. Barb uses professional
research suppliers to conduct and report on audience
research. It produces statistical research on TV
audiences for its subscribers. Audiences for TV
programmes are measured by electronic meters
attached to television sets in 4,485 homes. This panel,
which is one of the largest of its kind in the world,
includes some 10,500 people. The meters record the
state of each TV set or video. The information is
transmitted automatically each night by telephone into
a central computer and is used to calculate the size of
the audience. Since 1991, the meters have been able to
record video playbacks.

Broadcasting Complaints Commission
merged with Broadcasting Standards Commission

Bectu: Broadcasting, Entertainment, Cinematograph and Theatre Union
111 Wardour Street, London W1V 4AY
Fax 020-7437 8258   Tel 020-7437 8506
E-mail: bectu@geo2.poptel.org.uk
Website: www.bectu.org.uk

Midlands office	Tel 0121-632 5372
North west office	Tel 0161-274 3174
Scottish office	Tel 0141-248 9558
Wales office	Tel 029-2066 6557

BECTU is the main trade union for workers in
broadcasting, film, theatre and other sectors of the
entertainment and media industry. It offers a Student

Link-up Scheme to arts and media students, and an
introductory rate to course graduates. It can give some
careers advice (SAE please) but works with Skillset,
regional training consortia and FT2 in promoting
access, opportunity, training and employment
prospects. Publishes Stage, Screen & Radio monthly.

Broadcasting Press Guild
Tiverton, The Ridge, Woking, Surrey GU22 7EQ
Fax 01483-765882   Tel 01483-764895
Association of 100+ journalists writing about the media
in the national and trade press. Membership by
invitation. Holds monthly lunches and presents the
BPG TV and Radio Awards.

Broadcasting Research Unit
see Voice of the Listener and Viewer

Broadcasting Standards Commission
7 The Sanctuary, London SW1P 3JS
Fax 020-7233 0397   Tel 020-7808 1000
E-mail: bsc@bsc.org.uk
Website: www.bsc.org.uk
Statutory body for broadcasting standards and fairness.
It is the only organisation within the regulatory
framework of UK broadcasting to cover all TV and
radio. This includes BBC and commercial broadcasters
as well as text, cable, satellite and digital services.
The Commission has three main tasks, set out in the
1996 Broadcasting Act:
  * to produce codes of practice relating to standards and
    fairness;
  * to consider and adjudicate on complaints;
  * to monitor, research and report on standards and
    fairness in broadcasting

BSS
Union House, Shepherd's Bush, London W12 8UA
Fax 020-8735 5049   Tel 020-8735 5099
E-mail: marketing@bss.org
Website: www.bss.org
Broadcasting Support Services is an independent
charity providing telephone helplines, viewer's guides
and other services for listeners and viewers of radio and
TV programmes.

BSS Linklines
11 Portland Street, Manchester M1 3HU
Fax 0161-455 1266   Tel 0161-455 1206
E-mail: debra.garnett@bss.org
A telephone service for the voluntary sector,
broadcasters, the public and commercial organisations.

Campaign for Freedom of Information
Suite 102, 16 Baldwins Gardens, London EC1N 7RJ
Fax 020-7831 7461   Tel 020-7831 7477
E-mail: admin@cfoi.demon.co.uk
Website: www.cfoi.org.uk
The campaign is pressing for a Freedom of Information
Act to create a general right of access to official records
subject to exemptions protecting information whose
disclosure would cause real harm to essential interests
such as defence, law enforcement and privacy.
Campaigns for a public interest defence under the
Official Secrets Act. It also seeks disclosure in the
private sector on issues of public interest. It publishes
the newspaper Secrets, plus briefings.

Campaign for Press and Broadcasting Freedom
8 Cynthia Street, London N1 9JF
Fax 020-7837 8868   Tel 020-7278 4430
E-mail: freepress@cpbf.org.uk
Website: www.cpbf.org.uk
Campaigns for a democratic, diverse and accountable media, accessible to all. The CPBF opposes monopoly ownership of the press and seeks a Right of Reply. It organises events and publishes 6x pa journal Free Press, occasional pamphlets and the Media Catalogue of mail order books and postcards.

Celtic Film and Television Festival Company
149 West George Street, Glasgow G2 4QE
Fax 0141-302 1738   Tel 0141-302 1737
E-mail: mail@celticfilm.co.uk
Website: www.celticfilm.co.uk
Organises the annual International Celtic Festival of Film and Television, peripatetic in Scotland, Wales, Cornwall, Ireland and Brittany, including awards and conference. It supports development of TV and film in Celtic nations and indigenous languages.

Children's Film & Television Foundation
Elstree Film Studios, Borehamwood, Herts WD6 1JG
Fax 020-8207 0860   Tel 020-8953 0844
E-mail: annahome@cftf.onyxnet.co.uk
Non-profitmaking organisation which funds script development for quality film and television projects aimed at children and their parents. Holds an extensive film library, with a wide range of films made for children/family viewing. Founded 1951.

Churches Advisory Council for Local Broadcasting (CACLB)
PO Box 124, Westcliff-on-Sea, Essex SS0 0QU
Fax 01702-305121   Tel 01702-348369
E-mail: office@caclb.org.uk
Website: www.caclb.org.uk
A charity for the advancement of Christianity through radio and TV. Has an Association of Christian broadcasters, quarterly news bulletin, annual conference and awards.

Cinema and TV Benevolent Fund
22 Golden Square, London W1R 4AD
Fax 020-7437 7186   Tel 020-7437 6567
E-mail: charity@ctbf.co.uk
Trade charity for retired and serving employees and their dependents needing caring help, support and financial aid.

Commercial Radio Companies Association
77 Shaftesbury Avenue, London W1V 7AD
Fax 020-7470 0062   Tel 020-7306 2603
E-mail: info@crca.co.uk
Website: www.crca.co.uk
The trade body for UK commercial radio. It represents commercial radio to Government, the Radio Authority, Copyright Societies and other organisations concerned with radio. CRCA gives advice to members and acts as a clearing house for radio information. The CRCA jointly owns Radio Joint Audience Research (RAJAR) with the BBC, owns the Network Chart Show and is a member of the Association of European Radios which lobbies European institutions on behalf of commercial radio.

Commonwealth Broadcasting Association
17 Fleet Street, London EC4Y 1AA
Fax 020-7583 5549   Tel 020-7583 5550
E-mail: cba@cba.org.uk
Website: www.cba.org.uk
Non-profit association of broadcasters with a commitment to public service broadcasting in Commonwealth countries. Activities include training programmes and conferences.

Communication Workers Union
150 The Broadway, Wimbledon, London SW19 1RX
Fax 020-8971 7437   Tel 020-8971 7200
E-mail: c.proctor@cwu.org
Website: www.cwu.org
The largest trade union in posts, telecommunications and financial services. The CWU Voice is published monthly.

Community Media Association
15 Paternoster Row, Sheffield, S Yorks S1 2BX
Fax 0114-279 8976   Tel 0114-279 5219
E mail: cma@commedia.org.uk
Website: www.commedia.org.uk
London Office: The Resource Centre, 356 Holloway Road, London N7 6PA
Fax 020-7700 0099   Tel 020-7700 0100 x 234
E mail: cmalondon@commedia.org.uk
UK membership body, developing and campaigning for community-based media. It offers information, advice, training and consultancy, holds conferences and events and publishes the quarterly journals Airflash and London News.

Confederation of Aerial Industries
Fullerton House Business Centre, Fulton Road, Wembley Park, Middlesex HA9 0TF
Fax 020-8903 8719   Tel 020-8902 8998
E-mail: office@cai.org.uk
Trade association for aerials and satellite dish manufacturers.

Copyright Advice and Anti-Piracy Hotline
7 Victory Business Centre, Worton Road, Isleworth, Middlesex TW7 6DB
Fax 020-8847 5947   Tel 0845-6034567
E-mail: contact@copyright-info.org.uk
Website: www.copyright-info.org
Offers advice and information to anyone who wants to use film, music and software copyrights. It will also help identify and report piracy.

CSV Media
237 Pentonville Road, London N1 9NJ
Fax 020-7278 7912   Tel 020-7278 6601
E-mail: media@csv.org.uk
Website: www.csv.org.uk/media
CSV Media, part of the national charity Community Service Volunteers, specialises in social action broadcasting, media support services and media training. Services range from TV and radio programme production, broadcast back-up, including telephone helplines and training in TV and radio production.

Deaf Broadcasting Council
70 Blacketts Wood Drive, Chorleywood,
Rickmansworth, Herts WD3 5QQ
Fax 01923-283127
E-mail rmyers@waitrose.com
An umbrella organisation to which all the major
national bodies for and on behalf of deaf, deafened and
hard of hearing people are affiliated. Ensures that TV
companies and broadcasters are aware of their needs.
Publishes newsletter Mailshot 3-4x pa.

Different Voices
108 Portnall Road, London W9 3BG
Fax 020-8968 0991   Tel 020-8969 0109
E-mail: voices@twiza.demon.co.uk
Website: www.twiza.demon.co.uk
Contact: Cathy Aitchison
Non-profit making online information and support
network promoting greater media access for under-
represented groups. Different Voices runs the Online
Media Network, a directory for individuals and
organisations in the UK media.

Directors Guild of Great Britain
Acorn House, 314-320 Grays Inn Road, London
WC1X 8DP
Fax 020-7278 4742   Tel 020-7278 4343
E-mail: guild@dggb.co.uk
Website: www.dggb.co.uk
Union for directors in all media, including TV, film,
theatre and radio. Issues an advised schedule of rates,
code of practice and contract guides. Gives contractual
advice and holds workshops, conferences, public events
and social events. Publishes a magazine, Direct and an
annual directory of all members.

Directors and Producers' Rights Society
16-18 Strutton Ground, London SW1P 2HP
Fax 020-7227 4755   Tel 020-7227 4757
E-mail: info@dprs.org
A collecting society which administers authorial rights
payments on behalf of British film and television
directors.

Eclipse
18-20 Highbury Place, London N5 1QP
Fax 020-7354 8106   Tel 020-7354 5858
E-mail: publications@irseclipse.co.uk
Website: www.irseclipse.co.uk
Provides information on industrial relations practice,
health and safety legislation and employment law as
well as publishing journals and reports.

Equity
Guild House, Upper St Martins Lane, London WC2H
9EG
Fax 020-7379 7001   Tel 020-7379 6000
E-mail: info@equity.org.uk
Website: www.equity.org.uk/equity
British Actors' Equity Association is the trade union for
actors, stage managers, opera singers, dancers,
directors, designers, choreographers, variety artistes
and stunt performers working in theatre, film,
television, radio and variety venues. The union
publishes the quarterly magazine Equity which is
distributed to the membership of 35,000.

Euronews
60 Chemin des Moules, BP 161, 69131 Lyon, France
Fax: 0033 4 72 18 93 71 Tel: 0033 4 72 18 80 00
Website: www.euronews.net
A pan-European broadcaster which transmits TV news
in six languages to 43 countires. Controlled by ITN.

Fact
7 Victory Business Centre, Worton Road, Isleworth,
Middlesex TW7 6DB
Fax 020-8560 6364   Tel 020-8568 6646
Fact, the Federation Against Copyright Theft, is an
organisation funded by its members to combat
counterfeiting, piracy and misuse of their products.

Federation of Communication Services
207 Anerley Road, London SE20 8ER
Fax 020-8778 8402   Tel 020-8778 5656
E-mail: fcs@fcs.org.uk
Website: www.fcs.org.uk
Representative body for the UK mobile comms
industry. It is the focus for developments, issues and
legislation affecting moblie communications.

Federation of the Electronics Industry
Russell Square House, 10-12 Russell Square, London
WC1B 5EE
Fax 020-7331 2040   Tel 020-7331 2000
E-mail feedback@fei.org.uk
Website: www.fei.org.uk/fei
Trade association for information technology,
electronics, communications, business technology and
office furniture. Represents the industry's interests on
major European and international standards and
regulatory bodies, satellite and broadcasting groups. It
publishes annual statistics on electronic components.

Federation of Entertainment Unions
1 Highfield, Twyford, near Winchester, Hants SO21
1QR
Fax 01962-713288   Tel 01962-713134
E-mail: harris@interalpha.co.uk
Collective body of trade unions, representing the
interests of 150,000 members in the broadcasting and
entertainment industries. The unions are: BECTU,
Equity, Musicians Union, NUJ, Writers Guild, AEEU. It
provides liaison, representation, lobbying and co-
ordination services on issues of common concern.

Film Artistes' Association
111 Wardour Street, London W1 4AY
Fax 020-7287 8984   Tel 020-7437 8506
E-mail: bactu@geo2.poptel.org.uk
The trade union representing crowd artistes, stand-ins
and doubles.

Focal International: Federation of Commercial Audio Visual Libraries
See under Film Libraries

Gaelic Broadcasting Committee
4 Harbour View, Cromwell St Quay, Stornoway, Isle of
Lewis HS1 2DF
Fax 01851-706432   Tel 01851-705550
E-mail: comataidh@compuserve.com
Website: www.ccg.org.uk
Statutory body grant-funding Gaelic television sound
programmes, development and training.

Guardian Edinburgh International TV Festival
24 Neal Street, London WC2H 9PS
Fax 020-7836 0702   Tel 020-7379 4519
E-mail: info@geitf.co.uk
Website: www.geitf.co.uk
Britain's biggest international forum for the TV
industry attracts prominent speakers, many delegates
and widespread interest. Held over the English August
bank holiday, for four days, during the Edinburgh
Festival. Publishes an annual magazine.

Guild of British Animation
26 Noel Street, London W1V 3RD
Fax 020-7434 9002   Tel 020-7434 2651
E-mail: afvpa@easynet.co.uk
The Guild represents the interests of the growing
number of British animation companies.

Guild of British Camera Technicians
5-11 Taunton Road, Metropolitan Centre, Greenford,
Middlesex UB6 8UQ
Fax 020-8575 5972   Tel 020-8578 9243
E-mail: admin@gbct.org
The Guild represents film and video camera
technicians working in the UK entertainment industry.
It publishes the bimonthly news magazine Eyepiece.

Guild of British Film Editors
Travair, Spurlands End Road, Great Kingshill, High
Wycombe, Bucks HP15 6HY
Fax 01494-712313   Tel 01494-712313
E-mail: cox.gbfe@btinternet.com
The Guild of British Film Editors organises film shows
and technical visits for its members. It presents awards
for film and sound editing. It maintains a dialogue with
other technical guilds at home and abroad, publishes
newsletters.

Guild of Television Cameramen
1 Churchill Road, Tavistock, Devon PL19 9BU
Fax 01822-615785   Tel 01822-614405
Website: www.gtc.org.uk
Professional association aiming to preserve the working
status of TV camera operators. Publishes bi-annual
Zerb Magazine and newsletter. Holds regular
workshops.

Hospital Broadcasting Association
6 Abbots Grove, Pinglewick Hamlet, Belper,
Derbyshire DE56 1BX
Fax 0870-321 6013   Tel 0870-321 6000
E-mail: info@hbauk.com
Website: www.hbauk.com
The HBA is the national representative association for
hospital broadcasting. It is responsible for providing
advice and support to hospital radio stations, and for
promoting hospital broadcasting nationwide.

Independent Media Distribution
10 John Princes Street, London W1M 0AH
Fax 0120-7468 6869   Tel 0120-7468 6868
E-mail: shelby@imd.plc.uk
Distributes commercials, short form programmes and
new music releases to all radio stations in the UK and
Ireland.

Independent Television Commission (ITC)
HQ: 33 Foley Street, London W1P 7LB
Fax 020-7306 7800   Tel 020-7255 3000
Kings Worthy Court, Kings Worthy, Winchester, Hants
SO23 7QA.
Fax 01962-886141   Tel 01962-848600
E mail: publicaffairs@itc.org.uk
Website: www.itc.org.uk
National and regional offices:

Northern Ireland	028-9024 8733
Scotland	0141-226 4436
Wales	029-2038 4541
East of England	01603-623533
Midlands - Nottingham	0115-952 7333
North East England	0191-261 0148
North of England	0114-276 9091
North West England	0161-834 2707
S of England, Winchester	01962-883950
S of England, Plymouth	01752-663031

The ITC is the public body responsible for licensing
and regulating commercially funded television services
provided in and from the UK. These include Channel 3
(ITV), Channel 4, Channel 5, public teletext and a range
of cable, local delivery, satellite and digital television
services. They do not include services provided by the
BBC or by S4C, the fourth channel in Wales. The ITC
replaced the Independent Broadcasting Authority and
the Cable Authority in 1991.

ITC Engineering/Research/Finance:
Kings Worthy Court, Kings Worthy, Winchester,
Hants SO23 7QA
Fax 01962-886109   Tel 01962-848600

Institute of Broadcast Sound
27 Old Gloucester Street, London WC1N 3XX
Fax 020-8887 0167   Tel 01483 575450
E-mail: info@ibs.org.uk
Website: www.ibs.org.uk
Professional body for TV and radio sound broadcasters.
Publishes the bi-monthly trade magazine Line Up.

Institute of Local Television
27 Beaver Hall Road, Edinburgh EH7 4JE
Fax 0131-557 8608   Tel 0131-557 8610
E-mail: edinburghtv@ukonline.co.uk
Aims to increase local TV programming and maintain
high quality local service on cable. Through research
and consultancy supports development of the new
resticted service TV licence and the introduction of local
digital TV. Runs courses and conferences. Launched
Channel 6 as first local terrestrial TV service in
Edinburgh in spring 1997.

International Broadcasting Trust
2 Ferdinand Place, London NW1 8EE
Fax 020-7284 3374   Tel 020-7482 2847
E-mail: mail@ibt.org.uk
Website: www.ibt.org.uk
An TV company with charitable status specialising in
programmes on development, environment and
human rights issues. IBT is backed by a consortium of
70 aid and development agencies, educational bodies,
churches and trade unions. It publishes the bi-annual
newsletter Fast Forward and back-up material.

International Institute of Communications

3rd Floor, Westcott House, 35 Portland Place, London
W1N 3AG
Fax 020-7323 9623   Tel 020-7323 9622
E mail: enquiries@iicom.org
Website: www.iicom.org
Promotes the open debate of issues in the
communications field worldwide, in the interest of
human and social advancement. Specialises in
broadcasting, telecommunications and
communications policy. It publishes books, bimonthly
journal Intermedia, newsletter, reports, etc.

International Visual Communications
Association

5-6 Clipstone Street, London W1P 8LD
Fax 020-7436 2606   Tel 020-7580 0962
E-mail: info@ivca.org
A trade association representing the users and
suppliers of the corporate visual communications
industry. It publishes magazine and guides and
organises regular professional and social events.
Provides legal and information help.

ITV Association

200 Grays Inn Road, London, WC1X 8HF
Fax 020-7843 8155   Tel 020-7843 8000
The corporate political arm for the ITV. It lobbies MPs
about broadcasting standards and seeks to improve or
amend broadcasting bills.

ITV Network

200 Grays Inn Road, London WC1X 8HF
Fax 020-7843 8158   Tel 020-7843 8000
Website: www.itv.co.uk
Represents the interests of the regional ITV companies.
Set up in late 1992 to commission and schedule ITV's
networked programmes from 1 January 1993, as
required by the 1990 Broadcasting Act. Also
responsible for research, programme acquisitions and
financial, legal and business matters for ITV.

Local Independent Television Network

c/o Community Media Association, 15 Paternoster
Row, Sheffield S1 2BX
Fax 0114-279 8976   Tel 0114-279 5219
E-mail: cma@commedia.org.uk
Website: litn.org.uk
The trade body for those operating ITC Restricted
Service Licences.

London Film Commission

20 Euston Centre, Regent's Place, London NW1 3JH
Fax 020-7387 8788   Tel 020-7387 8787
E-mail: lfc@london-film.co.uk
The Commission encourages and assists film and TV
production in London and holds databases of locations,
personnel and facilities. Funded by government, the
film industry and other private sector sponsors, it works
to promote London as a first choice destination for
overseas film makers.

MDA

see Mobile Data Association

Mechanical Copyright Protection Society

41 Streatham High Road, London SW16 1ER
Fax 020-8769 8792   Tel 020-8664 4400
E mail: corpcomms@mcps.co.uk
Websitew: www.mcps.co.uk
Organisation of music publishers and composers,
collecting and distributing royalties from the recording
of copyright music onto CDs, cassettes, audio-visual
and broadcast material. The society's National
Discography, a database of commercial music and
records, offers a wide range of music information.
Publishes On the Right Track (a guide to starting in the
music business) and the magazine For the Record.

Media Antenna Scotland

294 West George Street, Glasgow G2 4QE
Fax 0141-357 2345   Tel 0141-302 1777
E-mail: louisescott@dial.pipex.com
Office in Scotland for the European Commission's
media programme.

Media Research Group

Starcom Worldwide, 24-27 Great Pulteney Street,
London W1R 3DB
                          Tel 020-7453 4593
E-mail: denise.gardner@starcomworldwide.co.uk
Website: www.telmar.co.uk
Provides forum for debating issues relating to media
planning and research. Holds bi-annual conference.

MediaTel

52 Poland Street, London W1V 4LQ
Fax 020-7734 0940   Tel 020-7439 7575
E-mail: info@mediatel.co.uk
Website: www.mediatel.co.uk
MediaTel is an on-line media news and information
database. There is free access to daily media news and
walkthrough screens but the media databases are only
available on an annual company subscription.

Media Trust

3-7 Euston Centre, Regents Place, London NW1 3JG
Fax 020-7874 7644   Tel 020-7874 7600
E-mail: info@mediatrust.org
Website: www.mediatrust.org
The Trust builds partnerships between the media and
the voluntary sector. It provides information, training
services, and on-line material. It also runs Media
Resource to match voluntary organisations with skills
and resources donated by the media.

Mobile Data Association

PO Box 2042, Wolverhampton WV10 7LJ
Fax 01922-413420   Tel 0704-134 0235
E-mail: info@mda-mobiledata.org
Website: www.mda-mobiledata.org
Association for the mobile data industry, representing
manufacturers, vendors, resellers and end users.

Musicians' Union

60-62 Clapham Road, London SW9 0JJ
Fax 020-7582 9805   Tel 020-7582 5566
E-mail: info@musiciansunion.org.uk
Website: www.musiciansunion.org.uk
The trade union which looks after the interests all styles
of musician. It publishes the quarterly journal Musician
plus a range of leaflets on the music biz.

National Communications Union
See Communication Workers Union

National Film and Television Archive
21 Stephen Street, London W1P 2LN
Fax 020-7436 7950 Tel 020-7255 1444
Website: www.bfi.org.uk
Founded in 1935 as a division of the British Film Institute. It acquires, preserves, catalogues and makes permanently available for study, research and screening a national and international collection of moving images of all kinds. Now holds over 350,000 titles, starting from 1895. Covers TV, documentary and feature films. The J Paul Getty Jnr Conservation Centre, in Berkhamsted is the location for the Archive's preservation work and for storage.

National Film Theatre
South Bank, Waterloo, London SE1 8XT
Fax 020-7815 1431 Tel 020-7815 1327
E-mail: brian.robinson@bfi.org.uk
Three cinemas owned by the British Film Institute (cf) showing the widest possible range of film and television from around the world.

National Sound Archive
See British Library National Sound Archive

National Viewers' and Listeners' Association
3 Willow House, Kennington Road, Ashford, Kent TN24 0NR
Fax 01233-633836 Tel 01233-633936
E-mail: info@nvala.org
Organisation founded by Mary Whitehouse. It campaigns to make the Obscene Publications Acts 1959 and 1964 effective, and encourages discussion and debate about the effects of the media on individuals, family and society. Publishes reports and the magazine The Viewer & Listener x3 p.a.

NetMedia
Haymarket House, 28-29 Haymarket, London SW1 4SP
Tel 020-7344 1236
E mail: msw@net-media.co.uk
Website: www.net-media.co.uk
NetMedia is the clearing house for UK media netheads which organises conferences and an annual award.

Networking
30-38 Dock Street, Leeds, West Yorks LS10 1JF
Fax 0113-245 1238 Tel 0113-242 8646
E mail: networking@vera-media.demon.co.uk
Membership organisation for women involved in any way, or hoping to work in film, video or television. Media departments, libraries,careers offices are welcome. It publishes a newsletter and contacts index and provides information and advice.

NTL
Crawley Court, Winchester, Hants SO21 2QA
Fax 01962-822374 Tel 01962-823434
E-mail: broadcast.tv@ntl.com
broadcast.radio@ntl.com
Website: www.ntl.com
Provides transmission service for ITV, Channel 4, S4C, Channel 5, Digital 3 & 4, SDN and most independent radio stations. NTL's uplinking facilities offer services to broadcasters including direct to home transmission.

OneWorld Online
Hedgerley Wood, 4 Red Lane, Chinnor Oxon OX9 4BW
Fax 01494-481751 Tel 01494-481629
E-mail: justice@oneworld.net
Website: www.oneworld.net
OneWorld is a community of over 100 websites devoted to human rights and sustainable development. It includes a library, a discussion forum, a news wire and a radio station offered free to local communities for rebroadcasting.

PACT (Producers Alliance for Cinema & Television)
45 Mortimer Street, London W1N 7TD
Fax 020-7331 6700 Tel 020-7331 6000
E-mail: enquiries@pact.co.uk
Website: www.pact.co.uk
Trade association and employers' body for feature film, independent television and new media productionn companies. Provides a range of services, including information and production advice. Lobbies Government and regulators on its members' behalf. Produces monthly members' magazine.

PACT Scotland
249 West George Street, Glasgow G2 4QE
Fax 0141-320 1721 Tel 0141-320 1720
E-mail: margaret@pactscot.co.uk
Website: www.pact.scot.co.uk

Production Managers Association
Ealing Studios, Ealing Green, London W5 5EP
Fax 020-8758 8647 Tel 020-8758 8699
E-mail: pma@pma.org.uk
Website: www.pma.org.uk
Offers a professional voice for both freelance and permanently employed production managers. Provides regular workshops, training courses and an employment register.

Radio Academy
5 Market Place, London W1N 7AH
Fax 020-7255 2029 Tel 020-7255 2010
E-mail: info@radioacademy.org
Website: www.radioacademy.org
Professional membership organisation for the radio industry. Organises the industry's annual conference, the Radio Festival plus seminars and workshops. Regional centres organise their own programme of events. Makes a number of awards for outstanding contributions to the radio industry.

Radio Advertising Bureau
77 Shaftesbury Avenue, London W1V 7AD
Fax 020-7306 2505 Tel 020-7306 2500
Website: www.rab.co.uk
The RAB is the marketing arm of the commercial radio industry. It aims to increase the levels of familiarity and favourability towards commercial radio as an advertising medium.

Radio Advertising Clearance Centre
46 Westbourne Grove, London W2 5SH
Fax 020-7229 0352 Tel 020-7727 2646
E-mail: adclear@racc.co.uk
Clears advertisements for radio.

Radio Authority

Holbrook House, 14 Great Queen Street, London WC2B 5DG
Fax 020-7405 7062   Tel 020-7430 2724
Website: www.radioauthority.org.uk
Statutory body licensing and regulating independent radio (all non-BBC services). Started in 1991, replacing part of the Independent Broadcasting Authority (see also Independent Television Commission). Publishes the annual Radio Authority Pocket Book and The Radio Authority complaints leaflet 'How Do I Complain?'.

Radio

PO Box 14880, London NW1 9ZD
Fax 020-7428 0541   Tel 020-7485 0873
A trade body representing independent radio producers to negotiate with the radio network, government and the unions. One of its aims is to increase the BBC's quota of independently produced programmes from around 10 per cent to some 25 per cent of output.

Radio Society of Great Britain

Lambda House, Cranborne Road, Potters Bar, Herts EN6 3JE
Fax 01707-645105   Tel 01707-659015
E-mail: ar.dept@rsgb.org.uk
The leading national organisation for amateur radio enthusiasts, offering a range of services to members. The society publishes: the monthly magazine Radio Communication, full of news, features, etc; and the annual Yearbook, a comprehensive guide to all organisations and the holder of every G call-sign.

Radiocommunications' Agency

Wyndham House, 189 Marsh Wall, London E14 9SX
Fax 020-7211 0507   Tel 020-7211 0211
E-mail: library.ra@gtnet.gov.uk
Website: www.radio.gov.uk
An executive agency of the DTI. It is responsible for the management of the civilian radio spectrum within the UK. It also represents UK radio interests internationally. Publishes an annual report and many useful information sheets on radio-related topics.

Rajar: Radio Joint Audience Research

Collier House, 163-169 Brompton Road, London SW3 1PY
Fax 020-7589 4004   Tel 020-7584 3003
Website: www.rajar.co.uk
Joint body involving the BBC and commercial radio which is responsible for controlling a system of audience research for radio in the UK.

Reel Women

57 Holmewood Gardens, London SW2 3NB
Fax 020-8678 7404   Tel 020-8678 7404
E-mail: rawlings@uwest.ac-uk
Brings together women working in television,film and video for discussions, seminars, screenings and workshops.

Researcher's Guide to British Film and Television Collections

British Universities Film and Video Council, 77 Wells Street, London W1P 3RE
Tel: 020-7393 1500
E-mail: ask@bufvc.ac.uk
Website: www.bufvc.ac.uk

Royal Television Society

100 Grays Inn Road, London WC1X 8AL
Fax 020-7430 0924   Tel 020-7430 1000
E-mail: info@rts.org.uk
Website: www.rts.org.uk
Promoting the art and science of television broadcasting, the Society provides a unique forum where all branches of the industry can meet and discuss major issues. Organises conferences, lectures, workshops, masterclasses and awards ceremonies. The RTS has regional centres, each running their own programme of events. Publishes Television magazine ten times a year and an annual handbook. Membership £62 pa, students £20.

Satellite and Cable Broadcasters' Group

64 West End, Northwold, Thetford, Norfolk IP26 5LG
Fax 01366-727411   Tel 01366-728795
E-mail: scbg.meiwes@care4free.net
Association of cable and satellite TV programme providers.

Satellite Media Services

Lawford Heath, Rugby, Warwickshire CV23 9EU
Fax 01788-523001   Tel 01788-523000
E mail info@sms.co.uk
SMS uses its dedicated lines, digital satellite and ISDN networks to distribute commericals, programmes, IRN and PA news services and record releases to independent commercial radio. It is also active in retail broadcasting, data communications networks and other commercial services distributed via satellite.

Scottish Association of Smallscale Broadcasters

Struan House, The Square, Aberfeldy, Perthshire PH15 2DD
Fax 01887-820038   Tel 01887-820956
E-mail: wwright@sol.co.uk
Co-operative umbrella for all individuals and organisations concerned with smallscale broadcast operations, RSLs (restricted service licences), training workshops, etc. Publishes quarterly newsletter. Formerly called the Scottish Community Broadcasting Group, set up in 1985.

Scottish Screen

2nd Floor, 249 West George Street, Glasgow G2 4QE
Fax 0141-302 1711   Tel 0141-302 1700
E-mail: info@scottishscreen.com
Website: www.scottishscreen.com
Information Officer: Isabella Edgar
Scottish Screen is responsible to the Scottish Parliament for developing all aspects of screen industry and culture in Scotland through script and company development, short film production, distribution of National Lottery finance, training, education, exhibition funding, the Film Commissions locations support and the Scottish Film and Television Archive.

Screenwriters' Workshop

Suffolk House, Whitfield Street, London W1P 5SW
Tel 020-7387 5511
Website: www.lsw.org.co.uk
Dedicated to helping screen and TV writers break into the industry. Courses and workshops with tuition at all stages.

Services Sound and Vision Group
Chalfont Grove, Gerrards Cross, Bucks SL9 8TN
Fax 01494-872982 Tel 01494-874461
Website: www.ssvc.com
Broadcasts radio and TV to the British armed forces via
BFBS (British Forces Broadcasting Service) around the
world. TLI (Teleport London International) provides
satellite services. Visua gives multimedia help.

Sgrin - Media Agency for Wales
The Bank, 10 Mount Stuart Square, Cardiff Bay,
Cardiff CF10 5EE
Fax 029-2033 3320 Tel 029-2033 3300
E-mail: sgrin@sgrin.co.uk
Website: www.sgrin.co.uk
Formulates a strategic vision for film, TV and new
media in Wales. It encourages industrial growth,
cultural development and public involvement and
houses the Wales Film and Television Archive and
Media Antenna Wales, the information centre for
European audiovisual funding and policy.

Society of Cable Telecommunication Engineers
Fulton House Business Centre, Fulton Road,
Wembley Park, Middlesex HA9 0TF
Fax 020-8903 8719 Tel 020-8902 8998
E-mail: office@scte.org.uk
Website: www.acte.org.uk
Technical body aiming to raise the standards of cable
telecommunication engineering and improve the status
of cable engineers. Publishes journal Cable
Telecommunication Engineering.

Society of Television Lighting Directors
E-mail: chairman@stld.org.uk
The Society promotes discussion on techniques and on
the use and design of equipment. It organises meetings
and produces a journal: Television Lighting.

Student Radio Association
c/o The Radio Academy, 5 Market Place, London
W1N 7AH
Fax 020-7255 2029 Tel 020-7255 2012
E-mail: exec@studentradio.org.uk
Website: www.studentradio.org.uk
The SRA is the representative body for student radio.
Run by an elected committee drawn from its 70
member stations. It holds three conferences and
organises the Student Radio Awards with Radio 1.

Telecommunications Users' Association
2-8 Games Road, Cockfosters EN4 9HN
Fax 020-8447 4901 Tel 020-8449 8844
E-mail: tua@dial.pipex.com
Website: www.tua.co.uk
An independent organisation representing its members
interests within the world's telecommunications
companies. Membership includes a help line,
consultancy, training, workshops and publications.

Television & Radio Industries Club
2 Duckling Lane, Sawbridgeworth, Herts CM21 9QA
Fax 01279-723100 Tel 01279-721100
Founded 1931 to promote goodwill amongst those
engaged in the audio, visual and allied industries. Its
primary role is arranging social events and it publishes
a yearbook and organises annual Celebrity Awards.

3WE (Third World & Environmental Broadcasting Project)
2 Ferdinand Place, London NW1 8EE
Fax 020-7284 3374 Tel 020-7482 2847
E-mail: ibt@gn.apc.org
3WE works for sustained and imaginative coverage of
global affairs on UK TV on behalf of Oxfam, WWF,
Amnesty International and a consortium of other
leading voluntary agencies.

Voice of the Listener and Viewer
101 King's Drive, Gravesend, Kent DA12 5BQ
Fax 01474-351112 Tel.01474-352835
E-mail: vlv@btinternet.com
An independent non-profit making, society working for
quality and diversity in British broadcasting which
speaks for viewers and listeners on all broadcasting
issues. VLV has no political, commercial or sectarian
affiliations and is concerned with the structures,
regulation and funding that under pin the British
broadcasting system. It does not handle complaints.
VLV has individual members, academic colleges and
university departments in membership. It publishes a
qurterly newsletter, reports and briefings. Arranges
public seminars, debates and conferences, including an
annual conference on children's television. Holds the
archives of the former Broadcasting Research Unit and
the British Action for Children's Television.

White Dot
PO Box 2116, Hove, East Sussex BN3 3LR
E-mail: info@whitedot.org
Website: www.spyinteractive.tv
A campaign against television which encourages people
to get a life and turn off their sets. It organises an
annual Turn Off TV Week. The next one is 23-29 April
2001. Recently launched the parody interactive TV
service on www.spyinteractive.tv

Wireless Preservation Society
52 West Hill Road, Ryde, Isle of Wight PO33 3LN
Fax 01983-564708 Tel 01983-567665
The society and the linked Communications and
Electronics Museum preserve a reference collection of
radio, TV and other electronic equipment in Museums
at Arreton Manor and Puckpool on the Isle of Wight
and at Bletchley Park, near Milton Keynes.

Women's Radio Group
Unit 13, 111 Power Road, London W4 5PY
Fax 020-8995 5442 Tel 020-8742 7802
E-mail: wrg@twiza.demon.co.uk
Website: www.twiza.demon.co.uk/wrg
Contact: Julie Hill
A training and networking charity for women
interested in radio. Activities include training courses,
seminars and radio related events.

The Writers' Guild of Great Britain
430 Edgware Road, London W2 1EH
Fax 020-7706 2413 Tel 020-7723 8074
E-mail: postie@wggb.demon.co.uk
Website: www.writers.org.uk/guild
The writers' union. It has agreements with Pact, BBC,
ITV, ITC, TMA and TAC. Provides support for
members, organises events and publishes a bi-monthly
magazine.

Ethnic media

First a few statistics. The UK's population is 56.5 million, of which 3.6 million - some 6.4 per cent - belong to an ethnic minority. Indians are the largest group, nearly half of them having a south Asian origin and the second largest group is black with West Indian origin. Within less than 15 years, Afro-Caribbeans and Asians will comprise at least 40 per cent of the youth populations in London and Birmingham.

These proportions are not reflected in the media. Under 2 per cent of London-based national press journalists are ethnic and the imbalance is greater on local papers. Broadcasting isn't much better and only the BBC and LWT employ more than 6.4 per cent ethnic staff. "In management roles that figure comes down to 2 per cent," says Greg Dyke. "The top of the BBC is very white."

The BBC director general began his tenure with a speech to the Commission for Racial Equality's (CRE) Race in the Media Awards. It is worth quoting at length. "Organisations that were riding high a few years ago are struggling because they failed to recognise the fundamental changes in our society. From Marks and Spencer right through to the Metropolitan Police you find institutions which have been slow to react to modern Britain and as a result have had problems. The BBC is no different ... the task during my time at the BBC is to make sure that we make public service broadcasting relevant to this new age. The danger for any broadcaster is to let your audience get ahead of you in ideas and attitudes. And I believe that in the area of race there is real evidence that one important part of our audience - the young - are already well ahead of us." Dyke pledged to up the proportion of ethnic employees to 10 per cent by 2003 and to operate incentives to at least double the number of ethnic managers. He continued: "Once we were the chosen career path for the public school, Oxbridge educated chap. But the BBC moved on from that a decade or so ago - which is just as well for me. This is an organisation that under John Birt's leadership really tried because John was really committed to this cause. It was John who drove through so much pioneering work in this area at LWT 20 years ago. It was John who created the 8 per cent target at the BBC. My concern is that it's more about the culture of the organisation - a culture that many from ethnic minorities do not find attractive or relevant. A culture that has to recognise and fully understand multi-cultural Britain. A culture that is rooted in another earlier Britain."

Meanwhile an old row at BBC World Service reached a head with allegations that the BBC was attempting to suppress correspondence relating to a CRE report which concluded procedures to monitor ethnic minority representation were "wholly inadequate" and revealing "widespread concern" among all staff about the lack of promotion beyond junior grades. The corporation responded with a "fresh blood" policy to recruit foreign journalists on three-year fixed term contracts. A Bectu spokesman said: "Many of the [African and central Asian] countries they come from are not ken on journalists ... The policy supposes these journalists can go stale, like a piece of meat."

In April 2000 a journalists' training course in Tower Hamlets collapsed when students were barred from claiming benefits because they were not available for work. David Thompson, a former Mirror journalist who had helped established the NCTJ-recognised course, wrote: "Most people entering journalism come from a narrower band of society than at any time in the past. They are, in the main, graduates, many from the older universities. They are largely from middle class homes because it is becoming harder for young people from working class homes, including those in the ethnic communities, to support themselves through university. In the end it is the newspaper industry which should ensure journalism doesn't become a middle class preserve like the law and doctoring. The weeklies and the tabloids in particular should recognise that they need reporters who understand how their readers live, what motivates them, what their ambitions are and how they can be championed. Nowhere is this truer than among the ethnic communities."

The Ali G Show

A north London Jewish boy made good as the media hit of the year by playing a thick Asian youth pretending to be a black. Sacha Baron Cohen's Ali G vaulted from a late night slot in autumn 1999 to his own show the following Spring by lampooning the Channel 4 audience which laughed hardest at his complex racial jokes. Cohen also parodied TV interview conventions and showed his understanding of the media by refusing to explain his intentions in a straight interview. "Is it because I is black?" was the catch line of a persona that spawned the best gags of the year.

"You was caned at school?" Ali G declared to a perplexed right wing educationist, Rhodes Boyson. "Respect." He had an inspired question for George Patton, the Orange Order's grandmaster in Northern Ireland. "What about marrying a Catholic girl?" he asked. "What if she was really fit? What if she had her own sound system and wasn't gonna be stealing money off you all the time?" James Whittaker, the most pompous of royal hacks, was asked: "Why was Diana knobbing that Pakistani?"

"Offensive," said the majority of comedians interviewed by New Nation newspaper. Felix Dexter, of The Real McCoy, said: "I appreciate the humour of an innocent confronting an expert and neither understanding what the other is on about. But a lot of the humour is laughing at black street culture, and it is being celebrated because it allows the liberal middle classes to laugh at that culture in a context where they can retain their sense of political correctness." Curtis Walker of the BBC2 show Urban Heat, said: "I don't like the idea of a white guy playing a black guy … and when he is playing to a stupid stereotype it is even worse."

The Ethnic Multicultural Media Awards didn't see it that way and awarded the Ali G Show the TV entertainment production of the year award. Let the Guardian's Gary Younge have the last word. "The issue is not whether we should be laughing at Ali G or not; we are. Even the black comedians who said he was offensive admit that he makes them laugh. Nor is the question whether some people should be uneasy at Ali G; they are. In such a nebulous, subjective and sensitive area the true mark of our racial sophistication will be whether we can have an intelligent discussion about what makes us laugh and what makes us uneasy."

Ali G: "Respect."

Gary Younge: "The issue is not whether we should be laughing at Ali G or not; we are. In such a nebulous, subjective and sensitive area the true mark of our racial sophistication will be whether we can have an intelligent discussion about what makes us laugh and what makes us uneasy."

ETHNIC PRESS

Ad-Diplomasi News Report
PO Box 138, London SW3 6BH
Fax 020-7266 1479   Tel 020-7286 1372
E-mail: ad-diplomasi@easynet.co.uk
Website:
www.easyweb.easynet.co.uk/~ad-diplomasi/
Arabic, bi-monthly with updates. Subscription only.
Editor: Raymond Atallah

The African
25 Hester Road, London N18 2RF
Fax 020-8351 0516   Tel 020-8350 0684
Monthly.
Editor: Zaya Yeebo

Akhbar-e-Watan
306-308a Hoe Street, London E17 9PX
Fax 020-8925 0446   Tel 020-8923 9222
E-mail: watan@wavenet.co,uk
Website: www.wavenet.co.uk/users/watan
Urdu. **Editor**: Taj Javaid

Al Ahram International
203-209 North Gower Street, London NW1 2NJ
Fax 020-7388 3130   Tel 020-7388 1155
Arabic daily.
Editor: Samir Mohamed

Al-Alaam
Banner House, 55-57 Banner Street, London EC1Y
8PX
Fax 020-7608 3581   Tel 020-7608 3454
E-mail: al.alaam@btinternet.com
Arabic weekly. **Editor**: Dr Sead Mahamed Shehabi

Al Arab
159 Acre Lane, London SW2 5UA
Fax 020-7326 1783   Tel 020-7274 9381
E-mail: editor@alarab.co.uk
Website: www.alarab.co.uk
Arabic daily.
Editor: A S Elhluni

Al Hayat
Kensington Centre, 66 Hammersmith Road, London
W14 8YT
Fax 020-7602 4963   Tel 020-7602 9988
Website: www.alhayat.com
Arabic daily.
Editor George Semaan

Al Muhajir
132 Mill Lane, London NW6 1NE
Fax 020-7813 6234   Tel 020-7813 5553
Arabic fortnightly.
Editor: M Assou

Amar Deep Hindi
36 Trent Avenue, London W5 4TL
Fax 020-8579 3180   Tel 020-8840 3534
Weekly.
Editor: J M Kaushal

The American in Britain
Yewlands House, Milbrook House, Nuttley, East
Sussex TN22 3PH
Fax 01825-713687   Tel 01825-713676

Ananda Bazar Patrika
48 Beverley Gardens, Wembley Middlesex HA9 9QZ
Fax 020-8908 2625   Tel 020-8904 2533
Bengali/English weekly.
Editor: Shrabani Basu

Asharq Al Awsat (Arab News)
Arab Press House, 184 High Holborn, London WC1V
7AP
Fax 020-7831 2310   Tel 020-7831 8181
E-mail: admin@arab.net
Editor: Abdul Rahaman Al Rashid

The Asian
Sunrise House, Sunrise Road, Southall, Middlesex
UB2 4AU
Fax 020-8574 9292   Tel 020-8574 9393
E-mail: editor@asianweekly.co.uk

Asian Age
Dolphin Media House, Spring Villa Park, Spring Villa
Road, London HAB 7EB
Fax 020-8951 4839   Tel 020-8951 4401
Daily.
Editor: Abhik Sen

Asian Convenience Retailer/Asian Voice
8-16 Coronet Street, London N1 6HD
Fax 020-8951 4839   Tel 020-8951 4878
E-mail: gujarat@samachar.com
Fortnightly.

Asian Entertainment Guide
18 Molyneux Street, London W1H 5HU
Fax 020-7724 2971   Tel 020-7723 6797
Weekly.
Editor: N Gosai

The Asian Express
211 Piccadilly, London W1V 9LD
Fax 020-7537 2141   Tel 020-7439 8985
Fortnightly.
Editor: Vallabh Kaviraj

Asian Hotel & Caterer
Garavi Gujarat House, 1 Silex Street, London SE1
0DW
Fax 020-7261 0055   Tel 020-7928 1234
E-mail: caterer@gujarat.demon.co.uk
Monthly.
Editor: Ramniklal Solanki

Asian Telegraph
21a Park Road, London NW1 6XN
Fax 020-7607 6705   Tel 020-7723 5042
Wesite: www.telegraph.com
Editor: Jafar Raza

Asian Times
148 Cambridge Heath Road, `London E1 5QJ
Fax 020-7702 7937   Tel 020-7702 8012
E-mail: name@eeye.demon.co.uk
Weekly.
Editor: Burhan Ahmad

Asian Trader
1 Silex Street, London SE1 0DW
Fax 020-7261 0055   Tel 020-7928 1234
E-mail: jaravi@gujarat.co.uk
English/Gujarati/Urdu. Fortnightly.
Editor: RC Solanki

Asian Voice (Scotland)
51 Forth Street, Glasgow G41 2SP
Fax 0141-420 6833   Tel 0141-420 6811
Weekly
Editor: Ian Stewart

Awaaz Asian Voice
PO Box 15, Batley, West Yorkshire WF17 7YY
Fax 01924-510513   Tel 01924-510512
E-mail: feedback@awaaz.demon.co.uk
Monthly, English/Gujarati/Urdu.
Editor: team

Awaze Quam
5b, Booth Street, Smethwick, Birmingham B66 2PF
Fax 0121-555 6899   Tel 0121-555 5921
E-mail: 106004,1160@compuserve.com
Weekly.
Editor: Raghbir Singh

Black Perspective
PO Box 246, London SE13 7DL
Fax 020-8692 6986   Tel 020-8692 6986
E-mail: editor@blackperspective.free-online.co.uk
Website: www.blackperspective.free-online.co.uk
Quarterly.

Caribbean Times
148 Cambridge Heath Road, London E1 5QJ
Fax 020-7702 7937   Tel 020-7702 8012
E-mail: emg@eeye.demon.co.uk
Weekly.
Editor: Michael Eboda

Cineblitz
Dolphin Media, Spring Villa Road, Edgware HA8 7EB
Fax 020-8381 1177   Tel 020-8381 1166
Monthly, Indian cinema news.
Editor: Rita Mehta

Cipher
184 Bridgewater Road, Alperton, Middlesex HA0 1AR
Fax 020-8795 0502   Tel 020-8903 6350
E-mail: ciphermag@aol.com
Website: www.ciphermusic.com
Bimonthly.
Editor: Joan Smith

Cronica Latina
PO Box 1269, London SW9 9RN
Fax 020-7326 1092   Tel 020-7326 0336
Spanish monthly. **Editor**: Juan Toledo

Cubi Si
Red Rose, 129 Seven Sisters Road, London N7 7QG
Fax 020-7561 0191   Tel 020-7263 6452
E-mail: cubasc@gn.apc.org.com
Quarterly magazine by the Cuban Solidarity Campaign.

Daily Jang
1 Sanctuary Street, London SE1 1ED
Fax 020-7378 1653   Tel 020-7403 5833
E-mail: jan@globalnet.co.uk
English and Urdu daily.
Editor: Zhoor Niazi

Daily Millat
2 Baynes Close, Enfield, Middlesex EN1 4BN
Fax 020-8367 6941   Tel 020-8366 5082
E-mail: MUS77SMI@aol.com
Press correspondent: S Mustafa

Des Pardes
8 The Crescent, Southall, Middlesex UB1 1BE
Fax 020-8571 2604   Tel 020-8571 1127
Weekly, news concerning Indian people, in Punjabi.
Editor: G Virk

The Diary
32 Bell Lane, London NW4 2AD
Fax 020-8922 5473   Tel 020-8772 4770
Monthly. Jewish listings.

Eastern Eye
Whitechapel Technology Centre, Whitechapel Road, London E1
Fax 020-7702 7937   Tel 020-7702 8012
E-mail: eeye@demon.co.uk
Weekly news for the Asian community.
Editor: Nadeem Khan

Eikoku News Digest
8-10 Long Street, London E2 8HQ
Fax 020-7256 0363   Tel 020-7739 2802
E-mail: info@newsdigest.co.uk
Website: www.newsdigest.co.uk
Weekly news in Japanese.
Editor: Tokuko Hashimoto

The Filipino
PO Box 20376, Golders Green, London NW11 8FE
Fax: 020-8458 1055   Tel 020-8731 7195
E-mail: editor@filipino.co.uk
Bimonthly.   **Editor**: Mrs B Foronzan

Garavi Gujarat
1-2 Silex Street, London SE1 0DW
Fax 020-7261 0055   Tel 020-7928 1234
E-mail garavi@Gujaratdemon.co.uk
English/Gujarati. Bi-monthly.
Editor: R C Solanki

The Gleaner
220-223 Elephant & Castle, London SE1 6TE
Fax 020-7277 1734   Tel 020-7277 1714
Website: www.jamaica-gleaner.com
Weekly Jamaican and Caribbean news.
Editor: Colette Hibbert

Gujarat Samachar/Asian Voice/Asian Business
8-16 Coronet Street, London N1 6HD
Fax 020-7739 0358   Tel 020-7729 5453
Website: www.gujarat-samachor.com
Gujarati/English weekly.

Hurriyet
35 D'Arblay Street, London W1V 3FE
Fax 020-7287 3101   Tel 020-7734 1211
E-mail: zabaltd@.aol.com
Turkish daily. **Editor**: Aysegul Richardson

Impact International
233 Seven Sisters Road, London N4 2BL
Fax 020-7272 8934   Tel 020-7263 1417
E-mail: impact@globalnet.co.uk
Fortnightly Muslim news.
Editor: Ahmad Irfan

India Abroad Newspaper
Flat 1, 2 Kendrick Place, London SW7 3HF
                    Tel 020-7581 5244
Editor: Sanjay Suri

India - Home and Abroad
1 Park Close, London NW2 6RQ
Fax 020-8452 4182   Tel 020-8452 4182
Quarterly. **Editor**: K K Singh

India Link International
42 Farm Avenue, North Harrow, Middx HA2 7LR
Fax 020-8723 5250   Tel 020-8866 8421
Monthly. **Editor**: Krishan Ralleigh

India Monitor
PO Box 25165, London SW1V 3WH
                        Tel 0956-568394
E-mail: MathurRak@aol.com
Website: www.rakeshmathur.com
Editor: Rakesh Mathur

India Times
90 Ascot Gardens, Southall UB1 2SB
Fax 020-8575 5661   Tel 020-8575 0151
Weekly, Asian magazine.
Editor: Ram Kumar

India Weekly
105 St John Street, London EC1M 4AS
Fax 020-7251 3289   Tel 020-7251 3290
E-mail: email@indiaweekly.co.uk
Website: www.indiaweekly.co.uk
Weekly.
Editor: Premen Addy

Irish Post
Cambridge House,Cambridge Grove, London W6 0LE
Fax 020-8741 3382   Tel 020-8741 0649
E-mail: irishpost@irishpost.co.uk
Website: www.irishpost.co.uk
Weekly.
Editor: Norah Casey

Irish Times
76 Shoe Lane, London EC4A 3JB
Fax 020-7353 8670   Tel 020-7353 8970
Website: www.irish-times.com
Editor: Frank Millar

Irish World
934 North Circular Road, London NW2 7RJ
Fax 020-8208 1103   Tel 020-8453 7800
E-mail: the-editor@theirishworld.com
Website: www.theirishworld.com
Weekly.
Editor: Karen Murray

Janomot
Unit 2, 20b Spelman Street, London E1 5LQ
Fax 020-7247 0141   Tel 020-7377 6032
E-mail: janomot@easynet.co.uk
Bengali weekly.
Editor: Mr N Uddin

Jewish Chronicle
25 Furnival Street, London EC4A 1JT
Fax 020-7405 9040   Tel 020-7415 1616
E-mail: jcadmin@jchron.co.uk
Website: www.jchron.co.uk
Editor: Barry Toberman

Jewish Quarterly
PO Box 2078, London W1A 1JR
Fax 020-7629 5110   Tel 020-7629 5004
Culture and Jewish life.   **Editor**: Matthew Reisz

Jewish Recorder
Jewish Cultural Society, 18 Oak Hill Drive, Edgbaston,
Birmingham B15 3UG
Fax 0121-766 8135   Tel 0121-766 6663
Editor: K Drapin

Jewish Telegraph
4 May Terrace, Gittnock, Glasgow G46 6DL
Fax 0141-621 4333   Tel 0141-621 4422
Editor: Paul Harris

Jewish Tribune
95-97 Stamford Hill, London N16 5DN
Fax 020-8800 5000   Tel 020-8800 6688
Weekly.   **Editor**: J Bentov

Lanka Vithki
PO Box 14373, London NW6 3WW
Fax 020-7428 9388   Tel 020-7428 9388
E-mail: lankavithki@sinha78.freeserve.co.uk
Monthly Sri Lankan magazine in Sinhala language.
Editor: Daya Ananda Ranasinghe

The Leader
2 Baynes Close, Enfield, Middlesex EN1 4BN
Fax 020-8367 6941   Tel 020-8366 5082
E-mail: MUS77SMI@aol.com
Editor: Syed Mustafa

London Irish Press
Unit 8, Concord Business Centre, London W3 0TR
Fax 020-8896 3654   Tel 020-8752 1202
Editor: Michael Hennessy

London Jewish News
50 Colindeep Lane, London NW9 6HB
Fax 020-8205 9121   Tel 020-8358 6520
E-mail: news@ljn.co.uk
Weekly
Editor: Stuart Brodkin

**London/Midland/Northern
   Asian/Black African/Caribbean**
10a Ellington Road, London E8 3PA
Fax 020-8525 1171   Tel 020-8985 4070
Quarterly.
Editor: Peter Patel

Mauritian International
PO Box 4100, London SW20 0XN
Fax 020-8947 1912   Tel 020-8947 1912
E-mail: jaclee@compuserve.com
Website: www.mauritiusworld.com
Quarterly. **Editor**: Jacques K Lee

Mauritius News
583 Wandsworth Road, London SW8 3JD
Fax 020-7627 8939   Tel 020-7498 3066
E-mail: editor@mauritius-news.co.uk
Website: www.mauritius-news.co.uk
Monthly. **Editor**: Peter Chellen

Melting Pot
PO Box 13258, London E1 2RR
Fax 020-8503 1555   Tel 020-8503 1414
Bi-monthly. Magazine for the multicultural society.

Middle East Expatriate
Crescent Court, 102 Victor Road, Teddington,
Middlesex TW11 8SS
Fax 020-8943 3701   Tel 020-8943 3630
Editor: Nick Horne

Milap Weekly
Masbro Centre, 87 Masbro Road, London W14 0LR
Tel: 020-7385 8966
Urdu weekly. **Editor**: R Soni

The Muslim News
PO Box 380, Harrow, Middlesex HA2 6LL
Fax 020-7608 1232 Tel 020-7608 2822
E-mail: info@muslimnews.co.uk
Website: www.muslimnews.co.uk
Monthly.
Editor: Ahmad J Versi

The Nation
96c Ilford Lane, Ilford, Essex IG1 2LD
Fax 020-8478 6200 Tel 020-8478 3200
E-mail: msarwar@thenation.demon.co.uk
Website: www.thenation.com
English/Urdu.
Editor Mr M Sarwar

Navin Weekly
Masbro Centre, 87 Masbro Rd, London W14 0LR
Tel: 020-7385 8966
Hindi weekly.
Editor: Ramesh Kumar

New Horizon
Icis House, 144-146 King's Cross Road, London
WC1X 9DH
Fax 020-7278 4797 Tel 020-7833 8275
E-mail icis@iibi.demon.co.uk
Website: www.islamic-banking.com
Monthly Muslim news, Islamic banking.
Editor: Ghazanfar Ali

New Impact Journal
Anser House of Marlow, Courtyard Offices, 3 High
Street, Marlow, Bucks SL7 1AX
Fax 01628-475570 Tel 01628-481581
E-mail: curious@newimpact.co.uk
Website: www.newimpact.co.uk
Bi-monthly on "enterprise and diversity".
Editor: Elaine Sihera

New Nation
1st Floor, 148 Cambridge Heath Road, London E1
5QJ
Fax 020-7702 7937 Tel 020-7702 8012
E-mail: emg@eeye.demon.co.uk
Weekly.
Editor: Michael Eboda

New World
234 Holloway Road, London N7 8DA
Fax 020-7607 6706 Tel 020-7700 2673
Fortnightly news on local and international affairs.
Editor: Dhiren Basu

The News
Jang Publications, 1 Sanctuary Street, London SE1
1ED
Fax 020-7378 1653 Tel 020-7403 5833
Editor: Mr Shahed Sadullah

Nigerian News
23 Aberdeen Court, Maida Vale, London W9 1AF
Fax 020-7266 4057 Tel 020-7266 4564
Fortnightly.
Editor: Olubiyi Ayodeji

North West Asian News
Observer Buildings, Drake Street, Rochdale OL16
1PH
Fax 020-7634 1595 Tel 020-7635 7086
Monthly.
Editor: Steve Hammond

Noticias Latin America
59 St Martin's Lane, London WC2N 4JS
Fax 020-7686 1662 Tel 020-7686 1633
E-mail: noticias@dial.pipex.com
Spanish language monthly.
Editor: Alberto Rojas

Notun Din
Room 5, Brady Centre, 192-196 Hanbury Street,
London E1 5HU
Fax 020-7247 2280 Tel 020-7247 6280
E-mail: nohin@din.demon.co.uk
Bengali, weekly.
Editor: M Chowdhury

Parikiaki
534a Holloway Road, London N7 6JP
Fax 020-7281 0127 Tel 020-7272 6777
Weekly, Greek.
Editor: George Georgiou

Perdesan Monthly
478 Lady Margaret Rd, Southall, Middlesex UB1 2NW
Fax 020-8575 8659 Tel 020-8575 8694
Monthly.
Editor: G K Bedi

Pride Magazine
Hamilton House, 55 Battersea Bridge Road, London
SW11 3AX
Fax 020-7288 3130 Tel 020-7228 3110
E-mail: aminat@pridemagazine.com
Website: www.pridemagazine.com
Monthly for women of colour.
Editor: Dionne Sainthill

Probashi Samachar
20 Orchard Avenue, London N14 4ND
Tel 020-8886 4231
Bengali quarterly. **Editor**: S Mazumdar

Punjab Mail International
66 Dames Road, London E7 0DR
Fax 020-8522 0901 Tel 020-8522 0901
Monthly magazine written in Punjabi and English "to
promote culture and heritage".
Editor: Gurdip Singh Sandhu

Punjab Times International
24 Cotton Brook Road, Derby DE23 8YJ
Fax 01332 372833 Tel 01332 372851
E-mail: punjabtimes@aol.com
Weekly.
Editor: Harjinder Singh Mandair

The Punjabi Guardian
Soho News Building, 129 Soho Road, Handsworth,
Birmingham B21 9ST
Fax 0121-507 1065 Tel 0121-554 3995
Monthly.
Editor: Inder Jit Singh Sandhu

Q News, The Muslim Magazine1
Dexion House, 2-4 Empire Way, Wembley HA9 0EF
Fax 020-8903 0820   Tel 020-8903 0819
E-mail: editor@q-news.com
Website: www.q-news.com
For British Muslims of all nationalities.
Monthly.
Editor: Fuad Nahdi

Ravi Asian News Weekly
Ravi House, 900 Leeds Road, Bradford BD3 8EZ
Fax 01274-666900   Tel 01274-666900
Urdu weekly. **Editor**: Mr Shappir Moughal

Ri-ra Magazine
39-41 North Road, London N7 5DP
Fax 020-7609 6716   Tel 020-7609 9010
Free magazine for Irish youth.
Editor: Micheal Coughla.Sean Scally

Sada Urdu Monthly
PO Box 630, Croydon CR0 2WN
Fax 020-8251 8689   Tel 020-8684 9429
Editor: Athar Raz

Salaam!
Unit 6, 5 Rockware Avenue, Greenford UB6 0AA
Fax 020-8930 2066   Tel 020-8357 0056
Monthly.
Publisher: Khan Iqbal Khan

Scotland's Oracle
575 Pollockshaws Road, Glasgow G41 2QQ
Fax 0141-423 9166   Tel 0141-423 9166
Editor: Ahsan ul haq

The Sikh Courier International
World Sikh Foundation, 33 Wargrave Road, South
Harrow HA2 8LL
Fax 020-8257 0359   Tel 020-8864 9228
Quarterly.
Editors: A S Chatwal

The Sikh Messenger
43 Dorset Road, London SW19 3EZ
Fax 020-8540 4148   Tel 020-8540 4148
Quarterly.
Editor: Indarjit Singh

Sing Tao (UK)
46 Dean Street, London W1V 5AP
Fax 020-7734 0828   Tel 020-7287 1525
E-mail: singtaoeu@yahoo.com
Website: www.singtaoeu.com
Chinese daily.
Editor: S T Wan

Spice Media
Suite 207, Keys Court, 82-84 Moseley Street,
Digbeth, Birmingham B12 0RT
Fax 0121-245 2434   Tel 0121-245 2424
E-mail: editorial@spicemagazine.com
Website: www.spicemagazine.com
Bi-monthly.
Editor: Parminder Singh

Surma
40 Wessex Street, London E2 0LB
Fax 020-8981 8829   Tel 020-8980 5544
E-mail: surmanews@l12.com
Bengali weekly. **Editor**: M E H Chowdhury

Ta Nea
8-10 Stamford Hill, London N16 6XS
Fax 020-8806 0160   Tel 020-8806 0169
Fortnightly. Greek.
Editor: Louis Vrakas

Teamwork
5 Westminster Bridge Road, London SE1 7XW
Fax 020-7928 0343   Tel 020-7928 7861
E-mail: wiscorg@aol.com
Bimonthly.
Editor: Mr W Trant

Toplum Postasi
117 Green Lanes, London N16 9OA
Fax 020-7354 0313   Tel 020-7354 4424
E-mail: toplum@aol.com
Website: www.toplumpostasi.com
Turkish weekly.
Editor: Artun Goksan

Touch Magazine
1st Floor, 51 Hoxton Square, London N1 6PB
Fax 020-7739 6504   Tel 020-7739 5727
E-mail: touchzine@aol.com
Monthly.   **Editor**: Vincent Jackson

Untold Magazine
Stratford Workshops, Burford Road, London E15 2SP
Fax 020-8739 6504   Tel 020-8519 1920
Bi-monthly.
Editor: Peter Akinti

La Voce Degli Italiani
20 Brixton Road, London SW9 6BU
Fax 020-7793 0385   Tel 020-7735 5164
E-mail ziliotto@dircon.co.uk
Fortnightly.
Editor: Giandomenico Ziliotto

The Voice Group
370 Coldharbour Lane, London SW9 8PL
Fax 020-7274 8994   Tel 020-7737 7377
E-mail: editorial@the-voice.co.uk
Weekly for Black British.
Editor-in-chief: Mike Best

Watan Weekend
Chamber Ho, 306-308a Hoe Street, London E17 9PX
Fax 020-8925 0446   Tel 020-8923 9222
E-mail: watan@wavenet.co.uk
Website: www.wavenet.co.uk/users/watan
Urdu.   **Editor**: Taj Javaid

Weekly Des Pardes
8 The Crescent, Southall, Middlesex UB1 1BE
Fax 020-8571 2604   Tel 020-8571 1127
Weekly, Punjabi.   **Editor**: Mr Virk

Weekly East
65 North Acton Road, London NW10 6PJ
Fax 020-8838 6300   Tel 020-8838 2112

Weekly Pakistan
65 North Acton Road, London NW10 6PJ
Fax 020-8838 6300   Tel 020-8838 2112

Weekly Potrika
218 Jubilee Street, London E1 3BS
Fax 020-7423 9122   Tel 020-7423 9270
E-mail: potrika786@easynet.co.uk
Bengali, weekly.
Executive editor: Syed Nahas Pasha

ETHNIC RADIO

Asian Sound Radio
Globe House, Southall Street, Manchester M3 1LG
Fax 0161-288 9000   Tel 0161-288 1000
Head of programmes: Paul Shah
Choice FM
291-299 Borough High Street, London SE1 1JG
Fax 020-7378 3936   Tel 020-7378 3969
Programme director: Patrick Berry
Galaxy 102.2
111 Broad Street, Birmingham B15 1AS
Fax 0121-616 1011   Tel 0121-616 1000
Programme director: Alex Carruthers
Galaxy 105
Joseph's Well, Westgate, Leeds LS3 1AB
Fax 0113-213 1054   Tel 0113-213 1053
Contact: Nick Walshe
Kiss 100 FM
Kiss House, 80 Holloway Road, London N7 8JG
Fax 020-7700 3979   Tel 020-7700 6100
Programme director: Matthew Matthews
London Greek Radio
Florentia Village, Vale Road, London N4 1TD
Fax 020-8880 8005   Tel 020-8880 8001
Programme controller: G Gregoriou
London Turkish Radio
185b High Road, London N22 6BA
Fax 020-8881 5151   Tel 020-8881 0606
Programme controller: Erkan Pastirmacioglu
Radio Asia
65 North Acton Road, London NW10 6RJ
                        Tel 020-8838 6300
Contact: Shanta Saluja
Radio Ceredigion
Yr Hen Ysgol Gymraeg, Aberystwyth, Dyfed SY23 1LF
Fax 01970-627206   Tel 01970-627999
General manager: Ellen ap Gwynn
Radio XL
KMS House, Bradford Street, Birmingham B12 0JD
Fax 0121-753 3111   Tel 0121-753 5353
Programme director: Barry Curtis
Sabras Sound
Radio House, 63 Melton Road, Leicester LE4 6PN
Fax 0116-268 7776   Tel 0116-261 0666
Contact: Don Kotak
Spectrum Chinese Programmes
PO Box 2JT, London W1A 2JT
Fax 020-7434 2836   Tel 020-7434 2835
Spectrum Radio
204-206 Queenstown Road, London SW8 3NR
Fax 020-7627 3409   Tel 020-7627 4433
Contact: Paul Hogan
Sunrise Radio
Merrick Road, Southall, Middlesex UB2 7AU
Fax 020-8893 5090   Tel 020-8893 5900
Chief executive: Avtar Lit
Sunrise Radio
Sunrise House, 30 Chapel Street, Bradford BD1 5DN
Fax 01274-728534   Tel 01274-375043
Programme controller: Ushar Parmar

ETHNIC TV STATIONS

APNA TV
42 Theobalds Road, London WC1X 8NW
Fax 020-7242 2860   Tel 020-7831 2525
E-mail: data@apnatv.freeserve.co.uk
Editor: Daxa Joshi
Asia Net
Elliott House, Victoria Road, London NW10 6NY
Fax 020-8930 0546   Tel 020-8930 0930
Chief executive: Dr Barnard Viswanath
Asia Net TV
PO Box 38, Greenford, Middlesex UB6 7SP
Fax 020-8810 5555   Tel 020-8566 9000
Website: www.asianet-tv.com
Contact: Luxmi Ghosh
Asian Television
PO Box 113, Oldham, Lancashire OL1 1LS
Fax 0161-665 2361   Tel 0161-627 1207
Station controller: Mr Shafaat Choudhry
Helenic TV
50 Clarendon Road, London N8 0DJ
Fax 020-8292 7042   Tel 020-8292 7037
General manager: Takis Fellas
Middle East Broadcasting Centre
80 Silverthorne Road, London SW8 3XA
Fax 020-7501 1110   Tel 020-7501 1111
Website: www.mbctvsat.com
Chief executive: Ian Ritchie
Namaste Asian Television
7 Trafalgar Business Centree, 77/87 Rriver Road,
Barking, Essex IG11 0JU
Fax 020-8507 0809   Tel 020-8507 8292
Network East
Room 714, BBC Pebble Mill, Pebble Mill Road,
Birmingham B5 7QQ
Fax 0121-432 8241   Tel 0121-432 8888
Head of Asian programming: Paresh Solanki
The Pakistani Channel
65 North Acton Road, London NW10 6PJ
Fax 020-8838 2122   Tel 020-8838 6300
E-mail: info.pak@btinternet.com
The Persian Channel
10 Pennine Parade, Pennine Drive, London NW2 1NT
Fax 020-8731 6971   Tel 020-8731 9333
News editor: Mahmood Taghi Sarabi
Phoenix Chinese News & Entertainment
Marvic House, Bishops Road, London SW6 7AD
Fax 020-7610 3118   Tel 020-7610 3880
E-mail: pcnetv@pcnetv.demon.co.uk
Editor: Poon Sui Mui
Sony Entertainment TV Asia
34 Fouberts Place, London W1V 2BH
Fax 020-7534 7585   Tel 020-7534 7575
Contact: Rajan Singh
Zee TV
64 Newman Street, London W1P 3HB
Fax 020-7436 0549   Tel 020-7436 0543
E-mail: anita.anand@zeetv.co.uk
Contact: Anita Anand

Republic of Ireland media

There are three things which mark out the Republic of Ireland media scene as odd. Firstly, much of its media originates overseas, with some 35 per cent of TV coming from the UK, and a third of Sunday papers plus half the daily circulations based in London. There is, however, a thriving indigenous media which - for the second oddity - is most heavily Irish where it's for the best educated. A well educated readership in a booming economy ensures the Irish Independent and Irish Times do well, despite VAT and competition from cheaper British rivals. The two leading Irish broadsheets have a combined daily circulation of over 250,000 for a population of four million. Of the two, the Irish Independent has the bigger sale with a large farming readership making it the stronger outside Dublin. The Irish Times is close in spirit to the Guardian, for it too is liberal left, urban and owned by a trust. Another oddity - at least for a dumbed down Brit - is that one in 14 of Irish people buys a heavyweight daily, compared with one in 24 in the UK. The Republic takes its media seriously, for the daily broadsheets outsell the tabloids which are in a market sector dominated by UK interests with a lightly regionalised Sun and Mirror and a more heavily regionalised Dublin-based Daily Star.

The third oddity is that the Republic's indigenous national press is more heavily dominated by one owner than in any other liberal democracy. Tony O'Reilly, the ex-international rugby star who is the Ireland's answer to Rupert Murdoch, owns Independent Newspapers which accounts for two thirds of Irish national morning and evening papers, most of the home-produced Sundays, plus a clutch of local papers. The market for locals is defined by longevity, stability and family ownership. In magazines, Magill and the satirical magazine Phoenix are must-reads. The RTÉ TV guide is the biggest seller.

While there is little sale of Belfast papers in Dublin (and vice versa) there is a clear demand for cross border television with UTV being the state's de facto third channel. UTV - which now favours initial letters for its title instead of the more politically loaded Ulster TV - has over 10 per cent of the Republic's viewing figures and is in the unique position of having more viewers outside its franchise area than in it. Irish Republic broadcasting is similarly regulated and structured to the UK. The 1960 Broadcasting Act established Radio Telefis Eireann (RTÉ), though as an advertising and licence revenue hybrid. RTÉ runs two English language TV stations (RTÉ 1 and Network 2), three national English language radio stations (Radio 1, 2FM, FM 3), a Gaelic TV station (formerly Teilifis Na Gaeilge or TNAG and recently rechristened TG4) and a Gaelic radio station (Raidio Na Gaeltachta). TV3 started broadcasting late in 1998 as the first fully commercial Irish television station. Its major shareholder is CanWest, the Canadian cable and entertainment conglomerate company which is the world's biggest purchaser of Hollywood movies. CanWest also has a stake in UTV and its strategy is to build upon an island of Ireland commercial TV tradition.

Republic of Ireland radio divides into three sections: first, the state-owned radio channels from RTÉ; second, the commercial channels which are led by Today FM (formerly 100FM) plus over 20 local stations which came into existence after the 1988 Broadcasting Act; and thirdly, community radio for which the Independent Radio and Television Commission started awarding licences in spring 1998. As in Britain, commercial radio has proved successful and secured itself nearly half the listening market. The stations have far more talk than their UK counterparts and thus provide sought after political platforms.

NATIONAL NEWSPAPERS

Evening Echo
Academy Street, Cork
Fax 00-353 21-275112 Tel 00-353 21-272722
Editor: Brian Feeney
Owner: Examiner Publications (Cork)
Evening Herald
Middle Abbey Street, Dublin 1
Fax 00-353 1-873 1787 Tel 00-353 1-873 1666
E-mail: herald.letters@independent.ie
Editor: Gerry O'Regen
Advertisement manager: Brendan McCabe
Owner: Independent Newspapers (Ireland)
The Examiner
PO Box 21, Academy Street, Cork
Fax 00-353 21-275112 Tel 00-353 21-272722
Dublin office: 96 Lower Baggot Street, Dublin 2
Fax 00-353 1-661 2737 Tel 00-353 1-661 2733
Editor: Brian Looney
Head of advertising: Padraig Mallon
Owner: Examiner Publications
Irish Independent
Middle Abbey Street, Dublin 1
Fax 00-353 1-873 1787 Tel 00-353 1-873 1333
Website: www.independent.ie
Managing editor: M Roche
Editor: V Doyle
Advertisement manager: Brendan McCabe
Owner: Independent Newspapers (Ireland)
The Irish Times
PO Box 74, 11-15 D'Olier Street, Dublin 2
Fax 00-353 1-677 2130 Tel 00-353 1-679 2022
E mail: postmaster@irish-times.ie
Website: www.irish-times.com
Editor: Conor Brady
Owner: Irish Times Trust
The Star
62A Terenure Road North, Dublin 6W
Fax 00-353 1-490 2193   Tel 00-353 1-490 1228
E mail: news@the-star.ie
Editor: Gerard O'Regan
Owner: Irish Independent

SUNDAY NEWSPAPERS

Ireland on Sunday
50 City Quay, Dublin 2
Fax 00-353 1-671 8882 Tel 00-353 1-671 8255
E mail: news@irelandonsunday.com
Editors: Liam Hayes, Cathal Dervan
Owner: Ireland on Sunday
Sunday Business Post
80 Harcourt Street, Dublin 2
Fax 00-353 1-679 6496 Tel 00-353 1-679 9777
E-mail: sbpost@iol.ie
Website: www.sbpost.ie
Editor: Damien Kiberd
Advertising manager: Deidre Hughes
Sunday Independent
Middle Abbey Street, Dublin 1
Fax 00-353 1-873 1787 Tel 00-353 1-873 1333
E-mail: sunday.letters@independent.ie
Website: www.independent.ie
Editor: Aengus Fanning
Owner: Independent Newspapers (Ireland)
Sunday Tribune
15 Lower Baggot Street, Dublin 2
Fax 00-353 1-661 5302 Tel 00-353 1-661 5555
E-mail: news@tribune.ie
Website: www.tribune.ie-classroom
Editor: Matt Cooper
Sunday World
Newspaper House, Rathfarnham Road, Dublin 6
Fax 00-353 1-490 1838 Tel 00-353 1-490 1980
Editor: Colm MacGinty
Advertising manager: Gerry Lennon
Owner: Sunday Newspapers

IRISH NATIONAL NEWSPAPER CIRCULATIONS

DAILIES	1988	1996	1997	1998	1999
1 Irish Independent	153,054	158,712	160,137	163,967	165,365
2 Evening Herald	108,702	115,983	112,546	103,583	105,386
3 Irish Times	87,855	101,841 1	107,839	111,729	113,835
4 The Star	69.819	85,976	88,840	89,938	
5 Cork Examiner	58,227	55,194	56,628	60,173	62,413
6 Cork Evening Echo	32,450	25,697	26,520	27,022	28,407
SUNDAYS					
1 Sunday Independent	230,794	339,501	327,153	310,505	317,193
2 Sunday World	360,138	296,085	307,162	312,402	309,604
3 Sunday Tribune	96,871	77,817	86,766	95,058	83,314
4 Ireland on Sunday			66,863	63,476	70,412
5 Sunday Business Post		37,429	43,698	47,232	49,035

Source: ABC

LOCAL PAPERS

CARLOW
Nationalist and Leinster Times w
00-353-503-31731
The Carlow People w
00-353-503-41877

CAVAN
The Anglo-Celt Weekly w
00-353-49-31100

CLARE
Clare Champion w
00-353-65-28105

CORK
The Corkman w
00-353-66-21666
Southern Star w
00-353-28-21200

DONEGAL
Derry People and Donegal News w
00-353-74-21014
Donegal Democrat w
00-353-72-51201
Donegal People's Press w
00-353-74-28000

CO. DUBLIN
Inner City News f 6xpa
00-353-1-836 3832
Local News Publications
00-353-1-453 4011

GALWAY
The Connacht Sentinel w
00-353-91-567251
The Connacht Tribune w
00-353-91-567251
Galway Advertiser w
00-353-91-567077
Tuam Herald w
00-353-93-24183

KERRY
The Kerryman w
00-353-66 21666
Kerry's Eye w
00-353-66-23199

KILDARE
Kildare Nationalist
00-353-45-432147
Leinster Leader w
00-353-45-897302
Liffey Champion
00-353-1-624 5533

KILKENNY
Kilkenny People w
00-353-56-21015

LEITRIM
Leitrim Observer w
00-353-78-20025

LEIX
Laois Nationalist w
00-353-502-60265
Leinster Express w
00-353-502-21666

LIMERICK
Limerick Chronicle w
00-353-61-315233
Limerick Leader 4xw
00-353-61-315233
Limerick Post
00-353-61-413322

LONGFORD
The Longford Leader w
00-353-43-45241
Longford News w
00-353-43-46342

LOUTH
Drogheda Independent w
00-353-41-38658
Dundalk Democrat w
00-353-42-34058

MAYO
Connaught Telegraph w
00-353-94-21711
Mayo News w
00-353-98-25311
The Western People w
00-353-96-21188

MEATH
Meath Chronicle w
00-353-46-21442
Cavan and Westmeath Herald w
00-353-46-21442
Meath Topic w
00-353-44-48868

MONAGHAN
Northern Standard w
00-353-47-81867

OFFALY
The Midland Tribune w
00-353-509-20003
Offaly Express w
00-353-506-21744
Offaly Topic w
00-353-506-41182
Tullamore Tribune w
00-353-506-21152

ROSCOMMON
Roscommon Champion w
00-353-903-25051
Roscomon Herald w
00-353-79-62622

SLIGO
Sligo Weekender
00-353-71-42140

TIPPERARY
Nationalist Newspaper w
00-353-52-22211
Nationalist & Munster Advertiser
00-353-52-22211
Nenagh Guardian w
00-353-67-31214
Tipperary Star w
00-353-504-21122

WATERFORD
Dungarvan Leader and Southern Democrat w
00-353-58-41203
Dungarvan Observer and Munster Industrial Advocate w
00-353-58-41205
The Munster Express wx2
00-353-51-872141
Waterford News & Star e
00-353-51-874951

WESTMEATH
The Westmeath Examiner w
00-353-44-48426
Westmeath Independent
00-353-902-72003
Westmeath Topic w
00-353-44 48868

WEXFORD
The Echo w
00-353-54-33231
Enniscorthy Guardian w
00-353-53-22155
Gorey Echo w
00-353-54-33231
The Guardian w
00-353-54-33833
New Ross Echo w
00-353-54-33231
New Ross Standard
00-353-514-21184
The People w
00-353-53-22155
Wexford Echo w
00-353-54-33231

WICKLOW
Wicklow People w
00-353-404-67198
Bray People w
00-353-1-286 7393

IRISH MAGAZINES

When phoning from the UK,
Republic of Ireland telephone
numbers begin: 00-353

A

Accountancy Ireland	
	1-668 0400
Administration	1-269 7011
Afloat Magazine	1-284 6161
Aisling Magazine, The	
	99-61245
Amnesty International	
	1-677 6361
AMT Magazine	1-284 7777
Arena	1-661-5588
Aspect	1-676 0774
Astronomy & Space	
	1-459 8883

B

Bakery World	1-280 0000
Big Issue, The	1-855 3969
Books Ireland	1-269 2185
An Bord Altranais News	
	1-676 0226
Bulletin	1-838 4167
Business & Finance	
	1-676 4587
Business Contact	1-855 0477
Buy & Sell	1-6080707

C

Car Driver Magazine	
	1-260 0899
Cara	1-662 3158
Catholic Standard	1-855 5619
Celtic Journey	1-296 0000
Checkout Magazine	
	1-280 2933
CIF Blue Pages	1-667-2885
CIRCA Art Magazine	
	1-676 5035
CIS Report	1-668 9494
Clar na nOg	1-478 4122
Comhar	1-678 5443
Commercial Law Practitioner	
	1-873 0101
Communications Today	
	1-284 7777
Communications Worker	
	1-836 6388
ComputerScope	1-830 3455
Construction	1-671 9244
Consumer Choice	1-668 6836
An Cosantoir	1-804 2690
CPA Journal of Accountancy	
	1-676 7353
Cuba Today	1-676 1213

D

Decision	1-283 6466
Doctor Desk Book	
	1-492 4034

E

Economic & Social Review	
	1-667 1525
Economic Series	1-661 3111
Education Today	1-872 2533
Employment Law Reports	
	1-873 0101
Engineers Journal	1-855 0477
Environmental Management	
Ireland	1-872 0734

F

Feasta	1-475 7401
Finance	1-660 6222
Finance Dublin	1-660 6222
Forum	1-280 3967
Futura	1-283 6782

G

Gaelic Sport	1-837 4311
Gaelic World	1-679 8655
Gaelsport Magazine	
	1-478 4322
Garda Review	1-830 3533
Gay Community News	
	1-671 9076
Golfers Companion	
	1-280 4077
Grocer's Magazine	1-280 9466
Guidelines	1-676 1975

H

Health & Safety	1-671 3500
Health Service News	
	1-668 6233
History Ireland	1-453 5730
Hot Press	1-679 5077
Hotel & Catering Review	
	1-280 0000

I

Image	1-280 8415
Impact News	1-855 0873
In Dublin	1-478 4322
Industrial Relations	1-497 2711
Industry & Commerce	
	1-671 3500
Inside Business	1-855 0477
Inside Ireland	1-493 1906
Insight Magazine	1-205 7200
IPA Journal	1-671 3500
IPU Review	1-493 1801
Ireland of the Welcomes	
	1-602 4000
Ireland's Eye	44-48868
Ireland's Own	53-22155
Iris Oifigiuil	1-661 3111
Irish Architect	1-295 8115
Irish Banking Review, The	
	1-671 5299
Irish Building Services News	
	1-288 5001
Irish Catholic	1-855 5169
Irish Criminal Law Journal	
	1-873 0101
Irish Current Law Monthly Digest	
	1-873 0101
Irish Dental Association, Journal of	
	1-283 0496
Irish Electrical Review	
	1-283 6755
Irish Emigrant, The	91-569158
Irish Farmers' Journal	
	1-450 1166
Irish Farmers' Monthly	
	1-289 3305
Irish Field, The	1-679 2022
Irish Food	1-289 3305
Irish Geography	1-708 3938
Irish Hardware Magazine	
	1-280 0000
Irish Homes Magazine	
	1-878 0444
Irish Journal of European Law	
	1-873 0101
Irish Marketing Journal	
	1-295 0088
Irish Medical Journal	
	1-676 7273
Irish Medical News	1-296 0000
Irish Medical Times	1-475 7461
Irish Pharmacy Journal	
	1-660 0551
Irish Racing Calender	45-441599
Irish Skipper, The	1-296 0000
Irish Social Worker	1-677 4838
Irish Travel Trade News	
	1-450 2422
IT	1-662 3158

IRISH MAGAZINES

When phoning from the UK, Republic of Ireland telephone numbers begin: 00-353

J
Journal, The   1-478 4141

L
LAN   1-872 0734
Law Society Gazette
                      1-671 0711
Licensing World   1-280 0000
Local Authority Times
                      1-668 6233

M
Marketing   1-280 7735
Medico-Legal Journal of Ireland
                      1-873 0101
Motoring Life   1-878 0444

N
New Music News   1-661 2105
Newmarket Business Report
                      1-668 9494
NODE News   1-475 1998
North County Leader
                      1-840 0200

O
Off Licence   1-280 0000

P
PC Live!   1-830 3455
Phoenix   1-661 1062
Plan - Building   1-295 8115
Poetry Ireland Review
                      1-671 4632
Provincial Farmer 46-21442
Public Sector Times
                      1-286 9111
Public Service Review
                      1-676 7271

R
Retail News   1-671 9244
RTE Guide   1-208 3111
Running Your Business
                      1-296 2244
Runway Airports   1-704 4170

S
Saol na nOilean   99-75096
Shelflife   1-284 7777
Socialist Voice   1-671 1943
Sporting Press   52-21422
Sportsworld   1-878 0444

T
Taxi News   1-855 5682
Technology Ireland
                      1-808 2287
Tillage Farmer, The
                      503-31487
Today's Farm   1-668 8188
Trade-Links Journal
                      1-454 2717
Tuarascail   1-872 2533

U
U Magazine   1-662 3158
Unity   1-671 1943
Updata   1-872 8800

V
Visitor   1-296 0000

W
WHERE Killarney   64-31108
Wicklow Times   1-286 9111
Wings   1-280 4322
Woman's Way   1-662 3158

IRISH TELEVISION

RTE - Radio Telefis Eireann
Donnybrook, Dublin 4
Fax 00-353 1-208 3080 Tel 00-353 1-208 3111
Website: www.rte.ie
RTE is the Irish national broadcasting organisation. It is a statutory corporation, created under the Broadcasting Authority Act, 1960. There are separate but interlinked divisions catering for radio and television programmes, news, engineering, sales and marketing, personnel, finance and public affairs. RTE's expenditure is funded from television licence fee income and from commercial revenue.
Director-general: Bob Collins
MD - organisation and development: Liam Miller
Managing director - television: Joe Mulholland
Managing director - commercial: Conor Sexton
Director of radio: Helen Shaw
Director of news: Edward Mulhall
Director of finance: Gerard O'Brien
Director of public affairs: Kevin Healy
Director of corporate affairs/secretary: Tom Quinn

SHARE OF TV AUDIENCE

	1997	1998	1999
RTE1	34%	33%	31%
Network 2	19%	18%	17%
UTV/HTV	11%	10%	10%
BBC1	10%	10%	9%
TV3			6%
C4/S4C	6%	6%	5%
Sky1/Sky News		6%	4%
BBC2	5%	4%	4%
TnaG (TG4)	1%	1%	1%
Others	15%	10%	11%

Source: AC Nielsen for 12 months to December 1999

Province 5 Television
Clogherboy House, Commons Road, Navan, Co Meath
Fax 00-353 46-27880   Tel 00-353 46-27880
Province 5 Television is a voluntary organsiation and is Ireland's only community television station. It operates under Cable Management in the Meath and north Dublin area. It provides 12 hours of local television and a 24 hour 7 day text service. The station is funded by sponsorship and fund-raising activities.
Station director: Kevin Mac Namidhe

IRISH TELEVISION

TV3
Westgate Business Park, Ballymount, Dublin 24
Fax 00-353 1-419 3317 Tel 00-353 1-419 3333
TV3 is Ireland's first independent national broadcaster.
TV3 began broadcasting in September 1998 as an
advertiser supported, national, free-to-air, entertainment
and information service. TV3 is a full service broadcast
network, providing news and information, sport,
entertainment, comedy, movies, drama, documentaries
and children's programming.
Chief exec/Managing director: Rick Hetherington
Chief financial officer: Ken Scott
Director of programming: Michael Murphy
Director of news: Andrew Hanlon
Director of sales: Pat Kiely

RADIO

SHARE OF RADIO AUDIENCE

	1997	1998	1999
Independents	43%	43%	45%
RTE Radio 1	31%	31%	28%
2FM	22%	20%	20%
Today FM	2%	6%	7%

Adult listeners tuned in weekdays between 7am-7pm
Source: JNLR/MRBI

3R Productions
36 Lower Leeson Street, Dublin 2
Fax 00-353 1-676 2984   Tel 00-353 1-676 8408
E-mail: 3rproductions@eircom.net

95 FM
88 O'Connell Street, Limerick
Fax 00-353 6-1419595   Tel 00-353 61-400195
Website: www.95FM.ie
Area: Limerick and city area

96 FM
Broadcasting House, Patrick's Place, Cork
Fax 00-353 21-4551500   Tel 00-353 21-551596
E-mail: info@96fm.ie
Website: www.96fm.ie

103 FM
Mallow, Co Cork
Fax 00-353 22-42488   Tel 00-353 22-42430

103 FM
Bandon, co Cork
Fax 00-353 23-44294   Tel 00-353 23-43103

Anna Livia FM
Griffith College, South Circular Road, Dublin 8
Fax 00-353 1-473 4445 Tel 00-353 1-677 8103
Area: Dublin   **Dial:** 103.2FM

Atlantic 252
Radio Tara, Mornington House, Summerhill Road,
Trim, co Meath
Fax 00 353 46-36644   Tel 00 353 46-36655
E-mail: studio@atlantic252.com
Website: www.atlantic252.com

CKR FM-Carlow Kildare Radio
Lismard House, Tullow Street, Carlow
Fax 00-353 503-41047 Tel 00-353 503-41044
Website: www.ckrfm.com
ACC House, 51 South Main Street, Naas, Co Kildare
Fax 00-353 45-897611 Tel 00-353 45-879666
Area: Leinster   **Dial:** 97.3FM, 97.6FM 107.4FM

Dublin's 98FM
The Malt House, Grand Canal Quay, Dublin 2
Fax 00-353 1-670 8969 Tel 00-353 1-670 8970
E-mail: info@98fm.ie
Website: www.98fm.ie

Community Radio Castlebar
Market Square, Castlebar, Co Mayo
Fax 00-353 94 25989   Tel 00-353 94 25555
E-mail: crcfm@eircom.net
Area: Castlebar   **Dial:** 102.9 FM

Community Radio Youghal
League of the Cross Hall, Catherine Street, Youghal,
Co Cork
Fax 00-353 24-91199   Tel 00-353 24-91199
E-mail: ycradio@iol.ie
Website: www.iol.ie/~ycradio
Area: Youghal   **Dial:** 105.1 FM

Connemara Community Radio
Connemara West Centre, Letterfrack, co Galway
Fax 00-353 95-41628   Tel 00-353 95- 41616
Area: North west Connemara   **Dial:** 106.1 FM, 87.8 FM

Cork Campus Radio
Level 3, Aras na MacLeinn, UCC, Cork
Fax 00-353 21-903108 Tel 00-353 21-902008
E-mail: radio@ucc.ie
Website: www.ucc.ie/ccr/
Area: Cork city   **Dial:** 97.4 FM

Donegal Highland Radio
Pinehill, Letterkenny, Co Donegal
Fax 00-353 74-25344   Tel 00-353 74-25000
E-mail: enquiries@highlandradio.com
Website: www.highlandradio.com

Dublin South Community Radio
Old School, Loreto Avenue, Rathfarnham, Dublin 14
Fax 00-353 1-493 0520 Tel 00-353 1-493 0377
E-mail: dscr@oceanfree.net
Area: Dublin S, Dun Laoghaire W   **Dial:** 104.9 FM

East Coast Radio
9 Prince of Wales Terrace, Bray, Co Wicklow
Fax 00-353 1-286 1219 Tel 00-353 1-286 6414
E-mail: seanashmore@eastcoastradio.fm
Website: www.eastcoastradio.fm

Flirt FM
c/o The Porter's Desk, Concourse, NUI, Galway
Fax 00-353 91-525700 Tel 00-353 91-750445
Area: Galway city   Dial: 105.6 FM

FM 104
3rd Floor, Hume House, Pembroke Road, Dublin 4
Fax 00-353 1-668 9401 Tel 00-353 1-668 9689
E-mail: info@fm104.ie
Website: www.fm104.ie

Galway Bay FM
Sandy Road, Galway
Fax 00-353 91-752689 Tel 00-353 91-770000
E-mail: gbfm@galway.net
Website: www.gbfm.galway.net
Area: Galway city and county
Dial: 95.8, 96.0, 96.8, 97.4 FM

Independent Network News
62 Lower Mount Street, Dublin 2
E-mail: inn@ireland.com
Fax 00-353 1-662 9556 Tel 00-353 1-662 9563

Long Wave Radio Atlantic 252
Mornington House, Summmerhill Road, Trim, Co
Meath
Fax 00-353 46 36644   Tel 00-353 46 36655
E-mail: studios@atlantic252.com
Webiste: www.atlantic252.com

Lyric FM
Cornmarket Square, Limerick

Mid and North West Radio
Abbey Street, Ballyhsunis, Co Mayo
Fax 00-353 907-30285 Tel 00-353 907-30553
E-mail: chris@mwr.ie
Website: www.mnwrfm.com
Area: Connaught, Donegal
Dial: 96.1 FM

Midlands Radio 3
The Mall, William Street, Tullamore, Co Offaly
Fax 00-353 506-52546 Tel 00-353 506-51333
E-mail: goodcompany@midlandsradio.fm
Website: www.midlandsradio.fm
Area: Westmeath, Laois, Offaly
Dial: 103.5 FM, 102.1 FM, 96.5 FM

N.E.A.R 101.6FM
The Development Centre, Bunratty Drive, Dublin 17
Fax 00-353 1-848 6111 Tel 00-353 1-848 5211
E-mail: nearfm@iol.ie
Website: www.nearfm.ie
Area: North east Dublin Dial: 101.6 FM

Radio County Sound
Broadcast House, Patricks Place, Cork, Co Cork
Fax 00-353 21-551500 Tel 00-353 21-551596
Website: www.96fm.ie
Area: Cork city and county   Dial: 96-103FM

Radio Kerry
Maine Street, Tralee, Co Kerry
Fax 00-353 66-7122282   Tel 00-353 66-7123666
E-mail: news@radiokerry.ie
Website: www.radiokerry.ie
Area: Kerry and SW   Dial: 97, 97.6, 96.2, 96.6 FM

Radio Kilkenny
Hebron Road, Kilkenny
Fax 00-353 56-63586   Tel 00-353 56-61577
E-mail: onair@radiokilkenny.tinet.ie
Area: Kilkenny city/county   Dial: 96.6, 96, 106.3 FM

Radio na Gaeltachta
Cashla, Co Galway
Fax 00-353 91-506666 Tel 00-353 91-506677
E-mail: rnag@rte.ie
Website: www.rnag.ie
Area: National   Dial: 92-94 agus, 102.7 FM

Radio na Life 102 FM
7 Merrion Square, Dublin 2
Fax 00-353 1-676 3966 Tel 00-353 1-661 6333
E-mail: e-thostrnl102@iol.ie
Website: www.iol.ie-~rnl102

Radio Telefis Eireann
Donnybrook, Dublin 4
Fax 00-353 1-208 3080 Tel 00-353 1-208 3111
Website: www.rte.ie.radio

South East Radio
Custom House Quay, Wexford
Fax 00-353 53-45295   Tel 00-353 53-45200
E-mail: wexford@iol.ie
Website: www.southeastradio.ie

Tipp FM
Co Tipperary Radio, Davis Road, Clonmel, Co
Tipperary
Fax 00-353 52-25447   Tel 00-353 52-25299
E-mail: breakfast@tippfm.com
Website: www.tippfm.com
Area: Tipperary   Dial: 97.1 FM, 103.9FM

Tipperary Mid-West Radio
St Michael's Street, Tipperary Town
Fax 00-353 62-52671   Tel 00-353 62-52555
E-mail: 1tipperarymidwest@eircom.net
Website: sss.localireland.ie
Area: SW County Tipperary   Dial: 104.8 FM

West Dublin Community Radio
Ballyfermot Road, Dublin 10
Fax 00-353 1-626 1167 Tel 00-353 1-626 1160
E-mail: w.d.c.r@indigo.ie
Area: West Dublin   Dial: 104.9 & 96 FM

Wired FM
c/o Mary Immaculate College, South Circular Road,
Limerick
Fax 00-353 61-315776 Tel 00-353 61-315103
E-mail: wiredFM@mic.ul.ie
Area: Limerick city   Dial: 96.8 FM, 106.8 FM

WLR FM
The Radio Centre, George's Street, Waterford
Fax 00-353 51 856731 Tel 00-353 51-843951
Website: www.wlr.fm.ie

SUPPORT ORGANISATIONS

Association of Advertisers in Ireland
Rock House, Main Street, Blackrock, Dublin
Fax 00-353 1-278 0488 Tel 00-353 1-278 0499
E-mail: assadvts@indigo.ie
Advisory and information service for advertisers, to
ensure the highest ethical standards.

Broadcasting Complaints Commission
PO Box 913, Dublin 2
Tel 00-3531- 676 7571
The Broadcasting Complaints Commission was
established in 1977. The objectives of the comission are
to deal with complaints relating to news, current affairs,
ministerial prohibitions, invasion of privacy, advertising
and published matters broadcast by RTE and local radio
stations.

The Independent Radio and Television Commission
Marine House, Clanwilliam Place, Dublin 2
Fax 00-353 1-676 0948 Tel 00-353 1-676 0966
Website: www.irtc.ie
The objectives of the Independent Radio and Television
Commission (IRTC) are to ensure the creation, and
monitoring of independent broadcasting. There are 21
local/regional stations operating in the country as well
as a community/special interest radio station and an
Irish language radio station in the Dublin area.
Working with the stations' management, the IRTC
seeks to ensure compliance with the laws of the land
and the maintenance of broadcasting and advertising
standards. The IRTC is a self-financing agency, drawing
its income from the levies paid by franchised stations.

Institute of Advertising Practioners in Ireland
8 Upper Fitzwilliam Street, Dublin 2
Fax 00-353 1-661 4589 Tel 00-353 1-676 5991
E-mail: info@iapi.com
Website: www.iapi.ie
Professional body representing advertising agencies,
providing a members advisory and information service.
Available to non-members.

ntl
10 Pembroke Place, Ballsbridge, Dublin 4
Fax 00 353 668 6766   Tel 00-353 1-799 8400
Website: www.ntl.ie

Public Relations Institute of Ireland
78 Merrion Square, Dublin 2
Fax 00-353 1-6764562 Tel 00-353 1-6618004
E-mail: prii@iol.ie
Website: www.prii.ie

Publicity Club of Ireland
c/o JGolden Pages, StMartins House, Waterloo Road,
Dublin 4
Fax 00-353 1-618 8046 Tel 00-353 1-618 8045
E-mail: margaret.mckeon@goldenpages.ie

Regional Newspapers Advertising Network
33 Parkgate Street, Dublin 8
Fax 00-353 1-677 9144 Tel 00-353 1-677 9049
E-mail: info@rnan.ie

Regional Newspapers Association of Ireland
33 Parkgate Street, Dublin 8
Fax 00-353 1-677 9144 Tel 00-353 1-677 9049
E-mail: info@rnan.ie

Windmill Lane Pictures
4 Windmill Lane, Dublin 2
Fax 00-353 1-671 8413 Tel 00-353 1-671 3444
E-mail: info@windmilllane.com
Ireland's leading independent television facility and
interactive media company.

NEWS AGENCIES

AP-Dow Jones News Wires
Longphort House, Earlsfort Centre, Dublin 2
Fax 00-353 1-662 1389 Tel 00-353 1-676 2189
E-mail: debra.marks@dowjones.com

BBC Dublin Office
36 Molesworth Place, Dublin 2
Shane Harrison
Fax 00-353 1-662 5712 Tel 00-353 1-662 5500
E-mail: mary.campbell@bbc.co.uk

Financial Times
20 Upper Merrion Street, Dublin 2
Fax 00-353 1-676 2125   Tel 00-353 1-676 2071

The Independent (London)
90 Middle Abbey Street, Dublin 1
Fax 00-353 1-705 5792 Tel 00-353 1-705 5710
E-mail: independent.news@independent.ie
Website: www.independent.ie

Independent Network News (INN)
62 Lower Mount Street, Dublin 2
Fax 00-353 1-662 9556 Tel 00-353 1-662 9555
National news syndicate for local radio stations.

Ireland International News Agency
51 Wellington Quay, Dublin 2
Fax 00-353 1-679 6586 Tel 00-353 1-671 2442
E-mail: diairmaidm@eircom.net

PA News
41 Silchester Road, Glenageary, co Dublin
Fax 00-353 1-280 4221   Tel 00-353 1-280 0936

Reuters Ireland
Kestrel House, Clanwilliam Place, Lower Mount Street,
Dublin 2
Fax 00-353 1-5001551 Tel 00-353 1-5001550
E-mail: reuters.ireland@reuters.iol.ie

Department for Culture, Media & Sport

On taking office Labour renamed the Tory-created Department of National Heritage as the Department for Culture, Media and Sport. Chris Smith, the new secretary of state, explained: "Heritage only explains a tiny bit of what we do and was backward looking. The new name gives a good sense of overall responsibilities, but isn't afraid to use the word culture."

Nomenclature aside, Smith went on to rule out any other immediate alterations. "We have no current plans to change the legislation that has been put in place by the previous government and to a certain extent I want to see how those rules bed down before making any changes. The only proviso I would add is that because the whole world of media is so fast-moving and fast-changing, putting legislation in place and hoping it will last forever is not necessarily the right way to approach these things."

Ministerial reticence has built Smith a reputation as a safe pair of hands and he has maintained a hands-off media policy which, apart from matters digital, has been laid back to the point of anonymity. He has reiterated the line that effective self-regulation is preferable to a privacy law. He has set a tentative date for the switch to digital television a decade away in 2010, refused to give the BBC its digital supplement and generally laid low with statements like: "Digital broadcasting will increase the level of choice for the consumer, provide opportunities for new broadcasters to enter the market, and enable more efficient use of the UK's broadcasting spectrum."

Labour's cautious adherence to the status quo changed early in 2000 with the announcement of a Communications Act to go onto the statute book by 2002. Whereas the 1996 Broadcasting Act came from a single heritage department, the media's political importance is now such that the next bill will be a combined effort assembled by the Department for Culture in tandem with the Department of Trade. Together they are answering a corporate clamour for an abandonment of ownership restrictions in the face of the web and converging technologies and

in February 2000 a cross-departmental memo included an invitation to comment on:
* the pace and direction of change in the communications market;
* the needs and demands of consumers;
* the objectives, principles and system for the economic regulation of communications services, including wider issues such as cross-media ownership rules affecting other media;
* the objectives, principles and system for content regulation;
* the role and regulation of public service broadcasters;
* the objectives, principles and system for spectrum management;
* the implications of conclusions on these issues for the organisational structure of regulation;
* the implication of policy at EU level.

As we went to press in the summer, it was open season for speculation about the autumn white paper so there is no point in repeating rumours here. Instead there is the panel over page extracted from a briefing paper presented by the Campaign for Press and Broadcasting Freedom to the Departments of Trade and Culture.

www.communicationswhitepaper.gov.uk
www.culture.gov.uk
www.dti.gov.uk

Department for Culture, Media and Sport

2-4 Cockspur Street, London SW1Y 5DH

DCMS: main number	020-7211 6000
Website	www.culture.gov.uk
Public enquiries	020-7211 6200

Secretary of State: Chris Smith
Ministers for: Art: Alan Howarth
Film, Tourism, Broadcasting: Janet Anderson
Sport: Kate Hoey

DCMS press office:
Fax 020-7211 6270   Tel 020-7211 6269/6267
Head of division:
Melanie Leech   020-7211 6463
General policy branch
(includes broadcasting appointments, BSC and broadcasting standards, sports rights):
Harry Reeves   020-7211 6461

COMMUNICATIONS WHITE PAPER

In announcing the communications white paper the words of the two government ministers concerned were predictable. What is new is that reform of the 1996 Broadcasting Act - something not mentioned in Labour's 1997 election manifesto - is now subject to Department of Trade as well as Department for Culture influence ...

CHRIS SMITH, DEPARTMENT FOR CULTURE
"The government's aim is to promote the global competitiveness of our media and communications industries, as well as protect the interests of the consumer. The white paper will be broad in scope, covering areas such as future regulation of broadcast content, media ownership rules, and the role of public service broadcasting."

International policy branch:
Carolyn Morrison — 020-7211 6444
Commercial broadcasting branch :
Abigail Thomas: — 020-7211 6456
Pubic service broadcasting:
Paul Heron — 020-7211 6468
Head of media division:
Janet Evans — 020-7211 6424
Policy on press freedom & regulation, cross media ownership:
Mark McGann — 020-7211 6432
Films branch, UK film industry and film culture:
Alan Sutherland — 020-7211 6447
National film and television school, film industry training, British Film Commission, media & media programmes:
Jon Zeff — 020-7211 6434

STEPHEN BYERS, DEPARTMENT OF TRADE
"As we move into the twenty-first century and the digital age, we need to ensure that regulations covering the converging IT, broadcasting and telecommunications industries are flexible and effective, foster competitive markets and ensure the UK remains a world leader in providing communications services."

Department for Trade and Industry
1 Victoria Street, London SW1H 0ET

DTI: main number	020-7215 5000
	www.dti.gov.uk
Central Desk (info)	020-7215 5952
News Director	020-7215 5970
Press	020-7215 2345
Secretary of State	Stephen Byers
Ministers of State: Energy	Helen Liddell
Small Business/E-Commerce	Patricia Hewitt
Trade	Richard Caborn
Under secretaries	Kim Howells, Lord Sainsbury
	Alan Johnson

The white paper

Below is an extract from the Campaign for Press and Broadcasting Freedom's submission to the Departments of Culture and Trade

"The media must be distinguished from other commercial products. The familiar argument for deregulation of ownership in broadcasting, often expressed by industry leaders and sometimes even by ministers, is that the industry must compete in a world market and that this requires ever bigger corporations to be allowed to form ... The argument is based on extremely shaky foundations, since the products of British television companies as they are now actually compete successfully on the world markets, and the government should not be misled by dubious and self-seeking arguments to the contrary from certain sections of the broadcasting industry. Nor should the media be considered simply as part of the export drive. The CPBF can see not the slightest reason why the UK government should not set limits to cross-media ownership and, even more importantly, on the degree to which trans-national corporations can own British media. Indeed, the whole logic of the review exercise demands that it should do so: why else even consider the matter? Why not just throw all regulations and restrictions to the wind? The answer, of course, is perfectly clear: public opinion would not accept it, and public opinion emanates from the 'consumers' whose interests, among others, this consultation exercise is supposed to be considering. And the public can see what the 'global market' produces and, though they are content to consume MTV, CNN, Neighbours and the X Files some of the time, they also want Jools Holland, ITN News at Ten, Brookside and Cracker. Which is why the CPBF supports ... quotas for domestic productions [and] insists that application to BSkyB and other operators is well overdue. Audiences, even conceived as 'consumers', are sold short by cross-ownership of different media through the inevitable process of cross-promotion."
www.cpbf.org.uk

Freedom of information

Peter Preston wrote this article in his Observer On the Press column in June 2000 under the headline 'Why papers won't say our freedom is in peril'

Welcome to question time on the Freedom Trail. Did you know that the Local Government Bill, now wending its way through Parliament, removes the statutory right of press and public to attend your local council's decision-making meetings? And to get agenda papers in advance? And to inspect the minutes when the decision's taken?

Did you know that the Regulation of Investigatory Powers Bill, in similar transition, hands MI5 the right to intercept any private email it chooses, without even prior clearance from a judge? Have you thought what that will mean for journalists' sources or for your own privacy?

Did you know that the Freedom of Information Bill is 'grudgingly drafted ... back to front: we haven't got anything at the front saying something like the Bill's purpose is to be as open as possible'? And that, pray, is the opinion of Elizabeth France, the first designated commissioner for the Freedom of Information?

Now, it's possible you might have been able to answer Yes every time. Perhaps you're preparing a university thesis on botched media law, or just a devourer of the Guardian. But, equally, some, and maybe all, of this will be news to you. Why isn't your paper keeping you abreast of such unpleasing events? Why (as the sainted Harry Evans, former editor of the Sunday Times, told the Society of Editors recently) does the press fight its battles so feebly? 'If we don't make a stand to maintain the freedoms of a half-free press, we shall be back to some of the worst periods of repression,' he said.

Here, not much for anyone's comfort, is one big reason why. The struggle against censorship keeps falling victim to self-censorship. And if that sounds bizarre, look at what journalists mean when they talk about self-censorship. British newspaper and broadcasting editors and reporters are not, by and large, an introspective lot. But, happily, US journalism and foundation funding can supply all the sociologically-honed introspection we could possibly need. The Columbia Journalism Review, along with the Pew Research centre, has just polled 300 leading professionals across the States on the reasons why stories they think should be covered aren't covered at all.

The third most regular reason why stories don't appear is, predictably, because they are 'damaging to the interests of the news organisation they are working for'. You can tell the truth, the whole truth and nothing but the truth: but not in your own backyard.

The second reason, cited by 43 per cent of national print men and 29 per cent of broadcasters, is that writing a particular story will expose you 'to ridicule by other journalists'. In short, don't break away from the pack. Conform: shape up, go with the gang. Or you'll be buying your own drinks next week. Some cynics may think that an everyday story of Westminster lobby folk.

Peter Preston

But the biggest reason why stories that the people involved think we need to know about seldom see the light of day, is something still more mundane. It's because they are 'too complicated'. Fully 62 per cent of the journalists polled thought, first hand, that 'too complex' stories which had considerable 'public interest' hit the spike or the cutting room floor because they were hard to tell or absorb. Eighty-four per cent said the same about stories which were 'important, but dull'. This is not dumbing down: it is dumbing out.

So: who wants to pick away at the intricacies of the Local Government Bill, apart from a few devoted local editors determined to find out what's going on? Who cares about email privacy until some editor finds he's got weevils in his own mail box? Who cares about the Freedom of Information Bill, clause by clause? It's all a migraine of complexity, a slaughterer of attention spans. Let's find something simpler.

Here, on reflection, is the ultimate irony. Big corporations employ large, expert teams to hone the news they think that papers and TV stations ought to carry. News management is a buoyant New Labour growth industry.

Yet the people who actually manage the news don't run the stories that affect them and their audiences most immediately because (implicitly) they deem them boring.

Any generalisation like this, of course, comes trailing honorable exceptions: reporters such as Nick Cohen, Richard Norton-Taylor, and Andrew Pierce among many others, editors around the land who see the point. But Harry Evans is still right to draw parallels with his own crusade long ago for the victims of thalidomide. That was protracted, expensive, difficult, complicated, and the rest of Fleet Street left it too feebly to the Sunday Times.

Is there a case for the defence? Naturally. Editors are paid to guess what their readers want in a highly competitive trade. Is 'self-censorship', in this quivering American definition, any more than the necessity of choice? And anyway, everybody knows, or hopes they know, that nasty media law in this country tends to get dropped when the heavyweight barons of our business call on Mr Straw or Mr Blair in private at the eleventh hour. Realpolitik.

But the trouble with that isn't just the difference between early warning and late bailing: it is that, as a process, it's exactly what the row about the Local Government Bill is all about. It leaves the reader as citizen in the cold, beyond a closed door: bereft of the questions, never mind the answers.

Law and the media

The media operates under many legal restraints. Broadcasters are governed by several statutory controls specific to them and operated via the Broadcasting Standards Council, the BBC Charter, the ITC and the Radio Authority. Although the press is not so tightly regulated, all forms of media must prepare material within five legally defined boundaries. These are:

DEFAMATION
OBSCENE PUBLICATION
INCITEMENT OF RACIAL HATRED
BLASPHEMY
SEDITION

DEFAMATION is the aspect of law which most affects journalists and it covers a multitude of sins. A statement is defamatory if it damages reputation by exposing a person to hatred, contempt, shame or ridicule or makes a person likely to be avoided or shunned. It is defamatory to attack a person's honour, to injure them (or a company) in following their trade. It is also defamatory to wrongly accuse somebody of criminal activity, dishonesty, cruelty, hypocrisy, incompetence, inefficiency or stupidity.

There are two sorts of defamation: slander is non-published and libel is published. There are five defences to accusations of defamatory libel:

> justification/truth
> fair comment
> privilege
> "innocent" defamation
> apology

Justification: truth is the first defence against a libel action. It is for the journalist to prove that what has been published or broadcast is true, rather than for a plaintiff to disprove it. Therefore, keep notes and background material for at least three years, after which libel claims are barred by statute through lapse of time.

Fair comment: this is a journalist's genuinely held opinion and one which is held without malice and in good faith on a matter of public interest. Malice means dishonest or improper motives as well as personal spite.

Privilege: defamation laws are, under certain circumstances, suspended. These are reports of public judicial proceedings; statements made in parliament; and public meetings. To avoid libel, a court would need to be convinced that a report of a privileged event was fair, accurate and contemporaneous.

"Innocent" defamation: the mere absence of an intention to defame is not defence enough against a charge of libel. However the 1952 Defamation Act allows journalists the defence of saying they did not know the circumstances which make a statement libellous. An offer of a correction and apology is a key to this defence.

Apology: this admits a libel without malice or gross negligence and offers recompense via published apology and sometimes a payment. It originates from the mid-19th century, and is a dangerous defence which must be met to the letter if a court is not to move immediately to its own assessment of damages.

OBSCENE PUBLICATION legislation makes it illegal to publish material which will tend to deprave and corrupt persons who are likely to read, see or hear it. The 1950 Obscene Publications Act allows expert evidence to be given using artistic, literary, scientific or other merits as a defence.

INCITEMENT TO RACIAL HATRED legislation is framed in the 1986 Public Order Act which forbids publication of material likely to incite hatred against any racial group.

BLASPHEMY- aka blasphemous libel - only applies where a piece of work is "so scurrilous and offensive as to pass the limit of decent controversy and to outrage Christian feeling". Under this law, only Christians can be outraged.

SEDITION is a little used catch-all to ban publication of material which either incites contempt or hatred for Parliament or the Monarch, or promotes reforms by violent or otherwise unconstitutional means.

Guardian newspaper libel headlines 1999 - 2000

"Editors win 'right to know defence' in libel"

29 OCTOBER 1999 Five law lords upheld a Sunday Times appeal against a high court ruling that the paper had libelled the former Irish PM, Albert Reynolds, for suggesting he had misled the Irish parliament. They allowed a defence of qualified privilege where information is so important that the interest in publishing it outweighs the right to safeguard reputations. A Guardian leader said: "The judgments have all the benefits and defects of pragmatism. Not for their lordships the ringing language of US jurists defending the First Amendment. They go instead for the "merit of elasticity". The problem with this - which they acknowledge - is that it entails uncertainty ... This will continue to have a chilling effect on free speech. Libel will remain an expensive lottery in this country for both plaintiff and defendant. However, the Reynolds judgment, combined with a proper respect for the European Convention, should help a bit."

"Police Federation faces £400,000 libel case bill"

4 NOVEMBER The Police Federation and Mirror Group Newspapers settled after the first day of a court case over a Mirror article alleging PC Robert Brindle, of the West Yorkshire police, had indecently assaulted two women colleagues and a civilian. The undisclosed settlement was thought to have included damages for Brindle. The litigious federation had won a hundred libel victories until the Guardian broke the run in 1998 when five officers lost an appeal at an estimated cost of £900,000.

"Dramatic end to Ashcroft and Times libel battle"

9 DECEMBER The Times declared it had no evidence that the billionaire Tory chairman, Michael Ashcroft, had ever "been suspected of money laundering or drug related crimes". So ended a potential court case with each side agreeing to pay its share of costs which were estimated at £500,000.

"A greedy corrupt liar"

22 DECEMBER The Guardian headline when a jury decided Neil Hamilton (above) had taken Mohamed Al Fayed's cash for posing parliamentary questions. Hamilton's failed libel action against Al Fayed faced him with a £2 million legal bill which brought an end to a saga which started with cash-for-questions allegations first published in the Guardian in 1994. "Why did he do it?" asked the Guardian editor Alan Rusbridger. "The answer is that the libel laws are stacked in favour of a plaintiff, so it is always well worth a last roll of the dice." A month later Hamilton said that he had failed to raise cash for his promised libel appeal.

"Irvine date for new damages law"

8 FEBRUARY 2000 The lord chancellor announced February 28 as the date for cheaper libel actions whereby newspaper are now able to avoid full-scale defamation actions by making an "offer of amends".

"Composer awarded £8,000 for paper's heckle libel"

3 MARCH The self-styled "romantic futurist" composer Keith Bursting won his libel battle against the Times' suggestion that he had organised heckling at atonal concerts.

"MP awarded £60,000 for wife-beating libel"

4 MARCH The Labour MP Jimmy Wary won his case against the Mail on Sunday's allegation that he had assaulted his ex-wife.

"Edwina Currie wins libel action"

10 MARCH An Express allegation that the novelist and former Tory minister was the "vilest lady in Britain" won Edwina Curie £30,000 in damages.

"ITN in £375,000 libel victory"

15 MARCH ITV's Penny Marshall and Channel 4's Ian Williams each won £150,000 in their case against LM (formerly Living Marxism) magazine questioning the credibility of their 1992 report about Serb-run camps in Bosnia. "The picture that fooled the world" was LM's headline describing footage of emaciated Muslim prisoners. The jury accepted that the camp was a prison and that the ITN pictures had not - as LM alleged - misrepresented the truth.

"Irving: consigned to history as a racist liar"

11 APRIL David Irving's libel action against the American academic Deborah Lipstadt and Penguin Books failed as he faced unequivocal condemnation from the high court. The judge ruled the right wing historian was "an active Holocaust denier; that he is anti-Semitic and racist and that he associates with right wing extremists who promote neo-Nazism". After the judgement - which cost Irving more than £2 million in legal bills - the litigant said: "If the British soldiers on the beaches of Normandy in 1944 could look forward to the end of the century and see what England has become, they would not have bothered to advance another 40 yards up the beach."

"Archer arrested over 'lie' "

8 APRIL Lord Archer (above) was arrested then bailed after admitting he had asked a friend to lie during his successful libel action against the Daily Star in 1987. The recent controversy forced Archer to withdraw as Tory candidate for London mayor and the possibility he had conspired to pervert the course of justice led the Daily Star to demand a £3 million repayment.

"Payout over fake TV guests libel"

18 APRIL Deborah Price, a TV researcher who had worked on the BBC's Vanessa Feltz show, accepted "large" damages after a Mirror article had alleged she had knowingly recruited bogus guests.

"Easy pickings in a town called Sue"

12 MAY The House of Lords ruled that two Russian businessmen could sue the American magazine Forbes in the English courts. A Guardian leader concentrated on Boris Berezovsky, and said: "He disdains to sue in Russia: he will not sue in the US, where Forbes sells a million copies. Instead, he has now been allowed to sue in London because the magazine sold a few hundred copies here. His motives are transparent; he wants to sue here because our libel law is loaded towards plaintiffs."

Libel insurance

Libel damages have fallen for several reasons. Since 1990 the Court of Appeal has been able to amend jury awards as happened when Elton John's £350,000 libel award from the Mirror was reduced on appeal to £75,000. On a more general level the Court of Appeal has ruled juries may be directed to bear in mind the £50,000 to £125,000 awards for pain and suffering in cases of bodily injury. Another factor is a decision by the European Court of Human Rights that the £1.5 million award in 1995 to Lord Aldington against Nikolai Tolstoy over allegations that he sent Cossacks to their death in 1945, breached the freedom of expression guarantee in the European Convention on Human Rights.

While the days of the £1 million are probably over, libel still blocks investigative journalism. The Guardian editor Alan Rusbridger says there should be three changes. First, that judges should not be allowed to dismiss the jury and make the final decision, as happened in Jonathan Aitken's action against the Guardian.

Second, that the innocent-until-guilty principle should apply instead of the defence having to prove its case. And third, withdrawal of qualified privilege, which sometimes allows individuals to speak without fear of a defamation action.

Meanwhile libel insurance is a booming business. The coverage typically provided within a media or libel policy includes libel, slander, malicious falsehood, passing off, infringement of copyright and trademark, false attribution of authorship, breach of confidence, trespass and invasion of privacy. Optional coverage may include withdrawal costs, errors and omissions or negligent statement and commercial printing exposures. Policies are written on a claims made basis or occurrence wording with limits in the aggregate or on an each and every event basis. Professional indemnity underwriters normally give a libel and slander extension where publishing or broadcasting is incidental to the main business of the insured. Specific libel policies are provided by the following insurers.

The web and the law

The world wide web is nothing if not global and two contradictory legal outcomes leave web law as confused as ever.

In March 2000 Demon Internet paid the university lecturer Laurence Godfrey £15,000 plus costs of around £250,000 because he was the subject of allegedly libellous postings. Although the settlement was made out of court, the threat of action was a warning to British internet service providers, and within days ISPs closed two sites, a gay one called Outcast and an anti-censorship site that claimed Outcast's closure was "Godfrey's first victim". Chris Evans of Internet Freedom said: "ISPs are surely not responsible for what internet users post to news groups or say on their web sites. Demon Internet was right to refuse to delete the posting. The internet affords Laurence Godfrey unprecedented opportunity to defend his reputation. With a little help from Britain's repugnant libel law, an ISP has ended up being forced to remove content because someone took offence. The consequence is that ISPs will end

up censoring content based on the principle of minimising risk."

Paul Hartman wrote a letter to the Guardian asking: "Is there any reason why I should not libel myself anonymously on the internet and then sue the service provider?"

Two months later a US supreme court ruled that ISPs should have protection against any libellous or obscene message transmitted via the web. After a case brought against the Prodigy ISP, the ruling said: "The public would not be well served by compelling an ISP to examine and screen millions of e-mail communications, on pain of liability or defamation. We are unwilling to deny Prodigy the common law qualified privilege afforded to telephone and telegraph companies."

A lawyer in Washington DC commented that US companies operating in Britain could apply to domestic courts if they were held liable under British law. "This is not going to disappear as a legal issue," said Stewart Baker, a partner at Steptoe and Johnson.

LIBEL INSURERS

Denham Syndicate ((Lloyd's Syndicate 990)
Holland House, 1-4 Bury Street, London EC3A 5HT
Fax 020-7623 8223   Tel 020-7283 0045
E-mail: all.enquiries@denham.e-market.net.uk
Website: www.denhamc.co.uk

ERC Frankona
7/8 Philpot Lane, London EC3M 8BQ
Fax 020-7617 6860   Tel 020-7617 6800
Website: www.ercgroup.com

Hiscox Underwriting Limited
1 Great St Helen's, London EC3A 6HX
Fax 020-7448 6900   Tel 020-7448 6000
Website: www.hiscox.co.uk

Media/Professional Insurance Agency
Bankside House, 107-112 Leadenhall Street, London
EC3A 4DA
Fax 020-7680 1177   Tel 020-7772 4700
Website: www.mediaprof.com

RE Brown & Others (Lloyd's Syndicate 702)
84 Fenchurch Street, London EC3M 4BH
Fax 020-7480 6920   Tel 020-7265 0071

Robert Fleming Professional and Financial Risks
Staple Hall, Stone House Court, 87-90 Hounsditch,
London EC3A 7AX
Fax 020-7623 6175   Tel 020-7621 1263

Royal & Sun Alliance
1 Leadenhall Street, London EC3V 1PP
Fax 020-7337 5922   Tel 020-7283 9000
Website: www.royal-and-sunalliance.com

D-Notices
MAY 2000 In a reversal of a secretive policy designed for the Cold War, the Ministry of Defence issued new Defence Advisory Notices to allow more extensive reporting on national security which do not, however, relieve the editor of responsibilities under the Official Secrets Act. The first section of the introduction said: "Public discussion of the UK's defence and counter-terrorist policy and overall strategy does not impose a threat to national security and is welcomed by the government. It is important however that such discussion should not disclose details which could damage national security."
For the full document, go to:
www.dnotice.org.uk

MEDIA LAW FIRMS

Allen & Overy
One New Change, London EC4M 9QQ
Fax 020-7330 9999   Tel 020-7330 3000
E-mail: infomahon@allenovery.com
Website: www.allenovery.com
Defamation; TV carrier.

Anderson Strathern WS
48 Castle Street, Edinburgh EH2 3LX
Fax 0131-226 7788   Tel 0131-220 2345
Website: www.andersonstrathern.co.uk
Entertainment and media; full service firm.

Ashurst Morris Crisp
Broadwalk House, 5 Appold Street, London EC2A 2HA
Fax 020-7972 7990   Tel 020-7638 1111
E-mail: postbox@ashurst.com
Website: www.ashurst.com
TV carrier.

Baker & McKenzie
100 New Bridge Street, London EC4V 6JA
Fax 020-7919 1999   Tel 020-7919 1000
E-mail: london.info@bakernet.com
Website: www.bakerinfo.com
Digital mixed media.

Bannatyne Kirkwood France & Co
16 Royal Exchange Square, Glasgow G1 3AG
Fax 0141-221 5120   Tel 0141-221 6020
E-mail: martin@b-k-f.demon.co.uk
Entertainment and media. Clients include: Associated Newspapers, Scotsman Publications, Equity and Guardian Newspapers Limited.

Beachcroft Wansbroughs
10-22 Victoria Street, Bristol BS99 7UD
Fax 0117-929 1582   Tel 0117-926 8981
Entertainment and media.

Bell & Scott WS
16 Hill Street, Edinburgh EH2 3LD
Fax 0131-226 7602   Tel 0131-226 6703
E-mail: maildesk@bellscott.co.uk
Entertainment and media.

Berwin Leighton
Adelaide House, London Bridge, London EC4R 9HA
Fax 020-7760 1111   Tel 020-7760 1000
Website: www.berwinleighton.com
TV carrier; TV content. Clients include: UNM, Walt Disney, Dream Works SKG, Endemol, Sovereign Pictures, Digital mixed media.

Bevan Ashford
35 Colston Avenue, Bristol BS1 4TT
Fax 0117-929 1865   Tel 0117-923 0111
Website: www.bevanashford.co.uk
Entertainment and media.

Biddle
1 Gresham Street, London EC2V 7BU
Fax 020-7606 3305   Tel 020-7606 9301
E-mail: law@biddle.co.uk
Website: www.biddle.co.uk
All media work including intellectual property, on-line matters and e-business. Clients include: Press Association and Border Television.

Bindman & Partners
275 Grays Inn Road, London WC1X 8QF
Fax 020-7837 9792   Tel 020-7833 4433
Defamation
Bird & Bird
90 Fetter Lane, London EC4A 1JP
Fax 020-7415 6111   Tel 020-7415 6000
Website: www.twobirds.com
Defamation, digital mixed media, publishing and
literary, entertainment and media, TV content, TV
carrier, intellectual property and computer games.
Bristows
3 Lincoln's Inn Fields, London WC2A 3AA
Fax 020-7400 8050   Tel 020-7400 8000
E-mail: info@bristows.com
Website: www.bristows.com
Computer games, digital mixed media, intellectual
property, publishing, e-business, internet, multimedia,
TV.
Burness Solicitors
50 Lothian Road, Festival Square, Edinburgh EH3 9WJ
Fax 0131-473 6006   Tel 0131-473 6000
E-mail: edinburgh@burness.co.uk
Entertainment,media, defamation, intellectual property,
publishing. Clients include: BBC Scotland, The Big
Issue in Scotland, Clyde & Forth Press, Greenock
Telegraph, BSkyB, Insider Publications.
Campbell Hooper
35 Old Queen Street, London SW1H 9JD
Fax 020-7222 5591   Tel 020-7222 9070
E-mail: ch@campbell-hooper.co.uk
Website: www.campbell-hooper.co.uk
TV carrier; TV content. Clients include: Virgin TV.
Charles Russell
8-10 New Fetter Lane, London EC4A 1RS
Fax 020-7203 0200   Tel 020-7203 5000
Website: www.charlesrussell.co.uk
TV carrier; TV content.
Clifford Chance
200 Aldersgate Street, London EC1A 4JJ
Fax 020-7600 5555   Tel 020-7600 1000
Website: www.cliffordchance.com
Defamation, digital mixed media, TV carrier.
Clients include: Reuters, Carlton, TeleWest.
Crockers Oswald Hickson
10 Gough Square, London EC4A 3NJ
Fax 020-7353 0743   Tel 020-7353 0311
Website: www.c-o-h.co.uk
Defamation. Clients include: Birmingham Post, The
Economist, FT, Hello!,International Herald Tribune,
Jewish Chronicle, Liverpool Echo, Magnum,Observer,
Telegraph Group.
Davenport Lyons
1 Old Burlington Street, London W1X 2NL
Fax 020-7437 8216   Tel 020-7468 2600
E-mail: dl@davenportlyons.com
Website: www.davenportlyons.com
Defamation; TV content; publishing and literary.
Clients include Private Eye, Telegraph, Express, MGN.

David Price & Co
5 Great James Street, London WC1N 3DA
Fax 020-7916 9910   Tel 020-7916 9911
E-mail: dp@davidpricesolicitors.com
Website: www.davidpricesolicitors.com
Defamation, freedom of speech, privacy issues.
Denton Wilde Sapte
5 Chancery Lane, Clifford's Inn, London EC4A 1BU
Fax 020-7404 0087   Tel 020-7242 1212
Website: www.dentonwildesapte.com
Digital mixed media, TV carrier, TV content,
publishing/literary.
DJ Freeman
43 Fetter Lane, London EC4A 1JU
Fax 020-7353 7377   Tel 020-7583 4055
E-mail: nal@djfreeman.co.uk
Website: www.djfreeman.co.uk
Digital media/defamation. Clients include: Channel 4,
Channel 5, Carlton, Reed Publishing, Bull Information
System.
Dundas & Wilson CS
191 West George Street, Glasgow G2 2LD
Fax 0141-222 2201   Tel 0141-222 2200
E-mail: DW-enquiries@dundas-wilson.com
Website: www.dundas-wilson.co.uk
Entertainment and media.
Edwards Geldard
Dumfries House, Dumfries Place, Cardiff CF10 3ZF
Fax 029-2023 7268   Tel 029-2023 8239
E-mail: info@geldard.co.uk
Intellectual property.
Eversheds
Fitzalan House, Fitzalan Road, Cardiff CF12 1XZ
Fax 020-7919 4919   Tel 029-2047 1147
Website: www.eversheds.com
Intellectual property.
Eversheds
85 Queen Victoria Street, London EC4V 4JC
Fax 020-7615 8080   Tel 020-7615 8000
Defamation, TV, publishing and literary.
Farrer & Co
66 Lincoln's Inn Fields, London WC2A 3LH
Fax 020-7831 9748   Tel 020-7242 2022
E-mail: media@farrer.co.uk
Website: www.farrer.co.uk
Defamation, intellectual property. Clients include: Sun,
News of the World, Haymarket, Sunday Telegraph.
Field, Fisher, Waterhouse
35 Vine Street, London EC3N 2AA
Fax 020-7488 0084   Tel 020-7481 4841
E-mail: info@ffwlaw.com
Clients include BBC.
Foot Anstey Sargent
Pynes Hill, Rydon Lane, Exeter EX2 5AZ
Fax 01392-203981   Tel 01392-203980
E-mail: arj@foot-bowden.co.uk
Defamation, contempt, court secrecy, challenges,
promotions. Clients include: Northcliffe Newspapers,
regional newspapers, publishers.

Freshfields
65 Fleet Street, London EC4Y 1HS
Fax 020-7832 7001   Tel 020-7936 4000
E-mail: email@freshfields.com
Website: www.freshfields.com
TV carrier, publishing, on-line services, new media, e-commerce

Garretts
180 Strand, London WC2R 2NN
Fax 020-7438 2518   Tel 020-7344 0344
Website: www.glegal.com
Digital mixed media, intellectual property, new media and e-commerce.

Goodman Derrick
90 Fetter Lane, London EC4A 1PT
Fax 020-7831 6407   Tel 020-7404 0606
E-mail: info@goodmanderrick.co.uk
Defamation; TV carrier; TV content; publishing and literary. Clients include: Carlton, Central, Yorkshire, Granada, ITV Network, ITV2, BSkyB, Channel 5.

Hammond Suddards
7 Devonshire Square, Cutlers Gardens, London EC2M 4YH
Fax 020-7655 1001   Tel 020-7655 1000
Website: www.hammondsuddards.com
TV content, publishing and literary, intellecttual property, entertainment and media.

Harbottle & Lewis
14 Hanover Square, London W1R 0BE
Fax 020-7667 5100   Tel 020-7667 5000
Website: www.harbottle.co.uk
Defamation, digital mixed media, TV/film/theatre, publishing/literary.

Hempsons
33 Henrietta Street, London WC2E 8NH
Fax 020-7836 2783   Tel 020-7836 0011
E-mail: london@hempsons.co.uk
Website: www.hempsons.co.uk
Defamation.

Henderson Boyd Jackson WS
19 Ainslie Place, Edinburgh EH3 6AU
Fax 0131-225 1103   Tel 0131-226 6881
E-mail: hlog@hbj.co.uk
Website: www.hbj.co.uk
Entertainment and media.

Henry Hepworth
5 John Street, London WC1N 2HH
Fax. 020-7539 7201   Tel 020-7539 7200
E-mail: hh@medialaw.co.uk
Defamation; digital mixed media; entertainment and media; TV carrier; TV content; publishing and literary. Clients include: BBC, BFI, Express Newspapers, John Wiley & Sons, Mirror Group Newspapers, S4C, Yorkshire Tyne Tees Television, Zenith Productions.

Herbert Smith
Exchange House, Primrose Street, London EC2A 2HS
Fax 020-7374 0888   Tel 020-7374 8000
E-mail: enquiries@herbertsmith.com
Defamation; TV carrier.
Clients include: WHSmith, Washington Post, International Herald Tribune, BSkyB.

Hobson Audley
7 Pilgrim Street, London EC4V 6LB
Fax 020-7450 4545   Tel 020-7450 4500
E-mail: lawyers@hobsonaudley.co.uk
Website: www.hobsonaudley.co.uk
Defamation, publishing, literary, intellectual property, electronic commerce.

Lee & Thompson
Green Garden House, 15-22 St Christopher's Place, London W1M 5HD
Fax 020-7486 2391   Tel 020-7935 4665
E-mail: mail@leeandthompson.com
TV content, media, entertainment, film.

Lewis Silkin
50 Victoria Street, London SW1H 0NW
Fax 020-7222 4633   Tel 020-7227 8000
E-mail: info@lewissilkin.com
Website: www.lewissilkin.com
Digital media, on line services, e-commerce, defamation including plaintiff/defendant newspaper.

Lovells
65 Holborn Viaduct, London EC1A 2DY
Fax 020-7296 2001   Tel 020-7296 2000
E-mail: information@lovells.com
Website: www.lovells.com
Defamation; digital media; TV content; publishing/literary. Clients include the Guardian.

Manches
Aldwych House, 81 Aldwych, London WC2B 4RP
Fax 020-7430 1133   Tel 020-7404 4433
E-mail: manchesmedia@manches.co.uk
Website: www.manches.com
Computer games, defamation, digital mixed media, TV and film, publishing and literary, intellectual property.

Marriott Harrison
12 Great James Street, London WC1N 3DR
Fax 020-7209 2001   Tel 020-7209 2000
E-mail: @marriottharrison.co.uk
Website: www.marriottharrison.com
TV content, TV production, publishing, intellectual property, mixed media, e-commerce.

Masons
30 Aylesbury Street, London EC1R 0ER
Fax 020-7490 2545   Tel 020-7490 4000
Website: www.masons.com
        www.out-law.com
Digital mixed media, e-commerce, online games.

McGrigor Donald
Pacific House, 70 Wellington Street, Glasgow G2 6SB
Fax 0141-204 1351   Tel 0141-248 6677
E-mail: enquiries@mcgrigors.com
Website: www.mcgrigors.com
Entertainment and defamation, digital, mixed media. TV and film contracts. Clients include Chrysalis and Mirror Group.

Mishcon de Reya
21 Southampton Row, London WC1B 5HS
Fax 020-7404 5982   Tel 020-7440 7000
E-mail: postmaster@mischon.co.uk
Website: www.mishhcon.co.uk
Defamation; digital mixed media; TV content; publishing and literary.

CROCKERS OSWALD HICKSON

LAWYERS

SPECIALISING IN MEDIA

LIBEL   SLANDER   COPYRIGHT
PASSING-OFF   CONTEMPT OF COURT
REPORTING RESTRICTIONS
PACE APPLICATIONS
PRE-PUBLICATIONS & PRE-BROADCASTING ADVICE
BREACH OF CONFIDENCE
LICENSING AGREEMENTS

TEL: 0207 353 0311 FAX: 0207 353 0743
E-MAIL: lawyers@c-o-h.co.uk WEBSITE: www.c-o-h.co.uk

10 GOUGH SQAURE, LONDON EC4A 3NJ

Morgan Cole
Princess House, Princess Way, Swansea SA1 3JL
Fax 01792 634500   Tel 01792-634634
E-mail: emyrlewis@morgan-cole.com
Website: www.morgan-cole.com
Film and TV production and financing, animation, TV content. Clients include: Fiction Factory, Agenda Media Group, Aaargh! Animation

Nellen & Co
19 Albemarle Street, London W1X 3HA
Fax 020-7493 0146   Tel 020-7499 8122
E-mail: nellenco@compuserve.com
Specialists in buying and selling magazines. Authors of PPA publication Guidelines for buying and Selling Magazine Titles - The Legal Framework.

Norton Rose
Kempson House, Camomile Street, London EC3A 7AN
Fax 020-7283 6500   Tel 020-7283 6000
Website: www.nortonrose.com
Telecommunications, e-commerce, sports, entyertainment and media, intellectual properrty and IT matters.Clients include Fox Kids Europe, Apple, Sportsworld Media Group.

Olswang
90 Long Acre, London WC2E 9TT
Fax 020-7208 8800   Tel 020-7208 8888
Website: www.olswang.com
Defamation; digital mixed media; TV carrier; TV and film content; publishing, intellectual property. Clients include: Guardian, Associated Newspapers, Daily Mirror, Daily Telegraph, IPC Magazines, MTV, Warner Bros, C4, Granada, Nickelodeon, BBC Worldwide, TalkSport and ITN.

Osborne Clarke
50 Queen Charlotte Street, Bristol BS1 4HE
Fax 0117-927 9209   Tel 0117-923 0220
26 Old Bailey, London EC4M 7HW
Fax 020-7809 1005   Tel 020-7809 1000
Apex Plaza, Fosbury Road, Reading RG1 1AX
Fax 0118-925 0038   Tel 0118-925 2000
E-mail: info@osborne-clarke.co.uk
Website: www.osborne-clarke.co.uk
Entertainment and media, marketing services, interactive media, IT and telecoms.
Clients include: Activision, Carlton Screen Advertising, Manning Gottlieb Media, Yahoo!

Peter Carter-Ruck & Partners
76 Shoe Lane, London EC4A 3JB
Fax 020-7353 5553   Tel 020-7353 5005
E-mail: lawers@carter-ruck.com
Website: www.carter-ruck.com
Defamation, media litigation, copyright, data base rights and on-line services, literary trusts and estates, sports media. Clients include: Express Newspapers, National Magazines, Pearson Education, United Broadcasting and Entertainment, high profile sporting, media and political individuals.

PricewaterhouseCoopers
1 Embankment Place, London WC2N 6NN
Fax 020-7822 4652   Tel 020-7583 5000
Digitiation, content management, royalty rights management, globalisation, shareholder value enhancement, internet assurances and post-merger integration.

Reid Minty & Co
19 Bourdon Place, Bourdon Street, London W1X 9HZ
Fax 020-7318 4445   Tel 020-7318 4444
Website: www.reidminty.co.uk
Defamation.

Reynolds Porter Chamberlain
278-282 High Holborn, London WC1V 7HA
Fax 020-7242 1431   Tel 020-7242 2877
E-mail: rmedia@rpc.co.uk
Website: www.rpc.co.uk
Defamation, publishing, pre-publication advice, TV content, internet, intellectual property, media litigation.

Richards Butler
Beaufort House, 15 St Botolph Street, London EC3A 7EE
Fax 020-7247 5091   Tel 020-7247 6555
Defamation; TV carrier; TV content.
Clients include: BBCWorldwide, Turner Broadcasting.

Rowe & Maw
20 Black Friars Lane, London EC4V 6HD
Fax 020-7248 2009   Tel 020-7248 4282
Website: www.roweandmaw.co.uk
Publishing and literary.

Russell Jones & Walker
324 Gray's Inn Road, London WC1X 8DH
Fax 020-7837 2941   Tel 020-7837 2808
Website: www.rjw.co.uk
Defamation.

Russells
1-4 Warwick Street, London W1R 6LJ
Fax 020-7494 3582   Tel 020-7439 8692
E-mail: media@russells.co.uk
TV content, music law.

Schilling & Lom and Partners
Royalty House, 72-74 Dean Street, London W1V 6AE
Fax 020-7453 2600   Tel 020-7453 2500
E-mail: legal@schillinglom.co.uk
Entertainment and media, defamation; TV content.
Clients include: LWT, Granada, Carlton, Yorkshire.

Sheridans
14 Red Lion Square, London WC1R 4QL
Fax 020-7831 1982   Tel 020-7404 0444
E-mail: general@sheridans.co.uk
Website: www.sheridans.co.uk
Digital mixed media.

The Simkins Partnership
45-51 Whitfield Street, London W1P 6AA
Fax 020-7907 3111   Tel 020-7907 3000
E-mail: simkins@simkins.com
Defamation; digital media; TV content; publishing/literary. Clients include: C4, FT.

Simmons & Simmons
21 Wilson Street, London EC2M 2TX
Fax 020-7628 2070   Tel 020-7628 2020
E-mail: enquiries@simmons-simmons.com
Website: www.simmons-simmons.com
Digital mixed media, TV carrier, TV interactive content,
e-commerce, IT, intellectual property, sports. Clients
include Broadcast Communications, the ITC, Telewest,
Time Warner and Vivendi.

Simons Muirhead & Burton
50 Broadwick Street, London W1V 1FF
Fax 020-7734 3263   Tel 020-7734 4499
E-mail: mail@smab.co.uk
Defamation. Clients include: Time Out, Random
House.

SJ Berwin & Co
222 Grays Inn Road, London WC1X 8HB
Fax 020-7533 2000   Tel 020-7533 2222
E-mail: info@sjberwin.com
Website: www.sjberwin.com
Digital mixed media; TV carrier; TV content.

Steedman Ramage WS
6 Alva Street, Edinburgh EH2 4QQ
Fax 0131-260 6610   Tel 0131-260 6600
E-mail: info@srws.co.uk
Entertainment and media.

Finers Stephens Innocent
179 Great Portland Street, London W1N 6LS
Fax 020-7580 7069   Tel 020-7323 4000
E-mail: marketinng@fsilaw.co.uk
Website: www.finersstephensinnocent.co.uk
Defamation, world wide web, registration of media, TV
content, publishing. Clients include: Wall Street
Journal, Washington Post, Society of Authors, ITN.

Swepstone Walsh
9 Lincolns Inn Fields London WC2A 3BP
Fax 020-7404 1493   Tel 020-7404 1499
E-mail: swepstone@compuserve.com
Defamation

Tarlo Lyons
Watchmaker Court, 33 St John's Lane, London EC1M
4DB
Fax 020-7814 9421   Tel 020-7405 2000
Website: www.tarlo-lyons.com
Film finance, theatre law. Clients include Children's
Film and TV Foundation, Adventures in Motion
Pictures, Cameron Mackintosh, Donmar Warehouse,
Roman Polanski.

Taylor Joynson Garrett
50 Victoria Embankment, London EC4Y 0DX
Fax 020-7300 7100   Tel 020-7300 7000
E-mail: enquiries@tjg.co.uk
Website: www.tjg.co.uk
Digital mixed media; TV carrier; TV content; publishing
and literary, entertainment and media, defamation.
Clients include: Associated Newspapers.

Theodore Goddard
150 Aldersgate Street, London EC1A 4EJ
Fax 020-7606 4390   Tel 020-7606 8855
E-mail: info@theodoregoddard.co.uk
Website: www.theodoregoddard.co.uk
Defamation; TV carrier; TV content, digital mixed
media, media litigation, publishing, film finance,
music, theatre. Clients include: HTV, Granada, Sky
Broadcasting, Columbia Pictures, Sony Music
Entertainment.

Titmuss Sainer Dechert
2 Serjeants' Inn, London EC4Y 1LT
Fax 020-7353 3683   Tel 020-7583 5353
E-mail: advice@titmuss-dechert.com
Website: www.titmus-sainier-dechert.com
Defamation; digital mixed media.

Tods Murray WS
33 Bothwell Street, Glasgow G2 6NL
Fax 0141-275 4781   Tel 0141-275 4771
66 Queen Street, Edinburgh EH2 4NE
Fax 0131-624 7170   Tel 0131-226 4771
E-mail: richard.findlay@todsmurray.co.uk
Entertainment and media.

Wiggin & Co
The Quadrangle, Imperial Square, Cheltenham,
Gloucestershire GL50 1YX
Fax 01242-224223   Tel 01242-224114
E-mail: law@wiggin.co.uk
52 Jermyn Street, London SW1Y 6LX
Fax 020-7290 2450   Tel 020-7290 2424
Entertainment and media, defamation, digital mixed
media, TV carrier, TV content, publishing and literary.

LEGAL PUBLICATIONS

**The Incorporated Council of Law Reporting
for England & Wales**
3 Stone Buildings, Lincoln's Inn, London WC2A 3XN
Fax 020-7831 5247   Tel 020-7242 6471
E-mail: postmaster@iclr.co.uk
The Council publishes the Weekly Law Reports etc and
produces law reports for The Times, The Law Society
Gazette and other titles.

The Legal 500
28-33 Cato Street, London W1H 5HS
Fax 020-7396 9300   Tel 020-7396 9292
Website: the_legal_500@link.org
The definitive guide to British law firms.

Media Lawyer
3 Broom Close, Broughton, Cumbria LA20 6JG
Fax 01229-716621   Tel 01229-716622
Newsletter for media lawyers and all concerned with
media law. Bi-monthly. £36 pa.

Nellen & Co
19 Albemarle Street, London W1X 3HA
Fax 020-7493 0146   Tel 020-7499 8122
E-mail: nellenco@compuserve.com
Authors of PPA publication Guidelines for Buying and
Selling Magazine Titles - The Legal Framework.

Sport and the media

Over 70 per cent of British men and just under 60 per cent of women take part in sport or physical recreation at least once a month. The Department for Culture, Media and Sport (DCMS) oversees sport and recreation from Whitehall. Immediately below it is UK Sport, the renamed UK Sports Council, which set up a Sports Cabinet for the DCMS in 1998. UK Sport oversees the four national Sports Councils, which in turn support the governing bodies of individual sports, manage the 13 National Sports Centres and distribute £20 million of National Lottery Sports Funds annually. UK Sport also oversees the Lottery-funded UK Sports Institute, set up in 1999 to provide facilities and integrated support services to all sports. Working with the Sports Councils are 400 governing bodies, each covering a specific sport. The Central Council of Physical Recreation (CCPR) represents the views of 306 English and UK sporting bodies. Equivalent federations are the Scottish and Welsh Sports Associations and the N Ireland Council of Physical Recreation.

Beyond participation is an even greater amount of armchair sporting activity, with nearly a quarter of newspaper coverage and tens of thousands of broadcasting hours devoted to sport. Most of the media sports news concentrated on the power of football to pull in media revenue. A good example was the ITV advertising bonanza for the England vs Portugal game on 12 June 2000 when slots were the most expensive yet, with 30 seconds during half time costing advertisers £340,000 to cover the network. It topped the previous record of £250,000 for the England vs Argentina game in 1998 and helped ITV pay for the Des Lynam transfer.

A bad year for the BBC. It lost the screening rights to Des Lynam, then the FA Cup, then the Ryder Cup and then Test cricket. And in May 2000 it had to cancel an afternoon's Grandstand for lack of anything to show. In June, BBC sports

GARY LINEKER'S PROMISE
"I have absolutely no intention of leaving the BBC. They have helped me make the transition from professional footballer to professional television presenter less painfully than I could have ever imagined. They have given me sound advice and protected me from mistakes I might have made. If necessary, I will go down with them. Not that I believe we will. We will bounce back because the ITV companies only have a temporary loan of 'our' programme."

news moved from bad to worse when 36 years of Match of the Day came to an end after ITV put in the higher bid for football highlights over the three years from August 2001.

Still, it's not all missed chances for the sporting Beeb. One of the first things Greg Dyke did on taking over as BBC director general was to face off the challenge from Talk Sport (which continued page 340 ...

had recently re-branded itself as a sports only radio station) and personally conduct successful negotiations to retain radio rights for ball-by-ball Test cricket commentaries. He's pinned a large part of his reputation on getting old sporting rights back to the corporation and it's a sign of the times that the BBC boss must give days over to securing sports rights - for the radio. There was a further very minor BBC coup during Euro 2000 when the corporation won a court order banning Talk Sport from passing off its coverage as live when, in fact, its commentators were away from the crowds watching games on TV screens.

Sky has made the running. In 1997 Rupert Murdoch said: "Sport absolutely overpowers film and everything else in the entertainment genre and football of all sports is number one." Murdoch's money was where his mouth was, for he'd just overseen Sky's signing of a record breaking £670 million four year deal to show twice-weekly live Premiership matches. The BBC picked up rights to highlights for another £70 million and ITV got the European Champions league. Murdoch's sporting "battering ram" was the making of Sky, and the money it poured into football's top flight resulted in high football wages paid to lots of foreign talent.

Fifty grand a week is the top footballer's whack at the moment, a figure which will soon seem modest now even more TV money sloshes into the game. The most recent figures are as follows: Sky paid £1.1 billion for up to 66 live Premiership games a season for three years; NTL paid £328 million for up to 40 pay-per-view games; and ITV paid £183 million for the Saturday night highlights package

Meanwhile - again following Sky's lead in its thwarted attempt to buy Manchester United for £625 million early in 1999 - media companies have been buying into English Premiership clubs, thus getting themselves the board level representation to argue for more generous television rights. The main such media purchases into football clubs are in the chart at the top of the next column.

Media football ownership

COMPANY	CLUB	PER CENT
Sky		
	Chelsea	9.9%
	Leeds United	9.9%
	Manchester City	9.9%
	Manchester United	9.9%
	Sunderland	5%
Granada		
	Liverpool	9.9%
NTL		
	Aston Villa	9.9%
	Newcastle United	9.9%
	Middlesbrough	5.5%
	Leicester City	9.9%

Chris Smith's 5 per cent TV levy

In October 1999 the culture secretary Chris Smith said: "Most of the money coming into sport has gone to pay top incomes. I would hope that we could see more of that money going into grassroots sports activity. There is now a need to spread it further down the pecking order. We have been watching what has been put in place in France. Clearly they have a successful national football profile. I think we can do as well as them, but I would want to do it by voluntary means. I'd rather not do it by statute." The following April he announced a 5 per cent levy on the TV income of football, cricket, rugby and tennis. Many MPs called for more, demanding support for struggling clubs and regulation of Premiership wages.

Presenter News in Briefs

Helen Rollason, the BBC presenter who was the first to breach the men-only sports broadcasting hierarchy, died of cancer. "She was the bravest of the brave," said Des Lynam, who had left the BBC for a four year ITV contract reportedly worth £5 million. The BBC rued the loss of their fifty-something sex symbol but the need to attract younger listeners meant that the test match batsman Fred Trueman was dismissed from the broadcasting filed of play after 25 years with the Beeb.

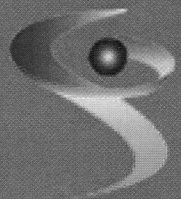

Sport and the web

Youth and sport equal big audiences which equals money, which is reason enough for the media to have been busy wooing netted-up youth. A pick of the best sites is listed immediately below and ... going beyond the media ... a host of dedicatted sporty web sites follows.

ONLINE SPORTS: NEWS/SCORES/EVENTS/ OFFICIALS/ODDS

BBC	www.bbb.co.uk/sport
Eurosport	www.eurosport.com
Express Newspapers	www.sportlive.net
Future fixtures data	www.sportcal.co.uk
Guardian	www.guardianunlimited.co.uk
PA	www.pa.press.net/sport
Reuters	www.sportsweb.com
Skysports (BSkyB)	www.skysports.co.uk
Sport England	www.english.sports.gov.uk
Sportcal (calendar)	www.sportcal.co.uk
Sporting Life	www.sporting-life.com
Sports.com	www.sports.com
Sports On Line	www.sportsonline.co.uk
Sports sites data	www.sportzine.co.uk
Ticket buying	www.ticketmaster.co.uk/sports
TV sport shows guide	www.sportlist.com

ONLINE SPORTS: ANGLING - YACHTING

Angling	www.fishing.co.uk
Archery	www.gnas.org
Athletics	www.iaaf.org
	www.ukathletics.org
Baseball	www.bbf.org
	www.majorleaguebaseball.com
Basketball	www.basketballengland.org.uk
Bets	www.bet.co.uk
	www.bluesq.com
	www.sportingbet.com
	www.victorchandler.com
	www.willhill.com
Boxing	www.boxing.com
	www.fightnews.com
Canoeing	www.bcu.org.uk
Cricket	www.cricinfo.com
	www.cricket.org
	www.cricketunlimited.co.uk
	www-uk.cricket.org
	www.wisden.com

Cycling	www.ctc.org.uk
	www.cycling.uk.com
	www.bikemagic.com
Darts	www.planetdarts.co.uk
Fencing	www.britishfencing.com
Football	www.fa2006.org
	www.fifa.com
	www.football365.co.uk
	www.footballnews.co.uk
	www.footballunlimited.co.uk
	www.planetfootball.com
	www.soccerbase.com
	www.soccer-links.com
	www.soccernet.com
	www.the-fa.org
	www.ukfootballnet.co.uk
Golf	www.golf.com
	www.golfcourses.org
	www.golf-foundation.org
	www.masters.org
	www.pga.com
Greyhounds	www.thedogs.co.uk
Gymnastics	www.baga.co.uk
Horse racing	www.bhs.org.uk
	www.equineworld.net
	www.racing-chronicle.co.uk
	www.racingpost.co.uk
	www.sporting-life.com
Judo	www.britishjudo.org.uk
Kung-fu	www.kungfu.cc
Martial arts	www.martialinfo.com
Motor cycling	www.acu.org.uk
Motor sports	www.formula1.com
	www.ukmotorsport.com
Mountaineering	www.mtn.co.uk
	www.thebmc.co.uk
Netball	www.netball.org
Olympic Games	www.olympics.org.uk
Paragliding	www.paragliding.net
Rugby	www.rfl.uk.com
	www.scrum.com
	www.planet-rugby.com
Show jumping	www.bsja.co.uk
Skateboarding	www.skateboard.com
Skiing	www.complete-skier.com
	www.skiclub.co.uk
Snooker	www.embassysnooker.com
	www.snookernet.com
Swimming	www.swimnet.co.uk
Squash	www.squash.co.uk
	www.squashplayer.co.uk
Surfing	www.britsurf.co.uk
Tennis	www.atptour.com
	www.itftennis.com
	www.lta.org.uk
	www.tennis.com
	www.wimbledon.org
Yachting/sailing	www.rya.org.uk

SPORTS COUNCILS

UK Sport	020-7273 1500
Sport England	020-7273 1500
East Midlands	0115-982 1887
East	01234-345222
London	020-8778 8600
North West	0161-834 0338
North	0191-384 9595
South East	020-8778 8600
South West	01460-73491
South	0118-948 3311
West Midlands	0121-456 3444
Yorkshire	0113-243 6443
Sports Council for Wales	01244-822600
Sport Scotland	0131-317 7200
Sports Council for N Ireland	028-9038 1222

NATIONAL BODIES

British Olympic Association	020-8871 2677
British Paralympic Association	020-8681 9655
British Universities Sports Fed	020-7357 8555
British Wheelchair Sports Foundation	01296-395995
Central Council of Physical Recreation	020-7828 3163
Commonwealth Games Fed	020-7383 5596
Dept of Culture, Media & Sport	020-7211 6000
Disability Sport England	020-7490 4919
Institute of Sport and Recreation	01664-565531
Institute of Sports Sponsorship	020-7233 7747
National Coaching Foundation	0113-274 4802
National Council for Schools Sports	01902-380302
National Lottery Charities Board	0345-919191
National Playing Fields Assoc	020-7584 6445
Physical Education Assoc	0118-931 6240
Sports Aid Foundation	020-7387 9380
Womens Sports Foundation	020-8697 5370
Youth Clubs UK	020-7242 4045

NATIONAL SPORTS CENTRES

Bisham Abbey, Bucks	01628-476911
Crystal Palace, South London	020-8778 0131
Cumbrae & Inverclyde, Ayrshire	01475-674666
Glenmore Lodge, Aviemore	01479-861256
Holme Pierrepont, Notts	0115-982 1212
Lilleshall, Shropshire	01952-603003
Plas Menai. Gwynedd	01248-670964
Plas y Brenin, Gwynedd	01690-720214
Welsh Institute, Cardiff	029-2030 0500
Tollymore, County Down	01396-722158

SPORTS BODIES

Royal **Aero** Club	0116-253 1051
Aircraft Owners & Pilots Assoc	020-7834 5631
British Microlight **Aircraft** Assoc	01869-338888
National Federation of **Anglers**	01283-734735
Scottish **Anglers** National Assoc	0131-339 8808
National Fed of Sea **Anglers**	01626-331330
Wales	01646-600313
Scotland	0131-317 7192
Grand National **Archery** Society	01952-677888
Scottish **Archery** Centre	01620 850401
Amateur **Athletic** Assoc	0121-456 5098
Scotland	0131-317 7320
N Ireland Sports Council	028-9038 1222
British **Athletic** Federation	0121-456 5098
Gaelic **Athletic** Assoc	020-8841 2468
Athletics Assoc of Wales	01792-456237
British **Automobile Racing** Club	01264-772607
Badminton Assoc	01908-268400
British **Balloon** & Airship Club	01604-870025
British **Baseball** Federation	01482-643551
English **Basketball** Assoc	0113-236 1166
Scottish **Basketball** Assoc	0131-317 7260
World Professional **Billiards** & Snooker Assoc	0117-974 4491
British **Bobsleigh** Assoc	01722-340014
British Crown Green **Bowling**	0151-648 5740
English **Bowling** Assoc	01903-820222
Wales	01446-733747
Scotland	0141-221 8999
Northern Ireland	01247-469374
English **Bowling** Federation	0114-247 7763
English Indoor **Bowling** Assoc	01664-481900
Wales	01656-841361
Scotland	01294-468372
Ireland	028-9079 4869
English Womens Indoor **Bowling**	01604-494163
English **Bowls** Council	01603-427551
Amateur **Boxing** Assoc	020-8778 0251
Wales	029-2062 3566
Scotland	01382-508261
Ireland	00353-4540777
British **Boxing** Board	020-7403 5879
British **Canoe** Union	0115-982 1100
Veteran **Car** Club (pre-1919)	01462-742818
Vintage Sports **Car** Club	01608-644777
Caravan Club	01342-326944
National **Caving** Assoc	01225-311364
British **Chess** Federation	01424-442500
Clay Pigeon Shooting Assoc	01536-443566
England & Wales **Cricket** Board	020-7432 1200
Marylebone **Cricket** Club (MCC)	020-7289 1611
Scottish **Cricket** Union	0131-317 7247

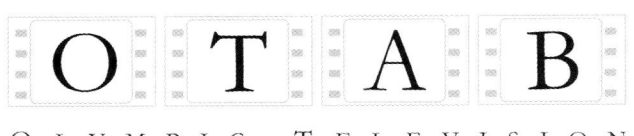

TWI *Archive*

A stunning wealth of images, covering a multitude of sports, as well as
a vast range of historical, scenic and cultural stockshots from around the globe.

contact: TWI Archive, Axis Centre, Burlington Lane, Chiswick, London W4 2TH
Togo Keynes - Sales and Marketing Manager
Tel: +44 (0)20 8233 5500/5300   Fax: +44 (0)20 8233 5301
E-mail: twiarchive@imgworld.com

Search engines can send you round the houses.

There is an easier way of finding accurate information about the UK than trawling web sites around the world with a search engine and ending up in an information cul-de-sac. After all, if you need details of the Housing Department in Birmingham why go to Alabama to find it? *KnowUK* is a unique service on the World Wide Web that provides key information on the people, places and institutions of the United Kingdom. It doesn't just point you in the right direction. It provides high quality information from respected sources such as *Who's Who, Debrett's People of Today, Hansard, The Municipal Year Book* and *Which?* If you would like to try *KnowUK* for youself, call our hotline on **0800 389 KNOW** (0800 389 5669) or visit the website and we can arrange a free trial. Alternatively, e-mail us at: **marketing@chadwyck.co.uk**

Know**UK**

will bring you home.

CHADWYCK-HEALEY

www.knowuk.co.uk

SPORTS BODIES CONTD.

Croquet Assoc	020-7736 3148
National **Crossbow** Federation	01902-758870
English **Curling** Assoc	01923-825004
Royal Caledonian **Curling** Club	0131-333 3003
British **Cycling** Federation	0161-230 2301
Northern Ireland	028-9181 7396
Welsh **Cycling** Union	01222 577052
Cyclists' Touring Club	01483-417217
Scottish **Cyclists** Union	0131-652 0187
British **Equestrian** Federation	01926-707700
British **Fencing** Assoc	020-8742 3032
English **Folk** Dance & Song Society	020-7485 2206
Football Association	020-7262 4542
Wales	029-2037 2325
Scotland	0141-332 6372
Northern Ireland	028-9066 9458
Football League	01772-325800
Scotland	0141-248 3844
Football Supporters Assoc	0151-737 2385
Football Trust	020-7832 0100
Womens **Football** Assoc	01707-651840
Scotland	0141-353 1162
British **Gliding** Assoc	0116-253 1051
English **Golf** Union	01526-354500
Wales	01633-430830
English Ladies **Golf** Assoc	0121-456 2088
Ladies **Golf** Union	01334-475811
Royal & Ancient **Golf** Club	01334-472112
Professional **Golfers** Assoc	01675-470333
British Amateur **Gymnastics**	01952-820330
Scotland	0131-458 5657
Irish	028-9038 3813
British Hang-**Gliding** Assoc	0116-261 1322
Hockey Association	01908-544644
English **Hockey**	01908-689290
Scottish **Hockey** Union	0131-312 8870
British **Horse** Society	01926-707700
British **Horseracing** Board	020-7396 0011
Jockey Club (**horse racing**)	020-7486 4921
Racecourse Assoc (**horse racing**)	01344-625912
British **Ice Hockey** Assoc	0115-915 9204
Scotland	01292-266203
National **Ice Skating** Assoc	020-7613 1188
British **Judo** Assoc	0116-255 9669
British **Ju-Jitsu** Assoc	0114-266 6733
English **Karate** Governing Body	01302-337645
Welsh **Karate** Federation	01834-813776
Keep Fit Assoc	020-7233 8898
English **Lacrosse** Assoc	0121-773 4422
British **Microlight** Aircraft Assoc	01869-338888
RAC **Motor Sports** Assoc	01753-681736
Auto-Cycle Union (**motorcycling**)	01788-540519
British **Motorcyclists** Federation	020-8942 7914
British **Mountaineering** Council	0161-445 4747
Scotland	01738-638227
Central Council for **Naturism**	01604-620361

All England **Netball** Assoc	01462-442344
Wales	029-2023 7048
Scotland	0141-570 4016
British **Orienteering** Federation	01629-734042
British **Parachute** Assoc	0116-278 5271
English **Pool** Assoc	01922-710218
National **Quoits** Assoc	01947-841100
Ramblers Assoc	020-7339 8500
British Federation of **Roller Skating**	01473-401430
National **Rounders** Assoc	0115-938 5478
Amateur **Rowing** Assoc	020-8748 3632
Wales	01600-714244
Scotland	01387-264233
Henley Royal Regatta (**rowing**)	01491-572153
British Amateur **Rugby** League	01484-544131
Rugby Football League	0113-232 9111
Rugby Football Union	020-8892 2000
Wales	029-2078 1700
Scotland	0131-346 5000
Camanachd Assoc (**shinty**)	01397-772772
Br Assoc for **Shooting**/Conservation	01244-573000
National Rifle Assoc (**shooting**)	01483-797777
British **Show Jumping** Assoc	024-7669 8800
Showmens' Guild	01784-461805
British **Ski** Federation	0131-445 7676
English **Ski** Council	0121-501 2314
Wales	029-2056 1904
Scotland	0131-317 7280
World Prof. Billiards & **Snooker**	0117-974 4491
British **Softball** Federation	01886-884204
British Racing & **Sports Car**	01732-848884
Squash Rackets Assoc	0161-231 4499
British **Surfing** Assoc	01736-360250
Amateur **Swimming** Assoc	01509-618700
Wales	029-2048 8820
Scotland	0141-641 8818
English **Table Tennis** Assoc	01424-722525
Wales	01495-756112
Scotland	0131-317 8077
Tennis & Rackets Assoc	020-7386 3448
Lawn **Tennis** Assoc	020-7381 7000
All England Club	020-8944 1066
Wales	029-2045 2000
Scotland	0131-444 1984
British **Ten-Pin Bowling** Assoc	020-8478 1745
British **Trampoline** Federation	020-8863 7278
Tug-of-War Assoc	01494-783057
English **Volleyball** Assoc	0115-981 6324
Northern Ireland	028-9066 7011
Long Distance **Walkers** Assoc	0113-264 2205
British **Water Ski** Federation	020-7833 2855
British **Weightlifters** Assoc	01865-200339
British Amateur **Wrestling** Assoc	0161-832 9209
British Federation of Sand & Land **Yacht**	
Clubs	01509-842292
Royal Ocean Racing Club (**yachting**)	020-7493 2248
Royal **Yachting** Assoc	023-8062 7400
British Wheel of **Yoga**	01529-306851

Advertising, PR and media analysts

New numbers

TV ad production budgets of £500,000 for half a minute of footage competes with the average TV drama budget of £70,000 an hour. Mere trifles - in June 2000 Advertising Association figures revealed a:

1999 UK ad spend = £15.3 billion

... which is 2 per cent of UK turnover ... or £485 a second ... or £250 a person every year

UK advertising expenditure

proportions of the £15.3 billion spent on ads in 1999

Television:	32.1%
Local papers:	22.9%
Magazines:	18.4%
National papers:	17.1%
Outdoor and transport:	5.4%
Radio:	4.0%

Source: Advertising Association, 2000

Old quotes

THE TIMES, 1999
"The Guinness surf ad is the most beautiful and powerful piece of film on our screens."
THE TIMES, 1986
"The incessant repetition of advertisers' moron-fodder has become so much a part of life that if we are not careful, we forget to be insulted by it."
JONATHAN PRICE, 1978
"Financially, commercials represent the pinnacle of our popular culture's artistic expression. More money per second goes into their making, more cash flows from their impact, more business thinking goes into each word than in any movie, opera, stage play, painting or videotape."
GEORGE ORWELL, 1946
"Advertising is the rattling of a stick inside a swill bucket."
NORMAN DOUGLAS, 1917
"You can tell the ideals of a nation by its advertising."

Press

Advertising in newspapers, magazines, posters, the cinema and direct mail is regulated by the Advertising Standards Authority, which is funded by a levy on display ads. It aims to enforce standards through a code which says ads should be: legal, decent, honest and truthful; prepared with a sense of responsibility to the consumer and society; and fair competition as generally accepted in business. The Authority's main sanction is to recommend that the ads it considers in breach of its code are not published. This is normally enough to make sure an offending ad is quashed. The Authority publishes monthly reports on the results of its investigations and, as a final resort, refers misleading adverts to the director general of fair trading who has the power to seek injunctions to prevent publication.

Broadcasting

The advertising rules for broadcasting are more complex than for the press. Advertising is allowed on independent television and radio, subject to controls laid down by the ITC and the Radio Authority. Both can impose heavy penalties on companies failing to comply with their codes. Advertisers are not allowed to influence programme content and their ads must be distinct from programmes. Television advertising is limited to an average of seven minutes an hour during the day and seven and a half minutes in the peak evening period. Adverts are forbidden in religious and school broadcasts, though religious advertising is now permitted. Political advertising is prohibited and gambling adverts are restricted to the football pools and the National Lottery. All tobacco adverts are banned on television (with the exception of ones that just happen to appear on Formula One racing cars) and cigarette ads are banned on radio.

TOP 30 AD AGENCIES*, BY BILLINGS
Listings on pages 354 - 355

1	Abbott Mead Vickers BBDO
2	Lowe Lintas
3	BMP DDB
4	J. Walter Thompson
5	McCann-Erickson UK
6	Saatchi & Saatchi
7	Publicis
8	Rainey Kelly Campbell Roalfe/Y&R
9	M&C Saatchi
10	TBWA GGT Simons Palmer
11	Ogilvy & Mather
12	Bates UK
13	D'Arcy
14	WCRS
15	Grey Advertising
16	Euro RSCG Worldwide
17	Leo Burnett
18	Bartle Bogle Hegarty
19	HHCL & Parters
20	Banks Hoggins O'Shea/FCB
21	BDH TBWA
22	St Luke's
23	Delaney Lund Knox Warren
24	Collett Dickenson Pearce
25	WWAV Rapp Collins Group
26	Golley Slater Group
27	Citigate Albert Frank
28	Roose & Partners
29	Leagas Delaney Partnership
30	Partners BDDH

Source: Campaign, Feb 2000

TOP 30 MEDIA AGENCIES* BY BILLINGS
Listings on pages 356 - 357

1	Zenith Media
2	Carat
3	BMP OMD
4	Universal McCann
5	Mediacom TMB
6	MindShare
7	MediaVest UK
8	Initiative Media London
9	New PHD
10	CIA Medianetwork
11	Optimedia
12	Starcom
13	Manning Gottlieb Media
14	Mediapolis
15	BBJ
16	Motive Communications
17	Western International Media
18	Walker Media
19	MBS Group
20	CDP Media Company
21	Feather Brooksbank Group
22	Mediavest (Manchester)
23	BJK&E Media
24	Brilliant
25	John Ayling & Associates
26	Media Campaign Services
27	WWAV Rapp Collins Media
28	New PHD Compass
29	Booth Lockett Makin Group
30	Collins Partnership

Source: Campaign, Feb 2000

* The advertising market used to be controlled by ad agencies, a situation which changed when media agencies emerged to negotiate prices with media owners. This has left the ad agencies to concentrate on what they call the "creative side".

AD/PR CONTACTS

AC Nielsen.MEAL
7 Harewood Avenue, London NW1 6JB
Fax 020-7393 5088   Tel 020-7393 5070
E-mail: john.purcell@acnielsen.co.uk
AC Nielsen.MEAL has provided the ad industry's standard measure of above-the-line advertising expenditure since 1968, with electronic data available to 1986 on TV, press, radio, cinema and outdoor media.

Advertising Association
Abford House, 15 Wilton Road, London SW1V 1NJ
Fax 020-7931 0376   Tel 020-7828 2771
E-mail: aa@adassoc.org.uk
Website: www.adassoc.org.uk
Promotes the rights, responsibilities, and role of advertising. It is committed to upholding the freedom to advertise in the UK and to self-regulation.

Advertising Film & Videotape Producers Association
26 Noel Street, London W1V 3RD
Fax 020-7434 9002   Tel 020-7434 2651
E-mail: afvpa@easynet.co.uk
TV commercials' production companies trade body.

Advertising Standards Authority
2 Torrington Place, London WC1E 7HW
Fax 020-7631 3051   Tel 020-7580 5555
E-mail: chrisr@asa.org.uk
Website: www.asa.org.uk
Adminsters and endorses the British Codes of Advertising and Sales Promotion, which states that non-broadcast advertisements should be legal, decent, honest and truthful. Financed by a levy on advertising spend, the ASA is independent of both the government and the advertising industry.

TOP 30 PR AGENCIES, BY BILLINGS
Listings on pages 357 - 358

1	**International Public Relations**
2	**Bell Pottinger Communications**
3	**Citigate Dewe Rogerson**
4	**Hill and Knowlton (UK)**
5	**Countrywide Peter Novelli**
6	**Burson-Marsteller**
7	**GCI UK/APCO**
8	**Medical Action Communications**
9	**BSMG Worldwide**
10	**Biss Lancaster**
11	**Edelman PR Worldwide**
12	**Ketchum**
13	**Grayling Group**
14	**Text 100**
15	**College Hill Associates**
16	**Fishburn Hedges**
17	**Freud Communications**
18	**Cohn and Wolfe**
19	**Key Communications**
20	**The Shire Hall Group**
21	**Beattie Media**
22	**Firefly Communications**
23	**Harrison Cowley**
24	**Brodeur Worldwide**
25	**Ogilvy Public Relations Worldwide**
26	**Harvard Public Relations**
27	**Manning Selvage and Lee**
28	**Richmond Towers**
29	**The Red Consultancy**
30	**Consolidated Comms Management**

Source: PR Week

Broadcast Advertising Clearance Centre
200 Grays Inn Road, London WC1X 8HF
Fax 020-7843 8154   Tel 020-7843 8265
E-mail: steph-ford@bacc.org.uk
Website: www.bacc.org.uk
Ensures that TV commercials comply with ITC codes
on behalf of the ITV and satellite companies.

Direct Marketing Association
1 Oxendon Street, London SW1Y 4EE
Fax 020-7321 0191   Tel 020-7321 2525
E-mail: dma@dma.org.uk
Website: www.dma.org.uk/members
Trade association for direct marketers which publishes
leaflets, a members' directory and a code of practice.

History of Advertising Trust
Hat House, 12 Raveningham Centre, Raveningham,
Norwich, Norfolk NR14 6NU
Fax 01508-548478   Tel 01508-548623
E-mail: hatadvert@email.msn.com
Website: www.hatads.org.uk
An archive of advertising material from the beginning
of the nineteenth century to the present day.

Incorporated Society of British Advertisers
44 Hertford Street, London W1Y 8AE
Fax 020-7629 5355   Tel 020-7499 7502
E-mail: ijackiem@isba.org.uk
Website: www.isba.org.uk
Represents British advertisers' interests across the
industry on all marketing communication issues.

Institute of Practitioners in Advertising
44 Belgrave Square, London SW1X 8QS
Fax 020-7245 9904   Tel 020-7201 8211
E-mail: tessa@ipa.co.uk
Website: www.ipa.co.uk
Trade and professional body for UK ad agencies.

Institute of Public Relations
15 Northburgh Street, London EC1V 0PR
Fax 020-7490 0588   Tel 020-7253 5151
E-mail: info@ipr.org.uk
Website: www.ipr.org.uk
The main professional association for all working in PR.

Market Research Society
15 Northburgh Street, London EC1V 0JR
Fax 020-7490 0608   Tel 020-7490 4911
E-mail: mrs@dial.pipex.com
Website: www.marketresearch.org.uk
Publishes a monthly magazine called the Journal of
Market Research Society and runs trainingcourses and
seminars, and holds an annual conference every March.

National Newspapers Mail Order Protection Scheme (MOPS)
16 Tooks Court, London EC4A 1LB
Fax 020-7404 0106   Tel 020-7269 0520
Website: www.mops.org.uk
Reimburses readers of member newspapers who lose
money when approved mail order advertisers enter
liquidation or bankruptcy, or cease to trade.

Public Relations Consultants' Association
Willow House, Willow Place, London SW1P 1JH
Fax 020-7828 4797   Tel 020-7233 6026
E-mail: chris@prca.org.uk
Website: www.prca.org.uk

Radio Advertising Bureau
77 Shaftesbury Avenue, London W1V 7AD
Fax 020-7306 2505   Tel 0171 306 2500
E-mail: rab@rab.co.uk
Website: www.rab.co.uk
Marketing company set up by the commercial radio
industry for advertisers and advertising agencies.

Radio Advertising Clearance Centre
46 Westbourne Grove, London W2 5SH
Fax 020-7229 0352   Tel 020-7727 2646
E-mail: adclear@racc.co.uk
Clears radio ad scripts and ensures compliance with the
Radio Authority's Advertising Code.

AD/PR MAGAZINES

Advertising Age International
Crain Communications, New Garden House, 78
Hatton Garden, London EC1N 8LD
Fax 020-7216 0053   Tel 020-7457 1419
Monthly media and marketing magazine.

Campaign
174 Hammersmith Road, London W6 7JP
Fax 020-8267 4914   Tel 020-8267 4656
Website: www.campaignlive.com
Publisher: Haymarket.
£2.10. Weekly news for the advertising industry.

Campaign Media Business
174 Hammersmith Road, London W6 7JP
Fax 020-8227 4726   Tel 020-8267 4745
Email: cmbiz@haynet.com
Glossy weekly paper for UK media executives and
media owners, media planners/buyers launched in
1999.

Creative Review
50 Poland Street, London W1V 4AX
Fax 020-7970 6713   Tel 020-7970 4000
Website: www.creativereview.com
Publisher: Centaur Communications.
£4.25. Monthly looking at the best in advertising and
design.

The Drum
3 Park Street South, Glasgow G3 6BG
Fax 0141-332 2012   Tel 0141-332 3255
Media and marketing magazine for Scotland.

The Marketeer
3 Park Street South, Glasgow G3 6BG
Fax 0141-332 2012   Tel 0141-332 3255
Media and marketing magazine for the English regions.

Marketing
Haymarket,174 Hammersmith Road, London W6 7JP
Fax 020-8267 4505   Tel 020-8267 4150
E-mail: editor@marketing.haynet.com
Website: www.marketing.haynet.com
Editor: Conor Dignam
£2.30. The weekly business newspaper for marketing.

Media & Marketing Europe
Emap,33-39 Bowling Green Lane, London EC1R 0DA
Fax 020-7505 8320   Tel 020-7505 8312
E-mail traceyt@media-emap.co.uk
£5.00. Monthly mag for advertising & marketing execs.

Media Week
Quantum, 19 Scarbrook Road, Croydon CR9 1LX
Fax 020-8565 4444   Tel 020-8565 4200
Weekly news magazine linking media and advertising .

New Media Age
50 Poland Street, London W1V 4AX
Fax 020-7943 8168   Tel 020-7970 4000
E-mail: nma.info@centaur.co.uk
Website: www.nma.co.uk
Business weekly for advertising, marketing and e-
commerce.

PR Week
Haymarket,174 Hammersmith Road, London W6 7JP
Fax 020-7413 4509   Tel 020-7413 4429
E-mail: prweek@haynet.com
Website: www.prweekuk.com
£1.70. The weekly news magazine for the PR industry.

AD/PR YEARBOOKS & GUIDES

Advertisers Annual/Blue Book
Harlequin House, 7 High Street, Teddington,
Middlesex TW11 8EL
Fax 020-8977 1133   Tel 020-8977 7711
Website: www.hollis-pr.co.uk
Publisher: Hollis Directories
Contact: Gary Zabel
£235. An ad directory from same stable as Willings
Press Guide. Covers: Agencies/advertiser brands; UK
media.

ALF
33-39 Bowling Green Lane, London EC1R 0DA
Fax 020-7505 8336   Tel 020-7505 8458
E-mail: joe@brad.co.uk
Website: www.brad.co.uk
Publisher: Emap Media
Contact: Jo Ellis
Monthly directory of 1,500 agencies, 1,000 advertisers -
all linked to 9,000 brands. All personnel are linked to
brands. £790 for 12 issues, £220 1 vol.

Benn's Media
Riverbank House, Angel Lane Tonbridge, Kent TN9
1SE
01732-367301   Tel 01732-362666
E-mail: bennsmedia@unmf.co,
Website: www.mfuk.com/mfinfo
Publisher: Benn Business Information Services
Contact: Debbie O'Neil
3 vols £310, 2 vols £290, 1 vol £145
Benn's has the most comprehensive of media listings.
Its three volumes cover the UK, Europe and the rest of
the world. Established 1846.

BRAD (British Rate & Data)
33-39 Bowling Green Lane, London EC1R 0DA
Fax 020-7505 8336   Tel 020-7505 8458
E-mail: judithm@brad.co.uk
Website: www.brad.co.uk
Publisher: Emap Media
Contact: Judith Mellor
Monthly guide to advertising in the UK. Over 12,000
media outlets covered. £495 for 12 issues, £260 1 vol.

Editors
34 Germain Street, Chesham Bucks HP5 1SJ
Fax 01494-797224   Tel 01494-797224
E-mail: editors@mediainfo.co.uk
Website: www.mediainfo.co.uk
Contact: James Scott
6 volumes for £495 pa.subscription
Directory of media contacts for the PR industry.

Hollis UK Press & PR Annual
Harlequin House, 7 High Street, Teddington,
Middlesex TW11 8EL
Fax 020-8977 1133   Tel 020-8977 7711
E-mail: orders@hollis-pr.co.uk
Website: www.hollis-pr.co.uk
Publisher: Hollis Directories
Contact: John Chambers
£97.50.Contacts throughout industry plus voluntary
organisations, PR consultancies and major media titles.

Institute of Public Relations Handbook
120 Pentonville Road, London N1 9JN
Fax 020-7837 6348   Tel 020-7278 0433
E-mail: kpinfo@kogan-page.co.uk
Publisher: Kogan Page
Contact: Don Edwards
£135. List of over 5,000 IPR members, plus other
information and articles.

IPO Directory
PO Box 30, Wetherby, West Yorkshire LS23 7YA
Fax 01937-541083   Tel 01937-541010
£15 annual subscription.
The official directory of information and press officers
in government departments and public corporations.
Published bi-annually.

LENA
33-39 Bowling Green Lane, London EC1R 0DA
Fax 020-7505 8336   Tel 020-7505 84458
E-mail: joe@brad.co.uk
Website: www.brad.co.uk
Publisher: Emap Media
Contact: Joe Ellis
Quarterly guide to the top 2,000 national advertisers.
Annual sub £580 for 4 issues, £310 1 vol.

Media Pocket Book
Farm Road, Henley-on-Thames, Oxfordshire RG9 1EJ
Fax 01491-571188   Tel 01491-574671
Publisher: Advertising Association
£26, each July. Key facts and figures on the media and
advertising, from newspaper circulations to TV
ownership. Other titles in this series are the Marketing,
Retail and Lifestyle Pocket Books.

Pims Media Directories
Pims House, Mildmay Avenue, London N1 4RS
Fax 020-7354 7053   Tel 020-7226 1000
E-mail: marketing@pims.co.uk
Website: www.pims.co.uk
Publisher: Pims UK
Contact: Susan Mears
Pims produces a range of detailed guides to editorial
media contacts, all regularly updated, aimed mainly at
the public relations sector. Titles include: UK Media
Directory (5 vols), A-Z Towns Directory (2 vols) and
several USA/European directories.

PR Planner UK & Europe
34 Germain Street, Chesham Bucks HP5 1SJ
Fax 01494-797224   Tel 01494-797224
E-mail: prplanner@mediainfo.co.uk
Website: www.mediainfo.co.uk
Loose-leaf guide to contacts in all media. The UK
edition is updated monthly and costs £370 pa, also
available on CD.The Euro edition is updated every other
month and costs £425 pa for Trade and Technical and
£250 the Consumer.

UK Media Yearbook
Bridge House, 63-65 North Wharf Road, London W2
1LA
Fax 020-7298 6902   Tel 020-7224 8500
E-mail: publications@zenithmedia.co.uk
Website: www.zenithmedia.com
Publisher: Zenith Media
£275. Facts and figures on the UK's advertising media
with commentary and analysis.

Willings Press Guide
Harlequin House, 7 High Street, Teddington,
Middlesex, TWII 8EL
Fax 020-8977 1133   Tel 020-8977 7711
E-mail: orders@hollis-pr.co.uk
Website: www.hollis-pr.co.uk
Contact: John Chambers
Publisher: Hollis Directories
Two vols £225. Alphabetical list detailing over 50,000
entries on newspapers and periodicals worldwide.
Available on web or CD for £275/£323.13 inc VAT. CD +
2 vols is £342.50 inc VAT.

World Advertising Trends
Farm Road, Henley on Thames, Oxfordshire RG9 1EJ
Fax 01491-571188   Tel 01491-574671
Publisher: Advertising Association
Contact: Toby Howard
£125. Statistical analysis of ad spends from 57 countries.

Three advertising lists

Below are three of the lists which the advertising trade is so good at generating:

Most popular TV ads ever

1 Surfing (Guinness, 1999)*
2 Martians (Smash, 1973)
3 Orange man (Tango, 1992)
4 Heat electric (Electricity Association, 1992)
5 Ice cream (Boddingtons, 1997)
6 Launderette (Levi's, 1985)
7 Secret lemonade drinker (R Whites, 1972)
8 Photo booth (Hamlet, 1986)
9 Gary Lineker (Walker's crisps, 1993)
10 Chance Encounter (Impulse, 1998)**

* 48 shots are packed into 51 seconds
** the first gay ad on British TV

Source: Channel 4/Sunday Times survey

Most irritating TV ads ever

1 Procter & Gamble Bounty kitchen towels
2 Chicken Tonight sauces with Ian Wright
3 Renault Scenic Sound of Music
4 ONdigital with Chris Tarrant
5 Citroen Xsara with Claudia Schiffer

Source: Marketing survey (Marketing: "There is some correlation between an irritating advert and its memorability.")

Top 20th century posters

1 "Labour isn't working" (Tories, 1978)
2 "Lord Kitchener Wants You" (1914)
3 Pyramids (B&H, 1977)
4 "For Strength" (Guinness, 1934)
5 "I never read The Economist" (Economist, 1989)
6 Pregnant man (Health Education Council, 1969)
7 "It also sticks handles to teapots" (Araldite, 1982)
8 "Careless talk costs lives" (1940)
9 New-born baby (Benetton, 1991)
10 "Hello boys" (Wonderbra, 1994)

Source: Campaign survey

ADVERTISING AGENCIES

Abbott Mead Vickers BBDO
151 Old Marylebone Road, London NW1 5QE
Fax 020-7616 3600   Tel 020-7616 3500
Website: www.amvbbdo.co.uk
Clients include: BT, Cellnet, Granada, Kiss FM

Banks Hoggins O'Shea/FCB
55 Newman Street, London W1P 3PG
Fax 020-7947 8801   Tel 020-7947 8000
E-mail: info@bho.fcb.com
Clients include: Coors, Travelstore.com, Chrysler.

Bartle Bogle Hegarty
60 Kingly Street, London, W1R 6DS
Fax 020-7437 3666   Tel 020-7734 1677
Website: www.bbh.co.uk

Bates UK
121-141 Westbourne Terrace, London, W2 6JR
Fax 020-7724 3075   Tel 020-7262 5077
Web: www.bates.uk.com
Clients include: Royal Mail, B&Q, Halifax.

BDH TBWA
Oaklands House, Talbot Road, Old Trafford,
Manchester M16 0AX
Fax 0161-908 8201   Tel 0161-908 8600
Clients include: Britannia Building Society, Brrother
UK, United Cinemas.

BMP DDB
12 Bishop's Bridge Road, London W2 6AA
Fax 020-7402 4871   Tel 020-7258 3979
Website: www.bmpddb.com
Clients include: Associated Newspapers, Barclays Bank,
boo.com Group, British Digital Broadcast, Sony United
Kingdom.

Citigate Albert Frank
26 Finsbury Square, London EC2A 1DS
Fax 020-7282 8070   Tel 020-7282 8000
E-mail: @citigate-group.co.uk

Collett Dickenson Pearce
33-34 Soho Square, London, W1V 6DP
Fax 020-7292 4010   Tel 020-7292 4000
Web: www.cdp-uk.com

D'Arcy Masius Benton & Bowles
123 Buckingham Palace Road, London SW1W 9DZ
Fax 020-7630 0033   Tel 020-7630 0000
Website: www.darcyww.co.uk
Clients include: Fiat UK, House of Fraser, Mars
Confectionary.

Delaney Lund Knox Warren
25 Wellington Street, London WC2E 7DA
Fax 020-7240 8739   Tel 020-7836 3474
Website: www.dlkw.co.uk
Clients include: Financial Times, IPC, UKTV.

EuroRSCG Worldwide
11 Great Newport Street, London WC2H 7JA
Fax 020-7465 0552   Tel 020-7240 4111
E-mail: info@eurorscg.co.uk
Web: www.eurorscg.co.uk
Clients include: Abbey National, Peugeot, Microsoft.

Golley Slater Group
Wharton Place, Wharton Street, Cardiff CF10 1GS
Fax 029-2023 8729   Tel 029-2038 8621
Clients include: Honda, Kodak, Western Mail & Echo.

Grey Advertising
215-227 Great Portland Street, London W1N 5HD
Fax 020-7637 7473   Tel 020-7636 3399
Website: www.greyen.com

HHCL & Partners
Kent House, 14-17 Market Place, Great Titchfield
Street, London, W1N 7AJ
Fax 020-7436 2677   Tel 020-7436 3333
Web: www.hhcl.com

J Walter Thompson
40 Berkeley Square, London W1X 6AD
Fax 020-7493 8432   Tel 020-7499 4040
Website: www.jwt.com

Leagas Delaney Partnership
233 Shaftsbury Avenue, London, WC2H 8EL
Fax 020-7240 9005   Tel 020-7836 4455
E-mail: uk@leagasdelaney.co.uk
Web: www.leagasdelaney.co.uk

Leo Burnett
The Leo Burnett Building, 60 Sloane Avenue, London,
SW3 3XB
Fax 020-7591 9126   Tel 020-7591 9111
Web: www.leoburnett.com

Lowe Lintas
3rd Floor West Wing, Bowater House, 68-114
Knightsbridge, London SW1X 7LT
Fax 020-7584 9557   Tel 020-7584 5033
Website: www.lowelintas.co.uk

M&C Saatchi
36 Golden Square, London W1R 4EE
Fax 020-7543 4501   Tel 020-7543 4500
Website: www.mcsaatchi.com
Clients include: British Airways, Dixons, Whiskas

McCann-Erickson
7-11 Hebrand Street, Londonn WC1N 1EX
Fax 020-7837 3773   Tel 020-7837 3737
Website: www.mcann.co.uk

Ogilvy and Mather
10 Cabot Sq, Canary Wharf, London E14 4QB
Fax 020-7345 9000   Tel 020-7345 3000
Website: www.ogilvy.com
Clients include: IBM, Ford, Unilever.

Partners BDDH
9-18 Maple Place, London W1P 5FX
Fax 020-7467 9210   Tel 020-7467 9200
Website: www.partnersbddh.co.uk
Clients include: Co-operative Bank, Guardian
Newspapers, Yellow Pages.

Publicis
82 Baker Street, London W1M 2AE
Fax 020-7487 5351   Tel 020-7935 4426
Website: www.publicis.co.uk
Clients include: Asda, Renault, United Biscuits

Rainey Kelly Campbell Roalfe
Greater London House, Hampstead Road, London
NW1 7QP
Fax 020-7611 6570   Tel 020-7404 2700

Roose & Partners
100 Gray's Inn Road, London WC1X 8AU
Fax 020-7831 8761   Tel 020-7831 7400
Clients include: MVC Entertaiment, Nestle UK -
Rowntree.

Saatchi and Saatchi
80 Charlotte Street, London W1A 1AQ
Fax 020-7637 8489   Tel 020-7636 5060
Website: www.saatchi-saatchi.com
Clients include: Procter & Gamble, Toyota, Sony.

St Luke's
22 Dukes Road, London, WC1H 9AD
Fax 020-7 380 8899   Tel 020-7380 8888
Web: www.stlukes.co.uk
Clients include: Sky, HSBC, IKEA

TBWA GGT Simons Palmer
76-80 Whitfield Street, London, W1P 5RQ
Fax 020-7573 6667   Tel 020-7573 6666
Website: www.tbwa.co.uk
Clients include: NatWest, Playstation, French Connection

WCRS
5 Golden Square, London, W1R 4BS
Fax 020-7806 5099   Tel 020-7806 5000
Website: www.wcrs.co.uk
Clients include: Orange, Land Rover, BMW

WWAV Rapp Collins Group
1 Riverside, Mambre Road, London W6 9WA
Fax 020-7735 8722   Tel 020-7727 3481
Clients include: 1st Line Communications, Channel
Four Television.

MEDIA AGENCIES

BBJ Media Services
Orion House, 5 Upper St Martins Lane, London, WC2H 9EA
Fax 020-7497 1177   Tel 020-7379 9000
Clients include Cable and Wireless and Audi.

BJK&E Media
25 Wellington Street, London, WC2E 7DA
Fax 020-7240 0792   Tel 020-7379 8080
E-mail: mpatterson@bjke.co.ul
Web: www.london.bozell.com
Clients include Financial Times, Daimler Chrysler, Save & Prosper.

BMP OMD
16 Bishops Bridge Road, Paddington, London, W2 6AA`
Fax 020-7258 4545   Tel 020-7893 4189
Website: www.bmpomd.co.uk
Formerly known as BMP DDB. Clients include Barclaycard, Boots, Vodafone.

Booth Lockett Makin Group
49/51 Carnaby Street, London W1V 1PF
Fax 020-7437 1287   Tel 020-7437 1317
Clients include: Blockbuster Entertainment, Dennis Publishing, EMAP Metro.

Brilliant Independent Media Specialists
Techno Centre, Station Road, Horsforth, Leeds LS18 5BJ
Fax 0113-258 7064   Tel 0113-259 0244
Clients include: Dunlop Slazenger, Sheffield Newspapers.

Carat
Parker Tower,43-49 Parker Street, London, WC2B 5PS
Fax 020-7430 6155   Tel 020-7430 6000
Website: www.carat.com
Clients include Royal Mail, Asda, Guinness.

CDP Media Company
33-34 Soho Square, London, W1V 6DP
Fax 020-7292 4010   Tel 020-7292 4000
Clients include Honda and Switch

CIA Medianetwork
1 Paris Garden, London, SE1 8NU
Fax 020-7803 2080   Tel 020-7633 9999
Clients include Odeon, Early Learning Centre.

Collins Partnership
11 Calico House, Plantation Wharf, London, SW11 3TN
Fax 020-7738 0014   Tel 020-7738 0177
E-mail: johnp@collins-p-ship.co.uk
Clients include: Tiny Computers, Alphatelecom, Mobiles Direct.

Feather Brooksbank Group
The Old Assembly Hall, 37 Constitution Street,Leith, Edinburgh EH6 7BG
Fax 0131-555 2556   Tel 0131-555 2554
Clients include: Bank of Scotland, DC Thomson & Co.

Initiative Media
84 Ecclestone Square, London, SW1V 1PX
Fax 020-7663 7003   Tel 020-7663 7000
Clients include Calvin Klein, Christian Dior and Peugeot

John Ayling and Associates
Level 2, 27 Soho Square, London, W1V 5FL
Fax 020-7437 8473   Tel 020-7439 6070
E-mail: jaa@jaa-media.co.uk
Clients include Dairycrest and Savacentre

Manning Gottlieb Media
Seymour Mews House, Wigmore Street, London, W1H 0AA
Fax 020-7412 0244   Tel 020-7470 5300
Clients include Eurostar, Nike and Virgin Direct.

MBS Group
84 Grovesnor Street, London, W1X 0LD
Fax 020-7409 0965   Tel 020-7493 1616

Media Campaign Services
20 Orange Street, London WC2H 7ED
Fax 020-7839 6997   Tel 020-7389 0800
Clients include: Abbey National, BMG Entertainment.

MediaCom TMB
180 North Gower Street, London NW1 2NB
Fax 020-7874 5999   Tel 020-7874 5500
E-mail: nick.lawson@mediacomtmb.com
Clients include BP, Mars, Procter & Gamble, Direct Line and Universal.

Mediapolis
1-19 New Oxford Street, London, WCA 1NQ
Fax 020-7393 2525   Tel 020-7393 9000
E-mail: mediaplanning.co.uk
Clients include Colgate, Mercedes Benz and Our Price.

Mediavest (Manchester)
117-119 Portland Street, Manchester M1 6ED
Fax 0161-228 3866   Tel 0161-228 3909

Mediavest UK
123 Buckingham Palace Road, London, SW1W 9DZ
Fax 020-7233 5677   Tel 020-7233 5678

MindShare
40 Strand, London, WC2N 5HZ
Fax 020-7969 4000   Tel 171-969 4040
Website: www.mindshareworld.com
The product of JWT and The Network merger. Clients include Kelloggs, Ford and Nestle Rowntree.

Motive Communications
24-27 Great Pulteney Street, London, W1R 3DB
Fax 020-7437 2401   Tel 020-7453 4444
Website: www.bbh.co.uk
Clients include Levi Strauss, Golden Wonder and Electrolux.

New PHD
5 North Crescent, Chenies Street, London, WC1E 7PH
Fax 020-7446 7100   Tel 020-7446 0555
E-mail: contact@newphd.co.uk
Clients include: BBC, BBC Worldwide, Midland Bank, BT and Toshiba

Optimedia UK
103 Wigmore Street, London W1H 9AB
Fax 020-7961 1001   Tel 020-7961 1000
Website: www.optimedia.co.uk
Clients include Renault and British Airways.

Starcom
60 Sloane Avenue, London SW3 3XB
Fax 020-7591 9126   Tel 020-7591 9999
Clients include: Hallmark Cards, HJ Heinz Company.

Universal McCann
7-11 Herbrand Street, London WC1N 1EX
Fax 020-7837 3773   Tel 020-7833 5858
Website: www.mccann.co.uk
Clients include Coke, Post Office and Black & Decker.

Walker Media
36 Golden Square, London, W1R 4EE
Fax 020-7543 4501   Tel 020-7447 7500
Web: www.mcsaatchi.com
Clients include British Airways, RAC and Quantas

Western International Media
Bowater House, 68-114 Knightsbridge, London, SW1X 7LT
Fax 020-7823 7115   Tel 020-7581 1455
E-mail: western@wim.co.uk
Clients include Vauxhall and Tesco.

WWAV Rapp Collins Media
1 Riverside, Mambre Road, London W6 9WA
Fax 020-7735 8722   Tel 020-7727 3481
Clients include: 1st Line Communications, Channel Four Television.

Zenith Media
63-65 North Wharf Road, London, W2 1LA
Fax 020-7706 2650   Tel 020-7224 8500
Website: www.zenithmedia.com
Clients include BMW, Rover and B&Q.
Zenith is jointly owned by Saatchi & Saatchi and Cordiant. It is the largest media buyer in the UK and has offices in 25 countries across Europe. Publishes UK Media Yearbook, Top 50 European Media Owners, Digital Media and Television in Europe to 2007.

PR AGENCIES

Beattie Media
18 Glasgow Road, Uddington, G71 7AS
Fax 01698 787879   Tel 01698-787878
Web: www.beattiemedia.co.uk
Top 3 clients: Hewlett Packard, Kwik-Fit, Marks & Spencer

Bell Pottinger Communications
7 Hertford Street, London W1Y 8LP
Fax 020-7629 1277   Tel 020-7495 4044

Biss Lancaster
69 Monmouth Street, London W2H 9DG
Fax 020-7497 8915   Tel 020-7497 3001

Brodeur Worldwide
23 Datchet Road, Slough, Berks, SL3 7PT
Fax 01753-790701   Tel 01753-790700
Web: www.brodeuruk.com

BSMG Worldwide
110 St Martins Lane, London WC2N 4DY
Fax 020-7841 5777   Tel 020-7841 5555
E-mail: nwilliams@bsmg.com
Website: www.charles.co.uk
Top 3 clients: IBM, Kingfisher, British Midland Airways

Burson-Marsteller
24-28 Bloomsbury Way, London WC1A 2PX
Fax 020-7430 1033   Tel 020-7831 6262
Website: www.bm.com
Clients include: Unilever, World Bank, McDonalds

Citigate Dewe Rogerson
3 London Wall Buildings, London EC2M 5SY
Fax 020-7628 3444   Tel 020-7638 9571
E-mail: info@citigatedr.co.uk
Website: www.citigate.com

Cohn and Wolfe
30 Orange Street, London, WC2H 7LZ
Fax 020-7331 9088   Tel 020-7331 5300
Web: www.cohnwolfe.com
Top 3 clients: Eli Lilly, Visa, Colgate-Palmolive

College Hill Associates
78 Cannon Street, London EC4N 6HH
Fax 020-7248 3295   Tel 020-7457 2020
E-mail: pr@collegehill.com
Top 3 clients: Old Mutual, Manpowerr, Waterford Wedgewood

Consolidated Communications Management
1 Poland Street, London W1
                         Tel 020-7287 2087
E-mail: alastair@consol.co.uk
Website: www.consol.co.uk

Countrywide Porter Novelli
South Bar House, Banbury, Oxfordshire OX16 9AD
Fax 01295-224444   Tel 01295-224400
Website: ww.countrywidepn.co.uk

Edelman PR Worldwide
28-29 Haymarket, London SW1Y 4SP
Fax 020-7344 1222   Tel 020-7344 1200
E-mail: central@edeluk.com
Website: www.edelman.com
Top 3 clients: Ericsson, UPS, CGU

Firefly Communications
The Coda Centre, 189 Munster Road, London, SW6 6AW
Fax 020-7385 4768   Tel 020-7386 1400
Web: www.firefly.co.uk
Top 3 clients: Compaq, ICL, Motorola

Fishburn Hedges
77 Kingsway, London WC2B 6ST
Fax 020-7242 4202   Tel 020-7839 4321
Website: www.fishburn-hedges.com

Freud Communications
19-21 Mortimer Street, London, W1N 8DX
Fax 020-7637 2626   Tel 020-7580 2626
Web: www.freud.co.uk

GCI UK/APCO
1 Chelsea Manor Gardens, London, SW3 5PN
Fax 020-7352 6244   Tel 020-7351 2400
Email: pr@gciuk.com
Web: www.gciuk.com

Grayling Group
4 Bedford Square, London WC1B 3RA
Fax: 020-7631 0602   Tel: 020-7255 1100
Website: www.graylinggroup.com
Top 3 clients: University for Industry, Equant, Amersham Pharmacia Biotech

Harrison Cowley
Dragon Court, 27 Macklin Street, London, WC2B 5LX
Fax 020-7404 6888   Tel 020-7404 6777
Web: www.harrisoncowley.com

Harvard Public Relations
Summerhouse Lane, Harmondsworth, Middx UB70AW
Fax 020-8 897 3242   Tel 020-8759 0005
E-mail: info@harvard.co.uk
Web: www.harvard.co.uk
Top 3 clients: Mattel Interactive, Siemens, Smithkline Beecham

Hill and Knowlton
35 Red Lion Square, London WC1R 4SG
Fax 020-7413 3111   Tel 020-7413 3000
E-mail: info@hillandknowlton.com
Website: www.hillandknowlton.com
Top 3 clients: Kelloggs, EDS, BT

International Public Relations
The Courtyard, 30 New Oxford Street, London WC1A 1AP
                    Tel 020-7898 3333
E-mail: jthorn@golinharris.com
Website: www.golinharris.com
Includes the Shandwick, Weber and Golin Harris groups of companies.

Ketchum
8-14 Southampton Street, London, WC2E 7HA
Fax 020-7836 3695   Tel 020-7836 6666
Web: www.ketchum.com

Key Communications
Kings Court, 2-16 Goodge Street, London, W1P 1SF
Fax 020-7580 0333   Tel 020-7580 0222
Web: www.keycommunications.co.uk

Manning, Selvage and Lee
123 Buckingham Palace Road, London, SW1W 9SH
Fax 020-7878 3030   Tel 020-7878 3000
Web: www.mslpr.com

Medical Action Communications
Medical Action House, Crabtree Office Village, Eversley Way, Surrey, TW20 8RY
Fax 01784-431323   Tel 01784-434353
Email: team@mac-uk.com
Web: www.medicalaction.com
Top 3 clients: Pfizer, Roche, Schering-Plough

Ogilvy Public Relations Worldwide
10 Cabot Square, Canary Wharf, London E14 4QB
Fax 020-7345 6618   Tel 020-7345 3023

The Red Consultancy
77 Wimpole Street, London W1M 7DD
Fax 020-7486 5260   Tel 020-7465 7700
E-mail: red@redconsultancy.com

Richmond Towers
26 Fitzroy Square, London, W1P 6BT
Fax 020-7388 7761   Tel 020-7388 7421
E-mail: mail@richmondtowers.com

The Shire Hall Group
3 Olaf Street, London, W11 4BE
Fax 020-7229 2989   Tel 020-7229 9922
Email: info@shirehall.co.uk   Web: www.shirehall.co.uk
Top 3 clients: Smithkline Beecham, Astra Zeneca, Schering

Text 100
Ariel Way (off Wood Lane), London, W12 7SL
Fax 020-8735 3215   Tel 020-8242 4100
Web: www.text100.co.uk

MEDIA ANALYSTS

Capel-Cure Sharp
The Registry, Royal Mint Court, London EC3N 4EY
Fax 020-7481 3798   Tel 020-7488 4000
Media analyst: David Liston

Credit Lyonnais Laing
Broadwalk House, 5 Appold Street, London, EC2A 2DA
Fax 020-7214 5752   Tel 020-7588 4000
Media analyst: Tobias Reeks, Edward Tetreau

CS First Boston
1 Cabot Square, London, E14 4QJ
Fax 020-7888 1600   Tel 020-7888 1616
Media analyst: Michael Picken

Goldman Sachs
Peterborough Court, 133 Fleet Street, EC4A 2BB
Fax 020-7774 5289   Tel 020-7774 1000
Media analyst: Guy Lamming

Henderson Crosthwaite
2 Gresham Street, London EC2V 7QP
Fax 020-7597 5090   Tel 020-7597 5000
Media analyst: Matthew Horsman

Kleinwort Benson
20 Fenchurch Street, London, EC3P 3DB
Fax 020-7475 9710   Tel 020-7623 8000

Merrill Lynch
Ropemaker Place, 25 Ropemaker Street, London, EC2Y 9LY
Fax 020-7867 2867   Tel 020-7867 2000
Media analyst: Neil Blackley

Panmure Gordon
New Broad Street House, 35 New Broad Street, London, EC2M 1SQ
Fax 020-7920 9305   Tel 020-7638 4010
Media analyst: Lorna Tilbian

Pricewaterhouse Coopers
1 Embankment Place, London WC2N 6NN
Fax 020-7378 0647   Tel 020-7939 3000
Head of entertainment and media: Ed Straw

Salomon Smith Barney
Victoria Plaza, 111 Buckingham Palace Road, London, SW1W 0SB
Fax 020-7222 7062   Tel 020-7721 2000
Media analyst: Richard Dale

Schroder
120 Cheapside, London, EC2V 6DS
Fax 020-7658 4032   Tel 020-7658 6000
Media analyst: Patrick Wellington

UBS Warburg Dillon Read
100 Liverpoool Street London EC2M 2RH
Fax 020-7568 4800   Tel 020-7567 8000
Media analyst: Colin Tennant

How to complain about the media

The first rule about complaining to a broadcaster or to the press is to make objections fast and then be prepared for a long drawn out resolution. For trivial complaints, write to the journalist who has caused offence or - if you are Alastair Campbell - simply get on the phone and shout. And if you are a member of the royalty, get in touch with Lord Wakeham, The Royal Nanny, c/o Press Complaints Commission.

In the press many newspapers have followed the Guardian's lead and now run a corrections and clarification section. Whether this is the case or not, it is still worth contacting the offending journalist and to sprinkle your complaints with praise about eloquence hard work, their other excellent articles and so on. Journalists - particularly on smaller publications - often respond to such flattery by writing a follow up where small wrongs are put right. More serious complaints warrant a phone call to the editor. Editors, especially if they sense lawyers looming, will be cagey and invariably ask for the complaint to be put in writing and a decently phrased letter has a good chance of being printed. And the last port of call - even for commoners - is the Press Complaints Commission.

With small complaints about a TV or radio programme, try going to journalists and then producers. As a general rule, a modicum of TV fame renders TV journalists more self-important and unresponsive than their print counterparts but it's still worth trying the direct route. If this stops at the switchboard, phone the BBC Complaints Unit or the Independent Television Commission and steel yourself for bureaucratic procedure. The most serious complaints should go to the Broadcasting Standards Commission.

The alternative is to go straight to your local solicitor or (for those who really enjoy spending money) to one of the media law firms listed on page 332-338 and sue for libel. The best advice here is: don't. It takes strong nerves and deep pockets, and litigants enter a territory where the opposition knows all the best tricks.

PRESS COMPLAINTS

Advertising Standards Authority
2 Torrington Place, London WC1E 7HW
Fax 020-7323 4339   Tel 020-7580 5555
Website: www.asa.org.uk
For complaints about newspaper and magazine ads.
National Newspapers Mail Order Protection Scheme (MOPS)
16 Tooks Court, London EC4A 1LB
Fax 020-7404 0106   Tel 020-7269 0520
Website: www.mops.org.uk
For repaying victims of mail order rip-offs.
Press Complaints Commission
1 Salisbury Square, London EC4Y 8JB
Fax 020-7353 8355   Tel 020-73531248
E-mail: pcc@pcc.org.uk
Website: www.pcc.org.uk
For complaints about the contents and conduct of newspapers and magazines. Upholds a Code of Practice and advises editors on journalistic ethics.

BROADCAST COMPLAINTS

BBC Programme Complaints Unit
BBC Broadcasting House, London W1A 1AA
If you think a programme has included specific and serious injustice, a serious invasion of privacy, a specific and serious inaccuracy or breach of accepted broadcasting standards, write to Fraser Steel at the above address.
Broadcasting Standards Commission
7 The Sanctuary, London SW1P 3JS
Fax 020-7222 3172   Tel 020-7233 0544
E-mail: bsc@bsc.org.uk
Website: www.bsc.org.uk
The 1996 Broadcasting Act established the BSC to replace the Broadcasting Complaints Commission and the Broadcasting Standards Council. The BSC started work on 1 April 1997 for those complaining of a breach of privacy or unjust or unfair treatment on radio or TV.
Independent Television Commission
33 Foley Street, London W1P 7LB
Fax 020-7306 7800   Tel 020-7255 3000
E-mail: publicaffairs@itc.org.uk
Complaints about ITV, C4, C5 and licensed cable, satellite or digital television.
Radio Authority
14 Great Queen Street, London WC2B 5DG
Fax 020-7405 7064   Tel 020-7430 2724
E-mail: info@radioauthority.org.uk
Website: www.radioauthority.org.uk
Complaints about commercial radio. Ask for the RA leaflet titled How Do I Complain?.

Media training and education

A decade ago students of journalism picked from 100 courses whereas there are now about 1,500. In consequence the number doing journalism and media studies courses has increased from 6,000 in 1990 to nearly 35,000 today. The job market has not expanded in proportion and the National Union of Journalists estimates there are about four times as many accepted at the institutions listed in the next pages as can possibly expect work in anything remotely connected to the media. So, be warned by the story in the panel below:

A salutary tale

This text below was sent as a letter to Bectu's Stage Screen & Radio magazine in April 2000 and is written by a former media production student who signed himself as "Karl Green BA (Hons) (?)"

"I wonder if governments past and present are contented with the fact that so many more people obtain degrees these days. I also wonder if the thousands upon thousands of media-related graduates are equally contented.

"I know of many fellow media graduates who work in shops, night clubs and bars, and some who have found themselves a job in a factory. I do not mock them: I have the utmost sympathy for the graduates who are probably taking any job they can get to pay for the debts amassed while studying. But I do feel very angry at the false hopes and dud degrees that thousands like me have been left with.

"On principle I will not work in a factory or a fast food outlet. No, I got a degree in media production and therefore I should be entitled to a job in that area. If the plain and simple fact is that there were never enough jobs for graduates - or even a reasonable percentage - then I think we should get our money back for being sold a product of unmerchantable quality."

Still interested? To earn a living in print journalism doesn't require compulsory qualifications and thus journalism is not really a profession. Once you've got started many - perhaps most - editors hire on the basis of hunch and evidence of past work. Formal qualifications don't count for much. The problem is getting started and a vocational postgraduate course - not a media studies first degree - is increasingly the best way to start, particularly in local papers or magazines. Local papers are once again a good place to start a career. Half run their own training departments, as do many magazine companies. The national papers - with the honourable exception of the Sun - hardly pay lip service to formal training and are more than happy to draw in the most talented recruits from magazines and locals.

Broadcasting demands specific technical skills which are not taught during a normal education. A more coherent and universally recognised training structure, which is co-ordinated by Skillset, is therefore in place. The best way into broadcasting is via one of the BBC or ITV in-house courses. Competition for places is intense and intensifies when even the best qualified are looking for work in an area where only about 5,000 people make a living as broadcast journalists. The BBC receives 80,000 enquiries a year about broadcasting jobs, and takes on around 2,000 a year at all grades. That said, the increase in channels is creating new jobs.

At the non-university end of the scale are National Vocational Qualifications, the closest the media has come to a start-off educational standard. NVQs are awarded by the RSA Examinations Board in partnership with the Newspapers Qualifications Council for newspapers, the Periodicals Training Council for magazines and Skillset in partnership with the Open University for broadcast journalism. They are open to those without formal qualifications (hence the nickname Not Very Qualified) and, being based on practical work and continual assessment, can be done at the candidate's pace. Their doubtful value as preparation for work in the media was further undermined when the

Periodical Training Council decided to abandon NVQs in favour of a new Professional Certificate.

Then there are media studies degrees. Some take the line they are valuable because they give systematic study to the way information mutates during the process of mediation. Within a business led by people who graduated in what they regard as more rigorous liberal arts degrees during the seventies and eighties, "media studies" is a phrase to evoke a sneer and the crusty observation that there's nothing really to learn except by way of doing an apprenticeship on the job.

Whether trained in some way or not, the iron law of the trade is that you are only as good as your last by-line. The best places for a first by-line are school and university newspapers, or by making a close study of the stories your local paper runs and offering them something similar for nothing. Ditto your favourite magazines. The rule in all cases is that the smaller the publication, the better the chance of a by-line. Aspiring journalists will find a degree in any subject is more or less mandatory. After that the ways into employment are many and vague, usually mundane, and always badly paid. It helps to have a parent in the business too.

The listings in the next dozen pages split into: general training contacts (which spell out the alphabet soups in the rest of this paragraph); group training centres run by local paper companies; press courses with NCTJ or PTC accreditation; TV and radio courses with BJTC or BKST or BECTU accreditation; and the media studies courses listed in the UCAS guide. (UCAS stands for University and Colleges Admissions and the full title of the book is University and Colleges Entrance: the Official Guide 2001 (The Big Guide) and it costs £21.95.)

Nearly all these courses last for at least a year. The National Union of Journalists reports an increased demand for evening courses and other shorter part time study. Many such courses do exist, though most do not have formal accreditation. However the NUJ (which itself organises short courses) was preparing a listing of these unaccredited courses as we went to press. Phone 020-7278 7916 for more details.

How to become a journalist

Tips from Peter Sands, former Northern Echo editor and a director of the Editorial Training Centre in St Leonards-on-Sea.

*Get educated. Most entrants are graduates.
*Learn to spell, and understand the importance of checking everything.
*Develop an obsessive enthusiasm for current affairs, newspapers and people.
*Get plenty of work experience and cuttings - editors want evidence of commitment.
*Get someone to pay for your training. Groups offering direct entry include Trinity Mirror, ECN, BUP, Newsquest, Johnston Press and Midland News Association.
*Identify your preferred newspapers and send editors a perfect CV and cuttings of your work.
*Don't be disheartened by rejection.
*If you have to pay for your training, check the available career-development loans and grants as well as courses. You will find many training centres listed in the Newspaper Society's Training to be a Journalist leaflet. Choose those which offer 100 wpm shorthand and deliver results. Find out what newspapers experience the tutors have and where previous trainees ended up.
*Be prepared to work strange hours and live frugally, at least for a year or two.

TRAINING TO GO ONLINE

Bibliotech Training
www.biblio-tech.net
University of Bournemouth
www.bournemouth.ac.uk
Nottingham Trent University Centre for Broadcast and Journalism
www.ntu.ac.uk
Cardiff University
www.cfy.ac.uk
City University
www.city.ac.uk
University of Central Lancashire
www.uclan.ac.uk

TRAINING CONTACTS

BBC TRAINING AND DEVELOPMENT:
Operations and Engineering Training
Wood Norton, Evesham, Worcestershire WR11 4TB
Fax 01386-420145   Tel 01386-420216
E-mail: woodnorton@bbc.co.uk
Website: www.bbctraining.co.uk
Production Training
35 Marylebone High Street, London W1M 4AA
Fax 020-7765 0006   Tel 020-7765 0005
E-mail: training@bbc.co.uk
Website: www.bbctraining.co.uk
BBC Training and Development offers training services
in all production, operations and engineering skills.
Training can be tailored to clients' requirements and is
provided at dedicated training centres (including Wood
Norton), or at clients' premises. Places for freelances on
some courses are subsidised by Skillset. BBC Training
and Development is only available to professionals
already working in the industry.

BKST - British Kinematograph Sound and TV Society
Walpole Court, Ealing Studios, London W5 5ED
Fax 020-8 758 8658   Tel 020-8567 6655
E-mail: movimage@bksts.demon.co.uk
Website: www.bksts.com
The BKSTS publishes Education, Training and
Working in Film, Television and Broadcasting. It
accredits courses and runs its own courses.

British Film Institute
21 Stephen Street, London W1P 2LN
Fax: 020-7436 7950   Tel 020-7255 1444
E-mail: helpdesk@bfi.org.uk
Website: www.bfi.org.uk
The BFI has an Education Department who also
publishes useful career guides

British Universities Film & Video Council
77 Wells Street, London W1P 3RE
Fax 020-7393 1555   Tel 020-7393 1500
E-mail: ask@bufvc.ac.uk
Website: www.bufvc.ac.uk
The Council promotes TV film and related media in
higher education. It runs an information service, has
editing facilities and organises conferences, courses and
research facilities. It publishes the Researcher's Guide
to British Film and TV Collections, the Researcher's
Guide to British Newsreels. Film and Television
Collections in Europe: The MAP-TV Guide and the
magazine Viewfinder.

Broadcast Journalism Training Council
39 Westbourne Gardens, London W2 5NR
Fax 020-7727 9522   Tel 020-7727 9522
E-mail: secretary@bjtc.org.uk
Website: www.bjtc.org.uk
The BJTC promotes professional standards in training
broadcast journalists. It is a charity whose subscribers
come from all sides of the radio and TV industry, the
NUJ and colleges offering broadcast journalism.
courses. It advises those hoping to become broadcast
journalists and developers of BJTC-recognised courses.

Bectu: Broadcasting Entertainment Cinematograph & Theatre Union
111 Wardour Street, London W1V 4AY
Fax 020-7437 8268   Tel 020-7437 8506
E-mail: bectu@geo2.poptel.org.uk
Website: www.bectu.org.uk
BECTU is the trade union for workers across the
entertainment and media industry. It offers a Student
Link-up Scheme to arts and media students, and an
introductory membership rate to course graduates. It
can give some careers advice (s.a.e. please), but works
with Skillset, regional training consortia and FT2 in
promoting access, equality of opportunity, quality
training, trainees' safety and optimum employment
prospects once training has ended. It publishes a
journal. Stage Screen & Radio, ten times a year.

Cyfle
Gronant, Penrallt Isaf, Caernarfon, Gwynedd LL55 1NS
Fax 01286-678831   Tel 01286-671000
E-mail: cyfle@cyfle-cyf.demon.co.uk
Website: www.cyfle.co.uk
Training for the Welsh film and TV industry.

Educational Television and Media Assoc.
37 Monkgate, York, YO31 7PB
Fax 01904-639212   Tel 01904-639212
E-mail Josie.key@etma.u-net.com
Website: www.etma.org.uk
Brings together organisations and individuals using TV
and other media for education and training. Holds an
annual conference and video competition. Publishes a
newsletter and the Journal of Educational Media.

Film Education
Alhambra House, 27-31 Charing Cross Road, London
WC2H 0AU
Fax 020-7839 5052   Tel 020-7976 2291
E-mail: postbox@filmeducation.org
Website: www.filmeducation.org
Film Education is a registered charity supported by the
UK film industry. Its aims are to develop the use of film
in the school curriculum and to facilitate the use of
cinemas by schools. To this end it publishes a variety of
free teaching materials, produces educational television
programmes, organises screenings and runs a range of
workshops, events and In Service Training courses.

FT2 - Film and Television Freelance Training
Warwick House, 9 Warwick Street, London W1R 5RA
Fax 020-7287 9899   Tel 020-7734 5141
E-mail: info@ft2.org.uk
Website: www.ft2.org.uk
FT2 provides new entrant training in the junior
construction, production and technical grades for the
freelance sector of the film and television industry. It is
funded by the Skillset Freelance Training Fund,
European Social fund and C4 and runs three projects:
FT2 New Entrant Technical Training A two year course
for young people to become technical assistants.
FT2 Setcrafts Apprenticeship Training Scheme For
young people to enter the freelance features and
commercials as carpenters, plasterers and set painters.
FT2 Freelance Access to Skillset NVQ Assessment To
enable existing freelances to undertake subsidised
assessments against the Skillset NVQs.

Skillset
103 Dean Street, London W1V 5RA
Fax 020-7534 5333   Tel 020-7534 5300
E-mail: info@skillset.org
Website: www.skillset.org
The National Training Organisation for broadcast, film, video and multi media. Recognised by Government as the voice of the industry in training. Operates at a strategic level to improve training and education policy and provision. Publishes a careers pack, plus employment and labour market trends, professional standards and qualifications and much more. Set up in 1993, Skillset is managed and funded by Advertising Film and Videotape Producers Association (AFVPA), BBC, Channel 4, Channel 5, the Federation of Entertainment Unions (FEU), International Visual Communications Association (IVCA), ITVA and the Producers Alliance for Film and Television (PACT).

Midlands Consortia Partner:
Midlands Media Training Consortium
Studio 11, the Nottingham Fashion Centre, Huntingdon Street, Nottingham NG1 3LF
Fax 0115-993 0151   Tel 0115-993 0151
Website: www.training@mmtc.co.uk
The Big Peg, 120 Vyse Street, The Jewellery Quarter, Birmingham B18 6NF
Fax 0121-248 1616   Tel 0121-248 1515

Northern Ireland Consortia Partner:
Northern Ireland Film Commission
21 Ormeau Avenue, Belfast BT2 8HD
Fax 028-9023 9918   Tel 028-9023 2444
E-mail: info@nifc.co.uk

Scottish Screen Training:
249 West George Street, Glasgow G2 4QE
Fax 0141-302 1711   Tel 0141-302 1700
E-mail: info@scottishscreen.com
Website: www.scottishscreen.com

Skillnet South West
59 Prince Street, Bristol BS1 4QH
Fax 0117-925 3511   Tel 0117-925 4011
E-mail: skillnetsw@bfv.co.uk

South & South East Consortia Partner:
12 Canal Ct, Mitcham Lane, London SW16 6LN
Fax 020-8769 2106   Tel 020-8769 6116
E-mail: skillstrain@magiclantern.co.uk

Wales Consortia Partner:
Media Skills Wales, Gronant, Penrallt
Isaf, Caernarfon, Gwynedd LL55 1NS
Fax 01286-678831   Tel 01286-671000
E-mail: cyfle@cyfle-cyf.demon.co.uk
Website: www.mediaskillswales.com

Yorkshire Consortia Partner:
40 Hanover Square, Leeds LS3 1BQ
Fax 0113-294 4989   Tel 0113-294 4410
E-mail: info@ymtc.co.uk
Website: www.ymtc.co.uk

First Film Foundation
9 Bourlet Close,London W1P 7PJ
Fax 020-7580 2116   Tel 020-7580 2111
E-mail: info@firstfilm.demon.co.uk
Website: www.firstfilm.co.uk
Development and training provider for new writing, producing and directing talent working on feature film projects. Schemes include a pan-European screen writers programme and the promotion of new British directors to the New York and LA film industries. The Foundation offers a script feedback service.

Institute of Communications Studies
University of Leeds, West Yorkshire LS2 9JT
Fax 0113-233 5820   Tel 0113-233 5820
E-mail: office3@ics-server.novell.leeds.ac.uk
Website: www.leeds.ac.uk/ics
Britain's oldest media research body looking mainly at the role of TV in political communications, now also a teaching department. Three year BA in Broadcasting Studies, three year BA in Broadcast Journalism, schemes in association with the BBC and a three year broadly based BA in Communications. MAs in communications and international communications.

National Association for Higher Education in the Moving Image (Nahemi)
Sir John Cass Department of Art, London Guildhall University, Central House, 59-63 Whitechapel High Street, London E1 7PF
                          Tel 020-7320 1000 x 1956
Website: www.lgu.ac.uk

Forum for debate on all aspects of film, video and TV education. Fosters links with industry, the professions and government. Represents all courses offering a major practical study in film, video or TV at higher education level.

National Council for the Training of Journalists
Latton Bush Centre, Southern Way, Harlow, Essex CM18 7BL
Fax 01279-438008   Tel 01279-430009
E-mail: NCTJtraining@aol.com
Website: www.nctj.com
The NCTJ is a charity which runs the most widely accepted independent training schemes for print journalists. It accredits courses at universities and colleges and should be the first point of contact for those who need to know more of the pre-entry, block and day release options for formal training. The NCTJ has three standard textbooks - Essential Law for Journalists, published by Butterworths, Essential Local Government for Journalists, and Essential Central Government for Journalists published by LGC Communications - and provides a mail order service of recommended books on many aspects of journalism. The Council's short course department has provided over 500 open courses for more than 7,000 journalists and distance courses for those not able to attend full time at college.

National Union of Journalists
Acorn House, 314-320 Grays Inn Road, London
WC1X 8DP
Fax 020-7837 8143   Tel 020-7278 7916
Website: www.nuj.org.uk
Mid-career training courses in editorial skills.
NCTBJ
See Broadcast Journalism Training Council
Newspaper Society
Bloomsbury House, 74-77 Great Russell Street,
London WC1B 3DA
Fax 020-7631 5119   Tel 020-7636 7014
E-mail: ns@newspapersoc.org.uk
Website: www.newspapersoc.org.uk
The Society takes a broad interest in local newspaper
training acting as industry training organisation and
lead body. Although the Society leaves course
accreditation to the NCTJ, it is a prime source of
information on all aspects of newspaper training and its
leaflet Training to be a Journalist, is recommended.
OCR
Westwood Way, Coventry CV4 8JQ
Fax 024-7642 1944   Tel 024-7647 0033
Website: www.ocr.org.uk
The vocational and academic awarding body.
Periodicals Training Council
55/56 Queen's House, Lincoln's Inn Fields, London
WC2A 3LJ
Fax 020-7404 4167   Tel 020-7404 4168
E-mail: training@ppa.co.uk
Website: www.ppa.co.uk/ptc
The PTC is the training arm of the Periodical
Publishers Association. It aims to enhance the
performance of the UK magazine industry and act as a
focus for training. It has accredited the vocational
courses in periodical journalism listed below. The
Council publishes PPA Training Programme,which has
full listings of all the courses run throughout the year at
the PPA; also Your Future in Magazines, which is
available free.
Scottish Daily Newspaper Society
48 Palmerston Place, Edinburgh EH12 5DE
Fax 0131-220 4344   Tel 0131-220 4353
E-mail: info@sdns.org.uk
Website: www.snpa.org.uk
The major training co-ordinator in Scotland.
Scottish Newspaper Publishers Association
48 Palmerston Place, Edinburgh EH12 5DE
Fax 0131-220 4344   Tel 0131-220 4353
E-mail: info@snpa.org.uk
Website: www.snpa.org.uk
Contact point for SVQ, the Scottish version of NVQs.
UCAS
Sheed and Ward, 14 Coopers Row, London EC3N
2BH   Tel 020-7610 2722
Publisher of University and College Entrance: the Official
Guide 2001. Price £21.95
WAVES
4 Wild Court, London WC2B 4AU
Fax 020-7242 2765   Tel 020-7430 1076
Website: www.waves.org.uk
Training for women in video and digital media.

GROUP TRAINING (PRESS)

These are the in-house courses run by the local
newspaper companies:

Bristol United Press
Temple Way, Bristol BS99 7HD
Fax 0117-934 3570   Tel 0117-934 3000

Eastern Counties Newspapers
Prospect House, Rouen Road, Norwich, Norfolk NR1
1RE
Fax 01603 772512   Tel 01603-772488/628311
Email: tont.moore@ecng.co.uk

Johnston Training Centre
Upper Mounts, Northampton NN1 3HR
Fax 01604-250186   Tel 01604-231528

Midland News Association
Rock House, Old Hill, Tettenhall Wolverhampton, West
Midlands WV6 8QB
Fax 01902-759478   Tel 01902-742126
NCTJ accredited. Mostly in-house but takes a few non-
company trainees. Couses start March and September.

Mirror Editorial Training Centre
Thomson House, Groat Market, Newcastle upon Tyne
NE1 1ED
Fax 0191-201 6014   Tel 0191-201 6043
E-mail: editorial@trinity-training.co.uk
Website: www.trinity-training.co.uk

Newsquest Media Group
Newspaper House, 34-44 London Road, Morden,
Surrey SM4 5BR
Fax 020-8646 3997   Tel 020-8640 8989

Press Association
292 Vauxhall Bridge Road, London SW1V 1AE
Fax 020-7963 7192   Tel 020-7963 7000

Regional Independent Media
Wellington Street, Leeds, West Yorks LS1 1RF
Fax 0113-242 1814   Tel 0113-243 2701
E-mai: vicky.blades@rim.co.uk
Accredited courses: Diplomas in Journalism and News
Writing to NVQ level

Trinity PLC
Kingsfield Court, Chester Business Park, Chester,
CH4 9RE
Fax 01244-687100   Tel 01244-350555
E-mail: trinity@trinity.plc.uk
Website: www.trinity.plc.uk

PRESS COURSES

Newspaper training courses are accredited by the National Council for Training of Journalists, and magazine courses are accredited by the PPA's training wing, the Periodical Training Council. Both these trade bodies support NVQs.

Bell College of Technology
Almada Street, Hamilton, Lanarkshire ML3 0JB
Fax 01698-282131   Tel 01698-283100
E-mail: enquiries@bell.ac.uk
Website: www.bell.ac.uk
NCTJ accredited two year Higher National Diploma.

Bournemouth University
Talbot Campus, Poole, Dorset BH12 5BB
Fax 01202-595530   Tel 01202-595745
E-mail: macugrad@bournemouth.ac.uk
Website: www.bournemouth.ac.uk
BA (Hons) multi-media journalism; MA/PG Dip multi-media journalism. The only undergraduate degree in the UK accredited by the NCTJ, the PTC. and the BJTC.

Brighton College of Technology
Pelham Street, Brighton BN1 4FA
Fax 01273-667703   Tel 01273-667788
E-mail: info@bricoltech.ac.uk
Website: www.bricoltech.ac.uk
NCTJ accredited

Cardonald College
690 Mosspark Drive, Glasgow G52 3AY
               Tel 0141-272 3242
Two year HND, but accredition process for NCTJ not yet complete.

City University
Department of Journalism, Northampton Square, London EC1V 0HB
Fax 020-7477 8594   Tel 020-7477 8221
E-mail: journalism@city.ac.uk
Web: www.city.ac.uk/journalism
PG Dip in newspaper journalism; PG Dip in periodical journalism (accredited by the PTC); MA in international journalism (print); MA in publishing studies; BA in journalism and a social science; BA in journalism and contemporary history; MA/MSc in electronic publishing.

Coleg Gwent
The Rhadyr, Usk NP15 1XJ
Fax 01495-333526   Tel 01495-333333
Website: www.gwent-tertiary.ac.uk
NCTJ accredited pre-entry academic year course in newspaper journalism. BTEC media, two years, full time. HND/HNC graphic design, a range of full and part time courses. BTEC photography and photo-media; BTEC graphic design course; GNVQ in media also HND and A level courses.

Cornwall College
Centre for Arts, Media & Social Sciences, Redruth, Cornwall TR15 3RD
Fax 01209-718802   Tel 01209 611611
E-mail: enquiries@cornwall.ac.uk
Website: www.cornwall.ac.uk
BJTC-accredited postgraduate diploma in broadcast journalism. NCTJ accredited postgraduate diploma in newspaper and magazine journalism.

Crawley College
College Road, Crawley, West Sussex RH10 1NR
               Tel 01293-442200
NCTJ accredited, pre-entry (academic year).

Darlington College of Technology
Cleveland Avenue, Darlington, Co. Durham DL3 7BB
Fax 01325-503000   Tel 01325-503050
Website: www.darlington.ac.uk
E-mail: enquire@darlington.ac.uk
NCTJ accredited pre-entry academic year, pre-entry calendar year and block release courses.

De Montfort University
The Gateway, Leicester LE1 9BH
Fax 0116-255 0307   Tel 0116-255 1551
E-mail: andiz@dmu.ac.uk
Website: www.dmu.ac.uk
One-year postgraduate diploma in journalism, NCTJ accredited.

Editorial Training Centre
Hanover House, Marine Court, St Leonards-on-Sea, East Sussex TN38 0DX
Fax 01424-445547   Tel 01424-435991
E-mail:editorial_centre@hinge.mistral.co.uk
Offers a range of journalism courses including pre-entry NVQ, starting 3 times a year.

Gloucestershire College of Arts & Tech.
Brunswick Campus, Brunswick Road, Gloucester GL1 1HU
Fax 01452-426601   Tel 01452-426602
E-mail: info@gloscat.ac.uk
NCTJ accredited pre-entry academic year course.

Goldsmiths College
Department of Media and Communications, University of London, New Cross, London SE14 6NW
Fax 020-7919 7616   Tel 020-7919 7600
u/grad programmes   020-7919 7766
postgrad   020-7919 7060
E-mail: admissions@gold.ac.uk
          media-comms@gold.ac.uk
Website: www.goldsmiths.ac.uk
BAs in media and communications; anthropology and comms; comms and sociology and comms, culture and society. Practical MAs in journalism; television journalism; TV documentary; TV drama; feature film; radio; image and comms. Theory MA programmes in media and comms; transnational comms and the global media; science, culture and technology.

TRAINEE JOURNALISTS

To become a journalist you need broad experience of writing, editing and DTP. We can help you to gain that essential experience with training that leads to an industry-recognised **Foundation Skills Certificate in Journalism**.

NATIONAL TRAINING AWARD MCMXCIV

Of the 64 delegates trained by us during the last year, 59 obtained jobs on a wide range of magazines or newspapers shortly after their course ended. Some former trainees work in broadcasting or freelance.

Our award-winning journalism course is accredited by the Periodicals Training Council and approved by the National Union of Journalists. Over 15 intensive weeks you discover how to write news and features at our well-equipped, modern, vocational training centre in Surrey. Every week you will write for or sub-edit and lay out the pages for three different types of publication. You also learn interviewing techniques, Teeline shorthand, media law, sub-editing and page design, and how to proofread. The course includes three weeks' work experience on another magazine or newspaper, plus expert tuition in QuarkXPress on Apple Macintosh computers.

We run three 15-week courses each year commencing January, May and December.

To take your first step towards a journalistic career, contact us for an information pack and application form (please quote ref: GMG) or visit our website.
- *telephone: 020-8640 3696*
- *email: enq@journalism-training-centre.co.uk*
- *website: http://www.journalism-training-centre.co.uk*
- *write to: Mike Bowen, Training Manager, Journalism Training Centre, Mill Green Business Park, Mill Green Road, Mitcham, Surrey, CR4 4HT*

Harlow College
Velizy Avenue, Town Centre, Harlow, Essex CM20 3LH
Fax 01279-868260   Tel 01279-868000
E-mail: learninglink@harlow-college.ac.uk
Website: www.harlow-college.ac.uk
Post graduate journalism in newspapers, 19 weeks, NCTJ accredited; post graduate journalism in magazines, 19 weeks; post A-level journalism in newspapers NCTJ accredited; BA in journalism in association with Middlesex University.

Harrow College
Lowlands Road, Harrow, Middlesex HA1 3AQ
Fax 020-8909 6050   Tel 020-8909 6400
E-mail: enquiries@harrow.ac.uk
NCTJ accredited college for pre-entry print journalism. Full time one year course.

Highbury College, Portsmouth
School of Media & Journalism, Dovercourt Road, Cosham, Portsmouth, Hants PO6 2SA
Fax 023-9237 8382   Tel 023-9231 3287
E-mail: glenne.martin@highbury.ac.uk
NCTJ and PTC accredited courses in newspaper journalism (20 weeks) and magazine journalism.

Journalism Training Centre
Unit G, Mill Green Business Park, Mill Green Road, Mitcham, Surrey CR4 4HT
Fax 020-8640 6266   Tel 020-8640 3696
E-mail: nvq@journalism-training-centre.co.uk
JTC foundations skills certificate in journalism, PTC accredited. NUJ approved. 3 courses per year, duration 14 weeks.

Lambeth College
Vauxhall Centre, Belmore Street, Wandsworth, London SW8 2JY
Fax 020-7501 5490   Tel 020-7501 5424
Website: www.lambethcollege.ac.uk
NCTJ accredited pre-entry academic year course. 18 week post-graduate.

Liverpool Community College
JournalismSchool, The Arts Centre, 9 Myrtle Street, Liverpool L7 7JA
Fax 0151-707 8528   Tel 0151 707 8528
E-mail: sandy.felton@aol.com
One year postgraduate diploma in print journalism (NCTJ); 18 week postgraduate fast-track (NCTJ); HNC professional media (journalism pathway) day-release for working journalists (NCTJ); NVQ level 4 journalism.

London College of Fashion
20 John Princes Street, London W1M 0BJ
Fax 020-7514 7484   Tel 020-7514 7400
Website: www.lcf.linst.ac.uk
PTC accredited fashion promotion degee with journalism, public relations and broadcast options.

London College of Printing
School of Media, 10 Back Hill, London EC1 5EN
Fax 020-7514 6848   Tel 020-7514 6500
E-mail: r.f.l.smith@lcp.linst.ac.uk
BA (Hons) in journalism; certificate in periodical journalism for graduates, BJTC recognised.

Napier University
Department of Print Media, Publishing and Communications. Craighouse Campus, Craighouse Road, Edinburgh EH10 5LG
Fax 0131-455 6193   Tel 0131-455 6150
E-mail: r.melville@napier.ac.uk
Website: www.napier.ac.uk
Four year BA (Hons) programme in journalism. MA/postgraduate diploma in newspaper journalism, periodical journalism, online journalism and international journalism.

PMA Training
PMA House, Free Church Passage, St Ives, Cambridgeshire PE27 4AY
Fax 01480-496022   Tel 01480-300653
E-mail: admin@pma-group.com
Website: www.pma-group.co.uk
PMA training was founded in 1980. It maintains close links with the Periodicals Training Council and now supplies most of the editorial training for the industry. PMA is based in Clerkenwell, central London. PMA is officially approved by the PTC, the Newspaper Society and the BACB. The five training rooms are registered as an assessment centre, and workshops are geared to professional qualifications. There are over 500 workshops per year covering editorial, internet, desktop publishing, law, design, new technology, marketing, PR, production, advertising, direct mail, radio and publishing management. PMA also runs two nine week post graduate course in magazine journalism each year.

School of Communication
See University of Westminster

Scottish Centre for Journalism Studies
University of Strathclyde, Glasgow G13 1PP
Fax 0141-950 3676   Tel 0141-950 3281
E-mail: gordon.j.smith@strath.ac.uk
NCTJ accredited one year postgradute course.

Sheffield College
Norton Centre, Dyche Lane, Sheffield S8 8BR
Fax 0114-2602 301   Tel 0114-2602 600
E-mail: mail@sheffcol.ac.uk
Website: www.sheffcol.ac.uk
NCTJ accredited block release, pre-entry academic year and January-December courses. 18 week "fast-track" graduate course. Also photojournalism and press photography.

South East Essex College
Carnarvon Road, Southend-on-Sea, Essex SS2 6LS
Tel 01702-220400
E-mail: learning@se-essex-college.ac.uk
BSc (hons) media production and technology - 3 years.
BSc (Hons) multimedia technology - 3 years. BTEC/
GNVQ broadcast media -2 years; print media.2 years.
NCTJ pre-entry one year news journalism certificate.

Staffordshire University
College Road, Stoke on Trent ST4 2DE
Fax 01782-292740   Tel 01782-292752
BA (Hons) in journalism, Not yet NCTJ accredited.

Surrey Institute of Art and Design
Falkner Road, Farnham, Surrey GU9 7DS
Tel 01252-722441
E-mail: registry@surrart.ac.uk
Website: www.surrart.ac.uk
BA (Hons) in journalism PTC/BJTC accredited; BA
(Hons) in film and video, BKSTS accredited; BA (Hons)
in animation; BA (Hons) in fashion journalism (subject
to validation);

Sutton Coldfield College
Lichfield Road, Sutton Coldfield, B74 2NW
Fax 0121-355 0799   Tel 0121-355 5671
E-mail: SCSE@sutcol.ac.uk
NCTJ accredited.

Training Direct International
Matlock, Derbyshire DE4 5AW
Fax 01629 534116   Tel 01629 534826
E-mail: peterhiscocks@tvtraining.freeserve.co.uk
A new non-profit NGO for the training and education
of all journalists. Not yet accredited.

Trinity and All Saints College
Brownberrie Lane, Horsforth, Leeds LS18 5HD
Fax 0113-283 7200   Tel 0113-283 7100
E-mail: M.Hampton@tasc.ac.uk
Website: www.tasc.ac.uk
NCTJ approved MA/PG diploma in print journalism.

University of Central Lancashire
Department of Journalism, Preston PR1 2HE
Fax 01772-892907   Tel 01772-894732
E-mail: n.atkinson@uclan.ac.uk
NCTJ and BJTC accredited courses: BA (Hons) course,
multi-media two years, print, broadcast or dissertation
final year. New media option for '99. Separate postgrad
diploma courses in newspaper and broadcast
journalism. New media postgraduate diploma course in
'99. IPR recognised BA (Hons) course in PR. Joint
honours BA (Hons) courses in journalism and PR

University of Sheffield
171 Northumberland Road, Sheffield S10 1DF
Fax 0114-266 8918   Tel 0114-222 2500
E-mail: jnlstudies@sheffield.ac.uk
NCTJ accredited. BA in journalism studies, masters
programme in journalism studies.

University of Ulster
Registry Office, Coleraine BT52 1SA
Tel 028-7032 4221
NCTJ accredited postgraduate diploma in newspaper
journalism, held at the Belfast Campus.

University of Wales
School of Journalism, Media and Cultural Studies,
Centre for Journalism Studies, Bute Building, King
Edward V11 Avenue, Cardiff CF10 3NB
Fax 029-2023 8832   Tel 029-2087 4041
E-mail: jomec@cardiff.ac.uk
Website: www.cf.ac.uk/uwcc/jomec/index.html
NCTJ recognised postgraduate diploma in newspaper
journalism; BJTC recognised course in broadcast (bi-
media) journalism; PTC recognised course in magazine
journalism, IPR recognised course in public and media
relations. Course in photojournalism. Euro MA course.

University of Westminster
School of Communication and Creative Industries,
Harrow Campus, Watford Road, Northwick Park,
Harrow HA1 3TP
Fax 020-7911 5955   Tel 020-7911 5903
E-mail: barrata@wmin.ac.uk
PTC postgraduate diploma in periodical journalism for
ethnic minorities. Part-time MA in journalism studies.
PG Dip in broadcast journalism, PG Dip in periodical
journalism, MA in public relations.

University of Wolverhampton
Molineux Street, Wolverhampton WV6 0DU
Tel 01902 321900
E-mail: info@bricoltech.ac.uk
Website: www.bricoltech.ac.uk
Degree course but NCTJ accreditation not yet complete.

Warrington Collegiate Institute
Padgate Campus, Warrington WA2 0DB
Fax 01925-816077   Tel 01925-494494
E-mail: wci@warr.ac.uk
Website: www.warr.ac.uk
NCTJ accredited.

Warwickshire College
Warwick New Road, Leamington Spa, Warwickshire
CV32 5JE
Tel 01926-318000
NCTJ accredited, pre-entry (academic year).

Wolverhampton College
Paget Road, Wolverhampton WV6 0DU
Fax 01902-423070   Tel 01902-317700
Website: www.wolverhamptoncollege.ac.uk
BA (Hons) in journalism and editorial design (with
Wolverhampton University). Day-release/pre-entry.
NCTJ, C &G and BTEC courses.

TV/RADIO COURSES

BBME Training, The Radio and Television School
7-9 The Broadway, Newbury, Berkshire RG14 1AS
Fax 01635-38802   Tel 016635-232800
E-mail: info@bbme.co.uk
Website: www.radiotvschool.co.uk
Short courses in radio and TV presentation to the public and corporate sector. Not yet accredited.

Bell College
Almada Street, Hamilton, Lanarkshire ML3 0JB
Fax 01698-457525   Tel 01698-283100
E-mail: enquiries@bell.ac.uk
Website: www.bell.ac.uk
Contact: Ronnie Bergman
BJTC recognised postgrad diploma in radio journalism.

The Arts Institute at Bournemouth
Wallisdown, Poole, Dorset BH12 5HH
Fax 01202-537729   Tel 01202-533011
E-mail: general@arts-inst-bournemouth.ac.uk
Website: www.arts-inst-bournemouth.ac.uk
BA (Hons) in film and TV or film & animation; National Diploma in sound and moving image.

Bournemouth University
Fern Barrow, Poole, Dorset BH12 5BB
Fax 01202-595099   Tel 01202-524111
E-mail: emcallis@bournemouth.ac.uk
Website: www.bournemouth.ac.uk
Degrees in media production, TV & video production. BJTC, NCTJ & PTC endorsed multi-media journalism degree. Postgrad in TV and video production. Postgrad in radio production and multi-media journalism.

Cardiff University of Wales
School of Journalism, Media and Cultural Studies, Centre for Journalism Studies, Bute Building, King Edward V11 Avenue, Cardiff CF10 3NB
Fax 029-2023 8832   Tel 029-2087 4041
E-mail: jomec-diploma@cardiff.ac.uk
Website: www.cf.ac.uk/uwcc/jomec/jomec
NCTJ recognised postgraduate diploma in newspaper journalism; BJTC recognised course in broadcast (bi-media) journalism; PTC recognised course in magazine journalism, IPR recognised course in public and media relations. Course in photojournalism. MAs in journalism and European journalism studies.

Centre for Journalism Studies
See University of Wales

City University
Department of Journalism, Northampton Square, London EC1V 0HB
Fax 020-7477 8594   Tel 020-7477 8221
E-mail: journalism@city.ac.uk
Web: www.city.ac.uk/journalism
Contaact: Elaine Da Costa
BJTC accredited PG Dip in broadcast journalism, MA international journalism (radio).

Coleg Gwent
The Rhadyr, Usk NP15 1XJ
Fax 01495-333526   Tel 01495-333333
Website: www.gwent-tertiary.ac.uk
BTEC Media, two years, full time. Emphasis on digital and linear TV/video. HND/HNC Graphic Design, a range of full and part time courses. BTEC graphic design and photography and photo-media; GNVQ in media also HND and A level courses.

Falmouth College of Arts
Woodlane, Falmouth, Cornwall TR11 4RH
Fax 01326-212205   Tel 01326-211077
E-mail: admissions@falmouth.ac.uk
BJTC recognised courses. Postgraduate diplomas in broadcast journalism and broadcast television. BA Hons in broadcasting studies. Plus English with media studies and journalism studies.Plus a postgrad diploma in professional writing. Broadcast television endorsed by BBC, ITV and Skillset.

Goldsmiths College
Department of Media and Communications, University of London, New Cross, London SE14 6NW
Fax 020-7919 7616   Tel 020-7919 7600
u/grad programmes   020-7919 7766
postgrad   020-7919 7060
E-mail: admissions@gold.ac.uk
          media-comms@gold.ac.uk
Website: www.goldsmiths.ac.uk
BAs in media and communications; anthropology and communitations; communications and sociology and communications, culture and society.
Practical MAs in journalism; television journalism; television documentary; television drama; feature film; radio; image and communications. Theory MA programmes in media and communications; transnational communications and the global media; science, culture and technology.

Highbury College, Portsmouth
School of Media & Journalism, Dovercourt Road, Cosham, Portsmouth, Hants PO6 2SA
Fax 023-9237 8382   Tel 023-9231 3287
E-mail: glenne.martin@highbury.ac.uk
Contact: Mark Thompson
BJTC recognised post-graduate diploma in broadcast journalism.

Institute of Communications Studies
University of Leeds, West Yorkshire LS2 9JT
Fax 0113-233 5820   Tel 0113-233 5820
E-mail: office3@ics-server.novell.leeds.ac.uk
Website: www.leeds.ac.uk/ics
BJTC recognised courses. Three year BA in Broadcasting Studies, three year BA in Broadcast Journalism, schemes in association with the BBC and a three year broadly based BA in Communications. MAs in communications and international communications.

London Institute
London College of Printing, School of Media, 10 Back Hill. Clerkenwell, London EC1R 5EN
Fax 020-7514 6848   Tel 020-7514 6500/6800
E-mail: s.cornes@lcp.linst.ac.uk
Website; www.lcp.linst.ac.uk
BA (Hons) film/video; PG Dip broadcast journalism.

London International Film School
24 Shelton Street, London WC2H 9HP
Fax 020-7497 3718   Tel 020-7836 9642
E-mail: film.school@lifs.org.uk
Website: www.lifs.org.uk

National Film and Television School
Beaconsfield Studios, Bucks HP9 1LG
Fax 01494-674042   Tel 01494-671234
E-mail: cad@nftsfilm-tv.ac.uk
10 full-time post graduate/post experience courses in all aspects of film and television arts and scienes.

Nottingham Trent University
York House, Nottingham NG1 3JB
Fax 0115-948 6632   Tel 0115-848 5858
E-mail: cbj@ntu.ac.uk
Website: www.cbj.ntu.ac.uk
BJTC recognised degree in broadcast journalism; and industry led MA in investigative journalism. Also MAs in online journalism; TV and newspaper journalism.

Plymouth College of Art and Design
Tavistock Place, Plymouth PL4 8AT
Fax 01752-203444   Tel 01752-203434
E-mail: enquiries@pcad.plym.ac.uk
HND course in film and TV with optional one year top up to BA (Hons). Plus professional diploma in photography, film and television.

Ravensbourne College of Design & Comms.
Walden Road, Chislehurst, Kent BR7 5SN
Fax 020-8325 8320   Tel 020-8289 4900
E-mail: info@rave.ac.uk
Website: www.rave.ac.uk
HND in technical ops, production and engineering. Degree courses in broadcast engineering and comms and technology. HNCs in post production and multi media; NC in broadcast engineering.

Salisbury College
Southampton Road, Salisbury, Wilts SP1 2LW
Fax 01722-344345   Tel 01722-344344
E-mail: @salcol.com Contact: Bill Shepley
HND in photography, film and TV and BA (Hons) degree in film and TV.

Sheffield Hallam University
Northern Media School, The Workstation, 15 Paternoster Row, Sheffield S1 2BX
Fax 0114-225 4606   Tel 0114-225 4648
E-mail: m.cherif@shu.ac.uk
Website: www.shu.ac.uk
BJTC post-grad broadcast journalism. MA screen arts.

South East Essex College
Carnarvon Road, Southend-on-Sea, Essex SS2 6LS
Tel 01702-220400
E-mail: marketing@se-essex-college.ac.uk
BSc (hons) media production and technology. BSc (Hons) multimedia technology. BTEC/GNVQ broadcast media; advanced media communications and production.

South Thames College
Wandsworth High Street, London SW18 2PP
Tel 020-8918 7777
Website: www.south-thames.ac.uk
BTEC in journalism; BTEC in television and video; BTEC in television and video production; BTEC in documentary video; BTEC in non-linear editing; BTEC in directing drama. HNC in media production.

Southampton Institute
East Park Terrace, Southampton SO14 0YN
Fax 023-8033 4441   Tel 023-8031 9555
E-mail: sef@solent.ac.uk
Contact: Roger Lownsborough
BKST accredited BSc (Hons) media technology programme.

Staffordshire University
College Road, Stoke on Trent ST4 2DE
Fax 01782-292740   Tel 01782-292752
BA Hons) in film, television and radio.

The Surrey Institute of Art & Design, University College
Falkner Road, Farnham, Surrey GU9 7DS
Fax 01252-892616   Tel 01252-722441
E-mail: registry@surrart.ac.uk
Website: www.surrart.ac.uk
BKSTS accredited degrees in film and video. PTC and BJTC accredited degree in journalism with radio and print options. New degrees in fashion journalism and animatioin subject to validation.

Trinity and All Saints College
Brownberrie Lane, Horsforth, Leeds LS18 5HD
Fax 0113-283 7200   Tel 0113-283 7100
E-mail: M.Hampton@tasc.ac.uk
Website: www.tasc.ac.uk
BJTC recognised MAs/postgraduate diplomas in broadcast (TV and radio) journalism and radio journalism.

University of Bradford
Richmond Road, Bradford BD7 1DP
Fax 01274-233727   Tel 01274-234011
E-mail: p.e.dale@brad.ac.uk
Website: www.eimc.brad.ac.uk
Contact: Paula Dale
BScs in: electronic imaging and media communications; media technology and production; computer animation & special effects; interactive systems & video games design; internet product design.

University of Bristol
Woodland Road, Bristol BS8 1UP
Fax 0117-928 7832   Tel 0117-928 7833
Website: www.bristol.ac.uk
Contact: Mark Sinfield
MA in television studies, MA in film and TV
production.

University of Central England in B'ham
Dept. of Media and Communication, Perry Bar,
Birmingham B42 2SU
Fax 0121-331 6501   Tel 0121-331 5719
E-mail: rod.pilling@uce.ac.uk
Website: www.uce.ac.uk
BJTC postgraduate course in broadcast journalism.

University of Central Lancashire
Department of Journalism, Preston PR1 2HE
Fax 01772-892907   Tel 01772-893730
E-mail: (.j.williams)@uclan.ac.uk
Website:
www.uclan.ac.uk/facs/lbs/depts/journ/index.htm
NCTJ and BJTC accredited courses: undergraduate BA
(Hons) course, multi-media two years,print, broadcast
online or dissertation final year. Separate one year
postgraduate diploma courses in newspaper, broadcast
and online journalism. IPR recognised undergraduate
BA (Hons) course in public relations. Joint honours
undergraduate BA (Hons) courses in journalism and
public relations.

University of Leeds
Institute of Communications Studies, Roger Stevens
building, University of Leeds, Leeds LS2 9JT
Fax 0113-233 5809   Tel 0113-233 5814
E-mail: j.stamper@leeds.ac.uk
Contact: Judith Stamper
BJTC recognised BA in broadcast journalism. Also non-
accredited courses in broadcast studies and
communications.

University of London
see Goldsmiths College

University of Westminster
School of Communication, Harrow Campus, Watford
Road, Harrow HA1 3TP
Fax 020-7911 5943   Tel 020-7911 5000
E-mail: barrata@wmin.ac.uk
BJTC accredited postgraduate diploma with periodical
and broadcast pathways. Many other courses available.

West Herts College
Hempstead Road, Watford, Herts WD1 3EZ
Fax 01923-812667   Tel 01923-812662
E-mail: viscom@westherts.ac.uk
Course in media production.

MEDIA STUDIES ETC

Anglia Polytechnic University
East Road, Cambridge, CB1 1PT
Fax 01223-576156   Tel 01223-363271
BA (Hons) communication studies/film studies.

Barnsley College
Old Mill Lane Site, Church Street, Barnsley S70 2AX
Fax 01226-216613   Tel 01226-730191

Bath Spa University College
Newton Park, Bath BA2 9BN
Fax 01225-875444   Tel 01225-875875

Bournemouth University
Studland House, 12 Christchurch Road,
Bournemouth, Dorset BH1 3NA
Fax 01202-503869   Tel 01202-524111

Brunel University
Uxbridge UB8 3PH
Fax 01895-203167   Tel 01895-274000

Bucks Chilterns University College
High Wycombe, Bucks HP11 2JZ
Fax 01494-603050   Tel 01494-603050
E-mail: caroline.bainbridge@bcuc.ac.uk

Canterbury Christ Church
North Holmes Road, Canterbury, KentCT1 1QU
Fax 01227-470442   Tel 01227-767700

Cardiff University of Wales
PO Box 494, Cardiff CF1 3YL
Fax 029-2087 4130   Tel 029-2087 4401

**Cheltenham and Glos College of Higher
Education**
The Park, Cheltenham, Gloucstershire GL50 2QF
Fax 01242-256759   Tel 01242-532824

Colchester Institute
Sheepen Road, Colchester, Essex CO3 3LL
Fax 01206-563041   Tel 01206-518777

College of Ripon & York
Lord Mayor's Walk, York YO31 7EX
Fax 01904-716931   Tel 01904-716672

Coventry University
Priory Street, Coventry CV1 5FB
Fax 024-7683 8667   Tel 024-7663 8248

Cumbria College of Art & Design
Brampton Road, Carlisle, Cumbria CA3 9AY
Fax 01228-514491   Tel 01228-400300

MEDIA STUDIES ETC

De Montfort University
The Gateway, Leicester LE1 9BH
Fax 0116-257 7515   Tel 0116-255 1551

Doncaster College
Waterdale, Doncaster DN1 3EX
Fax 01302-553559   Tel 01302-553718

Edge Hill College of Higher Education
Ormskirk, Lancashire L39 4QP
Fax 01695-579997   Tel 01695-584274

Falmouth College of Arts
Woodlane, Falmouth, Cornwall TR11 4RA
Fax 01326-212261   Tel 01326-211077

Farnborough College of Technology
Boundary Road, Farnborough, Hampshire GU14 6SB
Fax 01252-407271   Tel 01252-407270

Glasgow Caledonian University
City Campus, Glasgow G4 0BA
Fax 0141-331-3449   Tel 0141-331 3334

Goldsmiths College
University of London, New Cross, London SE14 6NW
Fax 020-7919 7509   Tel 020-7919 7281

King Alfred's Winchester
Winchester, Hampshire SO22 4NR
Fax 01962-827406   Tel 01962-841515

Lancaster University
University House, Lancaster LA1 4YW
Fax 01524-846243   Tel 01524-65201

Leeds, Trinity & All Saints College
Brownberrie Lane, Horsforth, Leeds LS18 5HD
Fax 0113-283 7321   Tel 0113-283 7123

Leeds Metropolitan University
Calverley Street, Leeds LS1 3HE
Fax 0113-283 3114   Tel 0113-283 3113

Liverpool John Moores University
Roscoe Court, 4 Rodney Street, Liverpool L1 2TZ
Fax 0151-231 3194   Tel 0151-231 5090

London Guildhall University
133 Whitechapel High Street, London E1 7QA
Fax 020-7320 1163   Tel 020-7320 1616

London Institute
London College of Printing, School of Media, 10 Back Hill, London EC1R 5LQ
Fax 020-7514 6131   Tel 020-7514 6129
BA (Hons) in media and cultural studies; BA (Hons) in photography; PG Dip in photojournalism; MA in documentary research; MA in photography; MA in photography: history and culture; MA in screenwriting.

Loughborough University
Ashby Road, Loughborough, Leicestershire LE11 3TU
Fax 01509-223905   Tel 01509-263171

Manchester Metropolitan University
Academic Division, All Saints, Manchester M15 6BH
Fax 0161-247 6871   Tel 0161-247 2966

Middlesex University
White Hart Lane, London N17 8HR
Fax 020-8362 5649   Tel 020-8362 5898

Napier University
Photography, Film and TV Department, 219 Colinton Road, Edinburgh EH14 1DJ
Fax 0131-455 4329   Tel 0131-444 2266

NE Wales Institute of Higher Education
Plas Coch, Mold Road, Wrexham LL11 2AW
Fax 01978-290008   Tel 01978-290666
BA (Hons) media studies, with other subject; BA (Hons) multi-media design; BA (Hons) animation.

Nottingham Trent University
Burton Street, Nottingham NG1 4BU
Fax 0115-848 6063   Tel 0115-941 8418

Oxford Westminster College
Oxford OX2 9AT
Fax 01865-251847   Tel 01865-247644

Oxford Brookes
Gipsy Lane Campus, Headington, Oxon OX3 0BP
Fax 01865-483983   Tel 01865-48304

Queen Margaret University College
Clerwood Terrace, Edinburgh EH12 8TS
Fax 0131-317 3248   Tel 0131-317 3247

Robert Gordon University
School of Information & Media, Aberdeen AB10 1FR
Fax 01224-262147   Tel 01224-263900

Roehampton Institute London
Roehampton Lane, London SW15 5PU
Fax 020-8392 3220   Tel 020-8392 3000

Royal Holloway, University of London
Education Office, Egham, Surrey TW20 0EX
Fax 01784-471381   Tel 01784-443399
E-mail: b.langford@rhbnc.ac.uk

Sheffield Hallam University
City Campus, Pond Street, Sheffield S1 1WB
Fax 0114-225 4023   Tel 0114-225 5555

South Bank University
103 Borough Road, London SE1 0AA
Fax 020-7815 6031   Tel 020-7815 7815

South Thames College
Wandsworth High Street, London SW18 2PP
                        Tel 020-8918 7777
BSc in media and society

Southampton Institute
East Park Terrace, Southampton SO14 0YN
Fax 023-8033 4161   Tel 023-8031 9039

St Helen's College
Brook Street, St Helens, Merseyside WA10 1PZ
Fax 01744-623400   Tel 01744-623338

St Martins College
Bowerham Road, Lancaster LA1 3JD
Fax 01524-384567   Tel 01524-384444

St Mary's College
Waldegave Road, Twickenham TW1 4SX
Fax 020-8240 4255   Tel 020-8240 4000
BA in media arts, as half a joint honours degree.

Staffordshire University
College Road, Stoke on Trent ST4 2DE
Fax 01782-292740   Tel 01782-292752
BA (Hons) in media studies; BA (Hons) in cultural
studies; BA Hons) in film, television and radio.

Suffolk College
Ipswich IP4 1LT
Fax 01473-230054   Tel 01473-255885

Surrey Institute of Art & Design
Falkner Road, Farnham, Surrey GU9 7DS
Fax 01252-892624   Tel 01252-892608

Swansea Institute of Higher Education
Mount Pleasant, Swansea SA1 6ED
Fax 01792-481085   Tel 01792-481094

Thames Valley University
911 University House, Ealing Green, London W5 5ED
Fax 020-8231 2744   Tel 020-8279 5000

Trinity College Carmarthen
College Road, Carmarthen SA31 3EP
Fax 01267-676766   Tel 01267-676767

University of Birmingham
Edgbaston, Birmingham B15 2TT
Fax 0121-414 3850   Tel 0121-414 3697

University of Bradford
Richmond Road, Bradford, West Yorkshire BD7 1DP
Fax 01274-233727   Tel 01274-234011

University of Brighton
Mithras House, Brighton, East Sussex BN2 4AT
Fax 01273-642825   Tel 01273-600900

University of Central England in B'ham
Academic Registry, Perry Barr, Birmingham B42 2SU
Fax 0121-331 6706   Tel 0121-331 6650

University of Central Lancashire
Foster Building, Preston, Lancashire PR1 2HE
Fax 01772-892935   Tel 01772-892400

University College Chichester
Bishop Otter Campus, Chichester, Sussex PO19 4PE
Fax 01243-816080   Tel 01243-816000
E-mail: m.ribbans@chihe.ac.uk
Media studies with: fine art, dance, English, geography,
history, music, related arts or study of religions.

University College Northampton
Park Campus, Northampton NN2 7AL
Fax 01604-713029   Tel 01604-735500

University College Warrington
Padgate Campus, Crab Lane, Warrington WA2 0DB
Fax 01925-494289   Tel 01925-494494

University College Worcester
Henwick Grove, Worcester WR2 6AJ
Fax 01905-855132   Tel 01905-855111

University of East Anglia
Norwich, Norfolk NR4 7TJ
Fax 01603-507728   Tel 01603-592283
BA in film and English or American studies.

University of East London
Longbridge Road, Dagenham, Essex RM8 2AS
Fax 020-8839 3438   Tel 020-8849 3443

University of Essex
Wivenhoe Park, Colchester, Esssex CO4 3SQ
Fax 01206-873003   Tel 01206-872200

MEDIA STUDIES ETC

University of Glamorgan
Pontypridd, Mid Glamorgan CF37 1DL
Fax 01443-482925   Tel 01443-482684
BA (Hons) in media practice; various joint schemes.

University of Greenwich
Wellington Street, Woolwich, London SE18 6PF
Fax 020-8331 8145   Tel 0800-005 006

University of Hertfordshire
College Lane, Hatfield, Hertfordshire AL10 9AB
Fax 01707-284870   Tel 01707-284800

University of Huddersfield
Queensgate, Huddersfield, West Yorkshire HD1 3DH
Fax 01484-516151   Tel 01484-422288

University of Leeds
Leeds LS2 9JT
Fax 0113-233 2334   Tel 0113-233 2332

University of Leicester
Leicester LE1 7RH
Fax 0116-252 2447   Tel 0116-252 5281

University of Lincolnshire & Humberside
Brayford Pool, Lincoln LN6 7TD
Fax 01522-886021   Tel 01522-882000

University of Liverpool
Liverpool L69 3BX
Fax 0151-708 6502   Tel 0151-794 2000

University of Luton
Park Square, Luton, Bedfordshire LU1 3JU
Fax 01582-489323   Tel 01582-489286

University of Newcastle
10 Kensington Terrace, Newcastle-on-Tyne NE1 7RU
Fax 0191-222 6139   Tel 0191-222 6138

University of North London
166-220 Holloway Road, London N7 8DB
Fax 020-7753 2677   Tel 020-7753 3355

University of Northumbria
Ellison Place, Newcastle upon Tyne NE18ST
Fax 0191-227 3009   Tel 0191-227 4064

University of Paisley
High Street Paisley PA1 2BE
Fax 0141-848 3623   Tel 0141-848 3859

University of Portsmouth
Winston Churchill Avenue, Portsmouth PO1 2UP
Fax 023-9284 3082   Tel 023-9287 6543

University of Sheffield
14 Favell Road, Sheffield S3 7QX
Fax 0114-222 8032   Tel 0114-222 8019

University of Southampton
Highfield, Southampton SO17 1BJ
Fax 023-8059 3037   Tel 023-8059 5000

University of Stirling
Stirling FK9 4LA
Fax 01786-466800   Tel 01786-467044
BA (Hons) film and media studies.

University of Sunderland
Edinburgh Building, Chester Road, Sunderland SR1 3SD
Fax 0191-515 3805   Tel 0191-515 3000

University of Sussex
Undergraduate Admissions, Sussex House, Brighton BN1 9RH
Fax 01273-678545   Tel 01273-678416

University of Teesside
Middlesborough TS1 3BA
Fax 01642-384201   Tel 01642-218121
BA (Hons) media studies and as a combined degree.

University of Ulster
Cromore Road, Coleraine, County Londonderry BT52 1SA
Fax 028-7032 4964   Tel 028-7032 4196

University of Wales, Bangor
Bangor, Gwynedd LL57 2DG
Fax 01248-383228   Tel 01248-383229
Welsh medium BA courses in comms & media; communication & journalism; theatre & media studies.

University of Wales, Lampeter
College Street, Lampeter, Ceredigion SA48 7ED
Fax 01570-423423   Tel 01570-423530
Single Hons degree in media studies; Single Hons degree in film studies.

University of the West of England, Bristol
Frenchay Campus, Bristol BS16 1QY
Fax 0117-976 3804   Tel 0117-965 6261
BA (Hons) cultural and media studies.

West Herts College
Hempstead Road, Watford, Hertfordshire WD1 3EZ
Fax 01923-812540   Tel 01923-812565

University of Westminster
Metford House, 115 New Cavendish Street, London W1M 8JS
Fax 020-7911 5858   Tel 020-7911 5000

University of Wolverhampton
Compton Road West, Wolverhampton WV3 9DX
Fax 01902-323744   Tel 01902-321000

Wirral Metropolitan College
Borough Road, Birkenhead, Merseyside L42 9QD
Fax 0151-551 7401   Tel 0151-551 7472

Media/PR recruitment agencies

1st Call Recruitment 01162-334404
1st Stop Careers   01276-683555

A
A F Selection   0121-355 0955
A.M.P   01908-222254
Abbey Recruitment Consultants
                   01625-530255
Action Staff Bureau 01892-542822
Albany Appointments
                   020-7493 8611
Allocate Recruitment
                   01789-262424
Andrew Fraser   01242-570262
Angela Mortimer   020-7287 7788
Annabelle Staff Bureau
                   0191-261 5135
Apex Recruitment Services
                   01926-424154
Apple Recruitment Services
                   028-9032 2602
Arrow Recruitment 01494-522226
Arw Recruitment   020-8669 7939
Ashley Search & Selection
                   0161-927 7290
At Your Service Agency
                   01553-771222
Atebion Employment Agency
                   01248-372112

B
Black Appointments 0131-226 0960
Brentvine   01590-679739
Bridge Executive Recruitment
                   01904-655266

C
Cam Consultants   020-7491 3944
Canto & Canto Recruitment
                   01527-402222
Careers & Jobs   01396-821600
Carreras Lathane Associates
                   020-7439 9634
Cathedral Appointments
                   01392-413577
Chiltern Recruitment
                   01494-459450
Choice Bureau   020-8367 6111
Creative Resource 0161-477 3221

D
Data Recruitment   020-8541 5455
Direct Staff & Calculating
                   020-8590 0074
Dovetail Employment Agency
                   01635-43100

E
Earl Street Employment Consultants
                   01622-755329
Excel Recruitment 020-7404 1010

F
Fletcher Schlaefli Media
                   020-8287 2777
Flexiskills Employment Agency
                   028-9032 4436
Future Recruitment 01293-432950

G
Grampian Network Services
                   01779-481900
Griffith Recruitment 01303-220844

H
Hales Personnel Services
                   01379-642276
Handle Recruitment 020-7935 3585
Highflyers Employment
                   01342-410111
HRM North   01309-676878
Human Resources Partnership
                   01908-696088

I
I P Recruitment   01992-450146
Industrial Workforce 0151-236 0831
Interactive Selection 020-8678 0870

J
J R Personnel   01509-211211
Jean McGhee Recruitment
                   0131-255 9911
Jencol Employment Agency
                   01332-812423
JKL & Hide Recruitment
                   0117-9250711
Judy Farquharson   020-7493 8824
Julia Ross Personnel
                   020-7836 5666
Jo Phillips   01227-455618

M
MacNeil Group Holdings
                   020-7629 8863
Marketplace Appointments
                   01923-243000
Mary Holland Associates
                   020-7726 4132
Matthews Personnel 01753-511688
Media Contacts Recruitment
                   020-7359 8244
Mediatec Recruitment
                   0121-634 6137

N
Nextep Ltd   020-7680 1001

O
Oasis Personnel   01243-533801

P
P & D Employment   01962-865152
Pamela Neave Employment
                   0117-921 1831
Parkway Search and Selection
                   01707-395200
Partners Employment Services
                   01225-760777
PIR Group   01480-493344
Pauline Kotschy Associates
                   01792-472725
PeopleBank Employment
                   020-7634 3255
Personnel Selection 01483-765546
Pertempts Caledonian
                   0131-225 7531
Phee Farrer Jones 020-7925 2250

P
Placing People   01908-671900
Price Jamieson   020-7580 7702
PSR Agency   020-8695 5777

Q
Quantum Staff Consultants
                   0131-220 6656

R
Raeburn Group   01224-625050
Rainbow Recruitment
                   020-7491 7252
Recruit Media   020-7704 1227
Recruiting for Scotland
                   0131-225 5000
Roberts Staff Bureau
                   01264 333888
Ross Campbell Consultants
                   01383-736163
Royds Raphael   020-7287 2050

S
Seka Media   020-7813 7713
Select Recruitment 028-9023 2328
Side-Kix   01753-857910
Southern Staff Services
                   01628-474474
Sovereign Recruitment
                   01661-822838
Stanley Staff Bureau 0151-355 1395
Status Appointments
                   01732-357747
Stop Gap Marketing 020-8332 7656
Sylvia Gray Staff Agency
                   028-9023 1682

T
TCB Recruitment   01905-613355
The Business Connection Group
                   01244-350303
The Davis Company 020-7580 4580
The Media Exchange
                   020-7636 6777
Travail Employment 01706-340202
TSU Recruitment   01732-355470

U
Upgrade Recruitment
                   020-8780 9922

V
Victoria Lewis Recruitment
                   01480-414898

W
Westray Recruitment Consultant
                   01642-247473
Working Wonders Recruitment
                   020-7930 9080

Y
Yvonne Palmer Associates
                   0115-9482244

List supplied by FRES - the
Federation of Recruitment and
Employment Services

Journalism awards 2000

NEWSPAPER AWARDS

British Press Awards

Press Gazette,19 Scarbrook Road, Croydon CR9 1LX
Fax 020-8565 4462   Tel 020-8565 4463
Newspaper: The Sunday Telegraph
Reporter: Nick Davies, The Guardian
Team reporting award: The Sunday Times, Kosovo
Feature writer: Ann Treneman, The Times
Financial journalist: Ben Laurence, The Observer
Interviewer: Nigel Farndale, Sunday Telegraph
Magazine
Foreign reporter: Jon Swain, The Sunday Times
Specialist writer: Lorraine Fraser, The Mail on Sunday
Business journalist: Hugo Dixon, Financial Times
Columnist: Brian Reade, The Mirror
Scoop: News of the World, Archer quits
Young journalist: Nick Paton Walsh, The Observer
Photographer: Ian Torrance, Daily Record/freelance
Sports photographer: Richard Pelham, The Sun
Cartoonist: Matt Pritchett, The Daily Telegraph
Critic: Richard Dorment, The Daily Telegraph
Sports journalist: Matt Dickinson, The Times
Front page: The eclipse, The Sun
On-line news service award: News Unlimited, The
Guardian
Supplement: The Mirror's M magazine
Gold award: Harold Evans
Hugh Cudlipp award: Hold Ye Front Page, The Sun

What the Papers Say

Granada Television, Manchester M60 9EA
Fax 0161-953 0291   Tel 0161-832 7211
E-mail: paul.tyrell@granadatv.careof.uk
Newspaper: The Times
Editor: Peter Stothard, The Times
Columnist: Deborah Orr, The Independent
Foreign correspondent : Robert Fisk, The Independent
Gerald Barry award: Clare Hollingworth
Peter Black award: AA Gill, The Sunday Times
Scoop: News of the World, Jeffrey Archer story
Interview: Ginny Dougray, The Times
Journalist of the decade: Paul Foot

Press Gazette Regional Press Awards

Press Gazette,19 Scarbrook Road, Croydon CR9 1LX
Fax 020-8565 4462   Tel 020-8565 4463
E-mail: sarahsj@qpp.co.uk
Regional newspaper of the year: Yorkshire Post
Weekly newspaper: South London Press
Free newspaper: Milton Keynes citizen
Campaign: Tamworth Herald, Colin Grazier
Evening newspaper: Evening Herald, Plymouth
Local newspaper week: Evening Press, York
Scoop: Darwin Templeton, Belfast Telegraph, The
Patten Report
Online news service: www.thisiswiltshire.co.uk
Young journalist: Bryn Jones, Daily Post, Liverpool
Business journalist: Jim Simpson, Yorkshire Post
Personal financial journalist: Peter Sharples,
Manchester Evening News
Reporter: Chris Bucktin, Hull Daily Mail
Photographer: Mike Urwin, Northern Echo
Sports photographer: Steve Ellis, The Star, Sheffield
Sports journalist: Matthew Reeeder, Evening Advertiser,
Swindon
Columnist: Martin Freeman, Evening Herald,
Plymouth
Feature writer: Gail Walker, Belfast Telegraph
Specialist reporter: Tracey Sparling, Evening Star,
Ipswich
Production team: Manchester Evening News, Harold
Shipman

MAGAZINE AWARDS

Magazines & Business to Business '00
Awards: PPA

Periodical Publishers Association, Queens House, 28
Kingsway, London WC2B 6JR
Fax 020-7404 4167   Tel 020-7404 4166
Next deadline: 28.1.2000
Consumer magazine: Ideal Home
Business magazine: Computer Weekly
International magazine (consumer): Wallpaper
International magazine (business): Traffic Technology
Customer magazine: the one-line guide
Consumer specialist magazine: Computer Active
Interactive magazine: EGi
Editor (consumer): Fiona McIntosh
Editor (business): Rufus Olins
Designer (consumer): Michelle Goodwin
Designer (business): Anne Braybon
Specialist writer (consumer): Charles Rangeley-Wilson
Columnist (business): Roger Evans
Writer (consumer): Michael Hodges
Writer (business): Tony Collins
Publisher (companies with less than 25 employees): Evo
Publisher (consumer): Rita Lewis
Publisher (business): Emma Roffey
Editorial campaign: Hospital Doctor, doctor
suspensions

Paul Foot, winner of the What the Papers Say journalist of the decade award

PHOTOGRAPHY AWARDS

Observer David Hodge Award
The Observer, 119 Farringdon Road, London EC1R 3ER
Set up in 1986 in memory of David Hodge, a photographer who died aged 29 of injuries sustained during the Brixton riots. This award for documentary photography is open to amateur, student and professional photographer under 30. First prize is £3,000 and an assignment for the Observer. Best Student wins £1,500 plus runners up. Past winners include Jonathan Olley (Network), Harriet Logan (Network) and Zoe Sinclair (The Girls')
1999 winner: Gunnar Knechtel
Best student: Rebecca Bradbury
(And Daisy Durham deserves special mention because - although born in 1988 - she shows remarkable fledgling talent.)

OTHER AWARDS

Guardian Student Media Awards
NUS, 461 Holloway Road London N7
The awards are one of the best established routes for journalists, editors and photographers to a successful career in media. The awards are launched in February and the winners announced in November. The latest roll of honour is:
Newspaper of the year: Leeds Student
Magazine: Pulp
Reporter: Guy Adams
Feature writer: Merope Mills, Student Direct
Photographer: Ed Alcock, London Student and Cub
Publication design: Dean Langley and Simon Griffin, Shout

Critic: SF Said, Varsity
Website: bloc
Shoestring award: Pulse
Diversity award: Steve Kilgallon, Cherwell

Ethnic Multicultural Media Awards
Hearsay Communications, 67-69 Whitfield Street, London W1P 5RL
Fax 020-7636 1255   Tel 020-7468 3527
E-mail: comms@hearsay.co.uk
Website: www.emma.co.uk
Best film: The Matrix
Actor: David Harewood, The Vice
Actress: Angela Griffin, Holby City
Radio DJ: DJ 279, Steve Phillips, Choice FM
British music act: Bally Sagoo
International music act: Santana
TV entertainment production: Da Ali G Show
Theatre production: RSC, Oroonoko
Book: Zadie Smith, White Teeth
Print journalist: Vikram Dodd, Guardian
Radio news journalist: Sanjivv Buttoo, BBC Radio Leeds
TV news journalist: Krishnan GuruMurthy, Channel 4 News
TV documentary: The Koran & the Kalashnikov, BBC
Female media newcomer: Zadie Smith
Male media newcomer: David Landu, Sunrise Radio
Publication: The Voice
Radio station: Kiss FM
Cable/digital channel: Zee TV
Public figure of the year: Mel B
Charity of the year: Blackliners - Aids awareness amongst the black community
Media personality: Yasmin Alibhai-Brown
Lifetime Achievement Award: Nelson Mandela

Online Journalism Awards
NetMedia, Haymarket House, 28/29 Haymarket,London SW1 4SP
                    Tel 020-7344 1236
E-mail: msw@net-media.co.uk
Website: www.net-media.co.uk
Best overall journalism service: BBC News Online
Internet journalist of the year: Miroslav Filipovic, Institute for War and Peace Reporting
Sports: BBC News Online
Best entertainment: Single is born, Helsingin Sanomat Verkkoliite
Best business: Dow Jones Newswires
Best general news: Kosovo conflict, BBC News Online
Science and technology: What is Life?, TimeEurope.com
Best news design and navigation: beme.com channel one, IPC Media
Best feature story: TIME Trail: Russian Democracy, TimeEurope.com
Best investigative reporting: Telepolis ENFOPOL special, Telepolis
Best news story broken on the net: Paddington rail crash, BBC News Online
Best financial reporting: European electricity market deregulation, Bloomberg News

BROADCAST AWARDS

BAFTA Performance Awards (TV Section)
British Academy of Film and Television Arts, 195
Piccadilly, London W1V 0LN
Fax 020-7734 1792   Tel 020-7734 0022
Best single drama: The Murder of Stephen Lawrence,
Granada Productions with Vanson Productions, ITV
Best drama series: The Cops, World Productions, BBC2
Best drama serial: Warriors, BBC Films
Best factual series: The Mayfair Set, BBC 2
Best light entertainment: Robbie the Reindeer, BBC 1
Best comedy: The League of Gentlemen, BBC 2
Best situation comedy: The Royle Family, BBC 2
Best presenter: Jeremy Paxman, Newsnight, BBC 2
Best actress: Thora Hird, Lost For Words, ITV
Best actor: Michael Gambon, Wives & Daughters, BBC 1
Best light entertainment performance: Graham Norton,
So Graham Norton, Channel 4
Best comedy performance: Caroline Aherne, The Royle
Family, BBC 2
Best arts programme: This is Modern Art, Oxford
Television Company, Channel 4
Best documentary: Divorce Iranian Style, 20th Century
Vixen Productions, Channel 4
Best news/current affairs: Coverage of the Kosovo
conflict, BBC 1
Best soap: East Enders, BBC 1
Best feature: Blood on the Carpet, BBC 2
Best sport: Test Cricket, Sunset & Vine, Channel 4
Best innovation: Walking With Dinosaurs, BBC 1
Outstanding creative achievement: Peter Kosminsky
Dennis Potter award: Tony Marchant
Lew Grade award (audience vote): A Touch of Frost, ITV
Special award: Honor Blackman, Joanna Lumley, Diana
Rigg, Linda Thorson, The Avengers series

Broadcast Production Awards
33-39 Bowling Green Lane, London EC1R 0DA
Fax 020-7505 8050   Tel 020-7505 8014
E-mail: bcast@media.emap.co.uk
Cable or satellite programme: Weekender, At It Produc-
tions for Sky One
Children's programme: Microsoap, BBC 1
Drama: Births, Marriaes and Deaths, Tiger Aspect Pro-
ductions for BBC 1
Documentary programme: True Stories: The Valley,
Mentorn Barraclough Carey for Channel 4
Documentary series: Shanghai Vice, River Films for
Channel 4
News programme: Nine O'Clock News, BBC 1
Comedy: The Royle Family, Granada Television for
BBC 1
Light entertainment: Don't Try This at Home, LWT for
ITV
Sports programme: Channel 4 Test Cricket, Sunset &
Vine, Channel 4
Popular factual programme: The Second World War in
Colour - A New World Order, TWI/Carlton for ITV
New programme: Walking with Dinosaurs, BBC 1
Independent production company: Wall to Wall
Television
Post production house: TSI

The Indies
Single Market Events, 23-24 George Street,
Richmond, Surrey TW9 1HY
Fax 020-8332 0495   Tel 020-8948 5522
The Indie: The 1900 House, Wall to Wall Television
Hat Trick Pioneer: Celador Productions
Drama: Queeer as Folk, Red Productions
Light entertainment: Smack the Pony, Talkback
Productions
Music and arts: This is Modern Art, Oxford Television
Communications
Factual: Time Team, The Picture House/Video Text
Communications
News: Staying Lost, October Films
Documentary: Shanghai Vice, River Films
Animation: Rex the Runt, Aardman Animation
Sport: Test Cricket, Sunset & Vine
Cable, digital and satellite: Robbie Williams Live, Done
& Dusted
Archive award: The Second World War in Colour, Trans
World International
Children: Teletubbies, Ragdoll Productions
The Indie-vidual award: Peter Bazalgette
Teh Global Indie: Who Wants to be a Millionaire?,
Celador Productions

One World
One World Broadcasting Trust, 3-7 Euston Centre,
Regent's Place, London NW1 3JG
Fax 020-7383 4238   Tel 020-7383 4248
E-mail: owbt@oneworld.org
TV news: Fergal Keene , Rwanda Genocide, Newsnight
UNICEF: Children in Arms, Radio 4
TV documentary: Sorious Samura with RonMcCullagh,
Out of Africa, Channel 4
ICRC dignity in conflict: Sorious Samura, Out of Africa,
Channel 4
Best NGO campaign: CAFOD's Kick Starting Global
Awareness
Radio news: Aids in Africa by Greg Barrow, BBC World
Service; From Our Own Correspondent, Mark Doyle,
BBC Radio 4
Radio documentary: In Touch with Africa, Gary
O'Donoghue, BBC Radio 4
Magazines, journals and periodicals: Tribes, Index on
Censorship
Special award: Jon Snow
Save the Children national press award: Ros Wynne-
Jones, Sudan, Express
Christian Aid lifestyle award: Jon Snow and Ekow
Eshun
ActionAid children and young people's award: RANT
magazine, Portsmouth Youth Service
International new media: The Scars of Brutality website
by Eric Beauchemin, Radio Netherlands

Rory Peck Award

Rory Peck Trust, 7 Southwick Mews, London W2 1JG
Fax 020-7262 2162   Tel 020-7262 5272
E-mail: rptrpa@dial.pipex.com
Website: www.oneworld.org/rorypeck
Honours the initiative, courage and skill of freelance
cameramen and women in TV newsgathering and
documentaries worldwide. The award is named after
Rory Peck a freelance cameraman killed whilst filming
the Moscow revolt in October 1993.
Winner: Sorius Samura from Sierra Leone. Freelance
(Freetown)

Royal Television Society Awards

Holborn Hall, 100 Grays Inn Road, London WC1X
8AL
Fax 020-7430 0924   Tel 020-7430 1000
Journalist of the year: John Simpson, BBC News
Young journalist of the year: Matthew Price, BBC
Newsround
Specialist journalism: Susan Watts, BBC News
Daily news magazine: Look North, BBC North East and
Cumbria
Regional current affairs: Soho Bombing - London
Tonight Special, London News Network
News (home): The Paddington Crash and Its Causes,
Channel 4 News
News (international): Dili Indonesia, BBC News
Current affairs (home): Why Stephen? - Black Britain
special, BBC News
Current affairs (International): Prime Suspects -
Dispatches, Channel 4
News event: Kosovo Liberation Day, Sky News
Television technician of the year: Miguel Gil, APTN
Interviewer of the year: Tim Sebastian, BBC News
Production award: Channel 4 News, ITN
Programme of the year: The Prime Suspects - Tonight
with Trevor McDonald, Granada Television
Judges award: Michael Brunson
Sports award: Test Cricket, Sunset & Vine for Channel
4
Live Outside Broadcast: Test Cricket, Sunset & Vine for
Channel 4
Sports news: Olympic Corruption, Channel 4 News
Sports documentary: Clash of the Titans: Benn v
Eubank, BBC Television
Regional sports news: Dougie Walker, Reporting
Scotland, BBC Scotland Sport
Regional sports documentary: Working Class Hero,
Neil Jenkins , BBC Wales
Sports presenter: Jim Rosenthal, ITV
Sports commentator: Peter Alliss, BBC Sport
Judges award: Bill McLaren, BBC

Sony Radio Awards

Zafer Productions, 47-48 Chagford Street, London
NW1 6EB
Fax 020-7724 6163   Tel 020-7723 0106
E-mail: zafer@compuserve.com
UK station of the year (500,00-12 mil listeners): Bam
Bam Breakfast, Kiss 100
UK station of the year (to UK): Jonathan Ross Show,
Radio 2
News gold award: Late Night Live, Soho bomb, Radio 5
Live
Event gold award: The Open, Radio 5 Live
Short form award: Woman's Hour inserts, Radio 4
Drama award: Plum's War, Radio 4
Comedy gold award: Blue Jam, Radio 1
Sport gold award: Super Sunday, GLR
Speech award: The Evacuation, The True Story, Radio 4
Lifetime achievement: Alan Freeman

Voice of the Listener and Viewer Awards

101 King's Drive, Gravesend, Kent DA12 5BQ
                    Tel 01474-352835
Best television contributor: John Sergeant, BBC1 & 2
Best radio contributor: Nick Clarke, BBC Radio 4
Best radio programme: From Our Own Correspon-
dent, BBC Radio 4
Best television programme: Hav I Got News for You,
BBC2
Best new television programme: Walking With
Dinosaurs, BBC2
Best new radio programme: Nicholas Nickleby, BBC
Special award: Shooting the Past, BBC2

AWARDS LISTINGS

Amnesty International UK media awards
Tel 020-7814 6278
For journalists who have contributed to the public's
understanding of human rights issues.

Anne Bolt Memorial Award
Tel 020-7843 3708
Photojournalists aged under 25.

BAFTA Awards
Tel 020-7440 3838
Film and television awards.

Bank of Scotland Press Awards
0141-333 1551
For journalists working on publications in Scotland and
Scottish based journalists working for publications out
of Scotland.

Bar Council Legal Journalists of the Year
Tel 020-7222 2525
Recognises print and broadcast journalists whose work
contributes to a greater understanding of legal issues.

Beer Writer of the Year Awards
Tel 020-7606 4455
Outstanding and innovative work on beer or brewing.

Bell's Scottish Photographer of the Year
Tel 0131-557 6767
Ten categories open to press and student photographers
based in Scotland,

BNFL North West Press Awards
Tel 01925-834036
Seven categories open to journalists in the north west.

**Bradford and Bingley Personal Finance
Media Awards**
Tel 01274-554712
Personal finance journalists in national and regional
newspapers, magazines, broadcast and new media.

**Britannia Building Society Housing
Journalist of the Year**
Tel 020-7393 2096
Journalists from national, regional or business
publications who have made a significant contribution
to the public awareness of housing.

The British Guild of Picture Editors' Awards
1-5 Poland Street, London W1V 4NA
Twelve categories for newspaper and agency
photographers.

British Guild of Travel Writers Awards
Tel 01761-411223
Various categories recognising excellence in travel
journalism. Open to Guild members only.

British Press Awards
Tel 020-8565 4463
National newspaper journalists in nineteen categories.

**British Sports Journalist and Sports
Photographer of the Year**
Tel 020-7273 1589

Broadcast Production Awards
Tel 020-7505 8300
For television production journalists in factual,
documentary and news categories.

**Bruce Kinlock Property Journalist of the
Year**
Tel 020-7428 8134
Property journalist of the year.

BSME Awards
020-8906 4664
13 awards in categories for consumer and business
magazines which publish at least four times per year.

BT Awards
Tel 0345-262624
Eight regional awards in thirteen categories.

Cartoon Art Trust Award
Tel 020-7278 7172
Awards for newspaper cartoonists in seven categories.

Catherine Pakenham Award
Tel 020-7538 6257
For women print journalists aged 18-25

Chris Cox Memorial Award
Tel 01325-503263
For the best student on the NCTJ accredited course at
Darlington University.

**Commission for Racial Equality, Race in the
Media Awards**
Tel 020-8864 2005
Criteria changes each year.

Ed Lacy Gibraltar Travel Award
Tel 020-8977-1105
For the best feature about Gibraltar.

Ethnic Multicultural Media Awards
Tel 020-7468 3527
Open to media professionals from ethnic minorities.

**Fine Art Trade Guild Awards for Art Journal-
ism**
Tel 020-7381 6616
For regional and local newspaper and magazine
journalists.

Freedom of Information Awards
16 Baldwin Gardens, London EC1 7RJ
For the exposure of unjustified official secrecy.

George Viner Memorial Fund Awards
Tel 020-7278 7916
Founded by the NUJ to sponsor black and ethnic
students on journalism courses.

Glaxo Wellcome Science Writers Awards
Tel 020-7439 1205
For science journalists.

Glenfiddich Food & Drink Awards
Tel 020-7255 1100
For excellence in writing and broadcasting on food and
drink.

Guardian Student Media Awards
Tel 020-7239 9936
For journalists on student publications. Ten categories
editors, reporters and designers on newspapers,
magazines and web sites.

Harold Wincott Awards
Tel 01923-242469
Five awards for journalists reporting on business and
finance.

The Indies: Independent Broadcast Production Awards
Tel 020-8948 5522
Various categories covering companies, programmes and individuals.

Industrial Society Work World Award
Tel 020-7262 2401
Celebrating journalism about the world of work.

International Consortium of Investigative work.
Website: www.icij.org/about/criteria
Reports must cover two countries.

James Cameron Memorial Awards
Tel 020-7477 8783
Award bestowed on journalists whose work has been in the tradition of James Cameron.

Jim Rodger Memorial Award for Young Scottish Sportswriters
Tel 0468-280021
For journalists aged 30 and under who have written for a Scottish newspaper.

KPMG Commercial Radio Awards
Tel 020-7306 2603
12 categories, including news and presenters.

Laurence Stern Fellowship
020-7477 8000
For young journalists who have worked on important national stories.

London Press Club Awards
Tel 020-7402 2566
Scoop of the year/Edgar Wallace award for outstanding writtng.

Mind Journalist of the Year
Tel 020-8522 1743
For reporting of mental health issues.

Neutrogena Beauty Journalism Awards
Tel 020-7465 7700
For print and broadcast journalists.

The Newspaper Awards
Tel 01442-233656
Sixteen categories for technical innovation and production.

Newspaper Society Weekly Newspaper Awards
Tel 020-7636 7014
Nine categories for weekly paid-for and free papers.

Nikon Press Photographer of the Year
Tel 020-8541 4440
Awards in nine categories.

North East Press Awards
Tell 01429-274441
25 awards for journalists working in the north east.

Northern Business Journalist
Tel 0113-247 2510
Three categories: newspapers, magazines and broadcast.

One World International Media Awards
Tel 020-7383 4248
For journalists and organisations who have furthred the cause of international affairs.

Plain English Media Awards
Tel 01663-744409
Regional and national categories for newspapers, radio and TV.

PPA magazines and B2B awards
Tel 020-7404 4166
Awards in nineteen categories for publishers, editors, writers and designers.

PPA Marcus Morris Awards
Tel 020-7404 4166
This award acknowledges the contribution of an individual to the magazine industry.

PTC New Journalist ot the Year Awards
Tel 020-7404 4168
Open to magazine journalists working in the industry for less than three years. Journalism, design and student categories.

Regional Press Awards
Tel 020-8565 4463
For ediitors and journalists working for daily and weekly regional newspapers.

Rory Peck Trust Awards
Tel 020-7262 5272
Honours the initiative, courage and skill of freelance camera operators in TV news and documentaries.

Rosmary Goodchild Award- Family Planning Association
Tel 020-7837 5432
For the best articles on sexual health and family planning.

Royal Television Journalism Awards
Tel 020-7430 1000
Sixteen categories for TV journalists.

Scottish Hydro-Electric Sport Photography Awards
Tel 020-8906 4664
Eight categories of awards.

Sony Radio Awards
Tel 01932-816000
Various categories covering stations, programmes and individuals.

Student Broadcast Journalist of the Year
Tel 020-7727 9522
Open to all students on BJTC courses.

Total Publishing Corporate Communication Awards
Tel 020-8565 4368
For the publication of customer and staff magazines.

Total Publishing Magazine Design Awards
Tel 020-8565 4368
For designers and art directors of magazines.

Travelex Travel Writers Awards
Tel 020-7405 7200
For travel journalists, in various media, in eight categories.

What the Papers Say Awards
Tel 0161-832 7211
Seven categories for national newspaper journalists.

Young Travel Writer of the Year
Tel 020-7861 6092
Print journalists aged 18-25

A year in the life of Rupert Murdoch

Rupert Murdoch

"I've been a catalyst for change in Britain, whether in the popular press, then later in the quality press, or fighting the unions. You can't be a successful outsider over 30 years without leaving a fair amount of scar tissue around the place. I think that's the price one pays. I'm not complaining, it's a fact of life."

Henry Porter

"Murdoch cares not the slightest for British institutions, nor for the health of its politics, nor for the rights of one of the oldest democracies in the world. As far as he is concerned we are just a little profitable territory with lenient tax authorities and politicians who will dance on hot coals for his support."

SEPTEMBER 1999
China ... Labour ... Europe ... James

While Murdoch told Vanity Fair of "the cynics who say the Dalai Lama is a very political old monk shuffling around in Gucci shoes", other cynics noted News Corp's very important Sino-TV interests might lead him to minimise Chinese repression of Tibet ... news leaked of Sky's £20,000 donation to Labour made (cynics said) in the weeks before the government blocked Sky's take-over of Manchester United in April 1999 ... Murdoch met the European Commission president Romano Prodi prompting speculation a) he was keen to patch up relations after Prodi (when the Italian PM) had blocked a News Corp take-over of the Mediaset TV network and b) he'd become a Euro enthusiast, change the Sun and Times stance and make life easier for Labour ... Letizia Moratti quit after less than a year as chairman of News Corp Europe after tiffing with her boss over "the group's European policy" ... James Murdoch, 26, joined Dad on the News Corp main board to push internet related business.

OCTOBER
Germany/France ... China ... movies

Murdoch, in his new role as Sky chairman, held negotiations with Deutsche Telecom and Kirch in Germany and Canal Plus in France but told shareholders he ruled out any mergers ... he met the Chinese president, Jiang Zemin, a man the Times described as "a man of peace and good will [and] a very friendly, very intelligent world statesman" ... Star Wars: the Phantom Menace was the third most successful movie ever but film profits at News Corp's 20th Century Fox still didn't match those made from Titanic.

NOVEMBER
Australia ... America ... Oxford

"The British monarchy has become irrelevant to this generation of Australians," declared Murdoch (an American citizen) in his paper The Australian in support of the Yes case in the Aussie republic referendum ... in Adelaide he told the News Corp AGM of his determination to expand into Europe, even at the price of issuing new shares in Sky ... back home in the States he told the 20th Century Fox AGM that he may sell off some of his 82 per cent Fox holding to fund online adventures ... and back at his old university in Oxford he gave a lecture where he said BBC people are "a self-appointed elite who hate anything changing in Britain". The twice divorced traveller also stood up for family values - "intergenerational values etc etc".

DECEMBER
Billions invested ... libel case ... immortality
Sky took a 24 per cent £1 billion stake in Kirch, Germany's biggest TV company in a deal giving new satellite access to a far larger market than Sky's British one ... the next day News Corp made a $1 billion investment for 10 per cent of the US Healtheon/WebMD online health-care company ... Murdoch held negotiations which led to a settlement of the libel battle between the Times and Michael Ashcroft, the Conservative chairman ... "He shows no sign of slowing down and will probably outlive all of us," said 48 year old Peter Chernin, News Corps' chief operating officer who is tipped as the man most likely to succeed ahead of Lachlan Murdoch.

JANUARY 2000
Phones in Australia and Finland ... French TV
Rupert Murdoch, 69, got into phones when News Corp bought a £124 million 25 per cent stake in One.tel, the Australian phone company ... News Corp execs were also on the line to Nokia, discussing how the mobile Rupert might work closely with the Finnish mobile phone company ... relations were more frosty with Vivendi, the French TV company which bought a quarter stake in Sky in a deal investigated by the Competition Commission but ratified in April.

FEBRUARY
The world ... Singapore
Murdoch used an interview on his Fox News TV Channel that he didn't want to become a snack for Yahoo ... with the AOL-Time Warner deal ringing in everybody's ears, the spin on the snack remark was that Murdoch would pursue a strategy of spinning off his satellite businesses into a separate company which would then go for stock market flotation ... at the end of the month News Corps execs were parleying with Yahoo with reports emerging the web giant might take a 5 per cent stake in News Corps' global satellite interest ... meanwhile News Corp invested $1 billion in Singapore Telecom.

MARCH
Hong Kong ... India
Far Eastern competition loomed large when Pacific Century Cyber Works bought Cable & Wireless Hong Kong and signalled its intent to move into Europe in partnership with the IMG sports marketing firm. "Everywhere we go, IMG got in there first," Murdoch complained as he saw the potential for his Hong Kong based Star TV diminish ... on a four day trip to India Murdoch boosted Star's Indian interests and said: "We'll certainly be investing in some companies. There are as many dot.coms here as anywhere yet at this stage it's a very small market."

APRIL
Cancer ... Vivendi
A bad month for Rupert Murdoch. Doctors in Los Angeles diagnosed a low grade prostate cancer and the British Competition Commission cleared Vivendi's 24.5 per cent stake in Sky. This move was despite rumours that the Department of Trade, under pressure from Downing Street, was prepared to block the deal.

MAY
Political values ... family values
Rupert Murdoch hinted at Sun and Times support for Labour at the next election when he told Le Figaro: "Tony Blair is a great man and an honest man [who] was the first Labour leader that we could support with enthusiasm." ... Elisabeth Murdoch resigned as Sky's network chief, upset - rumour had it - that Lachlan was the most favoured of the four Murdoch siblings. His daughter is secure in this world though. For she and her new partner Matthew Freud (the father of her third baby) have £12 million of shares in the Oxygen internet venture capitalists.

JUNE
Family values
Rupert promoted his youngest son James, 27, to head the Star TV Asian television business ... Murdoch indicated he would seek a flotation for his satellite TV interests

2001 news lines

The World Porridge Championship is on 2 Sepetember 2001. Details from Advance Media Information which supplies Britain's major news organisations with a daily-updated list of future events. For more info, see the AMI website www.amiplan.com or phone 020-8549 0799 ...

JANUARY

1 JANUARY Public records from 1970, declassified under 30 year rule, open to public. Public Records Office 020-8876 3444 Website: www.pro.gov.uk

50th anniversary of The Archers. BBC press 0121-432 8315 Website: www.bbc.co.uk/radio4/archers

200th anniversary of United Kingdom of Great Britain & Ireland formed with unveiling of new Union Jack at Dublin castle.

4 JANUARY Press and Preview Day, London International Boat Show, Earls Court, till Jan 14. Jenny Rawlinson, British Marine Industries Federation 01784 473 377 Website: www.bigblue.org.uk Email:jennyr@bmif.co.uk

8 JANUARY Trial in US of ex-Symbionese Liberation Army urban guerrilla Kathy Soliah (now Sarah Jane Olsen) for attempting to kill Los Angeles police officers in 1970s. Newspaper heiress Patty Hearst appears as a witness. Sara Olson Defense Fund Committee 001-612-822-1637 Website: www.saraolsondefense.com

16 JANUARY 10th anniversary of Operation Desert Storm - US-led allies v Iraq beginning at midnight, starting Gulf War. Website: www.desert-storm.com ck contact - Gulf Veterans Association, Sandra Scott secretary 0191-259 6091

20 JANUARY President Clinton leaves office. New US president inaugurated, Washington DC. White House press 001-202-456 9271 Website: www.whitehouse.gov

22 JANUARY 100th anniversary of Victoria's death. King Edward VII becomes king.

24 JANUARY Chinese New Year celebrations 2001: Year of Snake, Centered on Gerrard Street and Leicester Square. Organisers 020 7734 5161. Lili Jian Chao Press attaché Chinese Embassy 020 7636 0380/020 7636 0380

25 JANUARY World Economic Forum annual meeting, Davos, Switzerland, till Jan 30. WEF 0041 22 869 1212, fax 0041 22 786 2744 Website: www.weforum.org

27 JANUARY 100th anniversary of Italian composer Giuseppe Verdi's death. Website: www.rz-berlin.mpg.de/cmp/verdi.html

30 JANUARY 40th anniversary of the contraceptive pill being introduced to UK. Website: www.schering.co.uk

FEBRUARY

14 FEBRUARY National Impotence Day. Anne Craig, Impotence Association 020 8516 7724 Website: www.impotence.org.uk

18 FEBRUARY 100th anniversary of H Cecil Booth patenting a vacuum cleaner.

19 FEBRUARY Church of England General Synod, Church House, till Feb 21. Church House 020 -7898 1000 Website: www.church-of-england.org

25 FEBRUARY The BAFTAs - Orange British Academy Film Awards, Odeon, Leicester Sq. Diane Glynn, BAFTA Events 020- 7494 2751 Webs: www.bafta.org Email: dianeg@bafta.org

MARCH

6 MARCH Britain's Cleanest City awards on opening day of The Cleaning Show, NEC. Jay Grenby, British Cleaning Council press 01727 862101 Website: www.necgroup.co.uk

14 MARCH Press day for Daily Mail Ideal Home Show, Earls Court, till Apr 8. 020-8515 2000 Website: www.idealhomeshow.co.uk

24 MARCH Oxford v Cambridge boat race. Jenny Searl, Ketchum Communications 020 7465 2389 Website: www.boatrace.co.uk

25 MARCH Oscar awards ceremony, LA. Leslie Unter, Academy of Motion Pictures, Arts & Sciences, 001-310-247 3000 fax 001 310 859 9616 Website: www.oscars.org/academy

28 MARCH British Psychological Society Centenary annual conference, Scottish Exhibition and Conference Centre, Glasgow, till Mar 31. BPS press 0116 252 9500 Website: www.bps.org.uk

APRIL

10 APRIL 20th anniversary of Brixton riots, till Apr 12. Brixton area press, Metropolitan Police 020-8247 5009

22 APRIL Flora London Marathon. Marathon press 020 7620 4117 Website: www.london-marathon.com

28 APRIL Old mobile and pager code numbers that have been replaced by new ones cease to work. Number change press 0800 783 5260 Website: www.numberchange.org Email: press.office@numberchange.org

29 APRIL Confimed UK Census.65,000 census takers visit 30m households in England and Wales, with another 8000 in Scotland. Charlie Walker, National Statistics Census press 020-7533 5162 Craig Lindsay, General Register Office for Scotland 0131-314 4267 Website: www.statistics.gov.uk Email: charles.walker@ons.gov.uk

MAY

Cannes Film Festival. Festival International du Film 0033-145 61 66 08 Website: www.festival-cannes.fr

3 MAY County Council elections England & Wales. Jean Ward, Home Office press 020 7273 4640

5 MAY 20th anniversary of Bobby Sands death on hunger strike. Sinn Fein press 00353 1 872 2609 Website: www larkspirit.com/hungerstrikes/bios/sands.html

12 MAY Football: FA Cup Final. Steve Double Football Association press 020-7314 5301 Website: www.the-fa.org/index.htm Email: sdouble@the-fa.org

22 MAY Chelsea Flower Show, till May 25. (Press day May 21) Royal Horticultural Society press 020 7834 3043

25 MAY Hay-on-Wye Literature Festival, till June 3. Kate Phillips, Lit Fest press 01497 821 217 Website: www.hayfestival.co.uk

JUNE

BT Global Challenge round world yacht race ends, Southampton. James Mossman, Hill and Knowlton 020-7413 3000
Website: www.btchallenge.com

10 JUNE Duke of Edinburgh's 80th birthday celebrations. Buckingham Palace press 020-7930 4832
Website: www.royal.gov.uk

19 JUNE Royal Ascot, till June 22. Gill Nevin, British Horseracing Board press 020-7396 0011
Website: www.sportinglife.co.uk/ascot Email: GNevin@BHB.co.uk

25 JUNE Wimbledon Lawn Tennis Championships, till July 8. All England Lawn Tennis & Croquet Club 020 8944 1066
Email: info@aeltc.com
Website: http://www.wimbledon.org

JULY

17 JULY European Congress of Psychology, The Barbican Centre, London, till July 6. Sue Cavill, BPS press 0116-252 9500
Website: www.bps.org.uk
Email: ecp2001@thguk.com

2 JULY British Medical Association Annual Representative Meeting, Bournemouth, till July 5. BMA press 020-7383 6254
Website: www.bma.org.uk
Email: pressoffice@bma.org.uk

6 JULY Church of England General Synod, York, till Jul 10. Church House 020-7898 1000
Website: www.church-of-england.org

12 JULY Grand Order Of The Orange Lodge marches to mark Battle of the Boyne. Orange Lodge 01232 322801 Website: www.goli.demon.co.uk
Email: info@goli.demon.co.uk

AUGUST

4 AUGUST 100th anniversary of Louis Armstrong birth.
Website: www.allmusic.com

12 AUGUST 55th Edinburgh International Festival till Sept 1. Edinburgh Festival press 0131-473 2020 fax 0131-473 2002

26 AUGUST Notting Hill Carnival, till Aug 27. Carnival press 01342 851 001

27 AUGUST Bog-snorkelling championships, Neuadd Arms Hotel, Llanwrtyd Wells, Powys. Neuadd Arms 01591 610236
Web: www.benjerry.co.uk/bogsnork/index.htm

31 AUGUST World Conference against Racism, Racial Discrimination, Xenophobia and Related Intolerance, South Africa, till Sept 7. Office of the High Commissioner for Human Rights World Conference Secretariat 0041 22 917-9290 Website: www.un.org/rights/racism/bginfo.htm
Email: husbands@un.org

SEPTEMBER

1 SEPTEMBER Germany v England 2002 World Cup qualifier, Olympic Stadium, Munich. Steve Double, Football Association press 020 7314 5301
Website: www.the-fa.org/index.htm
Email: sdouble@the-fa.org

2 SEPTEMBER World Porridge Championships, Carrbridge. Dorothy Wederburn 01479 841613
Email: dmmw@aol.com

3 SEPTEMBER British Association for Advancement of Science Annual Festival of Science, Glasgow, till Sept 7. BAAS 020-7973 3079
Website: www.britassoc.org.uk/festival

10 SEPTEMBER Trades Union Congress conference in Brighton, till Sept 13. Liz Chinchen, TUC press 020 7467 1248 Email: lchinchen@tuc.org.uk

17 SEPTEMBER Royal Society of Medicine annual GP forum, London, till Sept 21. Rosamund Snow, RSM 020 7290 2904 Website: www.roysocmed.ac.uk Email: rosamund.snow@roysocmed.ac.uk

23 SEPTEMBER Liberal Democrats conference, Bournemouth, till Sept 27. Jeremy Browne, Liberal Democrat press 020 7227 1242 Website: www.libdems.org.uk Email: ldpressoffice@cix.co.uk

30 SEPTEMBER Labour Party conference, Brighton, till Oct 5. Labour Party press 020-7802 1393 Website: www.labour.org.uk

OCTOBER

1 OCTOBER Camelot's licence to run the National Lottery expires (Sept 30). Winner of bid begins operation, till 2008. Office of the National Lottery 020-7227 2000 Website: www.national-lottery.co.uk

4 OCTOBER Poetry Society National Poetry Day (provisional date). Various events around UK. Lisa Roberts, Poetry Society 020-7420 9880 Website: www.poetrysoc.com Email: poetrysoc@dial.pipex.com

5 OCTOBER National Courtesy Day. The Polite Society 01782 614 407

8 OCTOBER Conservative Party annual conference,Blackpool, till Oct 11. Conservative Party press 020-7984 8121 Website: www.conservative-party.org.uk

10 OCTOBER Frankfurt book fair, till Oct 15. Book Fair press 0049 69 21020 Website: www.frankfurt-book-fair.com Email: press@book-fair.com

18 OCTOBER British International Motor Show, NEC, till Oct 29. Society of Motor Manufacturers & Traders Exhibitions 020-7235 7000 Website: www.motorshow.co.uk Email: exhibitions@smmt.co.uk

NOVEMBER

1 NOVEMBER Fox Hunting season opens. Countryside Alliance. Paul Latham Countryside Alliance Press 020-7582 5432 Website: www.countryside-alliance.org Email: info@countryside-alliance.org

12 NOVEMBER Church of England General Synod, Church House, till Nov 16. Church House 020-7898 1000 Website: www.church-of-england.org

27 NOVEMBER 200th anniversary of Anders Celsius, Uppsala, Sweden, scientist/inventor (centigrade temp scale). Website: www.britannica.com/seo/a/anders-celsius

DECEMBER

1 DECEMBER 25th anniversary of Sex Pistols swearing on TV during Bill Grundy interview.

10 DECEMBER Nobel awards ceremony, Oslo. 100th anniversary of 1st Nobel Peace Prizes. Sigrid Lamgebraekke, Nobel Institute 0047 22 12 93 00 Website: www.nobelchannel.com

31 DECEMBER Sir Alex Ferguson 60

Advance Media Information 226 Strand, London WC2R 1BA Fax 020-8 286 2482   Tel 020-8 549 0799 E-mail: ami@easynet.co.uk Web site: www.amiplan.com

2001 anniversaries

All events listed here took place in multiples of five years ago. 2001 is the:

25th anniversary of 1976
50th anniversary of 1951
75th anniversary of 1926

JANUARY

1 The Act of Union unites Great Britain with all of Ireland, creating the Union Jack, 1801. The first British trademark is registered, for Bass Pale Ale, 1876. BBC launches The Archers, billed as "The daily events in the lives of country folk", 1951. Channel Four TV comes into official being, as a wholly-owned subsidiary of the Independent Broadcasting Association (IBA), 1981. Spain and Portugal join Common Market, 1986. Independent TV Commission and the Radio Authority replace IBA and Cable Authority as regulatory bodies, 1991; Broadcasting Standards Council assumes full statutory status.

2 Crowd barriers collapse at Glasgow's Ibrox Park football stadium, killing 66 people and injuring hundreds, 1971.

3 Three armed anarchists fight troops in the Siege of Sydney Street, in London's East End, 1911. The traitor William Joyce (Lord Haw Haw) is executed, 1946. The USA severs its diplomatic and consular relations with Fidel Castro's Cuba, 1961. Open University programmes begin on radio and TV, 1971.

4 American magazine Billboard publishes the first pop music chart based on national sales, 1936. Korean War: Chinese Communists capture Seoul, 1951.

5 German physicist Rontgen gives the first demonstration of X-rays, 1896. Ten Protestant workers shot dead when their works minibus is ambushed at a bogus road block at Kingsmills, South Armagh, 1976.

6 Harold II crowned King of England, 1066; killed at Battle of Hastings, 14 October, 1066. First widow's pensions are paid out at post offices, 1926. New Sadlers Wells Theatre opens, 1931. Start of ITV's long running current affairs programme This Week, 1956.

7 Television inventor John Logie Baird gives TV its first demonstration to the press, at 23 Frith Street in Soho, 1926; followed by the first-ever public demonstration, on 27 January. Launch of the ITV espionage fantasy series The Avengers, 1961 (ended 1969).

8 Britain occupies the former Dutch colony the Cape of Good Hope (Cape Town, South Africa), 1806. USA launches its biggest-ever offensive in the Vietnam War, 1966. ITV begins the first regular Sunday evening religious programmes, 1956.

9 First British X Certificate is awarded to a film, La Vie Commence Demain, 1951. Cabinet defence secretary Michael Heseltine resigns in bitter dispute with Downing Street over Mrs Thatcher's style of government, 1986; Leon Brittan resigns as trade and industry secretary on 24 January.

10 The Times publishes its first illustration, on the funeral of Lord Nelson, 1806.

11 Steamship London sinks in gale off France, killing 220 people, 1866. Radio Authority advertises the first Independent National Radio licence, 1991; it is awarded to Classic FM on 19 August.

12 Founding of the Royal Aeronautical Society, 1866. The Angry Brigade claims responsibility for bombing the home of Cabinet minister Robert Carr, 1971.

15 Death of Matthew Brady, American Civil War photographer and pioneer of photo journalism, 1896.

16 Former MP Bernadette McAliskey (nee Devlin) is shot and wounded by three loyalist gunmen, 1981. USA launches Western military onslaught - Operation Desert Storm, lasting until 28 February - on Iraq to retake invaded Kuwait, 1991.

19 Government announces closure of West India and Millwall Docks in London, 1976. A fire sweeps through a house in Deptford South London, killing 13 black people at a party, 1981. Robert Maxwell's sons Kevin and Ian are acquitted of mammoth pension fraud charges, 1996; the 131 day trial cost taxpayers over £25 million..

20 Hong Kong is occupied by the British, 1841. Death of King George V after 26 years on the throne, 1936. John F Kennedy becomes president of the USA, 1961. Postal workers go on strike for the first time ever, 1971. Britain and France agree to build today's Channel Tunnel, 1986.

21 Birth of the Liberal newspaper the Daily News, a parent of News Chronicle, with Charles Dickens as editor, 1846. Start of the first Monte Carlo car rally, 1911. Communist paper Daily Worker is suppressed by the government, 1941. Emley Moor, Britain's highest TV broadcasting tower, begins operation, 1971. Concorde makes its first commercial flight, London to Bahrain, 1976.

22 Death of Queen Victoria, after a 64-year reign, 1901.

24 World War One: Conscription introduced, 1916. Start of longest-running BBC radio programme The Week's Good Cause, 1926. The 270,000 ton tanker Olympic Bravery runs aground off France, being the world's largest shipwreck until then, 1976. News International suddenly moves the Sun, Times and Sunday Times from Fleet Street to a new print plant at Wapping, near Limehouse, 1986; print workers strike, but printing starts on 25 January; the Sun is relaunched on Monday 27th with the headline "A New Sun is Rising Today".

25 Limehouse Declaration by four former Labour cabinet ministers (the "Gang of Four"), including David Owen, leads to the formation of the Social Democratic Party, 1981.

27 Sunday opening of cinemas is declared illegal, 1931.

28 Death off Panama of Sir Francis Drake, first Englishman to sail round the world, 1596. First speeding fine is given to a British motorist, for driving at 8 mph, 1896. The space shuttle Challenger blows up after lift-off from Cape Canaveral, killing seven astronauts, 1986. TUC supports unions strike against News International moving to Wapping; the electrical union EETPU supplies the labour force, 1986.

29 Patenting of first successful petrol-driven car, by Karl Benz, 1886.

30 United Nations General Assembly meets for first time, London, 1946. Oral contraceptive pills go on sale in Britain, 1961. Joint US/UK naval force routs flotilla of Iraqi vessels off Kuwait, 1991.

31 Guy Fawkes, the man who tried to blow up the Houses of Parliament in 1605, is executed, 1606. All US "red indians" are ordered to move onto reservations or be declared hostile, 1876.

FEBRUARY

1 End of Crimean War, with defeat for Russia, 1856. Test flying begins at Heathrow, 1946. Licences for radios abolished, 1971.

2 Idi Amin declares himself the absolute ruler of Uganda, 1971. Government abolishes the radio-only annual licence, 1971.

3 A Soviet spacecraft makes the first controlled landing on the Moon, 1966.

4 The car makers Rolls Royce commission the famous figurehead The Spirit of Ecstasy, 1911. The firm goes bankrupt, same day, 1971.

5 Launch of Sunday Telegraph, the first new national Sunday paper for 43 years, 1961.

6 Britain's first police motorcycles equipped with radio telephones go on duty in London, 1951. Spurs captain Danny Blanchflower becomes first person to say "no" on air to the This is Your Life show, 1961. In the Northern Ireland Troubles, which began in 1969, the first British soldier is killed, 1971.

7 The Liberal party wins the general election and brings in legislation to start many of the 20th century's welfare services, 1906. On the same day, Labour wins its first significant number of MP seats (30). The hated Haiti dictator "Baby Doc" Duvalier flees an uprising, taking £100 million with him to France, 1986. The IRA fires a mortar bomb into the garden of 10 Downing Street while the Cabinet is meeting inside, 1991.

8 Big peaceful demonstration by unemployed people in Trafalgar Square is broken up by armed forces, 1886. BBC announces it is dropping its Children's Hour radio programme because of the increasing popularity of television, 1961. Freddie Laker forms his popular cutprice trans-Atlantic airline, 1966. In Angola, 14 British mercenaries are executed, 1976.

9 The Confederate States of America are formed in the run-up to the American Civil War that starts on 12 April in the same year, 1861.

10 Britain completes the conquest of India, with battle on this day at Sobraon in 1846. Britain's pioneer battleship Dreadnought is launched, 1906. High Court judge orders sequestration of the £17 million assets of trade union SOGAT '82 for defying court orders to stop blacking distribution of News International papers, 1986; but on 24 April Court of Appeal overturns decision and on 8 May Sogat retrieves its money after apologising. IRA ceasefire ends as huge bomb kills two people at Canary Wharf and severely damages several buildings, 1996.

12 First inter-club football match is held, at Sheffield, 1861.

13 Rupert Murdoch buys the Times and Sunday Times, 1981. During the Gulf War, American bombers kill hundreds in Baghdad bunker, 1991.

14 First-ever words are spoken over a telephone, by inventor Alexander Bell speaking to his assistant, in Boston, USA, 1876. IBM begins operating its computer, using 18,000 electronic valves, at Pennsylvania University, 1946. The Bank of England is nationalised, 1946. Fire inside a Dublin disco kills 49 young people, 1981.

15 Decimal currency replaces Britain's pounds/shillings/pence, 1971. Major oil pollution affects Pembroke coast following accident to 140,000 ton tanker Sea Express, 1996.

16 ITC advertises the 16 ITV channels (due to start on 1 January 1993), 1991. Trade unionists protesting against News International's move to its new plant at Wapping clash with police outside the building, 1986.

17 ATV starts the first commercial TV service for the Midlands, 1956, on weekdays; ABC Television begins the weekend service on 18th.

19 Another Cod War involving Britain and Iceland starts, 1976; it ends 1 June.

20 Ford admits four of its black assembly line workers were transformed into whites in a company advertising photo, 1996.

23 Military coup tries to restore the Spanish monarchy, 1981.

26 Hitler launches the longlife Volkswagen motorcar, 1936.

27 British defeated by Boers at Battle of Majuba, South Africa, 1881. The Gulf War comes to an end, 1991.

6,000 SACKED
NEWS
INTERNATIONAL
DISPUTE
SOGAT NGA AUEW UJ

nga

SOUTH
EAST

National Graphical Association

TUC

...DOCH IS BAD NEW...

THE TIM...

28 Oswald Mosley leaves Labour Party to launch the fascist New Party, 1931. Swedish prime minister Olaf Palme is assassinated, 1986.

MARCH

1 The wearing of car seat belts is made compulsory 1976. IRA prisoners in Northern Ireland begin seven-month hunger strike, 1981. Oracle Teletext starts, 1986. End of BBC/ITV monopoly of their programme details, 1991.

4 Start of Housewives' Choice, the record request programme for women at home, 1946; ended 1967. Eddie Shah's Today newspaper published for first time, the first national daily in Britain to carry colour pictures, 1986.

5 First flight takes place of prototype Spitfire fighter aircraft, 1936. Winston Churchill coins phrase "Iron Curtain", 1946. Government white paper on telecoms allows cable TV operators and telephone companies to diversify dramatically, 1991.

6 End of legendary Battle of the Alamo (Texans lose to Mexicans), 1836. Big women's liberation march is held, showing the spreading support for the movement, 1971.

7 Alexander Bell patents the first telephone capable of carrying sustained speech messages, 1876. The first cloned sheep have been produced, reveals Nature magazine, 1996.

8 British empire now covers a fifth of the Earth's land surface, says a government survey, 1906. East End gangster Ronnie Kray, one of the Kray twins, carries out a murder in a Whitechapel pub, 1966. Launch of Radio 210, ILR station for Reading area, 1976.

9 Accident at Bolton Wanderers football ground kills 33 people and injures 500 others in FA cup-tie, 1946. Harold Evans becomes editor of Times, 1981.

10 The first Cruft's Dog Show took place in London, 1886.

11 Birth in Australia of media mogul Rupert Murdoch, 1931. BBC World Service TV News service begins, 1991.

12 A former Scout leader shoots dead 16 children and a teacher at Dunblane Primary School, Scotland, in Britain's worst multiple murder in modern times, 1996.

13 The planet Uranus is discovered, 1781. Republic of Cyprus is formed, following the 1959 civil war, 1961. The Sun's front-page headline reveals "Freddie Starr Ate My Hamster", 1986.

14 First telephone cable laid across English Channel, 1891. New Liberal government approves starting old age pensions, 1906. Six men wrongly jailed for IRA bombing of a Birmingham pub in 1974 are freed, 1991.

16 Labour prime minister Harold Wilson announces his surprise resignation, 1976. House of Commons gives go-ahead for radio broadcasting of its proceedings, 1976. Launch of Downtown Radio, ILR station for Belfast area, 1976. Mike Tyson becomes WBC heavyweight champion, defeating UK's Frank Bruno, 1996.

17 The British are forced to evacuate Boston by George Washington, 1776. Britain's first birth control clinic, created by Marie Stopes, opens in north London, 1921.

18 The Communards start their uprising in Paris, eventually creating the world's first socialist government, 1871.

19 Married couple Princess Margaret and Earl of Snowdon announce separation plans, 1976.

21 Information on betting odds is broadcast before a horse race for first time, by BBC, 1961. British government announces end of its poll tax, after public opposition, 1991.

23 London's first tram cars begin operating, 1861. Pakistan is declared a republic, 1956. For the first time in 400 years, the heads of the Roman Catholic and Anglican churches meet officially, 1966.

24 Alistair Cooke's first Letter from America goes out on BBC radio, 1946. Argentina's president Isabel Peron is deposed in bloodless military coup, 1976.

25 European Commission imposers worldwide ban on British beef exports over fears of the "mad cow" disease BSE, 1996.

26 East Pakistan is declared the independent republic of Bangla Desh, starting nine months war, 1971.

27 Labour Party rejects the Communist Party's application for affiliation, 1946.

28 British novelist Virginia Woolf commits suicide, 1941.

29 Lancastrian forces defeat Yorkists, securing crown for Edward IV, 1461. Opening of Royal Albert Hall, 1871. Nazis win 99 per cent of the vote in German elections, 1936. Government announces Independent Television Authority will have responsibility for Independent Local Radio (ILR), 1971. Birth of first test-tube quintuplets, 1986.

30 President Ronald Reagan is shot and seriously wounded in Washington, 1981.

31 Coal miners launch a three-month national strike, unsuccessfully trying to stop the government giving the mines back into private hands after First World War state control, 1921. Labour wins general election, with bigger majority, 1966. Labour-controlled GLC (the world's largest local authority) comes to an end, 1986. Hampton Court Palace is severely damaged by fire, 1986. Trade unions are forced to agree Express Newspapers cutting its workforce by 2,500, just hours before a deadline which would have closed all its papers, 1986.

APRIL

1 All BBC commercial activities are brought together in a single organisation, BBC Enterprises, 1986. Sir Christopher Bland replaces Marmaduke Hussey as BBC chairman.

2 After a year's restructuring, British Telecom is relaunched as BT, 1991.

5 James Callaghan replaces Harold Wilson as Labour's prime minister following his sudden resignation on 16 March, 1976.

6 Opening of innovatory new railway up Snowdon mountain, with serious accident, 1896. First modern Olympic Games are held, in Athens, 1896. Germany invades Yugoslavia and Greece, with both countries surrendering 11 days later, 1941.

7 William (Billy) Butlin opens his first holiday camp, at Skegness, 1936.

9 Germany carries out a heavy air raid on Coventry, 1941. Soviet Union puts the first man into space, Major Yuri Gagarin, in a single satellite orbit, 1961. Bobby Sands is elected Sinn Fein MP for Fermanagh in by-election, 1981; he is on hunger strike in the Maze Prison, where he dies on 5 May, prompting widespread rioting in Northern Ireland.

12 Start of American Civil War, with Confederate forces bombarding Fort Sumter, South Carolina, 1861. Launch of Beacon Radio, ILR station for Wolverhampton and Black Country, 1976. Summer of inner-city rioting around UK begins in London's Brixton, 1981.

14 Ministry of Transport issues the first Highway Code, 1931. Spain is declared a republic following the abdication of King Alfonso III, 1931; he flees to Rome.

15 USA unsuccessfully carries out its "Bay of Pigs" military invasion of Cuba, 1961. USA attacks Libya, 1986. BBC World Service TV begins, 1991.

16 At the Battle of Culloden, the last real battle fought on British mainland soil, Bonnie Prince Charlie and the Highlanders are defeated by the English crown, 1746; the Highland clearances follow.

17 Prize-paying premium bonds are launched by the government, 1956.

18 Severe earthquake in San Francisco kills over 500 people, 1906.

19 First Miss World beauty contest is held, 1951. Vietnam Veterans Against the War stage week-long series of demonstrations in Washington, 1971.

21 Birth of Queen Elizabeth II, 1926. Launch of Sunday Business, 1996.

22 A revolt is staged by right-wing generals in Algeria, who threaten to invade France, but it is crushed in four days, 1961.

24 Five-day Easter Rising takes place in Dublin, with nationalists unsuccessfully challenging Britain's control of Ireland, 1916; about 450 people die in the city following assault by 5,000 British troops. Bradford lorry driver Peter Sutcliffe admits he is the "Yorkshire Ripper" who murdered 13 women, 1981.

25 Founding of the Newspaper Society, by 18 provincial paper owners, aimed at opposing legislation, 1836.

26 World's worst-ever nuclear accident takes place when a fire at Chernobyl nuclear power station in the Ukraine contaminates much of Europe with radioactive fall-out, 1986.

28 In Tasmania, 34 tourists at a visitors' centre are shot dead by local man, 1996.

29 Westward Television launches TV service for south-west England, 1961.

30 The hovercraft begins its first regular service across English Channel, 1966.

MAY

I Opening of the Great Exhibition, 1851. Opening of New York's Empire State Building, then the world's tallest structure, 1931. Fidel Castro proclaims Cuba a socialist nation, 1961. Betting shops legalised, 1961.

3 The nine-day General Strike begins, the most significant industrial dispute in British history, 1926; the Times is the only national newspaper to continue appearing; BBC broadcasts five radio news bulletins daily. Granada TV launches the weekday service for north of England, 1956; ABC Television starts the north's weekend service on 5 May.

4 Launch of Alfred Harmsworth's Daily Mail, immediately becoming the first of today's popular tabloids, 1896. The Festival of Britain opens on London's South Bank, 1951. News appears on the front page of the Times for the first time, 1966.

5 Birth of the Liberal newspaper Manchester Guardian (now The Guardian), 1821; lead article says "We are enemies of scurrility and slander". Italy takes over Ethiopia after militarily defeating native people following October 1935 invasion, 1936.

6 The Moors murderers Myra Hindley and Ian Brady are jailed for life for killing two children and a teenager, 1966.

7 German troops reoccupy Rhineland area, lost by them after the First World War, 1936.

9 The Horseless Carriage Show opens its doors to the motor trade for the first time, 1896. The German terrorist Ulrike Meinhof, a founder of Baader Meinhof, is found dead in her prison cell, 1976.

10 The House of Commons is destroyed by Germany's most devastating bombing raid on London in the whole of World War Two, 1941. Jeremy Thorpe MP, quits as leader of the Liberals, 1976.

12 Fifteen leaders of Ireland's Easter Rising are executed by the British, becoming the martyrs of the Irish War of Independence that soon begins, 1916. Frightened TUC leadership calls off General Strike, Britain's biggest ever industrial conflict, despite the possible success by trade unionists, 1926.

13 John Osborne's pioneering and highly controversial play Look Back in Anger opens at London's Royal Court theatre, 1956. Pope John Paul II shot and wounded in Vatican City, 1981.

16 British government unveils its plans for India's independence, 1946. Britain's seamen go on strike, 1966; government declares State of Emergency 23 May; strike ends 1 July.

18 BBC acquires its first female radio announcers, 1936.

20 USA explodes its first hydrogen bomb on the Pacific's Bikini atoll, 1956.

21 For the first time, clocks are put forward an hour to save more daylight, 1916.

23 The pirate Captain Kidd is hanged at London's Execution Docks, 1701.

24 In the Battle of the Atlantic, the leading German warship Bismarck sinks Royal Navy's pride HMS Hood, 1941; in retaliation, Bismarck is sunk on 27 May. First Eurovision Song Contest is held, in Switzerland, 1956.

25 Parliament passes Bank Holiday Act, creating the national annual holidays, 1871. Diplomats Donald Maclean and Guy Burgess disappear and are revealed as major Soviet spies, 1951. Bob Geldof's "Race Against Time" has 30 million people running in Sport Aid for the starving population of Africa, 1986.

26 News International makes £50 million offer to trade unions to end the 18-week dispute over moving to Wapping, 1986; but this is refused on 6 June.

27 Start of Southampton-New York maiden voyage of liner Queen Mary, 1936.

28 BBC radio broadcasts the first Goon Show, 1951.

29 BBC broadcasts the first TV interview with a member of the Royal Family (Duke of Edinburgh), 1961.

31 Launch of the Titanic, in Belfast, 1911; sinks on maiden voyage next year. First World War: Britain defeats Germany at the nautical Battle of Jutland, 1916. South Africa becomes a republic, withdrawing from the Commonwealth, 1961.

JUNE

1 First electric trolley buses begin running, in Leeds and Bradford, 1911. World's first scheduled experimental colour television service begins (by CBS, in New York), 1941. British television licences issued for the first time, costing £2, including radio service, 1946; estimated 7,500 sets. End of third Cod War between Britain and Iceland, 1976. Broadcasting Complaints Commission begins, 1981.

2 Broadcasting is born in the UK when Guglielmo Marconi patents his wireless system using electromagnetic waves, 1896; it is first publicly demonstrated on 27 July that year, with a transmission from GPO's London head-quarters. First live television pictures from the Moon, 1966.

3 Television pictures of the Derby race are transmitted (30--line) for the first time, 1931. First bikini bathing suit is unveiled in Paris, 1946. British Railways abolishes its Third Class seating, 1956.

4 Summer of serious rioting in Belfast begins with loss of life, 1886.

5 World War One: Warship HMS Hampshire, with Lord Kitchener aboard, sinks after striking a mine, 1916.

6 Launch of Cunard liner Lusitania, then world's largest passenger vessel, 1906. First publication of John Bull, a prominent news weekly magazine for many years, 1906. Gatwick Airport opens, 1936. Sitcom Till Death Us Do Part first televised by the BBC, 1966.

7 BBC re-opens its television service (closed since 1 September 1939), within range of about 40 miles from Alexandra Palace, 1946. Britain's national economic crisis forces the Labour government to borrow £3 billion from abroad and adopt right-wing policies ordered by International Monetary Fund, 1976. Israeli bombers attack and destroy an Iraqi nuclear reactor, 1981. Major reorganisation of BBC's internal bureaucracy announced, 1996.

8 First post-war outside television broadcast shows victory parade through London, 1946.

9 In The Garden: Freddy Streeter begins his weekly TV visit to the BBC gardens in the grounds of Ally Pally, 1946.

12 Derek Hatton, deputy leader of Liverpool Council, is expelled from Labour Party for membership of Militant Tendency, 1986.

13 Wat Tyler leads the Peasants' Revolt, the first popular rebellion in English history, 1381; he is beheaded two days later. Football's first European Cup is won by Real Madrid, 1956.

14 Death of John Logie Baird, the inventor of television, 1946.

15 USA and Canada agree the 49th parallel is the border between them, 1846. House of Lords votes in favour of televising itself, excluding Commons, 1966; but full coverage does not begin until January 1985. Massive IRA bomb devastates much of Manchester city centre, 1996.

16 Death of BBC's first director-general, Lord Reith, 1971; aged 81. At least 176 people killed in South Africa's worst-ever rioting, which starts today in Soweto near Johannesburg, 1976.

17 Breakfast-time television will start in May 1983, announces the IBA, 1981.

20 In India, 123 people die in the Black Hole of Calcutta, 1756. A former Kenyan man becomes Britain's first black police officer, 1966.

21 Foundation stone of Tower Bridge laid by Prince of Wales, 1886. Police seize the cartoon magazine Nasty Tales, 1971.

22 Coronation of King George V, 1911. Hitler launches his "Operation Barbarossa" invasion of Soviet Union, 1941.

23 Start of trial of three leading creators of Oz magazine, over alleged obscenity of its Schoolkids issue, 1971; they are found guilty and jailed, then bailed.

24 English Civil War: Royalists surrender to Parliamentarians, at Oxford, 1646. Britain agrees terms to join the Common Market 1971.

25 Sioux indians kill all 264 soldiers of the US 7th Cavalry, at "Custer's Last Stand", Little Big Horn, 1876. The world's first regular commercial colour TV service begins (by CBS in New York), 1951. Croatia and Slovenia declare independence from USSR, 1991.

26 First Grand Prix motor race takes place at Le Mans, 1906. Irish investigative journalist Veronica Guerin is assassinated in revenge killing while waiting at traffic lights in Dublin, 1996.

29 Britain carries out its first official census, 1801. Trade unions are legalised by an Act of Parliament, 1871. Hampstead Heath in north London is purchased by Metropolitan Board of Works, 1871. First British credit card (the Barclaycard) is introduced, 1966.

30 The Queen, riding her horse during the Trooping of the Colour, has blank shots fired at her by a protester against unemployment, 1981.

JULY

1 Start of Battle of the Somme, an unsuccessful British/French attack, leaving over 420,000 men dead when it ends on 13 November, 1916. World's first TV commercial (for a Bulova watch) is shown on NBC's WNBT station in New York, 1941. Home Secretary announces he has authorised purchase of 24 bullet-proof vehicles and 80 personnel carriers for police use in dealing with future rioting in London, 1986.

2 Author Ernest Hemingway commits suicide, 1961.

3 Launch of magazine Tatler, 1901. Israeli commandos rescue 103 hostages held on an airplane by Palestinian hijackers in Entebbe Airport, Uganda, 1976. Government Report of the Committee on Financing the BBC recommends a radical reorganisation of British television, sparking many of the major changes in coming years, 1986.

4 American Congress votes for independence from Britain, 1776. Philippine islands are given their independence from USA, 1946. Britain's worst week of rioting in living memory begins in Toxteth, Merseyside, 1981; a number of copy-cat riots follow.

6 First broadcast on TV of Hancock's Half Hour (on radio it began 2 November 1954), 1956; Tony Hancock committed suicide 1968.

7 Start of BBC's first children's TV programme For the Children, 1946.

9 Second World War comes to an official end nearly 12 years after its 1939 start, 1951.

10 A week of serious rioting culminates in "Britain's night of anarchy" in many inner-city areas, 1981.

11 British newspapers are banned from printing extracts from Peter Wright's book Spycatcher, about Soviet penetration of the security service, 1986.

14 Home Secretary authorises a further 25 new locations for ILR stations (bringing total up to 69), 1981.

17 The first edition of Punch magazine is published, 1841. This day in 1936 is the start of the three-year Spanish Civil War, when the right-wing military attacked the Republican government elected in 1931; Germany and Italy supported the fascists, the Soviet Union then organised the International Brigades and anarchists created their own volunteer bodies.

20 Football Association proposes start of FA Challenge Cup competition, 1871. Second World War: The "V for Victory" campaign is launched in Britain, 1941. The government tries to halt the rapid rise in inflation by freezing all pay and dividends, 1966. US spacecraft lands on Mars and sends back pictures, 1976.

21 British ambassador to Dublin, Sir Christopher Ewart-Biggs, is killed by an IRA bomb under his car, 1976. Setting up of new joint BBC/ITV system of audience research BARB 1981.

23 Dog licences are being abolished, announces government, 1986. Prince Andrew marries Sarah Ferguson, 1986.

25 USA starts using Bikini Atoll island in the Pacific for its nuclear bombs tests, 1946.

26 Birth of Irish playwright George Bernard Shaw, 1856. Launch of London paper Evening News, 1881; first printed on light blue paper. Egypt seizes control of Anglo-French Suez Canal, 1956. The Channel Islands become the last ITV area to receive colour 625-line UHF transmissions, 1976.

27 Jim Laker becomes first cricketer to take all ten wickets in a test innings, against Australia, 1956. Launch of NorthSound Radio, ILR station for Aberdeen area, 1981. A second bridge will be built over River Severn, announces government, 1986.

28 Potatoes arrive in Britain for first time, from Columbia, 1586. Government publishes its Marine Broadcasting (Offences) Bill that will make popular pirate radio illegal, 1966.

29 Prince Charles marries Lady Diana Spencer in St Paul's Cathedral, 1981.

30 Britain wins football World Cup for first time, defeating West Germany 4-2, 1966.

31 BBC Lime Grove studios close, 1991.

AUGUST

1 BBC Royal Charter expiring at the end of 1996 comes into force, 1981.

3 Irish nationalist and British diplomat Sir Roger Casement is hanged for high treason, at Pentonville Prison, 1916. First British traffic lights are installed at Piccadilly Circus, 1926. US comedian Lenny Bruce dies from drugs, 1966.

6 An American woman becomes the first female to swim English Channel, 1926.

7 First British motoring Grand Prix is run, at Brooklands, 1926.

8 Women launch a major, well-supported campaign to bring peace to Northern Ireland after three children are killed, 1976.

9 Internment without trial is introduced in Northern Ireland, sparking violent reaction by its Republican opponents, 1971.

10 Britain applies to join EEC, 1961. Launch of first US moon satellite Orbiter One, 1966.

11 Westward Television goes off the air after losing its ITV licence, 1981.

12 Three plain-clothes London policemen shot dead in street near Wormwood Scrubs, 1966.

13 Fierce rioting in Liverpool, 1911; part of the widespread and militant industrial unrest this year, aimed at creating a socialist society. Death of author HG Wells, 1946. East Germany closes frontier between East and West Berlin, and soon erects the Berlin Wall, 1961.

14 Death of US newspaper giant Randolph Hearst, 1951.

17 A Croydon woman becomes the first pedestrian to be killed by a car, 1896. The discovery of gold at Bonanza Creek in Canada's Yukon Territory leads to 1898 gold rush, 1896.

18 Australia and New Zealand withdraw their armed forces from the South Vietnam War, 1971.

19 France and Spain form alliance against Britain, 1796. Thousands die in India during rioting between Hindus and Moslems over Britain's plans for the country's independence, 1946. The Soviet premier Mikhail Gorbachev is arrested while on holiday in Crimea in unsuccessful coup attempt, 1991; in following months the USSR disintegrates.

24 Labour government falls because of severe economic crisis hitting Britain, 1931; Ramsay MacDonald forms coalition National Government to replace it.

25 British and Russian forces invade Iran, 1941.

26 England defeats France at Battle of Crecy, 1346. BBC experimentally transmits its first high-definition television pictures, from Alexandra Palace to the Radio Show at Olympia, 1936; its first announcer is Leslie Mitchell.

27 Francis Chichester sets off from Plymouth, to become the first old-age pensioner to sail around the world alone, 1966.

28 King Edward of England takes control of Scotland (temporarily) when 2,000 Scottish leaders submit, at Berwick, 1296.

29 The first electrical transformer is demonstrated, by Michael Faraday, at London's Royal Institute, 1831. Beatles play their last live concert, in San Francisco, 1966.

30 Germans lay siege to Leningrad, 1941. Traffic wardens are born, 1956.

31 Elizabeth Cowell becomes the first female announcer on television (BBC), 1936. One of Britain's worst ever (but most popular) sun-baked summer droughts is interrupted by the first showers, 1976.

SEPTEMBER

1 London's Cannon Street railway station opens, 1866. Twenty five councillors from Poplar are jailed for refusing to levy rates, 1921. Britain's first supermarket opens, in Earls Court, London, 1951. Borders Television launches the commercial television service for the England/Scotland border, 1961. Launch of Aire Radio, ILR station for Leeds area, 1981.

2 Great Fire of London starts in a bakery in Pudding Lane, lasting four days, 1666.

3 English Civil War: Battle of Worcester, 1651. Two British servicemen row across the Atlantic, 1966.

4 Surrender of Geronimo, the Chiricahua Apache leader of the last American Indian resistance, 1886.

5 Following the Parliamentary victory in the English Civil War, the offices of Archbishop of Canterbury and other bishops are abolished, 1646. World's first high-definition (240-line) TV outside broadcast made in Britain, from Alexandra Palace, 1936.

6 TUC condemns the widespread use of troops to quash widespread industrial unrest this summer, 1911. South African prime minister Hendrik Verwoerd assassinated by a white extremist, 1966. Launch of top BBC1 series Casualty, 1986.

8 Final length of the first trans-Atlantic telegraph cable is laid, 1866. Giant Japanese car makers Nissan open their new plant at Sunderland, 1986.

9 Start of the first BBC television documentary series Picture Post, 1936. Launch of Rediffusion's Starview pioneering cable TV service, in five towns, 1981; this is the first subscriber television service in Britain. Launch of Big Issue, the street-sold magazine for the homeless, 1991.

11 Installation of first TV set in a house, at Green Gables, Harrow, 1926.

12 Nobel prize winner Bertrand Russell is jailed for his active role in the Campaign for Nuclear Disarmament, 1961. Launch of Essex Radio, ILR station for Southend and Chelmsford area, 1981.

13 The Gold Coast will be Britain's first black colony in Africa to get independence, announces the government, 1956.

27 AUGUST 1966: PENSIONER PIONEER
Francis Chichester sails from Plymouth, becoming the first pensioner to sail alone round the world

14 Launch of Sunday Sport, by David Sullivan's Sport Newspapers, 1986.

15 Tanks go into action for the first time for British Army, in the Somme, 1916. Royal Navy "mutiny" at lnvergordon, 1931. The BBC produces the first televised church service, in St George's Chapel on Battle of Britain Sunday, 1946. Royal Navy's first nuclear submarine is launched, at Barrow, 1966.

17 A fleet of a hundred fishing boats sails up the Thames in protest at Britain joining the EEC, 1971.

18 First publication of New York Times, 1851. About 800 people are arrested in Britain's biggest ban-the-bomb CND demonstration so far, 1961. Dag Hammarskjold, head of UN, is killed in a mysterious air crash, 1961. France abolishes guillotine, 1981.

19 England defeats France at Battle of Poitiers, 1356.

20 Britain comes off gold standard, causing much industrial unrest, 1931. An Argentinian man becomes first person to swim non-stop across the English Channel and back again, 1961.

21 First television gardening programme begins on BBC, with CH Middleton, 1936. Ninety Russian diplomats are expelled from Britain for spying, 1971.

23 The planet Neptune is discovered, 1846.

29 The Third Programme begins on BBC radio, joining Home Service and Light Programme, 1946.

30 Opening of Hollywood-rival Pinewood Studios, near Iver in Buckinghamshire, 1936. Grampian TV launches a commercial TV service for north-east Scotland, 1961. Times is bought by Lord Thomson, already owner of the Sunday Times, 1966. Bechuanaland becomes independent nation of Botswana, 1966.

OCTOBER

1 General Franco takes over as head of Nationalist Government in Spain, 1936. First televising by the BBC of the Songs of Praise, 1961. First Disney World opens in Florida, 1971. Launch of Northants Radio, ILR station for Northampton area, 1986. Marmaduke Hussey named as new chairman of BBC by government, 1986.

2 First Royal Navy submarine launched. at Barrow, 1901. BBC shows Points of View for first time, 1961.

3 IRA hunger strike that began on 1 March ends after ten deaths, 1981.

4 Earls Court Underground station switches on Britain's first escalator, 1911.

6 President Sadat of Egypt assassinated in Cairo by Muslim extremists, 1981.

7 BBC radio launches Woman's Hour (theme tune: Oranges and Lemons) and Dick Barton, Special Agent, 1946. Launch of first satellite dish aerial for domestic use in Britain, at demonstration in a shop's roof garden in Kensington, 1981. First issue of Independent newspaper, 1986.

10 Anti-European rioting in Kowloon, the mainland area of Hong Kong, results in 51 people being killed, 1956.

11 British anti-Fascist demonstrations reach a climax, with 100,000 people trying to stop Sir Oswald Mosley marching through London's East End, 1936.

12 Opening of Holme Moss transmitter, bringing TV to the north of England, 1951. Launch of Ocean Sound, ILR station for Southampton/Portsmouth area, 1986.

14 Victory at Battle of Hastings allows the Normans to take over England, 1066. Launch of the underground magazine IT, 1966. BBC World Service TV launches Asian Service, which later becomes first BBC 24-hour TV channel, 1991.

15 Nazi war criminal Herman Goering commits suicide in Nuremberg Prison, 1946. First British party-political broadcast televised by the BBC (for the Liberals), 1951. Launch of Chiltern Radio, ILR station for Luton/Bedford area, 1976. Start of BBC World Service's news and information channel, 1991.

16 A medical anaesthetic is used successfully for the first time, Massachussets Hospital, 1846. First issue of Sunday paper the People, 1881. World's first birth control clinic opens, in New York, 1916. Express owner Lord Beaverbrook arranges with King Edward VIII there will be press silence about his Mrs Simpson affair, 1936. ITC awards the 1993 ten-year ITV licences, 1991; four existing licensees are losers.

17 The Queen opens Britain's first nuclear power electricity-generating station, at Calder Hall, Cumbria, 1956.

18 A pardon is granted to Timothy Evans, who was hanged in 1950 for the apparent, but unproved, murder at 10 Rillington Place, London, 1966.

19 Launch of SIBC, the ILR station for Shetland Islands, 1991.

20 Start of the Audit Bureau of Circulations (ABC), 1931. Launch by the BBC of kiddies television programme Muffin the Mule (with friend Oswald the Ostrich), 1946.

21 A coal tip engulfs a school in the Welsh village of Aberfan, killing 116 children and 28 adults, 1966. Two Tory MPs successfully sue the BBC over Panorama allegations that they had close links with right-wing groups, 1986.

22 Tit Bits magazine launched, 1881. George Blake, Soviet spy, escapes from UK prison and goes to East Berlin, 1966.

23 Start of the Hungarian revolt against Soviet control of the country, 1956; the USSR army invades on 4 November, crushing the liberation movement.

24 Eleven militant suffragettes are jailed after holding a demonstration at the House of Commons, 1906.

25 Last horsebus service in London, 1911. Post-war Labour government loses general election to Tories, with Winston Churchill becoming prime minister for first time, 1951. Launch of Private Eye magazine, 1961. New National Theatre on London's South Bank is opened by Queen, 1976.

26 Jeffrey Archer resigns as chairman of the Tory Party after then-unproved allegations of prostitute payment, 1986; he tries to become first mayor of London in May 2000, but further scandal forces him to withdraw.

27 First publication of the short-lived but influential radical news magazine Seven Days, 1971. Launch of Radio West (later GWR), the ILR station for the Bristol area, 1981. The Stock Exchange's "Big Bang" deregulation day creates a new computer-based dealing system, 1986. The BBC's Daytime Television service launches, 1986.

28 The Statue of Liberty is presented to the USA by France, 1886. The House of Commons votes in favour of the UK's entry into the EEC, 1971; the UK officially joins on 1 January 1973.

29 The new coalition National Government is re-elected at a general election, 1931.

31 Anglo-French forces invade Egypt to take control of the Suez Canal, 1956; a ceasefire begins on 7 November after USA condemns Britain's misguided action. An IRA bomb explodes at top of London's Post Office Tower, 1971; its popular tower-top restaurant then closes permanently

NOVEMBER

2 The world's first public high-definition television service begins, with BBC TV formally launched at 3pm from Alexandra Palace, on a hilltop in North London, using 405-line service, 1936 (the first transmission was on 26 August 1936); there were only 400 receiving sets in these early days.

5 First play goes out on BBC television: Marigold, a Scottish comedy by Harker and Pryor, 1936. Three London boroughs ordered by High Court to stop banning News International newspapers from their public libraries, 1986. Media magnate Robert Maxwell, owner of Mirror newspapers, is mysteriously found dead in the sea near Tenerife, 1991.

10 American scientists discover the secrets of the atomic nucleus, 1931. Death of 85-year old Marjorie Proops, the original newspaper agony aunt, 1996.

II The Jarrow Crusade of 200 unemployed workers marching from the Tyneside to London ends with prime minister Stanley Baldwin refusing to meet them, 1936; but many more jobs are soon created in the run-up to World War Two, which seems inevitable from 1937. Stevenage is designated the first new town in Britain, 1946. A special leaflet on the new Aids sickness will be distributed to 23 million homes, decides the government, 1986.

I3 Opening of the first underwater telegraph cable, from Dover to Calais, 1851. The Scottish explorer Dr David Livingstone is found alive in the central African jungle after going missing four years earlier, 1871. A television viewer undertaking a stunt for Noel Edmonds's Late Late Breakfast Show is killed during the rehearsals, 1986; the BBC cancels the show.

I4 The 4 mph speed limit for horseless carriages (aka cars) is lifted, 1896. An international agreement cuts the number of BBC radio wavelengths, forcing it to turn its local broadcasting into regional, 1926.

I5 The NBC (National Broadcasting Corporation) is inaugurated in USA, 1926.

I6 BBC1 televises Cathy Come Home, the landmark semi-documentary on homelessness, by Jeremy Sandford, 1966.

I9 Coal miners end their unsuccessful six month strike that had started the General Strike, 1926.

20 Rolls Royce car company formed by Charles Stewart Rolls and Frederick Henry Royce, 1906. Rolls Royce buys Bentley Motors, 1931.

24 The pop star Freddie Mercury, lead singer with Queen, dies of Aids, 1991.

29 Initial publication of Britain's first-ever weekly newspaper/magazine, called The Heads of Severall Proceedings in this Present Parliament, London, 1641

30 Crystal Palace, built 1851, is destroyed by fire, 1936; almost all John Logie Baird's pioneering TV equipment is lost there. First broadcast use of a video tape recorder, in Los Angeles, 1956.

DECEMBER

I Opening of world's first purpose-built picture palace, Cinema Omnia Pathe, in Paris, 1906.

2 Fidel Castro and a small group of revolutionaries land in Cuba, beginning three-year Cuban Revolution, 1956.

4 Britain's oldest Sunday newspaper, the Observer, is launched, 1791. Birth control pill becomes available on NHS, 1961. Fifteen people killed in Ulster Volunteer Force bomb attack on McGurk's Bar in north Belfast, 1971.

5 Britain's first woman judge is appointed, in Burnley, 1956.

6 Historic treaty creating the Irish Free State is signed, 1921, ending the War of Independence, but creating the 1921-22 Irish Civil War.

8 Britain and USA declare war on Japan the day after it attacks Pearl Harbour, 1941.

9 A cookery demonstration is televised for the first time, by BBC, 1936. British colony Tanganyika becomes independent Tanzania, 1961.

IO Britain's new king, Edward VIII, abdicates because of his love affair with American divorcee Wallis Simpson, 1936; he is succeeded by George VI.

II USA declares war on Germany and Italy, 1941. New rules mean television can be broadcast between 6pm and 7pm, 1956. British Satellite Broadcasting (BSB) is awarded the government's first contract for a British satellite TV service, 1986. Controversial Treaty of Maastricht emerges in EEC long-term integration planning, 1991.

12 An explosion in Oaks Colliery, near Barnsley, kills 340 men, 1866. Guglielmo Marconi gives the first large-scale public demonstration of radio, at London's Toynbee Hall, 1896; he makes the first transatlantic radio transmission, from Cornwall to Newfoundland, this same day in 1901.

14 Norwegian explorer Roald Amundsen leads first team to reach South Pole, 35 days ahead of Britain's Captain Scott, 1911; Amundsen survives, Scott does not.

16 The first football transfer deal takes place: Freddie Starr, Mansfield to Port Vale, 1951.

17 Cease-fire ends the successful struggle to set up independent Bangla Desh, following India's support over recent days in the India-Pakistan War, 1971. First ITV transmission to the Shetlands, 1977.

18 World War One: End of the ten-month Battle of Verdun, with a million casualties following Germany's unsuccessful attack on part of France, 1916. Nationalisation plans for the ports, railways and road haulage are agreed by MPs, 1946.

20 The eight crew of the Penlee lifeboat are killed while carrying out a ship rescue off Lands End, 1981.

21 First operation under general anaesthetic, when a man has a leg removed, using ether, 1846.

24 Radio telephone broadcasting is first demonstrated, from Brant Rock in Massachusetts to ships within an approx five-mile range, 1906.

25 William the Conqueror is crowned King of England, 1066. First Welsh eisteddford takes place, in Cardigan Castle, 1176. The Centigrade temperature scale is invented, by Anders Celsius, in Sweden, 1741. An American vessel is winner of first transatlantic yacht race, 1866. Hong Kong surrenders to Japanese, 1941.

2 NOVEMBER 1936: LIFT-OFF FOR THE BBC
The world's first public television service starts from Alexandra Palace, north London

29 Launch of the long-running BBC radio series Down Your Way, 1946.

30 Murder of Russian "Mad Monk" Gregory Rasputin, 1916.

31 The British Broadcasting Company Ltd (formed 18 October 1922) is dissolved, 1926; it becomes the BBC by Royal Charter tomorrow. Southern Television and ATV go off the air after losing their ITV licences, 1981.

UK facts and figures

The main source of basic UK data is National Statistics (NS), which collects, compiles and makes public all of Whitehall's statistical information. NS was launched in June 2000 as a revamp and renaming of much of the Office for National Statistics (ONS). The ONS was itself created in 1996 by merging the Central Statistical Office and the Office of Population Censuses and Surveys. NS makes data available in print and online. Its most comprehensive publication is the Annual Abstract of Statistics, containing tables on most aspects of UK life. A condensed version is Key Data. Handiest of all is the detailed leaflet UK in Figures (free), crammed full of the main statistics. None of these publications are analytical; for this, look at annuals such as Social Trends and the General Household Survey, helping paint pictures of UK life. Most readable is the annual hardback Britain: An Official Handbook. All are published by the Stationery Office (formerly HMSO) and should be in local reference libraries. ONS went online late, in July 1998, and NS is now making as much material available as quickly as possible. At the heart of NS - "the official UK statistics site" - is StatBase, a database and access point for items stored elsewhere. NS is based in London's Pimlico, near Vauxhall Bridge. It has its own shop, and a library, where all the official titles can be consulted; phone first. There is a second library in Newport. Below, most of these statistics come from NS sources.

National Statistics
1 Drummond Gate, London SW1V 2QQ.
Press 020-7533 5714   Enquiries 020-7533 5888
www.statistics.gov.uk

ENVIRONMENT

LAND AREAS	1,000 ACRES	SQ MILES
United Kingdom	60,319	94,248
England	32,225	50,351
Wales	5,129	8,015
Scotland	19,469	30,420
N Ireland	3,493	5,467

Features
UK's longest river: Severn, 220 miles.
Highest mountain: Ben Nevis, 4,406 feet.
Most northerly mainland point: Dunnet Head;
Most southerly: Lizard Point, Cornwall;
Most easterly: Lowestoft Ness, Suffolk;
Most westerly: Point of Ardnamurchan.
Total agricultural land: 18.6 million hectares.
The UK has 10,500 miles of coastline and
Nobody lives more than 75 miles from the sea.

POPULATIONS

World
The population reached 6 billion in 1999, and will reach at least 9 billion by 2050. It's doubled since 1960 and increased sevenfold since 1750. Almost half the population is under 25.

UK POPULATION		MALE	FEMALE
Total	59,237m	29.128m	30,108m
England	49,495m	24,378m	25,117m
Wales	2,933m	1,439m	1,495m
Scotland	5,120m	2,484m	2,636m
N Ireland	1,689m	827m	861m

The UK's population is the world's 18th largest. is expected to reach 63m in 2021, peak in 2036, and then fall. The population was 38.2m in 1801.

AGES	
Under 20	14,960m
20-64	34,770m
65-74	5,006m
75 plus	4,263m
Percentage under 16	20.5m
Percentage from 16 to retirement	61.4m
Percentage over retirement (60/65+)	18.1m

The UK is ageing: the number aged 65 and over increased by 25 per cent between 1971 and 1997, from 7.4 m to 9.3 m. The average mean age is expected to rise from 38.6 years in 1998 to 41.9 years in 2021 when the population should rise 3.3 m to 63.6 m with 856,000 fewer under 18 and 1.48 m more pensioners.

BRITISH ETHNIC MINORITIES

Total	3,702
Black (Caribbean)	485
Black (other)	665
Indian	942
Pakistani	591
Bangladeshi	257

HOUSEHOLDS

Ownership

Sixty seven per cent of the UK's 24.8 million dwellings are owner-occupied.

Just over 17 per cent are rented from local authorities and new towns, five per cent from registered social landlords, and 10 per cent from private landlords.

Sizes

British households are getting smaller: the average size has almost halved since the beginning of century, from 4.6 down to 2.4 people per household in 1998.

In 1901 five per cent of households in GB comprised one person, 11 per cent in 1961 and 29 per cent in 1999.

Just over one in ten people live alone, while nearly seven in ten live in a household headed by a couple.

MARRIED LIFE

Marriages

The number of marriages in England and Wales fell by 20 per cent between 1986 and 1997: down from 347,924 to 278,975.

The proportion of all non-married women aged 18 to 49 who were cohabiting in GB more than doubled between 1979 and 1999, from 11 per cent to 29 per cent.

The number of one-parent families is up from 750,000 in 1976 to 1.6 m in 1996. The number of children in one-parent families increased from 1.3 m to 2.8 m between 1976 and 1996.

Twenty four per cent of marriages entered into by teenage women ended in separation for 1985-9 marriages, compared with 11 per cent for 1965-9.

Divorce

The divorce rate fell to 12.9 per 1,000 married men and 12.8 per 1,000 married women in 1998, the lowest rate since 1990. In 1998 more divorces were granted on the grounds of separation than adultery; in 1991 it was the other way round. The average age at divorce continues to rise; in 1998 in England and Wales it was 40.4 years for men and 37.9 for women, compared with 39.7 and 37.2 respectively in 1997.

FROM BIRTH TO DEATH

BIRTHS (THOUSANDS)	1998	1900
United Kingdom	717	1,095
Male	366	558
Female	351	537
England and Wales	636	932
Scotland	57	132
N Ireland	24	--

Provisional figures indicate the number of births in 1999 will be down two per cent on 1998.

The average woman gave birth to 1.72 children in 1998.

Mothers giving birth are now, on average, nearly three years older than in the early 1970s. In 1999 the mean age was 29.0 years.

Childlessness is increasing, from one in 10 for women born in 1940 to one in five for those born in 1960.

The number of births outside marriage is increasing, from one in 10 in the 1970s, to four in 10 today.

The most popular names given to babies in 1999 were Jack and Chloe, as in the previous three years. Second were Thomas and Emily. The most common full names were David Jones (shared by 15,763) and Margaret Smith (7,640).

Deaths

There were 629,172 deaths in the UK in 1998.

The death rate is 10.3 per thousand population for men, 10.9 for women.

In 1900, during pregnancy and childbirth there were 4.71 maternal deaths per thousand live births; in 1998 it was 0.07 per thousand.

Male life expectancy at birth is 74.6 years, an increase of exactly five years in two decades; female life expectancy is 79.6 years, up 3.8.

Parliaments and politics

SCOTLAND

A Scottish referendum in September 1997 produced a clear majority in favour of establishing a Scottish Parliament. The Scotland Act received royal assent in November 1998, the first election was held on 6 May 1999 (as in Wales). Labour and the Liberal Democrats signed a coalition deal, neutralising the Scottish National Party. The four-year Parliament was officially opened by the Queen on 1 July. The summer recess began the next day, and in effect the new Scottish Parliament of 129 MSPs, plus mini-government, did not start work until it returned at the end of August. It has legislative control over roughly the same functions as those formerly run by the Scottish Office. Westminster retains power over the key issues of fiscal policy, foreign affairs, Europe, defence, energy, employment and social security. The May 1999 elections in Scotland and Wales were the first in Britain to be held under a system of proportional representation. Scotland's equivalent of the UK prime minister is the First Minister, Donald Dewar. Parliament is temporarily in buildings around The Mound in Edinburgh. Its expensive permanent home is being built at Holyrood at the other end of the Royal Mile. The Tories won the Labour seat of Ayr in a by-election in March 2000.

1999 SCOTTISH PARLIAMENT ELECTION

Labour	56
Scottish National Party	35
Conservative	18
Liberal Democrat	17
Green Party	1
Socialist Party	1
Individual	1

Contacts

Parliament HQ, George IV Bridge	0131-348 5000
	www.scottish.parliament.uk
General Enquiries	0845-278 1999
Media Relations	0131-348 5389
Cabinet secretariat	0131-244 5532
Scottish Executive , all departments	0131-556 8400

WALES

The National Assembly for Wales has less power than the Scottish Parliament. The vote in favour of devolution in September 1997 was also much smaller than in Scotland, just 0.6 per cent. In the first Assembly election, in May 1999, Plaid Cymru did unexpectedly well, and Labour failed to win a majority. Wales still has 40 Westminster MPs, 34 of them Labour. The Cardiff-based 60 Welsh members are more Westminster advisers than power-wielders. Taxation, defence, foreign affairs, social security, overall economic policy and broadcasting all remain in the hands of the Secretary of State for Wales and the UK cabinet. The Welsh First Secretary - mini prime minister - is Rhodri Morgan, who heads a cabinet of eight secretaries. The Assembly is temporarily based in Cardiff Bay, moving to a new Chamber in 2001.

1999 ASSEMBLY FOR WALES ELECTION

Labour	29
Plaid Cymru	17
Conservative	9
Liberal Democrat	6

Contacts

National Assembly for Wales	029-2082 5111
	www.wales.gov.uk
Public Information Line	029-2089 8200
Press	029-2082 5642/7
Members + UK Welsh Office	029-2082 5111

NORTHERN IRELAND

The Northern Ireland Assembly was set up by the Good Friday Agreement, of 10 April 1998. The referendum six weeks later voted overwhelmingly for the Assembly, with 108 members, plus a North-South Ministerial Council. Proportional representation elections took place in the 18 Westminster constituencies on 25 June, and the Assembly met for the first time on 1 July 1998. Proceedings started on 14 September, but the creation of the new government with devolved powers could not be achieved because no agreement could be reached on weapons decommissioning until late November 1999 The landmark ceremony took place on 2 December, when power was devolved to the Assembly and its Executive Committee of ten ministers, including two Sinn Fein. But the decommissioning conflict resumed, and in February 2000 Westminster suspended devolution until 30 May, when new agreement was reached. Continuing militant opposition by Unionist diehards left the future unknown. The Executive's First Minister is David Trimble. The British-Irish Council met for the first time on 17 December 1999. It provides a unique discussion forum for all sovereign and near-sovereign bodies in the British Isles, including Eire, the Channel Islands and the Isle of Man.

1998 N IRELAND ASSEMBLY ELECTION

Ulster Unionist Party	28
SDLP	24
Democratic Unionist Party	20
Sinn Fein	18
Six other parties	18

Contacts

Northern Ireland Assembly	028-9076 3210
	www.ni-assembly.gov.uk
Press	028-9052 1840
Parliament Buildings Info Office	028-9052 1333

ENGLAND

England at present does not have an elected national body of its own, although the Tories have hinted they may create one if they win the next election. This has aroused English nativism, which Labour have tried to defuse by creating nine Regional Development Agencies (RDAs) in 1999. These unelected quangos are meant to exert some influence over the policies of Westminster, working alongside the existing Government Offices for the Regions (GOs), which are responsible for implementing some government policies. But there has been little public interest so far in English regionalism, except in London, one of the nine regions.

1997 GENERAL ELECTION

The last UK general election was on 1 May 1997. The turnout was 31.3 million voters, 71.6 per cent of the 43.7 million registered electors. This was the lowest turnout since 1945. There was a 10.5 per cent national swing to Labour, which won 418 seats with 43.2 per cent of the turnout. But 77 per cent of the total UK population of 58.8m did not vote Labour. The Liberal Democrats had 12.1 per cent of the turnout, but only won 46 seats. The Labour majority was 177. Labour spent £13.7 million on the election. Labour's 418-seat win in 1997 was its highest-ever number; 1945 was next, with 393. A record number of woman MPs was elected: 120. The Tories had the lowest share of the vote since 1832 and the lowest number of MPs since 1906.

In the 13 by-elections to August 2000 only one seat changed hands: the Tories lost Romsey to the Lib Dems. The results for the three main parties in 1997 are shown at the foot of the page, not including the by-election. Seats won by other parties in 1997 were:

England: Independent (Martin Bell)	1
Wales: Plaid Cymru	4
Scotland: Scottish National Party	6
Northern Ireland: Ulster Unionist	10
SDLP	3
Democratic Unionist	2
Sinn Fein	2
UK Unionist	1

England had 529 seats; Labour won 329 of them, Tories 165 (all bar 17 of them in the

1997 GENERAL ELECTION RESULTS

	seats won	% of all seats	votes	% of turnout	% of electorate
Labour	418	63.6%	13.52m	43.2%	30.1%
Conservatives	165	25.0%	9.60m	30.7%	22.0%
Liberal Democrats	46	7.0%	5.24m	16.7%	12.1%
Total + other parties	659	100%	31.29m	100%	71.6%

South and Midlands), Liberal Democrats 34, Independent one. **Wales** had 40 seats; Labour won 34, Lib Dems 2, Plaid Cymru 4 (with 161,000 votes, 10 per cent of the total turnout in Wales), Tories none. **Scotland** had 72 seats; Labour won 56, Liberal Democrats 10, Scottish Nationalists 6, Tories none. **Northern Ireland** had 18 seats, all won by indigenous parties (see above). The Ulster Unionists took 56 per cent of the seats with only 33 per cent of the votes.

AND NEXT?

General elections can be held at any time, but by law the House of Commons has to be dissolved not later than five years to the day after its first meeting following an election, ie 7 May 1997. Election campaigns follow the dissolution and usually last for three weeks. So the next election deadline is around the end of May 2002. The Conservatives will need a swing of 11.6 per cent to win. In the 1997 election all the pollsters significantly over-predicted Labour support.

HOUSE OF COMMONS

Main number (all MPs)	020-7219 3000
	www.parliament.uk
Information office	020-7219 4272
Forthcoming business	020-7219 5532
Education Unit	020-7219 5839
Committees office	020-7219 4300
Library	020-7219 4272
Official report (Hansard)	020-7219 3764
Parliamentary Bookshop	020-7219 3890
Parliamentary Archives	020-7219 3074
Press Gallery/Lobby: Secretary	020-7219 4395
Superintendent	020-7219 5371
Publications	020-7219 4272
Serjeant at Arms	020-7219 3030
Whips offices: Government	020-7219 4400
Opposition (Conservative)	020-7219 3237
Liberal Democrat	020-7219 5654

Website for reading Commons publications:
www.publications.parliament.uk/pa/cm/cmpubns.htm

HOUSE OF LORDS

Six hundred years of history ended in November 1999 when the House of Lords Act came into force, abolishing the right of the 758 hereditary peers to make the country's laws. But the government allowed 102 of them to retain their power while it continued trying to make up its mind about how to reform the House. Lord Wakeham's royal commission recommendations in January 2000 were condemned by the Guardian as "a dog's dinner of a report ... a mumbled agreement among the Westminster club to keep things as they are." Tony Blair put the report on hold. Then in March he created 33 new life peerages making him the record holder, having set up a total of 209, six more than Margaret Thatcher. By mid-2000 the House of Lords had 676 members: 558 life peers, 92 peers under the 1999 House of Lords Act and 26 bishops and archbishops. The party strength was:

232	Conservative
186	Labour
56	Liberal Democrat
166	Crossbench
36	Others

Main Lords number	020-7219 3000
	www.parliament.uk
Lords Reform	www.lords-reform.org.uk
Information Office	020-7219 3107
Lords message services	020-7219 5353
Private bill office	020-7219 3231
Public bill office	020-7219 3153
Committees office	020-7219 3218
Judicial office	020-7219 3111
Library	020-7219 5242
Official report (Hansard)	020-7219 3031
Serjeant at Arms (Black Rod)	020-7219 3100
Whips offices: Government	020-7219 3131
Opposition (Conservative)	020-7219 4770
Liberal Democrat	020-7219 3114

UK PARLIAMENTS' PARTIES

Labour Party
London HQ	020-7802 1000
	www.labour.org.uk
Press	020-7802 1428
MEPs, London	020-7222 1719
Scottish Labour Party	0141-572 6900

Conservative Party
London HQ	020-7222 9000
	www.conservative-party.org.uk
Press	020-7896 4140
MEPs, London	020-7222 1720
Scottish Conservative Party	0131-555 2900
Welsh Conservative Party	029-2061 6031

Liberal Democrat Party

London HQ	020-7222 7999
	www.libdems.org.uk
Lib Dems Wales	029-2031 3400
Scottish Liberal Democrats	0131-337 2314
	www.scotlibdems.org.uk
Alliance Party of N Ireland	028-9032 4274

And the others ...

Plaid Cymru	029-2064 6000
	www.plaidcymru.org.uk
Scottish Green Party	0131-478 7896
	www.scottishgreens.org.uk
Scottish Socialist Party	0141-221 7714
	www.scotsocialistparty.org.uk
Scottish National Party	0131-226 3661
	www.snp.org.uk
Sinn Fein	028-9032 3214
	www.irlnet.com/sinnfein
Social Democratic & Labour Party	028-9024 7700
	www.indigo.ie/sdlp
Ulster Democratic Unionist Party	028-9047 1155
	www.dup.org.uk
Ulster Unionist Party	028-9032 4601
	www.uup.org
UK Unionist Party	028-9127 2994

UK ACTION POLITICS

An online starting point for political searching is the apolitical UK Politics (connected with Politico's Publishing), with a list of 2,500 websites. Other useful sites are GreenNet, Peoples' Global Action, Reclaim the Streets, Red Pepper, SchNews and Urban 75.

Actual Democracy	01268-792829
	www.gn.apc.org/actdem
The Agitator (activists directory)	020-8374 5027
Anarchist Black Cross	020-7837 1688
Anarchist Bookfair (annual, London)	020-8533 6936
Anarchist Federation	01523-78669
	www.afed.org.uk
Anti-Fascist Action	07000-569569
	www.geocities.com/CapitolHill/senate/5602
Anti-Nazi League	020-7924 0333
British National Party	020-8316 4721
Campaign for a Scottish Parliament	0131-225 7814
Campaign for an Independent Britain	020-8340 0314
Charter 88	020-7684 3888
Class War	01582-750601
	www.geocities.com/CapitolHill/9482
Communist League Party	020-7401 2293
Communist Party of Britain	020-7275 8162
	www.totalweb.co.uk/cp-of-britain
Communist Party of Gt Britain	020-8459 7146
	www.duntone.demon.co.uk/cpgb
Co-operative Party	020-7439 0123
Corporate Watch Magazine	01865-791391
	www.corporatewatch.org

Democracy Movement (anti-Euro)	020-7233 7351
	www.democracy-movement.org.uk
Democratic Left	020-7278 4443
	www.democratic-left.org.uk
Earth First!	07947-91841
	www.eco-action.org/efau
Eco-Action	www.eco-action.org
Electoral Reform Society	020-7928 1622
	www.electoral-reform.org.uk
English National Party	020-7278 5221
Fabian Society	020-7222 8877
Freedom Association	020-7793 4228
	www.tfa.net
Freedom Bookshop/Press (anarcho)	020-7247 9249
Freemasons	020-7831 9811
Global Grassroots Resistance Directory	
	www.geocities.com/CapitolHill/lobby/5217
Green Left	01422-844022
Green Party	020-7272 4474
	www.greenparty.org.uk
GreenNet	www.gn.apc.org
Hansard Society	020-7955 7478
Islamic Party of Britain	01908-671756
Left Direct	www.leftdirect.co.uk
Liberal Party (not Lib-Dems)	01704-500115
	www.libparty.demon.co.uk
London Socialist Alliance	020-8981 9243
Mayday 2000	020-8374 5027
	www.freespeech.org/mayday2k
Monday Club	020-72495368
Movement Against the Monarchy	01523-160145
	www.geocities.com/CapitolHill/lobby/1793
National Front (aka National Democrats)	07071-226074
	www.national-front.org.uk
Network of Socialist Alliances	01788-569766
Peoples' Global Action	www.agp.org
Reclaim the Streets	020-7281 4621
	www.reclaimthestreets.net
Red Pepper Magazine	020-7281 7024
	www.redpepper.org.uk
Referendum Movement	0990-110440
SchNews Magazine	01273-685913
	www.schnews.org.uk
Searchlight Magazine	020-284 4040
Socialist Party (ex-Militant Labour)	020-8533 3311
	www.socialistparty.org.uk
Socialist Party of Gt Britain	020-7622 3811
Socialist Workers Party	020-7538 5821
	www.swp.org.uk
Solidarity Federation	0161-232 7889
	www.gn.apc.org/solfed
St George Foundation	01303-850501
	www.camelotintl.com/stgeorge
UK Independence Party	020-7434 4559
UK Politics	www.ukpol.co.uk
Urban75	www.urban75.com/links
Welsh Community Resistance	029-2083 0029
	www.fanergoch.org
World Socialist Web Site	www.wsws.org
Workers Revolutionary Party	020-7928 3218
Yahoo! politics search: Capitol Hill	www.geocities.com

Departments of state

This is the government when it broke up for the long summer hols in late July 2000. The official (and widely recommended) website directory for all government and civil service organisations is www.open.gov.uk, run by the CCTA Government Information Service. Below, PUSS means Parliamentary Under-Secretary of State.

PRIME MINISTER'S OFFICE

10 Downing Street, London SW1A 2AA
Main number 020-7270 3000
www.cabinet-office.gov.uk
Press (24 hour) 020-7930 4433
Prime Minister Tony Blair
Deputy Prime Minister John Prescott
Press Secretary Alastair Campbell

AG., FISHERIES & FOOD

Nobel House, 17 Smith Square, London SW1P 3JR
MAFF: main number 020-7238 6000
www.maff.gov.uk
Information Division 020-7238 5603
Press Branch 020-7238 5599
Eves 020-7270 8960
Food safety, animal/plant health 020-7238 6094
Fisheries, countryside, floods 020-7238 6001
Agricultural/food industries, CAP 020-7238 6043
Helpline 0645-335577
Minister Nick Brown
Ministers of State Baroness Hayman, Joyce Quin
Minister for Fisheries/Countryside Elliot Morley

CABINET OFFICE

70 Whitehall, London SW1A 2AS
CO: main number 020-7270 1234
www.cabinet-office.gov.uk
Head of Information 020-7270 0516
Press 020-7270 0635
Minister for the Cabinet Office Marjorie Mowlam
Ministers of State Ian McCartney, Lord Falconer
Lord Privy Seal Baroness Jay
Parliamentary Secretary Graham Stringer

CULTURE, MEDIA & SPORT

2-4 Cockspur Street, London SW1Y 5DH
DCMS: main number 020-7211 6000
www.culture.gov.uk
Public enquiries 020-7211 6200
Information Division 020-7211 6263
Press 020-7211 6273
Secretary of State Chris Smith
Ministers for: Arts Alan Howarth
Film, Tourism, Broadcasting Janet Anderson
Sport Kate Hoey

MINISTRY OF DEFENCE

Horseguards Avenue, London SW1A 2HB
MOD: main number 020-7218 9000
www.mod.uk
Director of Information & News 020-7218 5317
Press 020-7218 2906
Eves 020-7218 7907
Army 020-7218 3256
Navy 020-7218 3258
RAF 020-7218 3254
Policy 020-7218 7925
Procurement 020-7218 7714
Tri-Service Joint HQ 01923-846029
Army HQ, Wilton 01722-433345
Navy HQ, Northwood 01923-837336
RAF HQ, High Wycombe 01494-496131
Chief of Defence Staff 020-7218 2116
D-Notice Committee 020-7218 2206
Secretary of State Geoff Hoon
Ministers of State: Armed Forces John Spellar
Defence Procurement Baroness Symons
PUSS Lewis Moonie

EDUCATION & EMPLOYMENT

Great Smith Street, London SW1P 3BT
DfEE: main number 020-7925 5000
www.dfee.gov.uk
Enquire Line 0870-000 2288
Information office 020-7925 5555
Press 020-7925 5615
Employment, disability, learning 020-7925 6487
Schools, regions, campaigns 020-7925 5105
Secretary of State David Blunkett
Ministers of State:
New Deal Tessa Jowell
School standards Estelle Morris
Education, employment Baroness Blackstone
PUSS Margaret Hodge, Malcom Wicks
Jacqui Smith, Michael Wills

ENVIRONMENT, TRANSPORT, REGIONS

Eland House, Bressenden Place,London SW1E 5DU
DETR: main number 020-7890 3000
www.detr.gov.uk
Communications Directorate 020-7890 3333
Eves 020-7873 1966
Press: Environment 020-7890 4607
Housing, local government 020-7890 4608
London 020-7944 4604
Planning, construction 020-7890 4603
Regions 020-7890 5274
Transport 020-7890 3231
Secretary of State John Prescott
Ministers of State: Environment Michael Meacher
Housing, Planning Nick Raynsford
Local Government Hilary Armstrong
Transport Lord Macdonald
PUSS Lord Whitty, Keith Hill
Chris Mullin, Beverley Hughes

FOREIGN & COMMONWEALTH

King Charles Street, London SW1A 2AL
FCO: main number 020-7270 3000
www.fco.gov.uk
Press 020-7270 3100
Europe/UN/human rights 020-7270 3105
Asia/Pacific/Americas/North Africa/
Middle East/travel 020-7270 3661
Consular/drugs/crime/media 020-7270 3103
Information Dept 020-7270 3909
Public enquiries 020-7270 1500
Secretary of State Robin Cook
Ministers of State John Battle, Peter Hain, Keith Vaz
PUSS Baroness Scotland

DEPARTMENT OF HEALTH

Richmond House, 79 Whitehall, London SW1A 2NS
DOH: main number 020-7210 3000
www.doh.gov.uk
Eves 020-7210 5368
Press 020-7210 5225
Central desk 020-7210 5221
NHS media group 020-7210 5656
Media Initiatives 020-7210 5436
NHS Executive 0113-254 5000
Public enquiries 020-7210 4850
Health Information Service 0800-665544
Secretary of State Alan Milburn
Minister for Public Health Yvette Cooper
Ministers of State Jack Denham, John Hutton
PUSS Lord Hunt, Gisela Stuart

HOME OFFICE

50 Queen Anne's Gate, London SW1H 9AT
HO: main number 020-7273 4000
www.homeoffice.gov.uk
Eves 020-7273 4595
Director, Communication 020-7273 3757
Press: Chief press officer 020-7273 4117
Police/emergencies/terrorism 020-7273 4610
Criminal justice/crime 020-7273 4600
Immigration/asylum/ID cards 020-7273 4620
Constitution/data/drugs/fire 020-7273 4640
Prison Service 020-7217 6633
Secretary of State Jack Straw
Ministers of State: Paul Boateng
Barbara Roche, Charles Clarke
PUSS Lord Bassam, Mike O'Brien

INTERNATIONAL DEV'MENT

94 Victoria Street, London SW1E 5JL
DFID: main number 020-7917 7000
www.dfid.gov.uk
Information Dept 020-7917 0435
Press 020-7917 0950
Secretary of State Clare Short
PUSS George Foulkes

LAW OFFICERS' DEPT

Attorney General's Chambers, 9 Buckingham Gate,
London SW1E 6JP
Main number 020-7271 2400
Press 020-7271 2405
Attorney General Lord Williams QC
Solicitor General Ross Cranston QC

LORD CHANCELLOR'S DEPT

House of Lords, London SW1A 0PW
LCD: main number 020-7210 8500
www.open.gov.uk/lcd
Eves 020-7210 8512
Press 020-7210 8512/3
Lord Chancellor Lord Irvine
Parliamentary Secretaries David Lock, Jane Kennedy

NORTHERN IRELAND EXEC

Castle Buildings, Stormont Estate, Belfast BT4 3SR
Main number 028-9052 8400
www.nics.gov.uk
First Minister David Trimble

NORTHERN IRELAND OFFICE

11 Millbank, London SW1P 4PN
Stormont Castle, Belfast BT4 3ST

NIO: main numbers: Belfast	028-9052 0700
London (24 hr)	020-7210 3000
	www.nio.gov.uk
NI Information Service, Belfast	028-9052 8211
Press	028-9052 8233
London press office	020-7210 6473
Public enquiries	020-7210 6454
Agriculture Dept	028-9052 4619
Economic Development Dept	028-9052 9900
Education Dept	028-9052 9277
Environment Dept	028-9054 0033
Finance Dept	028-9185 8175
Health & Social Services Dept	028-9052 0636
Police Authority	028-9023 0111
Secretary of State	Peter Mandelson
Ministers of State:	Adam Ingram
PUSS	George Howarth

PRIVY COUNCIL OFFICE

68 Whitehall, London SW1A 2AT

Office	020-7270 0472
Judicial Committee	020-7270 0485
President of the Council and Leader of the	
House of Commons	Margaret Beckett
Lord Privy Seal, Leader of the House of Lords and	
Minister for Women	Baroness Jay
PUSS	Paddy Tipping

SCOTLAND OFFICE

Dover House, Whitehall, London SW1A 2AU

Main number	020-7270 6754
	www.scottishsecretary.gov.uk
Press	020-7270 6745
Enquiry Point	0345-741741
Secretary of State	John Reid
Minister of State	Brian Wilson
Advocate General for Scotland	Lynda Clark QC

SCOTTISH EXECUTIVE

St Andrew's House, Regent Rd, Edinburgh EH1 3DG

Main number	0131-556 8400
	www.scotland.gov.uk
Enquiries	0845-278 1999
All departments	0131-556 8400
First Minister	Donald Dewar

DEPT OF SOCIAL SECURITY

79 Whitehall, London SW1A 2NS

DSS: main number	020-7238 3000
	www.dss.gov.uk
Public enquiries	020-7712 2171
Press	020-7238 0860
Chief press officer	020-7238 0748
Welfare reform	020-7238 0750
Child support	0191-238 0749
Benefit/support/poverty	020-7238 0752
Fraud/pensions/insurance	020-7238 0753
Child Support Agency	0191-225 0862
Freeline help	0800-882200
Secretary of State	Alistair Darling
Minister of State	Jeff Rooker
PUSS	Hugh Bayley, Baroness Hollis, Angela Eagle

TRADE AND INDUSTRY

1 Victoria Street, London SW1H 0ET

DTI: main number	020-7215 5000
	www.dti.gov.uk
Central Desk (info)	020-7215 5952
News Director	020-7215 5970
Press	020-7215 2345
Secretary of State	Stephen Byers
Ministers of State: Energy	Helen Liddell
Small Business/E-Commerce	Patricia Hewitt
Trade	Richard Caborn
PUSS	Kim Howells, Lord Sainsbury
	Alan Johnson

TREASURY

Parliament Street, London SW1P 3AG

HMT: main number	020-7270 3000
	www.hm-treasury.gov.uk
Public enquiries	020-7270 4860
Press	020-7270 5238
Public finances	020-7270 5245
Private finance	020-7211 1300
Taxation	020-7270 5187
Chancellor of the Exchequer	Gordon Brown
Chief Secretary	Andrew Smith
Paymaster General	Dawn Primarolo
Financial Secretary	Stephen Timms
Economic Secretary	Melonie Johnson
Parliamentary Secretary	Ann Taylor

WELSH OFFICE

Gwydyr House, Whitehall, London SW1A 2ER

WO: main number	020-7270 3000
	www.wales.gov.uk
Press	020-7270 0558
Enquiries	020-7270 0583
Secretary of State	Paul Murphy
PUSS	David Hanson

e-Government

New Labour promised a more open government when it came to power in 1997, but by 2000 it seemed that Whitehall was tightening up the management of official information, rather than freeing it. Early in 2000 the media revealed that Downing Street was designing an electronic Knowledge Network aimed at explaining the government's core message to the public without going through "the distorting prism of media reporting". The project will collect in one database every line for ministers and civil servants to take on every key government policy. The public will have only limited access to the Project. The Guardian said: "The world's most advanced government knowledge management system will tell the people who pay for it all about those aspects of government action likely to leave them satisfied ... while doing its highly professional best to stifle the rest."

At the same time Whitehall was imposing tighter statutory controls over public knowledge of official life by creating three new laws. The Freedom of Information Bill would give the central authorities the power to manage all information, freeing some trivia while legally imprisoning all the sensitive material. The Regulation of Investig-atory Powers Bill would allow the security services to intercept emails and to monitor traffic on the internet, thereby giving the government great power to abuse personal and commercial innovation. And the Local Government Bill would legitimise secret debate and decision-making by local councils. All three bills were being opposed as this book went to press, forcing changes on Downing Street. The 1998 Data Protection Act came into force in March 2000 giving the public some self-defence over private computer databanks, but allowing many government bodies to almost act at will.

Amidst all this tightening of state control over sensitive information there has been electronic liberalising of less contentious things. In late March 2000 Tony Blair said the government will try to offer all its services on a 24-hour, online basis by 2005. This is part of the "e-government strategy ... for public services in the information age". Its portal will be called UK Online, with the strategy coming into operation fully in 2001. Several government organisations are already providing data online and more should soon join them. The strategy is run on behalf of ministers by the "e-Envoy". Supporting him, and doing much of the ground-work for the strategy, is the Central IT Unit (CITU) in the Cabinet Office. Helping the e-Envoy create policies are the Information Age Government Champions (IAGC), 36 senior officials. Continuous news on "what's happening in e-government and information age public services" comes from Kable, the independent body sponsored by BT, Cable & Wireless and Oracle.

Before UK Online takes off, there are other Whitehall entry points. The key is the Government Information Service (GIS) website Open.gov.uk, run by the Central Computer and Telecommunications Agency (CCTA). This gateway to over 3,000 official organisations is one of the world's top sites. It is the essential tool for the public trying to discover something about central and local government. The CCTA is at the heart of the government's modernisation programme, and has its own website Another entry point is Inforoute, the HMSO's new gateway to information held by government departments. It aims to provide direct access to the government's Information Asset Register (IAR), an amalgamation of all the Whitehall databases . Other good websites are on the Quango page.

e-Government sites

Cabinet Office	www.cabinet-office.gov.uk
CCTA	www.ccta.gov.uk
CITU	www.citu.gov.uk
Civil Service Yearbook	www.civil-service.co.uk
DETR Local & Regional Government	www.local-regions.detr.gov.uk
e-Envoy	www.e-envoy.gov.uk
GIS	www.open.gov.uk
IAGC	www.iagchampions.gov.uk
Inforoute	www.inforoute.hmso.gov.uk
Kable	www.kablenet.com

GOVERNMENT PHONELINES

If your modem implodes, use the phone. Contact Whitehall via the Code of Practice on Access to Government Information - also called Open Government. This says that almost all government departments and bodies must respond to requests for information via the phoneline. But there are exemptions: policing, defence and the security services. Departmental contact points are listed below, under Openness Contacts. Enquirers may be told they have to write to the appropriate office; detailed replies should come within 20 days. The main Whitehall information-manager is the Central Office of Information. The COI has a wide remit, handling the flow of all information in and out of the government. Whitehall's specialist in processing raw facts and figures is the Office for National Statistics. This has its own library, open to the public, and runs a data-packed website, Statbase, on behalf of the Government Statistical Service. If the whole telecom system breaks down, try reading Britain: An Official Handbook (Stationery Office), the official annual picture of life in Britain, and Civil Service Yearbook (Stationery Office), the twice-yearly Whitehall directory.

Openness contacts

Code copies: Home Office CCP Dir	020-7273 4000
www.homeoffice.gov.uk/foi/ogcode981.htm	
Agriculture, Fisheries & Food	
Julie Sheen	0645-335577
Central Office of Information	
John Ellery	020-7261 8606
Charity Commissioners	
Frances Grey	0870-333 0123
Culture, Media & Sport, Dept of	
Enquiry Unit	020-7211 6200
Customs & Excise	
David Rennie	020-7865 5777
Data Protection Registrar	
Ruth Robinson	01625-545700
Defence, Ministry of	
Secretary of State's office	020-7218 6432
Education & Employment, Dept for	
Enquiry unit: John Quinn	020-7925 6572
Employment Service	
Dean Weston	020-7389 1529
Environment, Transport & Regions, Dept of	
Public Enquiry Point	020-7890 3000
Fair Trading, Office of	

Public Liaison Unit	020-7211 8000
Foreign & Commonwealth Office	
Enquiry Unit: Kate Crowe	020-7210 3865
Gas & Electricity, Office of (OFGEM)	
Mark Wiltshere	0207-932 1606
Health, Dept of	
Sarah Armstrong	020-7210 5787
Health & Safety Executive	
Infoline	0541-545500
Home Office	
Info Services: Alan King	020-7273 3818
Inland Revenue	
Jen Morgan	020-7438 6879
HM Land Registry	
Denise Reynolds	020-7917 8888
Legal Aid Board	
Jackie Collins	020-7813 1000
Lord Chancellor's Dept	
Kevin Fraser	020-7210 8533
National Lottery, Office of	
Mark Slattery	020-7227 2030
National Savings	
Sallie Randie	01344-784328
Northern Ireland Office	
Denis Carson	028-9052 7015
Ordnance Survey	
Mr A Warmington	023-8079 2605
Rail Regulator, Office of	
Ian Cooke	020-7282 2002
Royal Mint	
Judith Nichols	01443-222111
Scottish Office	
Paul Geoghan	0131-244 2656
Social Security, Dept of	
Info Management Policy Unit	020-7962 8142
Child Support Agency	0191-225 3154
Trade & Industry, Dept of	
Open Govt Enquiry Point	020-7215 3959
Transport, Dept of	
DVLA: Derek Bastin	01792-782318
Highways Agency: David Buxton	020-7921 4031
Water Services, Office of (OFWAT)	
Jane Fisher	0121-625 1361
Welsh Office	
Kate Cassidy	029-2082 5275

Central Office of Information
Hercules Road, London SE1 7DU

Main number	020-7928 2345
Enquiries	020-7261 8409
Press	020-7261 8795
Eves	020-7928 2345
	www.coi.gov.uk

Office for National Statistics
1 Drummond Gate, London SW1V 2QQ

Main number	020-7233 9233
Enquiries	020-7533 6363
ONS offices	www.ons.gov.uk
StatBase, via	www.statistics.gov.uk

Quangos

Quangos are public service bodies run as private businesses. The word "quango" is an abbreviation of "**QU**asi-**A**utonomous **N**on-**G**overnmental **O**rganisation". The Tory government began privatisation of the Civil Service in 1988, aiming to convert three-quarters of it into quangos within a decade. Labour opposed it in opposition, but the New Labour government of 1997 adopted a mellower attitude, and 77 per cent of all civil servants were working in quangos by mid-1999. The Civil Service steadily shrunk from its highest level of 751,000 staff in 1976, to 476,800 in 1999, but then rising to 481,200 in 2000.

The government officially calls most quangos either Non-Departmental Public Bodies (NDPBs) or Next Steps Executive Agencies (NSEAs). The NDPBs are almost separate from the government, while NSEAs are closer, being only semi-detached subsidiaries of departments. Whitehall defines an NDPB as: "A body which has a role in the process of national government, but is not a government department or part of one, and which accordingly operates to a greater or lesser extent at arms length from ministers". Examples are the Environment Agency, the Health and Safety Executive and the Low Pay Commission. In 1999 there were 98,400 staff in 1,057 NDPBs, with a turnover of £20.8 billion. Two-thirds of their 36,000 governors were men.

NSEAs are commonly known as "executive agencies", or just "agencies". They are the Next Steps Programme which was launched in 1988. NSEAs are less autonomous than the NDPBs. They are partially-independent organisations performing executive functions of government, while staying part of the civil service. Examples are the Prison Service, Land Registry, Office for National Statistics, Meteorological Office and Ordnance Survey. There were 139 NSEAs, or near-NSEAs, in 1999, employing 382,400 civil servants, with another 13 agencies in the pipeline.

At a local level, NDPBs, NSEAs and the various other types of quangos have taken over many services previously run by local authorities or by elected regional/national bodies, such as NHS hospitals, education and housing.

A major problem in understanding quangos is the similarity between semi-privatised and fully privatised bodies such as former gas, water and electricity boards, now the property of shareholders. It is often difficult to discover what formal status a quango has: is it an NSEA, private company, government department, trust, NDPB, public company, or a mixture of some of these ingredients? In addition, public accountability is hard to define, often being only personal, with just the chief exec responsible to the minister of the sponsoring government department. The Labour government has promised to make these organisations both more accountable and more efficient. In Whitehall, the quangos and Civil Service come under the Central Secretariat of the Cabinet Office.

QUANGONLINE

Cabinet Office
www.cabinet-office.gov.uk/quango
This is the official Cabinet Office guide to everything about quangos, including a directory of all NDPBs.

CCTA Government Information Service
www.open.gov.uk
For seekers of all central and local government organisations, including the fringe quangos.

Commissioner for Public Appointments
www.open.gov.uk/ocpa/ocpahome.htm
Lots of background information from, and about, the official responsible for monitoring quango operators.

Stationery Office
www.ukstate.com
www.official-documents.co.uk
Combined, these Stationery Office sites provide both a compendious official bookshop and a wide-ranging source of government info.

Technology Applications Group Information Superhighway
www.tagish.co.uk
Comprehensive online lists of public sector links, especially the local authorities outside Whitehall.

UK AND ENGLISH QUANGOS

These are NDPBs, NSEAs and other bodies run as quangos in some form. Included are the few remaining organisations that are still part of the Civil Service, other than the central government departments which are listed in full in the Departments of State section of this book. Many national quangos are hard to locate via phone directories because they come under the wings of a government department, and are only registered under that name, not their own. So, as many as possible of these shy organisations are included here. The initials are those of their overseeing department. For websites, look them up and access them directly via www.open.gov.uk.

ACAS - Advisory, Conciliation & Arbitration	
Service (DfEE)	020-7396 0022
ADAS (MAFF)	01902-754190
Advisory Committees on:	
Business & the Environment (DETR)	020-7890 6568
Conscientious Objectors (MoD)	020-7218 0509
Hazardous Substances (DETR)	020-7890 5265
Hill Farming (MAFF)	020-7238 6307
Historic Wreck Sites (DCMS)	020-7211 2099
NHS Drugs (DOH)	020-7210 5642
Pesticides (MAFF)	01904-455701
Public Lending Right (DCMS)	01642-604699
Telecommunications	020-7215 0319
Advisory Councils on:	
Public Records (LCD)	020-8876 3444
The Misuse of Drugs (HO)	020-7273 2994
Agricultural Land Tribunals (MAFF)	020-7238 5677
Agricultural Wages Board (MAFF)	020-7238 6540
Animal Procedures Cttee	020-7273 2861
Arts Council (DCMS)	020-7333 0100
Audit Commission for Local Authorities and	
the NHS (DETR)	020-7828 1212
Aviation Cttee (DTI)	020-7215 1128
Bank of England (HMT)	020-7601 4444
BBC (Press)	020-8576 1865
Biotechnology and Biological Research	
Council (CO)	01793-413200
Black Country Urban Development Corp	
(DETR)	020-7890 3748
Boards of Visitors to Prisons	020-7217 8388
Boundary Commissions - Local Government:	
England	020-7430 8400
Wales	029-2039 5031
Scotland	0131-538 7510
Boundary Commissions - Parliamentary:	
England & Wales	020-7533 5177
Scotland	0131-538 7500
Northern Ireland	020-7210 6569
British Antarctic Survey	01223-361188

British Coal (DTI)	01782-662052
British Council (FCO)	020-7930 8466
Press	020-7389 4878
British Energy	020-7389 3406
British Film Institute (DCMS)	020-7255 1444
Press	020-7957 8920
British Library (DCMS)	020-7412 7000
Press	020-7412 7116
British Museum (DCMS)	020-7636 1555
Press	020-7323 8779
British National Space Centre	020-7215 0806
British Nuclear Fuels (DTI)	01925-832000
Sellafield (press)	01946-785838
British Overseas Trade Board	see Trade Partners UK
British Standards Institution	020-8996 9000
British Tourist Authority (DCMS)	020-8846 9000
Press	020-8563 3034
British Waterways (DETR)	01923-226422
Broadcasting Complaints/Standards Commission	
(DCMS)	020-7233 0544
Building Regulations Advisory Cttee	020-7890 5742
Building Research Establishment	
(DETR)	01923-664000
Building Societies Commission	020-7676 1000
CCTA: Central Computer & Telecommunications	
Agency (OPS)	01603-704874
Central Office of Information (OPS)	020-7928 2345
Press	020-7261 8795
Emergency Planning	020-7261 8221
Films & Radio	020-7261 8895
New Media	020-7261 8691
News Distribution Service	020-7261 8445
Press & Pictures	020-7261 8422
Central Rail Users Consultative Committee	
(DETR)	020-7505 9090
Central Science Laboratory (MAFF)	01904-462000
Centre for Environment, Fisheries & Aquaculture	
Science (MAFF)	01502-562244
Charity Commission	020-7674 2333
Chemical & Biological Defence Establishment	
(MOD)	01980-613000
Citizens Charter Unit (CO)	020-7270 1234
Civil Aviation Authority (DETR)	020-7379 7311
Press	020-7832 5335
Civil Service College (CO)	01344-634000
Coal Authority (DTI)	01623-427162
Coastguard & Marine Safety Agency	
(DETR)	023-8032 9100
Commission for Racial Equality (HO)	020-7828 7022
Press	020-7932 5354
Commissioner for the Rights of Trade Union	
Members (DfEE)	01925-415771
Press	0161-952 4508
Committee for Monitoring Agreements on Tobacco	
Advertising/Sponsorship	020-7210 5658
Committees on:	
Carcinogenicity Food Chemicals	020-7210 5221
Medical Aspects of Food Policy	020-7210 5221
Safety of Medicines (DOH)	020-7273 0451
Standards in Public Life	020-7270 6345
Toxicity of Chemicals in Food	020-7210 5221

Commons Commissioners (DETR)	020-7222 0038
Commonwealth Institute (FCO)	020-7603 4535
Commonwealth Secretariat	020-7839 3411
Community Development Foundation (HO)	020-7226 5375
Companies House (DTI)	029-2038 8588
Press	029-2038 0526
Consumer Communications (OFTEL)	020-7634 8774
Copyright Tribunal	01633-814000
Council on Tribunals (LCD)	020-7947 6000
Countryside Agency/Commission	01242-521381
Court Service (LCD)	020-7210 2092
Customer service	020-7210 1793
Press	020-7210 8512
Covent Garden Market Auth (MAFF)	020-7720 2211
Crafts Council (DCMS)	020-7278 7700
Criminal Injuries Compensation Board (HO)	020-7842 6800
Crown Agents (FCO)	020-7834 3644
Crown Estate	020-7210 4210
Crown Prosecution Service	020-7796 8000
Customs & Excise (HMT)	020-7620 1313
Press	020-7865 5665
Investigations: press	020-7665 7829
Data Protection Registrar (HO)	01625-545700
Data Protection Tribunal (HO)	020-7273 3492
Defence Agencies (MOD):	
Armed Forces Personnel Admin	01452-712612
Army Personnel	0141-224 3010
Army Technical Support	01264-383753
Defence Analytical Services	020-7218 7950
Defence Animal Centre	020-7218 7950
Joint Air Reconnaissance Intelligence Centre	01480-52151x7230
Logistic Information	01264-382832
Military Survey	020-8890 3622
MOD Police	01371-854000
Naval Recruiting & Training	023-9272 7600
RAF Maintenance Group	01480-52151
RAF Training Group	01452-712612
Scientific Advisory Council	020-7218 0333
Specialist Procurement	0117-913 2724
Dental Practice Board (DOH)	01323-417000
Design Council (DTI)	020-7420 5200
Doctors/Dentists Review Body	020-7467 7229
Driver & Vehicle Licensing Agency (DOT)	01792-782318
Driving Standards Agency (DETR)	0115-901 2500
DSS Appeal Tribunals	020-7814 6500
Economic and Social Research Council (CO)	01793-413000
Press	01793-413122
Education Assets Board	0113-234 8888
(Electricity) National Consumers Consultative Cttee	0121-456 6359
Employment Appeal Tribunal (DfEE)	020-7273 1041
Employment Service (DfEE)	020-7273 6060
Engineering & Physical Science Research Council (CO)	01793-444000
English Heritage (DCMS)	020-7973 3000
Press	020-7973 3250
English Nature (DETR)	01733-455000
Press	01733-455193
English Partnerships (DETR)	020-7976 7070
English Tourist Board (DCMS)	020-8846 9000
Press	020-8563 3038
Environment Agency (DETR)	01454-624400
Press	020-7863 8600
Equal Opportunities Commission (DfEE)	0161-833 9244
Press	020-7222 1110
Export Credit Guarantee Dept	020-7512 7000
Farming/Rural Conservation (MAFF)	020-7238 5432
Financial Services Authority	020-7676 1000
Fire Service College (HO)	01608-650831
Fisheries Research (SO)	01224-876544
Food Advisory Committee (MAFF)	020-7238 6267
Food From Britain (MAFF)	020-7233 5111
Football Licensing Authority (DCMS)	020-7491 7191
Forensic Science Service (HO)	020-7230 6654
Forest Enterprise (SO)	0131-334 0303
Forestry Commission Research	0131-334 0303
Further Education Development Agency (DfEE)	020-7840 5400
Further Education Funding Council (DfEE)	024-7686 3000
Gaming Board (HO)	020-7306 6200
Gas Consumers Council	020-7931 0977
Government Car & Despatch (OPS)	020-7217 3838
Govt Property Lawyers (HMT)	01823-354695
Health & Safety Commission & Executive (DfEE)	020-7717 6000
Press	020-7717 6700
Health Education Authority (DOH)	020-7222 5300
Healthcare Advisory Service	0118-972 2696
Highways Agency (DETR)	020-7921 4443
Historic Royal Palaces (DCMS)	020-8781 9750
HMSO	01603-723014
Press	020-7270 0375
Copyright section	01603 723001
Horserace Betting Levy Board (HO)	020-7333 0043
Horserace Totalisator Board: The Tote (HO)	020-8874 6411
Horticultural Development Council (MAFF)	01732-848383
Housing Corporation (DETR)	020-7393 2000
Human Genetics Advisory Commission (DTI)	020-7271 2131
Hydrographic Office (MOD)	01823-337900
Immigration Appellate Auth (LCD)	020-7862 4200
Independent Television Commission (DCMS)	020-7255 3000
Industrial Development Advisory Board (DTI)	020-7215 5580
Industrial Injuries Advisory Council (DSS)	020-7962 8065
Industrial Tribunals:	
National Enquiry Line (DfEE)	0345-959775
Press	020-7215 5964
Inland Revenue (HMT)	020-7438 6622
Press	020-7438 6692
Innovation Unit (DTI)	020-7215 1705
Insolvency Service (DTI)	020-7637 1110
Intelligence Services Tribunal	020-7273 4383
Interception of Communications Tribunal	

(HO)	020-7273 4096
International Development	020-7917 7000
Press	020-7917 0950
Intervention Board (MAFF)	0118-958 3626
Joint Nature Conservation Committee	
(DETR)	01733-562626
Laboratory of the Government Chemist	
(DTI)	020-8943 7000
HM Land Registry (LCD)	020-7917 8888
Lands Tribunal (LCD)	020-7936 7200
Law Commission: England (LCD)	020-7453 1220
Scotland	0131-668 2131
Legal Aid Board (LCD)	020-7813 1000
Library & Information Commission	
(DCMS)	020-7411 0078
London Docklands Urban Development	
Corporation (DETR)	abolished 1998
London Transport (DETR)	020-7222 5600
Maritime & Coastguard Agency (DETR)	023-8032 9467
Meat Hygiene Service (MAFF)	01904-455501
Meat/Livestock Commission (MAFF)	01908-677577
Medical Devices Agency (DOH)	020-7972 8000
Medical Practices Committee (DOH)	020-7972 2930
Medical Research Council (CO)	020-7636 5422
Medicines Commission/Control Agency	
(DOH)	020-7273 0392
Mental Health Act Commission	0115-943 7100
Mental Health Review Tribunal	0115-929 4222
Merseyside Urban Development Corp	
(DETR)	020-7890 3748
Meteorological Office (MOD)	01344-420242
Press	01344-856655
Millennium Commission (DCMS)	020-8880 2001
Monopolies and Mergers Commission	
(DTI)	020-7324 1467
Museums & Galleries Commission	
(DCMS)	020-7233 4200
National Audit Office	020-7798 7000
National Biological Standards Board	
(DOH)	01707-654753
National Blood Authority (DOH)	01932-486800
National Consumer Council (DTI)	020-7730 3469
National Council for Vocational Qualifications	
(DfEE)	020-7229 1234
National Food Survey Committee	
(MAFF)	020-7270 8563
National Health Service Tribunal (DOH)	01444-881345
National Heritage Memorial Fund	
(DCMS)	020-7591 6000
National Lotteries Charity Board	
(DCMS)	020-747 5300
National Physical Laboratory (DTI)	020-8977 3222
National Radiological Protection Board	
(DOH)	01235-831600
National Savings Department	020-7605 9300
National Weights & Measures Laboratory	
(DTI)	020-8943 7272
National Youth Agency	0116-285 3700
Natural Environment Research Council	
(CO)	01793-411500
Natural Resources Institute (FCO)	01634-880088
New Millennium Experience Co (DCMS)	020-7808 8200
NHS Estates (DOH)	0113-254 7000
Nuclear Electric plc (DTI)	020-7389 3406
Nuclear Powered Warships/Weapons Safety	
Cttees (MOD)	020-72189433
Occupational Health & Safety (CO)	0131-220 9700
Occupational Pensions Regulatory Authority	
(DSS)	01273-627600
Office for National Statistics (HMT)	020-7533 5888
Ordnance Survey (DETR)	023-8079 2000
Parliamentary Boundary Commission	020-7533 5177
Parole Board (HO)	020-7217 3000
Particle Physics & Astronomy Research	
Council	01793-444000
Passport Agency (HO)	0990-210410
Patent Office (DTI)	01633-814000
Paymaster General	01293-560999
Pesticides Safety Directorate (MAFF)	01904 640500
Pensions Compensation Board (DSS)	020-7828 9794
Planning Inspectorate (DETR)	020-7890 3043
Poisons Board (HO)	020-7273 3627
Police Complaints Authority (HO)	020-7273 6450
Policyholders Protection Board (HMT)	020-7600 3333
Political Honours Scrutiny Committee	
(CO)	020-7219 4272
Post Office (DTI)	020-7490 2888
Press 24 hrs	020-7250 2468
Post Office Users National Council (DTI)	020-7928 9458
Prescription Pricing Authority	0191-232 5371
HM Prison Service (HO)	020-7217 6633
Property Advisers to Civil Estate (CO)	020-7271 2610
Public Health Laboratory (DOH)	020-8200 1295
Public Lending Right	01642-604699
Public Record Office (LCD)	020-8876 3444
Public Trust Office (LCD)	020-7664 7000
Qualifications Curriculum Auth (DfEE)	020-7509 5555
QEII Conference Centre	020-7798 4000
Queens Awards Office	020-7222 2277
Radio Authority (DCMS)	020-7430 2724
Radiocommunications Agency (DTI)	020-7211 0211
Railway Inspectorate	0113-483 4200
Recruitment & Assessment Services	01256-869555
Registered Homes Tribunals (DOH)	020-7972 4034
Registry of Friendly Societies	020-7676 1000
Remploy (DfEE)	020-8235 0500
Renewable Energy Advisory Committee	
(DTI)	020-7215 2651
Royal Commission on Environmental	
Pollution (DETR)	020-7276 2109
Royal Commission on Historical Monuments	
(DCMS)	020-7208 8200
Royal Mail	020-7250 2888
Royal Mint (HMT)	01443-222111
Royal Parks Agency(DCMS)	020-7298 2000
Royalty - press offices:	
Buckingham Palace	020-7930 4832
Clarence House	020-7930 3141
Duchy of Lancaster	020-7836 8277
Rural Development Commission - Countryside	
Agency (DETR)	01242-521381
School Teachers Review Body (DfEE)	020-7467 7244
Sea Fish Industry Authority (MAFF)	0131-558 3331
Securities & Investments Board	020-7676 1000

Security Commission (CO)	020-7270 5875
Security Facilities Executive (DETR)	020-7921 4813
Security Service Tribunal (HO)	020-7273 4095
Serious Fraud Office	020-7239 7272
Social Security (DSS):	
Advisory Committee	020-7412 1506
Child Support Agency	0191-225 0862
War Pensions Agency	01253-858858
Sports Council (DCMS)	020-7273 1500
Supreme Court Rule Cttee	020-7210 0730
Teacher Training Agency (DfEE)	020-7925 3700
Top Salaries Review Body	020-7467 7217
Trade Partners UK	020-7215 5000
Trade Unions & Employers Associations	
Certification Office	020-7210 3734
Traffic Commissioners	020-7676 2120
Traffic Director for London (DETR)	020-7222 4545
Transport Research Lab (DETR)	01344-773131
Treasury Solicitor's Dept (HMT)	020-7210 3079
Trinity House Lighthouses (DETR)	020-7481 6900
UK Atomic Energy Authority (DTI)	01235-821111
UK Nirex	01235-825500
UK Register of Organic Food Standards	
(MAFF)	020-7238 5915
Valuation Office (HMT)	020-7324 1033
Value Added Tax Tribunals (LCD)	020-7631 4242
Vehicle Certification Agency (DETR)	0117-951 5151
Vehicle Inspectorate (DETR)	0117-954 3200
Veterinary Laboratories Agency	
(MAFF)	01932-341111
Water Regs Advisory Cttee (DETR)	020-7890 5372
Wilton Park Conference Centre (FCO)	01903-815020
Womens National Commission (CO)	020-7238 0386

WELSH QUANGOS

Arts Council of Wales	029-2037 6500
Boundary Commission	020-7533 5177
Cadw: Historic Monuments	029-2050 0200
Cardiff Bay Development Corp	029-2058 5858
Countryside Council for Wales	01248-370444
Development Board for Rural Wales	01686-626965
Fourth Channel Authority	029-2074 7444
Further/Higher Education Funding Councils	
for Wales	029-2076 1861
Health Promotion Authority	029-2075 2222
Hill Farming Advisory Cttee	029-2082 5735
Housing for Wales	029-2082 5111
Land Authority	029-2022 3444
Local Government Boundary	029-2039 5031
National Library of Wales	01970-632800
National Museums of Wales	029-2039 7951
Patent Office	01633-814000
Place Names Advisory Cttee	029-2089 0534
Qualifications, Curriculum & Assessment	
Authority	029-2037 5400
Rail Users Consultative Cttee	029-2022 7247
Royal Commission on Ancient & Historical	
Monuments	01970-621233
Sports Council for Wales	029-2030 0500

Tai Cymru Housing for Wales	029-2082 5111
Wales Tourist Board	029-2049 9909
Welsh Development Agency	0345-775577
Welsh Funding Councils	029-2076 1861
Welsh Health Common Services Auth	029-2050 0500
Welsh Language Board	029-2022 4744

SCOTTISH QUANGOS

Accounts Commission	0131-447 1234
Caledonian MacBrayne	01475-650100
Children's Panel	0131-244 5444
Community Education Council	0131-313 2488
Council on the Curriculum	01382-455053
Crofters Commission	01463-663450
Deer Commission	01463-231751
Forest Enterprise	0131-334 0303
Forestry Commission Research	0131-334 0303
Health Boards	0131-244 3469
Health Service Committee	0131-556 8400
Higher Education Funding Council	0131-313 6500
Highlands & Islands Airports	01667-462445
Highlands & Islands Enterprise	01463-234171
Hill Farming Advisory Cttee	0131-244 6417
Historic Buildings Council	0131-244 4999
Historic Scotland	0131-668 8600
Lands Tribunal	0131-225 7996
Law Commission	0131-668 2131
Legal Aid Board	0131-226 7061
Local Govt Boundary Commission	0131-538 7510
Mental Welfare Commission	0131-222 6111
National Galleries	0131-556 8921
National Library	0131-226 4531
National Museum	0131-225 7534
NHS Tribunal	0131-244 2952
NHS Trusts	0131-244 3469
Parliamentary Boundary Commission	0131-244 2196
Parole Unit	0131-244 8528
Pensions Appeal Tribunal	0131-220 1404
Police Advisory Board	0131-556 8400
Rail Users Consultative Cttee	0141-221 7760
Registers of Scotland	0131-659 6111
Rent Assessment Panel	0131-226 1123
Royal Commission on Ancient & Historical	
Monuments	0131-662 1456
Royal Fine Art Commission	0131-556 6699
Scottish Agricultural Science	0131-244 8890
Scottish Arts Council	0131-226 6051
Scottish Court Service	0131-229 9200
Scottish Crop Research Institute	01382-562731
Scottish Enterprise	0141-248 2700
Scottish Environment Protection	01786-457700
Scottish Fisheries Protection	0131-244 6059
Scottish Homes	0131-313 0044
Scottish Hospital Trust	0131-228 8111
Scottish Nuclear	01355-262000
Scottish Natural Heritage	0131-447 4784
Scottish Prison Service	0131-244 8745
Scottish Qualifications Authority	0141-248 7900
Scottish Record Office	0131-535 1314

Scottish Screen	0141-334 4445
Scottish Transport Group	0131-226 7491
Sports Council	0131-317 7200
State Hospitals Board	01555-840293
Tourist Board	0131-332 2433

NORTHERN IRISH QUANGOS

Agricultural Research Institute	028-9268 2484
Arts Council	028-9038 5200
NI Child Support Agency	028-9089 6666
Boundary Commission	020-7210 6569
Central Services Agency (Health)	028-9032 4431
Compensation Agency	028-9024 9944
Construction Service	028-9025 0284
Court Service	028-9032 8594
Curriculum Council	028-9026 1200
Driver & Vehicle Testing	028-9068 1831
Economic Council	028-9023 2125
Education & Library Boards	028-9049 1461
Enterprise Ulster	028-9073 6400
Environment & Heritage Service	028-9054 6569
Equal Opportunities Commission	028-9024 2752
Fair Employment Commission	028-9024 0020
Fire Authority	028-9266 4221
Fishery Harbour Authority	028-4461 3844
Forensic Science Agency of NI	028-9036 1888
General Consumer Council	028-9067 2488
Health & Safety Agency	028-9024 3249

Health & Social Services Trusts	028-9052 0500
Health Promotion Agency	028-9031 1611
Higher Education Council	028-9127 9333
Historic Monuments Council	028-9023 5000
Housing Executive	028-9024 0588
Human Rights	028-9024 3987
Industrial Court	028-9032 7666
Industrial Development Board	028-9023 3233
Industrial Research & Tech	028-9052 9533
Land Registers of NI	028-9025 1515
Law Reform Advisory Committee	028-9054 2900
Local Enterprise Development Unit	028-9049 1031
Local Govt Staff Commission	028-9031 3200
Nature Conservation Council	028-9023 5000
Ordnance Survey of NI	028-9025 5755
Planning Service	028-9054 0677
Police Authority	028-9023 0111
Police Complaints Commission	028-9024 4821
Prison Service	028-9052 0700
Probation Board	028-9026 2400
Public Record Office of NI	028-9025 1318
Rate Collection Agency	028-9025 2252
Social Security Agency NI	028-9052 0520
Sports Council	028-9038 1222
Statistics and Research Agency	028-9052 0700
Tourist Board	028-9023 1221
Training/Employment Agency	028-9025 7777
Transport Holding Company	028-9024 3456
Valuation & Lands Agency	028-9025 0700
Water Service	028-9024 4711
Youth Council	028-9064 3882

Local and regional government

British local government was radically overhauled by the creation of unitary authorities from 1995 to 1998. These single-tier authorities, responsible for all local government services, replaced much of the two-tier structure set up in 1974. In Wales, 22 unitaries took over from all eight county councils and 37 district councils. In Scotland, the 12 regional and 56 district councils were replaced by 32 unitaries. These 32 included Scotland's three islands councils (Orkney, Shetland and the Western Isles), which were already unitary. In England a confusing mixture of authorities with differing structures and powers was created in a random selection of places, in marked contrast to Wales and Scotland. Three of 1974's new county councils - Avon, Cleveland and Humberside - were abolished, along with the traditional county of Berkshire.

Herefordshire and Worcestershire were split, becoming separate counties again. England now has 387 authorities:

ENGLISH LOCAL AUTHORITIES

34 county councils
36 metropolitan districts
32 London boroughs
1 City of London
46 new unitary councils
238 district councils

Northern Ireland has remained unchanged. Since 1973 it has had 26 single-tier district councils, but these have fewer functions than the new mainland unitaries.

ELECTIONS 2000

Voting took place in 152 councils on 4 May 2000. There was a big Conservative swing, gaining 594 seats and control of 17 councils;

Labour lost 574 seats and 17 councils; the Lib Dems lost 18 seats, took two councils and lost three; and the Green Party won four seats.

But the national centre of attention was London, where the first voting took place on 4 May for the new London Assembly and its directly-elected mayor, together setting up and running the Greater London Authority (GLA). A referendum in May 1998 had given the go-ahead for the new way of managing London, rudderless since the abolition of the GLC in 1986. The GLA Act was passed in May 1999. A South Bank site near Tower Bridge was agreed as its home, with temporary premises in Marsham Street near Westminster. Brent East's Labour MP and former GLC leader Ken Livingstone said in August 1998 he would like to be mayor. Downing Street suffered tremors of horror and launched a no-holds-barred campaign against him. Fixing of the Labour Party candidate selection process resulted in Frank Dobson being chosen in late February 2000. Livingstone then stood as an independent. Widespread public distaste with Labour Party tactics gave him a massive victory and produced an anti-Labour vote (or non-vote) in the local elections throughout the country. In the mayor election, London was one constituency, with voters having two votes. In the assembly election, there were 14 constituencies and voters had two votes, one for their constituency member and one for 11 London-wide members. The results were:

LONDON MAYORAL ELECTION

Ken Livingstone (Independent)	667,877
Steve Norris (Conservative)	464,434
Frank Dobson (Labour)	223,884
Susan Kramer (Lib Dem)	203,452

Greater London Assembly

Labour	9
Conservative	9
Lib Dems	4
Green Party	3

There were 44,755,889 local government electors in the UK early in 2000. On the electoral register, England had 37,301,107, Scotland 4,009,424, Wales 2,239,321, and Northern Ireland 1,206,037. London had 5,114,898, with 1,892,483 in Inner London and the other 3,222,415 in Outer London.

NEXT LOCAL ELECTIONS

Most UK councillors are elected for four years. In England county council seats are all polled at the same time, once every four years (next: 2001). In that year there are no district council elections. In district councils each authority can choose whether to elect all seats together once every four years, or ballot a third of seats every year, but in either case the district elections must not be in the year of county elections. All London boroughs and the Corporation of London are held together every four years (next: 2002). Metropolitan authority elections are in thirds (next: 2002, not 2001). Unitaries elect new councillors either every four years, like counties, or in the same way as the districts. Elections are also four-yearly in Wales (next: 2003) and Northern Ireland (next: 2001), but in Scotland they are three-yearly (next: 2002). Most elections are on the first Thursday in May. In the Isle of Man, the House of Keys vote is held every five years, on the third Thursday in November (next: 2001).

FUTURES

The Labour government began reshaping local authorities with minor changes in the 1999 Local Government Act. More radical proposals were in the 1998 white paper Modern Local Government: In Touch with the People. In this, Whitehall said its aim was to make councils more open and accountable to the public by changing the political management structures. Its options included having a directly elected mayor. But when the white paper appeared as the Local Government Bill in November 1999 it sparked major opposition from the media. The Bill wanted to scrap decision-making by public committees, replacing them with a government-style Cabinet system. Impotent "scrutiny panels" would superficially keep an eye on the decisions and policies of the cabinet, but in reality with no power. The Bill was consistently condemned by the media, fearing it would create a Downing Street-style secret elite, beyond the control of both non-cabinet councillors and the public, all barred from the main meetings. Some placatory changes were made to the Bill in mid-2000, but critcs remained cynical.

REGIONALISM

An experiment with regional government began in England in April 1999, with the launch of eight Regional Development Agencies (RDAs). The granting of new forms of independence to Wales, Scotland and Northern Ireland during 1997/8 had prompted subdividing England into regions, with the RDAs given the role of regenerating local economies, clearing derelict land and creating jobs. The RDAs are business-led quangos, run by small boards of local notables, appointed by the Minister for the Regions, with a third of them councillors. But Downing Street put on temporary hold the idea of adding elected assemblies to the RDAs following the anti-Labour votes in Wales and Scotland. The idea was revived in July 2000, when London became the ninth RDA with the new Greater London Authority. The RDAs have similar boundaries to the ten Government Offices (GOs) for the Regions set up in England in 1994. The GOs run the regional programmes of the DTI, DfEE, DETR and Home Office. Each regional director reports to the relevant Secretary of State for each department. The GOs Central Unit acts as the main coordinating point. The DETR is the leader.

Government Offices for the Regions

Central Unit	020-7890 5005
East Midlands (GOEM, Nottingham)	0115-971 2753
Eastern Region (GOER, Cambridge)	01223-346766
London (GOL, Millbank)	020-7217 3456
Merseyside (GOM, Liverpool)	0151-224 6300
North East (GONE, Newcastle)	0191-201 3300
North West (GONW, Manchester)	0161-952 4000
South East (GOSE, Guildford)	01483-882255
South West (GOSW, Bristol)	0117-900 1700
West Midlands (GOWM, Birmingham)	0121-212 5050
Yorks & Humber (GOYH, Leeds)	0113-280 0600

Regional Development Agencies

Advantage West Midlands	0121-380 3500
East Midlands DA	0115-988 8300
East of England DA	01223-713900
London (GLA)	020-7983 4000
North West DA	01925-400100
One North East	0191-261 2000
SEEDA (South East England DA)	01483-484226
South West of England RDA	01392-214747
Yorkshire Forward	0113-243 9222

ONLINE

Most UK authorities are online. They usually use their name, minus "Council" etc, plus the suffix "gov.uk", eg www.bedfordshire.gov.uk.

CCTA Government Information Service
www.open.gov.uk
For seekers of all government organisations, including the locals and regionals.

DETR
www.local-regions.detr.gov.uk
The Whitehall basecamp for everything official about local and regional government.

Local Government Association
www.lga.gov.uk
National voice of local authorities in England and Wales

Local Government Information Unit
www.lgiu.gov.uk
The independent research and info organisation. Wide-ranging material available, both online and in print.

Tagish
www.tagish.co.uk
Comprehensive online lists of public sector links, especially the local authorities.

LOCAL GOVT. CONTACTS

Assoc of Electoral Administrators	0116-267 2015
Assoc of Local Auth Chief Execs	01923-897630
Assoc of London Government	020-7222 7799
Audit Commission for Local Auths	020-7828 1212
Centre for Local Economic Strategies	0161-236 7036
Chartered Institute of Public Finance &	
Accountancy (CIPFA)	020-7543 5600
Commission (Ombudsman) for Local Admin in:	
England	020-7915 3210
Scotland	0131-225 5300
Wales	01656-661325
Convention of Scottish Local Auths	0131-474 9200
DETR	020-7890 3000
English Partnerships	020-7976 7070
Institute of Revenues/Rating/Valuation	020-7831 3505
Local Government Association	020-7664 3000
Local Government Commission for	
England	020-7430 8400
Local Government Boundary Commissions:	
Scotland	0131-538 7510
Wales	029-2039 5031
Local Govt Information Unit	020-7554 2800
Local Govt International Bureau	020-7664 3100
Local Govt Management Board	020-7296 6600
Municipal Yearbook	020-7973 6400
National Assoc of Local Councils	020-7637 1865
New Local Government Network	020-7357 0051

ENGLISH TWO-TIER COUNCILS

County and district councils.

Bedfordshire 01234-363222
Bedford   01234-267422
Mid Bedfordshire   01525-402051
S Bedfordshire   01582-472222

Berkshire
Abolished 1998. See under Other
English Unitary Councils.

Buckinghamshire
                     01296-395000
Aylesbury Vale   01296-585858
Chiltern   01494-729000
South Bucks   01753-533333
Wycombe   01494-461000

Cambridgeshire
                     01223-717111
Cambridge   01223-457000
East Cambs   01353-665555
Fenland   01354-654321
Huntingdonshire   01480-388388
South Cambs   01223-443000

Cheshire   01244-602424
Chester   01244-324324
Congleton   01270-763231
Crewe/Nantwich   01270-537777
Ellesmere Port   0151-356 6789
Macclesfield   01625-500500
Vale Royal   01606-862862

Cornwall & Scilly Isles
                     01872-322000
Caradon   01579-341000
Carrick   01872-224400
Isles of Scilly   01720-422537
Kerrier   01209-614000
North Cornwall   01208-893333
Penwith   01736-362341
Restormel   01726-74466

Cumbria   01228-606060
Allerdale   01900-326333
Barrow-in-Furness   01229-894900
Carlisle City   01228-817000
Copeland   01946-852585
Eden   01768-864671
South Lakeland   01539-733333

Derbyshire   01629-580000
Amber Valley   01773-570222
Bolsover   01246-240000
Chesterfield   01246-345345
Derbyshire Dales   01629-580580

Erewash   0115-944 0440
High Peak   01663-751751
NE Derbyshire   01246-231111
S Derbyshire   01283-221000

Devon   01392-382000
East Devon   01395-516551
Exeter   01392-277888
Mid Devon   01884-255255
North Devon   01271-327711
South Hams   01803-861234
Teignbridge   01626-361101
Torridge   01237-476711
West Devon   01822-615911

Dorset   01305-251000
Christchurch   01202-495000
East Dorset   01202-886201
Purbeck   01929-556561
West Dorset   01305-251010
Weymouth & Portland
                     01305-761222

Durham   0191-386 4411
Chester-le-Street   0191-387 1919
Derwentside   01207-218000
Durham City   0191-386 6111
Easington   0191-527 0501
Sedgefield   01388-816166
Teesdale   01833-690000
Wear Valley   01388-765555

East Sussex   01273-481000
Eastbourne   01323-410000
Hastings   01424-781066
Lewes   01273-471600
Rother   01424-787878
Wealden   01892-653311

Essex   01245-492211
Basildon   01268-533333
Braintree   01376-552525
Brentwood   01277-261111
Castle Point   01268-792711
Chelmsford   01245-606606
Colchester   01206-282222
Epping Forest   01992-564000
Harlow   01279-446611
Maldon   01621-854477
Rochford   01702-546366
Tendring   01255-425501
Uttlesford   01799-510510

Gloucestershire
                     01452-425000
Cheltenham   01242-262626
Cotswold   01285-643643
Forest of Dean   01594-810000
Gloucester City   01452-522232
Stroud   01453-766321
Tewkesbury   01684-295010

Hampshire   01962-841841
Basingstoke & Deane
                     01256-844844
East Hampshire   01730-266551
Eastleigh   023-8061 4646
Fareham   01329-236100
Gosport   023-9258 4242
Hart   01252-622122
Havant   023-9247 4174
New Forest   023-8028 5000
Rushmoor   01252-516222
Test Valley   01264-364144
Winchester   01962-840222

Herefordshire
See: Other English Unitary Councils.

Hertfordshire 01992-555555
Broxbourne   01992-631921
Dacorum   01442-260161
East Herts   01279-655261
Hertsmere   020-8207 2277
North Herts   01462-474000
St Albans   01727-866100
Stevenage   01438-356177
Three Rivers   01923-776611
Watford   01923-226400
Welwyn Hatfield   01707-357000

Kent   01622-671411
Ashford   01233-637311
Canterbury   01227-763763
Dartford   01322-343434
Dover   01304-821199
Gravesham   01474-564422
Maidstone   01622-602000
Sevenoaks   01732-741222
Shepway   01303-850388
Swale   01795-424341
Thanet   01843-225511
Tonbridge/Malling   01732-844522
Tunbridge Wells   01892 526121

Lancashire   01772-254868
Burnley   01282-425011
Chorley   01257-515151
Fylde   01253-721222
Hyndburn   01254-388111
Lancaster   01524-582000
Pendle   01282-661661
Preston   01772-906000
Ribble Valley   01200-425111
Rossendale   01706-217777
South Ribble   01772-421491
West Lancashire   01695-577177
Wyre   01253-891000

Leicestershire
                     0116-232 3232
Blaby   0116-275 0555
Charnwood   01509-263151

Harborough	01858-410000
Hinckley & Bosworth	
	01455-238141
Melton	01664-567771
NW Leicestershire	01530-833333
Oadby & Wigston	0116-288 8961

Lincolnshire 01522-552222

Boston	01205-314200
East Lindsey	01507-601111
Lincoln	01522-881188
North Kesteven	01529-414155
South Holland	01775-761161
South Kesteven	01476-406080
West Lindsey	01427-615411

Norfolk 01603-222222

Breckland	01362 695333
Broadland	01603-431133
Gt Yarmouth	01493-856100
Kings Lynn & West Norfolk	
	01553-692722
North Norfolk	01263-513811
Norwich	01603-622233
South Norfolk	01508-533633

Northamptonshire 01604-236236

Corby	01536-402551
Daventry	01327-871100
East Northants	01832-742000
Kettering	01536-410333
Northampton	01604-233500
South Northants	01327-350211
Wellingborough	01933-229777

Northumberland 01670-533000

Alnwick	01665-510505
Berwick-upon-Tweed	
	01289-330044
Blyth Valley	01670-542000
Castle Morpeth	01670-514351
Tynedale	01434-652200
Wansbeck	01670-814444

North Yorkshire 01609-780780

Craven	01756-700600
Hambleton	01609-779977
Harrogate	01423-568954
Richmondshire	01748-850222
Ryedale	01653-600666
Scarborough	01723-232323
Selby	01757-705101
York	01904-613161

Nottinghamshire 0115-982 3823

Ashfield	01623-450000
Bassetlaw	01909-533533
Broxtowe	0115-917 7777
Gedling	0115-901 3901
Mansfield	01623-463463
Newark & Sherwood	
	01636-605111
Rushcliffe	0115-981 9911

Oxfordshire 01865-792422

Cherwell	01295-252535
Oxford	01865-249811
South Oxfordshire	01491-835351
Vale of White Horse	
	01235-520202
West Oxfordshire	01993-702941

Shropshire 01743-251000

Bridgnorth	01746-713100
North Shropshire	01939-232771
Oswestry	01691-671111
Shrewsbury & Atcham	
	01743-232255
South Shropshire	01584-874941

Somerset 01823-355455

Mendip	01749-343399
Sedgemoor	01278-435435
South Somerset	01935-462462
Taunton Deane	01823-356356
West Somerset	01984-632291

Staffordshire 01785-223121

Cannock Chase	01543-462621
East Staffs	01283-508000
Lichfield	01543-414000
Newcastle-under-Lyme	
	01782-717717
South Staffs	01902-696000
Stafford	01785-619000
Staffs Moorlands	01538-483409
Tamworth	01827-709709

Suffolk 01473-583000

Babergh	01473-822801
Forest Heath	01638-719000
Ipswich	01473-262626
Mid Suffolk	01449-720711
St Edmundsbury	01284-763233
Suffolk Coastal	01394-383789
Waveney	01502-562111

Surrey 020-8541 8800

Elmbridge	01372-474474
Epsom & Ewell	01372-732000
Guildford	01483-505050
Mole Valley	01306-885001
Reigate/Banstead	01737-276000
Runnymede	01932-838383
Spelthorne	01784-451499
Surrey Heath	01276-686252
Tandridge	01883-722000

Waverley	01483-861111
Woking	01483-755855

Warwickshire 01926-410410

North Warwicks	01827-715341
Nuneaton & Bedworth	
	024-7637 6376
Rugby	01788-533533
Stratford-on-Avon	01789-267575
Warwick	01926-450000

West Sussex 01243-777100

Adur	01273-455566
Arun	01903-716133
Chichester	01243-785166
Crawley	01293-438000
Horsham	01403-215100
Mid Sussex	01444-458166
Worthing	01903-239999

Wiltshire 01225-713000

Kennet	01380-724911
North Wiltshire	01249-706111
Salisbury	01722-336272
West Wiltshire	01225-776655

Worcestershire 01905-763763

Bromsgrove	01527-873232
Malvern Hills	01684-892700
Redditch	01527-64252
Worcester City	01905-723471
Wychavon	01386-565000
Wyre Forest	01562-820505

LONDON

Greater London Authority

GLA, London Assembly
& Mayor 020-7983 4000
www.london.gov.uk

London boroughs

Barking & Dagenham	
	020-8592 4500
Barnet	020-8359 2000
Bexley	020-8303 7777
Brent	020-8904 1244
Bromley	020-8464 3333
Camden	020-7278 4444
Croydon	020-8686 4433
Ealing	020-8579 2424
Enfield	020-8366 6565
Greenwich	020-8854 8888
Hackney	020-8356 5000
Hammersmith & Fulham	
	020-8748 3020
Haringey	020-8975 9700
Harrow	020-8863 5611
Havering	01708-772222

Hillingdon	01895-250111
Hounslow	020-8583 2000
Islington	020-7226 1234
Kensington & Chelsea	020-7937 5464
Kingston-upon-Thames	020-8546 2121
Lambeth	020-7926 1000
Lewisham	020-8695 6000
Merton	020-8543 2222
Newham	020-8472 1430
Redbridge	020-8478 3020
Richmond-upon-Thames	020-8891 1411
Southwark	020-7237 6677
Sutton	020-8770 5000
Tower Hamlets	020-7364 5000
Waltham Forest	020-8527 5544
Wandsworth	020-8871 6000
Westminster	020-7641 6000
City of London	020-7606 3030

ENGLISH UNITARY COUNCILS

Metropolitan district councils

In 1986 the six metropolitan counties (Greater Manchester, Merseyside, South Yorks, Tyne & Wear, West Midlands and West Yorks) were scrapped, turning their 36 district councils into unitaries.

Barnsley	01226-770770
Birmingham	0121-303 9944
Bolton	01204-522311
Bradford	01274-752111
Bury	0161-253 5000
Calderdale	01422-357257
Coventry	024-7683 3333
Doncaster	01302-734444
Dudley	01384-818181
Gateshead	0191-477 1011
Kirklees	01484-221000
Knowsley	0151-489 6000
Leeds	0113-234 8080
Liverpool	0151-227 3911
Manchester	0161-234 5000
Newcastle/North Tyneside	0191-200 5151
Oldham	0161-911 3000
Rochdale	01706-647474
Rotherham	01709-382121
Salford	0161-794 4711
Sandwell	0121-569 2200
Sefton	01704-533133
Sheffield	0114-272 6444
Solihull	0121-704 6000
South Tyneside	0191-427 1717

St Helens	01744-456000
Stockport	0161-480 4949
Sunderland	0191-553 1000
Tameside	0161-342 8355
Trafford	0161-912 1212
Wakefield	01924-306090
Walsall	01922-650000
Wigan	01942-244991
Wirral	0151-638 7070
Wolverhampton	01902-556556

Other English unitary councils

All were created by the reorganisation of 1995-98, except Guernsey, Jersey and Isle of Man, which already existed.

Bath & North East Somerset	01225-477000
Blackburn with Darwen	01254-585585
Blackpool	01253-477477
Bournemouth	01202-451451
Bracknell Forest	01344-424642
Brighton & Hove	01273-290000
Bristol, City of	0117-922 2000
Darlington	01325-380651
Derby	01332-293111
East Riding of Yorkshire	01482-887700
Guernsey	01481-717000
Halton	0151-424 2061
Hartlepool	01429-266522
Herefordshire, County of	01432-260000
Isle of Man	01624-685685
Isle of Wight	01983-821000
Jersey	01534-603000
Kingston upon Hull, County of	01482-610610
Leicester	0116-254 9922
Luton	01582-746000
Medway	01634-306000
Middlesbrough	01642-245432
Milton Keynes	01908-691691
NE Lincolnshire	01472-313131
North Lincolnshire	01724-296296
North Somerset	01934-888888
Nottingham	0115-915 5555
Peterborough	01733-563141
Plymouth	01752-668000
Poole	01202-633633
Portsmouth	023-9282 2251
Reading	0118-939 0900
Redcar & Cleveland	01642-444000
Rutland	01572-722577
Slough	01753-552288
S Gloucestershire	01454-868686
Southampton	023-8022 3855
Southend-on-Sea	01702-215000

Stockton on Tees	01642-393939
Stoke-on-Trent	01782-234567
Swindon	01793-463000
Telford & Wrekin	01962-202100
Thurrock	01375-390000
Torbay	01803-201201
Warrington	01925-444400
West Berkshire	01635-42400
Windsor & Maidenhead	01628-798888
Wokingham	0118- 974 6000
York	01904-613161

WELSH UNITARY COUNCILS

Blaenau Gwent	01495-350555
Bridgend	01656-643643
Caerphilly	01443-815588
Cardiff	029-2087 2000
Carmarthenshire	01267-234567
Ceredigion	01545-570881
Conwy	01492-574000
Denbighshire	01824-706000
Flintshire	01352-704476
Gwynedd	01286-672255
Isle of Anglesey	01248-750057
Merthyr Tydfil	01685-725000
Monmouthshire	01633-644644
Neath Port Talbot	01639-763333
Newport	01633-244491
Pembrokeshire	01437-764551
Powys	01597-826000
Rhondda Cynon Taff	01443-424000
Swansea	01792-636000
Torfaen	01495-762200
Vale of Glamorgan	01446-700111
Wrexham	01978-292000

SCOTTISH UNITARIES

Aberdeen City	01224-522000
Aberdeenshire	01467-620981
Angus	01307-461460
Argyll & Bute	01546-602127
Clackmannanshire	01259-450000
Dumfries & Galloway	01387-261234
Dundee City	01382-434000
East Ayrshire	01563-576000
E Dunbartonshire	0141-578 8000
East Lothian	01620-827827
East Renfrewshire	0141-577 3000
Edinburgh, City of	0131-200 2000
Falkirk	01324-506070

Fife	01592-414141	Armagh	028-3752 9600
Glasgow City	0141-287 2000	Ballymena	028-2566 0300
Highland	01463-702000	Ballymoney	028-7066 2280
Inverclyde	01475-717171	Banbridge	028-4066 2991
Midlothian	0131-270 7500	Belfast	028-9032 0202
Moray	01343-543451	Carrickfergus	028-9335 1604
North Ayrshire	01294-324100	Castlereagh	028-9079 9021
North Lanarkshire	01698-302222	Coleraine	028-7035 2181
Orkney Islands	01856-873535	Cookstown	028-7976 2205
Perth & Kinross	01738-475000	Craigavon	028-3834 1199
Renfrewshire	0141-842 5000	Derry	028-7136 5151
Scottish Borders	01835-824000	Down	028-4461 0800
Shetland Islands	01595-693535	Dungannon	028-8772 5311
South Ayrshire	01292-612000	Fermanagh	028-6632 5050
South Lanarkshire	01698-454444	Larne	028-2827 2313
Stirling	01786-443322	Limavady	028-7172 2226
West Dunbartonshire	01389-737000	Lisburn	028-9268 2477
West Lothian	01506-777000	Magherafelt	028-7963 2151
Western Isles (Eilean Siar)	01851-703773	Moyle	028-7076 2225
		Newry & Mourne	028-3026 5411
		Newtownabbey	028-9335 2681
		North Down	028-9127 0371
		Omagh	028-8224 5321
		Strabane	028-7138 2204

NI DISTRICT COUNCILS

| Antrim | 028-9446 3113 |
| Ards | 028-9182 4000 |

European Union

The European Union grew out of trading organisations created by Belgium, France, Germany, Italy, Luxembourg and the Netherlands in the 1950s. These USA-backed groupings created the European Economic Community (EEC) in 1957. The EEC was also known as the Common Market. During the 1970s members often dropped the word "Economic" from the title, but it did not officially become the European Community (EC) until 1980. The title European Union (EU) was adopted in 1993 when the Maastricht Treaty was ratified. The UK, Denmark and Ireland joined in 1973, Greece 1981, Spain and Portugal 1986, and Austria, Finland and Sweden 1995. This brought membership to 15 states (population 371 million), with another 12 probably joining in the next decade

The aims of the EU are essentially economic, but broader social and political powers were given by the 1986 Single European Act, the 1992 Maastricht Treaty and the 1997 Amsterdam Treaty, aimed at eventually creating a single European state. The Euro currency was launched in January 1999 by 11 countries, excluding Britain, where a referendum is likely to be held before joining. The Euro coins and notes do not go into circulation until January 2002.

The 1992 Maastricht Treaty gave the EU three pillars. The first is made up of the then-established institutions and decision-making processes, described below: the Council of Ministers, European Council, Parliament, Commission, Court of Justice and Court of Auditors. The second pillar consists of defence and foreign policy, while the third encompasses policing, immigration, terrorism and legal co-operation. The second and third pillars are intergovernmental and therefore outside EU parliamentary control.

The Council of Ministers (CoM) is the most powerful decision-making body in the EU. Also known as the Council of the European Union, the CoM, consists of ministers from each state, whose meetings take place behind closed doors. The presidency rotates every six months, with Sweden then Belgium in 2001.

Separate from the CoM is the European Council, comprising heads of state of each member country meeting two or three times a year. It sets political guidelines for the Council of Ministers. The European Council and CoM should not be confused with the similarly-named Council of Europe (CoE). This is a political institution outside the EU, set up by ten states in 1949, and today having 39 members. Alongside the CoE is the European Court of Human Rights, based in the Parliament building in Strasbourg.

The European Parliament's main role is to scrutinise the activities of the CoM and the staff-run Commission. An Ombudsman, appointed by Parliament, investigates malad-ministration. Parliament has 626 members (MEPs), 87 of them in the UK. Elections have been held every five years since 1979, with the most recent in June 1999. This used a pro-portional voting system for the first time, with the 87 former constituencies replaced by 12 regions, each with between three and 11 MEPs. The electorate voted for parties, not individuals. The election was a victory for anti-Euro Tories, who doubled their seats while Labour lost over half theirs.

UK IN THE EURO PARLIAMENT

Conservatives	36
Labour	29
Liberal-Democrats	10
UK Independence Party	3
Plaid Cymru	2
Scottish Nationalist Party	2
Green Party	2
Northern Ireland: SDLP	1
Democratic Unionist Party	1
Ulster Unionist Party	1

Parliament meets 17 times each year. MEPs sit in political rather than national groupings. The largest is the centre-right European Peoples' Party with 233 members, including the UK Tories. Labour's Party of European Socialists has 180.

The main driving force of the EU is the European Commission, being both the EU's executive civil service and its legislature. The Commission drafts proposals, which are looked at by Parliament and decided by the CoM. In charge are 20 commissioners, non-MEPs recommended by member states for five-year renewable terms. All 20 were forced to resign in March 1999 when they were held responsible for massive fraud, corruption and cronyism being carried out at all levels of the EU bureaucracy. The EC's work is conducted by 30 Directorates-General and similar departments, employing 15,000 officials.

The Court of Justice is the legal administra-tor. Its 15 judges sit in Luxembourg. Their judgements are binding on member states and have primacy over national law. The Court of Auditors controls the EU's financial activities. Other influential EU bodies are the Economic and Social Committee, giving advice to the Commission; the Committee of the Regions, which must be consulted about regional interests; and the European Invest-ment Bank, the EU's financing institution.

The EU's institutions are spread between Brussels; Luxembourg, where Commission and Parliament have offices and the Court of Justice is based; and Strasbourg, where Parliament meets a week a month. The CoM has meetings in Luxembourg two months a year. The committees meet in Brussels.

RESEARCH

EU information can be hard to find. On the phone, starting points are the London offices of the Commission and Parliament. Some public libraries have information. The official EU guidebook is Interinstitutional Directory of the European Union, the Brussels equiva-lent to the UK's Civil Service Yearbook. More detail is in the quarterly Vacher's European Companion. Online, there are many official websites; the main one is Europa (European Commission), while the most helpful is European Parliament UK (especially its Links section). The only independent body in Europe monitoring the EU's secret activities and their effects on civil liberties Europe-wide is Statewatch, based in London.

MAIN EURO WEBSITES

Official websites

Council of Europe	www.coe.fr
Europa (European Commission)	www.europa.eu.int
Information services	/geninfo/icom-en.htm
Statistics, data	/eurostat.html
European Court of Human Rights	www.echr.coe.int
European Information Network	www.europe.org.uk
European Parliament	www.europarl.eu.int
UK	www.europarl.org.uk
European Union Council	www.ue.eu.int
EU Court of Auditors	www.eca.eu.int
EU Court of Justice	www.curia.eu.int
EU Office for Publications	www-eur-op.eu.int
EU Ombudsman	www.euro-ombudsman.eu.int
EU Police	www.europol.eu.int
Information Society Project Office	www.ispo.cec.be
OECD	www.oecd.org
UK Foreign Office	www.fco.gov.uk/europe

Unofficial websites

Business for Sterling	www.bfors.com
Democracy Movement	www.euroland.co.uk
Euroguide	www.euroguide.org
New Europe	www.new-europe.co.uk
Rough Guides	www.hotwired.com/rough/europe
Statewatch	www.statewatch.org

PARLIAMENT/MINISTERS

Parliament: UK Information Office	020-7227 4300
Info Office Scotland	0131-225 2058
Secretariat, Luxembourg	00-352 43001
Parliament, Strasbourg	00-333 88174001
Parliament, Brussels	00-322 2842111
Ombudsman	00-333 88174427
Council of Ministers: Secretariat	00-322 2856111
UK Representation, Brussels	00-322 2878211

EUROPEAN PARTIES

European People's Party (233 members):	
Brussels	00-322 2854144
Tory MEPs, London	020-7222 1994
Party of European Socialists (180):	
Brussels	00-322 2842111
Labour MEPs, London	020-7222 1719
European Liberal, Democratic and Reformist	
Party (50)	00-322 2842111
Greens/European Free Alliance (48)	00-322 2843045
European United Left (42)	00-322 2842683
Union for Europe of Nations (31)	00-322 2843920
Europe of Democracies (16)	00-322 2842111
Non-attached (26)	00-322 2842579

EUROPEAN COMMISSION

HQ general	00-322 2991111
Luxembourg	00-352 430134925
UK offices: London	020-7973 1992
Cardiff	029-20371631
Edinburgh	0131-225 2058
Belfast	028-9024 8241

OTHER EU OFFICIAL BODIES

Committee of the Regions	00-322 2822211
Economic/Social Committee	00-322 5469011
European Court of Auditors	00-352 43981
European Court of Justice	
Secretariat, Luxembourg	00-352 43031
European Investment Bank	020-7343 1200
European Monitoring Centre for Drugs and	
Drug Addiction	00-3512 8113000
Office for Official Publications	00-352 29291

OTHER ORGANISATIONS

Business in Europe - DTI Info Service	0117-944 4888
Consumers in Europe Group	020-7881 3021
Council of Europe	00-333 88412000
European Broadcasting Union	
(Geneva)	00-4122 7172111
European Cultural Foundation	00-3120 6760222
European Free Trade Association	
EFTA (Geneva)	00-4122 7491111
European Movement	020-7881 8989
European Patent Office (Munich)	00-4989 23990
European Round Table	00-322 5343100
European Trade Union Confederation	
(Brussels)	00-322 240121
GATT (Geneva)	00-4122 7395111
House of Commons Select Committee on	
European Legislation	020-7219 5465
International Federation of Newspaper	
Publishers (Paris)	00-331 47428500
International Press Centre	00-322 2850800
NATO (Brussels)	00-322 7074111
OECD (Paris)	00-331 45248200
Solidar	00-322 5001020
Statewatch	020-8802 1882
TUC European Information Service	020-7636 4030
United Nations (London)	020-7630 1981
Western European Union	00-322 5004411

EURO-SCEPTICS

Bruges Group	020-7287 4414
Business for Sterling	020-7931 7143
Campaign Against Euro Federalism	0151-638 2780
Campaign for an Independent Britain	020-8340 0314
Congress for Democracy	01372-453678
Democracy Movement (anti-Euro)	0990-110440
Euro Facts	020-8746 1206
European Foundation	020-7930 7319
Freedom Association	020-7793 4228
New Europe (anti-Euro)	020-7582 1001
Save Britain's Fish	01472-317686
UK Independence Party	020-7434 4559
Youth Against the EU	01795-539227

The legal system

There are separate legal systems in Scotland, England/Wales, and Northern Ireland, with significant differences in judicial procedures, the law and court structures. But the three systems share the common distinction between criminal law (dealing with offences against state laws) and civil law (settling disputes between individuals or organisations).

In England and Wales every criminal case starts in juryless magistrates courts, where most are also settled. Serious crimes move on to the 93 crown courts, where they are heard in front of a judge and jury. The leading crown court is the Central Criminal Court, best-known as the Old Bailey. Civil actions start in: the many local county courts; the magistrates courts in certain limited actions; or the Queens Bench, Chancery or Family Divisions of the High Court in more complicated cases. The High Court is based in the Royal Court of Justice in London's Strand. The biggest reform of the civil justice system for a century took place in April 1999.

Appeals are heard by the Criminal or Civil Divisions of the Court of Appeal, housed in the Royal Court of Justice. From the Court of Appeal, cases involving important points of law can ask to be heard by the House of Lords. The Criminal Cases Review Commission investigates suspected miscarriages of justice in England, Wales and Northern Ireland.

In Scotland, district courts are the equivalent of the magistrates courts. Above the districts are the sheriff courts, arranged in six sheriffdoms. They hear both criminal and civil cases, combining the roles of the crown and county courts south of the border. The Procurator Fiscal Service conducts public prosecutions. The final criminal court is the High Court of Justiciary, which is both a trial and appeal court; there is no appeal to the House of Lords. The supreme civil court is the Court of Session, but subject to the Lords.

The Northern Ireland legal system is similar to England and Wales, with magistrates, crown and county courts. The big difference is that terrorism cases are usually heard before judges without juries. Crown court appeals go to the Northern Ireland Court of Appeal, and then the House of Lords.

The primary source of law is Parliament, which has no legal limits on what it can do, although it must comply with European Union law. The UK's 1998 Human Rights Act came in to force in October 2000, requiring all public authorities to act in accordance with the European Convention on Human Rights.

LAW OFFICERS

Lord Chancellor's Dept	020-7210 8500
Press	020-7210 8512
	www.open.gov.uk/lcd
Attorney General & Solicitor General	020-7271 2400
Press	020-7271 2405
Scotland: Lord Advocate/Sol. Gen.	0131-226 2626
Northern Ireland: Law Barristers	028-9024 1523

APPEAL COURTS

Judicial Committee of Privy Council	020-7270 0483
House of Lords Appellate Committee	020-7219 3000
Lord Chancellor's secretary	020-7219 3232
Scotland: High Court	0131-225 2595
Court of Appeal, Royal Courts of:	
Justice, Strand	020-7947 6000
Civil Division	020-7947 6409
Criminal Division	020-7947 6011

SUPREME COURTS

England/Wales

Royal Courts of Justice, Strand	020-7947 6000
Crown Office	020-7947 6205
Lord Chief Justices clerk	020-7947 6001
Master of the Rolls clerk	020-7947 6371
Chancery Division	020-7947 6167
Family Division	020-7947 6540
Queens Bench Division	020-7947 6000
Court Service	020-7210 2092

Scotland

Court of Session and High Court of Justiciary	0131-225 2595
Crown Office (HQ, Procurator Fiscal)	0131-226 2626
Scottish Courts Administration	0131-229 9200

Northern Ireland

Supreme Court of Judicature	028-9023 5111
Court Service	028-9032 8594

CROWN COURTS

Crown Courts handle the most serious criminal cases. There are six circuits, each under an administrator responsible to the Lord Chancellor. The main court is the Central Criminal Court (Old Bailey) in the South East Circuit.

Midland and Oxford Circuit

Circuit Administrator (Birmingham)	0121-681 3200
Birmingham	0121-681 3300
Coventry	01203-536166
Derby	01332-622600
Grimsby	01472-311811
Hereford	01432-276118
Leicester	0116-222 2323
Lincoln	01522-883000
Northampton	01604-470400
Nottingham	0115-910 3500
Oxford	01865-264200
Peterborough	01733-349161
Shrewsbury	01743-355775
Stafford	01785-255217
Stoke-on-Trent	01782-854000
Warwick	01926-495428
Wolverhampton	01902-481000
Worcester	01905-730800

North Eastern Circuit

Circuit Administrator (Leeds)	0113-2511200
Bradford	01274-840274
Doncaster	01302-322211
Durham	0191-386 6714
Hull	01482-586161
Leeds	0113-283 0040
Newcastle-upon-Tyne	0191-383 5800
Sheffield	0114-281 2400
Teeside	01642-340000
York	01904-645121

Northern Circuit

Circuit Administrator (Manchester)	0161-833 1005
Barrow-in-Furness	01772-832300
Bolton	01204-392881
Burnley	01282-416899
Carlisle	01228-520619
Lancaster	01524-32454
Liverpool	0151-473 7373
Manchester	0161-954 1800
Preston	01772-832300

South Eastern Circuit

Circuit Administrator (London)	020-7947 6000
Aylesbury	01296-434401
Bury St Edmunds	01284-762676
Cambridge	01223-224666
Canterbury	01227-819200
Chelmsford	01245-603000
Chichester	01243-520700
Guildford	01483-468500
Ipswich	01473-213841
Kings Lynn	01553-760847
Lewes	01273-480400
London: Old Bailey	020-7248 3277
Croydon	020-8410 4700
Harrow	020-8424 2294
Inner London Sessions, SE1	020-7234 3100
Isleworth	020-8568 8811
Kingston-upon-Thames	020-8240 2500
Knightsbridge, SE1	020-7922 5800
Middlesex Guildhall, SW1	020-7799 2131
Snaresbrook, E11	020-8982 5500
Southwark, SE1	020-7522 7200
Wood Green, N22	020-8881 1400
Woolwich, SE28	020-8312 7000
Luton	01582-522000
Maidstone	01622-202000
Norwich	01603-728200
Reading	0118-9674400
St Albans	01727-834481
Southend	01268-458000

Wales and Chester Circuit

Circuit Administrator (Cardiff)	029-2041 5500
Caernarfon	01286-675200
Cardiff	029-2034 5931
Carmarthen	01267-236071
Chester	01244-317606
Dolgellau	01286-675200
Haverfordwest	01437-764782
Knutsford	01565-755486
Merthyr Tydfil	01685-358222
Mold	01352-754343
Newport	01633-266211
Swansea	01792-510200
Warrington	01925-256700
Welshpool	01938-553144

Western Circuit

Circuit Administrator (Bristol)	0117-974 3763
Barnstaple	01271-373286
Bournemouth	01202-502800
Bristol	0117-976 3030
Dorchester	01305-778684
Exeter	01392-210655
Gloucester	01452-529351
Newport	01983-526821
Plymouth	01752-208284
Portsmouth	023-9282 3000
Salisbury	01722-325444
Southampton	023-8021 3200
Swindon	01793-614848
Taunton	01823-335972
Truro	01872-222340
Winchester	01962-841212

N IRELAND CROWN COURTS

Court Service	028-9032 8594
Armagh	028-3752 2816

Ballymena	028-2564 9416
Belfast	028-90242099
Craigavon	028-3834 1324
Derry	028-7136 3448
Downpatrick	028-4461 4621
Enniskillen	028-6632 2356
Newtownards	028-9181 4343
Omagh	028-8224 2056

COUNTY COURTS

Midlands/Oxford
Birmingham	0121-681 4441
Nottingham	0115-910 3500
Stafford	01785-255217

North Eastern
Leeds	0113-283 0040
Newcastle-upon-Tyne	0191-201 2000
Sheffield	0114-281 2400

Northern
Liverpool	0151-473 7373
Manchester	0161-954 1800
Preston	01772-832300

South Eastern
Chelmsford	01245-264670
Kingston-upon-Thames	020-8546 8843
London	020-7917 5000
Maidstone	01622-202000

Wales & Chester
Cardiff	029-2037 6400
Chesterfield	01246-501200

Western
Bristol	0117-929 4414
Exeter	01392-210655
Winchester	01962-841212

SCOTTISH SHERIFF COURTS

Glasgow & Strathkelvin
Regional office	0141-429 5566
Sheriff courts	0141-429 8888

Grampian, Highlands & Islands
Regional office	01463 230782
Aberdeen	01224-648316
Banff	01261-812140
Dingwall	01349-863153
Dornoch	01862-810224
Elgin	01343-542505
Fort William	01397-702087
Inverness	01463-230782
Kirkwall	01856-872110
Lerwick	01595-693914
Lochmaddy	01876-500340
Peterhead	01779-476676
Portree	01478-612191
Stonehaven	01569-762758
Stornoway	01851-702231

Tain	01862-892518
Wick	01955-602846

Lothian & Borders
Regional office	0131-225 2525
Duns	01835-863231
Edinburgh	0131-225 2525
Haddington	01620-822936
Jedburgh	01835-863231
Linlithgow	01506-842922
Peebles	01721-720204
Selkirk	01750-21269

North Strathclyde
Regional office	0141-887 5225
Campbeltown	01586-552503
Dumbarton	01389-763266
Dunoon	01369-704166
Greenock	01475-787073
Kilmarnock	01563-520211
Oban	01631-562414
Paisley	0141-887 5291
Rothesay	01700-502982

South Strathclyde, Dumfries & Galloway
Regional office	01698-284000
Airdrie	01236-751121
Ayr	01292-268474
Dumfries	01387-262334
Hamilton	01698-282957
Kirkcudbright	01557-330574
Lanark	01555-661531
Stranraer	01776-702138

Tayside, Central & Fife
Regional office	01382-229961
Alloa	01259-722734
Arbroath	01241-876600
Cupar	01334-652121
Dundee	01382-229961
Dunfermline	01383-724666
Falkirk	01324-620822
Forfar	01307-462186
Kirkcaldy	01592-260171
Perth	01738-620546
Stirling	01786-462191

LAW CENTRES

Law centres provide free legal advice and representation. They are run by voluntary committees of local people, and are usually financed by local authorities. The centres are members of the Law Centres Federation.

Law Centres Federation
18-19 Warren St, London W1P 5DB
Fax 020-7387 8368   Tel 020-7387 8570
www.lawcentres.org.uk

Local law centres

Avon & Bristol	0117-924 8662
Birmingham (Saltley)	0121-328 2307
Bradford	01274-306617
Cardiff	029-2049 8117
Carlisle	01228-515129
Chesterfield	01246-550674
Coventry	024-7622 3051
Derby	01332-344557
Gateshead	0191-477 1109
Glasgow (SCastlemilk)	0141-634 0313
Gloucester	01452-423492
Humberside	01482-211180
Huddersfield (Kirklees)	01484-518525
Ireland: North (Belfast)	028-9032 1307
Leeds (Harehills)	0113-249 1100
Leicester	0116-255 3781
Liverpool Eight	0151-709 7222
London: Brent	020-8451 1122
Camberwell	020-7701 9499
Camden	020-7485 6672
Central London	020-7839 2998
Greenwich	020-8853 2550
Hackney	020-8985 8364
Hammersmith & Fulham	020-8741 4021
Hillingdon	020-8561 9400
Hounslow	020-8570 9505
Newham	020-8555 3331
North Islington	020-7607 2461
North Kensington	020-8969 7473
North Lambeth	020-7582 4373
North Lewisham	020-8692 5355
Paddington	020-8960 3155
Plumstead	020-8855 9817
Southwark	020-7732 2008
Springfield	020-8767 6884
Stockwell & Clapham	020-7720 6231
Tottenham	020-8347 9792
Tower Hamlets	020-7247 8998
Wandsworth & Merton	020-7228 9462
Luton	01582-481000
Manchester: North	0161-205 5040
South	0161-225 5111
Wythenshawe	0161-498 0905
Middlesbrough	01642-223813
Newcastle	0191-230 4777
Nottingham	0115-978 7813
Oldham	0161-627 0925
Rochdale	01706-657766
Salford	0161-736 3116
Scottish Association	0141-445 6451
Sheffield	0114-273 1888
Warrington	01925-651104
Wiltshire	01793-486926

LEGAL INFO/ADVICE

The government's Community Legal Service website Just Ask! gives help and advice, like the existing Legal Aid site. The Legal Action Group works to improve legal services for disadvantaged people. Statewatch monitors the legal activities of the state, focusing on Europe. Commercial (but free) legal info websites are appearing, eg Law.com, UK Legal.

Advice Services Alliance	020-7236 6022
British & Irish Legal Information Institute	www.bailii.org
Childrens Legal Centre	01206 873820
Citizens Advice Bureaux (HQ)	020-7833 2181
	www.adviceguide.org.uk
Community Legal Service	www.justask.org.uk
Disability Law Service	020-7791 9800
Earthrights (Environmental Law & Resource Centre)	07071-225011
Environmental Law Foundation	020-7404 1030
	www.greenchannel.com/elf/
Fed of Independent Advice Centres	020-7489 1800
	www.fiac.org.uk
FindLaw Legal Information	www.findlaw.com
Free Representation Unit	020-7831 0692
Inquest	020-8802 7430
Jurist Legal Education Network	www.law.cam.ac.uk
Justice	020-7329 5100
Law.com	www.law.com/uk
LawLinks: Legal Information on the Internet	http://library.ukc.ac.uk/library/lawlinks
Legal Action Group	020-7833 2931
	www.lag.org.uk
Legal Aid	020-7813 1000
	www.legal-aid.gov.uk
Legal Defence & Monitoring Group	020-8533 7116
Liberty	020-7403 3888
Lifers Campaign	01992-769632
Release	020-7729 9904
Rights of Women	020-7251 6577
Society of Voluntary Associates	020-7793 0404
Statewatch	020-8802 1882
	www.statewatch.org
UK Legal	www.uklegal.com

PROFESSIONAL BODIES

Bar Council	020-7242 0082
	www.barcouncil.org.uk
British Institute of International & Comparative Law	020-7636 5802
Coroners' Society	020-8979 6805
Court Services (Lord Chancellor Dept)	020-7210 2266
	www.courtservice.gov.uk
Criminal Cases Review Commission	0121-633 1800
Crown Prosecution Service	020-7796 8000
Enquiries	020-7334 8505
	www.cps.gov.uk
Law Commission	020-7453 1220
	www.lawcom.gov.uk
Law Society	020-7242 1222
	www.lawsociety.org.uk
Law Society of Scotland	0131-226 7411
Legal Services Commission	020-7759 0000
	www.legalservices.gov.uk
Magistrates Assoc	020-7383 4020
Serious Fraud Office	020-7239 7272

Prisons

There are 136 prisons in England and Wales, 22 in Scotland and four in Northern Ireland. They are run by separate prison services, listed below, which are executive agencies under the wing of the Home Office. England and Wales now have 64,800 prisoners, an increase of 30 per cent in a decade. Of these, 61,500 (95 per cent) are male, and 11,150 of them young offenders aged 15-21. Scotland has 6,000 prisoners, 97 per cent of them male, and Northern Ireland 1,500. There are 25,100 governors and officers, plus 18,400 other staff, including 257 chaplains. All prisons are full to overflowing, costing about £28,000 per prisoner per year. The last Tory government began privatising the prison system, giving eight prisons to contractors. The 1997 Labour government said it would bring them back into the public sector, but instead by mid-2000 it was using the threat of possible privatisation as a way of making prisons run themselves more cost-effectively. Over 70% of prisoners in England and Wales were found to have more than one of the main types of mental disorder in 1997, according to a survey carried out by the Department of Health. The conditions of prisoners are monitored and reported to Parliament by independent prisons inspectorates. They inspect about 20 prisons a year. There is also a prisons mbudsman covering England and Wales.

PRISON AGENCIES

HM Prison Service	020-7217 6000
	www.hmprisonservice.gov.uk
Press	020-7217 6633
Operations - North	020-7217 6677
Operations - South	020-7217 6447
Scottish Prison Service	0131-244 8745
	www.sps.gov.uk
Press	0131-244 8476
Prisons - South & West	0131-244 8546
Prisons - North & East	0131-244 8741
N Ireland Prison Service	028-9052 0700

GOVT. DEPARTMENTS

Home Office: Main number	020-7273 4000
	www.homeoffice.gov.uk

Parole Board, Eng & Wales	020-7217 5314
Prison Inspectorate, Eng & Wales	020-7273 3702
	www.homeoffice.gov.uk/hmipris.htm
Prisons Ombudsman	020-7276 2876
	www.homeoffice.gov.uk/prisons/prisomb.htm
Scottish Executive: Main number	0131-556 8400
	www.scotland.gov.uk
Press	0131-244 1111
Parole Board	0131-244 8755
Prison Inspectorate	0131-244 8481
Northern Ireland Office: Press	028-9052 8233

PRISON BODIES

Apex Trust	020-7638 5931
Howard League for Penal Reform	020-7281 7722
Inquest	020-8802 7430
Justice	020-7329 5100
NACRO (National Assoc for the Care & Resettlement of Offenders)	020-7582 6500
National Assoc of Prison Visitors	01234-359763
National Assoc of Probation Officers	020-7223 4887
National Council for Prisoners Abroad	020-7561 6820
National Prisoners Movement	020-8542 3744
Prison Governors Association	020-7217 8591
Prison Officers Association	020-8803 0255
Prison Reform Trust	020-7251 5070
Prison Watch	01332-756158
Prisoners Advice Service	020-7405 8090
Prisoners Families and Friends	020-7403 4091
Prisoners' Wives & Families Society	020-7278 3981
Women in Prison	020-7226 5879
Women Prisoners' Centre	020-8968 3121

MALE PRISONS

O = open prison

Acklington, Northumberland	01670-760411
Albany, Isle of Wight	01983-524055
Aldington, Kent	01233-720436
Ashwell, Leics	01572-774100
Bedford	01234-358671
Belmarsh, London SE28	020-8317 2436
Birmingham, Winson Green	0121-554 3838
Blakenhurst, Worcs	01527-543348
Blantyre House, Kent	01580-211367
Blundeston, Suffolk	01502-730591
Brinsford, Wolverhampton	01902-791118
Bristol	0117-980 8100
Brixton, London SW2	020-8674 9811
Brockhill, Worcs	01527-550314
Buckley Hall, Lancs	01706-861610
Bullingdon, Oxon	01869-322111
Camp Hill, Isle of Wight	01983-527661
Canterbury, Kent	01227-762244
Cardiff	029-2043 3100
Channings Wood, Devon	01803-812361
Chelmsford, Essex	01245-268651

Coldingley, Surrey	01483-476721
Dartmoor, Devon	01822-890261
Doncaster	01302-760870
Dorchester, Dorset	01305-266021
Downview, Surrey	020-8770 7500
Durham	0191-386 2621
Elmley, Kent	01795-880808
Erlestoke, Wilts	01380-813475
Everthorpe, Humberside	01430-422471
Exeter, Devon	01392-278321
Featherstone, Wolverhampton	01902-790991
Feltham, Middlesex	020-8890 0061
Ford (O), West Sussex	01903-717261
Frankland, Co Durham	0191-384 5544
Full Sutton, York	01759-375100
Garth, Lancs	01772-622722
Gartree, Leics	01858-410234
Glen Parva, Leics	0116-264 3100
Gloucester	01452-529551
Grendon & Spring Hill, Bucks	01296-770301
Guernsey, Channel Islands	01481-48376
Haslar, Hants	023-9258 0381
Haverigg, Cumbria	01229-772131
Hewell Grange (O), Worcs	01527-550843
High Down, Surrey	020-8643 0063
Highpoint (O), Suffolk	01440-823100
Hindley, Lancs	01942-866255
Holme House, Cleveland	01642-673759
Hull, N Humberside	01482-320673
Isle of Man	01624-621306
Jersey, Channel Islands	01534-44181
Kingston, Hants	023-9289 1100
Kirkham (O), Lancs	01772-684343
Kirklevington Grange, Cleveland	01642-781391
Lancaster	01524-385100
Latchmere House, Surrey	020-8948 0215
Leeds, West Yorks	0113-263 6411
Leicester	0116-254 6911
Lewes, East Sussex	01273-405100
Leyhill (O), Glos	01454-260681
Lincoln	01522-533633
Lindholme, South Yorks	01302-848700
Littlehey, Cambs	01480-812202
Liverpool	0151-525 5971
Long Lartin, Worcs	01386-830101
Low Newton, Co Durham	0191-386 1141
Maidstone, Kent	01622-755611
Manchester	0161-834 8626
Moorland, South Yorks	01302-351500
Morton Hall (O), Lincs	01522-866700
The Mount, Herts	01442-834363
North Sea Camp (O), Lincs	01205-760481
Norwich	01603-437531
Nottingham	0115-962 5022
Parkhurst, Isle of Wight	01983-523855
Pentonville, London N7	020-7607 5353
Preston, Lancs	01772-257734
Ranby, Notts	01777-706721
Reading, Berks	0118-958 7031
Risley, Cheshire	01925-763871
Rochester, Kent	01634-838100
Send, Surrey	01483-223048
Shepton Mallet, Somerset	01749-343377
Shrewsbury, Salop	01743-352511
Stafford	01785-254421

Standford Hill (O), Kent	01795-880441
Stocken, Leics	01642-673759
Sudbury (O), Derbys	01283-585511
Swaleside, Kent	01795-884100
Swansea	01792-464030
Usk, Gwent	01291-672411
Verne, Dorset	01305-820124
Wakefield, West Yorks	01924-378282
Wandsworth, London SW18	020-8874 7292
Wayland, Norfolk	01953-858100
Wealston (O), West Yorks	01937-844844
Wellingborough, Northants	01933-224151
Whatton, Notts	01949-850511
Whitemoor, Cambs	01354-660653
Winchester, Hants	01962-854494
Wolds, Humberside	01430-421588
Woodhill, Bucks	01908-501999
Wormwood Scrubs, W12	020-8743 0311
Wymott, Lancs	01772-421461

FEMALE PRISONS

Askham Grange (O), York	01904-704236
Bullwood Hall, Essex	01702-202515
Cookham Wood, Kent	01634-814981
Drake Hall (O), Staffs	01785-858100
Durham	0191-386 2621
East Sutton Park (O), Kent	01622-842711
Eastwood Park	01454-262100
Exeter, Devon	01392-278321
Holloway, London N7	020-7607 6747
Low Newton, Co Durham	0191-386 1141
New Hall, West Yorks	01924-848307
Risley, Cheshire	01925-763871
Styal, Cheshire	01625-532141

SCOTTISH PRISONS

Aberdeen	01224-876868
Barlinnie, Glasgow	0141-770 2000
Cornton Vale, Stirling	01786-832591
Dungavel, Lanarkshire	01357-440371
Edinburgh	0131-444 3000
Friarton, Perth	01738-625885
Glenochil, Clackmannanshire	01259-760471
Inverness	01463-233320
Longriggend, Lanarkshire	01236-830392
Low Moss, Glasgow	0141-762 4848
Noranside, Angus	01356-650217
Penninghame, Wigtownshire	01671-402886
Perth	01738-622293
Peterhead, Aberdeenshire	01779-479101
Shotts, Lanarkshire	01501-824000

N IRELAND PRISONS

Belfast: Crumlin Road	028-9074 1100
Maghaberry, Co Antrim	01846-611888
Magilligan, Co Londonderry	01504-763311
Maze, Co Antrim	01846-683111

International

Full details of the UK's 220 overseas diplomatic missions and all organisations in London representing foreign states are on www.fco.gov.uk/directory. Below, HCom = High Commission, Em = Embassy, Con = Consulate.

Afghanistan: London Em	020-7589 8891
Albania: London Em	020-7730 5709
Algeria: London Em	020-7221 7800
UK Em, Algiers	00-2132 30068
Angola: London Em	020-7495 1752
UK Em, Luanda	00-2442 392991
Antigua: London HCom	020-7486 7073
UK HCom, St Johns	00-1268 4620008
Argentina: London Em	020-7318 1300
UK Em, Buenos Aires	00-541 148037070
Australia: London HCom	020-7379 4334
UK HCom, Canberra	00-612 62706666
UK Con, Melbourne	00-613 96504155
UK Con, Perth	00-618 92215400
UK Con, Sydney	00-612 92477521
Austria: London Em	020-7235 3731
UK Em, Vienna	00-431 716130
Azerbaijan: London Em	020-7938 3412
Bahamas: London HCom	020-7408 4488
UK HCom, Nassau	00-1242 3257471
Bahrain: London Em	020-7370 5132
UK Em, Bahrain	00-973 534404
Bangladesh: London Em	020-7584 0081
UK HCom, Dhaka	00-8802 882705
Barbados: London HCom	020-7631 4975
UK HCom, Bridgetown	00-1246 4366694
Belarus: London Em	020-7937 3288
Belgium: London Em	020-7470 3700
UK Em, Brussels	00-322 2876211
Belize: London HCom	020-7499 9728
UK HCom, Belmopan	00-5018 22146
Bolivia: London Em	020-7235 4248
UK Em, La Paz	00-5912 433424
Bosnia: London Em	020-7255 3758
UK Em, Sarejevo	00-38771 444429
Botswana: London HCom	020-7499 0031
UK HCom, Gaborone	00-267 352841
Brazil: London Em	020-7499 0877
UK Con, Rio	00-5521 5533223
Brunei: London HCom	020-7581 0521
UK HCom, Begawan	00-6732 222231
Bulgaria: London Em	020-7584 9400
UK Em, Sofia	00-3592 4923335
Burma: London Em	020-7499 8841
UK Em, Rangoon	00-951 295300
Burundi: UK Con, Bujumbura	00-2564 1257054
Cameroon: London HCom	020-7727 0771
UK Em, Yaounde	00-237 220545
Canada: London HCom	020-7258 6600
UK HCom, Ottawa	00-1613 2371530
UK Con,Vancouver	00-1604 6834421
Chad: UK Em, Ndjamena	00-235 513064
Chile: London Em	020-7580 6392
UK Em, Santiago	00-562 2313737
China: London Em	020-7636 8845
UK Em, Beijing	00-8610 65321961
UK Con, Hong Kong	00-852 29013000
Colombia: London Em	020-7589 9177
UK Em, Bogota	00-571 2185111
Costa Rica: London Em	020-7706 8844
UK Em, San Jose	00-506 2215566
Cote d'Ivoire: London Em	020-7235 6991
UK Em, Abidjan (via operator)	225-226850
Croatia: London Em	020-7387 2022
UK Em, Zagreb	00-3851 4555310
Cuba: London Em	020-7240 2488
UK Em, Havana	00-537 241771
Cyprus: London HCom	020-7499 8272
UK HCom, Nicosia	00-3572 861100
Czech Republic: London Em	020-7243 1115
UK Em, Prague	00-4202 57320355
Denmark: London Em	020-7333 0200
UK Em, Copenhagen	00-45 35445200
Dominican Republic:UK HCom	020-7370 5194
UK Em, Santo Domingo	00-1809 4727111
Eastern Caribbean: London HCom	020-7937 9522
UK HCom, Castries	00-1758 4522484
Ecuador: London Em	020-7584 1367
UK Em, Quito	00-5932 560669
Egypt: London Em	020-7499 2401
UK Em, Cairo	00-202 3540850
El Salvador: London Em	020-7436 8282
UK Em, San Salvador	00-503 2239047
Estonia: London Em	020-7589 3428
UK Em, Tallinn	00-372 6313353
Ethiopia: London Em	020-7589 7212
UK Em, Addis Ababa	00-2511 612354
Fiji: London Em	020-7584 3661
UK Em, Suva	00-679 311033
Finland: London Em	020-7838 6200
UK Em, Helsinki	00-3589 22865100
France: London Em	020-7201 1000
UK Em, Paris	00-331 44513100
UK Con, Marseille	00-334 91157210
Gabon: London Em	020-7823 9986
UK Em, Libreville	00-241 762200
Gambia: London HCom	020-7937 6316
UK HCom, Banjul	00-220 495133
Georgia: London Em	020-7937 8233
UK Em, Tbilisi	00-99532 940578
Germany: London Em	020-7824 1300
UK Em, Bonn	00-49228 91670
UK Em, Berlin	00-4930 201840

UK Con, Frankfurt	00-4969 1700020
Ghana: London HCom	020-7235 4142
UK Em, Accra	00-23321 221665
Greece: London Em	020-7727 9934
UK Em, Athens	00-301 7236211
Grenada: London HCom	020-7373 7809
UK HCom, St Georges	00-1473 4403222
Guatemala: London Em	020-7351 3042
UK Em, Guatemala City	00-5023 321601
Guinea: UK Em, Conakry	00-224 442959
Guyana: London HCom	020-7229 7684
UK Em, Georgetown	00-5922 65881
Haiti: UK Em, Port au Prince	00-509 573969
Honduras: London Em	020-7486 4880
UK Em, Tegucigalpa	00-504 325429
Hungary : London Em	020-7235 5218
UK Em, Budapest	00-361 2662888
Iceland: London Em	020-7590 1100
UK Em, Reykjavik	00-354 5515883
India: London HCom	020-7836 8484
UK HCom, Bombay	00-9122 2830517
UK HCom, Calcutta	00-9133 2425171
Indonesia: London Em	020-7499 7661
UK Em, Jakarta	00-6221 330904
Iran: London Em	020-7225 3000
UK Em, Tehran	00-9821 675011
Iraq: London via Jordan Em	020-7937 3685
UK Em, Baghdad	00-9641 5372121
Irish Republic: London Em	020-7235 2171
UK Em, Dublin	00-3531 2053700
Israel: London Em	020-7957 9500
UK Em, Tel Aviv	00-9723 5429178
Italy: London Em	020-7312 2200
UK Con, Milan	00-3902 723001
Ivory Coast: London Em	020-7235 6991
UK Em, Abidjan	00-225 226850
Jamaica: London HCom	020-7823 9911
UK HCom, Kingston	00-1876 9269050
Japan: London Em	020-7465 6500
UK Em, Tokyo	00-813 52111100
Jerusalem: UK Con	00-9722 5828281
Jordan: London Em	020-7937 3685
UK Em, Amman	00-9626 823100
Kazakhstan: London Em	020-7581 4646
UK Em, Almaty	00-73272 506192
Kenya: London HCom	020-7636 2371
UK HCom, Nairobi	00-2542 335944
Korea: London Em	020-7227 5500
UK Em, Seoul	00-822 7357341
Kuwait: London Em	020-7590 3400
UK Em, Kuwait	00-965 2403324
Latvia: London Em	020-7312 0040
UK Em, Riga	00-371 7338126
Lebanon: London Em	020-7229 7265
UK Em, Beirut	00-9614 417007
Lesotho: London HCom	020-7235 5686
UK HCom	00-266 313961
Liberia: London Em	020-7221 1036
Libya: London via Saudi Arabian Em	
Libyan Interests Section	020-7589 6120
Lithuania: London Em	020-7486 6401
UK Em, Vilnius	00-3702 222070
Luxembourg: London Em	020-7235 6961
UK Em, Luxembourg	00-352 229864
Malawi: London HCom	020-7491 4172
UK HCom, Lilongwe	00-265 782400
Malaysia: London HCom	020-7235 8033
UK HCom, Kuala Lumpur	00-603 2482122
Malta: London HCom	020-7292 4800
UK HCom, Valletta	00-356 233134
Mauritius: London HCom	020-7581 0294
UK HCom, Port Louis	00-230 2111361
Mexico: London Em	020-7499 8586
UK Em, Mexico City	00-525 2072089
Mongolia: London Em	020-7937 0150
UK Em, Ulaan Bataar	00-9761 458133
Morocco: London Em	020-7581 5001
UK Em, Rabat	00-2127 720905
Mozambique: London Em	020-7383 3800
UK Em, Maputo	00-2581 420111
Namibia: London HCom	020-7636 6244
UK HCom, Windhoek	00-26461 223022
Nepal: London Em	020-7229 1594
UK Em, Kathmandu	00-9771 416460
Netherlands: London Em	020-7590 3200
UK Em, The Hague	00-3170 4270427
UK Con, Amsterdam	00-3120 6764343
New Zealand: London HCom	020-7930 8422
UK HCom, Wellington	00-644 4726049
Nicaragua: UK Em, Managua	00-5052 780014
Niger: UK Em, Niamey	00-227 732015
Nigeria: London HCom	020-7839 1244
UK HCom, Lagos	00-2341 2632903
Norway: London Em	020-7591 5500
UK Em, Oslo	00-4723 132700
UK Con, Bergen	00-4755 944705
Oman: London Em	020-7225 0001
UK Em, Muscat	00-968 693077
Pakistan: London HCom	020-7664 9200
UK HCom, Islamabad	00-9251 822131
UK HCom, Karachi	00-9221 5872436
Panama: London Em	020-7493 4646
UK Em, Panama City	00-507 2690866
Papua New Guinea: London HCom	020-7930 0922
UK HCom, Port Moresby	00-675 3251643
Paraguay: London Em	020-7937 1253
UK Em, Asuncion	00-59521 444472
Peru: London Em	020-7235 1917
UK Em, Lima	00-5114 334735
Philippines: London Em	020-7937 1600
UK Em, Manila	00-632 8167116
Poland: London Em	020-7580 4324
UK Em, Warsaw	00-4822 6253030
Portugal: London Em	020-7235 5331
UK Em, Lisbon	00-3511 3924000
Qatar: London Em	020-7493 2200
UK Em, Doha	00-974 421991
Romania: London Em	020-7937 9666
UK Em, Bucharest	00-401 3120305
Russian Fed. London Em	020-7229 3628

UK Em, Moscow	00-7503 9567200
Saudi Arabia: London Em	020-7917 3000
UK Em, Riyadh	00-9661 4880077
Senegal: London Em	020-7937 7237
UK Em, Dakar	00-221 8237392
Seychelles: London HCom	020-7224 1660
UK HCom, Victoria	00-248 225225
Singapore: London HCom	020-7235 8315
UK HCom, Singapore	00-65 4739333
Slovak Republic: London Em	020-7243 0803
UK Em, Bratislava	00-4217 54419632
Slovenia: London Em	020-7495 7775
UK Em, Ljubljona	00-38661 1257191
Somalia: UK HCom	00-2521 20288
South Africa: London Em	020-7451 7299
UK Em, Cape Town	00-2721 253670
UK Em, Pretoria	00-2712 342220
UK Con, Jo'burg	00-2711 3378940
Spain: London Em	020-7235 5555
UK Em, Madrid	00-3491 31085201
UK Con, Barcelona	00-3493 4199044
UK Con, Malaga	00-3495 2217571
Sri Lanka: London HCom	020-7262 1841
UK HCom, Colombo	00-941 437336
Sudan: London Em	020-7839 8080
UK Em, Khartoum	00-24911 777105
Swaziland: London HCom	020-7630 6611
UK HCom, Mbabane	00-268 4042581
Sweden: London Em	020-7917 6400
UK Em, Stockholm	00-468 6719000
Switzerland: London Em	020-7616 6000
UK Em, Berne	00-4131 3525021
UK Con, Geneva	00-4122 9182400
UK Con, Zurich	00-411 2611520
Syria: London Em	020-7245 9012
UK Em, Damascus	00-96311 3712561
Tanzania: London HCom	020-7499 8951
UK HCom, Dar es Salaam	00-25551 29601
Thailand: London Em	020-7589 2944
UK Em, Bangkok	00-662 2530191
Trinidad: London HCom	020-7245 9351
UK HCom, Port of Spain	00-1868 6229087
Tunisia: London Em	020-7584 8117
UK Em, Tunis	00-2161 341444
Turkey: London Em	020-7393 0202
UK Em, Ankara	00-90312 4686230
Uganda: London HCom	020-7839 5783
UK HCom, Kampala	00-25641 257054
Ukraine: London Em	020-7727 6312
UK Em, Kiev	00-38044 4620011
UAE London Em	020-7581 1281
UK Em, Abu Dhabi	00-9712 326600
United States: London Em	020-7499 9000
UK Em, Washington	00-1202 4621340
UK Con, Chicago	00-1312 3461810
UK Con, Dallas	00-1214 5214090
UK Con, Los Angeles	00-1310 4773322
UK Con, Miami	00-1305 3741522
UK Con, New York	00-1212 7450200
Uzbekistan: London Em	020-7229 7679

UK Em, Tashkent	00-998 716338416
Vanuatu: UK HCom, Vila	00-678 23100
Venezuela: London Em	020-7584 4206
UK Em, Caracas	00-582 9934111
Vietnam: London Em	020-7937 1912
UK Em, Hanoi	00-844 8252510
Yemen: London Em	020-7584 6607
UK Em, Sanaa	00-9671 264081
Yugoslavia: London Em	020-7370 6105
UK Em, Belgrade	00-38111 645055
Zaire: London Em	020-7235 6137
UK Em, Kinshasa	00-24312 34775
Zambia: London HCom	020-7589 6655
UK HCom Lusaka	00-2601 251133
Zimbabwe: London HCom	020-7836 7755
UK HCom, Harare	00-2634 793781

OVERSEAS TERRITORIES

The UK's Overseas Territories (OTs) are the last remnants of the British Empire. A century ago, Britain ruled 400 million people on a third of the planet. Today there are 180,000 people living in the 13 remaining colonies, fragments of land whose governors are still appointed by the Queen, and whose government is the responsibility of the Foreign and Commonwealth Office (FCO). Much of the old empire now forms the Commonwealth, an association bound by affinity rather than treaty. It comprises 54 states with 1.6 billion people, a quarter of the world's population. Several of the OTs play military, telecomms or strategy roles for the UK. The OTs were called Dependent Territories until early 1999, when the government aimed to reflect the independent character of the territories by giving them a clearer identity. A white paper began the process of granting full UK citizenship to the 125,000 residents who had lost it under the 1983 British Nationality Act. A new Overseas Territories Department was created inside the FCO, co-ordinating all government policies on the OTs. Separate from the FCO is the Department for International Development, the former Overseas Development Administration, rebuilt by the Labour government to help halve the proportion of people living in extreme poverty by 2015. Also aiming to overcome the injustices of the world is the information-packed website Oneworld.

Foreign & Commonwealth Office
Main number	020-7270 3000
	www.fco.gov.uk
Overseas Territories Dept	020-7270 2643
Press	020-7270 3100
Information dept	020-7270 3909

Dept for International Development
Main number	020-7917 7000
	www.dfid.gov.uk
Press	020-7917 0950
Information Dept	020-7917 0435

THE COLONIES

Anguilla
Small east Caribbean island. 37 sq miles, 10,700 pop.
Governor, Anguilla   00-1264 4972621

Bermuda
West Atlantic group of 100 small islands, 20 inhabited, 600 miles off North Carolina. 60,100 pop. 21 sq miles.
Governor, Hamilton   00-1441 2955151

British Antarctic Territory
Uninhabited section of Antarctica, including South Orkney and South Shetland islands. Run from London.
FCO Antarctic Dept   020-7270 2742

British Indian Ocean Territory
Large group of the small Chagos Archipelago islands in central Indian Ocean, south of India. Uninhabited, except for joint UK/USA military base on Diego Garcia.
Port Louis   00-230 2111361

British Virgin Islands
Eastern Caribbean group of 46 islands, 11 inhabited, near Anguilla. 59 sq miles, 19,100 pop.
Governor, Tortola   00-1284 4942345

Cayman Islands
Three tax-free, wealthy Caribbean islands south of Cuba. Home of 36,600 people and nearly as many companies, dodging everything. 100 sq miles.
Governor, George Town   00-1345 9497900

Falkland Islands
Largest islands in the South Atlantic, off southern Argentina. 4,700 sq miles, 2,220 pop, plus military.
FCO   020-7270 2749
Governor, Stanley   00-500 27433

Gibraltar
2.5 sq mile promontory of southernmost Spain, captured 1704. 27,200 pop.
FCO   020-7270 2975
Governor   00-350 45440

Hong Kong
Ceased being a dependent territory from 1 July 1997.

Montserrat
East Caribbean volcanic island, 39 sq miles, 3,500 pop.
Governor   00-1664 4912688

Pitcairn Islands
Eastern group in Pacific, midway between north New Zealand and Peru. 14 sq miles, 54 pop, all Seventh Day Adventists. Home of mutineers from the Bounty, 1790.
FCO   020-7270 2955
Governor   00-644 726049

St Helena
Island in the middle of the South Atlantic, 1,100 miles off Angola. Former prison of Napoleon. 47 sq miles. 5,000 pop, with dependencies.
FCO   020-7270 2749
Governor   00-290 2555

St Helena dependent: Ascension Island
700 miles NW of St Helena. 34 sq miles, 1,120 pop.
Administrator   00-247 6311

St Helena dependent: Tristan da Cunha
Island group 1,850 miles west of Cape Town. 285 pop.
Administrator   00-8741 4545435

South Georgia and South Sandwich Islands
Scattered islands east and south-east of Cape Horn. South Georgia is military, South Sandwich uninhabited volcanic.
Commissioner, Stanley   00-500 27433

Turks and Caicos Islands
Thirty Caribbean islands, north of Haiti. 20,000 pop.
Governor, Grand Turk   00-1649 9462308

INTERNATIONAL BODIES

The OneWorld website is the most wideranging alternative/supplement to the FCO's. See also the International section of the Action chapter at the back of this book.

British Council	020-7930 8466
	www.britcoun.org
Commonwealth Institute	020-7603 4535
	www.commonwealth.org.uk
Commonwealth Journalists Assoc	020-7486 3844
Commonwealth Press Union	020-7583 7733
	www.cpu.org.uk
Commonwealth Secretariat	020-7839 3411
	www.thecommonwealth.org
Federal Trust	020-7799 2818
Int. Fed. for Info & Documentation	00-3170 3140671
Int. Fed. of Newspaper Publishers	00-331 47428500
International Grains Council	020-7513 1122
	www.igc.org
International Labour Organisation	020-7828 6401
	www.ilo.org
International Maritime Organisation	020-7735 7611
	www.imo.org
International Mobile Satellite Org	020-7728 1000
	www.inmosat.org
International Sugar Organisation	020-7513 1144
International Whaling Commission	01223-233971
NATO	00-322 7074111
	www.nato.int
OneWorld	01494-481629
	www.oneworld.net
United Nations UK Info Centre	020-7630 1981
HQ, New York	00-1212 9634475
	www.un.org
World Bank Group	020-7930 8511
	www.worldbank.org

Disasters and emergencies

At national level, there is an emergency government system kept in readiness for the most serious disasters. It can be activated either as a whole or in part, and is most likely to be used during a foreign attack or mass civil unrest. The top layer consists of the prime minister, key ministers and top civil servants, plus chief military and police officers. In the most extreme emergency this would become the UK government, operating from a hardened communications base, especially the Crisis Management Centre, an expensive, high-tech nuclear-proofed bunker 20 metres below the main MoD building in Whitehall. This has special communications links with key central and local government organisations and the emergency services. The Emergency Powers Act 1920 gives the government extra authority when needed; it has been invoked so far on 12 occasions, all resulting from industrial disputes.

The Cabinet Office is responsible for creating disaster-handling policies, the Home Office for administering them. In charge is the Cabinet Office standing committee called the Civil Contingencies Committee (CCC), formerly known as the Civil Contingencies Unit. The committee comprises civil servants and some ministers, including representatives from the Treasury, Downing Street and the Cabinet Office, and is chaired by the Home Secretary. The CCC's terms of reference are: "To co-ordinate the preparation of plans for ensuring in an emergency the supplies and services essential to the life of the community, to keep these plans under regular review, to supervise their prompt and effective implementation in specific emergencies; and to report all necessary to the appropriate Ministerial Committee." The CCC appoints a government department (the "lead" department) to put plans into effect. The committee mounted its biggest planning operation in the run-up to the computer bug threat at the end of 1999. Widespread chaos was feared, including anarchist riots on the streets of the City of London. Nothing of significance actually happened, but the CCC carried out its first full-scale rehearsal for any type of disaster.

The Home Office Emergency Planning Division (EPD) runs the disaster system day-to-day on behalf of the CCC. The Division sets and maintains standards, represents the UK internationally and initiates central government arrangements. The EPD says: "Emergency planning involves assessing threats and where possible preventing them, tackling major emergencies, carrying on business as usual and restoring normality afterwards." At the core of the EPD is the Central and Local Government Group (CLGG), playing policy and operational roles. It operates the Emergency Operations Suite in the Home Office main building. The suite is maintained in a constant state of preparedness for any major disaster. The Suite has specially trained staff, supported by the latest high-tech equipment, supervised by another EPD unit, the Telecommunications Group (TG). This runs the Emergency Communications Network (ECN), a resilient, heavily-protected network, linking key elements of central government with regional and local emergency services, via its own telephone system. It is designed to ensure that Whitehall will maintain contact with, and therefore control of, all UK civil and military forces in the worst possible disasters. The creation of the ECN in the 1990s rendered redundant the post-war regional underground bunkers designed to set up devolved government in Cold War emergencies.

Home Office	020-7273 4000
	www.homeoffice.gov.uk
Press	020-7273 4610
Emergency Planning Division	020-7273 2577
	www.homeoffice.gov.uk/epd
Central & Local Govt Group	020-7273 3215
Telecommunications Group	020-7273 3195
International & Home Defence Group	020-7273 3310
Emergency Planning College	01347-821406
Cabinet Office	020-7270 1234
	www.cabinet-office.gov.uk
Press	020-7270 0635

REGIONS AND LEADERS

Below national level, Whitehall maintains regional control through the ten Government Offices in England. These have to replicate at regional and local level the work being done on the national infrastructure by the CCC.

Also spreading emergency planning out of Whitehall are the lead government departments. In an emergency, a specific department is the leader in co-ordinating affected departments in their handling of regional and local issues. The lead department acts as the focal point for communications between central government and any local Strategic Co-ordinating Group. Individual departments responsible for handling certain disasters are:

Flooding - MAFF or equivalents in Scottish, Welsh and Northern Ireland Offices.
Gas clouds - (DETR).
Marine and coastal pollution - DETR.
Marine: offshore installations - DETR.
Military - MoD.
Miscellaneous (building collapse, dam failures, earthquakes) - DETR or Scottish/Welsh/N Ireland Office.
Overseas disasters - FCO.
Radiation inside UK - Civil installations: DTI & Scottish Offices. Civil in transit: DETR. Military: MoD.
Radiation from outside UK - DETR.
Rivers, water services - DETR or Scottish/Welsh/N Ireland Offices.
Satellites - Home Office.
Search and rescue - Civil shipping: DETR (Coastguard Agency). Military shipping and aircraft, and civil aircraft at sea: MoD. Civil aircraft on land: DETR.
Sports accidents - DCMS, Scottish/Welsh Offices.
Transport accidents - DETR.
Weather - DETR (high winds: Home Office) or Scottish/Welsh/N Ireland Offices.

LOCAL PLANS

Local authorities have emergency planning duties. Each county-type authority has its own emergency planning officer (EPO), drawing up management plans. The EPOs are grant-aided local limbs of the Home Office EPD. The EPO is the starting point for inquiring about proposals for dealing with local disasters. Contact via the county councils, listed in this book under Local Government.

In the front line handling any disaster are the four emergency services, with the military in special reserve. All operate emergency procedures day-to-day, and have press offices for handling queries. They also have their own schemes for dealing with major incidents. These services and the EPOs operate within a three-level, Home Office-agreed management framework. In 1999 the Home Office reviewed this system, with the aim of creating joint 999 call centres and shared buildings for the three emergency services. Three local pilot projects were set up.

Many volunteer agencies help the official services, including the WRVS, RNLI, Red Cross, St John Ambulance, Raynet (a network of radio amateurs) and mountain rescue.

MEDIA

As the police normally take initial charge at a disaster, the Home Office says they should set up a media liaison point run by an experienced press officer. Media access to the disaster site would be controlled. If media relations are difficult, the regional office of the Central Office of Information can send a press officer. The Home Office is rethinking its relationship with the media following the 1999 Paddington rail disaster There is no single guidebook covering all contingency planning. The nearest is the Home Office handbook Dealing with Disaster covering emergency planning, as does the Home Office website.

EMERGENCY BODIES

Air Accidents Investigation, DTI	01252-510300
BASICS	01473-218407
British Airways Crisis Team, Gatwick	020-8513 0917
British Divers Marine Life Rescue	01634-281680
British Red Cross	020-7235 5454
British Safety Council	020-8741 1231
Casualties Union	020-7278 6264
Disasters Emergency Committee	020-7580 6550
Emergency Planning Society	020-8937 4984
International Rescue Corps	01324-665011
Marine Accident Investigation, DTI	023-80395500
National Centre for Volunteering	020-7520 8900
National Chemical Emergency Centre	01235-463060
National Voluntary Civil Aid Service	020-8977 2806
Royal Life Saving Society	01789-773994
Royal Society for the Prevention of Accidents	0121-248 2000
Search & Rescue Dog Assoc: Wales	01492-622195
England	0702-0960970
Lake District	01768-772463
Southern Scotland	01835-822211
Highlands	01721-721998
St John Ambulance	020-7235 5231
Underwater Search Unit	020-7275 4488

The military

The UK armed forces are run by the Defence Council, comprising Ministry of Defence (MoD) ministers and leading officers, including the Chief of the Defence Staff, the top militarist. Whitehall says: "The purpose of the MoD and the Armed Forces is to: defend the UK, and Overseas Territories, our people and interests; act as a force for good by strengthening international peace and security."

At the heart of this policy is NATO, to which most British forces are committed. NATO was set up in 1949 to unite Western Europe and North America in the anti-Soviet Cold War, which ended around 1990. In 1994 NATO adopted a more global perspective and the Combined Joint Task Force was set up to carry out a wider range of missions around the world. In 1997 military ties between NATO, all Europe, Russia and central Asia were created, and its membership increased to 19 in 1999. The multinational Allied Command Europe Rapid Reaction Corps (ARRC) has 55,000 UK troops and is commanded by a UK general. Britain's pre-Cold War NATO policies were transformed by the Strategic Defence Review of 1998. It committed the UK to a worldwide role with the ability to send large expeditionary forces to any kind of trouble spot, anticipating significant changes in the methods of warfare by 2015.

The total strength of the UK armed forces is 324,200, made up of: Army 109,700, RAF 55,200, Navy 43,700; plus 115,700 civilians. There are 60,900 regular reserves and 58,000 volunteer reserves The budget for 1999/2000 was £22.8 billion, 2.5 per cent of the GDP. Royal Navy equipment took £.3 billion, Army £1.7 billion and RAF £4.5 billion.

The MoD's administrative HQ is the Main Building (known by staff as "The Building") in Whitehall. At its core is a newly-renovated underground nuclear-proof bunker. This is called the Joint Operations Centre by militarists and the Crisis Management Centre by civilians. In the most severe crisis it would act as government HQ, and it has secure com

munications links with all departments.

Day-to-day military action is run from the new Permanent Joint Headquarters (PJHQ) in another bunker, next to the Navy's headquarters at Northwood, north-west London. PJHQ is the overall control centre for national military operations, superseding many former single-service bodies. It is also the control point of another new organisation, the Joint Rapid Reaction Forces (JRRF). This military fire brigade is a pool of all readily available forces with "real punch and protection" able to undertake any short-notice joint operation.

The Army's own operations centre is the Land Command, sited in (and under) the village of Wilton, just west of Salisbury. This is the hatching ground for any Army direct action inside the UK. The Royal Navy is run from Northwood and the Portsmouth Naval Base. The RAF is controlled by the Headquarters Strike Command, completely reorganised in early 2000. Its High Wycombe base is also home of the Combined Air Operations Centre, co-ordinating all RAF action.

The UK also has Special Forces, which the MoD says have "four primary roles: reconnaissance, offensive action, the provision of support to indigenous forces and counter-terrorism". Journalists are warned that operations are so sensitive that the MoD "will pursue all appropriate legal options to prevent the publication of information about the Special Forces which it considers to be potentially damaging". Inside the UK troops have three roles, jointly called Military Aid to the Civil Authorities. Military Aid to the Civil Power (MaC-P) is providing armed forces to help the police during violent civil challenges to state authority, as in Northern Ireland. Military Assistance to Civil Ministries (MaC-M) involves using troops to carry out specialised services for government departments, especially during strikes. Military Aid to the Civil Community (MaC-C) is arranging for service personnel to help the public during emergencies like the Millennium Bug scare.

MINISTRY OF DEFENCE

MoD + Army/RN/RAF	020-7218 9000
	www.mod.uk
Press office: Policy	020-7218 7925
Procurement	020-7218 7714
Army	020-7218 3256
Navy	020-7218 3258
RAF	020-7218 3254
Outside office hours	020-7218 7907
Chief of Defence Staff	020-7218 2116
Air Force: Chief of Staff	020-7218 6313
Army Department: Chief of Staff	020-7218 7873
Navy Department: First Sea Lord	020-7218 6193
UK CICC (Wilton)	01722-433208
Permanent Joint HQ	
At Northwood, Mdx	01923 826161
Press	01923-846029
24-hr duty officer	01923-846260
Army	www.army.mod.uk
HQ Land Command (Wilton)	01722-336222
HQ Northern Ireland (Lisburn)	01846-609261
HQ Scotland (Edinburgh)	0131-310 2092
London District	020-7414 2396
Second Division (York)	01904-662433
Third Division (Wilts)	01980-672946
Fourth Division (Aldershot)	01252-347011
Fifth Division (Shrewsbury)	01743-262252
Infantry HQ (Warminster)	01985-214000
Royal Navy	www.royal-navy.mod.uk
Commander-in-Chief Fleet (Northwood)	01923-837635

Naval Home Command (Portsmouth)	023-9272 3737
Surface Flotilla HQ (Portsmouth)	023-9272 2351
Aviation Command (Yeovilton)	01935-455548
Royal Marines (Plymouth)	01752-554558
	www.royal-marines.mod.uk
Naval Bases: Devonport	01752-554344
Faslane	01436-674321
RAF	www.raf.mod.uk
Strike Command (High Wycombe)	01494-461461
Logistics Command (Huntingdon)	01480-52151
Air Warfare Centre (Lincs)	01522-720271
No 1 Group	01494-461461
No 11/18 Group	020-8838 7000
No 38 Group	01494-461461
USAF HQ (Mildenhall)	01638-543000
Military Air Traffic Operations (Uxbridge)	01895-276009
Other MoD sections	
D Notice Committee	020-7218 2206
Defence Intelligence Staff	020-7218 2407
Magazines: Navy News	023-9282 6040
RAF News	01452-712612
Soldier Magazine	01252-347355
Ministry of Defence Police	01371-854000
Overseas forces: Cyprus	00357-2802505
Falkland Islands	00500-74204
Germany	004921-61472392
Gibraltar	003505-4231
NATO HQs: Supreme, Europe	003265-447111
Allied Forces NW Europe	01494-461461
Allied Forces Central Europe	003145-261111
Allied Forces South Europe	003981-5709053
Supreme Commander Atlantic	001757-4453258

Intelligence

Britain's three main intelligence agencies are MI5, MI6 and GCHQ. Parliamentary supervision of them comes from the all-party Intelligence and Security Committee, which has to "examine the expenditure, administration and policy" of the trio. It meets in secret and publishes an uninformative annual report. Chairman is Tory MP Tom King.

Management of the three agencies is supervised by the Cabinet Office's Joint Intelligence Organisation (JIO). It administers the Joint Intelligence Committee (JIC) which oversees MI6 and GCHQ, but not MI5. The JIC sets the UK's national intelligence priorities and produces regular assessments of raw material gathered by MI6 and GCHQ. The committee

is made up of officers from many departments and meets weekly. MI5 is monitored by another part of the JIO, the Sub-Committee on Security Service Priorities and Performance (SO-SSPP). Complaints against MI5 are investigated by the Security Service Tribunal, MI6's by the Intelligence Services Tribunal. MI5 is also overseen by the Intelligence and Security Liaison Unit of the Home Office.

Working alongside MI5, MI6 and GCHQ, but separately, is the military's Defence Intelligence Staff (DIS), part of the MoD. It analyses information from a "wide variety of sources", and passes it on as necessary. The DIS is buried deep within the MoD, and virtually impossible to contact.

MI5

Britain's internal counter-subversion organisation is MI5, officially called the Security Service. Set up in 1909, it currently holds 290,000 files on individuals. Only 17,500 of these are "open for inquiries" (ie, in active use; the rest are dormant). MI5's main role is: "The protection of national security and, in particular, its protection against threats from espionage, terrorism and sabotage, from the activities of agents of foreign powers and from actions intended to overthrow or undermine parliamentary democracy by political, industrial or violent means" and to "safeguard the economic well-being of the UK" (1989 Security Service Act). In 1996 MI5 was given a wider remit, allowing it to intervene in areas unrelated to "national security".

Since then MI5 has joined the police in fighting "serious crime". Its definition takes in "conduct by a large number of persons in pursuit of a common purpose", a catch-all description. The activities of some environmentalists are one of its areas of operation. In this and similar cases MI5 co-ordinates with the police via the new National Public Order Intelligence Unit, set up in 1999 in New Scotland Yard. MI5's main police contact point is the Special Branch (SB). All 55 police forces have their own SB, but in practice they are subsidiaries of the Metropolitan Police.

Stephen Lander is Director-General of MI5, with 1,900 staff. It is run on a budget of "less than £140 million", with 53 per cent spent on terrorism and 12 per cent on "protective security". This is MI5's most sensitive work, defending the core of the State from disruption. MI5 is based in Thames House, the former ICI headquarters on Millbank, bought and refurbished for £326 million in 1993/4 (original estimates were £100 million). In 1998, MI5 for the first time made public one of its phone numbers (but only for informants) and opened a website. It also publishes regularly a guide called MI5: The Security Service.

MI5 (for informants only)	020-7930 9000
	www.mi5.gov.uk
Security Service Tribunal	020-273 4095
Home Office press contacts	020-7273 4610
CIA (USA equivalent of MI5/6)	www.odci.gov

MI6

The Secret Intelligence Service (SIS, or MI6) is Britain's overseas spying agency. The 1994 Intelligence Services Act put MI6 and GCHQ on a statutory footing for the first time and widened MI6's role. It operates "in the interests of national security or of the economic well-being of the UK, or in support of the prevention or detection of serious crime", where "persons outside the British Islands" are suspects. The MI6 Chief is Richard Dearlove, appointed in 1999. He has 2,000 staff. The annual budget is £140 million. MI6 in 1994 moved into its new HQ Vauxhall Cross, next to Vauxhall Bridge, and almost facing MI5 across the Thames. It should have cost £152 million, but instead reached £221 million.

Foreign Office press contacts	020-7270 3100
FCO	www.fco.gov.uk
Intelligence Services Tribunal	020-7273 4383

GCHQ

The Government Communications Headquarters (GCHQ) is Britain's most powerful intelligence gathering agency. The secret eavesdropping centre, with 4,500 civilian staff and 2,000 military, is in Cheltenham. Its role is defined by the 1994 Intelligence Services Act. Its primary work is providing government departments and the military with signal intelligence (Sigint) and eavesdropping on all types of communication, including internet. This is in support of Whitehall's security, military, foreign and economic policies, and "the prevention or detection of serious crime". GCHQ works with its US equivalent, the National Security Agency (NSA), which together with Britain runs UKUSA, a worldwide intelligence operation. The NSA is the largest intelligence agency in the world. Its main listening post is on 560 acres of Menwith Hill, near Harrogate. Menwith intercepts all European phone, fax and e-mail communications. GCHQ, responsible to the Foreign Office, has an annual budget of £440 million. Its director is Kevin Tebbit. A high-tech superpower new HQ at Cheltenham costing £330 million should be completed by 2004.

GCHQ, Cheltenham	01242-221491
	www.gchq.gov.uk

Police

The UK has 52 police forces: 39 in England, four in Wales, eight in Scotland and one in Northern Ireland. Two of England's forces are in London: the Metropolitan (the "Met"), based at New Scotland Yard on Victoria Street; and the City of London, responsible only for the City, with its headquarters close to the Guildhall. There are about 127,000 police officers in England and Wales, 14,800 in Scotland and 8,500 in Northern Ireland. The Met is the biggest force, with 26,300 officers.

In England and Wales, all forces are maintained by local police authorities. By law, all these, except the Met, must have 17 members: nine local councillors, three magistrates and five "independents" (chosen by the other members from a short-list supplied by the Home Office). The Home Secretary directly controlled the Met as its authority until July 2000, when the new Greater London Authority took over, through its 23-member Metropolitan Police Authority. In Scotland, the police authorities are the new unitary councils. In Northern Ireland, the Royal Ulster Constabulary (RUC) is controlled by an authority appointed by the government. But under the 1998 Good Friday Agreement a new NI Police Service should be created and the RUC's name should be changed, a proposal that has aroused much controversy. Each police force is run by a chief constable, who is only nominally responsible to the police authority. The Home Office provides just over half the finance for the forces, thereby giving it more power than the authorities. This means Britain has a national police force in many respects, but one that is not acknowledged or directly controllable as such.

The Home Office oversees policing through its Police Policy Directorate. Much of the Home Office was reorganised in the mid-1990s to give it a more business-like structure, to tune it in more closely with new technology and to make policing more capable of responding to unpredictable internal security problems, such as the anti-capitalist movement. The Home Office has also played a prominent role in setting up and running Europol, the European police service which is outside the authority of the EU parliament.

The key police organisation is the Association of Chief Police Officers (ACPO), the professional body for ranks above chief superintendent. In practice, ACPO is the unofficial equivalent of the government's Cabinet, making strategy and policy decisions. The Police Federation represents the interests of the other officers. In 1999 ACPO introduced new, more secretive guidelines for police handling of the media and this prompted widespread condemnation by local newspaper editors whose access to basic information on crimes and accidents dried up.

Several police national services are provided by either the government or through co-operation between forces. A central organisation is the Police Information Technology Organisation (PITO), a Home Office section created in 1996. This oversees many operations, including the Police National Computer (PNC). The PNC provides all forces with 24-hour on-screen essential material, especially the Criminal Justice Record Service (Phoenix) of all criminal records. Another PITO unit is the Police National Network which gives a full range of telecommunications to all forces.

The National Criminal Intelligence Service (NCIS) plays a central role in collecting and analysing criminal intelligence. It was set up in 1992 and placed on an independent statutory basis in 1998. NCIS supplies the PNC with much of its information. The NCIS's London headquarters and regional offices gather, store and analyze a wide range of material. It also liaises with the International Criminal Police Organisation (Interpol). Also in 1998, the regional crime squads were replaced by the new independent National Crime Squad (NCS). The 1,400-strong NCS tries to solve the crimes the NCIS detects. Both also work on the Euro front, where a key body is the Schengen Information System, a

Europe-wide computerised database available to all police, immigration and border officials.

Official statistics show the number of "notifiable offences" recorded by the police in England and Wales rose from the half million of the early 1950s to 5.6 million in 1992. If correct, they then dropped until 1998, rising to 5.3 million in 2000. A Guardian investigation in 1999 showed police forces everywhere were taking part in a "huge fiddle" in which they pretended to have detected tens of thousands of crimes, while wiping from the records a mass of other petty crimes. The public inquiry into the death of Stephen Lawrence, published in February 1999, concluded there was "professional incompetence, institutional racism and a failure of leadership" in the Metropolitan Police. The home secretary Jack Straw then ordered a shake-up of the handling of complaints against the police. At present the police effectively investigate each other, but Straw wanted greater independence and openness. He commissioned public consultation until the end of June 2000, with a decision expected by the end of the year.

POLICE WEBSITES

The sites of all official police forces and police-related organisations are listed by the Police Information Technology Organisation on:

Police Services of the UK   www.police.uk

If you are searching for any police website, you need look no further than this (which is why none are listed here). The only official annual police directory in print is the Police and Constabulary Almanac (R Hazell & Co, 01491-641018), in many reference libraries.

GOVT. DEPARTMENTS

Home Office	020-7273 4000
	www.homeoffice.gov.uk
Press offices: Main	020-7273 4600
Directorates: Criminal Policy	020-7273 3183
Immigration Service Enforcement	020-8745 2400
Organised & International Crime	020-7273 2830
Police Policy	020-7273 3601
Northern Ireland Office	028-9052 0700
	www.nio.gov.uk
Police Division	028-9052 7547
NI Police Authority	028-9023 0111

Scottish Executive: Justice Dept	0131-556 8400
	www.scotland.gov.uk
Press	0131-244 2661
Crime Squad	0141-302 1000
Criminal Record Office	0141-532 2777

NATIONAL POLICE ORGS

Access to websites via www.police.uk.

Action Against Drugs Unit	020-7273 2185
Anti-Terrorist Hotline	0800-789321
Crown Prosecution Service	020-7796 8000
Outside office hours	020-7273 8341
Press office	020-7796 8106
Public enquiries	020-7334 8500
Customs & Excise Investigation	020-7283 5353
Forensic Science Service	0121-607 6800
HM Inspector of Constabulary: E&W	020-7273 4197
Scotland	0131-244 5614
HM Inspector of Probation	020-7273 3906
Intelligence & Security Liaison Unit	020-7273 2991
Interpol	020-7238 8600
Laboratory of the Govt Chemist	020-8943 7000
Missing Persons Helpline	020-8392 4545
National Crime Squad	020-7238 2500
Eastern Area	020-7238 8499
Northern Area	0161-848 5050
Western Area	01454-628301
National Criminal Intelligence Service	020-7238 8000
Press office	020-7238 8431
Enquiries	020-7238 8610
National Identification Service	020-7230 2780
National Police Training, Bramshill	01256-602200
Operational Policing Policy Unit	020-7273 2593
Parole Board (E&W)	020-7217 5314
Police Complaints Authority	020-7273 6450
Police Information Technology Org	020-8358 5555
Police National Computer	020-8200 3200
Police Science & Technology	020-7217 8609
Police Scientific Development Branch	01727-865051
Police Staff College, Bramshill	01256-602100
Policing & Organised Crime Unit	020-7273 3244
Serious Fraud Office	020-7239 7272

POLICE FORCES: ENGLAND

Access to websites via www.police.uk.

Metropolitan Police, London	020-7230 1212
24-hour press bureau	020-7230 2171/2/3/4
Voicebank	0891-900099
Metropolitan Police Authority	020-7944 8900
Race/violent crimes	020-7230 3382
Facility requests	020-7230 4094
Director, Public Affairs	020-7230 2691
Area headquarters:	
Central (at Victoria Embankment)	020-7925 1212
North (at Colindale)	020-8205 1212
South (at Kingston & Sidcup)	020-8541 1212

Avon/Somerset	01275-818181
Voicebanks:	
Bristol	01426-957011
Taunton	01426-950441
Bedfordshire	01234-841212
Voicebank	01426-925682
Berks/Bucks	see Thames Valley
Cambridgeshire	01480-456111
Voicebank	01426-950160
Cheshire	01244-350000
Voicebank	01426-955487
Cleveland	01642-326326
Voicebank	01426 979651
Cumbria	01768-891999
Voicebank	01426-972830
Derbyshire	01773-570100
Voicebank	01426-955020
Devon & Cornwall	0990-777444
Voicebank	01392-452198
Dorset	01929-462727
Voicebank	01426-932345
Durham	0191-386 4929
Voicebank	01426-984458
Essex	01245-491491
Voicebank	01426-925680
Gloucestershire	01242-521321
Voicebank	01426-955884
Guernsey	01481-725111
Hampshire	01962-841500
Voicebank	01426-932024
Herefordshire	see West Mercia
Hertfordshire	01707-354200
Voicebank	01426-934068
Humberside	01482-326111
Voicebank	01426-978223
Isle of Man	01624-631212
Jersey	01534-612612
Kent	01622-650100
Voicebank	01622-683932
Lancashire	01772-614444
Voicebank	01772-618194
Leicestershire	0116-222 2222
Lincolnshire	01522-532222
Voicebank	01426-957180
London, City of	020-7601-2222
Manchester, Gr	0161-872 5050
Voicebank	0891-335559
Merseyside	0151-709 6010
Voicebank	0891-557725
Norfolk	01603-768769
Voicebank	01426-952342
Northamptonshire	01604-700700
Voicebank	01426-952401
Northumbria	01661-872555
Voicebank	01426-979793
Nottinghamshire	0115-967 0999
Voicebank	01426-957125
Oxfordshire	see Thames Valley
Shropshire	see West Mercia
Staffordshire	01785-257717
Voicebank	01785-232525
Suffolk	01473-613500

Voicebank	01426-932403
Surrey	01483-571212
Voicebank	01426-953808
Sussex (E & W)	01273-475432
Voicebank	01273-479221
Thames Valley (Berks, Bucks,	
Oxon)	01865-846000
Voicebank	01426-932012
Warwickshire	01926-415000
Voicebank	01426-952404
West Mercia (Hereford, Salop,	
Worcs)	01905-723000
Voicebank	01426-913005
West Midlands	0121-626 5000
Voicebank	01426-952009
Wiltshire	01380-722341
Voicebank	01426-961045
Worcestershire	see West Mercia
Yorkshire - North	01609-783131
Voicebank	01426-979568
Yorkshire - South	0114-220 2020
Voicebank	01426-952018
Yorkshire - West	01924-375222
Voicebank	01426-979656

POLICE: SCOTLAND

Central Scotland	01786-456000
Clackman'shire	01259-723255
Falkirk	01324-634212
Stirling	01786-456000
Dumfries/Galloway	01387-252112
Fife	01592-418888
Grampian	01224-386000
Lothian & Borders	0131-311 3131
Borders	01450-375051
Edinburgh	0131-662 5000
Midlothian	0131-663 2855
West Lothian	01506-31200
Northern	01463-715555
Command areas:	
Badenoch	01479-810222
Caithness and	
Sutherland	01955-603551
Inverness/Nairn	01463-715555
Lochaber	01397-702361
Orkney	01856-872241
Ross, Cromarty and	
Skye	01349-862444
Shetland	01595-692110
Western Isles	01851-702222
Strathclyde	0141-532 2000
Dunbartonshire	01389-822000
East Ayrshire	1563-505000
Glasgow	0141-532 2000
Inverclyde	01475-492500
N Lanarkshire	01698-483000
S Lanarkshire	01698-483300
Paisley	0141-532 5900
S Ayrshire	01292-664000
Tayside	01382-223200

Divisions:	
Eastern (Angus)	01307-302200
Western (Perth and	
Kinross)	01738-621141
Central (Dundee)	01382-223200

POLICE: WALES

Dyfed-Powys	01267-222020
Divisions:	
Aberystwyth	01970-612791
Carmarthen	01267-222020
Eastern	01554-772222
Pembrokeshire	01437-763355
Powys, north	01686-625704
Powys, south	01874-622331
Gwent	01633-838111
Voicebank	01633-642219
Divisions:	
Blaenau Gwent	01495-350999
Caerphilly	029-2085 2999
Newport	01633-244999
Torfaen	01495-764711
North Wales	01492-517171
Voicebank	01426-950443
Divisions:	
Anglesey	01286-684950
Conwy	01492-511314
Denbighshire	01492-511336
Flintshire	01978-294710
Gwynedd	01286-673333
Wrexham	01978-294600
South Wales	01656-655555
Voicebank	01656-869292
Divisions:	
Bridgend	01656-655555
Cardiff	029-2022 2111
Merthyr Tydfil	01685-722541
Neath/Pt Talbot	01639-635321
Rhondda Cynon	
Taff	01443-485351
Swansea	01792-456999
Vale Glamorgan	01446-734451

POLICE: N IRELAND

Royal Ulster Constabulary	
(RUC)	028-9065 0222
Belfast Region	028-9065 0222
North Region:	
Ballymena	028-2565 3355
Coleraine	028-7034 4122
Londonderry	028-7136 7337
Enniskillen	028-6632 2823
South Region:	
Armagh	028-3752 3311
Dungannon	028-8775 2525
Newtownards	028-9181 8080
Portadown	028-3833 4411

SPECIALIST POLICE FORCES

British Transport Police
   Headquarters 020-7388 7541
   PR officer 020-7830 8854
   London Tube 020-7380 1400
Military
   MoD Police 01371-854000
   RAF Police 01452-712612
   Royal Marines 01752-836372
   Royal Military Police (Army) 01980-615653
   Royal Naval Regulating Branch
     (RN police) 023-9272 7243
Ports: Belfast 028-9055 3000
   Dover 01304-216084
   Falmouth 01326-212100
   Felixstowe 01394-604747
   Liverpool 0151-949 1212
   London (Tilbury) 01375-846781
   Tees 01642-277215
Royal Botanic Gardens Constabulary
   (Kew) 020-8332 5121
Royal Parks Constabulary 020-7298 2000
   Scotland 0131-668 8735
UK Atomic Energy Authority Police 01235-463760

OTHER ORGANISATIONS

Assoc of British Investigators 020-8546 3368
Assoc of Police Authorities 020-7664 3051
   www.apa.police.uk
Assoc of Police Suppliers 01428-602627
British Security Industry Assoc 01905-21464
BT Security & Investigation 0800-321999
Common Agricultural Policy Anti-Fraud
   Unit 0118-953 1086
Customs & Excise Investigation Service 020-7283 5353
Data Protection Registrar 01625-545745
Dept of Social Security Benefits Agency:
   Organised Fraud Units 0113-232 4419
Federation Against Copyright Theft 020-8568 6646
Federation Against Software Theft 01753-527999
Gaming Board 020-7306 6200
ICC Counterfeiting Intelligence Bureau 020-8591 3000
Immigration Service Intelligence and
   Investigation Unit 020-8745 2400
Inland Revenue Special Compliance
   Office 020-7234 3702
Institute of Professional Investigators 01254-680072
Jockey Club Security Dept 020-7343 3261
MAFF Food Investigation Branch 020-7270 8364
Medicines Control Agency 020-7273 06Q7
Parole Board 020-7217 5314
Personal Investment Authority 020-7676 1000
Post Office Investigation Dept 020-8681 9876
Radio Investigation Service (DTI) 020-7215 5961
Road Haulage Assoc Security 01932-841515
Sea Fisheries Inspectorate (MAFF) 020-7238 5798
Security Industry Inspectorate 01905-773131

STAFF BODIES

ACPO (Association of Chief Police Officers):
   England, Wales, N Ireland 020-7230 7184
   Scotland 0131-311 3051
Assoc of Chief Officers of Probation 020-7823 2551
British Assoc of Women Police 01543-276165
International Police Association 0115-981 3638
International Professional Security 01803-554849
Police Federation: England & Wales 020-8399 2224
   www.polfed.org
   N Ireland 028-9076 0831
   Scotland 0141-332 5234
   Police (magazine) 020-8335 2249
Police Superintendents Association:
   England & Wales 0118-984 4005
   Scotland 0141-221 5796
Charities: National Police Fund 020-7273 3684
   Police Dependents Trust 020-7273 2921
   Police Foundation 020-7582 3744

MONITORING GROUPS

Monitoring the police from a civil liberties perspective are Statewatch and Liberty. Inquest provides personal help following deaths in police or secure custody. The Police Complaints Authority has close links with the police and is therefore not believed by critics to be objective.

Earthrights (Environmental Law & Resource
   Centre) 07071-225011
Inquest 020-8802 7430
Justice 020-7329 5100
Legal Action Group 020-7833 2931
   www.lag.org.uk
Legal Defence & Monitoring Group 020-8533 7116
Liberty (NCCL) 020-7403 3888
Missing Persons Bureau 020-8392 4545
Police Complaints Authority 020-7273 6450
   www.pca.gov.uk
Police Review (magazine) 020-7851 9700
   www.police.janes.com
Release 020-7729 9904
Statewatch 020-8802 1882
   www.statewatch.org

Fire services

The UK's 64 fire services employ 50,000 staff and spend £1.4 billion a year responding to 865,000 fire calls and false alarms. In England they are run by county council authorities, or their equivalent in the metropolitan areas, while in Wales and Scotland they come under regional authority groups. In England and Wales, the services are overseen by the Fire Policy Unit of the Home Office's Fire and Emergency Planning Directorate. Fire services in Scotland come under the Justice Department of the Scottish Executive. Northern Ireland has a single fire authority, with its headquarters in Lisburn.

ENGLAND

Avon	0117-926 2061
Bedfordshire	01234-351081
Berkshire	0118-945 2888
Buckinghamshire	01494-786943
Cambridgeshire	01480-444500
Channel Islands - Guernsey	01481-724491
Jersey	01534-37444
Cheshire	01606-868700
Cleveland	01429-872311
Cornwall	01872-273117
Cumbria	01900-822503
Derbyshire	01332-771221
Devon	01392-872200
Dorset	01305-251133
Durham	0191-384 3381
Essex	01277-222531
Gloucestershire	01242-512041
Hampshire	023-80620000
Hereford & Worcester	01905-24454
Hertfordshire	01992-507507
Humberside	01482-565333
Isle of Man	01624-673333
Isle of Wight	01983-823194
Isles of Scilly	01872-273117
Kent	01622-692121
Lancashire	01772-862545
Leicestershire	0116-287 2241
Lincolnshire	01522-582222
London	020-7582 3811
Greater Manchester	0161-736 5866
Merseyside	0151-227 4466
Norfolk	01603-810351
Northamptonshire	01604-797000
Northumberland	01670-513161
Nottinghamshire	0115-967 0880
Oxfordshire	01865-842999
Shropshire	01743-260200
Somerset	01823-337222
Staffordshire	01785-813234
Suffolk	01473-588888
Surrey	01737-242444
Sussex - East	01273-406000
Sussex - West	01243-786211
Tyne and Wear	0191-232 1224
Warwickshire	01926-423231
West Midlands	0121-359 5161
Wiltshire	01380-731100
Yorkshire - North	01609-780150
Yorkshire - South	0114-272 7202
Yorkshire - West	01274-682311

WALES

Mid & West Wales	01267-221444
North Wales	01745-343431
South Wales	01443-232000

SCOTLAND

Central Scotland	01324-716996
Dumfries & Galloway	01387-252222
Fife	01592-774451
Grampian	01224-696666
Highland & Islands	01463-222722
Lothian & Borders	0131-228 2401
Strathclyde	01698-284200
Tayside	01382-322222

NORTHERN IRELAND

NI Fire Brigade HQ (Lisburn)	028-9266 4221
A Division (Belfast)	028-9031 0360
B Division (Bangor)	028-9127 1906
C Division (Portadown)	028-3833 2222
D Division (Derry)	028-7131 1162
E Division (Ballymena)	028-2564 3370
F Division (Omagh)	028-8224 1190

ORGANISATIONS

Home Office:	020-7273 4000
	www.homeoffice.gov.uk
Press Office	020-7273 4640
Fire Services Unit	020-7217 8749
Fire Services Inspectorate	020-7217 8728
Fire Brigades Union	020-8541 1765
Northern Ireland: Environment Dept	028-9054 0540
Fire Division	028-9025 0433
Scottish Executive Justice Dept	0131-556 8400
	www.scotland.gov.uk
Press Office	0131-244 2718
Fire Service	0131-244 2184

Ambulances

Ambulances in England are managed by NHS trusts, whose names are in brackets below if responsible for more than one county. Overseeing the services is the Department of Health. All Welsh ambulances come under the Welsh Ambulance Services, based in Cardiff, and Scottish ambulances under the Scottish Ambulance Service, with its HQ in Edinburgh. There are about 16,000 ambulance staff. Services cost £470 million in 1998, responding to 4.4 million calls. Demands rose 40% between 1990 and 1998.

ENGLAND

Avon	0117-927 7046
Bedfordshire	01234-408999
Berkshire	0118-977 1200
Bucks (Two Shires)	01908-262422
Cambridgeshire (East Anglian)	01603-424255
Channel Islands: Guernsey	01481-725211
Jersey	01534-622343
Cheshire (Mersey Regional)	0151-260 5220
Cleveland	01642-850888
Cornwall (Westcountry)	01392-261500
Cumbria	01228-596909
Derbyshire	01332-372441
Devon (Westcountry)	01392-261500
Dorset	01202-896111
Durham	0191-386 4488
Essex	01245-443344
Gloucestershire	01452-395050
Hampshire	01962-863511
Hereford & Worcester	01886-834200
Hertfordshire	01234-408999
Humberside	01482-561191
Isle of Man	01624-642642
Isle of Wight	01983-821655
Kent	01622-747010
Lancashire	01772-862666
Leicestershire	0116-275 0700
Lincolnshire	01522-545171
London	020-7928 0333
Greater Manchester	0161-796 7222
Merseyside (Mersey Regional)	0151-260 5220
Norfolk (East Anglian)	01603-424255
Northants (Two Shires)	01908-262422
Northumbria	0191-273 1212
Nottinghamshire	0115-929 6151
Oxfordshire	01865-740100
Scilly Isles	01884-254565
Shropshire	01743-364061
Somerset (Westcountry)	01823-278114
Staffordshire	01785-253521
Suffolk (East Anglian)	01603-424255
Surrey	01737-353333
Sussex	01273-489444
Warwickshire	01926-881331
West Midlands	01384-215555
Wiltshire	01249-443939
Yorkshire: North	01904-666000
South	01709-820520
West	01274-707070

WALES

Welsh Ambulance Services	0870-606 0029
East Dyfed	01267-233232
Mid-Glamorgan	01443-217005
North Wales	01745-585106
South & East Wales	01495-765400
West Wales	01792-562900

SCOTLAND

Scottish Ambulance Service HQ	0131-447 7711
North Region: HQ: Aberdeen	01224-662244
Inverness	01463-236611
Dundee	01382-817171
South East Region:HQ: Edinburgh	0131-447 8746
Motherwell	01698-276441
West Region: HQ: Glasgow	0141-353 6001
Ayr	01292-284101
Paisley	0141-848 1434

NORTHERN IRELAND

Dept of Health	028-9052 4309
Eastern (Belfast)	028-9024 6113
Northern (Antrim)	028-9442 8911
Western (Derry)	028-7134 8063

OFFICIAL ORGANISATIONS

Department of Health Press:	020-7210 5221
NHS Executive	0113-254 5000
	www.doh.gov.uk
Welsh Office Health Dept Press	029-2082 5647
Scottish Office Press	0131-244 2656
DoH Northern Ireland	028-9052 0500

SUPPORT ORGANISATIONS

Assoc of Ambulance Personnel	01749-344044
British Red Cross	020-7235 5454
Patients Association	020-8423 9111
Royal Life Saving Society	01789-295222
St Andrews Ambulance Assoc	0141-332 4031
St John Ambulance	020-7235 5231

Hospitals

The National Health Service (NHS) employs 990,000 staff, occupies 46,000 acres of land and oversees 1,600 hospitals with 270,000 beds. It spent £40.2 billion in 1998/9. Since 1991 self-governing trusts (quangos) have taken over most services, including hospitals, on a contractual basis. The trusts in England are monitored by the NHS Executive and its eight regional offices. These replaced the 14 regional health authorities (RHAs) in 1996. At the same time the district health authorities and family health services authorities below the RHAs were superseded by 100 all-purpose health authorities in England and five in Wales. About 75 per cent of the cost of the health service is met through general taxation, with National Insurance providing 13%. About 510 million prescriptions, worth £4.7 billion, are dispensed annually

Below are the hospitals with an accident and emergency department, plus some acute hospitals in larger towns without an emergency hospital.

ENGLISH HOSPITALS

Avon
Bath (Royal United)	01225-428331
Bristol (Frenchay)	0117-970 1212
Bristol (Royal Infirmary)	0117-923 0000
Bristol (Southmead)	0117-950 5050
Weston-super-Mare	01934-636363

Bedfordshire
Bedford	01234-355122
Luton & Dunstable	01582-491122

Berkshire
Ascot (Heatherwood)	01344-623333
Slough (Wexham Park)	01753-633000

Buckinghamshire
Aylesbury (Stoke Mandeville)	01296-315000
High Wycombe (Wycombe)	01494-526161

Cambridgeshire
Cambridge (Addenbrookes)	01223-245151
Huntingdon (Hinchingbrooke)	01480-416416
Peterborough	01733-874000

Channel Islands
Guernsey (Princess Elizabeth)	01481-725241
Jersey General	01534-59000

Cheshire
Chester (Countess)	01244-365000
Crewe (Leighton)	01270-255141
Macclesfield	01625-421000
Northwich (Victoria)	01606-564000
Warrington	01925-635911

Cleveland
Hartlepool	01429-266654
Middlesborough	01642-850850
North Tees	01642-617617

Cornwall
Penzance (West Cornwall)	01736-362382
Truro (Treviske)	01872-274242

Cumbria
Carlisle (Cumberland)	01228-523444
Furness, Cumbria	01229-870870

Derbyshire
Chesterfield	01246-277271
Derby (Derbyshire Royal)	01332-347141

Devon
Barnstaple (North Devon)	01271-322577
Exeter (Royal Devon)	01392-411611
Plymouth (Derriford)	01752-777111
Torbay	01803-614567

Dorset
Poole	01202-665511
Weymouth	01305-760022

Durham
Bishop Auckland, Co Durham	01388-454000
Darlington, Co Durham	01325-380100
Durham (Dryburn)	0191-333 2333
Shotley Bridge	01207-214444

Essex
Basildon, Essex	01268-533911
Chelmsford (Broomfield)	01245-440761
Epping (St Margarets)	01992-561666
Essex	01206-747474
Harlow (Princess Alexandra)	01279-444455
Harold Wood, Essex	01708-345533
Rochford/Southend	01702-435555

Gloucestershire
Cheltenham	01242-222222
Gloucester (Glos Royal)	01452-528555

Hampshire
Basingstoke	01256-473202
Portsmouth (Queen Alexandra)	023-9228 6000
Southampton	023-8077 7222
Winchester (Royal Hampshire)	01962-863535

Hereford & Worcester
Hereford	01432-355444
Kidderminster	01562-823424
Redditch (Alexandra)	01527-503030
Worcester Royal Infirmary	01905-763333

Hertfordshire

Hemel Hempstead	01442-213141
Stevenage (Lister)	01438-314333
Welwyn (Queen Elizabeth II)	01707-328111
Watford	01923-244366

Humberside

Bridlington	01262-606666
Grimsby	01472-874111
Hull (Royal Infirmary)	01482-328541
Scunthorpe	01724-282282

Isle of Man

Douglas (Nobles)	01624-642642

Isle of Wight

Newport (St Marys)	01983-524081

Kent

Ashford (William Harvey)	01233-633331
Canterbury (Kent & Canterbury)	01227-766877
Dartford (West Hill)	01322-223223
Gillingham (Medway)	01634-830000
Maidstone	01622-729000
Margate (Thanet)	01843-225544
Tunbridge Wells (Kent/Sussex)	01892-526111

Lancashire

Blackburn (Royal)	01254-263555
Blackpool (Victoria)	01253-300000
Burnley	01282-425071
Bury	0161-764 6081
Lancaster	01524-65944
Leigh	01942-672333
Ormskirk	01695-577111
Preston (Royal)	01772-716565
Southport	01704-547471

Leicestershire

Leicester	0116-254 1414

Lincolnshire

Boston (Pilgrim)	01205-364801
Grantham	01476-565232
Lincoln (County)	01522-512512
Louth (County)	01507-600100
Stamford	01780-764151

London - Emergency

Acton (Central Middlesex)	020-8965 5733
Ashford	01784-884488
Barnet	020-8216 4000
Bromley	020-8289 7000
Camberwell (Kings College)	020-7737 4000
Carshalton (St Helier)	020-8644 4343
City (St Bartholomews)	020-7601 8888
Ealing	020-8574 2444
Edgware	020-8952 2381
Edmonton (North Middlesex)	020-8887 2000
Enfield (Chase Farm)	020-8366 6600
Euston (University College)	020-7387 9300
Fulham (Charing Cross)	020-8846 1234
Greenwich	020-8858 8141
Hammersmith	020-8743 2030
Hampstead (Royal Free)	020-7794 0500
Harrow (Northwick)	020-8864 3232

Highgate (Whittington)	020-7272 3070
Hillingdon	01895-238282
Homerton	020-8510 5555
Ilford (King George)	020-8983 8000
Isleworth (West Middlesex)	020-8560 2121
Kingston	020-8546 7711
Lambeth (St Thomass)	020-7928 9292
Lewisham	020-8333 3000
Leytonstone (Whipps Cross)	020-8539 5522
Newham	020-7476 4000
North Kensington (St Charles)	020-8969 2488
Paddington (St Marys)	020-7886 6666
Roehampton (Queen Marys)	020-8789 6611
Romford (Oldchurch)	01708-746090
Sidcup (Queen Marys)	020-8302 2678
Southwark (Guys)	020-7955 5000
Thornton Heath (Mayday)	020-8401 3000
Tooting (St Georges)	020-8672 1255
Wembley	020-8903 1323
Westminster, SW1	020-8746 8000
Whitechapel (Royal London)	020-7377 7000
Woolwich (Queen Elizabeth)	020-8858 8141

London - Non-emergency

Brompton Heart, SW3	020-7352 8121
Eastman Dental, WC1	020-7915 1000
Eliz. Garrett Anderson, NW1	020-7387 2501
Gt Ormond St Childrens, WC1	020-7405 9200
London Homeopathic, WC1	020-7837 8833
Maudsley, SE5	020-7703 6333
Middlesex, W1	020-7636 8333
Moorfields Eye, EC1	020-7253 3411
National Orthopaedic	020-8954 2300
Neurology, WC1	020-7837 3611
Royal Marsden, SW3	020-7352 8171
Throat, Nose & Ear, WC1	020-7837 8855
Tropical Diseases, NW1	020-7387 4411

Greater Manchester

Ashton-under-Lyne (Tameside)	0161-331 6000
Bolton	01204-390390
Bury	0161-764 6081
Manchester Royal Infirmary	0161-276 1234
North Manchester	0161-795 4567
Royal Oldham	0161-624 0420
Rochdale Infirmary	01706-377777
Salford (Hope)	0161-789 7373
South Manchester (Withington)	0161-445 8111
Stockport	0161-483 1010
Wigan (Royal Albert Edward)	01942-244000
Wythenshawe	0161-998 7070

Merseyside

Liverpool (Alder Hay Childrens)	0151-228 4811
Liverpool (Broadgreen)	0151-282 6000
Liverpool (Royal)	0151-709 0141
Liverpool (Walton)	0151-525 3611
Whiston	0151-426 1600
Wirral	0151-678 5111

Norfolk

Gt Yarmouth (James Paget)	01493-452452
Kings Lynn (Queen Elizabeth)	01553-766266
Norfolk & Norwich	01603-286286

Northamptonshire
Kettering	01536-492000
Northampton	01604-634700

Northumberland
Ashington, Northumberland	01670-812541
Hexham, Northumberland	01434-606161

Nottinghamshire
Mansfield	01623-622515
Newark	01636-681681
Nottingham (City)	0115-969 1169
Nottingham (University)	0115-924 9924
Worksop	01909-500990

Oxfordshire
Banbury (Horton)	01295-275500
Headington (John Radcliffe)	01865-741166

Shropshire
Shrewsbury	01743-261000

Somerset
Bridgwater	01278-451501
Minehead	01643-707251
Taunton (Musgrove)	01823-333444
Yeovil	01935-475122

Staffordshire
Burton-upon-Trent (Queens)	01283-566333
Stafford	01785-257731
Stoke-on-Trent(North Staffs)	01782-715444

Suffolk
Ipswich	01473-712233
West Suffolk	01284-713000

Surrey
Ashford	01784-884488
Chertsey (St Petrs)	.01932-872000
Camberley (Frimley Park)	01276-604604
Epsom	01372-735735
Guildford (Royal Surrey)	01483-571120
Redhill & Dorking (E Surrey)	01737-768511

Sussex - East
Brighton (Royal Sussex)	01273-696955
Eastbourne	01323-417400
Hastings (Conquest)	01424-755255

Sussex - West
Chichester (St Richards)	01243-788122
Haywards Heath (Princess Royal)	01444-441881
Worthing	01903-205111

Tyne & Wear
Gateshead (Queen Elizabeth)	0191-482 0000
Newcastle	0191-273 8811
Newcastle (Royal Victoria)	0191-232 5131
North Tyneside	0191-259 6660
South Tyneside (South Shields)	0191-454 8888
Sunderland	0191-565 6256

Warwickshire
Nuneaton (George Eliot)	024-76351351
Rugby (St Cross)	01788-572831
Warwick(South Warwickshire)	01926-495321

West Midlands
Birmingham (Dudley Road)	0121-554 3801
Birmingham (Heartlands)	0121-766 6611
Coventry & Warwick	024-7622 4055
Dudley (Russells Hall)	01384-456111
Solihull	0121-711 4455
Sutton Coldfield (Good Hope)	0121-378 2211
University Hospital	0121-627 1627
West Bromwich (Sandwell)	0121-553 1831
Wolverhampton (Royal)	01902-307999

Wiltshire
Salisbury	01722-336262
Swindon (Princess Margaret)	01793-536231

Yorkshire -North
Harrogate	01423-885959
Northallerton (Friarage)	01609-779911
Scarborough	01723-368111
York	01904-631313

Yorkshire -South
Barnsley	01226-730000
Doncaster (Royal Infirmary)	01302-366666
Rotherham Hospital	01709-820000
Sheffield (Childrens)	0114-276 1111
Sheffield (Northern General)	0114-243 4343
Sheffield (Royal Hallamshire)	0114-271 1900

Yorkshire - West
Bradford (Royal)	01274-542200
Dewsbury	01924-465105
Halifax	01422-357222
Huddersfield (Royal Infirmary)	01484-422191
Keighley (Airedale)	01535-652511
Leeds (General Infirmary)	0113-243 2799
Leeds (St Jamess University)	0113-243 3144
Pontefract	01977-600600
Wakefield(Pinderfields)	01924-201688

SCOTTISH HOSPITALS

Borders
Melrose (Borders General)	01896-754333

Central
Falkirk (Royal)	01324-624000
Stirling (Royal)	01786-434000

Dumfries & Galloway
Dumfries (Royal Infirmary)	01387-246246

Fife
Dunfermline (Queen Margarets)	01383-623623

Grampian
Aberdeen (Royal)	01224-681818

Highland
Inverness (Raigmore)	01463-704000

Lothian
Edinburgh (Eastern General)	0131-536 7000
Edinburgh (Royal Infirmary)	0131-536 1000
Edinburgh (Western General)	0131-537 1000

Livingston (St Johns)	01506-419666

Orkney

Kirkwall (Balfour)	01856-885400

Shetland

Lerwick (Gilbert Bain)	01595-695678

Strathclyde

Airdrie (Monklands)	01236-748748
Ayr	01292-610555
Carluke (Law)	01698-361100
East Kilbride (Hairmyres)	01355-220292
Glasgow (Royal Infirmary)	0141-211 4000
Glasgow (Sick Children)	0141-201 0000
Glasgow (Southern)	0141-201 1100
Glasgow (Stobhill)	0141-201 3000
Glasgow (Victoria Infirmary)	0141-201 6000
Glasgow (Western Infirmary)	0141-211 2000
Greenock (Inverclyde)	01475-633777
Kilmarnock (Crosshouse)	01563-521133
Paisley (Royal Alexandra)	0141-887 9111

Tayside

Brechin (Stracathro)	01356-647291
Dundee (Royal Infirmary)	01382-660111
Perth (Royal)	01738-623311

Western Isles

Stornoway (Western Isles)	01851-704704

WELSH HOSPITALS

Clwyd

Rhyl (Clwyd)	01745-583910

Dyfed

Aberystwyth (Bronglais)	01970-623131
Carmarthen (West Wales)	01267-235151
Haverfordwest (Withybush)	01437-764545
Llanelli (Prince Phillip)	01554-756567

Glamorgan - Mid

Bridgend (Princess of Wales)	01656-752752
Merthyr Tydfil (Prince Charles)	01685-721721
Pontypridd (East Glamorgan)	01443-218218

Glamorgan - West

Swansea (Singleton)	01792-205666

Gwent

Abergavenny (Neill Hall)	01873-852091
Newport (Royal Gwent)	01633-234234

Gwynedd

Bangor (Gwynedd)	01248-384384
Llandudno	01492-860066

N IRELAND HOSPITALS

Antrim

Ballymena (Wavney)	028-9442 4000
Belfast City	028-9032 9241
Belfast (Musgrave Park)	028-9066 9501

Belfast (Royal Victoria)	028-9024 0503
Belfast (Ulster)	028-9048 4511
Larne (Moyle)	028-2827 5431
Lisburn (Lagan Valley)	028-9266 5141
Newtownabbey (Whiteabbey)	028-9086 5181
Newtownards (Ards)	028-9181 2661

Armagh

Craigavon	028-3833 4444

Down

Newry (Daisy Hill)	028-3026 5511

Fermanagh

Enniskillen (Erne)	028-6632 4711

Londonderry

Coleraine	028-7034 4177
Derry (Altnagelvin)	028-7186 0261
Magheragelt (Mid-Ulster)	028-7963 1031

Tyrone

Dungannon (South Tyrone)	028-8772 2821
Omagh (Tyrone County)	028-8224 5211

MILITARY HOSPITALS

Army

MoD Hospital Unit (Frimley Park)	01276-604320
Duchess of Kent, Catterick	01748-832521

Navy

Haslar, Gosport	023-9258 4255
Derford, Plymouth	01752-777111

SPECIAL HOSPITALS

Ashworth, Merseyside	0151-473 0303
Carstairs, Lanark	01555-840293
Broadmoor, Berkshire	01344-773111
Rampton, Notts	01777-248321

OFFICIAL ORGANISATIONS

Department of Health	020-7210 3000
	www.doh.gov.uk
Press office	020-7210 5221
Public enquiries	020-7210 4850
NHS Executive: HQ (Leeds)	0113-254 5000
Anglia & Oxford	01908-844400
Northern & Yorkshire	0191-301 1300
North Thames	020-7725 5300
North West	01925-704000
South Thames	020-7725 2500
South & West	0117-984 1750
Trent	0114-263 0300
West Midlands	0121-224 4600
Welsh Office	029-2082 5111
Scottish Office DoH	0131-244 2410
DoH Northern Ireland	028-9052 0500
Health & Safety Commission	020-7717 6000

The sea

HM Coastguard is responsible for Search and Rescue (SAR) operations in the 1.25 million square miles of UK seas and on the 10,500 miles of coastline. When accidents occur, the Coastguard can call on RNLI lifeboats, plus military and civilian aircraft, helicopters and ships, to provide assistance. There are about 500 professional Coastguard officers managing the service. In addition, 3,100 volunteer Auxiliary Coastguards carry out rescues on cliffs and beaches.

Seafarers in distress make radio calls on Channel 16, the distress and safety channel monitored by Coastguard control centres. In 1999 the Coastguard handled 12,220 incidents, assisting 6,581 people; 251 lives were lost. Coastguard officers need to have an international view of life; in 1997 they rescued off the Shetlands ten members of the crew of a ship which was registered in the Bahamas, managed from Norway, run by Croation officers and crewed by Filipinos.

The UK is divided into five Search and Rescue Regions, each of which is overseen by a large Maritime Rescue Co-ordination Centre (MRCC). Every region has subsidiary Maritime Rescue Sub-Centres (MRSCs). There are currently 21 of these MRCCs and MRSCs (listed below) around the UK coast, staffed 24-hours a day. Each has a liaison officer who specialises in talking to the press. The five regions have their coastlines divided into a total of 64 sectors, each run by one Sector Manager, who co-ordinates the work of the Auxiliaries in the area.

Since 1997 the Coastguard has been undergoing major controversial changes, some of them opposed by large sectors of the public. Despite widespread protests, three of the 21 co-ordination centres are scheduled to close by 2001: Oban, Pentland and Tyne Tees. But plans to shut Liverpool and merge two south coast MRSCs - Portland and Lee-on-Solent - were scrapped in 1999.

Auxiliary Coastguards are volunteers who are officially part of HM Coastguard. Some other volunteers in the mid-1990s formed the unofficial National Coastwatch Institution. Usually known as Coastwatch, the charity in certain places provides a coastal surveillance service to the Coastguard.

HM Coastguard operates the Channel Navigation Information Service (CNIS), a traffic separation scheme operating in the eastern English Channel. The Channel is the busiest shipping lane in the world, and CNIS is the world's most sophisticated radar surveillance and monitoring system. HM Coastguard hopes to revolutionise all ship rescue operations with the new satellite Global Maritime Distress and Safety System.

The work of HM Coastguard is administered on behalf of the Department of the Environment, Transport and Regions by the Maritime and Coastguard Agency (MCA), a quango based in Southampton. The MCA was created in April 1998 by the merger of the Coastguard Agency and the Marine Safety Agency, also quangos, which both started in 1994. A parliamentary select committee of MPs condemned the high level of bureaucracy in the MCA, and said it should be dismantled, but in mid-1999 the government announced it would just be rearranged.

The MCA has several other marine safety roles alongside HM Coastguard. Its Port State Control Section surveys merchant ships in UK waters to ensure they meet international standards. The Registry of Shipping and Seamen in Cardiff registers and keeps records on all UK merchant and fishing vessels. The Marine Pollution Control Unit (MPCU) deals with major spillages of oil and other hazardous substances, and maintains the National Contingency Plan which sets out the responsibilities of government departments and other organisations. In major events the Unit works in the Marine Operations Emergency Room in the Coastguard HQ at Southampton. The MCA also runs the marine safety services of the former Marine Safety Agency. The Receiver of Wreck, investigating the ownership of items found in the sea, is also based in the Coastguard building.

MCA

Maritime & Coastguard Agency, Spring Place,
105 Commercial Road, Southampton, SO15 1EG.
Main number   023-8032 9100
                                   www.mcagency.org.uk
24-hour information line   0870-6006505
Press   023-8032 9401
HM Coastguard   023-8032 9100
Marine Emergency Operations Room 023-8032 9445
Maritime Operations Director   023-8032 9444
Maritime Safety & Pollution Prevention 023-8032 9415
Receiver of Wreck   023-8032 9474
Registry of Shipping & Seamen   029-2074 7333
DETR   020-7890 3000
                                      www.detr.gov.uk
   Press: Transport   020-7890 3060
   Duty Officer   020-7276 5999

HM COASTGUARD CENTRES

North & East Scotland Region
MRCC, Aberdeen   01224-592334
MRSCs: Shetland   01595-692976
   Pentland   01856-873268
   Forth   01333-450666
Northern North Sea, from Scottish border to Shetlands
and then west to Cape Wrath, including oil and gas
installations.

Eastern Region
MRCC, Yarmouth   01493-851338
MRSCs: Tyne Tees   0191-257 2691
   Humber   01262-672317
Southern North Sea, from Scottish border to Aldeburgh,
including oil and gas installations.

Southern Region (east)
MRCC, Dover   01304-210008
MRSCs: Thames (Walton)   01255-675518
   Lee-on-Solent   023-9255 2100
South East coast from Aldeburgh to Bournemouth, includ-
ing eastern English Channel. The CNIS system is run from
Dover.

Southern Region (west)
MRCC, Falmouth   01326-317575
MRSCs: Portland   01305-760439
   Brixham   01803-882704
Southern Region Controller   01425-271700
From Bournemouth to Bude Bay, South West Atlantic
approaches. The controller for the whole region
(Aldeburgh to Bude Bay) is based in Christchurch.

Western Region
MRCC, Swansea   01792-366534
MRSCs: Milford Haven   01646-690909
   Holyhead   01407-762051
   Liverpool   0151-931 3341
Bristol Channel from Bude Bay, Irish Sea to North Channel
(excluding Northern Ireland coastal waters) and West
Atlantic approaches.

West of Scotland & Northern Ireland Region
MRCC, Clyde   01475-729988
MRSCs: Belfast   01247-463933
   Oban   01631-563720
   Stornoway   01851-702013
Northern Ireland, west of Scotland coast, North West
Atlantic approaches.

LIFEBOATS

The Royal National Lifeboat Institution (RNLI) is a voluntary body supported entirely by public donations. It has saved over 134,000 lives since it was set up in 1824. There were 6,521 launches in 1999, saving 1,028 lives and assisting 6,593 other people. The RNLI runs 223 lifeboat stations around the British Isles. It has a total of 306 operational boats, 128 of them all-weather vessels. The largest class is the 17-metre long Severn. In addition there are 114 relief boats. Each lifeboat station is run by a voluntary committee, whose honorary secretary authorises the launch of the boat, usually on the request of the local Coastguard. Larger lifeboats may have a paid officer; otherwise nearly all the crews are volunteers. During rescue operations the lifeboat is controlled by the coxswain, in liaison with the local Coastguard MRCC. The RNLI likes all press enquiries to go to the press office at its headquarters in Poole, Dorset. Out of hours, contact the central operations room.

RNLI headquarters, Poole   01202-663000
Central operations room   01202-668222
                                    www.rnli.org.uk

RNLI BOATHOUSES

Listed below are all the UK and Irish Republic stations with a large lifeboat (which is defined as being over 10 metres, and capable of off-shore work). The numbers are mainly for the boathouses themselves, rather than officers:

Aberdeen   01224-591658
Aith, Shetland   01595-810276
Aldeburgh,   Suffolk   01728-452552
Alderney, Channel Islands   01481-823456
Amble, Northumberland   01665-712460
Angle, Dyfed   01646-641204
Anstruther,   Fife   01333-310526
Appledore,   Devon   01237-473969
Arbroath,   Tayside   01241-873235

Arklow, Wicklow
00-353402 32850
Arranmore, Donegal
00-35375 21580
Ballycotton, Cork
00-35321 646903
Ballyglass, Mayo 00-35397 82072
Baltimore, Cork 00-35328 20174
Barmouth, Gwynedd
01341-280274
Barra Island, Western Isles
01871-810307
Barrow, Cumberland
01229-820941
Barry Dock, South Glamorgan
01446-735678
Beaumaris, Gwynedd
01248-810260
Bembridge, IoW 01983-872201
Berwick-upon-Tweed
01289-306217
Blyth, Northumberland
01670-352201
Bridlington, Humberside
01262-672450
Broughty Ferry, Tayside
01382-779956
Buckie, Grampian 01542-831289
Calshot, Hants 023-80893509
Campbeltown, Strathclyde
01586-552414
Clogher Head, Louth
00-35341 22600
Courtmacsherry, Cork
00-35323 46111
Cromer, Norfolk 01263-512237
Donaghadee, Down
028-9188 8556
Douglas, IoM 01624-621367
Dover, Kent 01304-204280
Dun Laoghaire, Dublin
00-3531 280 2667
Dunbar, Lothian 01368-863966
Dungeness, Kent 01797-321300
Dunmore East, Waterford
00-35351 383808
Eastbourne, East Sussex
01323-722648
Exmouth, Devon 01395-263579

Eyemouth, Borders 01890-750293
Falmouth, Cornwall 01326-374177
Fishguard, Dyfed 01348-873231
Flamborough, Humberside
01262-850947
Fleetwood, Lancs 01253-874000
Fowey, Cornwall 01726-832156
Fraserburgh, Grampian
01346-515162

Galway Bay, Galway
00-35399 61166
Girvan, Strathclyde 01465-714454
Gt Yarmouth, Norfolk
01493-662508
Hartlepool, Cleveland
01429-266103
Harwich, Essex 01255-502258
Hastings, East Sussex
01424-425502
Holyhead, Gwynedd
01407-762583
Howth, Dublin 00-3531 8393311
Hoylake, Merseyside
0151-632 2103
Humber 01964-650228
Ilfracombe, Devon 01271-863771
Invergordon, Highland
01349-853915
Islay, Strathclyde 01496-840242
Kilmore Quay, Wexford
00-35353 29690
Kirkwall, Orkney 01856-875201
Lerwick, Shetland 01595-693827
Lizard, Cornwall 01326-290451
Llandudno, Gwynedd
01492-875777
Lochinver, Highland
01571-844513
Longhope, Orkney 01856-701460
Lowestoft, Suffolk 01502-573757
Lytham St Annes, Lancs
01253-736316
Mallaig, Highland 01687-462579
Margate, Kent 01843-221613
Moelfre, Clwyd 01248-410367
Montrose, Tayside 01674-674341
Mumbles, West Glamorgan
01792-390424
Newcastle, Down 01396-725138
Newhaven, East Sussex
01273-514143
North Sunderland, Northmblnd
01665-720370
Oban, Strathclyde 01631-563733
Padstow, Cornwall 01841-520667
Penlee, Cornwall 01736-369246
Peterhead, Grampian
01779-473331
Plymouth, Devon 01752-662623
Poole, Dorset 01202-665607

Port Erin, IoM 01624-832154
Port St Mary, IoM 01624-835015
Porthdinllaen, Gwynedd
01758-720241
Portpatrick, Dumfries
01776-810251
Portree, Highland 01478-613610

Portrush, Antrim 028-7082 3216
Pwllheli, Gwynedd 01758-612200
Ramsey, IoM 01624-812169
Ramsgate, Kent 01843-227324
Rhyl, Clwyd 01745-344040
Rosslare, Wexford
00-35353 33249
St Davids, Dyfed 01437-720215
St Helier, Jersey 01534-24173
St Ives, Cornwall 01736-796422
St Marys, Scilly Isles
01720-422347
Salcombe, Devon 01548-842158
Scarborough, North Yorks
01723-360520
Selsey, West Sussex
01243-602833
Sennen Cove, Cornwall
01736-871222
Sheerness, Kent 01795-664624
Sheringham, Norfolk
01263-823212
Shoreham, West Sussex
01273-462670
Skegness, Lincs 01754-763011
Stornoway, Western Isles
01851-703987
Stromness, Orkney 01856-850204
Sunderland, Tyne & Wear
0191-567 3536
Swanage, Dorset 01929-423237
Teesmouth, Cleveland
01642-486636
Tenby, Dyfed 01834-842197
Thurso, Highland 01847-893433
Tobermory, Strathclyde
01688-302250
Torbay, Devon 01803-853136
Troon, Strathclyde 01292-314414
Tynemouth, Tyne & Wear
0191-257 0913
Valentia, Kerry 00-35366 76126
Walton, Essex 01255-675650
Wells, Norfolk 01328-710230
Weymouth, Dorset 01305-785817
Whitby, North Yorkshire
01947-602216
Wick, Highland 01955-603723
Wicklow 00-353404 67163
Workington, Cumberland
01900-604124
Yarmouth, IoW 01983-872201

Businesses

Britain has 3.7 million businesses. About 38 per cent of the 27.7 million workforce are employed by the 3,000 businesses employing over 500 people, while 2.3 million businesses are sole traders, and another 900,000 employ one to four people. UK companies are among the most profitable in the world. During the second half of the 1990s their annual level of profit was 12 per cent, higher than Japan, USA, Canada and Germany. The UK has 12 million shareholders, up a third following the demutualisation of several building societies in 1997. On the London Stock Exchange at the end of 1999 there were 2,292 UK companies listed (market value: £1,820 billion, up 28 per cent on 1998) and 499 international (value: £3,578 billion). The Stock Exchange suffered a disaster on 5 April 2000, the busy last day of the financial year, when its computer system crashed for nearly eight hours. The biggest takeover in the world took place on 3 February 2000, with Vodafone Airtouch paying £220 billion to merge with Germany's Mannesman. The largest UK companies are: BP Amoco, Glaxo Wellcome, BT, SmithKline Beecham and Lloyds TSB.

COMPANIES HOUSE

The main source of raw material for company research is Companies House. This is the official title of both the Department of Trade's company registry and of its regional offices. Its three statutory functions are: incorporating and dissolving companies; examining and holding company documents required under legislation; and making this information available to the public. All the 1.34 million registered companies must submit annual returns and other data to the registrars in the Companies House head offices in Cardiff (for England and Wales), Edinburgh (for Scotland) and Belfast (for Northern Ireland). Also on record are 250,000 dissolved companies.

The public can carry out personal research at these registries, and in the Information Centre in Bloomsbury St, London WC1 (at the junction of Bedford Avenue). Search facilities are also available in the satellite offices in Birmingham, Manchester, Leeds and Glasgow. All offices are open 9.00-4.00 (London 5.00) Mon-Fri. Basic information can be viewed free of charge on computer screens in the Search Rooms at these offices, or via the Companies House website. More detailed data is available in many ways - fax, phone, post, Internet, on-line, CD-ROM - but all at a charge. The key is the company's registration number, its identity tag.

The research starting point is the "standard search", a microfiche of the documents received by Companies House from the company over the last three years. The standard search costs £5.00 when bought in person, or £8 by post. Much company data is also available on-line via the Companies House Direct service, through which orders can be made. The one-off registration fee for Direct is £50, the monthly sub £7.50. Basic data is also on the Companies House Directory CD-ROM, updated monthly. Single copies are £30, an annual sub for 12 is £300.

Companies House: main offices

Cardiff Registry	029-2038 8588
Crown Way, Cardiff, CF14 3UZ	
Public enquiries (9-5 weekdays)	029-2038 0801
Online Direct help desk	0345-573991
Customer support helpline	029-2038 0668
Edinburgh Registry	0131-535 5800
37 Castle Terrace, EH1 2EB	
Belfast Registry	028-9023 4488
64 Chichester Street, BT1 4JX	
London Information Centre	029-2038 0801
21 Bloomsbury Street, WC1B 3XD.	
CH	www.companieshouse.gov.uk
DTI	www.dti.gov.uk

Satellite offices

Birmingham	0121-233 9047
Glasgow	0141-221 5513
Leeds	0113-233 8338
Manchester	0161-236 7500

Other company registries

Alderney	01481-822817
Guernsey/Sark	01481-725277
Isle of Man	01624-685233
Jersey	01534-603000

ONLINE INFO

The Corporation of London's wideranging website www.cityoflondon.gov.uk is a starting point for finding one's way around the business world. It includes access to all the main websites in the city. Also useful is the Bank of England's City Handbook, a nonprinted book only available on www.bankofengland.co.uk. This has an alphabetical listing of all the UK's main financial organisations. Another, less official source of general material is Find: the Financial Information Net Directory www.find.co.uk, providing a guide to all UK financial services. The latest business news, plus much other data, comes from sites such as Bloomberg www.bloomberg.com, the Financial Times www.ft.com, Reuters www.reuters.com and the Street www.thestreet.co.uk

Some company data can be obtained from the companies themselves. Nearly all larger companies have websites, most of which can be found by using the company name plus .co.uk or .com. All members of the Stock Exchange are listed on www.londonstockexchange.com/directory, along with City organisations. Quoted companies usually produce glossy annual reports, which can be obtained from the company itself, or consulted in London's City Business Library. Companies known by their type of business rather than their name can be found in the global stack of Yellow Pages www.worldyellowpages.com.

Company data is also available for a fee from a variety of online and CD-Rom services. Dunn & Bradstreet and Financial Times Electronic Publishing are the leading suppliers in these and other formats. The Office for National Statistics runs a Business Statistics Data Analysis Service. Personal details of four million directors are on a CD-Rom from i-CD Publishing. UK electronic specialists are:

Bloomberg	020-7330 7500
	www.bloomberg,com
Business Statistics (ONS)	0800-731 5761
Dun & Bradstreet	01494-422000
	www.dunandbrad.co.uk
Economist Intelligence Unit	020-7830 1007
	www.eiu.com
FT Electronic Publishing	0800-007777
ICC Information	020-8783 1122

	www.icc.co.uk
i-CD Publishing	0800-0192192
	www.192.com
Kompass/Reed Business Info	01342-335649
	www.kompass.co.uk
Lexis-Nexis	020-7464 1300
Reuters Business Briefing	020-7250 1122
	www.reuters.com
RM Online	020-7729 1234

Anti-capitalist perspectives

All the national media records the ups and downs of corporate life, but there is only one UK specialist publication focusing on global capitalism from an openly critical perspective. This is Corporate Watch, a quarterly magazine produced by a non-profit radical research group supporting activism against large corporations, especially multinationals. CW also publishes an online DIY guide called How to Research Companies. The group has a research division available on contract.
Corporate Watch   01865-791391
16b Cherwell Street, Oxford OX4 1BG.
www.corporatewatch.org

LIBRARIES

Most local reference libraries have a business section, which should contain at least some of the annual directories listed below. The main annuals are the Directory of Directors, Key British Enterprises, Macmillan's Unquoted Companies, the Stock Exchange Yearbook, UK Kompass and Who Owns Whom. The City Business Library is the starting point for research, containing many basic resources, including quoted company annual reports, directories, magazines, newspapers, CD-Roms, market reports, photocopiers - and toilets! But it's hard to find: it's in a basement on a walkway between London Wall and the north end of Aldermanbury, EC2.

British Library Business Information Service
96 Euston Road, London NW1 2DB.
BL-Lloyds TSB Business Line   020-7412 7454
Part of the British Library's St Pancras HQ. Free, but a Library pass is needed. Was off Chancery Lane till 1999.

City Business Library (City of London)
1 Brewers Hall Garden, London EC2V 5BX
Enquiries   020-7638 8215
Recorded details   020-7480 7638
Fee-paying research service   020-7600 1461
Open Monday-Friday 9.30-5.00.

DIRECTORIES

Directory of Directors
Annual. Reed Information
Details of 50,000 directors and the 14,000 companies they control.
Financial Times 500
Annual. FT Republishing.
Wide-ranging data on the top 500 companies.
Hemscott Company Guide
Quarterly. Hemmington Scott.
Latest details on stockmarket companies.
Key British Enterprises
Annual. Dun & Bradstreet
Six volumes covering the top 50,000 companies, with trade name sections. The best of its kind.
Macmillan's Unquoted Companies
Annual. Waterlow.
20,000 unquoted companies, turnovers above £15m.
Major UK Companies
Twice pa. Extel
Specialise in financial information. One of the best.
Stock Exchange Yearbook
Annual. Macmillan
A profile of 4,100 companies and securities listed on the London and Dublin Stock Exchanges.
UK Kompass Register
Annual. Kompass (Reed Information)
CBI-backed, four volumes, giving a wide range of data.
Who Owns Whom
Annual. Dun and Bradstreet
Detailing the corporate structures of over a million cos.

KEY CONTACTS

ACAS	020-7210 3613
	www.acas.org.uk
Audit Commission	020-7828 1212
	www.audit-commission.gov.uk
Bank of England	020-7601 4444
	www.bankofengland.co.uk
Press	020-7601 4411(-5)
Banking Ombudsman	020-7404 9944
	www.obo.org.uk
Bankruptcy Association	01524-64305
	www.theba.org.uk
British Bankers Association	020-7216 8800
	www.bba.org.uk
British Chambers of Commerce	020-7565 2000
	www.britishchambers.org.uk
British Institute of Management	01536-204222
Building Societies Association	020-7437 0655
	www.bsa.org.uk
CBI	020-7379 7400
	www.cbi.org.uk
Chamber of Shipping	020-7417 8400
City Information Group	020-8871 4284
	www.cityinfogroup.co.uk
Competition Commission (ex-Monopolies & Mergers Commission)	020-7324 1467

Corporation of London	020-7606 3030
	www.cityoflondon.gov.uk
Dept of Trade & Industry	020-7215 5000
	www.dti.gov.uk
Press	020-7215 5970
Company Law Directorate	020-7215 0403
Economist Intelligence Unit	020-7830 1007
	www.eiu.com
Ethical Investors Group	01242-604550
European Info Researchers Network	01509-268292
	www.eirne.com
Fair Trade	020-7405 5942
	www.fairtrade.org.uk
Federation of Small Businesses	020-7233 7900
	www.fsb.org.uk
Financial Services Authority	0845-606 1234
	www.fsa.gov.uk
FTSE	020-7448 1800
ICOM (Industrial Common Ownership Movement)	0113-246 1737
Industrial Common Ownership Fund)	0121-523 6886
	www.icof.co.uk
Industrial Society	020-7262 2401
	www.indsoc.co.uk
Inland Revenue	020-7438 6622
	www.inlandrevenue.gov.uk
Press office	020-7438 6692
Electronic Business Unit	01274-534555
Insolvency Service	020-7637 1110
Inst of Chartered Accountants	020-7920 8100
Institute of Directors	020-7839 1233
	www.iod.co.uk
Institute of Taxation	020-7235 9381
Investment Ombudsman	020-7796 3065
Lloyds of London	020-7327 1000
	www.lloydsoflondon.co.uk
London Chamber of Commerce	020-7248 4444
	www.londonchamber.co.uk
London Metal Exchange	020-7264 5555
Low Pay Unit	020-7713 7616
	www.lowpayunit.org
National Assoc of Pension Funds	020-7808 1300
	www.napf.co.uk
National Audit Office	020-7798 7000
	www.nao.gov.uk
Office of Fair Trading	020-7211 8000
	www.oft.gov.uk
Patent Office	01633-814000
Securities Institute	020-7645 0600
	www.securities-institute.org.uk
Serious Fraud Office	020-7239 7272
	www.sfo.org.uk
Eves	020-7239 7050
(London) Stock Exchange	020-7588 2355
	www.londonstockexchange.com
Takeovers & Mergers Panel	020-7382 9026
HM Treasury - press	020-7270 5238
	www.hm-treasury.gov.uk
TUC (Trades Union Congress)	020-7636 4030
	www.tuc.org.uk

TOP COMPANIES

Most of these have websites, usually using the company name plus .co.uk or .com.

Abbey National (banking)	0870-607 6000
Aegis Group (communications)	020-7838 9393
Agco (engineering)	024-7669 4400
Airtours	0161-232 0066
Alcan Aluminium	01753-233200
Alfred McAlpine (construction)	01565-756200
Alliance & Leicester (BS)	020-7629 6661
Alliance Trust (Investments)	01382-201700
Allied Domecq (alcohol)	0117-978 5000
Allied Bakeries	01784-451366
Allied Irish Bank	020-7629 8881
AMEC (construction)	01606-883885
Amerada Hess (fuel)	020-7823 2626
Amersham International	01494-544000
Amstrad (electronics)	01277-228888
Anglia Television	01603-615151
Anglian Water	01480-323000
Argos (retailing)	01908-690333
Arjo Wiggins Appleton (paper)	01256-723000
Asda (supermarkets)	0113-243 5435
Associated British Foods	020-7589 6363
Associated British Ports	020-7430 1177
Astrazeneca (chemicals)	020-7304 5000
Axa Insurance	020-7283 7101
B&Q (DIY)	023-8025 6256
BAA (airports)	020-7834 9449
Balfour Beatty (construction)	020-7216 6800
Bank of China	020-7282 8888
Bank of England	020-7601 4444
Bank of India	020-7628 3165
Bank of Ireland	020-7236 2000
Bank of Japan	020-7606 2454
Bank of Scotland	0131-442 7777
Barclays Bank	020-7699 5000
Barlow (construction)	020-7629 6243
Barratt Development (building)	0191-286 6811
Bass (alcohol)	020-7409 1919
BAT Industries (tobacco)	020-7845 1000
Benetton UK (clothing)	020-7495 5482
Bernard Matthews (food)	01603-872611
BG (ex-British Gas)	0118-935 3222
BICC (electrical)	020-7629 6622
Birds Eye Walls (food)	01932-263000
Birmingham Midshires BS	01902-302000
Blue Circle (building)	020-7828 3456
BOC (chemicals)	01276-477222
Body Shop (retailing)	01903-731500
Booker (agriculture/health)	020-7411 5500
Boots (retailing)	0115-9506111
Border Television	01228-541384
Bovis Construction	020-8422 3488
BP Mobil (oil)	01908-853000
BPB	01753-898800
Bradford & Bingley BS	01274-555555
Brent Walker (leisure)	020-7465 0111
Britannia Airways	01582-424155
Britannia BS	01538-399399

Britannic Assurance	01564-828888
British Aerospace	01252-373232
British Airways	020-8759 5511
British Bakeries	01753-857123
British Energy	0131-527 2000
British Land (property)	020-7486 4466
British Nuclear Fuels	020-7222 9717
British Petroleum (oil/gas)	020-7496 4000
British Railways Board	020-7928 5151
British Steel	020-7717 4444
British Sugar	01733-563171
British Telecommunications	020-7356 5000
BSkyB (media)	020-7705 3000
BTR (conglomerate)	020-7834 3848
Budgens (supermarkets)	020-8422 9511
Burmah Castrol (oil/gas)	01793-511521
Burton (retailing)	020-7636 8040
Cable & Wireless (telecomms)	020-7363 2000
Cadbury Schweppes (food)	020-7409 1313
Calor (oil/gas)	0118-933 2363
Camellia (agriculture)	020-7629 5728
Camelot (lottery)	01923-425000
Caradon (plastics)	01932-850850
Carlsberg-Tetley Brewing	01604-668866
Carlton Central Broadcasting (TV)	0121-643 9898
Carlton Communications (TV)	020-7663 6363
Cellnet (communications)	01753-565000
Centrica (gas)	01753-758000
Channel 4 (TV)	020-7396 4444
Channel 5 (TV)	020-7497 5225
Channel Television	01534-816816
Charter (engineering)	020-7838 7000
Chase Manhatten Bank	020-7777 2000
Cheltenham & Gloucester BS	01452-372372
Chevron (fuel)	020-7487 8100
Christian Salvesen (food)	01604-662600
Christie's (auctioneers)	020-7839 9060
Chubb Security	01332-202020
Ciba-Speciality Chemicals)	01625-421933
Clydesdale Bank	020-7699 6400
Coats Viyella (textiles)	020-7302 2300
Coca Cola & Schewppes Beverages	01895-231313
Comet (retailing)	01482-320681
Commercial Union (insurance)	020-7283 7500
Conoco (fuel)	01926-404000
Cookson (industry)	020-7766 4500
Co-operative Bank	0345-212212
Co-operative Retail Services	01706-713000
Co-operative Wholesale Society	0161-834 1212
Cordiant Communications (adverts)	020-7262 5077
Corus (ex-British Steel)	020-7717 4444
Costain (construction)	020-7705 8444
Courtaulds Textiles	020-7331 4500
Coutts & Co (banking)	020-7623 3434
Dalgety (food)	01454-201511
De La Rue (printing)	01256-329122
De Vere (leisure)	01925-651234
Debenhams (retailing)	020-7408 4444
Deutsche Morgan Grenfell (banking)	020-7545 8000
Diageo (ex-Grand Met, food)	020-7518 5200
Dixons (retailing)	020-7499 3494

Do-It-All (DIY)	01384-456456
Dow Chemical (oil)	020-8917 5000
Du Pont (chemicals)	01438-734000
Dunhill Holdings (consumer)	020-7838 8000
Dunlop (tyres)	024-7666 6655
Elementis (chemicals)	020-7711 1400
Elf Petroleum	020-7963 5000
EMI (electronics)	020-7355 4848
Engelhard (metals)	020-7456 7300
English China Clays (building)	0118-930 4010
Enterprise Oil	020-7925 4000
Ericsson (electronics)	01444-234567
Esso (oil/gas)	020-7834 6677
European Bank	020-7338 6000
Eurotunnel (transport)	020-7872 5496
Express Dairies	0116-281 6281
Ferranti (air systems)	0161-946 3600
First National Bank of Chicago	020-7388 3456
Firstgroup (bus operators)	01224-650000
Food Manufacturers	01753-693000
Ford (vehicles)	01277-253000
Forte (leisure)	020-7301 2000
Gallaher (tobacco)	01932-859777
GEC (electronics)	020-7493 8484
General Accident (insurance)	020-7626 8711
George Wimpey (building)	020-8748 2000
Girobank	020-7843 3000
GKN (engineering)	01527-517715
Glaxo Wellcome (household)	020-8966 8000
Glynwed (metals)	0121-742 2366
GMTV (television)	020-7827 7000
Goodyear (tyres)	01902-327000
Grampian Foods	01224-715454
Grampian Television	01224-846560
Granada (media/leisure)	020-7451 3000
Grand Metropolitan (Diadgeo, food)	020-7518 5200
Great Portland Estates	020-7580 3040
Greycoat (property)	020-7379 1000
Gt Universal Stores (retailing)	0161-273 8282
Guinness (aka Diadgeo, alcohol)	020-7927 5200
Halfords (retailing)	01527-517601
Halifax BS	01422-333333
Halliburton (engineering)	01372-865000
Hammerson (property)	020-7887 1000
Hanson (conglomerate)	020-7245 1245
Hawtin (fabrics)	029-2048 8961
Hewlett-Packard (electronics)	01344-360000
Hill Samuel Bank	020-7661 4861
Hillsdown (food)	020-7794 0677
Homebase (DIY)	01933-679679
House of Fraser (retailing)	020-7963 2000
HSBC Holdings (banking)	020-7260 8000
HTV (television)	029-2059 0590
Hyder (water)	029-2050 0600
IBM (computers)	023-9256 1000
ICI (chemicals)	020-7834 4444
Imperial Tobacco	0117-963 6636
IMI (metals)	0121-356 4848
Inchcape (transport)	020-7546 0022
Invensys (electronics)	020-7834 3848
Jaguar (motors)	024-7640 2121
John Laing (construction)	020-8959 3636
John Lewis (retailing)	020-7828 1000
John Menzies (retailing)	0131-225 8555
John Mowlem (construction)	020-8568 9111
John Swire & Sons (transport)	020-7834 7717
Johnson's Apparel Master	01455-238133
Kelda Group (water)	0113-234 3234
Kellog UK (food)	0161-869 2000
Kier Group (contruction)	01767-640111
Kimberly-Clark (paper)	01732-594000
Kingfisher (retailing)	020-7724 7749
Kleinwort Benson (banking)	020-7623 8000
Kodak	01442-261122
Kvaerner (mixture)	020-7262 8080
Kwik Save (supermarkets)	01745-887111
Ladbroke (leisure)	020-8459 8031
Land Securities (property)	020-7413 9000
Laporte (chemicals)	020-7399 2400
Lasmo (oil & gas)	020-7892 9000
Lawrie (agriculture)	01732-884488
Legal & General (insurance)	020-7528 6200
Liberty Int (property/finance)	020-7222 5496
Littlewoods (retailing)	0151-235 2222
Lloyds TSB Group	020-7626 1500
London Electricity	020-7242 9050
London Regional Transport	020-7222 5600
London Weekend Television	020-7620 1620
Lonrho (conglomerate)	020-7201 6000
Magnox Electric (electricity)	01453-810451
Marconi Communications	020-7493 8484
Marks & Spencer (retailing)	020-7935 4422
Marley (building materials)	01732-455255
Mars (food)	01753-550055
McCarthy & Stone (building)	01202-292480
McDonalds (fast food)	020-8700 7000
MEPC (property)	020-7911 5300
Meridian Broadcasting	023-8022 2555
MFI (furnishings)	020-8200 8000
Michelin Tyre	01782-402000
Midland Bank - aka HSBC	020-7260 8000
Milk Marque	01905-858500
Mirror Group (media)	020-7510 3000
Morgan Crucible (industrial)	01753-837000
Mothercare (parenting)	01923-241000
Motorola (electronics)	01293-404343
National Bank of Canada	020-7726 6581
National Grid (electricity)	024-7653 7777
National Power (electricity)	01793-877777
National Westminster Bank	020-7726 1000
Nationwide (BS)	01793-513513
Nestle (food)	020-8686 3333
News International (media)	020-7782 6000
Next (retailing)	0116-286 6411
NFC (transport)	01234-272222
NFU Mutual Insurance Society	01789-204211
Nissan UK (motors)	01903-268561
Nortel (communications)	01628-812000
North West Water	01925-234000
Northern Foods	01482-325432
Northern Rock (BS)	0191-285 7191
Northern Trust (banking)	020-7628 2233

Northumbrian Water	0191-284 3151	Smithkline Beecham (health)	020-8975 2000
Nuclear Electric - British Energy	01452-652222	Smiths Industries (engineers)	020-8458 3232
Orange (communications)	020-7984 1602	Societe Generale (banking)	020-7480 5000
P&O (transport)	020-7930 4343	Somerfield (supermarkets)	01745-887111
Paragon (loans)	0121-712 2323	South West Water	01392-446688
Pearson (media)	020-7411 2000	Southern Electric	01628-822166
Peugeot (vehicles)	024-7688 4000	Southern Water	01273-606766
Phillips Petroleum	01483-756666	St Ivel (food)	01793-848444
PIC International (agricultural)	01865-820654	Standard Chartered (banking)	020-7280 7500
Pilkington (glass)	01744-28882	Storehouse (retailing)	020-7262 3456
Pirelli (tyres)	020-7355 5080	Sunblest Bakeries (food)	01784-451366
Post Office (communications)	020-7490 2888	Superdrug (household/health)	020-8684 7000
Powell Duffryn (transport)	01344-666800	Syseca	0161-946 1001
Powergen (electricity)	024-7642 4000	T&N (engineering)	0161-955 5200
Press Association (media)	020-7963 7000	Tarmac (construction)	01902-353522
Prudential (insurance)	020-7334 9000	Tate & Lyle (food)	020-7626 6525
Racal Electronics	01344-481222	Taylor Woodrow (building)	020-7629 1201
Railtrack (transport)	020-7557 8000	Telewest (media)	01483-750900
Rank Organisation (leisure)	020-7706 1111	Tesco (supermarkets)	01992-632222
Rank Xerox (electronics)	01895-251133	Texaco (oil/gas)	020-7719 3000
Rechem (waste treatment)	01628-810011	Thames Water	020-7636 8686
Reckitt & Colman (household)	020-8994 6464	Thomson Corporation (media)	020-7437 9787
Redland (building materials)	01306-872000	Thomson Travel	020-7387 9321
Reed Elsevier (media)	020-7222 8420	Thorn EMI (leisure)	020-7355 4848
Rentokil (chemicals)	01342-833022	3i Group (investments)	020-7928 3131
Reuters (media)	020-7250 1122	TI Group (engineering)	01235-555570
Rexam (paper)	020-7584 7070	Tomkins (engineering)	020-8871 4544
Rhone Poulenc Rorer	01477-537112	Total Oil	020-7416 4200
Rio Tinton Zinc Corporation (mining)	020-7930 2399	Toyota (motors)	01737-768585
RJB Mining	01302-751751	TRW (engineering)	0121-556 1212
RMC (building materials)	01932-568833	TT Group (building materials)	01932-841310
Rolls-Royce (engineering)	020-7222 9020	Tyne Tees Television	0191-261 0181
Rosehaugh (property)	01463-811205	TXU (electricity)	01473-221331
Rothmans (tobacco)	01296-335000	Ulster Television	028-9032 8122
NM Rothschild (banking)	020-7280 5000	Unigate (food)	01892-534424
Rover (vehicles)	0121-475 2101	Unilever (food/household)	020-7822 5252
Royal Bank of Scotland	0131-556 8555	United Biscuits (food)	01895-432100
Royal & Sun Alliance (insurance)	020-7283 4300	United Distillers	0131-337 7373
Rugby Group (building)	01788-542666	United Utilities (water)	01925-285000
Saatchi & Saatchi (advertising)	020-7636 5060	Vauxhall (vehicles)	01582-721122
Safeway (supermarkets)	020-8848 8744	Vickers (engineering)	020-7828 7777
J Sainsbury (supermarkets)	020-7695 6000	Virgin Rail	020-7229 1282
Salomon Brothers (financial)	020-7721 2000	Virgin Travel	01293-562345
SBC Warburg (banking)	020-7606 1066	Vodafone (telecomms)	01635-33251
Schroders (banking)	020-7658 6000	Waitrose (supermarkets)	01344-424680
Scottish & Newcastle (beer)	0131-528 2000	Waste Management	020-8563 7000
Scottish Investment Trust	0131-225 7781	Welsh Water	01874-623181
Scottish Mortgage	0131-222 4000	Wessex Water	0117-929 0611
Scottish Nuclear - British Energy	01355-262000	WH Smith (retailing)	020-7242 0535
Scottish Power (electricity)	0141-568 2000	Whitbread (alcohol)	020-7606 4455
Scottish Television	0141-300 3000	Witan Investment	020-7638 5757
Sea Containers UK	020-7805 5265	Wolseley (building materials)	01905-774356
Sears (retailing)	020-7200 5999	Woolwich (building society)	020-8298 5000
Securicor (miscellaneous)	020-8770 7000	Woolworths (retailing)	020-7262 1222
Sentrica Management Graphics	0118-935 8222	WPP Group (advertising)	020-7408 2204
Severn Trent (water)	0121-722 4000	Xerox (office equipment)	01628-890000
Shell UK (oil/gas)	020-7257 3000	Yorkshire Electricity	0113-289 2123
Siebe (engineering)	01753-855411	Yorkshire Television	0113-243 8283
Signet Group	0870-909 0301	Zeneca (health)	020-7304 5000
SITA (ex-BFI, waste disposal)	01753-662700		
Slough Estates (property)	01753-537171		

Charities

England and Wales have about 188,000 registered charities. Of these, 159,400 are "main" charities and the other 27,200 are their subsidiaries. The total income of main charities in 1999 was £23 billion. The majority of all charities - 67 per cent - had an income below £10,000, with 90 per cent below £100,000. The top 5 per cent (8,600) received 89 per cent of the total income, £21 billion. Of these, just 312 charities took in £10.3 billion, 43 per cent of the total. The charities with the largest funds are the Wellcome Trust £11.3 billion, the Church Commissioners for England £4.4 billion, the Weston [Garfield] Foundation £1.8 billion and Leverhulme Trust £1.2 billion.

Charities come under the umbrella of the Charity Commission, which gives administrative advice to trustees and ensures they comply with legal rules. The Commissioners' powers were tightened up in the mid-1990s to try and stop malpractice and make charities more accountable. The Commission, established in 1853, is based in central London; it moved from the Haymarket to just off Fleet Street in 1999. There are regional offices in Liverpool and Taunton. These three centres together form the Central Register of Charities. They hold the public records of all charities, which can be inspected free of charge. Basic data on all charities is available on the website. Archive material is held by the Greater London Record Office, Clerkenwell.

In Scotland, charities are supervised by the Scottish Charities Office on behalf of the Lord Advocate. The Scottish Council for Voluntary Organisations is the charity acting as an umbrella body for voluntary organisations in Scotland. In Northern Ireland charities do not need to register, and are monitored by the DHSS Charities Branch.

The National Council for Voluntary Organisations (NCVO) is the leading co-ordinating body for charities and other public-spirited bodies. Its wide-ranging annual is the Voluntary Agencies Directory. The Charities Aid Foundation (CAF), an independent chari-

ty, is one of the main organisations that help the flow of funds to charities from companies, individuals and trusts. It runs an extensive website and publishes the annual Directory of Grant-Making Trusts, the best-known handbook on how to raise money for a charity. A fellow prominent organisation aiming to provide help is the Directory of Social Change, which runs the annual Charityfair and publishes the Guide to the Major Trusts, plus many other handbooks. Another reference annual is the Charities Digest, launched in 1882, published by Waterlow. The Association of Charitable Foundations provides support to grant-making bodies.

The National Lottery Charities Board dis tributes to charities 4.7 pence from every £1 spent on Lottery tickets. It has awarded grants totalling over £1.34 billion since the Lottery began in October 1995. Camelot Group plc, a private sector consortium, has the franchise to run the Lottery until October 2001. It is regulated by the National Lottery Commission.

CO-ORDINATORS

Charity Commission

Central helpline	0870-333 0123
13-15 Bouverie Street, London EC4Y 8DP	
	www.charity-commission.gov.uk
Press office	020-7674 2333
Liverpool	0151-703 1500
Taunton	01823-345000

Other organisations

Assoc of Charitable Foundations	020-7422 8600
	www.acf.org.uk
Card Aid	020-7794 9836
	www.cardaid.co.uk
Charities Aid Foundation	01732-520000
	www.cafonline.org
Charity Times magazine	020-7426 0424
Community Matters	020-7226 0189
	www.communitymatters.org.uk
Directory of Social Change	www.dsc.org.uk
Books	020-7209 5151
Charityfair/Charity Centre	020-7209 1015
Marketing/research	020-7209 4422
Funderfinder	0113-243 3008
	www.funderfinder.org.uk
Inst of Charity Fundraising Managers	020-7627 3436
	www.icfm.org.uk

London Metropolitan Archives	020-7606 3030
London Voluntary Service Council	020-7700 8107
Media Trust	020-7874 7600
	www.mediatrust.org
National Council for Voluntary Orgs	020-7713 6161
	www.ncvo-vol.org.uk
Helpdesk	0800-279 8798
National Lottery Charities Board	020-7747 5300
	www.nlcb.org.uk
N Ireland Charities Branch DHSS	028-9052 2780
Scottish Charities Office	0131-226 2626
	www.crownoffice.gov.uk
Scottish Council for Voluntary Orgs	0131-556 3882
	www.sol.co.uk/s/scvo
Voluntary Services Overseas	020-8780 7500
	www.vso.org.uk
Waterlow Information	020-7490 0049

MAIN CHARITIES

Actionaid	020-7281 4101
Action research	01403-210406
Afasic	020-7841 8900
Age Concern England	020-8679 8000
Alzheimer's Disease Society	020-7306 0606
Arthritis Research Campaign	01246-558033
Arts Council	020-7333 0100
Baring Foundation	020-7767 1348
Barnardo's	020-8550 8822
BBC Children in Need Appeal	020-8576 7788
Blue Cross	01993-822651
Bridge House Estate Fund	020-7332 3710
British Council	020-7930 8466
British Diabetic Association	020-7323 1531
British Film Institute	020-7255 1444
British Heart Foundation	020-7935 0185
British Library	020-7412 7000
British Museum	020-7636 1555
British Red Cross Society	020-7235 5454
British Youth Council	020-7422 8640
CAFOD	020-7733 7900
Cancer Relief Macmillan Fund	020-7351 7811
Cancer Research Campaign	020-7224 1333
Cats Protection League	01403-221900
Christ's Hospital	01403-211293
Christian Aid	020-7620 4444
Church Commissioners	020-7898 1000
City & Guilds of London	020-7294 2468
City Parochial Foundation	020-7606 6145
Community Foundation Network	020-7422 8611
Consumers Association	020-7830 6000
Construction Industry.Training Board	01485-577577
Distressed Gentlefolk's Aid Assoc	020-7396 6700
Dogs' Home Battersea	020-7622 3626
Donkey Sanctuary	01395-578222
English Churches Housing	020-8203 9233
Foundation for Sport and Arts	0151-259 5505
Garfield Weston Foundation	020-7589 6363
Gatsby Charitable Foundation	020-7410 0330
Great Ormond St Children's Hospital	020-7405 9200
Guide Dogs for the Blind	0118-983 5555
Help the Aged	020-7253 0253

Henry Smith's (Kensington Estate)	020-7242 1212
Imperial Cancer Research Fund	020-7242 0200
Independent Living Alternative	020-8906 9265
Institute of Cancer Research	020-7352 8133
Institute of Child Health	020-7242 9789
Institute of Psychiatry	020-7703 5411
International Planned Parenthood	020-7487 7900
Jewish Care	020-8922 2000
Jewish Philanthropic Assoc.	020-8446 1477
JNF Charitable Trust	020-8421 7600
John Ellerman Foundation	020-7930 8566
Joint Israel Appeal	020-8446 1477
Joseph Rowntree Foundation	01904-629241
JW Laing Trust	01225-427236
Leonard Cheshire Foundation	020-7802 8200
Leverhulme Trust	020-7822 6938
Ludwig Institute of Cancer Research	020-7878 4000
Marie Curie Foundation	020-7235 3325
Medecins sans Frontieres	020-7713 5600
MENCAP	020-7454 0454
Methodist Homes for the Aged	01332-296200
Monument Trust	020-7410 0330
MS Society	020-7610 7171
NACRO	020-7582 6500
National Canine Defence League	020-7837 0006
National Trust	020-7222 9251
Natural History Museum	020-7938 9123
NCH Action for Children	020-7226 2033
Norwood Ravenswood	020-8954 4555
NSPCC	020-7825 2500
Nuffield Foundation	020-7631 0566
Order of St John	020-7253 6644
Oxfam	01865-311311
Parkinson's Disease Society	020-7233 5373
Peabody Trust	020-7928 7811
Prince's Trust	0800-842842
Quantum Fund	020-7925 2555
RAF Benevolent Fund	020-7580 8343
Rank Foundation	020-7834 7731
RNLI	01202-663000
Robertson Trust	0141-352 6620
Royal British Legion	020-7973 7200
Royal College of Surgeons	020-7405 3474
Royal Horticultural Society	020-7834 4333
Royal National Institute for the Blind	020-7388 1266
Royal National Institute Deaf People	020-7296 8000
Royal Opera House	020-7240 1200
RSPB	01767-680551
RSPCA	01403-264181
Salvation Army Trust	020-7367 4500
Save the Children Fund	020-7703 5400
Scope	020-7619 7100
Sense	020-7272 7774
Soros Global Research	020-7451 2000
Stonham Housing Association	020-7401 2020
Stroke Association	020-7490 7999
Tear Fund	020-8977 9144
UNICEF-UK	020-7405 5592
Variety Club Children's Foundation	020-7428 8100
Wellcome Trust	020-7611 8888
WWF UK	01483-426444
YMCA	020-8520 5599

Consumer watchdogs

There are four breeds of consumer watchdog keeping an eye on human wildlife:

1) Regulatory bodies
2) Ombudsmen
3) Advisory committees
4) Pressure groups

REGULATORY BODIES

These are official or semi-official organisations ensuring that legal regulations are complied with by suppliers. The Office of Fair Trading (OFT) is the non-ministerial government department which safeguards shopping consumers by administering these regulations and monitoring competition. The OFT ensures all laws are enforced, especially the two most important ones: the 1979 Sale of Goods Act (amended 1994) and the 1968 Trades Description Act. Individual consumer problems are taken up by Trading Standards Departments in county councils, which handle nearly a million complaints annually.

The handling of problems for finance consumers is switching in mid-2001 from individual agencies, such as IMRO, OPRA, PIA, SFA and SIB, to a powerful new statutory body, the Financial Services Authority.

All Whitehall's consumer policies are supervised by the Consumer Affairs Directorate of the DTI Its website Consumer Gateway gives access to information and advice, plus links to other websites, official and unofficial. The government's two main auditing departments are the National Audit Office, which monitors the accounts of government departments and public bodies, and the Audit Commission, which examines the accounts of both the local authorities and the NHS. The Adjudicator's Office investigates how the Inland Revenue, Customs and Excise and National Insurance Contributions Agency handle their affairs. New consumer watchdog bodies are being formed to cover the gas, electricity, water and telecoms industries. OFGAS and OFFER will merge as OFGEM.

Adjudicator's Office	020-7930 2292
	www.open.gov.uk/adoff
Advertising Standards Authority	020-7580 5555
Audit Commission	020-7930 6077
British Standards Institution	020-8996 9000
Broadcasting Standards Commission	020-7233 0544
Building Societies Commission	020-7676 1000
Competition Commission (ex-Monopolies	
& Mergers Commission)	020-7324 1467
Data Protection Registrar	01625-545700
Dept of Trade & Industry	020-7215 5000
Consumer Gateway	www.consumer.gov.uk
Trade	020-7215 5960
Corporate & Consumer Affairs	020-7215 5971
Science & Technology	020-7215 5962
Industry & Employment	020-7215 5965
Financial Services Authority	020-7676 1000
Consumer Helpline	0845-606 1234
	www.fsa.gov.uk
Gaming Board	020-7306 6200
Investors Compensation Scheme	020-7947 6000
Lands Tribunal	020-7936 7200
National Audit Office	020-7798 7000
Occupational Pensions Regulatory	
Authority (OPRA)	01273-627600
Parliament Standards Commissioner	020-7219 0320
Patents Office	01633-814000
Personal Investment Authority (PIA)	020-7676 1000
Police Complaints Authority	020-7273 6450
Press Complaints Commission	020-7353 1248
Security and Futures Authority (SFA)	020-7676 1000
Office for the Supervision of Solicitors	01926-820082
Press	01926-822043
	www.lawsociety.org.uk

OFFICE OF:

Electricity Regulation (OFFER)	0845-601 3131
Scotland	0141-331 2678
Northern Ireland	028-9031 1575
Fair Trading (OFT)	020-7211 8000
Consumer Line	0345-224499
	www.oft.gov.uk
Gas Supply (OFGAS)	020-7828 0898
	www.ofgas.gov.uk
Health Economics	020-7930 9203
National Lottery (OFLOT)	020-7227 2000
Passenger Rail Franchising	
(OFPRAF)	020-7940 4200
Rail Regulator (ORR)	020-7282 2000
	www.rail-reg.gov.uk
Social Security Commissioners	020-7353 5145
Standards in Education (OFSTED)	020-7421 6800
	www.ofsted.gov.uk
Telecomms (OFTEL)	020-7634 8700
	www.oftel.gov.uk
Water Services (OFWAT)	0121-625 1300
	www.open.gov.uk/ofwat

OMBUDSMEN

Ombudsmen answer complaints from ordinary citizens about certain public bodies and private sector services. There are 24 recognised ombudsmen schemes. The majority of ombudsmen are government officers, appointed by statute to help enforce legal regulations. The others are non-statutory employees of industry sectors hoping to give an appearance of being publicly accountable, whether true or false. Eight ombudsman schemes were due to be merged into one during 2000 by the Financial Services Authority. All except the EU ombudsman are members of the British and Irish Ombudsman Association; its website www.bioa.org.uk has more details of them. All the entries below are ombudsmen, eg Banking = Banking Ombudsman.

Banking	020-7404 9944
British Waterways	01273-832624
Building Societies	020-7931 0044
Estate Agents	01722-333306
European Union	0033-388 172313
Funerals	020-7430 1112
Health Service: England	0845-015 4033
Wales	0845-601 0987
Scotland	0845-601 0456
Independent Housing	020-7836 3630
Insurance	020-7964 1480
Investment	020-7796 3065
Legal Services	0854-601 0794
Scotland	0131-556 5574
Local Government: SE England	020-7915 3210
North of England	01904-663200
Rest of England	024-7669 5999
Wales	01656-661325
Scotland	0131-225 5300
Northern Ireland	028-9023 3821
Parliamentary	020-7217 4163
Pensions	020-7834 9144
Personal Investment Authority	020-7216 0016
Prisons	020-7276 2876
Scottish Housing Association	0131-220 0599

ADVISORY COMMITTEES

These are the officially sponsored bodies giving consumers' views of industries and services to the government before decisions are made. The National Consumer Council (NCC) conducts research, lobbies policy makers and publishes reports. The NCC also helps run the Consumer Congress, the forum for consumer bodies, and publishes the annual Consumer Congress Directory.

Advisory Committees on Telecomms	020-7634 8700
Air Transport Users Council	020-7240 6061
Assoc of Community Health Councils	020-7609 8405
British Standards Institution Consumer	
Policy Committee	020-8996 7390
Central Rail Users Consultative Cttee	020-7505 9090
Electricity Regional Consumers Cttees	0121-456 6359
Food Advisory Cttee	020-7238 6289
Gas Consumers Council	020-7931 0977
General Consumer Council for NI	028-9067 2488
London Regional Passengers Cttee	020-7505 9000
Meat & Livestock Commission Consumers'	
Committee	01908-677577
National Consumer Council	020-7730 3469
Scottish CC	0131-556 5574
Welsh CC	029-2025 5454
Post Office Users National Council	020-7928 9458
Rail Users Consultative Cttees	020-7222 0391
Telecomms Advisory Cttees	020-7634 8774
Water Customer Service Cttees	0345-023953

ADVICE/PRESSURE GROUPS

The largest of the independent pressure groups is the million-member Consumers Association, publisher of the advert-free magazine Which? The 770 local Citizens Advice Bureaux deal with over six million problem-sufferers a year, including many consumers. There are two CAB websites, one giving background data and the other practical advice.

CAMRA (Campaign for Real Ale)	01727-867201
Consumer Credit Trade Assoc	020-7636 7564
Consumers' Association	020-7830 6000
	www.which.net
Consumers in Europe Group	020-7881 3021
Consumers International	020-7226 6663
Ethical Consumer (magazine)	0161-226 2929
Fed of Independent Advice Centres	020-7489 1800
Food Commission	020-7837 2250
Institute of Trading Standards Admin	01702-559922
Local Authorities Co-ordinating Body on	
Trading Standards	020-8688 1996
Money Advice Association	01822-855118
National Association of Citizens Advice	
Bureaux	020-7833 2181
CAB details	www.nacab.org.uk
Practical advice	www.adviceguide.org.uk
National Debtline	0121-359 8501
National Fed of Consumer Groups	0113-264 8341
National Food Alliance	020-7837 1228
Research Institute Consumer Affairs	020-7704 5200

Education

Britain has 27,600 state schools, 1,500 specials and 2,500 independents. They have 532,000 teachers and 9.97 million pupils. About 93 per cent of pupils attend publicly-funded state schools. These are primary schools for 5-11 year olds and secondary schools for 11-16. Most are controlled by Local Education Authorities (LEAs), except grant-maintained schools, which have opted out of LEA control and are overseen by the DfEE, and schools receiving public funds but run by voluntary bodies. Independent schools are not publicly-funded, charging fees to pupils. They are called: boarding, private, preparatory and public schools (in Scotland and most of the world "public" schools are actually publicly-funded schools); details from Independent Schools Information Service. Seventy per cent of pupils continue studying beyond the age of 16. About 864,000 become full-time students, with 1.62 million part-time, in further education colleges. These are mainly vocational, with exams to GCE Advanced level. Other exams here are GCSE and NVQ. Beyond "further" education is "higher" education, the shorthand for the 90 universities and 34 colleges examining above GCE A level. They have 1.23 million full-time students and 708,000 part-time.

EDUCATIONLINE

BBC
A wealth of material for all levels, including a search-able directory of over 3,000 educational websites (title: /webguide).   www.bbc.co.uk/education
The Guardian
The website of the Guardian's weekly education coverage.   www.educationunlimited.co.uk
Interactive curriculum lessons and learning materials for students, teachers and parents.   www.learn.co.uk
Higher Education Statistics Agency
Handy raw data.   www.hesa.ac.uk
Homework High
Popular Channel 4 site offering 9-16 year olds help with their homework.   www.homeworkhigh.com
Learnfree
Commercial site giving parents extensive help and information.   www.learnfree.co.uk
National Grid for Learning
A collection of resources brought together by White-hall to raise standards in education and support lifelong learning.   www.ngfl.gov.uk
NISS Information Gateway
Giving access to information for the UK academic community.   www.niss.ac.uk
Parents' Centre
User-friendly official help from the DfEE explaining all aspects of parent life.   www.parents.dfee.gov.uk
Qualifications and Curriculum Authority
Everything you need to know from the statutory organisation set up in 1997.   www.qca.org.uk
Social Science Information Gateway
One of the best information directories, covering wide-ranging education sources.   www.sosig.ac.uk
UCAS
Key starting point for anyone seeking admission to a university or college.   www.ucas.ac.uk

CENTRAL BODIES

Assoc of Colleges	020-7827 4600
Central Bureau for Educational Visits & Exchanges	020-7389 4004
	www.britcoun.org/cbeve
Convention of Scottish Local Auths	0131-474 9200
Dept for Education & Employment	020-7925 5000
Press	020-7925 5615
	www.dfee.gov.uk
Further Education Funding Council	024-7686 3000
General Teaching Council for England	0870-001 0308
	www.gtce.org.uk
Independent Schools Info Service (also Independent Schools Council)	020-7798 1500
National Curriculum Council	020-7229 1234
N Ireland Dept of Education	01247-279279
	www.nics.gov.uk/deni
Office for Standards in Education (OFSTED)	020-7421 6800
	www.ofsted.gov.uk
Qualifications & Curriculum Authority	020-7509 5555
	www.qca.org.uk
School Curriculum and Assessment Authority	020-7229 1234
Scottish Office Education	0131-556 8400
	www.scotland.gov.uk
Society of Education Officers	0161-236 5766
Welsh Joint Education Committee	029-2026 5000
Welsh Office Education Dept	029-2082 3207
	www.wales.gov.uk

UNIONS

Assoc of Teachers & Lecturers	020-7930 6441
Assoc of University Teachers	020-7670 9700
Headmasters Conference	0116-285 4810
National Assoc of Head Teachers	01444-472472
NAS/UWT	0121-453 6150

NATFHE	020-7837 3636
National Union of Students	020-7272 8900
National Union of Teachers	020-7388 6191
Prof Assoc of Teachers	01332-372337
Secondary Heads Assoc	0116-299 1122

UNIVERSITIES

Every university has a website, which all end with "ac.uk". Below, the word in brackets is the one between "www" and "ac.uk" on all the websites, eg Aberdeen is www.abdn.ac.uk.

Aberdeen (abdn)	01224-272000
Abertay Dundee (abertay-dundee)	01382-308000
Anglia Polytechnic (anglia)	01245-493131
Aston (aston)	0121-359 3611
Bath (bath)	01225-826826
Birmingham (bham)	0121-414 3344
Bournemouth (bournemouth)	01202-524111
Bradford (brad)	01274-232323
Brighton (bton)	01273-600900
Bristol (bris)	0117-928 9000
Brunel (brunel)	01895-274000
Buckingham (buck)	01280-814080
Cambridge (cam)	01223-337733
Central England in Birmingham (uce)	0121-331 5000
Central Lancashire (uclan)	01772-201201
City, London (city)	020-7477 8000
Coventry (coventry)	024-7663 1313
Cranfield (cranfield)	01234-750111
De Montfort, Leicester (dmu)	0116-255 1551
Derby (derby)	01332-622222
Dundee (dundee)	01382-223181
Durham (dur)	0191-374 2000
East Anglia (uea)	01603-456161
East London (uel)	020-8590 7722
Edinburgh (ed)	0131-650 1000
Essex (essex)	01206-873333
Exeter (ex)	01392-263263
Glamorgan (glam)	01443-480480
Glasgow (gla)	0141-339 8855
Glasgow Caledonian (gcal)	0141-331 3000
Greenwich (gre)	020-8331 8590
Heriot-Watt, Edinburgh (hw)	0131-449 5111
Hertfordshire (herts)	01707-284000
Huddersfield (hud)	01484-422288
Hull (hull)	01482-346311
Keele (keele)	01782-621111
Kent (ukc)	01227-764000
Kingston, London (kingston)	020-8547 2000
Lancaster (lancs)	01524-65201
Leeds (leeds	0113-233 2332
Leeds Metropolitan (lmu)	0113-283 2600
Leicester (le)	0116-252 2522
Lincolnshire & Humberside (ulh)	01482-440550
Liverpool (liv)	0151-794 2000
Liverpool John Moores (livjm)	0151-231 2121
London Guildhall (lgu)	020-7320 1000
University of London	020-7636 8000
Birkbeck College (bbk)	020-7631 6000

Courtauld Institute of Art (courtauld)	020-7872 0220
Goldsmiths College (gold)	020-7919 7171
Imperial College (ic)	020-7589 5111
Kings College (kd)	020-7836 5454
London School of Economics (lse)	020-7405 7686
Queen Mary College (qmw)	020-7975 5555
Royal Holloway (rhbnc)	01784-434455
Royal Veterinary College (rvc)	020-7468 5000
School of Oriental Studies (soas)	020-7637 2388
School of Pharmacy (ulsop)	020-7753 5800
School of Slavonic Studies (ssees)	020-7862 8519
St Georges Medical School (sghms)	020-8725 5992
University College (ucl)	020-7387 7050
Wye (wye)	01233-812401
Loughborough (lboro)	01509-263171
Luton (luton)	01582-734111
Manchester (man)	0161-275 2000
Manchester Metropolitan (mmu)	0161-247 2000
Middlesex (mdx)	020-8362 5000
Napier, Edinburgh (napier)	0131-444 2266
Newcastle-upon-Tyne (ncl	0191-222 6000
North London (unl)	020-7607 2789
Northumbria (unn)	0191-232 6002
Nottingham (nottingham)	0115-951 5151
Nottingham Trent (ntu)	0115-941 8418
Open University (open)	01908-274066
Oxford (ox)	01865-270000
Oxford Union	01865-241353
Oxford Brookes (brookes)	01865-741111
Paisley (paisley)	0141-848 3000
Plymouth (plym)	01752-600600
Portsmouth (port)	023-9287 6543
Queens, Belfast (qub)	028-9024 5133
Reading (rdg)	0118-987 5123
Robert Gordon, Aberdeen (rgu)	01224-262105
Royal Agricultural College (royagcol)	01285-652531
Salford (salford)	0161-295 5000
Sheffield (shef)	0114-222 2000
Sheffield Hallam (shu)	0114-272 0911
South Bank, London (sbu)	020-7928 8989
Southampton (soton)	023-8059 5000
St Andrews, Fife (st-and)	01334-476161
Staffordshire (staffs)	01782-294000
Stirling (stir)	01786-473171
Strathclyde (strath)	0141-552 4400
Sunderland (sunderland)	0191-515 2000
Surrey (surrey)	01483-300800
Sussex (sussex)	01273-606755
Teeside (tees)	01642-218121
Thames Valley, Ealing (tvu)	020-8579 5000
Ulster, Coleraine (ulst)	01265-44141
UMIST, Manchester (umist)	0161-236 3311
University of Wales	029-2038 2656
Aberystwyth (aber)	01970-623111
Bangor (bangor)	01248-351151
Cardiff (cf)	029-2087 4000
Lampeter (lampeter)	01570-422351
Swansea (swan)	01792-205678
Warwick (warwick)	024-7652 3523
West of England, Bristol (uwe)	0117-965 6261
Westminster (wmin)	020-7911 5000
Wolverhampton (wlv)	01902-321000
York (york)	01904-430000

Religion

The UK's largest religion is Christianity, primarily the Anglicans, Presbyterians (including the Church of Scotland), Roman Catholics and Free Churches. The second biggest is the Muslim religion, followed by the Sikhs, Jews, Buddhists and Hindus.

In the worldwide Anglican Communion group, the Church of England (CoE) is the leading body. England is divided into the provinces of Canterbury and York, each run by an archbishop: George Carey and David Hope respectively. There are 44 dioceses within the provinces, with 13,000 parishes. The CoE is governed by its General Synod, which itself is run Cabinet-style by the new Archbishop Council, set up in 1999. There are 16,000 churches and about 10,000 staff.

The other main Anglican churches in the UK are the Church in Wales, the Scottish Episcopal Church and the Church of Ireland. They are independent, but have strong links with the CoE. In Scotland, the leading religious body is the non-Anglican Church of Scotland. It has a Presbyterian structure, with 47 districts and about 660,000 members, and is governed by its General Assembly. Every ten years all Anglican bishops meet for the international Lambeth Conference to discuss common issues, although without any policy-making formal power. The next conference is in 2008.

Roman Catholics form by far the world's largest Christian movement, with nearly a billion members. The Roman Catholic Church is the global organisation run from the autonomous Vatican City State in Rome. The leading figure is the Pope, currently John Paul II. In England and Wales the governing body is the Bishops Conference, headed by the President, currently Michael Bowen, Archbishop of Southwark. In Scotland there is a similar Bishops Conference.

The Free Churches are Protestant churches which, unlike the Church of England and Church of Scotland, are not established, ie, officially recognised by the State. The largest of the Free is the Methodist Church. Others include the Salvation Army, Baptists and United Reformed Church.

Muslims are followers of the Islam. Many Muslims have come to Britain since the late nineteenth century, and there are now over 600 mosques. There is no central organisation, but the most influential bodies are the Islamic Cultural Centre (the London Central Mosque) and the Imams and Mosque Council. Sikhism grew up in the Punjab four centuries ago, coming to Britain in the 1950s. It has no central body, but the Sikh Missionary Society has an information service.

Christianity is declining, while many new religious movements, often called cults, are mushrooming. Paganism and Druidry have revived in England, and part of the anti-capitalist, pro-environment culture that aims to reshape politics. Leading bodies are the Pagan Federation and the British Druid Order.

The main religious directory is Religions in the UK (University of Derby/Inter Faith Network). Good websites listed below include the CoE, Roman Catholic, World Council of Churches, Christian Aid, Church Net, Jubilee 2000 and Pagan Federation.

ANGLICAN

Church of England	www.cofe.anglican.org
General Synod (main CoE contacts)	020-7898 1200
Archbishop of Canterbury	020-7928 8282
Archbishop of York	01904-707021
Church Commissioners	020-7898 1000
Record Centre	020-7231 1251
Church in Wales	029-2023 1638
	www.churchinwales.org.uk
Church of Ireland	00-3531 4978422
	www.ireland.anglican.org
Scottish Episcopal Church	0131-225 6357
	www.scotland.anglican.org
Anglican Communion	www.anglicancommunion.org

ROMAN CATHOLIC

Main website	www.tasc.ac.uk/cc
Bishops Conferences: E&W	020-7828 8709
Scotland	0141-221 1168
Archbishops: Westminster	020-7798 9033
Liverpool	0151-724 6398

Glasgow	0141-226 5898
Media offices: London	020-7828 8709
Glasgow	0141-221 1168
Dublin	00-3531 2885043
Catholic Enquiry Centre	020-8458 3316
	www.cms.org/ceo

OTHER CHRISTIAN

Baptist Union	01235-517700
	www.baptist.org.uk
Church of Jesus Christ of Latter-day	
Saints (Mormons)	0121-712 1200
Church of Scotland	0131-225 5722
Churches of Christ	01842 810357
Congregational Federation	0115-911 1460
Council of Churches for Britain	020-7620 4444
Eastern Orthodox Churches: Greek	020-7723 4787
Russian	020-8995 9503
Serbian	020-7727 8367
Free Church Federal Council	020-7387 8413
Free Church of England	0151-638 2564
Free Presbyterian Church of Scotland	0131-229 0649
Independent Methodist Churches	01942-223526
International Churches of Christ	020-7713 6028
Jehovah's Witnesses	020-8906 2211
Lutheran Council	020-7383 3081
Methodist Church	020-7222 8010
	www.methodist.org.uk
Moravian Church	020-8883 3409
Pentecostal Church bodies:	
Apostolic	01792-473992
Assemblies of God	0115-9811188
New Testament	01604-643311
Presbyterian Church in Ireland	028-9032 2284
Presbyterian Church of Wales	029-2049 4913
Quakers (Religious Society of Friends)	020-7663 1000
	www.quaker.org.uk
Salvation Army: E&W	020-7367 4500
Scotland	0131-443 4740
Seventh Day Adventist Church	01923-672251
Unification Church	020-7723 0721
Union of Welsh Independents	01792-467040
Unitarian Churches	020-7240 2384
United Reformed Church	020-7916 2020
	www.urc.org.uk
World Council of Churches	00-4122 7916111
	www.wcc-coe.org

OTHER RELIGIONS

Aetherius Society	020-7736 4187
Baha'i Community of UK	020-7584 2566
Buddhist:	
Buddhist Society	020-7834 5858
	www.buddsoc.org.uk
Friends of Western Buddhist Order	0121-449 8272
London Buddhist Vihara	020-8995 9493
Network of Buddhist Orgs	020-7582 5797
Church of Christ, Scientist	020-7384 8600
Church of Scientology	020-7580 3601

Hindu:	
Hindu Universe	www.hindunet.org
Int Soc for Krishna Consciousness	01923-856269
	www.iskcon.org.uk
Swaminarayan Hindu Mission	020-8965 2651
Jain Centre	0116-254 3091
Jesus Army	020-8992 0100
Jewish:	
Board of Deputies of British Jews	020-7543 5400
	www.bod.org.uk
United Synagogue	020-8343 6301
Jewish Care	020-8922 2000
Jewish Policy Research	020-7935 8266
Muslim:	
Al-Muhajiroun	020-8803 4541
Imama & Mosques Council	020-8993 7168
Islamic Centre England	020-7604 5500
	www.ic-el.org
Muslim Council of Britain	020-8903 9024
	www.mcb.org.uk
Muslim Information Centre	020-7272 5170
UK Action Cttee Islamic Affairs	020-8974 2780
World Ahl Ul-Bayt, Islamic League	020-8954 9881
Sikh Missionary Society	020-8574 1902
Sikh Temple	020-8854 1786
Theosophical Society	020-7935 9261

OTHER RELIGIOUS BODIES

British Druid Order	www.druidorder.demon.co.uk
British Humanist Assoc	020-7430 0908
	www.humanism.org.uk
Christian Aid	www.christian-aid.org.uk
Christian Research Assoc.	020-8294 1989
	www.christian-research.org.uk
Church Army	020-8318 1226
	www.churcharmy.org.uk
Church Commissioners	020-7898 1000
Church House Bookshop	020-7898 1000
Church Missionary Society	020-7928 8681
Church Net	www.churchnet.org.uk
Council of Christians & Jews	020-7820 0090
Cult Information Centre	01689-833800
	www.cultinformation.org.uk
Evangelical Alliance UK	020-7207 2100
Fellowship of Reconciliation	01832-720257
Inform (Information Network Focus on	
Religious Movements)	020-7955 7654
Inter Faith Network for the UK	020-7388 0008
	www.interfaith.org.uk
Jubilee 2000 Coalition	020-7739 1000
	www.jubilee2000uk.org
Lesbian and Gay Christians	020-7739 1249
Pagan Federation	01209-831519
	www.paganfed.demon.co.uk
Pagan Way Info Network	07930-833456
Spiritualist Assoc of Gt Britain	020-7235 3351
Spiritualists' National Union	01909-489828
	www.snu.org.uk
Three Faiths Forum	020-7485 2358
Transcendental Meditation	0990-143733

Shopping

In 1999 the UK had 203,000 retailing businesses, employing 2.4 million people, and 113,000 wholesalers, with 1.1 million staff. Retail annual turnover was £181.5 billion and wholesale £344 billion in 1996, the latest year for which figures are available. Eleven per cent of retailers have turnovers below £50,000, and another 25 per cent between £50,000 and £100,000. About 800 retailers (0.4 per cent of the total) have turnovers above £10 million, 250 of them over £50 million. Retailing accounts for 37 per cent of all consumer spending. The £90 billion grocery market is dominated by five supermarket groups, controlling three-quarters of trade. Tesco is the biggest, with a 1998 turnover of £16.2 billion and a profit of £882 million, followed by Sainsbury (£15.5b, £801m), Asda (£7.6b, £414m), Argyll-cum-Safeway (£7.0b, £427m) and Somerfield (£6.1b, £187m). The USA's cheap-goods giant Wal-mart bought Asda in mid-1999.

ONLINE SHOPS

Online shopping is mushrooming, and most businesses now have websites. The long-term effect on the shape of the retail industry is still unclear, with some experts predicting major upheavals. But a customer survey in April 2000 found many people unhappy with online services. Nervous e-shoppers are helped by the Guardian's book Guide to Shopping on the Internet, by Jim McClellan, and its partner website Shopping Unlimited. Basic advice is: If possible, shop at reputable companies you have heard about; be suspicious if no company address and phone number are given (if in any doubt - phone them); check on the site's security precautions; pay by credit card, but do not send its number via simple, unencrypted email (look for a closed padlock in the status bar on your screen, and the prefix "https:" rather than "http:"); don't be hoodwinked by a slick website; keep records, as though they were till receipts; and

don't hand over unnecessary personal information - when you are asked too much, go elsewhere. If you find that you are sinking in an e-mire, get help from this book's Consumer Watchdogs section. Official support comes from the DTI's Consumer Gateway, unofficial from the Consumers Association's internet traders vetting service, via Which?. Both are listed below, along with: shopping malls which sell a wide variety of products; directories providing links to the thousands of other shop sites; the two leading auctioneers; and the main supermarkets.

Auctions

eBay	www.ebay.co.uk
QXL	www.qxl.com

Helpers

Consumer Gateway	www.consumer.gov.uk
Which? Web Traders	www.which.net/webtrader

Malls and Directories

Barclay Square	www.barclaysquare.com
Best of British	www.bestofbritish.com
Big Save	www.bigsave.com
British Shopping Links	www.british-shopping.com
Daltons Web	www.daltons.co.uk
eDirectory	www.edirectory.co.uk
Home Town	www.hometown.co.uk
Internet Shopping	www.internetshopping.co.uk
My Taxi	www.mytaxi.co.uk
Netline	www.netline.co.uk
QVC	www.qvcuk.com
Safestreet	www.safestreet.co.uk
Shop Guide	www.shopguide.co.uk
Shop Smart	www.shopsmart.com
Shoppers Universe	www.shoppersuniverse.com
Shopping Centre	www.shoppingcentre.net
Shopping Centres	www.shopping-centres.com
Shopping Sites	www.shopping-sites.com
Shops on the Net	www.shopsonthenet.com
Shops-UK	www.shops-uk.com
The Guardian	www.shoppingunlimited.co.uk
UK Shopping City	www.ukshops.co.uk
UK Shopping Zone	www.ukshoppingzone.co.uk

Supermarkets

Asda	www.asda.co.uk
Co-op	www.co-op.co.uk
Iceland	www.iceland.co.uk
Safeway	www.safeway.co.uk
Sainsbury's	www.sainsburys.co.uk
Somerfield	www.somerfield.co.uk
Spar	www.spar.co.uk
Tesco	.www,tescodirect.com
Waitrose	www.waitrose.co.uk

LARGE RETAILERS

Many of these have their website listed on the directory www.retail.co.uk.

Allders	020-89295500
Allied Bakeries	01784-451366
Argos	01908-690333
Argyll (Safeway)	020-8848 8744
Asda	0113-243 5435
Associated British Foods	020-7589 6363
B & Q	023-8025 6256
BhS	020-7262 3288
Boots	0115-950 6111
Burton/Arcadia Group	020-7636 8040
Co-op (CRS - retail)	01706-713000
Co-op (CWS - wholesale)	0161-834 1212
Comet	01482-320681
Debenhams	020-7408 4444
Diadgeo (ex-Grand Metropolitan)	020-7518 5200
Dixons	01442-353000
Forte	0345-404040
Freemans	020-7735 7644
GatewaySomerfield	0117-935 9359
Great Universal Stores	0161-273 8282
Habitat	020-7255 2545
Halfords	01527-517601
Harrods	020-7730 1234
House of Fraser (Harrods, Army & Navy, Rackhams)	020-7963 2000
Iceland	01244-830100
John Lewis	020-7828 1000
John Menzies	0131-467 8070
Kingfisher (Comet, Woolworth, B&Q)	020-7724 7749
Kwik Save	01745-887111
Littlewoods (mail order)	0151-235 2222
Marks & Spencer	020-7935 4422
McDonalds Restaurants	020-8700 7000
MFI	020-8200 8000
Next	0116-286 6411
Owen Owen	0151-707 4000
Sainsbury	020-7695 6000
Sears (Freemans, Selfridges, Olympus)	020-7200 5999
WH Smith	01793-616161
Somerfield	0117-935 9359
Storehouse (Bhs, Habitat, Mothercare)	020-7262 3456
Superdrug	020-8684 7000
Tesco	01992-632222
Texas Homecare (Homebase)	01933-679679
EMI Group (HMV, Radio Rentals)	020-7355 4848
Toys R Us	01628-414141
Waitrose	01344-424680
FW Woolworth	020-7262 1222

LARGE SHOPPING CENTRES

Biggest centres (space for 1,500+ cars)

Basildon (Eastgate)	01268-533631
Belfast (Castle Court)	028-9023 4591
Birmingham (One Stop)	0121-344 3697
Birmingham (The Fort)	0121-386 4442
Bournemouth (Hampshire)	01202-516131
Brent Cross	020-8202 8095
Brighton (Churchill Square)	01273-327428
Bromley (Glades)	020-8313 9292
Crawley (County Mall)	01293-611975
Croydon (Whitgift)	020-8688 8522
Dartford (Bluewater Park)	01322-388989
Dudley (Merry Hill)	01384-481141
Edinburgh (Gyle)	0131-539 9000
Ellesmere Port	0151-357 2118
Gateshead (Metro)	0191-493 2040
Gillingham (Hempstead Valley)	01634-387076
Glasgow (Clyde)	0141-952 4594
Glasgow (Forge)	0141-556 6661
Hartlepool (Middleton Grange)	01429-861220
Hatfield (Galleria)	01707-278301
Leeds (White Rose)	01132-291234
Leicester (Fosse Park)	0116-263 0603
Livingston (Almondvale)	01506-432961
Luton (Arndale)	01582-412636
Milton Keynes (Central)	01908-678641
Nottingham (Broad Marsh)	0115-950 7133
Nottingham (Victoria)	0115-912 1111
Peterborough (Queensgate)	01733-311666
Redditch (Kingfisher)	01527-61355
Runcorn (Halton Lea)	01928-716363
Sheffield (Meadowhall)	0114-256 8800
Stockport (Mersey Way)	0161-480 2839
Swindon (Brunel)	01793-525857
Telford	01952-230032
Tunbridge Wells (Royal Victoria)	01892-514141
Warrington (Golden Square)	01925-655053
Washington (Galleries)	0191-416 7177
Watford (Harlequin)	01923-250292
Welwyn Garden (Howard)	01707-320026
West Thurrock (Lakeside)	01708-869933

Try www.shopping-centres.com for some of the smaller shopping centres

Britain's eight biggest shopping malls

Bluewater, near Dartford, Kent, M25/A2 junc.
   320 shops, 1.7 m sq ft. Opened March 1999.
MetroCentre, edge of Gateshead, Tyneside.
   320 shops, 1.4m sq ft.
Merry Hill, Dudley, West Midlands.
   260 shops, 1.8m sq ft.
Lakeside, West Thurrock, south Essex, M25.
   309 shops, 1.3m sq ft.
Trafford Centre, outskirts of Manchester.
   280 shops, 1.3m sq ft.
Meadowhall, on outskirts of Sheffield.
   285 shops, 1.2m sq ft.
Cribbs Causeway, near Bristol.
   140 shops, 725,000 sq ft.
Braehead, Renfrew, near Glasgow.
   100 shops, 600,000 sq ft.

Travel

TRAVELLING ONLINE

The starting point for all inside-UK travellers is UK Public Transport Information, with details of everything. Trainspotters can also use Railtrack and Train Line. Check out UK flights and airports on BAA, worldwide on Airwise. Travel agents are listed on ABTA. The Foreign Office gives useful travel advice.

Destination info

Lonely Planet	www.lonelyplanet.com
Rough Guides	www.travel.roughguides.com

Bookings/holidays/flights

A2bTravel	www.a2btravel.com
Bargain Holidays	www.bargainholidays.com
Cheapflights	www.cheapflights.co.uk
Deckchair	www.deckchair.com
Ebookers	www.ebookers.com
Expedia	www.expedia.co.uk
Green Earth Travel	www.vegtravel.com
InfoTravel	www.infotravelco.uk
Last Minute Holidays	www.lastminute.com
LinOne Travel	www.lineone.net
Teletext Holidays	www.teletext.co.uk/holidays
Travel Travel	www.travel-travel.co.uk
Travelocity	www.travelocity.co.uk
TravelSelect	www.travelselect.co.uk
TravelStore	www.travelstore.com

Boats

Canals	www.british-waterways.org
Coastguards, marine safety	www.mcagency.org.uk
Ferries	www.seaview.co.uk
Freight ferries	www.sailingschedules.co.uk

Buses/coaches/tube

Coach information	www.coach-hire.uk.com
London Transport	www.londontransport.co.uk
National Express	www.nationalexpress.co.uk
Stagecoach	www.stagecoachholdings.com

Maps

Altapedia (world atlas)	www.atlapedia.com
Mapquest (world roads)	www.mapquest.com
Multimaps (UK towns/streets)	www.multimap.com
Streetmap (London focus)	www.streetmap.co.uk

Planes

Airports guide	www.a2bairports.com
Airwise	www.airwise
Aviation industry data	www.inter-plane.com
BAA (flights/arrivals/news)	www.baa.co.uk

Trains

Eurostar (timetables/bookings)	www.eurstar.co.uk
Railtrack (UK timetables)	www.railtrack.co.uk
Rail industry contacts	www.railway-technology.com
TheTrainLine (UK bookings)	www.thetrainline.com
Wide-ranging rail news	www.rail.co.uk

Weather

UK Met Office	www.meto.gov.uk
BBC	www.bbc.co.uk/weather

And ...

ABTA (travel agents list)	www.abtanet.com
Currency conversions	www.oanda.com/converter
Foreign Office	www.fco.gov.uk/travel
Health advice	www.ukhealthnet.co.uk
Medicine Planet (health)	www.medicineplanet.com
UK Passport Agency	www.ukpa.gov.uk
UK Public Transport Information	www.pti.org.uk
Walking Britain	www.visitbritain.com/walking

TRAINS

Britain has 32,000 kilometres of rail track, 2,500 stations and 40,000 bridges, tunnels and viaducts. Passengers travelled 35.1 billion kilometres in 1998/9. Britain's busiest station is Victoria, with over 300,000 passengers daily. London's Underground in 1998/9 had 866 million passenger journeys, along 392 kilometres of track (171 subterranean), stopping at 246 stations. The Tory government's privatisation of British Rail was completed in 1997, splitting it into more than 90 separate businesses. The passenger services were divided into 25 regional units, which were franchised to private companies. BR's operational infrastructure was sold to Railtrack, which manages all track, signals, stations, bridges, tunnels and depots. Three companies franchised all British Rail's 11,000-strong rolling stock of passenger trains and carriages, which in turn were leased to the 25 passenger service operators. Freight services were split into seven components, which are now run by four companies. The Labour government tried to tighten up regulation by setting up the Strategic Rail Authority in early 2000, merging the British Railways Board and the Office of Passenger Rail Franchising.

RAIL TRAVEL ENQUIRIES

All national rail enquiries, 24-hour	0345-484950
Rail Europe	0990-848848
Channel Tunnel: Le Shuttle passengers	0990-353535
Eurostar passengers	0990-186186
London Transport/tube, 24-hour	020-7222 1234
Travel Check (recorded)	020-7222 1200
TBC (Train, Bus, Coach) Hotline	0891-910910

RAIL ORGANISATIONS

Assoc of Train Operating Companies	020-7928 5151
British Transport Police	020-7388 7541
Central Rail Users Consultative Cttee	020-7505 9090
Scotland	0141-221 7760
Wales	029-2022 7247
DETR	020-7890 3000
Railways Directorate	020-7944 3000
Office of Rail Regulator	020-7282 2000
Strategic Rail Authority	020-7960 1500

RAIL OPERATORS

Passenger train companies

Anglia	01473-693333
Cardiff	029-2043 0000
Central	020-7930 6655
Chiltern	01296-332100
Connex South Central	0870-603 0405
Connex South Eastern	020-7928 5151
Cross-Country (Virgin)	0121-654 7400
Eurostar	0345-303030
Gatwick Express	020-7973 5005
Great Eastern	020-7928 5151
Great North Eastern	01904-653022
Great Western	01793-499458
Heathrow Express	020-8745 0578
InterCity West Coast	0121-643 4444
Island Line (IoW)	01983-812591
LTS (London, Tilbury, Southend)	01702-357889
Merseyrail Electrics	0151-709 8292
Midland MainLine	01332-221125
North Spirit	01904-653022
North Western	0161-228 2141
ScotRail	0141-332 9811
Silverlink (North London)	01923-207258
South West	020-7928 5151
Thames	0118-908 3678
Thameslink	020-7620 6333
Wales & West	029-2043 0400
West Anglia Great Northern	0345-818919

Freight companies

Freightliner	020-7214 9491
English, Welsh & Scottish Railway	020-7713 2422
Railfreight Distribution	020-7922 9311

Railtrack plc

Company HQ	020-7557 8000
East Anglia	020-7904 4000
Great Western	01793-499500
London North Eastern	01904-522825
Midlands	0121-643 4444
North West	0161-228 2141
Scotland	0141-335 2424
Southern	020-7344 7292

BOATS

Britain's Merchant Navy was once the biggest commercial fleet in the world, but is now one of the smallest. From 1987 to 1998 the number of UK-owned merchant trading ships over 500 gross tons fell from 657 to 486. Total gross tonnage in 1998 was 7.6 million (11.3 million in 1987), deadweight tonnage 9.7 million. The biggest single type was the tanker, with 127 vessels of 2.4 million tons. In 1998 there were 530 million tons of traffic through major **British ports** (457 million in 1987). There are about 80 ports of commercial significance, plus several hundred smaller ones handling local cargo, fishing vessels, ferries and recreation. The largest in tonnage handling are (in descending order): London, Tees/Hartlepool, Grimsby/Immingham and Forth. Dover is Britain's main port for roll-on roll-off traffic. Britain's largest port owner and operator is Associated British Ports, with 23 under its control, handling nearly a quarter of traffic. The **Port of London Authority** (PLA) is responsible for 96 miles of the tidal Thames downriver from Teddington, and incorporating 82 operational wharves and terminals. It handles about 57 million tonnes of cargo a year. Britain has 3,200 kilometres of **inland waterways**, including canals with 22,000 canal boats, used by 10 million people a year.

WATER ORGANISATIONS

Associated British Ports	020-7430 1177
British Ports Association	020-7242 1200
British Waterways	01923-226422
Inland Waterways Assoc	01923-711114
Register of Shipping, Seamen & Fishing	
Boats	029-2074 7333
Westminster Passenger Services Fed	020-8977 5702

PORTS AND HARBOURS

Aberdeen, Grampian	01224-597000
Ardrossan, Strathclyde	01294-463972
Belfast	028-9055 4422
Bristol, Avon	0117-982 0000
Brixham, Devon	01803-853321
Cardiff	029-2040 0500
Clyde Ports	0141-221 8733
Cowes, Isle of Wight	01983-293952
Dover, Kent	01304-240400

Dundee, Tayside	01382-224121
Falmouth, Cornwall	01326-211376
Felixstowe, Suffolk	01394-604500
Fishguard, Dyfed	01348-404453
Fleetwood, Lancs	01253-872323
Folkestone, Kent	0990-755785
Forth Ports	0131-555 8750
Gt Yarmouth, Norfolk	01493-335500
Harwich, Essex	01255-243030
Heysham, Lancs	01524-852373
Holyhead, Anglesey	01407-762304
Grimsby, Humberside	01472-359181
Hull, Humberside	01482-327171
Immingham, Humberside	01469-571555
Ipswich, Suffolk	01473-231010
Isle of Man	01624-686628
Larne, Antrim	01574-872100
Lerwick, Shetland	01595-692991
Liverpool	0151-949 6000
London:	
Port of London Authority	020-7265 2656
Chief Harbour Master (Gravesend)	01474-562200
Duty Officer (Woolwich)	020-8855 0315
Port Controller (Gravesend)	01474-560311
Website	www.portoflondon.co.uk
London: Tilbury	01375-852200
Londonderry	028-7186 0555
Lowestoft, Suffolk	01502-572286
Manchester	0161-872 2411
Medway Ports, Kent	01795-561234
Milford Haven, Dyfed	01646-693091
Newhaven, East Sussex	01273-514131
Peterhead, Grampian	01779-483600
Poole, Dorset	01202-440200
Portsmouth, Hants	023-9229 7395
Ramsgate, Kent	01843-592277
Rye, East Sussex	01797-225225
Scarborough, North Yorks	01723-373530
Shoreham, West Sussex	01273-598100
Southampton, Hants	023-8033 0022
Stornoway, Western Isles	01851-702688
Sunderland, Tyne & Wear	0191-553 2100
Swansea, West Glamorgan	01792-633000
Tees & Hartlepool	01642-877000
Tyne	0191-455 2671
Weymouth, Dorset	01305-206421
Whitby, North Yorks	01947-602354
Workington, Cumbria	01900-602301

FERRY COMPANIES

Brittany Ferries:	
Portsmouth	023-9289 2207
Plymouth	01752-227941
Caledonian MacBrayne Ferries	01475-650100
Condor Ferries	01305-761555
Hoverspeed:	
Belfast/Stranraer	0990-523523
Dover/Folkestone	01304-865000
Irish Ferries:	

Dublin	00-3531 855 2222
Holyhead	01407-760223
Liverpool	0345-171717
Isle of Man Steam Packet Co	0990-523523
Isles of Scilly Steamship Co	01736-362009
Mersey Ferries	0151-630 1030
North Sea Ferries (Hull)	01642-431400
Orkney Ferries	01856-872044
P&O:	
All European ferries	0990-980980
Head office	020-7930 4343
Aberdeen	01224-572615
Cairnryan	01581-200276
Dover	0990-980980
Felixstowe	01394-604040
Fishguard	01348-404404
Larne	0870-242 4777
Portsmouth	0990-980555
Scrabster	01847-892052
Red Funnel Ferries (Southampton)	023-8033 3042
Holyman Sally Ferries	020-7401 7470
Scandanavian Seaways (Harwich)	01255-240240
Stena:	
All reservations	0990-707070
Harwich	01255-243333
Holyhead	01407-606666
Stranraer	01776-702531
Swansea Cork Ferries	01792-456116
Wightlink (Portsmouth)	01983-882432

PLANES

The UK has over 150 licensed civil airports, handling 143 million passengers in 1998. Three-quarters of the airports have less than a 100,000 passengers a year each, while 11 handle more than 2.5 million. The busiest are: Heathrow with 60.4 million in 1998, Gatwick 29.0 million, Manchester 17.2 million and Stansted 6.8 million. Heathrow is the busiest airport in the world for international passengers. Seven British airports, including Heathrow and Gatwick, are owned by BAA plc, and together handle 78 per cent of all passengers and 80 per cent of air cargo traffic in Britain. British Airways is the world's largest international airline, Britannia Airways the world's biggest charter airline. The Civil Aviation Authority (CAA) oversees all non-military flying and enforces all regulations, on behalf of the Civil Aviation Division of the DETR. The CAA subsidiary National Air Traffic Services (NATS) controls all air traffic and safety over Britain and its surrounding seas, in collaboration with the Ministry of

Defence. At the heart of NATS, which the government wants to privatise. is its Air Traffic Control Centre at West Drayton near Heathrow. A £600m new centre at Swanwick, Hants, should replace West Drayton in 2002.

FLIGHT ENQUIRIES

Aberdeen (Dyce)	01224-722331
Barra, Hebrides	01871-890283
Belfast (Aldergrove)	01849-422888
Belfast (City)	028-9045 7745
Benbecula, Outer Hebrides	01870-602051
Biggin Hill, Kent	01959-571111
Birmingham International	0121-767 5511
Blackpool, Lancs	01253-343434
Bournemouth (Hurn), Dorset	01202-364000
Bristol (Lulsgate), Avon	01275-474444
Brize Norton, Oxon (RAF)	01993-842551
Cambridge	01223-361133
Campbeltown (Strathclyde)	01586-553797
Cardiff	01446-711111
Carlisle	01228-573641
Channel Islands: Alderney	01481-822888
Guernsey	01481-237766
Jersey	01534-492000
Coventry, West Midlands	024-7630 1717
Culdrose, Cornwall (RAF)	01326-574121
Dundee, Tayside	01382-643242
East Midlands	01332-852852
Edinburgh (Turnhouse)	0131-333 1000
Exeter, Devon	01392-367433
Gatwick	01293-535353
Glasgow	0141-887 1111
Gloucester-Cheltenham	01452-857700
Heathrow	0870-000 0123
Inverness (Dalcross), Highland	01667-464000
Ipswich	0956-701015
Isle of Man (Ronaldsway)	01624-824313
Kent International (Manston)	01843-823333
Lands End	01736-788771
Leeds/Bradford (Yeadon)	0113-250 9696
Liverpool (Speke)	0151-288 4000
London: Battersea Heliport	020-7228 0181
City, Docklands	020-7646 0000
Gatwick, West Sussex	01293-535353
Heathrow, Middx	0870-000 0123
Stansted, Essex	01279-680500
Luton, Beds	01582-405100
Lydd, Kent	01797-322411
Manchester (Ringway)	0161-489 3000
Newcastle (Woolsington)	0191-286 0966
Northolt, Middx (RAF)	020-8845 2300
Norwich, Norfolk	01603-411923
Orkney: Kirkwall	01856-872421
Penzance Heliport, Cornwall	01736-363871
Plymouth, Devon	01752-772752
Prestwick, Strathclyde	01292-479822
St Mawgan, Cornwall	01637-860551
Scilly Isles: St Marys	01720-422646
Tresco Heliport	01720-422970
Shetland: Lerwick	01595-840246
Shoreham, West Sussex	01273-296900
Southampton (Eastleigh)	023-8062 9600
Southend, Essex	01702-608100
Stornoway, Western Isles	01851-702256
Teeside	01325-332811
Tiree, Argyll	01879-220456
Wick, Caithness	01955-602215

AIRLINES: BOOKINGS

Aer Lingus	020-8899 4747
Air Canada	0990-247226
Air France	020-8742 6600
Air New Zealand	020-8741 2299
Air UK	0990-074074
Alitalia	0870-544 8259
American Airlines	020-8572 5555
Britannia Airways	0990-502555
British Airways	0345-222111
British Midland	0870-607 0555
British World Airlines	01702-354435
Cathay Pacific	020-7747 8888
Easyjet	0870-6000000
El Al	020-7957 4100
Gulf Air	020-7408 1717
Icelandair	020-7874 1000
Japan Airlines	0345-747777
KLM	0990-750900
Lufthansa	0345-737747
Northwest Airlines	0990-561000
Qantas	0345-747767
Sabena	0845-607 2772
SAS	0870-608 8886
Singapore Airlines	020-8747 0007
South African Airways	020-7312 5000
Swissair	020-7434 7300
TWA	020-8814 0707
United	0845-8444777
Virgin Atlantic	01293-747747

AIR ORGANISATIONS

Airport Operators Assoc	020-7222 2249
Air Transport Users Council	020-7240 6061
Assoc of British Travel Agents (ABTA)	020-7637 2444
British Air Line Pilots Assoc	020-8476 4000
Civil Aviation Authority	020-7379 7311
DETR	020-7890 3000
International Air Transport Association	
(IATA) (Geneva)	00-4122 7992525
London	020-7240 9036
UK Passport Agency: enquiries	0870-521 0410
Applicants not receiving passport	0845-600 4646

ROADS

Britain has 230,800 miles of roads. The 2,052 miles of motorways and 7,600 miles of other trunk roads carry 34 per cent of all traffic and over half all goods vehicles. Motor traffic rose 22 per cent from 1988-98, with motorways increasing 49 per cent. There are 27.5 million licensed vehicles, 22.1 million of which are cars and 412,000 heavy goods vehicles. There are 63,800 taxis and 76,200 buses and coaches. Between 1987/8 and 1998/9 the number of local bus passenger journeys fell from 5.29 billion to 4.25 billion. Following privatisation, a handful of big companies now dominate the bus industry. The top five are Arriva, Stagecoach, National Express, Go-Ahead and and FirstBus. Most dynamic of all is Stagecoach, almost monopolising large areas of the country. The largest coach operator is National Express. Below are the main bus and coach groups, plus London Transport (LT), which is not an owner but a statutory corporation, responsible for providing public transport. Its day-to-day operations on all 700 bus routes are provided under contract by over 30 private companies, contactable via LT itself.

MOTORING ORGANISATIONS

AA: HQ	0990-448866
24-hr breakdown	0800-887766
AA Roadwatch	0990-500600
British Motorcyclists Fed	020-8942 7914
British Parking Assoc	01444-476300
British Roads Federation	020-7703 9769
Coach/bus companies:	
Arriva	020-8271 0101
Blazefield Holdings	01423-884020
EYMS Group	01482-327142
FirstBus	01224-650100
Go-Ahead Group	0191-232 3123
London Transport	020-7222 5600
National Express Group	0121-625 1122
Southern Vectis	01983-522456
Stagecoach Holdings	01738-442111
Yorkshire Traction	01226-202555
Department of Transport	020-7890 3000
DVLA Vehicles	01792-772134
Drivers	01792-772151
Greenflag: HQ	0113-239 3666
Breakdown service	0800-400600
Institute of Logistics & Transport	020-7467 9400
RAC: HQ	020-8917 2500
24-hr breakdown	0800-828282
Live road news: Website	www.rac.co.uk
Retail Motor Industry	020-7580 9122
Road Haulage Association	01932-841515
Road Operators Safety Council	01865-775552
Shires Public Transport Consortium	0117- 932 2771
Soc of Motor Manufacturers	020-7235 7000
Traffic Director for London	020-7222 454

Women

There are more women than men in the UK, and they live longer - but they are paid less and are more likely to be unemployed. There are 30.11 million females and 29.13 million males, and a baby girl can expect to reach the age of 79.4, while a male toddler can only make it to 74.1. In April 1999, men in full-time employment had average gross annual earnings of £23,000 - 42 per cent higher than women. Over 80 per cent of all crimes are committed by men. The Welsh cabinet in February 2000 became the first executive body in the western world to boast a majority of women ministers. But only 27 per cent of local councillors in Britain are women, and Parliament is 82 per cent male.

WOMEN'S ORGANISATIONS

Abortion Law Reform Assoc	020-7278 5539
	www.alra.mailbox.co.uk
Action for Sick Children	020-8542 4848
African & Caribbean Women Assoc	0141-341 0030
Amnesty International - Women's Action	
Network	020-7814 6200
Ash Women & Smoking Group	020-7840 8300
Asian Women's Advice Assoc	020-8533 5796
Assoc of Catholic Women	020-8399 1459
Assoc of Greater London Older	
Women	020-7281 3485
Assoc for Improvements in the Maternity	
Service	020-8960 5585
Assoc of Radical Midwives	01695-572776
Assoc for Teachers' Widows	01322-663833
Assoc of Women Solicitors	020-7320 5793
Bahai National Womens Committee	020-7584 2566
	www.bahai.org.uk
Baby Milk Action	01223-464420

Baby Products Assoc	01296-662789	Pro-Choice Alliance	020-7837 4792
Breast Cancer Care	020-7384 2984	Rape & Sexual Abuse Support Centre	020-8239 1122
www.breastcancercare.org.uk		Rape Crisis Centre	020-7837 1600
British Assoc of Women Entrepreneurs	020-7935 9455	Refuge	0990-995 4430
British Assoc of Women Police	01543-276165	Relate	01788-573241
British Fed of Women Graduates	020-7498 8037	www.relate.org.uk	
British Pregnancy Advisory Service	01564-793225	Rights of Women	020-7251 6577
Brook Advisory Centres	0800-018 5023	Royal College of Midwives	020-7872 5100
www.brook.org.uk		Royal College of Nursing	020-7409 3333
Campaign Against Domestic Violence	020-8520 5881	Scottish Women's Aid	0131-475 2372
Catholic Women's League	01689-891772	Scottish Women's Rural Institutes	0131-225 1724
Christian Women's Resource Centre	020-8693 1438	Sexwise	0800-282930
Co-operative Women's Guild	020-8804 5905	Society of Women Writers/Journalists	020-8529 0886
Conservative Women's National Cttee	020-7222 9000	Soroptimist International	0161-480 7686
Crossroads Womens Centre	020-7482 2496	Suffragette Fellowship	020-7222 2597
English Collective of Prostitutes	020-7482 2496	The 300 Group	01403-733797
Family Planning Assoc	020-7837 5432	Townswomen's Guilds	0121-456 3435
www.fpa.org.uk		UK Asian Women's Conference	020-8946 2858
Farm Women's Club	020-8652 4927	Victim Support	0845-303 0900
Fawcett Library	020-7320 1189	Wales Assembly of Women	01267-267428
Fawcett Society	020-7628 4441	WATCH (Women & the Church)	01763-848822
www.gn.apc.org/fawcett		Welsh Women's Aid	029-2039 0874
Feminist Library & Information Centre	020-7928 7789	West Indian Women's Assoc	020-8521 4456
Gingerbread	020-7336 8183	Womankind Worldwide	020-7588 6099
www.gingerbread.org		www.womankind.org.uk	
Guide Assoc	020-7834 6242	Women Against Rape	020-7482 2496
Jewish Women's Aid	0800-591203	Women Aid International	020-7925 1331
Justice for Women	020-8374 2948	Women & Medical Practice	020-8888 2782
League of Jewish Women	020-7387 7688	Women & Practical Conservation	020-7278 4294
Lesbian Employment Rights	020-7704 6067	Women in Film and TV	020-7240 4875
www.lager.dircon.co.uk		Women in Journalism	020-7274 2413
London Lesbian Line	020-7251 6911	Women in London www.gn.apc.org/womeninlondon	
London Rape Crisis	020-7837 1600	Women in Music	01449-736287
Marriage Counselling Scotland	0131-225 5006	Women in Prison	020-7226 5879
Maternity Alliance	020-7588 8583	Women Working Worldwide	0161-247 1760
Medical Women's Federation	020-7387 7765	WomenConnect www.womenconnect.org.uk	
Merched Y Wawr	01970-611661	Women's Advisory Council (UNA)	01395-263688
Microsyster	020-7684 3564	Women's Aid Federation	0117-944 4411
www.gn.apc.org/microsyster		www.womensaid.org.uk	
Mothers' Union	020-7222 5533	Women's Audio Visual Education	020-7430 1076
Muslim Women's Helpline	020-8908 3205	www.waves.org.uk	
National Abortion Campaign	020-7923 4976	Women's Environmental Network	020-7481 9004
National Alliance of Women's Orgs	020-8788 1051	www.gn.apc.org/wen	
National Assoc for Maternal & Child		Women's Farm & Garden Assoc	01285-658339
Welfare	020-7383 4117	Women's Health	020-7251 6580
National Assoc of Widows	01203-634848	Women's Health Concern	020-8780 3916
National Assoc of Women's Clubs	020-7837 1434	Women's Institutes	020-7371 9300
National Childbirth Trust	020-8992 8637	www.womensinstitute.org.uk	
National Childminding Assoc	020-8464 6164	Women's Inter-Church Council	020-7387 8413
www.ncma.org.uk		Women's Liberation (Lesbian Line)	020-7837 8602
National Council for One-Parent		Women's National Commission	020-7238 0386
Families	0800-018 5026	www.wnc.org.uk	
National Council of Women of GB	020-7354 2395	Women's Radio Group	020-8742 7802
www.ncwgb.org.uk		Women's Resource Centre	020-7729 4010
National Fed Women's Institutes	020-7371 9300	Women's Royal Voluntary Service	020-7793 9917
www.nfwi.org.uk		Women's Sports Foundation	020-8697 5370
National Free Church Womens Council	020-7387 8413	www.wsf.org.uk	
National Group on Homeworking	0113-245 4273	Women's Therapy Centre	020-7263 6200
Older Feminist Network	020-8346 1900	Women's Unit, Cabinet Office	020-7273 8880
One Parent Families Scotland	0131-556 3899	www.cabinet-office.gov.uk/womens-unit	
www.gn.apc.org/opfs			

The workers

The UK workforce is 29.54 million adults. In the first quarter of 2000, 1.71 million of these were "unemployed" - people out of work who have looked for a job in the last four weeks and are available to start within two weeks. This was a rate of 5.8 per cent. There were another 2.30 million who were economically inactive, while wanting a job. The average weekly hours worked were 32.6. A national minimum wage of £3.60 began in 1999.

Trade union membership peaked at 13.2 million in 1979, when the Tory government took over, falling to just under 7.8 million in 1998. The number of unions was halved from 453 in 1979, with many merging to cope with the effects of fewer members. Then New Labour sparked a tiny revival, with numbers increasing 0.6 per cent to just over 7.8 million in 1999, with more expected following the coming into effect of the Employment Relations Act in June 2000. Only about 30 per cent of employees are union members. In 1998 there were just 166 stoppages, the lowest number since records began in 1891. The number rose to 205 in 1999, but the amount of days lost fell, from 282,000 in 1998 to 242,000. There are 78 unions with 6.8 million members affiliated to the TUC. The largest are Unison, 1,272,330 members, TG-WU 881,625, AEEU 771,874, GMB 712,010 and MSF 416,000. AEEU and MSF should merge in 2001. The trade unions have been slow in tuning in to internet communications. There is more e-life at grassroots level, an example being LabourNet, "a medium for building international labour solidarity", set up following the Liverpool dockers' sacking.

There are three main employers organisations. The CBI (Confederation of British Industry) has 250,000 companies as members. It is based in Centrepoint, very near the TUC in Great Russell Street. The BCC (British Chambers of Commerce) represents 196 chambers, with their 200,000 local businesses. The IoD (Institute of Directors) looks after 35,000 company directors.

EMPLOYERS AND OFFICIALS

ACAS	020-7210 3911
British Chamber of Commerce (BCC)	020-7565 2000
CBI	020-7379 7400
Central Arbitration Committee	020-7210 3737
Certification Office for Trade Unions and Employers Assocs	020-7210 3734
Commissioners for the Rights of Trade Union Members /Protection Against Unlawful Industrial Action	01925-415771
Competition Commission (ex-Monopolies & Mergers Commission)	020-7324 1467
Dept for Education & Employment	020-7925 5000
Press	020-7925 5132
Dept of Trade & Industry	020-7215 5000
Press	020-7215 6424
Employment Appeal Tribunal	020-7273 1041
Employment Policy Unit	020-7735 0777
Federation of Small Businesses	020-7592 8100
Industrial Injuries Advisory Council	020-7962 8000
Industrial Society	020-7479 2000
Industrial Tribunals HQ	020-7273 8666
Help desk	0345-959775
Institute of Directors	020-7839 1233
Labour Markets Statistics Helpline	020-7533 6094

UNIONS AND ASSOCIATIONS

Many, but not all, of the bigger trade unions have websites. For their address most of them (listed here with *) use their initials followed by "org.uk", eg the AEEU is www.aeeu.org.uk. Exceptions are spelt out below.

Amalgamated Engineering & Electrical Union (AEEU*)	020-8462 7755
Associated Metalworkers Union (AMU)	01204-793245
Associated Society of Locomotive Engineers & Firemen (ASLEF)	020-7317 8600
Assoc of First Division Civil Servants	020-7343 1111 www.fda.org.uk
Assoc of Teachers & Lecturers (ATL*)	020-7930 6441
Assoc of University Teachers (AUT*)	020-7670 9700
Bakers, Food & Allied Workers Union	01707-260150
British Airline Pilots Assoc (BALPA*)	020-8476 4000
British Assoc of Journalists	020-7353 3003
British Assoc of Social Workers	0121-622 3911
British Medical Assoc (BMA)	020-7387 4499
Broadcasting, Entertainment, Cinematograph & Theatre Union (BECTU*)	020-7437 8506
Ceramic and Allied Trades Union	01782-272755
Chartered Society of Physiotherapy	020-7306 6666
Communication Managers Assoc	0118-934 2300
Communication Workers Union	020-8971 7200 www.cwu.org
Community & Youth Workers Union	0121-244 3344

Confederation of Insurance Trade
  Unions   020-7405 6798
Confederation of Shipbuilding & Engineering
  Unions   020-7703 2215
Connect (ex-STE)   020-8971 6000
                           wwwconnectuk.org
Council of Civil Service Unions   020-7924 2727
Educational Institute of Scotland (EIS*) 0131-225 6244
Engineers & Managers Assoc (EMA*) 01932-577007
Equity (British Actors Equity Assoc) 020-7379 6000
                           www.equity.org.uk
European Federation of Journalists 00-322 223 2265
European Trade Union Confederation
  (ETUC*)   00-322 224 0411
European Trade Union Institute 00-322 224 0470
Federation of Entertainment Unions 01962-713134
Fire Brigades Union   020-8541 1765
General Federation of Trade Unions
  (GFTU*)   020-7387 2578
GMB*   020-8947 3131
Graphical, Paper & Media Union
  (GPMU*)   01234-351521
Institute of Journalists (IOJ)   020-7252 1187
Institution of Professionals, Managers &
  Specialists (IPMS*)   020-7902 6600
International Confederation of Free Trade
  Unions (ICFTU*)   00-322 224 0211
International Federation of Chemical, Energy, Mine &
  General Workers Unions (ICEM) 00-322 626 2020
International Fed of Journalists 00-322 223 2265
International Labour Org   020-7828 6401
International Transport Workers Fed 020-7403 2733
Iron & Steel Trades Confederation 020-7837 6691
ISTC Community Union   020-7837 6691
                            www.istc-tu.org
Managerial & Professional Officers 01279-434444
Manufacturing Science Finance (MSF*) 020-7505 3000
Media & Entertainment International 00-322 223 5537
Musicians Union   020-7582 5566
                    www.musiciansunion.org.uk
National Assoc of Schoolmasters Union of
  Womens Teachers (NASUWT) 020-7420 9670
NATFHE* - Lecturers' Union   020-7837 3636
National Farmers Union (NFU)   020-7331 7200
National Union of Insurance Workers 020-7405 6798
National Union of Journalists (NUJ*) 020-7278 7916
National Union of Marine, Aviation & Shipping
  Transport Officers (NUMAST) 020-8989 6677
National Union of Mineworkers (NUM) 01226-215555
National Union of Rail, Maritime & Transport
  Workers (RMT)   020-7387 4771
National Union of Students (NUS*) 020-7272 8900
National Union of Teachers (NUT) 020-7388 6191
                        www.teachers.org.uk
Police Federation   020-8399 2224
Prison Officers Assoc (POA)   020-8803 0255
Professional Footballers Assoc   0161-236 0575
                          www.thepfa.co.uk
Public & Commercial Services Union
  (PCS*)   020-7924 2727
Royal College of Nursing   020-7409 3333

Royal College of Midwives   020-7872 5100
Society of Authors   020-7373 6642
Society of Radiographers   020-7740 7200
Trades Union Congress (TUC*) 020-7636 4030
  Information Service   020-7467 1304
  Brussels   00-322 224 0478
Transport & General Workers Union - T&G
  (TGWU*)   020-7611 2500
Transport Salaried Staffs' Association
  (TSSA*)   020-7387 2101
UNIFI* (ex-BIFU finance union) 020-8946 9151
Union of Construction, Allied Trades &
  Technicians (UCATT)   020-7622 2442
Union of Shop, Distributive & Allied
  Workers (USDAW)   0161-224 2804
                  www.poptel.org.uk/usdaw
Unions 21   020-7278 9944
Unison   020-7388 2366
                      www.unison.org.uk
United Road Transport Union   0161-881 6245
Writers Guild   020-7723 8074
                  www.writers.org.uk/guild

WORKERS' ACTION

Bootstrap Enterprises   020-7254 0775
Groundswell   01865-723750
Independent Labour Network 0115-978 4504
               www.iln.labournet.org.uk
Industrial Common Ownership Movement
  (ICOM)   0113-246 1737
Industrial Society   020-7479 2000
Industrial Workers of the World 0116-266 1835
Institute of Employment Rights 020-7498 6919
                           www.ier.org.uk
International Centre Trade Union Rights 020-7498 4700
              www.ictur.labournet.org.uk
Labour Research Dept   020-7928 3649
                        www.lrd.org.uk
LabourNet UK   www.labournet.net
Liberation   020-7254 6223
            www.labournet.org.uk/liberation
Low Pay Unit   020-7713 7616
                 www.lowpayunit.org.uk
National Museum of Labour History 0161-228 7212
New Ways to Work   020-7930 3355
                  www.new-ways.org.uk
Public Concern at Work   020-7404 6609
                www.pcaw.demon.co.uk
Tolpuddle Martyrs Museum   01305-848237
Trade Union News Magazine   01772-202779
               www.labournet.org.uk/tun
Unemployed Workers Charter 020-8965 0659
United Campaign for the Repeal of the
  Anti-Trade Union Laws   020-7638 7521
              www.ucratul.labournet.org
Voice of the Unions   020-8800 0454
           www.gn.apc.org/voiceoftheunions

Think tanks

Adam Smith Institute
23 Great Smith Street, London SW1P 3PL
Fax 020-7222 7544   020-7222 4995
www.adamsmith.org.uk
Established 1977. Promoting free market economics.

The Bow Group
92 Bishopsbridge Rd, London WC2   020-7431 6400

Centre for Economic Policy Research
90-98 Goswell Road, London EC1V.
Fax 020-7878 2999   020-7878 2900
Established 1983. Has many European contacts.

Centre for Policy Studies
57 Tufton Street, London SW1P 3QC
Fax 020-7222 4388   020-7222 4488
www.cps.org.uk
Director: Tessa Keswick. Established 1974 by Margaret
Thatcher and Keith Joseph. Very influential in the
formation and running of the 1979 government.

Centre for the Study of Financial Innovation
18 Curzon Street, London W1Y 7AD.
Fax 020-7493 0190   020-7493 0173
Established 1993. Sponsored by big business to explore
and influence evolving trends in international finance.

Demos
Paton House, 25 Haymarket, London SW1Y 4EN
Fax 0870-167 4861   020-7420 5252
www.demos.co.uk
Director: Tom Bentley. Established 1993 to help
reinvigorate public policy and political thinking.

Employment Policy Institute
Southbank House, Black Prince Rd, London SE1 7SJ
Fax 020-7793 8192   020-7735 0777
www.epi.org.uk
Director: John Philpott.

Fabian Society
11 Dartmouth Street, London SW1H 9BN
Fax 020-7976 7153   020-7222 8877
www.fabian-society.org.uk
General Secretary: Michael Jacobs.

Henley Centre for Forecasting
9 Bridewell Place, London EC4V 6AY
Fax 020-7353 2899   020-7955 1800
www.henleycentre.com
Chairman: Paul Edwards.

Institute of Economic Affairs
2 Lord North Street, London SW1P 3LB
Fax 020-7799 2137   020-7799 3745
www.iea.org.uk
General director: John Blundell. Established 1957 to
improve public understanding of economic principles.

Institute of Fiscal Studies
7 Ridgmount Street, London WC1E 7AE
Fax 020-7323 4780   020-7636 3784
www.ifs.org.uk
Director: Andrew Dilnot. Established 1969. A highly
regarded source of information.

Institute for Jewish Policy Research
79 Wimpole Street, London W1M 7DD
Fax 020-7935 3252   020-7935 8266
www.jpr.org.uk
Director: Barry Kosman.

Institute for Public Policy Research
30-32 Southampton Street, London WC2E 7RA
Fax 020-7470 6111   020-7470 6100
www.ippr.org.uk
Director: Mathew Taylor. Established 1988. IPPR
provides the main centre-left alternative to the free
market think tanks of the Right.

International Institute for Strategic Studies
13-15 Arundel St, Temple Place, London WC2R 3DX
Fax 020-7836 3108   020-7379 7676
www.isn.eth2.ch/iiss

Policy Studies Institute
100 Park Village East, London NW1 3SR
Fax 020-7388 0914   020-7468 0468
Director: Jim Skea. Established in 1978 to research all
aspects of policymaking.

Politeia
22 Charing Cross Road, London WC2H 0HR
Fax 020-7240 5095   020-7240 5070
Director: Sheila Lawlor.

Social Affairs Unit
314 Regent Street, London W1
Fax 020-7436 8530   020-7637 4356
Established 1980. Promotes education and research in
social and economic affairs.

Social Market Foundation
11 Tufton Street, London SW1P 3QB
Fax 020-7222 0310   020-7222 7060
Chairman: Professor Lord Skidelsky. Established 1989.
Influential free market think tank.

Royal Institute of International Affairs
10 St James Square, London SW1   020-7957 5700
www.riia.org
Aka Chatham House. Established 1920 to promote the
study of internationalism.

Action

ANIMALS, FARMING AND FOOD **484**
ANTI-CAPITALISM CULTURE **485**
COMMUNITY ACTION **485**
DRUGS AND ADDICTION **486**
EDUCATION AND FAMILY **486**
ENVIRONMENT AND ECOLOGY **487**
ETHNIC GROUPS **489**
HEALTH **489**
HELPLINES **490**
HISTORY **491**
HOUSING **491**
INTERNATIONAL/HUMAN RIGHTS **491**
ROADS AND TRANSPORT **492**
SCIENCE **493**
SEX **493**
WAR AND PEACE **493**

LEGAL **434**
CHARITIES **465**
CONSUMER WATCHDOGS **467**
RELIGION **471**
TRAVEL **475**
WOMEN **479**
WORK **481**
THINK TANKS **483**

WEBSITE DIRECTORIES

GreenNet	www.gn.apc.org/resources/web
Idealist	www.idealist.org
One World	www.oneworld.net/partners
Peoples' Global Action	www.agp.org
Red Pepper	www.redpepper.org.uk
SchNews	www.schnews.org.uk/database

ANIMALS, FARMING & FOOD

Animal Aid Society/Chickens Lib	01732-364546
	www.animalaid.org.uk
Animal Health Trust	01638-751000
	www.aht.org.uk
Animal Rights Coalition	01902-711935
	www.arcnews.co.uk
Arboricultural Assoc	01794-368717
	www.trees.org.uk
Bat Conservation Trust	020-7627 2629
	www.bats.org.uk
Breach Marine Protection	01405-769375
British Assoc for Shooting	01244-573000
	www.basc.org.uk
British Beekeepers Assoc	024-7669 6679
British Dietic Assoc	0121-616 4900
	www.vois.org.uk/bda

British Trust for Ornithology	01842-750050
British Union for Abolition of Vivisection	020-7700 4888
	www.helpthedogs.org.uk
Butterfly Conservation	01206-322342
	www.butterfly-conservation.org.uk
Campaign for Real Ale	01727-867201
	www.camra.org.uk
Cats Protection League	01403-221900
	www.cats.org.uk
Chickens' Lib	see Animal Aid Society
Community Composting Network	0114-258 0483
Compassion in World Farming	01730-264208
	www.ciwf.co.uk
Country Landowners Assoc	020-7235 0511
	www.cla.org.uk
Donkey Sanctuary	01395-578222
Earthkind	01202-682344
	www.earthkind.org.uk
Enough	0161-226 6668
Fairtrade Foundation	www.gn.apc.org/fairtrade
Farm Animal Welfare Council	020-7904 6000
Farm Animal Welfare Network	01484-688650
Farmers Union of Wales	01970-820820
	www.fuw.org.uk
Farming & Wildlife Advisory Gp	024-7669 6699
	www.fwag.org.uk
Food & Drink Federation	020-7836 2460
Game Conservancy Trust	01425-652381
	www.game-conservancy.org.uk
Glutamate Information Service	020-7631 3434
Hemp Seed Organics	020-8888 9277
	www.hempseedorganics.co.uk
Henry Doubleday Research Assoc	024-7630 3517
	www.hdra.org.uk
Herb Society	020-7823 5583
Hunt Saboteurs Assoc	01273-622827
International Dolphin Watch	01482-643403
International Fund for Animal Welfare	020-7587 6700
International Whaling Commission	01223-233971
Kennel Club	0870-606 6750
League Against Cruel Sports	020-7403 6155
	www.league.uk.com
London Animal Action	020-7278 3068
London Wildlife Trust	020-7261 0447
	www.wildlifetrust.org.uk/london
Mammal Society	020-7498 4358
	www.mammal.org.uk
National Anti-Vivisection Soc	020-8846 9777
	www.animaldefenders.org.uk
National Canine Defence	020-7837 0006
	www.ncdl.org.uk
National Farmers Union	020-7331 7200
	www.nfu.org.uk
National Fed of City Farms	0117-923 1800
National Fed of Badger Groups	020-7498 3220
National Food Alliance	020-7837 1228
National Org. Against Live Exports	01869-345243
National Society of Allotment	01536-266576
	www.nsalg.co.uk

Organics Direct	020-7729 2828
	www.organicsdirect.co.uk
Orkney Seal Rescue	01856-831463
Otter Trust	01986-893470
Passports for Pets	020-8870 5960
Peoples Dispensary for Sick Animals	01952-290999
Permaculture Assoc	0113-262 1718
Pesticide Action Network	020-7274 8895
	www.pan-uk.org
PETA (People for the Ethical Treatment	
of Animals)	020-8870 3966
Primal Seeds	www.primalseeds.org
Rare Breeds Survival Trust	024-7669 6551
	www.rare-breeds.com
Reforesting Scotland	0131-226 2496
Royal Agricultural Society	024-7669 6969
	www.rasc.org.uk
Royal Horticultural Society	020-7834 4333
	www.rhs.org.uk
RSPB (Birds)	01767 680551
	www.rspb.org.uk
RSPCA (Animals)	01403-264181
	www.rspca.org.uk
Scottish Environment Link	01738-630804
	www.scotlink.org
Scottish Landowners Federation	0131-653 5400
Scottish Wildlife Trust	0131-312 7765
Soil Assoc	0117-929 0661
	www.soilassociation.org
Sportsman's Association	01743-356868
	www.sportsmans-association.org
Sustain: Alliance for Better Food &	
Farming	020-7837 1228
	www.sustainweb.org
Ulster Wildlife Trust	01396-830282
Uncaged (against animal suffering)	0114-253 0020
	www.uncaged.co.uk
Vegan Society	01424-427393
	www.vegansociety.com
Vegetarian Society	0161-928 0793
	www.vegsoc.org
Veggies Catering Campaign	0115-958 5666
	www.veggies.org.uk
Whale & Dolphin Conservation	01225-334511
	www.wdcs.org
Wildfowl & Wetlands Trust	01453-890333
	www.wwt.org.uk
Womens Farming Union	024-7669 3171
Wood Green Animal Shelters	01763-838329
Working for Organic Growers	01273-476286
World Society Protection of Animals	020-7793 0540
World Wide Fund for Nature	01483-426444
	www.wwf-uk.org
WWOOF (Willing Workers on Organic	
Farms)	01273-476286
Zoo Federation	020-7586 0230
Zoological Society of London	020-7722 3333

ANTI-CAPITALISM CULTURE

Activists Networking	020-8341 3794
Anarchist Federation	www.afed.org.uk
Assoc of Festival Organisers	01296-394411
Big Green Gathering (annual event)	020-8941 6674
	www.big-green-gathering.com
Cannabis Hemp Information Club	0966-396444
Corporate Watch Magaziner	01865-791391
	www.corporatewatch.org
Creative Exchange	020-8532 8870
	www.gn.apc.org/creativeexchange
Earth First	www.eco-action.org/efau
Eco-Action	www.eco-action.org
Festival Eye (annual festival guide)	0870-737 1001
Freedom Trail	01935-863349
Frontline Magazine	09762-36216
Glastonbury Festival (late June)	0870-607 7380
Green Events	020-7267 2552
IndyMedia UK	www.indymedia.org.uk
Jubilee 2000 (due to close Dec 2000)	020-7739 1000
	www.jubilee2000uk.org
Notting Hill Carnival	www.nottinghillcarnival.net.uk
Pagan Federation	www.paganfed.demon.co.uk
Peoples' Global Action	www.agp.org
Reclaim the Streets	020-7281 4621
	www.reclaimthestreets.net
Red Pepper Magazine	020-7281 7024
	www.redpepper.org.uk
SchNews Magazine	01273-685913
	www.schnews.org.uk
Squall Magazine	www.squall.co.uk
Subvertise - Radical Advertising	www.subvertise,org
The Land is Ours	01865-722016
	www.oneworld.org/tlio
Undercurrents (alternative news videos)	01865-203661
	www.undercurrents.org
Urban 75	www.urban75.com

COMMUNITY ACTION & WORK

Advice Services Alliance	020-7236 6022
Assoc of British Credit Unions	0161-832 3694
	www.abcul.org
Centre for Alternative Industrial & Technological	
Systems	0114-266 5063
Charities Aid Foundation	01732-520000
	www.cafonline.org
Child Poverty Action Group	020-7837 7979
Childline-info	020-7239 1000
Citizen Organising Foundation	020-8981 6200
Citizens Advice Bureaux (HQ)	020-7833 2181
	www.nacab.org.uk
Communities Online	www.communities.org.uk
Communities That Care	020-7837 5900
Community Development Foundation	020-7226 5375
	www.cdf.org.uk
Community Organisations Forum	020-7426 9970
	www.towerhamlets.org.uk
Community Service Volunteers	020-7278 6601
	www.csv.org.uk

Direct Action Network	020-8889 1361
Directory of Social Change	020-7209 4949
	www.dsc.org.uk
Everyman Centre	020-7737 6747
Gamblers Anonymous	020-7384 3040
Inter-Action Trust	020-7583 2652
Law Centres Federation	020-7387 8570
	www.lawcentres.org.uk
Letslink UK	023-9273 0639
	www.letslinkuk.org
London Advice Services Alliance	020-7377 2748
	www.lasa.org.uk
London Hazards Centre	020-7267 3387
	www.lhc.org.uk
Low Pay Unit	020-7713 7616
	www.lowpayunit.org.uk
Marshmallow Employers' Project	020-8333 7306
National Council for Voluntary Orgs	020-7713 6161
	www.ncvo-vol.org.uk
National Fed. of Community Orgs	020-7226 0189
	www.communitymatters.org.uk
National Group on Homeworking	0113-245 4273
New Ways to Work	020-7930 3355
	www.new-ways.org.uk
Rotary International	01789-765411
	www.rivi.org.uk
Samaritans	01752-216500
	www.samaritans.org.uk
Saneline	0345-678000
Scottish Council for Voluntary Orgs	0131-556 3882
	www.scvo.org.uk
Scottish Crofters' Union	01471-822529
	www.scu.co.uk
Small World	020-7272 1394
	www.smallworldtv.co.uk
Unemployment Unit	020-7833 1222
Victim Support	020-7735 9166

DRUGS AND ADDICTION

Addaction	020-7251 5860
	www.addaction.org.uk
Alcohol Concern	020-7928 7377
	www.alcoholconcern.org.uk
Alcoholics Anonymous	01904-644026
	www.alcoholics-anonymous.org.uk
ASH (Action on Smoking and Health)	020-7224 0743
	www.ash.org.uk
Assoc for Nonsmokers Rights	01344-426252
Cannabis Hemp Info Club	0966-396444
Cannabis In Avalon	01458-833236
Drugscope	020-7928 1211
	www.drugscope.org.uk
Gamblers Anonymous	020-7384 3040
International Cannabis Coalition	020-7637 7467
Libra Trust	01273-480012
Mainliners	020-7582 5434
	www.members.aol.com/linersmain
Medical Council on Alcoholism	020-7487 4445
	www.medicouncil.demon.co.uk
Narcotics Anonymous	020-7251 4007
	www.ukna.org

National Drugs Helpline	0800-776600
Promis Helpline	0800-374318
	www.promis.demon.co.uk
Release	020-7729 9904
Helpline	020-7603 8654
	www.release.org.uk
Drugs in Schools Helpline	0808-8000800
Resolve	0808-8002345
Scottish Council on Alcohol	0141-333 9677
	www.drinkwise.co.uk
Transform (Campaign for Effective Drugs	
Laws)	0117-939 8052
	www.transform-drugs.org.uk

EDUCATION AND FAMILY

Abortion Law Reform Assoc	020-7637 7264
	www.alra.mailbox.co.uk
Active Birth Centre	020-7482 5554
Advisory Centre for Education	020-7354 8321
Age Concern	020-8679 8000
	www.ace.org.uk
Assoc of Radical Midwives	01695-572776
	www.midwifery.org.uk
Bliss (Baby Life Support Systems)	020-7520 9471
	www.bliss.org.uk
Baby Milk Action	01223-464420
	www.babymilkaction.org
Baby Products Association	01296-662789
Barnardos	020-8550 8822
	www.barnados.org.uk
British Pregnancy Advisory Service	01564-793225
	www.bpas.org.uk
Brook Advisory Centres	020-7284 6040
Campaign Against the Child Support	
Act	020-7482 2496
Campaign for State Education	020-8944 8206
	www.mandolin.demon.co.uk/case
Carers National Assoc	020-7490 8818
	www.carersuk.demon.co.uk
Child Poverty Action Group	020-7837 7979
Child Rescue	01273-692947
Childline	020-7239 1000
	www.childline.org.uk
Childrens Legal Centre	01206-872466
Childrens Society	020-7837 4299
	www.the-childrens-society.org.uk
EPOCH (End Physical Punishment of	
Children)	020-7700 0627
Families Need Fathers	020-7613 5060
Family Caring Trust	01693-64174
Family Planning Assoc	020-7837 5432
Family Rights Group	020-7923 2628
Family Welfare Assoc	020-7254 6251
Gingerbread	020-7336 8183
Guides Assoc	020-7834 6242
	www.guides.org.uk
Independent Schools Information	
Service	020-7798 1530
Inter-Action	020-7583 2652
	www.hmspresident.co.uk

International Planned Parenthood
   Federation   020-7487 7900
                www.ippf.org
Marie Stopes International   020-7574 7400
Mary Ward Centre   020-7831 7711
          www.marywardcentre.ac.uk
Message Home   0500-700740
Mothers Union   020-7222 5533
        www.themothersunion.org
National Abortion Campaign   020-7923 4976
National Childbirth Trust   020-8992 8637
National Childcare   020-7739 2866
National Childrens Bureau   020-7843 6000
             www.ncb.org.uk
National Council for One Parent
   Families   0800-0185026
National Infertility Support Network   01424-732361
NCH Action for Children   020-7226 2033
          www.nchasc.org.uk
NSPCC   020-7825 2500
          www.nspcc.org.uk
National Youth Agency   0116-285 3700
One Parent Families in Scotland   0131-556 3899
Parent Network   020-7284 5500
        www.parentlineplus.org.uk
Pensioners Voice   01254-52606
Pre-School Learning Alliance   020-7833 0991
Relate (Marriage Guidance)   01788-573241
          www.relate.org.uk
Save the Children Fund   020-7703 5400
        www.savethechildren.org.uk
Socialist Teachers Alliance   024-7633 2320
Watch? (What About the Children?)   01386-561635
Woodcraft Folk   020-8672 6031
       www.poptel.org.uk/woodcraft
Workers Educational Assoc   020-8983 1515
          www.wea.org.uk

ENVIRONMENT & ECOLOGY

Action with Rural England Communities 01285-653477
        www.acreciro.demon.co.uk
Advisory Cttee on Protection of Sea   020-7799 3033
          www.acops.org
Agenda 21 Network (London)   020-7296 6599
        www.la21-uk.org.uk
Assoc for Protection of Rural Scotland 0131-225 7012
        www.aprs.org.uk
Big Green Gathering (annual event)   020-8941 6674
       www.big-green-gathering.com
Black Environment Network   01286-870715
British Assoc of Nature Conservationists 01604-405285
British Earth Sheltering Assoc   01993 703619
British Ecological Society   020-8871 9797
        www.demon.co.uk/bes
British Mountaineering Council   0161-445 4747
        www.thebmc.co.uk
British Society of Dowsers   01233-750253
British Trust for Conservation Volunteers 01491-839766
        www.btcv.org.uk

British Unidentified Flying Object Research
   Association   020-8449 5908
Campaign for Environmentally Responsible
   Tourism   01268-795772
Campaign for Political Ecology   01793-790438
        www.gn.apc.org/eco
Campaign for Protection of Rural Wales 01938-552525
        www.cprw.org.uk
Centre for Alternative Technology   01654-702400
        www.cat.org.uk
Civic Trust   020-7930 9730
        www.civictrust.org.uk
   Wales   029-2048 4606
   Scotland   0141-221 1466
Clean Rivers Trust   01636-892627
Climate Action Network   020-7251 9199
        www.climatenetwork.org
Common Ground   020-7267 2144
Communities Against Toxics   0151-339 5473
Community Recycling Network   0117-942 0142
        www.crn.org.uk
Conservation Foundation   020-7591 3111
      www.conservationfoundation.co.uk
Council for Environmental Education   0118-950 2550
Council for National Parks   020-7924 4077
        www.cnp.org.uk
Council for the Protection of Rural England
   (CPRE)   020-7976 6433
      www.greenchannel.com/cpre
Dragon Environmental Network
        www.gn.apc.org/dragon
Earth First!   0161-224 4846
        www.eco-action.org/efau
Earthwatch Europe   01865-311600
Ecological Design Assoc   01453-765575
Ecology Building Society   01535-635933
Envirolink   www.envirolink.org
Environment Centre   0131-557 2135
Environment Council   020-7836 2626
Environmental Information Service   01603-871048
Environmental Investigation Agency   020-7490 7040
        www.eia-international.org
Environmental Law Foundation   020-7404 1030
      www.greenchannel.com/elf/
Farming & Wildlife Advisory Group   024-7669 6699
        www.fwag.org.uk
Fauna & Flora International   01223-571000
Fed of City Farms/Community Gdns   0117-923 1800
        www.farmgarden.org.uk
Forest Action Network UK   01603-611953
        www.fanweb.org/uk
Freedom Trail   01935-863349
Friends of the Earth   020-7490 1555
        www.foe.co.uk
   FoE Scotland   0131-554 9977
   FoE Cymru   029-2022 9577
Frontline Magazine   09762-36216
GenetiX Snowball   0161-834 0295
Georgian Group   020-7387 1720
Global Commons Institute   www.gci.org.uk

Global Witness 020-7272 6731
www.oneworld.org/globalwitness
Green Alliance 020-7233 7433
www.green-alliance.demon.co.uk
Green Events Magazine 020-7267 2552
Green Party 020-7272 4474
www.greenparty.org.uk
Green World Magazine 01252-330506
www.greenparty.org.uk/world
GreenNet 020-7713 1941
www.gn.apc.org
Greenpeace (London) 020-7713 1269
www.gn.apc.org
Greenpeace UK 020-7865 8100
Groundwork Foundation 0121-236 8565
www.groundwork.org.uk
Gypsy Council 01708-868986
Historic Churches Preservation Trust 020-7736 3054
Institute of Public Rights of Way 01535 637957
League Against Cruel Sports 020-7403 6155
www.league.uk.com
Local Agenda 21 Steering Group 020-7296 6600
London 21 www.london21.org
London Ecology Unit 020-7233 7433
London Thames Gateway 020-7377 1822
Marine Conservation Society 01989-566017
www.mcsuk.org
Marine Society 020-7261 9535
www.marine-society.org
Media Natura 020-7928 9556
Mountaineering Council of Scotland 01738-638227
www.mountaineering-scotland.org
National Council for the Conservation of
   Plants & Gardens 01483-211465
www.nccpg.org.uk
National Energy Action 0191-261 5677
www.nea.org.uk
National Pure Water Assoc 01924-254433
National Recycling Forum 020-7253 6266
National Small Woods Assoc 01743-792644
www.woodnet.org.uk/nswa
National Society for Clean Air 01273-326313
www.greenchannel.com/nsca
National Trust 020-7222 9251
www.nationaltrust.org.uk
National Trust for Scotland 0131-243 9300
Noise Abatement Society 01903-775578
N Ireland Environment Link 028-9031 4944
www.niel.demon.co.uk
Nukewatch UK 023-8055 4434
Oilwatch 020-7435 5000
Open Spaces Society 01491-573535
www.oss.org.uk
Oxleas Wood Hotline 01426-921900
Pedestrians Assoc 020-7820 1010
www.pedestrians.org.uk
Pesticides Action Network 020-7274 8895
www.pan-uk.org
Planning Exchange 0141-248 8541
www.planex.co.uk
Plantlife 020-7808 0100
www.plantlife.org.uk

Rainbow Centre 0115-958 5666
www.veggies.org.uk/rainbow
Ramblers Assoc 020-7339 8500
www.ramblers.org.uk
Reclaim the Streets 020-7281 4621
www.reclaimthestreets.net
Red Rope: Socialist Walkers/Climbers 01274-493995
www.gn.apc.org/redrope
Reforest the Earth 01603-611953
Reforesting Scotland 0131-554 4321
Royal Entomological Society 020-7584 8361
www.royensoc.demon.co.uk
Royal Forestry Society 01442-822028
www.rfs.org.uk
Royal Scottish Forestry Society 0138-737 1518
www.foresters.org/rsfs
Royal Town Planning Institute 020-7636 9107
www.rtpi.org.uk
Save Britains Heritage 020-7253 3500
Scottish Conservation Projects Trust 01786-479697
Scottish Crofters Union 01471-822529
Scottish Native Woods 01887-820392
Scottish Environment Link 01738-630804
www.scotlink.org
Sea Action 01273-626714
SERA (Socialist Environment & Resources
   Assoc) 020-7263 7389
www.users.aol.com/seraoffice
Society for the Protection of Ancient
   Buildings 020-7377 1644
www.spab.org.uk
Surfers Against Sewage 01872-553001
The Land is Ours 01865-722016
www.enviroweb.org/tlio
Tourism Concern 020-7753 3330
www.tourismconcern.org.uk
Town & Country Planning Assoc 020-7930 8903
www.tcpa.org.uk
Tree Council 020-7828 9928
www.treecouncil.org.uk
Trust for Urban Ecology 020-7237 9175
UK Environmental Law Assoc 01491-671631
www.ukela.greenchannel.com
Undercurrents Productions 01865-203661
Urban 75 www.urban75.com
Urban Pollution Research 020-8362 6374
www.mdx.ac.uk
Wales Green Party 01443-741242
Waste Watch 0870-243 0136
Waterwatch Network 01904-421588
www.waterwatch.org.uk
Waterway Recovery Group 01923-711114
Wild Flower Society 01509-215598
Wildfowl & Wetlands Trust 01453-890333
www.wwt.org.uk
Womens Environmental Network 020-7247 3327
www.gn.apc.org/wen
Woodland Trust 01476-581111
World Conservation Monitoring 01223-277314
www.wcmc.org.uk

ETHNIC GROUPS

Black Environment Network	01286-870715
Blink (Black Information Link)	020-7582 1990
	www.blink.org.uk
Civic Trust (Community Action)	020-7930 9730
	www.civictrust.org.uk
Commission for Racial Equality	020-7828 7022
Friends, Families and Travellers Group	01273-234777
Gandhi Foundation	020-8981 7628
Gypsy Council	01708-868986
Immigration Advisory Service	020-7357 6917
Indian Workers Assoc	020-8574 6019
Institute of Race Relations	020-7837 0041
	www.irr.org.uk
Joint Council for the Welfare of Immigrants (JCWI)	020-7251 8706
Kurdish Cultural Centre	020-7735 0918
Legal Advice for Travellers	029-2087 4580
Minority Rights Group	020-7978 9498
National Assembly Against Racism	020-7247 9907
National Group on Homeworking	0113-245 4273
	www.gn.apc.org/homeworking
National Gypsy Council	01928-723138
Newham Monitoring Project	020-8555 8151
Pakistan Welfare Assoc	020-8679 0924
Refugee Council	020-7820 3000
	www.refugeecouncil.org.uk
Refugee Legal Centre	020-7827 9090
Runnymede Trust	020-7600 9666
Scottish Asian Action Committee	0141-341 0025
Scottish Crofters Union	01471-822529
Searchlight Magazine	020-7284 4040
Standing Conference of West Indian Organisations	020-7928 7861
Survival	020-7242 1441
	www.survival-international.org
Traveller Law Research Unit	020-7833 4665
Youth Against Racism in Europe	020-8533 4533

HEALTH

Age Concern	020-8679 8000
	www.ace.org.uk
Alzheimers Disease Society	020-7306 0606
	www.alzheimers.org.uk
Arthritis Research Campaign	01246-558033
	www.arc.org.uk
ASH (Action on Smoking & Health)	020-7739 5902
	www.ash.org.uk
Body Positive	020-7287 8010
	www.bodypositive.org.uk
Breast Cancer Campaign	020-7749 3700
	www.bcc-uk.org
British Council of Disabled People	01332-295551
	www.bcodp.org.uk
British Deaf Assoc	020-7588 3520
	www.bda.org.uk
British Dental Health	01788-546365
	www.dentalhealth.org.uk
British Heart Foundation	020-7935 0185

	www.bhf.org.uk
British Holistic Medicine Assoc.	01743-261155
British Homeopathic Assoc	020-7935 2163
British Kidney Patient Assoc	01420-472021
British Lung Foundation	020-7831 5831
	www.lunguk.org
British Medical Assoc	020-7387 4499
	www.bma.org.uk
British Organ Donor Society	01223-893636
British Psychological Society	0116-254 9568
British Wheel of Yoga	01529-306851
Cancer Relief Macmillan Fund	020-7351 7811
	www.macmillan.org.uk
Cancer Research Campaign	020-7224 1333
	www.crc.org.uk
Casualties Union	020-7278 6264
Clic (Cancer and Leukaemia in Childhood)	0117 924 8844
Crusaid	020-7833 3939
	www.crusaid.org.uk
Direct Action Network	0121-247 6888
Disability Alliance	020-7247 8776
Disability Wales	029-2088 7325
Disabled Action Network	020-8889 1361
Downs Syndrome Assoc	020-8682 4001
	www.downs-syndrome.org.uk
Eating Disorders Assoc	01603-765050
Festival for Mind, Body, Spirit	020-7938 3788
Food Commission	020-7837 2250
	www.foodcomm.org.uk
Foundation for the Study of Infant Death	020-7222 8001
Genetics Forum	020-7837 9229
	www.geneticsforum.org.uk
GLAD (Greater London Assoc of Disabled People)	020-7346 5800
Haemophilia Society	020-7380 0600
Health Rights	020-7501 9856
Health Unlimited	020-7582 5999
	www.healthunlimited.org
Hearing Dogs for the Deaf	01844-353898
Help the Aged	020-7253 0253
	www.helptheaged.org.uk
Herpes Assoc	020-7609 9061
Imperial Cancer Research Fund	020-7242 0200
	www.icnet.uk
Inquest	020-8802 7430
Institute for Complementary Medicine	020-7237 5165
Leonard Cheshire Foundation	020-7802 8200
Leukaemia Research Fund	020-7405 0101
	www.lrf.org.uk
London Lighthouse	020-7792 1200
ME Assoc	01375-642466
Medic Alert	0800-581420
	www.medicalert.co.uk
Mediical Foundation	020-7813 9999
MENCAP	020-7454 0454
	www.mencap.org.uk
Mental After Care Assoc	020-7436 6194
	www.maca.org.uk
Mental Health Foundation	020-7535 7400
	www.mentalhealth.org.uk

Mental Health Media	020-7700 8173
	www.mhmedia.com
Migraine Action Assoc	01932-352468
Migraine Trust	020-7831 4818
	www.migrainetrust.org
MIND (National Assoc for Mental Health)	020-8519 2122
	www.mindex.org.uk
Multiple Sclerosis Society	020-7610 7171
National Aids Trust	020-7814 6767
	www.nat.org.uk
National Asthma Campaign	020-7226 2260
	www.asthma.org.uk
National Autistic Society	020-8813 8222
National Schizophrenia Fellowship	020-8547 3937
Natural Death Centre	020-8208 2853
	www.naturaldeath.org.uk
Natural Medicines Society	020-8974 1166
NDT (learning disabilities)	0161-228 7055
NHS Direct	0845-4647
	www.nhsdirect.nhs.uk
No Panic	01952-590005
Outset	0870-200 0001
	www.outset.org.uk
Overeaters Anonymous	01745-888127
Parkinsons Disease Society	020-7931 8080
Patients Assoc	020-8423 8999
Pregnancy Advisory Service	01564-743225
Pregnancy Calendar	www.pregnancycalendar.com
RADAR (Royal Assoc for Disability & Rehabilitation)	020-7250 3222
	www.radar.org.uk
Re-Solv (Society for the Prevention of Solvent Abuse)	01785-817885
	www.re-solv.org
Royal National Institute for the Blind	020-7388 1266
	www.rnib.org
Royal National Institute for the Deaf	020-7296 8000
	www.rnid.org.uk
Royal Society for the Prevention of Accidents (RSPCA)	029-2025 0600
Samaritans	01753-216500
	www.samaritans.org.uk
Sane	020-7375 1002
Scope	020-7619 7100
Scottish Council on Alcohol	0141-333 9677
Socialist Health Assoc	020-7377 0403
St John Ambulance Assoc	020-7235 5231
	www.stja.org.uk
Stillbirth & Neonatal Death Society	020-7436 5881
Terence Higgins Trust	020-7831 0330
	www.tht.org.uk
Voluntary Euthanasia Society	020-7937 7770
	www.ves.org.uk

TELEPHONE HELPLINES

Details from Telephone Helplines Association (website: www.helplines.org.uk).

Accident Legal Line	0500-192939
Advice Services Alliance	020-7236 6022
Advisory Service for Squatters	020-7359 8814
Age Concern	0800-731 4931
Aids Helpline	0800-567123
Alcoholics Anonymous Helpline	0845-769 7555
Anti-Bullying Campaign	020-7378 1446
Arthritis Care Helpline	0800-289170
Asthma Helpline	0345-010203
Asylum Aid	020-7359 4026
Bisexual Helpline	020-8569 7500
Breast Cancer Care Helpline	0500-245345
Cancer Information Service	0800-181199
Cancerlink	0800-132095
Careline (family counselling)	020-8514 1177
Carers Line	0808-808 7777
Cerebral Palsy Helpline	0800-626216
Child Death Helpline	0800-282986
Child Support Agency	0345-133133
ChildLine	0800-1111
Citizens Advice Bureaux (HQ)	020-7833 2181
Cot Death Helpline	020-7233 2090
Crimestoppers	0800-555111
Cruse Bereavement Line	020-8332 7227
Deafblind Helpline	0800-132320
Dept Social Security Disabilities Helpline	0800-882200
Dial Disability Helpline	01302-310123
Drinkline	0800-917 8282
Drugs in Schools Helpline	0345-366666
Environment Agency Emergencies	0800-807060
Epilepsy Helpline	0800-309030
Family Credit Helpline	01253-500050
Family Services Helpline	01543-468400
Fed of Independent Advice Centres	020-7489 1800
Floodline (for flood victims)	0845-988 1188
Gamblers Anonymous	020-7384 3040
Gamcare (gambling problems)	0845-600 0133
Gingerbread (lone parents)	020-7336 8183
Hearing Concern Helpline	01245-344600
Heartline	0800-858585
Hospice Information Service	020-8778 9252
Immigration Advisory Service	020-7378 9191
Law Centres Federation	020-7387 8570
Lesbian & Gay Switchboard	020-7837 7324
Leukaemia Care Society	01392-464848
London Marriage Guidance	020-7580 1087
Medic Alert	0800-581420
Medical Advisory Service	020-8994 9874
Message Home (from missing person)	0800-700740
Migraine Trust Helpline	020-7831 4818
Migrant Advisory Service	020-8574 4433
MIND	0345-660163
Missing Persons Helpline	0500-700700
Mobility Information Service	01743-761889
Money Advice Association	01822-855118

MS Helpline	020-7371 8000
Narcotics Anonymous Helpline	020-7730 0009
National Aids Helpline	0800-567123
National Assoc for Children of Alcoholics	0800-289061
National Debtline	0808-808 4000
National Drugs Helpline	0800-776600
Natural Death Centre	020-8208 2853
NHS Direct	0845-4647
NHS Health Information Service	0800-665544
NSPCC Helpline (child abuse)	0800-800500
Pain Concern Helpline	0345-413772
Parkinson's Helpline	020-7388 5798
Parentline	0808-8002222
Patients Helpline	020-8423 8999
Pregnancy Advisory Service	0345-304030
Promis Helpline (drugs/alcohol)	0800-374318
Rape Crisis Centre (London)	020-7837 1600
Rape & Sexual Abuse Helpline	020-8239 1122
Refuge (domestic violence)	0870-599 5443
Release Emergency (drugs)	020-7603 8654
Rights of Women Advice	020-7251 6577
RSPCA	0990-555999
Samaritans	0845-790 9090
SaneLine	0345-678000
Seafarers Benefits Advice Line	0345-413318
Seniorline (info for elderly)	0808-800 6565
Sexwise	0800-282930
Shelterline	0808-800 4444
Smokers Quitline	020-7487 3000
Telephone Helplines Assoc	020-7248 3388
Tenovus Cancer Helpline	0800-526527
Travellers Advice Team	0468-316755
Turning Point (drugs)	020-7702 2300
Victim Support (crime)	0845-303 0900
Womens Aid Helpline (violence)	0345-023468
Womens Health	020-7251 6580
Young Minds	0345-626376

HISTORY

Ancient Monuments Society	020-7236 3934
Architectural Heritage Fund	020-7925 0199
British Assoc of Friends of Museums	01276-66617
British Records Assoc	020-7833 0428
Council for British Archaeology	01904-671417
	www.britarch.ac.uk
English Civil War Society	01430-430695
Folklore Society	020-7387 5894
Historical Assoc	020-7735 3901
	www.history.org.uk
Rescue (British Archaeological Trust)	01992-553377
	www.rescue-archaeology.freeserve.co.uk
Society for Folk Life Studies	0113-275 6537
Subterranea Britannica	01737-823456
Victorian Society	020-8994 1019
	www.victorian-society.org.uk

HOUSING

Advisory Service for Squatters	020-7359 8814
	www.squat.freeserve.co.uk
Alone in London Service	020-7278 4486
Big Issue Magazine	020-7526 3200
	www.alone-in-London.gb.org
Building Industry Link Up	020-8534 5352
Centrepoint (Youth Homelessness)	020-7426 5300
Communities & Homes in Central	
London	020-7378 8300
Crisis (ex Crisis at Christmas)	020-7655 8300
	www.crisis.org.uk
Girls Alone Project	020-7383 4103
Homeless Information Project	020-7277 7639
Homes for Homeless People	01582-481426
	www.homeline.dircon.co.uk
Housing Law Practitioners Assoc	020-7233 8322
Institute of Housing	024-7685 1700
The Land is Ours	01865-722016
London Connection	020-7766 5544
	www.london-connection.org.uk
London Housing Unit	020-7428 4910
	www.lhu.org.uk
National Homeless Alliance	020-7833 2071
National Housing Federation	020-7278 6571
	www.housing.org.uk
National Housing & Town Planning	
Council	now Room, below
National Missing Persons Helpline	0500-700 700
New Horizon	020-7388 5560
Piccadilly Advice Centre	020-7437 1579
Room (National Council for Housing &	
Planning)	020-7251 2363
Rural Housing Trust	020-7793 8114
Save Our Building Societies (SOBS)	01727-847370
	www.sobs.org.uk
Scottish Crofters Union	01471-822529
SHAC (Housing Advice Line)	020-7404 6929
SHAC: Edinburgh	0131-466 8031
Shelter	020-7505 2000
	www.shelter.org.uk
Shelter Nightline	0808-800 4444
Simon Community	020-7485 6639

INTERNATIONAL AND RIGHTS

Action Aid: Fighting Poverty Together	020-7561 7561
	www.actionaid.org
Action for Southern Africa	020-7833 3133
Amnesty International	020-7814 6200
	www.amnesty.org.uk
Anti-Racist Alliance	020-8422 4849
Anti-Nazi League	020-7924 0333
	www.anl.org.uk
Anti-Slavery International	020-7501 8920
	www.antislavery.org
Article 19	020-7278 9292
	www.article19.org
British Humanist Assoc	020-7430 0908
	www.humanism.org.uk

British Irish Rights Watch 020-8772 9161
www.fhit.org/birw
British Red Cross Society 020-7235 5454
www.redcross.org.uk
Burma Campaign 020-7281 7377
www.burmacampaignuk.org.uk
Call for Peace (NI) 020-8372 6789
Campaign Against Asylum Bill 020-7247 9907
Campaign Against Racism & Fascism 020-7837 1450
www.carf.demon.co.uk
Campaign Against Racist Laws 020-8571 1437
Campaign for Freedom of Information 020-7831 7477
www.cfoi.org.uk
Campaign for Press and Broadcasting
  Freedom 020-7278 4430
www.cpbf.demon.co.uk
Canon Colins Educational Trust for
  Southern Africa 020-7354 1462
Charter 88 020-7684 3888
China Solidarity Campaign 020-8205 5781
Christian Aid 020-7620 4444
www.christian-aid.org.uk
CIIR (Catholic Institute for International
  Relations 020-7354 0883
Cuba Solidarity Campaign 020-7263 6452
www.poptel.org.uk/cuba-solidarity
Cymdeithas yr Iaith Gymraeg 01970-624501
www.cymdeithas.com
Freedom Press 020-7247 9249
Howard League for Penal Reform 020-7249 7373
www.howardleague.org
Human Rights Watch 020-7713 1995
www.hrw.org
Inquest 020-8802 7430
Intermediate Technology Development
  Group 020-7436 9761
www.oneworld.org/itdg
Internet Freedom 020-7681 1559
www.netfreedom.org
Interights 020-7278 3230
www.interights.org
International Alert 020-7793 8383
www.international-alert.org
International Assoc for Religious
  Freedom 01865-202744
www.iars-religiousfreedom.net
Iraqi National Congress 020-7629 2960
Irish Peace Initiative 020-8372 6789
Jubilee 2000 www.jubilee2000uk.org
Justice 020-7329 5100
Kashmir Freedom Movement 020-8810 0104
Kurdistan Solidarity Campaign 020-7586 5892
Labour Campaign for Travellers Rights 0113-248 6746
Latin America Bureau 020-7278 2829
www.lab.org.uk
Law Centres Federation 020-7387 8570
www.lawcentres.org.uk
Legal Action Group 020-7833 2931
www.lag.org.uk
Liberty (NCCL) 020-7403 3888
Minority Rights Group 020-7978 9498
www.minorityrights.org
National Assembly Against Racism 020-7247 9907

National Civil Rights Movement 020-8843 2333
New Internationalist Magazine 01865-728181
www.newint.org
Nicaragua Solidarity Campaign 020-7272 9619
www.gn.apc.org/nsc
Oxfam 01865-311311
www.oxfam.org.uk
Palestine Solidarity Campaign 020-7700 6192
People and Planet 01865-245678
www.peopleandplanet.org
Peoples Global Action Against Free Trade
www.agp.org
Peru Support Group 020-7620 1103
Philippine Resource Centre 020-7281 4561
Powerful Information 01908-666275
www.gn.apc.org/powerful-information
Prisoners Abroad 020-7561 6820
www.prisonersabroad.org.uk
Public Law Project 020-7467 9800
Redress 020-7278 9502
Release 020-7729 9904
www.release.org.uk
Returned Volunteer Action 020-7278 0804
Scottish Council for Civil Liberties 0141-332 5960
Statewatch 020-8802 1882
www.statewatch.org
Survival International 020-7242 1441
www.survival-international.org
Third World First - now People & Planet, cf
Tibet Information Network 020-7814 9011
www.tibetinfo.net
Tibet Society of the UK 020-7383 7533
www.tibet-society.org.uk
Tools for Self Reliance 023-8086 9697
www.tfsr.org
Travellers Support Group 01273-234777
War on Want 020-7620 1111
www.waronwant.org
WaterAid 020-7793 4500
www.wateraid.org.uk
World Development Movement 020-7737 6215
www.wdm.org.uk

ROADS AND TRANSPORT

Capital Transport Campaign 020-7388 2489
Cyclists Public Affairs Group 01483-417217
Environmental Transport Assoc 01932-828882
www.eta.co.uk
Freedom of the Skies 01570-493576
Freedom Trail 01935-863349
Heritage Railway Assoc 01233-712130
London Cycling Campaign 020-7928 7220
Motorcycle Action Group 0121-605 3553
No M11 Link Road Campaign 020-8530 7577
PACTS 020-7922 8112
www.pacts.org.uk
Pedestrians Assoc 020-7820 1010
Public Transport Campaign 0161-839 9040
Reclaim the Streets 020-7281 4621
www.reclaimthestreets.net

Platform	020-7613 0743
South Coast Against Road Building	01273-324455
Streetlife	020-7833 2071
Sustrans: Paths for People	0117-926 8893
	www.sustrans.org.uk
Transport 2000	020-7613 0743
Traveller Law Research Unit	029-2087 4580
Travellers Advice Team	0468-316755

SCIENCE

Assoc for Science Education	01707-283000
	www.ase.org.uk
Assoc for Advancement of Science	020-7973 3500
	www.britassoc.org.uk
British Astrological & Psychic Society	0906-4700827
	www.bapsoc.co.uk
British Society for History of Science	01367-718963
	www.bshs.org.uk
Centre for Alternative Technological	01142-665063
Centre for Alternative Technology	01654-702400
Centre for Exploitation of Science	020-7354 9942
	www.cest.org.uk
Institute for Social Inventions	020-82082853
	www.globalideasbank.org
Royal Society	020-7839 5561
	www.royalsoc.ac.uk
Science Policy Research Unit	01273-686758
Scientists for Global Responsibility	020-8871 5175
	www.sgr.uk

SEX

Albany Trust	020-8767 1827
Campaign Against Pornography	020-7263 1833
Campaign for Homosexual Equality	0402-326151
English Collective of Prostitutes	020-7482 2496
Gay Employment Rights	020-7704 6066
Gay Legal Advice	020-7837 5212
Gay & Lesbian Switchboard	020-7837 7324
Gay London Policing	020-7704 6767
Irish Gay Helpline	020-8208 2855
Jewish Lesbian & Gay Helpline	020-7706 3123
Lesbian & Gay Christian Movement	020-7739 1249
	www.members.aol.com/lgcm
Lesbian Employment Rights	020-7704 8066
Lesbian & Gay Christian Movement	
Helpline	020-7739 8134
Lesbian & Gay Switchboard	0121-622 6589
Lesbian Information Service	01706-817235
London Bisexual Group	020-8569 7500
London Lesbian Line	020-7251 6911
London Rape Crisis Centre	020-7916 5466
Men's Advice Line & Enquiries	020-8644 9914
Outrage	020-8240 0222
	www.outrage.org.uk
Sexual Compulsives Anon	020-8914 7599
Sexual Freedom Coalition	020-7460 1979
	www.sfc.org.uk
Stonewall - Lesbian & Gay Equality	020-7336 8860
	www.stonewall.org.uk
Terence Higgins Trust	020-7831 0330

WAR AND PEACE

Amnesty International	020-7814 6200
	www.amnesty.org.uk
At Ease	020-7247 5164
Bertrand Russell Foundation	0115-978 4504
Campaign Against Arms Trade	020-7281 0297
	www.caat.demon.co.uk
CND	020-7700 2393
	www.cnduk.org
Children and War	020-7424 9444
	www.ppu.org.uk
Clergy Against Nuclear Arms	01243-372428
Conscience Peace Tax Campaign	020-7561 1061
	www.gn.apc.org/conscience
Council for Arms Control	020-7848 2065
Faslane Peace Camp	01436-820901
Housmans Peace Resource Project	020-7278 4474
Institute for Law and Peace	020-7267 2153
International Institute for Strategic	
Studies	020-7379 7676
Labour Action for Peace	01604-491712
Landmines Working Group	020-7820 0222
Medical Action for Global Security	020-7272 2020
	www.medact.org
Moral Re-Armament	020-7828 6591
	www.mra.org.uk
National Peace Council	020-7354 5200
	www.gn.apc.org/npc
Non-Violent Resistance Network	020-7607 2302
Nukewatch UK	023-8055 4434
Pax Christi	020-8203 4884
Peace Brigades International	020-7713 0392
	www.igc.apc.org/pbi
Peace Education Project	020-7424 9444
	www.ppu.org.uk
Peace News	020-7278 3344
	www.gn.apc.org/peacenews
Peace Pledge Union	020-7424 9444
	www.ppu.org.uk
Quaker Peace & Service	020-7663 1000
	www.quaker.org.uk
Royal British Legion	020-7973 7200
	www.britishlegion.org.uk
Scientists for Global Responsibility	020-8871 5175
Scottish CND	0141-423 1222
Statewatch	020-8802 1882
	www.statewatch.org
War Child	020-7916 9276
	www.warchild.org.uk
War Resisters International	020-7278 4040
	www.gn.apc.org/warresisters
World Peace Movement	01276-24353
Youth Action for Peace	01903-528619

Media Guide index

This index is for all the media contacts listed to page 383. To find Outside Contacts, check the State, Disaster and Emergencies, and Society headings on the contents page

100 Arrows/Crosswords **123**
100.7 Heart FM/Galaxy 102.2 **273**
102.7 Hereward FM **273**
106 CTFM **271**
106.3 Bridge FM **269**
107 Oak FM **277**
107 SouthCity FM **279**
107.2 Wire FM **282**
107.3 Eagle **272**
107.4 Telford FM **281**
107.5 Cat FM **270**
107.6 Kestrel FM **274**
107.7 Chelmer FM **270**
107.7 WFM **268**
107.7 Wolf **282**
107.8 Arrow FM **268**
107.8 FM Thames Radio **281**
107.9 Dune FM **272**
107.9 Eagle **272**
123 Productions **251**
18 Plus Movies **232**
19 **123**
1A Productions **251**
1st Call Recruitment **377**
1st Stop Careers **377**
2.4 Media **251**
20/20 **123**
24/7 Media **139**
2CR FM **268**
2-Ten FM **268**
3+ **232**
3BM Television **251**
3Di TV Software **251**
3R Productions **316**
3WE Third World & Environmental
  Broadcasting Project **303**
400 Company **251**
421 Productions **251**
7YY **307**
95 FM **316**
96 3 QFM **278**
96 FM103 FM103FM **316**
96 Trent FM **281**
96.3 Aire FM **268**
96.4 Eagle **272**
96.4 FM BRMB **269**
96.4 FM Wave **282**
96.7 FM **268**
97.2 Stray FM **280**
97.4 Vale FM **281**

A

A Thomson Relay **239**
A&C Black **136**
A19 Film & Video **248**, **251**
A38 Films **251**
AA Magazine **123**
AA Publishing **136**
AA Roadwatch **244**
AAA Productions **251**
Aardman Animation **251**
Abbey Films **251**
Abbey Recruitment Consultants **377**
Abbott Mead Vickers BBDO **354**
ABC **164**, **166**
ABC Freight Guide **123**
ABC News Intercontinental **244**
ABCClio **136**
Aberdeen & District Independent **102**
Aberdeen Evening Express **76**, **102**
Aberdeen Herald & Post **102**
Aberdeen Press & Journal **102**
Abergavenny Chronicle **106**
Abergele Visitor **105**
Abingdon Herald **96**
About Face Media **251**
Absolute Press **136**
Absolutely Productions **251**
AC Nielsen.MEAL **158**, **350**
Acacia Productions **251**
Accolade **123**
Accountancy **123**
Accountancy Age **123**
Accountancy Ireland **315**
Accrington Observer **90**
Ace Photo Agency **146**
Ace TV **232**
Achievement Concepts **251**
Acorn User **123**
Action Images **146**
Action Plus **146**
Action Staff Bureau **377**
Action Time North **251**
Active 107.5 FM **268**
Active Life **123**
Adam and Eve Channel **240**
Adams Picture Library **146**
Adams Wooding TV **235**
Addax Media **110**
Addictive Television **251**
Ad-Diplomasi News Report **306**
Addison Wesley Longman **136**
Addlestone & Byfleet Review **97**
Administration **315**
Adnews **68**
Adscene Group **68**
Adult Channel **232**
Adval **251**
Advance Features **139**
Advance Media Information **164**
Advanstar Communications **110**
Adventure One **231**, **232**

Advertiser & Times Hants **68**
Advertisers Annual/Blue Book **352**
Advertising Age International **352**
Advertising Archives **146**
Advertising Association **350**
Advertising Film Producers Assoc **350**
Advertising Standards Authority **350**,
  359
AE Morgan **115**
AEEU **164**
Aerofilms **146**
Aeroplane Monthly **123**
Aerosol Review **123**
AF Selection **377**
Affinity Publishing **110**
AFI Research **139**
Afloat Magazine **315**
Africa Independent TV **232**
African **306**
African Affairs **123**
African Review of Business **123**
Afro Wisdom Films **251**
Afro-Caribbean Channel **240**
After Image **251**
AFX News **139**
Age Concern Books **136**
Agence France Presse **139**
Agency London **133**
Agenda Television **251**
The Agitator, **119**
Agran Barton TV **251**
Aidan Ellis **136**
Ailsa Productionns **251**
Aim Publications **110**
Aimimage Productions **251**
Air Forces Monthly **123**
Air International **123**
Air Mail **123**
Air Navigation International **123**
Air Pictorial **123**
Aircraft Illustrated **123**
Aircraft Technology **123**
Airdrie & Coatbridge Advertiser **104**
Airdrie & Coatbridge World **104**
Aire Valley Target **101**
Airflash **287**
Airforce Television **251**
Airlife Publishing **136**
Airline Business **123**
Airliners **123**
Airport Review **123**
Airport Television **240**
Airports International **123**
Airtrade **123**
Aisling Magazine **315**
AJ Focus **123**
AKG London **146**
Akhbar-e-Watan **306**
Al Aalam Magazine **123**
Al Ahram International **306**
Al Arab **306**
Al Hawadeth **123**
Al Hayat **306**

Al Majalla **123**
Al Muhajir **306**
Al Wasat **123**
Al-Alaam **306**
Alan Jones Photos **146**
Alan Torjussen **251**
Albany Appointments **377**
Alcibiades **251**
Aldershot Courier series **88**
Aldershot Mail **88**
Aldershot News series **88**
Aldridge Advertiser Weekly **99**
Alert Communications **139**
ALF **352**
Alfalfa Entertainments **251**
Alford Standard **91**
Alfreton & Ripley Echo **85**
Alfreton Chad **85**
Alhambra Films **251**
Alibi Communications **251**
A-Line Aberdeen **158**
Alive Productions **251**
Allen & Overy **332**
Allen Lane **136**
Allison & Busby **136**
Allocate Recruitment **377**
All-Party Media Group **294**
AllScot News & Features Agency **139**
Allsport UK **146**
Al-Mustakillah TV **232**
Alpha **103.2 268**
Alpha Channel **240**
Alpha Newspaper Group **68**
Alpha Photographic Press **148**
Al-Rashad **232**
Alton Gazette **88**
Alton Herald **88**
Alton Times & Mail **88**
AM Heath & Co **133**
Amalgamated Engineering & Electrical
    Union **164**
Amar Deep **123**
Amar Deep Hindi **306**
AMARC **294**
Amateur Gardening **123**
Amateur Photographer **123**
Amber Classic Gold **268**
Amenity Management **123**
American in Britain **306**
Amesbury Journal **100**
AMI **164**
Amiga Format **123**
Amirani Films **251**
Amnesty International **315**
Amnesty International **164, 294, 382**
AMP **377**
Ampthill & Flitwick Herald **83**
Amsat-UK **294**
AMT Magazine **315**
Amusement Business Europe **123**
An Bord Altranais News **315**
An Cosantoir **315**
An Phoblacht Sinn Fein/IRA **123**
Ananda Bazar Patrika **306**
Andersen Press **136**
Anderson Strathern WS **332**
Andes Press Agency **139, 148**

Andover Advertiser **88**
Andover Advertiser Midweek **88**
Andover Now **240**
Andre Deutsch **136**
Andrea Florence **251**
Andrew Fraser **377**
Andrew Lownie **133**
Andrew Mann **133**
Andrew Nurnberg Associates **133**
Andromeda Oxford **136**
Anfield & Walton Star **91**
Angel Business Communications **110**
Angel Express **251**
Angel Eye Film & TV **251**
Angel Films **251**
Angela Mortimer **377**
Angler's Mail **123**
Anglesey Chronicle **106**
Anglia Advertiser **68**
Anglia Polytechnic University **373**
Anglia Press Agency **139**
Anglia Television **216**
Angling Plus **123**
Angling Times **123**
Anglo-Celt Weekly **314**
Anglo-Danish Press Agency **139**
Angus County Press **68**
Animal Life/Action **123**
Animal Planet **232**
Animation Partnership **251**
Anjuman **232**
Anna Livia FM **316**
Annabelle Staff Bureau **377**
Annalogue **251**
Annandale Herald **103**
Anne Bolt Memorial Award **382**
Anness Publishing **136**
ANSA **139**
Antelope **251**
Antena Productions **251**
Antidote **251**
Antique Interiors **123**
Antiques & Art Ind **123**
Antiques Diary **123**
Antiques Trade Gazette **123**
Antonine Films **251**
Antrim Guardian **107**
AP Watt **133**
APA **166**
AP-Dow Jones News Wires **319**
Apex Photo Agency **148**
Apex Recruitment Services **377**
Apex TV **251**
APNA TV **311**
Apna TV Arab News Network **232**
Apollo **123**
Apple Recruitment Services **377**
Appletree Press **136**
Approaching Fish **251**
Appropriate Technology **123**
Apt Film & TV **251**
APTN **244**
Aquarius Picture Library **148**
Arable Farming **123**
Arbroath Herald **68, 102**
Arcade Channels **240**

Arcadi Books **136**
Arcadia Films **251**
Arcadian Productions **251**
Architectural Design **123**
Architecture Today **123**
Archive Films **248**
Ardea London **148**
Ardent Productions **251**
Ardrossan/Saltcoats Herald **103**
Arena **123, 315**
Argyll FM **268**
Ariel **287**
Aries Productions **251**
Ark Productions **251**
Arlesford & District Times **88**
Armadillo Films **251**
Armagh Down Observer **107**
Around the World Productions **251**
Arran Banner **103**
Arran Banner Printing & Publishing **68**
Arrow Books **136**
Arrow Recruitment **377**
Arsenal **240**
Art & Craft **123**
Art Business Today **123**
Art Monthly **123**
Art Quarterly **123**
Art Review **123**
Art Trade Press **136**
Article 19, Global Campaign for Free
    Expression **166, 294**
Artificial Eye **251**
Arts Institute at Bournemouth **371**
Artsworld **232**
ArtWork **123**
Arw Recruitment **377**
Ascot & Sunningdale Observer **83**
ASD Films **251**
ASDA FM National in-store radio **285**
Asda Magazine **123**
Ash Mail **97**
Asharq Al Awsat Arab News **306**
Ashboourne News Telegraph **85**
Ashby & Coalville Mail **90**
Ashby Times **90**
Ashfield Chad **95**
Ashford & Tenterden Adscene **89**
Ashford Extra **89**
Ashgate Publishing **136**
Ashley Search & Selection **377**
Ashton Advertiser **94**
Ashurst Morris Crisp **332**
Asia 1 TV **232**
Asia Image **287**
Asia Net TV **232, 311**
Asian **306**
Asian Age **306**
Asian Convenience Retailer **306**
Asian Entertainment Guide **306**
Asian Express **306**
Asian Hotel & Caterer **306**
Asian Music Channel **232**
Asian Programmes **232**

A

Asian Review of Business &Tech. **123**
Asian Sound Radio **268**, **285**, **311**
Asian Telegraph **306**
Asian Television **311**
Asian Times **306**
Asian Trade Publications **110**
Asian Trader **306**
Asian Voice Scotland **307**
Aslib **294**
Aspect **315**
Aspect Television **251**
Aspen Publishing **110**
Asset Television **232**
Assignments Photographers **148**
Associated Newspapers **68**
Associated Press AP **139**
Associated Press Television News **244**
Associated Sports
    Photography/Headline **148**
Assoc. of Advertisers in Ireland **319**
Association of American
    Correspondents in London **166**
Association of Authors' Agents **133**
Assoc. of British Science Writers **166**
Assoc. of Broadcasting Doctors **294**
Assoc. of European Journalists **166**
Association of Illustrators **166**
Assoc. of Investigative Journalists **166**
Association of Little Presses **166**
Association of Newspaper & Magazine
    Wholesalers **166**
Association of Photographers **166**
Assoc. of Publishing Agencies **166**
Association of Smallscale Scottish
    Broadcasters **294**
Assoc. of UK Media Librarians **166**
Astronomy & Space **315**
Astronomy Now **123**
Asylum Pictures **252**
At It Productions **252**
At Your Service Agency **377**
Atebion Employment Agency **377**
Atherstone Herald **99**
Athletics Weekly **123**
Athlone Press **136**
Atlantic **252 266**, **316**
Atlantic Europe **136**
Atlantic Eye **252**
Atlantic Productions **252**
Atlantic Telecom Group **238**, **239**
ATM **240**
Atomic TV **232**
ATP **148**
Attaboy TV **252**
Attic Futura **110**
Attic Press **136**
Attic Productions **252**
Atticus TV **252**
Attitude **123**
Auction Channel **232**
Auction sales **232**
Audience **123**
Audio Media **287**
Audio Visual **123**
Audio Visual Association **294**
Audit Bureau of Circulations **166**

Augustus Films **252**
Aurum Press **136**
Australia Pictures **148**
Australian Associated Press **139**
Author, The **123**, **160**
Authors' Licensing & Collecting **166**
Auto Express **123**
Auto Trader **110**, **123**
Autocar **123**
Autograph **148**
Automatic Pictures **252**
Automobile **123**
Automotive Digest **123**
Automotive Marketing Review **123**
Autosport **123**
AutoTrade **123**
AV Magazine **123**, **287**
Available Light **252**
Avalon TV **252**
AVC Media **252**
Avia Press Associates **110**
Avie Littler Assoc **252**
Avon Adv Hants & Dorset **86**
Avon Advertiser Hants/Dorset **88**
Avonbridge Film **252**
AVP Films **252**
Awaaz Asian Voice **307**
Award Publications **136**
Awaze Quam **307**
Axholme Herald **101**
Axiom Magazine **123**
Axminster News **86**
Axon Publishing **110**
Ayr Advertiser **103**
Ayr Leader **103**
Ayrshire Cable & Telecoms **239**
Ayrshire Post **103**
Ayrshire World **103**

B

B **123**
B&T Productions **252**
B4U **232**
B97 Chiltern FM **268**
Baby **123**
Baby Films **252**
Babylon Blue Bangla TV **232**
Back Hill Reporter **123**
Backbone Productions **252**
BAFTA **294**, **382**
Baker & McKenzie **332**
Baker Tilly **252**
Bakery World **315**
Ballantyne Ross **110**
Ballyclare Gazette **107**
Ballymena Chronicle **107**
Ballymena Guardian **107**
Ballymena Times **107**
Ballymoney Times **107**
Bamboo Film & TV **252**
Banbridge Chronicle **68**, **107**
Banbridge Leader **107**
Banbury Cake **96**
Banbury Citizen **96**
Banbury Guardian **96**
Band **123**

Banffshire Advertiser **102**
Banffshire Herald **105**
Banffshire Journal **102**
Bangaw Cyf **252**
Bangor & Caernarfon Chronicle **106**
Bangor Mail **106**
Bank of Scotland Press Awards **382**
Banker **123**
Banks Hoggins O'Shea/FCB **354**
Bannatyne Kirkwood France & Co **332**
Banstead Herald **97**
Bantam **136**
BAPLA **146**, **166**, **292**
Baptist Times **123**
Bar Channel **232**
Bar Council Journalists of the Year **382**
Barb **294**
Barbara Levy **133**
Barbie **123**
Barclay Bros **69**
Bard Entertainments **252**
Bare Faced Productions **252**
Barefoot Books **136**
Barker Service **232**
Barking & Dagenham Advertiser **92**
Barking & Dagenham Express **92**
Barking & Dagenham Post **92**
Barking & Dagenham Recorder **92**
Barnaby's Picture Library **148**
Barnardo's Film & Photographic **148**
Barnes, Mortlake Times **93**
Barnet & Finchley Press **92**
Barnet Advertiser **92**
Barnet Borough Times **92**
Barnsley Chronicle **68**, **78**, **101**
Barnsley College **373**
Barnsley Independent **101**
Barnsley Star **101**
Barraclough Carey **252**
Barratts Photopress **148**
Barrhead News **104**
Barrie & Jenkins **136**
Barrow N West Evening Mail **85**
Barry Gem **106**
Barry Rose Law **136**
Barry and District News **106**
Bartle Bogle Hegarty **354**
Basildon Evening Echo **87**
Basildon Standard Recorder **87**
Basildon Yellow Advertiser **87**
Basingstoke & N Hants Gaz. **88**
Basingstoke Observer **88**
Bassist **123**
Bates UK **354**
Bath & District Advertiser **96**
Bath Advertiser **83**
Bath Chronicle **96**
Bath FM **268**
Bath Oberserver **96**
Bath Spa University College **373**
Batley News **101**
Batsford **136**
Battersea News **93**
Bay **268**
Baylin Publications **136**
Baylis & Co **68**
Bazal **252**

BBC Asian Network **262**
BBC Belfast (National HQ) **205**
BBC B'ham (English Regions HQ) **205**
BBC Books **136**
BBC Bristol **205**
BBC Broadcast **202**
BBC Cardiff (National HQ) **205**
BBC Corporate HQ **202**
BBC Digital TV **228**
BBC Drama, Entertainment and
  Children **206**
BBC Dublin Office **319**
BBC Elstree **205**
BBC Factual and Learning **206**
BBC Gardener's World **123**
BBC Glasgow (National HQ) **205**
BBC GLR 94.9 London **262**
BBC GMR Talk Manchester **263**
BBC Good Food **123**
BBC Good Homes **123**
BBC Hereford & Worcestershire **262**
BBC Knowledge **229**
BBC Learning is Fun **123**
BBC Leeds **205**
BBC Main press office **202**
BBC Manchester **205**
BBC Match of the Day **123**
BBC Monitoring **263**
BBC Music Magazine **123**
BBC Network Television **202**
BBC New Media **206**
BBC Newcastle **205**
BBC News **202, 204**
BBC News Stills **148**
BBC Northern Ireland **205**
BBC Norwich **205**
BBC Nottingham **205**
BBC On Air **287**
BBC Parliament **244**
BBC Photograph Library **148**
BBC Plymouth **205**
BBC Prime **232**
BBC Production **202**
BBC Programme Complaints Unit **359**
BBC Radio Bristol **262**
BBC Radio Cambridgeshire **262**
BBC Radio Cleveland **263**
BBC Radio Cornwall **262**
BBC Radio Cumbria **263**
BBC Radio Derby **262**
BBC Radio Devon **262**
BBC Radio Essex **262**
BBC Radio Foyle **263**
BBC Radio Gloucestershire **262**
BBC Radio Guernsey **262**
BBC Radio HQ **262**
BBC Radio Humberside **263**
BBC Radio Jersey **262**
BBC Radio Kent **262**
BBC Radio Lancashire **263**
BBC Radio Leeds **263**
BBC Radio Leicester **262**
BBC Radio Lincolnshire **262**
BBC Radio Merseyside **263**
BBC Radio Nan Gaidheal **263**
BBC Radio Newcastle **263**

BBC Radio Norfolk **262**
BBC Radio Northampton **262**
BBC Radio Nottingham **262**
BBC Radio Scotland **263**
BBC Radio Sheffield **263**
BBC Radio Shropshire **263**
BBC Radio Solent **262**
BBC Radio Stoke **263**
BBC Radio Suffolk **263**
BBC Radio Ulster **263**
BBC Radio Wales **263**
BBC Radio WM West Midlands **263**
BBC Radio York **263**
BBC Resources **207**
BBC Scotland **205**
BBC Somerset Sound **262**
BBC Southampton **205**
BBC Sport **206**
BBC Televison Centre **204**
BBC Thames Valley **262**
BBC Three Counties Radio **263**
BBC Toybox **123**
BBC Training and Development **362**
BBC Wales **205**
BBC White City **202**
BBC Wildlife **123**
BBC World Service **202**
BBC World Service - HQ **263**
BBC Worldwide **110, 202, 207, 248**
BBC Written Archives **202**
BBJ Media Services **356**
BBME Radio and TV School **371**
BCB **282**
BCR FM **268**
BDH TBWA **354**
Beach **252, 268**
Beach House **252**
Beachcroft Wansbroughs **332**
Beacon FM/WABC Classic Gold **268**
Beano **123**
BEAP- Puzzle People **110**
Bearsden Milngavie Courier **104**
Beat **106 269**
Beattie Media **357**
Beautiful Homes **123**
Bebington News **91**
Beccles & Bungay Journal **97**
Beckett Communications **252**
Beckmann Productions **252**
BECTU **296, 362**
Bedford & Kempston Herald **83**
Bedford Square Press **136**
Bedford Times & Citizen series **83**
Bedfordshire on Sunday **81, 83**
Bedworth Echo **99**
Bee World **123**
Beekeeping & Development **123**
Beeley Productions **252**
Beer Writer of the Year Awards **382**
Belfast News Letter **107**
Belfast Sunday Life **107**
Belfast Telegraph **76, 107**
Belitha Press **136**
Bell & Scott WS **332**
Bell College of Technology **366, 371**

Bell Pottinger Communications **357**
Bell TV **252**
Bell's Photographer of the Year **382**
Bella **123**
Bellew Publishing **136**
Bellis News Agency **139**
Bellshill Speaker **104**
Belper Express **85**
Belper News **85**
Benn Business Publishing **118**
Benn's Media **162, 292, 352**
Bennett Publishing **110**
Berg Publishers **136**
Berkeley & Sharpness Gazette **87**
Berks & Bucks Observer **83**
Berlitz **136**
Bernard Babani **136**
Berrow's Worcester Journal **100**
Berwick & Borders Gazette **103**
Berwick Advertiser **95**
Berwick Gazette **95**
Berwick Universal Pictures **252**
Berwickshire Advertiser **103**
Berwickshire News **103**
Berwin Leighton **332**
Besom Productions **252**
Best **123**
Best Direct TV **232**
Best of Postman Pat **123**
Best of Rosie & Jim **123**
Best of Thomas Tank Engine **123**
Best of Tots TV **123**
Best Productions **252**
BET International **232**
BET on Jazz **240**
Better Satellite **123, 287**
Beulah **248**
Bevan Ashford **332**
Beverley Advertiser **100**
Bexhill Adnews **98**
Bexhill Observer **98**
Bexley Borough Mercury **93**
Bexley News Shopper **81, 93**
Bexley Leader **93**
Bexleyheath Mercury **93**
Bexleyheath/Welling Times **93**
Beyond International **252**
Beyond the Frame **252**
BFI Film and TV Handbook **292**
BFI **136, 252**
BFM Productions **252**
BIB **240**
Bible Society **136**
Bibliotech Training **361**
Bicester Advertiser **96**
Bicester Review **96**
Biddle **332**
Biddulph Chroicle **97**
Big **123, 269**
Big Bear Films **252**
Big Events Co **252**
Big Eye Film & TV **252**
Big Idea Productions **252**
Big Issue **110, 119, 123**
Big Issue Film Unit **252**
Big Strand **252**
Big Table Film Co, **252**

B

Big Talk Productions **252**
Biggin Hill News **94**
Biggleswade & Sandy Herald **83**
Biggleswade Chronicle **83**
Bike **123**
Billboard **123, 136**
Bindman & Partners **333**
Biochemist **123**
Biologist **123**
Bird & Bird **252, 333**
Bird Keeper **123**
Bird Life **123**
Bird Watching **123**
Birds **123**
Birdwatch **123**
Birkenhead News **91**
Birmingham Evening Mail **99**
Birmingham Metronews **99**
Birmingham News **99**
Birmingham Post **99**
Birmingham Press Club **166**
Birmingham Sunday Mercury **99**
Birmingham What's On **123**
Birstall News **101**
Bishops Stortford Citizen **88**
Biss Lancaster **357**
Bitcom International **252**
Bizarre **123**
BJK&E Media **356**
BKST **295, 362**
Black Appointments **377**
Black Bear **252**
Black Coral **252**
Black Flag **119**
Black Perspective **307**
Black Pudding Productions **252**
Blackbird Productions **252**
Blackburn Citizen **90**
Blackpool Gazette **90**
Blackstaff Press **136**
Blackstone Press **136**
Blackwatch Productions **252**
Blackwell Publishers **136, 110**
Blackwood & Risca News **105**
Blackwood Campaign **105**
Blairgowrie Advertiser **105**
Blake Friedmann **133**
Blake Publishing **136**
Blakeway Productions **252**
Blandford Press **136**
Blast! Films **252**
Blenheim Business Publications **110**
Blenheim TV Films **252**
Bliss **123**
Bloodaxe Books **136**
Bloomberg Info TV **232, 244**
Bloomberg News **139**
Bloomberg News Radio **285**
Bloomsbury **136**
Bloomsbury House **110**
Blow By Blow Productions **252**
Bloxwich Advertiser **99**
Blue Book of British Broadcasting **292**
Blue Heaven Productions **252**
Blue Horizon **252**
Blue Pages **123**

Blueprint **123**
Blues & Soul **123**
Blythe & Forsbrook Time **94, 97**
BMJ Publishing Group **110**
BMP DDB **354**
BMP OMD **356**
BNFL North West Press Awards **382**
Boat Angler **123**
Boatswain Press **136**
Bob Godfrey Films **252**
Bodley Head **136**
Bognor Chichester Journal **98**
Bognor Regis Observer **98**
Bolsover Advertiser **85**
Bolton Evening News **94**
Bolton Journal **94**
Bomb **123**
Bonhams Auction Guide **123**
Book & Magazine Collector **123**
Book Trust **166**
Books & Company **123**
Books in the Media **123, 287**
Books in Wales **123**
Books Ireland **315**
Bookseller **123, 160**
Booth Lockett Makin Group **356**
BoothClibborn **136**
Bootle Times **91**
Border Radio Holdings **266**
Border Telegraph **103, 216**
Bordon Herald **88**
Bordon Times & Mail **88**
Borehamwood Times **88**
Boro TV **240**
Boston & Sleaford Target **91**
Boston Standard **91**
Bounds Away **252**
Bour Productions **252**
Bourne Local **91**
Bournemouth Daily Echo **86**
Bournemouth News & Pictures **139**
Bournemouth University **366, 371, 373**
Bournemouth Advertiser **86**
Bowker Saur **111, 136**
Bowkers Video Directory **292**
Bowls International **123**
Box, The **232**
Boxing News **123**
Boxtree **136**
Boys Toys **123**
Boyz **123**
BPL Business Publications **111**
BPP Publishing **136**
Brackley & Towcester Advertiser **95**
Bracknell & Ascot Times **83**
Bracknell & Wokingham News **83**
Bracknell & Wokingham Std **83**
Bracknell News **83**
BRAD **124, 353**
Bradford & Bingley Media Awards **382**
Bradford Community Broadcasting **285**
Bradford Festival News **240**
Bradford Star **101**
Bradford Telegraph & Argus **101**
Braille Radio/TV Times **287**
Brainstorm Films **252**

Braintree & Witham Times **87**
Braintree & Witham Yellow Ad **87**
Bramhall & District Courier **84**
Brand Strategy **123**
Branded Film **252**
Brass Tacks Publishing **111**
Brassey's **136**
Bravo **232**
Bray People **314**
Breakthru **123**
Breathing Canyon **252**
Brechin Advertiser **102**
Brechin Productions **252**
Breedon Books **136**
Breeze **269**
Brenda Rowe Productions **252**
Brent & London Recorder **92**
Brent Leader **92**
Brentford, Chiswick Times **94**
Brentvine **377**
Brentwood Gazette **87**
Brentwood Recorder **92**
Brentwood Weekly News **87**
Brewin Books **136**
Brian Unwin **139**
Brian Waddell Productions **252**
Bride & Groom Magazine **123**
Brides & Setting Up Home **123**
Bridge Executive Recruitment **377**
Bridge Information Systems **140**
Bridgeman Art Library **148**
Bridgend Recorder **105**
Bridgend & Ogwr Post **105**
Bridgnorth Journal **96**
Bridgwater Mercury **96**
Bridgwater/Burnham Times **96**
Bridlington Free Press **100**
Bridport News **86**
Brighouse Echo **101**
Bright Thoughts Co **252**
Brighter Pictures **252**
Brighton & Hove Leader **98**
Brighton College of Technology **366**
Brighton Evening Argus **98**
Brighton Friday-Ad **98**
Brilliant Independent Media **356**
Brilliant Publications **136**
Bristol & West News Agency **140**
Bristol Evening Post **76**
Bristol Observer **83**
Bristol United Press **68, 365**
Bristol Western Daily Press **83**
Bristol's 107.3 Eagle **269**
Bristows **333**
Britannia Journalist of the Year **382**
British Academy of Composers **294**
British Academy of Film and Television Arts **294**
British Amateur Television Club **294**
British Archaeology **123**
British Association of Communicators in Business **166**
British Association of Journalists **166**
British Association of Picture Libraries and Agencies **146, 166**
British Baker **123**
British Birds **123**

British Board of Film Classification **295**
British Copyright Council **166**
British Dental Journal **123**
British European Publishers **111**
British Film Commission **295**
British Film Institute **136, 148, 248**
British Guild of Picture Editors **382**
British Guild of Travel Writers **166,382**
British Inst. of Photography **146, 166**
British Interactive Broadcasting **228**
British Interactive Multimedia **295**
British Internet Publishers' Alliance **295**
British Jeweller **123**
British Journal of Community Health **123**
British Journal of Community Hospital Medicine **123**
British Journal of Community Management **123**
British Journal of Community Midwifery **123**
British Journal of Community Nursing **123**
British Journal of Community Practice Nursing **123**
British Journal of Photography **123, 287**
British Journalism Review **160**
British Kinematograph, Sound and Television Society **295**
British Library Reproductions **148**
British Medical Journal **123**
British Movietone News **248**
British Museum Press **136**
British Pathe **248, 252**
British Press Awards **382**
British Printer **124, 160**
British Printing Industries **166**
British Radio & Electronic Equipment Manufacturers' Association **295**
British Rate & Data **124, 353**
British Screen **252**
British Screen Advisory Council **296**
British Screen Finance **296**
British Sky Broadcasting **228**
British Society of Cinematographers **296**
British Society of Magazine Editors **166**
British Sports Journalist and Sports Photographer of the Year **382**
British Universities Film & Video Council **362**
Britt Allcroft Company **252**
Broad Productions **252**
Broadbent Partnership **252**
Broadcast **124, 287**
Broadcast Advertising Clearance Centre **351**
Broadcast Books **136**
Broadcast Journalism Training Council **362**
Broadcast Production Awards **382**
Broadcasters Audience Research Board **296**
Broadcasting Complaints Commission **296, 319**

Broadcasting Press Guild **296**
Broadcasting Research Unit **296**
Broadcasting Standards Commission **296, 359**
Broadcasting Support Services **296**
Broadcasting, Entertainment, Cinematograph and Theatre Union **296, 362**
Broadland **269**
Brodeur Worldwide **357**
Bromley Leader **94**
Bromley News **94**
Bromley News Shopper **94**
Bromley, Beckenham Times **94**
Bromsgrove/Droitwich Standard **100**
Bronco Films **252**
Bronson Knight **252**
Brook Lapping Productions **252**
Brookside Productions **252**
Broughty& Carnoustie Gazette **103**
Brown Wells and Jacobs **136**
Brown, Son & Ferguson **136**
Brownhills Advertiser **97**
Bruce Coleman Collection **149**
Bruce Kinlock Property Journalist of the Year **382**
Brunel University **373**
BSkyB **231**
BSME Awards **382**
BSMG Worldwide **357**
BSS **296**
BSS Linklines **296**
BT Awards **382**
Buchan Observer **102**
Buckingham Advertiser **83**
Bucks Chilterns University College **373**
Bucks Examiner **83**
Bucks Free Press **83**
Bucks Herald **83**
Bude & Stratton Post **84**
Budgerigar World **124**
Buena Vista **252**
Buffalo Pictures **252**
Builder Group **111**
Building **124**
Building Design **124**
Building Homes **124**
Building Services **124**
Bulletin **315**
Bulletin International Video Library **149**
Bumper Films **252**
Bunty **124**
Bureau of Freelance Photographers **166**
Burgess Hill Leader **98**
Burlington Magazine **124**
Burness Solicitors **333**
Burnham & Highbridge News **96**
Burning Gold **252**
Burnley Citizen **90**
Burnley Express & News **90**
Burns & Oates **136**
Burntwood Mercury **97**
Burrill Productions **252**
Burry Port Star **105**
Burson-Marsteller **357**
Burton Advertiser **97**

Burton Daily Mail **97**
Burton Trader **97**
Bury Citizen **97**
Bury Free Press **97**
Bury Journal/Messenger **94**
Bury St Edmunds Mercury **97**
Bury Times **94**
Bus Fayre **124**
Business **307**
Business Africa/Asia/China/Latin America/Middle East/Russia **124**
Business & Finance **315**
Business and Technology **124**
Business Connection Group **377**
Business Contact **315**
Business Equipment Digest **124**
Business Franchise **124**
Business Information Channel **232**
Business Magazine Group **111**
Business Travel World **124**
Bute Newspapers **68**
Buteman **102**
Butterfly Conservation **124**
Butterworth **136**
Butterworth Tolley **136**
Butterworths Tolley **111**
Buxton Advertiser **85**
Buxton Raven **252**
Buxton Times **85**
Buy & Sell **315**
Buy a Boat **124**
Buying Cameras **124**
Buzz **124, 269**
BVTV **240**
BW Productions **252**
Byfleet News and Mail **98**

C

CB Radio Active **124**
C&T **238**
C7TV **232**
Cab Driver **124**
Cabal **111**
Cabinet Maker **124**
Cable & Satellite Europe **124, 287**
Cable & Satellite International **287**
Cable & Satellite Yearbook **292**
Cable & Telecoms **238**
Cable & Wireless Communications **238**
Cable 103.9 **285**
Cable 17 **240**
Cable and Wireless **228**
Cable Guide **124, 287**
Cable Radio Milton Keynes **285**
Cable Television Engineering **124**
Cablecom Investments **239**
Cactus Television **252**
CadCam **124**
Caernarfon Herald **105**
Caerphilly Campaign **105**
Cafe Productions **252**
Cage & Aviary Birds **124**
Caithness Courier **104**
Cake Decorating **124**
Cakes & Sugarcraft **124**

C

Calder Publications **136**
Calderdale News **101**
Calderdale TV **240**
Caledonia, Sterne & Wyld **252**
Caledonian Magazines **111**
Caledonian Newspaper Publishing **68**
Call TV **232**
Callister Commuications **252**
Calne Gazette & Herald **100**
Calyx Multimedia **149**
Cam Consultants **377**
Camberley & District Courier **97**
Camberley Mail **97**
Camberley News **97**
Camborne & Redruth Packet **84**
Cambrensis **252**
Cambrian News **68**, **105**
Cambridge Evening News **84**
Cambridge Film & TV **252**
Cambridge Interactive TV **240**
Cambridge Newspapers **63**
Cambridge Red Radio **269**
Cambridge University Press **111**, **136**
Cambridge Video **252**
Cambridge Weekly News **84**
Cambs Town Crier **84**
Camcorder User **124**
Camden New Journal **92**
Camden/St Pancras Chronicle **92**
Camelford & Delabole Post **84**
Camera Press **149**
Campaign **124**, **352**
Campaign for Freedom of Information
  166, **296**
Campaign for Press and Broadcasting
  Freedom **166**, **297**
Campaign Free Newspapers **106**
Campaign Media Business **352**
Campaigner **124**
Campbell Hooper **333**
Campbell Thomson & McLaughlin **133**
Campbeltown Courier **102**
Camping & Caravanning **124**
Canadian Press **140**
Canal & Riverboat **124**
Candis **124**
Candour **122**
Candover **68**
Cannock Chase Chronicle **97**
Cannock Mercury **97**
Canoeist **124**
Canongate Books **136**
Canopus Communications **252**
Canterbury Adscene **89**
Canterbury Christ Church **373**
Canterbury Extra **89**
Canto & Canto Recruitment **377**
Canvasback Productions **252**
Capel & Land **133**
Capel-Cure Sharp **358**
Capital FM/Capital Gold **269**
Capital Gold, Birmingham **269**
Capital Gold, Brighton **269**

Capital Pictures **149**
Capital Radio **266**
Capital Radio Digital **284**
Car & Accessory Trader **124**
Car Boot Calendar **124**
Car Driver Magazine **315**
Car Mechanics **124**
Car World **124**
Cara **315**
Carat **356**
Caravan Club Magazine **124**
Caravan Life **124**
Caravan Magazine **124**
Carcanet Press **136**
Cardiff Post **105**
Cardiff South Wales Echo **105**
Cardiff University of Wales **361**, **371**
Cardiff Western Mail **105**
Cardigan Advertiser **105**
Cardonald College **366**
Careers & Jobs **377**
Carey Films **252**
Carey Street Productions **252**
CARF **119**
Caribbean One TV **232**
Caribbean Times **124**, **307**
Caribbean World **124**
Carlisle News & Star **85**
Carlow People **314**
Carlton Books **136**
Carlton Communications **217**
Carlton Food Network **232**
Carlton International Media **248**
Carlton Kids/World **229**
Carlton Select **232**
Carlton Select/Food/Cinema **229**
Carlton Studios **218**
Carluke Gazette **104**
Carmarthen Citizen **105**
Carmarthen Journal **105**
Carnival Films **252**
Carnyx Group **111**
Carol Gould **252**
Caroline Sheldon Literary Agency **133**
Carreras Lathane Associates **377**
Carrick Gazette **103**
Carrick Herald **103**
Cars & Car Conversions **124**
CarSport **124**
Cartermill Int. **136**
Cartoon Art Trust **167**
Cartoon Art Trust Award **382**
Cartoon Network **228**, **229**, **232**
Cartoonist **124**
Cartoonists' Club of Great Britain **167**
Case TV **252**
Cash & Carry Management **124**
Cassell **136**
Cassidy & Leigh Southern News
  Service **140**
Castle Haven Digital **252**
CastlebarCommunity **316**
Castlepoint Recorder **87**
Castlepoint Yellow Advertiser **87**

Castlereagh Star **107**
Cat Ledger Literary Agency **133**
Cat, The **124**
Catalist Films **252**
Catalyst **124**
Catalyst TV **252**
Caterer & Hotelkeeper **124**
Caterham Mirror **97**
Catering Update **124**
Caters News Agency **140**
Cathedral Appointments **377**
Catholic Herald **111**, **124**
Catholic Standard **315**
Catholic Truth **136**
Cats **124**
Cause n Effect PH **252**
Cavan and Westmeath Herald **314**
Cavendish **136**
Cavendish Press **140**
Caves & Caving **124**
CBD Research **136**
CBS News **244**
CBTV **252**
CDA Communications **239**
CDP Media Company **356**
CE Digital **284**
Ceefax **243**
Celador Productions **252**
Celebrations in Cross Stitch **124**
Celtic Film and Television Festival
  Company **297**
Celtic Films **252**
Celtic Journey **315**
Celtic Productions **252**
Centaur Communications **111**
Centennial Publishing **111**
Central Broadcasting **218**
Central Criminal Court Journalists'
  Association **167**
Central Fife Times **104**
Central FM **270**
Central Independent News **68**
Central News Network **140**
Central Office of Information **140**, **248**
Central Press Features **140**
Central Press Lobby **140**
Central Reservation **252**
Centre FM **270**
Centre for Journalism Studies **371**
Centrepix **149**
Centrepoint **124**
Century Films **252**
Century Radio **270**
Cephas Picture Library **149**
Ceredigion **270**
CFM **270**
ChadwyckHealey **136**
Challenge TV **232**
Chambers Harrap **136**
Chameleon Television **252**
Champion FM **270**
Champion Newspapers **68**
Channale Pakeeza **232**

Channel 10 **240**
Channel 103 FM **270**
Channel 4 **224**, **232**
Channel 4 Clip Library **248**
Channel 5 **225**, **232**
Channel 7 **240**
Channel Business **124**
Channel East **232**
Channel Guide **240**
Channel One **240**
Channel Television **218**
Channel Travel Radio **270**
Channel X **252**
Chapman **136**
Chapman & Page **140**
Chapter One **252**
Chard & Ilminster News **96**
Chariot Productions **252**
Charles Pick Consultancy **133**
Charles Russell **333**
Charlotte Metcalf Productions **252**
Chartered Institute of Journalists **167**
Chartered Society of Designers **167**
Charterhouse Communications **111**
Chase Post **99**
Chat **124**
Chatsworth **252**
Chatto & Windus **136**
Cheadle & Post Times **97**
Cheadle District Advertiser **94**
Checkout **124**
Checkout Magazine **315**
Cheeky Ideas **252**
Cheerful Scout **252**
Cheerleader Productions **252**
Chelmsford Weekly News **87**
Chelmsford Yellow Advertiser **87**
Chelsea News **92**
Cheltenham and Glos College of Higher
  Education **373**
Cheltenham News **87**
Chemical Engineer **124**
Chemist & Druggist **124**
Chemistry in Britain **124**
Chemistry Review **124**
Chepstow News **106**
Cheriton Enterprises **252**
Cheshire Newspapers **68**
Chess **124**
Chester & District Standard **84 84**
Chester Chronicle **78, 84**
Chester le Street Advertiser **86**
Chester Mail **84**
Chester News Service **140**
Chester Press Bureaux **140**
Chester Standard Newspapers **68**
Chesterfield Advertiser **85**
Chesterfield Express **85**
Chesterfield Gazette **85**
Chew Valley Gazette **69**
Chichester Observer **78**
Child's Play **136**
Children's Express UK **167**
Children's Film and TV Foundation **297**

Children's Film Unit **252**
Children's Film/TV Foundation **252**
Childsplay Productions **252**
Chiltern FM/ClassicGold **270**
Chiltern Recruitment **377**
China Economic Review **124**
China In Focus **124**
Chingford Guardian **92**
Chippenham Gazette & Herald **100**
Chippenham News **100**
Chislehurst Times **94**
Chistera Productions **252**
Chobham & Windlesham News **97**
Choi & Co **252**
Choice **124**
Choice 107.1 **270**
Choice Bureau **377**
Choice FM **270, 311**
Choice Magazine **111**
Chorley Citizen **90**
Chorley Guardian **90**
Chris Cox Memorial Award **382**
Christchurch Advertiser **86**
Christian Aid Photo Library **149**
Christian Channel Europe **232**
Christian Channel London **240**
Christian Channel Shopping **232**
Christian Children's Channel **232**
Christian Communication Net **232**
Christian Family **124**
Christian Music Channel **232**
Christian programming **235**
Christian Socialist **124**
Christine Green **133**
Christmas TV & Film Co **252**
Christopher Little **133**
Christopher Swann Assocs **252**
Christopher Sykes Production **252**
Chronicle **99**
Chronicle Advertiserr **88**
Chronicle Publications **69**
Chrysalis Radio **266**
Chrysalis Sport **252**
Chrysalis Television **252**
Chrysalis Visual Entertainment **252**
Church Times **124**
Churches Advisory Council for Local
  Broadcasting **297**
C Hurst **136**
CIA Medianetwork **356**
Cicada Films **252**
Cicerone Press **136**
CIF Blue Pages **315**
Cinar Europe **252**
Cineblitz **307**
Cinecam Productions **252**
Cinecontact **253**
Cinecosse **253**
CinesiteEurope **253**
Cinnabar Films **253**
Cipher **307**
CIRCA Art Magazine **315**
Circulation Report **162**

CIS Information Services **158**
CIS Report **315**
Citigate Albert Frank **354**
Citigate Dewe Rogerson **357**
Citrus Publishing **111**
City Beat 96.7 **270**
City Broadcasting **253**
City Life **124**
City of London Dockland Times **92**
City of London Recorder **92**
City of Westminster Post **92**
City Post **92**
City University **361, 366, 371**
Civil Engineer International **124**
CKR FM-Carlow Kildare Radio **316**
Clacton & Frinton Gazette **87**
Clacton Coastal Express **87**
Clan FM **271**
Clanvisions **253**
Clar na nOg **315**
Clare Champion **314**
Clarion **86**
Clark **253**
Class **124**
Class Productions **253**
Classic & Sportscar **124**
Classic Bike **124**
Classic Boat **124**
Classic British Programmes **235**
Classic Car Weekly **124**
Classic CD **124**
Classic FM - INR**1 266**
Classic Gold **271**
Classic Stitches **124**
Claverdon Films **253**
Clear Definition **253**
Clevedon Mercury **83, 96**
Cleveland Clarion **101**
Clifford Chance **333**
Clipability **158**
Clipserver.com **158**
Clitheroe Advertiser & Times **90**
Club Mirror **124**
Club On **124**
Clyde & Forth Press **69**
Clyde 1/Clyde 2 **271**
Clyde Post **104**
Clyde Weekly News **103**
Clydebank Post **103**
CMR **285**
CN Group **68, 285**
CNBC **232**
CNE **232**
CNN International **232, 244**
Coach & Bus Week **124**
Coalville Leader **90**
Coalville/Ashby Echo **90**
Coarse Angling **124**
Coast FM **271**
Coat of Arms **124**
Coates & Parker **69**
Cobham News & Mail **97**
Cogent Pictures **253**
Cohn and Wolfe **357**
Col Regional Offices **140, 248**

C

Colchester Evening Gazette **87**
Colchester Express **87**
Colchester Institute **373**
Colchester Yellow Adv **87**
Coleg Gwent **366, 371**
Coleraine Chronicle **107**
Coleraine Leader **107**
Coleraine Times **107**
Coleridge **253**
Coleshill Herald **99**
Colin Smythe **136**
Collections **149**
College Hill Associates **357**
College of Ripon & York **373**
Collett Dickenson Pearce **354**
Collins & Brown **136**
Collins Partnership **356**
Colne Valley Chronicle **101**
Colorific! **149**
Colorsport **149**
Columbia Pictures **253**
Comagazine **124, 160**
Combat **124**
Combat & Survival **124**
Combined Service Publications **111**
Comedy House **253**
Comedy Unit, **253**
Comhar **315**
Commercial Law Practitioner **315**
Commercial Motor **124**
Commercial Radio Companies
  Association **297**
Commercial Vehicle Manager **124**
Commission for Racial Equality, Race in
  the Media Awards **382**
Common Cause **124**
Common Features **253**
Commonwealth Broadcaster **288**
Commonwealth Broadcasters'
  Directory **292**
Commonwealth Broadcasting
  Association **297**
Commonwealth Journalists Assoc.**167**
Commonwealth Press Union **167**
Communication Workers Union **297**
Communications Africa **124**
Communications International **124**
Communications Law **124, 160**
Communications Team **111**
Communications Today **315**
Communications Worker **315**
Communicopia Company TV **253**
Community Care **124**
Community Media Association **297**
Community Nurse **124**
Community Pharmacy **124**
Community Radio **316**
Community Transport Magazine **124**
Company **124**
Compulsive Viewing **253**
Computer & Video Games **124**
Computer Active **124**

Computer Arts **124**
Computer Buyer/Shopper **124**
Computer Music **124**
Computer Success **124**
Computer Video **124**
Computer Weekly **124**
Computer Wire **111**
ComputerScope **315**
Computing **124**
Comstock **149**
Conde Nast Publications **111**
Conde Nast Traveller **124**
Confederation of Aerial Industries **297**
Conference and Incentive Travel **124**
Congleton Adnews **84**
Congleton Chronicle series **84**
Congleton Guardian **84**
Connacht Sentinel **314**
Connacht Tribune **314**
Connaught Telegraph **314**
Connect FM **271**
Connemara Community Radio **316**
Conran Octopus **136**
Consett & Stanley Advertiser **86**
Consolidated Communications
Management **357**
Constable **136**
Construction **315**
Construction News **124**
Consumer Choice **315**
Consumers Association **111**
Containerisation International **124**
Contemporary Review **119**
Contemporary Visual Arts **124**
Contract Journal **124**
Contrast Films **253**
Control & Instrumentation **124**
Control Systems **124**
Convenience Store **124**
Convergence **288**
Convergence Group Convergence
  238
Convergence Productions **253**
Cool Crew Company **253**
Cool FM **271**
Coolbeans Films **253**
Copyright Advice and Anti-Piracy
  Hotline **297**
Copyright Licensing Agency **167**
Corby & District Citizen **95**
Corby Advertiser **95**
Corgi **136**
Cork Campus Radio **316**
Corkman **314**
Cornerstone Films **253**
Cornish and Devon Post **85**
Cornish Banner **124**
Cornish Guardian **78, 85**
Cornish Times **85**
Cornishman **85**
Cornwall College **366**
Coronet **136**
Corporate Money **124**

Corwen Times **105**
Cosgrove Hall Films **253**
Cosmopolitan **124**
Costcutter Radio **285**
Cotswold & Swindon News **140**
Cottonwood Films **253**
Couch Potato TV **253**
Council of Photographic News
  Agencies **146, 167**
Counter Culture **124**
Counterpoint Films **253**
Country Homes & Interiors **124**
Country Life **124**
Country Living **124**
Country Music International **124**
Country Music People **124**
Country Sports **124**
Country Walking **124**
Countryman **124**
Countryside **124**
Countryside Books **136**
Countrywide Films **253**
Countrywide Porter Novelli **357**
County Border News **89, 98**
County Border Times & Mail **98**
County Down Spectator **107**
County Echo & St Davids Chron **106**
County Echo Newspapers **106**
County Press **69**
County Sound Radio 1476 AM **271**
Couples **124**
Courier Newspapers Oxford **69**
Courtyard Productions **253**
Coventry & Warks. Journal **99**
Coventry Citizen **81, 99**
Coventry Evening Telegraph **99**
Coventry Evening Telegraph & Pink **76**
Coventry News Service **140**
Coventry University **373**
Cowboy Films **253**
Cowbridge Gem **106**
CPA Journal of Accountancy **315**
CPRE Voice **124**
Crafts **124**
Craftsman Magazine **124**
Craigavon Echo **107**
Cranleigh Times **98**
Craven Herald & Pioneer **101**
Crawley College **366**
Crawley News **98**
Crawley News Extra **98**
Crawley Observer **98**
Crawley Weekend Herald **98**
Creation **288**
Creation Company, **253**
Creation Video **253**
Creative Alliance **253**
Creative Film Productions **253**
Creative Law **253**
Creative Resource **377**
Creative Review **124, 352**

Creative Technology **124**
Credit Lyonnais Laing **358**
Crescent Moon **136**
Cressrelles **136**
Crewe & District Herald Post **84**
Crewe & Nantwich Guardian **84**
Crewe Chronicle **84**
Crewed Up **253**
Cricket Writers Club **167**
Cricketer International **124**
Crime Channel **232**
Crinkle Cut Motion Pictures **253**
Criss Cross **253**
Critics' Circle **167**
Croc Productions **253**
Crockers Oswald Hickson **333**
Croner **136**
Croner Publications **112**
Cronica Latina **307**
Cronk Dromgoole **253**
Crops **124**
Crosby Herald **91**
Cross Rhythms **285**
Cross Stitch **124**
Cross Stitcher **125**
Cross-Border Publishing **112**
Crossing the Line Films **253**
Crosstalk **288**
Crowood Press **136**
Crowthorne & Sandhurst Times **83**
Crowthorne Sandhurst Newsweek **83**
Croydon Advertiser series **78, 94**
Croydon Guardian **81, 94**
Croydon Post **81**
Croydon Post **94**
Cruickshank Cazenove **253**
Cruisin Pictures **253**
Crystal Media **253**
CS First Boston **358**
CSV Media **253, 297**
CTN **125**
CTV **232**
CTVC **253**
Cuba Today **315**
Cubi Si **307**
Cult Times **125**
Cultural Partnerships **253**
Cumberland & Westmorland Herald **69**
Cumberland Herald **85**
Cumberland News **78, 85**
Cumbernauld Advertiser **104**
Cumbernauld News **104**
Cumbria College of Art & Design **373**
Cumbrian Gazette **85**
Cumnock Chronicle **103**
Cunliffe & Franklyn **253**
Curious Productions **253**
Current Archaeology **125**
Curtis & Freud **253**
Curtis Brown **134**
Cuts Magazine **288**
Cutting Edge **253**

Cutting It Fine **158**
CW Daniel Co. **136**
CWC **238**
Cwmbran & Pontypool News **106**
Cycle Sport **125**
Cycle Touring & Campaigning **125**
Cycling Plus **125**
Cycling Weekly **125**
Cyfle **362**
Cynon Valley Leader **106**
Cyrus Productions **253**

D

D & J Croal **69**
D'Arcy Masius Benton & Bowles **354**
Dacorum Independent **88**
Dai Films **253**
Daily Express **60**
Daily Jang **307**
Daily Mail **60**
Daily Millat **307**
Daily Post **75**
Daily Record **75**
Daily Star **60**
Daily Telegraph **60**
Dairy Farmer **125**
Dakota Films **253**
Dalesman **136**
Dalesman Publishing **112**
Dalton's Weekly **125**
Dan Films **253**
Dance & Dancers **125**
Dance Express **125**
Dance News **125**
Dancing Times **125**
Dandy **125**
Dark Horse Productions **253**
Darley Anderson **134**
Darlington & N Yorks Herald **86**
Darlington & Stockton Times **86**
Darlington Advertiser **86**
Darlington College of Technology **366**
Darlington Northern Echo **86**
Darlington, Aycliffe & Sedgfield
  Advertiser **86**
Darlow Smithson Productions **253**
Dartford Leader **89**
Dartford News Shopper **89**
Dartford Times **89**
Dartford/Swanley Informer **89**
Dartmouth Chron/S Hams Gazette **86**
Darton, Longman & Todd **136**
Darts World **125**
Dashwood Productions **253**
Data Broadcasting International **243**
Data Recruitment **377**
Dave Knowles Films **253**
Davenhall **253**
David & Charles **136**
David & Charles Children's **136**
David Bennett **136**
David Fulton **136**

David Hickman **253**
David Higham Associates **134**
David Hoffman Photo Library **149**
David King Collection **149**
David Price & Co **333**
David Williams Picture Library **149**
Davis Company **377**
Dawkins Associates **253**
Dawlish Gazette **86**
Dawlish Post **86**
Day by Day **125**
DayLewis Productions **253**
Dazed & Confused **125**
DC Thomson & Co **74, 118**
De Montfort University **374, 366**
Deadpan **125**
Deaf Broadcasting Council **298**
Dealer Principal **125**
Dearne Valley Weekender **101**
Debenhams **125**
Deborah Owen **134**
Decanter **125**
Decision **315**
Deco Films & TV **253**
Decor **125**
Dedalus **136**
Dee News Service **140**
Deep Water **253**
Deeside Piper **102**
Defence Helicopter **125**
Defence Industry Digest **125**
Defence, Press & Broadcasting
  Advisory Committee **167**
Defence Upgrades **125**
Defence Weekly **125**
Delaney Lund Knox Warren **355**
Delta FM **271**
Demaine Associates **253**
Demon Dispatches **125**
Demos **136**
Denbighshire Free Press **105**
Denham Productions **253**
Denham Syndicate Lloyd's Syndicate
  990 **332**
Dennis Publishing **112**
Dennis Woolf Productions **253**
Dentist **125**
Denton Wilde Sapte **333**
Department for Culture, Media and
  Sport **320**
Department of Trade and Industry **321**
Derby Evening Telegraph **85**
Derby Express **85**
Derby Journal **85**
Derby Trader **85**
Derbyshire Times **78, 85**
Dereham & Fakenham Times **95**
Derry Journal **107**
Derry Journal Co **69**
Derry People and Donegal News **107,
  314**
Derwent Information **118**
Des Pardes **307**
Design Engineering **125**

D

Design Products & Applications **125**
Design Week **125**
Desmond Wilcox **253**
Deutsche Presse Agentur **140**
Devil **125**
Devizes Gazette & Herald **100**
Devizes News **100**
Devizes Star **100**
Devlin Morris Productions **253**
Devon News Agency **141**
Dewsbury Reporter **101**
Dewsbury Reporter series **69**
Dewsbury Weekly Adv **101**
Diamond Time **253**
Diary **307**
Dibb Directions **253**
Didcot Herald **96**
Didsbury & District Courier **84**
Diehard **136**
Diesel Car **125**
Different Voices **298**
Digital 3 and 4 Ltd **228**
Digital One **284**
Digital Photo FX **125**
Dimbleby Newspaper Group **69**
Dinah Wiener **134**
Dinnington Guardian **101**
Diplomat **125**
Diplomat Films **253**
Direct Marketing Association **351**
Direct Staff & Calculating **377**
Direct TV **253**
Director Publications **112**
Directors and Producers' Rights **298**
Directors Guild of Gt Britain **298**
Directors' Guild Directory **292**
Directory & Database Publishers
  Association **167**
Directory of Book Publishers,
  Distributors & Wholesalers **162**
Directory of International Film &
  Festivals **292**
Directory of Publishing **162**
Disability Now **125**
Disability Times **125**
Disckit **253**
Disco International DI **125**
Discovery Channel **233**
Disney & Me **125**
Disney Channel **233**
Disruptive Element Films **253**
Diss Express **95**
Diss Mercury **95**
Distinctive Publishing **112**
Diva **119**, **125**
Diva Pictures **253**
Diver Magazine **125**
Diverse Production **253**
DIY Week **125**
DJ **125**
DJ Freeman **333**
DLD Films **253**
DLT Entertainment **253**

DMG Business Media **112**
DMG Radio **266**
DNA Films **253**
Do Or Die **119**
Dobson Photo Agency **149**
Docklands Express **92**
Docklands Recorder **92**, **125**
Doctor **125**
Doctor Desk Book **315**
Doctor Who Magazine **125**
Document **125**
Dog World **112**, **125**
Dogs Today **125**
Domaine **253**
Domestic Films **253**
Domino Films **253**
Doncaster Advertiser **101**
Doncaster College **374**
Doncaster Courier **101**
Doncaster Free Press **101**
Doncaster Star **101**
Done & Dusted **253**
Donegal Democrat **314**
Donegal Highland Radio **316**
Donegal People's Press **314**
Donside Piper & Herlad **102**
Dorking Advertiser **98**
Dorling Kindersley **136**
Dorset Evening Echo **86**
Dorset Life **125**
Double Band Films **253**
Double E Productions **253**
Double Exposure **253**
Double Take **253**
Doubleday **136**
Douglas Chirnside **253**
Dover Express **89**
Dover Mercury **89**
Dover/Deal/Sandwich Adscene **89**
Dovetail Employment Agency **377**
Dow Jones Newswires **141**
Down Recorder **107**
Downtown Radio **271**
DOX Productions **253**
Dragon News & Picture Agency **141**
Dragon TV **253**
Dragonflair **136**
Drama House **253**
Dramatic Productions **253**
Drapers Record **125**
Dream 100 FM **272**
Dreamchaser **253**
Dref Wen **136**
Driffield Times **100**
Drogheda Independent **314**
Dromore Leader **107**
Dronfield Advertiser **85**
Druglink **125**
Drum **125**, **352**
Dublar Scripts **136**
Dublin South Community Radio **316**
Dublin's 98FM **316**
Duchess Productions **253**
Dudley Chronicle **99**

Dudley News **99**
Dumbarton Lennox Herald **103**
Dumbarton Reporter **103**
Dumfries & Galloway Standard **103**
Dumfries Courier **103**
Dumfriesshire Newspapers Group **69**
Duncan Baird **136**
Dundalk Democrat **314**
Dundas & Wilson CS **333**
Dundee Courier & Advertiser **103**
Dundee Courier & Advertiser **75**
Dundee Evening Telegraph **103**
Dundee Press Agency **141**
Dundee Sporting Post **103**
Dundee Sunday Post **103**
Dunfermline Herald & Post **104**
Dunfermline Press **104**
Dunfermline Press Group **69**
Dungannon About Town **107**
Dungannon Development Association
  69
Dungannon Observer **107**
Dungarvan Leader and Southern
  Democrat **314**
Dungarvan Observer and Munster
  Industrial Advocate **314**
Dunmow Broadcast **87**
Dunoon Observer **102**
Dunstable Gazette **83**
Durham Advertiser **86**
Durrants Press Cuttings **158**
Dursley County Independent **87**

E

E Music **233**
E! Entertainment TV **233**
E&R Inglis **69**
Edinburgh Scotland on Sunday **103**
Eagle & Eagle **253**
Eagles Productions **253**
Ealing & Acton Gazette **92**
Ealing & London Recorder **92**
Ealing & Southall Informer **92**
Ealing Leader **92**
Earl Street Emp. Consultants **377**
Early Music Today **125**
Earth First! Action Update **119**
Earth Matters **125**
Easingwold Weekly News **101**
East Anglian Daily Times **75**
East Anglian Film Archive **249**
East Antrim Guardian **107**
East Belfast Herald & Post **107**
East Belfast News **107**
East Cleveland Herald & Post **101**
East Coast Radio **319**
East Devon News series **86**
East Fife Mail **104**
East Grinstead Courier **98**
East Grinstead Observer **98**
East Kent Gazette **89**
East Kent Mercury **89**

East Kilbride News **104**
East Kilbride World **104**
East London Advertiser **92**
East Lothian Courier **104**
East Lothian News **104**
East Staffordshire Journal **97**
East Suffolk Mercury **97**
East Wind Films **253**
Eastbourne Advertiser **98**
Eastbourne Gazette **98**
Eastbourne Herald **98**
Eastern Counties Newspapers Group
  69, **365**
Eastern Daily Press **75**
Eastern Eye **125**, **307**
Eastleigh Gazette Extra **88**
East-West **233**
EastWest Publications **136**
Eastwood Advertiser **95**
Ebury Press **136**
ebusiness partner **125**
Echo **314**
Echo Newspaper series **69**
Eckington Leader **85**
Eclipse **298**
ECM Productions **253**
Ecologist, The **119**, **125**
Ecology Channel **233**
Economic & Social Review **315**
Economic Review **125**
Economic Series **315**
Economic Trends **125**
Economist **112**, **125**
Ecoscene **149**
Ecosse Films **253**
Ed Lacy Gibraltar Travel Award **382**
Ed Victor **134**
Edelman PR Worldwide **357**
Eden Productions **253**
Edenbridge Chronicle **89**
Edge **125**
Edge Hill College of Higher Education
  374
Edgware & Mill Hill Times **92**
Edinburgh Evening News **103**
Edinburgh Film & Video **253**
Edinburgh Herald & Post **103**
Edinburgh Herald and Post **81**
Edinburgh International Book Festival
  168
Edinburgh Press Club **168**
Edinburgh Scotsman **103**
Edinburgh University Press **136**
Editorial Training Centre **366**
Editors **353**
Education & Training Channel **240**
Education Channel **240**
Education Today **315**
Educational & Television Films **249**
Educational Broadcasting **253**
Educational Explorers **136**
Educational Programmes **229**
Educational Television and Media
  Association **362**
Edward Hodgett **70**

Edwards Fuglewicz **134**
Edwards Geldard **333**
EETPU **168**
EFirst **125**
EFS TV Production **253**
Egmont Children's **136**
Egmont Fleetway **112**
Ego **125**
Eight Syndicate **253**
Eikoku News Digest **307**
EIN **233**
Electric Sky **253**
Electrical Contractor **125**
Electrical Products **125**
Electrical Review **125**
Electrical Times **125**
Electronic Engineering **125**
Electronic Manufacture & Test **125**
Electronic Media Round Table **168**
Electronic Product Design **125**
Electronic Product Review **125**
Electronic Showcase **125**
Electronics **125**
Electronics & Wireless World **125**
Electronics Times **125**
Electronics Weekly **125**
Electronics World **125**
Element Books **136**
Element Films/Element Productions
  253
Elephant Productions **253**
eleven SEVENTY AM **272**
Elgin Productions **253**
Elle **125**
Elle Decoration **125**
Ellerman Investment **69**
Ellesmere Port Pioneer **84**
Ellesmere Press **69**
Elliot Right Way **136**
Elliott News Service **141**
Ellon & District Advertiser **102**
Ellon Times **102**
ELM Publications **136**
Elsevier Science Publishers **112**, **136**
Elstree Production Co **253**
Eltham & Greenwich Times **94**
Elvis Monthly **125**
Ely Standard **84**
Ely Weekly News **84**
Emap **112**, **136**
Emap Digital **284**
Emap Performance **266**
Eminent Management & Production
  150
Emme Productions **253**
Empics Sports Photo Agency **150**
Empire **125**
Employee Benefits **125**
Employer's Law **125**
Employment Law Reports **315**
Enchanted Lands **125**
Encyclopaedia Britannica **136**
Encyclopedia of the World Press **162**
Endboard Productions **253**
Endemol **253**

Endor Productions **253**
Energy Data Services **158**
Energy Film **249**
Energy Management **125**
Enfield Advertiser **92**
Enfield Gazette **92**
Enfield Independent **92**
Engineer **125**
Engineering **125**
Engineers Journal **315**
English & Pockett **253**
English Churchman **125**
English Garden **125**
English Review **125**
Enniscorthy Guardian **314**
Enterchoice **253**
Entertainment Film Production **253**
Entertainment Press Cuttings Agency
  158
Entertainment's News **246**
Environmental Health News **125**
Environmental Images **150**
Environmental Investigation Agency
  249
Environmental Investigation Agency
  Photo Library **150**
Environmental Management Ireland
  315
Environmental Politics **119**
Eo teilifis **253**
Eolas **253**
Eon Productions **253**
Eos Media **253**
Epicflow Films **253**
Epping Forest Community Channel
  240
Epping Forest Herald **87**
Epping Forest Independent **87**
Epping, Ongar & District Gazette **87**
Epping Yellow Advertiser **87**
Epsom & Ewell Herald **98**
Epsom/Banstead Informer **98**
Epworth Bells Advertiser **101**
Epworth Press **136**
Equity **298**
ERC Frankona **332**
Erith & Crayford Times **94**
Ernst & Young **253**
ES Magazine **125**
Eskdale & Liddesdale Ad. **103**
Eskdale & Liddesdale Newspapers **69**
Esquire **125**
Essential Playstation **125**
Essentials **125**
Essex Chronicle **78**, **87**
Essex Countryside **125**
Essex County Standard **87**
Essex FM **272**
Essex News Service **141**
Essex Weekly News **87**
Esta's TV Company **253**
Estate Agency News **125**
Estates Gazette **125**
Eternal Word UK **233**
Ethical Consumer **119**, **125**

E

Ethnic Multicultural Media Awards **382**
Euphoria Films **253**
EuroArt Media **253**
Eurobell **238**
Euroguy **125**
Euromonitor **136**
Euronews **298**
Europa **136**
European Chemical News **125**
European Film channel **233**
European Magazines **112**
European Network Broadcasting **233**
European Pig and Poultry Fair **125**
European Plastics News **125**
European Society for News Design **168**
Euro RSCG Worldwide **355**
Evans Brothers **136**
Evans Woolfe **253**
Evening Chronicle **76**
Evening Echo **319**
Evening Herald **319**
Evening News **76**
Evening Standard **76, 92**
Evening Times **76**
Events In Scotland **125**
Eversheds **333**
Everyday Practical Electronics **129**
Everyman's Library **136**
Evesham Journal wf **100**
Examiner **319**
Excalibur Productions **253**
Excel Recruitment **377**
Excelsior Group Productions **253**
Exchange & Mart **125**
Exe **125**
Executive Woman **125**
Exeter Express & Echo **86**
Exeter Leader **86**
Exeter Midweek Herald **86**
Exley Publications **136**
Exmouth Journal **86**
Expert Systems & Applications **125**
Express & Star **76, 99**
Extel Financial **141**
Extreme Film & TV **253**
Eye Eye **253**
Eye Film & TV **253**
Eye to Eye TV **253**
Eyepiece **288**

F

Faber & Faber **136**
Fabulous Fruits **253**
Face **125**
FACT **298**
Faction Films **253**
Fair Game Films **253**
Fairline **253**
Fairplay International Shipping **125**
Fairwater Films **253**
Faith Evans Associates **134**
Falcon Lodge Observer **99**
Falkirk Advertiser **103**
Falkirk Herald **103**
Falmouth College of Arts **371, 374**
Falmouth Packet **85**
Family Circle **125**
Family Tree Magazine **125**
Fantastic TV **233**
Fareham & Gosport Journal **88**
Farmers Guardian **125**
Farmers Weekly **125**
Farming News **125**
Farming Press **136**
Farnborough College of Technology **374**
Farnborough Courier **88**
Farnborough Mail **88**
Farnborough News **88**
Farnham Film **253**
Farnham Herald **98**
Farnham Mail **98**
Farrer & Co **333**
Fast Car **125**
Fast Ford **125**
Fat Pictures **253**
Faversham House Group **113**
Faversham News **89**
Faversham Times **89**
Feasta **315**
Feather Brooksbank Group **356**
Feature Films **254**
Features International **141**
Federation of Commercial Audio Visual Libraries **248**
Federation of Communication Services **298**
Federation of Entertainment Unions **168, 298**
Federation of the Electronics Industry **298**
Feel Good **125**
Feelgood Fiction **254**
Felicity Bryan **134**
Feline Films **254**
FEM FM/BHS Radio **286**
Feminist Review **119**
Feng Shui **125**
Fenland Citizen **84**
Fermanagh Herald **107**
Fermanagh News **107**
Fernhurst Books **136**
Ferrari Press Agency **141**
Festival Eye **119**
Festival Film & TV **254**
Festival Revue **240**
Fflic **254**

ffotograff **150**
FHM For Him Magazine **125**
The Field **125**
Field, Fisher, Waterhouse **333**
Fiesta **125**
Fife newspapers **104**
Figment Films **254**
Filipino **307**
Fillum **254**
Film & General Productions **254**
Film Artistes Association **298**
Film Company, **254**
Film Education **254, 362**
Film Form Productions **254**
Film Four **229**
Film Guide **125**
Film Master Film **254**
Film Research **249**
Film Review **125**
Film Video Multimedia **254**
FilmFair Animation **254**
FilmFour **228, 233**
Filmhouse **254**
FilmNOVA **254**
Films Of Record **254**
Filmsmith **254**
Filmworks **254**
Final Draft Films **254**
Finance **315**
Finance Dublin **315**
Financial Adviser **125**
Financial Director **125**
Financial Journalists' Group **168**
Financial Times **60, 319**
Financial Times Business **113, 288**
Financial Times Information **159**
Finchley & Hendon Advertisers **92**
Findlay Publications **113**
Fine Art Trade Guild Awards for Art Journalism **382**
Finers Stephens Innocent **338**
Finetake Productions **254**
FIPP **169**
Fire Prevention **125**
Firefly Communications **357**
First **125**
First Circle Films **254**
First Day Productions **254**
First Features Syndicate **141**
First Film Foundation **364**
First Freedom Productions **254**
First ONdigital Champions **229**
First Take Films **254**
Firstmile **254**
Fish Farming International **125**
Fishburn Hedges **357**
Fishguard County Echo **106**
Fishing News International **125**
Flag **122**
Flag Nat Dem **125**
Flagrant Films **254**
Flame Television **254**
Flashback Television **254**
Flat Dog Films **254**
Flatiron Films **254**
Fleet & District Courier **88**
Fleet Car **125**

Fleet Dealer **125**
Fleet Mail **88**
Fleet News **88, 125**
Fleet News Agency **141**
Fleet Street Motoring Group **168**
Fleetline News Service **141**
Fleetwood Weekly News **90**
Fletcher Schlaefli Media **377**
Flexiskills Employment Agency **377**
Flextech **239**
Flextech Telewest **228**
Flicks **125**
Flicks Books **136**
Flight International **125**
Flintshire Chroncile **106**
Flintshire Herald & Post **106**
Flintshire Leader **106**
Flipside **125**
Flipside Films **254**
Flirt FM **319**
Floris Books **136**
FLR 107.3 **272**
Flying Angel News **125**
Flying Brick Films **254**
Flying Elephant **254**
Flying Fox Films **254**
Flying Pictures **254**
Flying Saucer Review **125**
FM 102 Bear **268**
FM 103 Horizon **272**
FM 104 **319**
FM 107 Falcon **272**
FOCAL **248**
Focal Press **136**
Focus **125**
Focus Films **254**
Focus FM **286**
Focus International TV **254**
Focus on Africa **125**
Folens **136**
Folio Productions **254**
Folk Roots **125**
Folkestone & Hythe Adscene **89**
Folkestone Extra **89**
Folkestone Herald **89**
Fontana **136**
Food & Travel **126**
Food Channel **240**
Food Illustrated **125**
Food Manufacture **125**
Food Manufacture Ingredients &
    Machine Survey **126**
Food Processing **126**
Food Service Management **126**
Food Worker **126**
Foot Anstey Sargent **333**
Football Monthly **126**
Football Writers Association **168**
Footprint Films **254**
Footstep Productions **254**
For a Change **126**
Fore! **126**
Foreign Press Association in London
    168
Foreign Report **126**
Forest Journal **88**

Forest Life Picture Library **150**
Forest of Dean Newspapers **69**, **87**
Forester **87**
Forestry and British Timber **126**
Forfar Dispatch **102**
Forged Films **254**
Forget About It Films **254**
Format Photographers **150**
Formby Times **91**
Forme Communications **113**
Forres Gazette **105**
Fort William Extra **104**
Forth FM **285**
Forth FM/Forth AM **272**
Fortnight **119**, **126**
Fortune **126**
Forum **126, 315**
Forward Films/Altogether Now **254**
Fosseway Radio **272**
Foundation TV **254**
Foundry Productions **254**
Fountain TV **254**
Four Four Two **126**
Fourth Estate **136**
Fourth Estate Press Agency **141**
Fowlers Press Agency **141**
FOX FM **272**
Fox Kids **233**
Fox Kids Poland **233**
Fox Kids Scandinavia **233**
Fragile Films **254**
Frances Anderson Franklyn Films **254**
Frances Kelly **134**
Frances Lincoln **136**
Franchise Magazine **126**
Francis Frith Collection **150**
Frank **126**
Frank Cass **113**, **136**
Frank Ryan News Service **141**
Frank Spooner Pictures **150**
Frantic Productions **254**
Fraserburgh Herald **102**
Frederick Warne **136**
Free Association **136**
Free Church Chron **126**
Free Press **120**, **126**, **160**, **288**
Free Spirit Films **254**
Freedom **120**, **126**
Freedom Forum European Centre **168**
Freedom House Publications **113**
Freedom of Information Awards **382**
Freedom Today **122**
Freedom TV **254**
Freeform Productions **254**
Freelance Directory **162**
Freelance Film Partners **254**
Freelance Informer **126**
Freelance Market News **160**
Freelance Photographer's Market
    Handbook **163**
Freemans Press Agency **141**
Freemasonry Today **126**

Freestyle Publications **113**
Freeway Films **254**
Fresco channel **233**
Fresh **126**
Fresh AM **272**
Fresh Direction **126**
Freshfields **334**
Freud Communications **357**
Friction Films **254**
Friday Ad Group **69**
Friday Productions **254**
Friend **126**
Frinton & Walton Gazette **87**
Front **126**
Front Page Films **254**
Front Page News Agency **141**
Front Row **233**
Frontier Films **254**
Frontiers **126**
Frontrunner Films **254**
FSN-Feature Story Productions **244**
FT Media & Telecoms **113**
FT2 - Film and Television Freelance
    Training **362**
Fugitive Group **254**
Fuji International **254**
Fulcrum Productions **254**
Fulham Chronicle **92**
Fulmar West TV & Film **254**
Fun to Learn **126**
Funfax **136**
Furnishing **126**
Futerman Associates **134**
Futura **315**
Future Music **126**
Future Net **126**
Future Publishing **113**
Future Recruitment **377**
FW **126**
Fylde Extra **90**

G

G & J of the UK **113**
G H Smith & Son **73**
Gabriel Films **254**
Gabriel Productions **254**
Gabriela Productions **254**
Gael Media **254**
Gaelic Broadcasting Committee **298**
Gaelic Sport **315**
Gaelic World **315**
Gaelsport Magazine **315**
Gaia Books **136**
Gainsborough Productions **254**
Gainsborough Standard **91**
Gainsborough Target **91**
Gainsborough Trader News **91**
Galafilm **254**
Galaxy 102.2 **311**
Galloway Gazette **70**, **103**
Galloway News **103**
Galway Advertiser **314**
Galway Bay FM **319**
Games **229**
Games Today **126**

G

Gamesmaster **126**
Gannett **70**
Garavi Gujarat **126**, **307**
Garda Review **315**
Garden Trade News **126**
Garden/Garden Answers **126**
Gardeners World BBC **126**
Gardens Illustrated **126**
Garnet Publishingg **136**
Garnett Dickinson Publishing **70**
Garnock Valley Herald **103**
Garretts **334**
Garstang Courier **90**
Garstang Guardian **90**
Gatelodge **126**
Gateshead Herald & Post **99**
Gatwick News **126**
Gauvain Productions **254**
Gay Community News **315**
Gay Men's Press **136**
Gay Times **120**, **126**
Gaze International **150**
Gazette & Herald **101**
GCI UK/APCO **357**
Geddes & Grosset **136**
Gee & Son **136**
Geestor Productions **254**
Gemini FM **273**, **285**
Gemini News Service **141**
Genealogists Magazine **126**
General Entertainment **229**, **240**
General Practitioner **126**
Genisis Media Group **254**
Geofilms **254**
Geographical Magazine **126**
Geography Review **126**
George Philip **136**
George Ronald **136**
George Viner Memorial Fund Awards **382**
GeoScience Features Picture Library **150**
Geoscientist **126**
Gerald Duckworth **136**
Geriatric Medicine **126**
Getzels/Gordon **254**
Giles de la Mare **136**
Gillon Aitken Associates **133**
Gimlet Productions **254**
Ginger **254**
Girl About Town **126**
Girl Talk **126**
Give It Loads **254**
GJ Palmer & Sons **113**
Glamorgan Gazette **105**
Glamorgan Gem **106**
Glasgow Caledonian University **374**
Glasgow Daily Record **104**
Glasgow East End Independent **104**
Glasgow Film & Video Workshop **254**
Glasgow Film Office **254**
Glasgow Herald **104**
Glasgow South Extra **104**
Glasgow Sunday Mail **104**
Glasshead **254**
Glaswegian **81**, **104**

Glaxo Wellcome Science Writers Awards **382**
Gleaner **307**
Glenfiddich Food & Drink Awards **382**
Glenrothes Gazette **104**
Global Arts **254**
Global Net News Channel **233**
Global Productions **254**
Global Sports Productions **254**
Global Transport **126**
Glos & Avon Gazette **83**
Glossop Chronicle **85**
Gloucester News **87**
Gloucestershire Citizen **87**
Gloucestershire College of Arts & Tech. **366**
Gloucestershire County Gazette **87**
Gloucestershire Echo **88**
Gloucestershire News Service **141**
glowinthedark **254**
GM Partnership, **254**
GM Productions **254**
GMP Publishers **136**
GMTV **219**, **228**, **249**, **254**
GNU Productions **254**
Go Organic **126**
Godalming Times **98**
Godsfield Press **136**
Going Wild In London **126**
Golden Cockerell **136**
Golden Square Pics. **254**
Goldhawk Media **254**
Goldhawk Universal **254**
Goldman Sachs **358**
Goldsmiths College **366**, **371**, **374**
Golf Industry News **126**
Golf Monthly **126**
Golf Weekly **126**
Golf World **126**
Golfers Companion **315**
Golley Slater Group **355**
Gomer Press **136**
Good Food BBC **126**
Good Housekeeping **126**
Good Times **126**
Good Vibrations **126**
Good Woodworking **126**
Goodlife TV **233**
Goodman Derrick **334**
Goole HowdenThorne Courier **100**
Goole, Thorne & Howden Courier **101**
Gordon Getzels **254**
Gorey Echo **314**
Gorilla Entertainment **254**
Gosh! Films **254**
Gospel channel **233**
Gospel Magazine **126**
GQ **126**
Grade Company, **254**
Graham & Whiteside **136**
Gramophone Publications **113**, **126**
Grampian Network Services **377**
Grampian Television **219**
Granada **220**, **229**, **231**, **333**
Granada Sky Broadcasting DTT **228**
Grand Prix Review **126**
Granite Film & TV **254**

Grant Naylor Productions **254**
Grant Thornton **254**
Granta **126**
Granta Publications **113**, **136**
Grantham & Melton Trader **91**
Grantham Citizen **91**
Grantham Journal **91**
Graphical, Paper and Media Union **168**
Graphite Film & TV **254**
Grasshopper Productions **254**
Grassroots Campaigner **126**
Gravesend & Dartford Extra **89**
Gravesend Leader **89**
Gravesend Messenger **89**
Gravesend Reporter **89**
Grayling Group **357**
Grays Herald **87**
Great Barr Observer **99**
Great North News & Features **141**
Great Outdoors **126**
Great Scot International **141**
Great Yarmouth Advertiser **95**
Great Yarmouth Mercury **95**
Green Anarchist **120**
Green Books **136**
Green Futures **126**
Green House Productions **254**
Green Inc Productions **254**
Green Room **254**
Green Umbrella **254**
Green World **120**
Greene & Heaton **134**
Greenford & Northolt Gazette **92**
Greenhill Books **136**
Greenlit Productions **254**
Greenock Telegraph **104**
Greenpeace UK **150**
Greenpoint Films **254**
Greenwich Mercury **94**
Greg Evans International Photo Library **150**
Gregory & Radice **134**
Grey Advertising **355**
Griffith Recruitment **377**
Grimsby **240**
Grimsby Evening Telegraph **91**, **100**
Grimsby Target **91**, **100**
Grocer, The **126**
Grocer's Magazine **315**
Ground Engineering **126**
Grub Street **136**
Gruber Films **254**
GTI **113**
Guardian **60**
Guardian Edinburgh International TV Festival **299**
Guardian Media Group **70**
Guardian Series **78**
Guardian Student Media Awards **382**
Guardian Weekly **126**
Guardian/Observer News Services **141**
Guardian/Observer Photo Service **150**
Guernsey Evening Press & Star **84**
Guernsey Press Co **70**
Guernsey Weekly Press **84**

Guide **126**
Guidelines **315**
Guiding **126**
Guild of British Animation **299**
Guild of British Camera Technicians **299**
Guild of British Film Editors **299**
Guild of Food Writers **168**
Guild of Television Cameramen **299**
Guildford Times **98**
Guinness Publishing **136**
Guitar Techniques **126**
Guitarist **126**
Gujarat Samachar/Asian Voice/Asian **307**
Gurjari **233**
GW McKane & Son **70**
Gwent Gazette **105**
GWR FM **273**
GWR Group **266**
Gwyneth May Evans **239**
Gwynhelek Productions **254**

H

H Bauer Publishing **110**
Hackney Echo **92**
Hackney Gazette **92**
Hailsham Gazette **98**
Hair **126**
Hairdressers' Journal **126**
Hale, Altrincham Courier **94**
Hales Personnel Services **377**
Halesowen Chronicle **99**
Halesowen News **100**
Halifax Evening Courier **101**
Hallam FM **273**
Hallmark Entertainment Network **233**
Halo Productions **254**
Halstead Gazette&Advertiser **87**
Haltemprice Advertiser **101**
Ham Radio Today **126**
Hamilton Advertiser **104**
Hamilton People **104**
Hamilton TV **254**
Hamilton World **104**
Hamish Hamilton **137**
Hamlyn **137**
Hammersmith Chronicle **92**
Hammersmith Guardian **92**
Hammersmith/Fulham Times **92**
Hammond Suddards **334**
Hampshire Chronicle **88**
Hampshire Chronicle Group **70**
Hampstead & Highgate Express **92**
Hand Pict Productions **254**
Handle Recruitment **377**
Hanrahan TV Productions **254**
Hansard **126**
Hanson TV **254**
Harborough Mail **90**
Harbottle & Lewis **254**, **334**
Harbour Film & TV **254**
Harcourt Films **254**
Harcourt Publishers **113**, **137**
Harefield Gazette **92**
Haringey Advertiser **92**

Haringey Independent **92**
Haringey Weekly Herald **92**
Harlequin Mills & Boon **137**
Harlow & Epping Herald **87**
Harlow Citizen **87**
Harlow College **368**
Harlow/Epping Star **87**
Harold Starke **137**
Harold Wincott Awards **382**
Harpenden Advertiser **88**
HarperCollins **137**
Harpers & Queen **126**
Harrap **137**
Harris of Saltcoats **239**
Harrison Cowley **357**
Harrogate Advertiser **101**
Harrogate Herald **101**
Harrow College **368**
Harrow Independent **93**
Harrow Informer **93**
Harrow Leader **93**
Harrow Observer **93**
Hart Courier Series **88**
Hart Ryan Productions **254**
Hartlepool Mail **86**
Hartlepool Star **86**
Hartswood Films **254**
Harvard Public Relations **358**
Harvest Films **254**
Harvill **137**
Harwich Standard **87**
Hasan Shah Films **254**
Haslemere Herald **98**
Haslemere Messenger **98**
Hastings Ad News **98**
Hastings Friday-Ad **98**
Hastings Observer **98**
Hat Trick Productions **254**
Havant Journal **88**
Haverhill Echo **97**
Haverhill Weekly News **97**
Havering Community Channel **229**, **240**
Hawick News **70**, **103**
Hawk Books **137**
Hayes & Harlington Gazette **93**
Hayle Times **85**
Haymarket Group **113**
Haynes **137**
Hayter's Sports Agency **141**
Haywards Heath Friday-Ad **98**
Haywards Heath Leader **98**
Hazar Publishing **137**
Hazards Magazine **126**
HBO **233**
HD Thames **254**
HEADflicks **254**
Headlight **126**
Headlines **126**, **160**
Heads Congleton **70**
Healix **233**
Health & Beauty Salon **126**
Health & Fitness **126**
Health & Safety **315**
Health & Safety at Work **126**
Health Club Management **126**

Health Insurance **126**
Health Service Journal **126**
Health Service News **315**
Health Zone **233**
Heart 106.2 **273 286**
Heart of Wales Chronicle **106**
Heartland Films **254**
Heartland FM **273**
Heat **126**
Heathrow Villager **70**
Heavy Entertainment **254**
Heavy Horse World **126**
Hebden Bridge Times **102**
Heinemann **137**
Helen Langridge Associates **254**
Helenic TV **311**
Helensburgh Advertiser **102**
Helicon Publishing **137**
Helicopter International **126**
Helidata News **126**
Hellenic Television **229**, **240**
Hello! **113**, **126**
Helston & District Gazette **85**
Hemel Hempstead Express **88**
Hemming Group **113**
Hempsons **334**
Hemsworth Express **102**
Henderson Boyd Jackson WS **334**
Henderson Crosthwaite **358**
Hendon & Finchley Times **81**, **93**
Henley Standard **70**, **96**
Henry Hepworth **334**
Herald **75**
Herald Observer Newspapers **70**
Herbert Smith **334**
Here's Health **126**
Hereford & Leominster Jouranl **88**
Hereford Admag **88**
Hereford Times **78**, **88**
Heritage Scotland **126**
Heritage Today **126**
Herne Bay Gazette **89**
Herne Bay Times **89**
HertBeat FM **273**
Herts & Essex Observer **88**
Herts Advertiser **89**
Herts Mercury **88**
Herts Star **89**
Heswall News **91**
Hewland International **254**
Hexagon Productions **254**
Hexham Courant **95**
Heywood Advertiser **94**
HHCL & Partners **355**
Hibbert Ralph Entertainment **254**
HiFi Choice **126**
Higgs Group **70**
High Life **126**
High Peak Courier **84**, **85**
High Wycombe Leader **83**
Highbury and Islington Express **93**
Highbury College, Portsmouth **368**, **371**
Highbury House Communications **113**
Highflyer Productions **254**

H

Highflyers Employment **377**
Hightimes Prods **254**
Hill and Knowlton **358**
Hill Bros Leek **70**
Hill's Welsh Press **141**
Hilmarton Manor **137**
Hinckley Herald & Journal **90**
Hinckley Times **90**
Hindi Picture **254**
Hindsight **126**
Hip Hop Connection **126**
Hippopotamus **137**
Hirst, Kidd & Rennie **70**
Hiscox Underwriting Limited **332**
Historical Journal of Film, Radio and Television **288**
History Channel **231**
History Ireland **315**
History of Advertising Trust **351**
History Today **126**
History Workshop Journal **126**
Hit Entertainment **254**
HLA **254**
HMSO **113, 137**
HN **126**
Hobson Audley **334**
Hobson's Production **255**
Hobsons Publishing **137**
Hodder Headline **137**
Holderness Gazette **101**
Holderness Newspapers **70**
Hollis Directories **137**
Hollis UK Press & PR Annual **353**
Hollyoaks Productions **255**
Hollywood Reporter, **255**
Holme Valley Express **102**
Holmes Associates **255**
Holsworthy Post **86**
Holyhead Mail **106**
Holyrood **126**
Home Productions **255**
Home & Country **126**
Home & Family **126**
Home 107.9 **273**
Home Counties Newspapers **70**
Home Entertainment **126**
Home Furnishings **126**
Home Magic **126**
Home Shopping Channel **228, 233**
Homebase FM **286**
Homebase Living **126**
Homechoice **229, 240**
Homes & Antiques BBC **126**
Homes & Gardens **126**
Homes & Ideas **126**
Homestyle **126**
Honiton & Cullompton News **86**
Hopkinson News & Feature Service **142**
Horley and Gatwick Mirror **98**
Horley Publishing **70**
Horncastle News **91**
Horncastle Standard Series **91**
Hornsea Gazette **101**
Hornsey Journal **93**
Horoscope **126**

Horrod & Harris **255**
Horse **126**
Horse & Hound **126**
Horse & Pony **126**
Horse Exchange **126**
Horse Magazine **126**
Horsepower Productions **255**
Horsham Advertiser **98**
Horticulture Week **126**
Hospital Broadcasting Assoc. **299**
Hospital Doctor **126**
Hospital Equipment & Supplies **126**
Hot Press **315**
Hot Property Films **255**
Hot Shoe International **126, 288**
Hot Shot Films **255**
Hotel **126**
Hotel & Catering Review **315**
Hotel & Restaurant Magazine **126**
Hothouse **255**
Hounslow & Isleworth Leader **93**
Hounslow Borough Chronicle **93**
Hounslow Feltham Times **93**
Hounslow Guardian **93**
Hounslow/Chiswick Informer **93**
Hourglass Pictures **255**
House **126**
House & Garden **126**
House Beautiful **126**
House Magazine **126**
House of Cuttings **159**
Housewares **126**
Housing **126**
Housing Today **126**
How To Books **137**
Hoylake/West Kirkby News **91**
HRM North **377**
HSN/Screenshop **233**
HTV **220**
Hucknall & Bulwell Dispatch **95**
Huddersfield Daily Examiner **102**
Huddersfield District Chronicle **102**
Huddersfield Weekly News **102**
Huge Films **255**
Hugo's Language **137**
Hull Advertiser series **101**
Hull Daily Mail **76, 101**
Hull News & Pictures **142**
Hulton-Getty **150**
Human Resources Partnership **377**
Hungry Horse Pictures **255**
Hunter Productions **255**
Huntingdon Town Crier **84**
Huntingdon Weekly News **84**
Huntley Film Archives **249**
Huntly Express **102**
Hunts Post **84**
Hurriyet **307**
Hutchins Film Co **255**
Hutchinson Books **137**
Hutchison Picture Library **150**
Huw Brian Williams **255**
Huyton & Raby Star **92**
HVC **233**
Hyndburn Express **90**
Hyphen Films **255**
Hythe Herald **89**

I

I Feel Good **114**
Ian Allan Publishing **113, 137**
IB Tauris **137**
IBM Computer Today **126**
ICCE Photo Library **151**
Icom Publications **113**
Icon Films **255**
ID Magazine **126**
Ideal Home **126**
Ideal World **233**
Ideal World Productions **255**
IDG Communications **114**
Idler **126**
Ignition Films **255**
Ilford & Redbridge Post **93**
Ilford Forest Recorder **87**
Ilford Recorder **93**
Ilkeston Advertiser **85**
Ilkeston Express **85**
Ilkley Gazette **102**
Illuminations Films **255**
Illustrated London News **114, 126**
IP Recruitment **377**
Image **126, 288, 315**
Image Bank **151**
Image Bank Film **249**
Image Entertainment **255**
Image Technology **288**
Images of Africa Photobank **151**
Images of War **255**
Imagicians **255**
Imagine FM **273**
Imago Productions **255**
IML Group **114**
Impact International **307**
Impact News **315**
Impact Photos **151**
Impartial Reporter **107**
Imperial War Museum **151, 249**
Improve Your Coarse Fishing **126**
Improve Your Sea Angling **126**
In Balance **120, 126**
In Dublin **315**
In Print **137**
INCA **255**
Incorporated Council of Law Reporting for England & Wales **338**
Incorporated Society of British Advertisers **351**
Independent **60**
Independent Broadcast Production Awards **383**
Independent Image **255**
Independent London **319**
Independent Media Distribution **299**
Independent Network News **319**
Independent Newspapers Regionals **70**
Independent on Sunday **62**
Independent Publishers Guild **168**
Independent Radio and Television Commission **319**
Independent Radio Group **267**
Independent Retail News **127**
Independent Television Commission **299, 359**

Index Entertainment **255**
Index on Censorship **127**, **160**
Index Stock Shots **249**
India Abroad Newspaper **307**
India Link International **319**
India Monitor **319**
India Times **319**
India Weekly **127**, **319**
India-Home and Abroad **319**
Indies **383**
Indigo Television **255**
Individual Homes **127**
Industrial Exchange & Mart **127**
Industrial Relations **127**
Industrial Society Work World Award **383**
Industrial Workforce **377**
Industry & Commerce **315**
Infactuation Productions **255**
In-Focus **151**
Infonation **255**
Informa Publishing Group **114**, **160**
Information World Review **288**
Initial **255**
Initiative Media **356**
INK **168**
INN **319**
Inner City News f **6**xpa **314**
INP **255**
INS News Group **142**
Inside Broadcast **255**
Inside Business **315**
Inside Communications **114**
Inside Cosmetics **127**
Inside Eye **127**
Inside Ireland **315**
Inside Soap **127**
Insider Group **114**
Insight **114**
Insight ACR **151**
Insight Films **255**
Insight Magazine **315**
Inspiration Network **233**
Inspirations **127**
Insport International **151**
Institute of Advertising Practioners in Ireland **319**
Institute of Broadcast Sound **299**
Institute of Communications Studies **364**, **371**
Institute of Journalists **168**
Institute of Local Television **299**
Institute of Practitioners in Advertising **351**
Institute of Printing **168**
Institute of Printing Handbook **163**
Institute of Public Relations **351**, **353**
InStore Marketing **127**
Insurance Age **127**
Intelligence & National Security **127**
Intelligence Review **127**
Interactive Channel **229**, **240**
Interactive Media Publications **137**
Interactive Selection **377**
Inter-Continental Features **142**

Intercontinental Literary Agency **134**
Interesting Television **255**
InterMedia **127**, **255**, **288**
International Association of Women Sports Photographers **169**
International Broadcast Engineer **289**
International Broadcasting Trust **299**
International Consortium of Investigative Work **383**
International Defense Review **127**
International Express **127**
International Federation of the Periodical Press **169**
International Films **255**
International Food Ingredients **127**
International Food Manufacture **127**
International Freighting Weekly **127**
International Institute of Communications **300**
International Journal of Human Rights **120**
International Media Produuctions **255**
International Money Marketing **127**
International News Productions **255**
International Peacekeeping **120**
International Police Review **127**
International Press Cuttings Bureaux **159**
International Public Relations **358**
International Risk Management **127**
International Satellite Directory **292**
International Shopping **229**, **240**
International Socialism **127**
International Visual Communications Association **300**
Internet **127**
Internet Magazine **127**
Internet Works **127**
Intershop **233**
Interzone Science Fiction **127**
Invention Shop Channel **233**
Inverness & Highland News **104**
Inverness Courier **104**
Inverness Herald **104**
Inverurie Advertiser **102**
Inverurie Herald **102**
Investment Fund Index CD Rom **127**
Investor Relations **127**
Investors Chronicle **127**
Invicta FM/Capital Gold **273**
Invincible Films **255**
InVision Productions **255**
IoJ **168**
IOP Publishing **137**
IPA Journal **315**
IPC Magazines **114**
IPH **255**
IPO Directory **163**, **353**
Ipswich Advertiser **97**
Ipswich E Anglian Daily Times **97**
Ipswich Evening Star **97**
IPTV **255**
IPU Review **315**
Ireland International News Agency **319**
Ireland of the Welcomes **315**
Ireland on Sunday **319**

Ireland's Eye **315**
Ireland's Own **315**
IRIE TV Network **229**, **240**
Iris Oifigiuil **315**
Irish Architect **315**
Irish Banking Review **315**
Irish Building Services News **315**
Irish Catholic **315**
Irish Criminal Law Journal **315**
Irish Current Law Monthly Digest **315**
Irish Democrat **120**
Irish Dental Association Journal **315**
Irish Electrical Review **315**
Irish Emigrant, **315**
Irish Farmers' Journal **315**
Irish Farmers' Monthly **315**
Irish Field **315**
Irish Food **315**
Irish Geography **315**
Irish Hardware Magazine **315**
Irish Homes Magazine **315**
Irish Independent **319**
Irish Journal of European Law **315**
Irish Marketing Journal **315**
Irish Medical Journal **315**
Irish Medical News **315**
Irish News **70**
Irish News Belfast **75**
Irish Pharmacy Journal **315**
Irish Post **127**, **319**
Irish Racing Calender **315**
Irish Skipper, **315**
Irish Social Worker **315**
Irish Times **319**
Irish Travel Trade News **315**
Irish World **127**, **319**
IRN - Independent Radio News **244**
IRNA **142**
Iron Bridge/No Cake **255**
Iron Productions **255**
Irvine Herald **103**
Irvine Times **103**
Ishbel Maclean **255**
Isis Productions **255**
Islamic Republic News Agency **142**
Island FM **274**
Isle of Man Courier **89**
Isle of Man Examiner **89**
Isle of Thanet Gazette **89**
Isle of Wight Cable & Telephone Co **239**
Isle of Wight County Press **70**, **79**, **89**
Isle of Wight Radio **274**
Isles FM **274**
Islington Chronicle **93**
Islington Gazette **93**
IT **315**
ITC Engineering/Research/Finance **299**
ITC Head Office **208**
ITMag **127**
ITN **210**, **244**
ITN Archive **151**, **249**
ITV **249**
ITV Association **300**

I

ITV Network **300**
ITV Network Centre **210**
ITV Sport Archive **151**
ITV teletext **243**
ITV2 **228**
IVN Entertainment **249**
Ivybridge Gazette **86**
IWT TV **255**

J

J & M Entertainment **255**
J R Personnel **377**
J Walter Thompson **355**
J Whitaker & Sons **137**
J&M Publishing **71**
JA Allen **137**
Jacob & Johnson **71**
Jam **127**
James Cameron Memorial Awards **383**
James Clarke & Co **137**
James Currey **137**
James Nisbet **137**
Jane Balfour Films **255**
Jane Conway Gordon **134**
Jane Judd Literary Agency **134**
Jane Turnbull **134**
Jane Walmsley Productions **255**
Jane's **137**
Jane's Defence Weekly **127**
Janes Information Group **118**
Janine Wiedel Photolibrary **151**
Janomot Bengali Newsweekly **127, 319**
January Films **255**
Japan Forum **127**
Jarrold **137**
Jarrolds Press Agency **142**
Jay TV **255**
Jazz FM **274**
Jazz Journal International **127**
Jean McGhee Recruitment **377**
Jeito Films **255**
Jelly Wall **255**
Jencol Employment Agency **377**
Jenkins Group **142**
Jeremy Isaacs Productions **255**
Jersey Evening Post **84, 71**
Jersey Weekly Post **84**
Jerusalem **255**
Jessica Kingsley **137**
Jewish Chronicle **127, 319**
Jewish Quarterly **127, 319**
Jewish Recorder **319**
Jewish Socialist **120**
Jewish Telegraph **127, 319**
Jewish Tribune **127, 319**
Jezebel Films **255**
JHA Research Consultancy **159**
JICNARS **169**
JICREG **169**
Jiji Press **142**

Jim Henson Productions **255**
Jim Rodger Memorial Award for Young Scottish Sportswriters **383**
JKL & Hide Recruitment **377**
JM Dent & Sons **136**
Jo Phillips **377**
Job Met **127**
Jobson Publishing Corporation **114**
John Adams TV **255**
John Ayling and Associates **356**
John Brown Publishing **114**
John Cary Studios **255**
John Connor Press Associates **142**
John Donald **137**
John Farquharson **134**
John Frost Historical Newspaper Service **151**
John Gau Productions **255**
John H Hirst & Co **70**
John Hunt **137**
John Johnson **134**
John Jones **137**
John Lawrence Enterprises **255**
John Murray **137**
John O'Groats Journal **104**
John Penri Press **72**
John Sherratt **137**
John Wiley & Sons **114, 137**
Johnson Publications **137**
Johnston Press **71**
Johnston Training Centre **365**
Johnstone & Linwood Gazette **105**
Jonathan Cape **137**
Jonathan Clowes **134**
Jordan Publishing **137**
Journal of Educational Media **289**
Journal of Wound Care **127**
Journal, The **75, 316**
Journalism Studies **160**
Journalism Training Centre **368**
Journalist, The **127, 160**
Journalist's Handbook **162**
Journeyman Press **137**
JSTV **233**
Judith Chilcote **134**
Judy Farquharson **377**
Juice **274**
Julia Ross Personnel **377**
Julian Cotton Photo Library **151**
Jumping Jack Animation **255**
Junior **127**
Juniper **255**
Just **17 127**
Just Television **255**
JW Crabtree & Son **140**

K

Kagan World Media **289**
Kai Productions **255**
Kanal 5 **234**
Karen Hamilton **255**
Karnak House **137**
Katz Pictures **151**
Kays UK Production Manual **292**
KCR FM **274**
Keesing UK **114**
Keighley News **102**
Kelnat **255**
Kemps Film, TV & Video Yearbook **292**
Kenilworth Press **137**
Kenilworth Weekly News **99**
Kennedy Mellor **255**
Kennet Star **100**
Kenneth Mason **137**
Kensington & Chelsea Ind. **93**
Kensington & Chelsea Mail **93**
Kensington & Chelsea Post **93**
Kensington News **93**
Kent & Sussex Courier **89**
Kent and Sussex Courier **79**
Kent Messenger **71**
Kent Messenger **79, 89**
Kent Today **89**
Kentish Express **89**
Kentish Gazette **89**
Kentish Times Newspapers **71**
Keo Films **255**
Kerrang! **127**
Kerry's Eye **314**
Kerryman **314**
Kestrel Film Company **255**
Keswick Reminder **85**
Ketchum **358**
Kett's News Service **142**
Kettering & Disrict Citizen **95**
Kettering Herald & Post **95**
Kevin Fitzpatrick Photography **151**
Kevin Mayhew **137**
Key Communications **358**
Keystone Ealing **255**
Khalsa World Television **234**
Kick FM **274**
Kidderminster Chronicle **100**
Kidderminster Shuttle **100**
Kidderminster Why **100**
Kilburn & Brent Advertiser **93**
Kilburn Times **93**
Kildare Nationalist **314**
Kilkenny People **314**
Killen International Partnership **114**
Kilmarnock Leader **103**
Kilmarnock Standard **103**
Kilroy Television **255**
Kincardineshire Observer **102**
Kindred Spirit **127**
King Alfred's Winchester **374**
King Fisher Productions **255**
King Rollo Films **255**
Kingdom FM **274**

Kingfisher **137**, **255**
Kingsbridge Gazette **86**
Kingsfire Services **255**
Kingston Guardian **81**
Kingston Guardian series **94**
Kingston Informer **94**
Kingston, Surbiton Malden Times **94**
Kirkintilloch Herald **104**
Kirriemuir Herald **102**
Kiss **100**
Kitchens, Bedrooms & Bathrooms **127**
Kix 96 **274**
Kleinwort Benson **358**
KL-FM **274**
Kluwer **137**
Knaresborough Post **101**
Knave **127**
Knockabout **137**
Knowledge, The **292**
Knutsford Express Advertiser **84**
Knutsford Guardian **84**
Kobal Collection **154**
Kogan Page **137**
KPA TV **255**
KPMG Commercial Radio Awards **383**
Kriss Kross **127**
KTTV **234**
Kudos Productions **255**
Kugelblitz **255**
Kuwait News Agency **142**
KWTV **234**
Kyle Cathie **137**
Kyodo News **142**

L

La Plante Productions **255**
La Voce Degli Italiani **310**
Labour Left Briefing **120**, **127**
Labour Market Trends **127**
Labour Research **120**, **127**
Lady **114**, **127**
Ladybird Books **137**
Lakeland Echo **85**
Lakeland Press Agency **142**
Lakes Leader **85**
Lambent Productions **255**
Lambeth College **368**
LAN **316**
Lanark Gazette **104**
Lanarkshire People **104**
Lanarkshire Television **242**
Lanarkshire World **104**
Lancashire Evening Post **90**
Lancashire Evening Telegraph **90**
Lancaster Guardian **90**
Lancaster University **374**
Lancaster/Morecambe Citizen **90**
Lancet **114**, **127**
Lancing Herald **98**
Land Rover Owner International **127**
Landmark Productions **255**
Landscape Channel **234**

Landseer Film & TV **255**
Landworker **127**
Lanka Vithki **319**
Lantern FM **274**
Laois Nationalist **314**
Largs Weekly News **103**
Larne Gazette **107**
Larne Times **107**
Larousse **137**
Lashkara **319**
Last Ditch TV **255**
Launceston Gazette **85**
Laurel Productions **255**
Laurence King **137**
Laurence Stern Fellowship **383**
Law Society Gazette **316**
Law Society of England & Wales **114**
Law Society's Gazette **127**
Lawrence & Wishart **137**
Lawyer **127**
LBC 1152AM **274**
Lea Valley Star **89**
Leader **319**
Leading Ladies Film Co **255**
Leagas Delaney Partnership **355**
Leamington Review **99**
Leamington Spa Observer **99**
Learning Channel **229**, **240**
Learning Media **255**
Leather **127**
Leatherhead Advertiser **98**
Lebrecht Collection **154**
Lee & Thompson **334**
Leeds Express **102**
Leeds Metropolitan University **374**
Leeds Weekly News **81**, **102**
Leeds, Trinity & All Saints College **374**
Leek Post & Times **97**
LeeWright Productions **255**
Left Handed Pictures **255**
Legacy Films **255**
Legal 500 **338**
Legal Action **127**
Legal Business **127**
Leicester Community Channel **229**, **240**
Leicester Journal **90**
Leicester Mail **81**, **90**
Leicester Mercury **77**, **90**
Leicester News Service **142**
Leicester Sound **275**
Leigh & Tyldesley Journal **94**
Leigh Reporter/Golborne Star **94**
Leigh Times Co **71**
Leighton Buzzard Citizen **83**
Leighton Buzzard Herald **83**
Leighton Buzzard Observer **83**
Leila Films **255**
Leinster Express **314**
Leinster Leader **314**
Leisure Manager **127**
Leisure Painter **127**
Leisure Time Midlands **255**
Leisure Time Productions **255**
Leisure Week **127**

Leitrim Observer **314**
Leman Productions **255**
LENA **353**
Leo Burnett **355**
Letts Educational **137**
Level **127**
Lewis Silkin **334**
Lewisham & Catford News **94**
Lewisham Mercury **94**
Lewisham News Shopper **94**
Leyland Guardian **90**
Leyton Guardian **93**
Liba Productions **255**
Liberty Publishing **114**
Liberty Radio 963+972AM **275**
LIBRA TV **255**
Library Association **127**, **169**
Libris **137**
Licensing World **316**
Lichfield Chronicle **97**
Lichfield Mercury **71**, **97**
Lichfield Trader **97**
Life **234**
Lifeguard **127**
Lifewatch **127**
Liffey Champion **314**
Light & Lighting **127**
Like Minds **255**
Lilyville Productions **255**
Limelight Management **134**
Limerick Chronicle **314**
Limerick Leader **314**
Limerick Post **314**
Limited Company Limited **255**
Lincoln Chronicle **91**
Lincoln Target **91**
Lincolnshire Evening Echo **91**
Lincolnshire Free Press **91**
Lincolnshire Standard **91**
Lincs FM **266**, **275**
Lindley Stone **255**
Line Up **127**, **289**
Linedancer **127**
Link Entertainment **255**
Link House Magazines **114**
Linlithgow Gazette **104**
Lion Publishing **137**
Lion TV **255**
Lionsgate Media **255**
Liphook Times **98**
Liphook Times & Mail **88**
LIRE Media Group **169**
Lisa Eveleigh **135**
Lisburn Echo **107**
Liskeard Gazette **85**
List **127**
Lite FM **275**
Literary Review **127**
Little Aston Observer **100**
Little Bird **255**
Little Brown **137**
Little Dancer Films **255**
Little Ship **127**
Littlehampton Gazette **99**
Littlehampton Guardian **98**

L

Live & Kicking **127**
Live TV Local Network **229**, **240**
Liverpool **240**
Liverpool Community College **368**
Liverpool Daily Post **92**
Liverpool Echo **77**, **92**
Liverpool John Moores University **374**
Liverpool UP **137**
Living **127**, **234**
Lladudno Advertiser **105**
Llanelli Star **105**
Llantwit Major Gem **106**
Lloyd's List International **127**
LLP/Informa Publishing Group **114**
Lluniau Lliw Cyf **255**
LMI Pictures **255**
Loaded **127**
Lobster **120**, **127**
Local 8 **229**, **240**
Local Authority Times **316**
Local Channel Tellywest **229**, **240**
Local Government Chronicle **127**
Local Government News **104**
Local Government Tenders **127**
Local History Magazine **127**
Local Independent Television Network **242**, **300**
Local News Publications **314**
Local Peterborough/Norwich **229**
Local Publications Bourne **71**
Local Publications Saffron Walden **71**
Local Radio Company **267**
Local Sunday Newspapers Group **71**
Local Television Co **255**
Lochaber News **104**
Lochbroom FM **275**
Lodestar Productions **255**
Logisitic Europe **127**
Lomond TV **255**
London At Large **142**
London College of Fashion **368**
London College of Printing **368**
London Community Television **234**, **240**
London Cyclist **127**
London Film & Video Dev. **255**
London Film Archive **249**
London Film Commission **300**
London Gazette **127**
London Greek Radio **275**, **311**
London Guildhall University **374**
London Hotel Mag **127**
London Institute **372**, **374**
London International Film School **372**
London Irish Press **319**
London Jewish News **319**
London Magazine **127**
London Metropolitan Archives **154**
London News Network **246**
London Post **255**
London Press Club **169**, **383**
London Review of Books **127**

London Stockshots Library **250**
London Theatre Guide **127**
London Turkish Radio **275**, **311**
London Weekend Television **221**, **255**
London Weekly Times **93**
London West End Extra **93**
Londonderry NW Echo **107**
Londonderry Sentinel **107**
Londonzok **127**
Lonely Planet **137**
Long Eaton Advertiser **91**
Long Eaton Trader **91**
Longbow Productions **255**
Longeye **127**
Longford Leader **314**
Longford News **314**
Longman Group **137**
Longridge News **90**
Looks **127**
Loose Arrangement Film & TV **255**
Loose Moose **255**
Loot **114**, **127**
Lothian Times **103**
Lothian World **127**
Loud Mouse Productions **255**
Loughborough Echo **91**
Loughborough Herald & Post **91**
Loughborough Mail **91**
Loughborough University **374**
Loughton, Chigwell Gazette **87**
Louise Panton Productions **255**
Louth Leader **91**
Louth Standard **91**
Louth Target **91**
Lovells **334**
Lowe Lintas **355**
Lowestoft Journal **97**
Lucas Alexander Whitley **135**
Lucas Media **246**, **255**
Lucky World Productions **255**
Ludlow Advertiser **96**
Ludlow Journal **96**
Lunchtime Productions **255**
Lund Humphries **137**
Lurgan Examiner **107**
Lurgan Mail **107**
Lusia Films **255**
Lust For Life **255**
Luton Leader **83**
Luton News **83**
Luton on Sunday **81**
Luton/Dunstable Herald & Post **83**
Lutterworth Press **137**
Lutyens & Rubinstein **135**
LWT **221**
Lymington Times **88**
Lynn News **95**
Lyric FM **319**
Lytham St Annes Express **90**

M

M & E Design **127**
M & S Magazine **127**
M & Y News Agency **142**
M Factory **240**
M Magazine **127**
M&C Saatchi **355**
M4U **234**
Mablethorpe & Sutton Leader **91**
Mablethorpe & Sutton Standard **91**
Mac Format **127**
Macclesfield Express Adv. **84**
Macclesfield Messenger **84**
Macclesfield Times **84**
Macdonald's Young Books **137**
MacHeath Productions **255**
MacIntyre & Co **256**
Macmillan Magazines **115**, **137**, **256**
MacNeil Group Holdings **377**
MacQuitty International Collection **154**
MacUser **127**
MacWorld **127**
Mad About Dogs **127**
Madam **127**
Magazine Guide **127**
Magazine News **127**, **162**
Maggie Noach Literary Agency **135**
Maggie Pearlstine **135**
Maghull Star **92**
Magi Publications **137**
Magic **275**
Magic Lantern Productions **256**
Magic Stone **256**
Magnum Photos **154**
Maiden's Voyage **256**
Maidenhead Advertiser **83**
Maidstone Adscene **89**
Maidstone Extra **89**
Maidstone Star **89**
Mail on Sunday **62**
Mail Order Protection Scheme **351**
Mailout **127**
Mainstream Publishing **137**
Majesty **127**
Makar Productions **256**
Making Music **127**
Making Waves Film & TV **256**
Malachite Productions **256**
Maldon Standard **87**
Mallory Films **256**
Malmesbury Gazette **100**
Malone Gill Productions **256**
Malvern Gazette **100**
Man Alive Group **256**
Management Today **127**
Manches **334**
Manchester Evening News **77**, **94**
Manchester Metro News **94**
Manchester Metropolitan University **374**
Manchester Reporter Group **71**
Manchester United Magazine **127**
Manchester UP **137**
Mandarin **137**
Manga Max **127**
ManMade **256**

Manning Gottlieb Media **356**
Manning, Selvage and Lee **358**
Manor Publishing **115**
Mansell Publishing **137**
Mansfield & Sutton Observer **95**
Mansfield **103.2 276**
Mansfield Chad **95**
Mansfield Recorder **95**
Mansfield Weekly Post **95**
Mantra Publishing **137**
Manufacturing Chemist **127**
Manx Independent **89**
Manx Radio **276**
MAPA **142**
March Hare Productions **256**
Marcher Coast FM **276**
Marcher Gold **276**
Marcher Radio Group **267**
Margaret Hanbury **135**
Marie Claire **127**
Marine Conservation **127**
Marion Boyars **137**
Mark Film & TV **256**
Mark Allen Publishing **115**
Mark Paterson & Associates **135,
256**
Market Harborough Herald **91**
Market Research Society **351**
Marketeer **127, 352**
Marketing **127, 316, 352**
Marketing Direct **127**
Marketing Events **127**
Marketing Week **127**
Marketplace Appointments **377**
Marlborough Pewsey Gazette **100**
Marriott Harrison **334**
Marsh Agency **135**
Marshall Cavendish **137**
Marshall Publishing **137**
Martin Dunitz **137**
Martin Gates Productions **256**
Martin Pope Productions **256**
Marvel Comics **115**
Mary Clemmey **135**
Mary Evans Picture Library **154**
Mary Holland Associates **377**
Marylebone Mercury **93**
MASC Productions **256**
Masons **334**
Masons News Service **142**
Master Builder **127**
Masterbond Films **256**
Match **127**
Materials Recycling Week **127**
Matlock Mercury **85**
Matthews Personnel **377**
Mature Tymes **115**
MATV **242**
Mauritian International **319**
Mauritius News **319**
Maverick Television **256**
Max Power **127**
Maxim **127**
Maya Vision **256**
Mayfair **127**
Mayfair Productions **256**

Mayo News **314**
MBA Literary Agency **135**
MBC **234, 256**
MBC FM **286**
MBS Group **356**
MBS Productions **256**
MBUK **127**
McCallum Media Monitor **159**
McCann-Erickson **355**
McConnell Film Assoc **256**
McDougall Craig **256**
McGrawHill **137**
McGrigor Donald **334**
McKenzie Heritage Picture Archive
154
MDA **300**
MDB Magazine Directory **163**
Mearns Leader **102**
Meat Trades Journal **127**
Meath Chronicle **314**
Meath Topic **314**
Mechanical-Copyright Protection
Society **300**
Medeconomics **127**
Media & Marketing Europe **127, 352**
Media Antenna Scotland **300**
Media Campaign Services **356**
Media Circus **256**
Media Contacts Recruitment **377**
Media Disc **163**
Media Education Journal **289**
Media Europe **256**
Media Exchange **377**
Media International **128**
Media Lawyer **162, 338**
Media Mermaid **256**
Media Pictures **256**
Media Pocket Book **163, 353**
Media Research Group **169, 300**
Media Resource Service **169**
Media Shadowfax Europe **159**
Media Society **169**
Media Trust **300**
Media Ventures Group **115**
Media Week **128, 162, 289, 352**
Media, Culture & Society **128, 289**
Media/Professional Insurance Agency
332
MediaCom TMB **356**
Mediamark Publishing **115**
Mediapolis **356**
Mediatec Recruitment **377**
MediaTel **300**
Mediavest Manchester **356**
Mediavest UK **356**
Medical Action Communications **358**
Medical Imprint **128**
Medical Journalists' Association **169**
Medici Society **137**
MedicoLegal Journal of Ireland **316**
Meditel Productions **256**
Medway & Disrict Adscene **89**
Medway Extra **89**
Medway News **89**
Medway Standard **89**
Melody Maker **128**

Melrose Press **137**
Melting Pot **319**
Melton Citizen **91**
Memoir Film Productions **256**
Men & Motors **229**
Men Only **128**
Men's Health **128**
Men's Wear **128**
Mental Health Media **256**
Mentorn Barraclough Carey **256**
Mentorn **256**
Mercat Press **137**
Mercia FM/Classic Gold **1359 276**
Mercury FM **276**
Mercury Press Agency **142**
Merehurst **137**
Meridian Broadcasting **221**
Merioneth Express **106**
Merlin Films **256**
Merlin Press **137**
Merrell Holberton **137**
Merrill LynchPanmure Gordon **358**
Mersey Television **256**
Merthyr Campaign **106**
Merthyr Express **106**
Merthyr Tydfil **106, 115**
Metal Bulletin **128**
Metal Hammer **128**
Metalworking Production **128**
Metamedia Productions **256**
Methodist Publishing **137**
Methodist Recorder **128**
Methuen **137**
Metro **81**
Metro Cable Television Metro **239**
Metro FM **276**
Metro International **71**
Metro Networks **246**
Metro Publishing **137**
Metro South Wales **239**
Metrovision **240**
MFM **276**
Michael Cole Productions **256**
Michael Hurll TV **256**
Michael Joseph **137**
Michael O'Mara **137**
Michaelides & Bednash **256**
Michelin **137**
Michelle Kass Associates **135**
Micro Computer Mart **128**
Microsoft **228**
Microwave Engineering Europe **128**
Mid and North West Radio **319**
Mid Cornwall Advertiser **85**
Mid Devon Gazette **86**
Mid Suffolk Advertiser **97**
Mid Wales Journal **106**
Mid-Devon Advertiser series **86**
Mid-Devon Express & Star **86**
Middle East Broadcast & Satellite **289**
Middle East Broadcasting Centre **311**
Middle East Economic Digest **128**
Middle East Electricity **128**
Middle East Expatriate **319**
Middle East International **128**

M

Middlemarch Films **256**
Middlesbrough Evening Gazette **101**
Middlesbrough Herald & Post **101**
Middlesex University **374**
Middleton Guardian **94**
Middleton/Moston Express **94**
Middlewich Chronicle **84**
Midland Independent Newspapers **71**
Midland News Association **71, 365**
Midland Tribune **314**
Midlands Radio 3 **319**
Midlantic Films Inc UK **256**
Midlothian Advertiser **105**
Midnight Blue **234**
Mid-Somerset Gazette **96**
Mid-Sussex Citizen **99**
Mid-Sussex Times **99**
Mid-Ulster & S Derry Mail **107**
Mid-Ulster Echo **107**
Mid-Ulster Observer **107**
Midweek Magazine **128**
Migrant Media **256**
Mike Mansfield TV **256**
Milap Weekly **128, 309**
Milestone Pictures **256**
Militant **120**
Military Picture Library **154**
Millar Movies **256**
Millennium Radio **276**
Miller Freeman **115, 118, 137**
Mills & Boon **137**
Milngavie & Bearsden Herald **104**
Milton Keynes Citizen **83**
Milton Keynes on Sunday **81**
Mims UK **128**
Minaj Broadcast International **234**
Mind Journalist of the Year **383**
Mind Your Own Business **128**
MindShare **356**
Mine channel **234**
Minerva Picture Co **256**
Mining Journal **115**
Mining Magazine **128**
Ministry **128**
MiniWorld **128**
Minster FM **276**
Minster Sound Radio **267**
Mintai **256**
Minx **128**
Miracle Publishing **115**
Miramax Hal Films **256**
Mirfield Reporter **102**
Mirror **60**
Mirror Editorial Training Centre **365**
Mirror Syndication International **154**
MirrorTel Productions **256**
Mirus Production **256**
Mishcon de Reya **334**
Missles And Rockets **128**
Mitchell Beazley **137**

Mix **96**, 128, **276**
Mixmag **128**
Mizz **128**
MJW Productions **256**
ML International Pictures **255, 256**
MNE TV **256**
Mobile Data Association **300**
Model Rail **128**
Modern History Review **128**
Modern Times Group **71**
Moffat News **103**
Mogul TV **256**
Mojo **128**
Molesey News **98**
Molotov Productions **256**
Momentum Video **256**
Mon & Abergavenny News **106**
Money Management **128**
Money Marketing **128**
Money Marketing Focus Surveys **128**
Money Observer **128**
Moneyextra **128**
Moneywise **128**
Monitor Syndication **154**
Monmouthshire Beacon **106**
Monogram Productions **256**
Montrose Review Press **71**
Montrose/Brechin Review **102**
Moondance Films & TV **256**
Moondog Productions **256**
Moonstone Films **256**
MOPS **351**
Moray Firth **276**
More! **128**
Morecambe Guardian **90**
Morecambe Visitor **90**
Morgan Cole **337**
Morley Advertiser **102**
Morley Observer **102**
Morning Gazettef **99**
Morning News **71**
Morning Star **120**
Morpeth Herald/Leader **95**
Morton Newspapers Group **71**
Mortons of Horncastle **71**
Mosaic Films **256**
Mossley Reporter **94**
Mostly Movies **256**
Mother & Baby **128**
Motherwell People **104**
Motherwell Times **104**
Motive Communications **356**
Motor Cycle News **128**
Motor Industry Management **128**
Motor Ship **128**
Motor Sport **128**
Motor Trader **128**
Motor Transport **128**
Motorboat & Yachting **128**
Motorcaravan Monthly **128**
Motoring Life **316**
Motoring News **128**
Motoring Picture Library **154**

Mountain Bike Rider **128**
Mountain Bike UK **128**
Mountain Biker International **128**
Mourne Observer **71**, **107**
Move A Mountain **256**
Move On Up **256**
Movie Idols **128**
Movie International **128**
Moving Pictures International **128, 289**
Moving Still Productions **256**
MQ Publications **137**
MS London Magazine **128**
Mslexia **128**
MSTV **242**
MTV Networks **234**
MTV UK **229**
Multi Media Arts **256**
Multimedia and CD-ROM Directory **293**
Municipal Journal **128**
Munster Express **314**
Murfin Music International **267**
Musclemag International **128**
Museum of London Picture Library **154**
Museums Journal **128**
Music Asia **234**
Music Box **256**
Music Box Channel **234**
Music Choice **231**
Music Choice Europe **285**
Music Magazine **128**
Music Mall **256**
Music on Earth **256**
Music Week **128**
Musicians' Union **300**
Muslim News **309**
Muslim TV Ahmadiyya **234**
Muso **256**
Musselburgh News **104**
Mutual Films **256**
MUTV **231, 234**
Muzik **128**
Myrddin Productions **256**

N

N64 **128**
NAHEMI **364**
Nairnshire Telegraph Co **72**
Naked Ape **256**
Naked Film **256**
Namaste **234**
Namaste Asian Television **311**
Napier University **368, 374**
Narberth & Whitland Obs **106**
Nation **309**
National Artists Association **169**
National Association for Higher
   Education in the Moving Image **364**
National Association of Press Agencies **139, 169**
National Communications Union **301**

National Council for the Training of Journalists **362**
National Federation of Retail Newsagents **169**
National Film and Television Archive **301**
National Film and Television School **372**
National Film Theatre **301**
National Geographic **128, 231, 234**
National Geographic Society **115**
National Magazine Company **115**
National Maritime Museum **154**
National Monuments Record **154**
National Museum of Photography **154**
National News Press Agency **142**
National Newspapers Mail Order Protection Scheme MOPS **359**
National Printing Skills Centre **171**
National Railway Museum **154**
National Remote Sensing Centre **154**
National Small Press Centre **171**
National Small Press Centre Handbook **163**
National Sound Archive **301**
National Trust Magazine **128**
National Union of Journalists **171, 365**
National Viewers' and Listeners' Association **301**
Nationalist & Munster Advertiser **314**
Nationalist and Leinster Times **314**
Nationalist Newspaper **314**
Natural Health **240**
Natural World **128**
Nature **128**
Nautilus Films **256**
Navin Weekly **309**
Navy International **128**
Navy News **128**
NBC Channels **234**
NBC News Worldwide **246**
NCTBJ **365**
NCTJ **364**
NCTV **240, 256**
NE Wales Institute of Higher Education **374**
NEAR 101.6FM **319**
Neath & Port Talbot Guardian **106**
Nebraska Productions **256**
NECR **276**
Needlecraft **128**
Needmarsh Publishing **115**
Neil Setchfield Travel Picture Library **154**
Nellen & Co **337**
Nelson Leader Series **90**
Nelson Thomas **137**
Nelvana Enterprises **256**
Nenagh Guardian **314**
Neptune Radio 96.4 & 106.8FM **277**
Neston News **92**
.net **128**
NetMedia **301**

Network 021 **240**
Network Books **137**
Network East **311**
Network Five TV **256**
Network Photographers **154**
Network Week **128**
Networking **301**
Network World **128**
Neutrogena Beauty Journalism Awards **383**
Never Summer Productions **256**
Nevis Radio **277**
New Beacon Books **137**
New Cavendish Books **137**
New Christian Herald **128**
New Civil Engineer **128**
New Crane Publishing **115**
New Eden **128**
New English Library **137**
New Forest Post **88**
New Ground **120, 128**
New Holland **137**
New Horizon **309**
New Humanist **120, 128**
New Impact Journal **309**
New Internationalist **115, 120, 128**
New Journal Enterprises **72**
New Law Journal **128**
New Left Review **120, 128**
New Media Age **128, 162, 353**
New Media Companies 21st edition **163**
New Media Investor **162**
New Media TV **256**
New MediaFinance **128**
New Milton Advertiser **88**
New Music News **316**
New Musical Express **128**
New Nation **309**
New PHD **356**
New Ross Echo **314**
New Ross Standard **314**
New Rutland Times **72**
New Scientist **128**
New Statesman **115, 120, 128**
New Stitches **128**
New Street Productions **256**
New Theatre Publications **137**
New Times **121, 128**
New Woman **128**
New World **309**
New Zealand Press Association **142**
Newark Advertiser **72, 96**
Newark Trader News **96**
Newbury Local Mart **83**
Newbury Weekly News **83**
Newbury Weekly News Printers **72**
Newbury/Thatcham Chronicle **83**
Newcastle Evening Chronicle **99**
Newcastle Herald & Post **81**
Newcastle Herald & Post **99**
Newcastle Journal **99**
Newcastle Sunday Sun **99**

Newhall Publications **115**
Newham Recorder **94**
Newham Yellow Advertiser **94**
Newmarket Business Report **316**
Newmarket Journal **97**
Newmarket Weekly News **97**
Newport & Market Drayton Ad **96**
Newport Free Press **106**
Newport News **106**
News **309**
News Direct **246**
News Direct 97.3FM **277**
News Guardian **99**
News Letter **75**
News Line **121**
News of the World **62**
News of Willenhall, Wednesbury **100**
News Post Leader **95**
News Team International **142**
Newscom **72**
Newsflash Scotland **142**
NewsIndex **159**
Newsline **162**
Newspaper Awards **383**
Newspaper Library British Library **171**
Newspaper Licensing Agency **157**
Newspaper Makers **173**
Newspaper Press Fund **171**
Newspaper Publishers Association **171**
Newspaper Society **68, 171, 365**
Newspaper Society Weekly Newspaper Awards **383**
Newspapers in Education **171**
Newsquest Media Group **72, 365**
Newsweek **115, 128**
Newton & Golborne Guardian **92**
Newton Abbot Weekender **86**
Newtownards Chronicle **72, 107**
Newtownards Spectator **107**
Nextep Ltd **377**
Nexus **115, 137**
NFH **256**
Nicholas Brealey **137**
Nicholas Claxton Productions **256**
Nick Hern Books **137**
Nick Jr **231**
Nick Patten Productions **256**
Nickelodeon **231, 234**
Nigerian News **309**
Nikon Press Photographer of the Year **383**
Nimrooz **240**
Nine to Five **128**
Ninendo Official Mag **128**
Nineteen **128**
Nintendo Magazine **128**
NME **128**
NMTV **256**
Noble House Publishing **115**
Nobles Gate **256**
Noddy **128**
NODE News **316**
Noel Gay Motion Picture Co **256**

N

NoHo Digital **256**
Nomad Rush **256**
Nonviolent Action **121**
Norfolk Citizen **95**
Normanton Advertiser **72, 102**
North & West Wilts Star **100**
North Ayrshire Leader **103**
North Ayrshire World **103**
North Cheshire Herald **94**
North Cornwall Advertiser **85**
North County Leader **316**
North Devon Gazette & Advertiser **72, 86**
North Devon Journal **79, 86**
North Down Herald & Post **107**
North East Press Awards **383**
North Edinburgh News **72**
North Gwent Campaign **105**
North Newtownabbey Post **107**
North Norfolk News **95**
North Scot Press Agency **142**
North South Productions **256**
North Staffs Advertiser **97**
North Star **104**
North Tyneside Herald & Post **99**
North Wales Chronicle **106**
North Wales Newspapers **72**
North Wales Pioneer **105**
North Wales Press Agency **142**
North Wales Weekly News **105**
North West Asian News **309**
North West Film Archive **250**
North West News & Sports Agency **142**
North West One Films **256**
North Yorkshire Advertiser **101**
North Yorkshire News **101**
North Yorkshire Star **101**
Northallerton Times **101**
Northampton Chronicle & Echo **95**
Northampton Mercury **95**
Northamptonshire Evening Telegraph **95**
Northamptonshire Image **128**
Northants 96 **277**
Northants Herald & Post **95**
Northants Press Agency **142**
Northavon Gazette **83**
Northcliffe Newspapers Group **72**
Northcote House **137**
Northern Business Journalist **383**
Northern Constitution **107**
Northern Echo **76**
Northern Exposure TV Co **256**
Northern Ireland Information Service **142**
Northern Newspaper Group **72**
Northern Scot **105**
Northern Standard **314**
Northern Times **104**
Northlight Productions **256**
Northridge Entertainment **256**
NorthSound One/Two **277**
Northstar TV **256**
Northumberland Gazette **95**
Northumberland Herald & Post **95**

Northwich Chronicle **84**
Northwich Guardian **84**
Northwich Herald & Post **84**
Norton Radstock Advertiser **96**
Norton Rose **337**
Norwich Advertiser **95**
Norwich Eastern Daily Press **95**
Norwich Evening News **95**
Notes from the Borderland **121**
Notre Dame Films **256**
Notting Hill & Bayswater Ind. **93**
Nottingam Recorder **96**
Nottingham Evening Post **96**
Nottingham News Service **142**
Nottingham Recorder **81**
Nottingham Trent University **361, 372, 374**
Nottingham Weekly Post **96**
Nottingham/Trent Valley Journal **96**
Notun Din **309**
Nova Inc Fim & TV **256**
Nova Productions **250**
Novashop One/Two **234**
Novosti **142, 154**
Now **128, 284**
NRG **277**
NTC Publications **137**
NTL **228, 239, 301, 319**
Nu News **91**
Nuachtain News Group **72**
Nuneaton & District Newspapers **72**
Nuneaton Heartland Evening News **99**
Nuneaton Tribune **99**
Nunn Syndication Library **154**
Nursery Choice **128**
Nursery World **116, 128**
Nursing Standard **128**
Nursing Times **128**
NVC Arts **256**
NW Ireland Printing & Publishing Co **71**
NW Leicestershire Leader **91**

O

O Magazine **128**
Oadby & Wigston Mail **91**
Oasis Media **256**
Oasis Personnel **377**
Oban FM **277**
Oban Times **103**
Oban Times Group **72**
Objective Productions **256**
Observer **62**
Observer David Hodge Award **379**
Observer Life **128**
Observer Newspapers NI **72**
Occupational Health **128**
Ocean FM **277**
Ocicat **256**
Octagon Pictures **256**
Octagon Press **137**
October Films **256**
Octopus **256**
Octopus Publishing **137**
Off Licence **316**
Off-Air **289**

Offaly Express **314**
Offaly Topic **314**
Office Equipment News **128**
Official Playstation Magazine **128**
OffLicence News **128**
Offshore Engineer **128**
Offshore Financial Review **128**
Ogilvy and Mather **355**
Ogilvy Public Relations Worldwide **358**
Oil Factory **256**
OK! **128**
Okehampton Times **86**
Old Glory **128**
Old Street Films **256**
Oldham Advertiser **94**
Oldham Chronicle Weekend **94**
Oldham Evening Chronicle **94**
Oldie **128**
Oleander Press **137**
Olswang **337**
Olympic Television Archive Bureau **154**
Omnia **128**
Omnibus Press **137**
On Target **128**
ON TV **240, 256**
ONdigital **128, 228**
One Lung Productions **256**
One Shots **128**
One Way Film **256**
One World International Media Awards **383**
Oneword **286**
OneWorld Online **301**
Oneworld Publications **137**
Online Journalism Awards **379**
Onlywomen Press **137**
Open **231, 234**
Open Door Productions **256**
Open Gate Press **137**
Open Media **256**
Open Mike Productions **256**
Open Mind **256**
Open UP **137**
Opera **128**
Opera Now **128**
Optic Nerve **256**
Optician **128**
Optimedia UK **356**
Optomen TV **256**
Opus TV **256**
OR Media **256**
Oral History **128**
Orbit **128**
Orbit News Service **142**
Orcadian **72, 105**
Orchard FM **277**
Organise! **121**
Orion **137**
Orlando TV Productions **256**
Ormskirk Advertiser **90**
Ormskirk Visiter **90**
Orpheus Productions **256**
Orpington & Petts Wood Times **94**
Osborne Clarke **337**
Osprey **137**
Ossett & Horury Observer **102**
Oswestry Advertiser **96**

Otmoor Productions **256**
Our Baby **128**
Our Dogs **128**
Out of the Blue **256**
Outlook **107**
Outlook Press **72**
Outsider TV Production **256**
Outsourcing **128**
Oxford Brookes University **374**
Oxford Channel **242**
Oxford Courier **96**
Oxford Guardian **96**
Oxford Journal **96**
Oxford Mail **96**
Oxford Scientific Films **250, 256**
Oxford Star **96**
Oxford Television Company **256**
Oxford Times **96**
Oxford University Press **116, 137**
Oxford Westminster College **374**
Oxygen 107.9 **277**
Oxymoron Films **256**

P

P & D Employment **377**
PA News **319**
PA News Photo Library **154**
PA Regional Offices **138**
Pacemaker Press International **154**
Pacemaker Update **128**
Pacific 1 **257**
Packaging Magazine **128**
Packaging News **128**
Packet Series **85**
Pact **251**
Pact Magazine **289**
PACT **301**
Paddington Mercury **93**
Paddington Times **93**
Pagan Dawn **121**
Page One **142**
Pagnamenta Assoc **257**
Pagoda Film & TV **257**
Paisley **277**
Paisley & Renfrewshire News **105**
Paisley Daily Express **76, 105**
Paisley People **105**
Pakistani Channel **234, 311**
Paladin Books **137**
Paladin Pictures **257**
Palimpsest Productions **257**
Palindrome Productions **257**
Palm Pictures **257**
Pamela Neave Employment **377**
Pan Books **137**
Panache Pictures **257**
Pandora Press **137**
Pandora Productions **257**
Panel Building **128**
Panoptican Pictures **257**
Panos Pictures **154**
Paper Federation of Great Britain **171**
Paper Industry Technical Association **171**
Paperclip Partnership **159**
Parachute Pictures **154, 257**

Parallax Pictures **257**
Parallel Pictures **257**
Paramount **234**
Parents **128**
Parikiaki **128, 309**
Parker Mead **257**
Parkers Car Price Guide **128**
Parkhill Publishing **116**
Parkside Productions Partners in Production **257**
Parkway Search and Selection **377**
Parliament Magazine **128**
Parliamentary & EU News Service **144**
Parliamentary Channel **246**
Parliamentary Monitor **128**
Parliamentary Press Gallery/Lobby Journalists **171**
Parliamentry Communications **116**
Parragon Books **137**
Partners BDDH **355**
Partners Employment Services **377**
PASS **128**
Passion Pictures **257**
Pateley Bridge Herald **101**
Paternoster **137**
Pathe Productions **257**
Pathway Productions **257**
Paul Berriff Productions **257**
Paul Chapman **137**
Paul Raymond Publications **116**
Paul Trijbits Productions **257**
Pauline Kotschy Associates **377**
Pauline Muirhead Productions **257**
Pavilion Books **137**
PC magazines **128-129**
PCS Magazine **129**
PDP **257**
PDQ Publishing **137**
Peace News **121, 129**
Peak 107 FM **277**
Peakviewing Productions **257**
Pearson Education **137**
Pearson Television International Archive **250**
Pearson Television Stills Library **154**
Pearson TV **257**
Peebles Times **103**
Peeblesshire News **103**
Pelicula Films **257**
PEN **171**
Pen & Sword **137**
Penarth Times **106**
Penguin Books **137**
Peninsula Films **257**
Pensions Age **129**
Pensions Management **129**
Pensions Week **129**
Pensions World **129**
Penthouse **129**
Penthouse Channel **234**
Penumbra Productions **257**
Penwith Pirate **85**
People **314**
People, The **62**
People's Friend **129**
PeopleBank Employment **377**
Pepper's Ghost **257**

Perdesan Monthly **309**
Perfect Home **129**
Performance **234**
Performance Bike **129**
Performance Chemicals International **129**
Performance Films **257**
Pergamon Press **137**
Period Living **129**
Periodical Publishers Association **110, 172**
Periodicals Training Council **172, 365**
Periwinkle Productions **257**
Persian Channel **311**
Persian TV **240**
Personal Computer World **129**
Personnel Publications **116**
Personnel Selection **377**
Personnel Today **129**
Perspective Publishing **116**
Pertemps Caledonian **377**
Perth Shopper **105**
Perthshire Advertiser **105**
Perx Productions **257**
Pet Magic **129**
Pet Product Marketing **129**
Pet Reptile **129**
Peter Carter-Ruck & Partners **337**
Peter Collinns **137**
Peter Halban **137**
Peter Lowe **137**
Peter Sasdy Productions **257**
Peter Williams TV **257**
Peterborough Citizen **84**
Peterborough Evening Telegraph **84**
Peterborough Herald & Post **84 84**
Peterlee Star **86**
Petersfield & Bordon Post **88**
Petersfield Herald **88**
Petersfield Mail **88**
Petroleum Economist **129**
PFD **135**
PFI Report **129**
Phaidon Press **137**
Pharmaceutical Journal **129**
Pharmacy Today **129**
Phee Farrer Jones **377**
Philip Allan Publishers **116**
Philips **137**
Phillips Business Information **116**
Phoenix **234, 316**
Phoenix Chinese News & Entertainment **311**
Photo Technique **129**
Photofusion **154**
Photographer **129, 289**
Photonews Scotland **154**
Photoplay Productions **257**
Physics Review **129**
Physics World **129**
Piatkus **137**
Picador **137**
Picasso Pictures **257**
Piccadilly Key **103 277**
Piccadilly Press **137**
Pictor International **154**

P

Pictorial Heroes **257**
Picture Business **129**
Picture Factory **257**
Picture House Photography **154**
Picture House Productions **257**
Picture Palace Films **257**
Picture Perfect **257**
Picture Research Association **146, 172**
Picture This Independent Film **257**
Picturehead **257**
Pierrot Productions **257**
Pig Farming **129**
Pilgrim Films **257**
Pillarbox Productions **257**
Pilot Film & TV Productions **257**
Pims Media Directories **163, 353**
Pingu **129**
Pink Paper **129**
Pink Paper, The **121**
Pioneer Productions **257**
Pipedream Pictures **257**
Pipers'Ash **137**
PIR Group **377**
Pira International **172**
Pirate FM 102 **277**
Pirate Productions **257**
Pitkin Guides **137**
Pizazz Pictures **257**
Placing People **377**
Plain English Media Awards **383**
Plain English Publishing Company **116**
Plain Truth **129**
Plan Building **316**
Planet **129, 257**
Planet Playstation **129**
Planet Wild **257**
Planned Savings **129**
Planning **129**
Plant Managers Journal **129**
Plastics & Rubber Weekly **129**
Platinum Film & TV **257**
Play **129**
Playboy TV **234**
Playdays **129**
Playstation Plus **129**
Playstation Power **129**
Playststion Pro **129**
Plexus **137**
Pluto Press **137**
Plymouth College of Art and Design **372**
Plymouth Evening Herald **86**
Plymouth Extra **81, 86**
Plymouth Sound AM/FM **278**
Plympton News **86**
PM Publications **72**
PMA Training **368**
Pocket Arrows/Crosswords/Wordsearch **129**
Pocket Kidz! **129**
Poetry Ireland Review **316**
Point Sound & Vision **257**
Pola Jones Film **257**
Police **129**
Police Review **116, 129**

Policing Today **129**
Policy Press **137**
Polish service **235**
Political Quarterly **121**
Politics Review **129**
Polity Press **137**
Polkadot Productions **257**
Polygram Film **257**
Polygram Film and Television Library **250**
Pomegranate Pictures **257**
Pontefract Express **102**
Pontefract Weekend Times **102**
Pontypool & District Press **106**
Pontypridd Campaign **106**
Pontypridd Observer **106**
Poole Advertiser **86**
Poorhouse Productions **257**
Pop Culture Channel **234**
Popperfoto **154**
Popular Crafts **129**
Popular Films **257**
Popular Patchwork **129**
Portadown Times **107**
Portishead Admag **83**
Portishead AdvertiserSedgemoor Express & Star **96**
Portland Press **137**
Portman Entertainment **257**
Portobello Pictures **257**
Portsmouth & Sunderland Newspapers **73**
Portsmouth News **88**
Portsmouth News & Sports Mail **77**
Portsmouth/Southsea Journal **88**
Poseidon Productions **257**
Post Update **289**
Postgraduate Doctor **129**
Pot Black **129**
Potters Bar & Cuffley Press **89**
Potters Bar Times **89**
Poultry World **129**
Power FM **278**
Powerstation **129**
Powerstock Zefa **154**
Poynton Times **84**
Pozzitive **257**
PPA **172**
PPA Magazines and B2B awards **383**
PPA Marcus Morris Awards **383**
PR Newswire Europe Directories **163**
PR Planner UK & Europe **353**
PR Week **129, 352**
Practical (ly everything you can think of) **129**
Practice Nurse **129**
Practitioner **129**
Pre Press World **129**
Precise Media **257**
Precise Press Cuttings **159**
Precision Marketing **129**
Prediction **129**
Pregenancy & Birth **129**
Premier Christian Radio **278, 286**
Premier Media Partners **116**
Premiere **129**
Premises & Facilities Management **129**

PrePress News **162**
Prescot Reporter **92**
Presence Films **257**
Presentable Productions **257**
Press Agency Gatwick **144**
Press and Journal **76**
Press Association **144, 365**
Press Complaints Commission **172, 359**
Press Cutting Partnership **159**
Press Data Bureau **159**
Press Express **159**
Press Features Syndicate **154**
Press Gang News **144**
Press Gazette **129, 162**
Press Select **159**
Press Standards Board of Finance **172**
Press Team Scotland **144**
PressScan **159**
Pressure Cooker **257**
PressWise Trust **172**
Preston Citizen **90**
Preston Weekly Mail **90**
Prestwich Advertiser **95**
Prestwich Guide **95**
Preview Channel **240**
Price Jamieson **377**
Pricewaterhouse Coopers **358**
Pride **129**
Pride Magazine **309**
Prima **129**
Primary Source Media **118**
Prime Time Puzzles **129**
Princess **257**
Principal Media **257**
Print Week **129**
Printing Industries **162**
Printing Trades Directory **163**
Printing World **129, 162**
PrintWeek **162**
Prion Books **137**
Prism Press **137**
Private Eye **129, 162**
Pro Cycling **129**
Probashi Samachar **309**
Process Engineering **129**
Processing **129**
Producers Productions **257**
Producers' Alliance for Cinema and Television **250**
Production Guide **293**
Production Journal **129, 162**
Production Managers Association **301**
Production Solutions **129, 289**
Professional Engineering **129**
Professional Nurse **129**
Professional Printer **129, 162**
Professional Sport **154**
Profile Books **137**
Programme News **293**
Projector Productions **257**
Prominent Features **257**
Promotions and Incentives **129**
Proofreaders **173**

Property Direct **129**
Property Week **129**
Prospect **129**
Prospect Pictures **257**
Province 5 Television **316**
Provincial Farmer **316**
PSR Agency **377**
Psychic News **129**
Psychologist **129**
Psychology Review **129**
PTC New Journalist ot the Year Awards **383**
Public Administration **129**
Public Finance **129**
Public Record Office Image Library **154**
Public Relations Consultants' Association **351**
Public Relations Institute of Ireland **319**
Public Sector Times **316**
Public Service & Local Govt **129**
Public Service Review **316**
Public Treasurer **129**
Publican **129**
Publicis **355**
Publicity Club of Ireland **319**
Publishers' Association **172**
Publishers' Publicity Circle **172**
Publishing **162**
Publishing News **129**, **162**
Pudsey Times **102**
Pueblo Productions **257**
Puffin **137**
Pukka Films **257**
Pulmans Weekly News **86**
Pulp Books **137**
Pulse **129**
Pulse FM Classic Gold AM **278**
Pulse Productions **257**
Punch **129**
Punjab Mail International **309**
Punjab Times **129**
Punjab Times International **309**
Punjabi Guardian **309**
Puppetoon Productions **257**
Purple Frog **257**
Purple House **137**
Putney & Wimbledon Times **94**
Putney Chronicle **93**
Puzzle Compendium **129**
Puzzle Corner **129**
Puzzle Corner Special **129**
Puzzle Kids **129**
Puzzle Mix Special **129**
Puzzle Monthly **129**
Puzzle World **129**
Puzzler Collection/Puzzler **129**

Q

Q **129**
Q News, The Muslim Magazine **310**
Q102.9 FM **278**
Q103 FM **278**
Q24 **234**
Q97.2 Causeway Coast Radio **270**
Q97.2 FM **278**
Quadrant Broadcast **257**
Quadriga **257**
Quadrille Publishing **137**
Quadrillion **257**
Quality Time TV **257**
Quanta **257**
Quantum Home Shopping **234**
Quantum Publishing **116**
Quantum Staff Consultants **377**
Quartet Books **137**
Quarto **137**
Quay West Radio **278**
Queen Anne Press **137**
Queen Margaret University College **374**
QuesTV **234**
Quick and Easy Cross Stitch **129**
Quicksilver Films **257**
Quicksilver Media **144**
Quiller Press **137**
Quintessence Films **257**
Quirky Film & TV **257**
Quizkids **129**
Quizkids Special **129**
QVC - Shopping Channel **231**
QVC Deutschland **234**
QVC Shopping Channel **234**

R

Race and Class **129**
Racing & Football Outlook **129**
Racing Channel **234**
Radcliffe Times **95**
Radical History Review **121**
Radical Philosophy **121**
Radio **302**
Radio 1 **262**
Radio 2 **262**
Radio 3 **262**
Radio 4 **262**
Radio 5 Live **262**
Radio Academy **301**
Radio Academy Directory **293**
Radio Advertising Bureau **301**, **351**
Radio Advertising Clearance Centre **301**, **351**
Radio Advertising Handbook **293**
Radio Asia **311**
Radio Atlantic **252 319**
Radio Authority **265**, **302**, **359**
Radio Borders **278**
Radio Caroline **286**
Radio Ceredigion **311**
Radio City **285**
Radio Communication **129**
Radio Control Models **129**
Radio County Sound **319**
Radio Investments **267**
Radio Kerry **319**
Radio Kilkenny **319**
Radio Listener's Guide **293**
Radio Magazine **129**, **290**
Radio Maldwyn **276**
Radio Modeller **129**
Radio na Gaeltachta **319**
Radio na Life **102** FM **319**
Radio Phoenix **285**
Radio Review **290**
Radio Services **267**
Radio Society of Great Britain **302**
Radio Telefis Eireann **316**, **319**
Radio Times **129**, **290**
Radio Verulam **285**
Radio Victory **281**
Radio XL **311**
Radio XL **1296** AM **278**
Radio Youghal **316**
Radiocommunications Agency **302**
Radius Film Productions **257**
Raeburn Group **377**
RAF Museum **154**
Ragdoll Productions **257**
Raging Star Films **257**
Rail **129**
Railway Gazette International **129**
Railway Magazine **129**
Rainbow Recruitment **377**
Rainbow Television **234**
Rainey Kelly Campbell Roalfe **355**
Rajar: Radio Joint Audience Research **302**
Ram FM **278**
Rambling Today **129**
Random House **138**
RAP **257**
Raphael Associates **257**
Rapid Eye Movies **257**
Rapido TV **257**
Rapture TV **234**
Raven **129**
Raven, The **121**
Raven-Fox **116**
Ravensbourne College of Design & Comms. **372**
Ravi Asian News Weekly **310**
Raw Charm **257**
Raw Nerve Productions **257**
Rawle Partnership **257**
Rayleigh Recorder **87**
Rayleigh Times Group **87**
Raymonds Press Agency **144**
RCN Publishing **116**
RDF Television **257**
RE Brown & Others Lloyd's Syndicate 702 **332**
Reader's Digest Association **116**
Readers Digest **129**, **138**
Reading Chronicle **83**
Reading Chronicle Midweek **83**
Reading Evening Post **83**
Reading Standard **83**
Ready Steady Cook **129**

R

Real Homes **129**
Real Life Productions **257**
Real Money **129**
Real Radio **278**
Real World Pictures **257**
Reality Channel **234**
Reality Television **234**
Really Animated Productions **257**
Record Collector **129**
Recorded Picture Co **257**
Recorder Wales **73**
Recruit Media **377**
Recruiting for Scotland **377**
Red **130**
Red Balloo **257**
Red Consultancy **358**
Red Door Productions **257**
Red Dragon FM **278**
Red Galaxy Pictures **257**
Red Green and Blue Company **257**
Red Kite **121, 257**
Red Pepper **121, 130**
Red Production Co **257**
Redan Company **116**
Redbridge Community Channel **240**
Redbridge Guardian **87**
Reddish Reporter **95**
Redditch & Bromsgrove Jnl **100**
Redditch Advertiser **100**
Redditch/Alcester Standard **100**
Redline **130**
Redruth & Camborne Tinner **85**
Redwave Films **257**
Redweather Productions **257**
Redwood Publishing **116**
Reed Books **138**
Reed Business Information **116**
Reed Elsevier **117, 138**
Reel Life Television **257**
Reel Scoop **257**
Reel Women **302**
Regent Productions **257**
Regiment **130**
Regional Independent Media **73, 365**
Regional Newspapers Advertising
    Network **319**
Regional Newspapers Association of
    Ireland **319**
Regional Press Awards **383**
Reid Minty & Co **337**
Reigate & Banstead Ind. **98**
Reiner Moritz Associates **257**
Relationships Channel **234**
Remote Films **257**
Renaissance Films **257**
Renegade Films **257**
Renfrew & Erskine Gazette **105**
Renfrewshire World **105**
Researcher's Guide to British Film and
    TV Collections **248, 302**
Resident Abroad **130**
Resource Base **257**
Resurgence **121**
Resurgence **130**

Retail Jeweller **130**
Retail News **316**
Retford & Bawtry Guardian **96**
Retford & Bawtry Trader **96**
Retford & Worksop Times **96**
Retail Newsagent **130, 162**
Retail Technology **130**
Retail Week **130**
Retrograph Nostalgia Archive **154**
Reuters **144, 246**
Reuters Ireland **319**
Reuters Television **250**
Review Worldwide Insurance **130**
Review & Advertiser Newspaper Group
    73
Review Free Newspapers **73**
Review of Social Economy **130**
Revival Channel **234**
Revolution **130, 278**
Revolution Films **257**
Revs **130**
Rex Features **155**
Reynolds Porter Chamberlain **337**
Rhondda Campaign **106**
Rhondda Leader **106**
Rhyl/Prestatyn Journal **105**
Rhythm **130**
RIBA Journal **130**
Richard Butler **257**
Richards Butler **337**
Richmond Films & TV **257**
Richmond Informer **94**
Richmond Light Horse **257**
Richmond Towers **358**
Richmond/Twickenham Guardian **94**
Ride **130**
Ridings FM **278**
Ridings TV **240**
Right Now **122**
Right Start **130**
RIM Scotland **73**
Ripley & Heanor News **85**
Ripon Gazette **101**
Ri-ra Magazine **310**
Rishi Films **257**
RITZ 1035 **279**
River Publishing **117**
Riverchild Films **257**
Rivercourt Productions **257**
Riverfront Pictures **257**
Rivers Oram Press **138**
RM Associates **257**
RNA FM **279**
Robert Fleming Professional Risks **332**
Robert Gordon University **374**
Robert Hale **138**
Robert Harding Picture Library **155**
Roberts & Wykeham Films **257**
Roberts Staff Bureau **377**
Robinson Publishing **138**
Robson Books **138**
Rochdale Observer **95**
Rochdale/Heywood Express **95**
Rock FM **279**
Rock Sound films **257**
Rocket Pictures **257**
Rodale Press **117**

Roehampton Institute London **374**
Roger Bolton Productions **257**
Rogers, Coleridge & White **135**
RohanAsher Media **257**
Romantica **235**
Romeike & Curtice **159**
Romford & Havering Post **93**
Romford Recorder **93**
Romney Marsh Herald **90**
Romsey Advertiser **88**
Romsey Publishing Company **117**
Ronald Grant Archive **250**
Rooftop Productions **258**
Roose & Partners **355**
Rooster **117**
Rory Peck Trust Awards **383**
Roscommon Champion **314**
Roscomon Herald **314**
Rose Bay Film Productions **258**
Rosendale Press **138**
Rosetta Pictures **258**
Rosmary Goodchild Award- Family
    Planning Association **383**
Ross Campbell Consultants **377**
Ross Gazette **73, 88**
Rossendale Express **90**
Rossendale Free Press **90**
Rosso Productions **258**
Ross-shire Herald **104**
Rotherham Advertiser **101**
Rotherham Star **101**
Rough Sea Productions **258**
Round Organ **130**
Roundhouse Publishing **138**
Routledge **117, 138**
Rowe & Maw **337**
Royal & Sun Alliance **332**
Royal Geographical Society Picture
    Library **155**
Royal Holloway, University of London
    375
Royal National Institute for the Blind
    138
Royal Opera House Channel **240**
Royal Photographic Society Picture
    Library **155**
Royal Television Journalism Awards
    383
Royal Television Society **302, 293**
Royds Raphael **377**
Royston & Buntingford Crow **89**
Royston Weekly News **89**
RPM Arts **258**
RS Productions **258**
RSPB Moving Images **250**
RSPCA Photolibrary **155**
RTE **316**
RTE Guide **316**
Rugby Advertiser **99**
Rugby News **130**
Rugby Observer **99**
Rugby Review **99**
Rugby Vision Cyffro **258**
Rugby World **130**
Rugeley Mercury **97**
Ruislip Informer **93**
Runcorn Herald & Post **84**

Runcorn Weekly News **84**
Runcorn World **84**
Runners World **130**
Running Your Business **316**
Runway Airports **316**
Rupert Crew **135**
Rushmere **138**
RUSI Journal **130**
Russell Jones & Walker **337**
Russells **337**
Russian Information Agency - Novosti **144**
Rutherglen Reformer **104**
Rutland & Stamford Mercury **91**
Rutland Radio **279**
Rutland Times **91**
Rye & Battle Observer **98**
Ryland Peter & Small **138**

S

S2 **229**
S4C **225**
S4C2 **229, 235**
Saatchi and Saatchi **355**
Sabras Sound **279, 311**
Sada Urdu Monthly **310**
Safe and Sound Productions **258**
Safeway Magazine **130**
Saffron Walden Observer **87**
Saffron Walden Weekly News **87**
Safir Films **258**
Saga Magazine **130**
Saga Publishing **117, 138**
Sage Publications **117**
Sailing Today **130**
Sainsbury's: Magazine **130**
Saint Andrew Press **138**
Salaam! **310**
Salamander Books **138**
Sale & Altrincham Messenger **95**
Sale & District Courier **95**
Salford City Reporter **95**
Salisbury Advertiser **100**
Salisbury College **372**
Salisbury Journal **100**
Salisbury Review **122, 130**
Salisbury Times **100**
Sally and Richard Greenhill **155**
Sally Head Productions **258**
Salomon Smith Barney **358**
Salsa Rock Productions **258**
Salt Island Productions **258**
Samba Films **258**
Samuel French **138**
Samuels News & Photo Service **144**
Samuelson Productions **258**
Sandbach Chronicle **84**
Sandhurst/Crowthorne Mail **83**
Sandiacre and Stapleford News **96**
Sands Films **258**
Sandwell Chronicle **100**
Sankofa Film & Video **258**
Saol na nOilean **316**
Satellite & Cable Broadcasters' Group **302**
Satellite Information Services **235**

Satellite Media Services **302**
Satellite Times **130, 290**
Satellite Trader **130**
Satellite TV Europe **290**
SATV **258**
Saudi Press Agency **144**
Saunders & French Productions **258**
Sayidaty **130**
SB Publications **138**
SC Publishing Co **73**
Scala Productions **258**
Scarborough Evening News **101**
Scarborough Mercury **101**
Scarborough News/Ridings Press Agency **144**
Scase News Service **144**
Scene **130**
Scene One **235**
Schilling & Lom and Partners **337**
SchNews **121**
SchNews Magazine **130**
Schofield & Sims **138**
Scholastic **117, 138**
School of Communication **368**
Schroder **358**
Science and Society Picture Library **155**
Science Museum Publications **138**
Science Photo Library **155**
Science Pictures **258**
Sci-Fi Channel Europe **235**
SCM Press **138**
Scope Productions **258**
Score Digital **284**
Scorer Associates **258**
Scot FM **279**
Scotland on Sunday **79**
Scotland's Oracle **310**
Scots Law Times **130**
Scots Magazine **130**
Scotsman **76**
Scotsman Publications **73**
Scottish Academic Press **138**
Scottish and Universal Newspapers **73**
Scottish Association of Smallscale Broadcasters **302**
Scottish Book Trust **172**
Scottish Centre for Journalism Studies **368**
Scottish County Press **73**
Scottish Cultural Press **138**
Scottish Daily Newspaper Society **172, 365**
Scottish Daily Record & Sunday Mail **73**
Scottish Farmer **130**
Scottish Field **130**
Scottish Film & Television Archive **250**
Scottish Highland Photo Library **155**
Scottish Hydro-Electric Sport Photography Awards **383**
Scottish Media Group **73**
Scottish Media Newspapers Picture Library **155**
Scottish Memories **130**
Scottish News Agency **144**

Scottish Newspaper Publishers Association **172, 365**
Scottish Office Information Directorate **144**
Scottish Print Employers Federation **172**
Scottish Provincial Press **73**
Scottish Publishers Association **173**
Scottish Radio Holdings **267**
Scottish Screen **258, 302**
Scottish Television **222**
Scottish Television Enterprises **258**
Scottish Workers Republic **121**
Scouting **130**
Screen Digest **130, 290**
Screen First **258**
Screen International **130, 290**
Screen Partners **258**
Screen Resource **258**
Screen Ventures **258**
ScreenAge Pictures **258**
Screenbase Media **258**
Screenhouse Productions **258**
Screenwriters' Workshop **302**
Scripture Union **138**
Scunthorpe Evening Telegraph **91**
Scunthorpe Target **91**
Scunthorpe Trader News **91**
SDN **229**
Sea Angler **130**
Sea of Faith **130**
Seafarer Books **138**
Seaford Friday-Ad **98**
Seaford Gazette **98**
Seaham Star **99**
Search Press **138**
Searchlight **121, 130**
Seatrade Review **130**
Secker & Warburg **138**
Second Sight **258**
Secret Garden **258**
Security Management Today **130**
Seka Media **377**
Selby Times **101**
Select **130**
Select Recruitment **377**
Select TV Cable **229**
Selkirk Weekend Advertiser **103**
Sell-a-Vision Shopping **235**
Sentinel **77**
September Films **258**
Seren Books **138**
Serendipity Picture Company **258**
Serif **138**
Serpent's Tail **138**
Services Sound and Vision Group **303**
Setanta Sport **235**
Seven Day Press **144**
Seven Dials Films **258**
Sevenoaks & Tonbridge Leader **90**
Sevenoaks Chronicle **90**
Sevenoaks News in Focus **90**
Seventh Art Productions **258**
Severn House Publishers **138**
Severn Pictures **258**
Severn Sound FM **279**
Sewing World **130**

S

SFTV **258**
SFX **130**
SGR Colchester **279**
SGR FM **279**
Sgrin - Media Agency for Wales **303**
Shaker Films **258**
Sharp Image Productions **258**
Shattered Images **258**
She **130**
Shearman Productions **258**
Shed Productions **258**
Sheed & Ward **138**
Sheerness Times Guardian **90**
Sheffield College **368**
Sheffield Hallam University **372, 375**
Sheffield Independent Film **258**
Sheffield Mercury **101**
Sheffield Mercury Newspaper Baycro **73**
Sheffield Star **101**
Sheffield Telegraph **101**
Sheffield Weekly Gazette **81, 101**
Sheil Land Associates **135**
Sheldrake Press **138**
Shelflife **316**
Shelley Power Literary Agency **135**
Shepheard-Walwyn **138**
Shepherd Press **117**
Sheppey Gazette **90**
Shepshed Echo **91**
Sherbet **258**
Sheridans **337**
Shetland Times **73, 105**
Shipleys **258**
Shire Hall Group **358**
Shire Publications **138**
Shirely Stewart Literary Agent **135**
Shivers **130**
Shoot! **130**
Shooting & Conservation **130**
Shooting Partners **258**
Shooting Times **130**
Shop America **235**
Shop! **229, 235**
Shopping Centre **130**
Shoreham Herald **90**
Short Wave Magazine **130, 290**
Shots **290**
Show Time **235**
Showplay **258**
Shrewsbury Admag **96**
Shrewsbury Chronicle **96**
Shrewsbury Press Service **144**
Shropshire Magazine **130**
Shropshire Star **77, 96**
Sianel Pedwar Cymru **225**
SIBC **279**
Sidcup & Bexley Mercury **94**
Sidcup & Blackfen Times **94**
Side-Kix **377**
Sidgwick & Jackson **138**
Sidmouth Herald **86**
Sight & Sound **130, 290**
Sigma Films **258**
Sigma Press **138**
Sign **130**

Signal 1 **279**
Signals **258**
Siguy Films **258**
Sikh Courier International **310**
Sikh Messenger **310**
Silk FM **279**
Silverstone TV **240**
Sima TV **235**
Simkins Partnership **258, 337**
Simmons & Simmons **338**
Simon & Schuster **138**
Simons Muirhead & Burton **338**
SimpleActive **243**
Simply Money **235**
SIN **155**
Sing Tao UK **310**
Singer **130**
Siriol mm **258**
Sirius Media Services **144**
Sittingbourne Extra **90**
SJ Berwin & Co **338**
Skegness News **91**
Skelmersdale Advertiser **90**
Skelmersdale Champion **92**
Skillset **364**
Skin Deep **130**
Skoob Books **138**
Sky 5 Text **243**
Sky TV **229**
Sky Digital TV Guide **130**
Sky Movie Max **229**
Sky News Australia **231**
Sky News Library Sales **250**
Skyline Films **258**
Skyline Productions **258**
Skyscan Photolibrary **155**
Skyscraper Films **258**
SLCTV **240**
Sleaford Standard **91**
Sligo Weekender **314**
Slimming **130**
Slough & Langley Observer **83**
Slough Observer Group **73**
Smallholder **130**
Smash Hits **130**
SME Business **130**
SMG Publishing **73, 267**
Smith & Watson Productions **258**
Smith Davis Press **144**
Smith Willis Communications **159**
Smoke & Mirrors **258**
SNS **144**
SOA Photo Agency **155**
Soccer Stars **130**
Social Housing **130**
Socialism Today **130**
Socialist Affairs **121, 130**
Socialist Appeal **121**
Socialist Standard **122, 130**
Socialist Voice **316**
Socialist Worker **122, 130**
Socialist, The **121**
Society of Authors **173**
Society of Cable Telecommunication Engineers **303**
Society of Freelance Editors and **173**
Society of Indexers **173**

Society of Television Lighting Directors **303**
Society of Typographic Designers **173**
Society of Women Writers & Journalists **173**
Sociology Review **130**
SOI Film & TV **258**
Solent News & Photo Agency **144**
Solicitors Journal **130**
Solid Productions **258**
Solihull Times **100**
Solo **144**
Somerfield Mag **130**
Somerset & Avon Guardian **96**
Somerset & Dorset News **96**
Somerset County Gazette **96**
Somerset News Service **144**
Somerset Standard **96**
Somethin Else **258**
Songbird **258**
Sony Entertainment **235**
Sony Entertainment TV Asia **311**
Sony Radio Awards **383**
Sorted? **122, 130**
Soul Purpose Productions **258**
Soundings **122**
South Bank University **375**
South Bedfordshire News Agency **145**
South Belfast Herald and Post **107**
South Bucks Star **83**
South Cheshire Mail **84**
South Coast Leader **98**
South Coast Press Agency **145**
South Devon & Plymouth Times **86**
South Durham Herald **86**
South East Essex College **369, 372**
South East Radio **319**
South Hams Radio **279**
South Hants & Winchester Weekly News **88**
South Liverpool Merseymart **92**
South London Press **94**
South London Press Friday edition **79**
South Manchester Express **95**
South Manchester Reporter **95**
South Oxfordshire Courier **96**
South Shields Gazette **99**
South Thames College **372, 375**
South Tyneside Herald & Post **99**
South Tyne Star **99**
South Wales Argus **106**
South Wales Echo **77**
South Wales Evening Post **77, 106**
South Wales Guardian **105**
South West Media Development **258**
South West News Service **145**
South West Sound **279**
South Wirral News **84**
South Yorkshire Sport **145**
South Yorkshire Times **101**
Southall Gazette **93**
Southampton Advertiser **81, 88**
Southampton Institute **372, 375**
Southend on Sunday **87**
Southend Standard Recorder **87**
Southend Yellow Advertiser **87**
Southern Counties Radio **262**

Southern Daily Echo **88**
Southern FM **280**
Southern Newspapers **73**
Southern Reporter **103**
Southern Staff Services **377**
Southern Star **258**, **314**
Southnews **73**
Southport Champion **92**
Southport Midweek Visiter **92**
Southport Visiter **92**
Southwark News **74**, **94**
Souvenir Press **138**
Sovereign Radio **280**
Sovereign Recruitment **377**
Space Press **145**
Spalding & South Lincs Herald **74**
Spalding Guardian **91**
Spanish News Agency EFE **145**
Spark Magazine **122**
SPCK **138**
Speakeasy Productions **258**
Special Schools in Britain **130**
Specialist Crafts **138**
Specific Films **258**
Spectator Magazine **117**, **122**, **130**
Spectator Newspapers **74**
Spectrum **130**
Spectrum Chinese Programmes **311**
Spectrum Radio **280**, **311**
Spellmount **138**
Spenborough Guardian **102**
Spice Media **310**
Spike Island **258**
Spilsby Target **91**
Spire Films **258**
Spire FM **280**
Spirit **130**
Spirit Films **258**
Spirit FM **280**
Spitfire Films **258**
SPL **117**
Split Screen **258**
Spokesman **162**
Sport & General Press Agency **155**
Sporting Gun **130**
Sporting Pictures UK **155**
Sporting Press **316**
Sports Management **130**
Sports Marketing **130**
Sports Video Library **250**
Sports Writers Association of Gt Britain **173**
Sportsmedia Broadcasting **246**
Sportsphoto **155**
Sportsworld **316**
Spot **130**
Spotlight **130**
Springer-Verlag **138**
Sprocketeers **258**
Squall Download **122**
SR & VI Crane **69**
St Albans & Harpenden Observer **89**
St Andrews Citizen **104**
St Austell, Newquay Packet **85 85**
St Bride Printing Library **172**
St Elmo Films **258**

St Helen's College **375**
St Helens Reporter **92**
St Ives Printing & Publishing Co **74**
St Ives Times & Echo **85**
St Luke's **355**
St Martins College **375**
St Mary's College **375**
St Neots Weekly News **84**
St Pancras Films **258**
St Paul's Bibliographies **138**
St Pauls **138**
Stacey International **138**
Stafford Chronicle **97**
Stafford Post **97**
Staffordshire Newsletter **97**
Staffordshire University **369**, **372**, **375**
Stage **117**, **290**
Stage & Television Today **130**
Stage, Screen & Radio **130**, **290**
Stainer & Bell **138**
Staines Informer **98**
Stalybridge Reporter **95**
Stamford Citizen **91**
Stamford Herald **91**
Stampede **258**
Stanley Gibbons **138**
Stanley Staff Bureau **377**
Stanley Thornes **138**
Stanmore Observer **93**
Star **77**, **319**
Star Classified **89**
Star FM **280**
Star Newspapers Camberley **74**
Star Publishing **74**
Star Trek **130**
Starburst **130**
Starcom **356**
Stargirl **130**
Starlock Pictures **258**
Stars & Cars **130**
Statewatch **122**, **130**
Stationery Office **117**, **138**
Status Appointments **377**
Steam Railway **130**
Steam World **130**
Steedman Ramage WS **338**
Stephinson TV **258**
Sterling Publishing **138**
Sterling Publishing Group **117**
Steve Boulton **258**
Steve Hill Agency **145**
Steve Hill Photography **157**
Stevenage Comet **89**
Stevenage/Letchworth Herald **89**
Stewart Bonney News Agency **145**
Stewart Ferguson Photography **157**
Steyning Herald **99**
Sticks, The **130**
Still Moving Picture Co **157**
Still Pictures Whole Earth Photo Library **157**
Stillwater Trout Angler **130**
Stirling & Alloa Shopper **105**
Stirling Film **258**
Stirling News **105**

Stirling Observer **105**
Stockbridge Films **258**
Stockport Express Advertiser **95**
Stockport Messenger **95**
Stockport Times **95**
Stockton Herald & Post **101**
Stoke Sentinel **97**
Stone City Films **258**
Stop Gap Marketing **377**
Stories **258**
Storm TV **258**
Stornoway Gazette **103**, **105**
Storyland **130**
Storyline **258**
Stour Valley News **86**
Stourbridge Chronicle **100**
Stourbridge News **100**
Strabane Chronicle **107**
Strabane Weekly News **107**
Strad **130**
Straight Forward Productions **258**
Straight No Chaser **130**
Straight TV **258**
Strand News Service **145**
Strata Matrix **159**
Stratford & Newham Express **93**
Stratford Gazette **99**
Stratford Standard **99**
Strathearn Herald **105**
Strathspey/Badenoch Herald **104**
Strawberry Productions **258**
Stray Cat Motion Pictures **258**
Streatham Guardian **94**
Streatham Mercury **94**
Streetwise **130**
Streetwise TV **258**
Stretford Messenger **95**
Stroud News & Journal **88**
Structural Engineer **130**
Student Broadcast Journalist of the Year **383**
Student Broadcast Network **286**
Student Programming **240**
Student Radio Association **303**
Studies in Newspaper & Periodical History **163**
Studio Arts TV **258**
Studio Universal **235**
Style **235**
Style Publishing **117**
Subcon **130**
Suffolk Advertiser **97**
Suffolk College **375**
Suffolk Films **258**
Suffolk Free Press **97**
Suitcase Productions **258**
Summerhouse Publishing **117**
Summersdale Publishers **138**
Sun **60**
Sun FM **280**
Sunday Business **62**
Sunday Business Post **319**
Sunday Citizen **81**
Sunday Express **62**
Sunday Express Magazine **130**

S

Sunday Herald **79**
Sunday Independent **79, 86, 319**
Sunday Life Belfast **79**
Sunday Mail **79**
Sunday Mirror **62**
Sunday Mirror Magazine **130**
Sunday Post **79, 104**
Sunday Sport **62**
Sunday Sun **79**
Sunday Telegraph **62**
Sunday Times **62, 130**
Sunday Tribune **319**
Sunday World **319**
Sunderland Echo **99**
Sunderland Star **99**
Sundog Media **258**
Sunflower Books **138**
Sunrise FM **280**
Sunrise Radio **280, 286, 311**
Sunrise Radio Group **267**
Sunshine 855 **280**
Sunstone Films **258**
SuperMarketing **130**
Supershop **235**
Supervision **258**
Surf 107.7 **280**
Surma **310**
Surrey & Hants News **98**
Surrey & Hants Star **88**
Surrey Advertiser **79, 98**
Surrey Comet **94**
Surrey County Magazine **130**
Surrey Institute of Art & Design **369, 372, 375**
Surrey Mirror **98**
Surveyor **98**
Susan Young **258**
Sussex Academic Press **138**
Sussex Express & Herald **98**
Sussex Life **130**
Sutton Borough Guardian **94**
Sutton Coldfield College **369**
Sutton Coldfield News **100**
Sutton Coldfield Observer **100**
Sutton Publishing **138**
SVC Screen Entertainment **258**
Swadlincote Times **85**
Swanage & Wareham Adv **86**
Swanley Times **90**
Swansea Herald of Wales **106**
Swansea Institute of Higher Ed **375**
Swansea Sound **280**
Swarovski Magazine **130**
Sweet and Maxwell **118, 138**
Sweet FA **130**
Swepstone Walsh **338**
Swift Imagery **157**
Swindon Evening Advertiser **100**
Swindon Local **240**
Swindon Star **100**
Swing Productions **258**
Switchdigital **284**
Sygma **157**
Sylvia Gray Staff Agency **377**
Syndicated Features **157**

T

T&T Clarke **138**
T.V **235**
T3 **130**
Ta Nea **310**
Tablet **130**
Tablet Publishing Company **117**
Take Video Video & Film **258**
Take a Break **130**
Take One **240**
Take That **138**
Takeaway Media **258**
Talent Television **258**
Talisman Films **258**
Talkback **258**
Talking Newspaper Association **173**
talkSPORT **266**
Tall Order Productions **258**
Tall Stories **258**
Tamarind **138**
Tameside Reporter **84, 94, 95**
Tamil Radio and Television TRT **286**
Tamworth Herald **74, 97**
Tamworth Post **97**
Tandem Television **258**
Tangent Films **258**
Tango Films **258**
Tanja Howarth **135**
Tapecraft Productions **258**
Tarlo Lyons **338**
Tarquin Publications **138**
Tass/Itar **145**
Taste **130**
Tate Gallery Publishing **138**
Tatler **130**
Taunton Express & Star **96**
Taunton Midweek Gazette **96**
Tavistock Times Gazette **86**
Tawd Valley Cable **239**
Taxation **130**
Taxi News **316**
Tay FM/Radio Tay AM **280**
Taylor & Francis **138**
Taylor and Francis Carfax **118**
Taylor Joynson Garrett **338**
Taylored Productions **258**
TBWA GGT Simons Palmer **355**
TC TV **258**
TCB Recruitment **377**
TCC Nordic **235**
Teamwork **310**
Technical Review Middle East **130**
Technology Ireland **316**
Teddington & Hampton Times **94**
Teenage Magazine Arbitration Panel **173**
Teeny Weeny Families **130**
Teesdale Mercury **74, 87**
Teespress Agencies **145**
Teignmouth News **86**
Teignmouth Post **86**
Telecommunications Users' Association **303**
TeleG **229**
Telegraph Books **138**
Telegraph Magazine **130**
Telemagination **258**

Teletext **243**
Teletubbies **130**
Television **290**
Television & Radio Industries Club **303**
Television Asia **290**
Television Business International **130, 293**
Television Company, **258**
Television Europe **130, 291**
Television International **130, 291**
Television Junction **258**
Television Reed **130**
Television Sport & Leisure **258**
Television X **235**
Televisual **130, 291**
Telewest Communications **239**
Telford Journal **96**
Teliesyn **258**
Tell Sell **235**
TellAVision TV **258**
Tellex Monitors **159**
TellTale Productions **258**
TellyWest Avon area **240**
Tempest Films **258**
Ten 17 **281**
Tenby Observer **106**
Tern Television Productions **258**
Terra Firma Film Productions **258**
Tessa Sayle Agency **135**
Testimony Films **258**
Tewkesbury Admag **88**
Text **100**
TFM **281**
TG Scott **117**
Thames & Hudson **138**
Thames Publishing **138**
Thames Valley University **375**
Thanet Adscene **90**
Thanet Extra **90**
Thanet Times **90**
That 70's Co **258**
That's Life! **130**
The Money Channel **234**
the net **128**
Theodore Goddard **338**
Thetford & Watton Times **95**
Third Eye Productions **258**
Third Man Productions **258**
Third Text **130**
Third Way **122, 130**
Thomas Cook Magazine **130**
Thomas Nelson **138**
Thomson Corporation **118**
Thomson Financial Services **118**
Thornbury Gazette **83**
Thornton Cleveleys News **90**
Thura Film **258**
Thurrock & Lakeside Recorder **87**
Thurrock Gazette **87**
Thurrock Yellow Advertiser **87**
Thurrock, Lakeside, Grays Post **87**
Tidy Productions **258**
Tiger Aspect **258**
Tiger Lily Films **258**
Tigervision **258**
Tigress Productions **258**
TilesFM **286**

Tillage Farmer, **316**
Tilling Productions **258**
Tilt Films **258**
Tim Wood Agency **145**
Timber For Architects **130**
Timber Trades Journal **130**
Time Life International **118**, **130**
Time Out **118**, **130**
The Times **60**
Times Education Supplements **130**
Times Literary Supplement **130**
Times Supplements **118**
Timothy Benn Publishing **118**
Tindle Newspapers **74**
Tindle Radio **267**
Tipp FM **319**
Tipperary Mid-West Radio **319**
Tipperary Star **314**
Titan Books **138**
Titan Magazinel **118**
Titanic **258**
Titbits **130**
Titmuss Sainer Dechert **338**
TLR **281**
TMB Weekly **162**
TNT **235**
TNTV **258**
Today's Farm **316**
Today's Golfer **130**
Today's Runner **130**
Todmorden News **102**
Todmorden News & Advertiser **90**
Tods Murray WS **338**
Toledo **258**
Tomboy Films **258**
Tonbridge & District Friday-Ad **90**
Tonic Films **259**
Tonic Pictures **259**
Top Gear **130**
Top Left **259**
Top Of Pops **130**
Top Sante **130**
Top Sante Health & Beauty **130**
Topham Picturepoint **157**
Topical TV **259**
Toplum Postasi **310**
Topper Newspapers **74**
Torbay News Agency **145**
Torbay Weekender **86**
Torquay Herald Express **86**
Total 64 **131**
Total Bike **131**
Total Film **131**
Total Football **131**
Total Guitar **131**
Total Production **131**
Total Publishing Awards **383**
Total Rock Radio **286**
Totnes Times Series **86**
Tottenham & Wood Green Journal **93**
Touch **131**
Touch Magazine **310**
Touch Productions **259**

Tower FM **281**
Tower Hamlets **240**
Town FM **285**
Townswoman **131**
Toy Soldier & Model Figures **131**
Toy Trader **131**
Toybox **131**
TPD Publishing **118**
Track 29 **259**
Trade It **131**
Trade Marks Journal **131**
TradeLinks Journal **316**
Traditional Homes **131**
Trail **131**
Training **131**
Training Direct International **369**
Trans World International **259**
TransAtlantic Films **259**
Transit **131**
Transport Retort **131**
Transworld Publishers **138**
Travail Employment **377**
Travel **235**
Travel and exploration **235**
Travel Channel **235**
Travel Ink Photo & Feature Library **157**
Travel Trade Gazette **131**
Travelex Travel Writers Awards **383**
Trax FM **281**
Treasure Hunting **131**
Treasure Trove Pictures **259**
Treehouse Children's Books **138**
Trees **131**
Trees are News **131**
Trentham Books **138**
Trevor, Lavinia **135**
Tri Media Publishing **74**
Tribune **122**, **131**
Tricky Pictures **259**
Tricorn Associates **259**
Trident Midland Newspapers **74**
Triffic Films **259**
Trijbits Productions **259**
Trinity and All Saints College **369**, **372**
Trinity College Carmarthen **375**
Trinity PLC **365**
Trinity Publications **118**
Trinity-Mirror **74**
Triple Echo Productions **259**
Troon & Prestwick Times **103**
Tropix **157**
Trotman & Co **138**
Trouble **235**
Trouble and Strife **122**
Trout & Salmon **131**
Trout Fisherman **131**
Trowbridge/Melksham Adv **100**
Truck **131**
Truck & Driver **131**
True Corner Productions **259**
True TV and Film **259**
True Visions Productions **259**
Truro Packet **85**

Try Again **259**
TSU Recruitment **377**
Tuam Herald **314**
Tuarascail **316**
Tullamore Tribune **314**
Tullstar Productions **259**
Tumble Hill Productions **259**
Tunbridge Wells Adscene **90**
Tunbridge Wells Extra **90**
Tunbridge Wells Friday-Ad **90**
Tunbridge Wells Leader **90**
Tunbridge Wells News in Focus **90**
Tunnels and Tunnelling **131**
Turn On Television **259**
Turner Classic Movies **235**
Turnround **259**
Turriff & District Advertiser **102**
.tv **235**
TV & Satellite Week **131**, **291**
TV 21 **259**
TV 6 **259**
TV Danmark1 **235**
TV Hits **131**
TV Land **235**
TV News London **246**
TV Quick **131**, **291**
TV Shop **235**
TV Times **131**, **291**
TV Travel Shop **235**
TV World **131**
TV Zone **291**
TV12 **242**
TV3 **235**, **316**
TVBS Europe **235**
TVC9 **242**
TVF **259**
TVF International **259**
TV-You **229**
Tweeddale Press Group **74**
Twelfth House **259**
Twentieth Century Fox **259**
Twenty Twenty Television **259**
TWI Archive **157**, **250**
Twinkle **131**
Two Four Productions **259**
Two Sides TV **259**
Two-Can Design **138**
Two-Ten News Network **145**
TY FFILM **259**
Tyne Tees Television **222**
Tyro Films & TV **259**
Tyrone Constitution **74**, **107**
Tyrone Courier **107**
Tyrone Democrat **107**
Tyrone Times **107**

U

U Direct Films **235**
U Magazine **316**
U! **235**
UBS Warburg Dillon Read **358**
UCAS **365**
UCB United Christian Broadcasters **286**
Uckfield Friday-Ad **98**
Uden Associates **259**
UFO Times **131**
Ugly Duckling Productions **259**
UK Arena (BBC/Flextech) **235**
UK Gold **229, 235**
UK Horizons **229, 235**
UK Media Yearbook **353**
UK Newsletter and Electronic Publishers Association **173**
UK Play **229**
UK Play (BBC/Flextech) **235**
UK Press Directory - Newspapers **164**
UK Press gazette **131**
UK Radio Guide & Directory **291**
UK Style **229**
UK Style (BBC/Flextech) **235**
UKRD Group **267**
Ulrich's International Periodicals Directory **164**
Ulster Gazette **107**
Ulster Herald **107**
Ulster Nation **131**
Ulster Star **107**
Ulster Television **223**
Ultimate PC **131**
Umbrella Entertainment **259**
Umbrella Pictures **259**
Umbrella Productions **259**
Uncut **131**
Under Five Contact **131**
Undercurrents **122**
Unhooked Prods **259**
Unicorn Books **138**
Unicorn Organisation **259**
Union Pictures **259**
Union Review **131**
Unique's Business News/Unique **246**
United Advertising Publications **74, 118**
United Artists **259**
United Broadcasting **259**
United News and Media **118**
United Northern Photographers **157**
United Press International UPI **145**
United Provincial Newspapers **74**
Unity **316**
Unity Media **118**
Universal International Television **250**
Universal McCann **357**
Universal Pictorial Press & Agency **157**
Universal Pictures **259**
Universe **131**
University College London **372**
University College Chichester **375**
University College Northampton **375**
University College Warrington **375**
University College Worcester **375**
University of Birmingham **375**
University of Bournemouth **361**
University of Bradford **372, 375**

University of Brighton **375**
University of Bristol **373**
University of Central England in B'ham **373, 375**
University of Central Lancashire **361, 369, 373, 375**
University of East Anglia **375**
University of East London **375**
University of Essex **375**
University of Exeter Press **138**
University of Glamorgan **376**
University of Greenwich **376**
University of Hertfordshire **376**
University of Huddersfield **376**
University of Leeds **373, 376**
University of Leicester **376**
University of Lincolnshire & Humberside **376**
University of Liverpool **376**
University of London **373**
University of Luton **376**
University of Luton Press **138**
University of Manchester Broadcasting Symposia **293**
University of Newcastle **376**
University of North London **376**
University of Northumbria **376**
University of Paisley **376**
University of Plymouth **235**
University of Portsmouth **376**
University of Sheffield **369, 376**
University of Southampton **376**
University of Stirling **376**
University of Sunderland **376**
University of Sussex **376**
University of Teesside **376**
University of the West of England, Bristol **376**
University of Ulster **369, 376**
University of Wales **369**
University of Wales Press **138**
University of Wales, Bangor **376**
University of Wales, Lampeter **376**
University of Westminster **369, 373, 376**
University of Wolverhampton **369, 376**
Unlimited **131**
Unmanned Vehicles **131**
Untold **131**
Untold Magazine **310**
Updata **316**
Update **131**
Upfront Televsion **259**
Upgrade Recruitment **377**
Uptown Films **259**
Urban tv **259**
Usborne Publishing **138**
Used Car Dealer **131**
Utility Europe **131**
Uttoxeter Advertiser **97**
Uttoxeter Echo **97**
Uttoxeter Post & Times **97**
UTV **223**
Uxbridge & Hillingdon Leader **93**
Uxbridge Gazette **93**
Uxbridge Informer **93**

V

V&A Publications **138**
Vale Post **106**
Valleys Radio **281**
Vanessa Holt **135**
Vanguard **131**
Vanguard Films **259**
Vanity Fair **131**
Vegetarian Good Food BBC **131**
Vegetarian, The **131**
Ventura **138**
Ventura Productions **259**
Vera Productions **259**
Verso **138**
Vertigo **291**
Vesey Observer **100**
Veterinary Times **131**
VH**1 235**
Vibe FM **281**
Vibrant Productions **259**
Vicarious Productions **259**
Victor Film Co **259**
Victor Gollancz **138**
Victoria & Pimlico Times **93**
Victoria Lewis Recruitment **377**
Victoria Real **259**
Video Assignments **259**
Video Visuals **259**
Videotron Channel **240**
Viewfinder **291**
Viking **138**
Viking FM **281**
Vintage Motor Cycle **131**
Virago Press **138**
Virgin **1215 266**
Virgin Publishing **138**
Virgin Radio **286**
Virgin Radio London **281**
Virtue Books **138**
Visage Productions **259**
Visible Ink TV **259**
Visible Jazz **259**
Vision Channel **240**
Vision Paperbacks **138**
Vision Rams **240**
Visionworks **259**
Visitor **316**
Viva Films **259**
Viz **131, 259**
VNU Business Publications **118**
Vobavision **259**
Vogue **131**
Voice **131**
Voice Communications Group **118**
Voice Group **310**
Voice of the Listener & Viewer **291, 303**
Voice, The **122**
Volcano Films **259**
Volvo Magazine **131**
Vortex TV **259**
Voyager Television **259**
VT4 **235**

W

W Foulsham **138**
W Peters & Son **73**
W Y Crichton & Co **69**
Wakefield Express **102**
Walden Local **87**
Wales Film & Television Archive **250**
Wales News Service **145**
Wales on Sunday **79**, **105**
Walker Books **138**
Walker Media **357**
Wall to Wall Television **259**
Wallasey News **92**
Walmley Observer **100**
Walsall Advertiser **100**
Walsall Observer **100**
Waltham Abbey Gazette **87**
Waltham Forest **240**
Waltham Forest Guardian **93**
Waltham Forest Independent **93**
Walthamstow Guardian **93**
Walton & Hersham News & Mail **98**
Walton & Weybridge Leader **98**
Wanderlust **131**
Wandsworth Borough News **94**
Wandsworth Comet **93**
Wandsworth/Putney Guardian **94**
Wantage & Grove Herald **96**
War Cry **131**
Warburg Institute **138**
Ward Lock **138**
Ward Lock Educational **138**
Wark, Clements & Co **259**
Warminster Journal **100**
Warner Brothers **259**
Warner Sisters Film **259**
Warner/Chappell Plays **138**
Warners Group **118**
Warrington Collegiate Institute **369**
Warrington Guardian **79**, **84**
Warrington Mercury **84**
Warwick Courier **99**
Warwickshire College **369**
Warwickshire News Agency **145**
Washington Star **99**
Watan Weekend **310**
Watchmaker Productions **259**
Watchword **259**
Water **131**
Water Gardener **131**
Water Productions **259**
Waterford News & Star e **314**
Watermark Films **259**
Waterways **131**
Waterways Photo Library **157**
Watford Free Observer **89**
Watson, Little **135**
Watson's Press Agency **145**
Watts Publishing Group **138**
Wave **282**
Wave **102 282**
Waveney Advertiser **97**
WAVES **365**
Wax **131**
Wayland Publishers **138**
WCRS **355**
Wealden Advertiser **90**
Wear Valley Advertiser **87**
Websters International **138**

Wedding & Home **131**
Wedding Cakes **131**
Week, The **131,162**
Weekend Times **102**
Weekly Des Pardes **310**
Weekly East **310**
Weekly Law Digest **131**
Weekly News **104**, **131**
Weekly Pakistan **310**
Weekly Potrika **310**
Weidenfeld & Nicolson **138**
Weigall Productions **259**
Weight Watchers **131**
Wellcome Medical Science **157**
Wellingborough Citizen **95**
Wellingborough Herald & Post **95**
Wellington Weekly News **96**
Welsh Office - Information Division **145**
Welshpool County Times **106**
Welwyn & Hatfield Herald **89**
Welwyn & Hatfield Times **89**
Welwyn Garden Review **89**
Wembley & Kenton Recorder **93**
Wembley & Kingsbury Leader **93**
Wessex Film & Sound Archive **250**
Wessex FM **282**
Wessex News & Features Agency **145**
Wessex Photos **157**
West Briton **79**, **85**
West Cumberland Times & Star **85**
West Cumbrian Gazette **85**
West Derby Merseymart **92**
West Dublin Community Radio **319**
West FM **282**
West Herts & Watford Observer **89**
West Herts College **373**, **376**
West Highland Animation **259**
West Highland Free Press **104**
West Highland Publishing Co **74**
West Lothian Courier **105**
West Lothian Herald **105**
West Riding News & Sports **145**
West Somerset Free Press **96**
West Somerset Trader **96**
West Sound **282**
West Suffolk Mercury **97**
West Sussex County Times **99**
West Sussex Gazette **99**
West Wales Aerials **239**
West Wiltshire Advertiser **100**
Westbury/Warminster Adv **100**
Westcountry Television **223**
Western Daily Press **76**
Western Gazette **79**, **97**
Western International Media **357**
Western Mail **76**
Western Morning News **76**, **86**
Western People **314**
Western Telegraph **106**
Westlaw **118**
Westmeath Examiner **314**
Westmeath Independent **314**
Westmeath Topic **314**
Westminster & Pimlico News **93**
Westminster Mail **93**
Westminster Press **74**
Westmoreland Gazette **79**, **85**
Weston & Somerset Mercury **97**
Weston & Worle News **97**

Weston-Super-Mare Admag **97**
Westray Recruitment Consultant **377**
Westway Film Production **259**
Wetherby News **102**
Wexford Echo **314**
Wexford Guardian **314**
Weymouth Advertiser **86**
WH Freeman **138**
Wharfe Valley Times **102**
Wharfedale Observer **102**
What Bike? **131**
What Camcorder? **131**
What Car? **131**
What Digital Camera? **131**
What HiFi? **131**
What Investment? **131**
What Mobile & Cellphone **131**
What Mortgage? **131**
What PC & Software? **131**
What Plant? **131**
What Satellite TV **291**
What Satellite? **131**
What the Papers Say Awards **383**
What to Buy for Business **131**
What Video? **131**
What's in Store **235**
What's New in ??? **131**
What's On TV **131, 291**
When Saturday Comes **131**
WHERE Killarney **316**
Which Motorcaravan **131**
Which? **118**, **131**, **138**
Whisky Magazine **131**
Whitaker & Sons **138**
Whitby Davison **259**
Whitby Gazette **101**
Whitchurch Herald **96**
White Book **293**
White Dot **303**
White Magic **259**
Whitehaven News **85**
Whitehorse Films **259**
Whitehouse & Co **259**
Whitstable Gazette **90**
Whittet Books **138**
Who's Who in Digital, Cable & Satellite TV **293**
Wholesale Shopping Channel **235**
Whurr Publishers **138**
Wicklow People **314**
Wicklow Times **316**
Wide Eye Pictures **259**
Wide World **131**
Widnes Weekly News **84**
Widnes World **84**
Wigan Evening Post **95**
Wigan Observer **95**
Wigan Reporter **95**
Wiggin & Co **338**
Wigtown Free Press **74**, **103**
Wild Dream Films **259**
Wild Films **259**
Wild London **131**
Wild Rover Productions **259**
Wildcard Film and Television **259**
Wildcat Films **259**
Wildflower Productions **259**
Wildfowl and Wetlands **131**

W

Wildtrack TV **259**
Wiley Europe **138**
Willesden & Brent Chronicle **93**
William Heinemann **138**
William Morris Agency UK **135**
William Reed Publishing **118**
William Trimble **74**
Williams Worldwide Television **235**
Willings Press Guide **164, 353**
Wilmslow Express Advertiser **84**
Wilmslow Messenger **84**
Wilts & Glos.Standard Advertiser **88**
Wiltshire Gazette & Herald **100**
Wiltshire Sound **262**
Wiltshire Star **100**
Wiltshire Times **100**
Wimbledon Guardian **94**
Win 107.2 **282**
Winchester Entertainment **259**
Winchester Gazette Extra **88**
Windfall Films **259**
Windmill Lane Pictures **319**
Windows Expert **131**
Windrush Photos **157**
Windrush Press **138**
Windsor & Maidenhead Obs **83**
Windsor/Slough **83**
Wine **131**
Wings **316**
Wire **131**
Wire Productions **259**
Wired FM **319**
Wireless Group **267**
Wireless Preservation Society **303**
Wirral Globe **81, 92**
Wirral Metropolitan College **376**
Wisbech Standard **84**
Wisden Cricket Monthly **131**
Wish 102.4 **282**
Wishaw Press **104**
Wishaw World **104**
Wishbone Productions **259**
Witney & W Oxon Gazette **96**
Wizja Channels **235**
WLR FM **319**
WM **131**
Wobbly Picture Productions **259**
Woking Informer **98**
Woking News & Mail **98**
Woking Review **98**
Wokingham & Bracknell Times **83**
Wokingham News **83**
Wolverhampton Chronicle **100**
Wolverhampton College **369**
Woman **131**
Woman & Home **131**
Woman Alive **131**
Woman's Journal **131**
Woman's Own **131**
Woman's Realm **131**
Woman's Way **316**
Woman's Weekly **131**
Women & Golf **131**
Women in General Practice **131**
Women in Publishing **173**
Women Now Films **259**
Women Writers Network **173**

Women's Independent Cinema House **259**
Women's Radio Group **303**
Womens Press **138**
Wood Based Panels International **131**
Wood Green Herald **93**
Woodchester Productions **259**
Woodfall Wild Images **157**
Woodhall Spa Target **91**
Woodhead Publishing **138**
Woodley Chronicle **83**
Woodworker **131**
Woodworking News **131**
Woolwich/Charlton Mercury **94**
Worcester Evening News **100**
Worcester Why **100**
Word Search **131**
Wordsworth Editions **138**
Workers' Health **131**
Working Title Films **259**
Working Together **131**
Working Women **131**
Working Wonders Recruitment **377**
Works Management **131**
Worksop Midweek Guardian **96**
Worksop Trader News **96**
World Advertising Trends **353**
World International **138**
World Media **291**
World of Interiors **131**
World of Wonder **259**
World Productions **259**
World Radio & TV Handbook **293**
World Radio NetworkYouth fm **286**
World Service press office **202**
World Soccer **131**
World Television **259**
World Today **131**
World Wide Group **259**
World's End Productions **259**
World's Fair **131**
Worldmark Productions **259**
WorldWide Entertainment News **259**
Worldwide Television News WTN **246**
Worship Channel Europe **235**
Worshipful Company of Stationers **173**
Worthing Advertiser **99**
Worthing Guardian **99**
Worthing Herald **99**
Wrench & Franks **259**
Wrexham Evening Leader **106**
Wrexham Leader **106**
Writer's Handbook **164**
Writers' & Artists' Yearbook **164**
Writers & Readers **138**
Writers' Guild of Great Britain **173, 303**
Writing Magazine **131**
Writers' News **131, 162**
Writers' Newsletter **131, 162**
Writers' Republic **259**
WRN World Radio Network **246**
WW Norton **138**
WWAV Rapp Collins Group **355**
WWAV Rapp Collins Media **357**
Wymondham Mercury **95**
Wyvern FM **282**

X, Y & Z

X Files Monthly **131**
X Press **138**
X1 **235**
Xanadu Productions **259**
Xanthe Film & TV **259**
X-Cel FM **282**
Xfm **282**
Xinhua News Agency of China **145**
XL Entertainment **259**
XL for Men **131**
Xpose **131**
x-trax **246**
XYTV **259**
Y Cyfnod **106**
Y Cymro **106**
Y Dydd **106**
Y Tyst **106**
Yachting Monthly **131**
Yachting Press **118**
Yachting World **131**
Yaffa Newspaper Service **145**
Yale University Press **138**
Yately & District Courier wf **88**
Yately Mail **88**
Yattendon Investment Trust **74**
YCTV **240**
Yeovil Express & Star **97**
Yes Television **240**
YI Productions **259**
Yoda Productions **259**
York Star **102**
Yorkshire Coast Radio **282**
Yorkshire Evening Post **77, 102**
Yorkshire Evening Press **102**
Yorkshire Gazette & Herald **102**
Yorkshire Post **76, 102**
Yorkshire Television **223**
YorkshireTyne Tees TV **259**
You & Your Wedding **131**
You Magazine free **131**
Young Dancer **131**
Young Newspaper Executives' **173**
Young Travel Writer of the Year **383**
Your ?? **131**
Yours **131**
Youth Cable Television **240**
Yr Herald **106**
Yvonne Palmer Associated **377**
Zanzibar Film Productions **259**
ZCZ Films **259**
Zebra Productions **259**
Zed Books **138**
Zee TV **235, 311**
ZEF Productions **259**
Zenith Entertainments **259**
Zenith Media **259, 357**
Zephyr Films **259**
Zerb **291**
Zest **131**
Ziff-Davis UK **118**
Zin Zan Productions **259**
Zingaru Productionns **259**
Zipper **131**
Zit **131**
ZKK **259**
ZM **131**
Zoe Books **138**
ZTV **235**

COLLE

BRITISH

STAMPS

A STANLEY GIBBONS CHECKLIST OF
THE STAMPS OF GREAT BRITAIN

2003 (54th) Edition

STANLEY GIBBONS LTD

By Appointment to H.M. the Queen
Stanley Gibbons Ltd, London Philatelists.

London and Ringwood

COLLECT BRITISH STAMPS

The 2003 edition

From the famous Penny Black of 1840 to the absorbing issues of today, the stamps of Great Britain are highly popular with collectors. *Collect British Stamps* has been our message since very early days – but particularly since the First Edition of this checklist in September 1967. This 54th edition includes all the recent issues. Prices have been carefully revised to reflect today's market. Total sales of *Collect British Stamps* are now over 3·8 million copies.

Collect British Stamps appears in the autumn of each year. A more detailed Great Britain catalogue, the *Concise,* is published each spring. The *Great Britain Concise* incorporates many additional listings covering watermark varieties, phosphor omitted errors, missing colour errors, stamp booklets and special commemorative First Day Cover postmarks. It is ideally suited for the collector who wishes to discover more about GB stamps.

Listings in this edition of *Collect British Stamps* include all 2002 issues which have appeared up to the publication date.

Scope. *Collect British Stamps* comprises:

- All stamps with different watermark (*wmk*) or perforation (*perf*).

- Visible plate numbers on the Victorian issues.

- Graphite-lined and phosphor issues, including variations in the numbers of phosphor bands.

- First Day Covers for Definitives from 1936, Regionals and all Special Issues.

- Presentation, Gift and Souvenir Packs.

- Post Office Yearbooks.

- Regional issues and War Occupation stamps of Guernsey and Jersey.

- Postage Due and Official Stamps.

- Post Office Picture Cards (PHQ cards).

- Commemorative gutter pairs and 'Traffic Light' gutter pairs listed as mint sets.

- Royal Mail Postage Labels priced as sets and on P.O. First Day Cover.

Stamps of the independent postal administrations of Guernsey, Isle of Man and Jersey are contained in *Collect Channel Islands and Isle of Man Stamps.*

Layout. Stamps are set out chronologically by date of issue. In the catalogue lists the first numeral is the Stanley Gibbons catalogue number; the black (boldface) numeral alongside is the type number referring to the respective illustration. A blank in this column implies that the number immediately above is repeated. The denomination and colour of the stamp are then shown. Before February 1971 British currency was:

£1 = 20s   One pound = twenty shillings *and*
1s = 12d   One shilling = twelve pence.

Upon decimalisation this became:

£1 = 100p   One pound = one hundred (new) pence.

The catalogue list then shows two price columns. The left-hand is for unused stamps and the right-hand for used. Corresponding small boxes are provided in which collectors may wish to check off the items in their collection.

Our method of indicating prices is:
Numerals for pence, e.g. 10 denotes 10p (10 pence). Numerals for pounds and pence, e.g. 4·25 denotes £4·25 (4 pounds and 25 pence). For £100 and above, prices are in whole pounds and so include the £ sign and omit the zeros for pence.

Colour illustrations. The colour illustrations of stamps are intended as a guide only; they may differ in shade from the originals.

Size of illustrations. To comply with Post Office regulations stamp illustrations are three-quarters linear side. Separate illustrations of surcharges, overprints and watermarks are actual size.

Prices. Prices quoted in this catalogue are our selling prices at the time the book went to press. They are for stamps in fine condition; in issues where condition varies we may ask more for the superb and less for the sub-standard. The unused prices for stamps of Queen Victoria to King George V are for lightly hinged examples. Unused prices for King Edward VIII to Queen Elizabeth II are for unmounted mint (though when not available unmounted, mounted stamps are often supplied at a lower price). Prices for used stamps refer to postally used copies. All prices are subject to change without prior notice and we give no guarantee to supply all stamps priced, since it is not possible to keep every catalogued item in stock. Individual low value stamps sold at 399, Strand are liable to an additional handling charge. Commemorative issues may only be available in complete sets.

In the price columns:
† = Does not exist.
(—) or blank = Exists, or may exist, but price cannot be quoted.
* = Not normally issued (the so-called 'Abnormals' of 1862–80).

Perforations. The 'perforation' is the number of holes in a length of 2 cm, as measured by the Gibbons *Instanta* gauge. The stamp is viewed against a dark background with the transparent gauge put on top of it. Perforations are quoted to the nearest half. Stamps without perforation are termed 'imperforate'.

From 1992 certain stamps occur with a large elliptical (oval) hole inserted in each line of vertical perforations. The £10 definitive, No. 1658, is unique in having two such holes in the horizontal perforations.

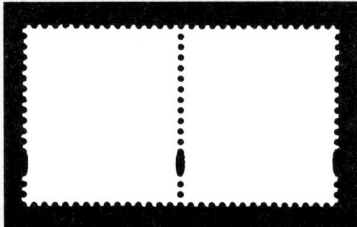

Elliptical perforations

Se-tenant combinations. *Se-tenant* means 'joined together'. Some sets include stamps of different design arranged *se-tenant* as blocks or strips and these are often collected unsevered as issued. Where such combinations exist the stamps are priced both mint and used, as singles or complete sets. The set price for mint refers to the unsevered combination plus singles of any other values in the set. The used set price is for single stamps of all values.

First day covers. Prices for first day covers are for complete sets used on plain covers (Nos. 430/8, 453/60, 462/78*b*, 485/90, and 503/12) or on special covers (Nos. 461, 479/84, 491/502 and 513 onwards), the stamps of which are cancelled with ordinary operational postmarks (1924–1962) or by the *standard* 'First Day of Issue' postmarks (1963 onwards). The British Post Office did not provide 'First Day' treatment for every definitive issued after 1963. Where the stamps in a set were issued on different days, prices are for a cover from each day.

Presentation Packs. Special packs comprising slip-in cards with printed information inside a protective covering, were introduced for the 1964 Shakespeare issue. Collectors packs, containing commemoratives from the preceding twelve months, were issued from 1967. Some packs with text in German from 1968–69 exist as does a Japanese version of the pack for Nos. 916/17. Yearbooks, hardbound and illustrated in colour within a slip cover, joined the product range in 1984.

PHQ cards. Since 1973 the Post Office has produced a series of picture cards, which can be sent through the post as postcards. Each card shows an enlarged colour reproduction of a current British stamp, either of one or more values from a set or of all values. Cards are priced here in fine mint condition for sets complete as issued. The Post Office gives each card a 'PHQ' serial number, hence the term. The cards are usually on sale shortly before the date of issue of the stamps, but there is no officially designated 'first day'.

Used prices are for cards franked with the stamp depicted, on the obverse or reverse; the stamp being cancelled with an official postmark for first day of issue.

For 1973–76 issues cards with stamps on the obverse are worth about 25% more than the prices quoted.

Gutter pairs. All modern Great Britain commemoratives are produced in sheets containing two panes of stamps separated by a blank horizontal or vertical margin known as a gutter. This feature first made its appearance on some supplies of the 1972 Royal Silver Wedding 3p, and marked the introduction of Harrison & Sons' new 'Jumelle' stamp-printing press. There are advantages for both the printer and the Post Office in such a layout which has now been used for almost all commemorative issues since 1974.

The term 'gutter pair' is used for a pair of stamps separated by part of the blank gutter margin.

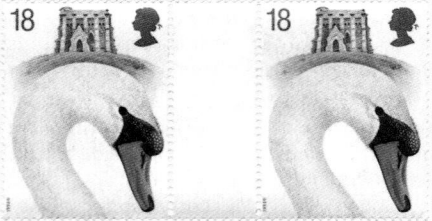

Gutter pair

Most printers include some form of colour check device on the sheet margins, in addition to the cylinder or plate numbers. Harrison & Sons used round 'dabs' or spots of colour, resembling traffic lights. For the period from the 1972 Royal Silver Wedding until the end of 1979 these colour dabs appeared in the gutter margin. Gutter pairs showing these 'traffic lights' are worth considerably more than the normal version.

Traffic light gutter pair

Catalogue numbers used. This checklist uses the same catalogue numbers as other current Stanley Gibbons catalogues.

Latest issue date for stamps recorded in this edition is 5 November 2002.

STANLEY GIBBONS LTD

Head Office: 399 Strand, London WC2R OLX.
Auction Room and Specialist Stamp Departments–
 Open Monday–Friday 9.30 a.m. to 5 p.m.
Shop – Open Monday to Friday 9 a.m. to 5.30 p.m.
 and Saturday 9.30 a.m. to 5.30 p.m.
Telephone 0207-836 8444 for all departments
E-mail: enquiries@stanleygibbons.co.uk
Website: www.stanleygibbons.com

Stanley Gibbons Publications:
 Parkside, Christchurch Road, Ringwood, Hants BH24 3SH. Telephone: 01425 472363
 Publications Mail Order, FREEPHONE: 0800 611622
 E-mail: info@stanleygibbons.co.uk

ISBN: 0-85259-533-6
© Stanley Gibbons Ltd 2002

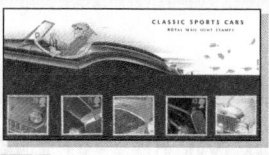

GB or All World we've got what you're looking for!

Looking to fill those awkward gaps in your collection through a reliable, one-stop supplier, without any fuss or bother?

Rick Warren Approvals are the solution.

We offer over 1/2 million individually priced stamps/sets so whatever you're looking for, we've probably got it. However, offering the best selection is only part of our service - take a look at what we offer!

- Selections when you want them.
- View at your leisure, at home, no pressure, no fuss.
- Prompt, personal service.
- Generous loyalty scheme.
- All major credit cards taken.
- See before you buy.

Fill those gaps in your collection with - Rick Warren Approvals

My interests are / I collect:

Please tick boxes as appropriate

Great Britain CI / IOM ☐	All World ☐	All BE ☐
QV / GV ☐	GVI ☐ QEII - 1970 ☐	QEII mod ☐

OTHER (please state) _____

_____

Mint & Used ☐   Mint Only ☐   Used Only ☐

YES. Please send me approval selections. I claim my £50* introductory vouchers. I am under no obligation and may cancel at any time.

CBS .03

NAME: _____

ADDRESS: _____

_____

_____

Credit Card No. _____

MasterCard VISA   Expiry Date _____

All approved selections governed by our Standard Terms & Conditions.
A copy sent with each selection.

Rick Warren Approvals FREEPOST Lingfield Surrey RH7 6ZA UK

Tel : +44 (0) 1342 833413   Fax : +44 (0) 1342 833892

www.apexstamps.com PTS

QUEEN VICTORIA

1837 (20 June)–1901 (22 Jan.)

IDENTIFICATION. In this checklist Victorian stamps are classified firstly according to which printing method was used –line-engraving, embossing or surface-printing.

Corner letters. Numerous stamps also have letters in all four, or just the lower corners. These were an anti-forgery device and the letters differ from stamp to stamp. If present in all four corners the upper pair are the reverse of the lower. Note the importance of these corner letters in the way the checklist is arranged.

Watermarks. Further classification depends on watermarks: these are illustrated in normal position, with stamps priced accordingly.

1 Line-engraved Issues

1

1a

1b

3 White lines added above and below head

2 Small Crown watermark

4 Large Crown watermark

Letters in lower corners

1840 *Wmk Small Crown Type* **2** *Imperforate*

Cat No.	Type		Unused	Used		
2	1	1d black	£3500	£200	□	□
5	1a	2d blue	£7500	£425	□	□

1841

8	1b	1d red-brown	£180	15·00	□	□
14	3	2d blue	£1500	60·00	□	□

1854–57 (*i*) *Wmk Small Crown Type* **2** *Perf* 16

17	1b	1d red-brown	£190	18·00	□	□
19	3	2d blue	£1800	85·00	□	□

(*ii*) *Wmk Small Crown Type* **2** *Perf* 14

24	1b	1d red-brown	£350	45·00	□	□
23	3	2d blue	£2500	£180	□	□

(*iii*) *Wmk Large Crown Type* **4** *Perf* 16

26	1b	1d red	£700	80·00	□	□
27	3	2d blue	£3500	£250	□	□

(*iv*) *Wmk Large Crown Type* **4** *Perf* 14

40	1b	1d red	40·00	9·00	□	□
34	3	2d blue	£1500	50·00	□	□

7

8

9 Watermark extending over three stamps

Letters in all four corners

Plate numbers. Stamps included a 'plate number' in their design and this affects valuation. The cheapest plates are priced here; see complete list of plate numbers overleaf.

1858–70 (*i*) *Wmk Type* **9** *Perf* 14

48	7	½d red	75·00	15·00	□	□

(*ii*) *Wmk Large Crown Type* **4** *Perf* 14

43	5	1d red	15·00	2·00	□	□
52	8	1½d red	£250	40·00	□	□
45	6	2d blue	£225	10·00	□	□

PLATE NUMBERS
on stamps of 1858–70 having letters in all four corners

Positions of Plate Numbers

Shows
Plate 9 (½d)

Shows
Plate 170 (1d, 2d)

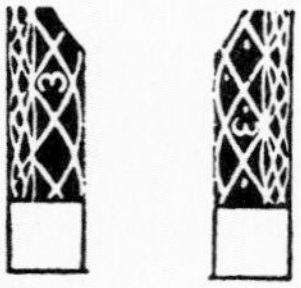

Shows
Plate 3 (1½d)

HALFPENNY VALUE (S.G. 48)

Plate	Un.	Used			Plate	Un.	Used		
1	£150	70·00	□	□	11	80·00	15·00	□	□
3	£125	35·00	□	□	12	80·00	15·00	□	□
4	£110	25·00	□	□	13	80·00	15·00	□	□
5	75·00	15·00	□	□	14	80·00	15·00	□	□
6	80·00	15·00	□	□	15	£125	35·00	□	□
8	£190	90·00	□	□	19	£140	50·00	□	□
9	£2500	£450	□	□	20	£160	70·00	□	□
10	90·00	15·00	□	□					

Plates 2, 7, 16, 17 and 18 were not completed, while Plates 21 and 22 though made were not used. Plate 9 was a reserve plate, not greatly used.

PENNY VALUE (S.G. 43)

Plate	Un.	Used			Plate	Un.	Used			Plate	Un.	Used			Plate	Un.	Used		
71	35·00	3·00	□	□	112	70·00	2·25	□	□	154	50·00	2·00	□	□	190	50·00	6·00	□	□
72	40·00	4·00	□	□	113	50·00	12·00	□	□	155	50·00	2·25	□	□	191	30·00	7·00	□	□
73	40·00	3·00	□	□	114	£250	12·00	□	□	156	45·00	2·00	□	□	192	50·00	2·00	□	□
74	40·00	2·00	□	□	115	90·00	2·25	□	□	157	50·00	2·00	□	□	193	30·00	2·00	□	□
76	35·00	2·00	□	□	116	75·00	9·00	□	□	158	30·00	2·00	□	□	194	50·00	8·00	□	□
77	£100000	£80000	□	□	117	45·00	2·00	□	□	159	30·00	2·00	□	□	195	50·00	8·00	□	□
78	90·00	2·00	□	□	118	50·00	2·00	□	□	160	30·00	2·00	□	□	196	50·00	5·00	□	□
79	30·00	2·00	□	□	119	45·00	2·00	□	□	161	60·00	7·00	□	□	197	55·00	9·00	□	□
80	45·00	2·00	□	□	120	15·00	2·00	□	□	162	50·00	7·00	□	□	198	40·00	6·00	□	□
81	45·00	2·25	□	□	121	40·00	9·50	□	□	163	50·00	3·00	□	□	199	55·00	6·00	□	□
82	90·00	4·00	□	□	122	15·00	2·00	□	□	164	50·00	3·00	□	□	200	60·00	2·00	□	□
83	£110	7·00	□	□	123	40·00	2·00	□	□	165	45·00	2·00	□	□	201	30·00	5·00	□	□
84	60·00	2·25	□	□	124	28·00	2·00	□	□	166	45·00	6·00	□	□	202	60·00	8·00	□	□
85	40·00	2·25	□	□	125	40·00	2·00	□	□	167	45·00	2·00	□	□	203	30·00	16·00	□	□
86	50·00	4·00	□	□	127	55·00	2·25	□	□	168	50·00	8·00	□	□	204	55·00	2·25	□	□
87	30·00	2·00	□	□	129	40·00	8·00	□	□	169	60·00	7·00	□	□	205	55·00	3·00	□	□
88	£130	8·00	□	□	130	55·00	2·25	□	□	170	35·00	2·00	□	□	206	55·00	9·00	□	□
89	40·00	2·00	□	□	131	65·00	16·00	□	□	171	15·00	2·00	□	□	207	60·00	9·00	□	□
90	40·00	2·00	□	□	132	£130	22·00	□	□	172	30·00	2·00	□	□	208	55·00	16·00	□	□
91	55·00	6·00	□	□	133	£110	9·00	□	□	173	70·00	9·00	□	□	209	50·00	9·00	□	□
92	35·00	2·00	□	□	134	15·00	2·00	□	□	174	30·00	2·00	□	□	210	65·00	12·00	□	□
93	50·00	2·00	□	□	135	95·00	26·00	□	□	175	60·00	3·50	□	□	211	70·00	20·00	□	□
94	45·00	5·00	□	□	136	90·00	20·00	□	□	176	60·00	2·25	□	□	212	60·00	11·00	□	□
95	40·00	2·00	□	□	137	28·00	2·25	□	□	177	40·00	2·00	□	□	213	60·00	11·00	□	□
96	45·00	2·00	□	□	138	18·00	2·00	□	□	178	60·00	3·50	□	□	214	65·00	18·00	□	□
97	40·00	3·50	□	□	139	60·00	16·00	□	□	179	50·00	2·25	□	□	215	65·00	18·00	□	□
98	50·00	6·00	□	□	140	18·00	2·00	□	□	180	60·00	5·00	□	□	216	70·00	18·00	□	□
99	55·00	5·00	□	□	141	£110	9·00	□	□	181	45·00	2·00	□	□	217	70·00	7·00	□	□
100	60·00	2·25	□	□	142	70·00	24·00	□	□	182	90·00	5·00	□	□	218	65·00	8·00	□	□
101	60·00	9·00	□	□	143	60·00	15·00	□	□	183	55·00	3·00	□	□	219	90·00	70·00	□	□
102	45·00	2·00	□	□	144	95·00	20·00	□	□	184	30·00	2·25	□	□	220	40·00	7·00	□	□
103	50·00	3·50	□	□	145	30·00	2·25	□	□	185	50·00	3·00	□	□	221	70·00	16·00	□	□
104	75·00	5·00	□	□	146	40·00	6·00	□	□	186	65·00	2·25	□	□	222	80·00	40·00	□	□
105	90·00	7·00	□	□	147	50·00	3·00	□	□	187	50·00	2·00	□	□	223	90·00	60·00	□	□
106	55·00	2·00	□	□	148	40·00	3·00	□	□	188	70·00	10·00	□	□	224	£100	50·00	□	□
107	60·00	7·00	□	□	149	40·00	6·00	□	□	189	70·00	7·00	□	□	225	£1250	£400	□	□
108	80·00	2·25	□	□	150	15·00	2·00	□	□										
109	85·00	3·50	□	□	151	60·00	9·00	□	□										
110	60·00	9·00	□	□	152	60·00	5·50	□	□										
111	50·00	2·25	□	□	153	£100	9·00	□	□										

Plates 69, 70, 75, 77, 126 and 128 were prepared but rejected. No stamps therefore exist, except for a very few from Plate 77 which somehow reached the public. Plate 177 stamps, by accident or design, are sometimes passed off as the rare Plate 77.

THREE-HALFPENNY VALUE (S.G. 52)

Plate	Un.	Used			Plate	Un.	Used		
(1)	£450	65·00	□	□	3	£250	40·00	□	□

Plate 1 did *not* have the plate number in the design. Plate 2 was not completed and no stamps exist.

TWOPENNY VALUE (S.G. 45)

Plate	Un.	Used			Plate	Un.	Used		
7	£650	45·00	□	□	13	£250	20·00	□	□
8	£600	32·00	□	□	14	£300	25·00	□	□
9	£225	10·00	□	□	15	£275	25·00	□	□
12	£1000	£110	□	□					

Plates 10 and 11 were prepared but rejected.

2 Embossed Issues

Prices are for stamps cut square and with average to fine embossing. Stamps with exceptionally clear embossing are worth more.

12

11

10

13

1847–54	*Wmk* 13 (6*d*), *no wmk* (*others*) *Imperforate*					
59	**12**	6d lilac	£4250	£550	□	□
57	**11**	10d brown	£3750	£725	□	□
54	**10**	1s green	£5000	£500	□	□

3 Surface-printed Issues

IDENTIFICATION. Check first whether the design includes corner letters or not, as mentioned for 'Line-engraved Issues'. The checklist is divided up according to whether any letters are small or large, also whether they are white (uncoloured) or printed in the colour of the stamp. Further identification then depends on watermark.

PERFORATION. Except for Nos. 126/9 all the following issues of Queen Victoria are perf 14.

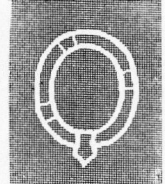

14

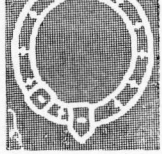

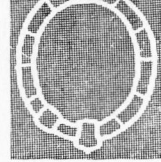

15 Small Garter   **16** Medium Garter   **17** Large Garter

18

19

20   Emblems

No corner letters

1855–57 (*i*) *Wmk Small Garter Type* **15**

62	**14**	4d red	£3250	£325	□	□

(*ii*) *Wmk Medium Garter Type* **16**

64	**14**	4d red	£2750	£300	□	□

(*iii*) *Wmk Large Garter Type* **17**

66*a*	**14**	4d red	£1000	90·00	□	□

(*iv*) *Wmk Emblems Type* **20**

70	**18**	6d lilac	£675	80·00	□	□
72	**19**	1s green	£1000	£225	□	□

Plate numbers. Stamps Nos. 90/163 should be checked for the 'plate numbers' indicated, as this affects valuation (the cheapest plates are priced here). The mark '*Pl.*' shows that several numbers exist, priced in separate list overleaf.

Plate numbers are the small numerals appearing in duplicate in some part of the frame design or adjacent to the lower corner letters (in the 5s value a single numeral above the lower inscription).

21

22

23

24

25

Small white corner letters

1862–64 *Wmk Emblems Type* **20**, *except* 4*d* (*Large Garter Type* **17**)

76	**21**	3d red	£1000	£225	□	□
80	**22**	4d red	£1000	80·00	□	□
84	**23**	6d lilac	£1100	80·00	□	□
87	**24**	9d bistre	£2500	£250	□	□
90	**25**	1s green *Pl.*	£1300	£140	□	□

26

27

28 (hyphen in SIX-PENCE)

32

33 Spray of Rose

34

29

30

31

Large white corner letters

1865–67 *Wmk Emblems Type* **20** *except 4d (Large Garter Type* **17**)

92	**26**	3d red (Plate 4)	£750	90·00	☐	☐
94	**27**	4d vermilion *Pl.*	£375	50·00	☐	☐
97	**28**	6d lilac *Pl.*	£500	70·00	☐	☐
98	**29**	9d straw *Pl.*	£1500	£350	☐	☐
99	**30**	10d brown (Plate 1) . . .	† £15000		☐	
101	**31**	1s green (Plate 4)	£1100	£150	☐	☐

1867–80 *Wmk Spray of Rose Type* **33**

103	**26**	3d red *Pl.*	£325	40·00	☐	☐
105	**28**	6d lilac (with hyphen) (Plate 6)	£725	75·00	☐	☐
109		6d mauve (without hyphen) *Pl.*	£450	65·00	☐	☐
110	**29**	9d straw (Plate 4)	£1000	£190	☐	☐
112	**30**	10d brown *Pl.*	£1700	£250	☐	☐
117	**31**	1s green *Pl.*	£550	30·00	☐	☐
119	**32**	2s blue *Pl.*	£1600	£125	☐	☐
121		2s brown (Plate 1) . . .	£9000	£1900	☐	☐

1872–73 *Wmk Spray of Rose Type* **33**

122b	**34**	6d brown *Pl.*	£500	45·00	☐	☐
125		6d grey (Plate 12)	£1000	£190	☐	☐

PLATE NUMBERS
on stamps of 1862–83

Cat No.		Plate No.	Un.	Used		

Small White Corner Letters (1862–64)

90	1s green	2	£1300	£140	☐	☐
		3	£15000		☐	☐

Plate 2 is actually numbered as '1' and Plate 3 as '2' on the stamps.

Large White Corner Letters (1865–83)

103	3d red	4	£650	£150	☐	☐
		5	£325	40·00	☐	☐
		6	£350	40·00	☐	☐
		7	£425	45·00	☐	☐
		8	£400	45·00	☐	☐
		9	£400	50·00	☐	☐
		10	£425	90·00	☐	☐
94	4d verm	7	£450	80·00	☐	☐
		8	£400	50·00	☐	☐
		9	£400	50·00	☐	☐
		10	£500	90·00	☐	☐
		11	£400	50·00	☐	☐
		12	£375	50·00	☐	☐
		13	£400	50·00	☐	☐
		14	£450	50·00	☐	☐
97	6d lilac	5	£500	70·00	☐	☐
		6	£1500	£130	☐	☐
109	6d mauve	8	£450	65·00	☐	☐
		9	£450	65·00	☐	☐
		10	*	£15000	☐	☐
122b	6d brown	11	£500	45·00	☐	☐
		12	£1500	£200	☐	☐
98	9d straw	4	£1500	£350	☐	☐
		5	£14000		☐	☐

112	10d brown	1	£1700	£250	☐	☐
		2	£15000	£3500	☐	☐
117	1s green	4	£550	32·00	☐	☐
		5	£600	30·00	☐	☐
		6	£750	30·00	☐	☐
		7	£750	60·00	☐	☐
119	2s blue	1	£1600	£125	☐	☐
		3	*	£4000	☐	☐
126	5s red	1	£4000	£400	☐	☐
		2	£5250	£525	☐	☐

Large Coloured Corner Letters (1873–83)

139	2½d mauve	1	£400	75·00	☐	☐
		2	£400	75·00	☐	☐
		3	£650	£110	☐	☐
141	2½d mauve	3	£675	80·00	☐	☐
		4	£350	40·00	☐	☐
		5	£350	40·00	☐	☐
		6	£350	40·00	☐	☐
		7	£350	40·00	☐	☐
		8	£350	40·00	☐	☐
		9	£350	40·00	☐	☐
		10	£375	50·00	☐	☐
		11	£350	40·00	☐	☐
		12	£350	40·00	☐	☐
		13	£350	40·00	☐	☐
		14	£350	40·00	☐	☐
		15	£350	40·00	☐	☐
		16	£350	40·00	☐	☐
		17	£1000	£200	☐	☐
142	2½d blue	17	£350	50·00	☐	☐
		18	£325	35·00	☐	☐
		19	£275	30·00	☐	☐
		20	£325	35·00	☐	☐

157	2½d blue	21	£325	30·00	☐	☐
		22	£275	25·00	☐	☐
		23	£275	25·00	☐	☐
143	3d red	11	£275	35·00	☐	☐
		12	£325	35·00	☐	☐
		14	£350	35·00	☐	☐
		15	£275	35·00	☐	☐
		16	£275	35·00	☐	☐
		17	£325	35·00	☐	☐
		18	£325	35·00	☐	☐
		19	£275	35·00	☐	☐
		20	£375	60·00	☐	☐
158	3d red	20	£425	£110	☐	☐
		21	£325	60·00	☐	☐
152	4d verm	15	£1200	£325	☐	☐
		16	*	£14000	☐	☐
153	4d green	15	£625	£200	☐	☐
		16	£550	£180	☐	☐
		17	*	£10000	☐	☐
160	4d brown	17	£275	45·00	☐	☐
		18	£275	45·00	☐	☐
147	6d grey	13	£350	50·00	☐	☐
		14	£350	50·00	☐	☐
		15	£350	50·00	☐	☐
		16	£350	50·00	☐	☐
		17	£500	£100	☐	☐
161	6d grey	17	£275	50·00	☐	☐
		18	£250	50·00	☐	☐
150	1s green	8	£475	75·00	☐	☐
		9	£475	75·00	☐	☐
		10	£475	80·00	☐	☐
		11	£475	80·00	☐	☐
		12	£400	60·00	☐	☐
		13	£400	60·00	☐	☐
		14	*	£16000	☐	☐
163	1s brown	13	£400	£100	☐	☐
		14	£350	£100	☐	☐

35

36

37

38

44

45

46

47 Small Anchor

48 Orb

Large coloured corner letters

1873–80 (*i*) *Wmk Small Anchor Type* **47**

139	41	2½d mauve *Pl.*	£400	75·00	☐	☐

(*ii*) *Wmk Orb Type* **48**

141	41	2½d mauve *Pl.*	£350	40·00	☐	☐
142		2½d blue *Pl.*	£275	30·00	☐	☐

(*iii*) *Wmk Spray of Rose Type* **33**

143	42	3d red *Pl.*	£275	35·00	☐	☐
145	43	6d pale buff (Plate 13) .	*	£9000	☐	☐
147		6d grey *Pl.*	£350	50·00	☐	☐
150	44	1s green *Pl.*	£400	60·00	☐	☐
151		1s brown (Plate 13) . . .	£2250	£400	☐	☐

(*iv*) *Wmk Large Garter Type* **17**

152	45	4d vermilion *Pl.*	£1200	£325	☐	☐
153		4d green *Pl.*	£550	£180	☐	☐
154		4d brown (Plate 17) . . .	£1100	£300	☐	☐
156	46	8d orange (Plate 1) . . .	£800	£250	☐	☐

49 Imperial Crown   **(50)** Surcharges in red **(51)**

1880–83 *Wmk Imperial Crown Type* **49**

157	41	2½d blue *Pl.*	£275	25·00	☐	☐
158	42	3d red *Pl.*	£325	60·00	☐	☐
159		3d on 3d lilac (surch Type 50)	£325	£110	☐	☐
160	45	4d brown *Pl.*	£275	45·00	☐	☐
161	43	6d grey *Pl.*	£250	50·00	☐	☐
162		6d on 6d lilac (surch Type 51)	£350	£110	☐	☐
163	44	1s brown *Pl.*	£350	£100	☐	☐

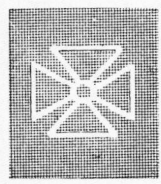

39 Maltese Cross

40 Large Anchor

1867–83 (*i*) *Wmk Maltese Cross Type* **39** *Perf* 15½ × 15

126	35	5s red *Pl.*	£4000	£400	☐	☐
128	36	10s grey (Plate 1)	£28000	£1400	☐	☐
129	37	£1 brown (Plate 1) . . .	£32000	£2000	☐	☐

(*ii*) *Wmk Large Anchor Type* **40** *Perf* 14

134	35	5s red (Plate 4)	£8000	£1800	☐	☐
135	36	10s grey (Plate 1)	£35000	£2200	☐	☐
132	37	£1 brown (Plate 1) . . .	£42000	£4500	☐	☐
137	38	£5 orange (Plate 1) . . .	£6500	£2500	☐	☐

41

42

43

52

53

54

55

56

1880–81 *Wmk Imperial Crown Type* **49**

164	52	½d green	. . . .	40·00	10·00	☐ ☐
166	53	1d brown	. . . .	15·00	10·00	☐ ☐
167	54	1½d brown	. . . .	£140	35·00	☐ ☐
168	55	2d red	. . . .	£175	70·00	☐ ☐
169	56	5d indigo	. . . .	£475	90·00	☐ ☐

57

Die I

Die II

1881 *Wmk Imperial Crown Type* **49**

(*a*) *14 dots in each corner, Die I*

171	57	1d lilac	. . . .	£125	25·00	☐ ☐

(*b*) *16 dots in each corner, Die II*

174	57	1d mauve	. . . .	2·50	1·50	☐ ☐

58

59

60

1883–84 *Wmk Anchor Type* **40**

179	58	2s 6d deep lilac	. . . .	£350	£110	☐ ☐
181	59	5s red	. . . .	£550	£140	☐ ☐
183	60	10s blue	. . . .	£1250	£375	☐ ☐

61

1884 *Wmk 3 Imperial Crowns Type* **49**

185	61	£1 brown	. . . .	£18000	£1500	☐ ☐

1888 *Wmk 3 Orbs Type* **48**

186	61	£1 brown	. . . .	£35000	£2750	☐ ☐

1891 *Wmk 3 Imperial Crowns Type* **49**

212	61	£1 green	. . . .	£2500	£450	☐ ☐

62

63

64

65

66

1883–84 *Wmk Imperial Crown Type* **49** (*sideways on horiz designs*)

187	52	½d blue	. . . .	20·00	7·00	☐ ☐
188	62	1½d lilac	. . . .	85·00	35·00	☐ ☐
189	63	2d lilac	. . . .	£140	65·00	☐ ☐
190	64	2½d lilac	. . . .	70·00	12·00	☐ ☐
191	65	3d lilac	. . . .	£175	85·00	☐ ☐
192	66	4d dull green	. . . . . .	£400	£175	☐ ☐
193	62	5d dull green	. . . . . .	£400	£175	☐ ☐
194	63	6d dull green	. . . . . .	£425	£200	☐ ☐
195	64	9d dull green	. . . . . .	£750	£375	☐ ☐
196	65	1s dull green	. . . . . .	£550	£200	☐ ☐

The above prices are for stamps in the true dull green colour. Stamps which have been soaked, causing the colour to run are virtually worthless.

71   72   73

74   75   76

77   78   79

80   81   82

'Jubilee' issue

1887–1900 *The bicoloured stamps have the value tablets, or the frames including the value tablets, in the second colour. Wmk Imperial Crown Type* **49**

197e	71	½d vermilion	1·50	1·00	☐	☐
213		½d green*	1·75	2·00	☐	☐
198	72	1½d purple and green . .	15·00	7·00	☐	☐
200	73	2d green and red	28·00	12·00	☐	☐
201	74	2½d purple on blue	22·00	3·00	☐	☐
203	75	3d purple on yellow . .	22·00	3·25	☐	☐
205	76	4d green and brown . .	30·00	13·00	☐	☐
206	77	4½d green and red	10·00	40·00	☐	☐
207a	78	5d purple and blue . . .	35·00	11·00	☐	☐
208	79	6d purple on red	30·00	10·00	☐	☐
209	80	9d purple and blue . . .	60·00	40·00	☐	☐
210	81	10d purple and red	45·00	38·00	☐	☐
211	82	1s green	£200	60·00	☐	☐
214		1s green and red	50·00	£125	☐	☐
	Set of 14	. . . .	£500	£325	☐	☐

*The ½d No. 213 in blue is a colour changeling.

KING EDWARD VII

1901 (22 Jan.)–1910 (6 May)

83   84   85

86   87   88

89   90   91

92   93

94   95   96

97

215	83	½d blue-green	2·00	1·50	□ □
217		½d yellow-green	2·00	1·50	□ □
219		1d red	2·00	1·50	□ □
221	84	1½d purple and green . .	35·00	18·00	□ □
291	85	2d green and red	25·00	20·00	□ □
231	86	2½d blue	20·00	10·00	□ □
234	87	3d purple on yellow . .	35·00	15·00	□ □
238	88	4d green and brown . .	40·00	18·00	□ □
240		4d orange	20·00	15·00	□ □
294	89	5d purple and blue . . .	28·00	20·00	□ □
245	83	6d purple	35·00	18·00	□ □
249	90	7d grey	10·00	18·00	□ □
307	91	9d purple and blue . . .	60·00	60·00	□ □
311	92	10d purple and red	60·00	60·00	□ □
314	93	1s green and red	50·00	35·00	□ □
260	94	2s 6d purple	£180	75·00	□ □
263	95	5s red	£210	£130	□ □
265	96	10s blue	£550	£325	□ □
266	97	£1 green	£1300	£500	□ □
		Set of 15 (*to* 1s)	£325	£275	□ □

(*b*) *Perf* 15 × 14

279	83	½d green	40·00	45·00	□ □
281		1d red	15·00	15·00	□ □
283	86	2½d blue	22·00	15·00	□ □
285	87	3d purple on yellow . .	40·00	15·00	□ □
286	88	4d orange	30·00	15·00	□ □
		Set of 5	£130	90·00	□ □

KING GEORGE V

1910 (6 May)–1936 (20 Jan.)

PERFORATION. All the following issues are Perf 15 × 14 except vertical commemorative stamps which are 14 × 15, unless otherwise stated.

98 (Hair dark)   **99** (Lion unshaded)   **100**

1911–12 *Wmk Imperial Crown Type* **49**

| 325 | 98 | ½d green . . . . | 4·50 | 1·50 | □ □ |
| 327 | 99 | 1d red . . . . | 4·50 | 2·50 | □ □ |

1912 *Wmk Royal Cypher* (*'Simple'*) *Type* **100**

| 335 | 98 | ½d green . . . . | 40·00 | 40·00 | □ □ |
| 336 | 99 | 1d red . . . . | 30·00 | 30·00 | □ □ |

101 (Hair light)   **102** (Lion shaded)   **103**

1912 *Wmk Imperial Crown Type* **49**

| 339 | 101 | ½d green . . . . | 15·00 | 8·00 | □ □ |
| 341 | 102 | 1d red . . . . | 5·00 | 2·00 | □ □ |

1912 *Wmk Royal Cypher* (*'Simple'*) *Type* **100**

| 344 | 101 | ½d green . . . . | 7·00 | 3·00 | □ □ |
| 345 | 102 | 1d red . . . . | 8·00 | 3·00 | □ □ |

1912 *Wmk Royal Cypher* (*'Multiple'*) *Type* **103**

| 346 | 101 | ½d green . . . . | 12·00 | 8·00 | □ □ |
| 350 | 102 | 1d red . . . . | 15·00 | 8·00 | □ □ |

104   **105**   **106**

107

108

111

1912–24 *Wmk Royal Cypher Type* 100

351	**105**	½d green	1·00	1·00 ☐ ☐
357	**104**	1d red	1·00	1·00 ☐ ☐
362	**105**	1½d brown	4·00	1·50 ☐ ☐
369	**106**	2d orange	5·00	3·00 ☐ ☐
371	**104**	2½d blue	12·00	4·00 ☐ ☐
377	**106**	3d violet	7·00	2·00 ☐ ☐
379		4d grey-green	15·00	2·00 ☐ ☐
381	**107**	5d brown	15·00	5·00 ☐ ☐
385		6d purple	15·00	7·00 ☐ ☐
		a. Perf 14	90·00	£110 ☐ ☐
387		7d olive-green	20·00	10·00 ☐ ☐
390		8d black on yellow . . .	32·00	11·00 ☐ ☐
392	**108**	9d black	20·00	6·00 ☐ ☐
393*a*		9d olive-green	£100	30·00 ☐ ☐
394		10d blue	22·00	20·00 ☐ ☐
395		1s brown	20·00	4·00 ☐ ☐
	Set of 15	. . . .	£260	95·00 ☐ ☐

1913 *Wmk Royal Cypher* ('*Multiple*') *Type* 103

397	**105**	½d green	£150	£180 ☐ ☐
398	**104**	1d red	£225	£225 ☐ ☐

See also Nos. 418/29.

109

110

T 109. *Background around portrait consists of horizontal lines*
1913–18 *Wmk Single Cypher Type* 110 *Perf* 11 × 12

413*a*	**109**	2s 6d brown	90·00	60·00 ☐ ☐
416		5s red	£225	90·00 ☐ ☐
417		10s blue	£300	£140 ☐ ☐
403		£1 green	£1300	£800 ☐ ☐
	Set of 4	. . . .	£1700	£950 ☐ ☐

See also Nos. 450/2.

1924–26 *Wmk Block Cypher Type* 111

418	**105**	½d green	1·00	1·00 ☐ ☐
419	**104**	1d red	1·00	1·00 ☐ ☐
420	**105**	1½d brown	1·00	1·00 ☐ ☐
421	**106**	2d orange	2·50	2·50 ☐ ☐
422	**104**	2½d blue	5·00	3·00 ☐ ☐
423	**106**	3d violet	10·00	2·50 ☐ ☐
424		4d grey-green	12·00	2·50 ☐ ☐
425	**107**	5d brown	20·00	3·00 ☐ ☐
426*a*		6d purple	3·00	1·50 ☐ ☐
427	**108**	9d olive-green	12·00	3·50 ☐ ☐
428		10d blue	35·00	40·00 ☐ ☐
429		1s brown	22·00	3·00 ☐ ☐
	Set of 12	. . . .	£110	60·00 ☐ ☐

112

112a

British Empire Exhibition
1924–25 *Wmk* 111 *Perf* 14 (*a*) 23.4.24. *Dated* '1924'

430	**112**	1d red	10·00	11·00 ☐ ☐
431	**112a**	1½d brown	15·00	15·00 ☐ ☐
	First Day Cover		£375 ☐

(*b*) 9.5.25. *Dated* '1925'

432	**112**	1d red	15·00	25·00 ☐ ☐
433	**112a**	1½d brown	40·00	65·00 ☐ ☐
	First Day Cover		£1300 ☐

113

114

115

116   St George and the Dragon

117

Ninth Universal Postal Union Congress

1929 (10 MAY) (*a*) *Wmk* **111**

434	**113**	½d green	. . . .	2·25	2·25	□	□
435	**114**	1d red	. . . .	2·25	2·25	□	□
436		1½d brown	. . . .	2·25	1·75	□	□
437	**115**	2½d blue	. . . .	10·00	10·00	□	□

(*b*) *Wmk* **117** *Perf* 12

438	**116**	£1 black	. . . .	£750	£550	□	□
434/7	*Set of* 4	. . . .		15·00	14·50	□	□
434/7 *First Day Cover* (4 *vals.*)	. . . . .				£500		□
434/8 *First Day Cover* (5 *vals.*)	. . . . .				£6500		□

118

119

120

121

122

1934–36 *Wmk* **111**

439	**118**	½d green	. . . .	50	50	□	□
440	**119**	1d red	. . . .	50	50	□	□
441	**118**	1½d brown	. . . .	50	50	□	□
442	**120**	2d orange	. . . .	75	75	□	□
443	**119**	2½d blue	. . . .	1·50	1·25	□	□
444	**120**	3d violet	. . . .	1·50	1·25	□	□
445		4d grey-green	. . . . . .	2·00	1·25	□	□
446	**121**	5d brown	. . . .	6·00	2·75	□	□
447	**122**	9d olive-green	. . . . . .	12·00	2·25	□	□
448		10d blue	. . . .	15·00	10·00	□	□
449		1s brown	. . . .	15·00	1·25	□	□
	Set of 11	. . . .		50·00	20·00	□	□

T 109 (re-engraved). Background around portrait consists of horizontal and diagonal lines

1934 *Wmk* **110**   *Perf* 11 × 12

450	**109**	2s 6d brown	. . . .	65·00	35·00	□	□
451		5s red	. . . .	£150	80·00	□	□
452		10s blue	. . . .	£325	75·00	□	□
	Set of 3	. . . .		£475	£180	□	□

123

123a

123b

123c

Silver Jubilee

1935 (7 MAY) *Wmk* **111**

453	**123**	½d green	. . . .	75	50	□	□
454	**123a**	1d red	. . . .	1·25	1·50	□	□
455	**123b**	1½d brown	. . . .	75	50	□	□
456	**123c**	2½d blue	. . . .	4·50	5·50	□	□
	Set of 4	. . . .		6·00	7·00	□	□
	First Day Cover	. . . .			£600		□

KING EDWARD VIII

1936 (20 Jan.–10 Dec.)

124

125

1936 *Wmk* **125**

457	**124**	½d green	30	30	☐	☐
458		1d red	60	50	☐	☐
459		1½d brown	30	30	☐	☐
460		2½d blue	30	85	☐	☐
	Set of 4	. . . .	1·25	1·75	☐	☐

First Day Covers

1 Sept. 1936	Nos. 457, 459/60	£150	☐
14 Sept. 1936	No. 458	£170	☐

KING GEORGE VI

1936 (11 Dec.)–1952 (6 Feb.)

126 King George VI and Queen Elizabeth   **127**

Coronation

1937 (13 MAY) *Wmk* **127**

461	**126**	1½d brown	30	30	☐	☐
		First Day Cover		35·00		☐

128   **129**   **130**

King George VI and National Emblems

1937–47 *Wmk* **127**

462	**128**	½d green	30	25	☐	☐
463		1d scarlet	30	25	☐	☐
464		1½d brown	20	25	☐	☐
465		2d orange	75	50	☐	☐
466		2½d blue	30	25	☐	☐
467		3d violet	3·75	1·00	☐	☐
468	**129**	4d green	60	75	☐	☐
469		5d brown	2·50	85	☐	☐
470		6d purple	1·25	60	☐	☐
471	**130**	7d green	4·25	60	☐	☐
472		8d red	3·75	80	☐	☐
473		9d deep green	5·50	80	☐	☐
474		10d blue	5·75	80	☐	☐
474*a*		11d plum	2·00	2·75	☐	☐
475		1s brown	6·00	75	☐	☐
	Set of 15	. . . .	32·00	10·00	☐	☐

First Day Covers

10 May 1937	Nos. 462/3, 466	5·00	☐
30 July 1937	No. 464	5·00	☐
31 Jan. 1938	Nos. 465, 467	25·00	☐
21 Nov. 1938	Nos. 468/9	45·00	☐
30 Jan. 1939	No. 470	45·00	☐
27 Feb. 1939	Nos. 471/2	60·00	☐
1 May 1939	Nos. 473/4, 475	£425	☐
29 Dec. 1947	No. 474*a*	40·00	☐

For later printings of the lower values in apparently lighter shades and different colours, see Nos. 485/90 and 503/8.

130a King George VI

131

132

132a

133

1939–48 *Wmk* **133** *Perf* 14

476	**130a**	2s 6d brown	. . . .	35·00	6·00 ☐ ☐
476*a*		2s 6d green	. . . .	4·50	1·50 ☐ ☐
477	**131**	5s red	. . . .	9·00	2·00 ☐ ☐
478	**132**	10s dark blue	. . . . . .	£225	20·00 ☐ ☐
478*a*		10s bright blue	. . . . .	20·00	5·00 ☐ ☐
478*b*	**132a**	£1 brown	. . . . . .	7·00	26·00 ☐ ☐
	Set of 6		. . . .	£275	55·00 ☐ ☐

First Day Covers

21 Aug. 1939	No. 477	. . . .	£625 ☐
4 Sept. 1939	No. 476	. . . .	£1100 ☐
30 Oct. 1939	No. 478	. . . .	£1900 ☐
9 Mar. 1942	No. 476*a*	. . . .	£1100 ☐
30 Nov. 1942	No. 478*a*	. . . .	£2500 ☐
1 Oct. 1948	No. 478*b*	. . . .	£225 ☐

134 Queen Victoria and King George VI

Centenary of First Adhesive Postage Stamps

1940 (6 MAY) *Wmk* **127** *Perf* 14½ × 14

479	**134**	½d green	. . . .	30	30 ☐ ☐
480		1d red	. . . .	1·00	40 ☐ ☐
481		1½d brown	. . . .	50	75 ☐ ☐
482		2d orange	. . . . . .	50	40 ☐ ☐
483		2½d blue	. . . .	2·25	50 ☐ ☐
484		3d violet	. . . .	3·00	3·50 ☐ ☐
	Set of 6		. . . .	6·50	5·25 ☐ ☐
	First Day Cover		. . . .		55·00 ☐

Head as Nos. 462–7, but lighter background

1941–42 *Wmk* **127**

485	**128**	½d pale green	. . . . .	30	30 ☐ ☐
486		1d pale red	. . . . . .	30	30 ☐ ☐
487		1½d pale brown	. . . . .	50	80 ☐ ☐
488		2d pale orange	. . . . .	50	50 ☐ ☐
489		2½d light blue	. . . . . .	30	30 ☐ ☐
490		3d pale violet	. . . . . .	2·00	1·00 ☐ ☐
	Set of 6			3·50	2·75 ☐ ☐

First Day Covers

21 July 1941	No. 489	. . . .	40·00 ☐
11 Aug. 1941	No. 486	. . . .	18·00 ☐
1 Sept. 1941	No. 485	. . . .	18·00 ☐
6 Oct. 1941	No. 488	. . . .	55·00 ☐
3 Nov. 1941	No. 490	. . . .	£100 ☐
28 Sept. 1942	No. 487	. . . .	50·00 ☐

135 Symbols of Peace and Reconstruction

136 Symbols of Peace and Reconstruction

Victory

1946 (11 JUNE) *Wmk* **127**

491	**135**	2½d blue	. . . .	20	15 ☐ ☐
492	**136**	3d violet	. . . .	20	40 ☐ ☐
	First Day Cover		. . . .		65·00 ☐

137 King George VI and Queen Elizabeth

138 King George VI and Queen Elizabeth

Royal Silver Wedding

1948 (26 APR.) *Wmk* **127**

493	**137**	2½d blue	. . . .	35	20 ☐ ☐
494	**138**	£1 blue	. . . .	38·00	38·00 ☐ ☐
	First Day Cover		. . . .		£425 ☐

1948 (10 MAY)

Stamps of 1d and 2½d showing seaweed-gathering were on sale at eight Head Post Offices elsewhere in Great Britain, but were primarily for use in the Channel Islands and are listed there (see after Regional Issues).

139 Globe and Laurel Wreath   **140** Speed

141 Olympic Symbol   **142** Winged Victory

Olympic Games
1948 (29 JULY) *Wmk* **127**

495	**139**	2½d blue	35	10	☐	☐
496	**140**	3d violet	35	55	☐	☐
497	**141**	6d purple	75	40	☐	☐
498	**142**	1s brown	1·40	1·60	☐	☐
		Set of 4	2·50	2·40	☐	
		First Day Cover		42·00	☐	

143 Two Hemispheres

145 Goddess Concordia,   **146** Posthorn and Globe
Globe and Points of
Compass

75th Anniversary of Universal Postal Union
1949 (10 OCT.) *Wmk* **127**

499	**143**	2½d blue	15	10	☐	☐
500	**144**	3d violet	15	50	☐	☐
501	**145**	6d purple	25	50	☐	☐
502	**146**	1s brown	60	1·25	☐	☐
		Set of 4	1·00	2·10	☐	
		First Day Cover		70·00	☐	

4d as No. 468 and others as Nos. 485/9, but colours changed
1950–51 *Wmk* **127**

503	**128**	½d pale orange	30	30	☐	☐
504		1d light blue	30	30	☐	☐
505		1½d pale green	65	60	☐	☐
506		2d pale brown	75	40	☐	☐
507		2½d pale red	60	40	☐	☐
508	**129**	4d light blue	2·00	1·75	☐	☐
		Set of 6	4·00	3·25	☐	☐

First Day Covers

2 Oct. 1950	No. 508	£110	☐
3 May 1951	Nos. 503/7	50·00	☐

147 HMS *Victory*   **148** White Cliffs of Dover

149 St George and the   **150** Royal Coat of Arms
Dragon

1951 (3 MAY) *Wmk* **133** *Perf* 11 × 12

509	**147**	2s 6d green	2·00	1·00	☐	☐
510	**148**	5s red	40·00	1·50	☐	☐
511	**149**	10s blue	10·00	8·50	☐	☐
512	**150**	£1 brown	48·00	20·00	☐	☐
		Set of 4	90·00	27·00	☐	☐
		First Day Cover		£850	☐	

151 Commerce and   **152** Festival Symbol
Prosperity

Festival of Britain
1951 (3 MAY) *Wmk* **127**

513	**151**	2½d red	15	20	☐	☐
514	**152**	4d blue	30	65	☐	☐
		First Day Cover		30·00	☐	

13

QUEEN ELIZABETH II
6 February, 1952

153 Tudor Crown   **154**

155   **156**   **157**

158   **159**   **160**

1952–54 *Wmk* 153

515	**154**	½d orange	. . . .	10	15	□ □
516		1d blue	. . . .	20	20	□ □
517		1½d green	. . . .	10	20	□ □
518		2d brown	. . . .	20	20	□ □
519	**155**	2½d red	. . . .	15	15	□ □
520		3d lilac	. . . .	70	70	□ □
521	**156**	4d blue	. . . .	3·25	1·25	□ □
		4½d (*See Nos.* 577, 594, 609 *and* 616b)				
522	**157**	5d brown	. . . .	70	3·50	□ □
523		6d purple	. . . . . .	4·00	95	□ □
524		7d green	. . . .	9·50	6·00	□ □
525	**158**	8d magenta	. . . . . .	70	85	□ □
526		9d bronze-green	. . . .	22·00	4·75	□ □
527		10d blue	. . . .	18·00	4·50	□ □
528		11d plum	. . . .	28·00	16·00	□ □
529	**159**	1s bistre	. . . .	80	55	□ □
530	**160**	1s 3d green	. . . . .	4·50	3·25	□ □
531	**159**	1s 6d indigo	. . . . .	14·00	3·75	□ □
		Set of 17	. . . .	95·00	42·00	□ □

First Day Covers

5 Dec. 1952	Nos. 517, 519	. . . .	15·00 □
6 July 1953	Nos. 522, 525, 529	. . . . .	45·00 □
31 Aug. 1953	Nos. 515/16, 518	. . . . . .	45·00 □
2 Nov. 1953	Nos. 521, 530/1	. . . .	£170 □
18 Jan. 1954	Nos. 520, 523/4	. . . . . .	£110 □
8 Feb. 1954	Nos. 526/8	. . . .	£200 □

See also Nos. 540/56, 561/6, 570/94 and 599/618a and for stamps as Types **154/5** and **157** with face values in decimal currency see Nos. 2031/3 and 2258/9.

161   **162**

163   **164**

Coronation

1953 (3 JUNE) *Wmk* **153**

532	**161**	2½d red	. . . .	20	25	□ □
533	**162**	4d blue	. . . .	90	2·00	□ □
534	**163**	1s 3d green	. . . . . .	4·00	3·25	□ □
535	**164**	1s 6d blue	. . . .	7·50	5·00	□ □
		Set of 4	. . . .	11·00	9·50	□ □
		First Day Cover	. . . .		70·00	□

For a £1 value as Type **163** see No. **MS**2147.

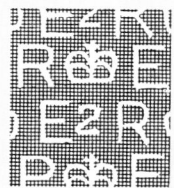 **165** St Edward's Crown

166 Carrickfergus Castle   **167** Caernarvon Castle

168 Edinburgh Castle   **169** Windsor Castle

1955 (1–23 SEPT.) *Wmk* **165** *Perf* 11 × 12

536	**166**	2s 6d brown	. . . .	9·00	2·00	□ □
537	**167**	5s red	. . . .	35·00	4·00	□ □

538	168	10s blue	85·00	15·00	□	□
539	169	£1 black	£130	35·00	□	□
		Set of 4	£225	50·00	□	□
		First Day Cover (Nos. 538/9)				
		(1 Sept.)		£750		□
		First Day Cover (Nos. 536/7)				
		(23 Sept.)		£550		□

See also Nos. 595a/8a and 759/62.

1955–58 Wmk **165**

540	154	½d orange	10	15	□	□
541		1d blue	30	15	□	□
542		1½d green	25	30	□	□
543		2d red-brown	25	35	□	□
543b		2d light red-brown	20	20	□	□
544	155	2½d red	20	25	□	□
545		3d lilac	25	30	□	□
546	156	4d blue	1·25	45	□	□
547	157	5d brown	5·00	5·75	□	□
548		6d purple	3·75	1·25	□	□
549		7d green	40·00	9·50	□	□
550	158	8d magenta	7·00	1·25	□	□
551		9d bronze-green	19·00	2·75	□	□
552		10d blue	19·00	2·75	□	□
553		11d plum	50	1·10	□	□
554	159	1s bistre	20·00	65	□	□
555	160	1s 3d green	30·00	1·60	□	□
556	159	1s 6d indigo	21·00	1·60	□	□
		Set of 18	£150	27·00	□	□

170 Scout Badge and 'Rolling Hitch'
171 'Scouts coming to Britain'

172 Globe within a Compass
173

World Scout Jubilee Jamboree
1957 (1 Aug.) Wmk **165**

557	170	2½d red	15	20	□	□
558	171	4d blue	30	90	□	□
559	172	1s 3d green	3·25	3·75	□	□
		Set of 3	3·25	4·50	□	□
		First Day Cover		20·00		□

46th Inter Parliamentary Union Conference
1957 (12 Sept.) Wmk **165**

560	173	4d blue	75	1·00	□	□
		First Day Cover		£110		□

Graphite-lined and Phosphor Issues

These are used in connection with automatic sorting machinery, originally experimentally at Southampton but now also operating elsewhere. In such areas these stamps were the normal issue, but from mid 1967 *all* low-value stamps bear phosphor markings.

The graphite lines were printed in black on the back, beneath the gum; two lines per stamp except for the 2d *(see below)*.

174 **175** (2d only)

(Stamps viewed from back)

In November 1959, phosphor bands, printed on the front, replaced the graphite. They are wider than the graphite, not easy to see, but show as broad vertical bands at certain angles to the light.

Values representing the rate for printed papers (and second class mail from 1968) have one band and others have two, three or four bands according to size and format. From 1972 onwards some commemorative stamps were printed with 'all-over' phosphor.

In the small stamps the bands are on each side with the single band at left (except where otherwise stated). In the large-size commemorative stamps the single band may be at left, centre or right varying in different issues. The bands are vertical on both horizontal and vertical designs except where otherwise stated.

See also notes on page 37.

Graphite-lined issue
1957 (19 Nov.) *Two graphite lines on the back, except 2d value, which has one line.* Wmk **165**

561	154	½d orange	25	25	□	□
562		1d blue	25	30	□	□
563		1½d green	1·00	1·40	□	□
564		2d light red-brown	1·40	2·25	□	□
565	155	2½d red	7·50	6·75	□	□
566		3d lilac	60	50	□	□
		Set of 6	10·00	10·50	□	□
		First Day Cover		85·00		□

See also Nos. 587/94.

176 Welsh Dragon
177 Flag and Games Emblem

178 Welsh Dragon

Sixth British Empire and Commonwealth Games, Cardiff

1958 (18 July) *Wmk* **165**

567	**176**	3d lilac	20	20	☐	☐
568 ·	**177**	6d mauve	40	45	☐	☐
569	**178**	1s 3d green	2·25	2·40	☐	☐
		Set of 3	2·50	2·75	☐	☐
		First Day Cover		70·00	☐	

179 Multiple Crowns

WATERMARK. All the following issues to No. 755 are Watermark **179** (sideways on the vertical commemorative stamps) unless otherwise stated.

1958–65 *Wmk* **179**

570	**154**	½d orange	10	10	☐	☐
571		1d blue	10	10	☐	☐
572		1½d green	10	15	☐	☐
573		2d light red-brown	10	10	☐	☐
574	**155**	2½d red	10	20	☐	☐
575		3d lilac	10	20	☐	☐
576a	**156**	4d blue	15	15	☐	☐
577		4½d brown	10	25	☐	☐
578	**157**	5d brown	30	40	☐	☐
579		6d purple	30	25	☐	☐
580		7d green	50	45	☐	☐
581	**158**	8d magenta	50	40	☐	☐
582		9d bronze-green	50	40	☐	☐
583		10d blue	90	50	☐	☐
584	**159**	1s bistre	45	30	☐	☐
585	**160**	1s 3d green	40	30	☐	☐
586	**159**	1s 6d indigo	3·50	55	☐	☐
		Set of 17	7·50	4·25	☐	☐
		First Day Cover (No. 577)				
		(9 Feb. 1959)		£250	☐	

For full information on all future British issues, collectors should write to Royal Mail, Freepost EH3647, 21 South Gyle Crescent, Edinburgh EH12 9PE.

Graphite-lined issue

1958–59 *Two graphite lines on the back, except* 2d *value, which has one line. Wmk* **179**

587	**154**	½d orange	3·25	3·75	☐	☐
588		1d blue	1·25	1·40	☐	☐
589		1½d green	38·00	35·00	☐	☐
590		2d light red-brown	6·25	2·75	☐	☐
591	**155**	2½d red	7·50	9·00	☐	☐
592		3d lilac	50	55	☐	☐
593	**156**	4d blue	4·00	4·75	☐	☐
594		4½d brown	6·00	4·75	☐	☐
		Set of 8	60·00	55·00	☐	☐

The prices quoted for Nos. 587 and 589 are for examples with inverted watermark. Stamps with upright watermark are priced at: ½d £8 *mint*, £9 *used* and 1½d £90 *mint*, £80 *used*.

1959–63 *Wmk* **179** *Perf* 11 × 12

595a	**166**	2s 6d brown	35	35	☐	☐
596a	**167**	5s red	90	45	☐	☐
597a	**168**	10s blue	4·00	4·00	☐	☐
598a	**169**	£1 black	11·00	6·50	☐	☐
		Set of 4	15·00	10·00	☐	☐

Phosphor-Graphite issue

1959 (18 Nov.) *Two phosphor bands on front and two graphite lines on back, except* 2d *value, which has one band on front and one line on back (a) Wmk* **165**

599	**154**	½d orange	3·25	3·50	☐	☐
600		1d blue	8·25	7·50	☐	☐
601		1½d green	3·25	3·25	☐	☐
		(b) Wmk **179**				
605	**154**	2d light red-brown (1 band)	4·25	4·00	☐	☐
606	**155**	2½d red	17·00	14·00	☐	☐
607		3d lilac	8·50	7·00	☐	☐
608	**156**	4d blue	15·00	16·00	☐	☐
609		4½d brown	24·00	18·00	☐	☐
		Set of 8	75·00	65·00	☐	☐

Phosphor issue

1960–67 *Two phosphor bands on front, except where otherwise stated. Wmk* **179**

610	**154**	½d orange	10	15	☐	☐
611		1d blue	10	10	☐	☐
612		1½d green	10	15	☐	☐
613		2d light red-brown (1 band)	18·00	18·00	☐	☐
613a		2d light red-brown (2 bands)	10	15	☐	☐
614	**155**	2½d red (2 bands)	20	30	☐	☐
614a		2½d red (1 band)	40	65	☐	☐
615		3d lilac (2 bands)	60	55	☐	☐
615c		3d lilac (1 side band)	60	55	☐	☐
615e		3d lilac (1 centre band)	40	45	☐	☐
616a	**156**	4d blue	25	25	☐	☐
616b		4½d brown	20	30	☐	☐

616c	157	5d brown	25	35 ☐ ☐
617		6d purple	30	30 ☐ ☐
617a		7d green	55	50 ☐ ☐
617b	158	8d magenta	40	45 ☐ ☐
617c		9d bronze-green	55	55 ☐ ☐
617d		10d blue	70	60 ☐ ☐
617e	159	1s bistre	35	35 ☐ ☐
618	160	1s 3d green	1·90	2·50 ☐ ☐
618a	159	1s 6d indigo	2·00	1·60 ☐ ☐
		Set of 17 (one of each value) . .	7·50	8·00 ☐ ☐

No. 615c exists with the phosphor band at the left or right of the stamp.

180 Postboy of 1660   **181** Posthorn of 1660

Tercentenary of Establishment of 'General Letter Office'
1960 (7 JULY)

619	**180**	3d lilac	20	20 ☐ ☐
620	**181**	1s 3d green	2·75	3·25 ☐ ☐
		Set of 2	2·75	3·25 ☐ ☐
		First Day Cover		42·00 ☐

182 Conference Emblem

First Anniversary of European Postal and Telecommunications Conference
1960 (19 SEPT.)

621	**182**	6d green and purple . .	50	50 ☐ ☐
622		1s 6d brown and blue . . .	6·50	5·00 ☐ ☐
		Set of 2	7·00	5·50 ☐ ☐
		First Day Cover		40·00 ☐

183 Thrift Plant

184 'Growth of Savings'

185 Thrift Plant

Centenary of Post Office Savings Bank
1961 (28 AUG.)

623A	**183**	2½d black and red	25	25 ☐ ☐
624A	**184**	3d orange-brown and violet	20	20 ☐ ☐
625A	**185**	1s 6d red and blue	2·25	2·25 ☐ ☐
		Set of 3	2·50	2·50 ☐ ☐
		First Day Cover		60·00 ☐

186 C.E.P.T. Emblem   **187** Doves and Emblem

188 Doves and Emblem

European Postal and Telecommunications (C.E.P.T.) Conference, Torquay
1961 (18 SEPT.)

626	**186**	2d orange, pink and brown	15	20 ☐ ☐
627	**187**	4d buff, mauve and ultramarine	15	25 ☐ ☐
628	**188**	10d turquoise, green and blue	15	80 ☐ ☐
		Set of 3	40	1·10 ☐ ☐
		First Day Cover		6·00 ☐

189 Hammer Beam Roof, Westminster Hall   **190** Palace of Westminster

Seventh Commonwealth Parliamentary Conference

1961 (25 Sept.)

629	**189**	6d purple and gold . . .	25	25 □ □
630	**190**	1s 3d green and blue . . .	2·40	2·50 □ □
		Set of 2	2·50	2·75 □ □
		First Day Cover		32·00 □

191 'Units of Productivity'   192 'National Productivity'

193 'Unified Productivity'

National Productivity Year

1962 (14 Nov.) *Wmk* **179** (*inverted on* 2½d *and* 3d)

631	**191**	2½d green and red	20	15 □ □
		p. Phosphor	70	60 □ □
632	**192**	3d blue and violet	25	15 □ □
		p. Phosphor	1·75	90 □ □
633	**193**	1s 3d red, blue and green .	1·75	2·00 □ □
		p. Phosphor	35·00	22·00 □ □
		Set of 3 (*Ordinary*)	2·00	2·10 □ □
		Set of 3 (*Phosphor*)	35·00	22·00 □ □
		First Day Cover (*Ordinary*)		48·00 □
		First Day Cover (*Phosphor*) . . .		£120 □

194 Campaign Emblem   195 Children of Three Races
and Family

Freedom from Hunger

1963 (21 Mar.) *Wmk* **179** (*inverted*)

634	**194**	2½d crimson and pink . .	10	10 □ □
		p. Phosphor	3·00	1·25 □ □
635	**195**	1s 3d brown and yellow . .	1·75	2·25 □ □
		p. Phosphor	30·00	23·00 □ □
		Set of 2 (*Ordinary*)	1·75	2·25 □ □
		Set of 2 (*Phosphor*)	32·00	24·00 □ □
		First Day Cover (*Ordinary*)		30·00 □
		First Day Cover (*Phosphor*) . . .		35·00 □

196 'Paris Conference'

Paris Postal Conference Centenary

1963 (7 May) *Wmk* **179** (*inverted*)

636	**196**	6d green and mauve . .	35	40 □ □
		p. Phosphor	6·00	6·00 □ □
		First Day Cover (*Ordinary*)		14·00 □
		First Day Cover (*Phosphor*) . . .		27·00 □

197 Posy of Flowers   198 Woodland Life

National Nature Week

1963 (16 May)

637	**197**	3d multicoloured	15	15 □ □
		p. Phosphor	55	60 □ □
638	**198**	4½d multicoloured	20	35 □ □
		p. Phosphor	2·75	3·00 □ □
		Set of 2 (*Ordinary*)	35	50 □ □
		Set of 2 (*Phosphor*)	3·25	3·50 □ □
		First Day Cover (*Ordinary*)		18·00 □
		First Day Cover (*Phosphor*) . . .		30·00 □

199 Rescue at Sea   200 19th-century Lifeboat

201 Lifeboatmen

Ninth International Lifeboat Conference, Edinburgh

1963 (31 May)

639	**199**	2½d blue, black and red .	15	20 □ □
		p. Phosphor	50	60 □ □
640	**200**	4d multicoloured	45	50 □ □
		p. Phosphor . . . . •	50	60 □ □

641 **201** 1s 6d sepia, yellow and
blue . . . . 2·50 2·75 □ □
p. Phosphor . . . . . 45·00 28·00 □ □
Set of 3 (Ordinary) . . . . . . 2·75 3·00 □ □
Set of 3 (Phosphor) . . . . . . 45·00 28·00 □ □
First Day Cover (Ordinary) . . . 35·00 □
First Day Cover (Phosphor) . . . 45·00 □

202 Red Cross   203

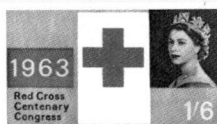

204

Red Cross Centenary Congress
1963 (15 AUG.)

642 **202** 3d red and lilac . . . . . 15 15 □ □
p. Phosphor . . . . 1·10 85 □ □
643 **203** 1s 3d red, blue and grey . . 2·75 3·00 □ □
p. Phosphor . . . . 35·00 32·00 □ □
644 **204** 1s 6d red, blue and bistre . 2·75 2·75 □ □
p. Phosphor . . . . 32·00 27·00 □ □
Set of 3 (Ordinary) . . . . . . 5·00 5·25 □ □
Set of 3 (Phosphor) . . . . . . 60·00 55·00 □ □
First Day Cover (Ordinary) . . . 35·00 □
First Day Cover (Phosphor) . . . 60·00 □

205 'Commonwealth Cable'

Opening of COMPAC (Trans-Pacific Telephone Cable)
1963 (3 DEC.)

645 **205** 1s 6d blue and black . . . . 2·25 2·50 □ □
p. Phosphor . . . . 18·00 18·00 □ □
First Day Cover (Ordinary) . . . 25·00 □
First Day Cover (Phosphor) . . . 30·00 □

206 Puck and Bottom
(*A Midsummer
Night's Dream*)

207 Feste (*Twelfth Night*)

208 Balcony Scene
(*Romeo and Juliet*)

209 'Eve of Agincourt'
(*Henry V*)

210 Hamlet contemplating
Yorick's skull (*Hamlet*)
and Queen Elizabeth II

Shakespeare Festival
1964 (23 APR.) Perf 11 × 12 (2s 6d) or 15 × 14 (others)

646 **206** 3d bistre, black and
violet-blue . . . . . . 15 15 □ □
p. Phosphor . . . . . . 25 30 □ □
647 **207** 6d multicoloured . . . . 30 30 □ □
p. Phosphor . . . . 75 1·00 □ □
648 **208** 1s 3d multicoloured . . . . 70 90 □ □
p. Phosphor . . . . 4·00 6·50 □ □
649 **209** 1s 6d multicoloured . . . . 1·00 85 □ □
p. Phosphor . . . . 8·00 8·00 □ □
650 **210** 2s 6d deep slate-purple . . 2·75 2·75 □ □
Set of 5 (Ordinary) . . . . 4·50 4·50 □ □
Set of 4 (Phosphor) . . . . . . 12·00 14·00 □ □
First Day Cover (Ordinary) . . . . 10·00 □
First Day Cover (Phosphor) . . . 16·00 □
Presentation Pack (Ordinary) . . 12·00 □

PRESENTATION PACKS were first introduced by the G.P.O. for the Shakespeare Festival issue. The packs include one set of stamps and details of the designs, the designer and the stamp printer. They were issued for almost all later definitive and special issues.

211 Flats near Richmond Park
('Urban Development')

212 Shipbuilding Yards, Belfast
('Industrial Activity')

213 Beddgelert Forest Park,
Snowdonia ('Forestry')

214 Nuclear Reactor, Dounreay
('Technological Development')

20th International Geographical Congress, London

1964 (1 July)

651	**211**	2½d multicoloured	10	10	□	□
		p. Phosphor	40	50	□	□
652	**212**	4d multicoloured	35	35	□	□
		p. Phosphor	1·25	1·25	□	□
653	**213**	8d multicoloured	75	80	□	□
		p. Phosphor	2·50	2·75	□	□
654	**214**	1s 6d multicoloured	3·00	3·00	□	□
		p. Phosphor	26·00	20·00	□	□
	Set of 4 (Ordinary)		3·75	3·75	□	□
	Set of 4 (Phosphor)		27·00	22·00	□	□
	First Day Cover (Ordinary) : . . .			20·00		□
	First Day Cover (Phosphor) . . .			30·00		□
	Presentation Pack (Ordinary) . .	£120			□	

215 Spring Gentian   **216** Dog Rose

217 Honeysuckle   **218** Fringed Water Lily

Tenth International Botanical Congress, Edinburgh

1964 (5 Aug.)

655	**215**	3d violet, blue and green	10	10	□	□
		p. Phosphor	40	40	□	□
656	**216**	6d multicoloured	30	35	□	□
		p. Phosphor	2·50	2·75	□	□
657	**217**	9d multicoloured	1·60	2·25	□	□
		p. Phosphor	4·25	4·00	□	□
658	**218**	1s 3d multicoloured	2·25	2·50	□	□
		p. Phosphor	23·00	20·00	□	□
	Set of 4 (Ordinary)		3·75	4·75	□	□
	Set of 4 (Phosphor)		27·00	24·00	□	□
	First Day Cover (Ordinary) . . .			22·00		□
	First Day Cover (Phosphor) . . .			32·00		□
	Presentation Pack (Ordinary) . .	£120			□	

219 Forth Road Bridge   **220** Forth Road and Railway Bridges

Opening of Forth Road Bridge

1964 (4 Sept.)

659	**219**	3d black, blue and violet	10	10	□	□
		p. Phosphor	50	50	□	□
660	**220**	6d blackish lilac, blue and red	40	40	□	□
		p. Phosphor	3·75	3·75	□	□
	Set of 2 (Ordinary)		50	50	□	□
	Set of 2 (Phosphor)		4·25	4·25	□	□
	First Day Cover (Ordinary)			7·00		□
	First Day Cover (Phosphor) . . .			12·00		□
	Presentation Pack (Ordinary) . .	£300			□	

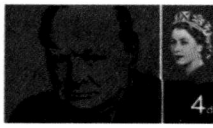 

221 Sir Winston Churchill   **221a** Sir Winston Churchill

Churchill Commemoration

1965 (8 July)

661	**221**	4d black and drab	15	10	□	□
		p. Phosphor	30	30	□	□
662	**221a**	1s 3d black and grey	35	40	□	□
		p. Phosphor	2·75	3·75	□	□
	Set of 2 (Ordinary)		50	50	□	□
	Set of 2 (Phosphor)		3·00	4·00	□	□
	First Day Cover (Ordinary)			6·00		□
	First Day Cover (Phosphor) . . .			7·00		□
	Presentation Pack (Ordinary) . .	18·00			□	

222 Simon de Montfort's Seal

223 Parliament Buildings (after engraving by Hollar, 1647)

700th Anniversary of Simon de Montfort's Parliament

1965 (19 July)

663	**222**	6d green	20	20	□	□
		p. Phosphor	75	90	□	□
664	**223**	2s 6d black, grey and drab	1·00	1·25	□	□
	Set of 2 (Ordinary)		1·10	1·25	□	□
	First Day Cover (Ordinary)			12·00		□
	First Day Cover (Phosphor) . . .			20·00		□
	Presentation Pack (Ordinary) . .	42·00			□	

224 Bandsmen and Banner

225 Three Salvationists

Salvation Army Centenary
1965 (9 Aug.)

665	**224**	3d multicoloured	10	15 □	□
		p. Phosphor	40	45 □	□
666	**225**	1s 6d multicoloured	75	1·10 □	□
		p. Phosphor	2·75	3·00 □	□
		Set of 2 (Ordinary)	85	1·25 □	□
		Set of 2 (Phosphor)	3·00	3·25 □	□
		First Day Cover (Ordinary)		22·00	□
		First Day Cover (Phosphor) . . .		28·00	□

226 Lister's Carbolic Spray

227 Lister and Chemical Symbols

Centenary of Joseph Lister's Discovery of Antiseptic Surgery
1965 (1 Sept.)

667	**226**	4d indigo, chestnut and grey	10	15 □	□
		p. Phosphor	30	30 □	□
668	**227**	1s black, purple and blue	80	1·10 □	□
		p. Phosphor	2·25	2·10 □	□
		Set of 2 (Ordinary)	90	1·25 □	□
		Set of 2 (Phosphor)	2·50	2·25 □	□
		First Day Cover (Ordinary)		12·00	□
		First Day Cover (Phosphor) . . .		14·00	□

228 Trinidad Carnival Dancers

229 Canadian Folk Dancers

Commonwealth Arts Festival
1965 (1 Sept.)

669	**228**	6d black and orange . .	20	20 □	□
		p. Phosphor	30	40 □	□
670	**229**	1s 6d black and violet . . .	80	1·10 □	□
		p. Phosphor	2·50	2·50 □	□
		Set of 2 (Ordinary)	1·00	1·25 □	□
		Set of 2 (Phosphor)	2·75	2·75 □	□
		First Day Cover (Ordinary)		14·00	□
		First Day Cover (Phosphor) . . .		18·00	□

230 Flight of Supermarine Spitfires

231 Pilot in Hawker Hurricane Mk I

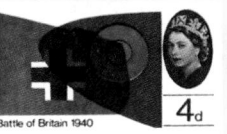
232 Wing-tips of Supermarine Spitfire and Messerschmitt Bf 109

233 Supermarine Spitfires attacking Heinkel HE 111H Bomber

234 Supermarine Spitfire attacking Junkers Ju 87B 'Stuka' Dive-bomber

235 Hawker Hurricanes Mk I over Wreck of Dornier Do-17Z Bomber

The above were issued together *se-tenant* in blocks of six (3 × 2) within the sheet.

236 Anti-aircraft Artillery in Action

237 Air Battle over St Paul's Cathedral

25th Anniversary of Battle of Britain
1965 (13 Sept.)

671	**230**	4d olive and black	50	70 □	□
		a. Block of 6. Nos. 671/6	6·00	10·00 □	□
		p. Phosphor	90	1·00 □	□
		pa. Block of 6. Nos. 671p/6p	10·00	15·00 □	□
672	**231**	4d olive, blackish olive and black	50	70 □	□
		p. Phosphor	90	1·00 □	□
673	**232**	4d multicoloured	50	70 □	□
		p. Phosphor	90	1·00 □	□
674	**233**	4d olive and black	50	70 □	□
		p. Phosphor	90	1·00 □	□
675	**234**	4d olive and black	50	70 □	□
		p. Phosphor	90	1·00 □	□

21

676	235	4d multicoloured	50	70	☐	☐
		p. Phosphor	90	1·00	☐	☐
677	236	9d violet, orange and purple	1·25	1·50	☐	☐
		p. Phosphor	1·25	1·50	☐	☐
678	237	1s 3d multicoloured	1·25	1·50	☐	☐
		p. Phosphor	1·25	1·50	☐	☐
		Set of 8 (Ordinary)	7·75	6·50	☐	☐
		Set of 8 (Phosphor)	11·50	8·00	☐	☐
		First Day Cover (Ordinary)		25·00		☐
		First Day Cover (Phosphor) . . .		28·00		☐
		Presentation Pack (Ordinary) . .	45·00		☐	

238 Tower and Georgian Buildings   **239** Tower and Nash Terrace, Regent's Park

Opening of Post Office Tower
1965 (8 Oct.)

679	238	3d yellow, blue and green	10	15	☐	☐
		p. Phosphor	15	15	☐	☐
680	239	1s 3d green and blue . . .	35	50	☐	☐
		p. Phosphor	30	50	☐	☐
		Set of 2 (Ordinary)	45	65	☐	☐
		Set of 2 (Phosphor)	45	65	☐	☐
		First Day Cover (Ordinary) . . .		6·00		☐
		First Day Cover (Phosphor) . . .		7·00		☐
		Presentation Pack (Ordinary) . .	4·00		☐	
		Presentation Pack (Phosphor) . .	4·00		☐	

240 U.N. Emblem   **241** I.C.Y. Emblem

20th Anniversary of UNO and International Co-operation Year
1965 (25 Oct.)

681	240	3d black, orange and blue	15	20	☐	☐
		p. Phosphor	25	30	☐	☐
682	241	1s 6d black, purple and blue	90	1·00	☐	☐
		p. Phosphor	3·25	3·25	☐	☐
		Set of 2 (Ordinary)	1·00	1·10	☐	☐
		Set of 2 (Phosphor)	3·50	3·50	☐	☐
		First Day Cover (Ordinary)		10·00		☐
		First Day Cover (Phosphor) . . .		12·00		☐

242 Telecommunications Network   **243** Radio Waves and Switchboard

I.T.U. Centenary
1965 (15 Nov.)

683	242	9d multicoloured	30	40	☐	☐
		p. Phosphor	60	75	☐	☐
684	243	1s 6d multicoloured	1·00	1·25	☐	☐
		p. Phosphor	4·25	5·25	☐	☐
		Set of 2 (Ordinary)	1·25	1·60	☐	☐
		Set of 2 (Phosphor)	4·75	6·00	☐	☐
		First Day Cover (Ordinary)		17·00		☐
		First Day Cover (Phosphor) . . .		20·00		☐

244 Robert Burns (after Skirving chalk drawing)   **245** Robert Burns (after Nasmyth portrait)

Burns Commemoration
1965 (25 Jan.)

685	244	4d black, indigo and blue	15	15	☐	☐
		p. Phosphor	25	40	☐	☐
686	245	1s 3d black, blue and orange	40	70	☐	☐
		p. Phosphor	2·25	1·75	☐	☐
		Set of 2 (Ordinary)	55	85	☐	☐
		Set of 2 (Phosphor)	2·50	2·10	☐	☐
		First Day Cover (Ordinary)		6·00		☐
		First Day Cover (Phosphor) . . .		7·00		☐
		Presentation Pack (Ordinary) . .	38·00		☐	

246 Westminster Abbey   **247** Fan Vaulting, Henry VII Chapel

900th Anniversary of Westminster Abbey
1966 (28 Feb.) *Perf* 15 × 14 (3d) *or* 11 × 12 (2s 6d)

| 687 | 246 | 3d black, brown and blue . . . . | 15 | 20 | ☐ | ☐ |
| | | p. Phosphor . . . . | 25 | 35 | ☐ | ☐ |

688	**247**	2s 6d black	70	1·00	☐	☐
		Set of 2	85	1·10	☐	☐
		First Day Cover (*Ordinary*)		8·00		☐
		First Day Cover (*Phosphor*) . . .		14·00		☐
		Presentation Pack (*Ordinary*) . .	17·00		☐	

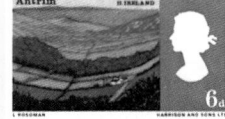

248 View near Hassocks, Sussex **249** Antrim, Northern Ireland

250 Harlech Castle, Wales **251** Cairngorm Mountains, Scotland

Landscapes
1966 (2 MAY)

689	**248**	4d black, yellow-green and blue	10	15	☐	☐
		p. Phosphor	10	15	☐	☐
690	**249**	6d black, green and blue	15	20	☐	☐
		p. Phosphor	15	20	☐	☐
691	**250**	1s 3d black, yellow and blue	25	40	☐	☐
		p. Phosphor	25	40	☐	☐
692	**251**	1s 6d black, orange and blue	40	50	☐	☐
		p. Phosphor	40	50	☐	☐
		Set of 4 (*Ordinary*)	80	1·10	☐	☐
		Set of 4 (*Phosphor*)	80	1·10	☐	☐
		First Day Cover (*Ordinary*)		7·00		☐
		First Day Cover (*Phosphor*) . . .		8·00		☐

252 Players with Ball

253 Goalmouth Mêlée **254** Goalkeeper saving Goal

World Cup Football Championship
1966 (1 JUNE)

693	**252**	4d multicoloured	10	10	☐	☐
		p. Phosphor	10	10	☐	☐
694	**253**	6d multicoloured	15	25	☐	☐
		p. Phosphor	15	25	☐	☐
695	**254**	1s 3d multicoloured	50	70	☐	☐
		p. Phosphor	50	70	☐	☐
		Set of 3 (*Ordinary*)	70	95	☐	☐
		Set of 3 (*Phosphor*)	70	95	☐	☐
		First Day Cover (*Ordinary*)		12·00		☐
		First Day Cover (*Phosphor*) . . .		15·00		☐
		Presentation Pack (*Ordinary*) . .	14·00		☐	

255 Black-headed Gull **256** Blue Tit

257 European Robin **258** Blackbird

The above were issued *se-tenant* in blocks of four within the sheet.

British Birds
1966 (8 AUG.)

696	**255**	4d multicoloured	10	20	☐	☐
		a. Block of 4. Nos. 696/9	80	2·00	☐	☐
		p. Phosphor	10	20	☐	☐
		pa. Block of 4. Nos. 696*p*/9*p*	75	2·00	☐	☐
697	**256**	4d multicoloured	10	20	☐	☐
		p. Phosphor	10	20	☐	☐
698	**257**	4d multicoloured	10	20	☐	☐
		p. Phosphor	10	20	☐	☐
699	**258**	4d multicoloured	10	20	☐	☐
		p. Phosphor	10	20	☐	☐
		Set of 4 (*Ordinary*)	80	70	☐	☐
		Set of 4 (*Phosphor*)	75	70	☐	☐
		First Day Cover (*Ordinary*)		12·00		☐
		First Day Cover (*Phosphor*) . . .		12·00		☐
		Presentation Pack (*Ordinary*) . .	9·00		☐	

259 Cup Winners

England's World Cup Football Victory
1966 (18 Aug.)

700	**259**	4d multicoloured	25	25 ☐ ☐
		First Day Cover		9·00 ☐

260 Jodrell Bank Radio Telescope

261 British Motor-cars

262 SR N6 Hovercraft

263 Windscale Reactor

British Technology
1966 (19 Sept.)

701	**260**	4d black and lemon . . .	10	10 ☐ ☐
		p. Phosphor	10	10 ☐ ☐
702	**261**	6d red, blue and orange	15	20 ☐ ☐
		p. Phosphor	15	20 ☐ ☐
703	**262**	1s 3d multicoloured	25	40 ☐ ☐
		p. Phosphor	35	40 ☐ ☐
704	**263**	1s 6d multicoloured	40	60 ☐ ☐
		p. Phosphor	50	60 ☐ ☐
		Set of 4 (Ordinary)	80	1·10 ☐ ☐
		Set of 4 (Phosphor)	1·00	1·10 ☐ ☐
		First Day Cover (Ordinary)		8·00 ☐
		First Day Cover (Phosphor) . . .		8·00 ☐
		Presentation Pack (Ordinary) . .	9·00	☐

264

265

266

267

268

269

The above show battle scenes, they were issued together *se-tenant* in horizontal strips of six within the sheet.

270 Norman Ship

271 Norman Horsemen attacking Harold's Troops

900th Anniversary of Battle of Hastings
1966 (14 Oct.) *Designs show scenes from Bayeux Tapestry* Wmk **179** (*sideways on 1s 3d*)

705	**264**	4d multicoloured	10	20 ☐ ☐
		a. Strip of 6. Nos. 705/10	1·90	6·00 ☐ ☐
		p. Phosphor	10	25 ☐ ☐
		pa. Strip of 6. Nos.		
		705p/10p	1·90	6·00 ☐ ☐
706	**265**	4d multicoloured	10	20 ☐ ☐
		p. Phosphor	10	25 ☐ ☐
707	**266**	4d multicoloured	10	20 ☐ ☐
		p. Phosphor	10	25 ☐ ☐
708	**267**	4d multicoloured	10	20 ☐ ☐
		p. Phosphor	10	25 ☐ ☐
709	**268**	4d multicoloured	10	20 ☐ ☐
		p. Phosphor	10	25 ☐ ☐
710	**269**	4d multicoloured	10	20 ☐ ☐
		p. Phosphor	10	25 ☐ ☐

711	**270**	6d multicoloured	10	20	☐	☐
		p. Phosphor	10	20	☐	☐
712	**271**	1s 3d multicoloured	20	40	☐	☐
		p. Phosphor	20	50	☐	☐
		Set of 8 (Ordinary)	2·00	1·60	☐	☐
		Set of 8 (Phosphor)	2·00	2·00	☐	☐
		First Day Cover (Ordinary)		8·00		☐
		First Day Cover (Phosphor) . . .		9·00		☐
		Presentation Pack (Ordinary) . .	9·00		☐	

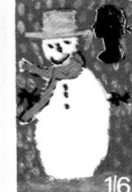

272 King of the Orient   **273** Snowman

Christmas

1966 (1 Dec.) *Wmk* **179** (*upright on* 1s 6d)

713	**272**	3d multicoloured	10	10	☐	☐
		p. Phosphor	10	10	☐	☐
714	**273**	1s 6d multicoloured	35	40	☐	☐
		p. Phosphor	30	35	☐	☐
		Set of 2 (Ordinary)	45	50	☐	☐
		Set of 2 (Phosphor)	40	45	☐	☐
		First Day Cover (Ordinary)		4·00		☐
		First Day Cover (Phosphor) . . .		4·00		☐
		Presentation Pack (Ordinary) . .	8·00		☐	

274 Sea Freight   **275** Air Freight

European Free Trade Association (EFTA)

1967 (20 Feb.)

715	**274**	9d multicoloured	15	20	☐	☐
		p. Phosphor	15	20	☐	☐
716	**275**	1s 6d multicoloured	30	45	☐	☐
		p. Phosphor	25	40	☐	☐
		Set of 2 (Ordinary)	45	65	☐	☐
		Set of 2 (Phosphor)	40	60	☐	☐
		First Day Cover (Ordinary)		4·00		☐
		First Day Cover (Phosphor) . . .		4·00		☐
		Presentation Pack (Ordinary) . .	3·00		☐	

276 Hawthorn and Bramble   **277** Larger Bindweed and Viper's Bugloss

278 Ox-eye Daisy, Coltsfoot and Buttercup   **279** Bluebell, Red Campion and Wood Anemone

The above sheet were issued together *se-tenant* in blocks of four within the sheet.

280 Dog Violet   **281** Primroses

British Wild Flowers

1967 (24 Apr.)

717	**276**	4d multicoloured	15	15	☐	☐
		a. *Block of* 4. *Nos.* 717/20	80	3·00	☐	☐
		p. Phosphor	10	15	☐	☐
		pa *Block of* 4. *Nos.* 717p/ 20p	50	2·75	☐	☐
718	**277**	4d multicoloured	15	15	☐	☐
		p. Phosphor	10	15	☐	☐
719	**278**	4d multicoloured	15	15	☐	☐
		p. Phosphor	10	15	☐	☐
720	**279**	4d multicoloured	15	15	☐	☐
		p. Phosphor	10	15	☐	☐
721	**280**	9d multicoloured	15	20	☐	☐
		p. Phosphor	15	25	☐	☐
722	**281**	1s 9d multicoloured	20	30	☐	☐
		p. Phosphor	20	30	☐	☐
		Set of 6 (Ordinary)	1·00	1·00	☐	☐
		Set of 6 (Phosphor)	75	1·00	☐	☐
		First Day Cover (Ordinary)		5·50		☐
		First Day Cover (Phosphor) . . .		7·00		☐
		Presentation Pack (Ordinary) . .	5·00		☐	
		Presentation Pack (Phosphor) . .	5·00		☐	

282 (value at left)

282a (value at right)

I   II

Two *types* of the 2d.

I. Value spaced away from left side of stamp.
II. Value close to left side from new multi-positive. This results in the portrait appearing in the centre, thus conforming with the other values.

1967–69 *Two phosphor bands, except where otherwise stated. No wmk.*

723	**282**	½d orange-brown	10	20 ☐	☐
724		1d olive (2 bands)	10	10 ☐	☐
725		1d olive (1 centre band)	30	35 ☐	☐
726		2d lake-brown (Type I) (2 bands)	10	15 ☐	☐
727		2d lake-brown (Type II) (2 bands)	15	20 ☐	☐
728		2d lake-brown (Type II) (1 centre band) . . .	70	90 ☐	☐
729		3d violet (1 centre band)	10	10 ☐	☐
730		3d violet (2 bands) . . .	30	35 ☐	☐
731		4d sepia (2 bands) . . .	10	10 ☐	☐
732		4d olive-brown (1 centre band)	10	10 ☐	☐
733		4d vermilion (1 centre band)	10	10 ☐	☐
734		4d vermilion (1 side band)	1·50	1·75 ☐	☐
735		5d blue	10	10 ☐	☐
736		6d purple	20	20 ☐	☐
737	**282a**	7d emerald	40	35 ☐	☐
738		8d vermilion	20	45 ☐	☐
739		8d turquoise-blue	50	60 ☐	☐
740		9d green	40	25 ☐	☐
741	**282**	10d drab	50	50 ☐	☐
742		1s violet	45	25 ☐	☐
743		1s 6d blue and deep blue .	50	50 ☐	☐
		c. Phosphorised paper .	80	80 ☐	☐
744		1s 9d orange and black .	50	45 ☐	☐
		Set of 16 (one of each value and colour)	4·00	4·00 ☐	☐
		Presentation Pack (one of each value)	7·00		☐
		Presentation Pack (German) . . .	45·00		☐

First Day Covers

5 June 1967	Nos. 731, 742, 744	. . . . .	3·00 ☐
8 Aug. 1967	Nos. 729, 740, 743	. . . . .	3·00 ☐
5 Feb. 1968	Nos. 723/4, 726, 736	. . . . .	3·00 ☐
1 July 1968	Nos. 735, 737/8, 741	. . . . .	3·00 ☐

No. 734 exists with phosphor band at the left or right.

283 'Master Lambton' (Sir Thomas Lawrence)

284 'Mares and Foals in a Landscape' (George Stubbs)

285 'Children Coming Out of School' (L. S. Lowry)

British Paintings

1967 (10 JULY) *Two phosphor bands. No wmk*

748	**283**	4d multicoloured	10	10 ☐	☐
749	**284**	9d multicoloured	15	15 ☐	☐
750	**285**	1s 6d multicoloured	25	35 ☐	☐
		Set of 3	45	50 ☐	☐
		First Day Cover		4·00	☐
		Presentation Pack	6·50		☐

286 *Gipsy Moth IV*

Sir Francis Chichester's World Voyage

1967 (24 JULY) *Three phosphor bands. No wmk*

751	**286**	1s 9d multicoloured	20	20 ☐	☐
		First Day Cover		2·00	☐

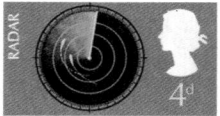

287 Radar Screen

288 *Penicillium notatum*

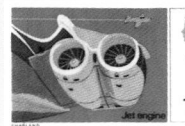

289 Vickers VC-10 Jet Engines   **290** Television Equipment

British Discovery and Invention

1967 (19 SEPT.) *Two phosphor bands (except 4d. three bands).*
Wmk **179** *(sideways on 1s 9d)*

752	**287**	4d yellow, black and vermilion	. . . .	10	10 □ □
753	**288**	1s multicoloured	. . . .	10	20 □ □
754	**289**	1s 6d multicoloured	. . . .	20	25 □ □
755	**290**	1s 9d multicoloured	. . . .	20	30 □ □
	Set of 4	. . . .		50	75 □ □
	First Day Cover	. . . .			3·50 □
	Presentation Pack	. . . .		2·75	□

NO WATERMARK. All the following issues are on un-watermarked paper unless otherwise stated.

291 'The Adoration of   **292** 'Madonna and
the Shepherds'   Child' (Murillo)
(School of Seville)

293 'The Adoration of the
         Shepherds' (Louis Le Nain)

Christmas

1967 *Two phosphor bands (except 3d, one phosphor band)*

756	·**291**	3d multicoloured			
		(27 Nov.)	. . . .	10	10 □ □
757	**292**	4d multicoloured			
		(18 Oct.)	. . . .	10	10 □ □

758	**293**	1s 6d multicoloured			
		(27 Nov.)	. . . .	15	30 □ □
	Set of 3	. . . .		30	45 □ □
	First Day Covers (2)	. . . .			3·50 □

Gift Pack 1967

1967 (27 NOV.) *Comprises Nos. 715p/22p and 748/58*

	Gift Pack	. . . .	2·75	□

1967–68 *No wmk. Perf* 11 × 12

759	**166**	2s 6d brown	. . . .	35	40 □ □
760	**167**	5s red	. . . .	80	90 □ □
761	**168**	10s blue	. . . .	5·00	6·75 □ □
762	**169**	£1 black	. . . .	4·75	6·25 □ □
	Set of 4	. . . .		9·75	12·50 □ □

294 Tarr Steps, Exmoor   **295** Aberfeldy Bridge

296 Menai Bridge   **297** M4 Viaduct

British Bridges

1968 (29 APR.) *Two phosphor bands*

763	**294**	4d multicoloured	. . . .	10	10 □ □
764	**295**	9d multicoloured	. . . .	10	15 □ □
765	**296**	1s 6d multicoloured	. . . .	15	25 □ □
766	**297**	1s 9d multicoloured	. . . .	20	30 □ □
	Set of 4	. . . .		50	70 □ □
	First Day Cover	. . . .			3·00 □
	Presentation Pack	. . . .		2·25	□

298 'TUC' and Trades Unionists   **299** Mrs Emmeline Pankhurst
                                      (statue)

300 Sopwith Camel and English   **301** Captain Cook's *Endeavour*
     Electric Lightning Fighters   and Signature

British Anniversaries. Events described on stamps

1968 (29 MAY) *Two phosphor bands*

767	**298**	4d multicoloured	10	10	□	□
768	**299**	9d violet, grey and black	10	15	□	□
769	**300**	1s multicoloured	15	25	□	□
770	**301**	1s 9d ochre and brown . .	35	40	□	□
		Set of 4	60	80	□	□
		First Day Cover		6·00		□
		Presentation Pack	2·75			□

302 'Queen Elizabeth I' (Unknown Artist)

303 'Pinkie' (Lawrence)

304 'Ruins of St Mary Le Port' (Piper)

305 'The Hay Wain' (Constable)

British Paintings

1968 (12 AUG.) *Two phosphor bands*

771	**302**	4d multicoloured	10	10	□	□
772	**303**	1s multicoloured	10	20	□	□
773	**304**	1s 6d multicoloured	20	30	□	□
774	**305**	1s 9d multicoloured	25	50	□	□
		Set of 4	50	1·00	□	□
		First Day Cover		3·00		□
		Presentation Pack	2·75			□
		Presentation Pack (*German*) . . .	6·00			□

Gift Pack 1968

1968 (16 SEPT.) *Comprises Nos. 763/74*

Gift Pack	8·00		□
Gift Pack (*German*)	20·00		□

Collectors Pack 1968

1968 (16 SEPT.) *Comprises Nos. 752/8 and 763/74*

Collectors Pack	9·00		□

306 Girl and Boy with Rocking Horse

307 Girl with Doll's House

308 Boy with Train Set

Christmas

1968 (25 NOV.) *Two phosphor bands (except 4d, one centre phosphor band)*

775	**306**	4d multicoloured	15	10	□	□
776	**307**	9d multicoloured	15	15	□	□
777	**308**	1s 6d multicoloured	15	30	□	□
		Set of 3	40	45	□	□
		First Day Cover		2·75		□
		Presentation Pack	3·00			□
		Presentation Pack (*German*) . . .	6·00			□

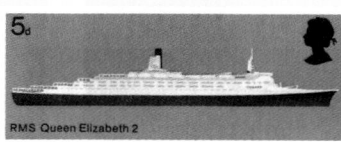

309 *Queen Elizabeth 2*

310 Elizabethan Galleon

311 East Indiaman

312 *Cutty Sark*

SS Great Britain

313   *Great Britain*

RMS Mauretania

314   *Mauretania I*

The 9d and 1s values were arranged in horizontal strips of three and pairs respectively throughout the sheet.

British Ships
1969 (15 JAN.) *One horiz phosphor band* (5d), *two phosphor bands* (9d) *or two vert phosphor bands at right* (1s)

778	**309**	5d multicoloured	10	15	☐	☐
779	**310**	9d multicoloured	10	25	☐	☐
		a. *Strip of 3. Nos. 779/81*	1·75	3·00	☐	☐
780	**311**	9d multicoloured	10	25	☐	☐
781	**312**	9d multicoloured	10	25	☐	☐
782	**313**	1s multicoloured	40	35	☐	☐
		a. *Pair. Nos. 782/3* . . .	1·50	2·50	☐	☐
783	**314**	1s multicoloured	40	35	☐	☐
		Set of 6	2·50	1·40	☐	☐
		First Day Cover		7·00		☐
		Presentation Pack	4·50		☐	
		Presentation Pack (*German*) . . .	20·00		☐	

315   Concorde in Flight

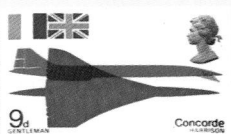

316   Plan and Elevation Views

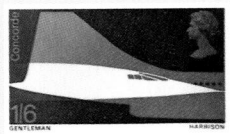

317   Concorde's Nose and Tail

First Flight of Concorde
1969 (3 MAR.) *Two phosphor bands*

784	**315**	4d multicoloured	10	10	☐	☐
785	**316**	9d multicoloured	15	25	☐	☐

786	**317**	1s 6d deep blue, grey and light blue	20	30	☐	☐
		Set of 3	40	60	☐	☐
		First Day Cover		3·00		☐
		Presentation Pack	3·00			☐
		Presentation Pack (*German*) . . .	18·00			☐

£1

318   (See also Type **357**)

1969 (5 MAR.) *P* 12

787	**318**	2s 6d brown	40	30	☐	☐
788		5s lake	2·00	60	☐	☐
789		10s ultramarine	6·50	6·00	☐	☐
790		£1 black	2·75	2·00	☐	☐
		Set of 4	10·50	8·00	☐	☐
		First Day Cover		9·50		☐
		Presentation Pack	16·00			☐
		Presentation Pack (*German*) . . .	42·00			☐

319   Page from the *Daily Mail*, and Vickers FB-27 Vimy Aircraft

320   Europa and C.E.P.T. Emblems

321   I.L.O. Emblem

322   Flags of N.A.T.O. Countries

323   Vickers FB-27 Vimy Aircraft and Globe showing Flight

Anniversaries. Events described on stamps
1969 (2 APR.) *Two phosphor bands*

791	**319**	5d multicoloured	10	10	☐	☐
792	**320**	9d multicoloured	15	20	☐	☐

793	**321**	1s claret, red and blue .	15	20 ☐ ☐	
794	**322**	1s 6d multicoloured	15	25 ☐ ☐	
795	**323**	1s 9d olive, yellow and turquoise-green . . .	20	35 ☐ ☐	
		Set of 5	65	95 ☐ ☐	
		First Day Cover		5·00 ☐	
		Presentation Pack	3·50	☐	
		Presentation Pack (German) . . .	42·00	☐	

324 Durham Cathedral

325 York Minster

326 St Giles' Cathedral, Edinburgh

327 Canterbury Cathedral

The above were issued together *se-tenant* in blocks of four within the sheet.

328 St Paul's Cathedral

329 Liverpool Metropolitan Cathedral

British Architecture (Cathedrals)
1969 (28 MAY) *Two phosphor bands*

796	**324**	5d multicoloured	10	15 ☐ ☐	
		a. Block of 4. Nos. 796/9	85	2·50 ☐ ☐	
797	**325**	5d multicoloured	10	15 ☐ ☐	
798	**326**	5d multicoloured	10	15 ☐ ☐	
799	**327**	5d multicoloured	10	15 ☐ ☐	
800	**328**	9d multicoloured	15	20 ☐ ☐	
801	**329**	1s 6d multicoloured	20	20 ☐ ☐	
		Set of 6	1·10	90 ☐ ☐	
		First Day Cover		5·00 ☐	
		Presentation Pack	3·50	☐	
		Presentation Pack (German) . . .	20·00	☐	

330 The King's Gate, Caernarvon Castle

331 The Eagle Tower, Caernarvon Castle

332 Queen Eleanor's Gate, Caernarvon Castle

333 Celtic Cross, Margam Abbey

The 5d values were printed *se-tenant* in strips of three throughout the sheet

334 Prince Charles

Investiture of H.R.H. The Prince of Wales
1969 (1 JULY) *Two phosphor bands*

802	**330**	5d multicoloured	10	15 ☐ ☐	
		a. Strip of 3. Nos. 802/4	30	1·50 ☐ ☐	
803	**331**	5d multicoloured	10	15 ☐ ☐	
804	**332**	5d multicoloured	10	15 ☐ ☐	
805	**333**	9d multicoloured	15	20 ☐ ☐	
806	**334**	1s black and gold	15	20 ☐ ☐	
		Set of 5	50	60 ☐ ☐	
		First Day Cover		2·50 ☐	
		Presentation Pack	2·50	☐	
		Presentation Pack (German) . . .	18·00	☐	

335 Mahatma Gandhi

Gandhi Centenary Year

1969 (13 Aug.) *Two phosphor bands*

807	**335**	1s 6d multicoloured	20	25	☐	☐
		First Day Cover		2·00		☐

Collectors Pack 1969

1969 (15 Sept.) *Comprises Nos. 775/86 and 791/807*

Collectors Pack . . . . 20·00   ☐

336   National Giro

337   Telecommunications —
International Subscriber
Dialling

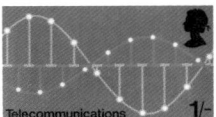

338   Telecommunications —
Pulse Code Modulation

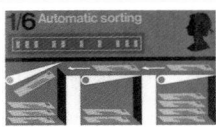

339   Postal Mechanisation —
Automatic Sorting

British Post Office Technology

1969 (1 Oct.) *Two phosphor bands. Perf* $13\frac{1}{2} \times 14$

808	**336**	5d multicoloured	10	10	☐	☐
809	**337**	9d green, blue and black	20	20	☐	☐
810	**338**	1s green, lavender and black	20	20	☐	☐
811	**339**	1s 6d multicoloured	20	35	☐	☐
		Set of 4	60	75	☐	☐
		First Day Cover		2·50		☐
		Presentation Pack	2·75			☐

340   Herald Angel

341   The Three Shepherds

342   The Three Kings

Christmas

1969 (26 Nov.) *Two phosphor bands (5d, 1s 6d) or one centre band (4d)*

812	**340**	4d multicoloured	10	10	☐	☐
813	**341**	5d multicoloured	15	15	☐	☐
814	**342**	1s 6d multicoloured	25	30	☐	☐
		Set of 3	45	50	☐	☐
		First Day Cover		2·00		☐
		Presentation Pack	2·75			☐

343   Fife Harling

344   Cotswold Limestone

345   Welsh Stucco

346   Ulster Thatch

British Rural Architecture

1970 (11 Feb.) *Two phosphor bands*

815	**343**	5d multicoloured	10	10	☐	☐
816	**344**	9d multicoloured	10	20	☐	☐
817	**345**	1s multicoloured	15	20	☐	☐
818	**346**	1s 6d multicoloured	20	30	☐	☐
		Set of 4	50	70	☐	☐
		First Day Cover		2·50		☐
		Presentation Pack	3·00			☐

347   Signing the Declaration
of Arbroath

348   Florence Nightingale
attending Patients

349   Signing of International
Co-operative Alliance

350   Pilgrims and *Mayflower*

351 Sir William Herschel, Francis Baily, Sir John Herschel and Telescope

Anniversaries. Events described on stamps

1970 (1 APR.) *Two phosphor bands*

819	**347**	5d multicoloured	. . . .	10	10	□	□
820	**348**	9d multicoloured	. . . .	15	15	□	□
821	**349**	1s multicoloured	. . . .	20	35	□	□
822	**350**	1s 6d multicoloured	. . . .	20	35	□	□
823	**351**	1s 9d multicoloured	. . . .	25	35	□	□
		Set of 5	. . . .	80	1·10	□	□
		First Day Cover	. . . .		3·00		□
		Presentation Pack	. . . .	3·00			□

352 'Mr Pickwick and Sam' (*Pickwick Papers*)

353 'Mr and Mrs Micawber' (*David Copperfield*)

354 'David Copperfield and Betsy Trotwood' (*David Copperfield*)

355 'Oliver asking for more' (*Oliver Twist*)

356 'Grasmere' (from engraving by J. Farrington, R.A.)

The 5d values were issued together *se-tenant* in blocks of four within the sheet.

Literary Anniversaries. Events described on stamps

1970 (3 JUNE) *Two phosphor bands*

824	**352**	5d multicoloured	. . . .	10	15	□	□
		a. Block of 4. Nos. 824/7		1·00	2·00	□	□
825	**353**	5d multicoloured	. . . .	10	15	□	□

826	**354**	5d multicoloured	. . . .	10	15	□	□
827	**355**	5d multicoloured	. . . .	10	15	□	□
828	**356**	1s 6d multicoloured	. . . .	30	35	□	□
		Set of 5	. . . .	1·10	85	□	□
		First Day Cover	. . . .		4·00		□
		Presentation Pack	. . . .	3·25			□

356a

357 (Value redrawn)

Decimal Currency

1970 (17 JUNE)–**72** *10p and some printings of the 50p were issued on phosphor paper. Perf 12*

829	**356a**	10p cerise	. . . . . .	50	75	□	□
830		20p olive-green	. . . . . .	50	25	□	□
831		50p ultramarine	. . . . .	1·00	40	□	□
831*b*	**357**	£1 black (6 Dec. 1972)	.	5·00	80	□	□
		Set of 4	. . . .	6·25	2·00	□	□
		First Day Cover (Nos. 829/31)	. .		2·75		□
		First Day Cover (No. 831b)	. . . .		3·00		□
		Presentation Pack (P.O Pack No. 18)					
		(*Nos. 829/31*)	. . . .	9·00			□
		Presentation Pack (P.O Pack No. 38)					
		(*Nos. 830/1, 790 or 831b*)	. . .	10·00			□

358 Runners

359 Swimmers

360 Cyclists

Ninth British Commonwealth Games, Edinburgh

1970 (15 JULY) *Two phosphor bands. Perf* 13½ × 14

832	**358**	5d pink, emerald, greenish yellow and yellow-green	10	10	□	□
833	**359**	1s 6d greenish blue, lilac, brown and Prussian blue	35	50	□	□

834	360	1s 9d yellow-orange, lilac, salmon and red-brown	35	50 ☐ ☐
		Set of 3	75	1·00 ☐ ☐
		First Day Cover		2·00 ☐
		Presentation Pack	2·50	☐

Collectors Pack 1970

1970 (14 SEPT.) *Comprises Nos. 808/28 and 832/4*
Collectors Pack . . . . 20·00 ☐

5^d Philympia 1970

9^d Philympia 1970

1/6 Philympia 1970

1840 first engraved issue   1847 first embossed issue   1855 first surface printed issue

| 361 | 1d Black (1840) | 362 | 1s Green (1847) | 363 | 4d Carmine (1855) |

'Philympia 70' Stamp Exhibition

1970 (18 SEPT.) *Two phosphor bands. Perf* $14 \times 14\frac{1}{2}$

835	361	5d multicoloured	10	10 ☐ ☐
836	362	9d multicoloured	20	30 ☐ ☐
837	363	1s 6d multicoloured	20	45 ☐ ☐
		Set of 3	45	80 ☐ ☐
		First Day Cover		2·25 ☐
		Presentation Pack	2·50	☐

| 364 | Shepherds and Apparition of the Angel | 365 | Mary, Joseph and Christ in the Manger |

| 366 | The Wise Men bearing Gifts |

Christmas

1970 (25 Nov.) *Two phosphor bands (5d, 1s 6d) or one centre phosphor band (4d)*

838	364	4d multicoloured	10	10 ☐ ☐
839	365	5d multicoloured	10	15 ☐ ☐
840	366	1s 6d multicoloured	20	30 ☐ ☐
		Set of 3	35	50 ☐ ☐
		First Day Cover		2·50 ☐
		Presentation Pack	2·50	☐

PRINTING PROCESSES

There is a basic distinction between stamps printed by photogravure and those printed by lithography. Sorting the two is not as difficult as it sounds and with a little experience it should become easy to tell which method of production was employed for a particular stamp.

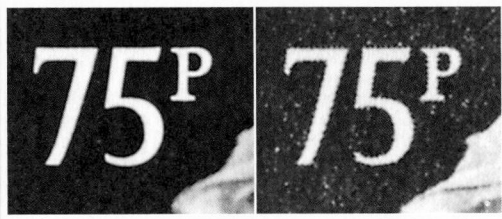

The tiny dots of the printing screen give uneven edges to the values on photogravure stamps (right). Litho values have clean, clear outlines (left).

All you need is a reasonably good glass giving a magnification of ×4 or more (×10 is even better!).

The image on a photogravure stamp is created from a pattern or 'screen', of minute dots which are not evident when looking at the stamp without a glass but show up quite clearly under magnification, especially in the Queen's face and around the margin of the stamp design where it meets the white background of the paper. Now look at the value; here also, what looks to the naked eye like a straight line is in fact made up of rows of tiny little dots.

'Screens' of dots are also used in the production of litho printed stamps but they are only required where the printer is attempting to produce shades and tints as is necessary in the Queen's head portion of the stamp. Where solid colour is used, as in the background of the majority of values, there is no need to resort to a screen of dots and the background is printed as a solid mass of colour. If you look at the margins or the values of stamps produced in this way you will not see any evidence of dots—just a clear clean break between the inked portion of the stamp and the uninked white of the paper.

367

367a

Decimal Currency

1971–96. *Type* **367**

(a) Printed in photogravure by Harrison and Sons (except for some ptgs of Nos. X879 and X913 which were produced by Enschedé) with phosphor bands. Perf 15 × 14

X841	½p turquoise-blue (2 bands)	10	10	□	□
X842	½p turquoise-blue (1 side band)	48·00	30·00	□	□
X843	½p turquoise-blue (1 centre band)	40	25	□	□
X844	1p crimson (2 bands) . . .	10	15	□	□
X845	1p crimson (1 centre band)	20	15	□	□
X846	1p crimson ('all-over' phosphor)	15	25	□	□
X847	1p crimson (1 side band) .	1·00	1·40	□	□
X848	1½p black (2 bands)	20	20	□	□
X849	2p myrtle-green (face value as in T **367**) (2 bands) .	10	20	□	□
X850	2p myrtle-green (face value as in T **367**) ('all-over' phosphor)	25	25	□	□
X851	2½p magenta (1 centre band)	20	15	□	□
X852	2½p magenta (1 side band) .	1·00	2·00	□	□
X853	2½p magenta (2 bands) . . .	30	60	□	□
X854	2½p rose-red (2 bands) . . .	50	70	□	□
X855	3p ultramarine (2 bands) .	20	25	□	□
X856	3p ultramarine (1 centre band)	15	20	□	□
X857	3p bright magenta (2 bands)	45	45	□	□
X858	3½p olive-grey (2 bands) . .	25	30	□	□
X859	3½p olive-grey (1 centre . . band)	30	25	□	□
X860	3½p purple-brown (1 centre band)	1·25	1·25	□	□
X861	4p ochre-brown (2 bands)	20	25	□	□
X862	4p greenish blue (2 bands)	1·75	2·00	□	□
X863	4p greenish blue (1 centre band)	1·50	1·90	□	□
X864	4p greenish blue (1 side band)	2·00	2·25	□	□
X865	4½p grey-blue (2 bands) . .	25	30	□	□
X866	5p pale violet (2 bands) . .	15	15	□	□
X867	5p claret (1 centre band) .	1·90	2·25	□	□
X868	5½p violet (2 bands)	30	30	□	□
X869	5½p violet (1 centre band) .	25	30	□	□
X870	6p light emerald (2 bands)	25	20	□	□
X871	6½p greenish blue (2 bands)	35	45	□	□
X872	6½p greenish blue (1 centre band)	30	15	□	□
X873	6½p greenish blue (1 side band)	60	70	□	□
X874	7p purple-brown (2 bands)	40	40	□	□
X875	7p purple-brown (1 centre band)	30	30	□	□
X876	7p purple-brown (1 side band)	45	70	□	□
X877	7½p chestnut (2 bands) . . .	25	30	□	□
X878	8p rosine (2 bands)	25	40	□	□
X879	8p rosine (1 centre band) .	25	40	□	□
X880	8p rosine (1 side band) . .	70	90	□	□
X881	8½p yellowish green (2 bands)	30	25	□	□
X882	9p yellow-orange and black (2 bands)	50	60	□	□
X883	9p deep violet (2 bands) .	35	30	□	□
X884	9½p purple (2 bands)	40	50	□	□
X885	10p orange-brown and chestnut (2 bands) . . .	30	25	□	□
X886	10p orange-brown (2 bands)	35	25	□	□
X887	10p orange-brown ('all-over' phosphor)	35	45	□	□
X888	10p orange-brown (1 centre band)	35	35	□	□
X889	10p orange-brown (1 side band)	70	90	□	□
X890	10½p yellow (2 bands)	45	50	□	□
X891	10½p blue (2 bands)	60	60	□	□
X892	11p brown-red (2 bands) . .	50	40	□	□
X893	11½p drab (1 centre band) . .	40	30	□	□
X894	11½p drab (1 side band) . . .	70	80	□	□
X895	12p yellowish green (2 bands)	45	45	□	□
X896	12p bright emerald (1 centre band)	45	45	□	□
X897	12p bright emerald (1 side band)	90	95	□	□
X898	12½p light emerald (1 centre band)	50	50	□	□
X899	12½p light emerald (1 side band)	80	80	□	□
X900	13p pale chestnut (1 centre band)	35	40	□	□
X901	13p pale chestnut (1 side band)	50	60	□	□
X902	14p grey-blue (2 bands) . .	75	80	□	□
X903	14p deep blue (1 centre band)	50	60	□	□
X904	14p deep blue (1 side band)	3·00	3·00	□	□
X905	15p bright blue (1 centre band)	75	75	□	□
X906	15p bright blue (1 side band)	3·25	3·25	□	□
X907	15½p pale violet (2 bands) . .	70	70	□	□
X908	16p olive-drab (2 bands) . .	1·40	1·50	□	□
X909	17p grey-blue (2 bands) . .	70	75	□	□
X910	17p deep blue (1 centre band)	1·00	1·00	□	□
X911	17p deep blue (1 side band)	2·00	2·00	□	□
X912	18p deep olive-grey (2 bands	80	1·00	□	□
X913	18p bright green (1 centre band)	60	50	□	□

34

X914	19p bright orange-red (2 bands)	1·50	1·75 □ □
X915	20p dull purple (2 bands) .	1·00	35 □ □
X916	20p brownish black (2 bands)	1·50	2·00 □ □
X917	22p bright orange-red (2 bands)	1·25	1·25 □ □
X917a	25p rose-red (2 bands) ...	5·00	3·50 □ □
X918	26p rosine (2 bands)	7·00	7·50 □ □
X919	31p purple (2 bands)	14·00	14·00 □ □
X920	34p ochre-brown (2 bands)	7·00	7·50 □ □
X921	50p ochre-brown (2 bands)	2·00	50 □ □
X922	50p ochre (2 bands)	5·00	5·00 □ □

(b) *Printed in photogravure by Harrison and Sons on phosphorised paper. Perf* 15 × 14

X924	½p turquoise-blue	10	15 □ □
X925	1p crimson	10	15 □ □
X926	2p myrtle-green (face value as in T **367**) ...	10	20 □ □
X927	2p deep green (smaller value as in T **367a**) ...	10	20 □ □
X928	2p myrtle-green (smaller value as in T **367a**)	2·75	2·75 □ □
X929	2½p rose-red	15	20 □ □
X930	3p bright magenta	10	30 □ □
X931	3½p purple-brown	50	60 □ □
X932	4p greenish blue	40	60 □ □
X933	4p new blue	20	25 □ □
X934	5p pale violet	25	30 □ □
X935	5p dull red-brown	25	30 □ □
X936	6p yellow-olive	30	30 □ □
X937	7p brownish red	1·25	1·50 □ □
X938	8½p yellowish green	40	50 □ □
X939	10p orange-brown	35	35 □ □
X940	10p dull orange	40	40 □ □
X941	11p brown-red	80	80 □ □
X942	11½p ochre-brown	50	60 □ □
X943	12p yellowish green	45	45 □ □
X944	13p olive-grey	45	50 □ □
X945	13½p purple-brown	50	70 □ □
X946	14p grey-blue	50	50 □ □
X947	15p ultramarine	60	60 □ □
X948	15½p pale violet	60	50 □ □
X949	16p olive-drab	50	50 □ □
X950	16½p pale chestnut	80	75 □ □
X951	17p light emerald	70	60 □ □
X952	17p grey-blue	60	60 □ □
X953	17½p pale chestnut	70	80 □ □
X954	18p deep violet	70	70 □ □
X955	18p deep olive-grey	75	60 □ □
X956	19p bright orange-red ...	90	60 □ □
X957	19½p olive-grey	1·50	1·50 □ □
X958	20p dull purple	85	50 □ □
X959	20p turquoise-green	75	70 □ □
X960	20p brownish black	90	90 □ □
X961	20½p ultramarine	1·25	1·25 □ □
X962	22p blue	85	70 □ □
X963	22p yellow-green	80	75 □ □
X964	22p bright orange-red ...	90	80 □ □
X965	23p brown-red	1·10	80 □ □
X966	23p bright green	80	80 □ □
X967	24p violet	1·50	1·50 □ □
X968	24p Indian red	1·90	1·40 □ □
X969	24p chestnut	80	85 □ □
X970	25p purple	1·00	1·00 □ □
X971	26p rosine	1·25	60 □ □
X972	26p drab	1·50	1·25 □ □
X973	27p chestnut	1·40	1·40 □ □
X974	27p violet	1·50	1·25 □ □
X975	28p deep violet	1·25	1·25 □ □
X976	28p ochre	1·40	1·25 □ □
X977	28p deep bluish grey	1·40	1·25 □ □
X978	29p ochre-brown	1·75	1·75 □ □
X979	29p deep mauve	2·00	1·60 □ □
X980	30p deep olive-grey	1·25	1·25 □ □
X981	31p purple	1·25	1·50 □ □
X982	31p ultramarine	1·60	1·50 □ □
X983	32p greenish blue	1·90	1·75 □ □
X984	33p light emerald	1·75	1·60 □ □
X985	34p ochre-brown	1·90	1·90 □ □
X986	34p deep bluish grey	2·00	1·90 □ □
X987	34p deep mauve	1·75	1·75 □ □
X988	35p sepia	1·75	1·75 □ □
X989	35p yellow	1·75	1·60 □ □
X990	37p rosine	2·00	1·75 □ □
X991	39p bright mauve	1·60	1·50 □ □

(c) *Printed in photogravure by Harrison and Sons on ordinary paper. Perf* 15 × 14

X992	50p ochre-brown	1·60	60 □ □
X993	75p grey-black (smaller values as T **367a**) ...	2·50	1·75 □ □

(d) *Printed in photogravure by Harrison and Sons on ordinary paper or phosphorised paper. Perf* 15 × 14

X994	50p ochre	1·75	80 □ □

(e) *Printed in lithography by John Waddington. Perf* 14

X996	4p greenish blue (2 bands)	25	30 □ □
X997	4p greenish blue (phosphorised paper) .	30	40 □ □
X998	20p dull purple (2 bands) .	1·25	90 □ □
X999	20p dull purple (phosphorised paper) .	1·75	90 □ □

(f) *Printed in lithography by Questa. Perf* 14 (*Nos* X1000, X1003/4 *and* X1023) *or* 15 × 14 (*others*)

X1000	2p emerald-green (face value as in T **367**) (phosphorised paper) .	20	20 □ □
	a. *Perf* 15 × 14	25	25 □ □
X1001	2p bright green and deep green (smaller value as in T **367a**) (phosphorised paper)	75	50 □ □
X1002	4p greenish blue (phosphorised paper) .	60	60 □ □

X1003	5p light violet (phosphorised paper) .	35	40	☐.	☐
X1004	5p claret (phosphorised paper)	50	50	☐	☐
	a. Perf 15 × 14	· 60	50	☐	☐
X1005	13p pale chestnut (1 centre band)	90	90	☐	☐
X1006	13p pale chestnut (1 side band)	80	80	☐	☐
X1007	14p deep blue (1 centre band)	1·60	1·60	☐	☐
X1008	17p deep blue (1 centre band)	80	80	☐	☐
X1009	18p deep olive-grey (phosphorised paper) .	1·00	90	☐	☐
X1010	18p deep olive-grey (2 bands)	6·50	6·50	☐	☐
X1011	18p bright green (1 centre band)	90	90	☐	☐
X1012	18p bright green (1 side band)	1·50	1·50	☐	☐
X1013	19p bright orange-red (phosphorised paper) .	2·00	2·25	☐	☐
X1014	20p dull purple (phosphorised paper) .	1·50	1·50	☐	☐
X1015	22p yellow-green (2 bands)	9·50	9·50	☐	☐
X1016	22p bright orange-red (phosphorised paper) .	90	1·00	☐	☐
X1017	24p chestnut (phosphorised paper)	1·50	1·75	☐	☐
X1018	24p chestnut (2 bands) . . .	1·40	1·50	☐	☐
X1019	33p light emerald (phosphorised paper) .	2·75	2·50	☐	☐
X1020	33p light emerald (2 bands)	1·25	1·50	☐	☐
X1021	34p bistre-brown (2 bands)	8·00	7·50	☐	☐
X1022	39p bright mauve (2 bands)	1·75	2·00	☐	☐
X1023	75p black (face value as T **367**) (ordinary paper)	3·00	2·50	☐	☐
	a. Perf 15 × 14	3·50	3·75	☐	☐
X1024	75p brownish grey and black (smaller value as T **367a**) (ordinary paper)	10·00	10·00	☐	☐

(g) Printed in lithography by Walsall. Perf 14

X1050	2p deep green (phosphorised paper) .	1·25	1·40	☐	☐
X1051	14p deep blue (1 side band)	4·25	4·25	☐	☐
X1052	19p bright orange-red (2 bands)	2·75	2·75	☐	☐
X1053	24p chestnut (phosphorised paper)	1·25	1·60	☐	☐
X1054	29p deep mauve (2 bands)	3·50	3·50	☐	☐
X1055	29p deep mauve (phosphorised paper) .	4·75	4·75	☐	☐
X1056	31p ultramarine (phosphorised paper) .	1·90	1·90	☐	☐
X1057	33p light emerald (phosphorised paper) .	1·60	1·60	☐	☐
X1058	39p bright mauve (phosphorised paper) .	2·00	2·00	☐	☐

Presentation Pack (P.O. Pack No. 26) (*contains* ½p (X841), 1p (X848), 1½p (X848), 2p (X849), 2½p (X851), 3p (X855), 3½p (X858), 4p (X861), 5p (X866), 6p (X870), 7½p (X877), 9p (X882)) . . . .   5·00   ☐

Presentation Pack (*'Scandinavia 71'*) (*contents as above*) . . . .   35·00   ☐

Presentation Pack (P.O. Pack No. 37) (*contains* ½p (X841), 1p (X844), 1½p (X848), 2p (X849), 2½p (X851), 3p (X855 *or* X856), 3½p (X858 *or* X859), 4p (X861), 4½p (X865), 5p (X866), 5½p (X868 *or* X869), 6p (X870), 6½p (X871 *or* X872), 7p (X874), 7½p (X877), 8p (X878), 9p (X882), 10p (X885)) . . .   5·00   ☐

Presentation Pack (P.O. Pack No. 90) (*contains* ½p (X841), 1p (X844), 1½p (X848), 2p (X849), 2½p (X851), 3p (X856), 5p (X866), 6½p (X872), 7p (X874 *or* X875), 7½p (X877), 8p (X878), 8½p (X881), 9p (X883), 9½p (X884), 10p (X886), 10½p (X890), 11p (X892), 20p (X915), 50p (X921)) . . .   6·00   ☐

Presentation Pack (P.O. Pack No. 129a) (*contains* 2½p (X929), 3p (X930), 4p (X996), 10½p (X891), 11½p (X893), 11½p (X942), 12p (X943), 13p (X944), 13½p (X945), 14p (X946), 15p (X947), 15½p (X948), 17p (X951), 17½p (X953), 18p (X954), 22p (X962), 25p (X970), 75p (X1023)) . . . .   18·00   ☐

Presentation Pack (P.O. Pack No. 1) (*contains* ½p (X924), 1p (X925), 2p (X1000), 3p (X930), 3½p (X931), 4p (X997), 5p (X1004), 10p (X888), 12½p (X898), 16p (X949), 16½p (X950), 17p (X952), 20p (X999), 20½p (X961), 23p (X965), 26p (X971), 28p (X975), 31p (X981), 50p (X992), 75p (X1023)) . .   30·00   ☐

Presentation Pack (P.O. Pack No. 5) (*contains* ½p (X924), 1p (X925), 2p (X1000a), 3p (X930), 4p (X997), 5p (X1004a), 10p (X939), 13p (X900), 16p (X949), 17p (X952), 18p (X955), 20p (X999), 22p (X963), 24p (X967), 26p (X971), 28p (X975), 31p (X981), 34p (X985), 50p (X992), 75p (X1023a))   25·00   ☐

Presentation Pack (*P.O. Pack No.* 9)
(*contains* 1p (X925), 2p (X1000*a*), 3p
(X930), 4p (X997), 5p (X1004*a*), 7p
(X937), 10p (X939), 12p (X896), 13p
(X900), 17p (X952), 18p (X955), 20p
(X999), 22p (X963), 24p (X967), 26p
(X971), 28p (X975), 31p (X981), 34p
(X985), 50p (X992), 75p (X1023*a*))   25·00   □

Presentation Pack (*P.O. Pack No.* 15)
(*contains* 14p (X903), 19p (X956),
20p (X959), 23p (X966), 27p (X973),
28p (X976), 32p (X983), 35p (X988))   11·00   □

Presentation Pack (*P.O. Pack No.* 19)
(*contains* 15p (X905), 20p (X960),
24p (X968), 29p (X979), 30p (X980),
34p (X986), 37p (X990)) . . . . . .   11·00   □

Presentation Pack (*P.O. Pack No.* 22)
(*contains* 10p (X940), 17p (X910),
22p (X964), 26p (X972), 27p (X974),
31p (X982), 33p (X984)) . . . . . .   10·00   □

Presentation Pack (*P.O. Pack No.* 24)
(*contains* 1p (X925), 2p (X927), 3p
(X930), 4p (X933), 5p (X935), 10p
(X940), 17p (X910), 20p (X959), 22p
(X964), 26p (X972), 27p (X974), 30p
(X980), 31p (X982), 32p (X983), 33p
(X984), 37p (X990), 50p (X994), 75p
(X993)) . . . .   20·00   □

Presentation Pack (*P.O. Pack No.* 25)
(*contains* 6p (X936), 18p (X913), 24p
(X969), 28p (X977), 34p (X987), 35p
(X989), 39p (X991)) . . . .   10·00   □

First Day Covers

15 Feb. 1971	½p, 1p, 1½p, 2p, 2½p, 3p, 3½p, 4p, 5p, 6p, 7½p, 9p (*Nos.* X841, X844, X848/9, X851, X855, X858, X861, X866, X870, X877, X882) (*Covers carry* 'POSTING DELAYED BY THE POST OFFICE STRIKE 1971' *cachet*)	3·50	□
11 Aug. 1971	10p (*No.* X885)	2·25	□
24 Oct. 1973	4½p, 5½p, 8p (*Nos.* X865, X868, X878)	2·00	□
4 Sept. 1974	6½p (*No.* X871)	3·00	□
15 Jan. 1975	7p (*No.* X874)	2·00	□
24 Sept. 1975	8½p (*No.* X881)	2·00	□
25 Feb. 1976	9p, 9½p, 10p, 10½p, 11p, 20p (*Nos.* X883/4, X886, X890, X892, X915)	3·00	□

2 Feb. 1977	50p (*No.* X921)	2·00	□
26 April 1978	10½p (*No.* X891)	2·00	□
15 Aug. 1979	11½p, 13p, 15p (*Nos.* X942, X944, X947)	2·25	□
30 Jan. 1980	4p, 12p, 13½p, 17p, 17½p, 75p (*Nos.* X996, X943, X945, X951, X953, X1023)	3·25	□
22 Oct. 1980	3p, 22p (*Nos.* X930, X962) . . .	2·00	□
14 Jan. 1981	2½p, 11½p, 14p, 15½p, 18p, 25p (*Nos.* X929, X893, X946, X948, X954, X970)	2·25	□
27 Jan. 1982	5p, 12½p, 16½p, 19½p, 26p, 29p (*Nos.* X1004, X898, X950, X957, X971, X978)	4·00	□
30 Mar. 1983	3½p, 16p, 17p, 20½p, 23p, 28p, 31p (*Nos.* X931, X949, X952, X961, X965, X975, X981)	5·00	□
28 Aug. 1984	13p, 18p, 22p, 24p, 34p (*Nos.* X900, X955, X963, X967, X985)	3·00	□
29 Oct. 1985	7p, 12p (*Nos.* X937, X896) . . .	7·00	□
23 Aug. 1988	14p, 19p, 20p, 23p, 27p, 28p, 32p, 35p (*Nos.* X903, X956, X959, X966, X973, X976, X983, X988)	6·00	□
26 Sept. 1989	15p, 20p, 24p, 29p, 30p, 34p, 37p (*Nos.* X905, X960, X968, X979/80, X986, X990)	5·50	□
4 Sept. 1990	10p, 17p, 22p, 26p, 27p, 31p, 33p (*Nos.* X940, X910, X964, X972, X974, X982, X984)	5·50	□
10 Sept. 1991	6p, 18p, 24p, 28p, 34p, 35p, 39p (*Nos.* X936, X913, X969, X977, X987, X989, X991)	6·00	□

For similar stamps, but with elliptical perforations see Nos. Y1667/1803 in 1993.

PHOSPHOR BANDS. See notes on page 15.
Phosphor bands are applied to the stamps, after the design has been printed, by a separate cylinder. On issues with 'all-over' phosphor the 'band' covers the entire stamp. Parts of the stamp covered by phosphor bands, or the entire surface for 'all-over' phosphor versions, appear matt.

Nos. X847, X852, X864, X873, X876, X880, X889, X894, X897, X899, X901, X906, X911, X1006 and X1012 exist with the phosphor band at the left or right of the stamp.

PHOSPHORISED PAPER. First introduced as an experiment for a limited printing of the 1s 6d value (No. 743*c*) in 1969, this paper has the phosphor, to activate the automatic sorting machinery, added to the paper coating before the stamps were printed. Issues on this paper have a completely shiny surface. Although not adopted after this first trial further experiments on the 8½p in 1976 led to this paper being used for new printings of current values.

368 'A Mountain Road'
(T. P. Flanagan)

369 'Deer's Meadow'
(Tom Carr)

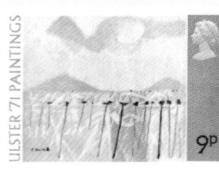

370 'Slieve na brock'
(Colin Middleton)

'Ulster '71' Paintings

1971 (16 June) *Two phosphor bands*

881	368	3p multicoloured	10	10	□	□
882	369	7½p multicoloured	45	55	□	□
883	370	9p multicoloured	50	55	□	□
		Set of 3	95	1·10	□	□
		First Day Cover		2·75	□	
		Presentation Pack	5·00		□	

371 John Keats
(150th Death Anniv)

372 Thomas Gray
(Death Bicentenary)

373 Sir Walter Scott (Birth
Bicentenary)

Literary Anniversaries. Events described above

1971 (28 July) *Two phosphor bands*

884	371	3p black, gold and blue . .	10	10	□	□
885	372	5p black, gold and olive .	45	50	□	□
886	373	7½p black, gold and brown	50	60	□	□
		Set of 3	95	1·10	□	□
		First Day Cover		3·50	□	
		Presentation Pack	5·00		□	

374 Servicemen and Nurse
of 1921

375 Roman Centurion

376 Rugby Football, 1871

British Anniversaries. Events described on stamps

1971 (25 Aug.) *Two phosphor bands*

887	374	3p multicoloured	10	10	□	□
888	375	7½p multicoloured	45	55	□	□
889	376	9p multicoloured	50	55	□	□
		Set of 3	95	1·10	□	□
		First Day Cover		2·75	□	
		Presentation Pack	5·00		□	

377 Physical Sciences
Building, University
College of Wales,
Aberystwyth

378 Faraday Building,
Southampton
University

379 Engineering Department,
Leicester University

380 Hexagon Restaurant,
Essex University

British Architecture (Modern University Buildings)

1971 (22 Sept.) *Two phosphor bands*

890	377	3p multicoloured	10	10	□	□
891	378	5p multicoloured	20	20	□	□

892	379	7½p ochre, black and purple-brown	. . . .	50	70 ☐ ☐
893	380	9p multicoloured	. . . .	80	1·00 ☐ ☐
		Set of 4		1·40	1·75 ☐ ☐
		First Day Cover			3·00 ☐
		Presentation Pack		5·50	☐

Collectors Pack 1971

1971 (29 SEPT.) *Comprises Nos. 835/40 and 881/93*

    Collectors Pack . . . .   27·00   ☐

381 Dream of the Wise Men

382 Adoration of the Magi

383 Ride of the Magi

Christmas

1971 (13 OCT.) *Two phosphor bands (3p, 7½p) or one centre phosphor band (2½p)*

894	381	2½p multicoloured	. . . . .	15	10 ☐ ☐
895	382	3p multicoloured	. . . . .	15	10 ☐ ☐
896	383	7½p multicoloured	. . . . .	70	90 ☐ ☐
		Set of 3		90	1·10 ☐ ☐
		First Day Cover			3·00 ☐
		Presentation Pack		4·50	☐

384 Sir James Clark Ross

385 Sir Martin Frobisher

386 Henry Hudson   **387** Capt. Robert F. Scott

British Polar Explorers

1972 (16 FEB.) *Two phosphor bands*

897	384	3p multicoloured	. . . .	10	10 ☐ ☐
898	385	5p multicoloured	. . . .	20	20 ☐ ☐
899	386	7½p multicoloured	. . . .	55	50 ☐ ☐
900	387	9p multicoloured	. . . .	85	90 ☐ ☐
		Set of 4		1·50	1·50 ☐ ☐
		First Day Cover			3·50 ☐
		Presentation Pack		4·75	☐

388 Statuette of Tutankhamun   **389** 19th-century Coastguard

390 Ralph Vaughan Williams and Score

Anniversaries. Events described on stamps

1972 (26 APR.) *Two phosphor bands*

901	388	3p multicoloured	. . . . .	10	10 ☐ ☐
902	389	7½p multicoloured	. . . . .	30	50 ☐ ☐
903	390	9p multicoloured	. . . . .	40	55 ☐ ☐
		Set of 3		80	1·10 ☐ ☐
		First Day Cover			3·00 ☐
		Presentation Pack		4·25	☐

For full information on all future British issues, collectors should write to Royal Mail, Freepost EH3647, 21 South Gyle Crescent, Edinburgh EH12 9PE.

391 St Andrew's, Greensted- juxta- Ongar, Essex

392 All Saints, Earls Barton, Northants

393 St Andrew's, Letheringsett, Norfolk

394 St Andrew's, Helpringham, Lincs

395 St Mary the Virgin, Huish Episcopi, Somerset

British Architecture (Village Churches)

1972 (21 June) *Two phosphor bands*

904	**391**	3p multicoloured	. . . . .	10		10	☐	☐
905	**392**	4p multicoloured	. . . . .	15		25	☐	☐
906	**393**	5p multicoloured	. . . . .	15		25	☐	☐
907	**394**	7½p multicoloured	. . . . .	75		90	☐	☐
908	**395**	9p multicoloured	. . . . .	75		1·00	☐	☐
		Set of 5	. . . .	1·75		2·25	☐	☐
		First Day Cover	. . . .			4·00		☐
		Presentation Pack	. . . .	6·00			☐	

'Belgica '72' Souvenir Pack

1972 (24 June) *Comprises Nos. 894/6 and 904/8*

	Souvenir Pack	. . . .	12·00	☐

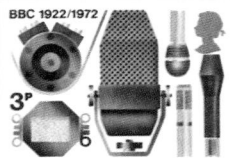

396 Microphones, 1924–69

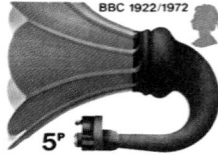

397 Horn Loudspeaker

398 TV Camera, 1972

399 Oscillator and Spark Transmitter, 1897

Broadcasting Anniversaries. Events described on stamps

1972 (13 Sept.) *Two phosphor bands*

909	**396**	3p multicoloured	. . . . .	10		10	☐	☐
910	**397**	5p multicoloured	. . . . .	10		25	☐	☐
911	**398**	7½p multicoloured	. . . . .	55		70	☐	☐
912	**399**	9p multicoloured	. . . . .	60		80	☐	☐
		Set of 4	. . . .	1·25		1·60	☐	☐
		First Day Cover	. . . .			4·00		☐
		Presentation Pack	. . . .	3·75			☐	

400 Angel holding Trumpet

401 Angel playing Lute

402 Angel playing Harp

Christmas

1972 (18 Oct.) *Two phosphor bands (3p, 7½p) or one centre phosphor band (2½p)*

913	**400**	2½p multicoloured	10	10	□	□
914	**401**	3p multicoloured	10	10	□	□
915	**402**	7½p multicoloured	60	90	□	□
		Set of 3	70	1·00	□	□
		First Day Cover		2·50		□
		Presentation Pack	2·50		□	

403 Queen Elizabeth II and Prince Philip **404** Europe

Royal Silver Wedding

1972 (20 Nov.) *3p 'all-over' phosphor, 20p without phosphor*

916	**403**	3p brownish black, deep blue and silver	15	15	□	□
917		20p brownish black, reddish purple and silver	65	85	□	□
		Set of 2	80	1·00	□	□
		First Day Cover		2·25		□
		Presentation Pack	2·25		□	
		Presentation Pack (Japanese) . .	6·00		□	
		Souvenir Book	5·00		□	
		Gutter Pair (3p)	60		□	
		Traffic Light Gutter Pair (3p) . . .	16·00		□	

Collectors Pack 1972

1972 (20 Nov.) *Comprises Nos. 897/918*

	Collectors Pack	27·00	□

Nos. 920/1 were issued horizontally *se-tenant* throughout the sheet.

Britain's Entry into European Communities

1973 (3 Jan.) *Two phosphor bands*

919	**404**	3p multicoloured	10	15	□	□
920		5p multicoloured (blue jigsaw)	30	50	□	□
		a. Pair. Nos. 920/1	1·00	1·75	□	□
921		5p multicoloured (green jigsaw)	30	50	□	□
		Set of 3	1·00	1·10	□	□
		First Day Cover		2·00		□
		Presentation Pack	2·50		□	

405 Oak Tree

British Trees (1st Issue)

1973 (28 Feb.) *Two phosphor bands*

922	**405**	9p multicoloured	40	50	□	□
		First Day Cover		2·50		□
		Presentation Pack	2·50		□	

See also No. 949

406 David Livingstone **407** H. M. Stanley

The above were issued horizontally *se-tenant* throughout the sheet.

408 Sir Francis Drake **409** Sir Walter Raleigh

410 Charles Sturt

British Explorers

1973 (18 Apr.) *'All-over' phosphor*

923	**406**	3p multicoloured	25	15	□	□
		a. Pair. Nos. 923/4	1·00	1·25	□	□

924	**407**	3p multicoloured	. . . .	25	15 □ □	
925	**408**	5p multicoloured	. . . .	25	35 □ □	
926	**409**	7½p multicoloured	. . . .	25	45 □ □	
927	**410**	9p multicoloured	. . . .	25	50 □ □	
		Set of 5		1·60	1·50 □ □	
		First Day Cover			3·50 □	
		Presentation Pack		4·00	□	

411 **412**

413

County Cricket 1873–1973

1973 (16 MAY) *Designs show sketches of W. G. Grace by Harry Furniss. Queen's head in gold. 'All-over' phosphor*

928	**411**	3p black and brown	. . . .	10	10 □ □	
929	**412**	7½p black and green	. . . .	70	90 □ □	
930	**413**	9p black and blue	. . . . .	90	1·10 □ □	
		Set of 3		1·60	1·90 □ □	
		First Day Cover			3·50 □	
		Presentation Pack		4·00	□	
		Souvenir Book		8·00	□	
		PHQ Card (No. 928)		60·00	£200 □ □	

The PHQ Card did not become available until mid-July. The used price quoted is for an example used in July or August 1973.

414 'Self-portrait' (Sir Joshua Reynolds)

415 'Self-portrait' (Sir Henry Raeburn)

416 'Nelly O'Brien' (Sir Joshua Reynolds)

417 'Rev R. Walker (The Skater)' (Sir Henry Raeburn)

Artistic Anniversaries. Events described on stamps

1973 (4 JULY) *'All-over' phosphor*

931	**414**	3p multicoloured	. . . .	10	10 □ □	
932	**415**	5p multicoloured	. . . .	15	25 □ □	
933	**416**	7½p multicoloured	. . . .	50	55 □ □	
934	**417**	9p multicoloured	. . . .	60	70 □ □	
		Set of 4		1·25	1·50 □ □	
		First Day Cover			2·25 □	
		Presentation Pack		3·00	□	

418 Court Masque Costumes

419 St Paul's Church, Covent Garden

420 Prince's Lodging, Newmarket

421 Court Masque Stage Scene

The 3p and 5p values were printed horizontally *se-tenant* within the sheet.

400th Anniversary of the Birth of Inigo Jones

1973 (15 AUG.) *'All-over' phosphor*

935	**418**	3p deep mauve, black and gold	. . . .	10	15 □ □
		a. Pair. Nos. 935/6	35	50 □ □
936	**419**	3p deep brown, black and gold	. . . .	10	15 □ □

937	**420**	5p blue, black and gold . .	40	50	☐	☐
		a. Pair. Nos. 937/8	1·25	1·50	☐	☐
938	**421**	5p grey-olive, black and				
		gold	40	50	☐	☐
	Set of 4		1·50	1·25	☐	☐
	First Day Cover			2·25	☐	
	Presentation Pack		3·50		☐	
	PHQ Card (No. 936)		£140	£150	☐	☐

422 Palace of Westminster seen from Whitehall   **423** Palace of Westminster seen from Millbank

19th Commonwealth Parliamentary Conference
1973 (12 Sept.) *'All-over' phosphor*

939	**422**	8p black, grey and pale				
		buff	55	60	☐	☐
940	**423**	10p gold and black	55	50	☐	☐
	Set of 2		1·10	1·10	☐	☐
	First Day Cover			2·00	☐	
	Presentation Pack		3·00		☐	
	Souvenir Book		6·00		☐	
	PHQ Card (No. 939)		40·00	£120	☐	☐

424 Princess Anne and Captain Mark Phillips

Royal Wedding
1973 (14 Nov.) *'All-over' phosphor*

941	**424**	3½p violet and silver	10	10	☐	☐
942		20p brown and silver . . .	70	90	☐	☐
	Set of 2		80	1·00	☐	☐
	First Day Cover			2·25	☐	
	Presentation Pack		2·25		☐	
	PHQ Card (No. 941)		8·00	40·00	☐	☐
	Set of 2 Gutter Pairs		3·00		☐	
	Set of 2 Traffic Light Gutter Pairs		85·00		☐	

425   426

427   428

429   430   'Good King Wenceslas, the Page and Peasant'

The 3p values depict the carol 'Good King Wenceslas' and were printed horizontally *se-tenant* within the sheet.

Christmas
1973 (28 Nov.) *One phosphor band (3p) or 'all-over' phosphor (3½p)*

943	**425**	3p multicoloured	20	25	☐	☐
		a. Strip of 5. Nos. 943/7 .	2·75	4·00	☐	☐
944	**426**	3p multicoloured	20	25	☐	☐
945	**427**	3p multicoloured	20	25	☐	☐
946	**428**	3p multicoloured	20	25	☐	☐
947	**429**	3p multicoloured	20	25	☐	☐
948	**430**	3½p multicoloured	20	25	☐	☐
	Set of 6		2·75	1·40	☐	☐
	First Day Cover			3·25	☐	
	Presentation Pack		3·75		☐	

Collectors Pack 1973
1973 (28 Nov.) *Comprises Nos. 919/48*

	Collectors Pack	27·00	☐

431   Horse Chestnut

British Trees (2nd issue)
1974 (27 Feb.) *'All-over' phosphor*

949	**431**	10p multicoloured	35	40	☐	☐
	First Day Cover			2·25	☐	
	Presentation Pack		2·50		☐	
	PHQ Card		£110	90·00	☐	☐
	Gutter Pair		3·00		☐	
	Traffic Light Gutter Pair		50·00		☐	

432 First Motor Fire-engine, 1904

433 Prize-winning Fire-engine, 1863

434 First Steam Fire-engine, 1830

435 Fire-engine, 1766

Bicentenary of Public Fire Services

1974 (24 APR.) *'All-over' phosphor*

950	**432**	3½p multicoloured	. . . .	10	10 □	□
951	**433**	5½p multicoloured	. . . .	30	35 □	□
952	**434**	8p multicoloured	. . . .	50	55 □	□
953	**435**	10p multicoloured	. . . .	50	55 □	□
		Set of 4	. . . .	1·25	1·40 □	□
		First Day Cover	. . . .		3·50	□
		Presentation Pack	. . . .	2·75		□
		PHQ Card (No. 950)	. . . .	£120	75·00 □	□
		Set of 4 Gutter Pairs	. . . . . .	3·50		□
		Set of 4 Traffic Light Gutter Pairs		50·00		□

436 P & O Packet Peninsular, 1888

437 Farman H.F. III Biplane, 1911

438 Airmail-blue Van and Postbox, 1930

439 Imperial Airways Short S.21 Flying Boat *Maia*, 1937

Centenary of Universal Postal Union

1974 (12 JUNE) *'All-over' phosphor*

954	**436**	3½p multicoloured	. . . .	10	10 □	□
955	**437**	5½p multicoloured	. . . .	25	35 □	□
956	**438**	8p multicoloured	. . . .	30	45 □	□
957	**439**	10p multicoloured	. . . .	45	50 □	□
		Set of 4	. . . .	1·00	1·25 □	□
		First Day Cover	. . . .		3·25	□
		Presentation Pack	. . . .	2·75		□
		Set of 4 Gutter Pairs	. . . .	3·00		□
		Set of 4 Traffic Light Gutter Pairs		40·00		□

440 Robert the Bruce

441 Owain Glyndŵr

442 Henry V

443 The Black Prince

Medieval Warriors

1974 (10 JULY) *'All-over' phosphor*

958	**440**	4½p multicoloured	. . . .	10	10 □	□
959	**441**	5½p multicoloured	. . . .	20	35 □	□
960	**442**	8p multicoloured	. . . .	50	60 □	□
961	**443**	10p multicoloured	. . . .	55	60 □	□
		Set of 4	. . . .	1·25	1·50 □	□
		First Day Cover	. . . .		4·25	□
		Presentation Pack	. . . .	4·00		□
		PHQ Cards (set of 4)	. . . .	30·00	42·00 □	□
		Set of 4 Gutter Pairs	. . . .	4·50		□
		Set of 4 Traffic Light Gutter Pairs		55·00		□

444 Churchill in Royal Yacht Squadron Uniform

445 Prime Minister, 1940

446 Secretary for War and Air, 1919

447 War Correspondent, South Africa, 1899

Birth Centenary of Sir Winston Churchill

1974 (9 Oct.) *Queen's head and inscription in silver. 'All-over' phosphor*

962	**444**	4½p green and blue	. . . .	20	15 □	□
963	**445**	5½p grey and black	. . . . .	35	40 □	□
964	**446**	8p rose and lake	. . . . .	65	70 □	□
965	**447**	10p stone and brown	. . .	70	70 □	□
	Set of 4	. . . .		1·75	1·75 □	□
	First Day Cover				3·00	□
	Presentation Pack			2·75		□
	Souvenir Book			4·00		□
	PHQ Card (No. 963)			6·00	20·00 □	□
	Set of 4 Gutter Pairs			4·50		□
	Set of 4 Traffic Light Gutter Pairs			40·00		□

448 Adoration of the Magi (York Minster, c 1355)

449 The Nativity (St Helen's Church, Norwich, c 1480)

450 Virgin and Child (Ottery St Mary Church, c 1350)

451 Virgin and Child (Worcester Cathedral, c 1224)

Christmas

1974 (27 Nov.) *Designs show church roof bosses. One phosphor band (3½p) or 'all-over' phosphor (others)*

966	**448**	3½p multicoloured	. . . .	10	10 □	□
967	**449**	4½p multicoloured	. . . .	10	10 □	□

968	**450**	8p multicoloured	. . . .	30	45 □	□
969	**451**	10p multicoloured	. . . .	40	55 □	□
	Set of 4	. . . .		80	1·10 □	□
	First Day Cover				3·00	□
	Presentation Pack			2·25		□
	Set of 4 Gutter Pairs			2·50		□
	Set of 4 Traffic Light Gutter Pairs			40·00		□

Collectors Pack 1974

1974 (27 Nov.) *Comprises Nos. 949/69*

	Collectors Pack		12·00	□

452 Invalid in Wheelchair

Health and Handicap Funds

1975 (22 Jan.) *'All-over' phosphor*

970	**452**	4½p + 1½p azure and blue	. .	20	20 □	□
	First Day Cover				2·00	□
	Gutter Pair			60		□
	Traffic Light Gutter Pair			1·25		□

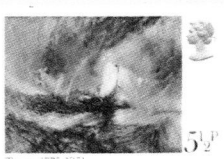

453 'Peace – Burial at Sea'

454 'Snowstorm – Steamer off a Harbour's Mouth'

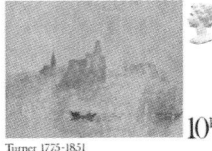

455 'The Arsenal, Venice'

456 'St Laurent'

Birth Bicentenary of J. M. W. Turner

1975 (19 Feb.) *'All-over' phosphor*

971	**453**	4½p multicoloured	. . . .	10	10 □	□
972	**454**	5½p multicoloured	. . . .	15	20 □	□

973	**455**	8p multicoloured	. . . . .	30	45	☐ ☐
974	**456**	10p multicoloured	. . . . .	40	50	☐ ☐
		Set of 4	. . . .	85	1·10	☐ ☐
		First Day Cover	. . . .		2·50	☐
		Presentation Pack	. . . .	2·50		☐
		PHQ Card (No. 972)	. . . .	40·00	25·00	☐ ☐
		Set of 4 Gutter Pairs	. . . .	2·25		☐
		Set of 4 Traffic Light Gutter Pairs		6·00		☐

457 Charlotte Square, Edinburgh

458 The Rows, Chester

The above were printed horizontally *se-tenant* throughout the sheet.

459 Royal Observatory, Greenwich

460 St George's Chapel, Windsor

461 National Theatre, London

European Architectural Heritage Year
1975 (23 APR.) *'All-over' phosphor*

975	**457**	7p multicoloured	. . . . .	25	30	☐ ☐
		a. Pair. Nos. 975/6	. . . .	1·00	1·25	☐ ☐
976	**458**	7p multicoloured	. . . . .	25	30	☐ ☐
977	**459**	8p multicoloured	. . . . .	25	35	☐ ☐
978	**460**	10p multicoloured	. . . . .	25	35	☐ ☐
979	**461**	12p multicoloured	. . . . .	30	40	☐ ☐
		Set of 5	. . . .	1·60	1·50	☐ ☐
		First Day Cover	. . . .		4·00	☐
		Presentation Pack	. . . .	3·00		☐
		PHQ Cards (Nos. 975/7)	. . . . .	10·00	25·00	☐ ☐
		Set of 5 Gutter Pairs	. . . .	5·50		☐
		Set of 5 Traffic Light Gutter Pairs		25·00		☐

462 Sailing Dinghies

463 Racing Keel Boats

464 Cruising Yachts

465 Multihulls

Sailing
1975 (11 JUNE) *'All-over' phosphor*

980	**462**	7p multicoloured	. . . . .	20	10	☐ ☐
981	**463**	8p multicoloured	. . . . .	30	30	☐ ☐
982	**464**	10p multicoloured	. . . . .	30	40	☐ ☐
983	**465**	12p multicoloured	. . . . .	45	60	☐ ☐
		Set of 4	. . . .	1·10	1·25	☐ ☐
		First Day Cover	. . . .		2·50	☐
		Presentation Pack	. . . .	2·50		☐
		PHQ Card (No. 981)	. . . .	6·00	20·00	☐ ☐
		Set of 4 Gutter Pairs	. . . .	2·75		☐
		Set of 4 Traffic Light Gutter Pairs		18·00		☐

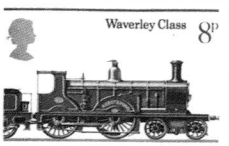

466 Stephenson's Locomotion, 1825

467 Abbotsford, 1876

468 Caerphilly Castle, 1923

469 High Speed Train, 1975

150th Anniversary of Public Railways
1975 (13 AUG.) *'All-over' phosphor*

984	**466**	7p multicoloured	. . . . .	20	10	☐ ☐
985	**467**	8p multicoloured	. . . . .	35	40	☐ ☐

986	**468**	10p multicoloured	45	45	☐	☐
987	**469**	12p multicoloured	50	50	☐	☐
		Set of 4	1·40	1·25	☐	☐
		First Day Cover		4·00		☐
		Presentation Pack	3·75		☐	
		Souvenir Book	6·00		☐	
		PHQ Cards (set of 4)	65·00	50·00	☐	☐
		Set of 4 Gutter Pairs	3·50		☐	
		Set of 4 Traffic Light Gutter Pairs	11·00		☐	

470   Palace of Westminster

62nd Inter-Parliamentary Union Conference

1975 (3 SEPT.) *'All-over' phosphor*

988	**470**	12p multicoloured	30	40	☐	☐
		First Day Cover		1·50		☐
		Presentation Pack	1·60		☐	
		Gutter Pair	75		☐	
		Traffic Light Gutter Pair	2·25		☐	

471   Emma and Mr
Woodhouse
(*Emma*)

472   Catherine Morland
(*Northanger Abbey*)

473   Mr Darcy
(*Pride and
Prejudice*)

474   Mary and Henry
Crawford (*Mansfield
Park*)

Birth Bicentenary of Jane Austen (novelist)

1975 (22 OCT.) *'All-over' phosphor*

989	**471**	8½p multicoloured	20	10	☐	☐
990	**472**	10p multicoloured	40	40	☐	☐

991	**473**	11p multicoloured	45	45	☐	☐
992	**474**	13p multicoloured	50	60	☐	☐
		Set of 4	1·40	1·40	☐	☐
		First Day Cover		4·00		☐
		Presentation Pack	2·50		☐	
		PHQ Cards (set of 4)	25·00	24·00	☐	☐
		Set of 4 Gutter Pairs	2·75		☐	
		Set of 4 Traffic Light Gutter Pairs	6·50		☐	

475   Angels with
Harp and Lute

476   Angel with Mandolin

477   Angel with Horn

478   Angel with Trumpet

Christmas

1975 (26 Nov.) *One phosphor band (6½p). phosphor-inked (8½p)
(background) or 'all-over' phosphor (others)*

993	**475**	6½p multicoloured	20	15	☐	☐
994	**476**	8½p multicoloured	30	35	☐	☐
995	**477**	11p multicoloured	40	45	☐	☐
996	**478**	13p multicoloured	45	45	☐	☐
		Set of 4	1·25	1·25	☐	☐
		First Day Cover		2·25		☐
		Presentation Pack	2·50		☐	
		Set of 4 Gutter Pairs	2·75		☐	
		Set of 4 Traffic Light Gutter Pairs	6·50		☐	

Collectors Pack 1975

1975 (26 Nov.) *Comprises Nos. 970/96*

	Collectors Pack	8·00		☐

479   Housewife

480   Policeman

481　District Nurse　　　482　Industrialist

487　Benjamin Franklin (bust by
　　　Jean-Jacques Caffieri)

Telephone Centenary
1976 (10 MAR.) *'All-over' phosphor*

997	**479**	8½p multicoloured	15	10	☐	☐
998	**480**	10p multicoloured	35	35	☐	☐
999	**481**	11p multicoloured	45	45	☐	☐
1000	**482**	13p multicoloured	50	50	☐	☐
		Set of 4	1·25	1·25	☐	☐
		First Day Cover		2·50		☐
		Presentation Pack	2·50		☐	
		Set of 4 Gutter Pairs	2·75		☐	
		Set of 4 Traffic Light Gutter Pairs	6·50		☐	

Bicentenary of American Revolution
1976 (2 JUNE) *'All-over' phosphor*

1005	**487**	11p multicoloured	40	40	☐	☐
		First Day Cover		1·50		☐
		Presentation Pack	1·50		☐	
		PHQ Card	4·00	15·00	☐	☐
		Gutter Pair	85		☐	
		Traffic Light Gutter Pair	2·00		☐	

483　Hewing Coal　　　　484　Machinery
　　　(Thomas Hepburn)　　　　(Robert Owen)

488　'Elizabeth of Glamis'　　489　'Grandpa Dickson'

485　Chimney Cleaning　　486　Hands clutching Prison
　　　(Lord Shaftesbury)　　　　Bars (Elizabeth Fry)

490　'Rosa Mundi'　　　491　'Sweet Briar'

Social Reformers
1976 (28 APR.) *'All-over' phosphor*

1001	**483**	8½p multicoloured	15	10	☐	☐
1002	**484**	10p multicoloured	30	35	☐	☐
1003	**485**	11p black, slate-grey and drab	35	40	☐	☐
1004	**486**	13p slate-grey, black and green	35	45	☐	☐
		Set of 4	1·00	1·10	☐	☐
		First Day Cover		2·50		☐
		Presentation Pack	2·50		☐	
		PHQ Card (No. 1001)	5·00	15·00	☐	☐
		Set of 4 Gutter Pairs	2·40		☐	
		Set of 4 Traffic Light Gutter Pairs	6·50		☐	

Centenary of Royal National Rose Society
1976 (30 JUNE) *'All-over' phosphor*

1006	**488**	8½p multicoloured	15	10	☐	☐
1007	**489**	10p multicoloured	30	35	☐	☐
1008	**490**	11p multicoloured	50	50	☐	☐
1009	**491**	13p multicoloured	60	60	☐	☐
		Set of 4	1·40	1·40	☐	☐
		First Day Cover		2·75		☐
		Presentation Pack	2·75		☐	
		PHQ Cards (set of 4)	25·00	26·00	☐	☐
		Set of 4 Gutter Pairs	3·25		☐	
		Set of 4 Traffic Light Gutter Pairs	9·00		☐	

492 Archdruid   **493** Morris Dancing

494 Scots Piper   **495** Welsh Harpist

British Cultural Traditions

1976 (4 Aug.) *'All-over' phosphor*

1010	**492**	8½p multicoloured	15	10	☐	☐
1011	**493**	10p multicoloured	35	35	☐	☐
1012	**494**	11p multicoloured	45	45	☐	☐
1013	**495**	13p multicoloured	50	50	☐	☐
		Set of 4	1·25	1·25	☐	☐
		First Day Cover		3·50		☐
		Presentation Pack	2·50		☐	
		PHQ Cards (set of 4)	15·00	18·00	☐	☐
		Set of 4 Gutter Pairs	2·75		☐	
		Set of 4 Traffic Light Gutter Pairs	8·00		☐	

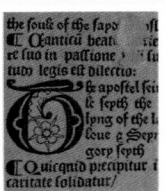

496 The Canterbury Tales   **497** The Tretyse of Love

For full information on all future British issues, collectors should write to Royal Mail, Freepost EH3647, 21 South Gyle Crescent, Edinburgh EH12 9PE.

498 *Game and Playe of Chesse*   **499** Early Printing Press

500th Anniversary of British Printing

1976 (29 Sept.) *'All-over' phosphor*

1014	**496**	8½p black, blue and gold .	20	10	☐	☐
1015	**497**	10p black, olive-green and gold	35	35	☐	☐
1016	**498**	11p black, grey and gold .	40	45	☐	☐
1017	**499**	13p brown, ochre and gold	45	50	☐	☐
		Set of 4	1·25	1·25	☐	☐
		First Day Cover		3·50		☐
		Presentation Pack	2·50		☐	
		PHQ Cards (set of 4)	12·00	18·00	☐	☐
		Set of 4 Gutter Pairs	2·75		☐	
		Set of 4 Traffic Light Gutter Pairs	8·00		☐	

500 Virgin and Child   **501** Angel with Crown

502 Angel appearing to Shepherds   **503** The Three Kings

Christmas

1976 (24 Nov.) *Designs show English medieval embroidery. One phosphor band (6½p) or 'all-over' phosphor (others)*

1018	**500**	6½p multicoloured	15	15	☐	☐
1019	**501**	8½p multicoloured	30	15	☐	☐
1020	**502**	11p multicoloured	35	45	☐	☐

1021	**503**	13p multicoloured	35	50	☐ ☐
		Set of 4	1·00	1·10	☐ ☐
		First Day Cover		3·50	☐
		Presentation Pack	2·50		☐
		PHQ Cards (set of 4)	4·50	16·00	☐ ☐
		Set of 4 Gutter Pairs	2·50		☐
		Set of 4 Traffic Light Gutter Pairs	6·50		☐

Collectors Pack 1976

1976 (24 Nov.) *Comprises Nos. 997/1021*

| | *Collectors Pack* . . . . | 12·00 | ☐ |

504   Lawn Tennis

505   Table Tennis

506   Squash

507   Badminton

Racket Sports

1977 (12 Jan.) *Phosphorised paper*

1022	**504**	8½p multicoloured	20	10	☐ ☐
1023	**505**	10p multicoloured	35	35	☐ ☐
1024	**506**	11p multicoloured	40	45	☐ ☐
1025	**507**	13p multicoloured	45	50	☐ ☐
		Set of 4	1·25	1·25	☐ ☐
		First Day Cover		3·50	☐
		Presentation Pack	2·50		☐
		PHQ Cards (set of 4)	7·00	16·00	☐ ☐
		Set of 4 Gutter Pairs	2·75		☐
		Set of 4 Traffic Light Gutter Pairs	6·50		☐

508

1977 (2 Feb.)–87 *Type* **508** *Ordinary paper*

1026		£1 green and olive	2·75	25	☐ ☐
1026b		£1·30 drab and deep greenish blue	5·50	6·00	☐ ☐
1026c		£1·33 pale mauve and grey-black	7·50	7·00	☐ ☐
1026d		£1·41 drab and deep greenish blue	8·00	8·50	☐ ☐
1026e		£1·50 pale mauve and grey-black	6·00	5·00	☐ ☐
1026f		£1·60 drab and deep greenish blue	6·50	7·00	☐ ☐
1027		£2 green and brown	6·00	50	☐ ☐
1028		£5 pink and blue	14·00	3·00	☐ ☐
		Set of 8	50·00	32·00	☐ ☐
		Presentation Pack (P.O. Pack No. 91 (small size)) (Nos. 1026, 1027/8)	24·00		☐
		Presentation Pack (P.O. Pack No.13 (large size)) (Nos. 1026, 1027/8)	80·00		☐
		Presentation Pack (P.O. Pack No. 14) (No. 1026f)	12·00		☐
		Set of 8 Gutter Pairs	£110		☐
		Set of 8 Traffic Light Gutter Pairs	£160		☐

First Day Covers

2 Feb. 1977	Nos. 1026, 1027/8	8·00	☐
3 Aug. 1983	No. 1026b	6·50	☐
28 Aug. 1984	No. 1026c	8·00	☐
17 Sept. 1985	No. 1026d	8·50	☐
2 Sept. 1986	No. 1026e	5·50	☐
15 Sept. 1987	No. 1026f	8·00	☐

509   Steroids — Conformational Analysis

510   Vitamin C — Synthesis

511   Starch — Chromatography

512   Salt — Crystallography

Centenary of Royal Institute of Chemistry

1977 (2 Mar.) *'All-over' phosphor*

1029	**509**	8½p multicoloured	15	10	☐ ☐
1030	**510**	10p multicoloured	40	45	☐ ☐
1031	**511**	11p multicoloured	40	45	☐ ☐

1032	512	13p multicoloured	40	40	☐	☐
		Set of 4	1·25	1·25	☐	☐
		First Day Cover		2·75		☐
		Presentation Pack	2·50		☐	
		PHQ Cards (set of 4)	7·00	12·00	☐	☐
		Set of 4 Gutter Pairs	2·75		☐	
		Set of 4 Traffic Light Gutter Pairs	6·50		☐	

513

Silver Jubilee

1977 (11 May–15 June) *'All-over' phosphor*

1033	513	8½p multicoloured	15	15	☐	☐
1034		9p multicoloured (15 June)	25	15	☐	☐
1035		10p multicoloured	25	25	☐	☐
1036		11p multicoloured	35	35	☐	☐
1037		13p multicoloured	40	40	☐	☐
		Set of 5	1·25	1·10	☐	☐
		First Day Covers (2)		4·00		☐
		Presentation Pack (ex 9p)	1·90		☐	
		Souvenir Book (ex 9p)	4·50		☐	
		PHQ Cards (set of 5)	12·00	15·00	☐	☐
		Set of 5 Gutter Pairs	2·75		☐	
		Set of 5 Traffic Light Gutter Pairs	4·00		☐	

517 'Gathering of Nations'

Commonwealth Heads of Government Meeting, London

1977 (8 June) *'All-over' phosphor*

1038	517	13p black, deep green, rose and silver	40	40	☐	☐
		First Day Cover		1·00		☐
		Presentation Pack	1·00		☐	
		PHQ Card	4·00	5·00	☐	☐
		Gutter Pair	90		☐	
		Traffic Light Gutter Pair	1·40		☐	

518   Hedgehog   519   Brown Hare

520   Red Squirrel   521   Otter

522   Badger

T **518/22** were printed together, *se-tenant*, throughout the sheet.

British Wildlife

1977 (5 Oct.) *'All-over' phosphor*

1039	518	9p multicoloured	25	20	☐	☐
		a. Strip of 5. Nos. 1039/43	1·50	2·00	☐	☐
1040	519	9p multicoloured	25	20	☐	☐
1041	520	9p multicoloured	25	20	☐	☐
1042	521	9p multicoloured	25	20	☐	☐
1043	522	9p multicoloured	25	20	☐	☐
		Set of 5	1·50	90	☐	☐
		First Day Cover		3·75		☐
		Presentation Pack	2·50		☐	
		PHQ Cards (set of 5)	5·00	6·00	☐	☐
		Gutter Strip of 10	3·75		☐	
		Traffic Light Gutter Strip of 10 .	4·00		☐	

523 'Three French Hens, Two Turtle Doves and a Partridge in a Pear Tree'

524 'Six Geese a laying, Five Gold Rings, Four Colly Birds'

525 'Eight Maids a-milking, Seven Swans a-swimming'

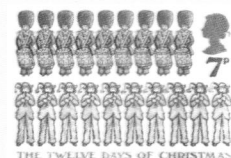

526 'Ten Pipers piping, Nine Drummers drumming'

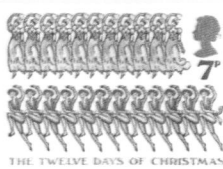

527 'Twelve Lords a-leaping, Eleven Ladies dancing'

528 'A Partridge in a Pear Tree'

T **523/8** depict the carol 'The Twelve Days of Christmas'.
T **523/7** were printed horizontally *se-tenant* throughout the sheet.

Christmas

1977 (23 Nov.) *One centre phosphor band (7p) or 'all-over' phosphor (9p)*

1044	**523**	7p multicoloured	25	15	☐	☐
		a. Strip of 5. Nos. 1044/8	1·50	2·00	☐	☐
1045	**524**	7p multicoloured	25	15	☐	☐
1046	**525**	7p multicoloured	25	15	☐	☐
1047	**526**	7p multicoloured	25	15	☐	☐
1048	**527**	7p multicoloured	25	15	☐	☐
1049	**528**	9p multicoloured	25	20	☐	☐
		Set of 6	1·50	85	☐	☐
		First Day Cover		3·50		☐
		Presentation Pack	2·50		☐	
		PHQ Cards (set of 6)	3·00	5·00	☐	☐
		Set of 6 Gutter Pairs	3·50		☐	
		Set of 6 Traffic Light Gutter Pairs	5·00		☐	

Collectors Pack 1977

1977 (23 Nov.) *Comprises Nos. 1022/5 1029/49*

	Collectors Pack	8·00	☐

529 Oil — North Sea Production Platform

530 Coal — Modern Pithead

531 Natural Gas — Flame Rising from Sea

532 Electricity — Nuclear Power Station and Uranium Atom

Energy Resources

1978 (25 Jan.) *'All-over' phosphor*

1050	**529**	9p multicoloured	20	10	☐	☐
1051	**530**	10½p multicoloured	20	25	☐	☐
1052	**531**	11p multicoloured	30	35	☐	☐
1053	**532**	13p multicoloured	35	40	☐	☐
		Set of 4	95	1·00	☐	☐
		First Day Cover		1·75		☐
		Presentation Pack	2·00		☐	
		PHQ Cards (set of 4)	2·00	4·00	☐	☐
		Set of 4 Gutter Pairs	2·25		☐	
		Set of 4 Traffic Light Gutter Pairs	4·00		☐	

533 Tower of London

534 Holyroodhouse

535 Caernarvon Castle

536 Hampton Court Palace

British Architecture (Historic Buildings)

1978 (1 MAR.) *'All-over' phosphor*

1054	**533**	9p multicoloured	20	10	□	□
1055	**534**	10½p multicoloured	20	30	□	□
1056	**535**	11p multicoloured	25	30	□	□
1057	**536**	13p multicoloured	25	30	□	□
		Set of 4	80	90	□	□
		First Day Cover		1·75	□	
		Presentation Pack	2·00		□	
		PHQ Cards (set of 4)	2·00	4·00	□	□
		Set of 4 Gutter Pairs	2·25		□	
		Set of 4 Traffic Light Gutter Pairs	4·00		□	
MS1058		121 × 90 mm. Nos. 1054/7 . .	1·50	1·60	□	□
		First Day Cover		2·00	□	

No. **MS**1058 was sold at 53½p, the premium being used for the London 1980 Stamp Exhibition.

537 State Coach

538 St Edward's Crown

539 The Sovereign's Orb

540 Imperial State Crown

25th Anniversary of Coronation

1978 (31 MAY) *'All-over' phosphor*

1059	**537**	9p gold and blue	20	10	□	□
1060	**538**	10½p gold and red	25	30	□	□
1061	**539**	11p gold and green	25	30	□	□
1062	**540**	13p gold and violet	30	35	□	□
		Set of 4	90	95	□	□
		First Day Cover		1·75	□	
		Presentation Pack	2·00		□	
		Souvenir Book	4·00		□	
		PHQ Cards (set of 4)	3·00	4·00	□	□
		Set of 4 Gutter Pairs	2·25		□	
		Set of 4 Traffic Light Gutter Pairs	4·00		□	

541 Shire Horse

542 Shetland Pony

543 Welsh Pony

544 Thoroughbred

Horses

1978 (5 JULY) *'All-over' phosphor*

1063	**541**	9p multicoloured	20	10	□	□
1064	**542**	10½p multicoloured	35	40	□	□
1065	**543**	11p multicoloured	35	45	□	□
1066	**544**	13p multicoloured	45	50	□	□
		Set of 4	1·25	1·25	□	□
		First Day Cover		1·75	□	
		Presentation Pack	2·00		□	
		PHQ Cards (set of 4)	2·25	5·00	□	□
		Set of 4 Gutter Pairs	2·75		□	
		Set of 4 Traffic Light Gutter Pairs	4·00		□	

545 Penny-farthing and
1884 Safety Bicycle

546 1920 Touring Bicycles

547 Modern Small-wheel
Bicycles

548 1978 Road-racers

Centenaries of Cyclists Touring Club and British Cycling Federation

1978 (2 Aug.) *'All-over' phosphor*

1067	**545**	9p multicoloured	20	10 ☐	☐
1068	**546**	10½p multicoloured	35	40 ☐	☐
1069	**547**	11p multicoloured	35	45 ☐	☐
1070	**548**	13p multicoloured	45	50 ☐	☐
		Set of 4	1·25	1·25 ☐	☐
		First Day Cover		2·00	☐
		Presentation Pack	2·00		☐
		PHQ Cards (*set of 4*)	2·25	5·00 ☐	☐
		Set of 4 Gutter Pairs	2·75		☐
		Set of 4 Traffic Light Gutter Pairs	4·00		☐

549 Singing Carols round the Christmas Tree

550 The Waits

551 18th-Century Carol Singers

552 'The Boar's Head Carol'

Christmas

1978 (22 Nov.) *One centre phosphor band* (7p) *or 'all-over' phosphor* (*others*)

1071	**549**	7p multicoloured	15	10 ☐	☐
1072	**550**	9p multicoloured	25	15 ☐	☐
1073	**551**	11p multicoloured	30	35 ☐	☐
1074	**552**	13p multicoloured	35	40 ☐	☐
		Set of 4	95	90 ☐	☐
		First Day Cover		1·60	☐
		Presentation Pack	1·90		☐
		PHQ Cards (*set of 4*)	1·75	4·25 ☐	☐
		Set of 4 Gutter Pairs	2·25		☐
		Set of 4 Traffic Light Gutter Pairs	3·50		☐

Collectors Pack 1978

1978 (22 Nov.) *Comprises Nos.* 1050/7, 1059/74

	Collectors Pack	8·00		☐

553 Old English Sheepdog   **554** Welsh Springer Spaniel

555 West Highland Terrier   **556** Irish Setter

Dogs

1979 (7 Feb.) *'All-over' phosphor*

1075	**553**	9p multicoloured	15	10 ☐	☐
1076	**554**	10½p multicoloured	30	30 ☐	☐
1077	**555**	11p multicoloured	30	40 ☐	☐
1078	**556**	13p multicoloured	30	40 ☐	☐
		Set of 4	95	1·10 ☐	☐
		First Day Cover		1·90	☐
		Presentation Pack	1·90		☐
		PHQ Cards (*set of 4*)	3·00	5·50 ☐	☐
		Set of 4 Gutter Pairs	2·25		☐
		Set of 4 Traffic Light Gutter Pairs	3·75		☐

557 Primrose   **558** Daffodil

559 Bluebell   **560** Snowdrop

Spring Wild Flowers

1979 (21 MAR.) *'All-over' phosphor*

1079	**557**	9p multicoloured	15	10	☐	☐
1080	**558**	10½p multicoloured	25	35	☐	☐
1081	**559**	11p multicoloured	30	35	☐	☐
1082	**560**	13p multicoloured	30	30	☐	☐
		Set of 4	90	1·00	☐	☐
		First Day Cover		1·75		☐
		Presentation Pack	1·90		☐	
		PHQ Cards (set of 4)	3·00	4·50	☐	☐
		Set of 4 Gutter Pairs	2·00		☐	
		Set of 4 Traffic Light Gutter Pairs	3·75		☐	

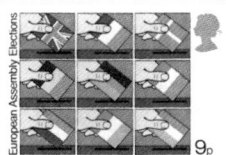

561

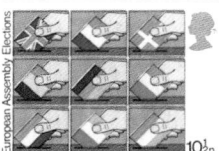

562

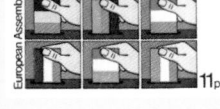

563

564

T **561/4** show hands placing the flags of the member nations into ballot boxes.

First Direct Elections to European Assembly

1979 (9 MAY) *Phosphorised paper*

1083	**561**	9p multicoloured	15	10	☐	☐
1084	**562**	10½p multicoloured	25	25	☐	☐
1085	**563**	11p multicoloured	30	30	☐	☐
1086	**564**	13p multicoloured	35	30	☐	☐
		Set of 4	95	85	☐	☐
		First Day Cover		1·75		☐
		Presentation Pack	1·90		☐	
		PHQ Cards (set of 4)	1·75	4·50	☐	☐
		Set of 4 Gutter Pairs	2·25		☐	
		Set of 4 Traffic Light Gutter Pairs	3·75		☐	

565 'Saddling "Mahmoud" for the Derby, 1936' (Sir Alfred Munnings)

566 'The Liverpool Great National Steeple Chase, 1839' (aquatint by F. C. Turner)

The First Spring Meeting, Newmarket 1793   11P

Racing at Dorsett Ferry, Windsor 1684   13P

567 'The First Spring Meeting, Newmarket, 1793' (J. N. Sartorius)

568 'Racing at Dorsett Ferry, Windsor, 1684' (Francis Barlow)

Horseracing Paintings and Bicentenary of The Derby (9p)

1979 (6 JUNE) *'All-over' phosphor*

1087	**565**	9p multicoloured	15	10	☐	☐
1088	**566**	10½p multicoloured	25	25	☐	☐
1089	**567**	11p multicoloured	30	30	☐	☐
1090	**568**	13p multicoloured	30	30	☐	☐
		Set of 4	90	85	☐	☐
		First Day Cover		1·75		☐
		Presentation Pack	2·00		☐	
		PHQ Cards (set of 4)	1·90	4·00	☐	☐
		Set of 4 Gutter Pairs	2·25		☐	
		Set of 4 Traffic Light Gutter Pairs	3·75		☐	

The Tale of Peter Rabbit
The Year of the Child   9p

The Wind in the Willows
The Year of the Child   10½p

569 The Tale of Peter Rabbit (Beatrix Potter)

570 The Wind in the Willows (Kenneth Grahame)

Winnie-the-Pooh
The Year of the Child   11p

Alice's Adventures in Wonderland
The Year of the Child   13p

571 Winnie-the-Pooh (A. A. Milne)

572 Alice's Adventures in in Wonderland (Lewis Carroll)

T **569/72** depict original illustrations from the four books.

International Year of the Child

1979 (11 July) *'All-over' phosphor*

1091	569	9p multicoloured	25	20	☐	☐
1092	570	10½p multicoloured	30	35	☐	☐
1093	571	11p multicoloured	40	40	☐	☐
1094	572	13p multicoloured	70	70	☐	☐
		Set of 4	1·50	1·50	☐	☐
		First Day Cover		2·25		☐
		Presentation Pack	2·00		☐	
		PHQ Cards (set of 4)	2·50	4·50	☐	☐
		Set of 4 Gutter Pairs	3·25		☐	
		Set of 4 Traffic Light Gutter Pairs	5·00		☐	

573 Sir Rowland Hill,
1795–1879

574 General Post,
c 1839

575 London Post,
c 1839

576 Uniform Postage,
1840

Death Centenary of Sir Rowland Hill (postal reformer)

1979 (22 Aug.–24 Oct.) *'All-over' phosphor*

1095	573	10p multicoloured	15	10	☐	☐
1096	574	11½p multicoloured	20	25	☐	☐
1097	575	13p multicoloured	30	35	☐	☐
1098	576	15p multicoloured	50	40	☐	☐
		Set of 4	1·00	1·00	☐	☐
		First Day Cover		1·75		☐
		Presentation Pack	1·90		☐	
		PHQ Cards (set of 4)	2·00	3·50	☐	☐
		Set of 4 Gutter Pairs	2·40		☐	
		Set of 4 Traffic Light Gutter Pairs	3·75		☐	
MS1099		89 × 121 mm. Nos. 1095/8 .	1·25	1·40	☐	☐
		First Day Cover (24 Oct.)		2·00		☐

No. **MS**1099 was sold at 59½p, the premium being used for the London 1980 Stamp Exhibition.

577 Policeman on the Beat

578 Policeman directing Traffic

579 Mounted Policewoman

580 River Patrol Boat

150th Anniversary of Metropolitan Police

1979 (26 Sept.) *Phosphorised paper*

1100	577	10p multicoloured	20	10	☐	☐
1101	578	11½p multicoloured	25	35	☐	☐
1102	579	13p multicoloured	30	40	☐	☐
1103	580	15p multicoloured	50	40	☐	☐
		Set of 4	1·10	1·10	☐	☐
		First Day Cover		1·75		☐
		Presentation Pack	2·00		☐	
		PHQ Cards (set of 4)	1·75	3·50	☐	☐
		Set of 4 Gutter Pairs	2·50		☐	
		Set of 4 Traffic Light Gutter Pairs	3·75		☐	

581 The Three Kings

582 Angel appearing to the Shepherds

583 The Nativity

584 Mary and Joseph travelling to Bethlehem

585 The Annunciation

Christmas

1979 (21 Nov.) *One centre phosphor band (8p) or phosphorised paper (others)*

1104	581	8p multicoloured	15	10	□	□
1105	582	10p multicoloured	20	15	□	□
1106	583	11½p multicoloured	30	30	□	□
1107	584	13p multicoloured	45	45	□	□
1108	585	15p multicoloured	50	50	□	□
		Set of 5	1·40	1·40	□	□
		First Day Cover		1·75	□	
		Presentation Pack	2·10		□	
		PHQ Cards (set of 5)	1·50	3·50	□	□
		Set of 5 Gutter Pairs	3·00		□	
		Set of 5 Traffic Light Gutter Pairs	4·00		□	

Collectors Pack 1979

1979 (21 Nov.) *Comprises Nos.* 1075/98, 1100/8

	Collectors Pack	10·00	□

586 Common Kingfisher   **587** Dipper

588 Moorhen   **589** Yellow Wagtails

Centenary of Wild Bird Protection Act

1980 (16 Jan.) *Phosphorised paper*

1109	586	10p multicoloured	20	10	□	□
1110	587	11½p multicoloured	40	35	□	□

1111	588	13p multicoloured	50	45	□	□
1112	589	15p multicoloured	50	45	□	□
		Set of 4	1·50	1·25	□	
		First Day Cover		1·75	□	
		Presentation Pack	2·00		□	
		PHQ Cards (set of 4)	1·60	4·00	□	□
		Set of 4 Gutter Pairs	3·75		□	

590 *Rocket* approaching Moorish Arch, Liverpool

591 First and Second Class Carriages passing through Olive Mount Cutting

592 Third Class Carriage and Sheep Truck crossing Chat Moss

593 Horsebox and Carriage Truck near Bridgewater Canal

594 Goods Truck and Mail-coach at Manchester

T **590/4** were printed together, *se-tenant*, in horizontal strips of 5 throughout the sheet.

150th Anniversary of Liverpool and Manchester Railway

1980 (12 Mar.) *Phosphorised paper*

1113	590	12p multicoloured	20	20	□	□
		a. Strip of 5. Nos. 1113/17	1·40	1·75	□	□
1114	591	12p multicoloured	20	20	□	□
1115	592	12p multicoloured	20	20	□	□
1116	593	12p multicoloured	20	20	□	□
1117	594	12p multicoloured	20	20	□	□
		Set of 5	1·40	90	□	
		First Day Cover		1·75	□	
		Presentation Pack	2·40		□	
		PHQ Cards (set of 5)	1·60	4·00	□	□
		Gutter block of 10	3·50		□	

INTERNATIONAL STAMP EXHIBITION

595 Montage of London Buildings

'London 1980' International Stamp Exhibition

1980 (9 APR.–7 MAY) *Phosphorised paper. Perf 14½ × 14*

1118	**595**	50p agate	1·60	1·25	☐	☐
		First Day Cover		2·25		☐
		Presentation Pack	2·00		☐	
		PHQ Card	80	2·25	☐	☐
		Gutter Pair	3·50		☐	
MS1119		90 × 123 mm. No. 1118 . . .	1·50	1·90	☐	☐
		First Day Cover (7 May)		2·25		☐

No. **MS**1119 was sold at 75p, the premium being used for the exhibition.

596 Buckingham Palace

597 The Albert Memorial

598 Royal Opera House

599 Hampton Court

600 Kensington Palace

London Landmarks

1980 (7 MAY) *Phosphorised paper*

1120	**596**	10½p multicoloured	20	10	☐	☐
1121	**597**	12p multicoloured	20	10	☐	☐
1122	**598**	13½p multicoloured	30	40	☐	☐
1123	**599**	15p multicoloured	40	55	☐	☐
1124	**600**	17½p multicoloured	50	55	☐	☐
		Set of 5	1·40	1·50	☐	☐
		First Day Cover		1·90		☐
		Presentation Pack	2·25		☐	
		PHQ Cards (set of 5)	1·60	3·00	☐	☐
		Set of 5 Gutter Pairs	3·50		☐	

601 Charlotte Brontë (*Jane Eyre*)

602 George Eliot (*The Mill on the Floss*)

603 Emily Brontë (*Wuthering Heights*)

604 Mrs Gaskell (*North and South*)

T **601/4** show authoresses and scenes from their novels. T **601/2** also include the 'Europa' C.E.P.T. emblem.

Famous Authoresses

1980 (9 JULY) *Phosphorised paper*

1125	**601**	12p multicoloured	25	10	☐	☐
1126	**602**	13½p multicoloured	30	35	☐	☐
1127	**603**	15p multicoloured	40	45	☐	☐
1128	**604**	17½p multicoloured	50	50	☐	☐
		Set of 4	1·25	1·25	☐	☐
		First Day Cover		1·75		☐
		Presentation Pack	2·25		☐	
		PHQ Cards (set of 4)	2·50	3·00	☐	☐
		Set of 4 Gutter Pairs	3·25		☐	

605 Queen Elizabeth the Queen Mother

80th Birthday of Queen Elizabeth the Queen Mother

1980 (4 Aug.) *Phosphorised paper*

1129	**605**	12p multicoloured	1·00	1·00	☐	☐
		First Day Cover		2·00		☐
		PHQ Card	1·00	1·50	☐	☐
		Gutter Pair	2·25		☐	

606 Sir Henry Wood

607 Sir Thomas Beecham

608 Sir Malcolm Sargent

609 Sir John Barbirolli

British Conductors

1980 (10 Sept.) *Phosphorised paper*

1130	**606**	12p multicoloured	20	10	☐	☐
1131	**607**	13½p multicoloured	40	45	☐	☐
1132	**608**	15p multicoloured	50	50	☐	☐
1133	**609**	17½p multicoloured	55	50	☐	☐
		Set of 4	1·50	1·40	☐	☐
		First Day Cover		1·90		☐
		Presentation Pack	2·25		☐	
		PHQ Cards (set of 4)	1·60	3·50	☐	☐
		Set of 4 Gutter Pairs	3·75		☐	

For full information on all future British issues, collectors should write to Royal Mail, Freepost EH3647, 21 South Gyle Crescent, Edinburgh EH12 9PE.

610 Running

611 Rugby

612 Boxing

613 Cricket

Sports Centenaries

1980 (10 Oct.) *Phosphorised paper. Perf* 14 × 14½

1134	**610**	12p multicoloured	20	10	☐	☐
1135	**611**	13½p multicoloured	50	50	☐	☐
1136	**612**	15p multicoloured	40	45	☐	☐
1137	**613**	17½p multicoloured	55	50	☐	☐
		Set of 4	1·50	1·40	☐	☐
		First Day Cover		1·90		☐
		Presentation Pack	2·25		☐	
		PHQ Cards (set of 4)	1·60	3·50	☐	☐
		Set of 4 Gutter Pairs	3·75		☐	

Centenaries:—12p Amateur Athletics Association; 13½p Welsh Rugby Union; 15p Amateur Boxing Association; 17½p First England v Australia Test Match.

614 Christmas Tree

615 Candles

616 Apples and Mistletoe

617 Crown, Chains and Bell

618   Holly

Christmas

1980 (19 Nov.) *One centre phosphor band (10p) or phosphorised paper (others)*

1138	**614**	10p multicoloured	. . . .	20	10 □ □
1139	**615**	12p multicoloured	. . . .	20	20 □ □
1140	**616**	13½p multicoloured	. . . .	40	40 □ □
1141	**617**	15p multicoloured	. . . .	55	55 □ □
1142	**618**	17½p multicoloured	. . . .	55	55 □ □
		Set of 5	. . . .	1·75	1·60 □ □
		First Day Cover	. . . .		1·90 □
		Presentation Pack	. . . .	2·25	□
		PHQ Cards (set of 5)	. . . . . .	1·60	4·50 □ □
		Set of 5 Gutter Pairs	. . . . .	4·25	□

Collectors Pack 1980

1980 (19 Nov.) *Comprises Nos. 1109/18, 1120/42*

	Collectors Pack	14·00	□

619   St Valentine's Day   620   Morris Dancers

621   Lammastide   622   Medieval Mummers

T **619/20** also include the 'Europa' C.E.P.T. emblem.

Folklore

1981 (6 Feb.) *Phosphorised paper*

1143	**619**	14p multicoloured	. . . .	25	10 □ □
1144	**620**	18p multicoloured	. . . .	35	50 □ □
1145	**621**	22p multicoloured	. . . .	60	55 □ □
1146	**622**	25p multicoloured	. . . .	70	65 □ □
		Set of 4	. . . .	1·75	1·60 □ □
		First Day Cover	. . . .		2·00 □
		Presentation Pack	. . . .	2·25	□
		PHQ Cards (set of 4)	. . . . . .	1·60	3·00 □ □
		Set of 4 Gutter Pairs	. . . . .	4·25	□

623   Blind Man with Guide Dog   624   Hands spelling 'Deaf' in Sign Language

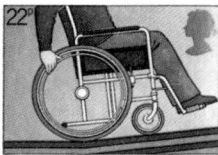   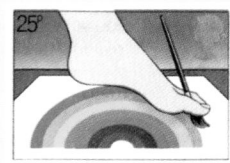

625   Disabled Man in Wheelchair   626   Disabled Artist painting with Foot

International Year of the Disabled

1981 (25 Mar.) *Phosphorised paper*

1147	**623**	14p multicoloured	. . . .	25	10 □ □
1148	**624**	18p multicoloured	. . . .	45	60 □ □
1149	**625**	22p multicoloured	. . . .	60	75 □ □
1150	**626**	25p multicoloured	. . . .	70	85 □ □
		Set of 4	. . . .	1·75	2·10 □ □
		First Day Cover	. . . .		2·40 □
		Presentation Pack	. . . .	2·40	□
		PHQ Cards (set of 4)	. . . . . .	1·60	3·00 □ □
		Set of 4 Gutter Pairs	. . . . .	4·25	□

627   *Aglais urticae*   628   *Maculinea arion*

629   *Inachis io*   630   *Carterocephalus palaemon*

Butterflies

1981 (13 MAY) *Phosphorised paper*

1151	**627**	14p multicoloured	25	10	☐	☐
1152	**628**	18p multicoloured	70	70	☐	☐
1153	**629**	22p multicoloured	80	75	☐	☐
1154	**630**	25p multicoloured	85	80	☐	☐
		Set of 4	2·40	2·10	☐	☐
		First Day Cover		2·75		☐
		Presentation Pack	2·75		☐	
		PHQ Cards (set of 4)	1·75	5·00	☐	☐
		Set of 4 Gutter Pairs	5·75		☐	

631 Glenfinnan, Scotland   **632** Derwentwater, England

633 Stackpole Head, Wales   **634** Giant's Causeway, N. Ireland

635 St Kilda, Scotland

50th Anniversary of National Trust for Scotland

1981 (24 JUNE) *Phosphorised paper*

1155	**631**	14p multicoloured	25	10	☐	☐
1156	**632**	18p multicoloured	45	40	☐	☐
1157	**633**	20p multicoloured	65	65	☐	☐
1158	**634**	22p multicoloured	70	70	☐	☐
1159	**635**	25p multicoloured	80	80	☐	☐
		Set of 5	2·50	2·40	☐	☐
		First Day Cover		2·75		☐
		Presentation Pack	2·75		☐	
		PHQ Cards (set of 5)	2·50	5·00	☐	☐
		Set of 5 Gutter Pairs	6·00		☐	

636 Prince Charles and Lady Diana Spencer

Royal Wedding

1981 (22 JULY) *Phosphorised paper*

1160	**636**	14p multicoloured	80	50	☐	☐
1161		25p multicoloured	1·60	2·00	☐	☐
		Set of 2	2·40	2·50	☐	☐
		First Day Cover		3·50		☐
		Presentation Pack	3·50		☐	
		Souvenir Book	5·00		☐	
		PHQ Cards (set of 2)	3·00	5·00	☐	☐
		Set of 2 Gutter Pairs	5·75		☐	

637 'Expeditions'   **638** 'Skills'

639 'Service'   **640** 'Recreation'

25th Anniversary of Duke of Edinburgh Award Scheme

1981 (12 AUG.) *Phosphorised paper. Perf 14*

1162	**637**	14p multicoloured	25	10	☐	☐
1163	**638**	18p multicoloured	45	50	☐	☐
1164	**639**	22p multicoloured	70	70	☐	☐
1165	**640**	25p multicoloured	80	80	☐	☐
		Set of 4	2·00	1·90	☐	☐
		First Day Cover		2·40		☐
		Presentation Pack	2·75		☐	
		PHQ Cards (set of 4)	1·75	4·00	☐	☐
		Set of 4 Gutter Pairs	5·00		☐	

641 Cockle-dredging from Linsey II

642 Hauling Trawl Net

643 Lobster Potting

644 Hoisting Seine Net

Fishing Industry

1981 (23 SEPT.) *Phosphorised paper*

1166	**641**	14p multicoloured	25	10	☐	☐
1167	**642**	18p multicoloured	45	50	☐	☐
1168	**643**	22p multicoloured	65	50	☐	☐
1169	**644**	25p multicoloured	75	60	☐	☐
		Set of 4	1·90	1·50	☐	☐
		First Day Cover		2·00		☐
		Presentation Pack	2·75		☐	
		PHQ Cards (set of 4)	1·75	4·00	☐	☐
		Set of 4 Gutter Pairs	4·75		☐	

Nos. 1166/9 were issued on the occasion of the centenary of Royal National Mission to Deep Sea Fishermen.

645 Father Christmas

646 Jesus Christ

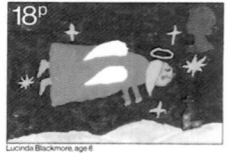

647 Flying Angel

648 Joseph and Mary arriving at Bethlehem

649 Three Kings approaching Bethlehem

Christmas. Children's Pictures

1981 (18 Nov.) *One phosphor band (11½p) or phosphorised paper (others)*

1170	**645**	11½p multicoloured	20	10	☐	☐
1171	**646**	14p multicoloured	30	10	☐	☐
1172	**647**	18p multicoloured	45	50	☐	☐
1173	**648**	22p multicoloured	65	60	☐	☐
1174	**649**	25p multicoloured	75	65	☐	☐
		Set of 5	2·10	1·75	☐	☐
		First Day Cover		2·25		☐
		Presentation Pack	3·00		☐	
		PHQ Cards (set of 5)	2·00	5·00	☐	☐
		Set of 5 Gutter Pairs	5·25		☐	

Collectors Pack 1981

1981 (18 Nov.) *Comprises Nos. 1143/74*

	Collectors Pack	16·00	☐

650 Charles Darwin and Giant Tortoises

651 Darwin and Marine Iguanas

652 Darwin, Cactus Ground Finch and Large Ground Finch

653 Darwin and Prehistoric Skulls

Death Centenary of Charles Darwin

1982 (10 FEB.) *Phosphorised paper*

1175	**650**	15½p multicoloured	35	10	☐	☐
1176	**651**	19½p multicoloured	55	50	☐	☐
1177	**652**	26p multicoloured	75	75	☐	☐
1178	**653**	29p multicoloured	80	80	☐	☐
		Set of 4	2·25	2·00	☐	☐
		First Day Cover		2·50		☐
		Presentation Pack	3·00		☐	
		PHQ Cards (set of 4)	2·50	6·50	☐	☐
		Set of 4 Gutter Pairs	5·50		☐	

654 Boys' Brigade

655 Girls' Brigade

656 Boy Scout Movement

657 Girl Guide Movement

Youth Organizations

1982 (24 MAR.) *Phosphorised paper*

1179	**654** 15½p multicoloured	. . . . .	25	10	☐ ☐
1180	**655** 19½p multicoloured	. . . . .	55	70	☐ ☐
1181	**656** 26p multicoloured	. . . . .	75	95	☐ ☐
1182	**657** 29p multicoloured	. . . . .	90	1·00	☐ ☐
	Set of 4		2·25	2·50	☐ ☐
	First Day Cover			3·00	☐
	Presentation Pack		3·25		☐
	PHQ Cards (set of 4)		2·50	6·50	☐ ☐
	Set of 4 Gutter Pairs		5·50		☐

Nos. 1179/82 were issued on the occasion of the 75th anniversary of the Boy Scout Movement, the 125th birth anniversary of Lord Baden-Powell and the centenary of the Boys' Brigade (1983).

658 Ballerina

659 Harlequin

660 Hamlet

661 Opera Singer

Europa. British Theatre

1982 (28 APR.) *Phosphorised paper*

1183	**658** 15½p multicoloured	. . . . .	25	10	☐ ☐
1184	**659** 19½p multicoloured	. . . . .	50	60	☐ ☐
1185	**660** 26p multicoloured	. . . . .	85	85	☐ ☐
1186	**661** 29p multicoloured	. . . . .	95	1·10	☐ ☐
	Set of 4		2·40	2·40	☐ ☐
	First Day Cover			3·00	☐
	Presentation Pack		3·00		☐
	PHQ Cards (set of 4)		2·50	6·50	☐ ☐
	Set of 4 Gutter Pairs		5·75		☐

662 Henry VIII and *Mary Rose*

663 Admiral Blake and *Triumph*

664 Lord Nelson and HMS *Victory*

665 Lord Fisher and HMS *Dreadnought*

666 Viscount Cunningham and HMS *Warspite*

Maritime Heritage

1982 (16 June) *Phosphorised paper*

1187	**662**	15½p multicoloured	40		10	□	□
1188	**663**	19½p multicoloured	60		55	□	□
1189	**664**	24p multicoloured	80		80	□	□
1190	**665**	26p multicoloured	90		90	□	□
1191	**666**	29p multicoloured	1·00		1·00	□	□
		Set of 5	3·25		3·00	□	□
		First Day Cover			3·50		□
		Presentation Pack	3·75			□	
		PHQ Cards (set of 5)	3·00		7·00	□	□
		Set of 5 Gutter Pairs	8·00			□	

667 'Strawberry Thief' (William Morris)

668 Untitled (Steiner and Co)

669 'Cherry Orchard' (Paul Nash)

670 'Chevron' (Andrew Foster)

British Textiles

1982 (23 July) *Phosphorised paper*

1192	**667**	15½p multicoloured	30		10	□	□
1193	**668**	19½p multicoloured	60		70	□	□
1194	**669**	26p multicoloured	80		90	□	□
1195	**670**	29p multicoloured	90		1·10	□	□
		Set of 4	2·40		2·50	□	□
		First Day Cover			3·00		□
		Presentation Pack	3·00			□	
		PHQ Cards (set of 4)	3·00		6·50	□	□
		Set of 4 Gutter Pairs	5·75			□	

Nos 1192/5 were issued on the occasion of the 250th birth anniversary of Sir Richard Arkwright (inventor of spinning machine).

671 Development of Communications

672 Modern Technological Aids

Information Technology

1982 (8 Sept.) *Phosphorised paper. Perf* 14 × 15

1196	**671**	15½p multicoloured	45		10	□	□
1197	**672**	26p multicoloured	70		1·00	□	□
		Set of 2	1·10		1·10	□	□
		First Day Cover			2·00		□
		Presentation Pack	1·75			□	
		PHQ Cards (set of 2)	1·50		4·50	□	□
		Set of 2 Gutter Pairs	2·75			□	

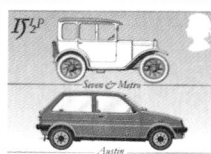

673 Austin 'Seven' and 'Metro'

674 Ford 'Model T' and 'Escort'

675 Jaguar 'SS1' and 'XJ6'

676 Rolls-Royce 'Silver Ghost' and 'Silver Spirit'

British Motor Industry

1982 (13 Oct.) *Phosphorised paper. Perf* 14½ × 14

1198	**673**	15½p multicoloured	35		10	□	□
1199	**674**	19½p multicoloured	65		65	□	□
1200	**675**	26p multicoloured	80		85	□	□
1201	**676**	29p multicoloured	1·25		1·10	□	□
		Set of 4	2·75		2·40	□	□
		First Day Cover			3·00		□
		Presentation Pack	3·25			□	
		PHQ Cards (set of 4)	3·00		6·75	□	□
		Set of 4 Gutter Pairs	6·50			□	

677 'While Shepherds Watched'

678 'The Holly and the Ivy'

679 'I Saw Three Ships'

680 'We Three Kings'

681 'Good King Wenceslas'

Christmas. Carols

1982 (17 Nov.) *One phosphor band (12½p) or phosphorised paper (others).*

1202	**677**	12½p multicoloured	25	10	☐	☐
1203	**678**	15½p multicoloured	35	10	☐	☐
1204	**679**	19½p multicoloured	75	80	☐	☐
1205	**680**	26p multicoloured	85	90	☐	☐
1206	**681**	29p multicoloured	90	1·00	☐	☐
		Set of 5	2·75	2·50	☐	☐
		First Day Cover		3·00		☐
		Presentation Pack	3·25		☐	
		PHQ Cards (set of 5)	3·00	7·00	☐	☐
		Set of 5 Gutter Pairs	6·50		☐	

Collectors Pack 1982

1982 (17 Nov.) *Comprises Nos.* 1175/1206

	Collectors Pack	22·00		☐

682 Atlantic Salmon

683 Northern Pike

684 Brown Trout

685 Eurasian Perch

British River Fishes

1983 (26 Jan.) *Phosphorised paper*

1207	**682**	15½p multicoloured	35	10	☐	☐
1208	**683**	19½p multicoloured	75	75	☐	☐
1209	**684**	26p multicoloured	90	90	☐	☐
1210	**685**	29p multicoloured	1·10	1·10	☐	☐
		Set of 4	2·75	2·50	☐	☐
		First Day Cover		3·00		☐
		Presentation Pack	3·00		☐	
		PHQ Cards (set of 4)	3·00	7·50	☐	☐
		Set of 4 Gutter Pairs	6·50		☐	

686 Tropical Island

687 Desert

688 Temperate Farmland

689 Mountain Range

Commonwealth Day. Geographical Regions

1983 (9 Mar.) *Phosphorised paper*

1211	**686**	15½p multicoloured	30	10	☐	☐
1212	**687**	19½p multicoloured	65	75	☐	☐
1213	**688**	26p multicoloured	85	90	☐	☐
1214	**689**	29p multicoloured	1·00	1·00	☐	☐
		Set of 4	2·50	2·50	☐	☐
		First Day Cover		3·00		☐
		Presentation Pack	3·25		☐	
		PHQ Cards (set of 4)	3·00	6·50	☐	☐
		Set of 4 Gutter Pairs	6·00		☐	

690 Humber Bridge

691 Thames Flood Barrier

692 *Iolair* (oilfield emergency support vessel)

697 Paratroopers, The Parachute Regiment (1983)

Europa. Engineering Achievements

1983 (25 MAY) *Phosphorised paper*

1215	**690**	16p multicoloured	35	10	☐	☐
1216	**691**	20½p multicoloured	1·00	1·25	☐	☐
1217	**692**	28p multicoloured	1·10	1·25	☐	☐
		Set of 3	2·25	2·40	☐	☐
		First Day Cover		2·75		☐
		Presentation Pack	3·25		☐	
		PHQ Cards (set of 3)	2·50	5·00	☐	☐
		Set of 3 Gutter Pairs	5·50		☐	

British Army Uniforms

1983 (6 JULY) *Phosphorised paper*

1218	**693**	16p multicoloured	35	10	☐	☐
1219	**694**	20½p multicoloured	55	75	☐	☐
1220	**695**	26p multicoloured	85	1·10	☐	☐
1221	**696**	28p multicoloured	90	1·10	☐	☐
1222	**697**	31p multicoloured	95	1·00	☐	☐
		Set of 5	3·25	3·75	☐	☐
		First Day Cover		4·00		☐
		Presentation Pack	4·25		☐	
		PHQ Cards (set of 5)	3·00	7·50	☐	☐
		Set of 5 Gutter Pairs	7·50		☐	

Nos. 1218/22 were issued on the occasion of the 350th anniversary of The Royal Scots, the senior line regiment of the British Army.

693 Musketeer and Pikeman, The Royal Scots (1633)

694 Fusilier and Ensign, The Royal Welch Fusiliers (mid-18th century)

695 Riflemen, 95th Rifles (The Royal Green Jackets) (1805)

696 Sergeant (khaki service uniform) and Guardsman full dress), The Irish Guards (1900).

698 20th-Century Garden, Sissinghurst

699 19th-Century Garden, Biddulph Grange

700 18th-Century Garden, Blenheim

701 17th-Century Garden, Pitmedden

British Gardens

1983 (24 Aug.) *Phosphorised paper. Perf* 14

1223	**698**	16p multicoloured	35	10	☐	☐
1224	**699**	20½p multicoloured	50	70	☐	☐
1225	**700**	28p multicoloured	95	1·10	☐	☐
1226	**701**	31p multicoloured	1·00	1·10	☐	☐
		Set of 4	2·50	2·75	☐	☐
		First Day Cover		3·00		☐
		Presentation Pack	3·75		☐	
		PHQ Cards (set of 4)	3·00	6·00	☐	☐
		Set of 4 *Gutter Pairs*	6·00		☐	

702 Merry-go-round

703 Big Wheel, Helter-skelter and Performing Animals

704 Side-shows

705 Early Produce Fair

British Fairs

1983 (5 Oct.) *Phosphorised paper*

1227	**702**	16p multicoloured	35	10	☐	☐
1228	**703**	20½p multicoloured	65	80	☐	☐
1229	**704**	28p multicoloured	80	90	☐	☐
1230	**705**	31p multicoloured	90	95	☐	☐
		Set of 4	2·40	2·50	☐	☐
		First Day Cover		2·75		☐
		Presentation Pack	3·75		☐	
		PHQ Cards (set of 4)	3·00	6·00	☐	☐
		Set of 4 *Gutter Pairs*	5·75		☐	

Nos. 1227/30 were issued to mark the 850th anniversary of St Bartholomew's Fair, Smithfield, London.

706 'Christmas Post' (pillar-box)

707 'The Three Kings' (chimney-pots)

708 'World at Peace' (Dove and Blackbird)

709 'Light of Christmas' (street lamp)

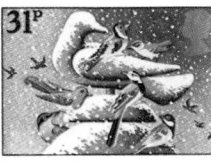

710 'Christmas Dove' (hedge sculpture)

Christmas

1983 (16 Nov.) *One phosphor band* (12½p) *or phosphorised paper* (*others*)

1231	**706**	12½p multicoloured	30	10	☐	☐
1232	**707**	16p multicoloured	35	10	☐	☐
1233	**708**	20½p multicoloured	70	95	☐	☐
1234	**709**	28p multicoloured	95	1·00	☐	☐
1235	**710**	31p multicoloured	1·10	1·25	☐	☐
		Set of 5	3·00	3·00	☐	☐
		First Day Cover		3·50		☐
		Presentation Pack	4·00		☐	
		PHQ Cards (set of 5)	3·00	6·00	☐	☐
		Set of 5 *Gutter Pairs*	6·50		☐	

Collectors Pack 1983

1983 (16 Nov.) *Comprises Nos.* 1207/35

	Collectors Pack	27·00	☐

711 Arms of the College of Arms

712 Arms of King Richard III (founder)

713 Arms of the Earl Marshal of England

714 Arms of the City of London

500th Anniversary of College of Arms

1984 (17 Jan.) *Phosphorised paper. Perf 14½*

1236	**711**	16p multicoloured	35	10	□	□
1237	**712**	20½p multicoloured	50	75	□	□
1238	**713**	28p multicoloured	1·00	1·00	□	□
1239	**714**	31p multicoloured	1·10	1·10	□	□
		Set of 4	2·75	2·75	□	□
		First Day Cover		3·25		□
		Presentation Pack	3·50		□	
		PHQ Cards (set of 4)	3·00	7·50	□	□
		Set of 4 Gutter Pairs	6·50		□	

715   Highland Cow   716   Chillingham Wild Bull

717   Hereford Bull   718   Welsh Black Bull

719   Irish Moiled Cow

British Cattle

1984 (6 Mar.) *Phosphorised paper*

1240	**715**	16p multicoloured	45	10	□	□
1241	**716**	20½p multicoloured	70	70	□	□
1242	**717**	26p multicoloured	90	85	□	□
1243	**718**	28p multicoloured	95	90	□	□
1244	**719**	31p multicoloured	1·25	1·00	□	□
		Set of 5	3·75	3·25	□	□
		First Day Cover		3·75		□
		Presentation Pack	4·00		□	
		PHQ Cards (set of 5)	3·00	7·00	□	□
		Set of 5 Gutter Pairs	8·00		□	

Nos. 1240/4 marked the centenary of the Highland Cattle Society and the bicentenary of the Royal Highland and Agricultural Society of Scotland.

720   Festival Hall, Liverpool   721   Milburngate Shopping Centre, Durham

722   Bush House, Bristol   723   Commercial Street Housing Scheme, Perth

Urban Renewal

1984 (10 Apr.) *Phosphorised paper*

1245	**720**	16p multicoloured	35	10	□	□
1246	**721**	20½p multicoloured	60	75	□	□
1247	**722**	28p multicoloured	1·10	1·25	□	□
1248	**723**	31p multicoloured	1·25	1·25	□	□
		Set of 4	3·00	3·00	□	□
		First Day Cover		3·50		□
		Presentation Pack	3·50		□	
		PHQ Cards (set of 4)	3·00	6·00	□	□
		Set of 4 Gutter Pairs	6·75		□	

Nos. 1245/8 marked the opening of the International Gardens Festival, Liverpool, and the 150th anniversaries of the Royal Institute of British Architects and the Chartered Institute of Building.

724   C.E.P.T. 25th Anniversary Logo   725   Abduction of Europa

Nos. 1249/50 and 1251/2 were each printed together, *se-tenant,* in horizontal pairs throughout the sheets.

For full information on all future British issues, collectors should write to Royal Mail, Freepost EH3647, 21 South Gyle Crescent, Edinburgh EH12 9PE.

Europa. 25th Anniversary of C.E.P.T. and 2nd European Parliamentary Elections

1984 (15 MAY) *Phosphorised paper*

1249	**724**	16p greenish slate, deep blue and gold	70	15	☐	☐
		a. *Horiz pair. Nos.* 1249/50	1·50	1·50	☐	☐
1250	**725**	16p greenish slate, deep blue, black and gold .	70	15	☐	☐
1251	**724**	20½p Venetian red, deep magenta and gold . .	1·60	1·00	☐	☐
		a. *Horiz pair. Nos.* 1251/2	3·25	2·75	☐	☐
1252	**725**	20½p Venetian red, deep magenta, black and gold	1·60	1·00	☐	☐
		Set of 4	4·25	2·10	☐	☐
		First Day Cover		4·50		☐
		Presentation Pack	4·75			☐
		PHQ Cards (set of 4)	3·00	6·00	☐	☐
		Set of 2 Gutter Blocks of 4 . . .	9·50			☐

726   Lancaster House

London Economic Summit Conference

1984 (5 JUNE) *Phosphorised paper*

1253	**726**	31p multicoloured	1·00	1·00	☐	☐
		First Day Cover		2·25		☐
		PHQ Card	1·00	3·25	☐	☐
		Gutter Pair	2·50		☐	

727   View of Earth from 'Apollo 11'

728   Navigational Chart of English Channel

729   Greenwich Observatory

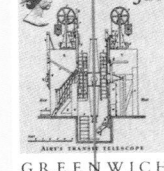

730   Sir George Airey's Transit Telescope

Centenary of Greenwich Meridian

1984 (26 JUNE) *Phosphorised paper. Perf* 14 × 14½

1254	**727**	16p multicoloured	45	10	☐	☐
1255	**728**	20½p multicoloured	70	70	☐	☐
1256	**729**	28p multicoloured	95	90	☐	☐
1257	**730**	31p multicoloured	1·25	1·10	☐	☐
		Set of 4	3·00	2·50	☐	☐
		First Day Cover		2·75		☐
		Presentation Pack	3·75			☐
		PHQ Cards (set of 4)	3·00	6·00	☐	☐
		Set of 4 Gutter Pairs	6·75			☐

731   Bath Mail Coach, 1784

732   Attack on Exeter Mail, 1816

733   Norwich Mail in Thunderstorm, 1827

734   Holyhead and Liverpool Mails leaving London, 1828

735   Edinburgh Mail Snowbound, 1831

T **731/5** were printed together, *se-tenant*, in horizontal strips of 5 throughout the sheet.

Bicentenary of First Mail Coach Run, Bath and Bristol to London

1984 (31 JULY) *Phosphorised paper*

1258	**731**	16p multicoloured	50	40 ☐ ☐
		a. Horiz strip of 5. Nos.		
		1258/62	3·00	3·50 ☐ ☐
1259	**732**	16p multicoloured	50	40 ☐ ☐
1260	**733**	16p multicoloured	50	40 ☐ ☐
1261	**734**	16p multicoloured	50	40 ☐ ☐
1262	**735**	16p multicoloured	50	40 ☐ ☐
		Set of 5	3·00	1·75 ☐ ☐
		First Day Cover		3·75 ☐
		Presentation Pack	3·50	☐
		Souvenir Book	7·00	☐
		PHQ Cards (set of 5)	3·00	7·50 ☐ ☐
		Gutter Block of 10	6·50	☐

736 Nigerian Clinic

737 Violinist and Acropolis, Athens

738 Building Project, Sri Lanka

739 British Council Library

50th Anniversary of The British Council

1984 (25 SEPT.) *Phosphorised paper*

1263	**736**	17p multicoloured	45	10 ☐ ☐
1264	**737**	22p multicoloured	65	90 ☐ ☐
1265	**738**	31p multicoloured	80	1·25 ☐ ☐
1266	**739**	34p multicoloured	90	1·10 ☐ ☐
		Set of 4	2·50	3·00 ☐ ☐
		First Day Cover		3·25 ☐
		Presentation Pack	3·50	☐
		PHQ Cards (set of 4)	3·00	6·00 ☐ ☐
		Set of 4 Gutter Pairs	6·00	☐

For full information on all future British issues, collectors should write to Royal Mail, Freepost EH3647, 21 South Gyle Crescent, Edinburgh EH12 9PE.

740 The Holy Family   **741** Arrival in Bethlehem

742 Shepherd and Lamb   **743** Virgin and Child

744 Offering of Frankincense

Christmas

1984 (20 Nov.) *One phosphor band (13p) or phosphorised paper (others)*

1267	**740**	13p multicoloured	25	15 ☐ ☐
1268	**741**	17p multicoloured	50	25 ☐ ☐
1269	**742**	22p multicoloured	60	85 ☐ ☐
1270	**743**	31p multicoloured	85	1·10 ☐ ☐
1271	**744**	34p multicoloured	1·10	1·25 ☐ ☐
		Set of 5	3·00	3·25 ☐ ☐
		First Day Cover		3·50 ☐
		Presentation Pack	4·25	☐
		PHQ Cards (set of 5)	3·00	6·00 ☐ ☐
		Set of 5 Gutter Pairs	6·50	☐

Collectors Pack 1984

1984 (20 Nov.) *Comprises Nos. 1236/71*

Collectors Pack	35·00	☐

Post Office Yearbook

1984 *Comprises Nos. 1236/71 in hardbound book with slip case*

Yearbook	90·00	☐

745 'Flying Scotsman'

746 'Golden Arrow'

747 'Cheltenham Flyer'

748 'Royal Scot'

749 'Cornish Riviera'

Famous Trains

1985 (22 Jan.) *Phosphorised paper*

1272	**745**	17p multicoloured	45	10	☐	☐
1273	**746**	22p multicoloured	80	95	☐	☐
1274	**747**	29p multicoloured	1·00	1·10	☐	☐
1275	**748**	31p multicoloured	1·25	1·40	☐	☐
1276	**749**	34p multicoloured	1·40	1·40	☐	☐
		Set of 5	4·50	4·50	☐	☐
		First Day Cover		6·00		☐
		Presentation Pack	5·50		☐	
		PHQ Cards (*set of 5*)	5·50	16·00	☐	☐
		Set of 5 Gutter Pairs	9·00		☐	

Nos. 1272/6 were issued on the occasion of the 150th anniversary of the Great Western Railway Company.

750 *Bombus terrestris* (bee)

751 *Coccinella septempunctata* (ladybird)

Wart-Biter Bush-Cricket

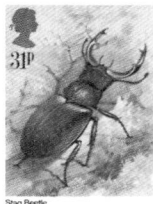

Stag Beetle

752 *Decticus verrucivorus* (bush-cricket)

753 *Lucanus cervus* (stag beetle)

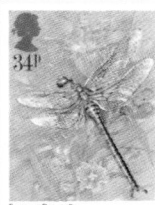

Emperor Dragonfly

754 *Anax imperator* (dragonfly)

Insects

1985 (12 Mar.) *Phosphorised paper*

1277	**750**	17p multicoloured	45	10	☐	☐
1278	**751**	22p multicoloured	70	70	☐	☐
1279	**752**	29p multicoloured	1·00	1·10	☐	☐
1280	**753**	31p multicoloured	1·25	1·25	☐	☐
1281	**754**	34p multicoloured	1·25	1·10	☐	☐
		Set of 5	4·25	3·75	☐	☐
		First Day Cover		4·25		☐
		Presentation Pack	4·75		☐	
		PHQ Cards (*set of 5*)	3·00	8·00	☐	☐
		Set of 5 Gutter Pairs	8·50		☐	

Nos. 1277/81 were issued on the occasion of the centenaries of the Royal Entomological Society of London's Royal Charter and of the Selborne Society.

SEVENTEEN·PENCE
WATER·MUSIC
George Frideric Handel

TWENTY·TWO·PENCE
THE·PLANETS·SUITE
Gustav Holst

755 'Water Music', by Handel

756 'The Planets', by Holst

757 'The First Cuckoo', by Delius

758 'Sea Pictures', by Elgar

Europa. European Music Year

1985 (14 MAY) *Phosphorised paper. Perf* 14½

1282	**755**	17p multicoloured	65	10 □ □
1283	**756**	22p multicoloured	90	1·10 □ □
1284	**757**	31p multicoloured	1·50	1·50 □ □
1285	**758**	34p multicoloured	1·60	1·60 □ □
		Set of 4	4·25	4·00 □ □
		First Day Cover		4·50 □
		Presentation Pack	4·75	□
		PHQ Cards (set of 4)	3·00	6·00 □ □
		Set of 4 Gutter Pairs	8·50	□

Nos. 1282/5 were issued on the occasion of the 300th birth anniversary of Handel.

759 R.N.L.I. Lifeboat and Signal Flags

760 Beachy Head Lighthouse and Chart

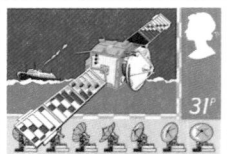

761 'Marecs A' Communications Satelite and Dish Aerials

762 Buoys

Safety at Sea

1985 (18 JUNE) *Phosphorised paper. Perf* 14

1286	**759**	17p multicoloured	45	10 □ □
1287	**760**	22p multicoloured	65	80 □ □

1288	**761**	31p multicoloured	1·00	1·10 □ □
1289	**762**	34p multicoloured	1·10	1·40 □ □
		Set of 4	3·00	3·00 □ □
		First Day Cover		4·25 □
		Presentation Pack	3·75	□
		PHQ Cards (set of 4)	3·00	6·00 □ □
		Set of 4 Gutter Pairs	6·75	□

Nos. 1286/9 were issued to mark the bicentenary of the unimmersible lifeboat and the 50th anniversary of Radar.

763 Datapost Motorcyclist, City of London

764 Rural Postbus

765 Parcel Delivery in Winter

766 Town Letter Delivery

350 Years of Royal Mail Public Postal Service

1985 (30 JULY) *Phosphorised paper*

1290	**763**	17p multicoloured	45	10 □ □
1291	**764**	22p multicoloured	65	85 □ □
1292	**765**	31p multicoloured	1·00	1·25 □ □
1293	**766**	34p multicoloured	1·25	1·25 □ □
		Set of 4	3·00	3·25 □ □
		First Day Cover		3·75 □
		Presentation Pack	3·75	□
		PHQ Cards (set of 4)	3·00	6·00 □ □
		Set of 4 Gutter Pairs	6·50	□

767 King Arthur and Merlin

768 The Lady of the Lake

769 Queen Guinevere and Sir Lancelot

770 Sir Galahad

Arthurian Legends

1985 (3 Sept.) *Phosphorised paper*

1294	**767**	17p multicoloured	. . . . .	40	10 ☐ ☐
1295	**768**	22p multicoloured	. . . . .	65	85 ☐ ☐
1296	**769**	31p multicoloured	. . . . .	1·10	1·40 ☐ ☐
1297	**770**	34p multicoloured	. . . . .	1·25	1·40 ☐ ☐
		Set of 4	. . . .	3·00	3·50 ☐ ☐
		First Day Cover	. . . .		4·00 ☐
		Presentation Pack	. . . .	4·50	☐
		PHQ Cards (set of 4)	. . . . . .	3·00	7·00 ☐ ☐
		Set of 4 Gutter Pairs	. . . . . .	6·50	☐

Nos. 1294/7 were issued to mark the 500th anniversary of the printing of Sir Thomas Malory's *Morte d'Arthur*.

771 Peter Sellers (from photo by Bill Brandt)

772 David Niven (from photo by Cornell Lucas)

773 Charlie Chaplin (from photo by Lord Snowdon)

774 Vivien Leigh (from photo by Angus McBean)

775 Alfred Hitchcock (from photo by Howard Coster)

British Film Year

1985 (8 Oct.) *Phosphorised paper. Perf* 14½

1298	**771**	17p multicoloured	. . . .	50	10 ☐ ☐
1299	**772**	22p multicoloured	. . . .	65	85 ☐ ☐
1300	**773**	29p multicoloured	. . . .	1·10	1·40 ☐ ☐
1301	**774**	31p multicoloured	. . . .	1·25	1·50 ☐ ☐
1302	**775**	34p multicoloured	. . . .	1·50	1·60 ☐ ☐
		Set of 5	. . . .	4·50	5·00 ☐ ☐
		First Day Cover	. . . .		5·25 ☐
		Presentation Pack	. . . .	6·50	☐
		Souvenir Book	. . . .	10·00	☐
		PHQ Cards (set of 5)	. . . . . .	3·00	9·50 ☐ ☐
		Set of 5 Gutter Pairs	. . . . . .	9·00	☐

776 Principal Boy

777 Genie

778 Dame

779 Good Fairy

780 Pantomime Cat

Christmas. Pantomime Characters

1985 (19 Nov.) *One phosphor band* (12p) *or phosphorised paper* (*others*)

1303	**776**	12p multicoloured	. . . . .	35	15 ☐ ☐
1304	**777**	17p multicoloured	. . . . .	40	25 ☐ ☐
1305	**778**	22p multicoloured	. . . . .	65	90 ☐ ☐
1306	**779**	31p multicoloured	. . . . .	1·00	1·10 ☐ ☐
1307	**780**	34p multicoloured	. . . . .	1·10	1·25 ☐ ☐
		Set of 5	. . . .	3·00	3·25 ☐ ☐
		First Day Cover	. . . .		4·00 ☐
		Presentation Pack	. . . .	4·25	☐
		PHQ Cards (Set of 5)	. . . . . .	3·00	8·00 ☐ ☐
		Set of 5 Gutter Pairs	. . . . . .	6·00	☐

Collectors Pack 1985

1985 (19 Nov.) *Comprises Nos.* 1272/1307

    Collectors Pack . . . . 35·00 ☐

Post Office Yearbook

1985 *Comprises Nos.* 1272/1307 *in hardbound book with slip case*

    Yearbook . . . . 80·00 ☐

17 PENCE · INDUSTRY YEAR 1986   22 PENCE · INDUSTRY YEAR 1986

781   Light Bulb and North Sea Oil Drilling Rig (Energy)

782   Thermometer and Pharmaceutical Laboratory (Health)

31 PENCE · INDUSTRY YEAR 1986   34 PENCE · INDUSTRY YEAR 1986

783   Garden Hoe and Steel Works (Steel)

784   Loaf of Bread and and Cornfield (Agriculture)

Industry Year

1986 (14 Jan.) *Phosphorised paper. Perf* $14\frac{1}{2} \times 14$

1308	781	17p multicoloured	45	10	☐	☐
1309	782	22p multicoloured	70	85	☐	☐
1310	783	31p multicoloured	1·10	1·25	☐	☐
1311	784	34p multicoloured	1·40	1·40	☐	☐
		Set of 4	3·25	3·25	☐	☐
		First Day Cover		4·00		☐
		Presentation Pack	4·00		☐	
		PHQ Cards (set of 4)	3·00	6·00	☐	☐
		Set of 4 Gutter Pairs	7·00		☐	

785   Dr Edmond Halley as Comet

786   *Giotto* Spacecraft approaching Comet

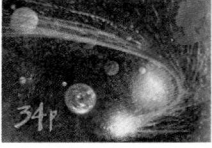

787   'Twice in a Lifetime'

788   Comet orbiting Sun and Planets

Appearance of Halley's Comet

1986 (18 Feb.) *Phosphorised paper*

1312	785	17p multicoloured	45	10	☐	☐
1313	786	22p multicoloured	75	95	☐	☐
1314	787	31p multicoloured	1·10	1·25	☐	☐
1315	788	34p multicoloured	1·25	1·25	☐	☐
		Set of 4	3·25	3·25	☐	☐
		First Day Cover		4·00		☐
		Presentation Pack	4·25		☐	
		PHQ Cards (set of 4)	4·00	6·00	☐	☐
		Set of 4 Gutter Pairs	7·00		☐	

HER MAJESTY THE QUEEN   HER MAJESTY THE QUEEN

Sixtieth Birthday   17p   Sixtieth Birthday   17p

789   Queen Elizabeth II in 1928, 1942 and 1952

790   Queen Elizabeth II in 1958, 1973 and 1982

Nos. 1316/17 and 1318/19 were each printed together, *se-tenant*, in horizontal pairs throughout the sheets.

60th Birthday of Queen Elizabeth II

1986 (21 Apr.) *Phosphorised paper*

1316	789	17p multicoloured	60	50	☐	☐
		a. Horiz pair. Nos. 1316/17	1·50	1·50	☐	☐
1317	790	17p multicoloured	60	50	☐	☐
1318	789	34p multicoloured	1·40	1·75	☐	☐
		a. Horiz pair. Nos. 1318/19	3·00	3·75	☐	☐
1319	790	34p multicoloured	1·40	1·75	☐	☐
		Set of 4	4·50	4·00	☐	☐
		First Day Cover		4·50		☐
		Presentation Pack	6·00		☐	
		Souvenir Book	9·00		☐	
		PHQ Cards (set of 4)	3·00	7·00	☐	☐
		Set of 2 Gutter Blocks of 4 . . .	9·50		☐	

For full information on all future British issues, collectors should write to Royal Mail, Freepost EH3647, 21 South Gyle Crescent, Edinburgh EH12 9PE.

791 Barn Owl

792 Pine Marten

793 Wild Cat

794 Natterjack Toad

Europa. Nature Conservation. Endangered Species

1986 (20 MAY) *Phosphorised paper. Perf* 14½ × 14

1320	**791**	17p multicoloured	. . . . .	50	10	☐	☐
1321	**792**	22p multicoloured	. . . . .	1·00	1·25	☐	☐
1322	**793**	31p multicoloured	. . . . .	1·50	1·60	☐	☐
1323	**794**	34p multicoloured	. . . . .	1·75	1·75	☐	☐
		Set of 4	. . . .	4·25	4·25	☐	☐
		First Day Cover	. . . .		4·75		☐
		Presentation Pack	. . . .	4·75		☐	
		PHQ Cards (set of 4)	. . . . . .	3·00	7·00	☐	☐
		Set of 4 Gutter Pairs	. . . . . .	8·50		☐	

795 Peasants Working in Fields

796 Freemen working at Town Trades

797 Knight and Retainers

798 Lord at Banquet

900th Anniversary of Domesday Book

1986 (17 JUNE) *Phosphorised paper*

1324	**795**	17p multicoloured	. . . . .	40	10	☐	☐
1325	**796**	22p multicoloured	. . . . .	70	85	☐	☐
1326	**797**	31p multicoloured	. . . . .	1·10	1·40	☐	☐
1327	**798**	34p multicoloured	. . . . .	1·25	1·40	☐	☐
		Set of 4	. . . .	3·00	3·50	☐	☐
		First Day Cover	. . . .		4·00		☐
		Presentation Pack	. . . .	4·00		☐	
		PHQ Cards (set of 4)	. . . . . .	3·00	6·00	☐	☐
		Set of 4 Gutter Pairs	. . . . . .	6·50		☐	

799 Athletics

800 Rowing

801 Weightlifting

802 Rifle-shooting

803 Hockey

Thirteenth Commonwealth Games, Edinburgh (Nos. 1328/31) and World Men's Hockey Cup, London (No. 1332)

1986 (15 JULY) *Phosphorised paper*

1328	**799**	17p multicoloured	. . . . .	50	10	☐	☐
1329	**800**	22p multicoloured	. . . . .	70	85	☐	☐
1330	**801**	29p multicoloured	. . . . .	90	1·00	☐	☐
1331	**802**	31p multicoloured	. . . . .	1·25	1·40	☐	☐
1332	**803**	34p multicoloured	. . . . .	1·40	1·40	☐	☐
		Set of 5	. . . .	4·25	4·25	☐	☐
		First Day Cover	. . . .		5·00		☐
		Presentation Pack	. . . .	5·00		☐	
		PHQ Cards (set of 5)	. . . . . .	4·00	8·00	☐	☐
		Set of 5 Gutter Pairs	. . . . . .	8·50		☐	

No. 1332 also marked the centenary of the Hockey Association.

804   Prince Andrew and Miss Sarah Ferguson 805

Royal Wedding

1986 (22 JULY) *One side band* (12p) *or phosphorised paper* (17p)

1333	804	12p multicoloured	50		30	☐	☐
1334	805	17p multicoloured	1·00		95	☐	☐
		Set of 2	1·50		1·25	☐	☐
		First Day Cover			2·25		☐
		Presentation Pack	2·00			☐	
		PHQ Cards (*set of 2*)	1·75		5·00	☐	☐
		Set of 2 Gutter Pairs	3·50			☐	

806   Stylised Cross on Ballot Paper

2nd Commonwealth Parliamentary Conference, London

1986 (19 AUG.) *Phosphorised paper. Perf* 14 × 14½

1335	806	34p multicoloured	1·10		1·10	☐	☐
		First Day Cover			1·75		☐
		PHQ Card	1·00		2·50	☐	☐
		Gutter Pair	2·50			☐	

807   Lord Dowding and   808   Lord Tedder and
       Hawker Hurricane Mk. I   Hawker Typhoon 1B

809   Lord Trenchard and   810   Sir Arthur Harris and
       De Havilland D.H.9A   Avro Type 683 Lancaster

811   Lord Portal and De
       Havilland D.H.98 Mosquito

History of the Royal Air Force

1986 (16th SEPT.) *Phosphorised paper. Perf* 14½ × 14

1336	807	17p multicoloured	70		10	☐	☐
1337	808	22p multicoloured	90		95	☐	☐
1338	809	29p multicoloured	1·25		1·10	☐	☐
1339	810	31p multicoloured	1·50		1·40	☐	☐
1340	811	34p multicoloured	1·75		1·50	☐	☐
		Set of 5	5·50		4·50	☐	☐
		First Day Cover			6·50		☐
		Presentation Pack	6·00			☐	
		PHQ Cards (*set of 5*)	4·00		10·00	☐	☐
		Set of 5 Gutter Pairs	11·00			☐	

Nos. 1336/40 were issued to celebrate the 50th anniversary of the first R.A.F. Commands.

812   The Glastonbury Thorn   813   The Tanad Valley Plygain

814   The Hebrides Tribute   815   The Dewsbury Church
                                       Knell

816   The Hereford Boy Bishop

Christmas. Folk Customs

1986 (18 Nov.–2 Dec.) *One phosphor band* (12p, 13p) *or phosphorised paper* (*others*)

1341	812	12p multicoloured (2 Dec.)	50	30	☐	☐
1342		13p multicoloured	25	10	☐	☐
1343	813	18p multicoloured	45	10	☐	☐
1344	814	22p multicoloured	80	95	☐	☐
1345	815	31p multicoloured	90	1·00	☐	☐
1346	816	34p multicoloured	1·10	1·10	☐	☐
		Set of 6	3·50	3·25	☐	☐
		First Day Covers (2)		6·00		☐
		Presentation Pack (Nos. 1342/6)	5·00		☐	
		PHQ Cards (set of 5) (Nos. 1342/6)	3·00	7·00	☐	☐
		Set of 6 Gutter Pairs	7·00		☐	

Collectors Pack 1986

1986 (18 Nov.) *Comprises Nos.* 1308/40, 1342/6

	Collectors Pack	35·00	☐

Post Office Yearbook

1986 *Comprises Nos.* 1308/40, 1342/6 *in hardbound book with slip case*

	Yearbook	75·00	☐

817   North American Blanket Flower

818   Globe Thistle

819   Echeveria

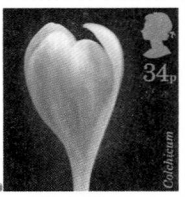

820   Autumn Crocus

Flower Photographs by Alfred Lammer

1987 (20 Jan.) *Phosphorised paper. Perf* $14\frac{1}{2} \times 14$

1347	817	18p multicoloured	40	10	☐	☐
1348	818	22p multicoloured	70	80	☐	☐
1349	819	31p multicoloured	1·00	1·25	☐	☐
1350	820	34p multicoloured	1·10	1·25	☐	☐
		Set of 4	3·00	3·25	☐	☐
		First Day Cover		4·00		☐
		Presentation Pack	4·50		☐	
		PHQ Cards (set of 4)	3·00	7·00	☐	☐
		Set of 4 Gutter Pairs	6·50		☐	

821   The Principia Mathematica

822   Motion of Bodies in Ellipses

823   Optick Treatise

824   The System of the World

300th Anniversary of The Principia Mathematica by Sir Isaac Newton

1987 (24 Mar.) *Phosphorised paper*

1351	821	18p multicoloured	55	10	☐	☐
1352	822	22p multicoloured	80	85	☐	☐
1353	823	31p multicoloured	1·25	1·50	☐	☐
1354	824	34p multicoloured	1·40	1·40	☐	☐
		Set of 4	3·75	3·50	☐	☐
		First Day Cover		4·00		☐
		Presentation Pack	4·50		☐	
		PHQ Cards (set of 4)	3·00	6·25	☐	☐
		Set of 4 Gutter Pairs	8·00		☐	

For full information on all future British issues, collectors should write to Royal Mail, Freepost EH3647, 21 South Gyle Crescent, Edinburgh EH12 9PE.

825 Willis Faber and Dumas 826 Pompidou Centre, Paris
Building, Ipswich

827 Staatsgalerie, Stuttgart 828 European Investment
Bank, Luxembourg

Europa. British Architects in Europe

1987 (12 May) *Phosphorised paper*

1355	825	18p multicoloured	50	10	□	□
1356	826	22p multicoloured	75	85	□	□
1357	827	31p multicoloured	1·25	1·40	□	□
1358	828	34p multicoloured	1·40	1·40	□	□
		Set of 4	3·50	3·50	□	□
		First Day Cover		3·50		□
		Presentation Pack	4·50		□	
		PHQ Cards (set of 4)	3·00	6·25	□	□
		Set of 4 Gutter Pairs	7·50		□	

829 Brigade Members 830 Bandaging Blitz
with Ashford Litter, 1887 Victim, 1940

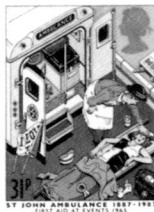

831 Volunteer with 832 Transport of Transplant
fainting Girl, 1965 Organ by Air Wing, 1987

Centenary of St John Ambulance Brigade

1987 (16 June) *Phosphorised paper. Perf* 14 × 14½

1359	829	18p multicoloured	50	10	□	□
1360	830	22p multicoloured	75	85	□	□
1361	831	31p multicoloured	1·25	1·40	□	□
1362	832	34p multicoloured	1·40	1·50	□	□
		Set of 4	3·50	3·50	□	□
		First Day Cover		4·00		□
		Presentation Pack	4·50		□	
		PHQ Cards (set of 4)	3·00	6·25	□	□
		Set of 4 Gutter Pairs	7·50		□	

833 Arms of the Lord 834 Scottish Heraldic Banner
Lyon King of Arms of Prince Charles

835 Arms of Royal 836 Arms of Royal Society
Scottish Academy of of Edinburgh
Painting, Sculpture
and Architecture

300th Anniversary of Revival of Order of the Thistle

1987 (21 July) *Phosphorised paper. Perf* 14½

1363	833	18p multicoloured	50	10	□	□
1364	834	22p multicoloured	75	90	□	□
1365	835	31p multicoloured	1·40	1·40	□	□
1366	836	34p multicoloured	1·50	1·40	□	□
		Set of 4	3·75	3·50	□	□
		First Day Cover		4·00		□
		Presentation Pack	4·50		□	
		PHQ Cards (set of 4)	3·00	7·50	□	□
		Set of 4 Gutter Pairs	7·50		□	

For full information on all future British issues, collectors
should write to Royal Mail, Freepost EH3647, 21 South Gyle
Crescent, Edinburgh EH12 9PE.

837 Crystal Palace, 'Monarch of the Glen' (Landseer) and Grace Darling

838 Great Eastern, Beeton's Book of Household Management and Prince Albert

839 Albert Memorial, Ballot Box and Disraeli

840 Diamond Jubilee Emblem, Morse Key and Newspaper Placard for Relief of Mafeking

150th Anniversary of Queen Victoria's Accession

1987 (8 SEPT.) Phosphorised paper

1367	**837**	18p multicoloured	50	10	☐	☐
1368	**838**	22p multicoloured	80	90	☐	☐
1369	**839**	31p multicoloured	1·50	1·50	☐	☐
1370	**840**	34p multicoloured	1·60	1·60	☐	☐
		Set of 4	4·00	3·75	☐	☐
		First Day Cover		4·25		☐
		Presentation Pack	5·00		☐	
		PHQ Cards (set of 4)	3·00	7·00	☐	☐
		Set of 4 Gutter Pairs	8·50		☐	

841 Pot by Bernard Leach

842 Pot by Elizabeth Fritsch

843 Pot by Lucie Rie

844 Pot by Hans Coper

Studio Pottery

1987 (13 OCT.) Phosphorised paper. Perf $14\frac{1}{2} \times 14$

1371	**841**	18p multicoloured	50	10	☐	☐
1372	**842**	26p multicoloured	70	70	☐	☐
1373	**843**	31p multicoloured	1·25	1·10	☐	☐
1374	**844**	34p multicoloured	1·40	1·40	☐	☐
		Set of 4	3·50	3·00	☐	☐
		First Day Cover		3·50		☐
		Presentation Pack	4·50		☐	
		PHQ Cards (set of 4)	3·00	6·00	☐	☐
		Set of 4 Gutter Pairs	7·50		☐	

Nos. 1371/4 also mark the birth centenary of Bernard Leach, the potter.

845 Decorating the Christmas Tree

846 Waiting for Father Christmas

847 Sleeping Child and Father Christmas in Sleigh

848 Child reading

849 Child playing Flute and Snowman

Christmas

1987 (17 Nov.) One phosphor band (13p) or phosphorised paper (others)

1375	**845**	13p multicoloured	30	10	☐	☐
1376	**846**	18p multicoloured	40	20	☐	☐
1377	**847**	26p multicoloured	80	1·00	☐	☐
1378	**848**	31p multicoloured	1·10	1·50	☐	☐
1379	**849**	34p multicoloured	1·25	1·50	☐	☐
		Set of 5	3·50	4·00	☐	☐
		First Day Cover		4·50		☐
		Presentation Pack	4·75		☐	
		PHQ Cards (set of 5)	3·00	6·00	☐	☐
		Set of 5 Gutter Pairs	7·50		☐	

Collectors Pack 1987

1987 (17 Nov.) Comprises Nos. 1347/79

    Collectors Pack . . . . 40·00 ☐

Post Office Yearbook

1987 Comprises Nos. 1347/79 in hardbound book with slip case

    Yearbook . . . . 40·00 ☐

850 Short-spined   851 Yellow Waterlily
     Seascorpion ('Bull-rout')   (Major Joshua Swatkin)
     (Jonathan Couch)

852 Whistling ('Bewick's')   853 Morchella esculenta
     Swan (Edward Lear)   (James Sowerby)

Bicentenary of Linnean Society. Archive Illustrations

1988 (19 Jan.) Phosphorised paper

1380	**850**	18p multicoloured	55	10	☐	☐
1381	**851**	26p multicoloured	85	1·00	☐	☐
1382	**852**	31p multicoloured	1·10	1·25	☐	☐
1383	**853**	34p multicoloured	1·25	1·40	☐	☐
		Set of 4	3·25	3·25	☐	☐
		First Day Cover		3·75		☐
		Presentation Pack	4·50		☐	
		PHQ Cards (set of 4)	3·00	6·00	☐	☐
		Set of 4 Gutter Pairs	7·00		☐	

854 Revd William   855 William Salesbury
     Morgan (Bible   (New Testament
     translator, 1588)   translator, 1567)

856 Bishop Richard   857 Bishop Richard Parry
     Davies (New   (editor of Revised
     Testament translator,   Welsh Bible, 1620)
     1567)

400th Anniversary of Welsh Bible

1988 (1 Mar.) Phosphorised paper. Perf $14\frac{1}{2} \times 14$

1384	**854**	18p multicoloured	40	10	☐	☐
1385	**855**	26p multicoloured	70	95	☐	☐
1386	**856**	31p multicoloured	1·25	1·25	☐	☐
1387	**857**	34p multicoloured	1·40	1·25	☐	☐
		Set of 4	3·25	3·25	☐	☐
		First Day Cover		3·50		☐
		Presentation Pack	4·25		☐	
		PHQ Cards (set of 4)	3·00	6·00	☐	☐
		Set of 4 Gutter Pairs	7·00		☐	

858 Gymnastics   859 Downhill Skiing
     (Centenary of British   (Ski Club of
     Amateur Gymnastics   Great Britain)
     Association)

860 Tennis (Centenary   861 Football (Centenary
     of Lawn Tennis   of Football League)
     Association)

Sports Organizations

1988 (22 MAR.) *Phosphorised paper. Perf* 14½

1388	858	18p multicoloured	40	15	☐	☐
1389	859	26p multicoloured	70	80	☐	☐
1390	860	31p multicoloured	1·10	1·25	☐	☐
1391	861	34p multicoloured	1·25	1·25	☐	☐
		Set of 4	3·25	3·25	☐	☐
		First Day Cover		3·50		☐
		Presentation Pack	4·25		☐	
		PHQ Cards (set of 4)	2·50	6·00	☐	☐
		Set of 4 Gutter Pairs	7·00		☐	

862 *Mallard* and Mailbags on Pick-up Arms

863 Loading Transatlantic Mail on Liner *Queen Elizabeth*

864 Glasgow Tram No. 1173 and Pillar Box

865 Imperial Airways Handley Page H.P.45 *Horatius* and Airmail Van

Europa. Transport and Mail Services in 1930's

1988 (10 MAY) *Phosphorised paper*

1392	862	18p multicoloured	45	15	☐	☐
1393	863	26p multicoloured	90	95	☐	☐
1394	864	31p multicoloured	1·10	1·50	☐	☐
1395	865	34p multicoloured	1·50	1·60	☐	☐
		Set of 4	3·50	3·75	☐	☐
		First Day Cover		4·00		☐
		Presentation Pack	4·50		☐	
		PHQ Cards (set of 4)	2·00	5·00	☐	☐
		Set of 4 Gutter Pairs	7·50		☐	

866 Early Settler and Sailing Clipper

867 Queen Elizabeth II with British and Australian Parliament Buildings

868 W. G. Grace (cricketer) and Tennis Racquet

869 Shakespeare, John Lennon (entertainer) and Sydney Landmarks

Nos. 1396/7 and 1398/9 were each printed together, *se-tenant,* in horizontal pairs throughout the sheets, each pair showing a background design of the Australian flag.

Bicentenary of Australian Settlement

1988 (21 JUNE) *Phosphorised paper. Perf* 14½

1396	866	18p multicoloured	60	25	☐	☐
		a. *Horiz pair. Nos.* 1396/7	1·50	1·50	☐	☐
1397	867	18p multicoloured	60	25	☐	☐
1398	868	34p multicoloured	1·25	80	☐	☐
		a. *Horiz pair. Nos.* 1398/9	2·75	2·75	☐	☐
1399	869	34p multicoloured	1·25	80	☐	☐
		Set of 4 . . ·.	4·25	1·90	☐	☐
		First Day Cover		3·50		☐
		Presentation Pack	4·50		☐	
		Souvenir Book	10·00		☐	
		PHQ Cards (set of 4)	2·00	6·50	☐	☐
		Set of 2 Gutter Blocks of 4 . . .	8·50		☐	

Stamps in similar designs were also issued by Australia. These are included in the Souvenir Book.

870 Spanish Galeasse off The Lizard

871 English Fleet leaving Plymouth

872 Engagement off Isle of Wight

873 Attack of English Fire-ships, Calais

ARMADA·NORTH SEA·30 JULY-2 AUG 1588

874　Armada in Storm,
　　　North Sea

Nos. 1400/4 were printed together, *se-tenant*, in horizontal strips of 5 throughout the sheet, forming a composite design.

400th Anniversary of Spanish Armada

1988 (19 JULY) *Phosphorised paper*

1400	870	18p multicoloured	70	40 □	□	
		a. Horiz strip of 5. Nos.				
		1400/4	3·50	3·75 □	□	
1401	871	18p multicoloured	70	40 □	□	
1402	872	18p multicoloured	70	40 □	□	
1403	873	18p multicoloured	70	40 □	□	
1404	874	18p multicoloured	70	40 □	□	
		Set of 5	3·50	1·75 □	□	
		First Day Cover		4·00	□	
		Presentation Pack	4·50		□	
		PHQ Cards (set of 5)	2·75	8·00 □	□	
		Gutter Block of 10	7·50		□	

The Owl and the Pussy-cat went to sea
In a beautiful pea-green boat,
EDWARD LEAR ● 1812-1888

875　'The Owl and the
　　　Pussy-cat'

Yours affectionately, Edward Lear ● 1812-1888

876　'Edward Lear as a Bird'
　　　(self-portrait)

C c Cc

C was a lovely Pussy Cat; its eyes were large and ...
EDWARD LEAR ● 1812-1888

877　'Cat' (from alphabet
　　　book)

There was a Young Lady whose bonnet,
Came untied when the birds sate upon it;
EDWARD LEAR ● 1812-1888

878　'There was a Young
　　　Lady whose Bonnet . . .'
　　　(limerick)

Death Centenary of Edward Lear (artist and author)

1988 (6–27 SEPT.) *Phosphorised paper*

1405	875	19p black, pale cream and carmine	65	20 □	□	
1406	876	27p black, pale cream and yellow	1·00	1·00 □	□	
1407	877	32p black, pale cream and emerald	1·25	1·40 □	□	
1408	878	35p black, pale cream and blue	1·40	1·40 □	□	
		Set of 4	4·00	3·50 □	□	
		First Day Cover		4·00	□	
		Presentation Pack	4·75		□	
		PHQ Cards (set of 4)	2·00	7·00 □	□	
		Set of 4 Gutter Pairs	8·50		□	
MS1409		122 × 90 mm. Nos. 1405/8 . .	7·00	8·00 □	□	
		First Day Cover (27 Sept.) . . .		8·50	□	

No. **MS**1409 was sold at £1·35, the premium being used for the 'Stamp World London 90' International Stamp Exhibition.

£1

CARRICKFERGUS CASTLE

879　Carrickfergus Castle

£1·50

CAERNARFON CASTLE

880　Caernarvon Castle

£2

EDINBURGH CASTLE

881　Edinburgh Castle

£5

WINDSOR CASTLE

882　Windsor Castle

1988 (18 OCT.) *Ordinary paper*

1410	879	£1 deep green	3·25	60 □	□	
1411	880	£1·50 maroon	4·00	1·25 □	□	
1412	881	£2 indigo	6·50	1·50 □	□	
1413	882	£5 deep brown	20·00	5·50 □	□	
		Set of 4	30·00	8·00 □	□	
		First Day Cover		35·00	□	
		Presentation Pack	35·00		□	
		Set of 4 Gutter pairs	65·00		□	

For similar designs, but with silhouette of Queen's head see Nos. 1611/14 and 1993/6.

Minimum Price. The minimum price quoted is 10p. This represents a handling charge rather than a basis for valuing common stamps. Where the actual value of a stamp is less than 10p this may be apparent when set prices are shown, particularly for sets including a number of 10p stamps. It therefore follows that in valuing common stamps the 10p catalogue price should not be reckoned automatically since it covers a variation in real scarcity.

883 Journey to Bethlehem

884 Shepherds and Star

885 Three Wise Men

886 Nativity

887 The Annunciation

888 Atlantic Puffin

889 Avocet

890 Oystercatcher

891 Northern Gannet

Christmas

1988 (15 Nov.) *One phosphor band (14p) or phosphorised paper (others)*

1414	**883**	14p multicoloured	45	20	☐	☐
1415	**884**	19p multicoloured	50	20	☐	☐
1416	**885**	27p multicoloured	90	1·00	☐	☐
1417	**886**	32p multicoloured	1·10	1·10	☐	☐
1418	**887**	35p multicoloured	1·40	1·10	☐	☐
		Set of 5	4·00	3·25	☐	☐
		First Day Cover		4·25		☐
		Presentation Pack	4·75		☐	
		PHQ Cards (set of 5)	2·50	7·00	☐	☐
		Set of 5 Gutter Pairs	8·50		☐	

Collectors Pack 1988

1988 (15 Nov.) *Comprises Nos. 1380/1408, 1414/18*

	Collectors Pack	40·00	☐

Post Office Yearbook

1988 *Comprises Nos. 1380/1404,* **MS**1409, *1414/18 in hardbound book with slip case*

	Yearbook	40·00	☐

Centenary of Royal Society for the Protection of Birds

1989 (17 Jan.) *Phosphorised paper*

1419	**888**	19p multicoloured	45	20	☐	☐
1420	**889**	27p multicoloured	1·25	1·25	☐	☐
1421	**890**	32p multicoloured	1·25	1·25	☐	☐
1422	**891**	35p multicoloured	1·40	1·40	☐	☐
		Set of 4	4·00	3·75	☐	☐
		First Day Cover		4·25		☐
		Presentation Pack	4·50		☐	
		PHQ Cards (set of 4)	2·50	8·00	☐	☐
		Set of 4 Gutter Pairs	8·50		☐	

892 Rose

893 Cupid

894 Yachts

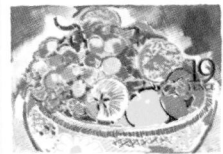
895 Fruit

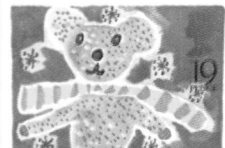

896   Teddy Bear

Nos. 1423/7 were printed together, *se-tenant*, in horizontal strips of five, two such strips forming the booklet pane with twelve half stamp-size labels.

Greetings Booklet Stamps

1989 (31 JAN.) *Phosphorised paper*

1423	**892**	19p multicoloured	5·50	4·50	☐	☐
		a. Booklet pane. Nos.				
		1423/7 × 2	50·00		☐	
1424	**893**	19p multicoloured	5·50	4·50	☐	☐
1425	**894**	19p multicoloured	5·50	4·50	☐	☐
1426	**895**	19p multicoloured	5·50	4·50	☐	☐
1427	**896**	19p multicoloured	5·50	4·50	☐	☐
		Set of 5	25·00	20·00	☐	☐
		First Day Cover		25·00		☐

897   Fruit and Vegetables   898   Meat Products

899   Dairy Produce   900   Cereal Products

Food and Farming Year

1989 (7 MAR.) *Phosphorised paper. Perf* 14 × 14½

1428	**897**	19p multicoloured	45	15	☐	☐
1429	**898**	27p multicoloured	90	85	☐	☐
1430	**899**	32p multicoloured	1·25	1·40	☐	☐
1431	**900**	35p multicoloured	1·40	1·50	☐	☐
		Set of 4	3·50	3·50	☐	☐
		First Day Cover		4·00		☐
		Presentation Pack	4·50		☐	
		PHQ Cards (set of 4)	2·00	6·00	☐	☐
		Set of 4 Gutter Pairs	7·50		☐	

901   Mortar Board   902   Cross on Ballot Paper
       (150th Anniv of   (3rd Direct Elections
       Public Education   to European Parliament)
       in England)

903   Posthorn (26th   904   Globe (Inter-
       Postal, Telegraph and   Parliamentary Union
       Telephone International   Centenary Conference,
       Congress, Brighton)   London)

Nos. 1432/3 and 1434/5 were each printed together, *se-tenant*, in horizontal pairs throughout the sheets.

Anniversaries

1989 (11 APR.) *Phosphorised paper. Perf* 14 × 14½

1432	**901**	19p multicoloured	1·00	50	☐	☐
		a. Horiz pair. Nos. 1432/3	2·00	2·00	☐	☐
1433	**902**	19p multicoloured	1·00	50	☐	☐
1434	**903**	35p multicoloured	1·50	1·75	☐	☐
		a. Horiz pair. Nos. 1434/5	3·00	4·00	☐	☐
1435	**904**	35p multicoloured	1·50	1·75	☐	☐
		Set of 4	4·50	4·00	☐	☐
		First Day Cover		4·75		☐
		Presentation Pack	6·50		☐	
		PHQ Cards (set of 4)	2·00	7·00	☐	☐
		Set of 2 Gutter Strips of 4 . . .	9·50		☐	

905   Toy Train and Airplane   906   Building Bricks
       Airplane

907   Dice and Board Games

908   Toy Robot, Boat and Doll's House

Europa. Games and Toys

1989 (16 MAY) *Phosphorised paper*

1436	**905**	19p multicoloured	65	20	□	□
1437	**906**	27p multicoloured	95	1·00	□	□
1438	**907**	32p multicoloured	1·40	1·40	□	□
1439	**908**	35p multicoloured	1·50	1·50	□	□
		Set of 4	4·00	3·75	□	□
		First Day Cover		4·25		□
		Presentation Pack	4·50		□	
		PHQ Cards (set of 4)	2·00	6·00	□	□
		Set of 4 *Gutter Pairs*	8·50		□	

909   Ironbridge, Shropshire

910   Tin Mine. St Agnes Head, Cornwall

911   Cotton Mills, New Lanark, Strathclyde

912   Pontcysylite Aqueduct, Clwyd

912a

Industrial Archaeology

1989 (4–25 JULY) *Phosphorised paper*

1440	**909**	19p multicoloured	60	15	□	□
1441	**910**	27p multicoloured	1·00	1·10	□	□
1442	**911**	32p multicoloured	1·10	1·25	□	□
1443	**912**	35p multicoloured	1·25	1·50	□	□
		Set of 4	3·50	3·50	□	□
		First Day Cover		4·25		□
		Presentation Pack	4·50		□	
		PHQ Cards (set of 4)	2·25	6·50	□	□
		Set of 4 *Gutter Pairs*	7·50		□	
MS1444		122 × 90 mm. **912a** As Nos.				
		1440/3 but designs horizontal .	6·00	6·00	□	□
		First Day Cover (25 July)		6·50		□

No. **MS**1444 was sold at £1·40, the premium being used for the 'Stamp World London 90' International Stamp Exhibition.

913   914

Booklet Stamps

1989 (22 AUG.)–92 (a) *Printed in photogravure by Harrison and Sons. Perf* 15 × 14

1445	**913**	(2nd) bright blue (1 centre band)	1·00	1·00	□	□
1446		(2nd) bright blue (1 side band) (20.3.90)	3·00	3·25	□	□
1447	**914**	(1st) black (phosphorised paper)	1·75	1·75	□	□
1448		(1st) brownish black (2 bands) (20.3.90)	3·00	3·00	□	□

(b) *Printed in lithography by Walsall. Perf* 14

1449	**913**	(2nd) bright blue (1 centre band)	1·00	90	□	□
1450	**914**	(1st) black (2 bands)	2·50	2·40	□	□

(c) Printed in lithography by Questa. Perf 15 × 14

1451	**913**	(2nd) bright blue (1 centre band) (19.9.89)	1·00	1·00 □ □
1451*a*		(2nd) bright blue (1 side band) (25.2.92)	3·50	3·50 □ □
1452	**914**	(1st) black (phosphorised paper) (19.9.89)	2·50	2·50 □ □
		First Day Cover (Nos. 1445, 1447)		4·00 □

For similar stamps showing changed colours see Nos. 1511/16, for those with elliptical perforations Nos. 1663*a*/6 and 1979 and for self-adhesive versions Nos. 2039/40.

No. 1451*a* exists with the phosphor band at the left or right of the stamp.

915   Snowflake (×10)

916   *Calliphora erythrocephala* (fly) (×5)

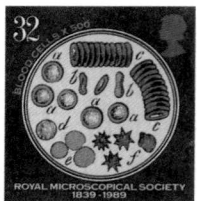

917   Blood Cells (×500)

918   Microchip (×600)

150th Anniversary of Royal Microscopical Society

1989 (5 Sept.) *Phosphorised paper. Perf 14½ × 14*

1453	**915**	19p multicoloured	45	15 □ □
1454	**916**	27p multicoloured	95	1·10 □ □
1455	**917**	32p multicoloured	1·10	1·40 □ □
1456	**918**	35p multicoloured	1·25	1·40 □ □
		Set of 4	3·50	3·75 □ □
		First Day Cover		4·25 □
		Presentation Pack	4·50	□
		PHQ Cards (set of 4)	2·00	6·00 □ □
		Set of 4 Gutter Pairs	7·50	□

919   Royal Mail Coach

920   Escort of Blues and Royals

921   Lord Mayor's Coach

922   Coach Team passing St Paul's

923   Blues and Royals Drum Horse

Nos. 1457/61 were printed together, *se-tenant,* in horizontal strips of 5 throughout the sheet, forming a composite design.

Lord Mayor's Show, London

1989 (17 Oct.) *Phosphorised paper*

1457	**919**	20p multicoloured	70	40 □ □
		a. Horiz strip of 5. Nos. 1457/61	3·50	3·50 □ □
1458	**920**	20p multicoloured	70	40 □ □
1459	**921**	20p multicoloured	70	40 □ □
1460	**922**	20p multicoloured	70	40 □ □
1461	**923**	20p multicoloured	70	40 □ □
		Set of 5	3·50	1·75 □ □
		First Day Cover		4·00 □
		Presentation Pack	4·00	□
		PHQ Cards (set of 5)	2·50	7·00 □ □
		Gutter Strip of 10	7·50	□

Nos. 1457/61 commemorate the 800th anniversary of the installation of the first Lord Mayor of London.

924 14th-century Peasants from Stained-glass Window

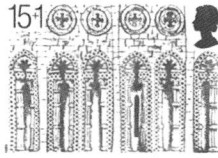

925 Arches and Roundels, West Front

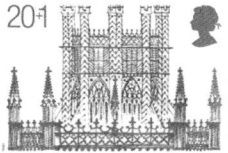

926 Octagon Tower

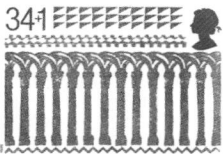

927 Arcade from West Transept

928 Triple Arch from West Front

Christmas. 800th Anniversary of Ely Cathedral

1989 (14 Nov.) *One phosphor band (Nos. 1462/3) or phosphorised paper (others)*

1462	**924**	15p gold, silver and blue .	50	15 ☐ ☐
1463	**925**	15p + 1p gold, silver and blue	60	40 ☐ ☐
1464	**926**	20p + 1p gold, silver and rosine	80	80 ☐ ☐
1465	**927**	34p + 1p gold, silver and emerald	1·60	1·75 ☐ ☐
1466	**928**	37p + 1p gold, silver and yellow-olive	1·75	1·90 ☐ ☐
		Set of 5	4·75	4·50 ☐ ☐
		First Day Cover		5·00 ☐
		Presentation Pack	5·25	☐
		PHQ Cards (set of 5)	2·50	7·00 ☐ ☐
		Set of 5 Gutter Pairs	9·50	☐

Collectors Pack 1989

1989 (14 Nov.) *Comprises Nos. 1419/22, 1428/43 and 1453/66*
Collectors Pack . . . . 42·00 ☐

Post Office Yearbook

1989 (14 Nov.) *Comprises Nos. 1419/22, 1428/44 and 1453/66 in hardback book with slip case*
Yearbook . . . . 42·00 ☐

929 Queen Victoria and Queen Elizabeth II

150th Anniversary of the Penny Black

1990 (10 JAN.–17 APR.) (*a*) *Printed in photogravure by Harrison and Sons (Nos. 1468, 1470, 1472 from booklets only). Perf 15 × 14*

1467	**929**	15p bright blue (1 centre band)	70	70 ☐ ☐
1468		15p bright blue (1 side band) (30 Jan.)	3·75	3·50 ☐ ☐
1469		20p brownish black and cream (phosphorised paper)	70	70 ☐ ☐
1470		20p brownish black and cream (2 bands) (30 Jan.)	3·00	3·00 ☐ ☐
1471		29p deep mauve (phosphorised paper)	1·75	1·75 ☐ ☐
1472		29p deep mauve (2 bands) (20 Mar.)	8·00	8·00 ☐ ☐
1473		34p deep bluish grey (phosphorised paper)	2·00	2·00 ☐ ☐
1474		37p rosine (phosphorised paper)	2·10	2·25 ☐ ☐
		Set of 5 (Nos. 1467, 1469, 1471, 1473/4)	6·50	6·50 ☐ ☐
		First Day Cover (Nos. 1467, 1469, 1471, 1473/4)		7·00 ☐
		Presentation Pack (Nos. 1467, 1469, 1471, 1473/4)	9·00	☐

(*b*) *Litho Walsall (booklets). Perf* 14 (30 Jan.)

1475	**929**	15p bright blue (1 centre band)	1·50	1·60 ☐ ☐
1476		20p brownish black and cream (phosphorised paper)	1·50	1·60 ☐ ☐

(*c*) *Litho Questa (booklets). Perf* 15 × 14 (17 Apr.)

1477	**929**	15p bright blue (1 centre band)	2·25	2·25 ☐ ☐
1478		20p brownish black (phosphorised paper)	1·75	2·00 ☐ ☐

No. 1468 exists with the phosphor band at the left or right of the stamp.

For Type **929** redrawn with "1st" face value see No. 2133.

930 Kitten

931 Rabbit

932 Duckling

933 Puppy

150th Anniversary of Royal Society for Prevention of Cruelty to Animals

1990 (23 JAN.) *Phosphorised paper. Perf* 14 × 14½

1479	**930**	20p multicoloured	75	15	☐	☐
1480	**931**	29p multicoloured	1·40	1·40	☐	☐
1481	**932**	34p multicoloured	1·60	1·60	☐	☐
1482	**933**	37p multicoloured	1·75	1·75	☐	☐
		Set of 4	5·00	4·50	☐	☐
		First Day Cover		5·00		☐
		Presentation Pack	5·50		☐	
		PHQ Cards (set of 4)	2·50	8·00	☐	☐
		Set of 4 Gutter Pairs	10·00		☐	

934 Teddy Bear

935 Dennis the Menace

936 Punch

937 Cheshire Cat

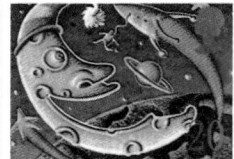

938 The Man in the Moon

939 The Laughing Policeman

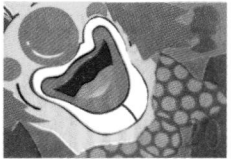

940 Clown

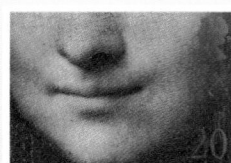

941 Mona Lisa

942 Queen of Hearts

943 Stan Laurel (comedian)

T **934/43** were printed together, *se-tenant,* in booklet panes of 10.

Greetings Booklet Stamps. 'Smiles'

1990 (6 FEB.) *Two phosphor bands*

1483	**934**	20p multicoloured	3·50	2·50	☐	☐
		a. Booklet pane. Nos.				
		1483/92	30·00		☐	
1484	**935**	20p multicoloured	3·50	2·50	☐	☐
1485	**936**	20p multicoloured	3·50	2·50	☐	☐
1486	**937**	20p multicoloured	3·50	2·50	☐	☐
1487	**938**	20p multicoloured	3·50	2·50	☐	☐
1488	**939**	20p multicoloured	3·50	2·50	☐	☐
1489	**940**	20p multicoloured	3·50	2·50	☐	☐
1490	**941**	20p multicoloured	3·50	2·50	☐	☐
1491	**942**	20p multicoloured	3·50	2·50	☐	☐
1492	**943**	20p gold and grey-black .	3·50	2·50	☐	☐
		Set of 10	30·00	22·00	☐	☐
		First Day Cover		25·00		☐

For these designs with the face value expressed as '1st' see Nos. 1550/9.

For full information on all future British issues, collectors should write to Royal Mail, Freepost EH3647, 21 South Gyle Crescent, Edinburgh EH12 9PE.

944 Alexandra Palace ('Stamp World London 90' Exhibition)

945 Glasgow School of Art

946 British Philatelic Bureau, Edinburgh

947 Templeton Carpet Factory, Glasgow

Europa (*Nos. 1493 and 1495*) *and 'Glasgow* 1990 *European City of Culture'* (*Nos. 1494 and 1496*)

1990 (6 MAR.) *Phosphorised paper*

1493	**944**	20p multicoloured	60	20	☐	☐
1494	**945**	20p multicoloured	60	20	☐	☐
1495	**946**	29p multicoloured	1·40	1·60	☐	☐
1496	**947**	37p multicoloured	1·50	1·60	☐	☐
		Set of 4	3·75	3·25	☐	☐
		First Day Cover		4·00		☐
		Presentation Pack	4·25		☐	
		PHQ Cards (set of 4)	2·50	6·50	☐	☐
		Set of 4 Gutter Pairs	7·50		☐	

948 Export Achievement Award

949 Technological Achievement Award

Nos. 1497/8 and 1499/500 were each printed together, *se-tenant*, in horizontal pairs throughout the sheets.

25th Anniversary of Queen's Awards for Export and Technology

1990 (10 APR.) *Phosphorised paper. Perf* 14 × 14½

1497	**948**	20p multicoloured	70	45	☐	☐
		a. Horiz pair. Nos. 1497/8	1·40	1·60	☐	☐
1498	**949**	20p multicoloured	70	45	☐	☐
1499	**948**	37p multicoloured	1·25	1·25	☐	☐
		a. Horiz pair. Nos. 1499/1500	2·50	3·25	☐	☐
1500	**949**	37p multicoloured	1·25	1·25	☐	☐
		Set of 4	3·50	3·00	☐	☐
		First Day Cover		4·00		☐
		Presentation Pack	5·00		☐	
		PHQ Cards (set of 4)	2·50	6·50	☐	☐
		Set of 2 Gutter Strips of 4 . . .	7·50		☐	

949a

'Stamp World 90' International Stamp Exhibition, London

1990 (3 MAY) *Sheet* 122 × 90 *mm. Phosphorised paper*

MS1501	**949a**	20p brownish black and cream	4·75	5·00	☐	☐
		First Day Cover		5·50		☐
		Souvenir Book (Nos. 1467, 1469, 1471, 1473/4 and MS1501 . .	22·00		☐	

No. **MS**1501 was sold at £1, the premium being used for the exhibition.

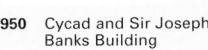

950 Cycad and Sir Joseph Banks Building

951 Stone Pine and Princess of Wales Conservatory

952 Willow Tree and Palm House

953 Cedar Tree and Pagoda

957 Elizabeth, Duchess of York

958 Lady Elizabeth Bowes-Lyon

150th Anniversary of Kew Gardens
1990 (5 JUNE) *Phosphorised paper*

1502	**950**	20p multicoloured	55	15	□	□
1503	**951**	29p multicoloured	90	1·00	□	□
1504	**952**	34p multicoloured	1·40	1·60	□	□
1505	**953**	37p multicoloured	1·60	1·50	□	□
		Set of 4	4·00	3·75	□	□
		First Day Cover		4·50		□
		Presentation Pack	4·50		□	
		PHQ Cards (set of 4)	2·50	6·50	□	□
		Set of 4 Gutter Pairs	8·50		□	

90th Birthday of Queen Elizabeth the Queen Mother
1990 (2 AUG.) *Phosphorised paper*

1507	**955**	20p multicoloured	95	20	□	□
1508	**956**	29p silver, indigo and grey-blue	1·40	1·25	□	□
1509	**957**	34p multicoloured	2·00	1·90	□	□
1510	**958**	37p silver, sepia and stone	2·25	2·00	□	□
		Set of 4	6·00	5·00	□	□
		First Day Cover		6·50		□
		Presentation Pack	7·00		□	
		PHQ Cards (set of 4)	4·75	7·50	□	□
		Set of 4 Gutter Pairs	12·00		□	

For these designs with Queen's head and frame in black see Nos. 2280/3.

954 Thomas Hardy and Clyffe Clump, Dorset

150th Birth Anniversary of Thomas Hardy (author)
1990 (10 JULY) *Phosphorised paper*

1506	**954**	20p multicoloured	80	50	□	□
		First Day Cover		1·40		□
		Presentation Pack	1·40		□	
		PHQ Card	1·00	2·00	□	□
		Gutter Pair	1·75		□	

Booklet Stamps
1990 (7 AUG.)–**92** *As Types* **913/14,** *but colours changed*

(a) Photo Harrison. Perf 15 × 14

1511	**913**	(2nd) deep blue (1 centre band)	1·25	1·25	□	□
1512	**914**	(1st) bright orange-red (phosphorised paper)	1·10	1·10	□	□

(b) Litho Questa. Perf 15 × 14

1513	**913**	(2nd) deep blue (1 centre band)	2·75	2·50	□	□
1514	**914**	(1st) bright orange-red (phosphorised paper)	90	1·00	□	□
1514a		(1st) bright orange-red (2 bands) (25.2.92) . . .	2·75	2·25	□	□

(c) Litho Walsall. Perf 14

1515	**913**	(2nd) deep blue (1 centre band)	80	80	□	□
1516	**914**	(1st) bright orange-red (phosphorised paper)	80	90	□	□
		c. Perf 13	2·50	3·00	□	□
		First Day Cover (Nos. 1515/16) .		5·00		□

For similar stamps with elliptical perforations see Nos. 1663a/6.

955 Queen Elizabeth the Queen Mother

956 Queen Elizabeth

For full information on all future British issues, collectors should write to Royal Mail, Freepost EH3647, 21 South Gyle Crescent, Edinburgh EH12 9PE.

959 Victoria Cross

960 George Cross

961 Distinguished Service Cross and Distinguished Service Medal

962 Military Cross and Military Medal

963 Distinguished Flying Cross and Distinguished Flying Medal

Gallantry Awards

1990 (11 SEPT.) *Phosphorised paper*

1517	959	20p multicoloured	80	60	☐	☐
1518	960	20p multicoloured	80	60	☐	☐
1519	961	20p multicoloured	80	60	☐	☐
1520	962	20p multicoloured	80	60	☐	☐
1521	963	20p multicoloured	80	60	☐	☐
		Set of 5	3·75	2·75	☐	☐
		First Day Cover		3·00		☐
		Presentation Pack	4·50		☐	
		PHQ Cards (set of 5)	3·00	7·50	☐	☐
		Set of 5 *Gutter Pairs*	8·00		☐	

964 Armagh Observatory, Jodrell Bank Radio Telescope and La Palma Telescope

965 Newton's Moon and Tides Diagram with Early Telescopes

966 Greenwich Old Observatory and Early Astronomical Equipment

967 Stonehenge, Gyroscope and Navigating by Stars

Astronomy

1990 (16 OCT.) *Phosphorised paper. Perf* 14 × 14½

1522	964	22p multicoloured	65	15	☐	☐
1523	965	26p multicoloured	1·00	1·10	☐	☐
1524	966	31p multicoloured	1·25	1·40	☐	☐
1525	967	37p multicoloured	1·50	1·40	☐	☐
		Set of 4	4·00	3·75	☐	☐
		First Day Cover		4·50		☐
		Presentation Pack	4·50		☐	
		PHQ Cards (set of 4)	2·50	7·00	☐	☐
		Set of 4 *Gutter Pairs*	8·50		☐	

Nos. 1522/5 commemorate the centenary of the British Astronomical Association and the bicentenary of the Armagh Observatory.

968 Building a Snowman

969 Fetching the Christmas Tree

970 Carol Singing

971 Tobogganing

972 Ice-skating

Christmas

1990 (13 Nov.) *One phosphor band (17p) or phosphorised paper (others)*

1526	**968**	17p multicoloured	50	15	☐	☐
1527	**969**	22p multicoloured	70	20	☐	☐
1528	**970**	26p multicoloured	95	1·10	☐	☐
1529	**971**	31p multicoloured	1·25	1·50	☐	☐
1530	**972**	37p multicoloured	1·40	1·50	☐	☐
		Set of 5	4·50	4·00	☐	☐
		First Day Cover		4·50		☐
		Presentation Pack	5·00		☐	
		PHQ Cards (set of 5)	3·25	7·00	☐	☐
		Set of 5 Gutter Pairs	9·00		☐	

Collectors Pack 1990

1990 (13 Nov.) *Comprises Nos. 1479/82, 1493/1510 and 1517/30*

Collectors Pack . . . . 55·00   ☐

Post Office Yearbook

1990 *Comprises Nos. 1479/82, 1493/1500, 1502/10 and 1517/30 in hardback book with slip case*

Yearbook . . . . 55·00   ☐

973 'King Charles Spaniel'   **974** 'A Pointer'

975 'Two Hounds in a Landscape'   **976** 'A Rough Dog'

977 'Fino and Tiny'

Dogs. Paintings by George Stubbs

1991 (8 JAN.) *Phosphorised paper. Perf 14 × 14½*

1531	**973**	22p multicoloured	85	15	☐	☐
1532	**974**	26p multicoloured	1·10	1·25	☐	☐
1533	**975**	31p multicoloured	1·25	1·25	☐	☐
1534	**976**	33p multicoloured	1·40	1·40	☐	☐
1535	**977**	37p multicoloured	1·50	1·40	☐	☐
		Set of 5	5·50	5·00	☐	☐
		First Day Cover		5·25		☐
		Presentation Pack	6·00		☐	
		PHQ Cards (set of 5)	3·50	7·00	☐	☐
		Set of 5 Gutter Pairs	11·00		☐	

978 Thrush's Nest   **979** Shooting Star and Rainbow

980 Magpies and Charm Bracelet   **981** Black Cat

982 Common Kingfisher with Key   **983** Mallard and Frog

984 Four-leaf Clover in Boot and Match Box   **985** Pot of Gold at End of Rainbow

986 Heart-shaped Butterflies   **987** Wishing Well and Sixpence

T **978/87** were printed together, *se-tenant*, in booklet panes of 10 stamps and 12 half stamp-size labels, the backgrounds of the stamps forming a composite design.

Greetings Booklet Stamps. 'Good Luck'

1991 (5 FEB.) *Two phosphor bands*

1536	**978**	(1st) multicoloured	1·90	1·90	☐	☐
		a. Booklet pane. Nos.				
		1536/45	17·00		☐	
1537	**979**	(1st) multicoloured	1·90	1·90	☐	☐
1538	**980**	(1st) multicoloured	1·90	1·90	☐	☐
1539	**981**	(1st) multicoloured	1·90	1·90	☐	☐
1540	**982**	(1st) multicoloured	1·90	1·90	☐	☐
1541	**983**	(1st) multicoloured	1·90	1·90	☐	☐
1542	**984**	(1st) multicoloured	1·90	1·90	☐	☐
1543	**985**	(1st) multicoloured	1·90	1·90	☐	☐
1544	**986**	(1st) multicoloured	1·90	1·90	☐	☐
1545	**987**	(1st) multicoloured	1·90	1·90	☐	☐
		Set of 10	17·00	17·00	☐	☐
		First Day Cover		19·00		☐

988 Michael Faraday (inventor of electric motor) (Birth Bicentenary)	**989** Charles Babbage (computer science pioneer) (Birth Bicentenary)

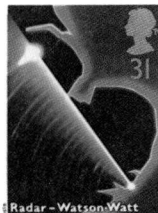 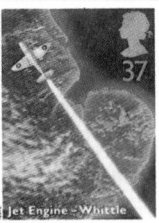

990 Radar Sweep of East Anglia (50th Anniv of Discovery by Sir Robert Watson-Watt)	**991** Gloster Whittle E28/39 Aircraft over East Anglia (50th Anniv of First Flight of Sir Frank Whittle's Jet Engine

Scientific Achievements

1991 (5 MAR.) *Phosphorised paper*

1546	**988**	22p multicoloured	50	15	☐	☐
1547	**989**	22p multicoloured	50	15	☐	☐
1548	**990**	31p multicoloured	95	1·10	☐	☐
1549	**991**	37p multicoloured	1·10	1·50	☐	☐
		Set of 4	2·75	2·50	☐	☐
		First Day Cover		3·50		☐
		Presentation Pack	3·75		☐	
		PHQ Cards (set of 4)	3·00	6·50	☐	☐
		Set of 4 Gutter Pairs	5·50		☐	

992 Teddy Bear

Nos. 1550/9 were originally printed together, *se-tenant*, in booklet panes of 10 stamps and 12 half stamp-size labels.

Greetings Booklet Stamps. 'Smiles'

1991 (26 MAR.) *As Nos. 1483/92, but inscribed '1st' as T 992. Two phosphor bands. Perf 15 × 14*

1550	**992**	(1st) multicoloured	1·25	1·50	☐	☐
		a. Booklet pane. Nos.				
		1550/9	11·00		☐	
1551	**935**	(1st) multicoloured	1·25	1·50	☐	☐
1552	**936**	(1st) multicoloured	1·25	1·50	☐	☐
1553	**937**	(1st) multicoloured	1·25	1·50	☐	☐
1554	**938**	(1st) multicoloured	1·25	1·50	☐	☐
1555	**939**	(1st) multicoloured	1·25	1·50	☐	☐
1556	**940**	(1st) multicoloured	1·25	1·50	☐	☐
1557	**941**	(1st) multicoloured	1·25	1·50	☐	☐
1558	**942**	(1st) multicoloured	1·25	1·50	☐	☐
1559	**943**	(1st) multicoloured	1·25	1·50	☐	☐
		Set of 10	11·00	13·50	☐	☐
		First Day Cover		14·00		☐

The stamps were re-issued in sheets of 10 each with *se-tenant* label on 22 May 2000 in connection with 'customised' stamps available at 'Stamp Show 2000'. The labels show either a pattern of ribbons or a personal photograph.

A similar sheet, but in lithography instead of photogravure, and perforated $14\frac{1}{2} \times 14$, appeared on 3 July 2001 with the labels showing either greetings or a personal photograph.

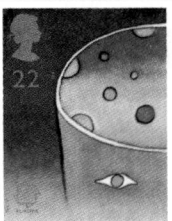 

993 Man looking at Space	**994**

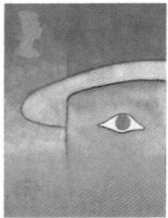

995 Space looking at Man **996**

Nos. 1560/1 and 1562/3 were each printed together, *se-tenant*, in horizontal pairs throughout the sheets, each pair forming a composite design.

Europa. Europe in Space
1991 (23 APR.) *Phosphorised paper*

1560	993	22p multicoloured	75	50	□	□
		a. Horiz pair. Nos. 1560/1	1·50	1·50	□	□
1561	994	22p multicoloured	75	50	□	□
1562	995	37p multicoloured	2·00	1·40	□	□
		a. Horiz pair. Nos. 1562/3	4·00	2·75	□	□
1563	996	37p multicoloured	2·00	1·40	□	□
		Set of 4	5·00	3·25	□	□
		First Day Cover		4·00		□
		Presentation Pack	5·50		□	
		PHQ Cards (set of 4)	3·00	6·50	□	□
		Set of 2 Gutter Strips of 4 . . .	10·00		□	

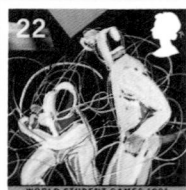

997 Fencing **998** Hurdling

999 Diving **1000** Rugby

World Student Games, Sheffield (Nos. 1564/6) and World Cup Rugby Championship, London (No. 1567)
1991 (11 JUNE) *Phosphorised paper. Perf* 14½ × 14

1564	997	22p multicoloured	60	20	□	□
1565	998	26p multicoloured	1·00	1·00	□	□
1566	999	31p multicoloured	1·25	1·25	□	□
1567	1000	37p multicoloured	1·50	1·50	□	□
		Set of 4	4·00	3·50	□	□
		First Day Cover		3·75		□
		Presentation Pack	4·25		□	
		PHQ Cards (set of 4)	2·50	6·50	□	□
		Set of 4 Gutter Pairs	8·00		□	

1001 'Silver Jubilee' **1002** 'Mme Alfred Carrière'

1003 Rosa moyesii **1004** 'Harvest Fayre'

1005 'Mutabilis'

9th World Congress of Roses, Belfast
1991 (16 JULY) *Phosphorised paper. Perf* 14½ × 14

1568	1001	22p multicoloured	95	20	□	□
1569	1002	26p multicoloured	1·10	1·25	□	□
1570	1003	31p multicoloured	1·25	1·25	□	□
1571	1004	33p multicoloured	1·50	1·50	□	□
1572	1005	37p multicoloured	1·60	1·50	□	□
		Set of 5	5·75	5·00	□	□
		First Day Cover		6·25		□
		Presentation Pack	6·25		□	
		PHQ Cards (set of 5)	3·00	8·50	□	□
		Set of 5 Gutter Pairs	11·50		□	

1006 Iguanodon

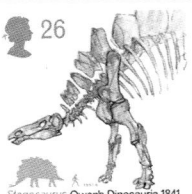

1007 Stegosaurus

1008 Tyrannosaurus

1009 Protoceratops

1010 Triceratops

150th Anniversary of Dinosaurs' Identification by Owen

1991 (20 Aug.) *Phosphorised paper. Perf* $14\frac{1}{2} \times 14$

1573	**1006**	22p multicoloured	90		20	☐	☐
1574	**1007**	26p multicoloured	1·10		1·25	☐	☐
1575	**1008**	31p multicoloured	1·25		1·25	☐	☐
1576	**1009**	33p multicoloured	1·50		1·50	☐	☐
1577	**1010**	37p multicoloured	1·60		1·50	☐	☐
		Set of 5	5·75		5·00	☐	☐
		First Day Cover			6·00		☐
		Presentation Pack	6·50			☐	
		PHQ Cards (*set of* 5)	3·25		8·50	☐	☐
		Set of 5 *Gutter Pairs*	11·50			☐	

1011 Map of 1816

1012 Map of 1906

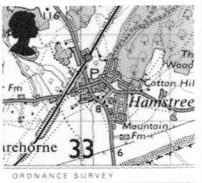

1013 Map of 1959

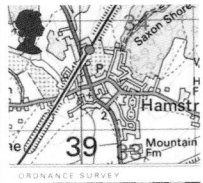

1014 Map of 1991

Bicentenary of Ordnance Survey. Maps of Hamstreet, Kent

1991 (17 Sept.) *Phosphorised paper. Perf* $14\frac{1}{2} \times 14$

1578	**1011**	24p multicoloured	60		20	☐	☐
1579	**1012**	28p multicoloured	1·00		95	☐	☐
1580	**1013**	33p multicoloured	1·25		1·40	☐	☐
1581	**1014**	39p multicoloured	1·50		1·40	☐	☐
		Set of 4	4·00		3·50	☐	☐
		First Day Cover			4·25		☐
		Presentation Pack	4·50			☐	
		PHQ Cards (*set of* 4)	3·00		6·00	☐	☐
		Set of 4 Gutter Pairs	8·50			☐	

1015 Adoration of the Magi

1016 Mary and Baby Jesus in Stable

1017 Holy Family and Angel

1018 The Annunciation

1019 The Flight into Egypt

Christmas. Illuminated Manuscripts from the Bodleian Library, Oxford

1991 (12 Nov.) *One phosphor band* (18p) *or phosphorised paper* (*others*)

1582	**1015**	18p multicoloured	75	10	☐	☐
1583	**1016**	24p multicoloured	90	10	☐	☐
1584	**1017**	28p multicoloured	95	1·25	☐	☐
1585	**1018**	33p multicoloured	1·10	1·40	☐	☐
1586	**1019**	39p multicoloured	1·25	1·60	☐	☐
		Set of 5	4·50	4·00	☐	☐
		First Day Cover		5·00		☐
		Presentation Pack	5·00		☐	
		PHQ Cards (*set of 5*)	3·00	7·50	☐	☐
		Set of 5 Gutter Pairs	8·50		☐	

Collectors Pack 1991

1991 (12 Nov.) *Comprises Nos. 1531/5, 1546/9 and 1560/86*

Collectors Pack . . . . 55·00   ☐

Post Office Yearbook

1991 *Comprises Nos. 1531/5, 1546/9 and 1560/86 in hardback book with slip case*

Yearbook . . . . 60·00   ☐

1020 Fallow Deer in Scottish Forest

1021 Hare on North Yorkshire Moors

1022 Fox in the Fens

1023 Redwing and Home Counties Village

1024 Welsh Mountain Sheep in Snowdonia

The Four Seasons. Wintertime

1992 (14 Jan.) *One phosphor band* (18p) *or phosphorised paper* (*others*)

1587	**1020**	18p multicoloured	50	15	☐	☐
1588	**1021**	24p multicoloured	70	20	☐	☐
1589	**1022**	28p multicoloured	90	1·10	☐	☐
1590	**1023**	33p multicoloured	1·10	1·40	☐	☐
1591	**1024**	39p multicoloured	1·25	1·60	☐	☐
		Set of 5	4·00	4·00	☐	☐
		First Day Cover		4·75		☐
		Presentation Pack	4·75		☐	
		PHQ Cards (*set of 5*)	3·00	8·00	☐	☐
		Set of 5 Gutter Pairs	8·50		☐	

1025 Flower Spray

1026 Double Locket

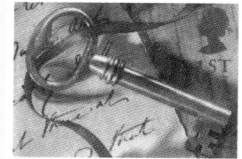

1027 Key

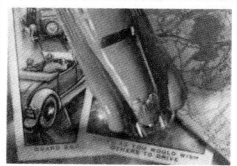

1028 Model Car and Cigarette Cards

1029 Compass and Map

1030 Pocket Watch

1031 1854 1d. Red Stamp and Pen

1032 Pearl Necklace

1033   Marbles

1034   Bucket, Spade and
       Starfish

T **1025/34** were printed together, *se-tenant*, in booklet panes of 10 stamps and 12 half stamp-size labels, the backgrounds of the stamps forming a composite design.

Greetings Stamps. 'Memories'

1992 (28 JAN.) *Two phosphor bands*

1592	**1025**	(1st) multicoloured	1·10	1·10	☐	☐
		a. Booklet pane. Nos.				
		1592/1601	10·00		☐	
1593	**1026**	(1st) multicoloured	1·10	1·10	☐	☐
1594	**1027**	(1st) multicoloured	1·10	1·10	☐	☐
1595	**1028**	(1st) multicoloured	1·10	1·10	☐	☐
1596	**1029**	(1st) multicoloured	1·10	1·10	☐	☐
1597	**1030**	(1st) multicoloured	1·10	1·10	☐	☐
1598	**1031**	(1st) multicoloured	1·10	1·10	☐	☐
1599	**1032**	(1st) multicoloured	1·10	1·10	☐	☐
1600	**1033**	(1st) multicoloured	1·10	1·10	☐	☐
1601	**1034**	(1st) multicoloured	1·10	1·10	☐	☐
		Set of 10	10·00	10·00	☐	☐
		First Day Cover		12·00		☐
		Presentation Pack	16·00		☐	

1035   Queen Elizabeth in
       Coronation Robes and
       Parliamentary Emblem

1036   Queen Elizabeth in
       Garter Robes and
       Archiepiscopal Arms

1037   Queen Elizabeth with
       Baby Prince Andrew and
       Royal Arms

1038   Queen Elizabeth at
       Trooping the Colour
       and Service Emblems

1039   Queen Elizabeth and
       Commonwealth Emblem

Nos. 1602/6 were printed together, *se-tenant*, in horizontal strips of 5 throughout the sheet.

40th Anniversary of Accession

1992 (6 FEB.) *Two phosphor bands. Perf* 14½ × 14

1602	**1035**	24p multicoloured	1·10	1·00	☐	☐
		a. *Horiz strip of* 5. *Nos.*				
		1602/6	6·00	7·00	☐	
1603	**1036**	24p multicoloured	1·10	1·00	☐	☐
1604	**1037**	24p multicoloured	1·10	1·00	☐	☐
1605	**1038**	24p multicoloured	1·10	1·00	☐	☐
1606	**1039**	24p multicoloured	1·10	1·00	☐	☐
		Set of 5	6·00	4·50	☐	☐
		First Day Cover		7·00		☐
		Presentation Pack	7·00		☐	
		PHQ Cards (set of 5)	3·50	7·50	☐	☐
		Gutter Block of 10	12·00		☐	

1040   Tennyson in 1888
       and 'The Beguiling
       of Merlin' (Sir Edward
       Burne-Jones)

1041   Tennyson in 1856
       and 'April Love'
       (Arthur Hughes)

1042   Tennyson in 1864
       and 'I am Sick of
       the Shadows'
       (John Waterhouse)

1043   Tennyson as a Young
       Man and 'Mariana'
       (Dante Gabriel Rossetti)

Death Centenary of Alfred, Lord Tennyson (poet)

1992 (10 MAR.) *Phosphorised paper. Perf* 14½ × 14

1607	**1040**	24p multicoloured	60	20 □ □
1608	**1041**	28p multicoloured	85	85 □ □
1609	**1042**	33p multicoloured	1·40	1·60 □ □
1610	**1043**	39p multicoloured	1·50	1·60 □ □
		Set of 4	4·00	3·75 □ □
		First Day Cover		4·25 □
		Presentation Pack	4·50	□
		PHQ Cards (set of 4)	2·50	6·50 □ □
		Set of 4 Gutter Pairs	8·50	□

£1

CARRICKFERGUS CASTLE

1044 Carrickfergus Castle

1992 (24 MAR.)–**95.** *Designs as Nos. 1410/13, but showing Queen's head in silhouette as T* **1044.** *Perf* 15 × 14 *(with one elliptical hole on each vertical side)*

1611	**1044**	£1 bottle green and gold†	5·50	1·00 □ □
1612	**880**	£1·50 maroon and gold†	5·00	1·00 □ □
1613	**881**	£2 indigo and gold† . . .	6·75	1·00 □ □
1613a	**1044**	£3 reddish violet and gold†	20·00	3·00 □ □
1614	**882**	£5 deep brown and gold†	17·00	3·00 □ □
		Set of 5	48·00	8·00 □ □
		First Day Cover (Nos. 1611/13, 1614)		35·00 □
		First Day Cover (22 Aug. 1995) (No. 1613a)		10·00 □
		Presentation Pack (P.O. Pack No. 27) (Nos. 1611/13, 1614) . . .	38·00	□
		Presentation Pack (P.O. Pack No. 33) (No. 1613a)	20·00	□
		PHQ Cards (Nos. 1611/14) . . .	4·00	□
		PHQ Card (No. 1613a)	2·00	16·00 □ □
		Set of 5 Gutter Pairs	95·00	□

†The Queen's head on these stamps is printed in optically variable ink which changes colour from gold to green when viewed from different angles.

PHQ cards for Nos. 1611/13 and 1614 were not issued until 16 February 1993.

Nos. 1611/14 were printed by Harrison. For stamps with different lettering by Enschedé see Nos. 1993/6.

For full information on all future British issues, collectors should write to Royal Mail, Freepost EH3647, 21 South Gyle Crescent, Edinburgh EH12 9PE.

1045 British Olympic Association Logo (Olympic Games, Barcelona)

1046 British Paralympic Association Symbol (Paralympics '92, Barcelona)

1047 *Santa Maria* (500th Anniv of Discovery of America by Columbus)

1048 *Kaisei* (Japanese cadet brigantine) (Grand Regatta Columbus, 1992)

1049 British Pavilion, 'EXPO 92', Seville

Nos. 1615/16 were printed together, *se-tenant,* in horizontal pairs throughout the sheet.

Europa. International Events

1992 (7 APR.) *Phosphorised paper. Perf* 14 × 14½

1615	**1045**	24p multicoloured	1·00	60 □ □
		a. Horiz pair. Nos. 1615/16	2·25	1·75 □ □
1616	**1046**	24p multicoloured	1·00	60 □ □
1617	**1047**	24p multicoloured	1·00	50 □ □
1618	**1048**	39p multicoloured	1·25	1·25 □ □
1619	**1049**	39p multicoloured	1·40	1·25 □ □
		Set of 5	5·25	3·75 □ □
		First Day Cover		5·25 □
		Presentation Pack	5·75	□
		PHQ Cards (set of 5)	3·00	6·50 □ □
		Set of 3 Gutter Pairs and a Gutter Strip of 4	10·50	□

1050   Pikeman

1051   Drummer

1052   Musketeer

1053   Standard Bearer

350th Anniversary of the Civil War

1992 (16 JUNE) *Phosphorised paper. Perf* 14½ × 14

1620	**1050**	24p multicoloured	60	20	□	□
1621	**1051**	28p multicoloured	85	85	□	□
1622	**1052**	33p multicoloured	1·40	1·40	□	□
1623	**1053**	39p multicoloured	1·50	1·50	□	□
	Set of 4		4·00	3·50	□	□
	First Day Cover			4·25		□
	Presentation Pack		4·50		□	
	PHQ Cards (set of 4)		2·50	6·00	□	□
	Set of 4 Gutter Pairs		8·00		□	

1054   *The Yeomen of the Guard*

1055   *The Gondoliers*

1056   *The Mikado*

1057   *The Pirates of Penzance*

1058   *Iolanthe*

150th Birth Anniversary of Sir Arthur Sullivan (composer). Gilbert and Sullivan Operas

1992 (21 JULY) *One phosphor band* (18p) *or phosphorised paper* (others). *Perf* 14½ × 14

1624	**1054**	18p multicoloured	50	20	□	□
1625	**1055**	24p multicoloured	80	20	□	□
1626	**1056**	28p multicoloured	95	1·00	□	□
1627	**1057**	33p multicoloured	1·50	1·60	□	□
1628	**1058**	39p multicoloured	1·60	1·60	□	□
	Set of 5		4·75	4·25	□	□
	First Day Cover			5·00		□
	Presentation Pack		5·25		□	
	PHQ Cards (set of 5)		3·00	6·00	□	□
	Set of 5 Gutter Pairs		9·50		□	

1059   'Acid Rain Kills'

1060   'Ozone Layer'

1061   'Greenhouse Effect'

1062   'Bird of Hope'

Protection of the Environment. Children's Paintings

1992 (15 SEPT.) *Phosphorised paper. Perf* 14 × 14½

1629	**1059**	24p multicoloured	70	20	□	□
1630	**1060**	28p multicoloured	1·10	1·10	□	□
1631	**1061**	33p multicoloured	1·25	1·25	□	□
1632	**1062**	39p multicoloured	1·40	1·25	□	□
	Set of 4		4·00	3·50	□	□
	First Day Cover			4·50		□
	Presentation Pack		4·75		□	
	PHQ Cards (set of 4)		2·50	5·50	□	□
	Set of 4 Gutter Pairs		8·00		□	

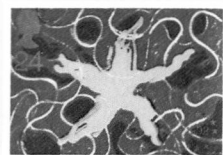

1063 European Star

Single European Market

1992 (13 Oct.) *Phosphorised paper*

1633	**1063**	24p multicoloured		90	80	□	□
		First Day Cover			1·90		□
		Presentation Pack		1·90		□	
		PHQ Card		90	3·50	□	□
		Gutter Pair		2·00		□	

1064 'Angel Gabriel', St James's, Pangbourne

1065 'Madonna and Child', St. Mary's, Bibury

1066 'King with Gold', Our Lady and St Peter, Leatherhead

1067 'Shepherds', All Saints, Porthcawl

1068 'Kings with Frankincense and Myrrh', Our Lady and St Peter, Leatherhead

Christmas. Stained Glass Windows

1992 (10 Nov.) *One phosphor band (18p) or phosphorised paper (others)*

1634	**1064**	18p multicoloured		45	15	□	□
1635	**1065**	24p multicoloured		75	15	□	□
1636	**1066**	28p multicoloured		90	1·10	□	□
1637	**1067**	33p multicoloured		1·10	1·50	□	□
1638	**1068**	39p multicoloured		1·25	1·40	□	□
		Set of 5		4·00	4·00	□	□
		First Day Cover			5·00		□
		Presentation Pack		4·75		□	
		PHQ Cards (set of 5)		3·00	7·50	□	□
		Set of 5 Gutter Pairs		8·00		□	

Collectors Pack 1992

1992 (10 Nov.) *Comprises Nos. 1587/91, 1602/10 and 1615/38*

Collectors Pack . . . . 55·00 □

Post Office Yearbook

1992 (11 Nov.) *Comprises Nos. 1587/91, 1602/10 and 1615/38 in hardback book with slip case*

Yearbook . . . . 60·00 □

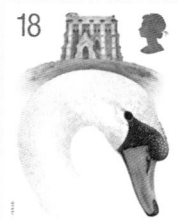

1069 Mute Swan Cob and St Catherine's, Abbotsbury

1070 Cygnet and Decoy

1071 Swans and Cygnet

1072 Eggs in Nest and Tithe Barn, Abbotsbury

1073 Young Swan and the Fleet

600th Anniversary of Abbotsbury Swannery

1993 (19 Jan.) *One phosphor band* (18p) *or phosphorised paper* (*others*)

1639	**1069**	18p multicoloured	1·50	25	☐	☐
1640	**1070**	24p multicoloured	1·40	25	☐	☐
1641	**1071**	28p multicoloured	1·60	1·75	☐	☐
1642	**1072**	33p multicoloured	2·25	2·40	☐	☐
1643	**1073**	39p multicoloured	2·40	2·40	☐	☐
		Set of 5	8·25	6·25	☐	☐
		First Day Cover		7·50		☐
		Presentation Pack	9·00		☐	
		PHQ Cards (set of 5)	3·00	8·50	☐	☐
		Set of 5 Gutter Pairs	17·00		☐	

1074 Long John Silver and Parrot (*Treasure Island*)

1075 Tweedledum and Tweedledee (*Alice Through the Looking-Glass*)

1076 William (*William* books)

1077 Mole and Toad (*The Wind in the Willows*)

1078 Teacher and Wilfrid ('The Bash Street Kids')

1079 Peter Rabbit and Mrs Rabbit (*The Tale of Peter Rabbit*)

1080 Snowman (*The Snowman*) and Father Christmas (*Father Christmas*)

1081 The Big Friendly Giant and Sophie (*The BFG*)

1082 Bill Badger and Rupert Bear

1083 Aladdin and the Genie

T **1074/83** were printed together, *se-tenant,* in booklet panes of 10 stamps and 20 half stamp-size labels.

Greetings Stamps. 'Gift Giving'

1993 (2 Feb.) *Two phosphor bands. Perf* 15 × 14 (*with one elliptical hole on each vertical side*)

1644	**1074**	(1st) multicoloured	1·10	1·10	☐	☐
		a. Booklet pane. Nos. 1644/53	10·00		☐	
1645	**1075**	(1st) gold, cream and black	1·10	1·10	☐	☐
1646	**1076**	(1st) multicoloured	1·10	1·10	☐	☐
1647	**1077**	(1st) multicoloured	1·10	1·10	☐	☐
1648	**1078**	(1st) multicoloured	1·10	1·10	☐	☐
1649	**1079**	(1st) multicoloured	1·10	1·10	☐	☐
1650	**1080**	(1st) multicoloured	1·10	1·10	☐	☐
1651	**1081**	(1st) multicoloured	1·10	1·10	☐	☐
1652	**1082**	(1st) multicoloured	1·10	1·10	☐	☐
1653	**1083**	(1st) multicoloured	1·10	1·10	☐	☐
		Set of 10	10·00	10·00	☐	☐
		First Day Cover		12·00		☐
		Presentation Pack	15·00		☐	
		PHQ Cards (set of 10)	7·00	20·00	☐	☐

1084 Decorated Enamel Dial

1085 Escapement, Remontoire and Fusee

1086 Balance, Spring and Temperature Compensator

1087 Back of Movement

300th Birth Anniversary of John Harrison (inventor of the marine chronometer). Details of 'H4' Clock

1993 (16 Feb.) Phosphorised paper. Perf 14½ × 14

1654	1084	24p multicoloured	. . .	60	20	☐	☐
1655	1085	28p multicoloured	. . .	1·00	1·10	☐	☐
1656	1086	33p multicoloured	. . .	1·40	1·25	☐	☐
1657	1087	39p multicoloured	. . .	1·50	1·40	☐	☐
		Set of 4	. . . .	4·00	3·50	☐	☐
		First Day Cover	. . . .		4·25		☐
		Presentation Pack	. . . .	4·25		☐	
		PHQ Cards (set of 4)	. . . . . .	2·50	7·50	☐	☐
		Set of 4 Gutter Pairs	. . . . . .	8·00		☐	

1088 Britannia

1993 (2 Mar.) Granite paper. Perf 14 × 14½ (with two elliptical holes on each horizontal side)

1658	1088	£10 multicoloured	. . . .	26·00	12·00	☐	☐
		First Day Cover	. . . .		22·00		☐
		Presentation Pack	. . . .	28·00		☐	
		PHQ Card	. . . .	2·50	30·00	☐	☐

1089 Dendrobium hellwigianum

1090 Paphiopedilum Maudiae 'Magnifcum'

1091 Cymbidium lowianum

1092 Vanda Rothschildiana

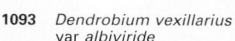

1093 Dendrobium vexillarius var albiviride

1093a

14th World Orchid Conference, Glasgow

1993 (16 Mar.) One phosphor band (18p) or phosphorised paper (others)

1659	1089	18p multicoloured	. . . .	45	20	☐	☐
1660	1090	24p multicoloured	. . . .	75	20	☐	☐
1661	1091	28p multicoloured	. . . .	1·00	1·10	☐	☐
1662	1092	33p multicoloured	. . . .	1·25	1·50	☐	☐
1663	1093	39p multicoloured	. . . .	1·60	1·40	☐	☐
		Set of 5	. . . .	4·50	4·00	☐	☐
		First Day Cover	. . . .		5·50		☐
		Presentation Pack	. . . .	5·50		☐	
		PHQ Cards (set of 5)	. . . . . .	3·00	7·50	☐	☐
		Set of 5 Gutter Pairs	. . . . . .	9·00		☐	

Booklet Stamps

1993 (6 Apr.)–99 As T 913/14 and 1093a, but Perf 14 (No. 1663b) or 15 × 14 (others) (both with one elliptical hole on each vertical side)

(a) Photo
    Harrison (No. 1664)
    Questa (Nos. 1663ab, 1664ab)
    Walsall (No. 1663b)
    Harrison (later De La Rue), Questa or Walsall (No. 1664a)
    Harrison (later De La Rue), Enschedé, Questa or Walsall (Nos. 1663a, 1664b)

1663a	913	(2nd) bright blue (1 centre band)	. . . .	30	35	☐	☐
		ab. Perf 14	1·00	1·00	☐	☐
1663b		(2nd) bright blue (1 side band)	. . . .	1·00	1·00	☐	☐
1664	914	(1st) bright orange-red (phosphorised paper)	1·75	1·25	☐	☐
1664a		(1st) bright orange-red (2 phosphor bands) . .	40	45	☐	☐
		ab. Perf 14	1·40	1·40	☐	☐
1664b	1093a	(E) deep blue (2 phosphor bands)	55	60	☐	☐

(b) Litho Questa or Walsall (No. 1666 also Enschedé)

1665	913	(2nd) bright blue (1 centre band)	. . . .	75	75	☐	☐
1666	914	(1st) bright orange-red (2 phosphor bands) . .	80	90	☐	☐
		First Day Cover (No. 1664b)				
		(19.1.99)		3·00		☐

Nos. 1663a, 1664a, 1664b and 1665/6 also come from sheets.

No. 1663b exists with the phosphor band at the left or right of the stamp and was only issued in booklets.

No. 1664*b* was valid for the basic European airmail rate, initially 30p.

For 1st in gold see Nos. 1979 and 2295.

For self-adhesive versions in these colours see Nos. 2039/40 and 2296.

1993–2002 As Nos. X841 *etc, but perf* 14 (*No.* Y1676) *or* 15 × 14 (*others*) (*both with one elliptical hole on each vertical side*)

(*a*) *Photo*

Enschedé:— 20p (Y1677), 29p, 35p (Y1688), 36p, 38p (Y1692), 41p (Y1696), 43p (Y1699)

Harrison (later De La Rue):— 7p, 8p, 20p (Y1679/80), 25p (Y1681), 33p, 35p (Y1689), 37p (Y1691a), 41p (Y1697/8), 42p, 43p (Y1700), 44p, 45p, 47p, 68p

Walsall:— 10p (Y1674a), 19p (Y1676), 38p (Y1693a), 43p (Y1700a)

Enschedé or Harrison (later De La Rue):— 4p, 5p, 6p, 10p (Y1674), 25p (Y1682), 31p, 39p, 50p, £1

Enschedé, Harrison (later De La Rue) or Questa:— 1p, 2p

Enschedé, Harrison (later De La Rue) or Walsall:— 30p, 37p (Y1691), 63p

Harrison (later De La Rue) or Questa:— 19p (Y1675), 20p (Y1678), 26p

De La Rue or Walsall:— 38p (Y1693), 40p, 64p, 65p

Y1667	**367**	1p crimson (2 bands) .	10	10	☐	☐
Y1668		2p deep green (2 bands)	10	10	☐	☐
Y1669		4p new blue (2 bands) .	10	10	☐	☐
Y1670		5p dull red-brown (2 bands)	10	10	☐	☐
Y1671		6p yellow-olive (2 bands)	25	25	☐	☐
Y1672		7p grey (2 bands)	30	25	☐	☐
Y1673		8p yellow (2 bands) . .	10	15	☐	☐
Y1674		10p dull orange (2 bands)	15	10	☐	☐
		a. Perf 14	1·90	2·00	☐	☐
Y1675		19p bistre (1 centre band)	30	35	☐	☐
Y1676		19p bistre (1 side band) .	2·00	2·00	☐	☐
Y1677		20p turquoise-green (2 bands)	90	90	☐	☐
Y1678		20p bright green (1 centre band)	70	70	☐	☐
Y1679		20p bright green (1 side band)	1·40	1·40	☐	☐
Y1680		20p bright green (2 bands)	30	35	☐	☐
Y1681		25p rose-red (phosphorised paper)	1·10	1·10	☐	☐
Y1682		25p rose-red (2 bands) .	1·10	1·10	☐	☐
Y1683		26p red-brown (2 bands)	1·00	1·00	☐	☐
Y1684		29p grey (2 bands)	1·25	1·25	☐	☐
Y1685		30p deep olive-grey (2 bands)	1·10	1·10	☐	☐
Y1686		31p deep mauve (2 bands)	1·10	1·10	☐	☐
Y1687		33p grey-green (2 bands)	50	55	☐	☐
Y1688		35p yellow (2 bands) . .	1·40	1·50	☐	☐
Y1689		35p yellow (phosphorised paper)	5·50	5·50	☐	☐
Y1690	**367**	36p bright ultramarine (2 bands)	1·50	1·50	☐	☐
Y1691		37p bright mauve (2 bands)	1·40	1·40	☐	☐
Y1691a		37p grey-black (2 bands)	60	65	☐	☐
Y1692		38p rosine (2 bands) . . .	1·50	1·50	☐	☐
Y1693		38p ultramarine (2 bands)	1·40	1·40	☐	☐
		a. Perf 14	3·75	3·75	☐	☐
Y1694		39p bright magenta (2 bands)	1·25	1·40	☐	☐
Y1695		40p deep azure (2 bands)	60	65	☐	☐
Y1696		41p grey-brown (2 bands)	1·40	1·25	☐	☐
Y1697		41p drab (phosphorised paper)	4·75	4·75	☐	☐
Y1698		41p rosine (2 bands) . . .	65	70	☐	☐
Y1698a		42p deep olive-grey (2 bands)	65	70	☐	☐
Y1699		43p deep olive-brown (2 bands)	2·00	2·00	☐	☐
Y1700		43p sepia (2 bands) . . .	1·75	1·75	☐	☐
		a. Perf 14	2·00	2·00	☐	☐
Y1701		44p grey-brown (2 bands)	2·00	2·00	☐	☐
Y1702		45p bright mauve (2 bands)	70	75	☐	☐
Y1702a		47p turquoise-green (2 bands)	75	80	☐	☐
Y1703		50p ochre (2 bands) . . .	75	80	☐	☐
Y1704		63p light emerald (2 bands)	2·00	1·90	☐	☐
Y1705		64p turquoise-green (2 bands)	2·00	2·00	☐	☐
Y1706		65p greenish blue (2 bands)	1·00	1·10	☐	☐
Y1706a		68p grey-brown (2 bands)	1·10	1·25	☐	☐
Y1707		£1 bluish violet (2 bands)	1·50	1·60	☐	☐

(*b*) *Litho Walsall* (37p, 60p, 63p), *Questa or Walsall* (25p, 35p, 41p), *Questa* (*others*)

Y1743	**367**	1p lake (2 bands)	40	40	☐	☐
Y1748		6p yellow-olive (2 bands)	12·00	13·00	☐	☐
Y1749		10p dull orange (2 bands)	4·50	4·50	☐	☐
Y1750		19p bistre (1 side band) .	1·75	1·75	☐	☐
Y1751		20p bright yellow-green (1 centre band) . . .	1·50	1·50	☐	☐
Y1752		25p red (2 bands)	1·00	1·00	☐	☐
Y1753		26p chestnut (2 bands) .	1·00	1·00	☐	☐
Y1754		30p olive-grey (2 bands)	3·50	3·50	☐	☐
Y1755		35p yellow (2 bands) . .	1·60	1·60	☐	☐
Y1756		37p bright mauve (2 bands)	2·40	2·40	☐	☐
Y1757		41p drab (2 bands) . . .	1·75	1·75	☐	☐
Y1758		60p dull blue-grey (2 bands)	2·50	2·50	☐	☐
Y1759		63p light emerald (2 bands)	3·00	3·00	☐	☐

(c) Recess Enschedé or De La Rue

Y1800	**367**	£1·50 red	2·25	2·00	☐	☐
Y1801		£2 dull blue	3·00	2·25	☐	☐
Y1802		£3 dull violet	4·50	3·00	☐	☐
Y1803		£5 brown	7·50	5·00	☐	☐

PHQ Card (No. Y1707) . . . . . 40 3·00 ☐ ☐

Presentation Pack (P.O. Pack No. 30) (contains 19p (Y1675), 25p (Y1681), 29p (Y1684), 36p (Y1690), 38p (Y1692), 41p (Y1696)) . . 8·00 ☐

Presentation Pack (P.O. Pack No. 34) (contains 1p (Y1667), 2p (Y1668), 4p (Y1669), 5p (Y1670), 6p (Y1671), 10p (Y1674), 19p (Y1675), 20p (Y1677), 25p (Y1682), 29p (Y1684), 30p (Y1685), 35p (Y1688), 36p (Y1690), 38p (Y1692), 41p (Y1696), 50p (Y1703), 60p (Y1758), £1 (Y1707)) . . . . . 17·00 ☐

Presentation Pack (P.O. Pack No. 35) (contains 20p (Y1678), 26p (Y1683), 31p (Y1686), 37p (Y1691), 39p (Y1694), 43p (Y1699), 63p (Y1704)) . . . . 8·00 ☐

Presentation Pack (P.O. Pack No. 41) (contains 2nd (1663a), 1st (1664a), 1p (Y1667), 2p (Y1668), 4p (Y1669), 5p (Y1670), 6p (Y1671), 10p (Y1674), 20p (Y1678), 26p (Y1683), 30p (Y1685), 31p (Y1686), 37p (Y1691), 39p (Y1694), 43p (Y1700), 50p (Y1703), 63p (Y1704), £1 (Y1707)) . . . . 12·00 ☐

Presentation Pack (P.O. Pack No. 43 or 43a) (contains £1·50 (Y1800), £2 (Y1801), £3 (Y1802), £5 (Y1803)) 18·00 ☐

Presentation Pack (P.O. Pack No. 44) contains 7p (Y1672), 19p (Y1675), 38p (Y1693), 44p (Y1701), 64p (Y1705)) . . . . . 3·25 ☐

Presentation Pack (P.O. Pack No. 49) (contains 8p (Y1673), 33p (Y1687), 40p (Y1695), 41p (Y1698), 45p (Y1702), 65p (Y1706)) . . . . 4·00 ☐

Presentation Pack (P.O. Pack No. 57) (contains 2nd (1663a), 1st (1664a), E (1664b), 1p (Y1667), 2p (Y1668), 4p (Y1669), 5p (Y1670), 8p (Y1673), 10p (Y1674), 20p (Y1680), 33p (Y1687), 40p (Y1695), 41p (Y1698), 45p (Y1702), 50p (Y1703), 65p (Y1706), £1 (Y1707)) . . . . 8·00 ☐

Presentation Pack (P.O. Pack No. 58) (contains 37p (Y1691a), 42p (Y1698a), 47p (Y1702a), 68p (Y1706a) . . . . 3·50 ☐

First Day Covers

26 Oct. 1993	19p, 25p, 29p, 36p, 38p, 41p (Nos. Y1675, Y1681, Y1684, Y1690, Y1692, Y1696)	6·00	☐
9 Aug. 1994	60p (No. Y1758)	4·00	☐
22 Aug. 1995	£1 (No. Y1707)	3·50	☐
25 June 1996	20p, 26p, 31p, 37p, 39p, 43p, 63p (Nos. Y1678, Y1683, Y1686, Y1691, Y1694, Y1699, Y1704)	8·00	☐
9 Mar. 1999	£1·50, £2, £3, £5 (Nos. Y1800/3)	27·00	☐
20 Apr. 1999	7p, 38p, 44p, 64p (Nos. Y1672, Y1693, Y1701, Y1705)	5·00	☐
25 Apr. 2000	8p, 33p, 40p, 41p, 45p, 65p (Nos. Y1673, Y1687, Y1695, Y1698, Y1702, Y1706)	4·75	☐
4 July 2002	37p, 42p, 47p, 68p, (Nos. Y1691a, Y1698a, Y1702a, Y1706a) . . .	4·00	☐

No. Y1707 is printed in Iriodin ink which gives a shiny effect to the solid part of the background behind the Queen's head.

Nos. Y1689 and Y1697 were only issued in coils and Nos. Y1674a, Y1676, Y1679, Y1693a, Y1700a, Y1743 and Y1748/59 only in booklets.

No. Y1750 exists with the phosphor band at the left or right of the stamp, but Nos. Y1676 and Y1679 exist with band at right only.

For 26p in gold see No. 1978.

For self-adhesive versions of the 42p and 68p see Nos. 2297/8.

1094 'Family Group'
(bronze sculpture)
(Henry Moore)

1095 'Kew Gardens'
(lithograph)
(Edward Bawden)

1096 'St Francis and the
Birds' (Stanley Spencer)

1097 'Still Life: Odyssey I'
(Ben Nicholson)

Europa. Contemporary Art

1993 (11 MAY) *Phosphorised paper. Perf* 14 × 14½

1767	**1094**	24p multicoloured	60	20	☐	☐
1768	**1095**	28p multicoloured	90	1·00	☐	☐
1769	**1096**	33p multicoloured	1·25	1·40	☐	☐
1770	**1097**	39p multicoloured	1·40	1·40	☐	☐
		Set of 4	3·75	3·50	☐	☐
		First Day Cover		4·00		☐
		Presentation Pack	4·50		☐	
		PHQ Cards (*set of* 4)	2·50	6·50	☐	☐
		Set of 4 *Gutter Pairs*	8·00		☐	

1098 Emperor Claudius
(from gold coin)

1099 Emperor Hadrian
(bronze head)

1100 Goddess Roma
(from gemstone)

1101 Christ (Hinton
St Mary mosaic)

Roman Britain

1993 (15 JUNE) *Phosphorised paper with two phosphor bands.*
Perf 14 × 14½

1771	**1098**	24p multicoloured	50	20	☐	☐
1772	**1099**	28p multicoloured	80	90	☐	☐
1773	**1100**	33p multicoloured	1·25	1·25	☐	☐
1774	**1101**	39p multicoloured	1·40	1·40	☐	☐
		Set of 4	3·50	3·50	☐	☐
		First Day Cover		4·00		☐
		Presentation Pack	4·50		☐	
		PHQ Cards (*set of* 4)	2·50	6·50	☐	☐
		Set of 4 *Gutter Pairs*	7·50		☐	

1102 *Midland Maid* and
other Narrow Boats,
Grand Junction Canal

1103 *Yorkshire Maid* and
other Humber Keels,
Stainforth and Keadby
Canal

1104 *Valley Princess* and
other Horse-drawn
Barges, Brecknock and
Abergavenny Canal

1105 Steam Barges including
Pride of Scotland and
and Fishing Boats,
Crinan Canal

Inland Waterways

1993 (20 JULY) *Two phosphor bands. Perf* 14½ × 14

1775	**1102**	24p multicoloured	60	20	☐	☐
1776	**1103**	28p multicoloured	95	1·00	☐	☐
1777	**1104**	33p multicoloured	1·25	1·25	☐	☐
1778	**1105**	39p multicoloured	1·50	1·40	☐	☐
		Set of 4	4·00	3·50	☐	☐
		First Day Cover		4·25		☐
		Presentation Pack	4·50		☐	
		PHQ Cards (*set of* 4)	2·50	7·50	☐	☐
		Set of 4 *Gutter Pairs*	8·50		☐	

Nos. 1775/8 commemorate the bicentenaries of the Acts of
Parliament authorising the canals depicted.

1106 Horse Chestnut

1107 Blackberry

1108 Hazel

1109 Rowan

1110 Pear

The Four Seasons. Autumn. Fruits and Leaves

1993 (14 SEPT.) *One phosphor band* (18p) *or phosphorised paper* (*others*)

1779	**1106**	18p multicoloured	50	20 ☐ ☐
1780	**1107**	24p multicoloured	75	20 ☐ ☐
1781	**1108**	28p multicoloured	1·10	1·25 ☐ ☐
1782	**1109**	33p multicoloured	1·40	1·50 ☐ ☐
1783	**1110**	39p multicoloured	1·50	1·50 ☐ ☐
		Set of 5	4·75	4·25 ☐ ☐
		First Day Cover		5·00 ☐
		Presentation Pack	5·25	☐
		PHQ Cards (*set of 5*)	2·50	7·50 ☐ ☐
		Set of 5 Gutter Pairs	9·50	☐

SHERLOCK HOLMES & DR WATSON
"THE REIGATE SQUIRE"

1111 *The Reigate Squire*

SHERLOCK HOLMES & SIR HENRY
"THE HOUND OF THE BASKERVILLES"

1112 *The Hound of the Baskervilles*

SHERLOCK HOLMES & LESTRADE
"THE SIX NAPOLEONS"

1113 *The Six Napoleons*

SHERLOCK HOLMES & MYCROFT
"THE GREEK INTERPRETER"

1114 *The Greek Interpreter*

SHERLOCK HOLMES & MORIARTY
"THE FINAL PROBLEM"

1115 *The Final Problem*

T **1111/15** were printed together, *se-tenant*, in horizontal strips of 5 throughout the sheet.

Sherlock Holmes. Centenary of the Publication of The Final Problem

1993 (12 OCT.) *Phosphorised paper. Perf* 14 × 14½

1784	**1111**	24p multicoloured	1·10	1·10 ☐ ☐
		a. Horiz strip of 5. Nos. 1784/8	5·50	5·50 ☐ ☐
1785	**1112**	24p multicoloured	1·10	1·10 ☐ ☐
1786	**1113**	24p multicoloured	1·10	1·10 ☐ ☐
1787	**1114**	24p multicoloured	1·10	1·10 ☐ ☐
1788	**1115**	24p multicoloured	1·10	1·10 ☐ ☐
		Set of 5	5·50	5·00 ☐ ☐
		First Day Cover		6·50 ☐
		Presentation Pack	6·00	☐
		PHQ Cards (*set of 5*)	3·00	10·00 ☐ ☐
		Gutter Strip of 10	11·00	☐

1116

Self-adhesive Booklet Stamp

1993 (19 OCT.) *Litho Walsall. Two phosphor bands. Die-cut perf* 14 × 15 (*with one elliptical hole on each vertical side*)

1789	**1116**	(1st) orange-red	1·25	1·40 ☐ ☐
		First Day Cover		4·50 ☐
		Presentation Pack (*booklet pane of 20*)	20·00	☐
		PHQ Card	2·50	7·50 ☐ ☐

For similar 2nd and 1st designs printed in photogravure by Enschedé see Nos. 1976/7.

1117 Bob Cratchit and Tiny Tim

1118 Mr and Mrs Fezziwig

1119   Scrooge

1120   The Prize Turkey

1121   Mr Scrooge's Nephew

Christmas. 150th Anniversary of Publication of A Christmas Carol

1993 (9 Nov.) *One phosphor band* (19p) *or phosphorised paper* (*others*)

1790	**1117**	19p multicoloured	60	15	□	□
1791	**1118**	25p multicoloured	90	15	□	□
1792	**1119**	30p multicoloured	1·25	1·50	□	□
1793	**1120**	35p multicoloured	1·40	1·60	□	□
1794	**1121**	41p multicoloured	1·50	1·60	□	□
		Set of 5	5·00	4·50	□	□
		First Day Cover		5·50		□
		Presentation Pack	5·75		□	
		PHQ Cards (set of 5)	3·00	7·50	□	□
		Set of 5 Gutter Pairs	10·00		□	

Collectors Pack 1993

1993 (9 Nov.) *Comprises Nos.* 1639/43, 1654/7, 1659/63, 1767/88 *and* 1790/4

	Collectors Pack	60·00	□

Post Office Yearbook

1993 (9 Nov.) *Comprises Nos.* 1639/43, 1654/7, 1659/63, 1767/88 *and* 1790/4 *in hardback book with slip case*

	Yearbook	65·00	□

1122   Class 5 No. 44957 and Class B1 No. 61342 on West Highland Line

1123   Class A1 No. 60149 *Amadis* at Kings Cross

1124   Class 4 No. 43000 on Turntable at Blyth North

1125   Class 4 No. 42455 near Wigan Central

1126   Class Castle No. 7002 *Devizes Castle* on Bridge crossing Worcester and Birmingham Canal

The Age of Steam. Railway Photographs by Colin Gifford

1994 (18 Jan.) *One phosphor band* (19p) *or phosphorised paper with two bands* (*others*). *Perf* 14½

1795	**1122**	19p deep blue-green, grey-black and black	55	25	□	□
1796	**1123**	25p slate-lilac, grey-black and black	90	95	□	□
1797	**1124**	30p lake-brown, grey-black and black . . .	1·40	1·40	□	□
1798	**1125**	35p deep claret, grey-black and black . . .	1·50	1·60	□	□
1799	**1126**	41p indigo, grey-black and black	1·60	1·50	□	□
		Set of 5	5·50	5·00	□	□
		First Day Cover		5·75		□
		Presentation Pack	6·25		□	
		PHQ Cards (set of 5)	3·00	8·00	□	□
		Set of 5 Gutter Pairs	11·00		□	

1127   Dan Dare and the Mekon

1128   The Three Bears

1129   Rupert Bear

1130   Alice (*Alice in Wonderland*)

1131 Noggin and the Ice Dragon

1132 Peter Rabbit posting Letter

1133 Red Riding Hood and Wolf

1134 Orlando the Marmalade Cat

1135 Biggles

1136 Paddington Bear on Station

T **1127/36** were printed together, *se-tenant,* in booklet panes of 10 stamps and 20 half stamp-size labels.

Greeting Stamps. 'Messages'
1994 (1 FEB.) *Two phosphor bands. Perf* 15 × 14 (*with one elliptical hole on each vertical side*)

1800	**1127**	(1st) multicoloured	1·00	90	□	□
		a. Booklet pane. Nos.				
		1800/9	11·00		□	
1801	**1128**	(1st) multicoloured	1·00	90	□	□
1802	**1129**	(1st) multicoloured	1·00	90	□	□
1803	**1130**	(1st) gold, bistre-yellow				
		and black	1·00	90	□	□
1804	**1131**	(1st) multicoloured	1·00	90	□	□
1805	**1132**	(1st) multicoloured	1·00	90	□	□
1806	**1133**	(1st) multicoloured	1·00	90	□	□
1807	**1134**	(1st) multicoloured	1·00	90	□	□
1808	**1135**	(1st) multicoloured	1·00	90	□	□
1809	**1136**	(1st) multicoloured	1·00	90	□	□
		Set of 10	11·00	8·00	□	
		First Day Cover		12·00		□
		Presentation Pack	20·00		□	
		PHQ Cards (set of 10)	9·00	20·00	□	□

1137 Castell Y Waun (Chirk Castle), Clwyd, Wales

1138 Ben Arkle, Sutherland, Scotland

1139 Mourne Mountains, County Down, Northern Ireland

1140 Dersingham, Norfolk, England

1141 Dolwyddelan, Gwynedd, Wales

25th Anniversary of Investiture of the Prince of Wales. Paintings by Prince Charles
1994 (1 MAR.) *One phosphor band* (19p) *or phosphorised paper* (*others*)

1810	**1137**	19p multicoloured	55	20	□	□
1811	**1138**	25p multicoloured	1·00	20	□	□
1812	**1139**	30p multicoloured	1·10	1·40	□	□
1813	**1140**	35p multicoloured	1·40	1·50	□	□
1814	**1141**	41p multicoloured	1·50	1·50	□	□
		Set of 5	5·00	4·50	□	□
		First Day Cover		5·00		□
		Presentation Pack	5·25		□	
		PHQ Cards (set of 5)	3·00	7·50	□	□
		Set of 5 Gutter Pairs	10·00		□	

1142 Bather at Blackpool

1143 'Where's my Little Lad?'

1144 'Wish You were Here!'

1145 Punch and Judy Show

1146 'The Tower Crane' Machine

Centenary of Picture Postcards

1994 (12 APR.) *One side band* (19p) *or two phosphor bands* (*others*). *Perf* 14 × 14½

1815	**1142**	19p multicoloured	60		20	□	□
1816	**1143**	25p multicoloured	90		20	□	□
1817	**1144**	30p multicoloured	1·10		1·25	□	□
1818	**1145**	35p multicoloured	1·40		1·50	□	□
1819	**1146**	41p multicoloured	1·50		1·50	□	□
		Set of 5	5·00		4·25	□	□
		First Day Cover			4·75		□
		Presentation Pack	5·50			□	
		PHQ Cards (set of 5)	3·00		7·50	□	□
		Set of 5 Gutter Pairs	10·00			□	

1147 British Lion and French Cockerel over Tunnel

Minimum Price. The minimum price quoted is 10p. This represents a handling charge rather than a basis for valuing common stamps. Where the actual value of a stamp is less than 10p this may be apparent when set prices are shown, particularly for sets including a number of 10p stamps. It therefore follows that in valuing common stamps the 10p catalogue price should not be reckoned automatically since it covers a variation in real scarcity.

1148 Symbolic Hands over Train

Nos. 1820/1 and 1822/3 were printed together, *se-tenant*, in horizontal pairs throughout the sheets.

Opening of Channel Tunnel

1994 (3 MAY) *Phosphorised paper. Perf* 14 × 14½

1820	**1147**	25p multicoloured	80	70	□	□
		a. Horiz pair. Nos. 1820/1	1·75	1·60	□	□
1821	**1148**	25p multicoloured	80	70	□	□
1822	**1147**	41p multicoloured	1·50	1·50	□	□
		a. Horiz pair. Nos. 1822/3	3·25	3·25	□	□
1823	**1148**	41p multicoloured	1·50	1·50	□	□
		Set of 4	4·50	4·00	□	□
		First Day Cover		5·50		□
		Presentation Pack	5·50		□	
		Souvenir Book	27·00		□	
		PHQ Cards (set of 4)	3·00	7·50	□	□

Stamps in similar designs were also issued by France and these are included in the Souvenir Book.

1149 Groundcrew replacing Smoke Canisters on Douglas Boston of 88 Sqn

1150 H.M.S. *Warspite* (battleship) shelling Enemy Positions

1151 Commandos landing on Gold Beach

1152 Infantry regrouping on Sword Beach

1153 Tank and Infantry advancing, Ouistreham

Nos. 1824/8 were printed together, *se-tenant*, in horizontal strips of 5 throughout the sheet.

50th Anniversary of D-Day

1994 (6 JUNE) *Two phosphor bands. Perf* $14\frac{1}{2} \times 14$

1824	**1149**	25p multicoloured	1·00	1·10	☐	☐
		a. Horiz strip of 5. Nos.				
		1824/8	5·00	5·50	☐	☐
1825	**1150**	25p multicoloured	1·00	1·10	☐	☐
1826	**1151**	25p multicoloured	1·00	1·10	☐	☐
1827	**1152**	25p multicoloured	1·00	1·10	☐	☐
1828	**1153**	25p multicoloured	1·00	1·10	☐	☐
		Set of 5	5·00	5·00	☐	☐
		First Day Cover		5·25		☐
		Presentation Pack	5·50		☐	
		PHQ Cards (set of 5)	3·00	7·50	☐	☐
		Gutter Block of 10	11·00		☐	

1158 The 9th Hole, Turnberry

Scottish Golf Courses

1994 (5 JULY) *One phosphor band* (19p) *or phosphorised paper* (*others*). *Perf* $14\frac{1}{2} \times 14$

1829	**1154**	19p multicoloured	50	20	☐	☐
1830	**1155**	25p multicoloured	75	20	☐	☐
1831	**1156**	30p multicoloured	1·10	1·40	☐	☐
1832	**1157**	35p multicoloured	1·25	1·40	☐	☐
1833	**1158**	41p multicoloured	1·40	1·40	☐	☐
		Set of 5	4·50	4·25	☐	☐
		First Day Cover		5·00		☐
		Presentation Pack	5·25		☐	
		PHQ Cards (set of 5)	3·00	7·50	☐	☐
		Set of 5 Gutter Pairs	10·00		☐	

Nos. 1829/33 commemorate the 250th anniversary of golf's first set of rules produced by the Honourable Company of Edinburgh Golfers.

1154 The Old Course, St Andrews

1155 The 18th Hole, Muirfield

AMSER HAF/SUMMERTIME *Llanelwedd*

1159 Royal Welsh Show, Llanelwedd

SUMMERTIME *Wimbledon*

1160 All England Tennis Championships, Wimbledon

1156 The 15th Hole ('Luckyslap'), Carnoustie

1157 The 8th Hole ('The Postage Stamp'), Royal Troon

SUMMERTIME *Cowes*

1161 Cowes Week

SUMMERTIME *Lord's*

1162 Test Match, Lord's

1163   Braemar Gathering

The Four Seasons. Summertime. Events

1994 (2 Aug.) *One phosphor band* (19p) *or phosphorised paper* (*others*)

1834	**1159**	19p multicoloured	50	20	☐	☐
1835	**1160**	25p multicoloured	75	20	☐	☐
1836	**1161**	30p multicoloured . . .	1·10	1·25	☐	☐
1837	**1162**	35p multicoloured . . .	1·25	1·60	☐	☐
1838	**1163**	41p multicoloured . . .	1·40	1·60	☐	☐
		Set of 5	4·50	4·25	☐	☐
		First Day Cover		4·75		☐
		Presentation Pack	5·00		☐	
		PHQ Cards (set of 5)	3·00	7·50	☐	☐
		Set of 5 Gutter Pairs	9·00		☐	

1164   Ultrasonic Imaging

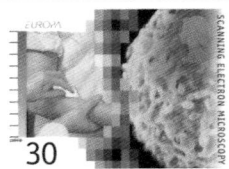

1165   Scanning Electron Microscopy

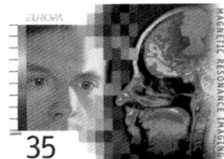

1166   Magnetic Resonance Imaging

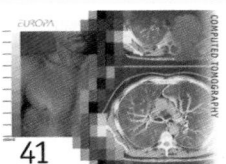

1167   Computed Tomography

Europa. Medical Discoveries

1994 (27 Sept.) *Phosphorised paper. Perf* 14 × 14½

1839	**1164**	25p multicoloured	80	20	☐	☐
1840	**1165**	30p multicoloured	1·25	1·10	☐	☐
1841	**1166**	35p multicoloured	1·25	1·40	☐	☐
1842	**1167**	41p multicoloured	1·50	1·40	☐	☐
		Set of 4	4·25	3·75	☐	☐
		First Day Cover		4·50		☐
		Presentation Pack	4·75		☐	
		PHQ Cards (set of 4)	2·50	7·50	☐	☐
		Set of 4 Gutter Pairs	8·50		☐	

1168   Virgin Mary and Joseph

1169   Three Wise Men

1170   Virgin and Child

1171   Shepherds

1172   Angels

Christmas. Children's Nativity Plays

1994 (1 Nov.) *One phosphor band* (19p) *or phosphorised paper* (*others*)

1843	**1168**	19p multicoloured	65	15	☐	☐
1844	**1169**	25p multicoloured	90	15	☐	☐
1845	**1170**	30p multicoloured	1·10	1·40	☐	☐
1846	**1171**	35p multicoloured	1·25	1·40	☐	☐
1847	**1172**	41p multicoloured	1·50	1·40	☐	☐
		Set of 5	4·75	4·00	☐	☐
		First Day Cover		4·50		☐
		Presentation Pack	5·25		☐	
		PHQ Cards (set of 5)	3·00	7·50	☐	☐
		Set of 5 Gutter Pairs	9·50		☐	

Collectors Pack 1994

1994 (14 Nov.) *Comprises Nos.* 1795/1847

	Collectors Pack	55·00	☐

Post Office Yearbook

1994 (14 Nov.) *Comprises Nos.* 1795/9 *and* 1810/47 *in hardback book with slip case*

	Yearbook	60·00	☐

1173　Sophie (black cat)

1174　Puskas (Siamese) and Tigger (tabby)

1175　Chloe (ginger cat)

1176　Kikko (tortoiseshell) and Rosie (Abyssinian)

1177　Fred (black and white cat)

Cats

1995 (17 Jan.) *One phosphor band (19p) or two phosphor bands (others). Perf* $14\frac{1}{2} \times 14$

1848	1173	19p multicoloured	80	20	☐	☐
1849	1174	25p multicoloured	95	25	☐	☐
1850	1175	30p multicoloured	1·10	1·40	☐	☐
1851	1176	35p multicoloured	1·25	1·50	☐	☐
1852	1177	41p multicoloured	1·60	1·60	☐	☐
		Set of 5　.	5·00	4·50	☐	☐
		First Day Cover　.		5·00		☐
		Presentation Pack　.	5·50		☐	
		PHQ Cards (set of 5)　.	3·50	9·00	☐	☐
		Set of 5 Gutter Pairs　.	10·00		☐	

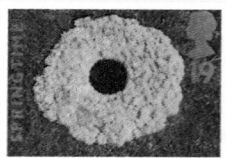

1178　Dandelions

1179　Sweet Chestnut Leaves

1180　Garlic Leaves

1181　Hazel Leaves

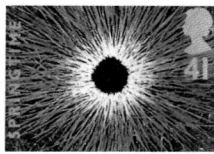

1182　Spring Grass

The Four Seasons. Springtime. Plant Sculptures by Andy Goldsworthy

1995 (14 Mar.) *One phosphor band (19p) or two phosphor bands (others)*

1853	1178	19p multicoloured	80	15	☐	☐
1854	1179	25p multicoloured	95	15	☐	☐
1855	1180	30p multicoloured	1·25	1·40	☐	☐
1856	1181	35p multicoloured	1·25	1·40	☐	☐
1857	1182	41p multicoloured	1·60	1·60	☐	☐
		Set of 5　.	5·25	4·25	☐	☐
		First Day Cover　.		5·00		☐
		Presentation Pack　.	5·50		☐	
		PHQ Cards (set of 5)　.	3·00	6·50	☐	☐
		Set of 5 Gutter Pairs　.	10·50		☐	

1183　'La Danse a la Campagne' (Renoir)

1184　'Troilus and Criseyde' (Peter Brookes)

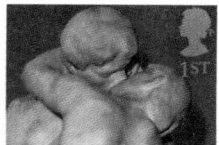

1185　'The Kiss' (Rodin)

1186　'Girls on the Town' (Beryl Cook)

1187 'Jazz'
(Andrew Mockett)

1188 'Girls performing a
Kathal Dance'
(Aurangzeb period)

1189 'Alice Keppel with
her Daughter'
(Alice Hughes)

1190 'Children Playing'
(L. S. Lowry)

1191 'Circus Clowns'
(Emily Firmin and
Justin Mitchell)

1192 Decoration from
'All the Love Poems of
Shakespeare' (Eric Gill)

T **1183/92** were printed together, *se-tenant,* in booklet panes of 10 stamps and 20 half stamp-size labels.

Greetings Stamp. 'Greetings in Art'

1995 (21 MAR.) *Two phosphor bands. Perf 14½ × 14 (with one elliptical hole on each vertical side)*

1858	**1183**	(1st) multicoloured	1·00	80	☐	☐
		a. Booklet pane. Nos.				
		1858/67	11·00		☐	
1859	**1184**	(1st) multicoloured	1·00	80	☐	☐
1860	**1185**	(1st) multicoloured	1·00	80	☐	☐
1861	**1186**	(1st) multicoloured	1·00	80	☐	☐
1862	**1187**	(1st) multicoloured	1·00	80	☐	☐
1863	**1188**	(1st) multicoloured	1·00	80	☐	☐
1864	**1189**	(1st) purple-brown and				
		silver	1·00	80	☐	☐
1865	**1190**	(1st) multicoloured	1·00	80	☐	☐
1866	**1191**	(1st) multicoloured	1·00	80	☐	☐
1867	**1192**	(1st) black, greenish				
		yellow and silver . .	1·00	80	☐	☐
		Set of 10	11·00	7·25	☐	☐
		First Day Cover		10·00		☐
		Presentation Pack	12·00		☐	
		PHQ Cards (set of 10)	9·00	20·00	☐	☐

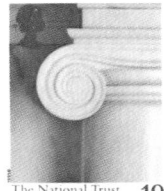

The National Trust
Celebrating 100 Years 19

1193 Fireplace Decoration,
Attingham Park,
Shropshire

The National Trust
Protecting Land 25

1194 Oak Seedling

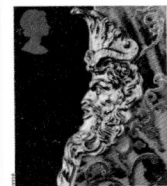

The National Trust
Conserving Art 30

1195 Carved Table Leg,
Attingham Park

The National Trust
Saving Coast 35

1196 St David's Head,
Dyfed, Wales

The National Trust
Repairing Buildings 41

1197 Elizabethan Window,
Little Moreton Hall,
Cheshire

Centenary of The National Trust

1995 (11 APR.) *One phosphor band (19p), two phosphor bands (25p, 35p) or phosphorised paper (30p, 41p)*

1868	**1193**	19p multicoloured	60	20	☐	☐
1869	**1194**	25p multicoloured	80	20	☐	☐
1870	**1195**	30p multicoloured	1·00	1·25	☐	☐
1871	**1196**	35p multicoloured	1·25	1·50	☐	☐
1872	**1197**	41p multicoloured	1·40	1·50	☐	☐
		Set of 5	4·50	4·25	☐	☐
		First Day Cover		4·75		☐
		Presentation Pack	5·25		☐	
		PHQ Cards (set of 5)	3·00	7·50	☐	☐
		Set of 5 Gutter Pairs	9·00		☐	

1198 British Troops and French Civilians celebrating

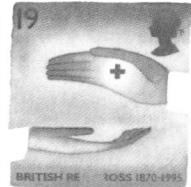

1199 Symbolic Hands and Red Cross

1203 The Time Machine

1204 The First Men in the Moon

1200 St Paul's Cathedral and Searchlights

1201 Symbolic Hand releasing Peace Dove

1205 The War of the Worlds

1206 The Shape of Things to Come

Science Fiction. Novels by H. G. Wells

1995 (6 JUNE) *Two phosphor bands. Perf* 14½ × 14

1878	**1203**	25p multicoloured	. . . .	95	25 □	□
1879	**1204**	30p multicoloured	. . . .	1·40	1·50 □	□
1880	**1205**	35p multicoloured	. . . .	1·50	1·60 □	□
1881	**1206**	41p multicoloured	. . . .	1·60	1·60 □	□
		Set of 4	. . . .	5·00	4·50 □	
		First Day Cover	. . . .		5·25	□
		Presentation Pack	. . . .	5·50		□
		PHQ Cards (set of 4)	. . . . . .	2·50	10·00 □	□
		Set of 4 Gutter Pairs	. . . . . .	10·00		□

Nos. 1878/81 commemorate the centenary of publication of Wells's *The Time Machine*.

1202 Symbolic Hands

Europa. Peace and Freedom

1995 (2 MAY) *One phosphor band* (Nos. 1873/4) *or two phosphor bands* (others). Perf 14½ × 14

1873	**1198**	19p silver, bistre-brown and grey-black	. . .	70	40 □	□
1874	**1199**	19p multicoloured	. . .	70	40 □	□
1875	**1200**	25p silver, blue and grey-black	. . . . . .	1·00	60 □	□
1876	**1201**	25p multicoloured	. . .	1·00	60 □	□
1877	**1202**	30p multicoloured	. . . .	1·25	1·75 □	□
		Set of 5	. . . .	4·25	3·50 □	□
		First Day Cover	. . . .		4·00	□
		Presentation Pack	. . . .	5·00		□
		PHQ Cards (set of 5)	. . . . . .	3·00	8·00 □	□
		Set of 5 Gutter Pairs	. . . . .	8·50		□

Nos. 1873 and 1875 commemorate the 50th anniversary of the end of the Second World War, No. 1874 the 125th anniversary of the British Red Cross Society and Nos. 1876/7 the 50th anniversary of the United Nations.

Nos. 1876/7 include the 'EUROPA' emblem.

1207 The Swan, 1595

1208 The Rose, 1592

For full information on all future British issues, collectors should write to Royal Mail, Freepost EH3647, 21 South Gyle Crescent, Edinburgh EH12 9PE.

1209 The Globe, 1599

1210 The Hope, 1613

1211 The Globe, 1614

T **1207/11** were printed together, *se-tenant*, in horizontal strips of 5 throughout the sheet, the backgrounds forming a composite design.

Reconstruction of Shakespeare's Globe Theatre

1995 (8 Aug.) *Two phosphor bands. Perf* 14½

1882	**1207**	25p multicoloured	90	90	□	□
		a. *Horiz strip of 5. Nos.*				
		1882/6	4·25	4·25	□	□
1883	**1208**	25p multicoloured	90	90	□	□
1884	**1209**	25p multicoloured	90	90	□	□
1885	**1210**	25p multicoloured	90	90	□	□
1886	**1211**	25p multicoloured	90	90	□	□
		Set of 5	4·25	4·00	□	□
		First Day Cover		5·50		□
		Presentation Pack	5·25		□	
		PHQ Cards (set of 5)	3·00	8·00	□	□
		Gutter Strip of 10	8·50		□	

1212 Sir Rowland Hill
and Uniform Penny
Postage Petition

1213 Hill and Penny Black

1214 Guglielmo Marconi
and Early Wirelesss

1215 Marconi and Sinking
of *Titanic* (liner)

Pioneers of Communications

1995 (5 Sept.) *One phosphor band* (19p) *or phosphorised paper* (*others*). *Perf* 14½ × 14

1887	**1212**	19p silver, red and black	65	30	□	□
1888	**1213**	25p silver, brown and				
		black	90	35	□	□
1889	**1214**	41p silver, grey-green and				
		black	1·50	1·60	□	□
1890	**1215**	60p silver, deep ultra-				
		marine and black . .	1·75	1·90	□	□
		Set of 4	4·25	3·75	□	□
		First Day Cover		4·50		□
		Presentation Pack	4·50		□	
		PHQ Cards (set of 4)	2·50	7·50	□	□
		Set of 4 Gutter Pairs	8·50		□	

Nos. 1887/8 mark the birth bicentenary of Sir Rowland Hill and Nos. 1889/90 the centenary of the first radio transmissions.

1216 Harold Wagstaff

1217 Gus Risman

1218 Jim Sullivan

1219 Billy Batten

1220   Brian Bevan

Centenary of Rugby League

1995 (3 OCT.) *One phosphor band* (19*p*) *or two phosphor bands* (*others*). *Perf* 14 × 14½

1891	**1216**	19p multicoloured	85		20	□	□
1892	**1217**	25p multicoloured	1·00		25	□	□
1893	**1218**	30p multicoloured	1·25		1·50	□	□
1894	**1219**	35p multicoloured	1·25		1·60	□	□
1895	**1220**	41p multicoloured	1·60		1·75	□	□
		Set of 5	5·25		4·75	□	□
		First Day Cover			5·25		□
		Presentation Pack	6·00			□	
		PHQ Cards (set of 5)	3·00		7·00	□	□
		Set of 5 Gutter Pairs	10·50			□	

1221   European Robin in Mouth of Pillar Box

1222   European Robin on Railings and Holly

1223   European Robin on Snow-covered Milk Bottles

1224   European Robin on Road Sign

1225   European Robin on Door Knob and Christmas Wreath

Christmas. Christmas Robins

1995 (30 OCT.) *One phosphor band* (19p) *or two phosphor bands* (*others*)

1896	**1221**	19p multicoloured	60	20	□	□
1897	**1222**	25p multicoloured	85	30	□	□
1898	**1223**	30p multicoloured	1·25	1·40	□	□
1899	**1224**	41p multicoloured	1·60	1·60	□	□
1900	**1225**	60p multicoloured	1·75	1·90	□	□
		Set of 5	5·50	4·75	□	□
		First Day Cover		5·25		□
		Presentation Pack	6·00		□	
		PHQ Cards (set of 5)	3·00	7·50	□	□
		Set of 5 Gutter Pairs	11·00		□	

The 19p value was re-issued on 3 October 2000 in sheets of 20 each with *se-tenant* label, in connection with 'customised' stamps available from the Philatelic Bureau. The labels show either Christmas greetings or a personal photograph.

Collectors Pack 1995

1995 (30 OCT.) *Comprises Nos.* 1848/1900

	Collectors Pack	55·00	□

Post Office Yearbook

1995 (30 OCT.) *Comprises Nos.* 1848/57 *and* 1868/1900 *in hardback book with slip case*

	Yearbook	60·00	□

1226   Opening Lines of 'To a Mouse' and Fieldmouse

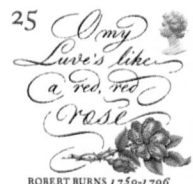

1227   'O my Luve's like a red, red rose' and Wild Rose

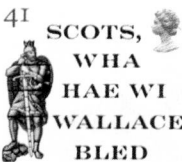

1228   'Scots, wha hae wi Wallace bled' and Sir William Wallace

1229   'Auld Lang Syne' and Highland Dancers

Death Bicentenary of Robert Burns (*Scottish poet*)

1996 (25 Jan.) *One phosphor band* (19p) *or two phosphor bands* (*others*)*. Perf* 14½

1901	**1226**	19p cream, bistre-brown and black	60	25	□	□
1902	**1227**	25p multicoloured	90	25	□	□
1903	**1228**	41p multicoloured	1·40	1·40	□	□
1904	**1229**	60p multicoloured	1·75	1·75	□	□
		Set of 4	4·25	3·25	□	□
		First Day Cover		5·00		□
		Presentation Pack	5·00		□	
		PHQ Cards (*set of 4*)	3·00	6·00	□	□
		Set of 4 *Gutter Pairs*	8·50		□	

1230 'MORE! LOVE' (Mel Calman)

1231 'Sincerely' (Charles Barsotti)

1232 'Do you have something for the HUMAN CONDITION?' (Mel Calman)

1233 'MENTAL FLOSS (Leo Cullum)

1234 '4.55 P.M.' (Charles Barsotti)

1235 'Dear lottery prize winner (Larry)

1236 'I'm writing to you because...' (Mel Calman)

1237 'FETCH THIS, FETCH THAT' (Charles Barsotti)

1238 'My day starts before I'm ready for it' (Mel Calman)

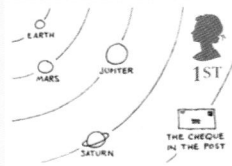

1239 'THE CHEQUE IN THE POST' (Jack Ziegler)

T **1230/9** were printed together, *se-tenant,* in booklet panes of 10 stamps and 20 half stamp-size labels.

Greetings Stamps. Cartoons

1996 (26 Feb.–11 Nov.) *'All-over' phosphor. Perf* 14½ × 14 (*with one elliptical hole on each vertical side*)

1905	**1230**	(1st) black and mauve	80	75	□	□
		a. Booklet pane. Nos. 1905/14	9·00		□	
		p. Two phosphor bands	90	90	□	□
		pa. Booklet pane. Nos. 1905p/14p (11 Nov.)	10·00		□	
1906	**1231**	(1st) black and blue-green	80	75	□	□
		p. Two phosphor bands	90	90	□	□
1907	**1232**	(1st) black and new blue .	80	75	□	□
		p. Two phosphor bands	90	90	□	□
1908	**1233**	(1st) black and bright violet	80	75	□	□
		p. Two phosphor bands	90	90	□	□
1909	**1234**	(1st) black and vermilion .	80	75	□	□
		p. Two phosphor bands	90	90	□	□
1910	**1235**	(1st) black and new blue .	80	75	□	□
		p. Two phosphor bands	90	90	□	□
1911	**1236**	(1st) black and vermilion .	80	75	□	□
		p. Two phosphor bands	90	90	□	□
1912	**1237**	(1st) black and bright violet	80	75	□	□
		p. Two phosphor bands	90	90	□	□
1913	**1238**	(1st) black and blue-green	80	75	□	□
		p. Two phosphor bands	90	90	□	□
1914	**1239**	(1st) black and bright mauve	80	75	□	□
		p. Two phosphor bands	90	90	□	□
		Set of 10 (*Nos. 1905/14*)	9·00	6·75	□	□
		Set of 10 (*Nos. 1905p/14p*) . . .	10·00	8·00	□	□
		First Day Cover (*Nos. 1905/14*) .		8·00		□
		Presentation Pack (*Nos. 1905/14*)	10·00		□	
		PHQ Cards (*set of 10*)	9·00	20·00	□	□

Nos. 1905/14 were re-issued on 18 December 2001, each stamp with a *se-tenant* label showing cartoon titles or a personal photograph. Such sheets are perforated without elliptical holes.

For full information on all future British issues, collectors should write to Royal Mail, Freepost EH3647, 21 South Gyle Crescent, Edinburgh EH12 9PE.

1240 'Muscovy Duck'

1241 'Lapwing'

1242 'White-fronted Goose'

1243 'Bittern'

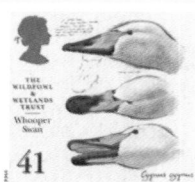

1244 'Whooper Swan'

50th Anniversary of the Wildfowl and Wetlands Trust. Bird Paintings by C. F. Tunnicliffe

1996 (12 Mar.) *One phosphor band* (19p) *or phosphorised paper* (others). *Perf* 14 × 14½

1915	**1240**	19p multicoloured	. . . .	70	20	☐	☐
1916	**1241**	25p multicoloured	. . . .	90	20	☐	☐
1917	**1242**	30p multicoloured	. . . .	1·00	1·25	☐	☐
1918	**1243**	35p multicoloured	. . . .	1·10	1·50	☐	☐
1919	**1244**	41p multicoloured	. . . .	1·50	1·60	☐	☐
		Set of 5	. . . .	4·75	4·25	☐	☐
		First Day Cover	. . . .		5·00		☐
		Presentation Pack	. . . .	5·25		☐	
		PHQ Cards (set of 5)	. . . . . .	3·00	7·50	☐	☐
		Set of 5 Gutter Pairs	. . . . . .	9·50		☐	

1245 The Odeon, Harrogate

1246 Laurence Olivier and Vivien Leigh in *Lady Hamilton* (film)

1247 Old Cinema Ticket

1248 Pathé News Still

1249 Cinema Sign, The Odeon, Manchester

Centenary of Cinema

1996 (16 Apr.) *One phosphor band* (19p) *or two phosphor bands* (others). *Perf* 14 × 14½

1920	**1245**	19p multicoloured	. . . .	50	25	☐	☐
1921	**1246**	25p multicoloured	. . . .	70	25	☐	☐
1922	**1247**	30p multicoloured	. . . .	90	1·00	☐	☐
1923	**1248**	35p black, red and silver		1·25	1·25	☐	☐
1924	**1249**	41p multicoloured	. . . .	1·60	1·60	☐	☐
		Set of 5	. . . .	4·50	4·00	☐	☐
		First Day Cover	. . . .		5·00		☐
		Presentation Pack	. . . .	5·00		☐	
		PHQ Cards (set of 5)	. . . . . .	3·00	7·50	☐	☐
		Set of 5 Gutter Pairs	. . . . . .	9·00		☐	

1250 Dixie Dean

1251 Bobby Moore

1252 Duncan Edwards

1253 Billy Wright

1254 Danny Blanchflower

European Football Championship

1996 (14 MAY) *One phosphor band* (19p) *or two phosphor bands* (*others*). *Perf* 14½ × 14

1925	**1250**	19p multicoloured	40	20	□	□
1926	**1251**	25p multicoloured	70	20	□	□
1927	**1252**	35p multicoloured	1·25	1·60	□	□
1928	**1253**	41p multicoloured	1·40	1·60	□	□
1929	**1254**	60p multicoloured	1·75	1·90	□	□
		Set of 5	5·00	5·00	□	□
		First Day Cover		5·50		□
		Presentation Pack	5·50		□	
		PHQ Cards (*set of 5*) ...	3·00	8·00	□	□
		Set of 5 Gutter Pairs	10·00		□	

1255 Athlete on Starting Blocks

1256 Throwing the Javelin

1257 Basketball

1258 Swimming

1259 Athlete celebrating and Olympic Rings

T **1255/9** were printed together, *se-tenant,* in horizontal strips of 5 throughout the sheet.

Olympic and Paralympic Games, Atlanta

1996 (9 JULY) *Two phosphor bands. Perf* 14½ × 14

1930	**1255**	26p multicoloured	90	1·00	□	□
		a. *Horiz strip of 5. Nos.* 1930/4	5·00	5·50	□	□
1931	**1256**	26p multicoloured	90	1·00	□	□
1932	**1257**	26p multicoloured	90	1·00	□	□
1933	**1258**	26p multicoloured	90	1·00	□	□
1934	**1259**	26p multicoloured	90	1·00	□	□
		Set of 5	5·00	4·50	□	□
		First Day Cover		5·75		□
		Presentation Pack	5·50		□	
		PHQ Cards (*set of 5*)	3·00	7·50	□	□
		Gutter Strip of 10	10·00		□	

1260 Prof. Dorothy Hodgkin (scientist)

1261 Dame Margot Fonteyn (ballerina)

1262 Dame Elisabeth Frink (sculptress)

1263 Dame Daphne du Maurier (novelist)

1264 Dame Marea Hartman (sports administrator)

Europa. Famous Women

1996 (6 AUG.) *One phosphor band* (20p) *or two phosphor bands* (*others*). *Perf* 14½

1935	**1260**	20p dull blue-green, brownish grey and black	60	25	□	□
1936	**1261**	26p dull mauve, brownish grey and black ...	75	25	□	□
1937	**1262**	31p bronze, brownish grey and black ...	95	1·10	□	□

1938	**1263**	37p silver, brownish grey and black	1·25	1·40	☐	☐
1939	**1264**	43p gold, brownish grey and black	1·40	1·50	☐	☐
		Set of 5	4·50	4·50	☐	☐
		First Day Cover		5·50		☐
		Presentation Pack	5·25		☐	
		PHQ Cards (set of 5)	3·00	7·50	☐	☐
		Set of 5 *Gutter Pairs*	9·00		☐	

Nos. 1936/7 include the 'EUROPA' emblem.

1265 *Muffin the Mule*

1266 *Sooty*

1267 *Stingray*

1268 *The Clangers*

1269 *Dangermouse*

50th Anniversary of Children's Television

1996 (3 SEPT.)–**97** *One phosphor band* (20p) *or two phosphor bands* (*others*). *Perf* 14½ × 14

1940	**1265**	20p multicoloured	55	20	☐	☐
		a. Perf 15 × 14 (23.9.97)	2·00	2·00	☐	☐
1941	**1266**	26p multicoloured	80	20	☐	☐
1942	**1267**	31p multicoloured	1·00	1·50	☐	☐
1943	**1268**	37p multicoloured	1·40	1·60	☐	☐
1944	**1269**	43p multicoloured	1·60	1·75	☐	☐
		Set of 5	4·75	4·75	☐	☐
		First Day Cover		5·50		☐
		Presentation Pack	5·25		☐	
		PHQ Cards (set of 5)	3·00	7·50	☐	☐
		Set of 5 *Gutter Pairs*	9·50		☐	

No. 1940a comes from stamp booklets.

1270 Triumph TR3

1271 MG TD

1272 Austin-Healey 100

1273 Jaguar XK120

1274 Morgan Plus 4

Classic Sports Cars

1996 (1 OCT.) *One phosphor band* (20p) *or two phosphor bands* (*others*). *Perf* 14½

1945	**1270**	20p multicoloured	55	20	☐	☐
1946	**1271**	26p multicoloured	70	20	☐	☐
1947	**1272**	37p multicoloured	1·10	1·50	☐	☐
1948	**1273**	43p multicoloured	1·10	1·50	☐	☐
1949	**1274**	63p multicoloured	1·50	1·50	☐	☐
		Set of 5	4·50	4·50	☐	☐
		First Day Cover		5·75		☐
		Presentation Pack	5·50		☐	
		PHQ Cards (set of 5)	3·00	8·00	☐	☐
		Set of 5 *Gutter Pairs*	9·00		☐	

1275 The Three Kings

1276 The Annunciation

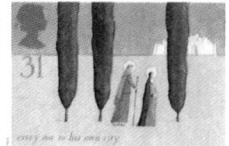

1277 The Journey to Bethlehem

1278 The Nativity

1279 The Shepherds

Christmas

1996 (28 OCT.) *One phosphor band* (2nd) *or two phosphor bands* (*others*)

1950	**1275**	(2nd) multicoloured	. . .	75	20 ☐	☐
1951	**1276**	(1st) multicoloured	. . .	1·00	25 ☐	☐
1952	**1277**	31p multicoloured	. . .	1·10	1·50 ☐	☐
1953	**1278**	43p multicoloured	. . .	1·25	1·40 ☐	☐
1954	**1279**	63p multicoloured	. . .	1·60	1·75 ☐	☐
		Set of 5	. . . .	5·25	4·50 ☐	☐
		First Day Cover	. . . .		5·50	☐
		Presentation Pack	. . . .	5·75		☐
		PHQ Cards (*set of 5*)	. . . . . .	3·00	7·00 ☐	☐
		Set of 5 Gutter Pairs	. . . . . .	10·50		☐

Collectors Pack 1996

1996 (28 OCT.) *Comprises Nos.* 1901/4 *and* 1915/54
    Collectors Pack . . . . 55·00   ☐

Post Office Yearbook

1996 (28 OCT.) *Comprises Nos.* 1901/4 *and* 1915/54 *in hardback book with slip case*
    Yearbook . . . . 65·00   ☐

1280 Gentiana acaulis (Georg Ehret)

1281 Magnolia grandiflora (Ehret)

1282 Camellia japonica (Alfred Chandler)

1283 Tulipa (Ehret)

1284 Fuchsia 'Princess of Wales' (Augusta Withers)

1285 Tulipa gesneriana (Ehret)

1286 Guzmania splendens (Charlotte Sowerby)

1287 Iris latifolia (Ehret)

1288 Hippeastrum rutilum (Pierre-Joseph Redoute)

1289 Passiflora coerulea (Ehret)

T **1280/9** were printed together, *se-tenant,* in booklet panes of 10 stamps and 20 half stamp-size labels.

Greeting Stamps. 19th-century Flower Paintings

1997 (6 JAN.) *Two phosphor bands. Perf* 14½ × 14 (*with one elliptical hole on each vertical side*)

1955	**1280**	(1st) multicoloured	. . . .	85	85 ☐	☐
		a. Booklet pane. Nos.				
		1955/64	. . . . . .	9·00		☐
1956	**1281**	(1st) multicoloured	. . . .	85	85 ☐	☐
1957	**1282**	(1st) multicoloured	. . . .	85	85 ☐	☐
1958	**1283**	(1st) multicoloured	. . . .	85	85 ☐	☐
1959	**1284**	(1st) multicoloured	. . . .	85	85 ☐	☐
1960	**1285**	(1st) multicoloured	. . . .	85	85 ☐	☐
1961	**1286**	(1st) multicoloured	. . . .	85	85 ☐	☐
1962	**1287**	(1st) multicoloured	. . . .	85	85 ☐	☐

1963	**1288**	(1st) multicoloured	85	85	□	□
1964	**1289**	(1st) multicoloured	85	85	□	□
		Set of 10	9·00	7·75	□	□
		First Day Cover		10·00		□
		Presentation Pack	10·00		□	
		PHQ Cards (set of 10)	9·00	18·00	□	□

1290 'King Henry VIII'

1291 'Catherine of Aragon'

1292 'Anne Boleyn'

1293 'Jane Seymour'

1294 'Anne of Cleves'

1295 'Catherine Howard'

1296 'Catherine Parr'

T **1290/6** were printed together, *se-tenant*, in horizontal strips of 6 throughout the sheet.

450th Death Anniversary of King Henry VIII

1997 (21 JAN.) *Two phosphor bands. Perf 15 (No. 1965) or 14 × 15 (others)*

1965	**1290**	26p multicoloured	1·00	80	□	□
1966	**1291**	26p multicoloured	1·25	85	□	□
		a. Horiz strip of 6. Nos.				
		1966/71	7·50	8·50	□	□
1967	**1292**	26p multicoloured	1·25	85	□	□
1968	**1293**	26p multicoloured	1·25	85	□	□
1969	**1294**	26p multicoloured	1·25	85	□	□
1970	**1295**	26p multicoloured	1·25	85	□	□
1971	**1296**	26p multicoloured	1·25	85	□	□
		Set of 7	7·75	5·50	□	□
		First Day Cover		9·00		□
		Presentation Pack	8·50		□	
		PHQ Cards (set of 7)	7·00	12·00	□	□
		Gutter Pair and Gutter Block of 12	17·00		□	

1297 St Columba in Boat

1298 St Columba on Iona

1299 St Augustine with King Ethelbert

1300 St Augustine with Model of Cathedral

Religious Anniversaries

1997 (11 MAR.) *Two phosphor bands. Perf 14½*

1972	**1297**	26p multicoloured	75	35	□	□
1973	**1298**	37p multicoloured	1·10	1·50	□	□
1974	**1299**	43p multicoloured	1·50	1·50	□	□
1975	**1300**	63p multicoloured	2·00	2·10	□	□
		Set of 4	4·75	5·00	□	□
		First Day Cover		6·00		□
		Presentation Pack	5·25		□	
		PHQ Cards (set of 4)	2·50	7·25	□	□
		Set of 4 Gutter Pairs	9·50		□	

Nos. 1972/3 commemorate the 1400th death anniversary of St Columba and Nos. 1974/5 the 1400th anniversary of the arrival of St Augustine of Canterbury in Kent.

1301

1302

Self-adhesive Coil Stamps

1997 (18 MAR.) *Photo Enschedé. One centre phosphor band (2nd) or two phosphor bands (1st). Perf 14 × 15 die-cut (with one elliptical hole on each vertical side)*

1976	**1301**	(2nd) bright blue	2·25	2·50	☐	☐
1977	**1302**	(1st) bright orange-red .	2·75	2·75	☐	☐
		Set of 2	5·00	5·25	☐	☐
		First Day Cover		5·50		☐
		Presentation Pack		4·00		☐

Nos. 1976/7, which were priced at 20p and 26p, were each sold in rolls of 100 with the stamps separate on the backing paper.

Royal Golden Wedding (1st issue)

1997 (21 APR.) *Designs as T 367 and 914 but colours changed. Printed in photogravure by Harrison (26p), Harrison or Walsall (1st). Two phosphor bands. Perf 15 × 14 (with one elliptical hole on each vertical side)*

1978	**367**	26p gold	90	90	☐	☐
1979	**914**	(1st) gold	90	90	☐	☐
		Set of 2	1·75	1·75	☐	☐
		First Day Cover		3·50		☐
		Presentation Pack		3·00		☐

See also Nos. 2011/14

For self-adhesive version of No. 1979 see No. 2295

1303 *Dracula*

1305 *Dr Jekyll and Mr Hyde*

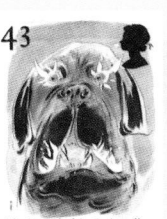

1304 *Frankenstein*

1306 *The Hound of the Baskervilles*

Europa. Tales and Legends. Horror Stories

1997 (13 MAY) *Two phosphor bands. Perf 14 × 15*

1980	**1303**	26p multicoloured	90	40	☐	☐
1981	**1304**	31p multicoloured	1·00	1·40	☐	☐
1982	**1305**	37p multicoloured	1·25	1·50	☐	☐
1983	**1306**	43p multicoloured	1·50	1·60	☐	☐
		Set of 4	4·25	4·50	☐	☐
		First Day Cover		6·00		☐
		Presentation Pack	5·00			☐
		PHQ Cards (set of 4)	3·00	6·50	☐	☐
		Set of 4 Gutter Pairs	8·50			☐

Nos. 1980/3 commemorate the birth bicentenary of Mary Shelley (creator of Frankenstein) with the 26p and 31p values incorporating the 'EUROPA' emblem.

1307 Reginald Mitchell and Supermarine Spitfire MkIIA

1308 Roy Chadwick and Avro Lancaster MkI

1309 Ronald Bishop and De Havilland Mosquito B MkXVI

1310 George Carter and Gloster Meteor T Mk7

1311 Sir Sidney Camm and Hawker Hunter FGA Mk9

British Aircraft Designers

1997 (10 JUNE) *One phosphor band (20p) or two phosphor bands (others)*

1984	**1307**	20p multicoloured	55	40	☐	☐
1985	**1308**	26p multicoloured	95	1·10	☐	☐
1986	**1309**	37p multicoloured	1·25	1·10	☐	☐
1987	**1310**	43p multicoloured	1·40	1·40	☐	☐
1988	**1311**	63p multicoloured	1·90	1·90	☐	☐
		Set of 5	5·50	5·25	☐	☐
		First Day Cover		6·25		☐
		Presentation Pack	6·00			☐
		PHQ Cards	3·50	9·00	☐	☐
		Set of 5 Gutter Pairs	11·00			☐

1312 Carriage Horse and Coachman

1313 Lifeguards Horse and Trooper

1314 Household Cavalry Drum Horse and Drummer

1315 Duke of Edinburgh's Horse and Groom

'All The Queen's Horses'. 50th Anniv of the British Horse Society
1997 (8 July) *One phosphor band (20p) or two phosphor bands (others). Perf 14½*

1989	1312	20p multicoloured	75	45	☐	☐
1990	1313	26p multicoloured	1·10	1·40	☐	☐
1991	1314	43p multicoloured	1·40	1·50	☐	☐
1992	1315	63p multicoloured	1·90	2·00	☐	☐
		Set of 4	4·75	4·75	☐	☐
		First Day Cover		5·75		☐
		Presentation Pack	5·50		☐	
		PHQ Cards (set of 4)	2·50	6·75	☐	☐
		Set of 4 Gutter Pairs	9·50		☐	

CASTLE

Harrison printing (Nos. 1611/14)

CASTLE

Enschedé printing (Nos. 1993/6)

Differences between Harrison and Enschedé printings:
    Harrison – 'C' has top serif and tail of letter points to right. 'A' has flat top. 'S' has top and bottom serifs.
    Enschedé – 'C' has no top serif and tail of letter points upwards. 'A' has pointed top. 'S' has no serifs.

1997 (29 July) *Designs as Nos. 1612/14 with Queen's head in silhouette as T 1044, but re-engraved as above. Perf 15 × 14 (with one elliptical hole on each vertical side).*

1993	880	£1·50 deep claret and gold†	5·50	3·75	☐	☐
1994	881	£2 indigo and gold† ...	7·00	2·00	☐	☐
1995	1044	£3 violet and gold† ...	10·00	3·50	☐	☐
1996	882	£5 deep brown and gold†	18·00	10·00	☐	☐
		Set of 4	35·00	17·00	☐	☐
		Set of 4 Gutter Pairs	70·00		☐	
		Presentation Pack (P.O Pack No. 40)	40·00		☐	

† The Queen's head on these stamps is printed in optically variable ink which changes colour from gold to green when viewed from different angles.

1316 Haroldswick, Shetland

1317 Painswick, Gloucestershire

1318 Beddgelert, Gwynedd

1319 Ballyroney, County Down

Sub-Post Offices
1997 (12 Aug.) *One phosphor band (20p) or two phosphor bands (others). Perf 14½*

1997	1316	20p multicoloured	65	50	☐	☐
1998	1317	26p multicoloured	85	50	☐	☐
1999	1318	43p multicoloured	1·40	1·50	☐	☐
2000	1319	63p multicoloured	1·90	2·10	☐	☐
		Set of 4	4·25	4·00	☐	☐
		First Day Cover		5·50		☐
		Presentation Pack	5·00		☐	
		PHQ Cards (set of 4)	2·50	7·00	☐	☐
		Set of 4 Gutter Pairs	8·50		☐	

Nos. 1997/2000 also mark the centenary of the National Federation of Sub-Postmasters.

1320 Noddy

1321 Famous Five

Enid Blyton's *Secret Seven*

1322   *Secret Seven*

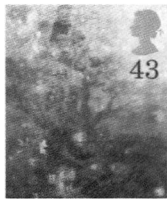

Enid Blyton's *Faraway Tree*

1323   *Faraway Tree*

Enid Blyton's *Malory Towers*

1324   *Malory Towers*

Birth Centenary of Enid Blyton (children's author)

1997 (9 SEPT.) *One phosphor band* (20p) *or two phosphor bands* (*others*). Perf 14 × 14½

2001	**1320**	20p multicoloured	. . . .	60	45	☐ ☐
2002	**1321**	26p multicoloured	. . . .	1·00	1·25	☐ ☐
2003	**1322**	37p multicoloured	. . . .	1·25	1·25	☐ ☐
2004	**1323**	43p multicoloured	. . . .	1·50	1·50	☐ ☐
2005	**1324**	63p multicoloured	. . . .	2·00	2·00	☐ ☐
	Set of 5	. . . .		5·75	5·75	☐ ☐
	First Day Cover	. . . .			6·50	☐
	Presentation Pack	. . . .		6·00		☐
	PHQ Cards (*set of* 5)	. . . . . .		3·50	9·00	☐ ☐
	Set of 5 *Gutter Pairs*	. . . . . .		11·50		☐

1325   Children and Father Christmas pulling Cracker

1326   Father Christmas with Traditional Cracker

1327   Father Christmas riding Cracker

1328   Father Christmas on Snowball

1329   Father Christmas and Chimney

Christmas. 150th Anniversary of the Christmas Cracker

1997 (27 OCT.) *One phosphor band* (2nd) *or two phosphor bands* (*others*)

2006	**1325**	(2nd) multicoloured	. . . .	75	20	☐ ☐
2007	**1326**	(1st) multicoloured	. . . .	90	25	☐ ☐
2008	**1327**	31p multicoloured	. . . .	1·00	1·50	☐ ☐
2009	**1328**	43p multicoloured	. . . .	1·25	1·50	☐ ☐
2010	**1329**	63p multicoloured	. . . .	1·60	1·90	☐ ☐
	Set of 5	. . . .		5·00	4·75	☐ ☐
	First Day Cover	. . . .			5·50	☐
	Presentation Pack	. . . .		5·75		☐
	PHQ Cards (*set of* 5)	. . . . . .		3·00	8·50	☐ ☐
	Set of 5 *Gutter Pairs*	. . . . . .		10·00		☐

The 1st value was re-issued on 3 October 2000, in sheets, each stamp with a *se-tenant* label, in connection with 'customised' service available from the Philatelic Bureau. The labels show either Christmas greetings or a personal photograph.

1330   Wedding Photograph, 1947

1331   Queen Elizabeth II and Prince Philip, 1997

Royal Golden Wedding (2nd issue)

1997 (13 NOV.) *One phosphor band* (20p) *or two phosphor bands* (*others*). Perf 15

2011	**1330**	20p gold, yellow-brown and grey-black	. . .	85	45	☐ ☐
2012	**1331**	26p multicoloured		1·10	70	☐ ☐
2013	**1330**	43p gold, bluish green and grey-black	. . .	1·90	2·25	☐ ☐
2014	**1331**	63p multicoloured	. . . .	2·50	3·00	☐ ☐
	Set of 4			5·75	5·75	☐ ☐
	First Day Cover	. . . .			6·50	☐
	Presentation Pack	. . . .		6·25		☐
	Souvenir Book (*contains Nos.* 1979, 1989/92 *and* 2011/14)	. .		18·00		☐
	PHQ Cards (*set of* 4)	. . . . . .		2·50	7·00	☐ ☐
	Set of 4 *Gutter Pairs*	. . . . . .		12·00		☐

Collectors Pack 1997

1997 (13 Nov.) *Comprises Nos. 1965/75, 1980/92 and 1997/2014*

      Collectors Pack . . . . 60·00   □

Post Office Yearbook

1997 (13 Nov.) *Comprises Nos. 1965/75, 1980/92 and 1997/2014 in hardback book with slip case*

      Yearbook . . . . 60·00   □

 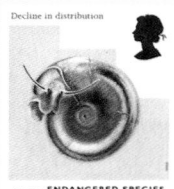

| 1332 | Common Doormouse | 1333 | Lady's Slipper Orchid |

| 1334 | Song Thrush | 1335 | Shining Ram's-horn Snail |

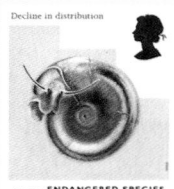

| 1336 | Mole Cricket | 1337 | Devil's Bolete |

Endangered Species

1998 (20 Jan.) *One side phosphor band* (20p) *or two phosphor bands* (others). *Perf* 14 × 14½

2015	**1332**	20p multicoloured	. . . .	60	40	□	□
2016	**1333**	26p multicoloured	. . . .	75	40	□	□
2017	**1334**	31p multicoloured	. . . .	1·00	1·00	□	□
2018	**1335**	37p multicoloured	. . . .	1·25	1·10	□	□

2019	**1336**	43p multicoloured	. . . .	1·40	1·25	□	□
2020	**1337**	63p multicoloured	. . . .	1·90	1·75	□	□
		Set of 6	. . . .	6·25	5·25	□	□
		First Day Cover	. . . .		5·75		□
		Presentation Pack	. . . . . .	6·75		□	
		PHQ Cards (Set of 6)	. . . . . .	3·00	9·00	□	□
		Set of 6 Gutter Pairs	. . . . .	13·50		□	

| 1338 | Diana, Princess of Wales (photo by Lord Snowdon) | 1339 | At British Lung Foundation Function, April 1997 (photo by John Stillwell) |

| 1340 | Wearing Tiara, 1991 (photo by Lord Snowdon) | 1341 | On Visit to Birmingham, October 1995 (photo by Tim Graham) |

1342   In Evening Dress, 1987 (photo by Terence Donovan)

T **1338/42** *were printed together,* se-tenant, *in horizontal strips of 5 throughout the sheet.*

Diana, Princess of Wales Commemoration

1998 (3 Feb.) *Two phosphor bands*

2021	**1338**	26p multicoloured	. . . .	90	90	□	□
		a. Horiz strip of 5. Nos.					
		2021/5	. . . .	4·00	4·50	□	□
2022	**1339**	26p multicoloured	. . . .	90	90	□	□
2023	**1340**	26p multicoloured	. . . .	90	90	□	□

2024	**1341**	26p multicoloured	. . . .	90	90	☐	☐
2025	**1342**	26p multicoloured	. . . .	90	90	☐	☐
		Set of 5	. . . .	4·00	4·00	☐	☐
		First Day Cover	. . . .		6·00		☐
		Presentation Pack	. . . .	15·00		☐	
		Presentation Pack (Welsh)	. . .	80·00		☐	
		Gutter Strip of 10	. . . .	8·00		☐	

1343 Lion of England and Griffin of Edward III

1344 Falcon of Plantagenet and Bull of Clarence

1345 Lion of Mortimer and Yale of Beaufort

1346 Greyhound of Richmond and Dragon of Wales

1347 Unicorn of Scotland and Horse of Hanover

T **1343**/7 were printed together, *se-tenant,* in horizontal strips of 5 throughout the sheet.

650th Anniversary of the Order of the Garter. The Queen's Beasts

1998 (24 FEB.) *Two phosphor bands*

2026	**1343**	26p multicoloured	. . . .	90	90	☐	☐
		a. Horiz strip of 5. Nos.					
		2026/30	. . . . . .	4·00	4·50	☐	☐
2027	**1344**	26p multicoloured	. . . .	90	90	☐	☐
2028	**1345**	26p multicoloured	. . . .	90	90	☐	☐
2029	**1346**	26p multicoloured	. . . .	90	90	☐	☐
2030	**1347**	26p multicoloured	. . . .	90	90	☐	☐
		Set of 5	. . . .	4·00	4·00	☐	☐
		First Day Cover	. . . .		5·25		☐
		Presentation Pack	. . . .	5·00		☐	
		PHQ Cards (set of 5)	. . . . .	3·00	8·00	☐	☐
		Gutter Block of 10	. . . . . .	8·00		☐	

The phosphor bands on Nos. 2026/30 are only half the height of the stamps and do not cover the silver parts of the designs.

1348

Booklet Stamps

1998 (10 MAR.) *Design as T* 157 *(issued 1952–54), but with face values in decimal currency as T* **1348**. *One side phosphor band (20p) or two phosphor bands (others). Perf 14 (with one elliptical hole on each vertical side)*

2031	**1348**	20p light green	. . . . . .	70	75	☐	☐
2032		26p red-brown	. . . . . .	90	95	☐	☐
2033		37p light purple	. . . . .	2·50	2·50	☐	☐
		Set of 3	. . . .	3·75	3·75	☐	☐

1349 St John's Point Lighthouse, County Down

1350 Smalls Lighthouse, Pembrokeshire

1351 Needles Rock Lighthouse, Isle of Wight, c 1900

1352 Bell Rock Lighthouse, Arbroath, mid-19th-century

1353 Eddystone Lighthouse, Plymouth, 1698

Lighthouses

1998 (24 MAR.) *One side phosphor band (20p) or two phosphor bands (others). Perf 14½ × 14*

2034	**1349**	20p multicoloured	50	40	□	□
2035	**1350**	26p multicoloured	75	50	□	□
2036	**1351**	37p multicoloured	1·10	1·25	□	□
2037	**1352**	43p multicoloured	1·50	1·50	□	□
2038	**1353**	63p multicoloured	2·10	2·10	□	□
		Set of 5	5·50	5·25	□	□
		First Day Cover		5·75	□	
		Presentation Pack	6·00		□	
		PHQ Cards (set of 5)	3·50	9·00	□	□
		Set of 5 Gutter Pairs	11·00		□	

Nos. 2034/8 commemorate the 300th anniversary of the first Eddystone Lighthouse and the final year of manned light-houses.

Self-adhesive stamps

1998 (6 APR.) *Photo Enschedé, Questa or Walsall. Designs as T* **913/14.** *One centre phosphor band (2nd) or two phosphor bands (1st). Perf 15 × 14 die-cut (with one elliptical hole on each vertical side)*

2039	(2nd) bright blue	30	35	□	□
	b. Perf 14½ × 14 die-cut	30·00		□	□
2040	(1st) bright orange-red	40	45	□	□
	b. Perf 14½ × 14 die-cut	30·00		□	□
	Set of 2	70	80	□	□

Nos. 2039/40 were initially priced at 20p and 26p, and were available in coils of 200 (Enschedé), sheets of 100 (Enschedé, Questa or Walsall) or self-adhesive booklets (Questa or Walsall). See also Nos. 2295/8.

1354   Tommy Cooper

1355   Eric Morecambe

1356   Joyce Grenfell

1357   Les Dawson

1358   Peter Cook

Comedians

1998 (23 APR.) *One phosphor band (20p) or two phosphor bands (others). Perf 14½ × 14*

2041	**1354**	20p multicoloured	50	50	□	□
2042	**1355**	26p multicoloured	90	85	□	□
2043	**1356**	37p multicoloured	1·25	1·25	□	□
2044	**1357**	43p multicoloured	1·50	1·50	□	□
2045	**1358**	63p multicoloured	2·10	2·10	□	□
		Set of 5	5·75	5·50	□	□
		First Day Cover		6·50	□	
		Presentation Pack	6·00		□	
		PHQ Cards (set of 5)	3·50	10·00	□	□
		Set of 5 Gutter Pairs	11·50		□	

1359   Hands forming Heart

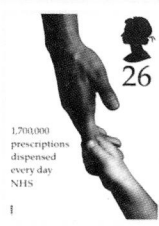

1360   Adult and Child holding Hands

1361   Hands forming Cradle

1362   Hands taking Pulse

50th Anniversary of National Health Service

1998 (23 JUNE) *One side phosphor band (20p) or two phosphor bands (others). Perf 14 × 14½*

2046	**1359**	20p multicoloured	50	50	□	□
2047	**1360**	26p multicoloured	80	80	□	□
2048	**1361**	43p multicoloured	1·40	1·40	□	□
2049	**1362**	63p multicoloured	2·10	2·10	□	□
		Set of 4	4·25	4·25	□	□
		First Day Cover		5·00	□	
		Presentation Pack	4·50		□	
		PHQ Cards (set of 4)	2·50	6·00	□	□
		Set of 4 Gutter Pairs	8·50		□	

For full information on all future British issues, collectors should write to Royal Mail, Freepost EH3647, 21 South Gyle Crescent, Edinburgh EH12 9PE.

1363 *The Hobbit*
(J. R. R. Tolkien)

1364 *The Lion, The Witch and the Wardrobe*
(C. S. Lewis)

1365 *The Phoenix and the Carpet* (E. Nesbit)

1366 *The Borrowers*
(Mary Norton)

1367 *Through the Looking Glass* (Lewis Carroll)

Famous Children's Fantasy Novels

1998 (21 July) *One phosphor band* (20p) *or two phosphor bands (others)*

2050	**1363**	20p multicoloured	50	45	□	□
2051	**1364**	26p multicoloured	85	55	□	□
2052	**1365**	37p multicoloured	1·25	1·50	□	□
2053	**1366**	43p multicoloured	1·40	1·50	□	□
2054	**1367**	63p multicoloured	2·10	2·00	□	□
		Set of 5	5·50	5·50	□	□
		First Day Cover		6·25		□
		Presentation Pack	6·00		□	
		PHQ Cards (set of 5)	3·00	9·00	□	□
		Set of 5 Gutter Pairs	11·00		□	

Nos. 2050/4 commemorate the birth centenary of C. S. Lewis and the death centenary of Lewis Carroll.

1368 Woman in Yellow
Feathered Costume

1369 Woman in Blue
Costume and Headdress

1370 Group of Children in
White and Gold Robes

1371 Child in 'Tree' Costume

Europa. Festivals. Notting Hill Carnival

1998 (25 Aug.) *One centre phosphor band* (20p) *or two phosphor bands (others). Perf* 14 × 14½

2055	**1368**	20p multicoloured	75	45	□	□
2056	**1369**	26p multicoloured	95	55	□	□
2057	**1370**	43p multicoloured	1·50	1·60	□	□
2058	**1371**	63p multicoloured	2·00	2·10	□	□
		Set of 4	4·75	4·25	□	□
		First Day Cover		5·00		□
		Presentation Pack	5·25		□	
		PHQ Cards (set of 4)	2·50	6·00	□	□
		Set of 4 Gutter Pairs	9·50		□	

Nos. 2055/6 include the 'EUROPA' emblem.

1372 Sir Malcolm Campbell's
Bluebird, 1925

1373 Sir Henry Segrave's
Sunbeam, 1926

1374 John G. Parry Thomas's
Babs, 1926

1375 John R. Cobb's
Railton Mobil Special, 1947

1376 Donald Campbell's
Bluebird CN7, 1964

British Land Speed Record Holders

1998 (29 SEPT.–13 OCT.) *One phosphor band (20p) or two phosphor bands (others). Perf 15 × 14*

2059	**1372**	20p multicoloured (centre band)	70	25	□	□
		a. Perf 14½ × 13½ (side band) (13 Oct.) . . .	1·00	1·00	□	□
2060	**1373**	26p multicoloured	85	30	□	□
2061	**1374**	30p multicoloured	1·25	1·50	□	□
2062	**1375**	43p multicoloured	1·50	1·60	□	□
2063	**1376**	63p multicoloured	2·25	2·40	□	□
		Set of 5	6·00	5·50	□	□
		First Day Cover		6·50		□
		Presentation Pack	6·50		□	
		PHQ Cards (set of 5)	3·00	7·50	□	□
		Set of 5 Gutter Pairs	12·00		□	

No. 2059*a*, which occurs with the phosphor band at the left or right of the stamp, comes from stamp booklets. There are minor differences of design between No. 2059 and No. 2059*a*, which also omits the copyright symbol and date.

Nos. 2059/63 commemorate the 50th death anniversary of Sir Malcolm Campbell.

1377 Angel with Hands raised in Blessing

1378 Angel praying

1379 Angel playing Flute

1380 Angel playing Lute

1381 Angel praying

Christmas. Angels

1998 (2 Nov.) *One phosphor band (20p) or two phosphor bands (others)*

2064	**1377**	20p multicoloured	70	50	□	□
2065	**1378**	26p multicoloured	85	60	□	□
2066	**1379**	30p multicoloured	1·25	1·50	□	□
2067	**1380**	43p multicoloured	1·40	1·60	□	□
2068	**1381**	63p multicoloured	2·00	2·25	□	□
		Set of 5	5·50	5·75	□	□
		First Day Cover		6·00		□
		Presentation Pack	6·00		□	
		PHQ Cards (set of 5)	3·00	7·50	□	□
		Set of 5 Gutter Pairs	11·00		□	

Collectors Pack 1998

1998 (2 Nov.) *Comprises Nos. 2015/30, 2034/8 and 2041/68*

Collectors Pack	55·00	□

Post Office Yearbook

1998 (2 Nov.) *Comprises Nos. 2015/30, 2034/8 and 2041/68 in hardback book with slip case*

Yearbook	60·00	□

1382 Greenwich Meridian and Clock (John Harrison's chronometer)

1383 Industrial Worker and Blast Furnace (James Watt's discovery of steam power)

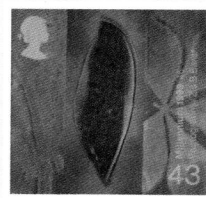
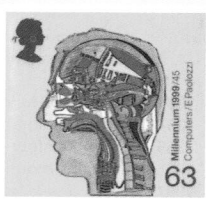

1384 Early Photos of Leaves (Henry Fox-Talbot's photographic experiments)

1385 Computer inside Human Head (Alan Turing's work on computers)

Millennium Series. The Inventors' Tale

1999 (12 JAN.–21 SEPT.) *One centre phosphor band (20p) or two phosphor bands (others). Perf 14 × 14½*

2069	**1382**	20p multicoloured	65	65	□	□
2070	**1383**	26p multicoloured	85	95	□	□
2071	**1384**	43p multicoloured	1·40	1·50	□	□
2072	**1385**	63p multicoloured	2·00	2·25	□	□
		a. Perf 13½ × 14 (21 Sept.)	3·00	3·00	□	□
		Set of 4	4·50	4·75	□	□
		First Day Cover		6·00		□
		Presentation Pack	5·00		□	
		PHQ Cards (set of 4)	3·00	10·00	□	□
		Set of 4 Gutter Pairs	9·00		□	

No. 2072*a* comes from stamp booklets.

1386 Airliner hugging Globe (International air travel)

1387 Woman on Bicycle (Development of the bicycle)

1388 Victorian Railway Station (Growth of public transport)

1389 Captain Cook and Maori (Captain James Cook's voyages)

Millennium Series. The Travellers' Tale

1999 (2 FEB.) *One centre phosphor band* (20p) *or two phosphor bands* (*others*)*. Perf* 14 × 14½

2073	**1386**	20p multicoloured	65	65	□	□
2074	**1387**	26p multicoloured . . .	85	95	□	□
2075	**1388**	43p grey-black, stone and bronze	1·40	1·50	□	□
2076	**1389**	63p multicoloured	2·00	2·25	□	□
	Set of 4		4·50	4·75	□	□
	First Day Cover			6·00		
	Presentation Pack		5·00		□	
	PHQ Cards (*set of 4*)		3·00	9·00	□	□
	Set of 4 Gutter Pairs		9·00		□	

1390

1999 (16 FEB.) (*a*) *Embossed and litho Walsall. Self-adhesive. Die-cut perf* 14 × 15

2077	**1390**	(1st) grey (face value) (Queen's head in colourless relief) (phosphor background around head)	2·00	2·00	□	□

(*b*) *Recess Enschedé. Perf* 14 × 14½

2078	**1390**	(1st) grey-black (2 phosphor bands)	2·00	2·00	□	□

(*c*) *Typo Harrison. Perf* 14 × 15

2079	**1390**	(1st) black (2 phosphor bands)	2·00	2·00	□	□
	Set of 3		5·50	5·50	□	□

Nos. 2077/9 were only issued in £7·54 stamp booklets.

1391 Vaccinating Child (pattern in cow markings) (Jenner's development of smallpox vaccine)

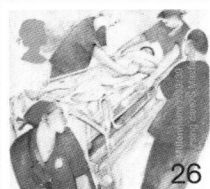

1392 Patient on Trolley (nursing care)

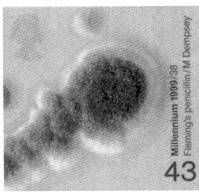

1393 Penicillin Mould (Fleming's discovery of penicillin)

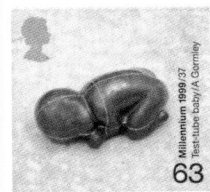

1394 Sculpture of Test-tube Baby (development of in vitro fertilization)

Millennium Series. The Patients' Tale

1999 (2 MAR.) *One centre phosphor band* (20p) *or two phosphor bands* (*others*)*. Perf* 13½ × 14

2080	**1391**	20p multicoloured	65	65	□	□
2081	**1392**	26p multicoloured	85	95	□	□
2082	**1393**	43p multicoloured	1·40	1·50	□	□
2083	**1394**	63p multicoloured	2·00	2·25	□	□
	Set of 4		4·50	4·75	□	□
	First Day Cover			6·00		
	Presentation Pack		5·00		□	
	PHQ Cards (*set of 4*)		3·00	9·00	□	□
	Set of 4 Gutter Pairs		9·00		□	

Minimum Price. The minimum price quoted is 10p. This represents a handling charge rather than a basis for valuing common stamps. Where the actual value of a stamp is less than 10p this may be apparent when set prices are shown, particularly in sets including a number of 10p stamps. It therefore follows that in valuing common stamps the 10p catalogue price should not be reckoned automatically since it covers a variation in real scarcity.

1395 Dove and Norman Settler (medieval migration to Scotland)

1396 Pilgrim Fathers and Red Indian (17th-century migration to America)

1397 Sailing Ship and Aspects of Settlement (19th-century migration to Australia)

1398 Hummingbird and Superimposed Stylised Face (20th-century migration to Great Britain)

Millennium Series. The Settlers' Tale

1999 (6 APR.) *One centre phosphor band* (20p) *or two phosphor bands* (*others*). *Perf* 14 × 14½

2084	1395	20p multicoloured	65	65	☐	☐
2085	1396	26p multicoloured	85	95	☐	☐
2086	1397	43p multicoloured	1·40	1·50	☐	☐
2087	1398	63p multicoloured	2·00	2·25	☐	☐
		Set of 4	4·50	4·75	☐	☐
		First Day Cover		6·00		☐
		Presentation Pack	5·00		☐	
		PHQ Cards (set of 4)	3·00	9·00	☐	☐
		Set of 4 Gutter Pairs	9·00		☐	

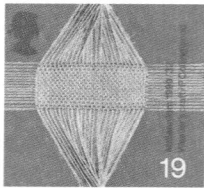

1399 Woven Threads (woollen industry)

1400 Salts Mill, Saltaire (worsted cloth industry)

1401 Hull on Slipway (shipbuilding)

1402 Lloyd's Building (City of London finance centre)

Millennium Series. The Workers' Tale

1999 (4 MAY) *One centre phosphor band* (19p) *or two phosphor bands* (*others*). *Perf* 14 × 14½

2088	1399	19p multicoloured	65	65	☐	☐
2089	1400	26p multicoloured	85	95	☐	☐
2090	1401	44p multicoloured	1·40	1·50	☐	☐
2091	1402	64p multicoloured	2·00	2·25	☐	☐
		Set of 4	4·50	4·75	☐	☐
		First Day Cover		6·00		☐
		Presentation Pack	5·00		☐	
		PHQ Cards (set of 4)	3·00	9·00	☐	☐
		Set of 4 Gutter Pairs	9·00		☐	

1403 Freddie Mercury (lead singer of Queen) ('Popular Music')

1404 Bobby Moore with World Cup, 1966 ('Sport')

1405 Dalek from *Dr Who* (science-fiction series) ('Television')

1406 Charlie Chaplin (film star) ('Cinema')

Millennium Series. The Entertainers' Tale

1999 (1 JUNE) *One centre phosphor band* (19p) *or two phosphor bands* (*others*). *Perf* 14 × 14½

2092	1403	19p multicoloured	65	65	☐	☐
2093	1404	26p multicoloured	85	95	☐	☐

2094	1405	44p multicoloured	1·40	1·50	☐	☐
2095	1406	64p multicoloured	2·00	2·25	☐	☐
		Set of 4	4·50	4·75	☐	☐
		First Day Cover		6·00		☐
		Presentation Pack	5·00			☐
		PHQ Cards (set of 4)	3·00	9·00	☐	☐
		Set of 4 Gutter Pairs	9·00			☐

1407 Prince Edward and Miss Sophie Rhys-Jones **1408**
(from photos by John Swannell)

Royal Wedding

1999 (15 JUNE) *Two phosphor bands*

2096	1407	26p multicoloured	85	85	☐	☐
2097	1408	64p multicoloured	1·90	1·90	☐	☐
		Set of 2	2·75	2·75	☐	☐
		First Day Cover		4·25		☐
		Presentation Pack	3·25			☐
		PHQ Cards (set of 2)	1·50	5·50	☐	☐
		Set of 2 Gutter Pairs	5·50			☐

 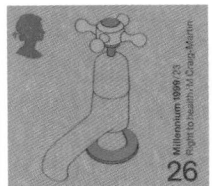

1409 Suffragette behind Prison Window ('Equal Rights for Women')

1410 Water Tap ('Right to Health')

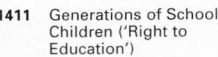 

1411 Generations of School Children ('Right to Education')

1412 'MAGNA CARTA' ('Human Rights')

Millennium Series. The Citizens' Tale

1999 (6 JULY) *One centre phosphor band* (19p) *or two phosphor bands* (others). *Perf* 14 × 14½

2098	1409	19p multicoloured	65	65	☐	☐
2099	1410	26p multicoloured	85	95	☐	☐

2100	1411	44p multicoloured	1·40	1·50	☐	☐
2101	1412	64p multicoloured	2·00	2·25	☐	☐
		Set of 4	4·50	4·75	☐	☐
		First Day Cover		6·00		☐
		Presentation Pack	5·00			☐
		PHQ Cards (set of 4)	3·00	9·00	☐	☐
		Set of 4 Gutter Pairs	9·00			☐

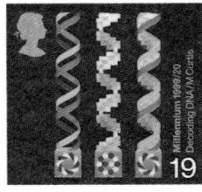 

1413 Molecular Structures ('DNA decoding')

1414 Galapagos Finch and Fossilized Skeleton ('Darwin's theory of evolution')

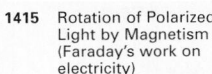 

1415 Rotation of Polarized Light by Magnetism (Faraday's work on electricity)

1416 Saturn (development of astronomical telescopes)

Millennium Series. The Scientists' Tale

1999 (3 AUG.–21 SEPT.) *One centre phosphor band* (19p) *or two phosphor bands* (others). *Perf* 13½ × 14 (19p, 64p) *or* 14 × 14½ (26p, 44p)

2102	1413	19p multicoloured	65	65	☐	☐
2103	1414	26p multicoloured	85	95	☐	☐
		b. Perf 14½ × 14 (21 Sept.)	2·50	2·50	☐	☐
2104	1415	44p multicoloured	1·40	1·50	☐	☐
		a. Perf 14½ × 14 (21 Sept.)	2·75	2·75	☐	☐
2105	1416	64p multicoloured	2·00	2·25	☐	☐
		Set of 4	4·50	4·75	☐	☐
		First Day Cover		6·00		☐
		Presentation Pack	5·00			☐
		PHQ Cards (set of 4)	3·00	9·00	☐	☐
		Set of 4 Gutter Pairs	9·00			☐

Nos. 2103b and 2104a come from stamp booklets.

For full information on all future British issues, collectors should write to Royal Mail, Freepost EH3647, 21 South Gyle Crescent, Edinburgh EH12 9PE.

1416a

Solar Eclipse

1999 (11 Aug.) *Sheet 89 × 121 mm. Two phosphor bands. Perf 14 × 14½*

MS2106	**1416a**	64p × 4 multicoloured	15·00	15·00 □	□
	First Day Cover			16·00	□

1417 Upland Landscape (Strip farming)

1418 Horse-drawn Rotary Seed Drill (Mechanical farming)

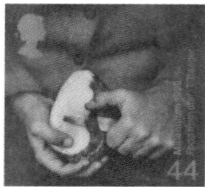

1419 Man peeling Potato (Food imports)

1420 Aerial View of Combine Harvester (Satellite agriculture)

Millennium Series. The Farmers' Tale

1999 (7 Sept.) *One centre phosphor band (19p) or two phosphor bands (others). Perf 14 × 14½*

2107	**1417**	19p multicoloured	65	65	□	□
2108	**1418**	26p multicoloured	85	95	□	□
2109	**1419**	44p multicoloured	1·40	1·50	□	□
2110	**1420**	64p multicoloured	2·00	2·25	□	□
		Set of 4	4·50	4·75	□	□
		First Day Cover		6·00		□
		Presentation Pack	5·00		□	
		PHQ Cards (set of 4)	3·00	9·00	□	□
		Set of 4 Gutter Pairs	9·00		□	

No. 2107 includes the 'EUROPA' emblem.

1421 Robert the Bruce (Battle of Bannockburn, 1314)

1422 Cavalier and Horse (English Civil War)

1423 War Graves Cemetery, The Somme (World Wars)

1424 Soldiers with Boy (Peace-keeping)

Millennium Series. The Soldiers' Tale

1999 (5 Oct.) *One centre phosphor band (19p) or two phosphor bands (others). Perf 14 × 14½*

2111	**1421**	19p black, stone and silver	65	65	□	□
2112	**1422**	26p multicoloured	85	95	□	□
2113	**1423**	44p grey-black, black and silver	1·40	1·50	□	□
2114	**1424**	64p multicoloured	2·00	2·25	□	□
		Set of 4	4·50	4·75	□	□
		First Day Cover		6·00		□
		Presentation Pack	5·00		□	
		PHQ Cards (set of 4)	3·00	9·00	□	□
		Set of 4 Gutter Pairs	9·00		□	

For full information on all future British issues, collectors should write to Royal Mail, Freepost EH3647, 21 South Gyle Crescent, Edinburgh EH12 9PE.

1425 'Hark the herald angels sing', and Hymnbook (John Wesley)

1426 King James I and Bible (Authorised Version of Bible)

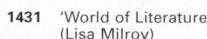

1431 'World of Literature' (Lisa Milroy)

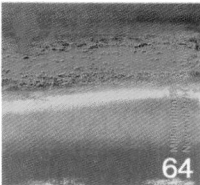

1432 'New Worlds' (Sir Howard Hodgkin)

Millennium Series. The Artists' Tale

1999 (7 Dec.) *One centre phosphor band* (19p) *or two phosphor bands* (others). *Perf* 14 × 14½

2119	**1429**	19p multicoloured	65		65	☐	☐
2120	**1430**	26p multicoloured	85		95	☐	☐
2121	**1431**	44p multicoloured	1·40		1·50	☐	☐
2122	**1432**	64p multicoloured	2·00		2·25	☐	☐
		Set of 4	4·50		4·75	☐	☐
		First Day Cover			6·00		☐
		Presentation Pack	5·00			☐	
		PHQ Cards (*set of* 4)	3·00		9·00	☐	☐
		Set of 4 *Gutter Pairs*	9·00			☐	

Collectors Pack 1999

1999 (7 Dec.) *Comprises Nos.* 2069/76, 2080/105 *and* 2107/22
Collectors Pack . . . . 55·00 ☐

1427 St Andrews Cathedral, Fife ('Pilgrimage')

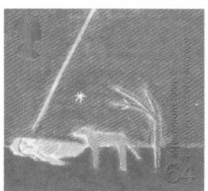

1428 Nativity ('First Christmas')

Millennium Series. The Christians' Tale

1999 (2 Nov.) *One centre phosphor band* (19p) *or two phosphor bands* (others). *Perf* 14 × 14½

2115	**1425**	19p multicoloured	65		65	☐	☐
2116	**1426**	26p multicoloured	85		95	☐	☐
2117	**1427**	44p multicoloured	1·40		1·50	☐	☐
2118	**1428**	64p multicoloured	2·00		2·25	☐	☐
		Set of 4	4·50		4·75	☐	☐
		First Day Cover			6·00		☐
		Presentation Pack	5·00			☐	
		PHQ Cards (*set of* 4)	3·00		9·00	☐	☐
		Set of 4 *Gutter Pairs*	9·00			☐	

Post Office Yearbook

1999 (7 Dec.) *Comprises Nos.* 2069/76, 2080/105 *and* 2107/22 *in hardback book with slip case*
Yearbook . . . . 60·00 ☐

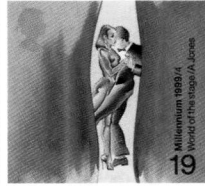

1429 'World of the Stage' (Allen Jones)

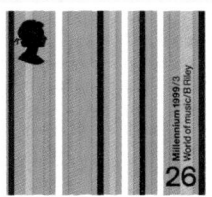

1430 'World of Music' (Bridget Riley)

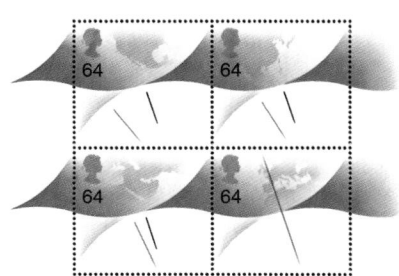

1433*a*

Millennium Series. 'Millennium Timekeeper'

1999 (14 Dec.) *Sheet* 120 × 89 *mm. Multicoloured. Two phosphor bands. Perf* 14 × 14½

MS2123	**1433***a*	64p Clock face and map of North America; 64p Clock face and map of Asia; 64p Clock face and map of Middle East; 64p Clock face and map of Europe	9·00	9·00	□	□
		First Day Cover		10·00		□
		Presentation Pack	10·00		□	
		PHQ Cards (set of 5)	3·00	16·00	□	□

No. **MS**2123 also exists overprinted 'EARLS COURT, LONDON 22–28 MAY 2000 THE STAMP SHOW 2000' from Exhibition Premium Passes, costing £10, available from 1 March 2000.

1437 Queen Elizabeth II

New Millennium

2000 (6 Jan.) *Photo De La Rue, Questa or Walsall (No. 2124); Questa or Walsall (No. 2124d). Two phosphor bands. Perf* 15 × 14 *(with one elliptical hole on each vertical side)*

2124	**1437**	(1st) olive-brown	80	80	□	□
	d.	Perf 14	80	80	□	□
		First Day Cover		2·00		□
		Presentation Pack	3·00		□	
		PHQ Card (23 May)	50		□	

No. 2124 comes from sheets or stamp booklets and No. 2124d from booklets only.

1438 Barn Owl (World Owl Trust, Muncaster)

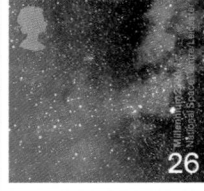

1439 Night Sky (National Space Science Centre, Leicester)

1440 River Goyt and Textile Mills (Torrs Walkway, New Mills)

1441 Cape Gannets (Seabird Centre, North Berwick)

Millennium Projects (1st series). 'Above and Beyond'

2000 (18 Jan.–26 May) *One centre phosphor band* (19p) *or two phosphor bands* (others). *Perf* 14 × 14½ (1st, 44p) *or* 13½ × 14 (others)

2125	**1438**	19p multicoloured	65	65	□	□
2126	**1439**	26p multicoloured	85	95	□	□
2126*a*		(1st) multicoloured (26 May)	1·00	1·00	□	□
2127	**1440**	44p multicoloured	1·40	1·50	□	□
2128	**1441**	64p multicoloured	2·00	2·25	□	□
		Set of 4 (ex No. 2126a)	4·50	4·75	□	□
		First Day Cover		6·00		□
		Presentation Pack	5·00		□	
		PHQ Cards (set of 4)	3·00	9·00	□	□
		Set of 4 Gutter Pairs	9·00		□	

No. 2126a was only issued in stamp booklets.

1442 Millennium Beacon (Beacons across the Land)

1443 Garratt Steam Locomotive No. 143 pulling Train (Rheilffordd Eryri, Welsh Highland Railway)

1444 Lightning (Dynamic Earth Centre, Edinburgh)

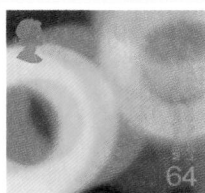

1445 Multicoloured Lights (Lighting Croydon's Skyline)

Millennium Projects (2nd series). 'Fire and Light'

2000 (1 Feb.) *One centre phosphor band* (19p) *or two phosphor bands* (others). *Perf* 14 × 14½

2129	**1442**	19p multicoloured	65	65	□	□
2130	**1443**	26p multicoloured	85	95	□	□
2131	**1444**	44p multicoloured	1·40	1·50	□	□
2132	**1445**	64p multicoloured	2·00	2·25	□	□
		Set of 4	4·50	4·75	□	□
		First Day Cover		6·00		□
		Presentation Pack	5·00		□	
		PHQ Cards (set of 4)	3·00	9·00	□	□
		Set of 4 Gutter Pairs	9·00		□	

1446 Queen Victoria and Queen Elizabeth II

2000 (15 Feb.) *Design T 929, but redrawn with '1st' face value as T 1446. Two phosphor bands. Perf 14 (with one elliptical hole on each vertical side)*

2133	**1446**	(1st) brownish black and cream	. . . . .	1·10	1·25 □ □

No. 2133 was only issued in stamp booklets.

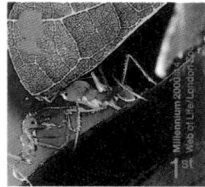

1451 Reed Beds, River Braid (ECOS, Ballymena)

1452 South American Leaf-cutter Ants ('Web of Life' Exhibition, London Zoo)

1447 Beach Pebbles (Turning the Tide, Durham Coast)

1448 Frog's Legs and Water Lilies (National Pondlife Centre, Merseyside)

1453 Solar Sensors (Earth Centre, Doncaster)

1454 Hydroponic Leaves (Project SUZY, Teesside)

Millennium Projects (4th series). 'Life and Earth'

2000 (4 Apr.) *One centre phosphor band* (2nd) *or two phosphor bands* (*others*). *Perf* 14 × 14½

2138	**1451**	(2nd)	multicoloured . . .	65	65 □ □
2139	**1452**	(1st)	multicoloured . . .	85	95 □ □
2140	**1453**	44p	multicoloured . . .	1·40	1·50 □ □
2141	**1454**	64p	multicoloured . . .	2·00	2·25 □ □
	Set of 4		. . . .	4·50	4·75 □ □
	First Day Cover		. . . .		6·00 □
	Presentation Pack		. . . .	5·00	□
	PHQ Cards (set of 4)		. . . . . .	3·00	9·00 □ □
	Set of 4 Gutter Pairs		. . . . . .	9·00	□

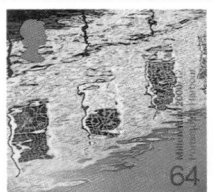

1449 Cliff Boardwalk (Parc Arfordirol, Llanelli Coast)

1450 Reflections in Water (Portsmouth Harbour Development)

Millennium Projects (3rd series). 'Water and Coast'

2000 (7 Mar.) *One centre phosphor band* (19p) *or two phosphor bands* (*others*). *Perf* 14 × 14½

2134	**1447**	19p multicoloured	65	65 □ □
2135	**1448**	26p multicoloured	85	95 □ □
2136	**1449**	44p black, grey and silver	1·40	1·50 □ □
2137	**1450**	64p multicoloured	2·00	2·25 □ □
	Set of 4	. . . .	4·50	4·75 □ □
	First Day Cover	. . . .		6·00 □
	Presentation Pack	. . . .	5·00	□
	PHQ Cards (set of 4)	. . . . . .	3·00	9·00 □ □
	Set of 4 Gutter Pairs	. . . . . .	9·00	□

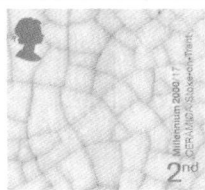

1455 Pottery Glaze (Ceramica Museum, Stoke-on-Trent)

1456 Bankside Galleries (Tate Modern, London)

1457 Road Marking (Cycle Network Artworks)

1458 People of Salford (Lowry Centre, Salford)

Millennium Projects (5th series). 'Art and Craft'

2000 (2 MAY) *One centre phosphor band* (2nd) *or two phosphor bands* (others). *Perf* 14 × 14½

2142	**1455**	(2nd) multicoloured . . .	65	65	☐	☐
2143	**1456**	(1st) multicoloured . . .	85	95	☐	☐
2144	**1457**	45p multicoloured . . .	1·40	1·50	☐	☐
2145	**1458**	65p multicoloured . . .	2·00	2·25	☐	☐
		Set of 4	4·50	4·75	☐	☐
		First Day Cover		6·00		☐
		Presentation Pack	5·00		☐	
		PHQ Cards (set of 4)	3·00	9·00	☐	☐
		Set of 4 Gutter Pairs	9·00		☐	

'Stamp Show 2000' International Stamp Exhibition, London. Jeffrey Matthews Colour Palette

2000 (22 MAY) *Sheet,* 124 × 70 *mm, containing stamps as T* **367** *with two labels. Phosphorised paper. Perf* 15 × 14 (*with one elliptical hole on each vertical side*)

MS2146   4p new blue; 5p dull red-brown;
6p yellow-olive; 10p dull orange;
31p dp mauve; 39p brt magenta;
64p turq-green; £1 bluish violet

	10·00	10·00	☐	☐
First Day Cover		10·00		☐
Exhibition Card (wallet, sold at £4.99, containing one mint sheet and one cancelled on postcard)	18·00		☐	

The £1 value is printed in Iriodin ink which gives a shiny effect to the solid part of the background behind the Queen's head.

1459

'Stamp Show 2000' International Stamp Exhibition, London. 'Her Majesty's Stamps'

2000 (23 MAY) *Sheet* 121 × 89 *mm. Phosphorised paper. Perf* 15 × 14 (*with one elliptical hole on each vertical side of stamps as T* **1437**)

MS2147   **1459**   (1st) olive-brown (Type **1437**) × 4; £1 slate-green (as Type **163**)

. . . .	10·00	10·00	☐	☐
First Day Cover		12·00		☐
Presentation Pack	35·00		☐	
PHQ Cards (set of 2)	6·00	20·00	☐	☐

The £1 value is an adaptation of the 1953 Coronation 1s. 3d. stamp. It is shown on one of the PHQ cards with the other depicting the complete miniature sheet.

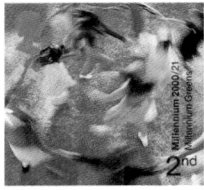 

1460 Children playing (Millennium Greens Project)

1461 Millennium Bridge, Gateshead

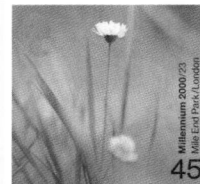 

1462 Daisies (Mile End Park, London)

1463 African Hut and Thatched Cottage ('On the Meridian Line' Project)

Millennium Projects (6th series). 'People and Places'

2000 (6 JUNE) *One centre phosphor band* (2nd) *or two phosphor bands* (others). *Perf* 14 × 14½

2148	**1460**	(2nd) multicoloured . . .	65	65	☐	☐
2149	**1461**	(1st) multicoloured . . .	85	95	☐	☐
2150	**1462**	45p multicoloured . . .	1·40	1·50	☐	☐
2151	**1463**	65p multicoloured . . .	2·00	2·25	☐	☐
		Set of 4	4·50	4·75	☐	☐
		First Day Cover		6·00		☐
		Presentation Pack	5·00		☐	
		PHQ Cards (set of 4)	3·00	9·00	☐	☐
		Set of 4 Gutter Pairs	9·00		☐	

1464 Raising the Stone (Strangford Stone, Killyleagh)

1465 Horse's Hooves (Trans Pennine Trail, Derbyshire)

1466 Cyclist (Kingdom of Fife Cycle Ways, Scotland)

1467 Bluebell Wood (Groundwork's 'Changing Places' Project)

Millennium Projects (7th series). 'Stone and Soil'

2000 (4 JULY) *One centre phosphor band* (2nd) *or two phosphor bands* (others). *Perf* 14 × 14½

2152	**1464**	(2nd) brownish black, grey-black and silver	65	65	☐	☐
2153	**1465**	(1st) multicoloured . . .	85	95	☐	☐
2154	**1466**	45p multicoloured . . .	1·40	1·50	☐	☐
2155	**1467**	65p multicoloured . . .	2·00	2·25	☐	☐
	Set of 4		4·50	4·75	☐	☐
	First Day Cover			6·00		☐
	Presentation Pack		5·00		☐	
	PHQ Cards (*set of* 4)		3·00	9·00	☐	☐
	Set of 4 *Gutter Pairs*		9·00		☐	

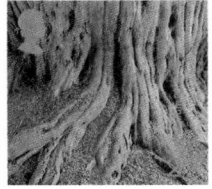

1468 Tree Roots ('Yews for the Millennium' Project)

1469 Sunflower ('Eden' Project, St. Austell)

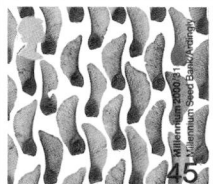

1470 Sycamore Seeds (Millennium Seed Bank, Wakehurst Place, Surrey)

1471 Forest, Doire Dach ('Forest for Scotland')

Millennium Projects (8th series). 'Tree and Leaf'

2000 (1 AUG.) *One centre phosphor band* (2nd) *or two phosphor bands* (others). *Perf* 14 × 14½

2156	**1468**	(2nd) multicoloured . . .	65	65	☐	☐
2157	**1469**	(1st) multicoloured . . .	85	95	☐	☐
2158	**1470**	45p multicoloured . . .	1·40	1·50	☐	☐
2159	**1471**	65p multicoloured . . .	2·00	2·25	☐	☐
	Set of 4		4·50	4·75	☐	☐
	First Day Cover			6·00		☐
	Presentation Pack		5·00		☐	
	PHQ Cards (*set of* 4)		3·00	9·00	☐	☐
	Set of 4 *Gutter Pairs*		9·00		☐	

1472 Queen Elizabeth the Queen Mother

1472a Royal Family on Queen Mother's 99th Birthday (from photo by J. Swannell)

Queen Elizabeth the Queen Mother's 100th Birthday

2000 (4 Aug.) *Phosphorised paper plus two phosphor bands. Perf 14½*

2160	**1472**	27p multicoloured . . .	1·50	1·25	☐	☐
MS2161	121 × 89 mm. **1472a** 27p Queen Elizabeth II; 27p Prince William; 27p Queen Elizabeth the Queen Mother; 27p Prince Charles		6·00	7·00	☐	☐
	First Day Cover (**MS**2161)			8·00		☐
	Presentation Pack (**MS**2161) . .		9·00		☐	
	PHQ Cards (set of 5)		4·50	15·00	☐	☐

No. 2160 was only issued in stamp booklets and in No. **MS**2161.

The complete miniature sheet is shown on one of the PHQ cards with the others depicting individual stamps.

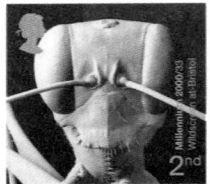

1473 Head of *Gigantiops destructor* (Ant) (Wildscreen at Bristol)

1474 Gathering Water Lilies on Broads (Norfolk and Norwich Project)

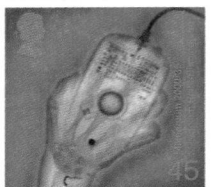

1475 X-ray of Hand holding Computer Mouse (Millennium Point, Birmingham)

1476 Tartan Wool Holder (Scottish Cultural Resources Access Network)

Millennium Projects (9th series). 'Mind and Matter'

2000 (5 Sept.) *One centre phosphor band* (2nd) *or two phosphor bands* (others). *Perf* 14 × 14½

2162	**1473**	(2nd) multicoloured . . .	65	65	☐	☐
2163	**1474**	(1st) multicoloured . . .	85	95	☐	☐
2164	**1475**	45p multicoloured . . .	1·40	1·50	☐	☐
2165	**1476**	65p multicoloured . . .	2·00	2·25	☐	☐
	Set of 4	. . . .	4·50	4·75	☐	☐
	First Day Cover			6·00		☐
	Presentation Pack		5·00		☐	
	PHQ Cards (set of 4)		3·00	9·00	☐	☐
	Set of 4 Gutter Pairs		9·00		☐	

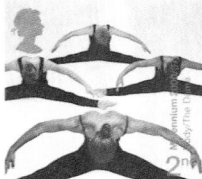

1477 Acrobatic Performers (Millennium Dome)

1478 Football Players (Hampden Park, Glasgow)

1479 Bather (Bath Spa Project)

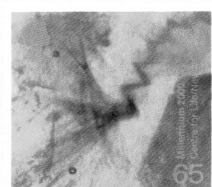

1480 Hen's Egg under Magnification (Centre for Life, Newcastle)

Millennium Projects (10th series). 'Body and Bone'

2000 (3 Oct.) *One centre phosphor band* (2nd) *or two phosphor bands* (others). *Perf* 14 × 14½ (2nd) *or* 13½ × 14 (others)

2166	**1477**	(2nd) black, slate-blue and silver	65	65	☐	☐
2167	**1478**	(1st) multicoloured . . .	85	95	☐	☐
2168	**1479**	45p multicoloured . . .	1·40	1·50	☐	☐
2169	**1480**	65p multicoloured . . .	2·00	2·25	☐	☐
	Set of 4	. . . .	4·50	4·75	☐	☐
	First Day Cover			6·00		☐
	Presentation Pack		5·00		☐	
	PHQ Cards (set of 4)		3·00	9·00	☐	☐
	Set of 4 Gutter Pairs		9·00		☐	

1481 Virgin and Child Stained Glass Window, St. Edmundsbury Cathedral (Suffolk Cathedral Millennium Project)

1482 Floodlit Church of St. Peter and St. Paul, Overstowey (Church Floodlighting Trust)

1483 12th-cent. Latin Gradual (St. Patrick Centre, Downpatrick)

1484 Chapter House Ceiling, York Minster (York Millennium Mystery Plays)

Millennium Projects (11th series). 'Spirit and Faith'

2000 (7 Nov.) *One centre phosphor band* (2nd) *or two phosphor bands* (others). *Perf* 14 × 14½

2170	**1481**	(2nd) multicoloured . . .	65	65	☐	☐
2171	**1482**	(1st) multicoloured . . .	85	95	☐	☐
2172	**1483**	45p multicoloured . . .	1·40	1·50	☐	☐
2173	**1484**	65p multicoloured . . .	2·00	2·25	☐	☐
	Set of 4		4·50	4·75	☐	☐
	First Day Cover			6·00		☐
	Presentation Pack		5·00		☐	
	PHQ Cards (set of 4)		3·00	9·00	☐	☐
	Set of 4 Gutter Pairs		9·00		☐	

Post Office Yearbook

2000 (7 Nov.) *Comprises Nos.* **MS**2125/6, 2127/32, 2134/45, 2148/59 *and* **MS**2161/81 *in hardback book with slip case*

	Yearbook	75·00	☐

The last two issues in the Millennium Projects Series were supplied for insertion into the above at a later date.

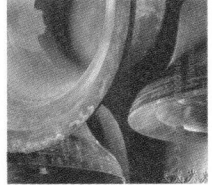

1485 Church Bells (Ringing in the Millennium)

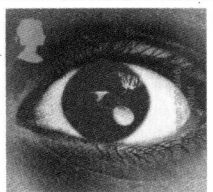

1486 Eye (Year of the Artist)

1487 Top of Harp (Canolfan Mileniwm, Cardiff)

1488 Figure within Latticework (TS2K Creative Enterprise Centres, London)

Millennium Projects (12th series). 'Sound and Vision'

2000 (5 Dec.) *One centre phosphor band* (2nd) *or two phosphor bands* (others). *Perf* 14 × 14½

2174	**1485**	(2nd) multicoloured . . .	65	65	☐	☐
2175	**1486**	(1st) multicoloured . . .	85	95	☐	☐
2176	**1487**	45p multicoloured . . .	1·40	1·50	☐	☐
2177	**1488**	65p multicoloured . . .	2·00	2·25	☐	☐
	Set of 4		4·50	4·75	☐	☐
	First Day Cover			6·00		☐
	Presentation Pack		5·00		☐	
	PHQ Cards (set of 4)		3·00	9·00	☐	☐
	Set of 4 Gutter Pairs		9·00		☐	

Collectors Pack 2000

2000 (5 Dec.) *Comprises Nos.* MS2125/6, 2127/32, 2134/45, 2148/59 *and* **MS**2161/81

	Collectors Pack	65·00	☐

1489 'Flower' ('Nurture Children')

1490 'Tiger' ('Listen to Children')

1491 'Owl' ('Teach Children')

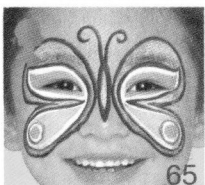

1492 'Butterfly' ('Ensure Children's Freedom')

New Millennium. Rights of the Child. Face Paintings

2001 (16 Jan.) *One centre phosphor band* (2nd) *or two phosphor bands* (others). *Perf* 14 × 14½

2178	**1489**	(2nd) multicoloured . . .	65	65	☐	☐
2179	**1490**	(1st) multicoloured . . .	85	95	☐	☐
2180	**1491**	45p multicoloured . . .	1·40	1·50	☐	☐
2181	**1492**	65p multicoloured . . .	2·00	2·25	☐	☐
	Set of 4		4·50	4·75	☐	☐
	First Day Cover			6·00		☐
	Presentation Pack		5·00		☐	
	PHQ Cards (set of 4)		3·00	9·00	☐	☐
	Set of 4 Gutter Pairs		9·00		☐	

1493 'Love'

1494 'THANKS'

1495 'abc' (New Baby)

1496 'WELCOME'

1497 'Cheers'

'Occasions' Greetings Stamps

2001 (6 FEB.) *Two phosphor bands. Perf* 14½ × 14

2182	**1493**	(1st) multicoloured	. . . .	70	80 □	□
2183	**1494**	(1st) multicoloured	. . . .	70	80 □	□
2184	**1495**	(1st) multicoloured	. . . .	70	80 □	□
2185	**1496**	(1st) multicoloured	. . . .	70	80 □	□
2186	**1497**	(1st) multicoloured	. . . .	70	80 □	□
		Set of 5	. . . .	3·25	3·50 □	□
		First Day Cover			4·50	□
		Presentation Pack (13 Feb.) . . .		3·75		□
		PHQ Cards (*set of 5*)	. . . . .	3·00	7·50 □	□
		Set of 5 Gutter Pairs		6·50		□

The silver-grey backgrounds are printed in Iriodin ink which gives a shiny effect.

Nos. 2182/6 were printed in photogravure. They were subsequently re-issued on 1 May, as sheets of 20, including a *se-tenant* format, printed in lithography with each stamp accompanied by a half stamp-size label showing either postal symbols or a personal photograph.

1498 Dog and Owner on Bench

1499 Dog in Bath

1500 Boxer at Dog Show

1501 Cat in Handbag

1502 Cat on Gate

1503 Dog in Car

1504 Cat at Window

1505 Dog behind Fence

1506 Cat watching Bird

1507 Cat in Washbasin

T **1498**/**1507** were printed together in sheetlets of 10 (5 × 2), with the surplus self-adhesive paper around each stamp retained.

Cats and Dogs

2001 (13 FEB.) *Self-adhesive. Two phosphor bands. Die-cut perf* 15 × 14

2187	**1498**	(1st) black, grey and silver	70	80 □	□
		a. Sheetlet. Nos. 2187/96	6·25	□	
2188	**1499**	(1st) black, grey and silver	70	80 □	□
2189	**1500**	(1st) black, grey and silver	70	80 □	□
2190	**1501**	(1st) black, grey and silver	70	80 □	□
2191	**1502**	(1st) black, grey and silver	70	80 □	□
2192	**1503**	(1st) black, grey and silver	70	80 □	□
2193	**1504**	(1st) black, grey and silver	70	80 □	□
2194	**1505**	(1st) black, grey and silver	70	80 □	□
2195	**1506**	(1st) black, grey and silver	70	80 □	□
2196	**1507**	(1st) black, grey and silver	70	80 □	□
		Set of 10	6·25	7·25 □	□
		First Day Cover		8·00	□
		Presentation Pack	7·00		□
		PHQ Cards (*set of 10*)	5·00	10·00 □	□

1508 'RAIN'

1509 'FAIR'

1510 'STORMY'

1511 'VERY DRY'

Nos. 2197/200 show the four quadrants of a barometer dial which are combined on the miniature sheet.

The Weather

2001 (13 MAR.) *One side phosphor band* (19p) *or two phosphor bands (others). Perf* 14½

2197	**1508**	19p multicoloured	. . . .	55	60 ☐ ☐
2198	**1509**	27p multicoloured	. . . .	75	85 ☐ ☐
2199	**1510**	45p multicoloured	. . . .	1·25	1·40 ☐ ☐
2200	**1511**	65p multicoloured	. . . .	1·90	2·00 ☐ ☐
		Set of 4		4·00	4·50 ☐ ☐
		First Day Cover			6·00 ☐
		Presentation Pack		5·00	☐
		Set of 4 Gutter Pairs		8·00	☐
MS2201	105 × 105 mm. Nos. 2197/200			4·50	4·75 ☐ ☐
		First Day Cover			6·00 ☐
		PHQ Cards (set of 5)		3·50	9·00 ☐ ☐

The reddish violet on both the 27p and the miniature sheet is printed in thermochromic ink which changes from reddish violet to light blue when exposed to heat.

The PHQ cards depict the four values and the miniature sheet.

1512 *Vanguard* Class Submarine, 1992

1513 *Swiftsure* Class Submarine, 1973

1514 *Unity* Class Submarine, 1939

1515 'Holland' Type Submarine, 1901

1516 White Ensign

1517 Union Jack

1518 Jolly Roger flown by H.M.S. *Proteus* (submarine)

1519 Flag of Chief of Defence Staff

Centenary of Royal Navy Submarine Service

2001 (10 APR.–22 OCT.) *One centre phosphor band* (2nd) *or two phosphor bands (others).* (*a*) *Submarines. PVA gum. Perf* 15 × 14

2202	**1512**	(2nd) multicoloured	50	50 ☐ ☐
		a. Perf 15½ × 15 (22 Oct.)	90	95 ☐ ☐
2203	**1513**	(1st) multicoloured	70	80 ☐ ☐
		a. Perf 15½ × 15 (22 Oct.)	1·40	1·50 ☐ ☐
2204	**1514**	45p multicoloured	1·10	1·25 ☐ ☐
		a. Perf 15½ × 15 (22 Oct.)	2·25	2·40 ☐ ☐
2205	**1515**	65p multicoloured	1·75	1·90 ☐ ☐
		a. Perf 15½ × 15 (22 Oct.)	3·00	3·25 ☐ ☐
		Set of 4	3·75	4·00 ☐
		First Day Cover		5·25 ☐
		Presentation Pack	4·25	☐
		PHQ Cards (set of 4)	3·00	8·00 ☐ ☐
		Set of 4 Gutter Pairs	7·50	☐

(*b*) *Flags. Sheet* 92 × 97 mm. *PVA gum. Perf* 14½

MS2206	**1516** (1st) multicoloured; **1517** (1st) multicoloured; **1518** (1st) multicoloured; **1519** (1st) multicoloured (22 Oct.)	3·25	3·50 ☐ ☐
	First Day Cover		7·50 ☐
	Presentation Pack	4·00	☐
	PHQ Cards (set of 5)	3·50	9·00 ☐ ☐

(c) *Self-adhesive. Die-cut perf* 15½ × 14 (*No.* 2207)
or 14½ (*others*)

2207	**1513**	(1st) multicoloured (17 Apr.)	15·00	15·00	☐	☐
2208	**1516**	(1st) multicoloured (22 Oct.)	5·00	5·00	☐	☐
2209	**1518**	(1st) multicoloured (22 Oct.)	5·00	5·00	☐	☐

Nos. 2202*a*/5*a* only come from stamp booklets.

The five PHQ cards depict the four designs and the complete miniature sheet.

Nos. 2207/9 only come from two different £1.62 booklets.

1520 Leyland X2 Open-top, London General B Type, Leyland Titan TD1 and AEC Regent 1

1521 AEC Regent 1, Daimler COG5, Utility Guy Arab Mk II and AEC Regent III RT Type

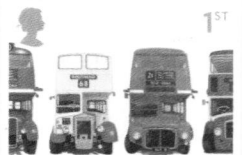

1522 AEC Regent III RT Type, Bristol KSW5G Open-top, AEC Routemaster and Bristol Lodekka FSF6G

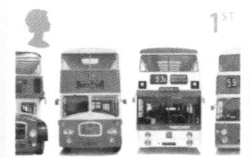

1523 Bristol Lodekka FSF6G, Leyland Titan PD3/4, Leyland Atlantean PDR1/1 and Daimler Fleetline CRG6LX-33

1524 Daimler Fleetline CRG6LX-33, MCW Metrobus DR102/43, Leyland Olympian ONLXB/1R and Dennis Trident

T **1520**/4 were printed together, *se-tenant*, in horizontal strips of 5 throughout the sheet. The illustrations of the first bus on No. 2210 and the last bus on No. 2214 continue onto the sheet margins.

150th Anniversary of First Double-decker Bus

2001 (15 MAY) *'All-over' phosphor. Perf* 14½ × 14

2210	**1520**	(1st) multicoloured	95	1·00	☐	☐
		a. Horiz strip of 5. *Nos.*				
		2210/14	4·50	4·75	☐	☐
2211	**1521**	(1st) multicoloured	95	1·00	☐	☐
2212	**1522**	(1st) multicoloured	95	1·00	☐	☐
2213	**1523**	(1st) multicoloured	95	1·00	☐	☐
2214	**1524**	(1st) multicoloured	95	1·00	☐	☐
		Set of 5	4·50	4·75	☐	☐
		First Day Cover		5·50		☐
		Presentation Pack	5·00		☐	
		PHQ Cards (*set of* 5)	4·00	12·00	☐	☐
		Gutter Strip of 10	5·00		☐	
MS2215	120 × 105 mm. Nos. 2210/14		4·50	4·75	☐	☐
		First Day Cover		5·50		☐

In No. **MS**2215 the illustrations of the AEC Regent III RT Type and the Daimler Fleetline CRG6LX-33 appear twice.

1525 Toque Hat by Pip Hackett

1526 Butterfly Hat by Dai Rees

1527 Top Hat by Stephen Jones

1528 Spiral Hat by Philip Treacy

Fashion Hats

2001 (19 JUNE) *'All-over' phosphor. Perf* 14½

2216	**1525**	(1st) multicoloured	75	85	☐	☐
2217	**1526**	(E) multicoloured	90	1·00	☐	☐
2218	**1527**	45p multicoloured	1·25	1·40	☐	☐
2219	**1528**	65p multicoloured	1·90	2·00	☐	☐
		Set of 4	4·25	4·75	☐	☐
		First Day Cover		5·00		☐
		Presentation Pack	4·75		☐	
		PHQ Cards (*set of* 4)	3·00	9·00	☐	☐
		Set of 4 *Gutter Pairs*	8·50		☐	

1529 Common Frog

1530 Great Diving Beetle

1531 Three-spined Stickleback

1532 Southern Hawker Dragonfly

Europa. Pond Life

2001 (10 July) *Two phosphor bands*

2220	**1529**	(1st) multicoloured . . .	70	80	□	□
2221	**1530**	(E) multicoloured . . .	85	90	□	□
2222	**1531**	45p multicoloured . . .	1·10	1·25	□	□
2223	**1532**	65p multicoloured . . .	1·90	2·00	□	□
	Set of 4		4·00	4·50	□	□
	First Day Cover			5·50		□
	Presentation Pack		4·75		□	
	PHQ Cards (set of 4)		3·00	9·00	□	□
	Set of 4 Gutter Pairs		8·00		□	

The 1st and E values incorporate the 'EUROPA' emblem.

The bluish silver on all four values is in Iriodin ink and was use〔
as a background for those parts of the design below the water lin〔

1533 Policeman

1534 Clown

1535 Mr. Punch

1536 Judy

1537 Beadle

1538 Crocodile

Nos. 2224/9 were printed together, *se-tenant*, in horizontal strips of 6 throughout the sheet.

Punch and Judy Show Puppets

2001 (4 Sept.) *Two phosphor bands.* (*a*) *PVA gum. Perf* 14 × 15

2224	**1533**	(1st) multicoloured . . .	65	70	□	□
		a. Horiz strip of 6.				
		Nos. 2224/9	3·50	4·25	□	□
2225	**1534**	(1st) multicoloured . . .	65	70	□	□
2226	**1535**	(1st) multicoloured . . .	65	70	□	□
2227	**1536**	(1st) multicoloured . . .	65	70	□	□
2228	**1537**	(1st) multicoloured . . .	65	70	□	□
2229	**1538**	(1st) multicoloured . . .	65	70	□	□
	Set of 6		3·50	3·75	□	□
	First Day Cover			4·75		□
	Presentation Pack		4·50		□	
	PHQ Cards (set of 6)		3·50	10·50	□	□
	Gutter Block of 12		7·25		□	

(*b*) *Self-adhesive. Die-cut perf* 14 × 15½

2230	**1535**	(1st) multicoloured . . .	2·75	2·75	□	□
2231	**1536**	(1st) multicoloured . . .	2·75	2·75	□	□

Nos. 2230/1 were only issued in £1.62 stamp booklets.

For full information on all future British issues, collectors should write to Royal Mail, Freepost EH3647, 21 South Gyle Crescent, Edinburgh EH12 9PE.

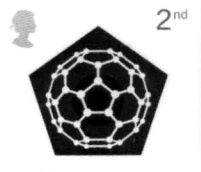

2nd

CHEMISTRY
Nobel Prize 100th Anniversary

1539 Carbon 60 Molecule (Chemistry)

1st

ECONOMIC SCIENCES
Nobel Prize 100th Anniversary

1540 Globe (Economic Sciences)

E

Nobel Prize 100th Anniversary

1541 Embossed Dove (Peace)

40

PHYSIOLOGY OR MEDICINE
Nobel Prize 100th Anniversary

1542 Crosses (Physiology or Medicine)

45

Nobel Prize 100th Anniversary

1543 Poem 'The Addressing of Cats' by T. S. Eliot in Open Book (Literature)

65

Nobel Prize 100th Anniversary

1544 Hologram of Boron Molecule (Physics)

Centenary of Nobel Prizes

2001 (2 Oct.) *One side phosphor band (2nd) or phosphor frame (others). Perf* 14½

2232	**1539**	(2nd) black, silver and grey-black	50	55	☐	☐
2233	**1540**	(1st) multicoloured . . .	70	80	☐	☐
2234	**1541**	(E) black, silver and bright green	90	1·00	☐	☐
2235	**1542**	40p multicoloured . . .	90	1·00	☐	☐
2236	**1543**	45p multicoloured . . .	1·25	1·40	☐	☐
2237	**1544**	65p black and silver . .	1·90	2·00	☐	☐
		Set of 6	5·50	6·00	☐	☐
		First Day Cover		7·00		☐
		Presentation Pack	6·50		☐	
		PHQ Cards (set of 6)	3·50	10·50	☐	☐
		Set of 6 Gutter Pairs	11·00		☐	

The grey-black on No. 2232 is printed in thermochromic ink which temporarily changes to pale grey when exposed to heat.
The centre of No. 2235 is coated with a eucalyptus scent.

2nd

1545 Robins with Snowman

1st

1546 Robins on Bird Table

E

1547 Robins skating on Bird Bath

45

1548 Robins with Christmas Pudding

65

1549 Robins in Paper Chain Nest

Christmas. Robins

2001 (6 Nov.) *Self-adhesive. One centre phosphor band (2nd) or two phosphor bands (others). Die-cut perf* 14½

2238	**1545**	(2nd) multicoloured . . .	50	55	☐	☐
2239	**1546**	(1st) multicoloured . . .	70	80	☐	☐
2240	**1547**	(E) multicoloured . . .	90	1·00	☐	☐
2241	**1548**	45p multicoloured . . .	1·25	1·40	☐	☐
2242	**1549**	65p multicoloured . . .	1·90	2·00	☐	☐
		Set of 5	4·75	5·25	☐	☐
		First Day Cover		5·75		☐
		Presentation Pack	5·50		☐	
		PHQ Cards (set of 5)	3·50	7·50	☐	☐

Collectors Pack 2001

2001 (6 Nov.) *Comprises Nos.* 2178/2200, 2202/**MS**2206, 2210/14, 2216/29 *and* 2232/42

	Collectors Pack	55·00	☐

Post Office Yearbook

2001 (6 Nov.) *Comprises Nos.* 2178/96, **MS**2201/6, **MS**2215/29 *and* 2232/42 *in hardback book with slip case*

	Yearbook	60·00	☐

1550 'How the Whale got
his Throat'

1551 'How the Camel got
his Hump'

1552 'How the Rhinoceros
got his Skin'

1553 'How the Leopard
got his Spots'

1554 'The Elephant's Child'

1555 'The Sing-Song of
Old Man Kangaroo'

1556 'The Beginning of
the Armadillos'

1557 'The Crab that played
with the Sea'

1558 'The Cat that walked
by Himself'

1559 'The Butterfly that
stamped'

T 1550/9 were printed together in sheetlets of 10 (5×2), w
the surplus self-adhesive paper around each stamp retained

Centenary of Publication of Rudyard Kipling's *Just So Stories*

2002 (15 Jan.) *Self-adhesive. Two phosphor bands. Die-cut perf
15 × 14*

2243	1550	(1st) multicoloured	45	50	☐	☐
		a. Sheetlet. Nos. 2243/				
		52	4·50		☐	
2244	1551	(1st) multicoloured	45	50	☐	☐
2245	1552	(1st) multicoloured	45	50	☐	☐
2246	1553	(1st) multicoloured	45	50	☐	☐
2247	1554	(1st) multicoloured	45	50	☐	☐
2248	1555	(1st) multicoloured	45	50	☐	☐
2249	1556	(1st) multicoloured	45	50	☐	☐
2250	1557	(1st) multicoloured	45	50	☐	☐
2251	1558	(1st) multicoloured	45	50	☐	☐
2252	1559	(1st) multicoloured	45	50	☐	☐
		Set of 10	4·50	5·00	☐	☐
		First Day Cover		5·50		☐
		Presentation Pack	4·50		☐	
		PHQ Cards (set of 10)	3·75	5·75	☐	☐

1560 Queen Elizabeth II, 1952
(Dorothy Wilding)

1561 Queen Elizabeth II, 1968
(Cecil Beaton)

1562 Queen Elizabeth II, 1978
(Lord Snowdon)

1563 Queen Elizabeth II, 1984
(Yousef Karsh)

1564 Queen Elizabeth II, 1996
(Tim Graham)

1565

147

Golden Jubilee. Studio portraits of Queen Elizabeth II by photographers named

2002 (6 Feb.) *One centre phosphor band* (2nd) *or two phosphor bands* (others). W **1565**. *Perf* 14½ × 14

2253	**1560**	(2nd) multicoloured	. . . .	30	35 □ □
2254	**1561**	(1st) multicoloured	. . . .	45	50 □ □
2255	**1562**	(E) multicoloured	. . . .	60	65 □ □
2256	**1563**	45p multicoloured	. . . .	70	75 □ □
2257	**1564**	65p multicoloured	. . . .	1·00	1·10 □ □
		Set of 5	. . . .	3·00	3·25 □ □
		First Day Cover	. . . .		4·00 □
		Presentation Pack	. . . .	3·50	□
		PHQ Cards (set of 5)	. . . . . .	1·90	4·75 □ □
		Set of 5 Gutter Pairs	. . . . . .	6·25	□

Stamps from sheets had the watermark sideways: those from stamp booklets had the watermark upright.

1566

Booklet Stamps

2002 (6 Feb.) *Designs as 1952-54 issue, but with service indicator as T* **1566**. *One centre phosphor band* (2nd) *or two phosphor bands* (1st). W **1565**. *Uncoated paper. Perf* 15 × 14 (*with one elliptical hole on each vertical side*)

2258	**1566**	(2nd) carmine-red	. . . . .	30	35 □ □
2259	**154**	(1st) green	. . . .	45	50 □ □
		Set of 2	. . . .	75	85 □ □

Nos. 2258/9 were only issued in £7.29 stamp booklets.

1567 Rabbits ('a new baby')

1568 'LOVE'

1569 Aircraft Sky-writing 'hello'

1570 Bear pulling Potted Topiary Tree (Moving Home)

1571 Flowers ('best wishes')

'Occasions' Greetings Stamps

2002 (5 Mar.) *Two phosphor bands. Perf* 15 × 14

2260	**1567**	(1st) multicoloured	. . . .	45	50 □ □
2261	**1568**	(1st) multicoloured	. . . .	45	50 □ □
2262	**1569**	(1st) multicoloured	. . .	45	50 □ □
2263	**1570**	(1st) multicoloured	. . . .	45	50 □ □
2264	**1571**	(1st) multicoloured	. . . .	45	50 □ □
		Set of 5	. . . .	2·25	2·50 □ □
		First Day Cover	. . . .		3·00 □
		Presentation Pack	. . . .	2·50	□
		PHQ Cards (set of 5)	. . . . . .	1·90	3·75 □ □
		Set of 5 Gutter Pairs	. . . . . .	5·00	□

Nos. 2260/4 were subsequently available in sheets of 20 perforated 14½ × 14, either of one design or *se-tenant*, with each stamp accompanied by a half stamp-size label showing either greetings or a personal photograph.

1572 Studland Bay, Dorset

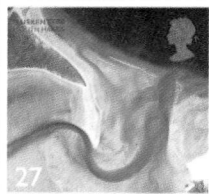

1573 Luskentyre, South Harris

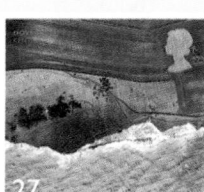

1574 Cliffs, Dover, Kent

1575 Padstow Harbour, Cornwall

1576 Broadstairs, Kent

1577 St. Abb's Head, Scottish Borders

1578 Dunster Beach, Somerset

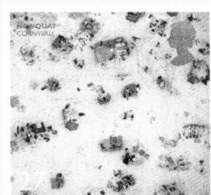

1579 Newquay Beach, Cornwall

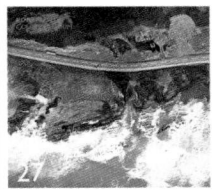

1580 Portrush, County Antrim

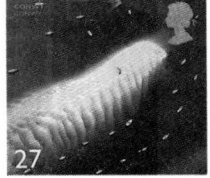

1581 Sand-spit, Conwy

T **1572/81** were printed together, *se-tenant*, in blocks of 10 (5 × throughout the sheet.

British Coastlines

2002 (19 Mar.) *Two phosphor bands. Perf* 14½

2265	**1572**	27p multicoloured	45	50	☐
		a. Block of 10.			
		Nos. 2265/74	4·50		☐
2266	**1573**	27p multicoloured	45	50	☐
2267	**1574**	27p multicoloured	45	50	☐
2268	**1575**	27p multicoloured . . .	45	50	☐
2269	**1576**	27p multicoloured . . .	45	50	☐
2270	**1577**	27p multicoloured . . .	45	50	☐
2271	**1578**	27p multicoloured . . .	45	50	☐
2272	**1579**	27p multicoloured . . .	45	50	☐
2273	**1580**	27p multicoloured . . .	45	50	☐
2274	**1581**	27p multicoloured . . .	45	50	☐
		Set of 10	4·50	5·00	☐
		First Day Cover		5·50	
		Presentation Pack	4·50		☐
		PHQ Cards (*set of* 10)	3·75	6·25	☐
		Gutter Block of 20	9·50		☐

1582 Slack Wire Act

1583 Lion Tamer

1584 Trick Tri-cyclists

1585 Krazy Kar

1586 Equestrienne

Europa. Circus

2002 (10 Apr.) *One centre phosphor band* (2nd) *or two phosphor bands* (*others*). *Perf* 14½

2275	**1582**	(2nd) multicoloured	30	35	☐	☐
2276	**1583**	(1st) multicoloured	45	50	☐	☐
2277	**1584**	(E) multicoloured	60	65	☐	☐
2278	**1585**	45p multicoloured	70	75	☐	☐
2279	**1586**	65p multicoloured	1·00	1·10	☐	☐
		Set of 5	3·00	3·25	☐	☐
		First Day Cover		4·00	☐	☐
		Presentation Pack	3·50		☐	
		PHQ Cards (*set of* 5)	1·90	4·75	☐	☐
		Set of 5 Gutter Pairs	6·25		☐	

The 1st and E values incorporate the "EUROPA" emblem.

Due to the funeral of the Queen Mother, the actual issue of Nos. 2275/9 was delayed from 9 April which is the date that appears on first day covers.

1587 Queen Elizabeth the Queen Mother

Queen Elizabeth the Queen Mother Commemoration

2002 (25 Apr.) *Vert designs as T* **955/8** *with changed face values and showing both the Queen's head and frame in black as in T* **1587**. *Two phosphor bands. Perf* 14 × 15

2280	**1587**	(1st) multicoloured	45	50	☐	☐
2281	**956**	(E) black and indigo . .	60	65	☐	☐
2282	**957**	45p multicoloured	70	75	☐	☐
2283	**958**	65p black, stone and sepia	1·00	1·10	☐	☐
	Set of 4	. . . .	2·75	3·00	☐	☐
	First Day Cover		3·75		☐
	Presentation Pack	3·00		☐
	Set of 4 Gutter Pairs	5·75		☐

50th Anniversary of Passenger Jet Aviation. Airliners

2002 (2 May) *One centre phosphor band* (2nd) *or two phosphor bands* (others). *Perf* 14½. (*a*) *Photo De La Rue. PVA gum*

2284	**1588**	(2nd) multicoloured	30	35	☐	☐
2285	**1589**	(1st) multicoloured	45	50	☐	☐
2286	**1590**	(E) multicoloured	60	65	☐	☐
2287	**1591**	45p multicoloured	70	75	☐	☐
2288	**1592**	65p multicoloured	1·00	1·10	☐	☐
	Set of 5	. . . .	3·00	3·25	☐	☐
	First Day Cover		4·00		☐
	Presentation Pack	3·50		☐
	Set of 5 Gutter Pairs	6·25		☐
MS2289	120 × 105 mm. Nos. 2284/8 .	3·00	3·25	☐	☐
	First Day Cover		4·00	☐
	PHQ Cards (*set of 6*)	2·25	4·75	☐	☐

(*b*) *Photo Questa. Self-adhesive*

2290	**1589**	(1st) multicoloured	45	50	☐	☐

The complete miniature sheet is shown on one of the PHQ cards with the others depicting individual stamps.

No. 2290 was only issued in £1.62 stamp booklets.

1588 Airbus A340-600 (2002)

1589 Concorde (1976)

1593 Crowned Lion with Shield of St. George

1590 Trident (1964)

1591 VC 10 (1964)

1594 Top Left Quarter of English Flag, and Football

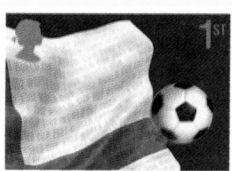

1595 Top Right Quarter of English Flag, and Football

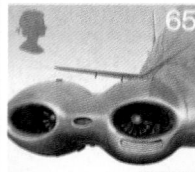

1592 Comet (1952)

1596 Bottom Left Quarter of English Flag, and Football

1597 Bottom Right Quarter of English Flag, and Football

World Cup Football Championship, Japan and Korea

2002 (21 MAY) *Two phosphor bands. Perf* 14½ *(a) PVA gum*

2291	**1593**	(1st) deep turquoise-blue, scarlet-vermilion and silver	......	45	50 □	□

MS2292 145 × 74 mm. No. 2291; **1594** (1st) multicoloured; **1595** (1st) multicoloured; **1596** (1st) multicoloured;

1597 (1st) multicoloured	....	2·00	2·50 □	□
First Day Cover (**MS**2292)	...		3·00	□
Presentation Pack (**MS**2292)	..	2·50		□
PHQ Cards (set of 6)	......	2·25		□
Gutter Pair (No. 2291)	......	95		□

(b) Self-adhesive. Die-cut perf 15 × 14

2293	**1594**	(1st) multicoloured	...	45	50 □	□
2294	**1595**	(1st) multicoloured	....	45	50 □	□

The complete miniature sheet is shown on one of the PHQ cards with the others depicting individual stamps from **MS**2292 and No. 2291.

Nos. 2293/4 were only issued in £1.62 stamp booklets.

Stamps as Type **1597** were also issued in sheets of 20, setenant with half stamp-sized labels, printed by lithography and perforated 14 × 14½. The labels show either match scenes or personal photographs.

Booklet Stamps

2002 (5 JUNE–4 JULY) *Self-adhesive. Photo Questa, Walsall or Enschedé* (No. 2295) *or Walsall* (others). *Two phosphor bands. Perf* 15 × 14 *die-cut* (*with one elliptical hole on each vertical side*)

2295	**914**	(1st) gold		45	50 □	□
2296	**1093a**	(E) deep blue (4 July)	...	60	65 □	□
2297	**367a**	42p deep olive-grey (4 July)	......	65	70 □	□
2298		68p grey-brown (4 July)	.	1·10	1·25 □	□
		Set of 4	......	2·75	3·00 □	□

A further printing of No. 2295 in sheets of 100 appeared on July 2002 produced by Enschedé.

1598 Swimming

1599 Running

1600 Cycling

1601 Long Jumping

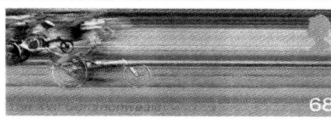

1602 Wheelchair Racing

17th Commonwealth Games, Manchester

2002 (16 JULY) *One side phosphor band* (2nd) *or two phosphor bands* (others). *Perf* 14½

2299	**1598**	(2nd) multicoloured	....	30	35 □	□
2300	**1599**	(1st) multicoloured	....	45	50 □	□
2301	**1600**	(E) multicoloured	....	60	65 □	□
2302	**1601**	47p multicoloured	....	75	80 □	□
2303	**1602**	68p multicoloured	....	1·10	1·25 □	□
		Set of 5	......	3·00	3·50 □	□
		First Day Cover			4·00	□
		Presentation Pack	......	3·50		□
		PHQ Cards (set of 5)	......	1·90	4·75 □	□
		Set of 5 Gutter Pairs	......	6·25		□

1603 Tinkerbell

1604 Wendy, John and Michael Darling in front of Big Ben

1605 Crocodile and Alarm Clock

1606 Captain Hook

151

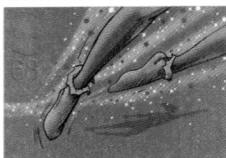

1607 Peter Pan

150th Anniversary of Great Ormond Street Children's Hospital.
Peter Pan by Sir James Barrie

2002 (20 Aug.) *One centre phosphor band (2nd) or two phosphor bands (others). Perf 15×14*

2304	**1603**	(2nd) multicoloured	30	35	☐	☐
2305	**1604**	(1st) multicoloured	45	50	☐	☐
2306	**1605**	(E) multicoloured	60	65	☐	☐
2307	**1606**	47p multicoloured	75	80	☐	☐
2308	**1607**	68p multicoloured	1·10	1·25	☐	☐
	Set of 5		3·00	3·50	☐	☐
	First Day Cover			4·00		☐
	Presentation Pack		3·50		☐	
	PHQ Cards (set of 5) ...		1·90	4·75	☐	☐
	Set of 5 Gutter Pairs		6·25		☐	

1608 Millennium Bridge, 2001

1609 Tower Bridge, 1894

1610 Westminster Bridge, 1864

1611 'Blackfriars Bridge, c1800' (William Marlow)

1612 'London Bridge, c1670' (Wenceslaus Hollar)

Bridges of London

2002 (10 Sept.) *One centre phosphor band (2nd) or two phosphor bands (others). (a) Litho. PVA gum. Perf 15 × 14*

2309	**1608**	(2nd) multicoloured	30	35	☐	☐
2310	**1609**	(1st) multicoloured	45	50	☐	☐
2311	**1610**	(E) multicoloured	60	65	☐	☐
2312	**1611**	47p multicoloured	75	80	☐	☐
2313	**1612**	68p multicoloured	1·10	1·25	☐	☐
	Set of 5		3·00	3·50	☐	☐
	First Day Cover			4·00		☐
	Presentation Pack		3·50		☐	
	PHQ Cards (set of 5)		1·90	4·75	☐	☐
	Set of 5 Gutter Pairs		6·25		☐	

(*b*) *Photo. Self-adhesive. Die-cut perf 14½ × 14*

2314	**1609**	(1st) multicoloured	45	50	☐	☐

No. 2314 was only issued in £1.62 stamp booklets.

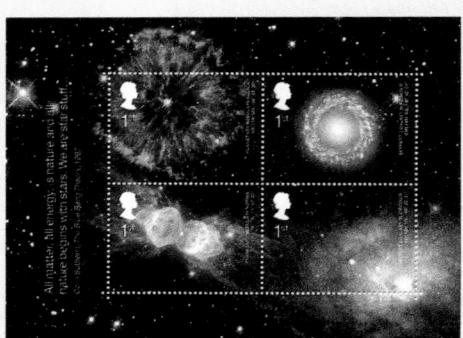

1613 Galaxies and Nebula

Astronomy

2002 (24 Sept.) *Sheet* 120 × 89 *mm. Multicoloured. Two phosphor bands. Perf 14½ × 14*

MS2315	**1613**	(1st) Planetary nebula in Aquila; (1st) Seyfert 2 galaxy in Pegasus; (1st) Planetary nebula in Norma; (1st) Seyfert 2 galaxy in Circinus	1·60	1·75	☐ ☐
	First Day Cover			2·50	☐
	Presentation Pack		2·10		☐
	PHQ Cards (set of 5)		1·90	3·25	☐ ☐

The five PHQ cards depict the four designs and the complete miniature sheet.

1614 Green Pillar Box, 1857

1615 Horizontal Aperture Box, 1874

1616 Air Mail Box, 1934

1617 Double Aperture Box, 1939

1618 Modern Style Box, 1980

150th Anniversary of the First Pillar Box

2002 (8 Oct.) *One centre phosphor band (2nd) or two phosphor bands (others). Perf* $14 \times 14\frac{1}{2}$

2316	**1614**	(2nd)	multicoloured	30	35	☐ ☐
2317	**1615**	(1st)	multicoloured	45	50	☐ ☐
2318	**1616**	(E)	multicoloured	60	65	☐ ☐
2319	**1617**	47p	multicoloured	75	80	☐ ☐
2320	**1618**	68p	multicoloured	1·10	1·25	☐ ☐
	Set of 5		. . . .	3·00	3·50	☐ ☐
	First Day Cover		. . . .		4·00	☐
	Presentation Pack		. . . .	3·50		☐
	PHQ Cards (set of 5)		. . . . . .	1·90	4·75	☐ ☐
	Set of 5 Gutter Pairs		. . . . . .	6·25		☐

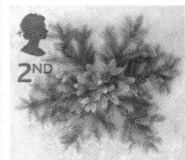

1619 Blue Spruce Star

1620 Holly

1621 Ivy

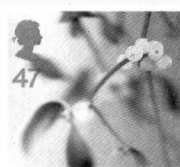

1622 Mistletoe

1623 Pine Cone

Christmas

2002 (5 Nov.) *Self-adhesive. One centre phosphor band (2nd) or two phosphor bands (others). Die-cut perf* $14\frac{1}{2} \times 14$

2321	**1619**	(2nd)	multicoloured	30	35	☐ ☐
2322	**1620**	(1st)	multicoloured	45	50	☐ ☐
2323	**1621**	(E)	multicoloured	60	65	☐ ☐
2324	**1622**	47p	multicoloured	75	80	☐ ☐
2325	**1623**	68p	multicoloured	1·10	1·25	☐ ☐
	Set of 5		. . . .	3·00	3·50	☐ ☐
	First Day Cover		. . . .		4·00	☐
	Presentation Pack		. . . .	3·50		☐
	PHQ Cards (set of 5)		. . . . . .	1·90	4·75	☐ ☐

Collectors Pack 2002

2002 (5 Nov.) *Comprises Nos.* 2243/57, 2260/88, 2291/2, 2299/313 *and* **MS**2315/25

	Collectors Pack	. . . .	40·00	☐

Post Office Yearbook

2002 (5 Nov.) *Comprises Nos.* 2243/57, 2260/88, 2291//2, 2299/313 *and* **MS**2315/25 *in hardback book with slip case*

	Yearbook	. . . .	48·00	☐

REGIONAL ISSUES

PERFORATION AND WATERMARK. All the following Regional stamps are perforated 15 × 14, unless otherwise stated.
For listing of First Day Covers see pages 164/6.

1 England

EN **1**   Three Lions

EN **2**   Crowned Lion with Shield of St. George

EN **3**   Oak Tree

EN **4**   Tudor Rose

2001 (23 APR.)–**02** *Printed in photogravure by De La Rue or Questa* (*Nos.* EN1/2), *De La Rue* (*others*). *One centre phosphor band* (2nd) *or two phosphor bands* (*others*). *Perf* 15 × 14 (*with one elliptical hole on each vertical side*)

EN1	EN **1**	(2nd) slate-green and silver	30	35	☐	☐
EN2	EN **2**	(1st) lake-brown and silver	45	50	☐	☐
EN3	EN **3**	(E) olive-green and silver	60	65	☐	☐
EN4	EN **4**	65p deep reddish lilac and silver	1·00	1·10	☐	☐
EN5		68p deep reddish lilac and silver	1·10	1·25	☐	☐
	Presentation Pack (*P.O. Pack No. 54*) (*Nos.* EN1/4)		2·75		☐	
	PHQ Cards (*set of 4*) (*Nos.* EN1/4)		1·50	10·00	☐	☐

Nos. EN1/3 were initially sold at 19p, 27p and 36p, the latter representing the basic European airmail rate.

Combined Presentation Packs for England, Northern Ireland, Scotland and Wales

Presentation Pack (*P.O. Pack No.* 59) (*contains 68p from England, Northern Ireland, Scotland and Wales* (*Nos.* EN5, NI93, S99, W88)) . . . . . .   4·50   ☐

2 Northern Ireland

N **1**

N **2**

N **3**

N **4**

1958–67 *Wmk* **179**

NI1	N **1**	3d lilac	15	10	☐	☐
		p. One centre phosphor band	15	15	☐	☐
NI2		4d blue	15	15	☐	☐
		p. Two phosphor bands	15	15	☐	☐
NI3	N **2**	6d purple	20	25	☐	☐
NI4		9d bronze-green (2 phosphor bands) . .	30	70	☐	☐
NI5	N **3**	1s 3d green	30	70	☐	☐
NI6		1s 6d blue (2 phosphor bands)	30	70	☐	☐

1968–69 *One centre phosphor band* (*Nos.* NI8/9) *or two phosphor bands* (*others*). *No wmk*

NI7	N **1**	4d blue	15	15	☐	☐
NI8		4d sepia	15	15	☐	☐
NI9		4d vermilion	20	20	☐	☐
NI10		5d blue	20	20	☐	☐
NI11	N **3**	1s 6d blue	2·25	2·50	☐	☐
		Presentation Pack (*comprises Nos.* NI1p, NI4/6, NI8/10) . . .	3·25		☐	

Decimal Currency
1971–91 *Type* N **4**. *No wmk*
(*a*) *Printed in photogravure with phosphor bands*

NI12	2½p magenta (1 centre band)		70	45	☐	☐
NI13	3p ultramarine (2 bands) . . .		25	25	☐	☐
NI14	3p ultramarine (1 centre band)		20	15	☐	☐
NI15	3½p olive-grey (2 bands)		20	25	☐	☐
NI16	3½p olive-grey (1 centre band)		20	25	☐	☐
NI17	4½p grey-blue (2 bands)		30	25	☐	☐
NI18	5p violet (2 bands)		1·25	1·25	☐	☐
NI19	5½p violet (2 bands)		20	20	☐	☐
NI20	5½p violet (1 centre band) . . .		20	25	☐	☐
NI21	6½p blue (1 centre band)		20	20	☐	☐
NI22	7p brown (1 centre band) . .		35	25	☐	☐
NI23	7½p chestnut (2 bands)		2·00	2·00	☐	☐
NI24	8p rosine (2 bands)		35	35	☐	☐
NI25	8½p yellow-green (2 bands) . .		35	40	☐	☐
NI26	9p violet (2 bands)		40	40	☐	☐
NI27	10p orange-brown (2 bands) .		40	50	☐	☐
NI28	10p orange-brown (1 centre band)		40	50	☐	☐
NI29	10½p blue (2 bands)		50	50	☐	☐
NI30	11p scarlet (2 bands)		50	50	☐	☐

NI31	12p yellowish green	50	50 □ □
NI32	13½p purple-brown	60	70 □ □
NI33	15p ultramarine	60	70 □ □

(c) Printed in lithography. Perf 14 (11½p, 12½p, 14p (No. NI38
15½p, 16p, 18p, (No. NI45), 19½p, 20½p, 22p (No. NI53), 26
(No. NI60), 28p (No. NI62)) or 15 × 14 (others)

NI34	11½p drab (1 side band)	85	85 □ □
NI35	12p bright emerald (1 side band)	70	80 □ □
NI36	12½p light emerald (1 side band)	60	60 □ □
	a. Perf 15 × 14	4·50	4·25 □ □
NI37	13p pale chestnut (1 side band)	80	50 □ □
NI38	14p grey-blue (phosphorised paper)	75	75 □ □
NI39	14p deep blue (1 centre band)	75	60 □ □
NI40	15p bright blue (1 centre band)	90	60 □ □
NI41	15½p pale violet (phosphorised paper)	80	80 □ □
NI42	16p drab (phosphorised paper)	1·00	1·00 □ □
	a. Perf 15 × 14	9·00	7·50 □ □
NI43	17p grey-blue (phosphorised paper)	90	95 □ □
NI44	17p deep blue (1 centre band)	1·00	80 □ □
NI45	18p deep violet (phosphorised paper)	1·00	1·00 □ □
NI46	18p olive-grey (phosphorised paper)	1·00	90 □ □
NI47	18p bright green (1 centre band)	1·00	95 □ □
	a. Perf 14	1·90	1·60 □ □
NI48	18p bright green (1 side band)	2·50	2·50 □ □
NI49	19p bright orange-red (phosphorised paper) . . .	1·00	1·00 □ □
NI50	19½p olive-grey (phosphorised paper)	1·90	1·90 □ □
NI51	20p brownish black (phosphorised paper) . . .	1·00	80 □ □
NI52	20½p ultramarine (phosphorised paper)	3·75	3·75 □ □
NI53	22p blue (phosphorised paper)	1·10	1·10 □ □
NI54	22p yellow-green (phosphorised paper)	1·10	1·10 □ □
NI55	22p bright orange-red (phosphorised paper) . . .	1·25	90 □ □
NI56	23p bright green (phosphorised paper)	1·25	1·10 □ □
NI57	24p Indian red (phosphorised paper)	1·50	1·00 □ □
NI58	24p chestnut (phosphorised paper)	1·10	90 □ □
NI59	24p chestnut (2 bands)	2·50	2·75 □ □
NI60	26p rosine (phosphorised paper)	1·25	1·25 □ □
	a. Perf 15 × 14	4·50	3·50 □ □
NI61	26p drab (phosphorised paper)	1·50	1·25 □ □
NI62	28p deep violet-blue (phosphorised paper) . . .	1·40	1·25 □ □
	a. Perf 15 × 14	1·50	1·25 □ □
NI63	28p deep bluish grey (phosphorised paper) . . .	1·60	1·40 □ □
NI64	31p bright purple (phosphorised paper) . . .	1·60	1·60 □ □
NI65	32p greenish blue (phosphorised paper) . . .	1·75	1·75 □ □
NI66	34p deep bluish grey (phosphorised paper) . . .	1·90	1·90 □ □
NI67	37p rosine (phosphorised paper)	1·90	1·90 □ □
NI68	39p bright mauve (phosphorised paper) . . .	1·90	1·90 □ □

Nos. NI48 and NI59 were only issued in stamp booklets.

Presentation Pack (P.O. Pack No. 29) (contains 2½p (NI12), 3p (NI13), 5p (NI18), 7½p (NI23))	4·25	□
Presentation Pack (P.O. Pack No. 61) (contains 3p (NI14), 3½p (NI15), 5½p (NI19), 8p (NI24) later with 4½p (NI17) added) .	2·75	□
Presentation Pack (P.O. Pack No. 84) (contains 6½p (NI21), 8½p (NI25), 10p (NI27), 11p (NI30))	2·00	□
Presentation Pack (P.O. Pack No. 129d) (contains 7p (NI22), 9p (NI26), 10½p (NI29), 11½p (NI34), 12p (NI31), 13½p (NI32), 14p (NI38), 15p (NI33), 18p (NI45), 22p (NI53))	9·00	□
Presentation Pack (P.O. Pack No. 4) (contains 10p (NI28), 12½p (NI36), 16p (NI42), 20½p (NI52), 26p (NI60), 28p (NI62))	10·00	□
Presentation Pack (P.O. Pack No. 8) (contains 10p (NI28), 13p (NI37), 16p (NI42a), 17p (NI43), 22p (NI54), 26p (NI60), 28p (NI62), 31p (NI64))	17·00	□
Presentation Pack (P.O. Pack No. 12) (contains 12p (NI35), 13p (NI37), 17p (NI43), 18p (NI46), 22p (NI54), 26p (NI60a), 28p (NI62a), 31p (NI64))	15·00	□

Combined Presentation Packs for Northern Ireland,
Scotland and Wales

Presentation Pack (P.O. Pack No. 17) (contains 14p, 19p, 23p, 32p from Northern Ireland, Scotland and Wales (Nos. NI39, NI49, NI56, NI65, S54, S62, S67, S77, W40, W50, W57, W66))	16·00	□

Presentation Pack (*P.O. Pack No. 20*) (*contains* 15p, 20p, 24p, 34p *from Northern Ireland, Scotland and Wales* (*Nos.* NI40, NI51, NI57, NI66, S56, S64, S69, S78, W41, W52, W58, W67)) . . . . 18·00 □

Presentation Pack (*P.O. Pack No. 23*) (*contains* 17p, 22p, 26p, 37p *from Northern Ireland, Scotland and Wales* (*Nos.* NI44, NI55, NI61, NI67, S58, S66, S73, S79, W45, W56, W62, W68)) . . . . 18·00 □

Presentation Pack (*P.O. Pack No. 26*) (*contains* 18p, 24p, 28p, 39p *from Northern Ireland, Scotland and Wales* (*Nos.* NI47, NI58, NI63, NI68, S60, S70, S75, S80, W48, W59, W64, W69)) . . . . 18·00 □

1993 (7 Dec.)–**2000** (*a*) *Printed in lithography by Questa. Perf* 15 × 14 (*with one elliptical hole on each vertical side*)

NI69	N **4**	19p bistre (1 centre band)	90	80	□	□
NI70		19p bistre (1 side band) . .	2·75	2·50	□	□
NI71		20p bright green (1 centre band)	1·50	1·25	□	□
NI72		25p red (2 bands)	75	75	□	□
NI73		26p red-brown (2 bands) .	1·50	1·50	□	□
NI74		30p deep olive-grey (2 bands)	1·60	1·40	□	□
NI75		37p bright mauve (2 bands)	2·25	2·25	□	□
NI76		41p grey-brown (2 bands)	1·75	1·75	□	□
NI77		63p light emerald (2 bands)	3·50	3·25	□	□

(*b*) *Printed in photogravure by Walsall* (19*p*, 20*p*, 26*p* (*No.* NI81*b*), 38*p*, 40*p*, 63*p*, 64*p*, 65*p*), *Harrison or Walsall* (26*p* (*No.* NI81), 37*p*). *Perf* 14 (*No.* NI80) *or* 15 × 14 (*others*) (*both with one elliptical hole on each vertical side*)

NI78	N **4**	19p bistre (1 centre band)	1·75	70	□	□
NI79		20p bright green (1 centre band)	85	70	□	□
NI80		20p bright green (1 side band)	1·90	1·90	□	□
NI81		26p chestnut (2 bands) . .	1·25	1·00	□	□
		b. Perf 14	2·25	1·75	□	□
NI82		37p bright mauve (2 bands)	1·25	1·00	□	□
NI83		38p ultramarine (2 bands)	1·75	1·75	□	□
NI84		40p deep azure (2 bands)	90	90	□	□
NI85		63p light emerald (2 bands)	2·25	2·00	□	□
NI86		64p turquoise-green (2 bands)	2·25	2·00	□	□
NI87		65p greenish blue (2 bands)	2·00	2·00	□	□

Nos. NI70, NI80 and NI81*b* were only issued in stamp booklets. No. NI70 exists with the phosphor band at the left or right of the stamp.

Presentation Pack (*P.O. Pack No. 47*) (*contains* 19p, 26p, 38p, 64p (*Nos.* NI78, NI81, NI83 NI86)) . . . . 4·00 □

Presentation Pack (*P.O. Pack No. 52*) (*contains* 1st, 40p, 65p) (*Nos.* NI84, NI87, NI88*b*) . . 3·75 □

Combined Presentation Packs for Northern Ireland, Scotland and Wales

Presentation Pack (*P.O. Pack No. 31*) (*contains* 19p, 25p, 30p, 41p *from Northern Ireland, Scotland and Wales* (*Nos.* NI69, NI72, NI74, NI76, S81, S84, S86, S88, W70, W73, W75, W77)) . . . . 18·00 □

Presentation Pack (*P.O. Pack No. 36*) (*contains* 20p, 26p, 37p, 63p *from Northern Ireland, Scotland and Wales* (*Nos.* NI71, NI73, NI75, NI77, S83, S85, S87, S89, W72, W74 W76, W78)) . . . . 22·00 □

Presentation Pack (*P.O. Pack No. 42*) (*contains* 20p (1 centre band), 26p, 37p, 63p *from Northern Ireland, Scotland and Wales* (*Nos.* NI79, NI81/2, NI85, S90/3, W79/82)) 12·00 □

N 5

2000 (15 Feb.–25 Apr.) *Type* N **4** *redrawn with* '1st' *face value as Type* N **5**. *Two phosphor bands. Perf* 14 (*with one elliptical hole on each vertical side*)

NI88	N **5**	(1st) bright orange-red . .	1·10	1·10	□	□
		b. Perf 15 ×14 (25 Apr.)	1·25	1·25	□	□

No. NI88 was only issued in stamp booklets. No. NI88*b* was issued in sheets on 25 April.

N **6** Basalt Columns, Giant's Causeway

N **7** Aerial View of Patchwork Fields

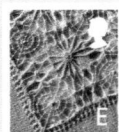

N 8   Linen Pattern   N 9   Vase Pattern
                              from Belleck

2001 (6 Mar.)–**02** *Printed in lithography by De La Rue (68p),*
La Rue or Walsall (E) or Walsall (others). One centre phosph
band (2nd) or two phosphor bands (others). Perf 15 × 14 (w
one elliptical hole on each vertical side)

NI89	N 6	(2nd) black, new blue, bright magenta and greenish yellow . . .	30	35 ☐
NI90	N 7	(1st) black, new blue and greenish yellow . . .	45	50 ☐
NI91	N 8	(E) black, new blue and pale orange	60	70 ☐
NI92	N 9	65p black, bright magenta and greenish yellow	1·00	1·10 ☐
NI93		68p black, bright magenta and greenish yellow	1·10	1·25 ☐
		Presentation Pack (P.O. Pack No. 53) (Nos. NI89/92)	2·75	☐
		PHQ Cards (set of 4) (Nos. NI89/92)	1·50	10·00 ☐

Nos. NI89, NI90 and NI91 were initially sold at 19p, 27p an
36p, the latter representing the basic European airmail rate.

For combined presentation packs for all four Regions, s
under England.

3 Scotland

S 1   S 2   S 3   S 4

1958–67 *Wmk 179*

S1	S 1	3d lilac	15	15 ☐ ☐
		p. Two phosphor bands	16·00	2·00 ☐ ☐
		pa. One side band . . .	20	25 ☐ ☐
		pb. One centre band . .	15	15 ☐ ☐
S2		4d blue	15	15 ☐ ☐
		p. Two phosphor bands	15	15 ☐ ☐
S3	S 2	6d purple	20	15 ☐ ☐
		p. Two phosphor bands	20	20 ☐ ☐
S4		9d bronze-green (2 phosphor bands) . .	35	40 ☐ ☐
S5	S 3	1s 3d green	40	40 ☐ ☐
		p. Two phosphor bands	40	40 ☐ ☐
S6		1s 6d blue (2 phosphor bands) . .	45	50 ☐ ☐

No. S1*pa* exists with the phosphor band at the left or right of
the stamp.

1967–70 *One centre phosphor band (Nos. S7, S9/10) or two*
phosphor bands (others). No wmk

S7	S 1	3d lilac	10	15 ☐ ☐
S8		4d blue	10	15 ☐ ☐
S9		4d sepia	10	10 ☐ ☐
S10		4d vermilion	10	10 ☐ ☐
S11		5d blue	20	10 ☐ ☐
S12	S 2	9d bronze-green	4·00	4·50 ☐ ☐
S13	S 3	1s 6d blue	1·40	1·40 ☐ ☐
		Presentation Pack (containing Nos. S3, S5p, S7, S9/13) . . .	10·00	☐

Decimal Currency
1971–93 *Type S 4. No wmk*
(*a*) *Printed in photogravure by Harrison and Sons with phos-*
phor bands. Perf 15 × 14

S14		2½p magenta (1 centre band) .	25	20 ☐ ☐
S15		3p ultramarine (2 bands) . . .	30	15 ☐ ☐
S16		3p ultramarine (1 centre band)	15	15 ☐ ☐
S17		3½p olive-grey (2 bands)	20	25 ☐ ☐
S18		3½p olive-grey (1 centre band)	20	25 ☐ ☐
S19		4½p grey-blue (2 bands)	30	25 ☐ ☐
S20		5p violet (2 bands)	85	1·00 ☐ ☐
S21		5½p violet (2 bands)	20	20 ☐ ☐
S22		5½p violet (1 centre band) . . .	20	25 ☐ ☐
S23		6½p blue (1 centre band)	20	20 ☐ ☐
S24		7p brown (1 centre band) . .	30	30 ☐ ☐
S25		7½p chestnut (2 bands)	95	1·25 ☐ ☐
S26		8p rosine (2 bands)	45	40 ☐ ☐

S27	8½p yellow-green (2 bands) . .	40	40 □ □	
S28	9p violet (2 bands)	40	40 □ □	
S29	10p orange-brown (2 bands) .	45	50 □ □	
S30	10p orange-brown (1 centre band)	40	50 □ □	
S31	10½p blue (2 bands)	45	50 □ □	
S32	11p scarlet (2 bands)	50	50 □ □	

(b) *Printed in photogravure by Harrison and Sons on phosphorised paper. Perf* 15 × 14

S33	12p yellowish green	50	50 □ □
S34	13½p purple-brown	70	80 □ □
S35	15p ultramarine	60	70 □ □

(c) *Printed in lithography by John Waddington. One side phosphor band* (11½p, 12p, 12½p, 13p) *or phosphorised paper* (others). *Perf* 14

S36	11½p drab	80	80 □ □
S37	12p bright emerald	2·00	1·60 □ □
S38	12½p light emerald	60	70 □ □
S39	13p pale chestnut	75	75 □ □
S40	14p grey-blue	75	65 □ □
S41	15½p pale violet	80	80 □ □
S42	16p drab	80	85 □ □
S43	17p grey-blue	1·25	1·00 □ □
S44	18p deep violet	80	80 □ □
S45	19½p olive-grey	1·50	1·50 □ □
S46	20½p ultramarine	3·75	3·75 □ □
S47	22p blue	1·10	1·10 □ □
S48	22p yellow-green	3·00	3·25 □ □
S49	26p rosine	1·25	1·25 □ □
S50	28p deep violet-blue	1·25	1·25 □ □
S51	31p bright purple	2·25	2·25 □ □

(d) *Printed in lithography by Questa. Perf* 15 × 14

S52	12p bright emerald (1 side band)	2·00	2·00 □ □
S53	13p pale chestnut (1 side band)	70	75 □ □
S54	14p deep blue (1 centre band)	60	70 □ □
S55	14p deep blue (1 side band) . .	80	90 □ □
S56	15p bright blue (1 centre band)	70	70 □ □
S57	17p grey-blue (phosphorised paper)	4·00	4·00 □ □
S58	17p deep blue (1 centre band)	1·00	1·10 □ □
S59	18p olive-grey (phosphorised paper)	1·10	85 □ □
S60	18p bright green (1 centre band)	1·25	90 □ □
	a. *Perf* 14	1·40	1·50 □ □
S61	18p bright green (1 side band)	2·50	2·50 □ □
S62	19p bright orange-red (phosphorised paper) . . .	80	80 □ □
S63	19p bright orange-red (2 bands)	1·75	1·75 □ □
S64	20p brownish black (phosphorised paper) . . .	95	95 □ □
S65	22p yellow-green (phosphorised paper)	1·40	1·50 □ □
S66	22p bright orange-red (phosphorised paper) . . .	1·25	90 □ □

S67	23p bright green (phosphorised paper)	1·25	1·10 □ □
S68	23p bright green (2 bands) . .	12·00	12·00 □ □
S69	24p Indian red (phosphorised paper)	1·50	1·00 □ □
S70	24p chestnut (phosphorised paper)	1·40	1·25 □ □
	a. *Perf* 14	2·75	2·75 □ □
S71	24p chestnut (2 bands)	3·00	2·75 □ □
S72	26p rosine (phosphorised paper)	3·25	3·00 □ □
S73	26p drab (phosphorised paper)	1·25	1·25 □ □
S74	28p deep violet-blue (phosphorised paper) . . .	1·25	1·25 □ □
S75	28p deep bluish grey (phosphorised paper) . . .	1·50	1·40 □ □
	a. *Perf* 14	5·50	4·50 □ □
S76	31p bright purple (phosphorised paper)	2·00	1·90 □ □
S77	32p greenish blue (phosphorised paper) . . .	1·75	1·60 □ □
S78	34p deep bluish grey (phosphorised paper) . . .	1·90	1·90 □ □
S79	37p rosine (phosphorised paper)	1·90	1·90 □ □
S80	39p bright mauve (phosphorised paper)	2·00	1·90 □ □
	a. *Perf* 14	3·50	3·50 □ □

Nos. S55, S61, S63, S68 and S71 were only issued in stamp booklets.

Presentation Pack (P.O. Pack No. 27) (contains 2½p (S14), 3p (S15), 5p (S20), 7½p (S25)) . .	4·25	□
Presentation Pack (P.O. Pack No. 62) (contains 3p (S16), 3½p (S17), 5½p (S21), 8p (S26), later with 4½p (S19) added) .	2·75	□
Presentation Pack (P.O. Pack No. 85) (contains 6½p (S23), 8½p (S27), 10p (S29), 11p (S32)) .	2·00	□
Presentation Pack (P.O. Pack No. 129b) (contains 7p (S24), 9p (S28), 10½p (S31), 11½p (S36), 12p (S33), 13½p (S34), 14p (S40), 15p (S35), 18p (S44), 22p (S47))	9·00	□
Presentation Pack (P.O. Pack No. 2) (contains 10p (S30), 12½p (S38), 16p (S42), 20½p (S46), 26p (S49), 28p (S50))	10·00	□
Presentation Pack (P.O. Pack No. 6) (contains 10p (S30), 13p (S39), 16p (S42), 17p (S43), 22p (S48), 26p (S49), 28p (S50), 31p (S51))	13·00	□

Presentation Pack (P.O. Pack No.
10) (*contains* 12p (S52), 13p
(S53), 17p (S57), 18p (S59),
22p (S65), 26p (S72), 28p (S74),
31p (S76)) . . . .   15·00   □

For combined packs containing values from all three Regio
see under Northern Ireland.

1993 (7 DEC.)–**98** (a) *Printed in lithography by Questa. P*
15 × 14 (*with one elliptical hole on each vertical side*)

S81	S 4	19p bistre (1 centre band)	80	70	□
S82		19p bistre (1 side band)	3·00	2·50	□
S83		20p bright green (1 centre band)	1·25	1·00	□
S84		25p red (2 bands)	1·25	1·00	□
S85		26p red-brown (2 bands)	1·50	1·50	□
S86		30p deep olive-grey (2 bands)	1·50	1·25	□
S87		37p bright mauve (2 bands)	2·50	2·25	□
S88		41p grey-brown (2 bands)	1·90	1·90	□
S89		63p light emerald (2 bands)	3·50	3·25	□

(b) *Printed in photogravure by Walsall* (20p, 26p (No. S91
63p), Harrison or Walsall (26p (No. S91), 37p). Perf 14 (N
S90a) *or* 15 × 14 (*others*) (*both with one elliptical hole*
each vertical side)

S90	S 4	20p bright green (1 centre band)	60	60	□
S90a		20p bright green (1 side band)	2·00	1·75	□
S91		26p chestnut (2 bands) .	1·00	1·00	□
		a. Perf 14	2·25	2·00	□
S92		37p bright mauve (2 bands)	1·25	90	□
S93		63p light emerald (2 bands)	2·25	2·00	□

Nos. S82, S90a and S91a were only issued in stamp bookle
For combined presentation packs for all three Regions, s
under Northern Ireland.

S 5   Scottish Flag   S 6   Scottish Lion

S 7   Thistle   S 8   Tartan

1999 (8 JUNE)–**2002** *Printed in photogravure by De La Rue* (68p),
De La Rue, Questa or Walsall (2nd, 1st) *or Walsall* (*others*). *One*
centre phosphor band (2nd) *or two phosphor bands* (*others*).
Perf 15 × 14 (*with one elliptical hole on each vertical side*)

S94	S 5	(2nd) new blue, blue and silver	30	35	□ □
S95	S 6	(1st) greenish yellow, deep rose-red, rose-red and silver	40	45	□ □
S96	S 7	(E) bright lilac, deep lilac and silver	60	70	□ □
S97	S 8	64p greenish yellow, bright magenta, new blue, grey-black and silver	2·50	2·25	□ □
S98		65p greenish yellow, bright magenta, new blue, grey-black and silver	1·00	1·10	□ □
S99		68p greenish yellow, bright magenta, new blue, grey-black and silver	1·10	1·25	□ □
		Presentation Pack (P.O. Pack No. 45) (*contains 2nd, 1st, E, 64p*) (*Nos. S94/7*)	4·00		□
		Presentation Pack (P.O. Pack No. 50) (*contains 65p*) (*No. S98*)	3·00		□
		Presentation Pack (P.O. Pack No. 55) (*contains 2nd, 1st, E, 65p*) (*Nos. S94/6, S98*)		2·75	□
		PHQ Cards (*Nos. S94/7*)	1·50	10·00	□ □

Nos. S94, S95 and S96 were initially sold at 19p, 26p and 30p,
the latter representing the basic European airmail rate.

For combined presentation packs for all four Regions, see
under England.

S 9

2000 (15 FEB.) *Type* S 5 *redrawn with* '1st' *face value as Type*
S 9. *Two phosphor bands. Perf* 14 (*with one elliptical hole on*
each vertical side)

S108	S 9	(1st) bright orange-red . .	1·25	1·25	□ □

No. S108 was only issued in stamp booklets.

4 Wales and Monmouthshire

W 1   W 2   W 3

1958–67 *Wmk* **179**

W1	W 1	3d lilac	15	15	☐	☐
		p. One centre phosphor band	20	15	☐	☐
W2		4d blue	20	15	☐	☐
		p. Two phosphor bands	20	15	☐	☐
W3	W 2	6d purple	35	30	☐	☐
W4		9d bronze-green (2 phosphor bands) . .	40	35	☐	☐
W5	W 3	1s 3d green	40	40	☐	☐
W6		1s 6d blue (2 phosphor bands)	40	40	☐	☐

1967–69 *One centre phosphor band (Nos.* W7, W9/10) *or two phosphor bands (others). No wmk*

W7	W 1	3d lilac	10	15	☐	☐
W8		4d blue	10	15	☐	☐
W9		4d sepia	15	15	☐	☐
W10		4d vermilion	15	15	☐	☐
W11		5d blue	15	15	☐	☐
W12	W 3	1s 6d blue	3·50	3·50	☐	☐
		Presentation Pack (comprises Nos. W4, W6/7, W9/11)	3·75		☐	

W 4 With 'p'    W 5 Without 'p'

Decimal Currency
1971–92 *Type* W 4. *No wmk*

(a) Printed in photogravure with phosphor bands

W13	2½p magenta (1 centre band) .	20	20	☐	☐
W14	3p ultramarine (2 bands)	25	20	☐	☐
W15	3p ultramarine (1 centre band)	25	25	☐	☐
W16	3½p olive-grey (2 bands)	20	30	☐	☐
W17	3½p olive-grey (1 centre band)	20	30	☐	☐
W18	4½p grey-blue (2 bands)	30	30	☐	☐
W19	5p violet (2 bands)	1·00	1·10	☐	☐
W20	5½p violet (2 bands)	25	30	☐	☐
W21	5½p violet (1 centre band) . . .	25	30	☐	☐
W22	6½p blue (1 centre band)	20	20	☐	☐
W23	7p brown (1 centre band) . .	25	25	☐	☐

W24	7½p chestnut (2 bands)	90	1·25	☐	☐
W25	8p rosine (2 bands)	30	35	☐	☐
W26	8½p yellow-green (2 bands) . .	30	35	☐	☐
W27	9p violet (2 bands)	40	40	☐	☐
W28	10p orange-brown (2 bands) .	40	40	☐	☐
W29	10p orange-brown (1 centre band)	40	40	☐	☐
W30	10½p blue (2 bands)	40	45	☐	☐
W31	11p scarlet (2 bands)	40	45	☐	☐

(b) Printed in photogravure on phosphorised paper

W32	12p yellow-green	40	50	☐	☐
W33	13½p purple-brown	60	70	☐	☐
W34	15p ultramarine	60	70	☐	☐

(c) Printed in lithography. Perf 14 (11½p, 12½p, 14p (No. W39), 15½p. 16p, 18p (No. W46), 19½p, 20½p, 22p (No. W54), 26p (No. W61), 28p (No. W63)) or 15 × 14 (others)

W35	11½p drab (1 side band)	90	80	☐	☐
W36	12p bright emerald (1 side band)	1·50	1·25	☐	☐
W37	12½p light emerald (1 side band)	70	70	☐	☐
	a. Perf 15 × 14	4·50	5·00	☐	☐
W38	13p pale chestnut (1 side band)	60	60	☐	☐
W39	14p grey-blue (phosphorised paper)	70	70	☐	☐
W40	14p deep blue (1 centre band)	75	75	☐	☐
W41	15p bright blue (1 centre band)	80	75	☐	☐
W42	15½p pale violet (phosphorised paper)	75	75	☐	☐
W43	16p drab (phosphorised paper)	1·50	1·60	☐	☐
	a. Perf 15 × 14	1·75	1·90	☐	☐
W44	17p grey-blue (phosphorised paper)	70	80	☐	☐
W45	17p deep blue (1 centre band)	90	80	☐	☐
W46	18p deep violet (phosphorised paper)	1·00	95	☐	☐
W47	18p olive-grey (phosphorised paper)	95	90	☐	☐
W48	18p bright green (1 centre band)	75	75	☐	☐
	b. Perf 14	4·50	4·50	☐	☐
W49	18p bright green (1 side band)	2·25	2·25	☐	☐
W50	19p bright orange-red (phosphorised paper) . . .	1·00	80	☐	☐
W51	19½p olive-grey (phosphorised paper)	1·50	1·50	☐	☐
W52	20p brownish black (phosphorised paper)	90	90	☐	☐
W53	20½p ultramarine (phosphorised paper)	3·25	3·25	☐	☐
W54	22p blue (phosphorised paper)	1·25	1·25	☐	☐
W55	22p yellow-green (phosphorised paper)	1·25	1·25	☐	☐
W56	22p bright orange-red (phosphorised paper) . . .	1·25	1·10	☐	☐
W57	23p bright green (phosphorised paper)	1·25	1·25	☐	☐
W58	24p Indian red (phosphorised paper)	1·40	1·10	☐	☐

W59	24p chestnut (phosphorised		
	paper)	1·10	1·10 ☐
	b. Perf 14	3·50	3·75 ☐
W60	24p chestnut (2 bands) . . .	1·40	1·40 ☐
W61	26p rosine (phosphorised		
	paper)	1·25	1·10 ☐
	a. Perf 15 × 14	5·50	5·00 ☐
W62	26p drap (phosphorised paper)	1·50	1·25 ☐
W63	28p deep violet-blue (phos-		
	phorised paper)	1·25	1·25 ☐
	a. Perf 15 × 14	1·50	1·25 ☐
W64	28p deep bluish grey		
	(phosphorised paper) . . .	1·50	1·25 ☐
W65	31p bright purple (phosphorised		
	paper)	1·40	1·40 ☐
W66	32p greenish blue (phos-		
	phorised paper)	1·60	1·40 ☐
W67	34p deep bluish grey		
	(phosphorised paper) . . .	1·60	1·60 ☐
W68	37p rosine (phosphorised		
	paper)	1·90	1·90 ☐
W69	39p bright mauve (phos-		
	phorised paper)	2·00	2·00 ☐

Nos. W49 and W60 were only issued in stamp booklets. Tl former exists with the phosphor band at the left or right of tl stamp.

Presentation Pack (P.O. Pack No.			
28) (contains 2½p (W13), 3p			
(W14), 5p (W19), 7½p (W24)) .	4·25		☐
Presentation Pack (P.O. Pack No.			
63) (contains 3p (W15), 3½p			
(W16), 5½p (W20), 8p (W25),			
later with 4½p (W18) added) .	2·75		☐
Presentation Pack (P.O. Pack No.			
86) (contains 6½p (W22), 8½p			
(W26), 10p (W28), 11p (W31))	2·00		☐
Presentation Pack (P.O. Pack No.			
129c) (contains 7p (W23), 9p			
(W27), 10½p (W30), 11½p			
(W35), 12p (W32), 13½p (W33),			
14p (W39), 15p (W34), 18p			
(W46), 22p (W53))	9·00		☐
Presentation Pack (P.O. Pack No.			
3) (contains 10p (W29), 12½p			
(W37), 16p (W43), 20½p (W53),			
26p (W61), 28p (W63))	10·00		☐
Presentation Pack (P.O. Pack No.			
7) (contains 10p (W29), 13p			
(W38), 16p (W43a), 17p			
(W44), 22p (W55), 26p (W61),			
28p (W63), 31p (W65))	13·00		☐
Presentation Pack (P.O. Pack No.			
11) (contains 12p (W36), 13p			
(W38), 17p (W44), 18p (W47),			
22p (W55), 26p (W61a), 28p			
(W63a), 31p (W65))	15·00		☐

For combined packs containing values from all three Regio see under Northern Ireland.

1993 (7 Dec.)–**96** *Printed in lithography by Questa. Perf* 15 × 14 (*with one elliptical hole on each vertical side*)

W70	W 4	19p bistre (1 centre band)	80	70 ☐ ☐
W71		19p bistre (1 side band) .	3·25	3·00 ☐ ☐
W72		20p bright green (1 centre		
		band)	1·25	1·40 ☐ ☐
W73		25p red (2 bands)	1·25	1·00 ☐ ☐
W74		26p red-brown (2 bands)	1·60	1·50 ☐ ☐
W75		30p deep olive-grey (2		
		bands)	1·10	1·25 ☐ ☐
W76		37p bright mauve (2		
		bands)	2·40	2·40 ☐ ☐
W77		41p grey-brown (2 bands)	1·75	1·90 ☐ ☐
W78		63p light emerald (2		
		bands)	3·75	3·75 ☐

No. W71 was only issued in stamp booklets.

For combined presentation packs for all three Regions see under Northern Ireland.

1997 (1 July)–**98** *Printed in photogravure by Walsall* (20p, 26p (*No.* W80a), 63p), *Harrison or Walsall* (26p (*No.* W80), 37p) *Perf* 14 (*No.* W79a) *or* 15 × 14 (*both with one elliptical hole on each vertical side*)

W79	W 5	20p bright green (1 centre		
		band)	80	80 ☐ ☐
W79a		20p bright green (1 side		
		band)	2·25	2·00 ☐ ☐
W80		26p chestnut (2 bands) .	1·00	1·00 ☐ ☐
		a. Perf 14	2·00	2·00 ☐ ☐
W81		37p bright mauve (2		
		bands)	1·25	1·25 ☐ ☐
W82		63p light emerald (2		
		bands)	2·25	2·00 ☐ ☐
		Presentation Pack (P.O. Pack No.		
		39) (Nos. W79 and W80/2) . .	5·75	☐

Nos. W79a and W80a were only issued in stamp booklets.

W 6   Leek

W 7   Welsh Dragon

W 8   Daffodil

W 9   Prince of Wales Feathers

1999 (8 June)–**2002** *Printed in photogravure by De La Rue* (68p),
or Walsall (others). One phosphor band (2nd) *or two phosphor
bands* (others). *Perf* 14 (*No.* W83a) *or* 15 × 14 (*others*) (*both
with one elliptical hole on each vertical side*)

W83	W 6	(2nd) orange-brown, yellow-orange and black (1 centre band) . . .	30	35	□	□
W83a		(2nd) orange-brown, yellow-orange and black (1 side band)	1·50	1·50	□	□
W84	W 7	(1st) blue-green, greenish yellow, silver and black	40	45	□	□
W85	W 8	(E) greenish blue, deep greenish blue and grey-black	60	70	□	□
W86	W 9	64p violet, gold, silver and black	2·50	2·25	□	□
W87		65p violet, gold, silver and black	1·00	1·10	□	□
W88		68p violet, gold, silver and black	1·10	1·25	□	□
		Presentation Pack (*P.O. Pack No. 46*) (*contains* 2nd, 1st, E, 64p) (*Nos.* W83, W84/6))	4·00		□	
		Presentation Pack (*P.O. Pack No. 51*) (*contains* 65p) (*No.* W87))	3·00		□	
		Presentation Pack (*P.O. Pack No. 56*) (*contains* 2nd, 1st, E, 65p) (*Nos.* W83, W84/5, W87)) . . .	2·75		□	
		PHQ Cards (*Nos.* W83, W84/6) .	1·50	10·00	□	□

Nos. W83, W84 and W85 were initially sold at 19p, 26p and
30p, the latter representing the basic European airmail rate.

No. W83a was only issued in stamp booklets.

For combined presentation packs for all four Regions, see
under England.

W **10**

2000 (15 Feb.) *Type* W **4** *redrawn with* '1af/st' *face value as Type*
W **10**. *Two phosphor bands. Perf* 14 (*with one elliptical hole on
each vertical side*)

W97	W **10**	(1st) bright orange-red .	1·25	1·25	□	□

No. W97 was only issued in stamp booklets.

ISLE OF MAN

Regional Issues

1   2   3

1958–67 *Wmk* **179**. *Perf* 15 × 14

1	**1**	2½d red	40	1·25	☐	☐
2	**2**	3d lilac	20	20	☐	☐
		p. One centre phosphor				
		band	20	50	☐	☐
3		4d blue	1·40	1·40	☐	☐
		p. Two phosphor bands . .	20	30	☐	☐

1968–69 *One centre phosphor band* (*Nos.* 5/6) *or two phospho* *bands* (*others*). *No wmk*

4	**2**	4d blue	25	30	☐	☐
5		4d sepia	25	40	☐	☐
6		4d vermilion	45	75	☐	☐
7		5d blue	45	75	☐	☐

Decimal Currency

1971 (7 July) *One centre phosphor band* (2½p) *or two phospho* *bands* (*others*). *No wmk*

8	**3**	2½p magenta	20	15	☐	☐
9		3p ultramarine	20	15	☐	☐
10		5p violet	40	60	☐	☐
11		7½p chestnut	40	75	☐	☐
		Presentation Pack	2·75		☐	

For comprehensive listings of the Independent Administratio issues of the Isle of Man, see Stanley Gibbons *Collect Channe Islands and Isle of Man Stamps.*

CHANNEL ISLANDS
1 General Issue

C **1** Gathering Vraic   C **2** Islanders gathering Vraic

Third Anniversary of Liberation

1948 (10 May) *Wmk Type* **127**. *Perf* 15 × 14

C1	C **1**	1d red	25	30	☐	☐
C2	C **2**	2½d blue	25	30	☐	☐
		First Day Cover	35·00		☐	

2 Guernsey

(a) War Occupation Issues

Stamps issued under British authority during the German Occupation.

1   2   3

1941–44 *Rouletted.* (*a*) *White paper. No wmk*

1d	**1**	½d green	3·00	1·75	☐	☐
2		1d red	2·00	90	☐	☐
3		2½d blue	3·25	4·00	☐	☐
		(*b*) *Bluish French bank-note paper. Wmk loops*				
4	**1**	½d green	20·00	18·00	☐	☐
5		1d red	10·00	16·00	☐	☐

(b) Regional Issues

1958–67 *Wmk* **179**. *Perf* 15 × 14

6	**2**	2½d red	35	40	☐	☐
7	**3**	3d lilac	30	30	☐	☐
		p. One centre phosphor				
		band	15	20	☐	☐
8		4d blue	25	30	☐	☐
		p. Two phosphor bands . .	15	20	☐	☐

1968–69 *One centre phosphor band* (*Nos.* 10/11) *or two phosphor bands* (*others*). *No wmk*

9	**3**	4d blue	10	20	☐	☐
10		4d sepia	10	15	☐	☐
11		4d vermilion	20	25	☐	☐
12		5d blue	20	30	☐	☐

For comprehensive listings of the Independent Postal Administration issues of Guernsey, see Stanley Gibbons *Collect Channel Islands and Isle of Man Stamps.*

3 Jersey

(a) War Occupation Issues

Stamps issued under British authority during the German Occupation.

1   2 Old Jersey Farm   3 Portelet Bay

4 Corbière Lighthouse

5 Elizabeth Castle

6 Mont Orgueil Castle

7 Gathering Vraic (seaweed)

1941–42 *White paper. No wmk Perf 11*

1	**1**	½d green	4·00	3·25	☐	☐
2		1d red	4·50	2·50	☐	☐

1943 *No wmk Perf 13½*

3	**2**	½d green	7·50	5·50	☐	☐
4	**3**	1d red	2·00	75	☐	☐
5	**4**	1½d brown	3·50	3·25	☐	☐
6	**5**	2d orange	4·75	3·25	☐	☐
7a	**6**	2½d blue	1·00	1·10	☐	☐
8	**7**	3d violet	1·25	3·00	☐	☐
		Set of 6	18·00	15·00	☐	☐

(b) Regional Issues

8

9

1958–67 *Wmk* **179***. Perf* 15 × 14

9	**8**	2½d red	20	45	☐	☐
10	**9**	3d lilac	20	25	☐	☐
		p. One centre phosphor band	15	15	☐	☐
11		4d blue	25	30	☐	☐
		p. Two phosphor bands . .	15	25	☐	☐

1968–69 *One centre phosphor band (4d values) or two phosphor bands (5d). No wmk*

12	**9**	4d sepia	15	25	☐	☐
13		4d vermilion	15	35	☐	☐
14		5d blue	15	50	☐	☐

For comprehensive listings of the Independent Postal Adminstration issues of Jersey, see Stanley Gibbons *Collect Channel Islands and Isle of Man Stamps.*

REGIONAL FIRST DAY COVERS

PRICES for First Day Covers listed below are for stamps, as indicated, used on illustrated envelopes and postmarked with operational cancellations (before 1964) or with special First Day of Issue cancellations (1964 onwards). First Day postmarks of 8 June 1964 and 7 February 1966 were of the machine cancellation 'envelope' type.

£sd Issues

18 Aug. 1958	Guernsey 3d (*No.* 7)	17·00	☐
	Isle of Man 3d (*No.* 2)	32·00	☐
	Jersey 3d (*No.* 10)	17·00	☐
	Northern Ireland 3d (*No.* NI1) .	30·00	☐
	Scotland 3d (*No.* S1)	12·00	☐
	Wales 3d (*No.* W1)	12·00	☐
29 Sept. 1958	Northern Ireland 6d, 1s 3d (*Nos.* NI3, NI5)	35·00	☐
	Scotland 6d, 1s 3d (*Nos.* S3, S5)	25·00	☐
	Wales 6d, 1s 3d (*Nos.* W3, W5)	25·00	☐
8 June 1964	Guernsey 2½d (*No.* 6)	30·00	☐
	Isle of Man 2½d (*No.* 1)	45·00	☐
	Jersey 2½d (*No.* 9)	30·00	☐
7 Feb. 1966	Guernsey 4d (*No.* 8)	8·00	☐
	Isle of Man 4d (*No.* 3)	10·00	☐
	Jersey 4d (*No.* 11)	8·00	☐
	Northern Ireland 4d (*No.* NI2) .	7·00	☐
	Scotland 4d (*No.* S2)	7·00	☐
	Wales 4d (*No.* W2)	7·00	☐
1 March 1967	Northern Ireland 9d, 1s 6d (*Nos.* NI4, NI6)	4·00	☐
	Scotland 9d, 1s 6d (*Nos.* S4, S6)	4·00	☐
	Wales 9d, 1s 6d (*Nos.* W4, W6)	4·00	☐
4 Sept. 1968	Guernsey 4d, 5d (*Nos.* 10, 12)	3·00	☐
	Isle of Man 4d, 5d (*Nos.* 5, 7) .	4·00	☐
	Jersey 4d, 5d (*Nos.* 12, 14) . .	3·00	☐
	Northern Ireland 4d, 5d (*Nos.* NI8, NI10)	3·00	☐
	Scotland 4d, 5d (*Nos.* S9, S11).	3·00	☐
	Wales 4d, 5d (*Nos.* W9, W11) .	3·00	☐

Decimal Issues

7 July 1971	Isle of Man 2½p, 3p, 5p, 7½p (*Nos.* 8/11)	3·00	☐
	Northern Ireland 2½p, 3p, 5p, 7½p (*Nos.* NI12/13, NI18, NI23) .	3·75	☐
	Scotland 2½p, 3p, 5p, 7½p (*Nos.* S14/15, S20, S25)	3·00	☐
	Wales 2½p, 3p, 5p, 7½p (*Nos.* W13/14, W19, W24)	3·00	☐
23 Jan. 1974	Northern Ireland 3p, 3½p, 5½p, 8p (*Nos.* NI14/15, NI19, NI24) .	2·00	☐
	Scotland 3p, 3½p, 5½p, 8p (*Nos.* S16/17, S21, S26)	2·00	☐
	Wales 3p, 3½p, 5½p, 8p (*Nos.* W15/16, W20, W25)	2·00	☐

6 Nov. 1974	Northern Ireland 4½p (No. NI17)	1·50	☐
	Scotland 4½p (No. S19)	1·50	☐
	Wales 4½p (No. W18)	1·50	☐
14 Jan. 1976	Northern Ireland 6½p, 8½p (Nos. NI21, NI25)	1·50	☐
	Scotland 6½p, 8½p (Nos. S23, S27)	1·50	☐
	Wales 6½p, 8½p (Nos. W22, W26)	1·50	☐
20 Oct. 1976	Northern Ireland 10p, 11p (Nos. NI27, NI30)	1·50	☐
	Scotland 10p, 11p (Nos. S29, S32)	1·50	☐
	Wales 10p, 11p (Nos. W28, W31)	1·50	☐
18 Jan. 1978	Northern Ireland 7p, 9p, 10½p (Nos. NI22, NI26, NI29)	1·75	☐
	Scotland 7p, 9p, 10½p (Nos. S24, S28, S31	1·75	☐
	Wales 7p, 9p, 10½p (Nos. W23, W27, W30)	1·75	☐
23 July 1980	Northern Ireland 12p, 13½p, 15p (Nos. NI31/3)	2·25	☐
	Scotland 12p, 13½p, 15p (Nos. S33/5)	2·25	☐
	Wales 12p, 13½p, 15p (Nos. W32/4)	2·25	☐
8 April 1981	Northern Ireland 11½p, 14p, 18p, 22p (Nos. NI34, NI38, NI45, NI53)	3·50	☐
	Scotland 11½p, 14p, 18p, 22p (Nos. S36, S40, S44, S47) . . .	3·50	☐
	Wales 11½p, 14p, 18p, 22p (Nos. W35, W39, W46, W54)	3·75	☐
24 Feb. 1982	Northern Ireland 12½p, 15½p, 19½p, 26p (Nos. NI36, NI41, NI50, NI60)	5·00	☐
	Scotland 12½p, 15½p, 19½p, 26p (Nos. S38, S41, S45, S49) . . .	4·50	☐
	Wales 12½p, 15½p, 19½p, 26p (Nos. W37, W42, W51, W61) .	4·50	☐
27 April 1983	Northern Ireland 16p, 20½p, 28p (Nos. NI42, NI52, NI62)	6·00	☐
	Scotland 16p, 20½p, 28p (Nos. S42, S46, S50)	6·00	☐
	Wales 16p, 20½p, 28p (Nos. W43, W53, W63)	6·50	☐
23 Oct. 1984	Northern Ireland 13p, 17p, 22p, 31p (Nos. NI37, NI43, NI54, NI64)	4·75	☐
	Scotland 13p, 17p, 22p, 31p (Nos. S39, S43, S48, S51) . . .	7·50	☐
	Wales 13p, 17p, 22p, 31p (Nos. W38, W44, W55, W65)	4·25	☐
7 Jan. 1986	Northern Ireland 12p (No. NI35)	1·50	☐
	Scotland 12p (No. S37)	1·50	☐
	Wales 12p (No. W36)	1·50	☐
6 Jan. 1987	Northern Ireland 18p (No. NI46)	1·50	☐
	Scotland 18p (No. S59)	1·50	☐
	Wales 18p (No. W47)	1·50	☐
8 Nov. 1988	Northern Ireland 14p, 19p, 23p, 32p (Nos. NI39, NI49, NI56, NI65)	4·00	☐
	Scotland 14p, 19p, 23p, 32p (Nos. S54, S62, S67, S77) . . .	4·25	☐
	Wales 14p, 19p, 23p, 32p (Nos. W40, W50, W57, W66)	4·50	☐
28 Nov. 1989	Northern Ireland 15p, 20p, 24p, 34p (Nos. NI40, NI51, NI57, NI66)	4·50	☐
	Scotland 15p, 20p, 24p, 34p (Nos. S56, S64, S69, S78) . . .	4·75	☐
	Wales 15p, 20p, 24p, 34p (Nos. W41, W52, W58, W67)	4·75	☐
4 Dec. 1990	Northern Ireland 17p, 22p, 26p, 37p (Nos. NI44, NI55, NI61, NI67)	4·75	☐
	Scotland 17p, 22p, 26p, 37p (Nos. S58, S66, S73, S79) . . .	4·75	☐
	Wales 17p, 22p, 26p, 37p (Nos. W45, W56. W62, W68)	4·75	☐
3 Dec. 1991	Northern Ireland 18p, 24p, 28p, 39p (Nos. NI47, NI58, NI63, NI68)	5·50	☐
	Scotland 18p, 24p, 28p, 39p (Nos. S60, S70, S75, S80) . . .	5·50	☐
	Wales 18p, 24p, 28p, 39p (Nos. W48, W59, W64, W69)	5·50	☐
7 Dec 1993	Northern Ireland 19p, 25p, 30p, 41p (Nos. NI69, NI72, NI74, NI76)	5·50	☐
	Scotland 19p, 25p, 30p, 41p (Nos. S81, S84, S86, S88) . . .	5·50	☐
	Wales 19p, 25p, 30p, 41p (Nos. W70, W73, W75, W77)	5·75	☐
23 July 1996	Northern Ireland 20p (1 centre band), 26p, 37p, 63p (Nos. NI71, NI73, NI75, NI77)	8·75	☐
	Scotland 20p (1 centre band), 26p, 37p, 63p (Nos. S83, S85, S87, S89)	8·75	☐
	Wales 20p, 26p, 37p, 63p (Nos. W72, W74, W76, W78)	9·50	☐
1 July 1997	Wales 20p (1 centre band), 26p, 37p, 63p (Nos. W79/82)	5·50	☐
8 June 1999	Northern Ireland 38p, 64p (Nos. NI83, NI86)	4·00	☐
	Scotland 2nd, 1st, E, 64p (Nos S94/7)	4·00	☐
	Wales 2nd, 1st, E, 64p (Nos. W83, W84/6)	4·00	☐

25 Apr 2000	Northern Ireland 1st, 40p, 65p (Nos. NI84, NI87, NI88b)	4·25	☐
	Scotland 65p (No. S98)	1·90	☐
	Wales 65p (No. W87)	1·90	☐
6 Mar 2001	Northern Ireland 2nd, 1st, E, 65p (Nos. NI89/92)	3·25	☐
23 Apr 2001	England 2nd, 1st, E, 65p (Nos. EN1/4)	3·25	☐
4 July 2002	England 68p (No. EN5)	1·75	☐
	Northern Ireland 68p (No. NI93)	1·75	☐
	Scotland 68p (No. S99)	1·75	☐
	Wales 68p (No. W88)	1·75	☐

POSTAGE DUE STAMPS

PERFORATION. All postage due stamps to No. D101 are perf
14 × 15.

D 1    D 2

1914–22 *Wmk Type* **100** (*Royal Cypher* ('Simple') *sideways*

D1	D **1**	½d green	50	25	□	□
D2		1d red	50	25	□	□
D3		1½d brown	48·00	20·00	□	□
D4		2d black	50	25	□	□
D5		3d violet	5·00	75	□	□
D6		4d green	18·00	5·00	□	□
D7		5d brown	6·00	3·50	□	□
D8		1s blue	40·00	4·75	□	□
	Set of 8		£110	32·00	□	□

1924–31 *Wmk Type* **111** (*Block* G v R) *sideways*

D10	D **1**	½d green	1·25	75	□	□
D11		1d red	60	25	□	□
D12		1½d brown	45·00	18·00	□	□
D13		2d black	1·00	25	□	□
D14		3d violet	1·50	25	□	□
D15		4d green	15·00	3·00	□	□
D16		5d brown	32·00	28·00	□	□
D17		1s blue	10·00	1·00	□	□
D18	D **2**	2s 6d purple/*yellow*	45·00	2·00	□	□
	Set of 9		£140	48·00	□	□

1936–37 *Wmk Type* **125** (E 8 R) *sideways*

D19	D **1**	½d green	7·50	8·00	□	□
D20		1d red	1·50	2·00	□	□
D21		2d black	7·00	11·00	□	□
D22		3d violet	1·50	2·25	□	□
D23		4d green	23·00	35·00	□	□
D24*a*		5d brown	16·00	23·00	□	□
D25		1s blue	11·00	9·00	□	□
D26	D **2**	2s 6d purple/*yellow*	£275	9·00	□	□
	Set of 8		£325	90·00	□	□

1937–38 *Wmk Type* **127** (G vi R) *sideways*

D27	D **1**	½d green	9·00	5·00	□	□
D28		1d red	3·00	75	□	□
D29		2d black	2·50	75	□	□
D30		3d violet	12·00	1·00	□	□
D31		4d green	75·00	13·00	□	□
D32		5d brown	14·00	75	□	□
D33		1s blue	75·00	2·00	□	□
D34	D **2**	2s 6d purple/*yellow*	75·00	2·50	□	□
	Set of 8		£250	23·00	□	□

1951–52 *Colours changed and new value* (1½d) *Wmk Type* **127**
(G vi R) *sideways*

D35	D **1**	½d orange	1·00	3·00	□	□
D36		1d blue	1·50	1·50	□	□
D37		1½d green	1·75	3·00	□	□
D38		4d blue	32·00	12·00	□	□
D39		1s brown	38·00	14·00	□	□
	Set of 5		70·00	30·00	□	□

1954–55 *Wmk Type* **153** (*Mult Tudor Crown and* E 2 R) *sideways*

D40	D **1**	½d orange	4·50	8·00	□	□
D41		2d black	10·00	12·00	□	□
D42		3d violet	55·00	38·00	□	□
D43		4d blue	20·00	23·00	□	□
D44		5d brown	25·00	12·00	□	□
D45	D **2**	2s 6d purple/*yellow*	£110	7·00	□	□
	Set of 6		£200	90·00	□	□

1955–57 *Wmk Type* **165** (*Mult St Edward's Crown and* E 2 R)
sideways

D46	D **1**	½d orange	2·00	4·00	□	□
D47		1d blue	5·50	1·75	□	□
D48		1½d green	6·00	5·00	□	□
D49		2d black	45·00	3·75	□	□
D50		3d violet	7·00	2·00	□	□
D51		4d blue	20·00	4·00	□	□
D52		5d brown	32·00	2·25	□	□
D53		1s brown	70·00	2·00	□	□
D54	D **2**	2s 6d purple/*yellow*	£150	10·00	□	◻
D55		5s red/*yellow*	80·00	26·00	□	□
	Set of 10		£375	55·00	□	□

1959–63 *Wmk Type* **179** (*Mult St Edward's Crown*) *sideways*

D56	D **1**	½d orange	15	1·25	□	□
D57		1d blue	15	50	□	□
D58		1½d green	90	3·50	□	□
D59		2d black	1·10	50	□	□
D60		3d violet	30	30	□	□
D61		4d blue	30	30	□	□
D62		5d brown	45	60	□	□
D63		6d purple	50	30	□	□
D64		1s brown	90	30	□	□
D65	D **2**	2s 6d purple/*yellow*	4·75	75	□	□
D66		5s red/*yellow*	6·50	1·00	□	□
D67		10s blue/*yellow*	10·00	5·50	□	□
D68		£1 black/*yellow*	40·00	7·50	□	□
	Set of 13		60·00	20·00	□	□

1968–69 *Design size* 22½ × 19 mm. *No wmk*

D69	D **1**	2d black	25	75	□	□
D70		3d violet	30	75	□	□
D71		4d blue	40	75	□	□
D72		5d orange-brown	5·00	10·00	□	□
D73		6d purple	60	1·00	□	□
D74		1s brown	2·00	1·00	□	□
	Set of 6		7·50	13·00	□	□

1968–69 *Design size* 21½ × 17½ mm. *No wmk*

D75	D **1**	4d blue	6·00	6·00	□	□
D76		8d red	1·25	1·00	□	□

D 3   D 4

Decimal Currency
1970–77 *No wmk*

D77	D 3	½p turquoise-blue	. . .	15	50 □ □	
D78		1p reddish purple	. . .	15	15 □ □	
D79		2p myrtle-green	. . . .	20	15 □ □	
D80		3p ultramarine	. . . . .	20	15 □ □	
D81		4p yellow-brown	. . . .	25	15 □ □	
D82		5p violet	. . . .	25	15 □ □	
D83		7p red-brown	. . . . . .	35	80 □ □	
D84	D 4	10p red	. . . .	30	30 □ □	
D85		11p green	. . . .	50	1·00 □ □	
D86		20p brown	. . . .	60	25 □ □	
D87		50p ultramarine	. . . . .	1·75	25 □ □	
D88		£1 black	. . . .	3·25	50 □ □	
D89		£5 orange-yellow and black	. . . .	35·00	1·50 □ □	
	Set of 13	. . . .		38·00	5·25 □ □	

*Presentation Pack (P.O. Pack No.
36) (Nos. D77/82, D84, D86/8)*   9·00   □

*Presentation Pack (P.O. Pack No.
93) (Nos. D77/88)* . . . .   9·00   □

D 5   D 6   D 7

1982 *No wmk*

D90	D 5	1p lake	. . . .	10	30 □ □	
D91		2p bright blue	. . . . .	30	30 □ □	
D92		3p deep mauve	. . . . .	15	30 □ □	
D93		4p deep blue	. . . . . .	15	25 □ □	
D94		5p sepia	. . . .	20	25 □ □	
D95	D 6	10p light brown	. . . . .	30	40 □ □	
D96		20p olive-green	. . . . .	50	60 □ □	
D97		25p deep greenish blue	.	80	90 □ □	
D98		50p grey-black	. . . . . .	1·50	1·10 □ □	
D99		£1 red	. . . .	3·00	1·25 □ □	
D100		£2 turquoise-blue	. . .	6·00	2·40 □ □	
D101		£5 dull orange	. . . . .	14·00	2·00 □ □	
	Set of 12	. . . .		24·00	8·50 □ □	
	Set of 12 *Gutter Pairs*	. . . . . .		48·00	□	
	Presentation Pack	. . . .		26·00	□	

For full information on all future British issues, collectors
should write to Royal Mail, Freepost EH3647, 21 South Gyle
Crescent, Edinburgh EH12 9PE.

1994 (15 FEB.) *Perf* 15 × 14 (*with one elliptical hole on each
vertical side*)

D102	D 7	1p red, yellow and black	10	50 □ □	
D103		2p magenta, purple and black	. . . .	10	50 □ □
D104		5p yellow, red-brown and black	. . . . . .	15	35 □ □
D105		10p yellow, emerald and black	. . . .	30	45 □ □
D106		20p blue-green, violet and black	. . . .	50	70 □ □
D107		25p cerise, rosine and black	. . . .	70	75 □ □
D108		£1 violet, magenta and black	. . . .	3·00	2·50 □ □
D109		£1.20 greenish blue, blue-green and black	3·75	3·50 □ □	
D110		£5 greenish black, blue-green and black	14·00	12·00 □ □	
	Set of 9	. . . .	20·00	19·00 □ □	
	Presentation Pack	. . . .	28·00	□	

ROYAL MAIL POSTAGE LABELS

These imperforate labels were issued as an experiment by the Post Office. Special microprocessor-controlled machines were installed at post offices in Cambridge, London, Shirley (Southampton) and Windsor to provide an after-hours sales service to the public. The machines printed and dispensed the labels according to the coins inserted and the buttons operated by the customer. Values were initially available in ½p steps to 16p and in addition, the labels were sold at philatelic counters in two packs containing either 3 values (3½, 12½, 16p) or 32 values (½p to 16p).

From 28 August 1984 the machines were adjusted to provide values up to 17p. After 31 December 1984 labels including ½p values were withdrawn. The machines were taken out of service on 30 April 1985.

Machine postage-paid impression in red on phosphorised paper with grey-green background design. No watermark, imperforate.

1984 (1 May–28 Aug.)

Set of 32 (½p to 16p)	13·00	22·00 □ □
Set of 3 (3½p, 12½p, 16p)	2·50	3·00 □ □
Set of 3 on First Day Cover		
(1 May)	6·50 □
Set of 2 (16½p, 17p) (28 August)	4·00	3·00 □ □

OFFICIAL STAMPS

Various stamps of Queen Victoria and King Edward V overprinted in Black.

I.R. **OFFICIAL** (O 1)	**I. R.** **OFFICIAL** (O 2)	**O.W.** **OFFICIAL** (O 3)
ARMY **OFFICIAL** (O 4)	**ARMY** **OFFICIAL** (O 5)	**GOVT PARCELS** (O 7)

BOARD OF EDUCATION (O 8)

R.H. OFFICIAL (O 9)

ADMIRALTY OFFICIAL (O 10)

1 Inland Revenue

Overprinted with Types O 1 or O 2 (5s, 10s, £1)

1882–1901 *Queen Victoria*

O 1	52	½d green	50·00	20·00 □ □
O 5		½d blue	50·00	22·00 □ □
O13	67	½d vermilion	2·50	1·50 □ □
O17		½d green	6·00	4·50 □ □
O 3	57	1d lilac (Die II)	4·00	2·00 □ □
O 6	64	2½d lilac	£180	65·00 □ □
O14	70	2½d purple on blue	70·00	6·00 □ □
O 4	43	6d grey (Plate 18)	£190	50·00 □ □
O18	75	6d purple on red	£190	45·00 □ □
O 7	65	1s green	£2750	£575 □ □
O15	78	1s green	£240	£100 □ □
O19		1s green and red	£950	£350 □ □
O 9	59	5s red	£1800	£500 □ □
O10	60	10s blue	£3250	£850 □ □
O11	61	£1 brown (Wmk Crowns)	£24000	□
O12		£1 brown (Wmk Orbs) . .	£32000	□
O16		£1 green	£4500	£750 □ □

1902–04 *King Edward VII*

O20	79	½d blue-green	22·00	3·00 □ □
O21		1d red	15·00	2·00 □ □
O22	82	2½d blue	£475	£100 □ □
O23	79	6d purple	£90000	£70000 □ □
O24	89	1s green and red	£700	£170 □ □
O25	91	5s red	£5250	£3500 □ □
O26	92	10s blue	£17000	£10000 □ □
O27	93	£1 green	£14000	£9000 □ □

2 Office of Works

Overprinted with Type O 3

1896–1902 *Queen Victoria*

O31	67	½d vermilion	£110	60·00 □ □
O32		½d green	£200	£100 □ □
O33	57	1d lilac (Die II)	£200	60·00 □ □
O34	74	5d dull purple and blue	£900	£250 □ □
O35	77	10d dull purple and red . .	£1800	£400 □ □

1902–03 *King Edward VII*

O36	79	½d blue-green	£425	£110 □ □
O37		1d red	£425	£110 □ □
O38	81	2d green and red	£800	£250 □ □
O39	82	2½d blue	£850	£300 □ □
O40	88	10d purple and red	£6000	£2400 □ □

3 Army

Overprinted with Types O 4 (½d, 1d) or O 5 (2½d, 6d)

1896–1901 *Queen Victoria*

O41	67	½d vermilion	2·50	1·50	☐	☐
O42		½d green	2·50	4·50	☐	☐
O43	57	1d lilac (Die II)	2·50	1·50	☐	☐
O44	70	2½d purple on blue	6·00	3·50	☐	☐
O45	75	6d purple on red	22·00	24·00	☐	☐

Overprinted with Type O 4

1902 *King Edward VII*

O48	79	½d blue-green	3·00	1·50	☐	☐
O49		1d red	3·00	1·50	☐	☐
O50		6d purple	80·00	35·00	☐	☐

4 Government Parcels

Overprinted with Type O 7

1883–1900 *Queen Victoria*

O69	57	1d lilac (Die II)	30·00	9·00	☐	☐
O61	62	1½d lilac	£125	30·00	☐	☐
O65	68	1½d purple and green . . .	25·00	3·00	☐	☐
O70	69	2d green and red	50·00	8·00	☐	☐
O71	73	4½d green and red	£125	90·00	☐	☐
O62	63	6d green	£925	£300	☐	☐
O66	75	6d purple on red	60·00	18·00	☐	☐
O63	64	9d green	£675	£190	☐	☐
O67	76	9d purple and blue	70·00	20·00	☐	☐
O64	44	1s brown (Plate 13)	£500	90·00	☐	☐
O64c		1s brown (Plate 14)	£825	£140	☐	☐
O68	78	1s green	£150	80·00	☐	☐
O72		1s green and red	£190	65·00	☐	☐

1902 *King Edward VII*

O74	79	1d red	25·00	9·00	☐	☐
O75	81	2d green and red	70·00	18·00	☐	☐
O76	79	6d purple	£130	20·00	☐	☐
O77	87	9d purple and blue	£275	60·00	☐	☐
O78	89	1s green and red	£425	£100	☐	☐

5 Board of Education

Overprinted with Type O 8

1902 *Queen Victoria*

O81	74	5d dull purple and blue .	£600	£160	☐	☐
O82	78	1s green and red	£1800	£1000	☐	☐

1902–04 *King Edward VII*

O83	79	½d blue-green	90·00	30·00	☐	☐
O84		1d red	90·00	30·00	☐	☐
O85	82	2½d blue	£600	90·00	☐	☐
O86	85	5d purple and blue	£3000	£1500	☐	☐
O87	89	1s green and red	£45000		☐	

6 Royal Household

Overprinted with Type O 9

1902 *King Edward VII*

O91	79	½d blue-green	£190	£130	☐	☐
O92		1d red	£160	£110	☐	☐

7 Admiralty

Overprinted with Type O 10

1903 *King Edward Vii*

O107	79	½d blue-green	12·00	7·00	☐	☐
O102		1d red	7·00	4·00	☐	☐
O103	80	1½d purple and green . . .	90·00	55·00	☐	☐
O104	81	2d green and red	£140	70·00	☐	☐
O105	82	2½d blue	£150	55·00	☐	☐
O106	83	3d purple on yellow . . .	£140	55·00	☐	☐

Notes

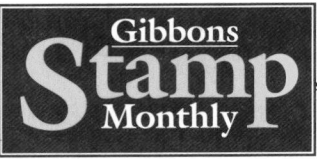

Visit the world's most famous stamp shop - 399 Strand

- Browse through our stockbooks which contain over 4 million stamps. Over half a million of which are GB stamps!

- The biggest range of stamp literature, albums and accessories

- We have everything from the Penny Black to Queen Elizabeth II's Golden Jubilee

Strand Savers Card

Only £20.00 a year to join.
Entitles you to 10% discount on all purchases from 399 Strand.
You will also be invited to double discount days where you can enjoy even greater savings of up to 20%.
Monthly special prize draws for card holders. When your card expires you can rejoin for just £15.00.

Opening times:
9.00am - 5.30pm Monday to Friday
9.30am - 5.30pm Saturday
Do not miss the Manager's Weekly Specials, plus many more fantastic offers

Stanley Gibbons Limited
399 Strand, London WC2R 0LX
Tel: +44 (0)20 7836 8444
Fax: +44 (0)20 7836 7342
Email: stampsales@stanleygibbons.co.uk

Quote ref.: CBS02

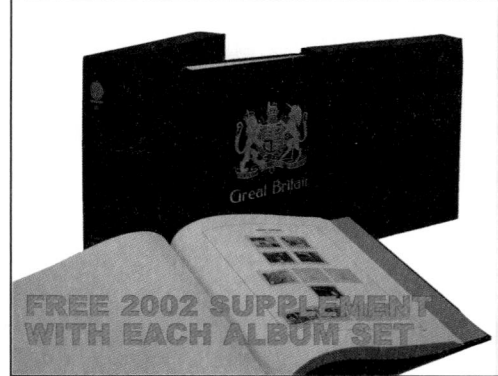

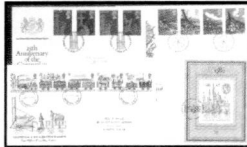

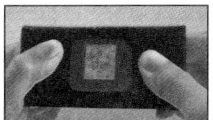